Complete Solutions Guide

Precalculus with Limits: A Graphing Approach

Fifth Edition

and

Precalculus Functions and Graphs: A Graphing Approach

Fifth Edition

Larson/Hostetler/Edwards

Bruce H. Edwards

University of Florida
Gainesville, Florida

Houghton Mifflin Company Boston New York

Publisher: Richard Stratton
Sponsoring Editor: Cathy Cantin
Marketing Manager: Jennifer Jones
Editorial Associate: Jeannine Lawless
Editorial Assistant: Jill Clark

Printed in the United States of America.

ISBN 13: 978-0-618-85447-9
ISBN 10: 0-618-85447-9

3456789-???-11 10 09

Preface

This *Complete Solutions Guide* is a supplement to *Precalculus with Limits: A Graphing Approach*, Fifth Edition and *Precalculus Functions and Graphs: A Graphing Approach*, Fifth Edition by Ron Larson, Robert Hostetler, and Bruce H. Edwards.

Solutions to the exercises in the text are given in two parts. Part I contains worked-out solutions to all Section and Review Exercises; summaries of the chapters; and Practice Tests with solutions. Part II contains solutions to the Chapter and Cumulative Tests from the textbook.

This *Complete Solutions Guide* is the result of the efforts of Larson Texts, Inc. If you have any corrections or suggestions for improving this guide, we would appreciate hearing from you.

Bruce H. Edwards
358 Little Hall
University of Florida
Gainesville, FL 32611
be@math.ufl.edu

Contents

Part I **Solutions to Exercises and Practice Tests**

Chapter 1 Functions and Their Graphs 1
Chapter 2 Polynomial and Rational Functions 87
Chapter 3 Exponential and Logarithmic Functions 192
Chapter 4 Trigonometric Functions 271
Chapter 5 Analytic Trigonometry 378
Chapter 6 Additional Topics in Trigonometry 465
Chapter 7 Linear Systems and Matrices 548
Chapter 8 Sequences, Series, and Probability 689
Chapter 9 Topics in Analytic Geometry 771
Chapter 10 Analytic Geometry in Three Dimensions 887
Chapter 11 Limits and an Introduction to Calculus 928
Appendices 990

Solutions to Chapter Practice Tests 1080

Part II **Solutions to Chapter and Cumulative Tests** 1106

PART I

CHAPTER 1
Functions and Their Graphs

Section 1.1 Lines in the Plane 2

Section 1.2 Functions 14

Section 1.3 Graphs of Functions 24

Section 1.4 Shifting, Reflecting, and Stretching Graphs 35

Section 1.5 Combinations of Functions 43

Section 1.6 Inverse Functions 54

Section 1.7 Linear Models and Scatter Plots 68

Review Exercises 72

Practice Test 86

CHAPTER 1
Functions and Their Graphs

Section 1.1 Lines in the Plane

You should know the following important facts about lines.

- The graph of $y = mx + b$ is a straight line. It is called a linear equation.
- The slope of the line through (x_1, y_1) and (x_2, y_2) is
  $$m = \frac{y_2 - y_1}{x_2 - x_1}.$$
- (a) If $m > 0$ the line rises from left to right. (b) If $m = 0$, the line is horizontal.
  (c) If $m < 0$,, the line falls from left to right. (d) If m is undefined, the line is vertical.
- Equations of Lines
  (a) Slope-Intercept: $y = mx + b$ (b) Point-Slope: $y - y_1 = m(x - x_1)$
  (c) Two-Point: $y - y_1 = \frac{y_2 - y_1}{x_2 - x_1}(x - x_1)$ (d) General: $Ax + By + c = 0$
  (e) Vertical: $x = a$ (f) Horizontal: $y = b$
- Given two distinct nonvertical lines
  $$L_1: y = m_1x + b_1 \quad \text{and} \quad L_2: y = m_2x + b_2$$
  (a) L_1 is parallel to L_2 if and only if $m_1 = m_2$ and $b_1 \neq b_2$.
  (b) L_1 is perpendicular to L_2 if and only if $m_1 = -1/m_2$.

Vocabulary Check

1. (a) iii (b) i (c) v (d) ii (e) iv

2. slope

3. parallel

4. perpendicular

5. linear extrapolation

1. (a) $m = \frac{2}{3}$. Since the slope is positive, the line rises. Matches L_2.

(b) m is undefined. The line is vertical. Matches L_3.

(c) $m = -2$. The line falls. Matches L_1.

2. (a) $m = 0$. The line is horizontal. Matches L_2.

(b) $m = -\frac{3}{4}$. Because the slope is negative, the line falls. Matches L_1.

(c) $m = 1$. Because the slope is positive, the line rises. Matches L_3.

3.

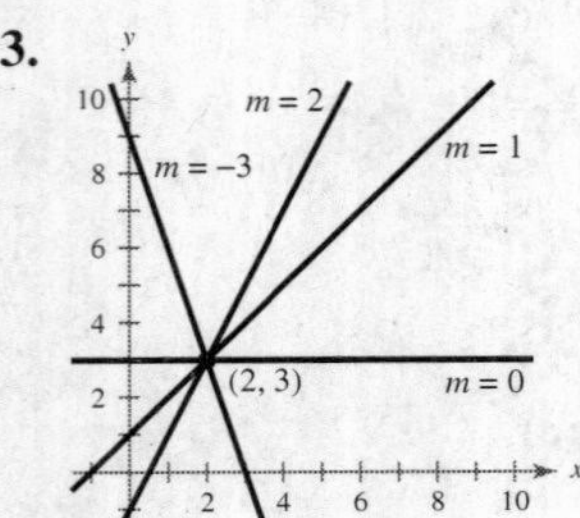

4.

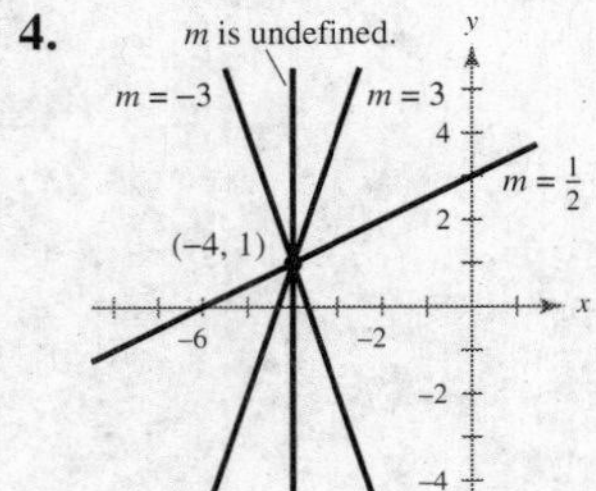

5. Slope $= \dfrac{\text{rise}}{\text{run}} = \dfrac{3}{2}$

6. The line appears to go through (0, 8) and (2, 0).

Slope $= \dfrac{8-0}{0-2} = -4$

7. Slope $= \dfrac{0-(-10)}{-4-0} = \dfrac{10}{-4} = -\dfrac{5}{2}$

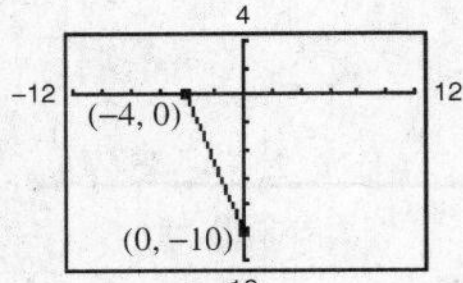

8. Slope $= \dfrac{-4-4}{4-2} = -4$

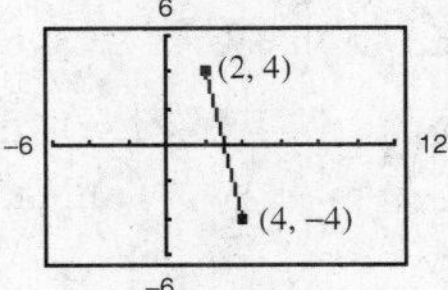

9.

Slope is undefined.

10. Slope $= \dfrac{6-(-2)}{1-(-3)} = \dfrac{8}{4} = 2$

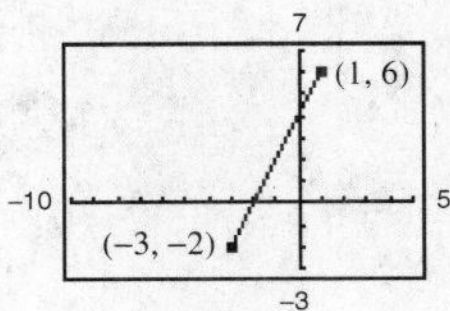

11. Since $m = 0$, y does not change. Three points are $(0, 1)$, $(3, 1)$, and $(-1, 1)$.

12. Since $m = 0$, y does not change. Three additional points: $(0, -2)$, $(1, -2)$, $(4, -2)$.

13. Since m is undefined, x does not change and the line is vertical. Three points are $(1, 1)$, $(1, 2)$, and $(1, 3)$.

14. Because m is undefined, x does not change. Three other points are: $(-4, 0)$, $(-4, 3)$, $(-4, 5)$.

15. Since $m = -2$, y decreases 2 for every unit increase in x. Three points are $(1, -11)$, $(2, -13)$, and $(3, -15)$.

16. Since $m = 2$, y increases 2 for every unit increase in x. Three points are: $(-4, 6)$, $(-3, 8)$, and $(-2, 10)$.

17. Since $m = \frac{1}{2}$, y increases 1 for every increase of 2 in x. Three points are $(9, -1)$, $(11, 0)$,and $(13, 1)$.

18. Since $m = -\frac{1}{2}$, y decreases 1 for every increase of 2 units in x. Three points are $(1, -7)$, $(3, -8)$, $(5, -9)$.

19. $5x - y + 3 = 0$

$$y = 5x + 3$$

(a) Slope: $m = 5$

y-intercept: $(0, 3)$

(b)

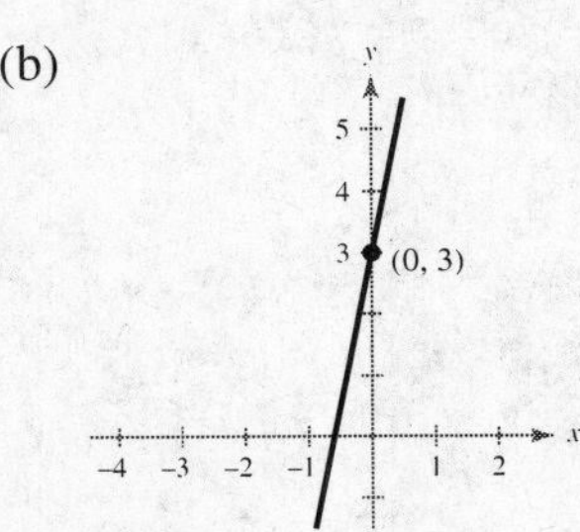

20. $2x + 3y - 9 = 0$

$$3y = -2x + 9$$

$$y = -\tfrac{2}{3}x + 3$$

(a) Slope: $m = -\frac{2}{3}$

y-intercept: $(0, 3)$

(b)

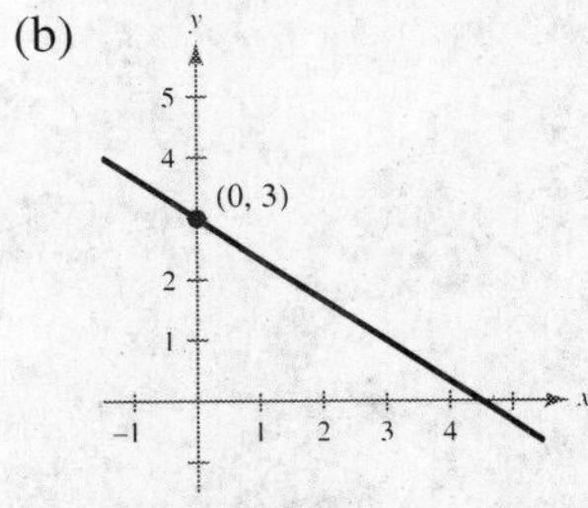

21. $5x - 2 = 0$

$x = \frac{2}{5}$

(a) Slope: undefined

No y-intercept

(b)

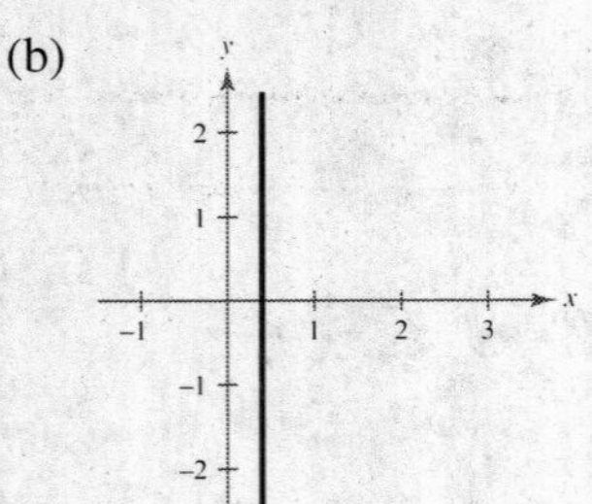

22. $3x + 7 = 0$

$x = -\frac{7}{3}$

(a) Slope: undefined

y-intercept: none

(b)

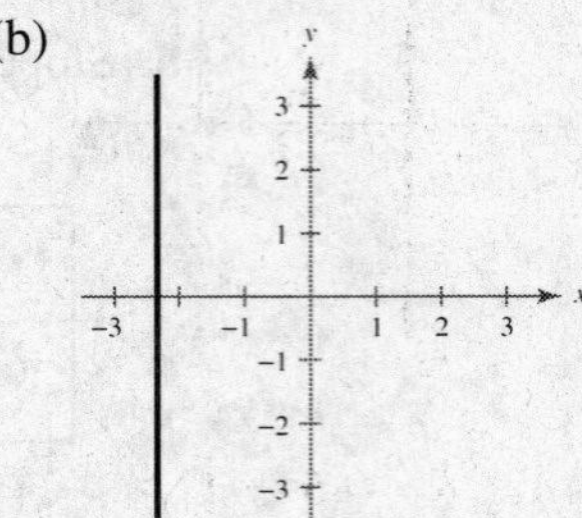

23. $3y + 5 = 0$

$y = -\frac{5}{3}$

(a) Slope: $m = 0$

y-intercept: $\left(0, -\frac{5}{3}\right)$

(b)

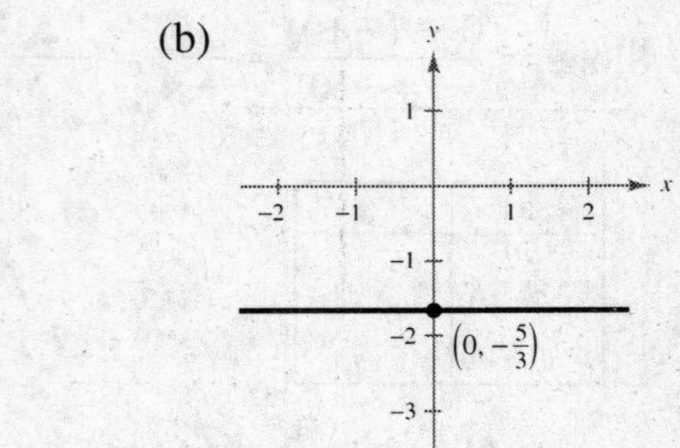

24. $-11 - 8y = 0$

$8y = -11$

$y = -\frac{11}{8}$

(a) Slope: $m = 0$

y-intercept: $\left(0, -\frac{11}{8}\right)$

(b)

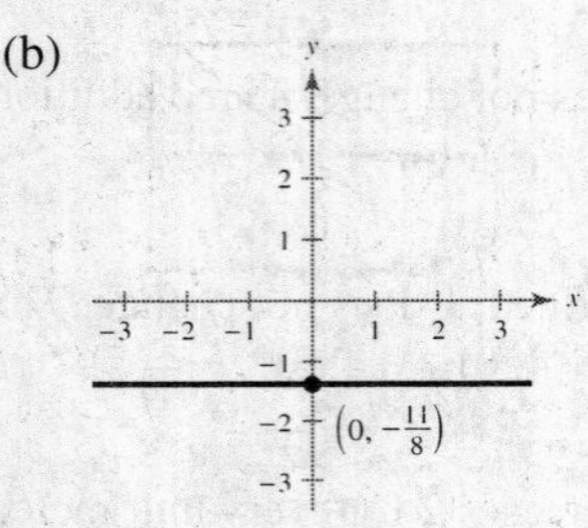

25. $y + 2 = 3(x - 0)$

$y = 3x - 2 \implies 3x - y - 2 = 0$

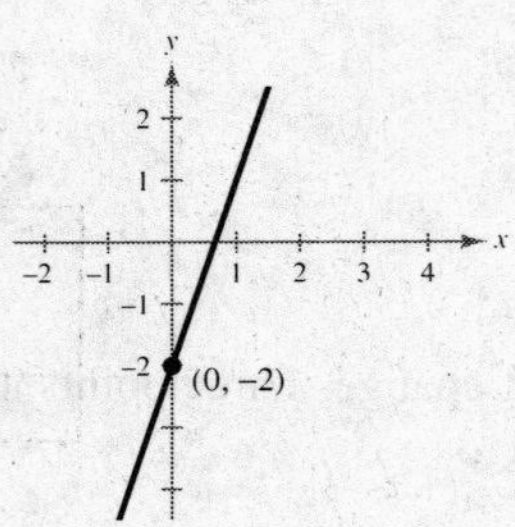

26. (a) $m = -2, \quad (-3, 6)$

$y - 6 = -2(x + 3)$

$y = -2x$

$2x + y = 0$

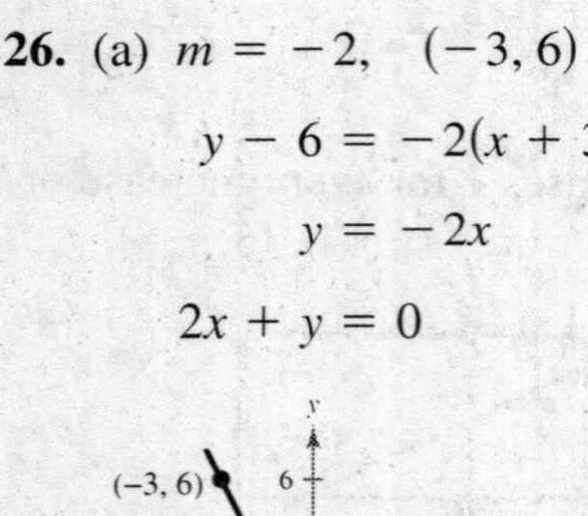

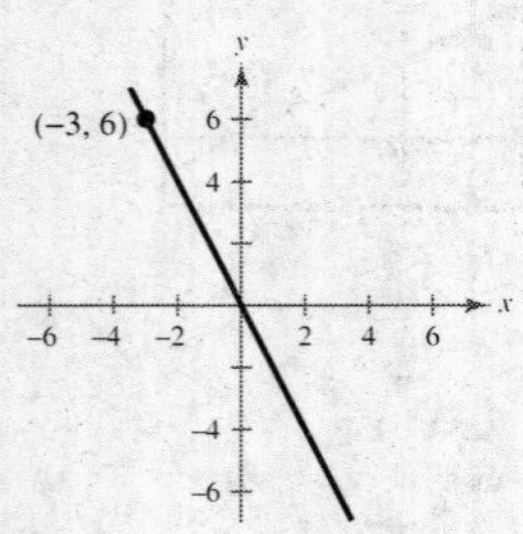

27. $y - (-3) = -\frac{1}{2}(x - 2)$

$y + 3 = -\frac{1}{2}x + 1$

$2y + 4 = -x$

$x + 2y + 4 = 0$

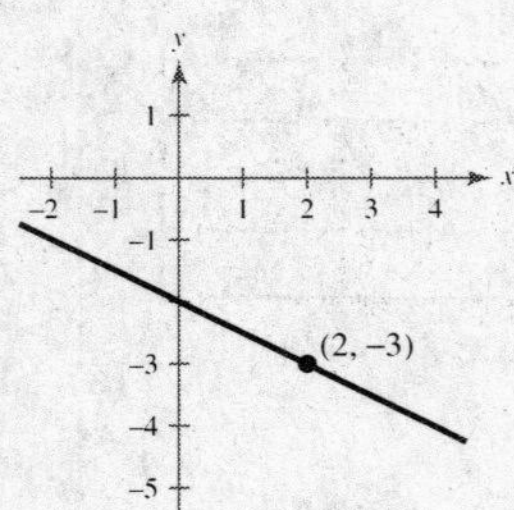

28. $m = \frac{3}{4}, (-2, -5)$

$y + 5 = \frac{3}{4}(x + 2)$

$4y + 20 = 3x + 6$

$0 = 3x - 4y - 14$

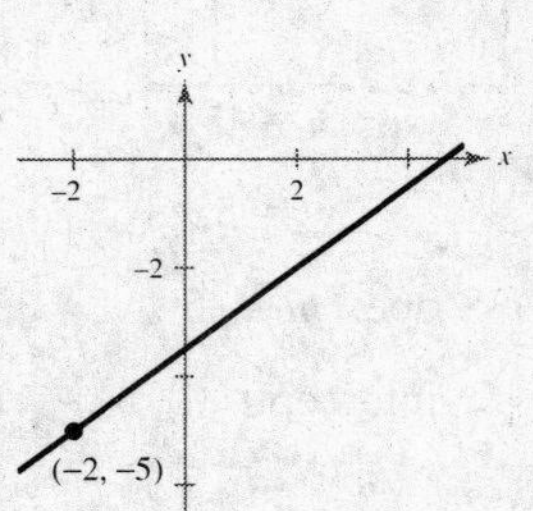

29. $x = 6$

$x - 6 = 0$

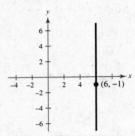

30. m undefined. Line is vertical.

$x + 10 = 0$

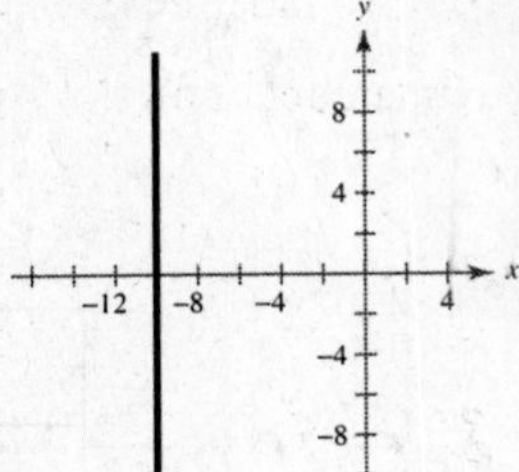

31. $y - \frac{3}{2} = 0\left(x + \frac{1}{2}\right)$

$y - \frac{3}{2} = 0$ horizontal line

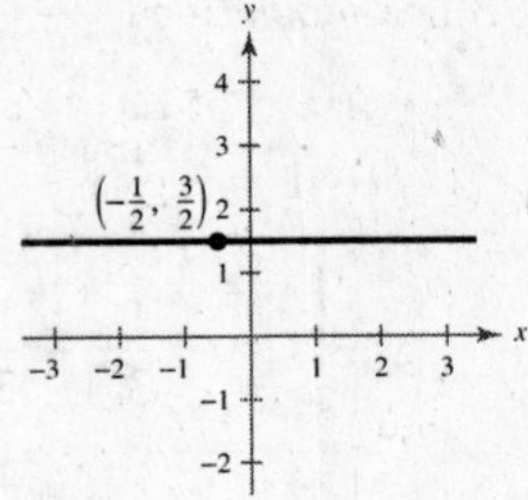

32. $m = 0$. Line is horizontal.

$y + 8.5 = 0$

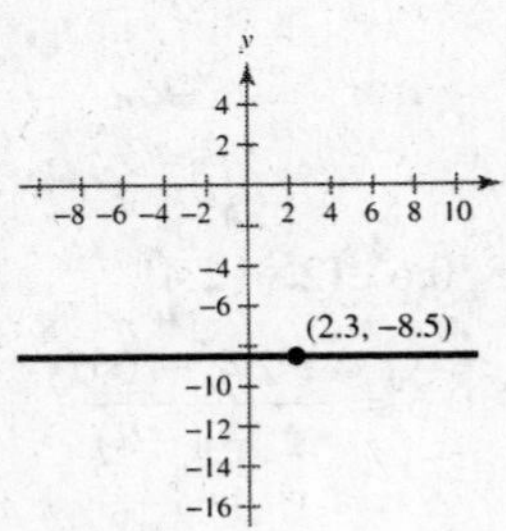

33. $y + 1 = \dfrac{5 + 1}{-5 - 5}(x - 5)$

$y = -\dfrac{3}{5}(x - 5) - 1$

$y = -\dfrac{3}{5}x + 2$

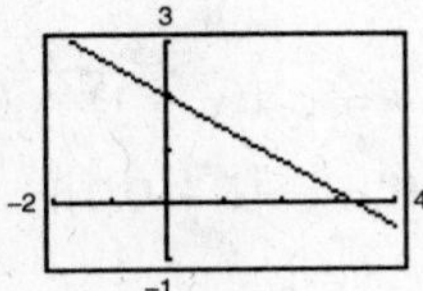

34. $(4, 3), (-4, -4)$

$y - 3 = \dfrac{-4 - 3}{-4 - 4}(x - 4)$

$y - 3 = \dfrac{7}{8}(x - 4)$

$y = \dfrac{7}{8}x - \dfrac{1}{2}$

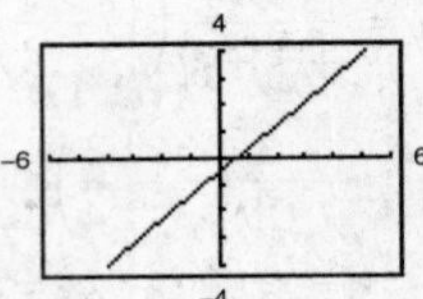

35. Since both points have $x = -8$, the slope is undefined.

$x = -8$

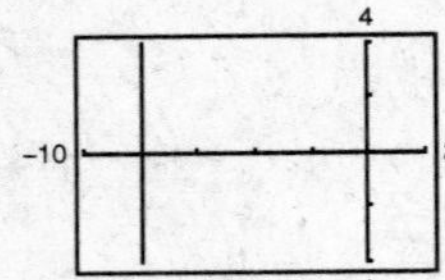

36. $(-1, 4), (6, 4)$

$y - 4 = \dfrac{4 - 4}{6 - (-1)}(x + 1)$

$y - 4 = 0(x + 1)$

$y - 4 = 0$

$y = 4$

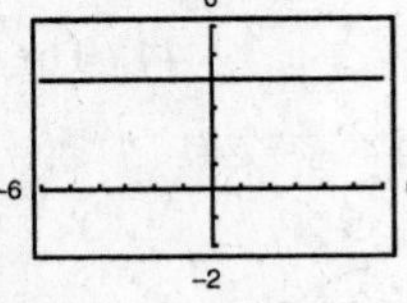

37. $y - \dfrac{1}{2} = \dfrac{\frac{5}{4} - \frac{1}{2}}{\frac{1}{2} - 2}(x - 2)$

$y = -\dfrac{1}{2}(x - 2) + \dfrac{1}{2}$

$y = -\dfrac{1}{2}x + \dfrac{3}{2}$

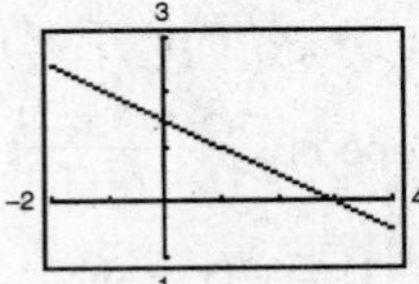

38. $(1, 1), \left(6, -\frac{2}{3}\right)$

$$y - 1 = \frac{-\frac{2}{3} - 1}{6 - 1}(x - 1)$$

$$y - 1 = -\frac{1}{3}(x - 1)$$

$$y - 1 = -\frac{1}{3}x + \frac{1}{3}$$

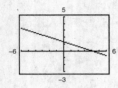

$$y = -\frac{1}{3}x + \frac{4}{3}$$

39. $y + \frac{3}{5} = \frac{-\frac{9}{5} + \frac{3}{5}}{\frac{9}{10} + \frac{1}{10}}\left(x + \frac{1}{10}\right)$

$$y + \frac{3}{5} = -\frac{6}{5}\left(x + \frac{1}{10}\right)$$

$$y = -\frac{6}{5}x - \frac{18}{25}$$

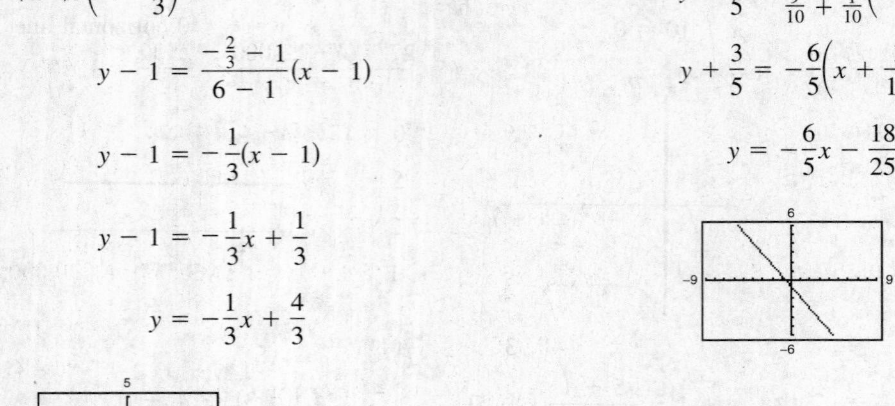

40. $\left(\frac{3}{4}, \frac{3}{2}\right), \left(-\frac{4}{3}, \frac{7}{4}\right)$

$$y - \frac{3}{2} = \frac{\frac{7}{4} - \frac{3}{2}}{-\frac{4}{3} - \frac{3}{4}}\left(x - \frac{3}{4}\right)$$

$$y - \frac{3}{2} = -\frac{3}{25}\left(x - \frac{3}{4}\right)$$

$$y - \frac{3}{2} = -\frac{3}{25}x + \frac{9}{100}$$

$$y = -\frac{3}{25}x + \frac{159}{100}$$

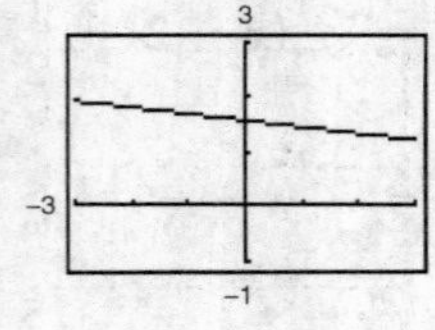

41. $y - 0.6 = \frac{-0.6 - 0.6}{-2 - 1}(x - 1)$

$$y = 0.4(x - 1) + 0.6$$

$$y = 0.4x + 0.2$$

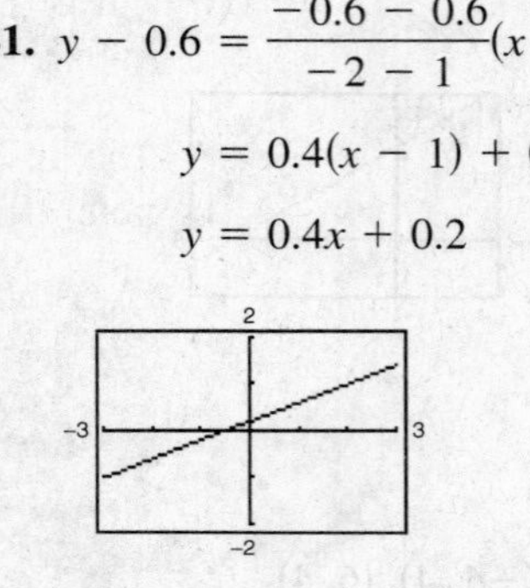

42. $(-8, 0.6), (2, -2.4)$

$$y - 0.6 = \frac{-2.4 - 0.6}{2 - (-8)}(x + 8)$$

$$y - 0.6 = -\frac{3}{10}(x + 8)$$

$$y = -\frac{3}{10}x - \frac{9}{5}$$

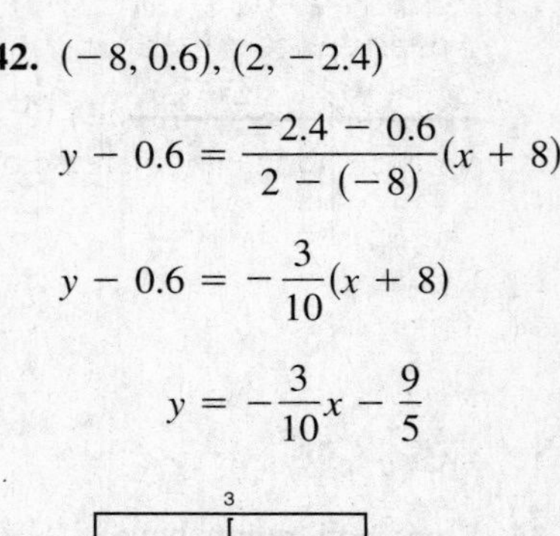

43. The slope is $\frac{-3 - (-7)}{1 - (-1)} = \frac{4}{2} = 2.$

$$y - (-3) = 2(x - 1)$$

$$y + 3 = 2x - 2$$

$$y = 2x - 5$$

44. The slope is $\frac{-1 - \frac{3}{2}}{4 - (-1)} = \frac{-\frac{5}{2}}{5} = \frac{-1}{2}.$

$$y - (-1) = -\frac{1}{2}(x - 4)$$

$$y + 1 = -\frac{1}{2}x + 2$$

$$y = -\frac{1}{2}x + 1$$

45. Using the points (2004, 28,500) and (2006, 32,900), you have

$$m = \frac{32{,}900 - 28{,}500}{2006 - 2004} = \frac{4400}{2} = 2200$$

$$S - 28{,}500 = 2200(t - 2004)$$
$$S = 2200t - 4{,}380{,}300.$$

When $t = 2008$,

$$S = 2200(2008) - 4{,}380{,}300 = \$37{,}300.$$

46. Using the points (2004, 25,000) and (2006, 27,500), you have

$$m = \frac{27{,}500 - 25{,}000}{2006 - 2004} = \frac{2500}{2} = 1250$$

$$S - 25{,}000 = 1250(t - 2004)$$
$$S = 1250t - 2{,}480{,}000.$$

When $t = 2008$,

$$S = 1250(2008) - 2{,}480{,}000 = \$30{,}000.$$

47. $x - 2y = 4$

$$-2y = -x + 4$$
$$y = \frac{1}{2}x - 2$$

Slope: $\frac{1}{2}$

y-intercept: $(0, -2)$

The graph passes through $(0, -2)$ and rises 1 unit for each horizontal increase of 2.

48. $3x + 4y = 1$

$$4y = -3x + 1$$
$$y = \frac{-3}{4}x + \frac{1}{4}$$

Slope: $-\frac{3}{4}$

y-intercept: $\left(0, \frac{1}{4}\right)$

The line slopes downward and passes through the point $\left(0, \frac{1}{4}\right)$.

49. $x = -6$

slope is undefined

no y-intercept

The line is vertical and passes through $(-6, 0)$.

50. $y = 12$

Slope: 0

y-intercept: $(0, 12)$

The line is horizontal and passes through $(0, 12)$.

51. $y = 0.5x - 3$

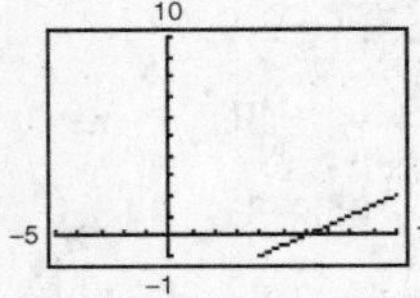

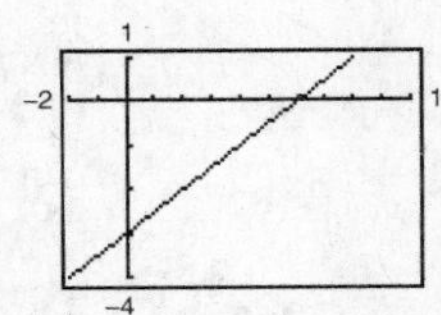

The second setting shows the x- and y-intercepts more clearly.

52.

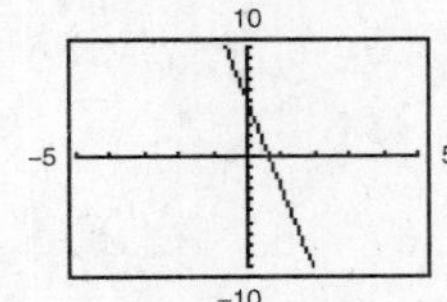

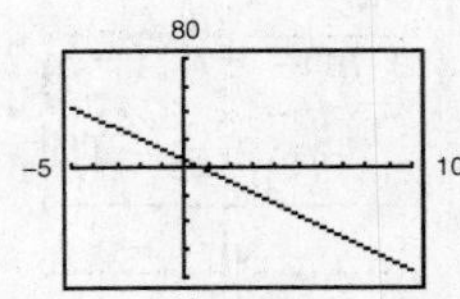

The first setting shows the x- and y-intercepts more clearly.

53. $m_{L_1} = \frac{9 + 1}{5 - 0} = 2$

$$m_{L_2} = \frac{1 - 3}{4 - 0} = -\frac{1}{2} = -\frac{1}{m_{L_1}}$$

L_1 and L_2 are perpendicular.

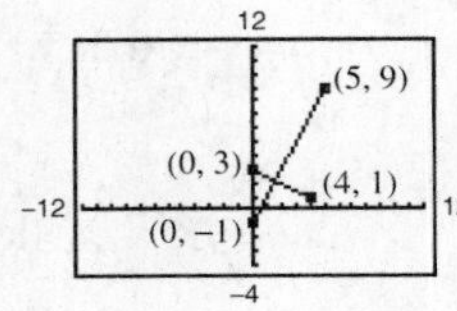

54. L_1: $(-2, -1), (1, 5)$

$m_1 = \dfrac{5 - (-1)}{1 - (-2)} = \dfrac{6}{3} = 2$

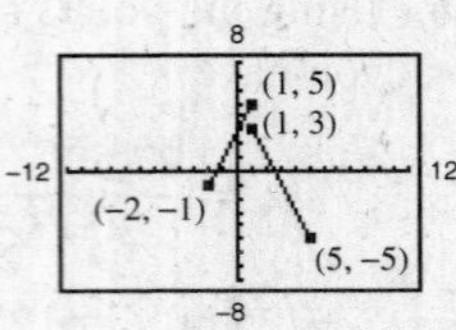

L_2: $(1, 3), (5, -5)$

$m_2 = \dfrac{-5 - 3}{5 - 1} = \dfrac{-8}{4} = -2$

The lines are neither parallel nor perpendicular.

55. $m_{L_1} = \dfrac{0 - 6}{-6 - 3} = \dfrac{2}{3}$

$m_{L_2} = \dfrac{\frac{7}{3} + 1}{5 - 0} = \dfrac{2}{3} = m_{L_1}$

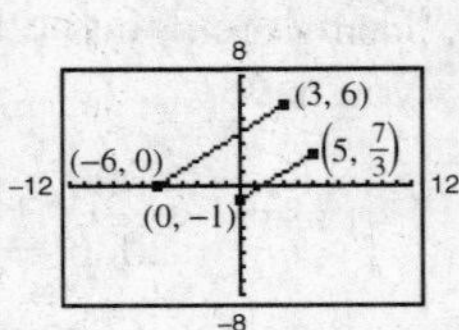

L_1 and L_2 are parallel.

56. L_1: $(4, 8), (-4, 2)$

$m_1 = \dfrac{2 - 8}{-4 - 4} = \dfrac{-6}{-8} = \dfrac{3}{4}$

L_2: $(3, -5), \left(-1, \dfrac{1}{3}\right)$

$m_2 = \dfrac{(1/3) - (-5)}{-1 - 3} = \dfrac{16/3}{-4} = -\dfrac{4}{3}$

The lines are perpendicular.

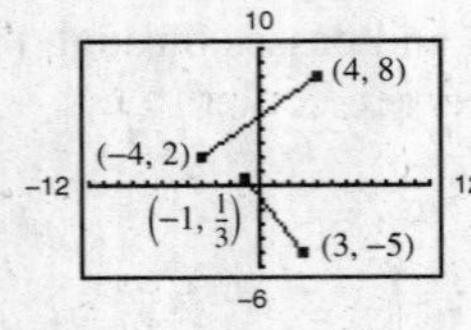

57. $4x - 2y = 3$

$y = 2x - \dfrac{3}{2}$

Slope: $m = 2$

(a) $y - 1 = 2(x - 2)$

$y = 2x - 3$

(b) $y - 1 = -\dfrac{1}{2}(x - 2)$

$y = -\dfrac{1}{2}x + 2$

58. $x + y = 7$

$y = -x + 7$

Slope: $m = -1$

(a) $m = -1, (-3, 2)$

$y - 2 = -1(x + 3)$

$y = -x - 1$

(b) $m = 1, (-3, 2)$

$y - 2 = 1(x + 3)$

$y = x + 5$

59. $3x + 4y = 7$

$y = -\frac{3}{4}x + \frac{7}{4}$

Slope: $m = -\frac{3}{4}$

(a) $y - \frac{7}{8} = -\frac{3}{4}\left(x + \frac{2}{3}\right)$

$y = -\frac{3}{4}x + \frac{3}{8}$

(b) $y - \frac{7}{8} = \frac{4}{3}\left(x + \frac{2}{3}\right)$

$y = \frac{4}{3}x + \frac{127}{72}$

60. $6x + 2y = 9$

$2y = -6x + 9$

$y = -3x + \frac{9}{2}$

Slope: $m = -3$

(a) $m = -3, (-3.9, -1.4)$

$y + 1.4 = -3(x + 3.9)$

$y = -3x - 13.1$

(b) $m = \frac{1}{3}, (-3.9, -1.4)$

$y + 1.4 = \frac{1}{3}(x + 3.9)$

$y = \frac{1}{3}x - \frac{1}{10}$

61. $x - 4 = 0$ vertical line

slope not defined

(a) $x - 3 = 0$ passes through $(3, -2)$

(b) $y = -2$ passes through $(3, -2)$ and is horizontal

62. $y + 2 = 0$

$y = -2$

Slope: $m = 0$

(a) $m = 0, \quad (-4, 1)$

$y = 1$

(b) m undefined (vertical line)

$x = -4$

63. The slope is 2 and $(-1, -1)$ lies on the line. Hence,

$$y - (-1) = 2(x - (-1))$$
$$y + 1 = 2(x + 1)$$
$$y = 2x + 1.$$

64. The slope is -2 and $(-1, 1)$ lies on the line. Hence,

$$y - 1 = -2(x - (-1))$$
$$y - 1 = -2(x + 1)$$
$$y = -2x - 1.$$

65. The slope of the given line is 2. Then l has slope $-\frac{1}{2}$. Hence,

$$y - 2 = -\tfrac{1}{2}(x - (-2))$$
$$y - 2 = -\tfrac{1}{2}(x + 2)$$
$$y = -\tfrac{1}{2}x + 1.$$

66. The slope of the given line is 3. Then l has slope $-\frac{1}{3}$. Hence,

$$y - 5 = -\tfrac{1}{3}(x - (-3))$$
$$y - 5 = -\tfrac{1}{3}(x + 3)$$
$$y = -\tfrac{1}{3}x + 4.$$

67. (a) $y = 2x$ (b) $y = -2x$ (c) $y = \frac{1}{2}x$

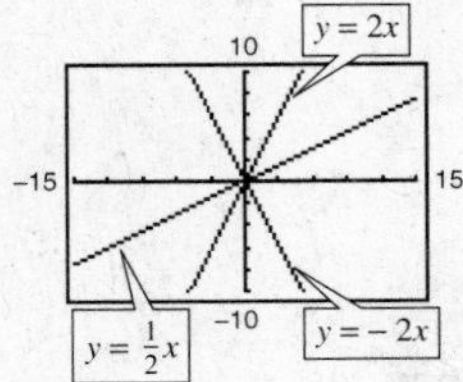

(b) and (c) are perpendicular.

68. L_1: $y = \frac{2}{3}x$; L_2: $y = -\frac{3}{2}x$; L_3: $y = \frac{2}{3}x + 2$

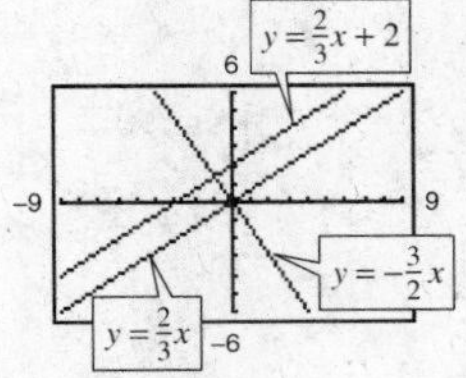

L_1 is parallel to L_3. L_2 is perpendicular to L_1 and L_3.

69. (a) $y = -\frac{1}{2}x$ (b) $y = -\frac{1}{2}x + 3$
(c) $y = 2x - 4$

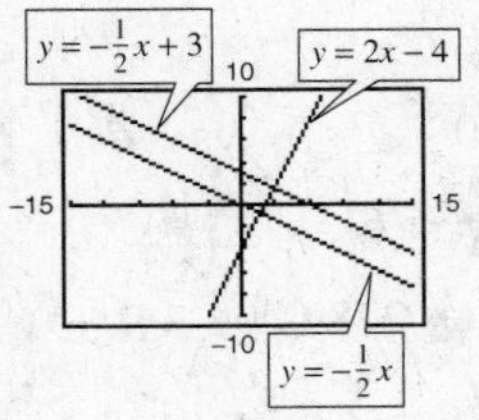

(a) and (b) are parallel.
(c) is perpendicular to (a) and (b).

70. L_1: $y = x - 8$; L_2: $y = x + 1$;
L_3: $y = -x + 3$

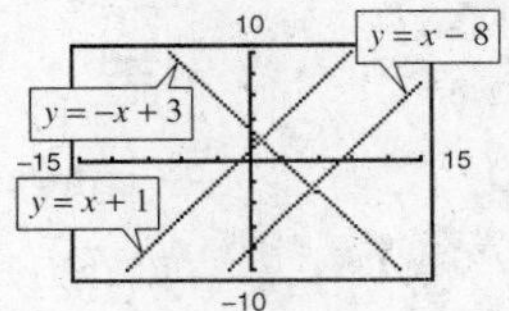

L_1 is parallel to L_2. L_3 is perpendicular to L_1 and L_2.

71. (a)

Years	*Slope*
1995–1996	$0.69 - 0.91 = -0.22$
1996–1997	$0.57 - 0.69 = -0.12$
1997–1998	$0.74 - 0.57 = 0.17$
1998–1999	$1.60 - 0.74 = 0.86$
1999–2000	$0.82 - 1.60 = -0.78$
2000–2001	$0.92 - 0.82 = 0.10$
2001–2002	$0.20 - 0.92 = -0.72$
2002–2003	$0.00 - 0.20 = -0.20$
2003–2004	$0.31 - 0.00 = 0.31$

Greatest increase: 1998–1999 (0.86)

Greatest decrease: 1999–2000 (−0.78)

(b) (5, 0.91), (14, 0.31):

$$y - 0.91 = \frac{0.31 - 0.91}{14 - 5}(x - 5)$$
$$y = -\frac{1}{15}(x - 5) + \frac{91}{100} = -\frac{1}{15}x + \frac{373}{300}$$
$$y \approx -0.07x + 1.24$$

(c) Between 1995 and 2004, the earnings per share decreased at the rate of 0.07 per year.

(d) For 2010, $x = 20$ and $y = -0.07(20) + 1.24 = -0.16$, which is reasonable.

72. (a)

Years	*Slope*
1995–1996	$13.1 - 13.2 = -0.1$
1996–1997	$13.2 - 13.1 = 0.1$
1997–1998	$12.6 - 13.2 = -0.6$
1998–1999	$12.9 - 12.6 = 0.3$
1999–2000	$14.4 - 12.9 = 1.5$
2000–2001	$14.1 - 14.4 = -0.3$
2001–2002	$13.9 - 14.1 = -0.2$
2002–2003	$15.1 - 13.9 = 1.2$
2003–2004	$18.4 - 15.1 = 3.3$

Greatest increase: 2003–2004 (3.3)

Smallest increase: 1996–1997 (0.1)

(b) (5, 13.2), (14, 18.4)

$$y - 13.2 = \frac{18.4 - 13.2}{14 - 5}(x - 5)$$

$$y = \frac{26}{45}x + \frac{464}{45}$$

$$y \approx 0.58x + 10.31$$

(c) Between 1995 and 2004, the sales (in billions of dollars) increased at the rate of 0.58 per year.

(d) For 2010, $x = 20$ and $y = 0.58(20) + 10.31 = 21.91$ (billion), which seems reasonable.

73. $\dfrac{\text{rise}}{\text{run}} = \dfrac{3}{4} = \dfrac{x}{\frac{1}{2}(32)}$

$$\frac{3}{4} = \frac{x}{16}$$

$$4x = 48$$

$$x = 12$$

The maximum height in the attic is 12 feet.

74. $\text{Slope} = \dfrac{\text{rise}}{\text{run}}$

$$\frac{-12}{100} = \frac{-2000}{x}$$

$$-12x = (-2000)(100)$$

$$x = 16{,}666\tfrac{2}{3}\text{ ft} \approx 3.16\text{ miles}$$

75. $(6, 2540)$, $m = 125$

$$V - 2540 = 125(t - 6)$$

$$V = 125t + 1790$$

76. $(6, 156)$, $m = 4.50$

$$V - 156 = 4.50(t - 6)$$

$$V = 4.50t + 129$$

77. $(6, 20{,}400)$, $m = -2000$

$$V - 20{,}400 = -2000(t - 6)$$

$$V = -2000t + 32{,}400$$

78. $(6, 245{,}000)$, $m = -5600$

$$V - 245{,}000 = -5600(t - 6)$$

$$V = -5600t + 278{,}600$$

79. The slope is $m = -10$. This represents the decrease in the amount of the loan each week. Matches graph (b).

80. The y-intercept is 12.5 and the slope is 1.5, which represents the increase in hourly wage per unit produced. Matches graph (c).

81. The slope is $m = 0.35$. This represents the increase in travel cost for each mile driven. Matches graph (a).

82. The y-intercept is 600 and the slope is -100, which represents the decrease in the value of the word processor each year. Matches graph (d).

83. (a) $(0, 25{,}000), (10, 2000)$

$$V - 25{,}000 = \frac{2000 - 25{,}000}{10 - 0}(t - 0)$$

$$V - 25{,}000 = -2300t$$

$$V = -2300t + 25{,}000$$

(b) 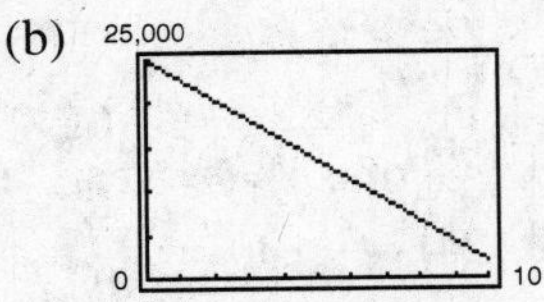

t	0	1	2	3	4	5	6	7	8	9	10
V	25,000	22,700	20,400	18,100	15,800	13,500	11,200	8900	6600	4300	2000

(c) $t = 0$: $V = -2300(0) + 25{,}000 = 25{,}000$

$t = 1$: $V = -2300(1) + 25{,}000 = 22{,}700$

etc.

84. (a) Using the points (0, 32) and (100, 212), we have

$$m = \frac{212 - 32}{100 - 0} = \frac{180}{100} = \frac{9}{5}$$

$$F - 32 = \frac{9}{5}(C - 0)$$

$$F = \frac{9}{5}C + 32.$$

(b) $F = \frac{9}{5}C + 32$

$F = 0°$: $0 = \frac{9}{5}C + 32$

$-32 = \frac{9}{5}C$

$-17.8 \approx C$

$C = 10°$: $F = \frac{9}{5}(10) + 32$

$F = 18 + 32$

$F = 50$

$F = 90°$: $90 = \frac{9}{5}C + 32$

$58 = \frac{9}{5}C$

$32.2 \approx C$

$C = -10°$: $F = \frac{9}{5}(-10) + 32$

$F = -18 + 32$

$F = 14$

$F = 68°$: $68 = \frac{9}{5}C + 32$

$36 = \frac{9}{5}C$

$20 = C$

$C = 177°$: $F = \frac{9}{5}(177) + 32$

$F = 318.6 + 32$

$F = 350.6$

C	−17.8°	−10°	10°	20°	32.2°	177°
F	0°	14°	50°	68°	90°	350.6°

85. (a) $C = 36{,}500 + 5.25t + 11.50t$

$= 16.75t + 36{,}500$

(b) $R = 27t$

(c) $P = R - C$

$= 27t - (16.75t + 36{,}500)$

$= 10.25t - 36{,}500$

(d) $0 = 10.25t - 36{,}500$

$36{,}500 = 10.25t$

$t \approx 3561$ hours

86. (a) (580, 50), (625, 47)

$$x - 50 = \frac{47 - 50}{625 - 580}(p - 580)$$

$$x - 50 = \frac{-1}{15}(p - 580)$$

$$x = \frac{-1}{15}p + \frac{266}{3}$$

(b)

100

0 1500

0

If $p = 655$, $x = 45$, units.

Algebraically, $x = -\frac{1}{15}(655) + \frac{266}{3} = 45.$

(c) If $p = 595$, $x = 49$ units.

Algebraically, $x = -\frac{1}{15}(595) + \frac{266}{3} = 49.$

87. (a) $\frac{80{,}124 - 75{,}349}{2005 - 1991} = \frac{4775}{14} \approx 341$ students per year

(b) 1984: $75{,}349 - 341(7) \approx 72{,}962$ students

1997: $75{,}349 + 341(6) \approx 77{,}395$ students

2000: $75{,}349 + 341(9) \approx 78{,}418$ students

(Answers could vary.)

(c) Let $t = 0$ represent 1990.

(1, 75,349), (15, 80,124)

$$y - 75{,}349 = \frac{80{,}124 - 75{,}349}{15 - 1}(t - 1)$$

$$y = \frac{4775}{14}(t - 1) + 75{,}349$$

$$y \approx 341t + 75{,}008$$

The slope 341 represents the annual increase in students. It is positive, indicating that Penn State University increased its students from 1991 to 2005.

88. Answers will vary. The slope is 341 which is equivalent to the rate of change.

89. False. The slopes are different:

$$\frac{4 - 2}{-1 + 8} = \frac{2}{7}$$

$$\frac{7 + 4}{-7 - 0} = -\frac{11}{7}$$

90. False.

The equation of the line joining $(10, -3)$ and $(2, -9)$ is

$$y + 3 = \frac{-9 + 3}{2 - 10}(x - 10)$$

$$y + 3 = \frac{3}{4}(x - 10)$$

$$y = \frac{3}{4}x - \frac{21}{2}.$$

For $x = -12$, $y = \frac{3}{4}(-12) - \frac{21}{2}$

$$= -19.5$$

$$\neq \frac{-37}{2}$$

$$= -18.5$$

91. $\frac{x}{5} + \frac{y}{-3} = 1$

$$-3x + 5y + 15 = 0$$

$a = 5$ and $b = -3$ are the x- and y-intercepts.

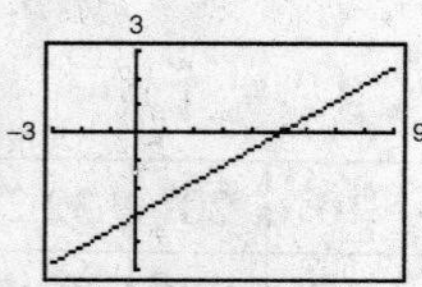

92. $\frac{x}{a} + \frac{y}{b} = 1$

$\frac{x}{-6} + \frac{y}{2} = 1$

$y = 2\left(1 + \frac{x}{6}\right)$

$y = \frac{x}{3} + 2$

a and b are the x- and y-intercepts.

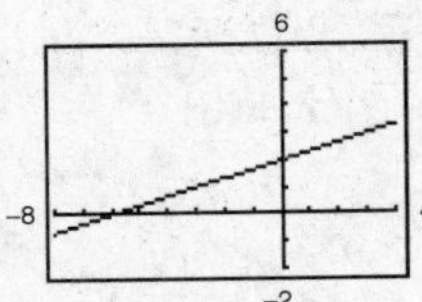

93. $\frac{x}{4} + \frac{y}{-\frac{2}{3}} = 1$

$-\frac{2}{3}x + 4y = \frac{-8}{3}$

$-2x + 12y = -8$

intercepts: $(4, 0), \left(0, -\frac{2}{3}\right)$

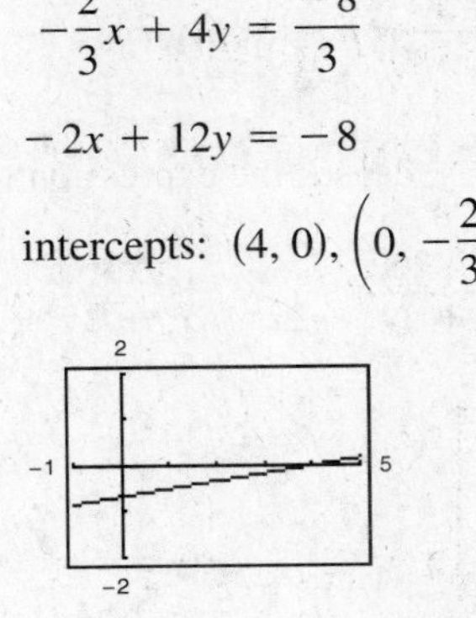

94. $\frac{x}{\frac{1}{2}} + \frac{y}{5} = 1$

$5x + \frac{1}{2}y = \frac{5}{2}$

$10x + y = 5$

Intercepts: $\left(\frac{1}{2}, 0\right), (0, 5)$

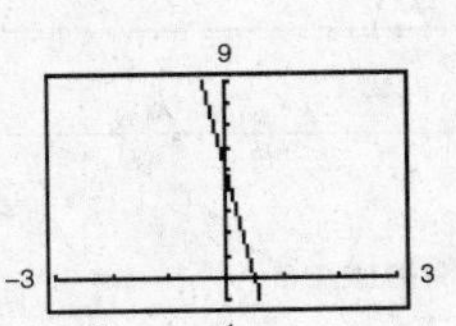

95. $\frac{x}{2} + \frac{y}{3} = 1$

$3x + 2y - 6 = 0$

96. $\frac{x}{a} + \frac{y}{b} = 1$

$\frac{x}{-5} + \frac{y}{-4} = 1$

$4x + 5y + 20 = 0$

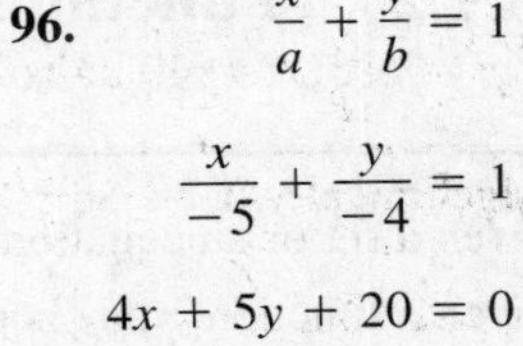

97. $\frac{x}{-1/6} + \frac{y}{-2/3} = 1$

$-6x - \frac{3}{2}y = 1$

$12x + 3y + 2 = 0$

98. $\frac{x}{a} + \frac{y}{b} = 1$

$\frac{x}{3/4} + \frac{y}{4/5} = 1$

$\frac{4}{5}x + \frac{3}{4}y = \frac{3}{5}$

$16x + 15y - 12 = 0$

99. The slope is positive and the y-intercept is positive. Matches (a).

100. The slope is negative and the y-intercept is negative. Matches (b).

101. Both lines have positive slope, but their y-intercepts differ in sign. Matches (c).

102. The lines intersect in the first quadrant at a point (x, y) where $x < y$. Matches (a).

103. No. The line $y = 2$ does not have an x-intercept.

104. No. $x = 1$ cannot be written in slope-intercept form because the slope is undefined.

105. Yes. Answers will vary.

106. Yes. Answers will vary.

107. Yes. $x + 20$

108. Yes. $3x - 10x^2 + 1 = -10x^2 + 3x + 1$

109. No. The term $x^{-1} = \frac{1}{x}$ causes the expression to not be a polynomial.

110. Yes. $2x^2 - 2x^4 - x^3 + 2 = -2x^4 - x^3 + 2x^2 + 2$

111. No. This expression is not defined for $x = \pm 3$.

112. No.

113. $x^2 - 6x - 27 = (x - 9)(x + 3)$

114. $x^2 - 11x + 28 = (x - 4)(x - 7)$

115. $2x^2 + 11x - 40 = (2x - 5)(x + 8)$

116. $3x^2 - 16x + 5 = (3x - 1)(x - 5)$

117. Answers will vary.

Section 1.2 Functions

- Given a set or an equation, you should be able to determine if it represents a function.
- Given a function, you should be able to do the following.
  (a) Find the domain.
  (b) Evaluate it at specific values.

Vocabulary Check

1. domain, range, function

2. independent, dependent

3. piecewise-defined

4. implied domain

5. difference quotient

1. Yes, it does represent a function. Each domain value is matched with only one range value.

2. No, it is not a function. The domain value of -1 is matched with two output values.

3. No, it does not represent a function. The domain values are each matched with three range values.

4. Yes, it does represent a function. Every domain value is matched with only one range value.

5. Yes, the relation represents y as a function of x. Each domain value is matched with only one range value.

6. No, the table does not represent a function. The input values of 0 and 1 are each matched with two different output values.

7. No, it does not represent a function. The input values of 10 and 7 are each matched with two output values.

8. Yes, the table does represent a function. Each input value is matched with only one output value.

9. (a) Each element of A is matched with exactly one element of B, so it does represent a function.

(b) The element 1 in A is matched with two elements, -2 and 1 of B, so it does not represent a function.

(c) Each element of A is matched with exactly one element of B, so it does represent a function.

(d) The element 2 of A is not matched to any element of B, so it does not represent a function.

10. (a) The element c in A is matched with two elements, 2 and 3 of B, so it is not a function.

(b) Each element of A is matched with exactly one element of B, so it does represent a function.

(c) This is not a function from A to B (it represents a function from B to A instead).

(d) Each element in A is matched with exactly one element of B, so it does represent a function.

11. Each are functions. For each year there corresponds one and only one circulation.

12. $f(2003) = 7.7$ million newspapers

13. $x^2 + y^2 = 4 \implies y = \pm\sqrt{4 - x^2}$

Thus, y *is not* a function of x. For instance, the values $y = 2$ and -2 both correspond to $x = 0$.

14. $x = y^2 + 1$

$y = \pm\sqrt{x - 1}$

This *is not* a function of x. For example, the values $y = 2$ and $y = -2$ both correspond to $x = 5$.

15. $y = \sqrt{x^2 - 1}$

This *is* a function of x.

16. $y = \sqrt{x + 5}$

This *is* a function of x.

17. $2x + 3y = 4 \implies y = \frac{1}{3}(4 - 2x)$

Thus, y *is* a function of x.

18. $x = -y + 5 \implies y = -x + 5.$

This *is* a function of x.

19. $y^2 = x^2 - 1 \implies y = \pm\sqrt{x^2 - 1}$

Thus, y *is not* a function of x. For instance, the values $y = \sqrt{3}$ and $-\sqrt{3}$ both correspond to $x = 2$.

20. $x + y^2 = 3 \implies y = \pm\sqrt{3 - x}$

Thus, y *is not* a function of x.

21. $y = |4 - x|$

This *is* a function of x.

22. $|y| = 4 - x \implies y = 4 - x$ or $y = -(4 - x)$

Thus, y *is not* a function of x.

23. $x = -7$ does not represent y as a function of x. All values of y correspond to $x = -7$.

24. $y = 8$ is a function of x, a constant function.

25. $f(x) = \dfrac{1}{x + 1}$

(a) $f(4) = \dfrac{1}{(4) + 1} = \dfrac{1}{5}$

(b) $f(0) = \dfrac{1}{(0) + 1} = 1$

(c) $f(4t) = \dfrac{1}{(4t) + 1} = \dfrac{1}{4t + 1}$

(d) $f(x + c) = \dfrac{1}{(x + c) + 1} = \dfrac{1}{x + c + 1}$

26. $g(x) = x^2 - 2x$

(a) $g(2) = (2)^2 - 2(2) = 0$

(b) $g(-3) = (-3)^2 - 2(-3) = 15$

(c) $g(t + 1) = (t + 1)^2 - 2(t + 1) = t^2 - 1$

(d) $g(x + c) = (x + c)^2 - 2(x + c)$

$= x^2 + 2cx + c^2 - 2x - 2c$

27. $f(t) = 3t + 1$

(a) $f(2) = 3(2) + 1 = 7$

(b) $f(-4) = 3(-4) + 1 = -11$

(c) $f(t + 2) = 3(t + 2) + 1 = 3t + 7$

28. $g(y) = 7 - 3y$

(a) $g(0) = 7 - 3(0) = 7$

(b) $g\left(\frac{7}{3}\right) = 7 - 3\left(\frac{7}{3}\right) = 0$

(c) $g(s + 2) = 7 - 3(s + 2)$

$= 7 - 3s - 6 = 1 - 3s$

29. $h(t) = t^2 - 2t$

(a) $h(2) = 2^2 - 2(2) = 0$

(b) $h(1.5) = (1.5)^2 - 2(1.5) = -0.75$

(c) $h(x + 2) = (x + 2)^2 - 2(x + 2) = x^2 + 2x$

30. $V(r) = \frac{4}{3}\pi r^3$

(a) $V(3) = \frac{4}{3}\pi(3)^3 = 36\pi$

(b) $V\left(\frac{3}{2}\right) = \frac{4}{3}\pi\left(\frac{3}{2}\right)^3 = \frac{4}{3} \cdot \frac{27}{8}\pi = \frac{9\pi}{2}$

(c) $V(2r) = \frac{4}{3}\pi(2r)^3 = \frac{32\pi r^3}{3}$

31. $f(y) = 3 - \sqrt{y}$

(a) $f(4) = 3 - \sqrt{4} = 1$

(b) $f(0.25) = 3 - \sqrt{0.25} = 2.5$

(c) $f(4x^2) = 3 - \sqrt{4x^2} = 3 - 2|x|$

32. $f(x) = \sqrt{x + 8} + 2$

(a) $f(-8) = \sqrt{(-8) + 8} + 2 = 2$

(b) $f(1) = \sqrt{(1) + 8} + 2 = 5$

(c) $f(x - 8) = \sqrt{(x - 8) + 8} + 2 = \sqrt{x} + 2$

33. $q(x) = \frac{1}{x^2 - 9}$

(a) $q(0) = \frac{1}{0^2 - 9} = -\frac{1}{9}$

(b) $q(3) = \frac{1}{3^2 - 9}$ is undefined.

(c) $q(y + 3) = \frac{1}{(y + 3)^2 - 9} = \frac{1}{y^2 + 6y}$

34. $q(t) = \frac{2t^2 + 3}{t^2}$

(a) $q(2) = \frac{2(2)^2 + 3}{(2)^2} = \frac{8 + 3}{4} = \frac{11}{4}$

(b) $q(0) = \frac{2(0)^2 + 3}{(0)^2}$ Division by zero is undefined.

(c) $q(-x) = \frac{2(-x)^2 + 3}{(-x)^2} = \frac{2x^2 + 3}{x^2}$

35. $f(x) = \frac{|x|}{x}$

(a) $f(3) = \frac{|3|}{3} = 1$

(b) $f(-3) = \frac{|-3|}{-3} = -1$

(c) $f(t) = \frac{|t|}{t} = \begin{cases} 1 & \text{if } t > 0 \\ -1 & \text{if } t < 0 \end{cases}$

$f(0)$ is undefined.

36. $f(x) = |x| + 4$

(a) $f(4) = |4| + 4 = 8$

(b) $f(-4) = |-4| + 4 = 4 + 4 = 8$

(c) $f(t) = |t| + 4$

37. $f(x) = \begin{cases} 2x + 1, & x < 0 \\ 2x + 2, & x \geq 0 \end{cases}$

(a) $f(-1) = 2(-1) + 1 = -1$

(b) $f(0) = 2(0) + 2 = 2$

(c) $f(2) = 2(2) + 2 = 6$

38. $f(x) = \begin{cases} 2x + 5, & x \le 0 \\ 2 - x^2, & x > 0 \end{cases}$

(a) $f(-2) = 2(-2) + 5 = 1$

(b) $f(0) = 2(0) + 5 = 5$

(c) $f(1) = 2 - 1^2 = 1$

39. $f(x) = \begin{cases} x^2 + 2, & x \le 1 \\ 2x^2 + 2, & x > 1 \end{cases}$

(a) $f(-2) = (-2)^2 + 2 = 6$

(b) $f(1) = (1)^2 + 2 = 3$

(c) $f(2) = 2(2)^2 + 2 = 10$

40. $f(x) = \begin{cases} x^2 - 4, & x \le 0 \\ 1 - 2x^2, & x > 0 \end{cases}$

(a) $f(-2) = (-2)^2 - 4 = 4 - 4 = 0$

(b) $f(0) = 0^2 - 4 = -4$

(c) $f(1) = 1 - 2(1^2) = 1 - 2 = -1$

41. $f(x) = \begin{cases} x + 2, & x < 0 \\ 4, & 0 \le x < 2 \\ x^2 + 1, & x \ge 2 \end{cases}$

(a) $f(-2) = (-2) + 2 = 0$

(b) $f(1) = 4$

(c) $f(4) = 4^2 + 1 = 17$

42. $f(x) = \begin{cases} 5 - 2x, & x < 0 \\ 5, & 0 \le x < 1 \\ 4x + 1, & x \ge 1 \end{cases}$

(a) $f(-2) = 5 - 2(-2) = 9$

(b) $f\left(\frac{1}{2}\right) = 5$

(c) $f(1) = 4(1) + 1 = 5$

43. $h(t) = \frac{1}{2}|t + 3|$

t	-5	-4	-3	-2	-1
$h(t)$	1	$\frac{1}{2}$	0	$\frac{1}{2}$	1

44. $f(s) = \dfrac{|s - 2|}{s - 2}$

$$f(0) = \frac{|0 - 2|}{0 - 2} = \frac{2}{-2} = -1$$

$$f(1) = \frac{|1 - 2|}{1 - 2} = \frac{1}{-1} = -1$$

$$f\left(\frac{3}{2}\right) = \frac{\left|\frac{3}{2} - 2\right|}{\frac{3}{2} - 2} = \frac{\frac{1}{2}}{-\frac{1}{2}} = -1$$

$$f\left(\frac{5}{2}\right) = \frac{\left|\frac{5}{2} - 2\right|}{\frac{5}{2} - 2} = \frac{\frac{1}{2}}{\frac{1}{2}} = 1$$

$$f(4) = \frac{|4 - 2|}{4 - 2} = \frac{2}{2} = 1$$

s	0	1	$\frac{3}{2}$	$\frac{5}{2}$	4
$f(s)$	-1	-1	-1	1	1

45. $f(x) = \begin{cases} -\frac{1}{2}x + 4, & x \le 0 \\ (x - 2)^2, & x > 0 \end{cases}$

x	-2	-1	0	1	2
$f(x)$	5	$\frac{9}{2}$	4	1	0

46. $h(x) = \begin{cases} 9 - x^2, & x < 3 \\ x - 3, & x \ge 3 \end{cases}$

$h(1) = 9 - (1)^2 = 8$

$h(2) = 9 - (2)^2 = 5$

$h(3) = (3) - 3 = 0$

$h(4) = (4) - 3 = 1$

$h(5) = (5) - 3 = 2$

x	1	2	3	4	5
$h(x)$	8	5	0	1	2

47. $f(x) = 15 - 3x = 0$

$3x = 15$

$x = 5$

48. $f(x) = 5x + 1 = 0$

$5x = -1$

$x = -\frac{1}{5}$

49. $f(x) = \dfrac{3x - 4}{5} = 0$

$3x - 4 = 0$

$3x = 4$

$x = \dfrac{4}{3}$

50. $f(x) = \dfrac{2x - 3}{7} = 0$

$2x - 3 = 0$

$2x = 3$

$x = \dfrac{3}{2}$

51. $f(x) = g(x)$

$x^2 = x + 2$

$x^2 - x - 2 = 0$

$(x + 1)(x - 2) = 0$

$x = -1$ or $x = 2$

52. $f(x) = g(x)$

$x^2 + 2x + 1 = 7x - 5$

$x^2 - 5x + 6 = 0$

$(x - 3)(x - 2) = 0$

$x = 3$ or $x = 2$

53. $f(x) = 5x^2 + 2x - 1$

Since $f(x)$ is a polynomial, the domain is all real numbers x.

54. $g(x) = 1 - 2x^2$

Because $g(x)$ is a polynomial, the domain is all real numbers x.

55. $h(t) = \dfrac{4}{t}$

Domain: All real numbers except $t = 0$

56. $s(y) = \dfrac{3y}{y + 5}$

$y + 5 \neq 0$

$y \neq -5$

The domain is all real numbers $y \neq -5$.

57. $f(x) = \sqrt[3]{x - 4}$

Domain: all real numbers

58. $f(x) = \sqrt[4]{x^2 + 3x}$. $x^2 + 3x = x(x + 3) \geq 0$

Domain: $x \leq -3$ or $x \geq 0$

59. $g(x) = \dfrac{1}{x} - \dfrac{3}{x + 2}$

Domain: All real numbers except

$x = 0,\ x = -2$

60. $h(x) = \dfrac{10}{x^2 - 2x}$

$x^2 - 2x \neq 0$

$x(x - 2) \neq 0$

The domain is all real numbers $x \neq 0$ and $x \neq 2$.

61. $g(y) = \dfrac{y + 2}{\sqrt{y - 10}}$

$y - 10 > 0$

$y > 10$

Domain: all $y > 10$.

62. $f(x) = \dfrac{\sqrt{x + 6}}{6 + x}$. $x + 6 \geq 0$ for numerator, and $x \neq -6$ for denominator. Domain: $x > -6$.

63. $f(x) = \sqrt{4 - x^2}$

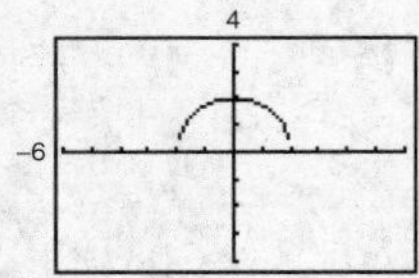

Domain: $[-2, 2]$

Range: $[0, 2]$

64. $f(x) = \sqrt{x^2 + 1}$

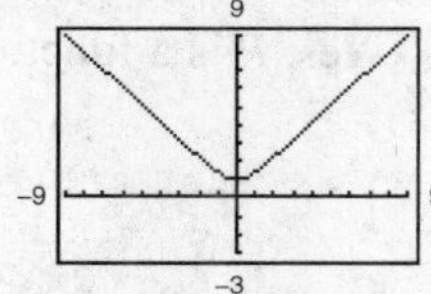

Domain: all real numbers

Range: $1 \le y$

65. $g(x) = |2x + 3|$

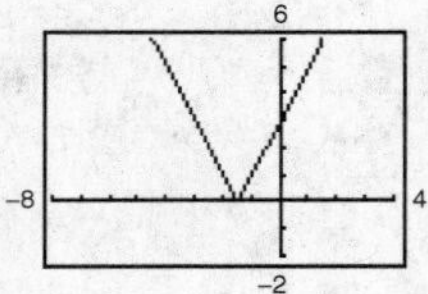

Domain: $(-\infty, \infty)$

Range: $[0, \infty)$

66. $g(x) = |x - 5|$

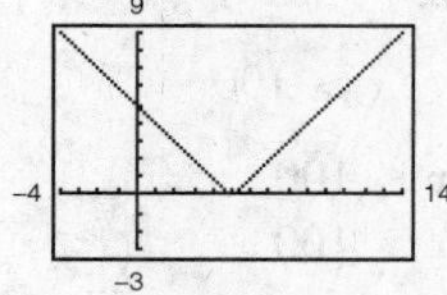

Domain: all real numbers

Range: $y \ge 0$

67. $f(x) = x^2$

$\{(-2, 4), (-1, 1), (0, 0), (1, 1), (2, 4)\}$

68. $f(x) = x^2 - 3$

$\{(-2, 1), (-1, -2), (0, -3), (1, -2), (2, 1)\}$

69. $f(x) = |x| + 2$

$\{(-2, 4), (-1, 3), (0, 2), (1, 3), (2, 4)\}$

70. $f(x) = |x + 1|$

$\{(-2, 1), (-1, 0), (0, 1), (1, 2), (2, 3)\}$

71. $A = \pi r^2, \quad C = 2\pi r$

$$r = \frac{C}{2\pi}$$

$$A = \pi\left(\frac{C}{2\pi}\right)^2 = \frac{C^2}{4\pi}$$

72. $A = \frac{1}{2}bh$, in an equilateral triangle $b = s$ and:

$$s^2 = h^2 + \left(\frac{s}{2}\right)^2$$

$$h = \sqrt{s^2 - \left(\frac{s}{2}\right)^2}$$

$$h = \sqrt{\frac{4s^2}{4} - \frac{s^2}{4}} = \frac{\sqrt{3}s}{2}$$

$$A = \frac{1}{2}s \cdot \frac{\sqrt{3}s}{2} = \frac{\sqrt{3}s^2}{4}$$

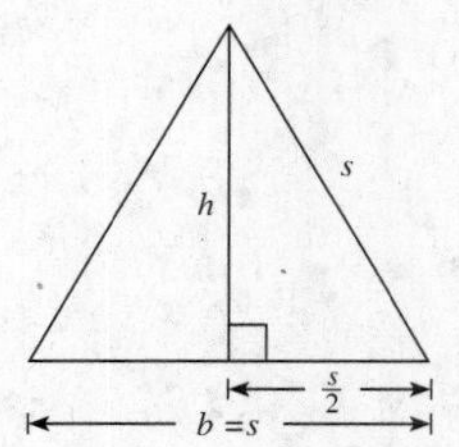

73. (a) According to the table, the maximum profit is 3375 for $x = 150$.

(b) Yes, P is a function of x.

(c) Profit = Revenue − Cost

$$= \text{(price per unit)(number of units)} - \text{(cost)(number of units)}$$

$$= [90 - (x - 100)(0.15)]x - 60x$$

$$= (105 - 0.15x)x - 60x$$

$$= 45x - 0.15x^2, \quad x > 100$$

$$P = \begin{cases} 30x, & x \le 100 \\ 45x - 0.15x^2, & x > 100 \end{cases}$$

74. (a) From the table, the maximum volume seems to be 1024, corresponding to $x = 4$.

(b)

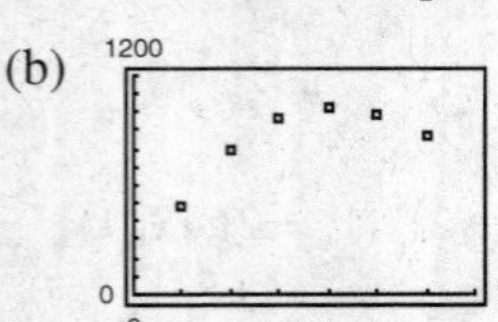

Yes, V is a function of x.

(c) $V = \text{length} \times \text{width} \times \text{height}$

$$= (24 - 2x)(24 - 2x)x$$

$$= x(24 - 2x)^2 = 4x(12 - x)^2$$

Domain: $0 < x < 12$

(d)

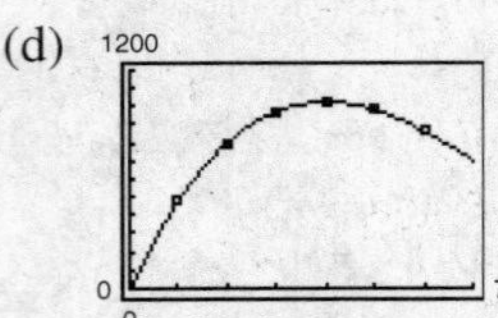

The function is a good fit. Answers will vary.

75. $A = \frac{1}{2}(\text{base})(\text{height}) = \frac{1}{2}xy.$

Since $(0, y)$, $(2, 1)$ and $(x, 0)$ all lie on the same line, the slopes between any pair of points are equal.

$$\frac{1 - y}{2 - 0} = \frac{1 - 0}{2 - x}$$

$$1 - y = \frac{2}{2 - x}$$

$$y = 1 - \frac{2}{2 - x} = \frac{x}{x - 2}$$

Therefore, $A = \frac{1}{2}xy = \frac{1}{2}x\left(\frac{x}{x - 2}\right) = \frac{x^2}{2x - 4}.$

The domain is $x > 2$, since $A > 0$.

76. $A = l \cdot w = (2x)y = 2xy$

But $y = \sqrt{36 - x^2}$, so $A = 2x\sqrt{36 - x^2}$, $0 < x < 6$.

77. (a) $V = (\text{length})(\text{width})(\text{height}) = yx^2$

But, $y + 4x = 108$, or $y = 108 - 4x$.

Thus, $V = (108 - 4x)x^2$.

Since $y = 108 - 4x > 0$

$$4x < 108$$

$$x < 27.$$

Domain: $0 < x < 27$

(b)

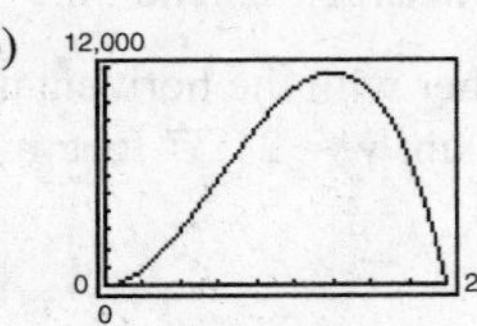

(c) The highest point on the graph occurs at $x = 18$. The dimensions that maximize the volume are $18 \times 18 \times 36$ inches.

78. (a) Cost = variable costs + fixed costs

$$C = 12.30x + 98{,}000$$

(b) Revenue = price per unit × number of units

$$R = 17.98x$$

(c) Profit = Revenue − Cost

$$P = 17.98x - (12.30x + 98{,}000)$$

$$P = 5.68x - 98{,}000$$

79. The domain of $-1.97x + 26.3$ is $7 \le x \le 12$.

The domain of $0.505x^2 - 1.47x + 6.3$ is $1 \le x \le 6$.

You can tell by comparing the models to the given data. The models fit the data well on the domains above.

80. $f(5) = 0.505(5^2) - 1.47(5) + 6.3 = 11.575$, which means \$11, 575 in monthly revenue.

81. $f(11) = -1.97(11) + 26.3 = 4.63$

\$4,630 in monthly revenue for November.

82. The values obtained from the model are a close fit for the actual data.

83. $n(t) = \begin{cases} -6.13t^2 + 75.8t + 577, & 0 \le t \le 6 \\ 24.9t + 672, & 6 < t \le 13 \end{cases}$

$t = 0$ corresponds to 1990.

t	0	1	2	3	4	5	6	7	8	9	10	11	12	13
Model	577	647	704	749	782	803	811	846	871	896	921	946	971	996

84. (a) $R = (\text{rate})(\text{number of people})$

$$= [8 - 0.05(n - 80)]n$$

$$= (12 - 0.05n)n = \frac{240n - n^2}{20}, \quad n \ge 80$$

(b)

n	90	100	110	120	130	140	150
$R(n)$	675	700	715	720	715	700	675

The revenue increases, and then decreases.

The maximum revenue occurs when $n = 120$.

(c)

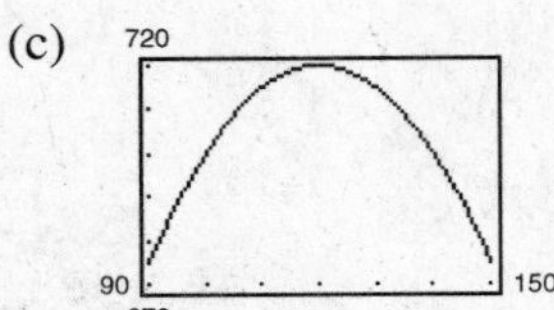

The maximum occurs at $n = 120$.

85. (a) $F(y) = 149.76\sqrt{10}y^{5/2}$

y	5	10	20	30	40
$F(y)$	2.65×10^4	1.50×10^5	8.47×10^5	2.33×10^6	4.79×10^6

(Answers will vary.)

F increases very rapidly as y increases.

(b)

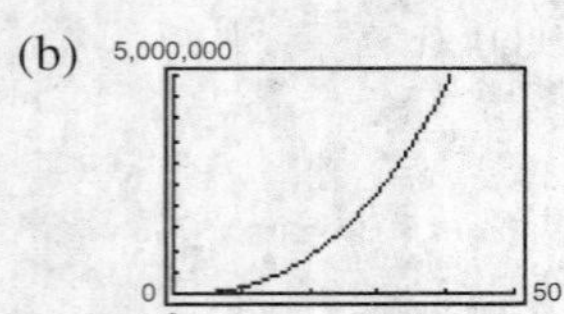

(c) From the table, $y \approx 22$ ft (slightly above 20). You could obtain a better approximation by completing the table for values of y between 20 and 30.

(d) By graphing $F(y)$ together with the horizontal line $y_2 = 1{,}000{,}000$, you obtain $y \approx 21.37$ feet.

86. (a) $f(2000) \approx 145.6$ billion dollars

(b) $\dfrac{f(2004) - f(1995)}{2004 - 1995} \approx \dfrac{221 - 72.2}{9} \approx 16.5$ billion dollars/year

This is the average yearly change from 1995 and 2004.

(c)

t	5	6	7	8	9	10	11	12	13	14
$P(t)$	72.4	81.6	94.1	109.1	126.1	144.6	163.9	183.5	202.7	221.0

The model approximates the data well.

(d)

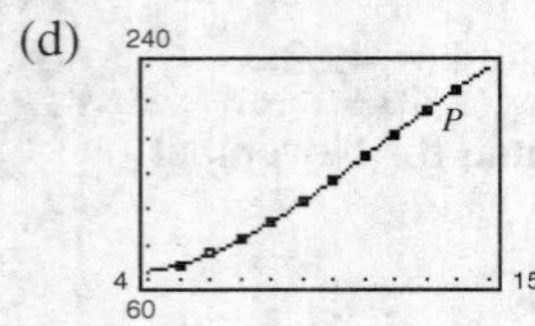

87.
$$f(x) = 2x$$
$$\frac{f(x + c) - f(x)}{c} = \frac{2(x + c) - 2x}{c} = \frac{2c}{c} = 2, \quad c \neq 0$$

88.
$$g(x) = 3x - 1$$
$$g(x + h) = 3(x + h) - 1 = 3x + 3h - 1$$
$$g(x + h) - g(x) = (3x + 3h - 1) - (3x - 1) = 3h$$
$$\frac{g(x + h) - g(x)}{h} = \frac{3h}{h} = 3, h \neq 0$$

89. $f(x) = x^2 - x + 1, \quad f(2) = 3$
$$\frac{f(2 + h) - f(2)}{h} = \frac{(2 + h)^2 - (2 + h) + 1 - 3}{h}$$
$$= \frac{4 + 4h + h^2 - 2 - h + 1 - 3}{h}$$
$$= \frac{h^2 + 3h}{h} = h + 3, \quad h \neq 0$$

90. $f(x) = x^3 + x$

$$f(x + h) = (x + h)^3 + (x + h) = x^3 + 3x^2h + 3xh^2 + h^3 + x + h$$

$$\begin{aligned} f(x + h) - f(x) &= (x^3 + 3x^2h + 3xh^2 + h^3 + x + h) - (x^3 + x) \\ &= 3x^2h + 3xh^2 + h^3 + h \\ &= h(3x^2 + 3xh + h^2 + 1) \end{aligned}$$

$$\frac{f(x + h) - f(x)}{h} = \frac{h(3x^2 + 3xh + h^2 + 1)}{h} = 3x^2 + 3xh + h^2 + 1, h \neq 0$$

91. $f(t) = \frac{1}{t}, \quad f(1) = 1$

$$\frac{f(t) - f(1)}{t - 1} = \frac{\frac{1}{t} - 1}{t - 1} = \frac{1 - t}{t(t - 1)} = \frac{-1}{t}, \quad t \neq 1$$

92. $f(x) = \frac{4}{x + 1}$

$$f(7) = \frac{4}{7 + 1} = \frac{1}{2}$$

$$\frac{f(x) - f(7)}{x - 7} = \frac{\frac{4}{x + 1} - \frac{1}{2}}{x - 7} = \frac{8 - (x + 1)}{2(x + 1)(x - 7)} = \frac{7 - x}{2(x + 1)(x - 7)} = \frac{-1}{2(x + 1)}, x \neq 7$$

93. False. The range of $f(x)$ is $[-1, \infty)$.

94. True. The first number in each ordered pair corresponds to exactly one second number.

95. $f(x) = \begin{cases} x + 4, & x \leq 0 \\ 4 - x^2, & x > 0 \end{cases}$

96. $f(x) = \begin{cases} 1 - x^2, & x \leq 0 \\ x + 1, & x > 0 \end{cases}$

97. $f(x) = \begin{cases} 2 - x, & x \leq -2 \\ 4, & -2 < x < 3 \\ x + 1, & x \geq 3 \end{cases}$

98. $f(x) = \begin{cases} x^2, & x \leq 1 \\ 1, & 1 < x < 4 \\ 5 - x, & x \geq 4 \end{cases}$

99. The domain is the set of inputs of the function and the range is the set of corresponding outputs.

100. An advantage of function notation is that it gives a name to the relationship so it can easily be referenced. When evaluating a function, you see both the input and output values.

101. $12 - \frac{4}{x + 2} = \frac{12(x + 2) - 4}{x + 2} = \frac{12x + 20}{x + 2}$

102.
$$\begin{aligned} \frac{3}{x^2 + x - 20} + \frac{x}{x^2 + 4x - 5} &= \frac{3}{(x + 5)(x - 4)} + \frac{x}{(x + 5)(x - 1)} \\ &= \frac{3(x - 1)}{(x + 5)(x - 4)(x - 1)} + \frac{x(x - 4)}{(x + 5)(x - 1)(x - 4)} \\ &= \frac{3x - 3 + x^2 - 4x}{(x + 5)(x - 4)(x - 1)} = \frac{x^2 - x - 3}{(x + 5)(x - 4)(x - 1)} \end{aligned}$$

103. $\dfrac{2x^3 + 11x^2 - 6x}{5x} \cdot \dfrac{x + 10}{2x^2 + 5x - 3} = \dfrac{x(2x^2 + 11x - 6)(x + 10)}{5x(2x - 1)(x + 3)}$

$$= \frac{(2x - 1)(x + 6)(x + 10)}{5(2x - 1)(x + 3)}$$

$$= \frac{(x + 6)(x + 10)}{5(x + 3)}, x \neq 0, \frac{1}{2}$$

104. $\dfrac{x + 7}{2(x - 9)} \div \dfrac{x - 7}{2(x - 9)} = \dfrac{x + 7}{2(x - 9)} \cdot \dfrac{2(x - 9)}{x - 7} = \dfrac{x + 7}{x - 7}, \quad x \neq 9$

Section 1.3 Graphs of Functions

- You should be able to determine the domain and range of a function from its graph.
- You should be able to use the vertical line test for functions.
- You should be able to determine when a function is constant, increasing, or decreasing.
- You should be able to find relative maximum and minimum values of a function.
- You should know that f is
  (a) Odd if $f(-x) = -f(x)$.
  (b) Even if $f(-x) = f(x)$.

Vocabulary Check

1. ordered pairs
2. Vertical Line Test
3. decreasing
4. minimum
5. greatest integer
6. even

---

1. Domain: All real numbers

Range: $(-\infty, 1]$

$f(0) = 1$

2. Domain: all real numbers, $(-\infty, \infty)$

Range: all real numbers, $(-\infty, \infty)$

$f(0) = 2$

3. Domain: $[-4, 4]$

Range: $[0, 4]$

$f(0) = 4$

4. Domain: all real numbers, $(-\infty, \infty)$

Range: $[-3, \infty)$

$f(0) = -3$

5. $f(x) = 2x^2 + 3$

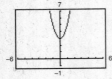

7

-6 6

-1

Domain: All real numbers

Range: $[3, \infty)$

6. $f(x) = -x^2 - 1$

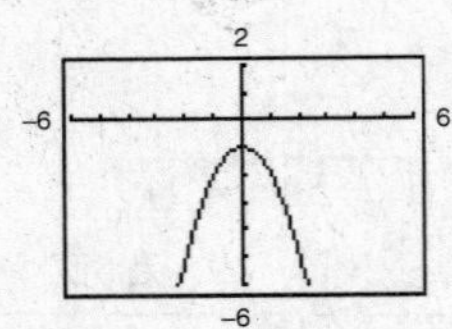
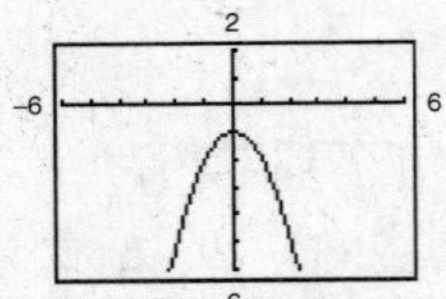

Domain: $(-\infty, \infty)$

Range: $(-\infty, -1]$

7. $f(x) = \sqrt{x - 1}$

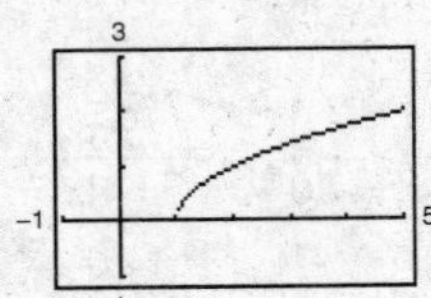

Domain: $x - 1 \geq 0 \Rightarrow x \geq 1$ or $[1, \infty)$

Range: $[0, \infty)$

8. $h(t) = \sqrt{4 - t^2}$

$4 - t^2 \geq 0 \Rightarrow t^2 \leq 4$

Domain: $[-2, 2]$

Range: $[0, 2]$

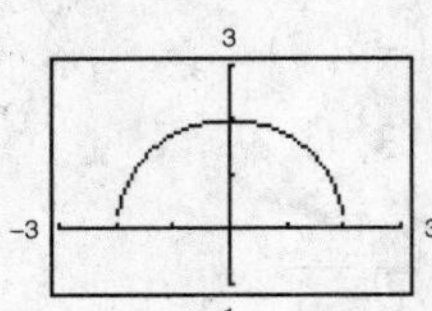

9. $f(x) = |x + 3|$

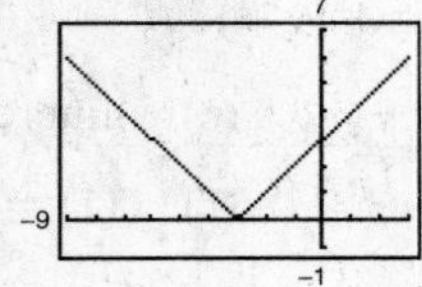

Domain: All real numbers

Range: $[0, \infty)$

10. $f(x) = -\frac{1}{4}|x - 5|$

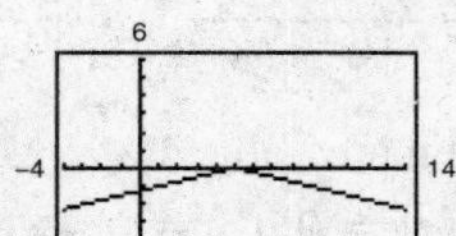

Domain: $(-\infty, \infty)$

Range: $(-\infty, 0]$

11. $f(x) = x^2 - x - 6$

(a) Domain: all real numbers

(b) $f(x) = x^2 - x - 6 = (x - 3)(x + 2) = 0 \quad \Rightarrow \quad x = 3, -2$

(c) These are the x-intercepts of f.

(d) $f(0) = -6$

(e) This is the y-intercept of f.

(f) $f(1) = 1^2 - 1 - 6 = -6$. The coordinates are $(1, -6)$

(g) $f(-1) = (-1)^2 - (-1) - 6 = -4$. The coordinates are $(-1, -4)$.

(h) $f(-3) = (-3)^2 - (-3) - 6 = 6$. $(-3, f(-3)) = (-3, 6)$.

12. $f(x) = x^3 - 4x$

(a) Domain: all real numbers

(b) $f(x) = x^3 - 4x = x(x^2 - 4) = x(x - 2)(x + 2) = 0 \quad \Rightarrow \quad x = 0, 2, -2$

(c) These are the x-intercepts of f.

(d) $f(0) = 0$

(e) This is the y-intercept (and x-intercept) of f.

(f) $f(1) = 1 - 4 = -3$. The coordinates are $(1, -3)$.

(g) $f(-1) = -1 - 4(-1) = 3$. The coordinates are $(-1, 3)$.

(h) $f(-3) = (-3)^3 - 4(-3) = -27 + 12 = -15$. $(-3, f(-3)) = (-3, -15)$.

13. $f(x) = |x - 1| - 2$

(a) Domain: all x

(b) $|x - 1| - 2 = 0 \quad \Rightarrow \quad |x - 1| = 2 \quad \Rightarrow \quad x = -1, 3$

(c) x-intercepts

(d) $f(0) = |0 - 1| - 2 = -1$

(e) y-intercept

(f) $f(1) = |1 - 1| - 2 = -2, \quad (1, -2)$

(g) $f(-1) = |-1 - 1| - 2 = 0, \quad (-1, 0)$

(h) $f(-3) = |-3 - 1| - 2 = 2, \quad (-3, 2)$

14. $f(x) = \begin{cases} x + 4, & x \le 0 \\ 4 - x^2, & x > 0 \end{cases}$

(a) Domain: all x

(b) $f(x) = 0$ if $x = -4$ or $x = 2$

(c) x-intercepts

(d) $f(0) = 0 + 4 = 4$

(e) y-intercept

(f) $f(1) = 4 - 1^2 = 3, \quad (1, 3)$

(g) $f(-1) = (-1) + 4 = 3, \quad (-1, 3)$

(h) $f(-3) = -3 + 4 = 1, \quad (-3, 1)$

15. $y = \frac{1}{2}x^2$

A vertical line intersects the graph just once, so y is a function of x. Graph $y_1 = \frac{1}{2}x^2$.

16. $x - y^2 = 1 \implies y = \pm\sqrt{x - 1}$

y is not a function of x. The vertical line $x = 2$ intersects the graph twice. Graph $y_1 = \sqrt{x - 1}$ and $y_2 = -\sqrt{x - 1}$.

17. $x^2 + y^2 = 25$

A vertical line intersects the graph more than once, so y is not a function of x. Graph the circle as

$y_1 = \sqrt{25 - x^2}$

$y_2 = -\sqrt{25 - x^2}$.

18. $x^2 = 2xy - 1$

A vertical line intersects the graph just once, so y is a function of x. Solve for y and graph

$$y = \frac{x^2 + 1}{2x}.$$

19. $f(x) = \dfrac{3}{2}x$

f is increasing on $(-\infty, \infty)$.

20. $f(x) = x^2 - 4x$

The graph is decreasing on $(-\infty, 2)$ and increasing on $(2, \infty)$.

21. $f(x) = x^3 - 3x^2 + 2$

f is increasing on $(-\infty, 0)$ and $(2, \infty)$.

f is decreasing on $(0, 2)$.

22. $f(x) = \sqrt{x^2 - 1}$

The graph is decreasing on $(-\infty, -1)$ and increasing on $(1, \infty)$.

23. $f(x) = 3$

(a)

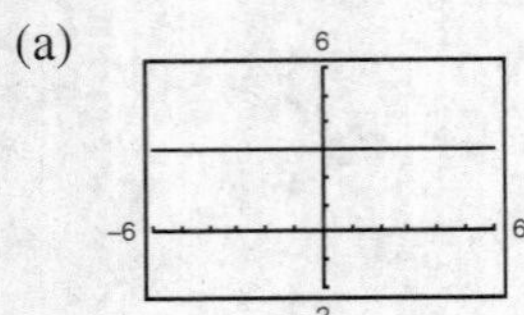

(b) f is constant on $(-\infty, \infty)$.

24. $f(x) = x$

(a)

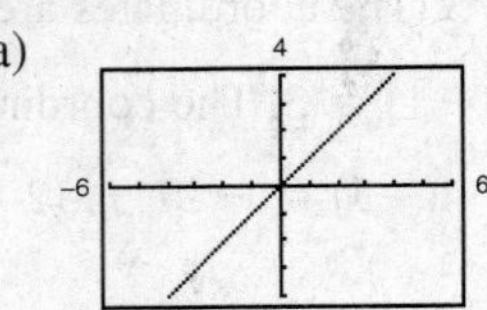

(b) The graph is increasing on $(-\infty, \infty)$.

25. $f(x) = x^{2/3}$

(a)

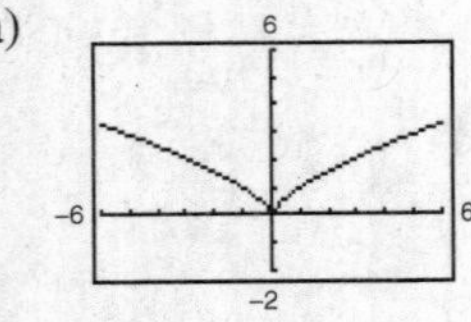

(b) Increasing on $(0, \infty)$

Decreasing on $(-\infty, 0)$

26. $f(x) = -x^{3/4}$

(a)

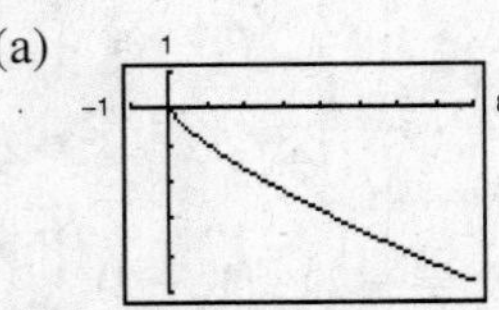

(b) The graph is decreasing on $(0, \infty)$.

27. $f(x) = x\sqrt{x + 3}$

(a)

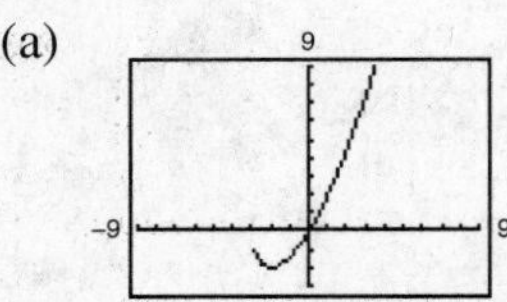

(b) Increasing on $(-2, \infty)$

Decreasing on $(-3, -2)$

28. $f(x) = \sqrt{1 - x}$

(a)

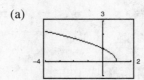

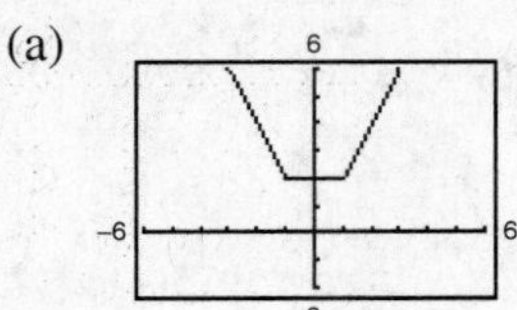

(b) f is decreasing on $(-\infty, 1)$.

29. $f(x) = |x + 1| + |x - 1|$

(a)

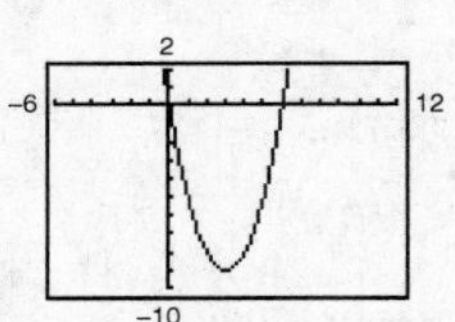

(b) Increasing on $(1, \infty)$, constant on $(-1, 1)$, decreasing on $(-\infty, -1)$

30. $f(x) = -|x + 4| - |x + 1|$

(a)

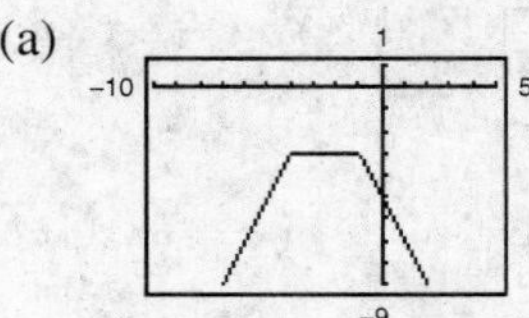

(b) The graph is increasing on $(-\infty, -4)$, constant on $(-4, -1)$, and decreasing on $(-1, \infty)$.

31. $f(x) = x^2 - 6x$

Relative minimum: $(3, -9)$

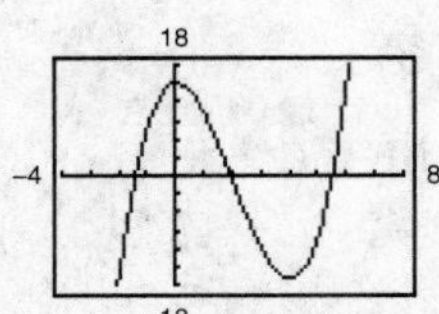

32. $f(x) = 3x^2 - 2x - 5$

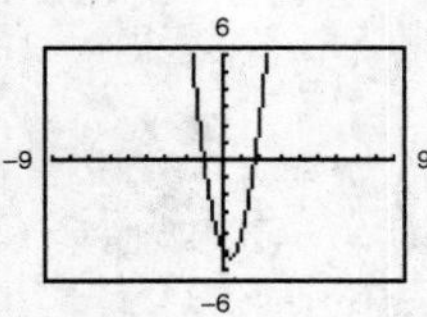

Relative minimum: $(0.33, -5.33)$

33. $y = 2x^3 + 3x^2 - 12x$

Relative minimum: $(1, -7)$

Relative maximum: $(-2, 20)$

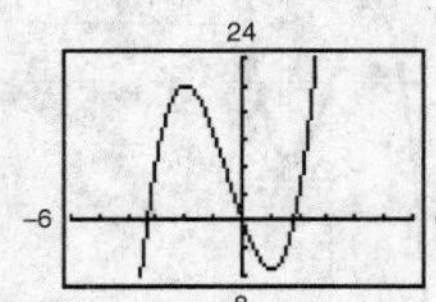

34. $y = x^3 - 6x^2 + 15$

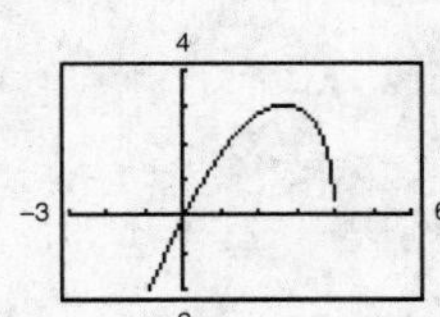

Relative minimum: $(4, -17)$

Relative maximum: $(0, 15)$

35. $h(x) = (x - 1)\sqrt{x}$

Relative minimum: $(0.33, -0.38)$

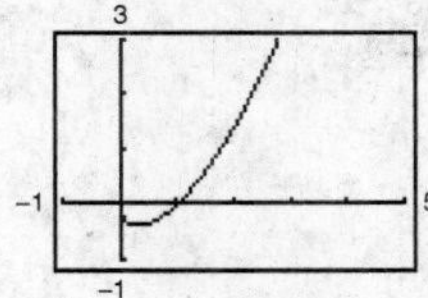

$(0, 0)$ is not a relative maximum because it occurs at the endpoint of the domain $[0, \infty)$.

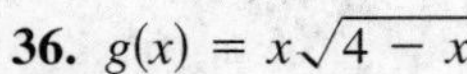

36. $g(x) = x\sqrt{4 - x}$

Maximum: $(2.67, 3.08)$

37. $f(x) = x^2 - 4x - 5$

(a)

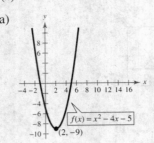

Minimum: $(2, -9)$

(b) 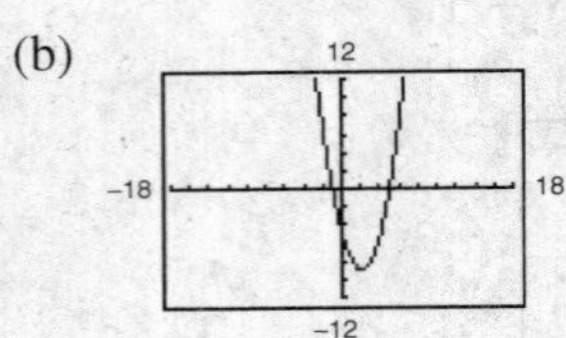

Minimum: $(2, -9)$

(c) Answers are the same.

38. $f(x) = 3x^2 - 12x$

(a)

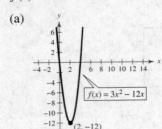

Relative minimum: $(2, -12)$

(b) Relative minimum: $(2, -12)$

(c) Answers are the same.

39. $f(x) = x^3 - 3x$

(a) 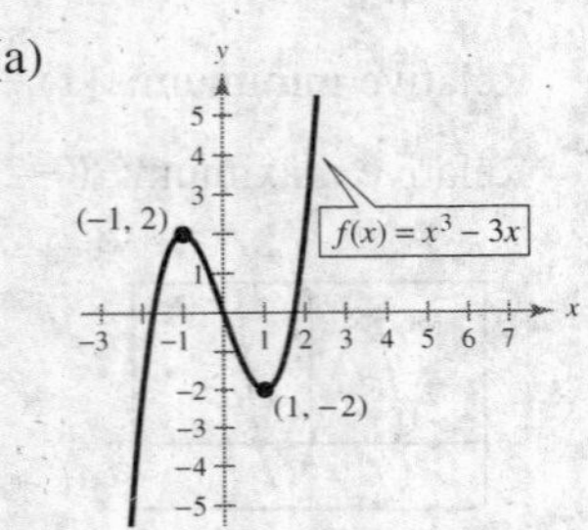

Relative maximum: $(-1, 2)$

Relative minimum: $(1, -2)$

(b) Relative maximum: $(-1, 2)$

Relative minimum: $(1, -2)$

(c) Answers are the same.

40. $f(x) = -x^3 + 3x^2$

(a) 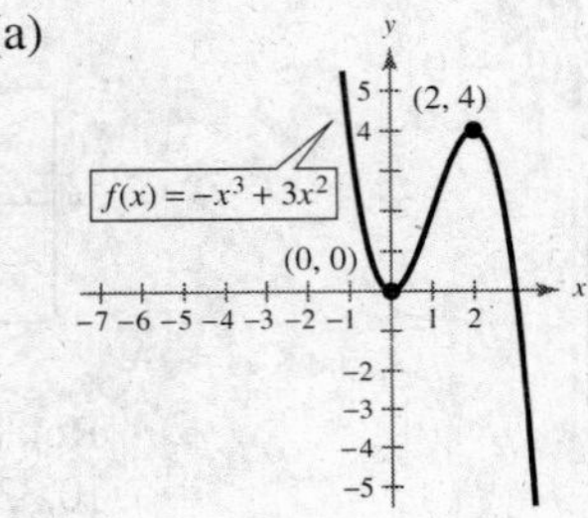

Relative maximum: $(2, 4)$

Relative minimum: $(0, 0)$

(b) Relative maximum: $(2, 4)$

Relative minimum: $(0, 0)$

(c) Answers are the same.

41. $f(x) = 3x^2 - 6x + 1$

(a) 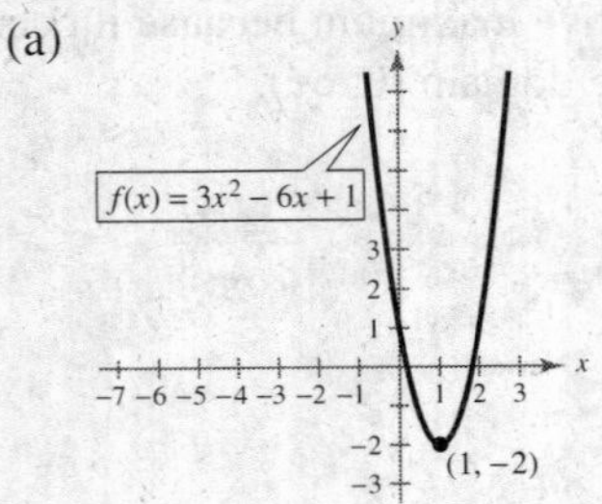

Relative minimum: $(1, -2)$

(b) Relative minimum: $(1, -2)$

(c) Answers are the same.

42. $f(x) = 8x - 4x^2$

(a) 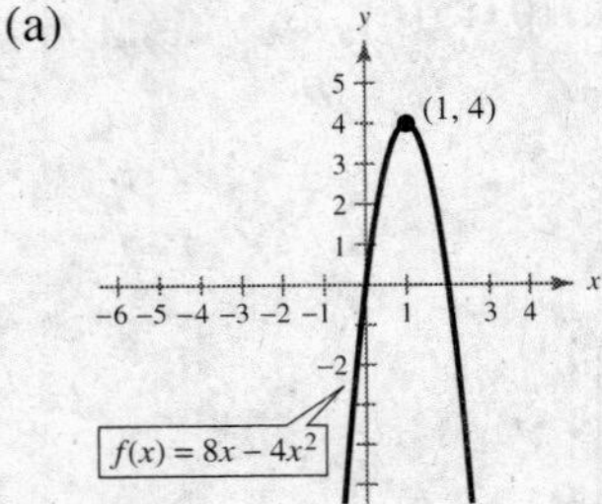

Relative maximum: $(1, 4)$

(b) Relative maximum: $(1, 4)$

(c) Answers are the same.

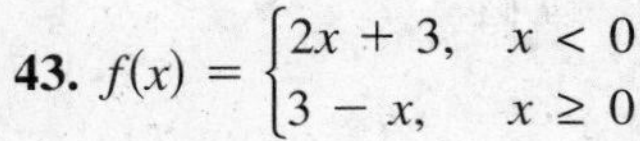

43. $f(x) = \begin{cases} 2x + 3, & x < 0 \\ 3 - x, & x \geq 0 \end{cases}$

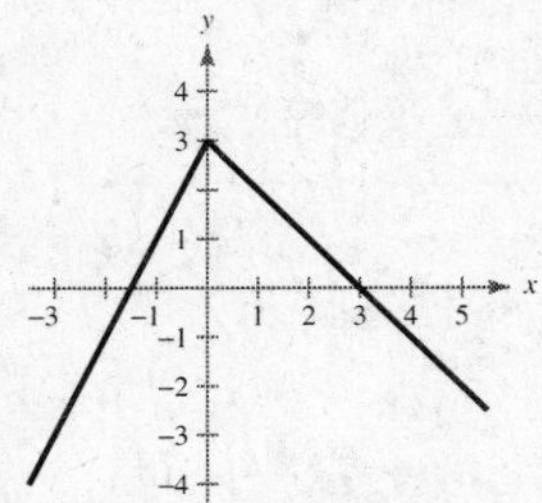

44. $f(x) = \begin{cases} x + 6, & x \leq -4 \\ 2x - 4, & x > -4 \end{cases}$

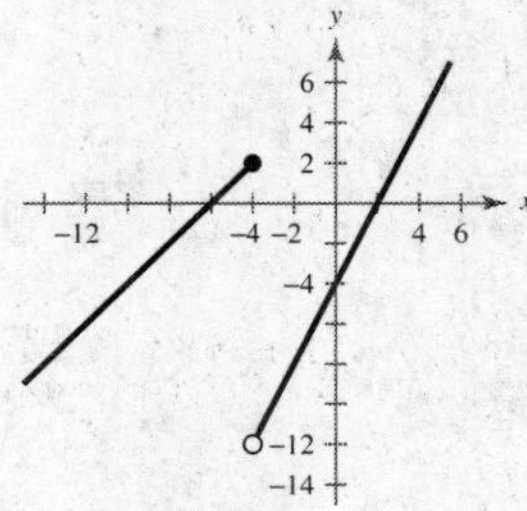

45. $f(x) = \begin{cases} \sqrt{x + 4}, & x < 0 \\ \sqrt{4 - x}, & x \geq 0 \end{cases}$

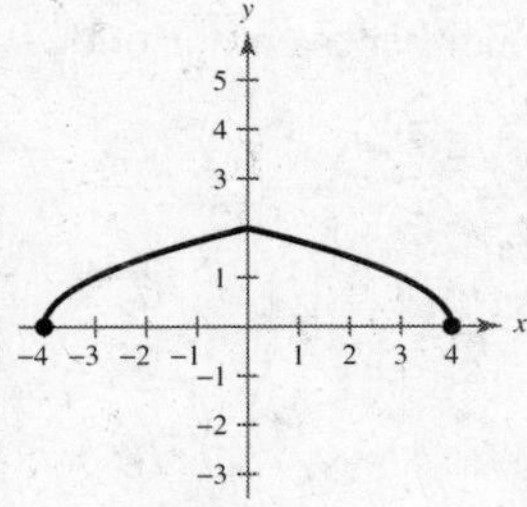

46. $f(x) = \begin{cases} 1 - (x - 1)^2, & x \leq 2 \\ \sqrt{x - 2}, & x > 2 \end{cases}$

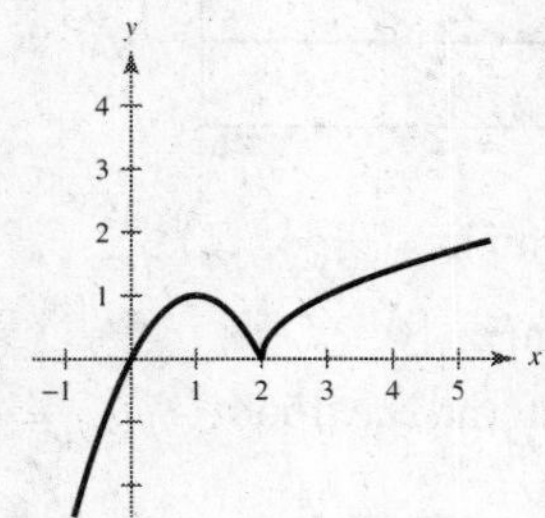

47. $f(x) = \begin{cases} x + 3, & x \leq 0 \\ 3, & 0 < x \leq 2 \\ 2x - 1, & x > 2 \end{cases}$

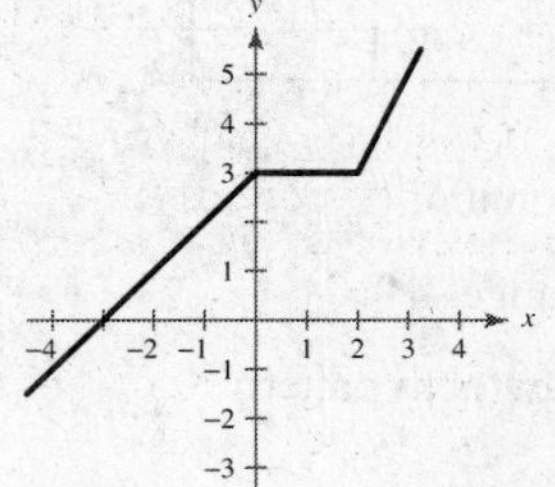

48. $g(x) = \begin{cases} x + 5, & x \leq -3 \\ -2, & -3 < x < 1 \\ 5x - 4, & x \geq 1 \end{cases}$

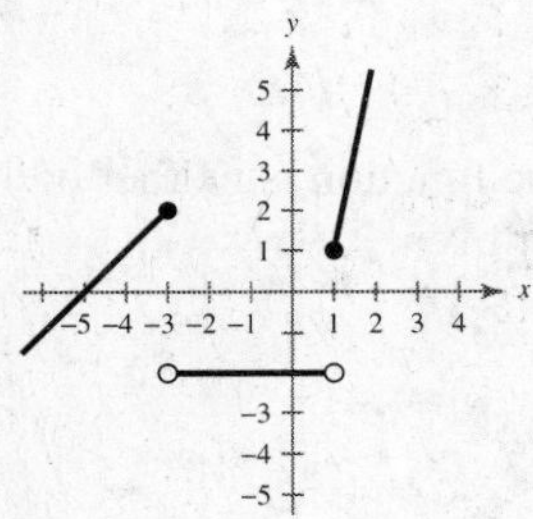

49. $f(x) = \begin{cases} 2x + 1, & x \leq -1 \\ x^2 - 2, & x > -1 \end{cases}$

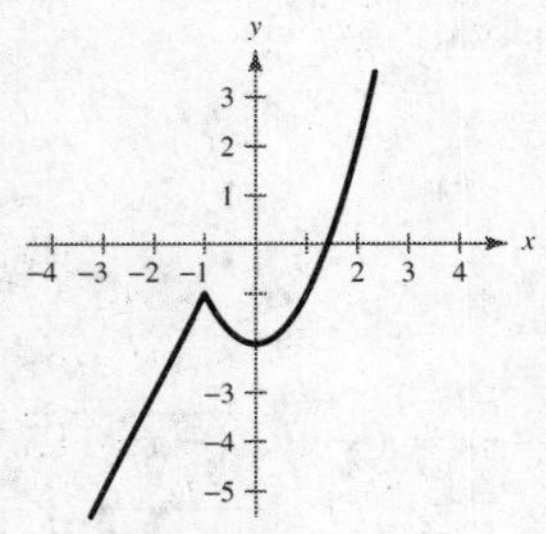

50. $h(x) = \begin{cases} 3 + x, & x < 0 \\ x^2 + 1, & x \geq 0 \end{cases}$

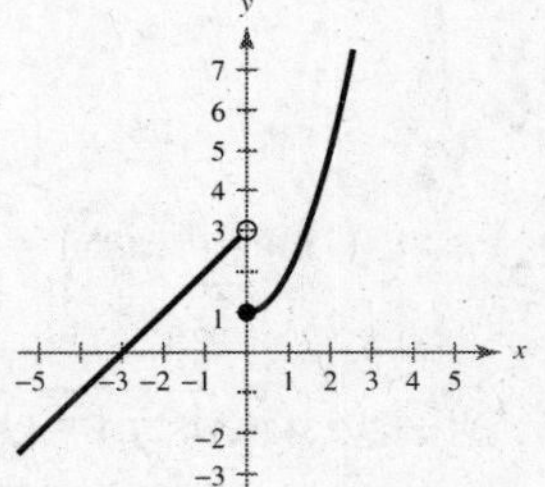

51. $f(x) = [\![x]\!] + 2$

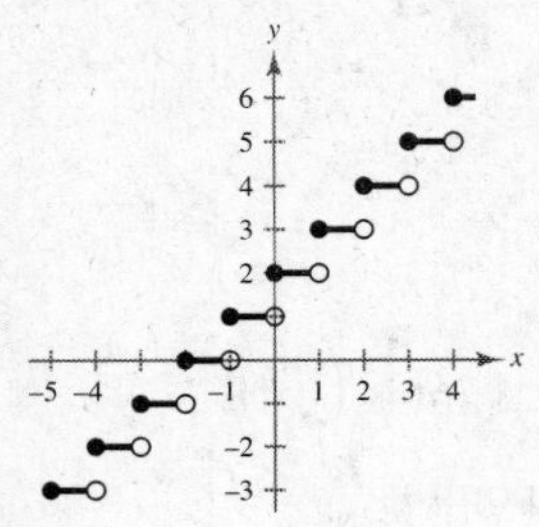

52. $f(x) = [\![x]\!] - 3$

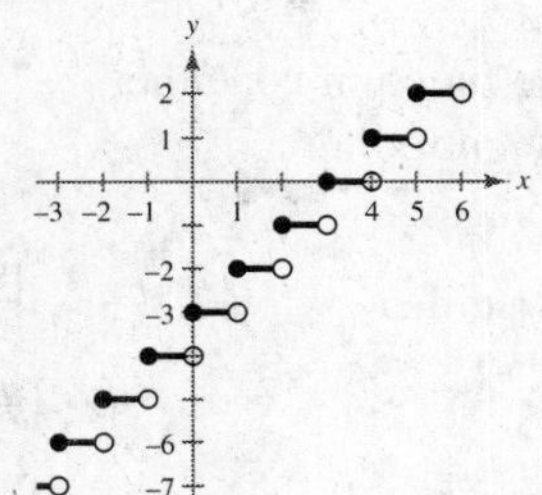

53. $f(x) = [\![x - 1]\!] + 2$

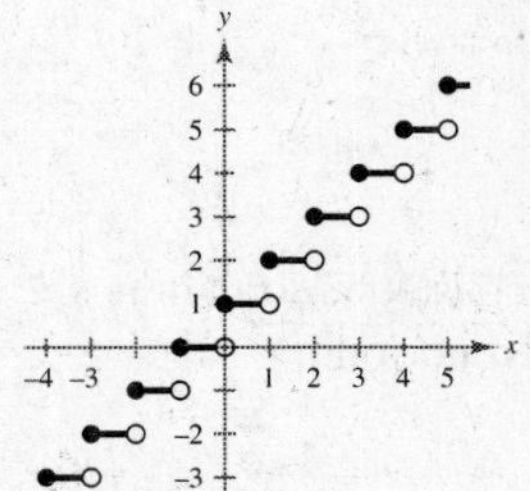

54. $f(x) = [\![x - 2]\!] + 1$

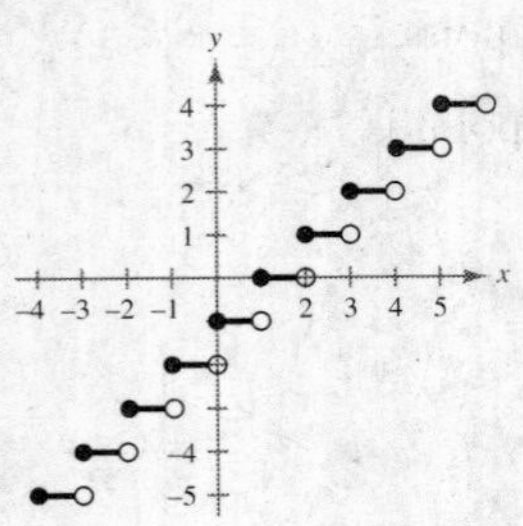

55. $f(x) = [\![2x]\!]$

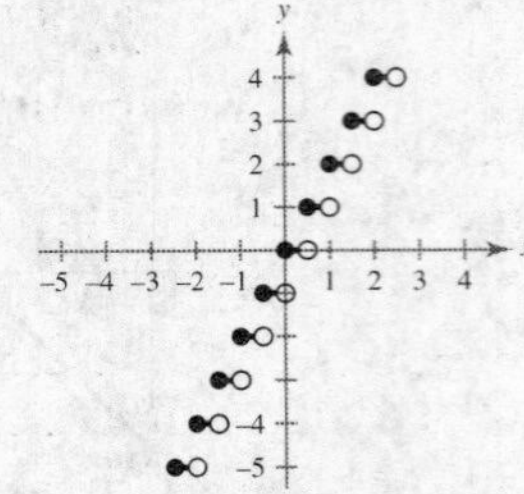

56. $f(x) = [\![4x]\!]$

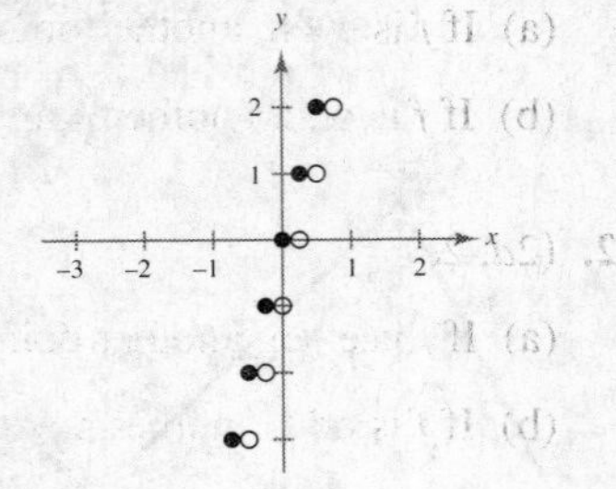

57. $s(x) = 2\left(\frac{1}{4}x - [\![\frac{1}{4}x]\!]\right)$

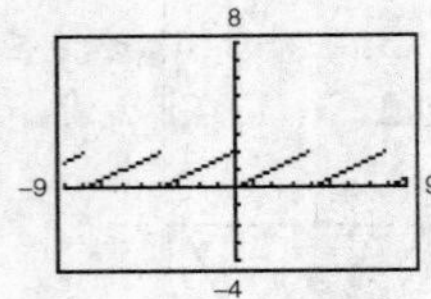

Domain: $(-\infty, \infty)$

Range: $[0, 2)$

Sawtooth pattern

58. $g(x) = 2\left(\frac{1}{4}x - [\![\frac{1}{4}x]\!]\right)^2$

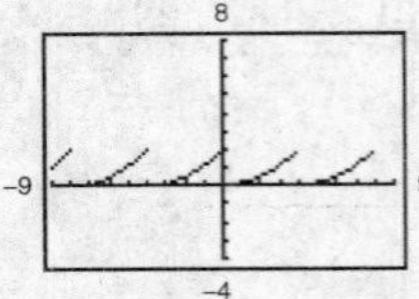

Domain: $(-\infty, \infty)$

Range: $[0, 2)$

Pattern: Sawtooth

59. $f(-t) = (-t)^2 + 2(-t) - 3$

$= t^2 - 2t - 3$

$\neq f(t) \neq -f(t)$

f is neither even nor odd.

60. $f(-x) = (-x)^6 - 2(-x)^2 + 3$

$= x^6 - 2x^2 + 3 = f(x).$

f is even.

61. $g(-x) = (-x)^3 - 5(-x)$

$= -x^3 + 5x$

$= -g(x)$

g is odd.

62. $h(x) = x^3 - 5$

$h(-x) = (-x)^3 - 5$

$= -x^3 - 5$

$\neq h(x)$

$\neq -h(x)$

The function is neither odd nor even.

63. $f(-x) = (-x)\sqrt{1 - (-x)^2}$

$= -x\sqrt{1 - x^2}$

$= -f(x)$

The function is odd.

64. $f(-x) = (-x)\sqrt{(-x) + 5}$

$= -x\sqrt{-x + 5}$

$\neq f(x)$

$\neq -f(x)$

The function is neither even nor odd.

65. $g(-s) = 4(-s)^{2/3}$

$= 4s^{2/3}$

$= g(s)$

The function is even.

66. Because the domain is $s \geq 0$, the function is neither even nor odd.

67. $\left(-\frac{3}{2}, 4\right)$

(a) If f is even, another point is $\left(\frac{3}{2}, 4\right)$.

(b) If f is odd, another point is $\left(\frac{3}{2}, -4\right)$.

68. $\left(-\frac{5}{3}, -7\right)$

(a) If f is even, another point is $\left(\frac{5}{3}, -7\right)$.

(b) If f is odd, another point is $\left(\frac{5}{3}, 7\right)$.

69. $(4, 9)$

(a) If f is even, another point is $(-4, 9)$.

(b) If f is odd, another point is $(-4, -9)$.

70. $(5, -1)$

(a) If f is even, another point is $(-5, -1)$.

(b) If f is odd, another point is $(-5, 1)$.

71. $(x, -y)$

(a) If f is even, another point is $(-x, -y)$.

(b) If f is odd, another point is $(-x, y)$.

72. $(2a, 2c)$

(a) If f is even, another point is $(-2a, 2c)$.

(b) If f is odd, another point is $(-2a, -2c)$.

73. $f(x) = 5$, even

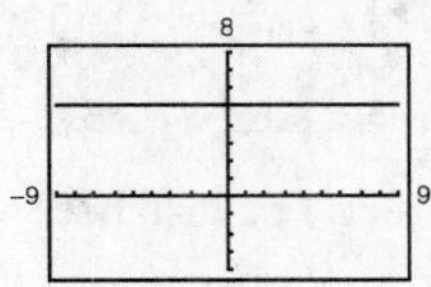

74. $f(x) = -9$

f is even.

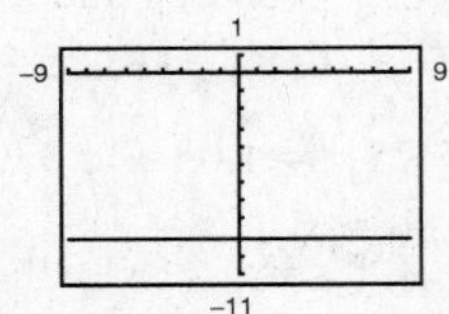

75. $f(x) = 3x - 2$ is neither even nor odd.

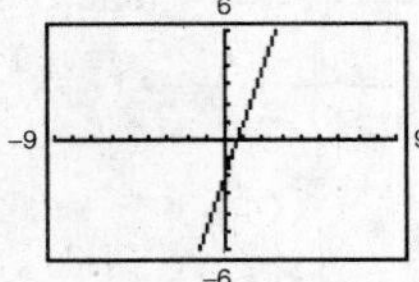

76. $f(x) = 5 - 3x$ is neither even nor odd.

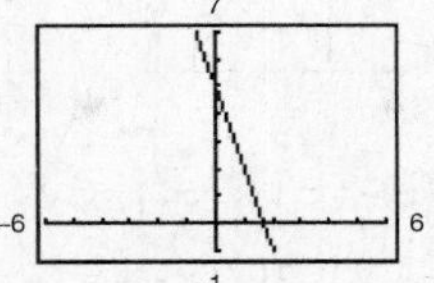

77. $h(x) = x^2 - 4$, even

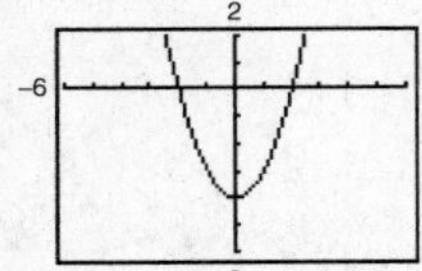

78. $f(x) = -x^2 - 8$ is even.

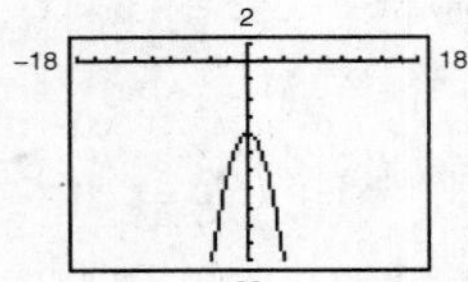

79. $f(x) = \sqrt{1 - x}$ is neither even nor odd.

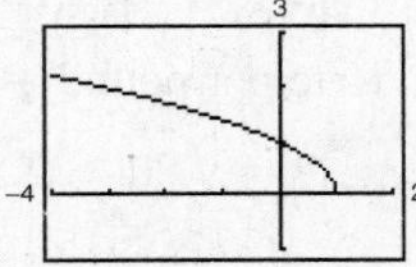

80. $g(t) = \sqrt[3]{t - 1}$ is neither even nor odd.

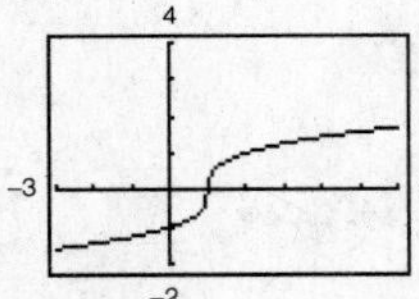

81. $f(x) = |x + 2|$ is neither even nor odd.

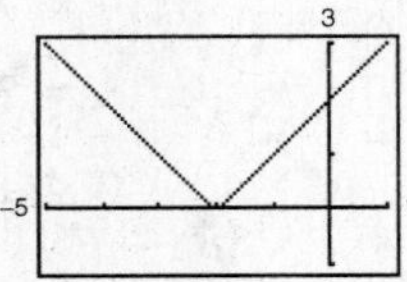

82. $f(x) = -|x - 5|$ is neither even nor odd.

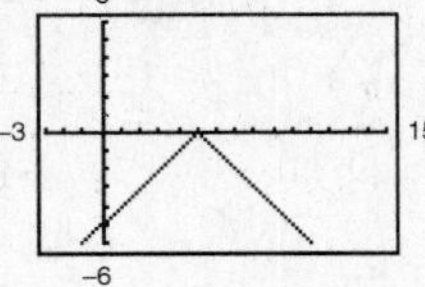

83. $f(x) = 4 - x \geq 0$

$4 \geq x$

$(-\infty, 4]$

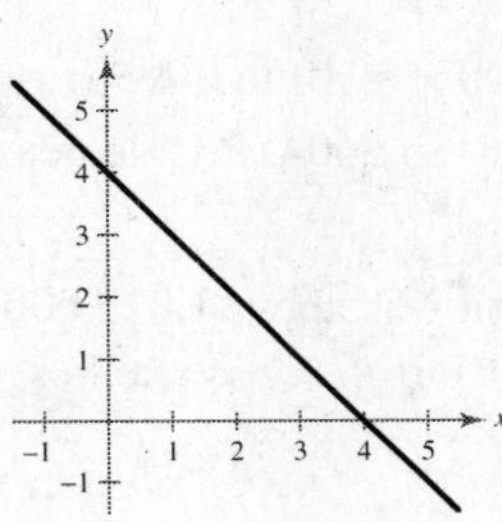

84. $f(x) = 4x + 2$

$f(x) \geq 0$

$4x + 2 \geq 0$

$4x \geq -2$

$x \geq -\frac{1}{2}$

$\left[-\frac{1}{2}, \infty\right)$

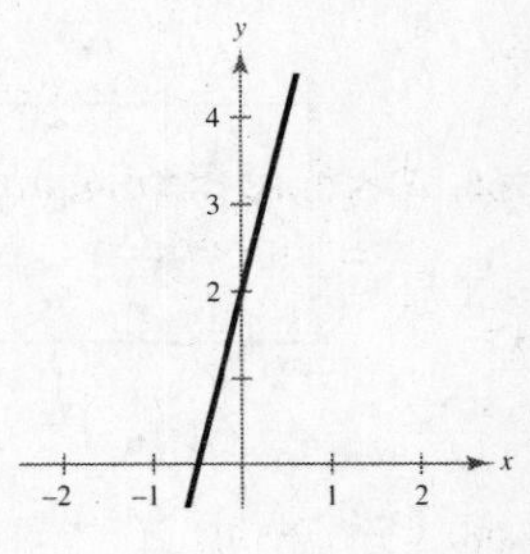

85. 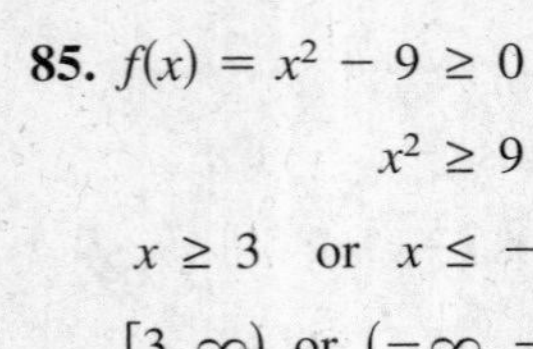
$f(x) = x^2 - 9 \geq 0$

$x^2 \geq 9$

$x \geq 3$ or $x \leq -3$

$[3, \infty)$ or $(-\infty, -3]$

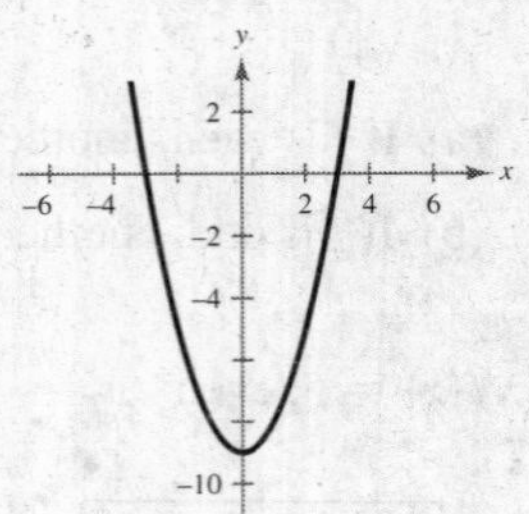

86. $f(x) = x^2 - 4x$

$f(x) \geq 0$

$x^2 - 4x \geq 0$

$x(x - 4) \geq 0$

$(-\infty, 0], [4, \infty)$

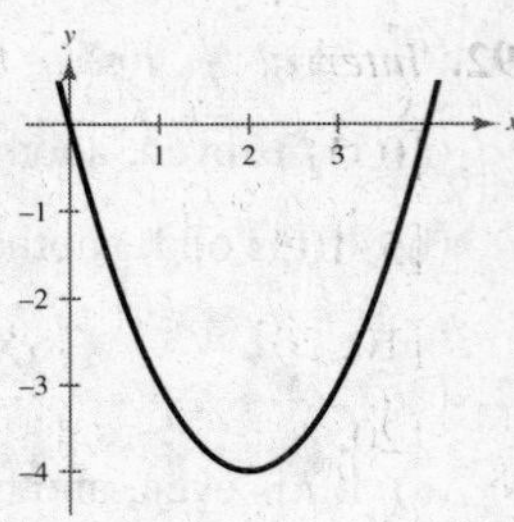

87. (a) The second model is correct. For instance,

$$C_2\left(\tfrac{1}{2}\right) = 1.05 - 0.38[[-(\tfrac{1}{2} - 1)]]$$

$$= 1.05 - 0.38[[\tfrac{1}{2}]] = 1.05.$$

(b) 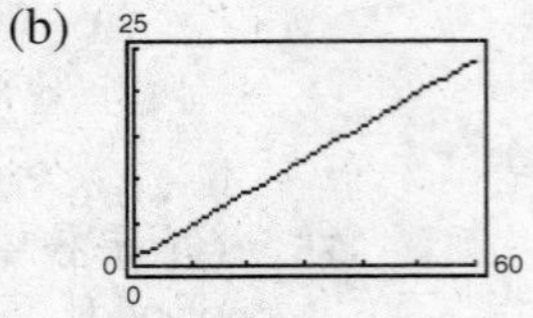

The cost of an 18-minute 45-second call is

$$C_2\left(18\tfrac{45}{60}\right) = C_2(18.75) = 1.05 - 0.38[[-(18.75 - 1)]]$$

$$= 1.05 - 0.38[[-17.75]] = 1.05 - 0.38(-18)$$

$$= 1.05 + 0.38(18) = \$7.89.$$

88. *Model*: (Total cost) = (Flat rate) + (Rate per pound)

Labels: Total cost $= C$

Flat rate $= 9.80$

Rate per pound $= 2.50[\![x]\!],\ x > 0$

Equation: $C = 9.80 + 2.50[\![x]\!],\ x > 0$

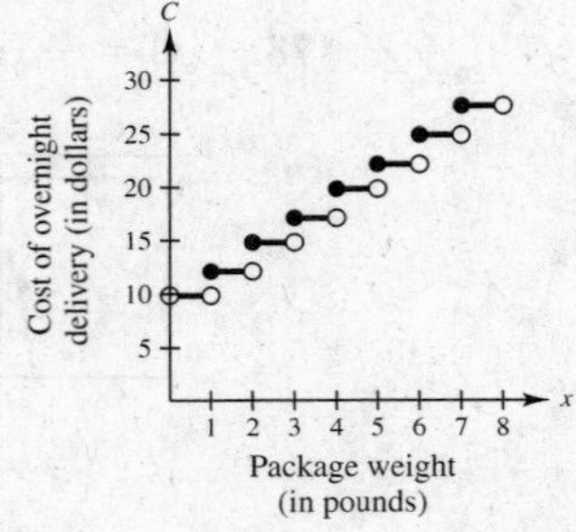

89. $h = \text{top} - \text{bottom}$

$= (-x^2 + 4x - 1) - 2$

$= -x^2 + 4x - 3,\ 1 \leq x \leq 3$

90. $h = \text{top} - \text{bottom}$

$= 3 - (4x - x^2)$

$= 3 - 4x + x^2,$

$0 \leq x \leq 1$

91. $P(t) = 0.0108t^4 - 0.211t^3 + 0.40t^2 + 7.9t + 1791$

$0 \leq t \leq 14$

(a) 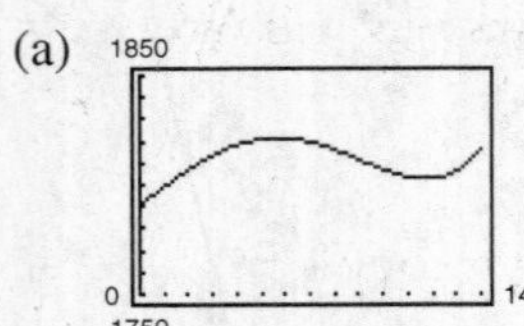

(b) P is increasing from 1990 ($t = 0$) to 1995 ($t \approx 5.7$), and from 2001 ($t \approx 11.8$) to 2004. P is decreasing from 1995 to 2001.

(c) The maximum population was about 1,821,000 in 1995 ($t \approx 5.7$).

92.

Interval	*Intake Pipe*	*Drainpipe 1*	*Drainpipe 2*
[0, 5]	Open	Closed	Closed
[5, 10]	Open	Open	Closed
[10, 20]	Closed	Closed	Closed
[20, 30]	Closed	Closed	Open
[30, 40]	Open	Open	Open
[40, 45]	Open	Closed	Open
[45, 50]	Open	Open	Open
[50, 60]	Open	Open	Closed

93. False. The domain of $f(x) = \sqrt{x^2}$ is the set of all real numbers.

94. False. The domain must be symmetric about the y-axis.

95. c **96.** d **97.** b **98.** e **99.** a **100.** f

101.
$$f(x) = a_{2n+1}x^{2n+1} + a_{2n-1}x^{2n-1} + \cdots + a_3x^3 + a_1x$$
$$f(-x) = a_{2n+1}(-x)^{2n+1} + a_{2n-1}(-x)^{2n-1} + \cdots + a_3(-x)^3 + a_1(-x)$$
$$= -a_{2n+1}x^{2n+1} - a_{2n-1}x^{2n-1} - \cdots - a_3x^3 - a_1x = -f(x)$$

Therefore, $f(x)$ is odd.

102.
$$f(x) = a_{2n}x^{2n} + a_{2n-2}x^{2n-2} + \cdots + a_2x^2 + a_0$$
$$f(-x) = a_{2n}(-x)^{2n} + a_{2n-2}(-x)^{2n-2} + \cdots + a_2(-x)^2 + a_0$$
$$= a_{2n}x^{2n} + a_{2n-2}x^{2n-2} + \cdots + a_2x^2 + a_0 = f(x)$$

$f(-x) = f(x)$; thus, $f(x)$ is even.

103. f is an even function.

(a) $g(x) = -f(x)$ is even because $g(-x) = -f(-x) = -f(x) = g(x)$.

(b) $g(x) = f(-x)$ is even because $g(-x) = f(-(-x)) = f(x) = f(-x) = g(x)$.

(c) $g(x) = f(x) - 2$ is even because $g(-x) = f(-x) - 2 = f(x) - 2 = g(x)$.

(d) $g(x) = -f(x - 2)$ is neither even nor odd because $g(-x) = -f(-x - 2) = -f(x + 2) \neq g(x)$ nor $-g(x)$.

104. Yes, $x = y^2 + 1$ defines x as a function of y. (But not y as a function of x)

105. No, $x^2 + y^2 = 25$ does not represent x as a function of y. For instance, $(-3, 4)$ and $(3, 4)$ both lie on the graph.

106. Answers will vary.

107. $-2x^2 + 8x$

Terms: $-2x^2, 8x$

Coefficients: $-2, 8$

108. Terms: $3x$, 10

Coefficient: 3

109. $\frac{x}{3} - 5x^2 + x^3$

Terms: $\frac{x}{3}, -5x^2, x^3$

Coefficients: $\frac{1}{3}, -5, 1$

110. Terms: $7x^4$, $\sqrt{2}x^2$

Coefficient: 7, $\sqrt{2}$

111. (a) $d = \sqrt{(6-(-2))^2 + (3-7)^2}$

$= \sqrt{64+16} = \sqrt{80} = 4\sqrt{5}$

(b) midpoint $= \left(\frac{-2+6}{2}, \frac{7+3}{2}\right) = (2, 5)$

112. (a) $d = \sqrt{(-5-3)^2 + (0-6)^2} = \sqrt{64+36} = \sqrt{100} = 10$

(b) midpoint $= \left(\frac{-5+3}{2}, \frac{0+6}{2}\right) = (-1, 3)$

113. (a) $d = \sqrt{\left(-\frac{3}{2} - \frac{5}{2}\right)^2 + (4-(-1))^2} = \sqrt{16+25} = \sqrt{41}$

(b) midpoint $= \left(\frac{\frac{5}{2} - \frac{3}{2}}{2}, \frac{-1+4}{2}\right) = \left(\frac{1}{2}, \frac{3}{2}\right)$

114. (a) $d = \sqrt{\left(-6 - \frac{3}{4}\right)^2 + \left(\frac{2}{3} - \frac{1}{6}\right)^2} = \sqrt{\left(\frac{-27}{4}\right)^2 + \left(\frac{1}{2}\right)^2} = \frac{\sqrt{733}}{4}$

(b) midpoint $= \left(\frac{-6+\frac{3}{4}}{2}, \frac{\frac{2}{3}+\frac{1}{6}}{2}\right) = \left(\frac{-21}{8}, \frac{5}{12}\right)$

115. $f(x) = 5x - 1$

(a) $f(6) = 5(6) - 1 = 29$

(b) $f(-1) = 5(-1) - 1 = -6$

(c) $f(x-3) = 5(x-3) - 1 = 5x - 16$

116. $f(x) = -x^2 - x + 3$

(a) $f(4) = -(4)^2 - 4 + 3 = -17$

(b) $f(-2) = -(-2)^2 - (-2) + 3 = 1$

(c) $f(x-2) = -(x-2)^2 - (x-2) + 3$

$= -(x^2 - 4x + 4) - x + 2 + 3$

$= -x^2 + 3x + 1$

117. $f(x) = x\sqrt{x-3}$

(a) $f(3) = 3\sqrt{3-3} = 0$

(b) $f(12) = 12\sqrt{12-3}$

$= 12\sqrt{9} = 12(3) = 36$

(c) $f(6) = 6\sqrt{6-3} = 6\sqrt{3}$

118. $f(x) = -\frac{1}{2}x|x+1|$

(a) $f(-4) = -\frac{1}{2}(-4)|-4+1| = 2(3) = 6$

(b) $f(10) = -\frac{1}{2}(10)|10+1| = -5(11) = -55$

(c) $f\left(-\frac{2}{3}\right) = -\frac{1}{2}\left(-\frac{2}{3}\right)\left|-\frac{2}{3}+1\right| = \frac{1}{3}\left(\frac{1}{3}\right) = \frac{1}{9}$

119. $f(x) = x^2 - 2x + 9$

$f(3+h) = (3+h)^2 - 2(3+h) + 9 = 9 + 6h + h^2 - 6 - 2h + 9$

$= h^2 + 4h + 12$

$f(3) = 3^2 - 2(3) + 9 = 12$

$\frac{f(3+h) - f(3)}{h} = \frac{(h^2 + 4h + 12) - 12}{h} = \frac{h(h+4)}{h} = h + 4, h \neq 0$

120. $f(x) = 5 + 6x - x^2$

$$f(6 + h) = 5 + 6(6 + h) - (6 + h)^2 = 5 + 36 + 6h - (36 + 12h + h^2) = -h^2 - 6h + 5$$

$$f(6) = 5 + 6(6) - 6^2 = 5$$

$$\frac{f(h + 6) - f(6)}{h} = \frac{(-h^2 - 6h + 5) - 5}{h} = \frac{h(-h - 6)}{h} = -h - 6, h \neq 0$$

Section 1.4 Shifting, Reflecting, and Stretching Graphs

- You should know the graphs of the most commonly used functions in algebra, and be able to reproduce them on your graphing utility.
  - (a) Constant function: $f(x) = c$
  - (b) Identity function: $f(x) = x$
  - (c) Absolute value function: $f(x) = |x|$
  - (d) Square root function: $f(x) = \sqrt{x}$
  - (e) Squaring function: $f(x) = x^2$
  - (f) Cubing function: $f(x) = x^3$
- You should know how the graph of a function is changed by vertical and horizontal shifts.
- You should know how the graph of a function is changed by reflection.
- You should know how the graph of a function is changed by nonrigid transformations, like stretches and shrinks.
- You should know how the graph of a function is changed by a sequence of transformations.

Vocabulary Check

1. quadratic function **2.** absolute value function **3.** rigid transformations

4. $-f(x), f(-x)$ **5.** $c > 1, 0 < c < 1$ **6.** (a) ii (b) iv (c) iii (d) i

1.

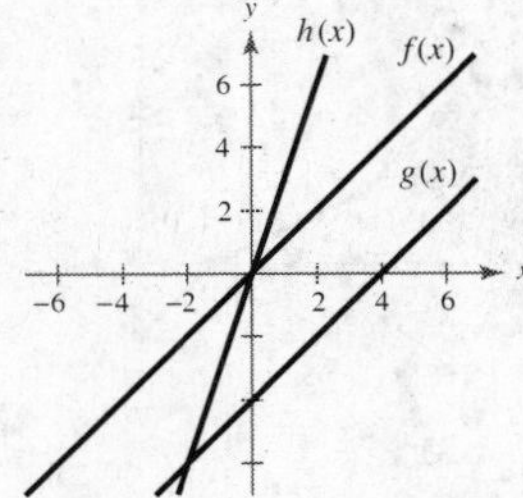

2.

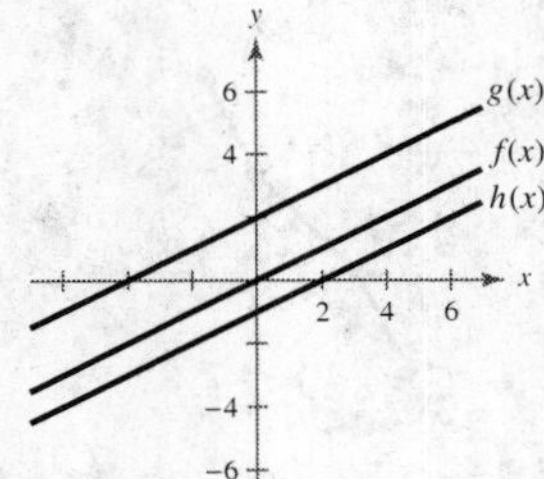

3.

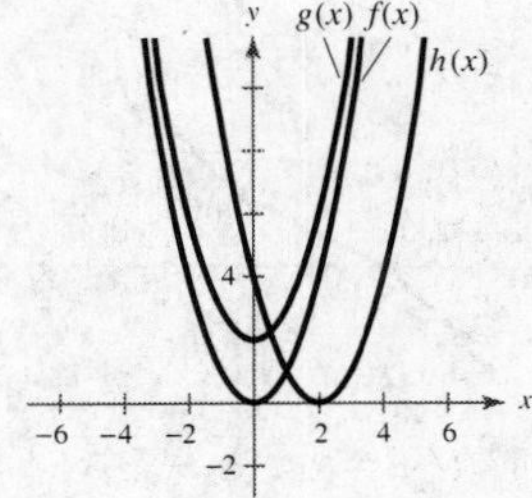

4.

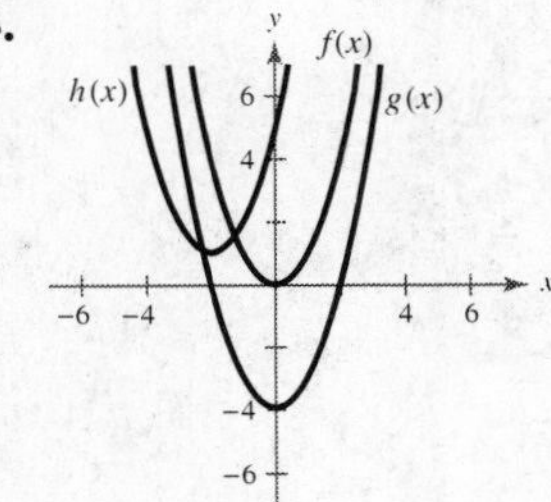

5.

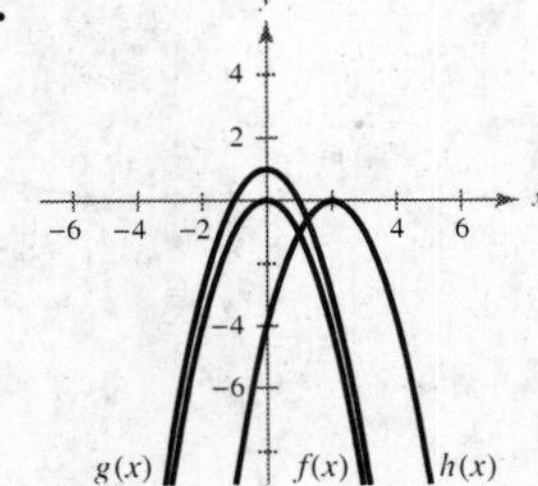

6.

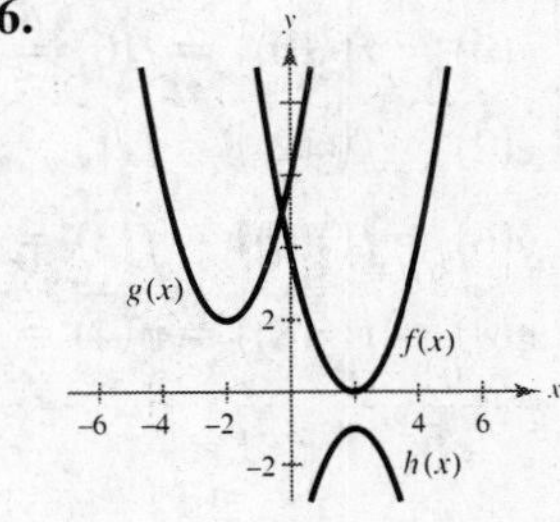

7.

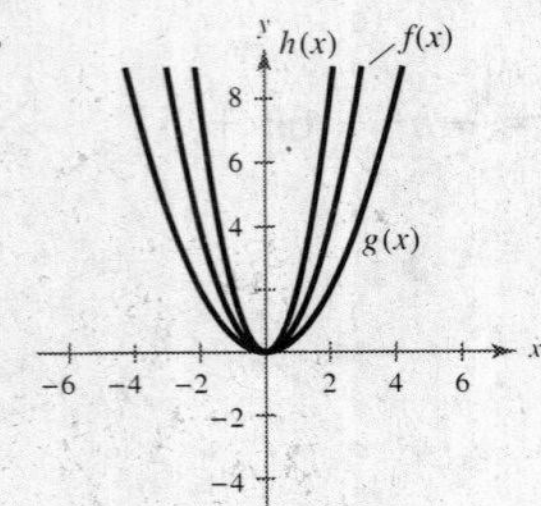

8.

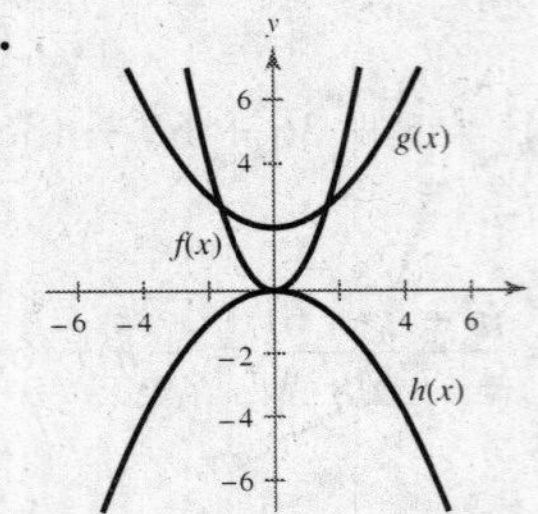

9.

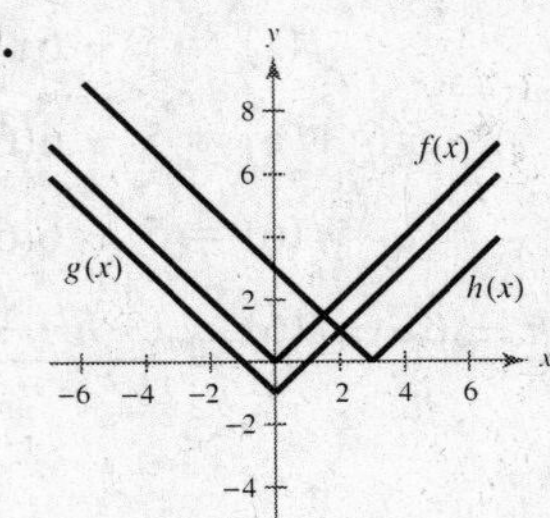

10.

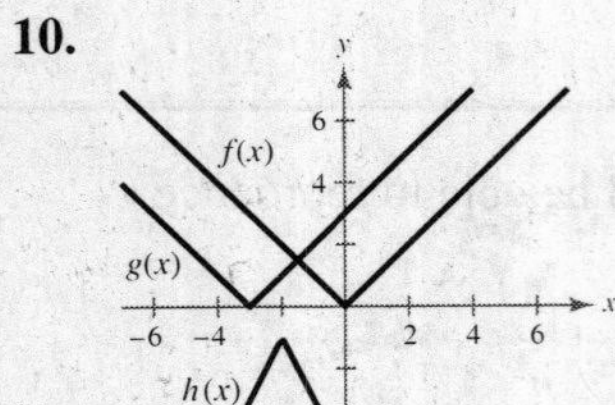

11.

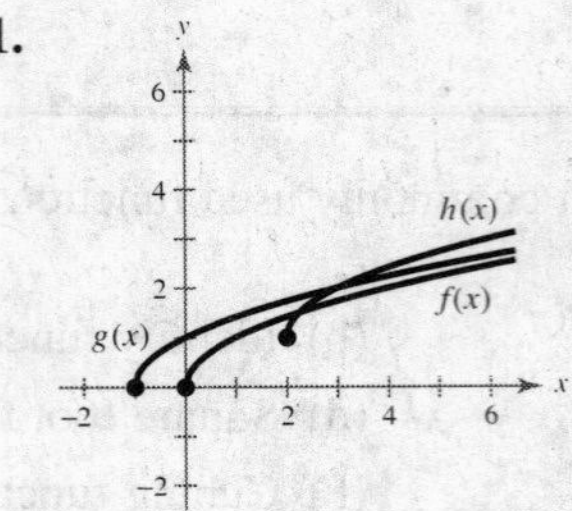

12.

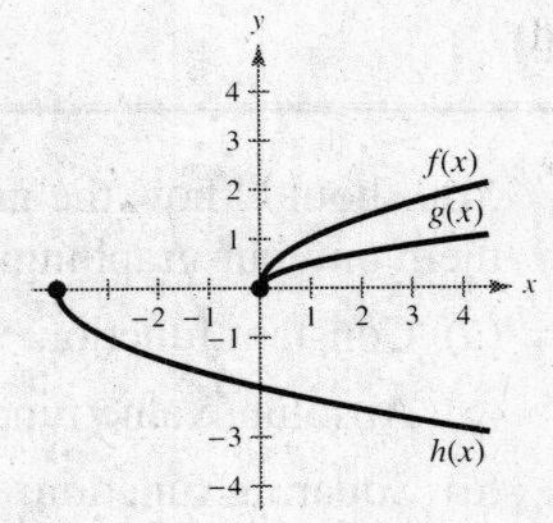

13. (a) $y = f(x) + 2$

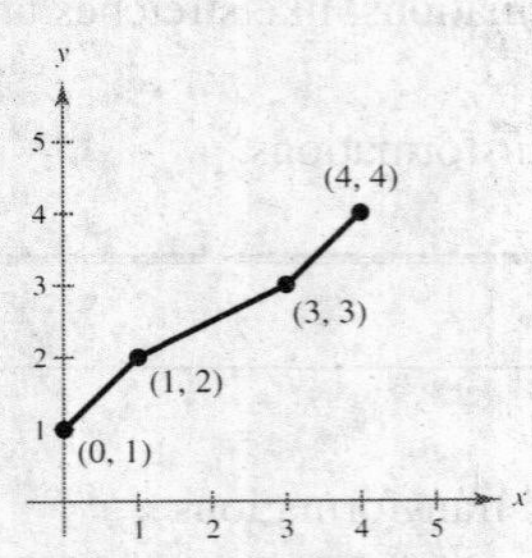

(b) $y = -f(x)$

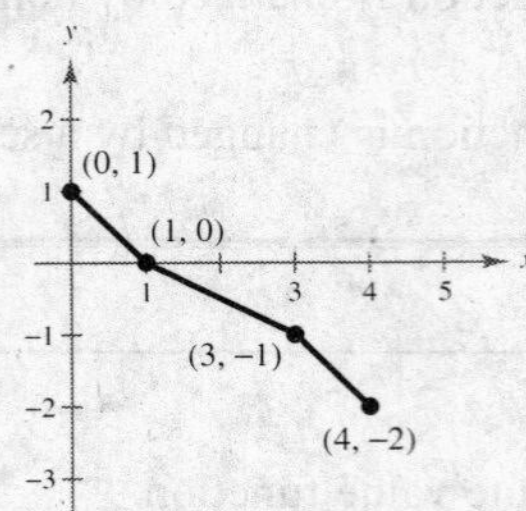

(c) $y = f(x - 2)$

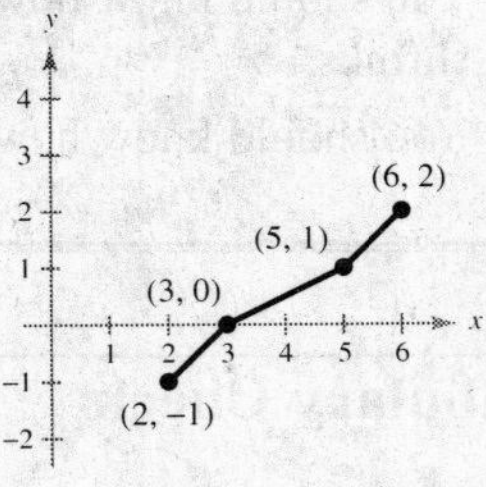

(d) $y = f(x + 3)$

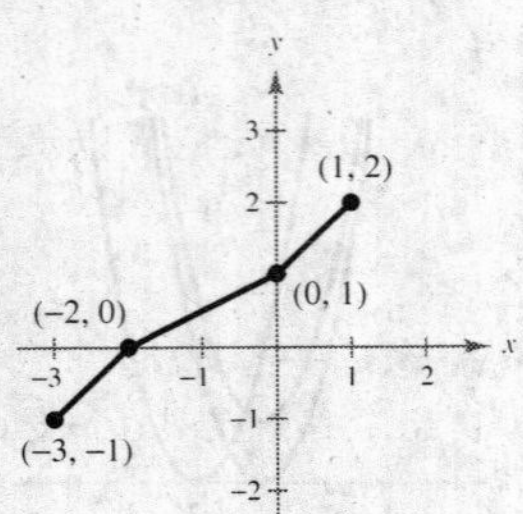

(e) $y = 2f(x)$

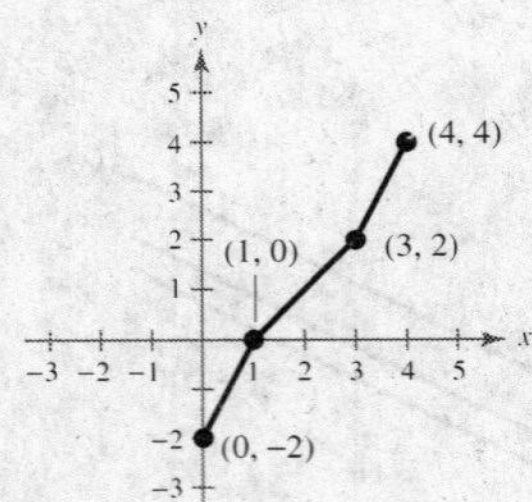

(f) $y = f(-x)$

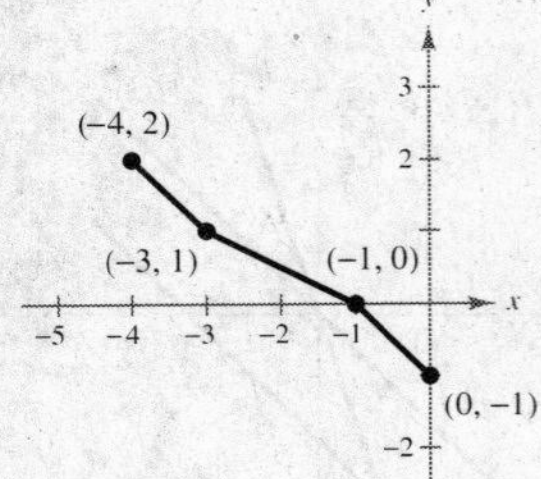

(g) Let $g(x) = f\left(\frac{1}{2}x\right)$. Then from the graph,

$g(0) = f\left(\frac{1}{2}(0)\right) = f(0) = -1$

$g(2) = f\left(\frac{1}{2}(2)\right) = f(1) = 0$

$g(6) = f\left(\frac{1}{2}(6)\right) = f(3) = 1$

$g(8) = f\left(\frac{1}{2}(8)\right) = f(4) = 2$

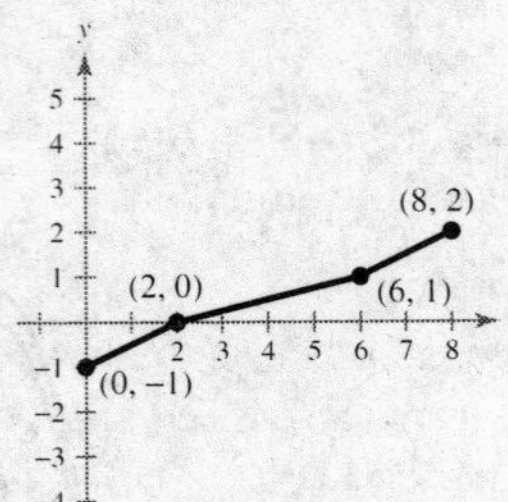

14. (a)

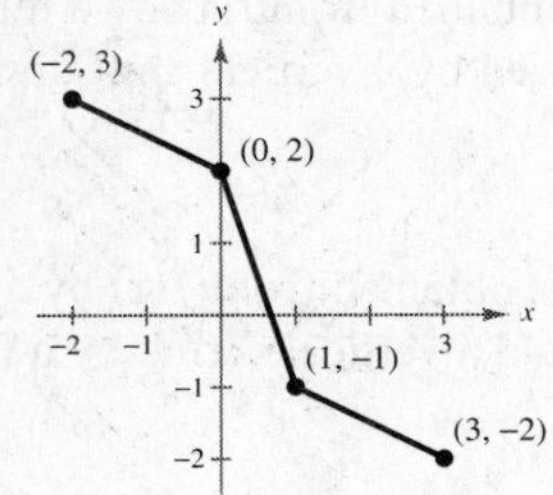

(b)

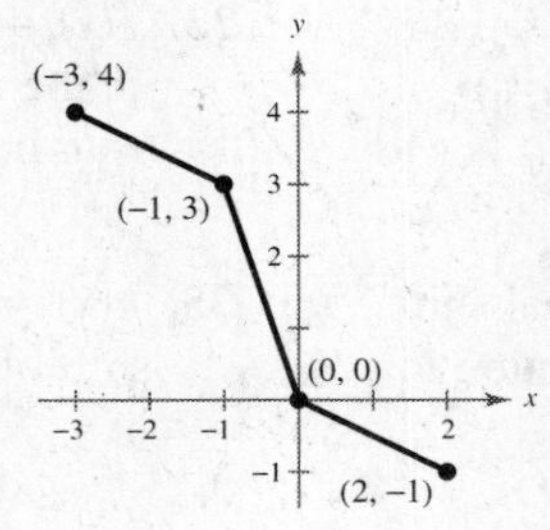

(c)

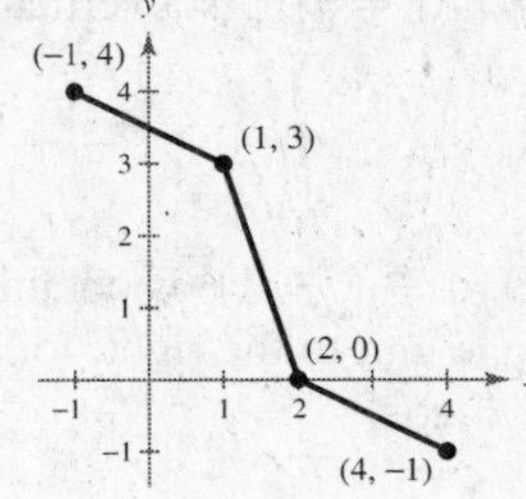

(d)

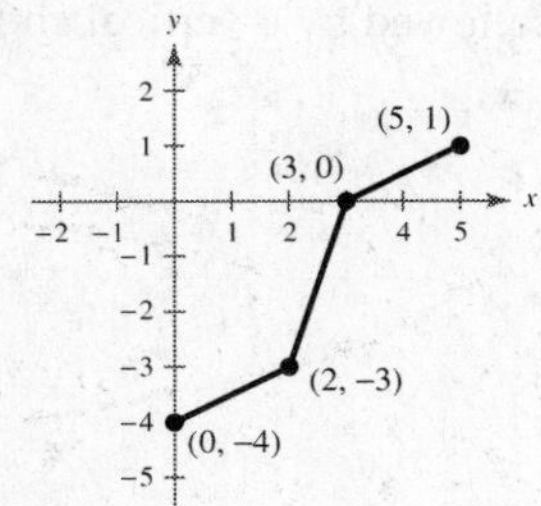

(e)

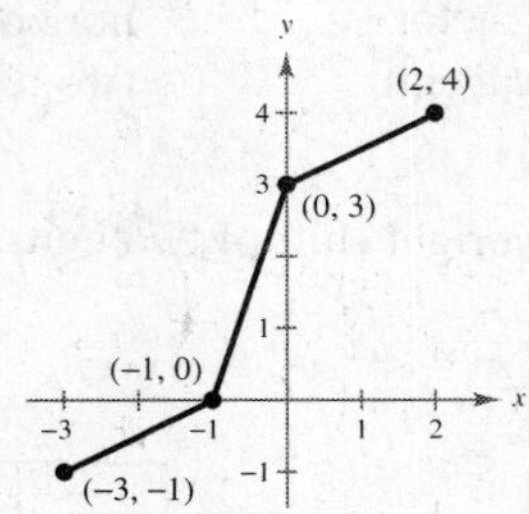

(f)

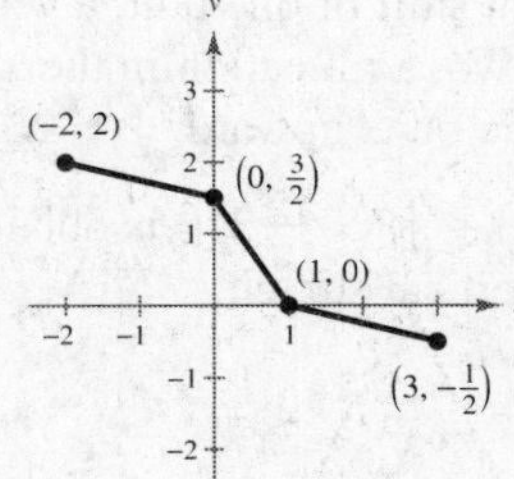

(g) Let $g(x) = f(2x)$. Then from the graph,

$$g(-1) = f(2(-1)) = f(-2) = 4$$

$$g(0) = f(2(0)) = f(0) = 3$$

$$g\left(\tfrac{1}{2}\right) = f\left(2\left(\tfrac{1}{2}\right)\right) = f(1) = 0$$

$$g\left(\tfrac{3}{2}\right) = f\left(2\left(\tfrac{3}{2}\right)\right) = f(3) = -1$$

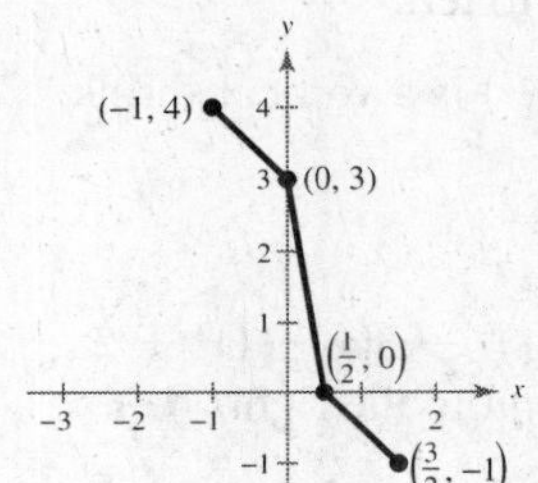

15. Horizontal shift three units to left of $y = x$: $y = x + 3$ (or vertical shift three units upward)

16. Constant function: $y = 7$

17. Vertical shift one unit downward of $y = x^2$

$y = x^2 - 1$

18. Horizontal shift of $y = |x|$: $y = |x + 2|$

19. Reflection in the x-axis and a vertical shift one unit upward of $y = \sqrt{x}$: $y = 1 - \sqrt{x}$

20. Reflection in the x-axis and a vertical shift one unit upward of $y = x^3$: $y = 1 - x^3$

21. $y = -\sqrt{x} - 1$ is $f(x)$ reflected in the x-axis, followed by a vertical shift one unit downward.

22. $y = \sqrt{x} + 2$ is $f(x) = \sqrt{x}$ shifted vertically upwards two units.

23. $y = \sqrt{x - 2}$ is $f(x)$ shifted right two units.

24. $y = \sqrt{x + 4}$ is $f(x)$ shifted left four units.

25. $y = 2\sqrt{x}$ is a vertical stretch of $f(x) = \sqrt{x}$.

26. $y = \sqrt{-x + 3}$ is $f(x)$ reflected in the y-axis, followed by a horizontal shift to the right three units.

27. $y = |x + 5|$ is $f(x)$ shifted left five units.

28. $y = |x| - 3$ is $f(x) = |x|$ shifted down three units.

29. $y = -|x|$ is $f(x)$ reflected in the x-axis.

30. $y = |-x|$ is a reflection in the y-axis. In fact $y = |-x| = |x|$.

31. $y = 4|x|$ is a vertical stretch of $f(x)$.

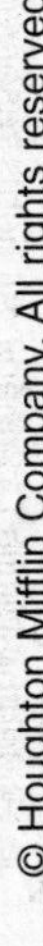

32. $y = \left|\frac{1}{2}x\right| = \frac{1}{2}|x|$ is a vertical shrink.

33. $g(x) = 4 - x^3$ is obtained from $f(x)$ by a reflection in the x-axis followed by a vertical shift upward of four units.

34. $g(x) = -(x - 1)^3$ is obtained by a horizontal shift of one unit to the right, followed by a reflection in the x-axis.

35. $h(x) = \frac{1}{4}(x + 2)^3$ is obtained from $f(x)$ by a left shift of two units and a vertical shrink by a factor of $\frac{1}{4}$.

36. $h(x) = -2(x - 1)^3 + 3$ is obtained from $f(x)$ by a right shift of one unit, a vertical stretch by a factor of two, a reflection in the x-axis, and a vertical shift three units upward.

37. $p(x) = \left(\frac{1}{3}x\right)^3 + 2$ is obtained from $f(x)$ by a horizontal stretch followed by a vertical shift two units upward.

38. $p(x) = [3(x - 2)]^3$ is obtained from $f(x)$ by a right shift of two units, followed by a vertical stretch.

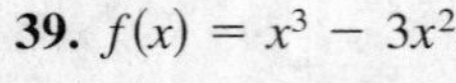

39. $f(x) = x^3 - 3x^2$

$g(x) = f(x + 2) = (x + 2)^3 - 3(x + 2)^2$ is a horizontal shift two units to left.

$h(x) = \frac{1}{2}f(x) = \frac{1}{2}(x^3 - 3x^2)$ is a vertical shrink.

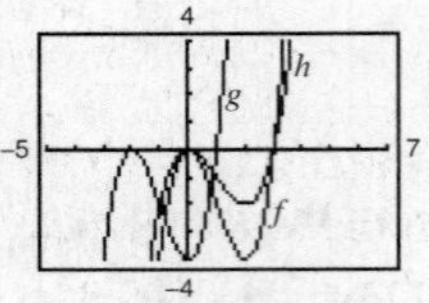

40. $f(x) = x^3 - 3x^2 + 2$

$g(x) = f(x - 1) = (x - 1)^3 - 3(x - 1)^2 + 2$ is a horizontal shift one unit to the right.

$h(x) = f(3x) = (3x)^3 - 3(3x)^2 + 2$ is a horizontal shrink.

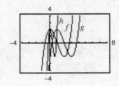

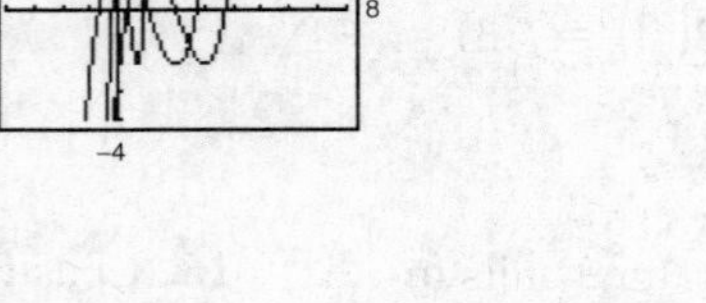

41. $f(x) = x^3 - 3x^2$

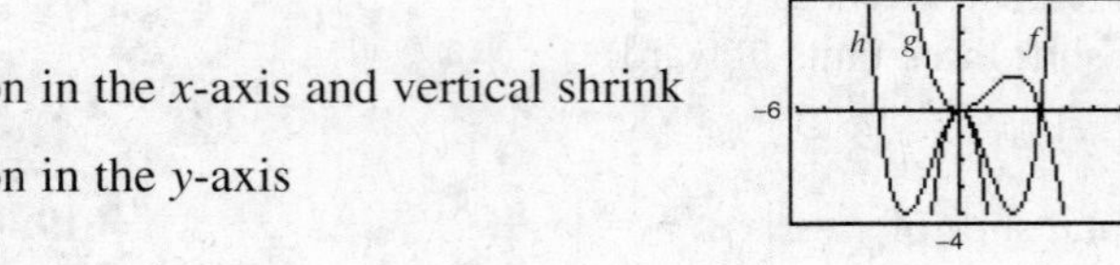

$g(x) = -\frac{1}{3}f(x) = -\frac{1}{3}(x^3 - 3x^2)$ reflection in the x-axis and vertical shrink

$h(x) = f(-x) = (-x)^3 - 3(-x)^2$ reflection in the y-axis

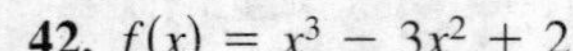

42. $f(x) = x^3 - 3x^2 + 2$

$g(x) = -f(x) = -(x^3 - 3x^2 + 2)$ is a reflection in the x-axis.

$h(x) = f(2x) = (2x)^3 - 3(2x)^2 + 2$ is a horizontal shrink.

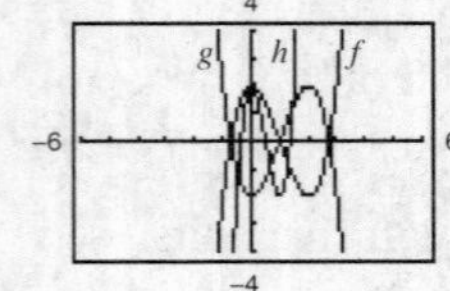

43. (a) $f(x) = x^2$

(b) $g(x) = 2 - (x + 5)^2$ is obtained from f by a horizontal shift to the left five units, a reflection in the x-axis, and a vertical shift upward two units.

(c)

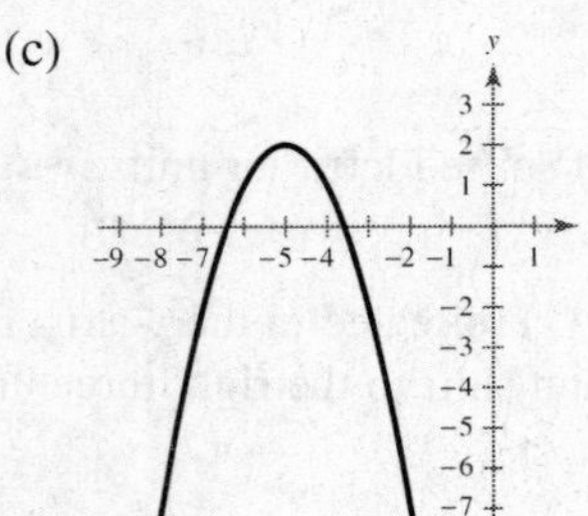

(d) $g(x) = 2 - f(x + 5)$

44. (a) $f(x) = x^2$

(b) $g(x) = -(x + 10)^2 + 5$ is obtained from f by a horizontal shift 10 units to the left, a reflection in the x-axis, and a vertical shift 5 units upward.

(c)

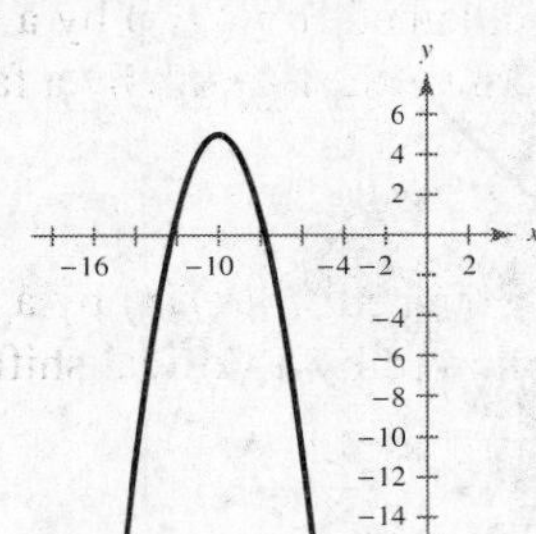

(d) $g(x) = -f(x + 10) + 5$

45. (a) $f(x) = x^2$

(b) $g(x) = 3 + 2(x - 4)^2$ is obtained from f by a horizontal shift four units to the right, a vertical stretch of 2, and a vertical shift upward three units.

(c)

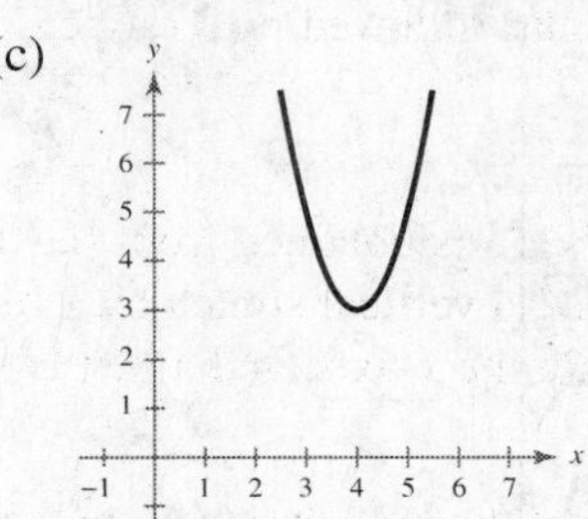

(d) $g(x) = 3 + 2f(x - 4)$

46. (a) $f(x) = x^2$

(b) $g(x) = -\frac{1}{4}(x + 2)^2 - 2$ is obtained from f by a horizontal shift two units to the left, a vertical shrink of $\frac{1}{4}$, a reflection in the x-axis, and a vertical shift two units downward.

(c)

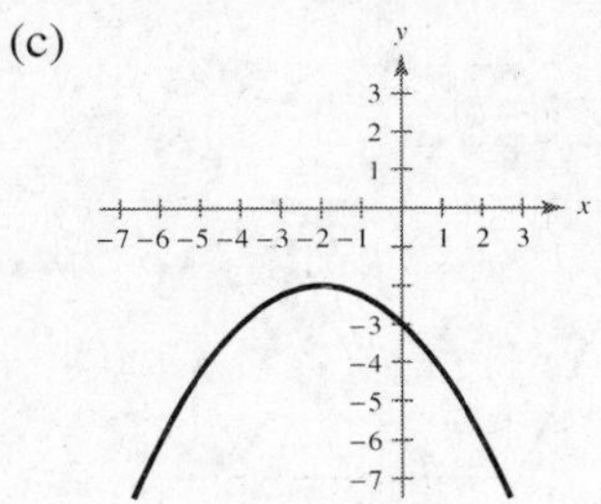

(d) $g(x) = -\frac{1}{4}f(x + 2) - 2$

47. (a) $f(x) = x^3$

(b) $g(x) = 3(x - 2)^3$ is obtained from f by a horizontal shift two units to the right followed by a vertical stretch of 3.

(c)

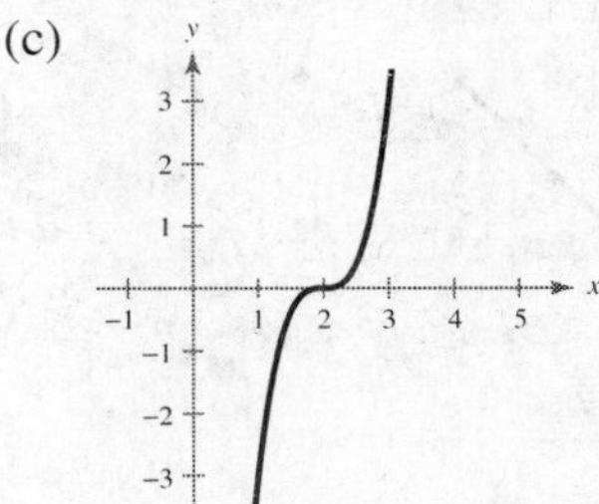

(d) $g(x) = 3f(x - 2)$

48. (a) $f(x) = x^3$

(b) $g(x) = -\frac{1}{2}(x + 1)^3$ is obtained from f by a horizontal shift one unit to the left, a vertical shrink, and a reflection in the x-axis.

(c)

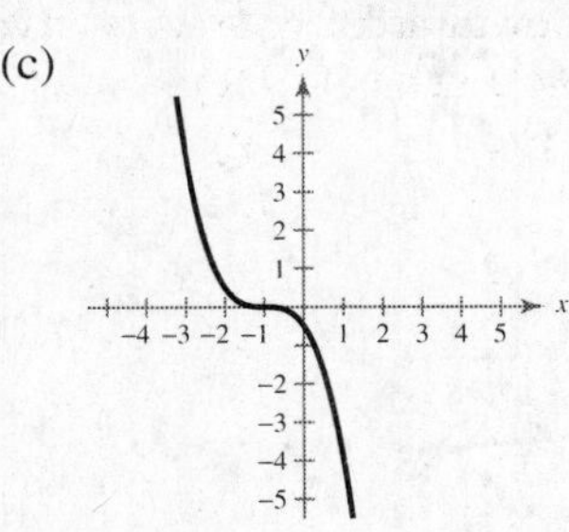

(d) $g(x) = -\frac{1}{2}f(x + 1)$

49. (a) $f(x) = x^3$

(b) $g(x) = (x - 1)^3 + 2$ is obtained from f by a horizontal shift one unit to the right, and a vertical shift upward two units.

(c)

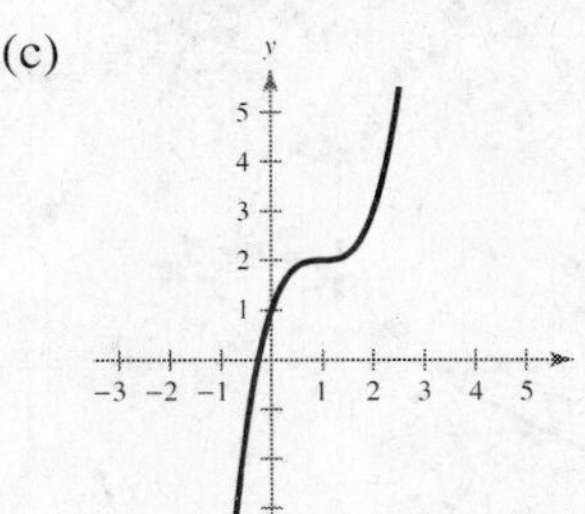

(d) $g(x) = f(x - 1) + 2$

50. (a) $f(x) = x^3$

(b) $g(x) = -(x + 3)^3 - 10$ is obtained from f by a horizontal shift 3 units to the left, a reflection in the x-axis, and a vertical shift 10 units downward.

(c)

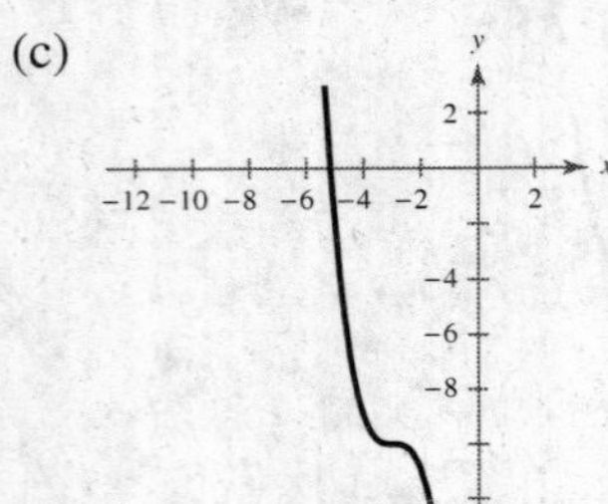

(d) $g(x) = -f(x + 3) - 10$

51. (a) $f(x) = |x|$

(b) $g(x) = |x + 4| + 8$ is obtained from f by a horizontal shift four units to the left, followed by a vertical shift eight units upward.

c)

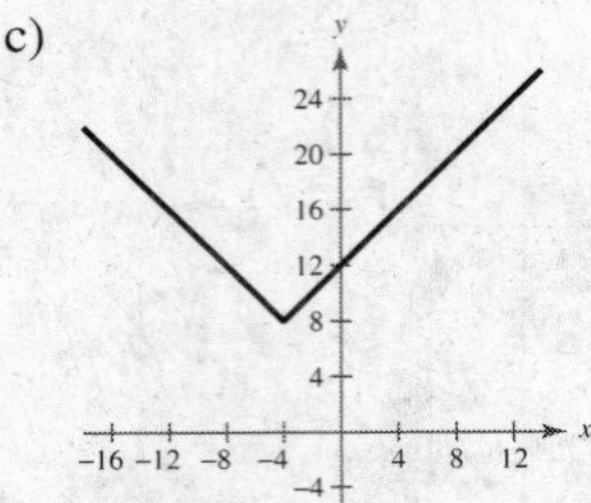

(d) $g(x) = f(x + 4) + 8$

52. (a) $f(x) = |x|$

(b) $g(x) = |x + 3| + 9$ is obtained from f by a horizontal shift three units to the left, followed by a vertical shift nine units upward.

(c)

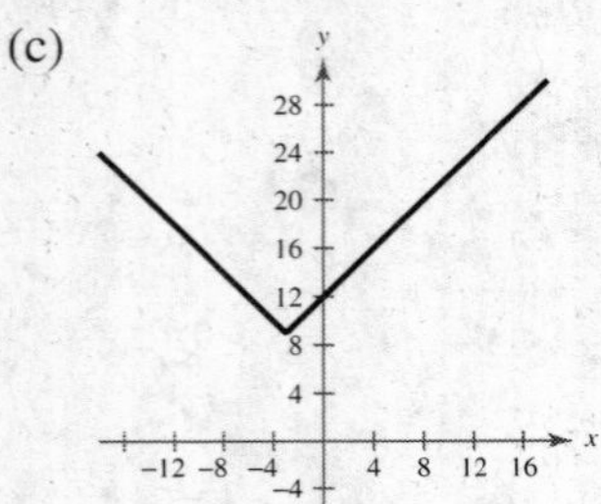

(d) $g(x) = f(x + 3) + 9$

53. (a) $f(x) = |x|$

(b) $g(x) = -2|x - 1| - 4$ is obtained from f by a horizontal shift one unit to the right, a vertical stretch of 2, a reflection in the x-axis, and a vertical shift downward four units.

(c)

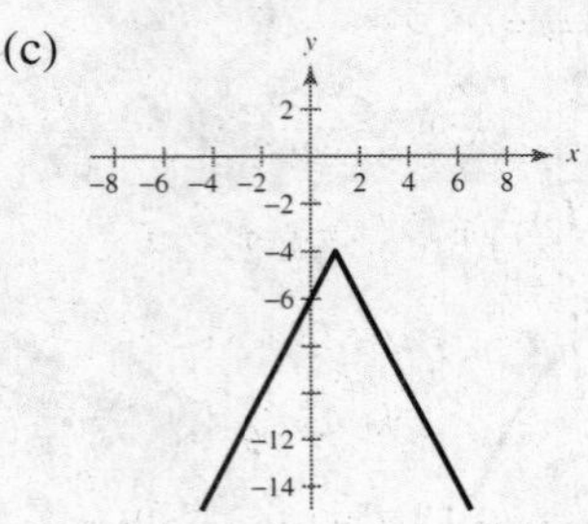

(d) $g(x) = -2f(x - 1) - 4$

54. (a) $f(x) = |x|$

(b) $g(x) = \frac{1}{2}|x - 2| - 3$ is obtained from f by a horizontal shift two units to the right, a vertical shrink, and a vertical shift three units downward.

(c)

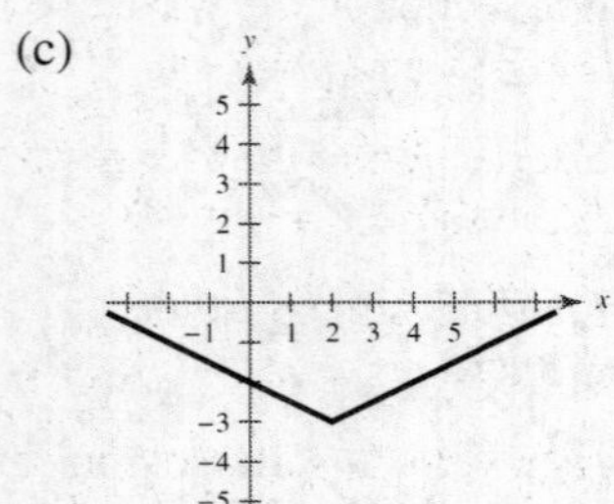

(d) $g(x) = \frac{1}{2}f(x - 2) - 3$

55. (a) $f(x) = \sqrt{x}$

(b) $g(x) = -\frac{1}{2}\sqrt{x + 3} - 1$ is obtained from f by a horizontal shift three units to the left, a vertical shrink, a reflection in the x-axis, and a vertical shift one unit downward.

(c)

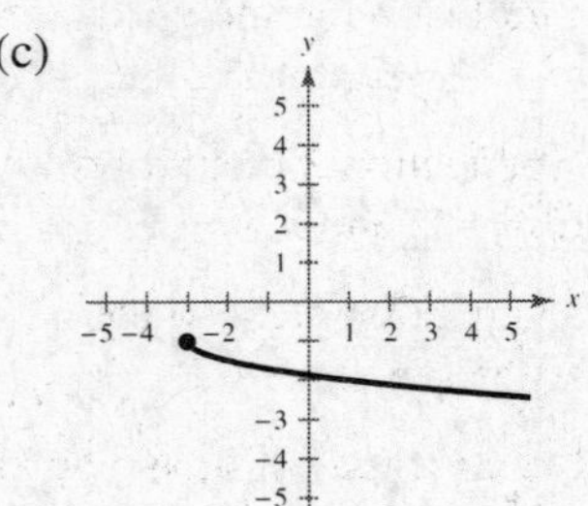

(d) $g(x) = -\frac{1}{2}f(x + 3) - 1$

56. (a) $f(x) = \sqrt{x}$

(b) $g(x) = -\sqrt{x+1} - 6$ is obtained from f by a horizontal shift one unit to the left, a reflection in the x-axis, and a vertical shift six units downward.

(c)

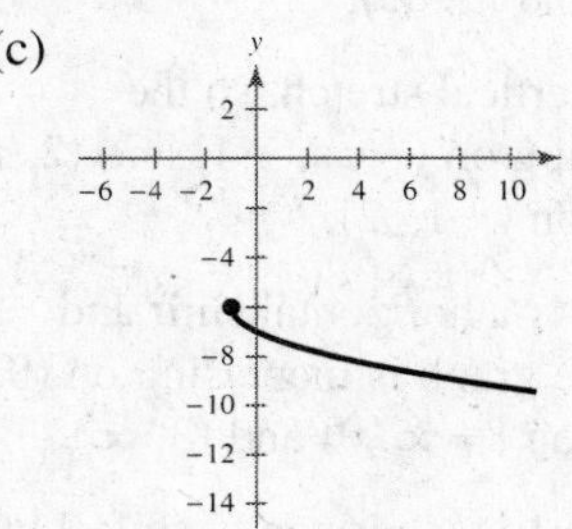

(d) $g(x) = -f(x+1) - 6$

57. (a) $F(t) = 33.0 + 6.2\sqrt{t}$ is a vertical stretch of $f(t) = \sqrt{t}$, followed by a vertical shift of 33.0.

(b)

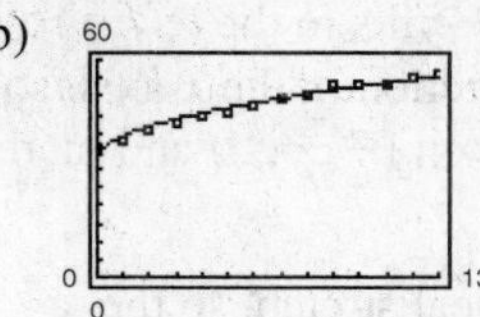

(c) $G(t) = F(t+13) = 33.0 + 6.2\sqrt{t+13}$,

$-13 \le t \le 0$.

$G(-13) = F(0)$ corresponds to 1990.

$G(0) = F(13)$ corresponds to 2003.

58. (a) $M(t) = 32.3t^2 + 3769$ is a vertical stretch of $f(t) = t^2$ by 32.3, followed by a vertical shift of 3769.

(b)

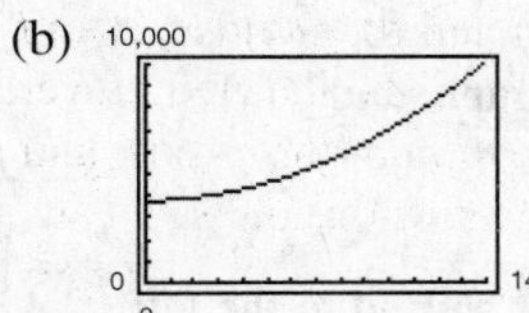

(c) $M(t) = 32.3t^2 + 3769 > 10{,}000$

$32.3t^2 > 6231$

$t^2 > 192.91$

$t > 13.9$

The debt will exceed 10 trillion dollars in 2003.

(d) $G(t) = M(t+10) = 32.3(t+10)^2 + 3769, \quad -10 \le t \le 4$

$G(0) = M(10)$ corresponds to 2000.

$G(-10) = M(0)$ corresponds to 1990.

59. False. $y = f(-x)$ is a reflection in the y-axis.

60. False. $y = -f(x)$ is a reflection in the x-axis.

61. (a) $y = f(-x)$ is a reflection in the y-axis, so the x-intercepts are $x = -2$ and $x = 3$.

(b) $y = -f(x)$ is a reflection in the x-axis, so the x-intercepts are $x = 2$ and $x = -3$.

(c) $y = 2f(x)$ is a vertical stretch, so the x-intercepts are the same: $x = 2, -3$.

(d) $y = f(x) + 2$ is a vertical shift, so you cannot determine the x-intercepts.

(e) $y = f(x-3)$ is a horizontal shift 3 units to the right, so the x-intercepts are $x = 5$ and $x = 0$.

62. (a) $y = f(-x)$ is a reflection in the y-axis, so the x-intercepts are $x = 1$ and $x = -4$.

(b) $y = -f(x)$ is a reflection in the x-axis, so the x-intercepts are the same $x = -1, 4$.

(c) $y = 2f(x)$ is a vertical stretch, so the x-intercepts are the same: $x = -1, 4$.

(d) $y = f(x) - 1$ is a vertical shift, so you cannot determine the x-intercepts.

(e) $y = f(x-2)$ is a horizontal shift 2 units to the right, so the x-intercepts are $x = 1$ and $x = 6$.

63. (a) $y = f(-x)$ is a reflection in the y-axis, so the graph is increasing on $(-\infty, -2)$ and decreasing on $(-2, \infty)$.

(b) $y = -f(x)$ is a reflection in the x-axis, so the graph is decreasing on $(-\infty, 2)$ and increasing on $(2, \infty)$.

(c) $y = 2f(x)$ is a vertical stretch, so the graph is increasing on $(-\infty, 2)$ and decreasing on $(2, \infty)$.

(d) $y = f(x) - 3$ is a vertical shift, so the graph is increasing on $(-\infty, 2)$ and decreasing on $(2, \infty)$.

(e) $y = f(x + 1)$ is a horizontal shift one unit to the left, so the graph is increasing on $(-\infty, 1)$ and decreasing on $(1, \infty)$.

64. (a) $y = f(-x)$ is a reflection in the y-axis, so the graph is increasing on $(-2, 1)$ and decreasing on $(-\infty, -2)$ and $(1, \infty)$.

(b) $y = -f(x)$ is a reflection in the x-axis, so the graph is increasing on $(-1, 2)$ and decreasing on $(-\infty, -1)$ and $(2, \infty)$.

(c) $y = \frac{1}{2}f(x)$ is a vertical stretch, so the graph is increasing on $(-\infty, -1)$ and $(2, \infty)$, and decreasing on $(-1, 2)$.

(d) $y = -f(x - 1)$ is a horizontal shift and reflection, so the graph is increasing on $(0, 3)$ and decreasing on $(-\infty, 0)$ and $(3, \infty)$.

(e) $y = f(x - 2) + 1$ is a horizontal shift 2 units to the right, and a vertical shift, so the graph is increasing on $(-\infty, 1)$ and $(4, \infty)$, and decreasing on $(1, 4)$.

65. The vertex is approximately at $(2, 1)$ and the graph opens upward. Matches (c).

66. The domain is $[0, -\infty)$ and $(0, -4)$ is approximately on the graph, and $f(x) < 0$. Matches (a) and (b).

67. The vertex is approximately $(2, -4)$ and the graph opens upward. Matches (c).

68. The graph of f is $y = x^3$ shifted to the left approximately four units, reflected in the x-axis, and shifted upward approximately two units. Matches (b).

69. Slope L_1: $\dfrac{10 + 2}{2 + 2} = 3$

Slope L_2: $\dfrac{9 - 3}{3 + 1} = \dfrac{3}{2}$

Neither parallel nor perpendicular

70. Slope L_1: $\dfrac{3 - (-7)}{4 - (-1)} = \dfrac{10}{5} = 2$

Slope L_2: $\dfrac{-7 - 5}{-2 - 1} = \dfrac{-12}{-3} = 4$

Neither parallel nor perpendicular

71. Domain: All $x \neq 9$

72. $f(x) = \dfrac{\sqrt{x - 5}}{x - 7}$

Domain: $x \geq 5$ and $x \neq 7$

73. Domain:
$100 - x^2 \geq 0 \Rightarrow x^2 \leq 100 \Rightarrow -10 \leq x \leq 10$

74. $f(x) = \sqrt[3]{16 - x^2}$

Domain: all real numbers

Section 1.5 Combinations of Functions

■ Given two functions, f and g, you should be able to form the following functions (if defined):

1. Sum: $(f + g)(x) = f(x) + g(x)$
2. Difference: $(f - g)(x) = f(x) - g(x)$
3. Product: $(fg)(x) = f(x)g(x)$
4. Quotient: $(f/g)(x) = f(x)/g(x),\ g(x) \neq 0$
5. Composition of f with g: $(f \circ g)(x) = f(g(x))$
6. Composition of g with f: $(g \circ f)(x) = g(f(x))$

Vocabulary Check

1. addition, subtraction, multiplication, division

2. composition

3. $g(x)$

4. inner, outer

1.

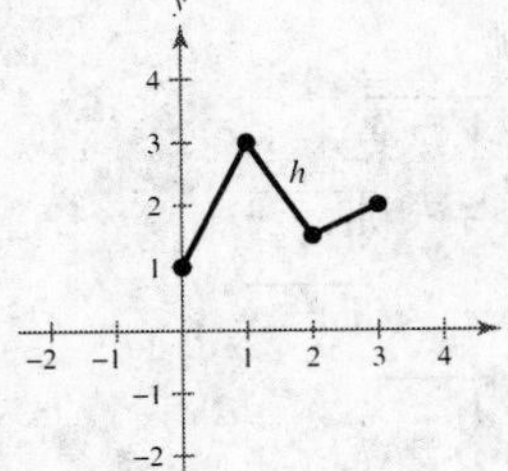

2.

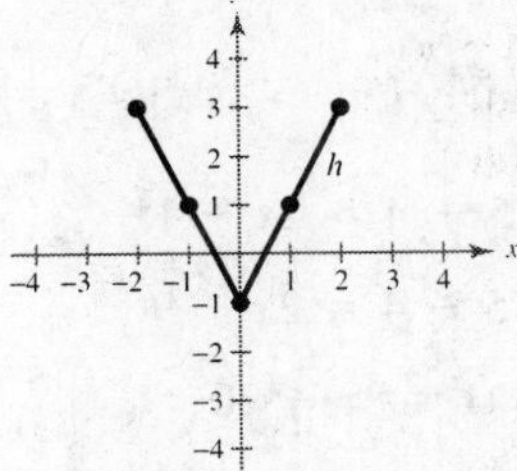

3.

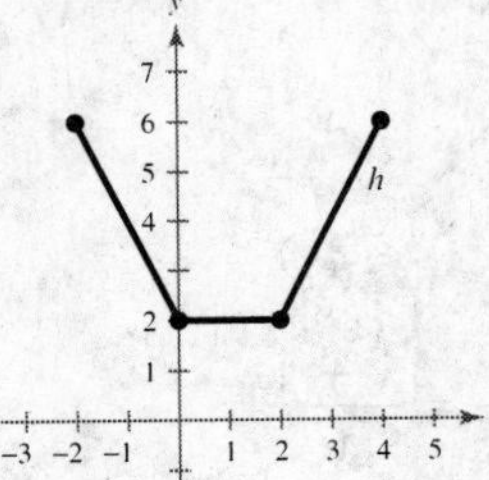

4.

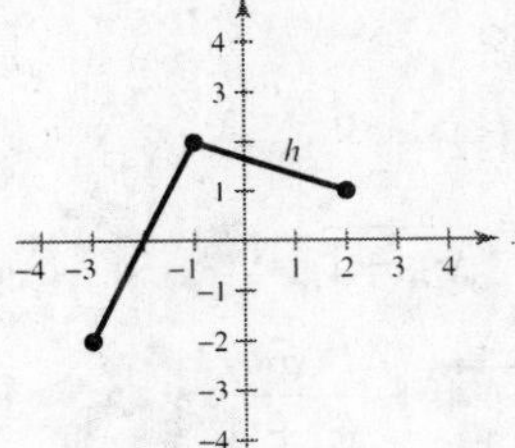

5. $f(x) = x + 3, \quad g(x) = x - 3$

(a) $(f + g)(x) = f(x) + g(x) = (x + 3) + (x - 3) = 2x$

(b) $(f - g)(x) = f(x) - g(x) = (x + 3) - (x - 3) = 6$

(c) $(fg)(x) = f(x)g(x) = (x + 3)(x - 3) = x^2 - 9$

(d) $\left(\frac{f}{g}\right)(x) = \frac{f(x)}{g(x)} = \frac{x + 3}{x - 3}, \quad x \neq 3$

Domain: all $x \neq 3$

6. $f(x) = 2x - 5,\; g(x) = 1 - x$

(a) $(f + g)(x) = 2x - 5 + 1 - x = x - 4$

(b) $(f - g)(x) = 2x - 5 - (1 - x)$

$= 2x - 5 - 1 + x$

$= 3x - 6$

(c) $(fg)(x) = (2x - 5)(1 - x)$

$= 2x - 2x^2 - 5 + 5x$

$= -2x^2 + 7x - 5$

(d) $\left(\frac{f}{g}\right)(x) = \frac{2x - 5}{1 - x}$

Domain: $1 - x \neq 0$

$x \neq 1$

7. $f(x) = x^2, g(x) = 1 - x$

(a) $(f + g)(x) = f(x) + g(x) = x^2 + (1 - x) = x^2 - x + 1$

(b) $(f - g)(x) = f(x) - g(x) = x^2 - (1 - x) = x^2 + x - 1$

(c) $(fg)(x) = f(x) \cdot g(x) = x^2(1 - x) = x^2 - x^3$

(d) $\left(\frac{f}{g}\right)(x) = \frac{f(x)}{g(x)} = \frac{x^2}{1 - x}, x \neq 1$

Domain: all $x \neq 1$.

8. $f(x) = 2x - 5,\; g(x) = 4$

(a) $(f + g)(x) = 2x - 5 + 4 = 2x - 1$

(b) $(f - g)(x) = 2x - 5 - 4 = 2x - 9$

(c) $(fg)(x) = (2x - 5)(4) = 8x - 20$

(d) $\left(\frac{f}{g}\right)(x) = \frac{2x - 5}{4} = \frac{1}{2}x - \frac{5}{4}$

Domain: $-\infty < x < \infty$

9. $f(x) = x^2 + 5, g(x) = \sqrt{1 - x}$

(a) $(f + g)(x) = x^2 + 5 + \sqrt{1 - x}$

(b) $(f - g)(x) = x^2 + 5 - \sqrt{1 - x}$

(c) $(fg)(x) = (x^2 + 5)\sqrt{1 - x}$

(d) $\left(\frac{f}{g}\right)(x) = \frac{x^2 + 5}{\sqrt{1 - x}}$

Domain: $x < 1$

10. $f(x) = \sqrt{x^2 - 4},\; g(x) = \frac{x^2}{x^2 + 1}$

(a) $(f + g)(x) = \sqrt{x^2 - 4} + \frac{x^2}{x^2 + 1}$

(b) $(f - g)(x) = \sqrt{x^2 - 4} - \frac{x^2}{x^2 + 1}$

(c) $(fg)(x) = \left(\sqrt{x^2 - 4}\right)\left(\frac{x^2}{x^2 + 1}\right) = \frac{x^2\sqrt{x^2 - 4}}{x^2 + 1}$

Domain: $x^2 - 4 \geq 0$

$x^2 \geq 4 \Rightarrow x \geq 2 \text{ or } x \leq -2$

(d) $\left(\frac{f}{g}\right)(x) = \sqrt{x^2 - 4} \div \frac{x^2}{x^2 + 1}$

$= \frac{(x^2 + 1)\sqrt{x^2 - 4}}{x^2}$

Domain: $x^2 - 4 \geq 0$ and $x \neq 0$

$x \geq 2 \text{ or } x \leq -2$

11. $f(x) = \frac{1}{x}, g(x) = \frac{1}{x^2}$

(a) $(f + g)(x) = \frac{1}{x} + \frac{1}{x^2} = \frac{x + 1}{x^2}$

(b) $(f - g)(x) = \frac{1}{x} - \frac{1}{x^2} = \frac{x - 1}{x^2}$

(c) $(fg)(x) = \frac{1}{x} \cdot \frac{1}{x^2} = \frac{1}{x^3}$

(d) $\left(\frac{f}{g}\right)(x) = \frac{1/x}{1/x^2} = x, x \neq 0$

Domain: $x \neq 0$

12. $f(x) = \dfrac{x}{x+1},\ g(x) = x^3$

(a) $(f+g)(x) = \dfrac{x}{x+1} + x^3 = \dfrac{x + x^4 + x^3}{x+1}$

(b) $(f-g)(x) = \dfrac{x}{x+1} - x^3 = \dfrac{x - x^4 - x^3}{x+1}$

(c) $(fg)(x) = \dfrac{x}{x+1} \cdot x^3 = \dfrac{x^4}{x+1}$

(d) $\left(\dfrac{f}{g}\right)(x) = \dfrac{x}{x+1} \div x^3$

$= \dfrac{x}{x+1} \cdot \dfrac{1}{x^3} = \dfrac{1}{x^2(x+1)}$

Domain: $x \neq 0, x \neq -1$

13. $(f+g)(3) = f(3) + g(3)$

$= (3^2 - 1) + (3 - 2)$

$= 8 + 1 = 9$

14. $(f-g)(-2) = f(-2) - g(-2)$

$= ((-2)^2 - 1) - (-2 - 2)$

$= 3 - (-4) = 7$

15. $(f-g)(0) = f(0) - g(0)$

$= (0 - 1) - (0 - 2)$

$= 1$

16. $(f+g)(1) = f(1) + g(1)$

$= (1 - 1) + (1 - 2)$

$= -1$

17. $(fg)(4) = f(4)g(4)$

$= (4^2 - 1)(4 - 2)$

$= 15(2)$

$= 30$

18. $(fg)(-6) = f(-6)g(-6)$

$= ((-6)^2 - 1)(-6 - 2)$

$= 35(-8)$

$= -280$

19. $\left(\dfrac{f}{g}\right)(-5) = \dfrac{f(-5)}{g(-5)}$

$= \dfrac{(-5)^2 - 1}{-5 - 2}$

$= \dfrac{24}{-7}$

$= -\dfrac{24}{7}$

20. $\left(\dfrac{f}{g}\right)(0) = \dfrac{f(0)}{g(0)}$

$= \dfrac{0 - 1}{0 - 2}$

$= \dfrac{1}{2}$

21. $(f-g)(2t) = f(2t) - g(2t)$

$= ((2t)^2 - 1) - (2t - 2)$

$= 4t^2 - 2t + 1$

22. $(f+g)(t-4) = f(t-4) + g(t-4)$

$= ((t-4)^2 - 1) + (t - 4 - 2)$

$= t^2 - 8t + 15 + t - 6$

$= t^2 - 7t + 9$

23. $(fg)(-5t) = f(-5t)g(-5t)$

$= ((-5t)^2 - 1)(-5t - 2)$

$= (25t^2 - 1)(-5t - 2)$

$= -125t^3 - 50t^2 + 5t + 2$

24. $(fg)(3t^2) = f(3t^2)g(3t^2)$

$= ((3t^2)^2 - 1)(3t^2 - 2)$

$= (9t^4 - 1)(3t^2 - 2)$

$= 27t^6 - 18t^4 - 3t^2 + 2$

25. $\left(\dfrac{f}{g}\right)(-t) = \dfrac{f(-t)}{g(-t)}$

$= \dfrac{(-t)^2 - 1}{-t - 2}$

$= \dfrac{t^2 - 1}{-t - 2} = \dfrac{1 - t^2}{t + 2},\quad t \neq -2$

26. $\left(\frac{f}{g}\right)(t + 2) = \frac{f(t + 2)}{g(t + 2)}$

$= \frac{(t + 2)^2 - 1}{(t + 2) - 2}$

$= \frac{t^2 + 4t + 3}{t}, \quad t \neq 0$

27.

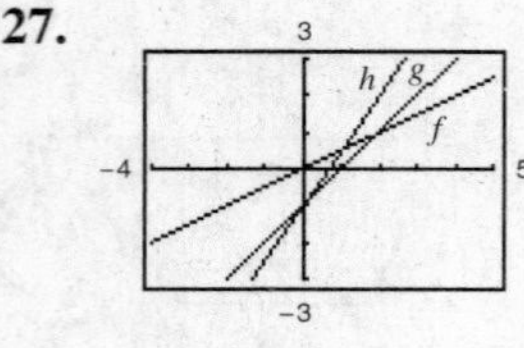
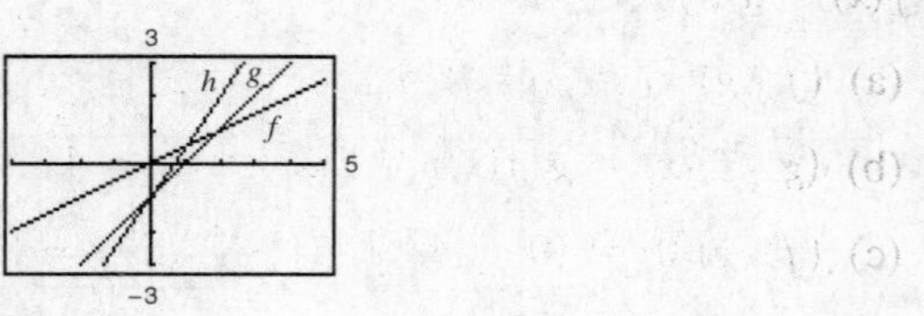

28.

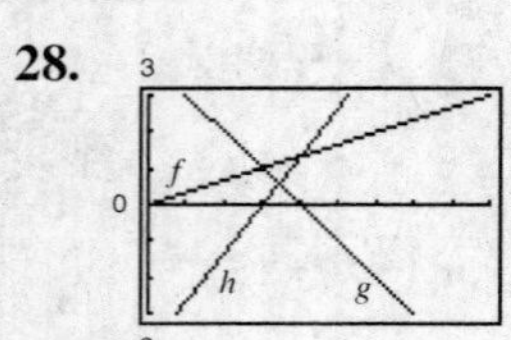

29.

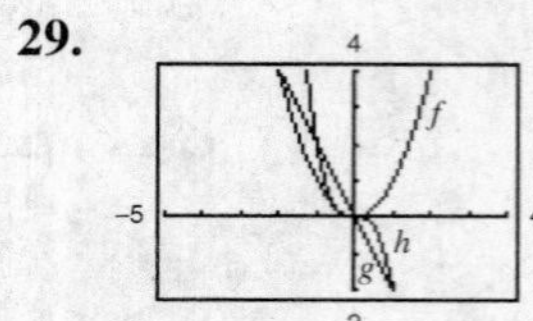

30.

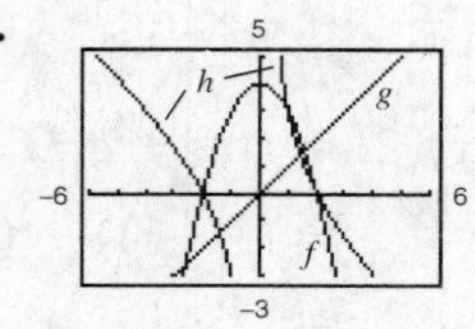

31. $f(x) = 3x,\ g(x) = -\frac{x^3}{10},\ (f + g)(x) = 3x - \frac{x^3}{10}$

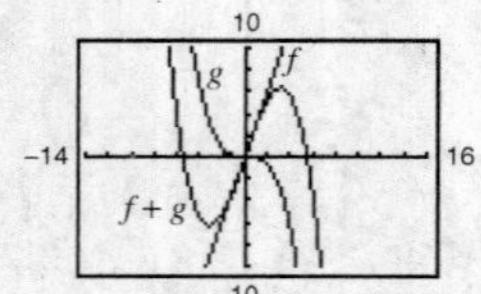

For $0 \leq x \leq 2$, $f(x)$ contributes more to the magnitude.

For $x > 6$, $g(x)$ contributes more to the magnitude.

32. $f(x) = \frac{x}{2},\ g(x) = \sqrt{x}$

$(f + g)(x) = \frac{x}{2} + \sqrt{x}$

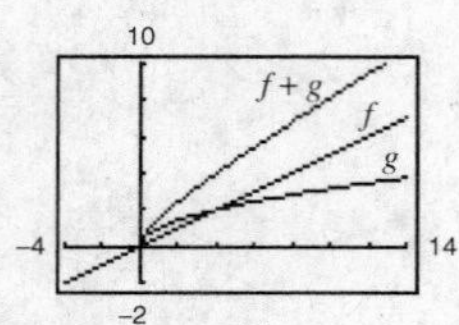

$g(x)$ contributes more to the magnitude of the sum for $0 \leq x \leq 2$. $f(x)$ contributes more to the magnitude of the sum for $x > 6$.

33. $f(x) = 3x + 2,\ g(x) = -\sqrt{x + 5}$,

$(f + g)(x) = 3x + 2 - \sqrt{x + 5}$

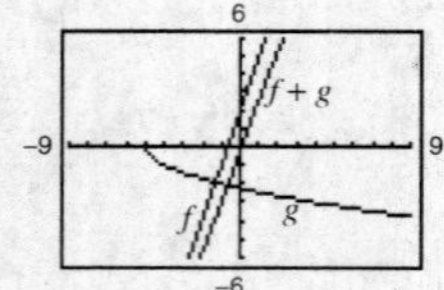

$f(x) = 3x + 2$ contributes more to the magnitude in both intervals.

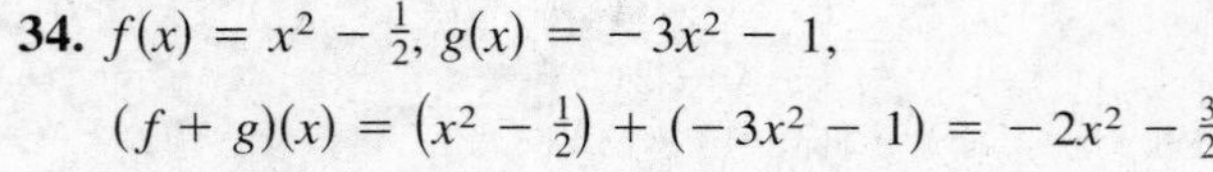

34. $f(x) = x^2 - \frac{1}{2},\ g(x) = -3x^2 - 1$,

$(f + g)(x) = \left(x^2 - \frac{1}{2}\right) + (-3x^2 - 1) = -2x^2 - \frac{3}{2}$

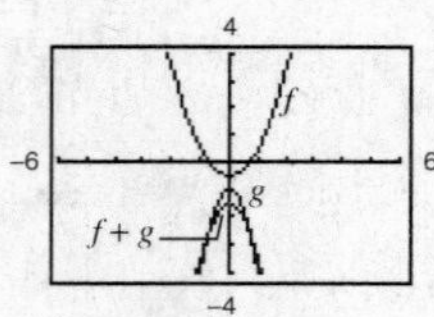

g contributes more on both intervals.

35. $f(x) = x^2, g(x) = x - 1$

(a) $(f \circ g)(x) = f(g(x)) = f(x - 1) = (x - 1)^2$

(b) $(g \circ f)(x) = g(f(x)) = g(x^2) = x^2 - 1$

(c) $(f \circ g)(0) = (0 - 1)^2 = 1$

36. $f(x) = \sqrt[3]{x - 1},\ g(x) = x^3 + 1$

(a) $(f \circ g)(x) = f(g(x))$

$= f(x^3 + 1)$

$= \sqrt[3]{(x^3 + 1) - 1}$

$= \sqrt[3]{x^3} = x$

(b) $(g \circ f)(x) = g(f(x))$

$= g\left(\sqrt[3]{x - 1}\right)$

$= \left(\sqrt[3]{x - 1}\right)^3 + 1$

$= (x - 1) + 1 = x$

(c) $(f \circ g)(0) = 0$

37. $f(x) = 3x + 5, g(x) = 5 - x$

(a) $(f \circ g)(x) = f(g(x)) = f(5 - x) = 3(5 - x) + 5 = 20 - 3x$

(b) $(g \circ f)(x) = g(f(x)) = g(3x + 5) = 5 - (3x + 5) = -3x$

(c) $(f \circ g)(0) = 20$

38. $f(x) = x^3,\ g(x) = \dfrac{1}{x}$

(a) $(f \circ g)(x) = f(g(x)) = f\left(\dfrac{1}{x}\right) = \left(\dfrac{1}{x}\right)^3 = \dfrac{1}{x^3}$

(b) $(g \circ f)(x) = g(f(x)) = g(x^3) = \dfrac{1}{x^3}$

(c) $(f \circ g)(0)$ is not defined.

39. (a) The domain of $f(x) = \sqrt{x + 4}$ is $x + 4 \geq 0$ or $x \geq -4$.

(b) The domain of $g(x) = x^2$ is all real numbers.

(c) $(f \circ g)(x) = f(g(x)) = f(x^2) = \sqrt{x^2 + 4}$.

The domain of $(f \circ g)$ is all real numbers.

40. (a) Domain of f: $x + 3 \geq 0 \Rightarrow x \geq -3$

(b) Domain of g: all real numbers

(c) Domain of $(f \circ g)(x) = f\left(\dfrac{x}{2}\right) = \sqrt{\dfrac{x}{2} + 3}$:

$\dfrac{x}{2} + 3 \geq 0 \Rightarrow x \geq -6$

41. (a) The domain of $f(x) = x^2 + 1$ is all real numbers.

(b) The domain of $g(x) = \sqrt{x}$ is all $x \geq 0$.

(c) $(f \circ g)(x) = f(g(x)) = f\left(\sqrt{x}\right)$

$= \left(\sqrt{x}\right)^2 + 1 = x + 1, \quad x \geq 0$

The domain of $f \circ g$ is $x \geq 0$.

42. $f(x) = x^{1/4},\quad g(x) = x^4$

(a) Domain of f: $x \geq 0$

(b) Domain of g: all x

(c) $(f \circ g)(x) = f(g(x)) = f(x^4) = (x^4)^{1/4} = x$

Domain: all x

43. (a) The domain of $f(x) = \dfrac{1}{x}$ is all $x \neq 0$.

(b) The domain of $g(x) = x + 3$ is all real numbers.

(c) The domain of $(f \circ g)(x) = f(x + 3) = \dfrac{1}{x + 3}$ is all $x \neq -3$.

44. (a) Domain of f: all $x \neq 0$

(b) Domain of g: all $x \neq 0$

(c) Domain of $(f \circ g)(x) = f\left(\dfrac{1}{2x}\right) = 2x, \quad x \neq 0,$ is all $x \neq 0$.

45. (a) The domain of $f(x) = |x - 4|$ is all real numbers.

(b) The domain of $g(x) = 3 - x$ is all real numbers.

(c) $(f \circ g)(x) = f(g(x)) = f(3 - x) = |(3 - x) - 4| = |-x - 1| = |x + 1|$

Domain: all real numbers

46. $f(x) = \dfrac{2}{|x|}, \quad g(x) = x - 1$

(a) Domain of f: all $x \neq 0$

(b) Domain of g: all x

(c) $(f \circ g)(x) = f(g(x)) = f(x - 1) = \dfrac{2}{|x - 1|}$

Domain: all $x \neq 1$

47. (a) The domain of $f(x) = x + 2$ is all real numbers.

(b) The domain of $g(x) = \dfrac{1}{x^2 - 4}$ is all $x \neq \pm 2$

(c) $(f \circ g)(x) = f(g(x)) = f\left(\dfrac{1}{x^2 - 4}\right) = \dfrac{1}{x^2 - 4} + 2$

Domain: $x \neq \pm 2$

48. (a) Domain of f: all $x \neq \pm 1$

(b) Domain of g: all real numbers

(c) Domain of $(f \circ g)(x) = f(x + 1) = \dfrac{3}{(x + 1)^2 - 1}$

$= \dfrac{3}{x^2 + 2x} = \dfrac{3}{x(x + 2)}$

is all real numbers $\neq 0, -2$.

49. (a) $(f \circ g)(x) = f(g(x)) = f(x^2) = \sqrt{x^2 + 4}$

Domain: all x

$(g \circ f)(x) = g(f(x)) = g\left(\sqrt{x + 4}\right) = \left(\sqrt{x + 4}\right)^2$

$= x + 4, \; x \geq -4$

(b)

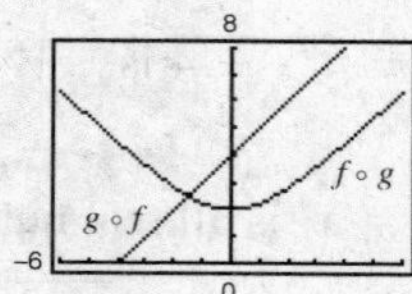

They are not equal.

50. (a) $(f \circ g)(x) = f(g(x)) = f(x^3 - 1)$

$= \sqrt[3]{(x^3 - 1) + 1} = \sqrt[3]{x^3} = x$

Domain: all x

$(g \circ f)(x) = g(f(x)) = g\left(\sqrt[3]{x + 1}\right)$

$= \left[\sqrt[3]{x + 1}\right]^3 - 1$

$= (x + 1) - 1 = x$

They are equal. $(f \circ g)(x) = (g \circ f)(x) = x$

(b)

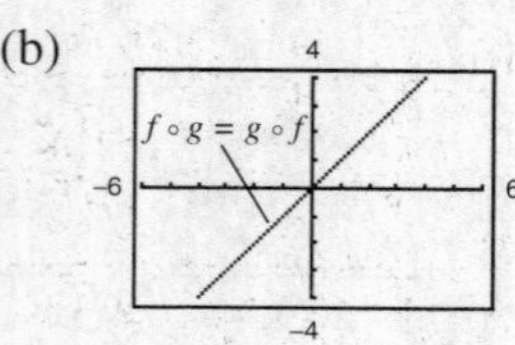

51. (a) $(f \circ g)(x) = f(g(x)) = f(3x + 9)$

$= \frac{1}{3}(3x + 9) - 3 = x$

Domain: all x

$(g \circ f)(x) = g(f(x)) = g\left(\frac{1}{3}x - 3\right)$

$= 3\left(\frac{1}{3}x - 3\right) + 9 = x$

The domain of $f \circ g$ is all real numbers.

(b)

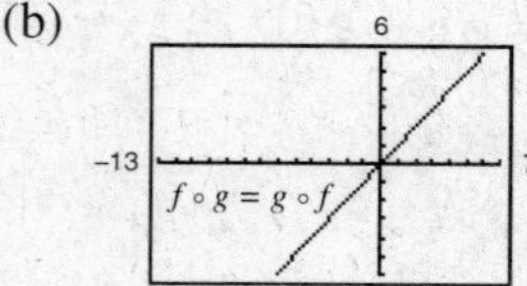

They are equal.

52. (a) $(f \circ g)(x) = (g \circ f)(x) = \sqrt{\sqrt{x}} = x^{1/4}$

Domain: $x \geq 0$

(b) 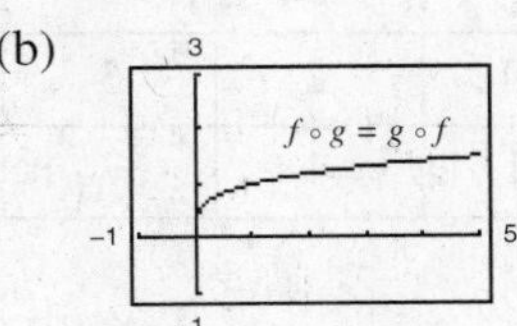

They are equal.

53. (a) $(f \circ g)(x) = f(g(x)) = f(x^6) = (x^6)^{2/3} = x^4$

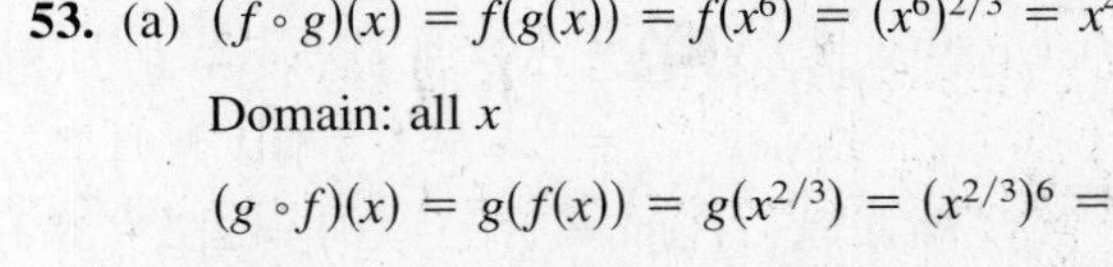

Domain: all x

$(g \circ f)(x) = g(f(x)) = g(x^{2/3}) = (x^{2/3})^6 = x^4$

(b) 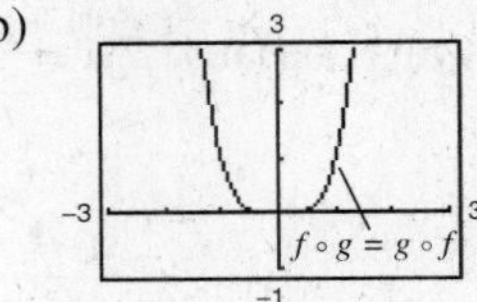

They are equal.

54. (a) $(f \circ g)(x) = f(g(x)) = f(-x^2 + 1) = |-x^2 + 1|$

Domain: all x

$(g \circ f)(x) = g(f(x)) = g(|x|) = -|x|^2 + 1$

(b) 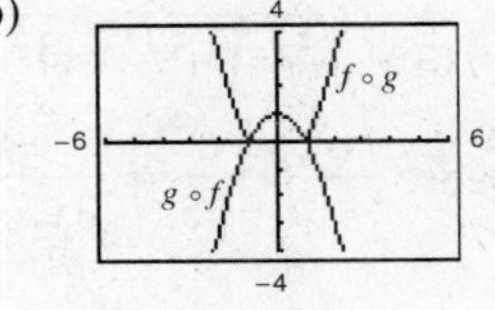

$f \circ g \neq g \circ f$

55. (a) $(f \circ g)(x) = f(g(x)) = f(4 - x) = 5(4 - x) + 4 = 24 - 5x$

$(g \circ f)(x) = g(f(x)) = g(5x + 4) = 4 - (5x + 4) = -5x$

(b) No, $(f \circ g)(x) \neq (g \circ f)(x)$ because $24 - 5x \neq -5x$.

(c)

x	$f(g(x))$	$g(f(x))$
0	24	0
1	19	−5
2	14	−10
3	9	−15

56. (a) $(f \circ g)(x) = f(4x + 1) = \frac{1}{4}[(4x + 1) - 1] = \frac{1}{4}[4x] = x$

$(g \circ f)(x) = g\left(\frac{1}{4}(x - 1)\right) = 4\left[\frac{1}{4}(x - 1)\right] + 1 = (x - 1) + 1 = x$

(b) They are equal because $x = x$.

(c)

x	$f(g(x))$	$g(f(x))$
−1	−1	−1
0	0	0
1	1	1
2	2	2
3	3	3

57. (a) $(f \circ g)(x) = f(g(x)) = f(x^2 - 5) = \sqrt{(x^2 - 5) + 6} = \sqrt{x^2 + 1}$

$(g \circ f)(x) = g(f(x)) = g\left(\sqrt{x + 6}\right) = \left(\sqrt{x + 6}\right)^2 - 5$

$= (x + 6) - 5 = x + 1, x \geq -6$

(b) No, $(f \circ g)(x) \neq (g \circ f)(x)$ because $\sqrt{x^2 + 1} \neq x + 1$.

(c)

x	$f(g(x))$	$g(f(x))$
0	1	1
−2	$\sqrt{5}$	−1
3	$\sqrt{10}$	4

58. (a) $(f \circ g)(x) = f\left(\sqrt[3]{x + 10}\right) = \left[\sqrt[3]{x + 10}\right]^3 - 4$

$= (x + 10) - 4 = x + 6$

$(g \circ f)(x) = g(x^3 - 4) = \sqrt[3]{(x^3 - 4) + 10} = \sqrt[3]{x^3 + 6}$

(b) They are not equal because $x + 6 \neq \sqrt[3]{x^3 + 6}$.

(c)

x	$f(g(x))$	$g(f(x))$
−2	4	$\sqrt[3]{-2}$
0	6	$\sqrt[3]{6}$
1	7	$\sqrt[3]{7}$
2	8	$\sqrt[3]{14}$
3	9	$\sqrt[3]{33}$

59. (a) $(f \circ g)(x) = f(g(x)) = f(2x - 1) = |(2x - 1) + 3|$

$= |2x + 2| = 2|x + 1|$

$(g \circ f)(x) = g(f(x)) = g(|x + 3|) = 2|x + 3| - 1$

(b) No, $(f \circ g)(x) \neq (g \circ f)(x)$ because $2|x + 1| \neq 2|x + 3| - 1$.

(c)

x	$f(g(x))$	$g(f(x))$
-1	0	3
0	2	5
1	4	7

60. (a) $(f \circ g)(x) = f(g(x)) = f(-x) = \dfrac{6}{3(-x) - 5} = \dfrac{6}{-3x - 5}$

$(g \circ f)(x) = g\left(\dfrac{6}{3x - 5}\right) = -\left(\dfrac{6}{3x - 5}\right) = \dfrac{-6}{3x - 5}$

(b) They are not equal because $\dfrac{6}{-3x - 5} \neq \dfrac{-6}{3x - 5}$.

(c)

x	$f(g(x))$	$g(f(x))$
0	$-\frac{6}{5}$	$\frac{6}{5}$
1	$-\frac{3}{4}$	3
2	$-\frac{6}{11}$	-6
3	$-\frac{3}{7}$	$-\frac{3}{2}$

61. (a) $(f + g)(3) = f(3) + g(3) = 2 + 1 = 3$

(b) $\left(\dfrac{f}{g}\right)(2) = \dfrac{f(2)}{g(2)} = \dfrac{0}{2} = 0$

62. (a) $(f - g)(1) = f(1) - g(1) = 2 - 3 = -1$

(b) $(fg)(4) = f(4) \cdot g(4) = 4 \cdot 0 = 0$

63. (a) $(f \circ g)(2) = f(g(2)) = f(2) = 0$

(b) $(g \circ f)(2) = g(f(2)) = g(0) = 4$

64. (a) $(f \circ g)(1) = f(g(1)) = f(3) = 2$

(b) $(g \circ f)(3) = g(f(3)) = g(2) = 2$

65. Let $f(x) = x^2$ and $g(x) = 2x + 1$, then $(f \circ g)(x) = h(x)$. This is not a unique solution. For example, if $f(x) = (x + 1)^2$ and $g(x) = 2x$, then $(f \circ g)(x) = h(x)$ as well.

66. $h(x) = (1 - x)^3$

One possibility: Let $g(x) = 1 - x$ and $f(x) = x^3$.

$(f \circ g)(x) = f(1 - x) = (1 - x)^3 = h(x)$

67. Let $f(x) = \sqrt[3]{x}$ and $g(x) = x^2 - 4$, then $(f \circ g)(x) = h(x)$. This answer is not unique. Other possibilities may be:

$f(x) = \sqrt[3]{x - 4}$ and $g(x) = x^2$ or

$f(x) = \sqrt[3]{-x}$ and $g(x) = 4 - x^2$ or

$f(x) = \sqrt[9]{x}$ and $g(x) = (x^2 - 4)^3$

68. $h(x) = \sqrt{9 - x}$

One possibility: Let $g(x) = 9 - x$ and $f(x) = \sqrt{x}$.

$(f \circ g)(x) = f(9 - x) = \sqrt{9 - x} = h(x)$

69. Let $f(x) = 1/x$ and $g(x) = x + 2$, then $(f \circ g)(x) = h(x)$. Again, this is not a unique solution. Other possibilities may be:

$f(x) = \dfrac{1}{x + 2}$ and $g(x) = x$

or $f(x) = \dfrac{1}{x + 1}$ and $g(x) = x + 1$

70. $h(x) = \dfrac{4}{(5x + 2)^2}$

One possibility:

Let $g(x) = 5x + 2$ and $f(x) = \dfrac{4}{x^2}$.

$(f \circ g)(x) = f(5x + 2) = \dfrac{4}{(5x + 2)^2}$

71. Let $f(x) = x^2 + 2x$ and $g(x) = x + 4$. Then $(f \circ g)(x) = h(x)$. (Answer is not unique.)

72. $h(x) = (x + 3)^{3/2} + 4(x + 3)^{1/2}$

One possibility:

Let $g(x) = x + 3$ and $f(x) = x^{3/2} + 4x^{1/2}$.

$$\begin{aligned}(f \circ g)(x) &= f(g(x)) = f(x + 3)\\ &= (x + 3)^{3/2} + 4(x + 3)^{1/2} = h(x)\end{aligned}$$

73. (a) $T(x) = R(x) + B(x) = \frac{3}{4}x + \frac{1}{15}x^2$

(b)

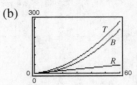

(c) $B(x)$ contributes more to $T(x)$ at higher speeds.

74. (a)
$$\begin{aligned}R_3 &= R_1 + R_2\\ &= (480 - 8t - 0.8t^2) + (254 + 0.78t)\\ &= 734 - 7.22t - 0.8t^2, \quad t = 0, 1, 2, 3, 4, 5, 6\end{aligned}$$

(b)

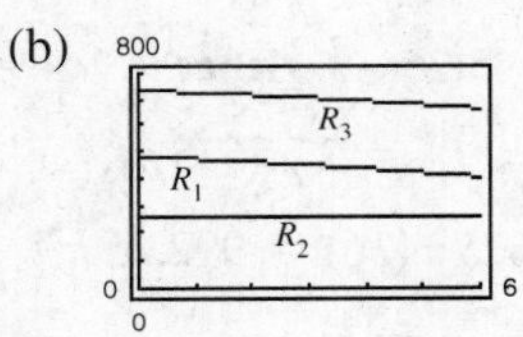

75. $t = 5$ corresponds to 1995.

Year	1995	1996	1997	1998	1999	2000	2001	2002	2003	2004	2005
y_1	140	151.4	162.8	174.2	185.6	197	208.4	219.8	231.2	242.6	254
y_2	325.8	342.8	364.4	390.6	421.5	457	497.1	541.8	591.2	645.2	703.8
y_3	458.8	475.3	497.9	526.5	561.2	602	648.8	701.7	760.7	825.7	896.8

76.

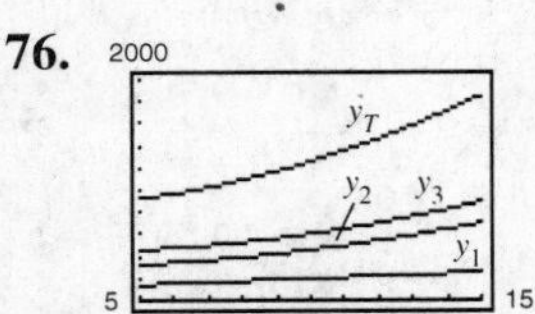

y_T represents the total out-of-pocket payments, insurance premiums and other types of premiums in billions of dollars.

77. $(A \circ r)(t)$ gives the area of the circle as a function of time.

$$\begin{aligned}(A \circ r)(t) &= A(r(t))\\ &= A(0.6t)\\ &= \pi(0.6t)^2 = 0.36\pi t^2\end{aligned}$$

78. (a) $r(x) = \dfrac{x}{2}$

(b) $A(r) = \pi r^2$

(c) $(A \circ r)(x) = A(r(x))$

$= A\left(\dfrac{x}{2}\right) = \pi\left(\dfrac{x}{2}\right)^2 = \dfrac{1}{4}\pi x^2$

$A \circ r$ represents the area of the circular base of the tank with edge x.

79. $C(x) = 60x + 750$

$x(t) = 50t$

(a) $C(x(t)) = C(50t)$

$= 60(50t) + 750$

$= 3000t + 750$

$C(x(t))$ represents the cost after t hours.

(b) $x(4) = 50(4) = 200$ units

(c) 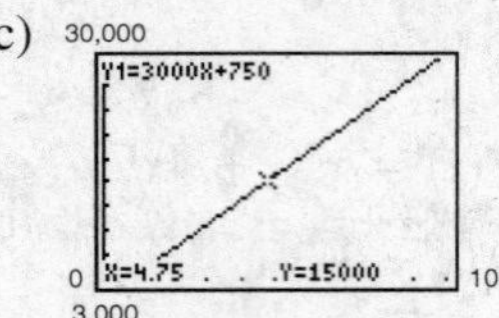

$t = 4.75$, or 4 hours 45 minutes

80. $x = 150$ miles $-$ (450 mph)(t hours)

$y = 200$ miles $-$ (450 mph)(t hours)

$s = \sqrt{x^2 + y^2} = \sqrt{(150 - 450t)^2 + (200 - 450t)^2} = 50\sqrt{162t^2 - 126t + 25}$

81. (a) $(N \circ T)(t) = N(T(t))$

$= N(2t + 1)$

$= 10(2t + 1)^2 - 20(2t + 1) + 600$

$= 40t^2 + 590$

$N \circ T$ represents the number of bacteria as a function of time.

(b) $(N \circ T)(6) = 10(13^2) - 20(13) + 600 = 2030$

At time $t = 6$, there are 2030 bacteria.

(c) $N = 800$ when $t \approx 2.3$ hours.

82. (a) Area $= \pi r^2$, $r(t) = 5.25\sqrt{t}$. Hence

$(A \circ r)(t) = \pi\left[5.25\sqrt{t}\right]^2 = 27.5625\pi t, \quad t \geq 0$

(b) $(A \circ r)(36) = 27.5625\pi(36) = 992.25\pi$

≈ 3117 square meters

(c) $A = 6250 = 27.5625\pi t \implies t \approx 72.2$ hours

83. $g(f(x)) = g(x - 500{,}000) = 0.03(x - 500{,}000)$ represents 3 percent of the amount over \$500,000.

84. (a) $R = p - 1200$

(b) $S = 0.92p$

(c) $(R \circ S)(p) = 0.92p - 1200$

$(S \circ R)(p) = 0.92(p - 1200)$

(d) $(R \circ S)(18{,}400) = 15{,}728$

$(S \circ R)(18{,}400) = 15{,}824$

The discount first yields a lower cost.

85. False. $(f \circ g)(x) = f(6x) = 6x + 1$, but $(g \circ f)(x) = g(x + 1) = 6(x + 1)$.

86. True. $(f \circ g)(x) = f(g(x))$ is only defined if $g(x)$ is in the domain of f.

87. Let A, B, and C be the three siblings, in decreasing age. Then $A = 2B$ and $B = \frac{1}{2}C + 6$.

(a) $A = 2B = 2(\frac{1}{2}C + 6) = C + 12$

(b) If $A = 16$, then $B = 8$ and $C = 4$.

88. From Exercise 87, $A = 2B$ and $B = \frac{1}{2}C + 6$.

(a) $2(B - 6) = C$ and $B = \frac{1}{2}A$. Hence,

$C = 2(\frac{1}{2}A - 6) = A - 12$.

(b) If $C = 2$, then $B = 7$ and $A = 14$.

89. Let $f(x)$ and $g(x)$ be odd functions, and define $h(x) = f(x)g(x)$. Then,

$$\begin{aligned} h(-x) &= f(-x)g(-x) \\ &= [-f(x)][-g(x)] \quad \text{since } f \text{ and } g \text{ are both odd} \\ &= f(x)g(x) = h(x). \end{aligned}$$

Thus, h is even.

Let $f(x)$ and $g(x)$ be even functions, and define $h(x) = f(x)g(x)$. Then,

$$\begin{aligned} h(-x) &= f(-x)g(-x) \\ &= f(x)g(x) \quad \text{since } f \text{ and } g \text{ are both even} \\ &= h(x). \end{aligned}$$

Thus, h is even.

90. The product of an odd function and an even function is odd. Let f be odd and g even. Then

$(fg)(-x) = f(-x)g(-x) = -f(x)g(x) = -(fg)(x)$

Thus, fg is odd.

91. $g(-x) = \frac{1}{2}[f(-x) + f(-(-x))] = \frac{1}{2}[f(-x) + f(x)] = g(x)$,

which shows that g is even.

$$\begin{aligned} h(-x) &= \tfrac{1}{2}[f(-x) - f(-(-x))] = \tfrac{1}{2}[f(-x) - f(x)] \\ &= -\tfrac{1}{2}[f(x) - f(-x)] = -h(x), \end{aligned}$$

which shows that h is odd.

92. (a) $$f(x) = \underbrace{\frac{1}{2}[f(x) + f(-x)]}_{g(x)} + \underbrace{\frac{1}{2}[f(x) - f(-x)]}_{h(x)}$$

$$= \qquad g(x) \qquad + \qquad h(x)$$

where g is even and h is odd.

(b) $$f(x) = \frac{1}{2}[(x^2 - 2x + 1) + (x^2 + 2x + 1)] + \frac{1}{2}[(x^2 - 2x + 1) - (x^2 + 2x + 1)]$$

$$= \frac{1}{2}[2x^2 + 2] + \frac{1}{2}[-4x] = [x^2 + 1] + [-2x]$$

$$g(x) = \frac{1}{2}\left[\frac{1}{x + 1} + \frac{1}{-x + 1}\right] + \frac{1}{2}\left[\frac{1}{x + 1} - \frac{1}{-x + 1}\right]$$

$$= \frac{-1}{(x + 1)(x - 1)} + \frac{x}{(x + 1)(x - 1)}$$

93. $(0, -5), (1, -5), (2, -7)$ (other answers possible)

94. Three points on the graph of $y = \frac{1}{5}x^3 - 4x^2 + 1$ are $(0, 1), (1, -2.8)$ and $(-1, -3.2)$.

95. $(\sqrt{24}, 0), (-\sqrt{24}, 0), (0, \sqrt{24})$
(other answers possible)

96. Three points on the graph of $y = \dfrac{x}{x^2 - 5}$ are $(0, 0), \left(1, -\dfrac{1}{4}\right)$ and $\left(-1, \dfrac{1}{4}\right)$.

97.
$$y - (-2) = \frac{8 - (-2)}{-3 - (-4)}(x - (-4))$$
$$y + 2 = 10(x + 4)$$
$$y - 10x - 38 = 0$$

98.
$$y - 5 = \frac{2 - 5}{-8 - 1}(x - 1)$$
$$y - 5 = \frac{1}{3}(x - 1)$$
$$3y - x - 14 = 0$$

99.
$$y - (-1) = \frac{4 - (-1)}{-(1/3) - (3/2)}\left(x - \frac{3}{2}\right)$$
$$y + 1 = \frac{5}{-11/6}\left(x - \frac{3}{2}\right) = -\frac{30}{11}\left(x - \frac{3}{2}\right)$$
$$11y + 11 = -30x + 45$$
$$30x + 11y - 34 = 0$$

100.
$$y - 1.1 = \frac{3.1 - 1.1}{-4 - 0}(x - 0)$$
$$y - 1.1 = -\frac{1}{2}x$$
$$2y + x - 2.2 = 0$$

Section 1.6 Inverse Functions

- Two functions f and g are inverses of each other if $f(g(x)) = x$ for every x in the domain of g and $g(f(x)) = x$ for every x in the domain of f.
- Be able to find the inverse of a function, if it exists.
  1. Replace $f(x)$ with y.
  2. Interchange x and y.
  3. Solve for y. If this equation represents y as a function of x, then you have found $f^{-1}(x)$. If this equation does not represent y as a function of x, then f does not have an inverse function.
- A function f has an inverse function if and only if no **horizontal** line crosses the graph of f at more than one point.
- A function f has an inverse function if and only if f is one-to-one.

Vocabulary Check

1. inverse, f^{-1} **2.** range, domain **3.** $y = x$

4. one-to-one **5.** Horizontal

1.
$$f(x) = 6x$$
$$f^{-1}(x) = \tfrac{1}{6}x$$
$$f(f^{-1}(x)) = f\left(\tfrac{1}{6}x\right) = 6\left(\tfrac{1}{6}x\right) = x$$
$$f^{-1}(f(x)) = f^{-1}(6x) = \tfrac{1}{6}(6x) = x$$

2.
$$f(x) = \tfrac{1}{3}x$$
$$f^{-1}(x) = 3x$$
$$f(f^{-1}(x)) = f(3x) = \tfrac{1}{3}(3x) = x$$
$$f^{-1}(f(x)) = f^{-1}\left(\tfrac{1}{3}x\right) = 3\left(\tfrac{1}{3}x\right) = x$$

3. $f(x) = x + 7$

$f^{-1}(x) = x - 7$

$f(f^{-1}(x)) = f(x - 7) = (x - 7) + 7 = x$

$f^{-1}(f(x)) = f^{-1}(x + 7) = (x + 7) - 7 = x$

4. $f(x) = x - 3$

$f^{-1}(x) = x + 3$

$f(f^{-1}(x)) = f(x + 3) = (x + 3) - 3 = x$

$f^{-1}(f(x)) = f^{-1}(x - 3) = (x - 3) + 3 = x$

5. $f^{-1}(x) = \dfrac{x - 1}{2}$

$$f(f^{-1}(x)) = f\left(\frac{x - 1}{2}\right) = 2\left(\frac{x - 1}{2}\right) + 1 = (x - 1) + 1 = x$$

$$f^{-1}(f(x)) = f^{-1}(2x + 1) = \frac{(2x + 1) - 1}{2} = \frac{2x}{2} = x$$

6. $f(x) = \dfrac{x - 1}{4}$

$f^{-1}(x) = 4x + 1$

$$f(f^{-1}(x)) = f(4x + 1) = \frac{(4x + 1) - 1}{4} = \frac{4x}{4} = x$$

7. $f^{-1}(x) = x^3$

$f(f^{-1}(x)) = f(x^3) = \sqrt[3]{x^3} = x$

$f^{-1}(f(x)) = f^{-1}\left(\sqrt[3]{x}\right) = \left(\sqrt[3]{x}\right)^3 = x$

8. $f(x) = x^5$

$f^{-1}(x) = \sqrt[5]{x}$

$f(f^{-1}(x)) = f\left(\sqrt[5]{x}\right) = \left(\sqrt[5]{x}\right)^5 = x$

$f^{-1}(f(x)) = f^{-1}(x^5) = \sqrt[5]{x^5} = x$

9. (a) $$f(g(x)) = f\left(-\frac{2x + 6}{7}\right) = -\frac{7}{2}\left(-\frac{2x + 6}{7}\right) - 3 = \frac{2x + 6}{2} - 3 = (x + 3) - 3 = x$$

$$g(f(x)) = g\left(-\frac{7}{2}x - 3\right) = -\frac{2\left(-\frac{7}{2}x - 3\right) + 6}{7} = -\frac{-7x - 6 + 6}{7} = \frac{7x}{7} = x$$

(b)

x	2	0	-2	-4	-6
$f(x)$	-10	-3	4	11	18

x	-10	-3	4	11	18
$g(x)$	2	0	-2	-4	-6

Note that the entries in the tables are the same except that the rows are interchanged.

10. (a) $$f(g(x)) = f(4x + 9) = \frac{(4x + 9) - 9}{4} = \frac{4x}{4} = x$$

$$g(f(x)) = g\left(\frac{x - 9}{4}\right) = 4\left(\frac{x - 9}{4}\right) + 9$$

$$= (x - 9) + 9 = x$$

(b)

x	1	5	9	13	17
$f(x)$	-2	-1	0	1	2

x	-2	-1	0	1	2
$g(x)$	1	5	9	13	17

The entries are the same except that the rows are interchanged.

11. (a) $f(g(x)) = f(\sqrt[3]{x-5}) = [\sqrt[3]{x-5}]^3 + 5 = (x-5) + 5 = x$

$g(f(x)) = g(x^3+5) = \sqrt[3]{(x^3+5)-5} = \sqrt[3]{x^3} = x$

(b)

x	-3	-2	-1	0	1
$f(x)$	-22	-3	4	5	6

x	-22	-3	4	5	6
$g(x)$	-3	-2	-1	0	1

Note that the entries in the tables are the same except that the rows are interchanged.

12. (a) $f(g(x)) = f(\sqrt[3]{2x}) = \dfrac{(\sqrt[3]{2x})^3}{2} = \dfrac{2x}{2} = x$

$g(f(x)) = g\left(\dfrac{x^3}{2}\right) = \sqrt[3]{2\left(\dfrac{x^3}{2}\right)} = \sqrt[3]{x^3} = x$

(b)

x	-2	-1	0	1	2
$f(x)$	-4	$-\frac{1}{2}$	0	$\frac{1}{2}$	4

x	-4	$-\frac{1}{2}$	0	$\frac{1}{2}$	4
$g(x)$	-2	-1	0	1	2

The entries are the same except that the rows are interchanged.

13. (a) $f(g(x)) = f(8+x^2) = -\sqrt{(8+x^2)-8} = -\sqrt{x^2} = -(-x) = x \quad x \le 0$

[Since $x \le 0$, $\sqrt{x^2} = -x$]

$g(f(x)) = g(-\sqrt{x-8}) = 8 + [-\sqrt{x-8}]^2 = 8 + (x-8) = x$

(b)

x	8	9	12	17	24
$f(x)$	0	-1	-2	-3	-4

x	0	-1	-2	-3	-4
$g(x)$	8	9	12	17	24

Note that the entries in the tables are the same except that the rows are interchanged.

14. (a) $f(g(x)) = f\left(\dfrac{x^3+10}{3}\right) = \sqrt[3]{3\left(\dfrac{x^3+10}{3}\right) - 10} = \sqrt[3]{(x^3+10)-10} = \sqrt[3]{x^3} = x$

$g(f(x)) = g(\sqrt[3]{3x-10}) = \dfrac{[\sqrt[3]{3x-10}]^3 + 10}{3} = \dfrac{(3x-10)+10}{3} = \dfrac{3x}{3} = x$

(b)

x	$\frac{2}{3}$	3	$\frac{10}{3}$	$\frac{11}{3}$	6
$f(x)$	-2	-1	0	1	2

x	-2	-1	0	1	2
$g(x)$	$\frac{2}{3}$	3	$\frac{10}{3}$	$\frac{11}{3}$	6

The entries in the table are the same except that the rows are interchanged.

15. $f(g(x)) = f(\sqrt[3]{x}) = (\sqrt[3]{x})^3 = x$

$g(f(x)) = g(x^3) = \sqrt[3]{x^3} = x$

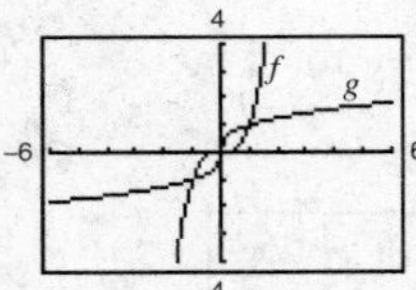

Reflections in the line $y = x$

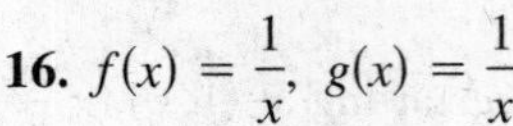

16. $f(x) = \dfrac{1}{x},\ g(x) = \dfrac{1}{x}$

$$f(g(x)) = f\left(\frac{1}{x}\right) = \frac{1}{1/x} = 1 \div \frac{1}{x} = 1 \cdot \frac{x}{1} = x$$

$$g(f(x)) = g\left(\frac{1}{x}\right) = \frac{1}{1/x} = 1 \div \frac{1}{x} = 1 \cdot \frac{x}{1} = x$$

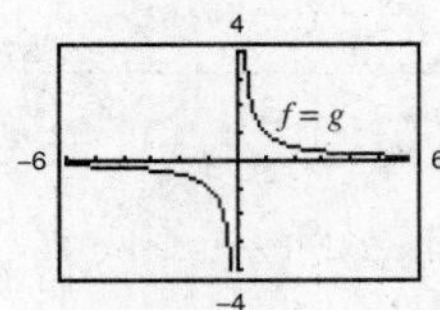

Reflections in the line $y = x$

17. $f(g(x)) = f(x^2 + 4),\ x \geq 0$

$= \sqrt{(x^2 + 4) - 4} = x$

$g(f(x)) = g(\sqrt{x - 4})$

$= (\sqrt{x - 4})^2 + 4 = x$

Reflections in the line $y = x$

18. $f(x) = 9 - x^2, x \geq 0$

$g(x) = \sqrt{9 - x}, x \leq 9$

$f(g(x)) = f(\sqrt{9 - x}) = 9 - (\sqrt{9 - x})^2 = 9 - (9 - x) = x$

$g(f(x)) = g(9 - x^2) = \sqrt{9 - (9 - x^2)} = \sqrt{x^2} = x$

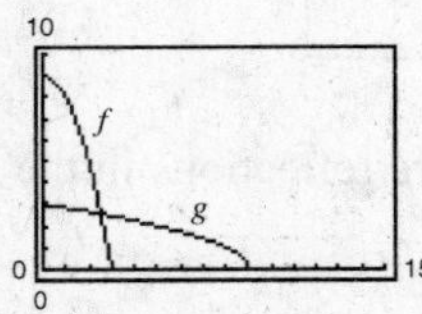

Reflections in the line $y = x$

19. $f(g(x)) = f(\sqrt[3]{1 - x}) = 1 - (\sqrt[3]{1 - x})^3 = 1 - (1 - x) = x$

$g(f(x)) = g(1 - x^3) = \sqrt[3]{1 - (1 - x^3)} = \sqrt[3]{x^3} = x$

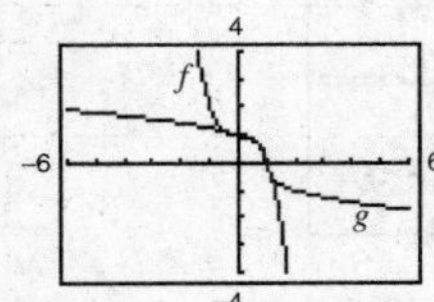

Reflections in the line $y = x$

20. $f(x) = \dfrac{1}{1 + x},\ x \geq 0;\ g(x) = \dfrac{1 - x}{x},\ 0 < x \leq 1$

$$f(g(x)) = f\left(\frac{1 - x}{x}\right) = \frac{1}{1 + \left(\dfrac{1 - x}{x}\right)} = \frac{1}{\dfrac{x}{x} + \dfrac{1 - x}{x}} = \frac{1}{\dfrac{1}{x}} = x$$

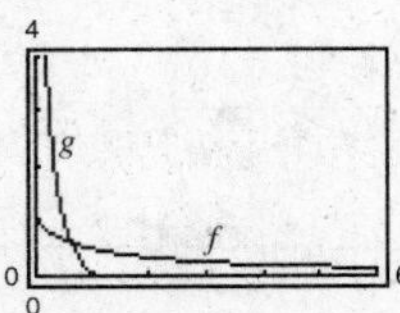

Reflections in the line $y = x$

$$g(f(x)) = g\left(\frac{1}{1 + x}\right) = \frac{1 - \left(\dfrac{1}{1 + x}\right)}{\left(\dfrac{1}{1 + x}\right)} = \frac{\dfrac{1 + x}{1 + x} - \dfrac{1}{1 + x}}{\dfrac{1}{1 + x}} = \frac{\dfrac{x}{1 + x}}{\dfrac{1}{1 + x}} = \frac{x}{1 + x} \cdot \frac{x + 1}{1} = x$$

21. The inverse is a line through $(-1, 0)$.

Matches graph (c).

22. The inverse is a line through $(0, 6)$ and $(6, 0)$.

Matches graph (b).

23. The inverse is half a parabola starting at (1, 0).

Matches graph (a).

24. The inverse is a reflection in $y = x$ of a third-degree equation through (0, 0).

Matches graph (d).

25. $f(x) = 2x, \quad g(x) = \dfrac{x}{2}$

(a)

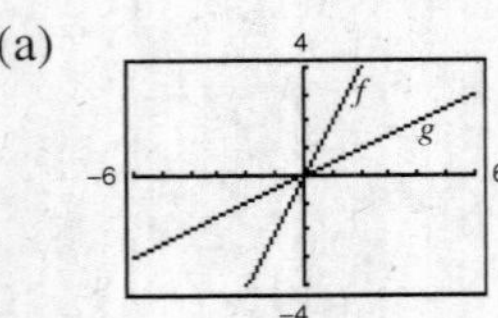

Reflection in the line $y = x$

(b)

x	-2	-1	0	1	2
$f(x)$	-4	-2	0	2	4

x	-4	-2	0	2	4
$g(x)$	-2	-1	0	1	2

The entries in the tables are the same, except that the rows are interchanged.

26. $f(x) = x - 5$

$g(x) = x + 5$

(a)

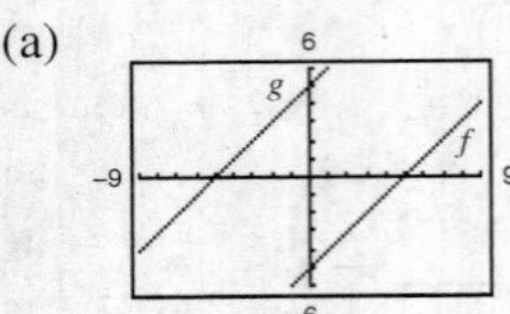

The graphs are reflections in the line $y = x$.

(b)

x	-5	-3	0	3	5
$f(x)$	-10	-8	-5	-2	0

x	-10	-8	-5	-2	0
$g(x)$	-5	-3	0	3	5

The entries in the table are the same except that the rows are interchanged.

27. $f(x) = \dfrac{x - 1}{x + 5}, \quad g(x) = -\dfrac{5x + 1}{x - 1} = \dfrac{5x + 1}{1 - x}$

(a)

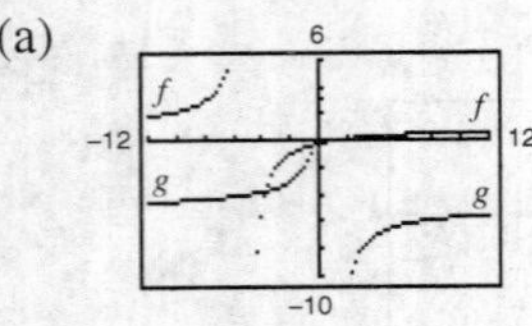

Reflection in the line $y = x$

(b)

x	-2	-1	0	3	5
$f(x)$	-1	$-\frac{1}{2}$	$-\frac{1}{5}$	$\frac{1}{4}$	$\frac{2}{5}$

x	-1	$-\frac{1}{2}$	$-\frac{1}{5}$	$\frac{1}{4}$	$\frac{2}{5}$
$g(x)$	-2	-1	0	3	5

The entries in the tables are the same, except that the rows are interchanged.

28. $f(x) = \dfrac{x + 3}{x - 2}$

$g(x) = \dfrac{2x + 3}{x - 1}$

(a)

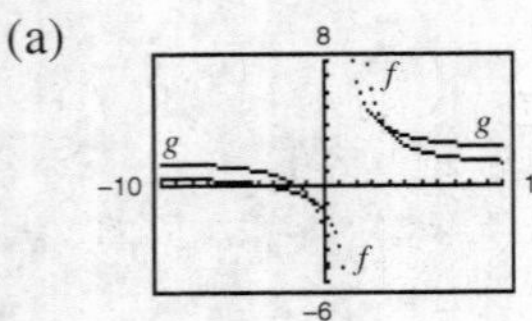

Reflection in the line $y = x$.

(b)

x	-4	-3	0	3	6
$f(x)$	$\frac{1}{6}$	0	$-\frac{3}{2}$	6	$\frac{9}{4}$

x	$\frac{1}{6}$	0	$-\frac{3}{2}$	6	$\frac{9}{4}$
$g(x)$	-4	-3	0	3	6

The entries in the table are the same except that the rows are interchanged.

29. Not a function

30. It is the graph of a function, but not one-to-one.

31. It is the graph of a one-to-one function.

32. It is the graph of a one-to-one function.

33. It is the graph of a one-to-one function.

34. It is the graph of a one-to-one function.

35. $f(x) = 3 - \frac{1}{2}x$

f is one-to-one because a horizontal line will intersect the graph at most once.

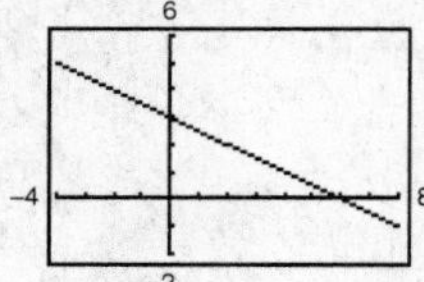

36. $f(x) = \frac{1}{4}(x + 2)^2 - 1$

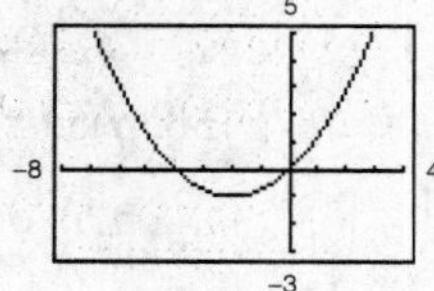

f does not pass the Horizontal Line Test, so f is not one-to-one.

37. $h(x) = \dfrac{x^2}{x^2 + 1}$

h is not one-to-one because some horizontal lines intersect the graph twice.

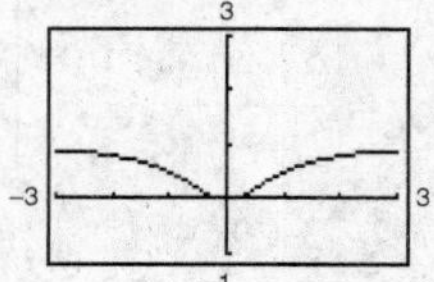

38. $g(x) = \dfrac{4 - x}{6x^2}$

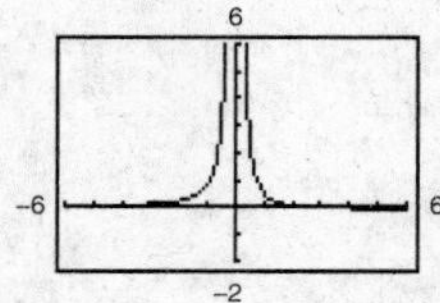

g does not pass the Horizontal Line Test, so g is not one-to-one.

39. $h(x) = \sqrt{16 - x^2}$

h is not one-to-one because some horizontal lines intersect the graph twice.

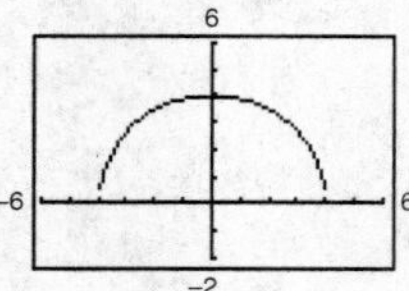

40. $f(x) = -2x\sqrt{16 - x^2}$

is not one-to-one because it does not pass the Horizontal Line Test.

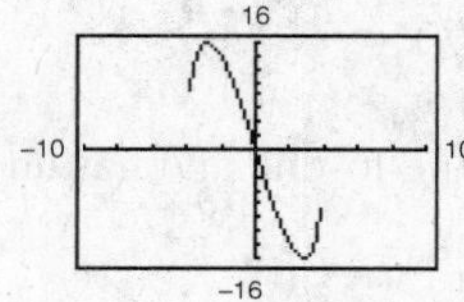

41. $f(x) = 10$

f is not one-to-one because the horizontal line $y = 10$ intersects the graph at every point on the graph.

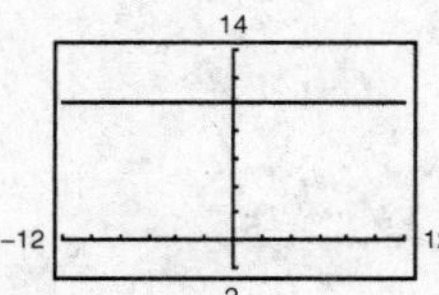

42. $f(x) = -0.65$

is not one-to-one because it does not pass the Horizontal Line Test.

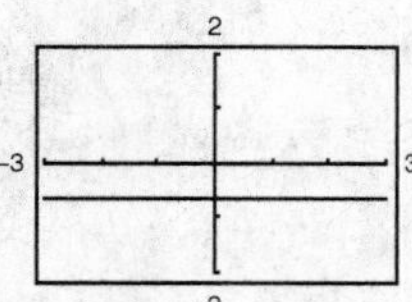

43. $g(x) = (x + 5)^3$

g is one-to-one because a horizontal line will intersect the graph at most once.

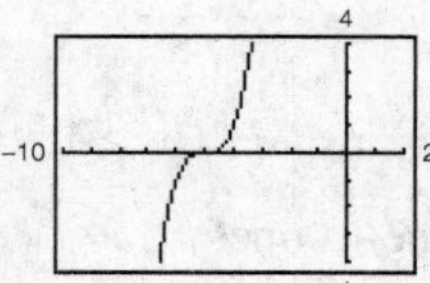

44. $f(x) = x^5 - 7$

is one-to-one because it passes the Horizontal Line Test.

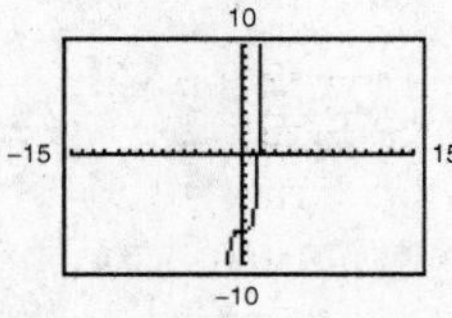

45. $h(x) = |x + 4| - |x - 4|$

h is not one-to-one because some horizontal lines intersect the graph more than once.

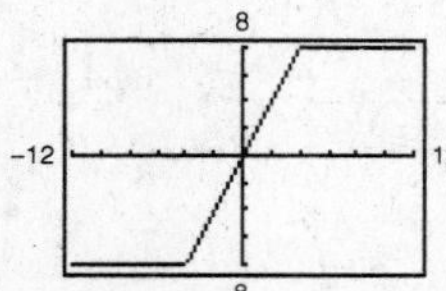

46. $f(x) = -\dfrac{|x - 6|}{|x + 6|}$

is not one-to-one because it does not pass the Horizontal Line Test.

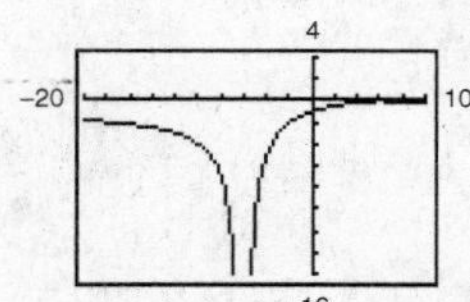

47. $f(x) = x^4$

$y = x^4$

$x = y^4$

$y = \pm\sqrt[4]{x}$

f is not one-to-one.

This does not represent y as a function of x. f does not have an inverse.

48. g is not one-to-one.

For example, $g(1) = g(-1) = 0$.

49. $f(x) = \dfrac{3x + 4}{5}$

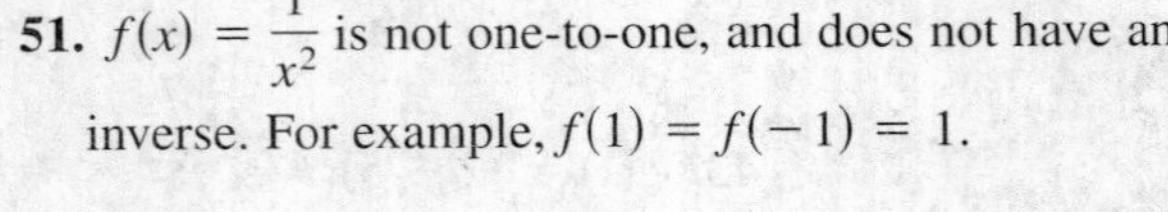

$y = \dfrac{3x + 4}{5}$

$x = \dfrac{3y + 4}{5}$

$5x = 3y + 4$

$5x - 4 = 3y$

$\dfrac{5x - 4}{3} = y$

$f^{-1}(x) = \dfrac{5x - 4}{3}$

f is one-to-one and has an inverse.

50. $f(x) = 3x + 5$

f is one-to-one.

$y = 3x + 5$

$x = 3y + 5$

$x - 5 = 3y$

$\dfrac{x - 5}{3} = y$

$f^{-1}(x) = \dfrac{x - 5}{3}$

51. $f(x) = \dfrac{1}{x^2}$ is not one-to-one, and does not have an inverse. For example, $f(1) = f(-1) = 1$.

52. $h(x) = \dfrac{4}{x^2}$ is not one-to-one.

For example, $h(1) = h(-1) = 4$.

53. $f(x) = (x + 3)^2,\ x \geq -3,\ y \geq 0$

$y = (x + 3)^2,\ x \geq -3,\ y \geq 0$

$x = (y + 3)^2,\ y \geq -3,\ x \geq 0$

$\sqrt{x} = y + 3,\ y \geq -3,\ x \geq 0$

$y = \sqrt{x} - 3,\ x \geq 0,\ y \geq -3$

f is one-to-one.

This is a function of x, so f has an inverse.

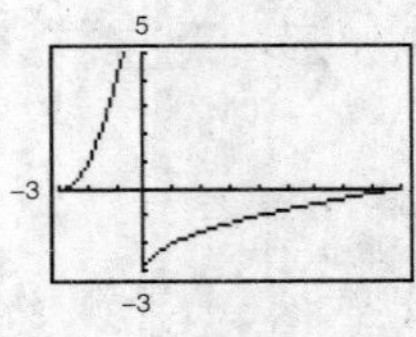

$f^{-1}(x) = \sqrt{x} - 3,\ x \geq 0$

54. $q(x) = (x - 5)^2,\ x \leq 5$ is one-to-one.

$y = (x - 5)^2,\ x \leq 5$

$x = (y - 5)^2,\ y \leq 5$

$-\sqrt{x} = y - 5,\ y \leq 5$

$y = -\sqrt{x} + 5$

The inverse is $q^{-1}(x) = -\sqrt{x} + 5$.

55. $f(x) = \sqrt{2x+3} \implies x \geq -\frac{3}{2}, y \geq 0$

$y = \sqrt{2x+3},\ x \geq -\frac{3}{2},\ y \geq 0$

$x = \sqrt{2y+3},\ y \geq -\frac{3}{2},\ x \geq 0$

$x^2 = 2y + 3,\ x \geq 0,\ y \geq -\frac{3}{2}$

$y = \frac{x^2 - 3}{2},\ x \geq 0,\ y \geq -\frac{3}{2}$

f is one to one.

This is a function of x, so f has an inverse.

$f^{-1}(x) = \frac{x^2 - 3}{2},\ x \geq 0$

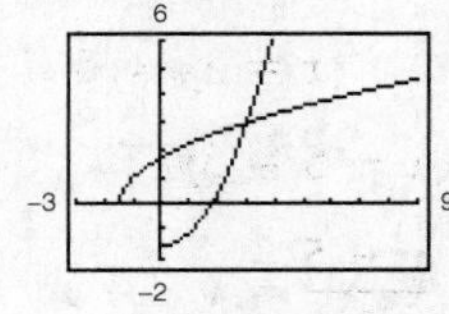

56. $f(x) = \sqrt{x-2} \implies x \geq 2,\ y \geq 0$

$y = \sqrt{x-2},\ x \geq 2,\ y \geq 0$

$x = \sqrt{y-2},\ y \geq 2,\ x \geq 0$

$x^2 = y - 2,\ x \geq 0,\ y \geq 2$

$x^2 + 2 = y,\ x \geq 0,\ y \geq 2$

f is one-to-one, so f has an inverse.

$f^{-1}(x) = x^2 + 2,\ x \geq 0$

57. $f(x) = |x - 2|,\ x \leq 2, y \geq 0$

$y = |x - 2|$

$x = |y - 2|,\quad y \leq 2,\quad x \geq 0$

$x = -(y - 2)$ since $y - 2 \leq 0$.

$x = -y + 2$

$y = -x + 2,\quad x \geq 0,\quad y \leq 2$

$f^{-1}(x) = -x + 2,\quad x \geq 0$

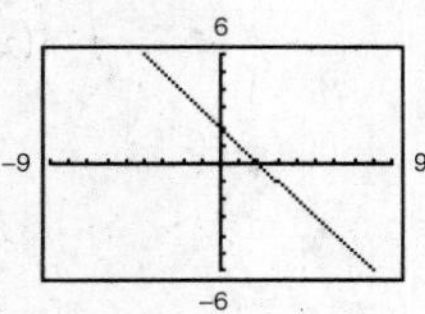

58. $f(x) = \frac{x^2}{x^2 + 1}$

f is not one-to-one.
For instance $f(1) = f(-1)$.
Hence, f does not have an inverse.

59. $f(x) = 2x - 3$

$y = 2x - 3$

$x = 2y - 3$

$y = \frac{x+3}{2}$

$f^{-1}(x) = \frac{x+3}{2}$

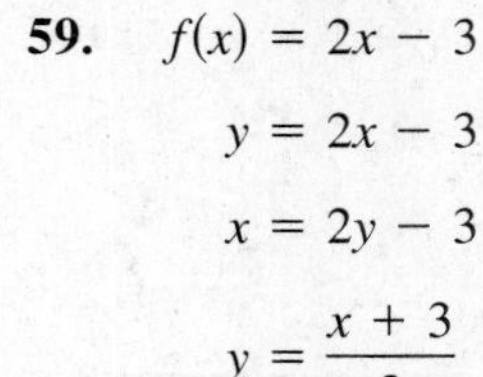

Reflections in the line $y = x$

60. $f(x) = 3x$

$y = 3x$

$x = 3y$

$\frac{x}{3} = y$

$f^{-1}(x) = \frac{x}{3}$

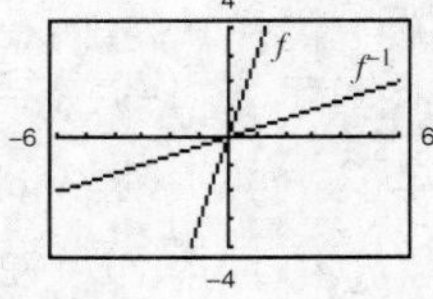

Reflections in the line $y = x$

61. $f(x) = x^5$

$y = x^5$

$x = y^5$

$y = \sqrt[5]{x}$

$f^{-1}(x) = \sqrt[5]{x}$

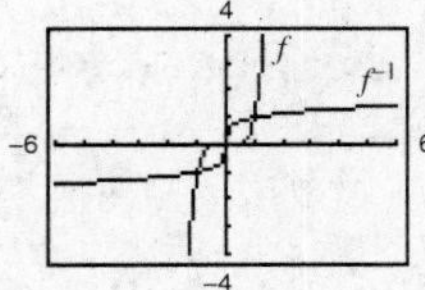

Reflections in the line $y = x$

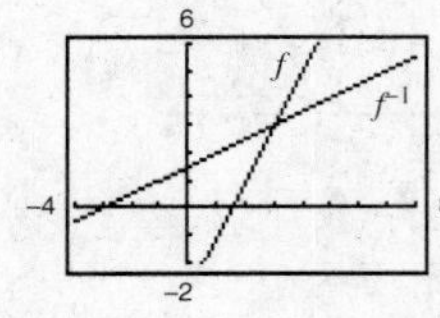

62. $f(x) = x^3 + 1$

$y = x^3 + 1$

$x = y^3 + 1$

$x - 1 = y^3$

$\sqrt[3]{x - 1} = y$

$f^{-1}(x) = \sqrt[3]{x - 1}$

Reflections in the line $y = x$

63. $f(x) = x^{3/5}$

$y = x^{3/5}$

$x = y^{3/5}$

$y = x^{5/3}$

$f^{-1}(x) = x^{5/3}$

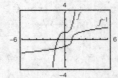

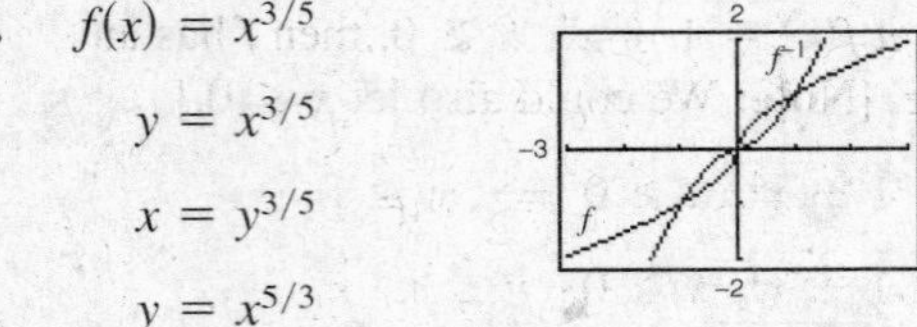

Reflections in the line $y = x$

64. $f(x) = x^2, x \geq 0$

$y = x^2$

$x = y^2$

$\sqrt{x} = y$

$f^{-1}(x) = \sqrt{x}$

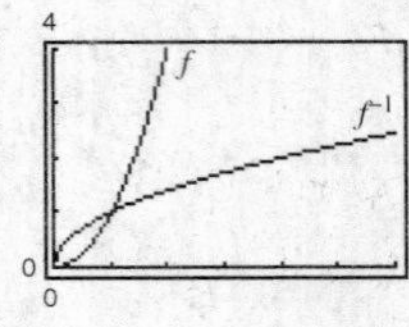

Reflections in the line $y = x$

65. $f(x) = \sqrt{4 - x^2}, 0 \leq x \leq 2$

$y = \sqrt{4 - x^2}$

$x = \sqrt{4 - y^2}$

$x^2 = 4 - y^2$

$y^2 = 4 - x^2$

$y = \sqrt{4 - x^2}$

$f^{-1}(x) = \sqrt{4 - x^2}, 0 \leq x \leq 2$

Reflections in the line $y = x$

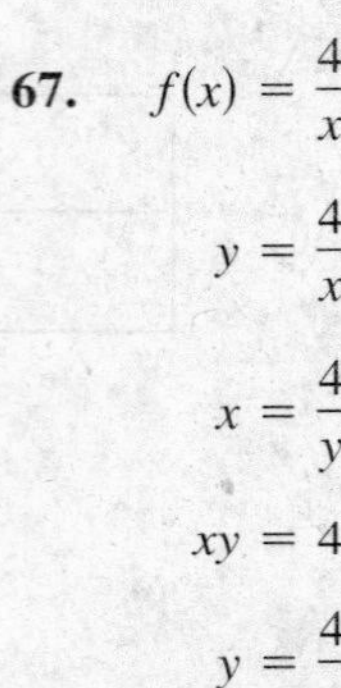

66. $f(x) = \sqrt{16 - x^2}, \quad -4 \leq x \leq 0$

$y = \sqrt{16 - x^2}$

$x = \sqrt{16 - y^2}, -4 \leq y \leq 0$

$x^2 = 16 - y^2$

$y^2 = 16 - x^2$

$y = -\sqrt{16 - x^2}, \quad 0 \leq x \leq 4$

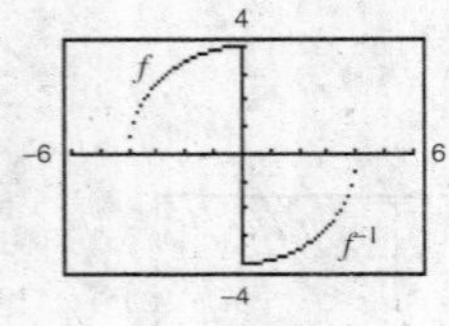

67. $f(x) = \dfrac{4}{x}$

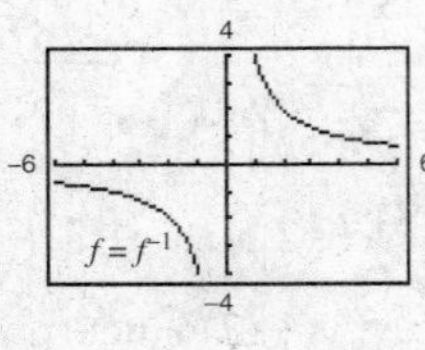

$y = \dfrac{4}{x}$

$x = \dfrac{4}{y}$

$xy = 4$

$y = \dfrac{4}{x}$

$f^{-1}(x) = \dfrac{4}{x}$

Reflections in the line $y = x$

68. $f(x) = \dfrac{6}{\sqrt{x}}$

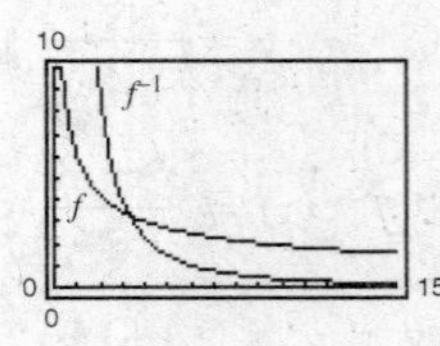

$y = \dfrac{6}{\sqrt{x}}$

$x = \dfrac{6}{\sqrt{y}}$

$x^2 = \dfrac{36}{y}$

$y = \dfrac{36}{x^2}, \ x > 0$

$f^{-1}(x) = \dfrac{36}{x^2}, \ x > 0$

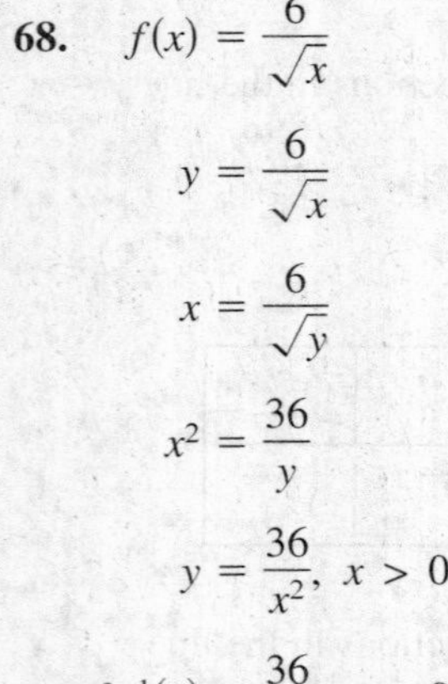

69. If we let $f(x) = (x - 2)^2, \ x \geq 2$, then f has an inverse. [**Note:** We could also let $x \leq 2$.]

$f(x) = (x - 2)^2, \ x \geq 2, \ y \geq 0$

$y = (x - 2)^2, \ x \geq 2, \ y \geq 0$

$x = (y - 2)^2, \ x \geq 0, \ y \geq 2$

$\sqrt{x} = y - 2, \quad x \geq 0, \ y \geq 2$

$\sqrt{x} + 2 = y, \quad x \geq 0, \ y \geq 2$

Thus, $f^{-1}(x) = \sqrt{x} + 2, \ x \geq 0.$

70. If we let $f(x) = 1 - x^4,\ x \ge 0$, then f has an inverse. [**Note:** We could also let $x \le 0$.]

$$f(x) = 1 - x^4,\ x \ge 0 \Rightarrow y \le 1$$
$$y = 1 - x^4,\ x \ge 0,\ y \le 1$$
$$x = 1 - y^4,\ y \ge 0,\ x \le 1$$
$$y^4 = 1 - x,\ y \ge 0,\ x \le 1$$
$$y = \sqrt[4]{1-x},\ x \le 1,\ y \ge 0$$

Thus, $f^{-1}(x) = \sqrt[4]{1-x},\ x \le 1$.

71. If we let $f(x) = |x + 2|,\ x \ge -2$, then f has an inverse. [**Note:** We could also let $x \le -2$.]

$$f(x) = |x + 2|,\quad x \ge -2$$
$$f(x) = x + 2 \text{ when } x \ge -2$$
$$y = x + 2,\ x \ge -2,\quad y \ge 0$$
$$x = y + 2,\ x \ge 0,\quad y \ge -2$$
$$x - 2 = y,\quad x \ge 0,\ y \ge -2$$

Thus, $f^{-1}(x) = x - 2,\ x \ge 0$.

72. If we let $f(x) = |x - 2|,\ x \ge 2$, then f has an inverse. [**Note:** We could also let $x \le 2$.]

$$f(x) = |x - 2|,\ x \ge 2$$
$$f(x) = x - 2 \text{ when } x \ge 2.$$
$$y = x - 2,\ x \ge 2,\ y \ge 0$$
$$x = y - 2,\ x \ge 0,\ y \ge 2$$
$$x + 2 = y,\ x \ge 0,\ y \ge 2$$

Thus, $f^{-1}(x) = x + 2,\ x \ge 0$.

73. Let $f(x) = (x + 3)^2,\quad x \ge -3$.

$$y = (x + 3)^2$$
$$x = (y + 3)^2$$
$$\sqrt{x} = y + 3$$
$$y = \sqrt{x} - 3$$
$$f^{-1}(x) = \sqrt{x} - 3$$

Domain f: $x \ge -3$ Range f: $y \ge 0$

Domain f^{-1}: $x \ge 0$ Range f^{-1}: $y \ge -3$

74. Let $f(x) = (x - 4)^2,\quad x \ge 4$.

$$y = (x - 4)^2$$
$$x = (y - 4)^2$$
$$\sqrt{x} = y - 4$$
$$y = \sqrt{x} + 4$$
$$f^{-1}(x) = \sqrt{x} + 4$$

Domain f: $x \ge 4$ Range f: $y \ge 0$

Domain f^{-1}: $x \ge 0$ Range f^{-1}: $y \ge 4$

75. Let $f(x) = -2x^2 + 5,\quad x \ge 0$.

$$y = -2x^2 + 5$$
$$x = -2y^2 + 5$$
$$x - 5 = -2y^2$$
$$y^2 = \frac{x-5}{-2} = \frac{5-x}{2}$$
$$y = \sqrt{(5-x)/2}$$
$$f^{-1}(x) = \sqrt{\frac{5-x}{2}}$$

Domain f: $x \ge 0$ Range f: $y \le 5$

Domain f^{-1}: $x \le 5$ Range f^{-1}: $y \ge 0$

76. Let $f(x) = \frac{1}{2}x^2 - 1,\quad x \ge 0$.

$$y = \tfrac{1}{2}x^2 - 1$$
$$x = \tfrac{1}{2}y^2 - 1$$
$$2(x + 1) = y^2$$
$$f^{-1}(x) = \sqrt{2x + 2}$$

Domain f: $x \ge 0$ Range f: $y \ge -1$

Domain f^{-1}: $x \ge -1$ Range f^{-1}: $y \ge 0$

77. Let $f(x) = |x - 4| + 1,\quad x \ge 4$ and $y \ge 1$.

$$y = |x - 4| + 1$$
$$y = x - 3 \text{ because } x \ge 4.$$
$$x = y - 3$$
$$y = x + 3$$
$$f^{-1}(x) = x + 3,\quad x \ge 1$$

Domain f: $x \ge 4$ Range f: $y \ge 1$

Domain f^{-1}: $x \ge 1$ Range f^{-1}: $y \ge 4$

78. Let $f(x) = -|x - 1| - 2, \quad x \geq 1$ and $y \leq -2$.

$$y = -|x - 1| - 2 = -(x - 1) - 2 \text{ because } x \geq 1.$$

$$y = -x - 1$$

$$x = -y - 1$$

$$x + 1 = -y$$

$f^{-1}(x) = -x - 1, \quad x \leq -2$

Domain f: $x \geq 1$ Range f: $y \leq -2$

Domain f^{-1}: $x \leq -2$ Range f^{-1}: $y \geq 1$

79. 

x	$f(x)$
-2	-4
-1	-2
1	2
3	3

x	$f^{-1}(x)$
-4	-2
-2	-1
2	1
3	3

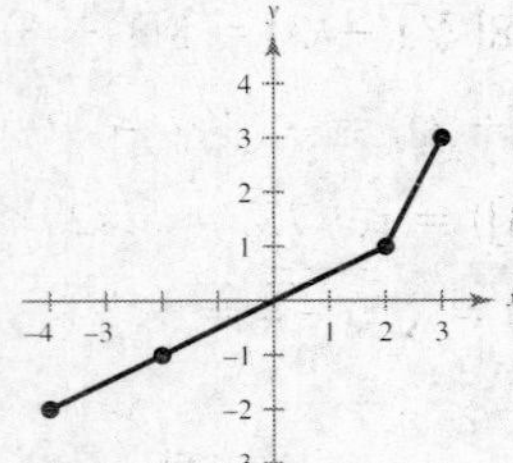

80.

x	$f(x)$
4	-3
3	-2
-1	0
-2	6

x	$f^{-1}(x)$
-3	4
-2	3
0	-1
6	-2

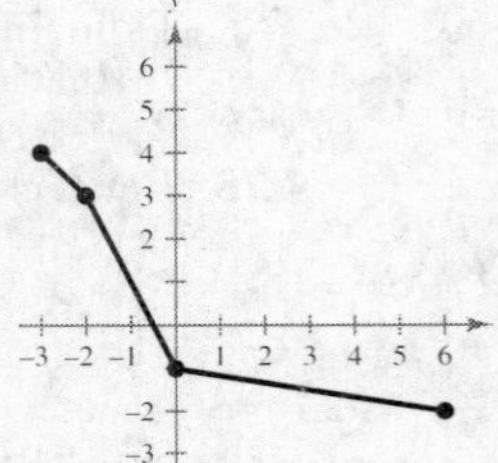

81. $f^{-1}(0) = \frac{1}{2}$ because $f\left(\frac{1}{2}\right) = 0$.

82. $g^{-1}(0) = -2$ because $g(-2) = 0$.

83. $(f \circ g)(2) = f(3) = -2$

84. $g(f(-4)) = g(4) = 6$

85. $f^{-1}(g(0)) = f^{-1}(2) = 0$

86. $(g^{-1} \circ f)(3) = g^{-1}(-2) = -3$

87. $(g \circ f^{-1})(2) = g(0) = 2$

88. $(f^{-1} \circ g^{-1})(-2) = f^{-1}(-3) = 1$

89. $f(x) = x^3 + x + 1$

The graph of the inverse relation is an inverse function since it satisfies the Vertical Line Test.

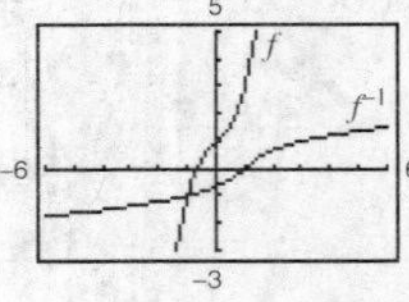

90. (a) and (b)

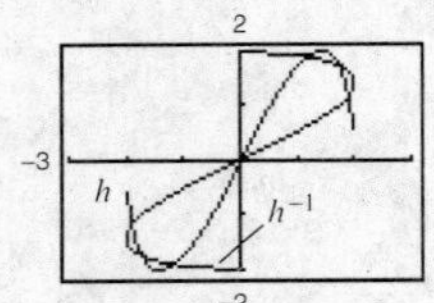

(c) Not an inverse function since it does not satisfy the Vertical Line Test.

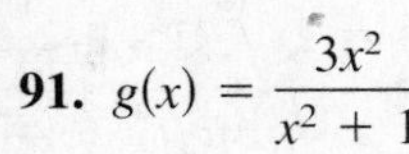

91. $g(x) = \dfrac{3x^2}{x^2 + 1}$

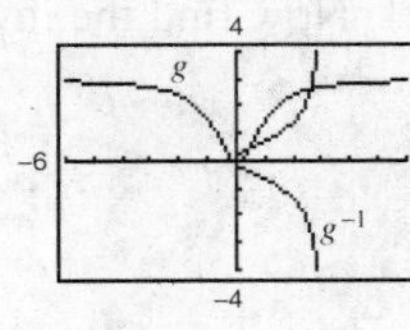

The graph of the inverse relation is not an inverse function since it does not satisfy the Vertical Line Test.

92. (a) and (b)

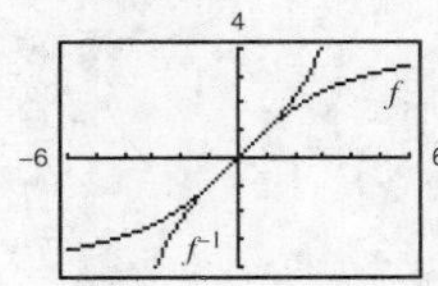

(c) Inverse function since it satisfies the Vertical Line Test.

In Exercises 93–98, $f(x) = \frac{1}{8}x - 3$, $f^{-1}(x) = 8(x + 3)$, $g(x) = x^3$, $g^{-1}(x) = \sqrt[3]{x}$.

93. $(f^{-1} \circ g^{-1})(1) = f^{-1}(g^{-1}(1)) = f^{-1}(\sqrt[3]{1}) = 8(\sqrt[3]{1} + 3) = 8(1 + 3) = 32$

94. $(g^{-1} \circ f^{-1})(-3) = g^{-1}(f^{-1}(-3)) = g^{-1}(8(-3 + 3)) = g^{-1}(0) = \sqrt[3]{0} = 0$

95. $(f^{-1} \circ f^{-1})(6) = f^{-1}(f^{-1}(6)) = f^{-1}(8[6 + 3]) = f^{-1}(72) = 8(72 + 3) = 600$

96. $(g^{-1} \circ g^{-1})(-4) = g^{-1}(g^{-1}(-4)) = g^{-1}(\sqrt[3]{-4}) = \sqrt[3]{\sqrt[3]{-4}} = -\sqrt[9]{4}$

97. $(fg)(x) = f(g(x)) = f(x^3) = \frac{1}{8}x^3 - 3$

Now find the inverse of $(f \circ g)(x) = \frac{1}{8}x^3 - 3$:

$$\begin{aligned} y &= \tfrac{1}{8}x^3 - 3 \\ x &= \tfrac{1}{8}y^3 - 3 \\ x + 3 &= \tfrac{1}{8}y^3 \\ 8(x + 3) &= y^3 \\ \sqrt[3]{8(x + 3)} &= y \\ (f \circ g)^{-1}(x) &= 2\sqrt[3]{x + 3} \end{aligned}$$

Note: $(f \circ g)^{-1} = g^{-1} \circ f^{-1}$

98.
$$\begin{aligned} (g^{-1} \circ f^{-1})(x) &= g^{-1}(f^{-1}(x)) \\ &= g^{-1}(8(x + 3)) \\ &= \sqrt[3]{8(x + 3)} \\ &= 2\sqrt[3]{x + 3} \end{aligned}$$

In Exercises 99–102, $f(x) = x + 4$, $f^{-1}(x) = x - 4$, $g(x) = 2x - 5$, $g^{-1}(x) = \dfrac{x + 5}{2}$.

99.
$$\begin{aligned} (g^{-1} \circ f^{-1})(x) &= g^{-1}(f^{-1}(x)) \\ &= g^{-1}(x - 4) \\ &= \frac{(x - 4) + 5}{2} \\ &= \frac{x + 1}{2} \end{aligned}$$

100.
$$\begin{aligned} (f^{-1} \circ g^{-1})(x) &= f^{-1}(g^{-1}(x)) \\ &= f^{-1}\left(\frac{x + 5}{2}\right) \\ &= \frac{x + 5}{2} - 4 \\ &= \frac{x + 5 - 8}{2} \\ &= \frac{x - 3}{2} \end{aligned}$$

101. $(f \circ g)(x) = f(g(x)) = f(2x - 5) = (2x - 5) + 4 = 2x - 1$. Now find the inverse of $(f \circ g)(x) = 2x - 1$:

$$y = 2x - 1$$
$$x = 2y - 1$$
$$x + 1 = 2y$$
$$y = \frac{x + 1}{2}$$
$$(f \circ g)^{-1}(x) = \frac{x + 1}{2}$$

Note that $(f \circ g)^{-1}(x) = (g^{-1} \circ f^{-1})(x)$; see Exercise 99.

102. $(g \circ f)(x) = g(f(x)) = g(x + 4) = 2(x + 4) - 5 = 2x + 8 - 5 = 2x + 3$. Now find inverse:

$$y = 2x + 3$$
$$x = 2y + 3$$
$$x - 3 = 2y$$
$$\frac{x - 3}{2} = y$$
$$(g \circ f)^{-1}(x) = \frac{x - 3}{2}$$

Note that $(g \circ f)^{-1} = f^{-1} \circ g^{-1}$.

103. (a) Yes, f is one-to-one. For each European shoe size, there is exactly one U.S. shoe size.

(b) $f(11) = 45$

(c) $f^{-1}(43) = 10$ because $f(10) = 43$.

(d) $f(f^{-1}(41)) = f(8) = 41$

(e) $f^{-1}(f(13)) = f^{-1}(47) = 13$

104. (a) Yes, g is one-to-one. For each European shoe size, there is exactly one U.S. shoe size.

(b) $g(6) = 38$

(c) $g^{-1}(42) = 9$ because $g(9) = 42$.

(d) $g(g^{-1}(39)) = g(7) = 39$

(e) $g^{-1}(g(5)) = g^{-1}(37) = 5$

105. (a) Yes, f is one-to-one, so f^{-1} exists.

(b) f^{-1} gives the year corresponding to the 10 values in the second column.

(c) $f^{-1}(650.3) = 10$ because $f(10) = 650.3$.

(d) No, because $f(11) = f(15) = 690.4$.

106. (a)

$$y = 8 + 0.75x$$
$$x = 8 + 0.75y$$
$$x - 8 = 0.75y$$
$$\frac{x - 8}{0.75} = y$$
$$y = f^{-1}(x) = \frac{x - 8}{0.75}$$

$x =$ hourly wage

$y =$ number of units produced

(b)

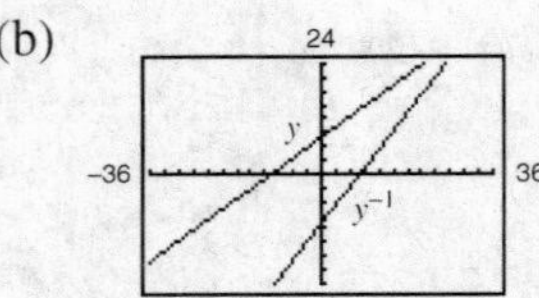

(c) If 10 units are produced, then

$y = 8 + 0.75(10) = \$15.50$.

(d) If the hourly wage is \$22.25, then

$y = \frac{22.25 - 8}{0.75} = 19$ units.

107. False. $f(x) = x^2$ is even, but f^{-1} does not exist.

108. True. If $(0, b)$ is the y-intercept of f, then $(b, 0)$ is the x-intercept of f^{-1}.

109. We will show that $(f \circ g)^{-1}(x) = (g^{-1} \circ f^{-1})(x)$ for all x in their domains.
Let $y = (f \circ g)^{-1}(x) \implies (f \circ g)(y) = x$ then $f(g(y)) = x \implies f^{-1}(x) = g(y)$.
Hence, $(g^{-1} \circ f^{-1})(x) = g^{-1}(f^{-1}(x)) = g^{-1}(g(y)) = y = (f \circ g)^{-1}(x)$.
Thus, $g^{-1} \circ f^{-1} = (f \circ g)^{-1}$.

110. If f is one-to-one, then f^{-1} exists. If f is odd, then $f(-x) = -f(x)$. Consider $f(x) = y \leftrightarrow f^{-1}(y) = x$.
Then $f^{-1}(-y) = f^{-1}(-f(x)) = f^{-1}(f(-x)) = -x = -f^{-1}(y)$. Thus, f^{-1} is odd.

111. No, the graphs are not reflections of each other in the line $y = x$.

112. Yes, the graphs are reflections of each other in the line $y = x$.

113. Yes, the graphs are reflections of each other in the line $y = x$.

114. Yes, the graphs are reflections of each other in the line $y = x$.

115. Yes. The inverse would give the time it took to complete n miles.

116. Yes, assuming that the population is increasing between 1960 and 2005. The inverse would give the year corresponding to a given population.

117. No. The function oscillates.

118. No, because heights remain constant, or even decrease, after many years.

119. $\dfrac{27x^3}{3x^2} = 9x, \ x \neq 0$

120. $\dfrac{5x^2y}{xy + 5x} = \dfrac{5x^2y}{x(y + 5)} = \dfrac{5xy}{y + 5}, \ x \neq 0$

121. $\dfrac{x^2 - 36}{6 - x} = \dfrac{(x - 6)(x + 6)}{-(x - 6)} = \dfrac{x + 6}{-1} = -x - 6, \ x \neq 6$

122. $\dfrac{x^2 + 3x - 40}{x^2 - 3x - 10} = \dfrac{(x - 5)(x + 8)}{(x - 5)(x + 2)} = \dfrac{x + 8}{x + 2}, \ x \neq 5$

123. $4x - y = 3$

$y = 4x - 3$

Yes, y is a function of x.

124. $x = 5$. No. Does not pass Vertical Line Test

125. $x^2 + y^2 = 9$

$y = \pm\sqrt{9 - x^2}$

No, y is not a function of x.

126. $x^2 + y = 8$

$y = -x^2 + 8$

Yes, y is a function of x.

127. $y = \sqrt{x + 2}$

Yes, y is a function of x.

128. $x - y^2 = 0$

$y^2 = x$

$y = \pm\sqrt{x}$

No, y is not a function of x.

Section 1.7 Linear Models and Scatter Plots

- You should know how to construct a scatter plot for a set of data
- You should recognize if a set of data has a positive correlation, negative correlation, or neither.
- You should be able to fit a line to data using the point-slope formula.
- You should be able to use the regression feature of a graphing utility to find a linear model for a set of data.
- You should be able to find and interpret the correlation coefficient of a linear model.

Vocabulary Check

1. positive **2.** negative **3.** fitting a line to data **4.** $-1, 1$

1. (a)

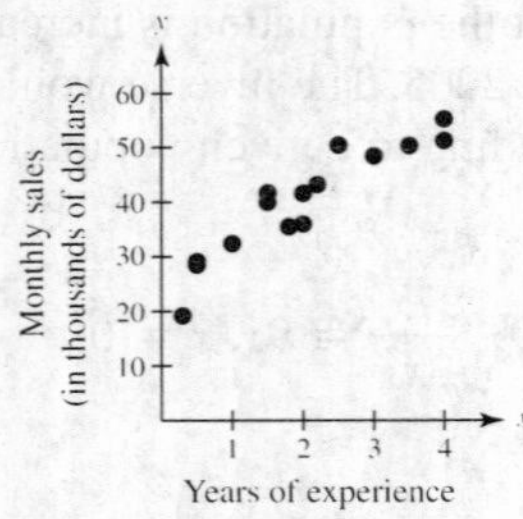

(b) Yes, the data appears somewhat linear. The more experience, x, corresponds to higher sales, y.

2. (a)

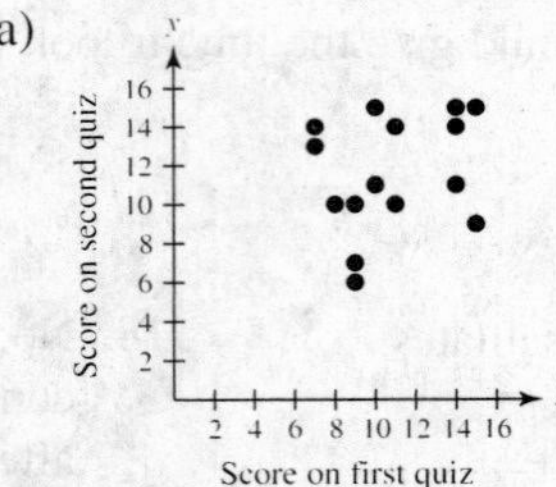

(b) No. Quiz scores are dependent on several variables, such as study time, class attendance, etc.

3. Negative correlation—y decreases as x increases.

4. No correlation

5. No correlation

6. Positive correlation

7. (a)

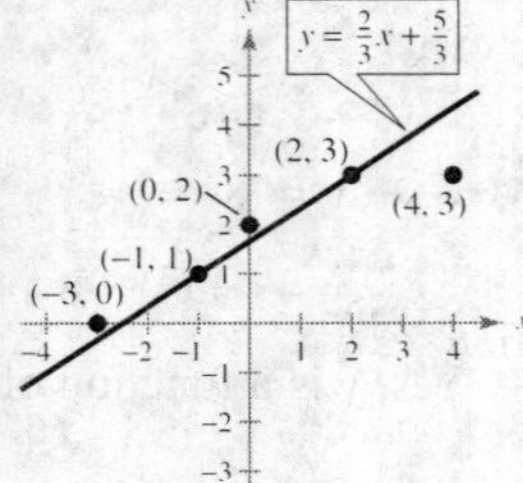

(b) $y = 0.46x + 1.62$

Correlation coefficient: 0.95095

(c)

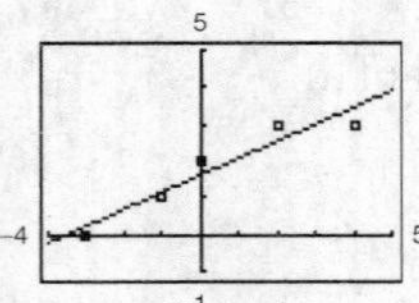

(d) Yes, the model appears valid.

8. (a)

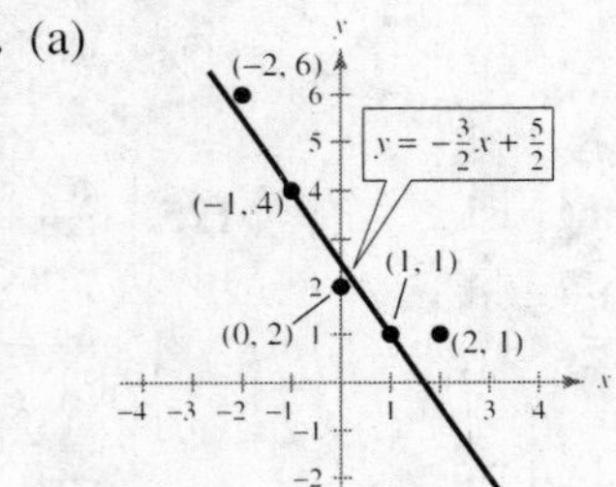

(b) $y = -1.3x + 2.8$

Correlation coefficient: -0.94812

(c)

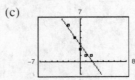

(d) The model appears valid.

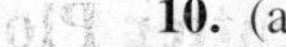

9. (a)

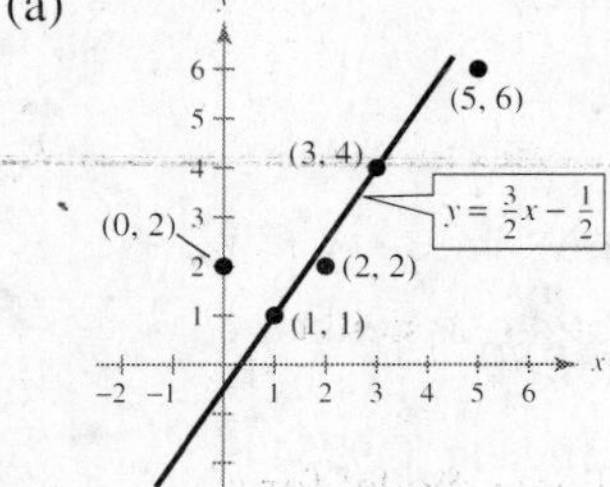

(b) $y = 0.95x + 0.92$

Correlation coefficient: 0.90978

(c)

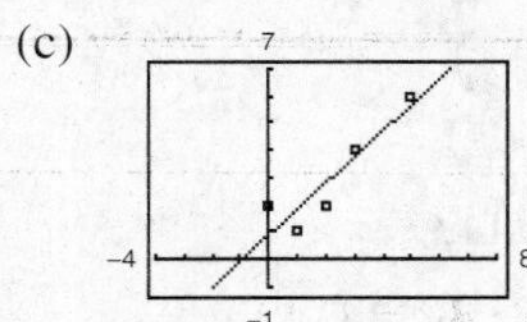

(d) Yes, the model appears valid.

10. (a)

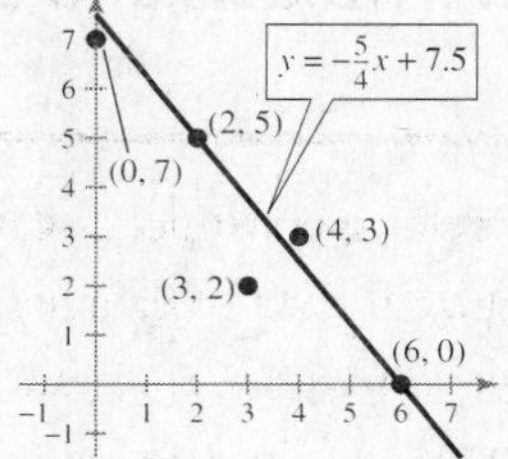

(b) $y = -1.15x + 6.85$

Correlation coefficient: -0.95175

(c)

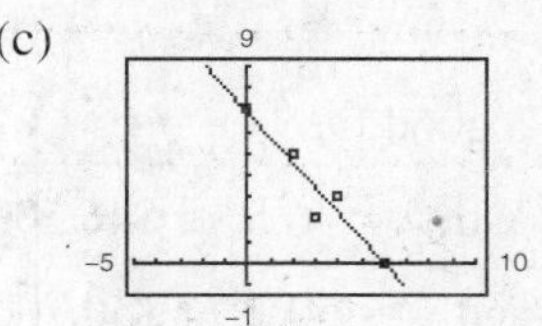

(d) The model is somewhat valid.

11. (a)

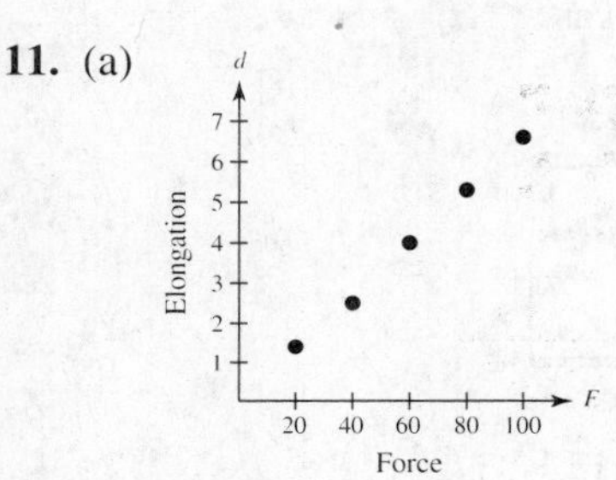

(b) $d = 0.07F - 0.3$

(c) $d = 0.066F$ or $F = 15.13d + 0.096$

(d) If $F = 55$, $d = 0.066(55) \approx 3.63$ cm.

12. (a)

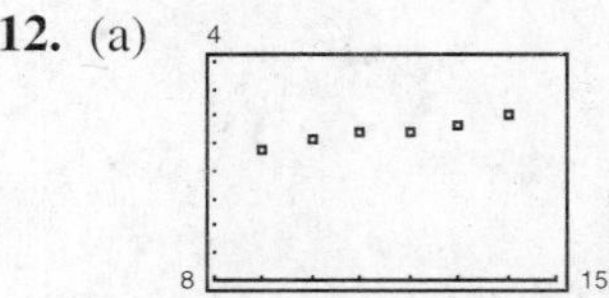

(b) $y = 0.122t + 1.32$

(c)

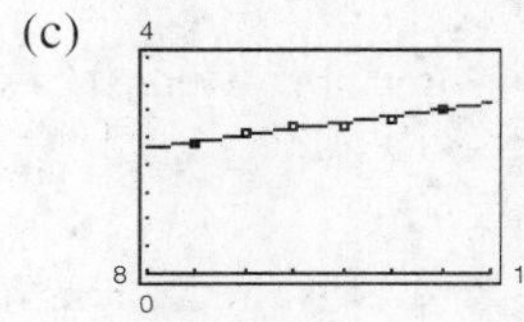

Yes, the model is a good fit.

(d) For 2010, $t = 20$ and $y \approx 3.76$ minutes.

For 2015, $t = 25$ and $y \approx 4.37$ minutes.

Yes, the answers seem reasonable.

13. (a)

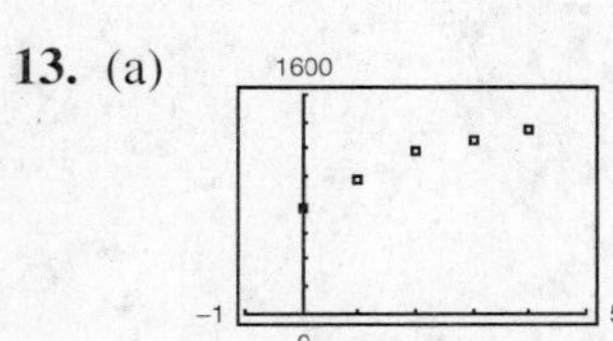

(b) $y = 136.1t + 836$

(c)

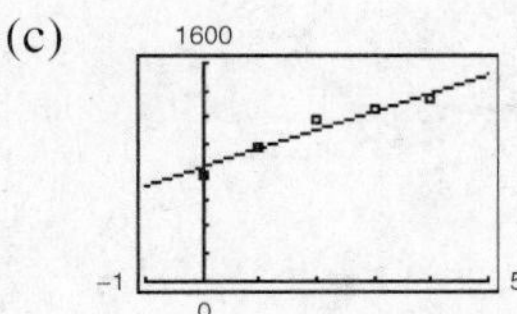

Yes, the model is a good fit.

(d) For 2005, $t = 5$ and $y \approx 1516.5$, or \$1,516,500.

For 2010, $t = 10$ and $y \approx 2197$, or \$2,197,000.

Yes, the answers seem reasonable.

(e) The slope is 136.1. It says that the mean salary increases by \$136,100 per year.

14. (a)

(b) $y = 0.84t + 33.9$

(c)

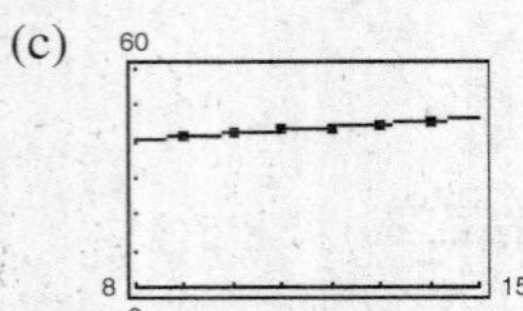

Yes, the model is a good fit.

(d) For 2005, $t = 15$ and $y \approx 46.5$, or \$46,500.

For 2010, $t = 20$ and $y \approx 50.7$, or \$50,700.

Yes, the answers seem reasonable.

15. (a)

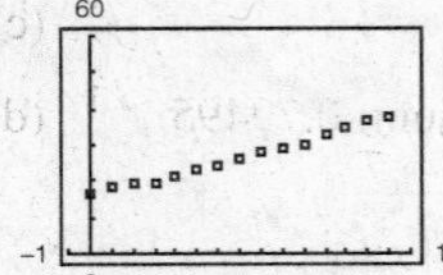

(b) $C = 1.552t + 15.70$

Correlation coefficient: 0.99544

(c)

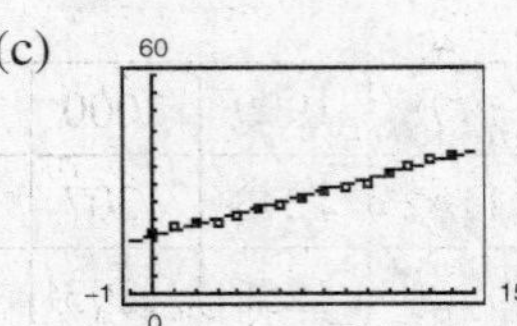

(d) The model is a good fit.

(e) For 2005, $t = 15$, $y_1 \approx \$38.98$.

For 2010, $t = 20$, $y_1 \approx \$46.74$.

(f) Answers will vary.

16. (a)

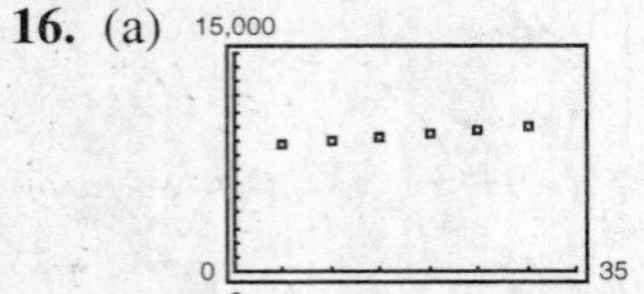

(b) $P = 42.0t + 8585$

(c)

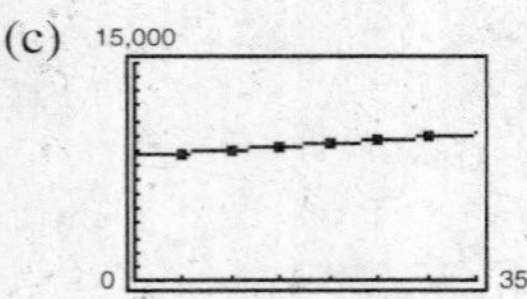

The model is a good fit.

(d) For 2050, $t = 50$ and $P = 10{,}685$, or 10,685,000 people. Answers will vary.

17. (a)

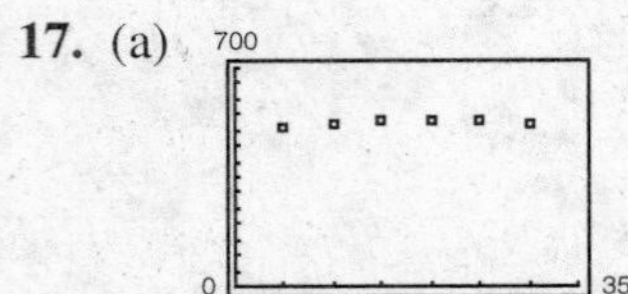

(b) $P = 0.6t + 512$

(c)

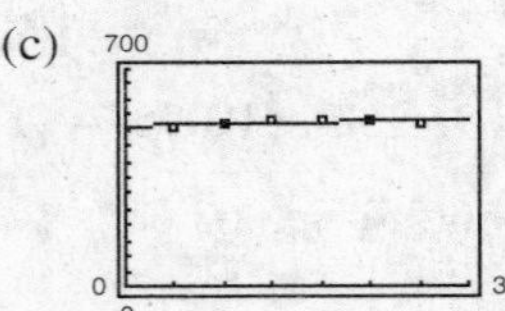

The model is not a good fit.

(d) For 2050, $t = 50$ and $P = 542$, or 542,000 people. Answers will vary.

18. (a) $y = 47.77x + 103.8$

Correlation coefficient: 0.81238

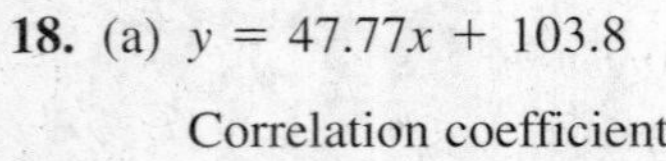

(b)

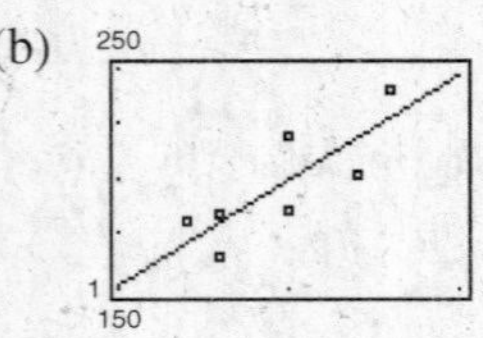

(c) The slope represents the increase in sales due to increased advertising.

(d) For \$1500, $x = 1.5$ and $y = 175.455$ or \$175,455.

19. (a) $T = 36.7t + 926$

Correlation coefficient: 0.79495

(b)

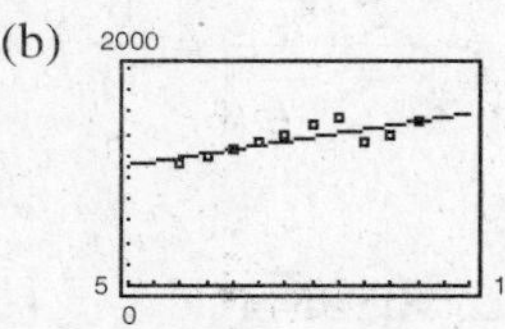

(c) The slope indicated the number of new stores opened per year.

(d) $T = 36.7t + 926 > 1800$

$36.7t > 874$

$t > 23.8$

The number of stores will exceed 1800 near the end of 2013.

(e)

Year	1997	1998	1999	2000	2001	2002	2003	2004	2005	2006
Data	1130	1182	1243	1307	1381	1475	1553	1308	1400	1505
Model	1183	1220	1256	1293	1330	1366	1403	1440	1477	1513

The model is not a good fit, especially around $t = 14$.

20. (a) $y = -0.022t + 5.03$

(b) The negative slope indicates that the times are decreasing.

(c)

(d) The model is not very accurate.

(e) Answers will vary.

21. True. To have positive correlation, the y-values tend to increase as x increases.

22. False. The closer to 1 or -1, the better the fit.

23. Answers will vary.

24. Answers will vary.

25. $f(x) = 2x^2 - 3x + 5$

(a) $f(-1) = 2 + 3 + 5 = 10$

(b) $f(w + 2) = 2(w + 2)^2 - 3(w + 2) + 5$

$= 2w^2 + 5w + 7$

26. $g(x) = 5x^2 - 6x + 1$

(a) $g(-2) = 5(4) - 6(-2) + 1 = 33$

(b) $g(z - 2) = 5(z - 2)^2 - 6(z - 2) + 1$

$= 5z^2 - 26z + 33$

27. $h(x) = \begin{cases} 1 - x^2, & x \le 0 \\ 2x + 3, & x > 0 \end{cases}$

(a) $h(1) = 2(1) + 3 = 5$ (b) $h(0) = 1 - 0 = 1$

28. (a) $k(-3) = 5 - 2(-3) = 11$

(b) $k(-1) = (-1)^2 + 4 = 5$

29. $6x + 1 = -9x - 8$

$15x = -9$

$x = -\frac{9}{15} = -\frac{3}{5}$

30. $3(x - 3) = 7x + 2$

$-11 = 4x$

$x = -\frac{11}{4}$

31. $8x^2 - 10x - 3 = 0$

$(4x + 1)(2x - 3) = 0$

$x = -\frac{1}{4}, \frac{3}{2}$

32. $10x^2 - 23x - 5 = 0$

$(2x - 5)(5x + 1) = 0$

$x = \frac{5}{2}, -\frac{1}{5}$

33. $2x^2 - 7x + 4 = 0$

$x = \frac{7 \pm \sqrt{49 - 4(4)(2)}}{4}$

$= \frac{7 \pm \sqrt{17}}{4}$

34. $2x^2 - 8x + 5 = 0$

$x = \frac{8 \pm \sqrt{64 - 40}}{4}$

$= 2 \pm \frac{\sqrt{6}}{2}$

Review Exercises for Chapter 1

1.

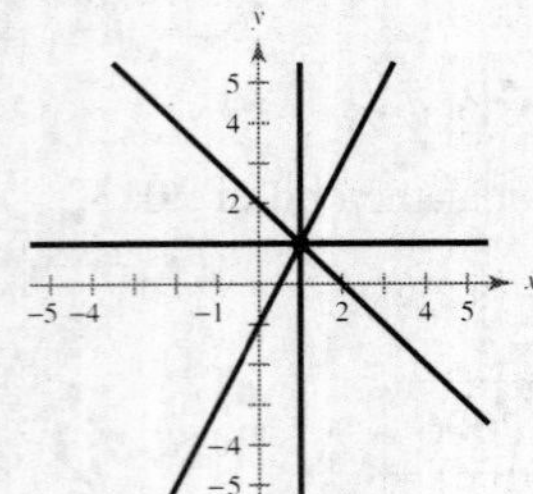

2.

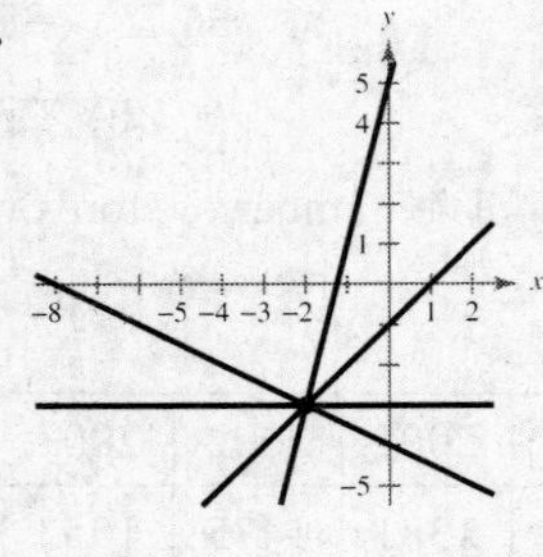

3. $m = \dfrac{2 - 2}{8 - (-3)} = \dfrac{0}{11} = 0$

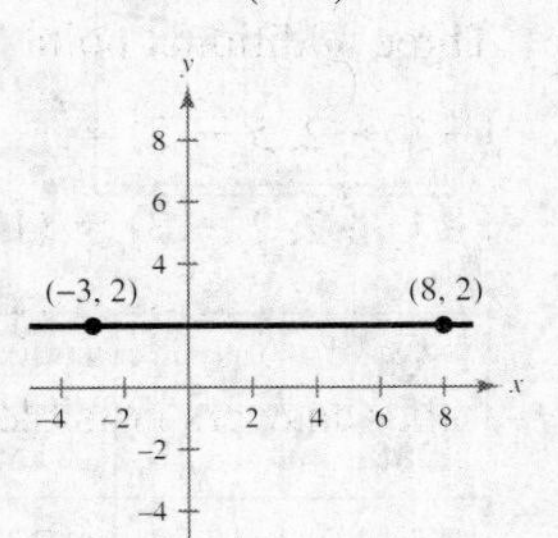

4. Slope $= \dfrac{12 - (-1)}{7 - 7}$, undefined

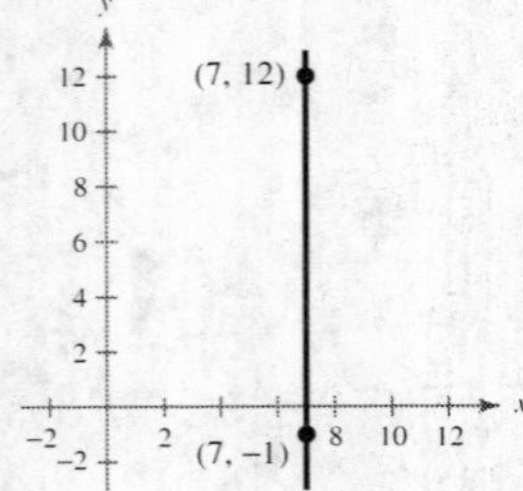

5. $m = \dfrac{(5/2) - 1}{5 - (3/2)} = \dfrac{3/2}{7/2} = \dfrac{3}{7}$

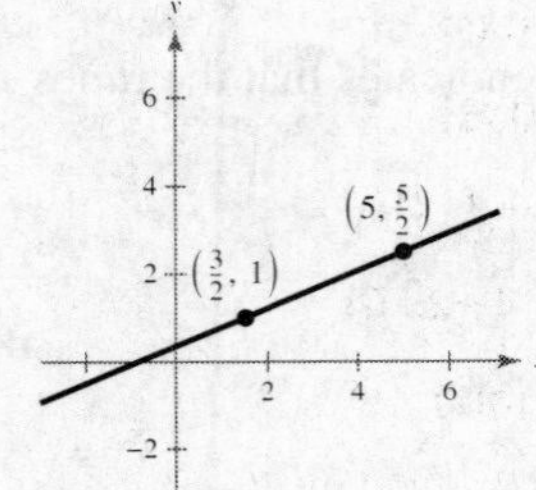

6. Slope $= \dfrac{\frac{5}{6} - \left(-\frac{5}{2}\right)}{-\frac{3}{4} - \frac{1}{2}} = \dfrac{\frac{5}{6} + \frac{15}{6}}{-\frac{3}{4} - \frac{2}{4}} = \dfrac{\frac{10}{3}}{-\frac{5}{4}}$

$= -\dfrac{10}{3} \cdot \dfrac{4}{5} = -\dfrac{8}{3}$

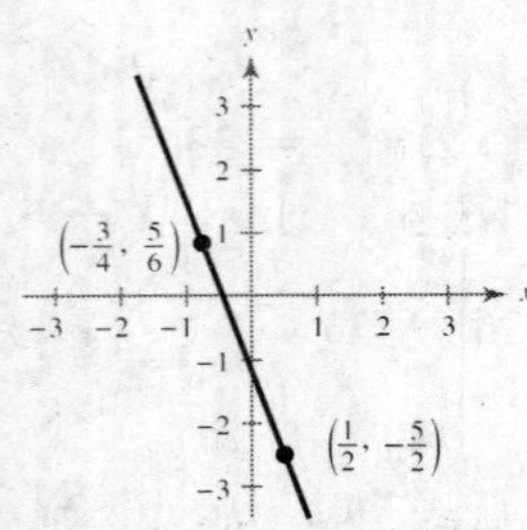

7. $(-4.5, 6), (2.1, 3)$

$m = \dfrac{3 - 6}{2.1 - (-4.5)} = \dfrac{-3}{6.6} = -\dfrac{30}{66} = -\dfrac{5}{11}$

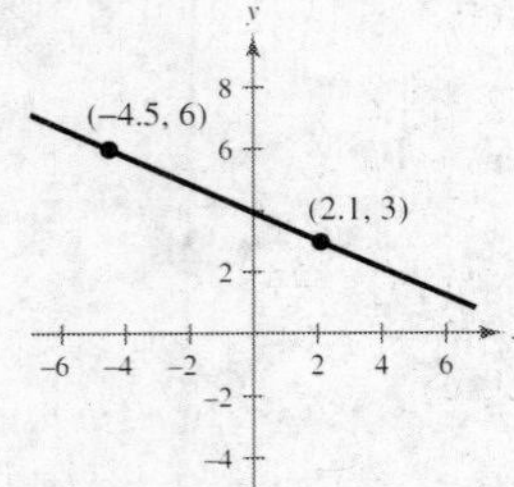

8. Slope $= \dfrac{-1.2 + 6.3}{-1 + 2.7} = \dfrac{5.1}{1.7} = \dfrac{51}{17} = 3$

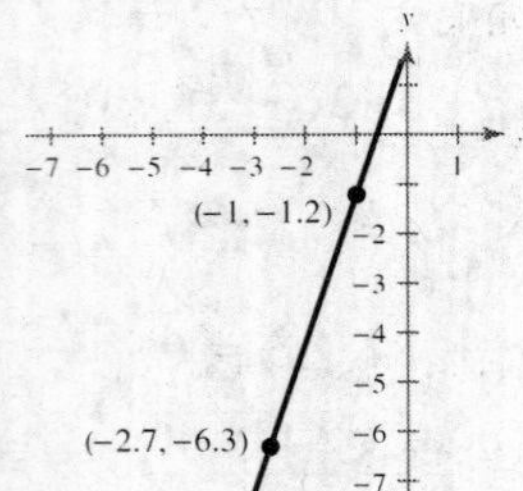

9. (a) $y + 1 = \dfrac{1}{4}(x - 2)$

$4y + 4 = x - 2$

$-x + 4y + 6 = 0$

(b) Three additional points:

$(2 + 4, -1 + 1) = (6, 0)$

$(6 + 4, 0 + 1) = (10, 1)$

$(10 + 4, 1 + 1) = (14, 2)$

(other answers possible)

10. (a) $y - 5 = -\frac{3}{2}(x + 3)$

$2y - 10 = -3x - 9$

$3x + 2y - 1 = 0$

(b) Three additional points:

$(-3 + 2, 5 - 3) = (-1, 2)$

$(-1 + 2, 2 - 3) = (1, -1)$

$(1 + 2, -1 - 3) = (3, -4)$

(other answers possible)

11. (a) $y + 5 = \frac{3}{2}(x - 0)$

$2y + 10 = 3x$

$-3x + 2y + 10 = 0$

(b) Three additional points:

$(0 + 2, -5 + 3) = (2, -2)$

$(2 + 2, -2 + 3) = (4, 1)$

$(4 + 2, 1 + 3) = (6, 4)$

(other answers possible)

12. (a) $y - 0 = -\frac{2}{3}(x - 3)$

$3y = -2x + 6$

$2x + 3y - 6 = 0$

(b) Three additional points:

$(3 - 3, 0 + 2) = (0, 2)$

$(0 - 3, 2 + 2) = (-3, 4)$

$(-3 - 3, 4 + 2) = (-6, 6)$

(other answers possible)

13. (a) $y + 5 = -1\left(x - \frac{1}{5}\right)$

$y + 5 = -x + \frac{1}{5}$

$5y + 25 = -5x + 1$

$5x + 5y + 24 = 0$

(b) Three additional points:

$\left(\frac{1}{5} + 1, -5 - 1\right) = \left(\frac{6}{5}, -6\right)$

$\left(\frac{6}{5} + 1, -6 - 1\right) = \left(\frac{11}{5}, -7\right)$

$\left(\frac{11}{5} + 1, -7 - 1\right) = \left(\frac{16}{5}, -8\right)$

(other answers possible)

14. (a) $y - \frac{7}{8} = -\frac{4}{5}(x - 0)$

$40y - 35 = -32x$

$32x + 40y - 35 = 0$

(b) Three additional points:

$\left(0 + 5, \frac{7}{8} - 4\right) = \left(5, -\frac{25}{8}\right)$

$\left(5 + 5, -\frac{25}{8} - 4\right) = \left(10, -\frac{57}{8}\right)$

$\left(10 + 5, -\frac{57}{8} - 4\right) = \left(15, -\frac{89}{8}\right)$

(other answers possible)

15. (a) $y - 6 = 0(x + 2)$

$y - 6 = 0$

(b) Three additional points:

$(0, 6), (1, 6), (2, 6)$

(other answers possible)

16. (a) $y - 8 = 0(x + 8) = 0$

$y = 8$ (horizontal line)

$y - 8 = 0$

(b) Three additional points: $(0, 8), (1, 8), (2, 8)$

(other answers possible)

17. (a) m is undefined means that the line is vertical.

$x - 10 = 0$

(b) Three additional points: $(10, 0), (10, 1), (10, 2)$

(other answers possible)

18. (a) Slope is undefined, line is vertical: $x = 5$ or $x - 5 = 0$

(b) Three additional points: $(5, 0), (5, 1), (5, 2)$

(other answers possible)

19. $y + 1 = \dfrac{-1 + 1}{4 - 2}(x - 2)$

$= 0(x - 2) = 0 \Rightarrow y = -1$

(Slope = 0)

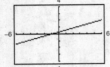

20. Slope is undefined.

Line is vertical.

$x = 0$

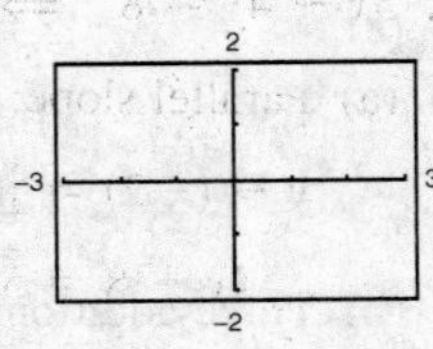

21. $y - 0 = \dfrac{2 - 0}{6 - (-1)}(x + 1)$

$= \dfrac{2}{7}(x + 1) = \dfrac{2}{7}x + \dfrac{2}{7} \Rightarrow y = \dfrac{2}{7}x + \dfrac{2}{7}$

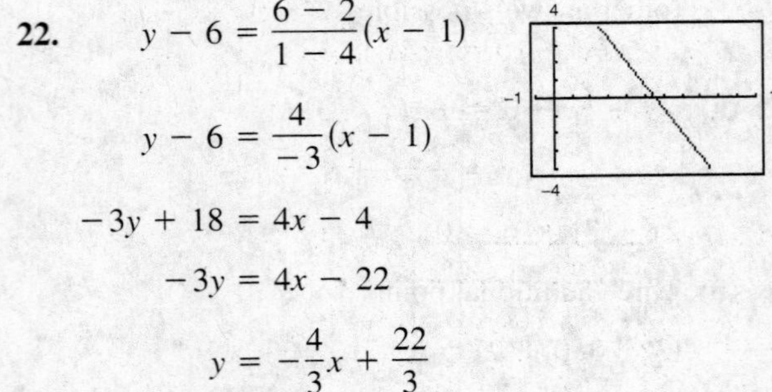

22. $y - 6 = \dfrac{6 - 2}{1 - 4}(x - 1)$

$y - 6 = \dfrac{4}{-3}(x - 1)$

$-3y + 18 = 4x - 4$

$-3y = 4x - 22$

$y = -\dfrac{4}{3}x + \dfrac{22}{3}$

23. $t = 8$ corresponds to 2008.

Point: (8, 12,500), slope: 850

$V - 12{,}500 = 850(t - 8)$

$V = 850t + 5700$

24. $m = -115$

Point: (8, 3795)

$V - 3795 = -115(t - 8)$

$V = -115t + 4715$

25. $m = 42.70$

Point: (8, 625.50)

$V - 625.50 = 42.70(t - 8)$

$V = 42.70t + 283.90$

26. $t = 8$ corresponds to 2008.

Point: (8, 72.95), slope: −5.15

$V - 72.95 = -5.15(t - 8)$

$V = -5.15t + 114.15$

27. (2, 160,000), (3, 185,000)

$m = \dfrac{185{,}000 - 160{,}000}{3 - 2} = 25{,}000$

$S - 160{,}000 = 25{,}000(t - 2)$

$S = 25{,}000t + 110{,}000$

For the fourth quarter let $t = 4$. Then we have

$S = 25{,}000(4) + 110{,}000 = \$210{,}000.$

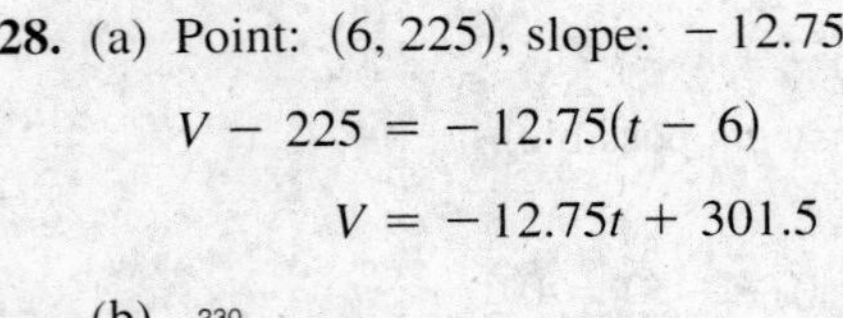

28. (a) Point: (6, 225), slope: −12.75

$V - 225 = -12.75(t - 6)$

$V = -12.75t + 301.5$

(b)

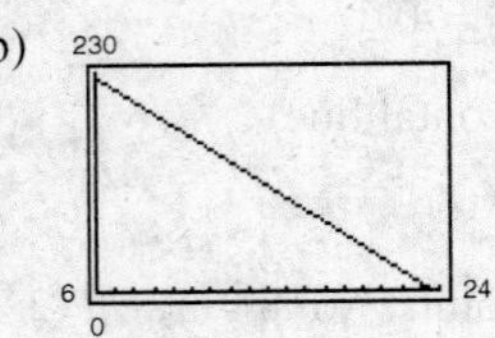

(c) In 2010, $t = 10$ and $V = 174$ dollars.

(d) $V = 0$ when $t \approx 23.6$, (2023).

Algebraically,

$V = -12.75t + 301.5 = 0$

$t = \dfrac{301.5}{12.75} \approx 23.6.$

29. $5x - 4y = 8 \Rightarrow y = \frac{5}{4}x - 2$ and $m = \frac{5}{4}$

(a) Parallel slope: $m = \frac{5}{4}$

$$y - (-2) = \frac{5}{4}(x - 3)$$
$$4y + 8 = 5x - 15$$
$$0 = 5x - 4y - 23$$
$$y = \frac{5}{4}x - \frac{23}{4}$$

(b) Perpendicular slope: $m = -\frac{4}{5}$

$$y - (-2) = -\frac{4}{5}(x - 3)$$
$$5y + 10 = -4x + 12$$
$$4x + 5y - 2 = 0$$
$$y = -\frac{4}{5}x + \frac{2}{5}$$

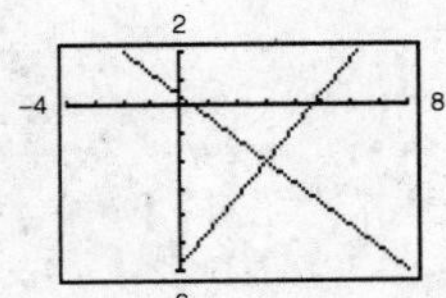

30. Slope of given line: $m = -\frac{2}{3}$

(a) $y - 3 = -\frac{2}{3}(x + 8) \Rightarrow 3y - 9 = -2x - 16$

$\Rightarrow 2x + 3y + 7 = 0$

$$y = -\frac{2}{3}x - \frac{7}{3}$$

(b) $y - 3 = \frac{3}{2}(x + 8) \Rightarrow 2y - 6 = 3x + 24$

$\Rightarrow 3x - 2y + 30 = 0$

$$y = \frac{3}{2}x + 15$$

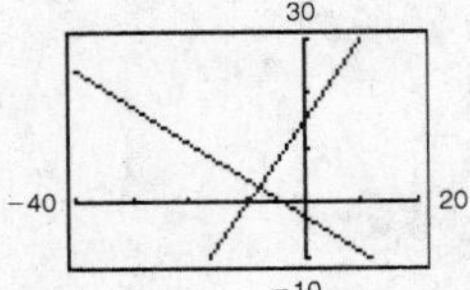

31. $x = 4$ is a vertical line; the slope is not defined.

(a) Parallel line: $x = -6$

(b) Perpendicular slope: $m = 0$

Perpendicular line: $y - 2 = 0(x + 6)$

$= 0 \Rightarrow y = 2$

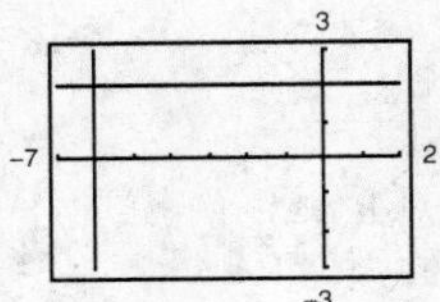

32. $y = 2$ is a horizontal line.

(a) Parallel line through $(3, -4)$: $y = -4$

(b) Perpendicular line through $(3, -4)$: $x = 3$

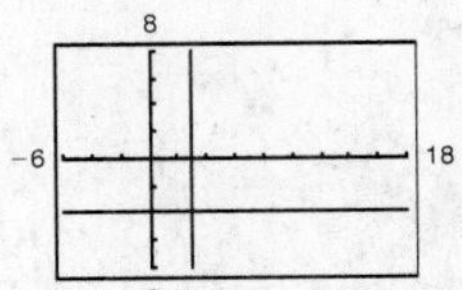

33. (a) Not a function. 20 is assigned two different values.

(b) Function

(c) Function

(d) Not a function. No value is assigned to 30.

34. (a) Not a function. u is assigned two different values.

(b) Function

(c) Function

(d) Not a function. w is assigned two different values and u is unassigned.

35. No, y is not a function of x. Some x-values correspond to two y-values. For example, $x = 1$ corresponds to $y = 4$ and $y = -4$.

36. Yes, $y = 2x - 3$.

37. $y = \sqrt{1 - x}$

Each x value, $x \leq 1$, corresponds to only one y-value so y is a function of x.

38. No, does not pass Vertical Line Test.

39. $f(x) = x^2 + 1$

(a) $f(1) = 1^2 + 1 = 2$

(b) $f(-3) = (-3)^2 + 1 = 10$

(c) $f(b^3) = (b^3)^2 + 1 = b^6 + 1$

(d) $f(x - 1) = (x - 1)^2 + 1 = x^2 - 2x + 2$

40. $g(x) = x^{4/3}$

(a) $g(8) = 8^{4/3} = 2^4 = 16$

(b) $g(t + 1) = (t + 1)^{4/3}$

(c) $g(-27) = (-27)^{4/3} = (-3)^4 = 81$

(d) $g(-x) = (-x)^{4/3} = x^{4/3}$

41. $h(x) = \begin{cases} 2x + 1, & x \le -1 \\ x^2 + 2, & x > -1 \end{cases}$

(a) $h(-2) = 2(-2) + 1 = -3$

(b) $h(-1) = 2(-1) + 1 = -1$

(c) $h(0) = 0^2 + 2 = 2$

(d) $h(2) = 2^2 + 2 = 6$

42. $f(x) = \dfrac{3}{2x - 5}$

(a) $f(1) = \dfrac{3}{2(1) - 5} = -1$

(b) $f(-2) = \dfrac{3}{2(-2) - 5} = \dfrac{3}{-9} = -\dfrac{1}{3}$

(c) $f(t) = \dfrac{3}{2t - 5}$

(d) $f(10) = \dfrac{3}{2(10) - 5} = \dfrac{3}{15} = \dfrac{1}{5}$

43. The domain of $f(x) = \dfrac{x - 1}{x + 2}$ is all real numbers $x \neq -2$.

44. The domain of $f(x) = \dfrac{x^2}{x^2 + 1}$ is the set of all real numbers.

45. $f(x) = \sqrt{25 - x^2}$

Domain: $\quad 25 - x^2 \ge 0$

$(5 + x)(5 - x) \ge 0$

Domain: $[-5, 5]$

46. The domain of $f(x) = \sqrt{x^2 - 16}$ is given by

$x^2 - 16 \ge 0$

$x^2 \ge 16.$

The domain is $(-\infty, -4] \cup [4, \infty)$.

47. The domain of $g(5) = \dfrac{5s + 5}{3s - 9}$ is all real numbers $s \neq 3$.

48. The domain of $f(x) = \dfrac{2x + 1}{3x + 4}$ is all real numbers $\neq -\dfrac{4}{3}$.

49. (a) $C(x) = 16{,}000 + 5.35x$

(b) $P(x) = R(x) - C(x)$

$= 8.20x - (16{,}000 + 5.35x)$

$= 2.85x - 16{,}000$

50. $R(t)$ in billions of dollars

Year	1997	1998	1999	2000	2001	2002	2003	2004
$R(t)$	6.744	7.744	8.996	10.5	12.699	11.994	10.448	8.929

51.
$$f(x) = 2x^2 + 3x - 1$$
$$f(x + h) = 2(x + h)^2 + 3(x + h) - 1$$
$$= 2x^2 + 4xh + 2h^2 + 3x + 3h - 1$$
$$\frac{f(x + h) - f(x)}{h} = \frac{(2x^2 + 4xh + 2h^2 + 3x + 3h - 1) - (2x^2 + 3x - 1)}{h}$$
$$= \frac{4xh + 2h^2 + 3h}{h}$$
$$= 4x + 2h + 3, \quad h \neq 0$$

52.
$$f(x + h) = (x + h)^3 - 5(x + h)^2 + (x + h)$$
$$= x^3 + 3x^2h + 3xh^2 + h^3 - 5x^2 - 10xh - 5h^2 + x + h$$
$$f(x + h) - f(x) = 3x^2h + 3xh^2 + h^3 - 10xh - 5h^2 + h$$
$$\frac{f(x + h) - f(x)}{h} = \frac{h(3x^2 + 3xh + h^2 - 10x - 5h + 1)}{h}$$
$$= 3x^2 + 3xh + h^2 - 10x - 5h + 1, \quad h \neq 0$$

53. Domain: All real numbers

Range: $y \leq 3$

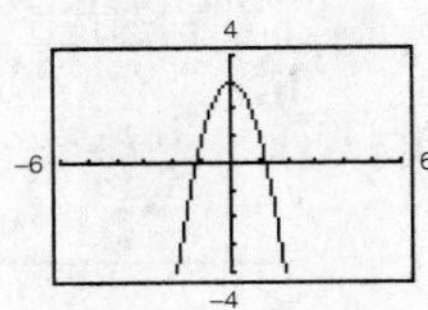

54. Domain: $2x^2 - 1 \geq 0 \Rightarrow x^2 \geq \frac{1}{2} \Rightarrow \left(-\infty, -\frac{\sqrt{2}}{2}\right] \cup \left[\frac{\sqrt{2}}{2}, \infty\right)$

Range: $[0, \infty)$

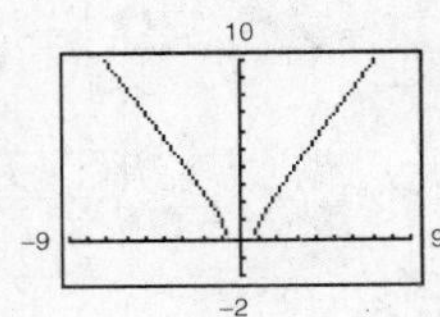

55. Domain: $36 - x^2 \geq 0 \Rightarrow x^2 \leq 36 \Rightarrow -6 \leq x \leq 6$

Range: $0 \leq y \leq 6$

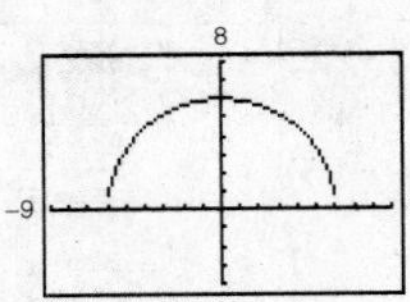

56. Domain: all real numbers

Range: $[0, \infty)$

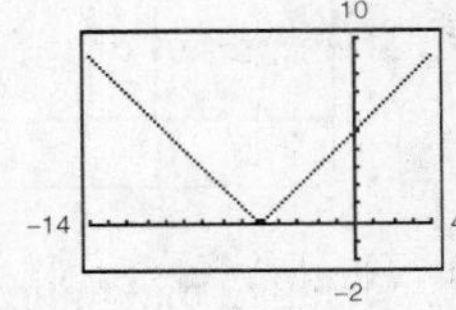

57. (a) $y = \dfrac{x^2 + 3x}{6}$

(b) y is a function of x.

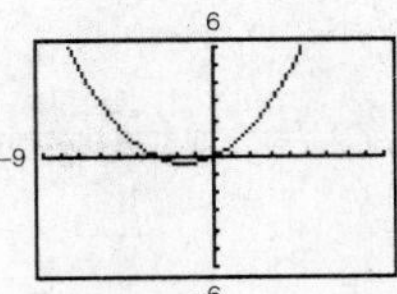

58. (a) $y = -\frac{2}{3}|x + 5|$

(b) y is a function of x.

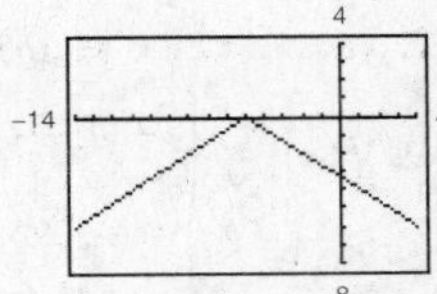

59. (a) $3x + y^2 = 2$

$$y^2 = 2 - 3x$$
$$y = \pm\sqrt{2 - 3x}$$

(b) y is not a function of x.

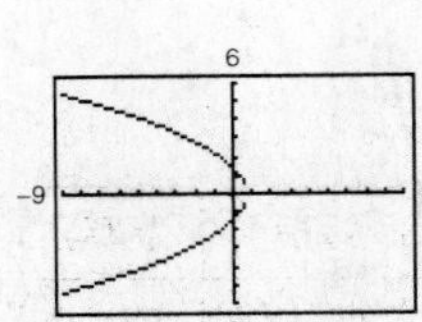

60. (a) $x^2 + y^2 = 49$

(b) y is not a function of x.

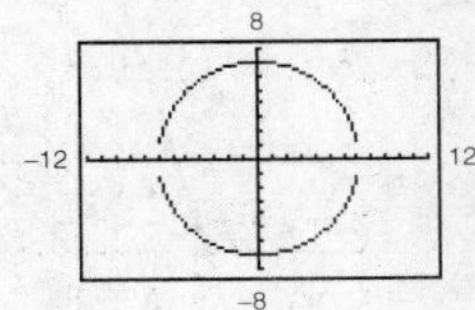

61. $f(x) = x^3 - 3x$

(a)

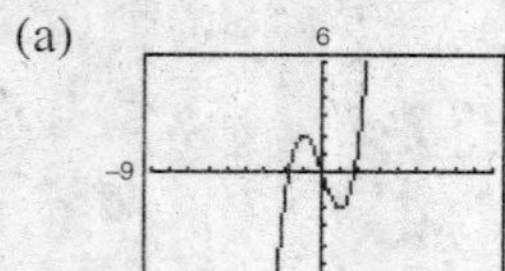

(b) Increasing on $(-\infty, -1)$ and $(1, \infty)$

Decreasing on $(-1, 1)$

62. $f(x) = \sqrt{x^2 - 9}$

(a)

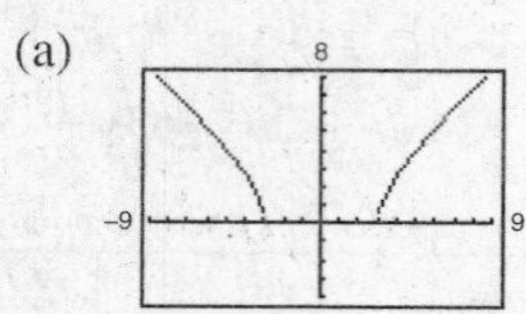

(b) Increasing on $(3, \infty)$

Decreasing on $(-\infty, -3)$

63. $f(x) = x\sqrt{x - 6}$

(a)

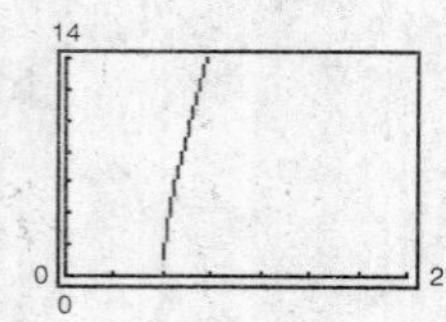

(b) Increasing on $(6, \infty)$

64. $f(x) = \dfrac{|x + 8|}{2}$

(a)

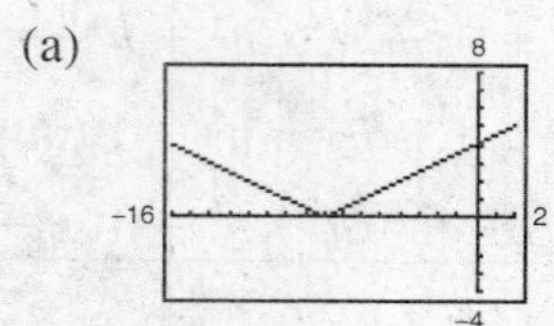

(b) Increasing on $(-8, \infty)$

Decreasing on $(-\infty, -8)$

65. $f(x) = (x^2 - 4)^2$

Relative minima: $(-2, 0)$ and $(2, 0)$

Relative maximum: $(0, 16)$

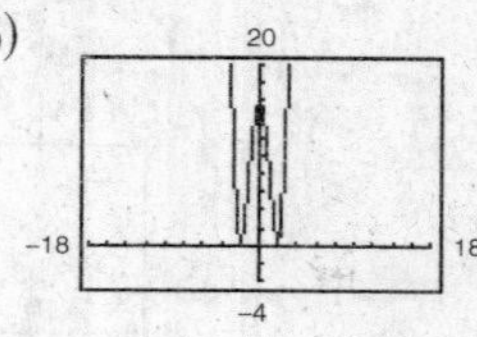

66. $f(x) = x^2 - x - 1$

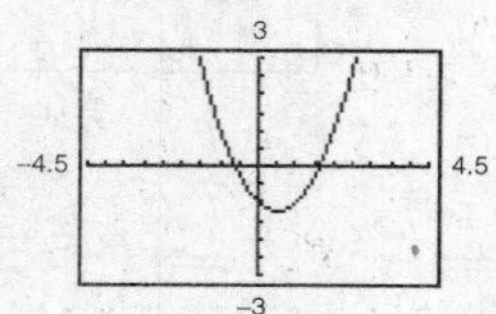

Relative minimum: $(0.5, -1.25)$

67. $h(x) = 4x^3 - x^4$

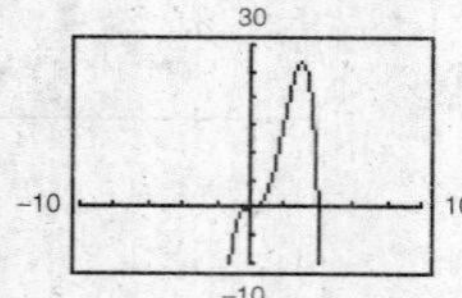

Relative maximum: $(3, 27)$

68. $f(x) = x^3 - 4x^2 - 1$

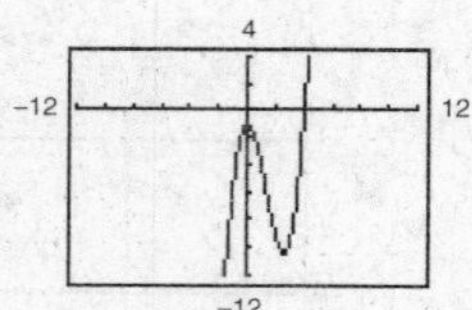

Relative maximum: $(0, -1)$

Relative minimum: $(2.67, -10.48)$

69. $f(x) = \begin{cases} 3x + 5, & x < 0 \\ x - 4, & x \geq 0 \end{cases}$

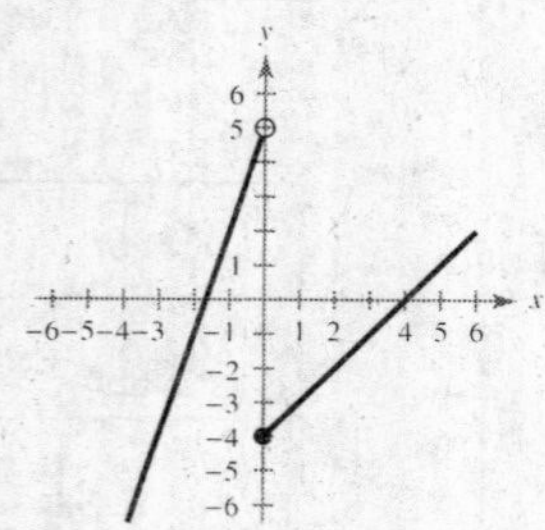

70. $f(x) = \begin{cases} x^2 + 7, & x < 1 \\ x^2 - 5x + 6, & x \geq 1 \end{cases}$

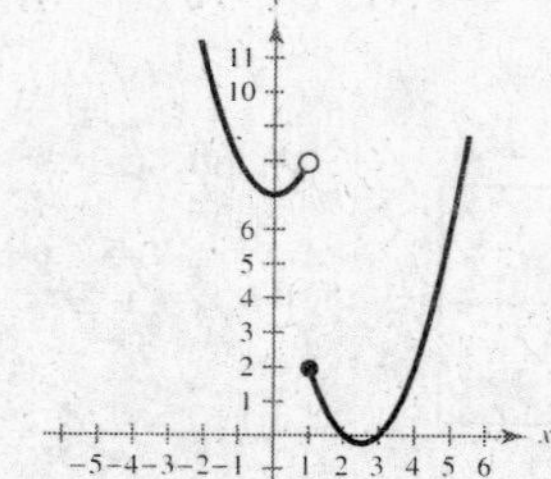

71. $f(x) = [\![x]\!] + 3$

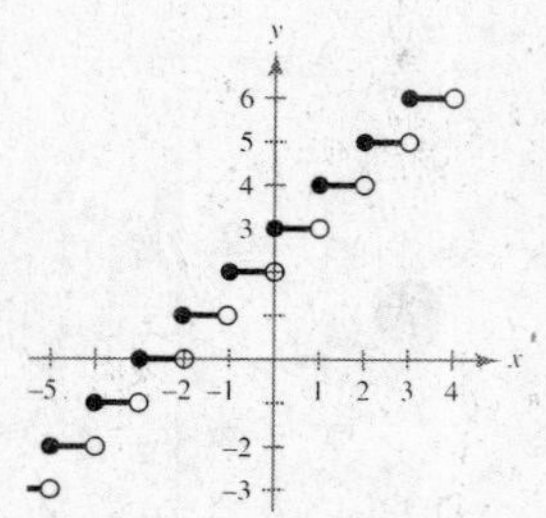

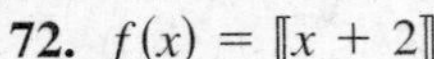

72. $f(x) = [\![x + 2]\!]$

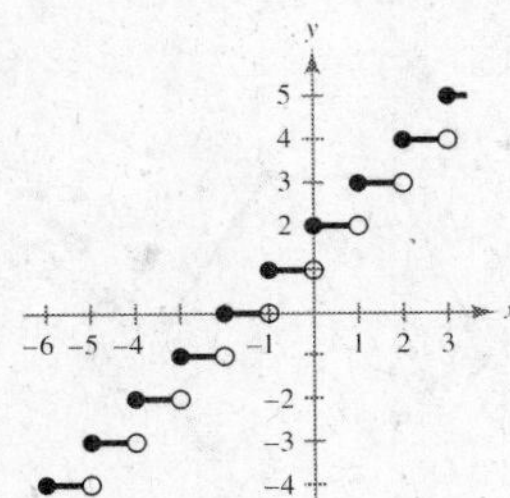

73. $f(-x) = (-x)^2 + 6$

$= x^2 + 6$

$= f(x)$

Even

74. $f(-x) = (-x)^2 - (-x) - 1$

$= x^2 + x - 1$

$\neq f(x)$

and $f(-x) \neq -f(x)$

Neither even nor odd

75. $f(-x) = ((-x)^2 - 8)^2$

$= (x^2 - 8)^2$

$= f(x)$

f is even.

76. $f(x) = 2x^3 - x^2$ is neither even nor odd.

77. $f(-x) = 3(-x)^{5/2} \neq f(x)$ and $f(-x) \neq -f(x)$

Neither even nor odd

(Note that the domain of f is $x \geq 0$.)

78. $f(-x) = 3(-x)^{2/5} = 3x^{2/5} = f(x)$

Even

79. $f(x) = -2$ is a constant function.

80. $g(x) = x$ is the parent function. f is obtained from g by a reflection in the x-axis, followed by a vertical shift five units upward.

$f(x) = -x + 5 = -g(x) + 5$

81. $g(x) = x^2$ is the parent function. f is obtained from g by a horizontal shift two units to the right, followed by a vertical shift one unit upward.

$f(x) = (x - 2)^2 + 1 = g(x - 2) + 1$

82. $g(x) = -x^3 - 2$ is obtained from $f(x) = x^3$ by a reflection in the x-axis, followed by a vertical shift two units downward.

$g(x) = -f(x) - 2$

83. $g(x) = |x| + 3$ is obtained from $f(x) = |x|$ by a vertical shift three units upward.

$g(x) = f(x) + 3$

84. $g(x) = -\sqrt{x - 3}$ is obtained from $f(x) = \sqrt{x}$ by a horizontal shift three units to the right followed by a reflection in the x-axis.

$g(x) = -f(x - 3)$

85.

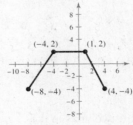

$y = f(-x)$ is a reflection in the y-axis.

86.

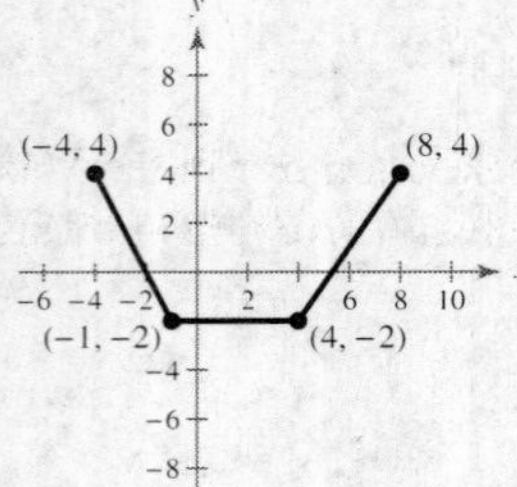

$y = -f(x)$ is a reflection in the x-axis.

87.

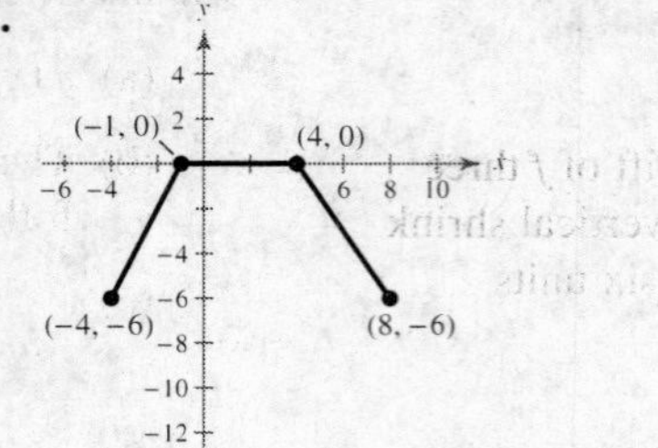

$y = f(x) - 2$ is a vertical shift two units downward.

88.

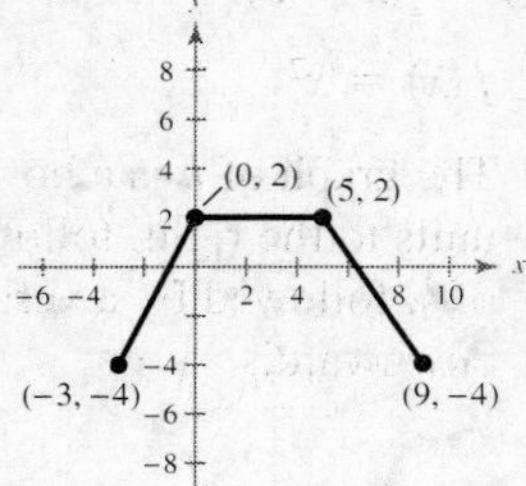

$y = f(x - 1)$ is a horizontal shift one unit to the right.

89. (a) $f(x) = x^2$

(b) h is a vertical shift six units downward.

(c)

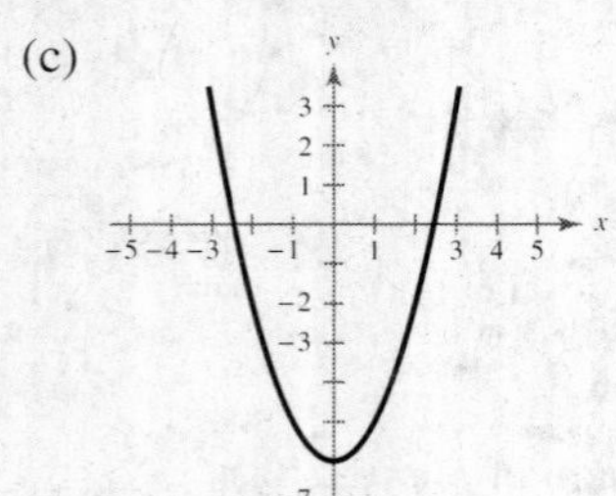

(d) $h(x) = f(x) - 6$

90. (a) $f(x) = x^2$

(b) h is a reflection in the x-axis, followed by a vertical shift three units downward.

(c)

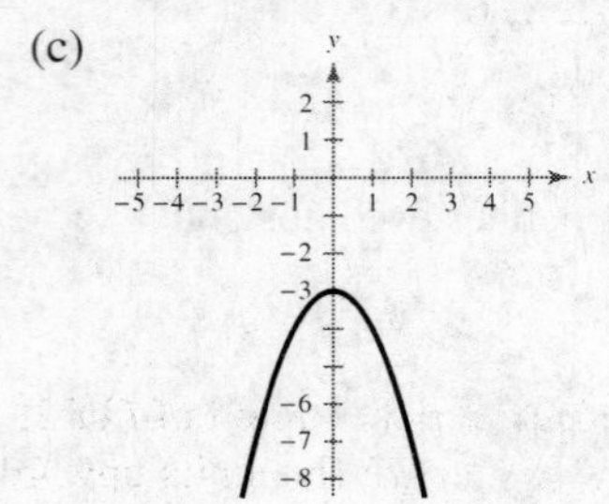

(d) $h(x) = -f(x) - 3$

91. $h(x) = (x - 2)^3 + 5$

(a) $f(x) = x^3$

(b) The graph of h is a horizontal shift of f two units to the right, followed by a vertical shift five units upward.

(c)

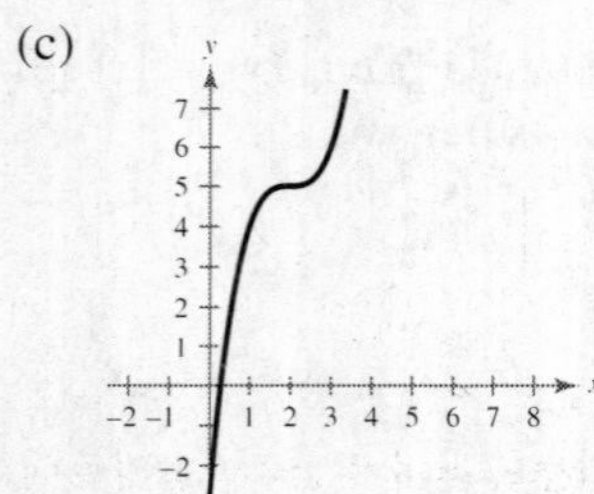

(d) $h(x) = (x - 2)^3 + 5 = f(x - 2) + 5$

92. $h(x) = -(x + 2)^2 - 8$

(a) $f(x) = x^2$

(b) The graph of h is a horizontal shift of f two units to the left, followed by a reflection in the x-axis, followed by a vertical shift eight units downward.

(c)

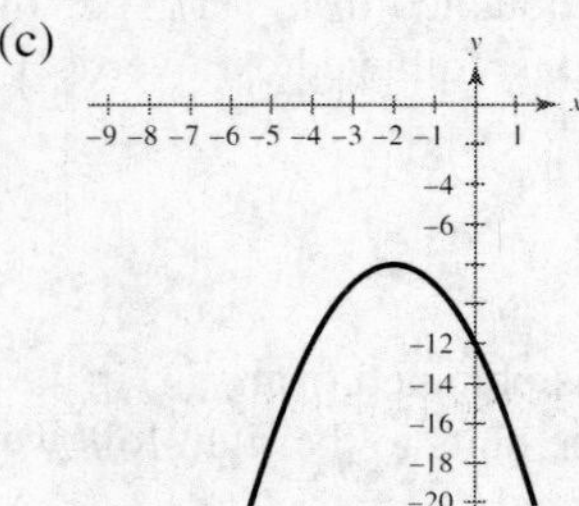

(d) $h(x) = -(x + 2)^2 - 8 = -f(x + 2) - 8$

93. (a) $f(x) = x^2$

(b) h is a horizontal shift two units to the right, a reflection in the x-axis, followed by a vertical shift eight units downward.

(c)

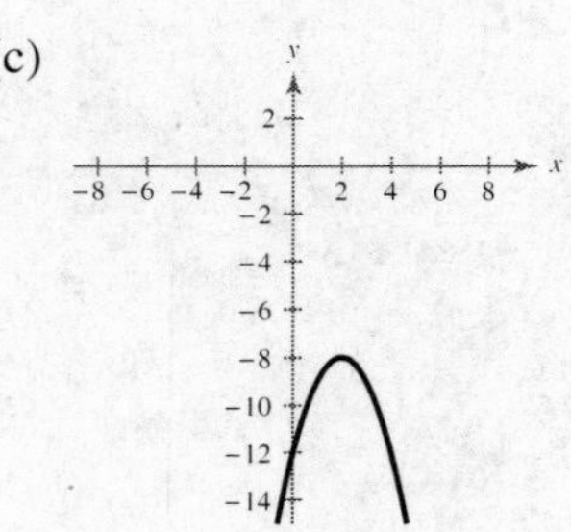

(d) $h(x) = -f(x - 2) - 8$

94. $h(x) = \frac{1}{2}(x - 3)^2 - 6$

(a) $f(x) = x^2$

(b) The graph of h is a horizontal shift of f three units to the right, followed by a vertical shrink of $\frac{1}{2}$, followed by a vertical shift six units downward.

(c)

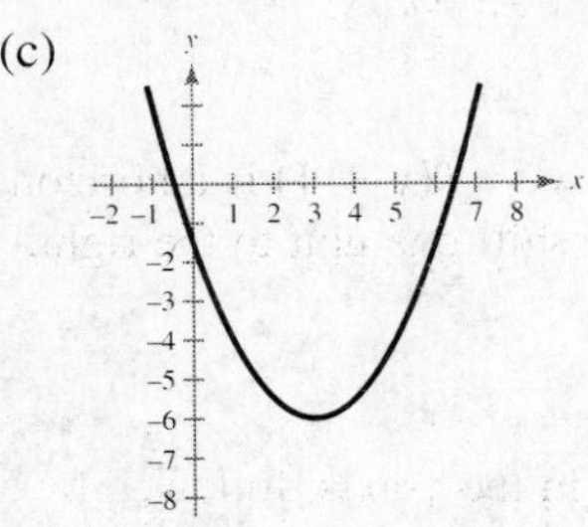

(d) $h(x) = \frac{1}{2}(x - 3)^2 - 6$

$= \frac{1}{2}f(x - 3) - 6$

95. $h(x) = -\sqrt{x} + 5$

(a) $f(x) = \sqrt{x}$

(b) The graph of h is a reflection of f in the x-axis, followed by a vertical shift five units upward.

(c)

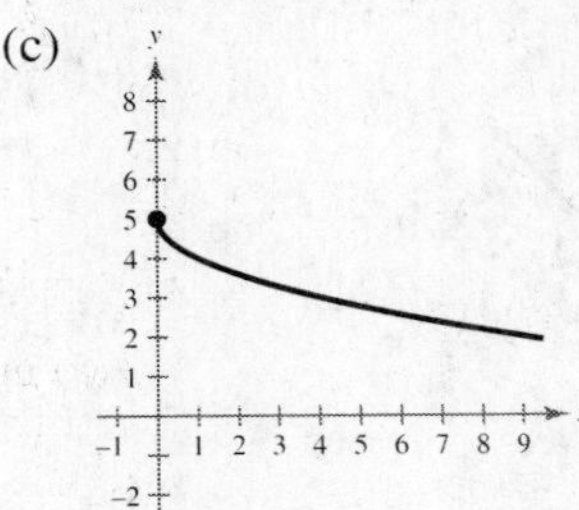

(d) $h(x) = -\sqrt{x} + 5$

$= -f(x) + 5$

96. $h(x) = 2\sqrt{x} + 5$

(a) $f(x) = \sqrt{x}$

(b) The graph of h is a vertical stretch of f of 2, followed by a vertical shift five units upward.

(c)

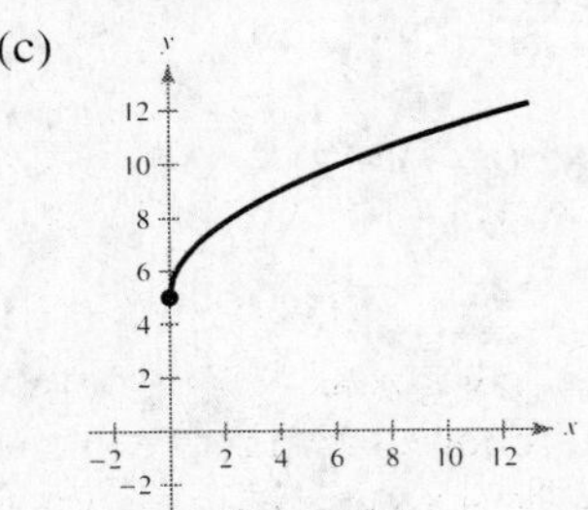

(d) $h(x) = 2\sqrt{x} + 5$

$= 2f(x) + 5$

97. $h(x) = \sqrt{x - 1} + 3$

(a) $f(x) = \sqrt{x}$

(b) The graph of h is a horizontal shift of one unit to the right, followed by a vertical shift three units upward.

(c)

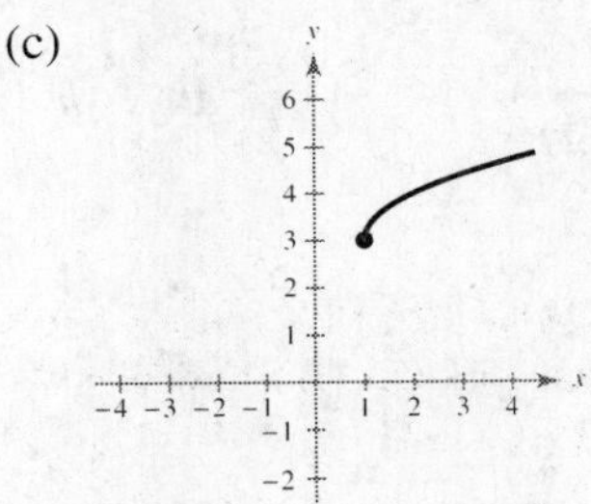

(d) $h(x) = f(x - 1) + 3$

98. $h(x) = |x| + 9$

(a) $f(x) = |x|$

(b) The graph of h is a vertical shift of f nine units upward.

(c)

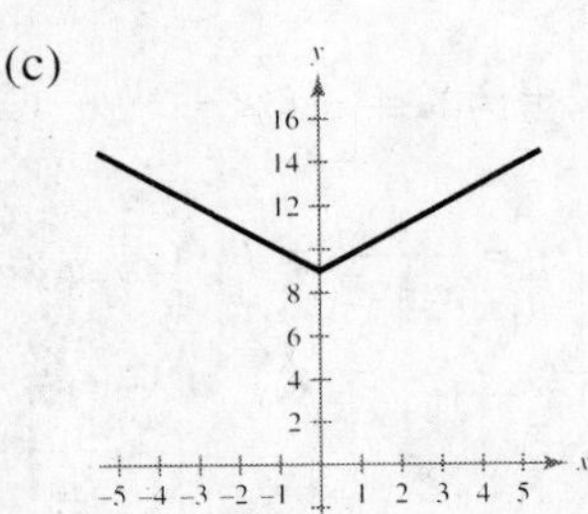

(d) $h(x) = |x| + 9$

$= f(x) + 9$

99. $h(x) = -\frac{1}{2}|x| + 9$

(a) $f(x) = |x|$

(b) h is a vertical shrink, followed by a reflection in the x-axis, followed by a vertical shift nine units upward.

(c)

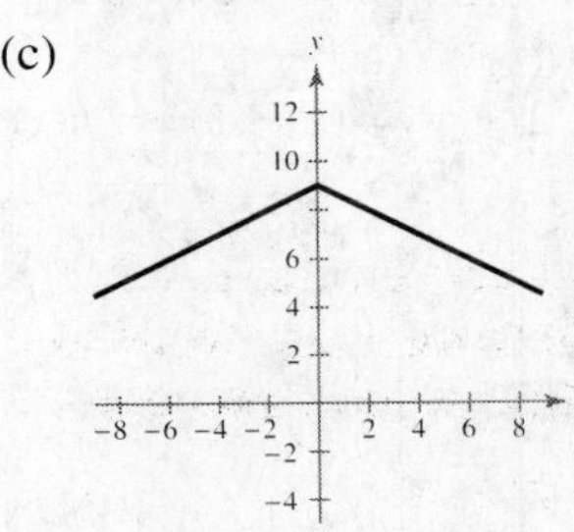

(d) $h(x) = -\frac{1}{2}f(x) + 9$

100. $h(x) = |x + 8| - 1$

(a) $f(x) = |x|$

(b) h is a horizontal shift eight units to the left, followed by a vertical shift one unit downward.

(c)

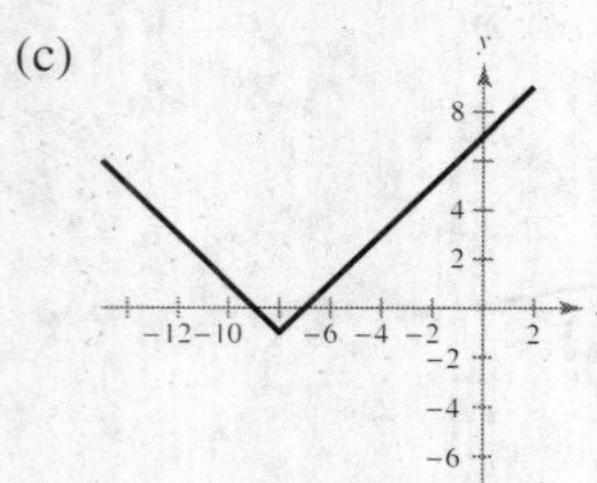

(d) $h(x) = f(x + 8) - 1$

101. $(f - g)(4) = f(4) - g(4)$
$= [3 - 2(4)] - \sqrt{4}$
$= -5 - 2$
$= -7$

102. $(f + h)(5) = f(5) + h(5)$
$= -7 + 77$
$= 70$

103. $(f + g)(25) = f(25) + g(25)$
$= -47 + 5$
$= -42$

104. $(g - h)(1) = g(1) - h(1) = 1 - 5 = -4$

105. $(fh)(1) = f(1)h(1) = (3 - 2(1))(3(1)^2 + 2)$
$= (1)(5) = 5$

106. $\left(\frac{g}{h}\right)(1) = \frac{g(1)}{h(1)} = \frac{1}{5}$

107. $(h \circ g)(7) = h(g(7))$
$= h(\sqrt{7})$
$= 3(\sqrt{7})^2 + 2$
$= 23$

108. $(g \circ f)(-2) = g(7) = \sqrt{7}$

109. $(f \circ h)(-4) = f(h(-4))$
$= f(50)$
$= -97$

110. $(g \circ h)(6) = g(h(6))$
$= g(110)$
$= \sqrt{110}$

111. $f(x) = x^2, g(x) = x + 3$
$(f \circ g)(x) = f(x + 3)$
$= (x + 3)^2 = h(x)$

112. $f(x) = x^3, g(x) = 1 - 2x$
$(f \circ g)(x) = f(1 - 2x) = (1 - 2x)^3 = h(x)$

113. $f(x) = \sqrt{x}, g(x) = 4x + 2$
$(f \circ g)(x) = f(4x + 2) = \sqrt{4x + 2} = h(x)$

114. $f(x) = \sqrt[3]{x}, g(x) = (x + 2)^2$
$(f \circ g)(x) = f((x + 2)^2) = \sqrt[3]{(x + 2)^2} = h(x)$

115. $f(x) = \frac{4}{x}, g(x) = x + 2$
$(f \circ g)(x) = f(x + 2) = \frac{4}{x + 2} = h(x)$

116. $f(x) = \frac{6}{x^3}, g(x) = 3x + 1$
$(f \circ g)(x) = f(3x + 1) = \frac{6}{(3x + 1)^3} = h(x)$

117.

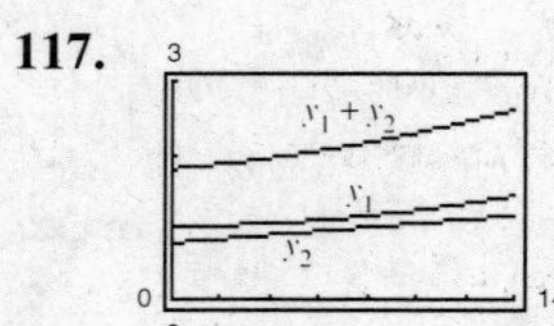

118. $y_1 + y_2 = (0.00204t^2 + 0.0015t + 1.021) + (0.0274t + 0.785)$

For 2008, let $t = 18$.

$(y_1 + y_2)(18) \approx 2.987$, or about 2,987,000 students.

119. $f(x) = 6x$

$f^{-1}(x) = \frac{1}{6}x$

$f(f^{-1}(x)) = f\left(\frac{1}{6}x\right) = 6\left(\frac{1}{6}x\right) = x$

$f^{-1}(f(x)) = f^{-1}(6x) = \frac{1}{6}(6x) = x$

120. $f(x) = x + 5$

$f^{-1}(x) = x - 5$

$f(f^{-1}(x)) = f(x - 5) = (x - 5) + 5 = x$

$f^{-1}(f(x)) = f^{-1}(x + 5) = (x + 5) - 5 = x$

121. $f(x) = \frac{1}{2}x + 3 \Rightarrow f^{-1}(x) = 2(x - 3) = 2x - 6$

$$f(f^{-1}(x)) = f(2(x - 3)) = \frac{1}{2}(2(x - 3)) + 3 = x - 3 + 3 = x$$

$$f^{-1}(f(x)) = f^{-1}\left(\frac{1}{2}x + 3\right) = 2\left(\frac{1}{2}x + 3 - 3\right) = 2\left(\frac{1}{2}x\right) = x$$

122. $f(x) = \dfrac{x - 4}{5} \Rightarrow f^{-1}(x) = 5x + 4$

$$f(f^{-1}(x)) = f(5x + 4) = \frac{5x + 4 - 4}{5} = \frac{5x}{5} = x$$

$$f^{-1}(f(x)) = f^{-1}\left(\frac{x - 4}{5}\right) = 5\left(\frac{x - 4}{5}\right) + 4 = x - 4 + 4 = x$$

123. (a)

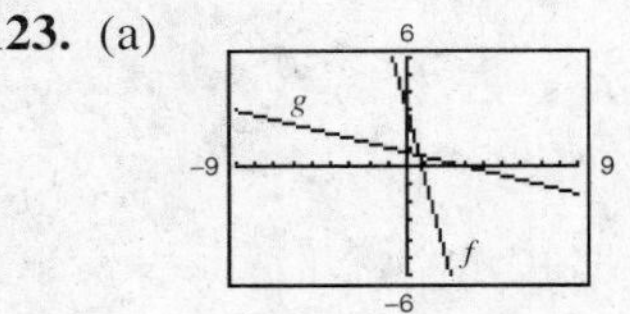

Reflection in the line $y = x$

(b)

x	-5	-1	0	1	3
$f(x)$	23	7	3	-1	-9

x	23	7	3	-1	-9
$g(x)$	-5	-1	0	1	3

The entries in the table are the same except that their rows are interchanged.

124. $f(x) = \sqrt{x + 1}, \quad g(x) = x^2 - 1, \quad x \geq 0$

(a)

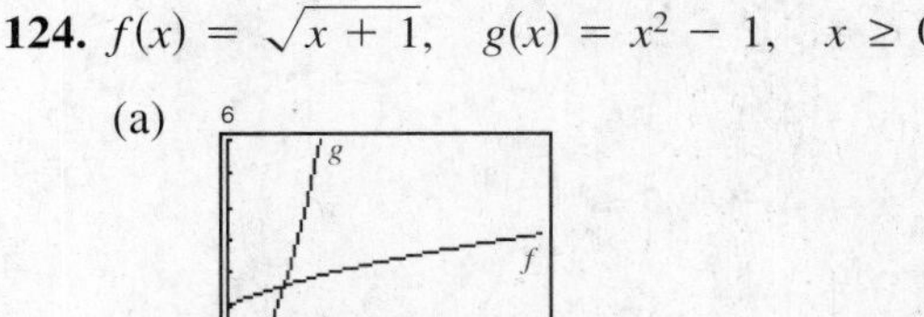

Reflections in $y = x$

(b)

x	-1	0	3	8	15
$f(x)$	0	1	2	3	4

x	0	1	2	3	4
$g(x)$	-1	0	3	8	15

The entries are the same, except that the rows are interchanged.

125.

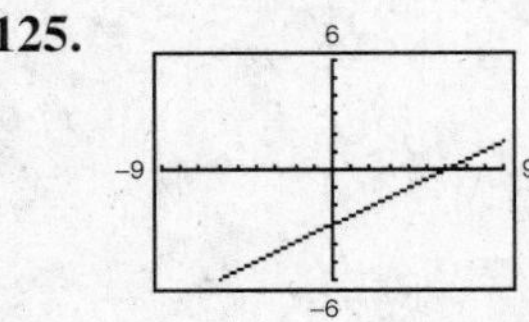

$f(x) = \frac{1}{2}x - 3$ passes the Horizontal Line Test, and hence is one-to-one and has an inverse $(f^{-1}(x) = 2(x + 3))$.

126.

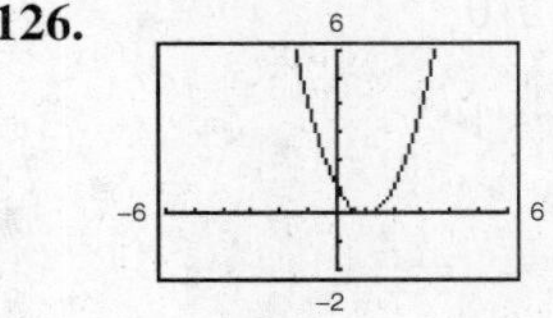

$f(x) = (x - 1)^2$ does not pass the Horizontal Line Test. Not one-to-one

127.

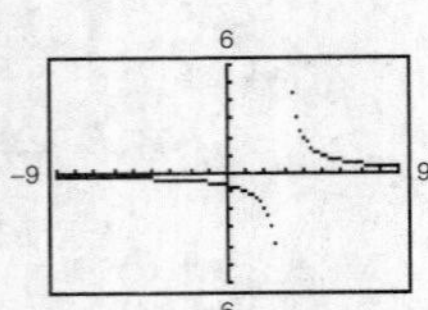

$h(t) = \dfrac{2}{t-3}$ passes the Horizontal Line Test, and hence is one-to-one.

128.

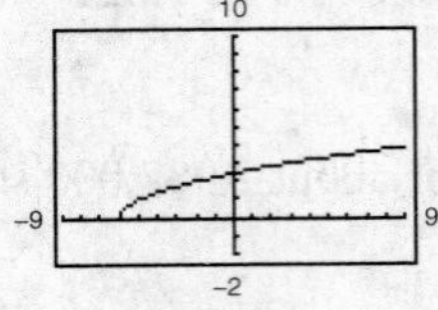

$g(x) = \sqrt{x+6}$ passes the Horizontal Line Test. It is one-to-one.

129.

$$y = \frac{1}{2}x - 5$$
$$x = \frac{1}{2}y - 5$$
$$x + 5 = \frac{1}{2}y$$
$$y = 2(x + 5)$$
$$f^{-1}(x) = 2x + 10$$

130.

$$f(x) = \frac{7x + 3}{8}$$
$$y = \frac{1}{8}(7x + 3)$$
$$x = \frac{1}{8}(7y + 3)$$
$$8x = 7y + 3$$
$$8x - 3 = 7y$$
$$f^{-1}(x) = \frac{1}{7}(8x - 3)$$

131.

$$f(x) = 4x^3 - 3$$
$$y = 4x^3 - 3$$
$$x = 4y^3 - 3$$
$$x + 3 = 4y^3$$
$$\frac{x + 3}{4} = y^3$$
$$f^{-1}(x) = \sqrt[3]{\frac{x + 3}{4}}$$

132.

$$y = 5x^3 + 2$$
$$x = 5y^3 + 2$$
$$x - 2 = 5y^3$$
$$\frac{x - 2}{5} = y^3$$
$$f^{-1}(x) = \sqrt[3]{\frac{x - 2}{5}}$$

133.

$$f(x) = \sqrt{x + 10}$$
$$y = \sqrt{x + 10},\ x \ge -10,\ y \ge 0$$
$$x = \sqrt{y + 10},\ y \ge -10,\ x \ge 0$$
$$x^2 = y + 10$$
$$x^2 - 10 = y$$
$$f^{-1}(x) = x^2 - 10,\ x \ge 0$$

134.

$$f(x) = 4\sqrt{6 - x},\ x \le 6,\ y \ge 0$$
$$y = 4\sqrt{6 - x}$$
$$x = 4\sqrt{6 - y},\ y \le 6,\ x \ge 0$$
$$x^2 = 16(6 - y) = 96 - 16y$$
$$16y = 96 - x^2$$
$$y = \frac{96 - x^2}{16}$$
$$f^{-1}(x) = \frac{96 - x^2}{16},\ x \ge 0$$

135. Negative correlation

136. No correlation

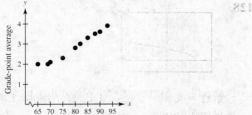

137. (a)

(b) Yes, the relationship is approximately linear. Higher entrance exam scores, x, are associated with higher grade-point averages, y.

138. (a)

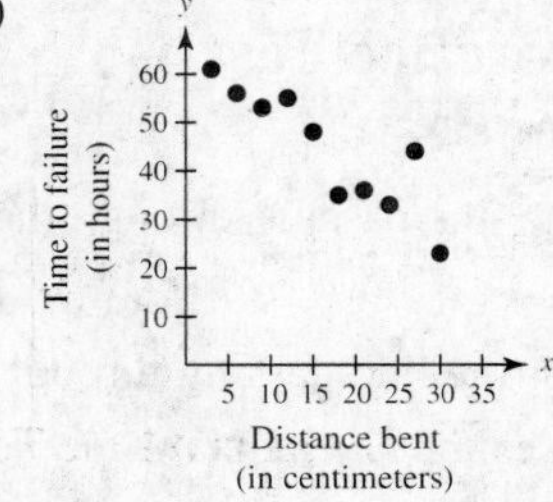

(b) Answers will vary.

139. (a)

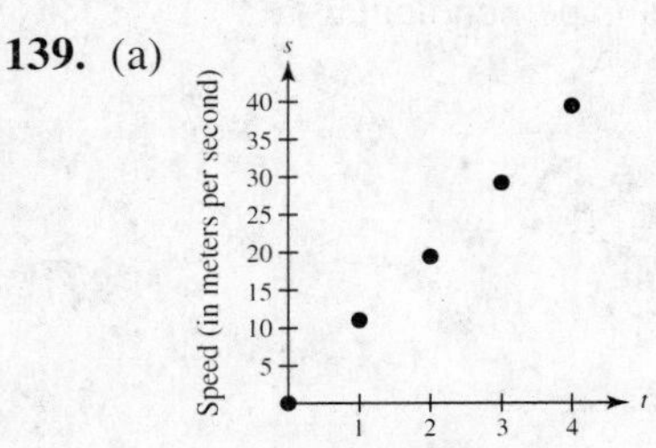

(b) $s \approx 10t$ (Approximations will vary.)

(c) $s = 9.7t + 0.4$; 0.99933

(d) For $t = 2.5$, $S \approx 24.7$ m/sec.

140. (a) $y = -0.0119t + 4.164$, linear model; -0.91997

(b)

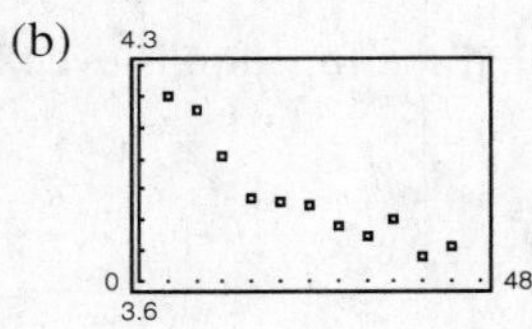

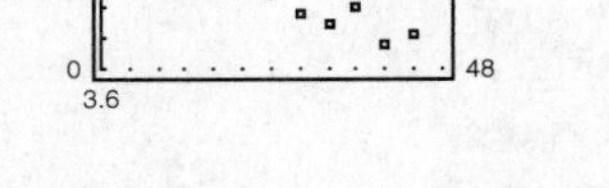

(c)

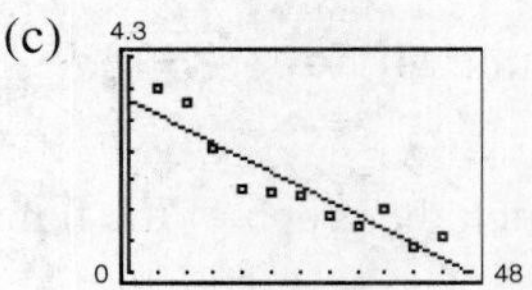

(d), (e) Answers will vary.

141. $y = 95.174x - 458.423$

142. $y = 95.174x - 458.423$

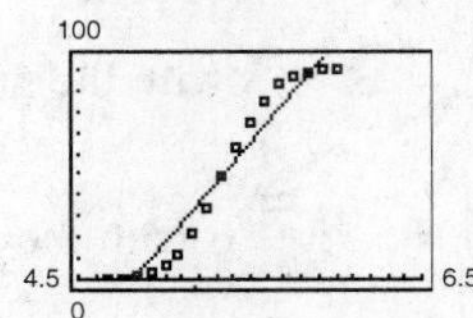

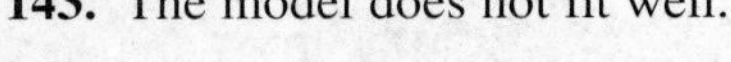

143. The model does not fit well.

144. No. The data stops at (6.00, 100.0).

145. False. $g(x) = -[(x-6)^2 + 3] = -(x-6)^2 - 3$ and $g(-1) = -52 \neq 28$

146. True. $f^{-1}(x) = x^{1/n}$, n odd

147. False. $f(x) = \dfrac{1}{x}$ or $f(x) = x$ satisfies $f = f^{-1}$.

148. False. The slope can be positive, negative, or 0.

Chapter 1 Practice Test

1. Find the slope of the line passing through the points $(-2, 2)$ and $(1, 3)$.

2. Find an equation for the line passing through the points $(3, -2)$ and $(4, -5)$. Use a graphing utility to sketch a graph of the line.

3. Find an equation of the line that passes through the point $(-1, 5)$ and has slope -3. Use a graphing utility to sketch a graph of the line.

4. Find the slope-intercept form of the line that passes through the point $(-3, 2)$ and is perpendicular to $3x + 5y = 7$.

5. Does the equation $x^4 + y^4 = 16$ represent y as a function of x?

6. Evaluate the function $f(x) = |x - 2|/(x - 2)$ at the points $x = 0$, $x = 2$, and $x = 4$.

7. Find the domain of the function $f(x) = 5/(x^2 - 16)$.

8. Find the domain of the function $g(t) = \sqrt{4 - t}$.

9. Use a graphing utility to sketch the graph of the function $f(x) = 3 - x^6$ and determine if the function is even, odd, or neither.

10. Determine the open interval(s) on which the function $f(x) = 12x - x^3$ is increasing.

11. Use a graphing utility to approximate any relative minimum or maximum values of the function $y = 4 - x + x^3$.

12. Compare the graph of $f(x) = x^3 - 3$ with the graph of $y = x^3$.

13. Compare the graph of $f(x) = \sqrt{x - 6}$ with the graph of $y = \sqrt{x}$.

14. Find $g \circ f$ if $f(x) = \sqrt{x}$ and $g(x) = x^2 - 2$. What is the domain of $g \circ f$?

15. Find f/g if $f(x) = 3x^2$ and $g(x) = 16 - x^4$. What is the domain of f/g?

16. Show that $f(x) = 3x + 1$ and $g(x) = \dfrac{x - 1}{3}$ are inverse functions algebraically and graphically.

17. Find the inverse of $f(x) = \sqrt{9 - x^2}$, $0 \le x \le 3$. Graph f and f^{-1} in the same viewing rectangle.

18. Use a graphing utility to find the least squares regression line for the points $(-1, 0)$, $(0, 1)$, $(3, 3)$, $(4, 5)$. Graph the points and the line.

CHAPTER 2
Polynomial and Rational Functions

Section 2.1 Quadratic Functions 88

Section 2.2 Polynomial Functions of Higher Degree 99

Section 2.3 Real Zeros of Polynomial Functions 112

Section 2.4 Complex Numbers 126

Section 2.5 The Fundamental Theorem of Algebra 132

Section 2.6 Rational Functions and Asymptotes 142

Section 2.7 Graphs of Rational Functions 150

Section 2.8 Quadratic Models 165

Review Exercises 170

Practice Test 191

CHAPTER 2
Polynomial and Rational Functions

Section 2.1 Quadratic Functions

You should know the following facts about parabolas.

- $f(x) = ax^2 + bx + c,\ a \neq 0$, is a quadratic function, and its graph is a parabola.
- If $a > 0$, the parabola opens upward and the vertex is the minimum point. If $a < 0$, the parabola opens downward and the vertex is the maximum point.
- The vertex is $(-b/2a, f(-b/2a))$.
- To find the x-intercepts (if any), solve

  $ax^2 + bx + c = 0.$
- The standard form of the equation of a parabola is

  $f(x) = a(x - h)^2 + k$

  where $a \neq 0$.

  (a) The vertex is (h, k).

  (b) The axis is the vertical line $x = h$.

Vocabulary Check

1. nonnegative integer, real **2.** quadratic, parabola **3.** axis

4. positive, minimum **5.** negative, maximum

1. $f(x) = (x - 2)^2$ opens upward and has vertex $(2, 0)$. Matches graph (c).

2. $f(x) = 3 - x^2$ opens downward and has vertex $(0, 3)$. Matches graph (d).

3. $f(x) = x^2 + 3$ opens upward and has vertex $(0, 3)$. Matches graph (b).

4. $f(x) = -(x - 4)^2$ opens downward and has vertex $(4, 0)$. Matches graph (a).

5.

(a) $y = \frac{1}{2}x^2$, vertical shrink

(b) $y = \frac{1}{2}x^2 - 1$, vertical shrink and vertical shift one unit downward

(c) $y = \frac{1}{2}(x + 3)^2$, vertical shrink and horizontal shift three units to the left

(d) $y = -\frac{1}{2}(x + 3)^2 - 1$, horizontal shift three units to the left, vertical shrink, reflection in x-axis, and vertical shift one unit downward

6.

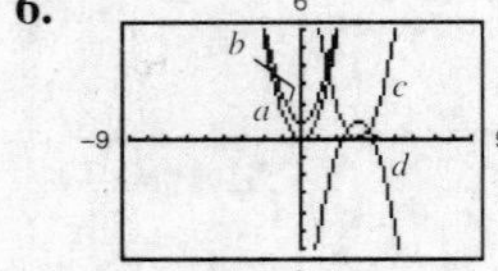

(a) $y = \frac{3}{2}x^2$, vertical stretch

(b) $y = \frac{3}{2}x^2 + 1$, vertical stretch, followed by a vertical shift upward one unit

(c) $y = \frac{3}{2}(x - 3)^2$, horizontal shift three units to the right, followed by a vertical stretch

(d) $y = -\frac{3}{2}(x - 3)^2 + 1$, horizontal shift three units to the right, a vertical stretch, a reflection in the x-axis, and a vertical shift one unit upward

7. $f(x) = 25 - x^2$

Vertex: $(0, 25)$

x-intercepts: $(-5, 0), (5, 0)$

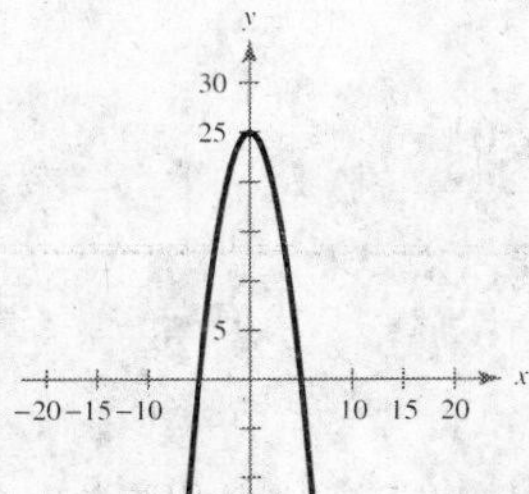

8. $f(x) = x^2 - 7$

Vertex: $(0, -7)$

Intercepts: $(\pm\sqrt{7}, 0)$

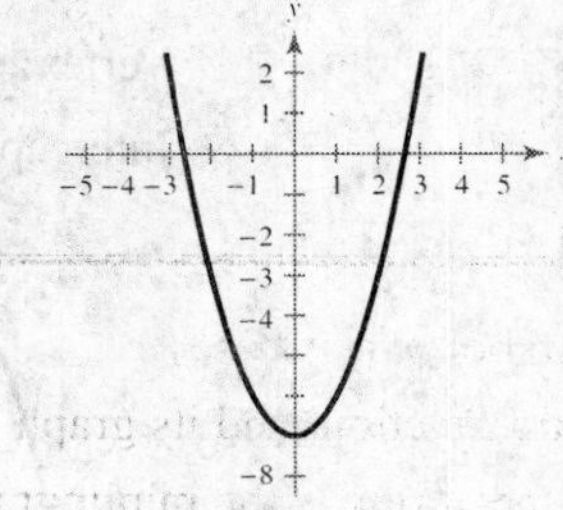

9. $f(x) = \frac{1}{2}x^2 - 4$

Vertex: $(0, -4)$

x-intercepts: $(\pm 2\sqrt{2}, 0)$

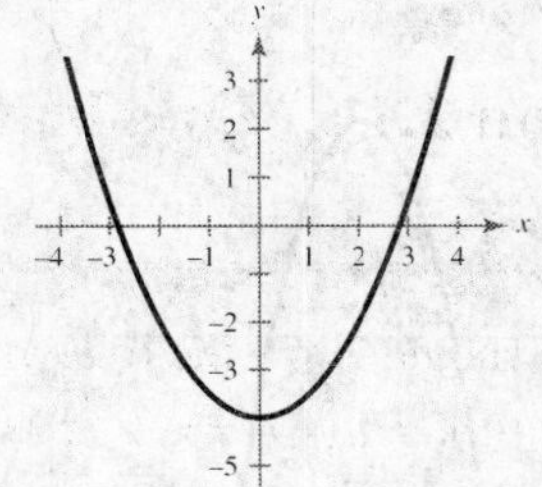

10. $f(x) = 16 - \frac{1}{4}x^2$

Vertex: $(0, 16)$

Intercepts: $(\pm 8, 0)$

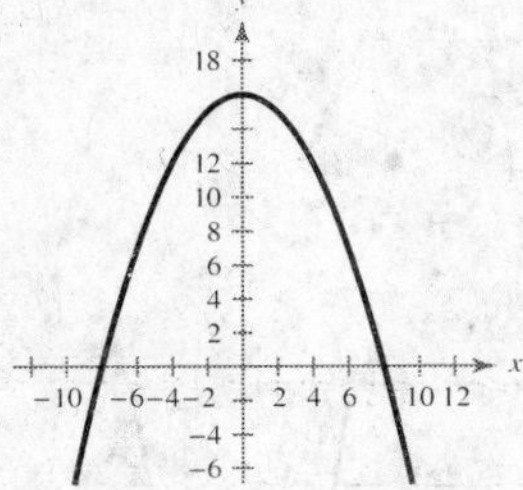

11. $f(x) = (x + 4)^2 - 3$

Vertex: $(-4, -3)$

x-intercepts: $(-4 \pm \sqrt{3}, 0)$

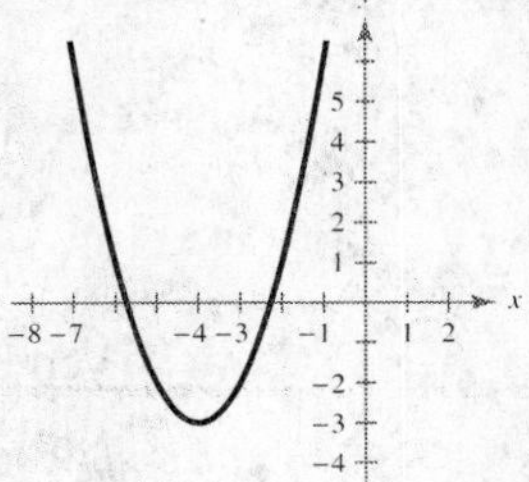

12. $f(x) = (x - 6)^2 + 3$

Vertex: $(6, 3)$

No x-intercepts

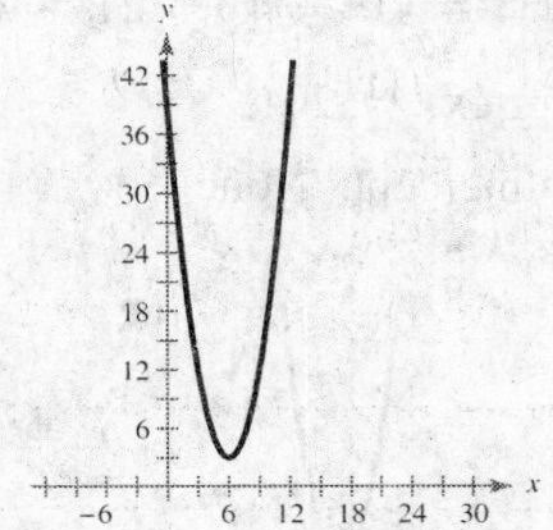

13. $h(x) = x^2 - 8x + 16 = (x - 4)^2$

Vertex: $(4, 0)$

x-intercepts: $(4, 0)$

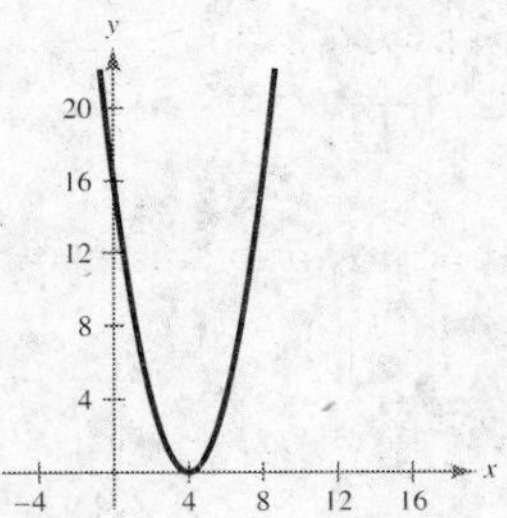

14. $g(x) = x^2 + 2x + 1 = (x + 1)^2$

Vertex: $(-1, 0)$

Intercept: $(-1, 0)$

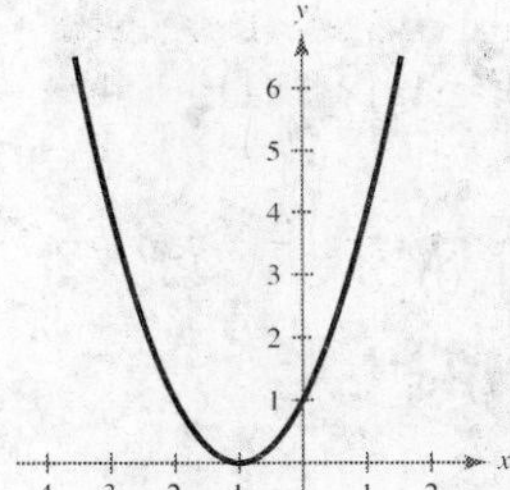

15. $f(x) = x^2 - x + \frac{5}{4} = \left(x - \frac{1}{2}\right)^2 + 1$

Vertex: $\left(\frac{1}{2}, 1\right)$

x-intercepts: None

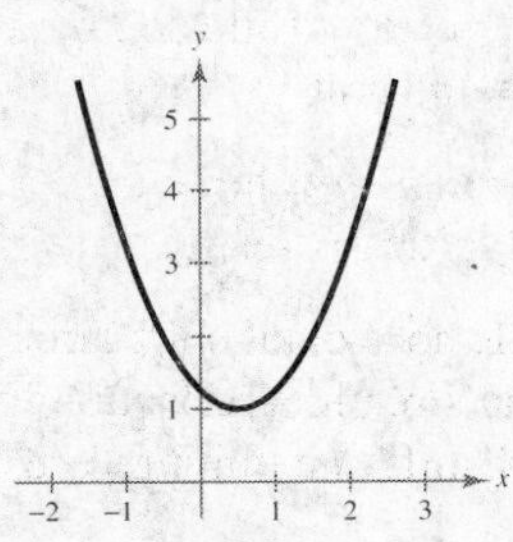

16. $f(x) = x^2 + 3x + \frac{1}{4} = \left(x + \frac{3}{2}\right)^2 - 2$

Vertex: $\left(-\frac{3}{2}, -2\right)$

Intercepts: $\left(-\frac{3}{2} \pm \sqrt{2}, 0\right)$

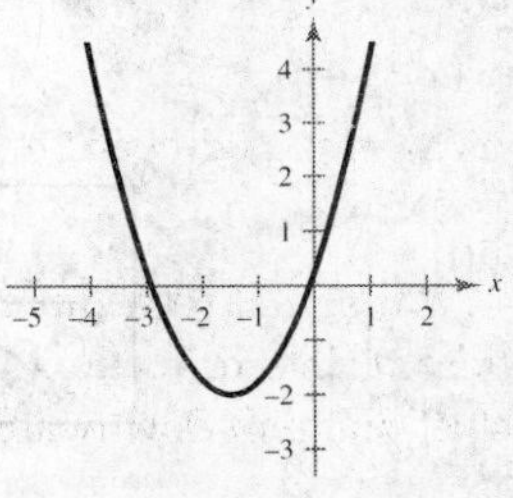

17. $f(x) = -x^2 + 2x + 5 = -(x - 1)^2 + 6$

Vertex: $(1, 6)$

x-intercepts: $(1 - \sqrt{6}, 0), (1 + \sqrt{6}, 0)$

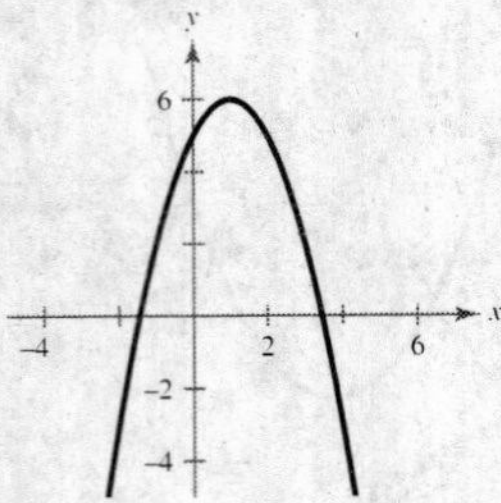

18. $f(x) = -x^2 - 4x + 1 = -1(x^2 + 4x - 1)$

$= -1[(x + 2)^2 - 5]$

$= -(x + 2)^2 + 5$

Vertex: $(-2, 5)$

Intercepts: $(-2 \pm \sqrt{5}, 0)$

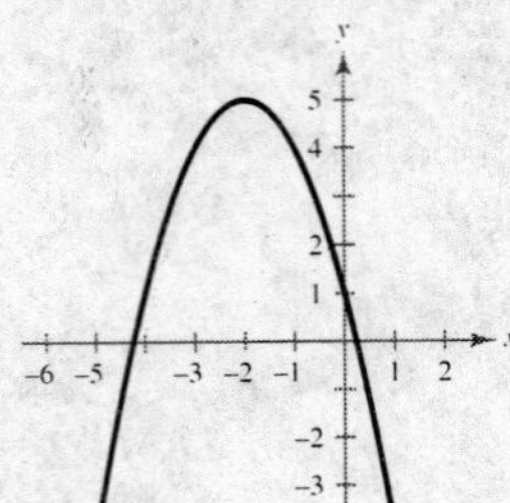

19. $h(x) = 4x^2 - 4x + 21 = 4\left(x - \frac{1}{2}\right)^2 + 20$

Vertex: $\left(\frac{1}{2}, 20\right)$

x-intercept: None

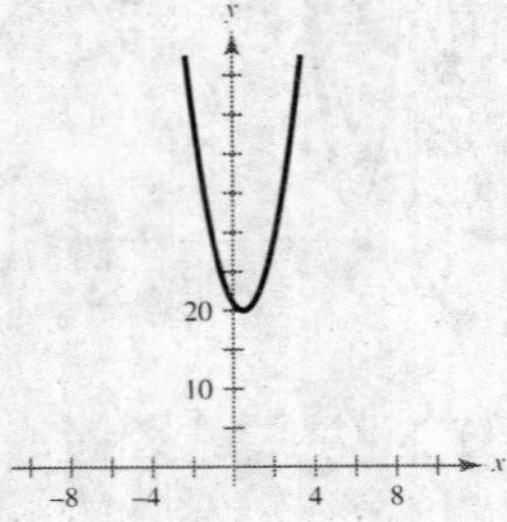

20. $f(x) = 2x^2 - x + 1$

$= 2\left(x^2 - \frac{1}{2}x\right) + 1$

$= 2\left(x - \frac{1}{4}\right)^2 - \frac{1}{8} + 1$

$= 2\left(x - \frac{1}{4}\right)^2 + \frac{7}{8}$

Vertex: $\left(\frac{1}{4}, \frac{7}{8}\right)$

No x-intercepts

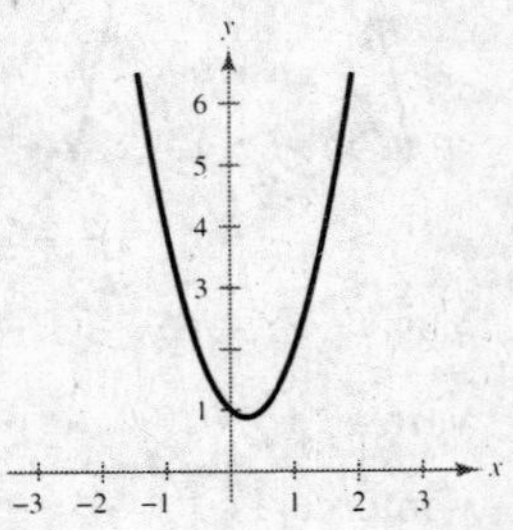

21. $f(x) = -(x^2 + 2x - 3) = -(x + 1)^2 + 4$

Vertex: $(-1, 4)$

x-intercepts: $(-3, 0), (1, 0)$

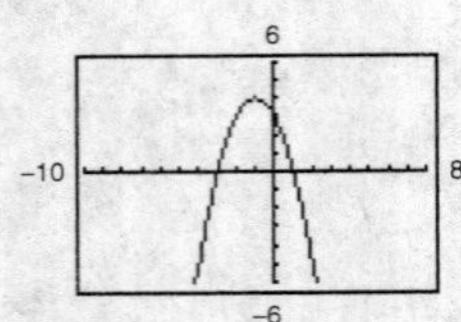

22.

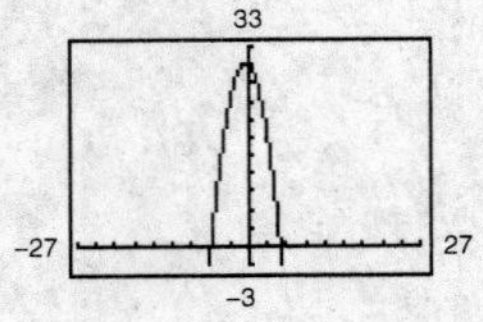

Vertex: $\left(-\frac{1}{2}, \frac{121}{4}\right)$

Intercepts: $(5, 0), (-6, 0)$

$f(x) = -(x^2 + x - 30)$

$= -\left(x^2 + x + \frac{1}{4}\right) + \frac{1}{4} + 30$

$= -\left(x + \frac{1}{2}\right)^2 + \frac{121}{4}$

23. $g(x) = x^2 + 8x + 11 = (x + 4)^2 - 5$

Vertex: $(-4, -5)$

x-intercepts: $(-4 \pm \sqrt{5}, 0)$

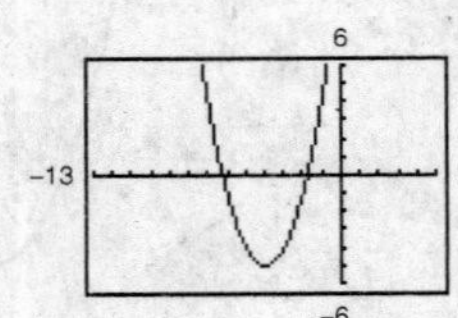

24.

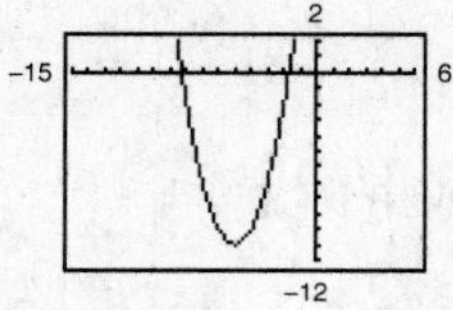

Vertex: $(-5, -11)$

Intercepts: $(-1.683, 0), (-8.317, 0)$

$$\begin{aligned} f(x) &= x^2 + 10x + 14 \\ &= (x^2 + 10x + 25) - 11 \\ &= (x + 5)^2 - 11 \end{aligned}$$

25. $$\begin{aligned} f(x) &= -2x^2 + 16x - 31 \\ &= -2\left(x^2 - 8x + \tfrac{31}{2}\right) \\ &= -2\left(x^2 - 8x + 16 - \tfrac{1}{2}\right) \\ &= -2(x - 4)^2 + 1 \end{aligned}$$

Vertex: $(4, 1)$

x-intercept: $\left(4 \pm \frac{1}{2}\sqrt{2}, 0\right)$

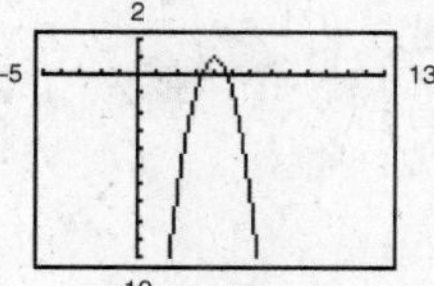

26.

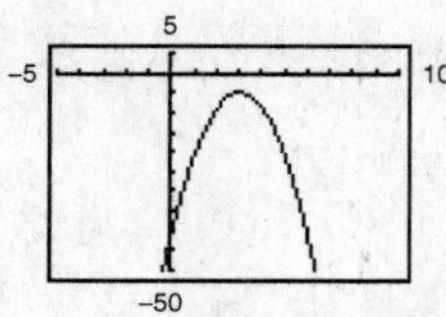

Vertex: $(3, -5)$

No x-intercepts

$$\begin{aligned} f(x) &= -4x^2 + 24x - 41 \\ &= -4(x^2 - 6x + 9) + 36 - 41 \\ &= -4(x - 3)^2 - 5 \end{aligned}$$

27. $(-1, 4)$ is the vertex.

$f(x) = a(x + 1)^2 + 4$

Since the graph passes through the point $(1, 0)$, we have:

$$\begin{aligned} 0 &= a(1 + 1)^2 + 4 \\ 0 &= 4a + 4 \\ -1 &= a \end{aligned}$$

Thus, $f(x) = -(x + 1)^2 + 4$. Note that $(-3, 0)$ is on the parabola.

28. $(-2, -1)$ is the vertex.

$f(x) = a(x + 2)^2 - 1$

Since the graph passes through $(0, 3)$, we have:

$$\begin{aligned} 3 &= a(0 + 2)^2 - 1 \\ 3 &= 4a - 1 \\ 4 &= 4a \\ 1 &= a \end{aligned}$$

Thus, $y = (x + 2)^2 - 1$.

29. $(-2, 5)$ is the vertex.

$f(x) = a(x + 2)^2 + 5$

Since the graph passes through the point $(0, 9)$, we have:

$$\begin{aligned} 9 &= a(0 + 2)^2 + 5 \\ 4 &= 4a \\ 1 &= a \end{aligned}$$

$f(x) = 1(x + 2)^2 + 5 = (x + 2)^2 + 5$

30. $(4, 1)$ is the vertex.

$f(x) = a(x - 4)^2 + 1$

Since the graph passes through the point $(6, -7)$, we have:

$$\begin{aligned} -7 &= a(6 - 4)^2 + 1 \\ -7 &= 4a + 1 \\ -8 &= 4a \\ -2 &= a \end{aligned}$$

$f(x) = -2(x - 4)^2 + 1$

31. $(1, -2)$ is the vertex.

$f(x) = a(x - 1)^2 - 2$

Since the graph passes through the point $(-1, 14)$, we have:

$$\begin{aligned} 14 &= a(-1 - 1)^2 - 2 \\ 14 &= 4a - 2 \\ 16 &= 4a \\ 4 &= a \end{aligned}$$

$f(x) = 4(x - 1)^2 - 2$

32. $(-4, -1)$ is the vertex.

$f(x) = a(x + 4)^2 - 1$

Since the graph passes through the point $(-2, 4)$, we have:

$4 = a(-2 + 4)^2 - 1$

$5 = 4a$

$a = \frac{5}{4}$

$f(x) = \frac{5}{4}(x + 4)^2 - 1$

33. $\left(\frac{1}{2}, 1\right)$ is the vertex.

$f(x) = a\left(x - \frac{1}{2}\right)^2 + 1$

Since the graph passes through the point $\left(-2, -\frac{21}{5}\right)$, we have:

$-\frac{21}{5} = a\left(-2 - \frac{1}{2}\right)^2 + 1$

$-\frac{21}{5} = \frac{25}{4}a + 1$

$-\frac{26}{5} = \frac{25}{4}a$

$-\frac{104}{125} = a$

$f(x) = -\frac{104}{125}\left(x - \frac{1}{2}\right)^2 + 1$

34. $\left(-\frac{1}{4}, -1\right)$ is the vertex.

$f(x) = a\left(x + \frac{1}{4}\right)^2 - 1$

Since the graph passes through the point $\left(-1, \frac{-17}{16}\right)$, we have:

$-\frac{17}{16} = a\left(0 + \frac{1}{4}\right)^2 - 1$

$-\frac{17}{16} = \frac{1}{16}a - 1$

$-\frac{1}{16} = \frac{1}{16}a$

$a = -1$

$f(x) = -\left(x + \frac{1}{4}\right)^2 - 1$

35. $y = x^2 - 4x - 5$

x-intercepts: $(5, 0), (-1, 0)$

$0 = x^2 - 4x - 5$

$0 = (x - 5)(x + 1)$

$x = 5$ or $x = -1$

36. $y = 2x^2 + 5x - 3$

x-intercepts: $\left(\frac{1}{2}, 0\right), (-3, 0)$

$0 = 2x^2 + 5x - 3$

$0 = (2x - 1)(x + 3)$

$x = \frac{1}{2}, -3$

37. $y = x^2 + 8x + 16$

x-intercept: $(-4, 0)$

$0 = x^2 + 8x + 16$

$0 = (x + 4)^2$

$x = -4$

38. $y = x^2 - 6x + 9$

x-intercept: $(3, 0)$

$0 = x^2 - 6x + 9$

$0 = (x - 3)^2$

$x = 3$

39. $y = x^2 - 4x$

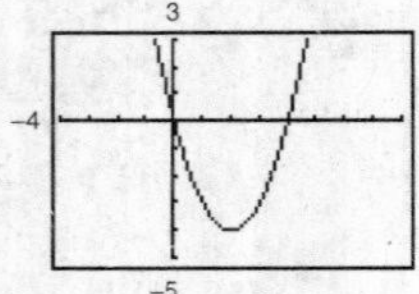

$0 = x^2 - 4x$

$0 = x(x - 4)$

$x = 0$ or $x = 4$

x-intercepts: $(0, 0), (4, 0)$

40. $y = -2x^2 + 10x$

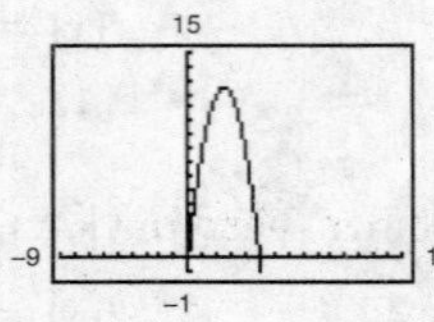

x-intercepts: $(0, 0), (5, 0)$

$0 = -2x^2 + 10x$

$0 = x(-2x + 10)$

$x = 0, x = 5$

41. $y = 2x^2 - 7x - 30$

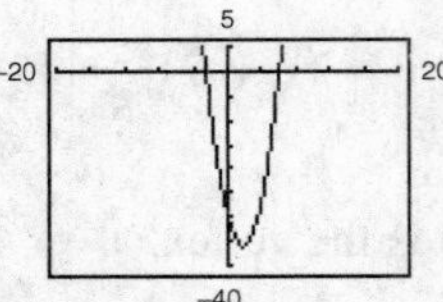

$0 = 2x^2 - 7x - 30$

$0 = (2x + 5)(x - 6)$

$x = -\frac{5}{2}$ or $x = 6$

x-intercepts: $\left(-\frac{5}{2}, 0\right), (6, 0)$

42. $y = 4x^2 + 25x - 21$

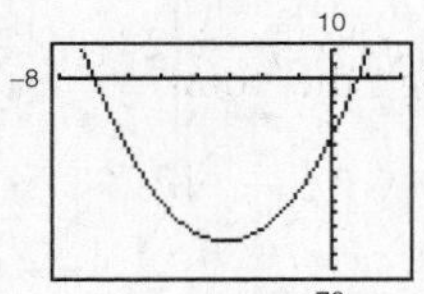

x-intercepts: $(-7, 0), (0.75, 0)$

$0 = 4x^2 + 25x - 21$

$= (x + 7)(4x - 3)$

$x = -7, \frac{3}{4}$

43. $y = -\frac{1}{2}(x^2 - 6x - 7)$

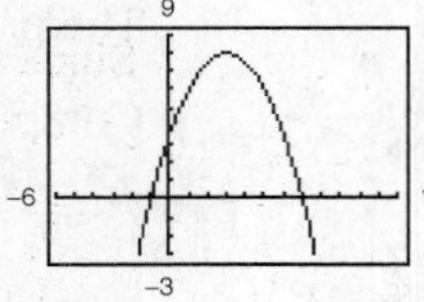

$0 = -\frac{1}{2}(x^2 - 6x - 7)$

$0 = x^2 - 6x - 7$

$0 = (x + 1)(x - 7)$

$x = -1, 7$

x-intercepts: $(-1, 0), (7, 0)$

44. $y = \frac{7}{10}(x^2 + 12x - 45)$

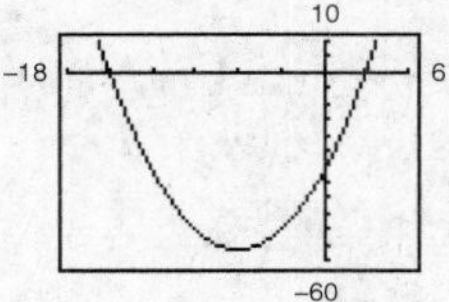

x-intercepts: $(3, 0), (-15, 0)$

$0 = \frac{7}{10}(x^2 + 12x - 45)$

$0 = x^2 + 12x - 45$

$= (x - 3)(x + 15)$

$x = 3, -15$

45. $f(x) = [x - (-1)](x - 3)$, opens upward

$= (x + 1)(x - 3)$

$= x^2 - 2x - 3$

$g(x) = -[x - (-1)](x - 3)$, opens downward

$= -(x + 1)(x - 3)$

$= -(x^2 - 2x - 3)$

$= -x^2 + 2x + 3$

Note: $f(x) = a(x + 1)(x - 3)$ has x-intercepts $(-1, 0)$ and $(3, 0)$ for all real numbers $a \neq 0$.

46. $f(x) = a(x - 0)(x - 10) = ax(x - 10)$

Many correct answers.

$f(x) = x(x - 10) = x^2 - 10x$ opens upward.

$f(x) = -x(x - 10) = -x^2 + 10x$ opens downward.

47. $f(x) = [x - (-3)]\left[x - \left(-\frac{1}{2}\right)\right](2)$, opens upward

$= (x + 3)\left(x + \frac{1}{2}\right)(2)$

$= (x + 3)(2x + 1)$

$= 2x^2 + 7x + 3$

$g(x) = -(2x^2 + 7x + 3)$, opens downward

$= -2x^2 - 7x - 3$

Note: $f(x) = a(x + 3)(2x + 1)$ has x-intercepts $(-3, 0)$ and $\left(-\frac{1}{2}, 0\right)$ for all real numbers $a \neq 0$.

48. $f(x) = 2\left[x - \left(-\frac{5}{2}\right)\right](x - 2)$

$= 2\left(x + \frac{5}{2}\right)(x - 2)$

$= 2x^2 + x - 10$, opens upward

$g(x) = -f(x)$, opens downward

$g(x) = -2x^2 - x + 10$

Many other answers possible.

49. Let $x =$ the first number and $y =$ the second number. Then the sum is

$x + y = 110 \implies y = 110 - x.$

The product is

$P(x) = xy = x(110 - x) = 110x - x^2.$

$P(x) = -x^2 + 110x$

$= -(x^2 - 110x + 3025 - 3025)$

$= -[(x - 55)^2 - 3025]$

$= -(x - 55)^2 + 3025$

The maximum value of the product occurs at the vertex of $P(x)$ and is 3025. This happens when $x = y = 55$.

50. Let $x =$ first number and $y =$ second number. Then, $x + y = S$, $y = S - x$. The product is

$$P(x) = xy = x(S - x).$$

$$P(x) = Sx - x^2$$

$$= -x^2 + Sx$$

$$= -\left(x^2 - Sx + \frac{S^2}{4} - \frac{S^2}{4}\right)$$

$$= -\left(x - \frac{S}{2}\right)^2 + \frac{S^2}{4}$$

The maximum value of the product occurs at the vertex of $P(x)$ and is $S^2/4$. This happens when $x = y = S/2$.

51. Let x be the first number and y be the second number. Then $x + 2y = 24 \implies x = 24 - 2y$.

The product is $P = xy = (24 - 2y)y = 24y - 2y^2$.

Completing the square,

$$P = -2y^2 + 24y$$

$$= -2(y^2 - 12y + 36) + 72$$

$$= -2(y - 6)^2 + 72.$$

The maximum value of the product P occurs at the vertex of the parabola and equals 72. This happens when $y = 6$ and $x = 24 - 2(6) = 12$.

52. Let $x =$ first number and $y =$ second number. Then $x + 3y = 42$, $y = \frac{1}{3}(42 - x)$. The product is

$$P(x) = xy = x\tfrac{1}{3}(42 - x) = 14x - \tfrac{1}{3}x^2.$$

$$P(x) = -\tfrac{1}{3}x^2 + 14x$$

$$= -\tfrac{1}{3}(x^2 - 42x)$$

$$= -\tfrac{1}{3}(x^2 - 42x + 441) + 147$$

$$= -\tfrac{1}{3}(x - 21)^2 + 147.$$

The maximum value of the product is 147, and occurs when $x = 21$ and $y = \frac{1}{3}(42 - 21) = 7$.

53. (a)

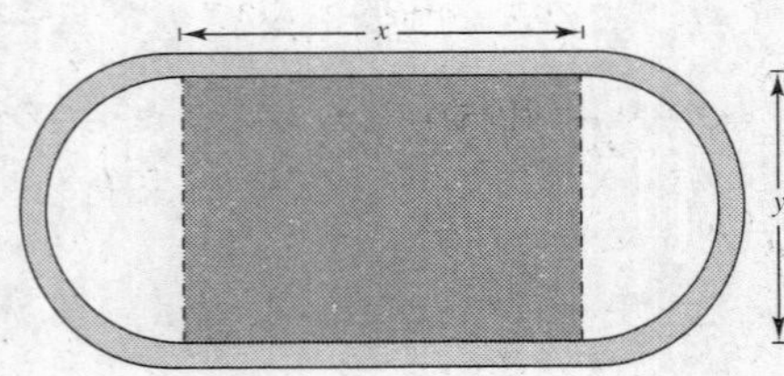

(b) Radius of semicircular ends of track: $r = \frac{1}{2}y$

Distance around two semicircular parts of track:

$$d = 2\pi r = 2\pi\left(\frac{1}{2}y\right) = \pi y$$

(c) Distance traveled around track in one lap:

$$d = \pi y + 2x = 200$$

$$\pi y = 200 - 2x$$

$$y = \frac{200 - 2x}{\pi}$$

(d) Area of rectangular region:

$$A = xy = x\left(\frac{200 - 2x}{\pi}\right)$$

$$= \frac{1}{\pi}(200x - 2x^2)$$

$$= -\frac{2}{\pi}(x^2 - 100x)$$

$$= -\frac{2}{\pi}(x^2 - 100x + 2500 - 2500)$$

$$= -\frac{2}{\pi}(x - 50)^2 + \frac{5000}{\pi}$$

The area is maximum when $x = 50$ and

$$y = \frac{200 - 2(50)}{\pi} = \frac{100}{\pi}.$$

(e)

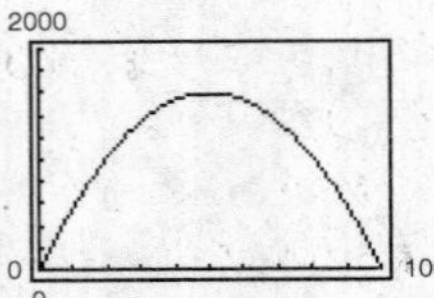

The area is maximum when $x = 50$ and

$$y = \frac{200 - 2(50)}{\pi} = \frac{100}{\pi}.$$

54. (a) $4x + 3y = 200 \Rightarrow y = \frac{1}{3}(200 - 4x) \Rightarrow A = 2xy = 2x\frac{1}{3}(200 - 4x) = \frac{8x}{3}(50 - x)$

(b)

x	y	Area
2	$\frac{1}{3}[200 - 4(2)]$	$2xy = 256$
4	$\frac{1}{3}[200 - 4(4)]$	$2xy \approx 491$
6	$\frac{1}{3}[200 - 4(6)]$	$2xy = 704$
8	$\frac{1}{3}[200 - 4(8)]$	$2xy = 896$
10	$\frac{1}{3}[200 - 4(10)]$	$2xy \approx 1067$
12	$\frac{1}{3}[200 - 4(12)]$	$2xy = 1216$

x	y	Area
20	$\frac{1}{3}[200 - 4(20)]$	$2xy = 1600$
22	$\frac{1}{3}[200 - 4(22)]$	$2xy \approx 1643$
24	$\frac{1}{3}[200 - 4(24)]$	$2xy = 1664$
26	$\frac{1}{3}[200 - 4(26)]$	$2xy = 1664$
28	$\frac{1}{3}[200 - 4(28)]$	$2xy \approx 1643$
30	$\frac{1}{3}[200 - 4(30)]$	$2xy = 1600$

Maximum area if $x = 25$, $y = 33\frac{1}{3}$

(c) $A = \dfrac{8x(50 - x)}{3}$

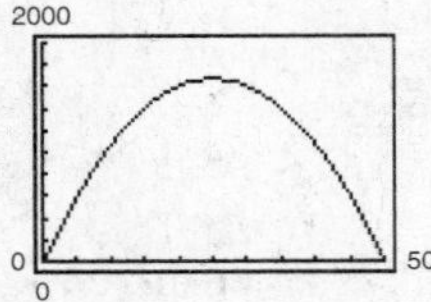

Maximum if $x = 25$, $y = 33\frac{1}{3}$

(d)
$$\begin{aligned} A &= \frac{8}{3}x(50 - x) \\ &= -\frac{8}{3}(x^2 - 50x) \\ &= -\frac{8}{3}(x^2 - 50x + 625 - 625) \\ &= -\frac{8}{3}[(x - 25)^2 - 625] \\ &= -\frac{8}{3}(x - 25)^2 + \frac{5000}{3} \end{aligned}$$

The maximum area occurs at the vertex and is $5000/3$ square feet. This happens when $x = 25$ feet and $y = (200 - 4(25))/3 = 100/3$ feet. The dimensions are $2x = 50$ feet by $33\frac{1}{3}$ feet.

(e) The results are the same.

55. (a)

(b) When $x = 0$, $y = \frac{3}{2}$ feet.

(c) The vertex occurs at

$$x = \frac{-b}{2a} = \frac{-9/5}{2(-16/2025)} = \frac{3645}{32} \approx 113.9.$$

The maximum height is

$$y = \frac{-16}{2025}\left(\frac{3645}{32}\right)^2 + \frac{9}{5}\left(\frac{3645}{32}\right) + \frac{3}{2}$$
$$\approx 104.0 \text{ feet.}$$

(d) Using a graphing utility, the zero of y occurs at $x \approx 228.6$, or 228.6 feet from the punter.

56. $y = -\frac{4}{9}x^2 + \frac{24}{9}x + 12$

The maximum height of the dive occurs at the vertex, $x = \dfrac{-b}{2a} = -\dfrac{24/9}{2(-4/9)} = 3$.

The height at $x = 3$ is

$-\frac{4}{9}(3)^2 + \frac{24}{9}(3) + 12 = 16.$

The maximum height of the dive is 16 feet.

57. $C = 800 - 10x + 0.25x^2$

x	10	15	20	25	30
C	725	706.25	700	706.25	725

From the table, the minimum cost seems to be at $x = 20$.

The minimum cost occurs at the vertex.

$$x = \frac{-b}{2a} = -\frac{(-10)}{2(0.25)} = \frac{10}{0.5} = 20$$

$C(20) = 700$ is the minimum cost.

Graphically, you could graph $C = 800 - 10x + 0.25x^2$ in the window $[0, 40] \times [0, 1000]$ and find the vertex $(20, 700)$.

58. (a) 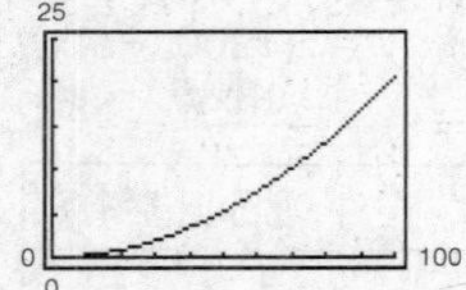

$0.002s^2 + 0.05s - 0.029$

(b) The parabola intersects $y = 10$ at $s \approx 59.4$. Thus, the maximum speed is 59.4 mph. Analytically,

$$0.002s^2 + 0.05s - 0.029 = 10$$

$$2s^2 + 50s - 29 = 10{,}000$$

$$2s^2 + 50s - 10{,}029 = 0.$$

Using the Quadratic Formula,

$$s = \frac{-50 \pm \sqrt{50^2 - 4(2)(-10{,}029)}}{2(2)}$$

$$= \frac{-50 \pm \sqrt{82{,}732}}{4} \approx -84.4, 59.4.$$

The maximum speed is the positive root, 59.4 mph.

59. (a) $R(20) = -25(20)^2 + 1200(20)$

$= \$14{,}000$ thousand

$R(25) = -25(25)^2 + 1200(25)$

$= \$14{,}375$ thousand

$R(30) = -25(30)^2 + 1200(30)$

$= \$13{,}500$ thousand

(b) The vertex occurs at

$$p = \frac{-b}{2a} = \frac{-1200}{2(-25)} = \$24.$$

(c) $R(24) = -25(24)^2 + 1200(24)$

$= \$14{,}400$ thousand

(d) Answers will vary.

60. (a) $R(4) = -12(4)^2 + 150(4) = \$408$

$R(6) = -12(6)^2 + 150(6) = \$468$

$R(8) = -12(8)^2 + 150(8) = \$432$

(b) The vertex occurs at

$$p = \frac{-b}{2a} = \frac{-150}{2(-12)} = \frac{25}{4} = 6.25.$$

The price is \$6.25 per pet.

(c) The maximum revenue is

$$R\left(\frac{25}{4}\right) = -12\left(\frac{25}{4}\right)^2 + 150\left(\frac{25}{4}\right) = \$468.75.$$

(d) Answers will vary.

61. $C(t) = 4306 - 3.4t - 1.32t^2, 0 \le t \le 44$

($t = 0$ corresponds to 1960.)

(a) 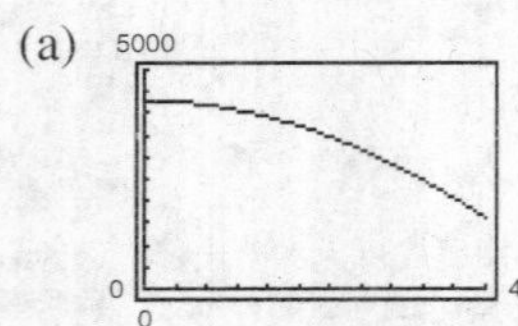

(b) The maximum consumption per year of 4306 cigarettes per person per year occurred in 1960 ($t = 0$). Answers will vary.

(c) For 2000, $C(40) = 2058$.

$$(2058)\frac{209{,}117{,}000}{48{,}306{,}000} \approx 8909 \text{ cigarettes per smoker per year,}$$

$$\frac{8909}{365} \approx 24 \text{ cigarettes per smoker per day}$$

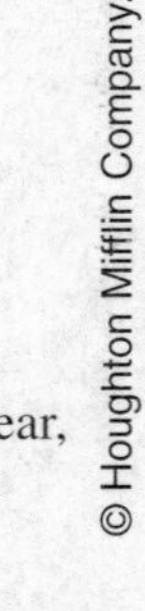

62. $S = -28.40t^2 + 218.1t + 2435,\ 0 \le t \le 14$

(a) The vertex is $\dfrac{-b}{2a} = \dfrac{-218.1}{2(-28.4)} \approx 3.8$, or 1993.

(b) For 2004, $t = 14$ and $S \approx -78$, or $-\$78{,}000{,}000$. Clearly the model is not accurate past 2003.

(c) Probably not. Answers will vary.

63. True

$-12x^2 - 1 = 0$

$12x^2 = -1$, impossible

64. True. For $f(x)$, $\dfrac{-b}{2a} = -\dfrac{-10}{2(-4)} = -\dfrac{10}{8} = -\dfrac{5}{4}$.

For $g(x)$, $\dfrac{-b}{2a} = \dfrac{-30}{2(12)} = \dfrac{-30}{24} = \dfrac{-5}{4}$.

In both cases, $x = -\frac{5}{4}$ is the axis of symmetry.

65. The parabola opens downward and the vertex is $(-2, -4)$. Matches (c) and (d).

66. The parabola opens upward and the vertex is $(1, 3)$. Matches (a).

67. For $a < 0$, $f(x) = a\left(x + \dfrac{b}{2a}\right)^2 + \left(c - \dfrac{b^2}{4a}\right)$ is a maximum when $x = \dfrac{-b}{2a}$. In this case, the maximum value is $c - \dfrac{b^2}{4a}$. Hence,

$$25 = -75 - \frac{b^2}{4(-1)}$$

$$-100 = 300 - b^2$$

$$400 = b^2$$

$$b = \pm 20.$$

68. For $a < 0$, $f(x) = a\left(x + \dfrac{b}{2a}\right)^2 + \left(c - \dfrac{b^2}{4a}\right)$ is a maximum when $x = \dfrac{-b}{2a}$. In this case, the maximum value is $c - \dfrac{b^2}{4a}$. Hence,

$$48 = -16 - \frac{b^2}{4(-1)}$$

$$-192 = 64 - b^2$$

$$b^2 = 256$$

$$b = \pm 16.$$

69. For $a > 0$, $f(x) = a\left(x + \dfrac{b}{2a}\right)^2 + \left(c - \dfrac{b^2}{4a}\right)$ is a minimum when $x = \dfrac{-b}{2a}$. In this case, the minimum value is $c - \dfrac{b^2}{4a}$. Hence,

$$10 = 26 - \frac{b^2}{4}$$

$$40 = 104 - b^2$$

$$b^2 = 64$$

$$b = \pm 8.$$

70. For $a > 0$, $f(x) = a\left(x + \dfrac{b}{2a}\right)^2 + \left(c - \dfrac{b^2}{4a}\right)$ is a minimum when $x = \dfrac{-b}{2a}$. In this case, the minimum value is $c - \dfrac{b^2}{4a}$. Hence,

$$-50 = -25 - \frac{b^2}{4}$$

$$-200 = -100 - b^2$$

$$b^2 = 100$$

$$b = \pm 10.$$

71. Model (a) is preferable. $a > 0$ means the parabola opens upward and profits are increasing for t to the right of the vertex,

$$t \geq -\frac{b}{(2a)}.$$

72. $y = ax^2 + bx - 4$

$(1, 0)$ on graph: $0 = a + b - 4$

$(4, 0)$ on graph: $0 = 16a + 4b - 4$

From the first equation, $b = 4 - a$.

Thus, $0 = 16a + 4(4 - a) - 4 = 12a + 12 \Rightarrow a = -1$ and hence $b = 5$, and $y = -x^2 + 5x - 4$.

73. $x + y = 8 \Rightarrow y = 8 - x$

Then $-\frac{2}{3}x + y = -\frac{2}{3}x + (8 - x) = 6 \Rightarrow -\frac{5}{3}x = -2 \Rightarrow x = \frac{6}{5}$ and $y = 8 - \frac{6}{5} = \frac{34}{5}$.

$(1.2, 6.8)$

74. $y = 3x - 10 = \frac{1}{4}x + 1$

$$12x - 40 = x + 4$$

$$11x = 44$$

$$x = 4$$

The graphs intersect at $(4, 2)$.

75. $y = x + 3 = 9 - x^2$

$$x^2 + x - 6 = 0$$

$$(x + 3)(x - 2) = 0$$

$$x = -3, x = 2$$

Thus, $(-3, 0)$ and $(2, 5)$ are the points of intersection.

76. $y = x^3 + 2x - 1 = -2x + 15$

$$x^3 + 4x - 16 = 0$$

$$(x - 2)(x^2 + 2x + 8) = 0$$

$$x = 2$$

The graphs intersect at $(2, 11)$.

77. Answers will vary. (Make a Decision)

Section 2.2 Polynomial Functions of Higher Degree

- You should know the following basic principles about polynomials.
- $f(x) = a_n x^n + a_{n-1}x^{n-1} + \cdots + a_2x^2 + a_1x + a_0$, $a_n \neq 0$, is a polynomial function of degree n.
- If f is of odd degree and
  - (a) $a_n > 0$, then
    1. $f(x) \to \infty$ as $x \to \infty$.
    2. $f(x) \to -\infty$ as $x \to -\infty$.
  - (b) $a_n < 0$, then
    1. $f(x) \to -\infty$ as $x \to \infty$.
    2. $f(x) \to \infty$ as $x \to -\infty$.
- If f is of even degree and
  - (a) $a_n > 0$, then
    1. $f(x) \to \infty$ as $x \to \infty$.
    2. $f(x) \to \infty$ as $x \to -\infty$.
  - (b) $a_n < 0$, then
    1. $f(x) \to -\infty$ as $x \to \infty$.
    2. $f(x) \to -\infty$ as $x \to -\infty$.
- The following are equivalent for a polynomial function.
  - (a) $x = a$ is a zero of a function.
  - (b) $x = a$ is a solution of the polynomial equation $f(x) = 0$.
  - (c) $(x - a)$ is a factor of the polynomial.
  - (d) $(a, 0)$ is an x-intercept of the graph of f.
- A polynomial of degree n has at most n distinct zeros.
- If f is a polynomial function such that $a < b$ and $f(a) \neq f(b)$, then f takes on every value between $f(a)$ and $f(b)$ in the interval $[a, b]$.
- If you can find a value where a polynomial is positive and another value where it is negative, then there is at least one real zero between the values.

Vocabulary Check

1. continuous

2. Leading Coefficient Test

3. n, $n - 1$, relative extrema

4. solution, $(x - a)$, x-intercept

5. touches, crosses

6. Intermediate Value

1. $f(x) = -2x + 3$ is a line with y-intercept $(0, 3)$. Matches graph (f).

2. $f(x) = x^2 - 4x$ is a parabola with intercepts $(0, 0)$ and $(4, 0)$ and opens upward. Matches graph (h).

3. $f(x) = -2x^2 - 5x$ is a parabola with x-intercepts $(0, 0)$ and $\left(-\frac{5}{2}, 0\right)$ and opens downward. Matches graph (c).

4. $f(x) = 2x^3 - 3x + 1$ has intercepts $(0, 1)$, $(1, 0)$, $\left(-\frac{1}{2} - \frac{1}{2}\sqrt{3}, 0\right)$ and $\left(-\frac{1}{2} + \frac{1}{2}\sqrt{3}, 0\right)$. Matches graph (a).

5. $f(x) = -\frac{1}{4}x^4 + 3x^2$ has intercepts $(0, 0)$ and $\left(\pm 2\sqrt{3}, 0\right)$. Matches graph (e).

6. $f(x) = -\frac{1}{3}x^3 + x^2 - \frac{4}{3}$ has y-intercept $\left(0, -\frac{4}{3}\right)$. Matches graph (d).

7. $f(x) = x^4 + 2x^3$ has intercepts $(0, 0)$ and $(-2, 0)$. Matches graph (g).

8. $f(x) = \frac{1}{5}x^5 - 2x^3 + \frac{9}{5}x$ has intercepts $(0, 0)$, $(1, 0)$, $(-1, 0)$, $(3, 0)$, $(-3, 0)$. Matches (b).

9. $y = x^3$

(a) $f(x) = (x - 2)^3$

Horizontal shift two units to the right

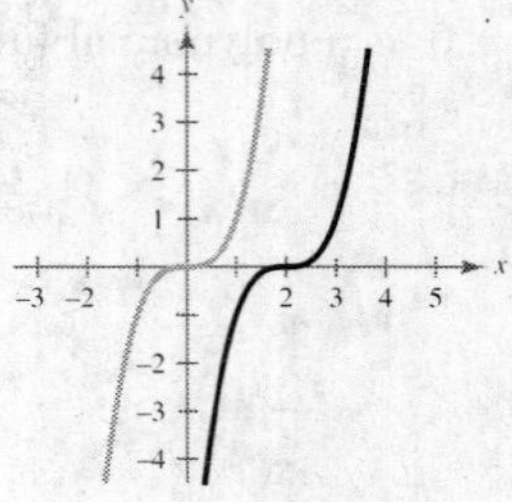

(b) $f(x) = x^3 - 2$

Vertical shift two units downward

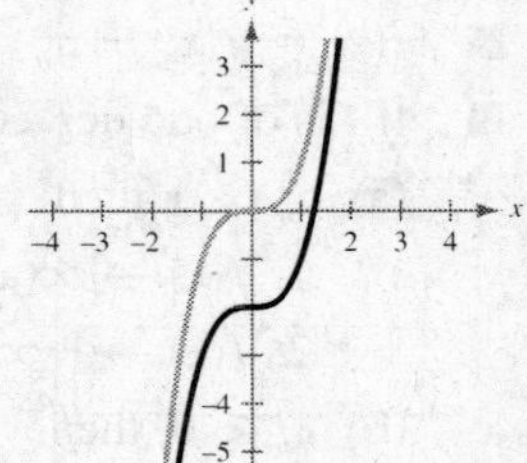

(c) $f(x) = -\frac{1}{2}x^3$

Reflection in the x-axis and a vertical shrink

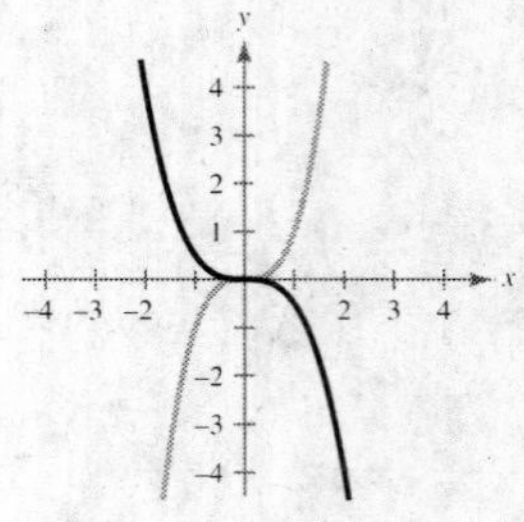

(d) $f(x) = (x - 2)^3 - 2$

Horizontal shift two units to the right and a vertical shift two units downward

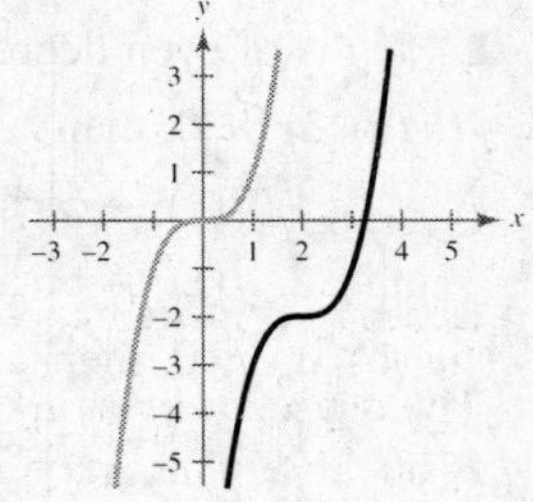

10. $y = x^4$

(a) $f(x) = (x + 5)^4$

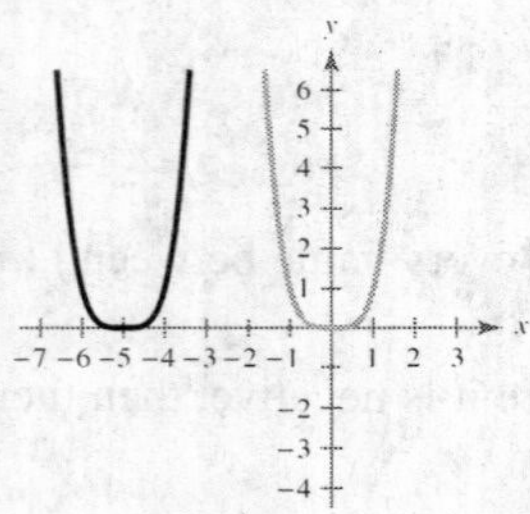

Horizontal shift five units to the left

(b) $f(x) = x^4 - 5$

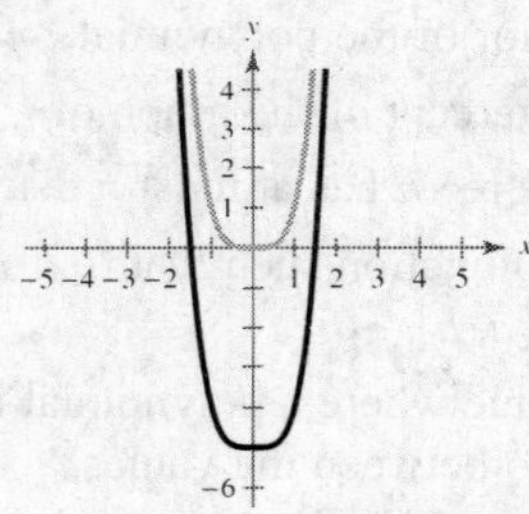

Vertical shift five units downward

(c) $f(x) = 4 - x^4$

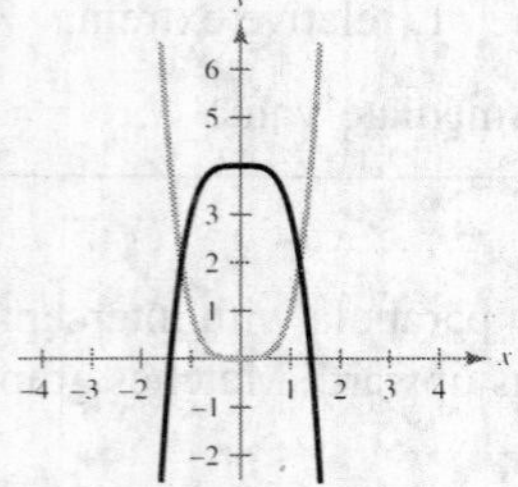

Reflection in the x-axis and then a vertical shift four units upward

(d) $f(x) = \frac{1}{2}(x - 1)^4$

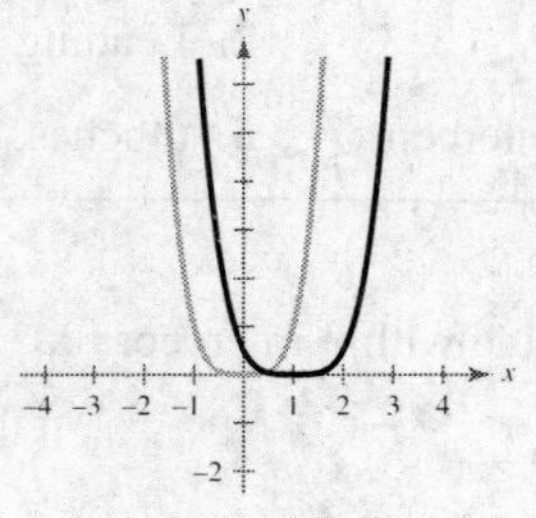

Horizontal shift one unit to the right and a vertical shrink

11. $f(x) = 3x^3 - 9x + 1;\ g(x) = 3x^3$

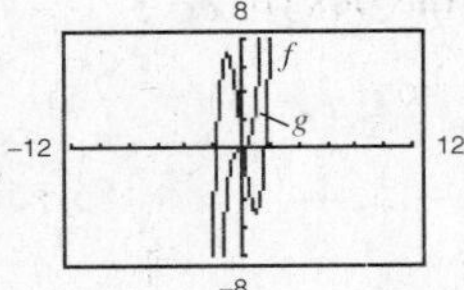

12. $f(x) = -\frac{1}{3}(x^3 - 3x + 2),\ g(x) = -\frac{1}{3}x^3$

13. $f(x) = -(x^4 - 4x^3 + 16x);\ g(x) = -x^4$

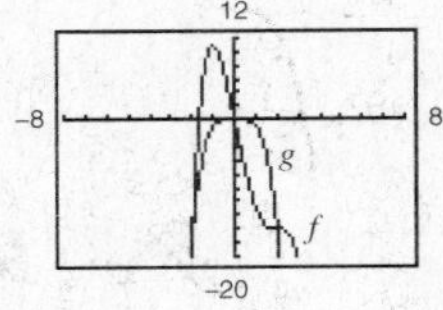

14. $f(x) = 3x^4 - 6x^2,\ g(x) = 3x^4$

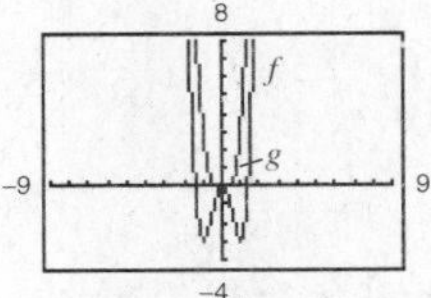

15. $f(x) = 2x^4 - 3x + 1$

Degree: 4

Leading coefficient: 2

The degree is even and the leading coefficient is positive. The graph rises to the left and right.

16. $h(x) = 1 - x^6$

Degree: 6

Leading coefficient: -1

The degree is even and the leading coefficient is negative. The graph falls to the left and right.

17. $g(x) = 5 - \frac{7}{2}x - 3x^2$

Degree: 2

Leading coefficient: -3

The degree is even and the leading coefficient is negative. The graph falls to the left and right.

18. $f(x) = \frac{1}{3}x^3 + 5x$

Degree: 3

Leading coefficient: $\frac{1}{3}$

The degree is odd and the leading coefficient is positive. The graph falls to the left and rises to the right.

19. Degree: 5 (odd)

Leading coefficient: $\frac{6}{3} = 2 > 0$

Falls to the left and rises to the right

20. Degree: 7 (odd)

Leading coefficient: $\frac{3}{4} > 0$

Falls to the left and rises to the right

21. $h(t) = -\frac{2}{3}(t^2 - 5t + 3)$

Degree: 2

Leading coefficient: $-\frac{2}{3}$

The degree is even and the leading coefficient is negative. The graph falls to the left and right.

22. $f(s) = -\frac{7}{8}(s^3 + 5s^2 - 7s + 1)$

Degree: 3

Leading coefficient: $-\frac{7}{8}$

The degree is odd and the leading coefficient is negative. The graph rises to the left and falls to the right.

23. $f(x) = x^2 - 25$

$= (x + 5)(x - 5)$

$x = \pm 5$

24. $f(x) = 49 - x^2$

$= (7 - x)(7 + x)$

$x = \pm 7$

25. $h(t) = t^2 - 6t + 9$

$= (t - 3)^2$

$t = 3$ (multiplicity 2)

26. $f(x) = x^2 + 10x + 25$
$= (x + 5)^2$
$x = -5$ (multiplicity 2)

27. $f(x) = x^2 + x - 2$
$= (x + 2)(x - 1)$
$x = -2, 1$

28. $f(x) = 2x^2 - 14x + 24$
$= 2(x^2 - 7x + 12)$
$= 2(x - 3)(x - 4)$
$x = 3, 4$

29. $f(t) = t^3 - 4t^2 + 4t$
$= t(t - 2)^2$
$t = 0, 2$ (multiplicity 2)

30. $f(x) = x^4 - x^3 - 20x^2$
$= x^2(x^2 - x - 20)$
$= x^2(x + 4)(x - 5)$
$x = -4, 5, 0$ (multiplicity 2)

31. $f(x) = \frac{1}{2}x^2 + \frac{5}{2}x - \frac{3}{2}$
$= \frac{1}{2}(x^2 + 5x - 3)$
$x = \frac{-5 \pm \sqrt{25 - 4(-3)}}{2} = -\frac{5}{2} \pm \frac{\sqrt{37}}{2}$
$\approx 0.5414, -5.5414$

32. $f(x) = \frac{5}{3}x^2 + \frac{8}{3}x - \frac{4}{3}$
$= \frac{1}{3}(5x^2 + 8x - 4)$
$= \frac{1}{3}(5x - 2)(x + 2)$
$x = \frac{2}{5}, -2$

33. (a)

(b) $x \approx 3.732, 0.268$
(c) $f(x) = 3x^2 - 12x + 3$
$= 3(x^2 - 4x + 1)$
$x = \frac{4 \pm \sqrt{16 - 4}}{2} = 2 \pm \sqrt{3}$

34. $g(x) = 5x^2 - 10x - 5$
(a)

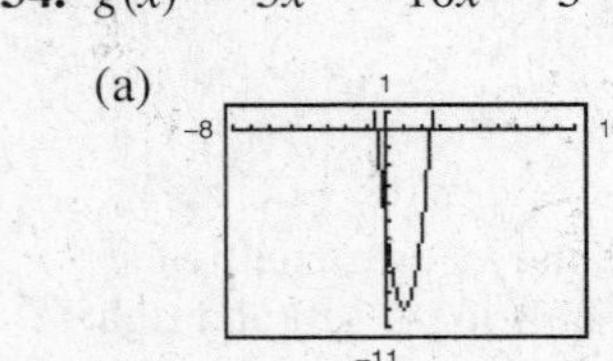

(b) Zeros: $-0.414, 2.414$
(c) $g(x) = 5(x^2 - 2x - 1)$
$x = \frac{2 \pm \sqrt{4 - 4(-1)}}{2} = 1 \pm \sqrt{2}$
$(\approx -0.414, 2.414)$
$(1 \pm \sqrt{2}, 0)$

35. (a)

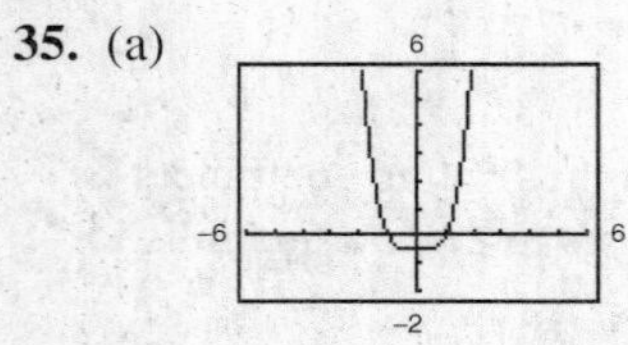

(b) $t = \pm 1$
(c) $g(t) = \frac{1}{2}t^4 - \frac{1}{2}$
$= \frac{1}{2}(t + 1)(t - 1)(t^2 + 1)$
$t = \pm 1$

36. $y = \frac{1}{4}x^3(x^2 - 9)$
(a)

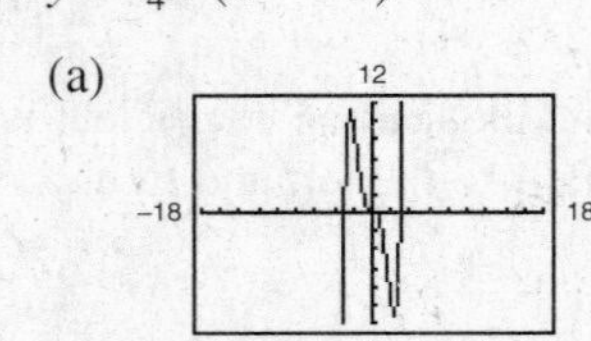

(b) Zeros: $0, \pm 3$
(c) $0 = \frac{1}{4}x^3(x^2 - 9)$
$x = 0, \pm 3$
x-intercepts: $(0, 0), (\pm 3, 0)$

37. (a)

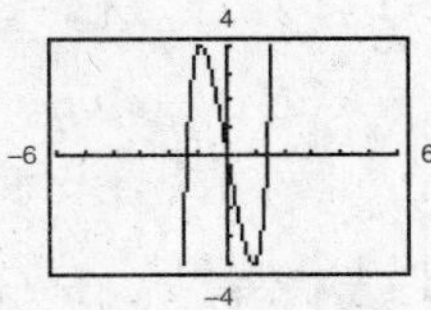

(b) $x = 0, 1.414, -1.414$

(c) $f(x) = x^5 + x^3 - 6x$

$= x(x^4 + x^2 - 6)$

$= x(x^2 + 3)(x^2 - 2)$

$x = 0, \pm\sqrt{2}$

38. $g(t) = t^5 - 6t^3 + 9t$

(a)

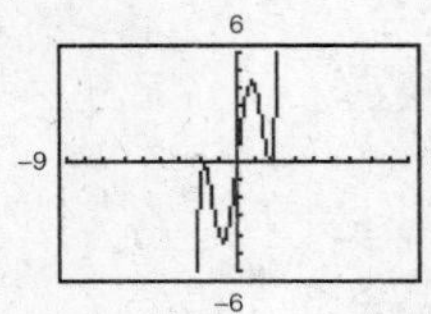

(b) Zeros: $0, \pm 1.732$

(c) $g(t) = t^5 - 6t^3 + 9t$

$= t(t^4 - 6t^2 + 9)$

$= t(t^2 - 3)^2$

$t = 0, \pm\sqrt{3} \quad (\approx 0, \pm 1.732)$

$(0, 0), (\pm\sqrt{3}, 0)$

39. (a)

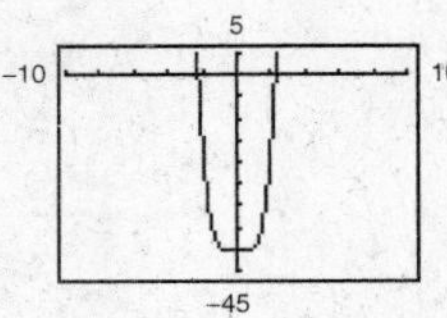

(b) $2.236, -2.236$

(c) $f(x) = 2x^4 - 2x^2 - 40$

$= 2(x^4 - x^2 - 20)$

$= 2(x^2 + 4)(x + \sqrt{5})(x - \sqrt{5})$

$x = \pm\sqrt{5}$

40. $f(x) = 5x^4 + 15x^2 + 10$

(a)

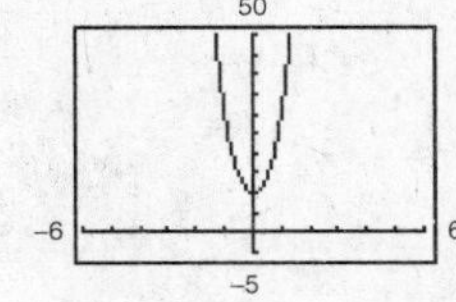

(b) No real zeros

(c) $f(x) = 5(x^4 + 3x^2 + 2)$

$= 5(x^2 + 1)(x^2 + 2) > 0$

No real zeros

41. (a)

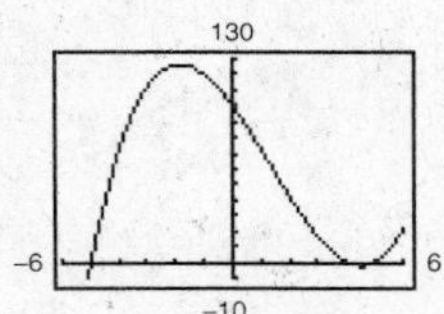

(b) $x = 4, 5, -5$

(c) $f(x) = x^3 - 4x^2 - 25x + 100$

$= x^2(x - 4) - 25(x - 4)$

$= (x^2 - 25)(x - 4)$

$= (x - 5)(x + 5)(x - 4)$

$x = \pm 5, 4$

42. $y = 4x^3 + 4x^2 - 7x + 2$

(a)

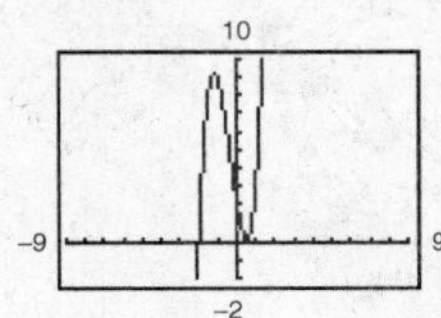

(b) Zeros: $-2, \frac{1}{2}$

(c) $0 = 4x^3 + 4x^2 - 7x + 2$

$= (2x - 1)(2x^2 + 3x - 2)$

$= (2x - 1)(2x - 1)(x + 2)$

$x = -2, \frac{1}{2}$

x-intercepts: $(-2, 0), \left(\frac{1}{2}, 0\right)$

43. (a)

(b) $x = 0, \frac{5}{2}$

(c) $y = 4x^3 - 20x^2 + 25x$

$0 = 4x^3 - 20x^2 + 25x$

$0 = x(2x - 5)^2$

$x = 0$ or $x = \frac{5}{2}$ (multiplicity 2)

44. $y = x^5 - 5x^3 + 4x$

(a)

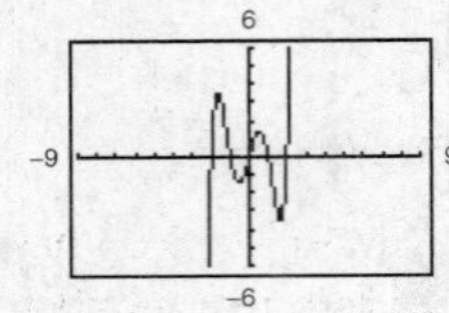

(b) Zeros: $0, \pm 1, \pm 2$

(c) $y = x^5 - 5x^3 + 4x$

$= x(x^4 - 5x^2 + 4)$

$= x(x^2 - 4)(x^2 - 1)$

$= x(x - 2)(x + 2)(x - 1)(x + 1)$

Zeros: $0, \pm 1, \pm 2$

$(0, 0), (\pm 1, 0), (\pm 2, 0)$

45. $f(x) = 2x^4 - 6x^2 + 1$

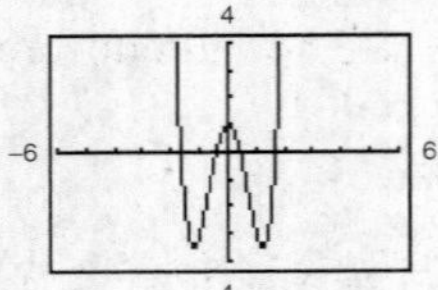

Zeros: $x \approx \pm 0.421, \pm 1.680$

Relative maximum: $(0, 1)$

Relative minimums:
$(1.225, -3.5), (-1.225, -3.5)$

46. $f(x) = -\frac{3}{8}x^4 - x^3 + 2x^2 + 5$

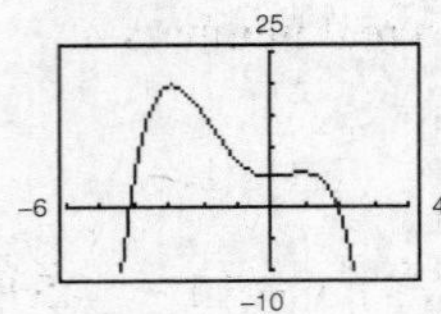

Real zeros: $-4.142, 1.934$

Relative maximums: $(0.915, 5.646)$,
$(-2.915, 19.688)$

Relative minimum: $(0, 5)$

47. $f(x) = x^5 + 3x^3 - x + 6$

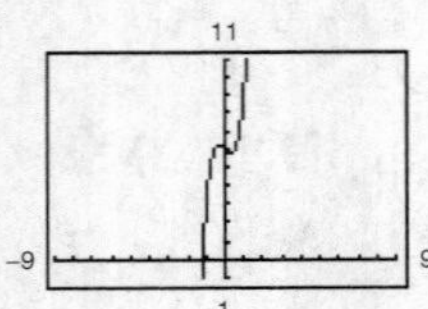

Zeros: $x \approx -1.178$

Relative maximum: $(-0.324, 6.218)$

Relative minimum: $(0.324, 5.782)$

48. $f(x) = -3x^3 - 4x^2 + x - 3$

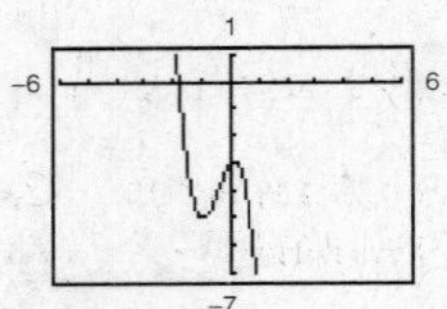

Real zero: -1.819

Relative maximum: $(0.111, -2.942)$

Relative minimum: $(-1, -5)$

49. $f(x) = (x - 0)(x - 4) = x^2 - 4x$

Note: $f(x) = a(x - 0)(x - 4) = ax(x - 4)$ has zeros 0 and 4 for all nonzero real numbers a.

50. $f(x) = (x + 7)(x - 2) = x^2 + 5x - 14$

51. $f(x) = (x - 0)(x + 2)(x + 3) = x^3 + 5x^2 + 6x$

Note: $f(x) = ax(x + 2)(x + 3)$ has zeros $0, -2$, and -3 for all nonzero real numbers a.

52. $f(x) = (x - 0)(x - 2)(x - 5) = x^3 - 7x^2 + 10x$

53. $f(x) = (x - 4)(x + 3)(x - 3)(x - 0)$

$= (x - 4)(x^2 - 9)x$

$= x^4 - 4x^3 - 9x^2 + 36x$

Note: $f(x) = a(x^4 - 4x^3 - 9x^2 + 36x)$ has zeros 4, -3, 3, and 0 for all nonzero real numbers a.

54. $f(x) = (x - (-2))(x - (-1))(x - 0)(x - 1)(x - 2)$

$= x(x + 2)(x + 1)(x - 1)(x - 2)$

$= x(x^2 - 4)(x^2 - 1)$

$= x(x^4 - 5x^2 + 4)$

$= x^5 - 5x^3 + 4x$

Note: $f(x) = ax(x + 2)(x + 1)(x - 1)(x - 2)$ has zeros $-2, -1, 0, 1, 2$ for all nonzero real numbers a.

55. $f(x) = \left[x - \left(1 + \sqrt{3}\right)\right]\left[x - \left(1 - \sqrt{3}\right)\right]$

$= \left[(x - 1) - \sqrt{3}\right]\left[(x - 1) + \sqrt{3}\right]$

$= (x - 1)^2 - \left(\sqrt{3}\right)^2$

$= x^2 - 2x + 1 - 3$

$= x^2 - 2x - 2$

Note: $f(x) = a(x^2 - 2x - 2)$ has zeros $1 + \sqrt{3}$ and $1 - \sqrt{3}$ for all nonzero real numbers a.

56. $f(x) = \left(x - \left(6 + \sqrt{3}\right)\right)\left(x - \left(6 - \sqrt{3}\right)\right)$

$= \left((x - 6) - \sqrt{3}\right)\left((x - 6) + \sqrt{3}\right)$

$= (x - 6)^2 - 3$

$= x^2 - 12x + 36 - 3$

$= x^2 - 12x + 33$

Note: $f(x) = a\left(x - \left(6 + \sqrt{3}\right)\right)\left(x - \left(6 - \sqrt{3}\right)\right)$ has zeros $6 + \sqrt{3}$ and $6 - \sqrt{3}$ for all nonzero real numbers a.

57. $f(x) = (x - 2)\left[x - \left(4 + \sqrt{5}\right)\right]\left[x - \left(4 - \sqrt{5}\right)\right]$

$= (x - 2)\left[(x - 4) - \sqrt{5}\right]\left[(x - 4) + \sqrt{5}\right]$

$= (x - 2)[(x - 4)^2 - 5]$

$= x^3 - 10x^2 + 27x - 22$

Note: $f(x) = a(x - 2)[(x - 4)^2 - 5]$ has zeros 2, $4 + \sqrt{5}$, and $4 - \sqrt{5}$ for all nonzero real numbers a.

58. $f(x) = (x - 4)\left(x - \left(2 + \sqrt{7}\right)\right)\left(x - \left(2 - \sqrt{7}\right)\right)$

$= (x - 4)\left((x - 2) - \sqrt{7}\right)\left((x - 2) + \sqrt{7}\right)$

$= (x - 4)\left((x - 2)^2 - 7\right)$

$= (x - 4)(x^2 - 4x - 3)$

$= x^3 - 8x^2 + 13x + 12$

Note: $f(x) = a(x - 4)(x^2 - 4x - 3)$ has zeros 4, $2 \pm \sqrt{7}$ for all nonzero real numbers a.

59. $f(x) = (x + 2)^2(x + 1) = x^3 + 5x^2 + 8x + 4$

Note: $f(x) = a(x + 2)^2(x + 1)$ has zeros $-2, -2$, and -1 for all nonzero real numbers a.

60. $f(x) = (x - 3)(x - 2)^3$

$= x^4 - 9x^3 + 30x^2 - 44x + 24$

Note: $f(x) = a(x - 3)(x - 2)^3$ has zeros 3, 2, 2, 2 for all nonzero real numbers a.

61. $f(x) = (x + 4)^2(x - 3)^2$

$= x^4 + 2x^3 - 23x^2 - 24x + 144$

Note: $f(x) = a(x + 4)^2(x - 3)^2$ has zeros $-4, -4$, 3, 3 for all nonzero real numbers a.

62. $f(x) = (x + 5)^3(x - 0)^2$

$= x^5 + 15x^4 + 75x^3 + 125x^2$

Note: $f(x) = a(x + 5)^3x^2$ has zeros $-5, -5, -5$, 0, 0 for all nonzero real numbers a.

63. $f(x) = -(x + 1)^2(x + 2)$

$= -x^3 - 4x^2 - 5x - 2$

Note: $f(x) = a(x + 1)^2(x + 2)^2$, $a < 0$, has zeros $-1, -1, -2$, rises to the left, and falls to the right.

64. $f(x) = -(x + 1)^2(x - 4)^2$

$= -x^4 + 6x^3 - x^2 - 24x - 16$

Note: $f(x) = a(x + 1)^2(x - 4)^2$, $a < 0$, has zeros $-1, -1, 4, 4$, falls to the left and falls to the right.

65.

$y = -x^3 + 3x - 2$

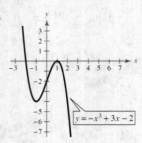

For example,

$f(x) = -(x + 2)(x - 1)^2 = -x^3 + 3x - 2.$

66.

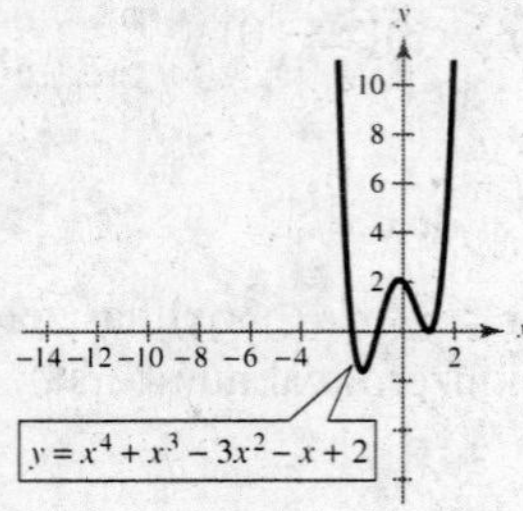

For example, $f(x) = (x + 2)(x + 1)(x - 1)^2$.

67.

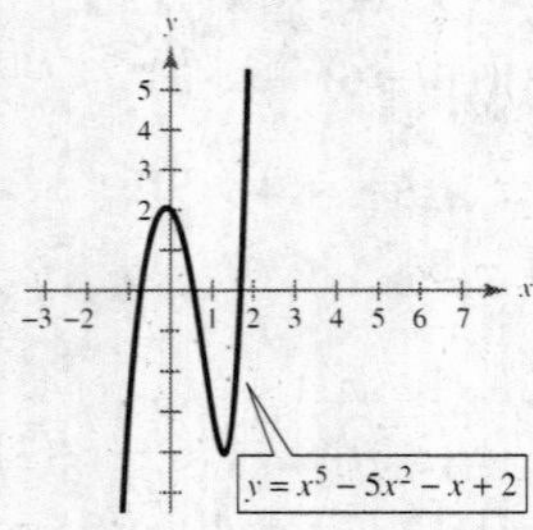

68.

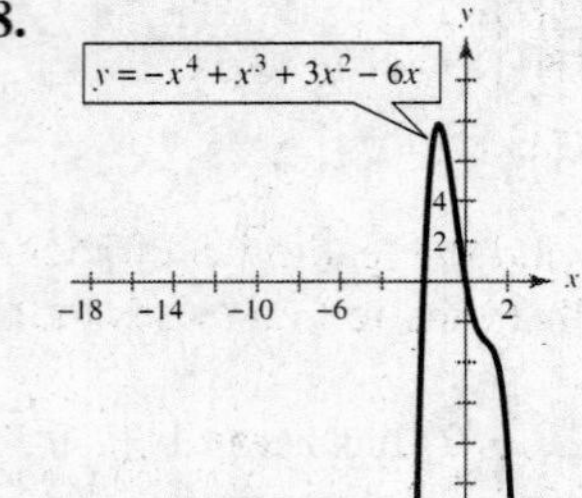

69. (a) The degree of f is odd and the leading coefficient is 1. The graph falls to the left and rises to the right.

(b) $f(x) = x^3 - 9x = x(x^2 - 9) = x(x - 3)(x + 3)$

Zeros: $0, 3, -3$

(c) and (d)

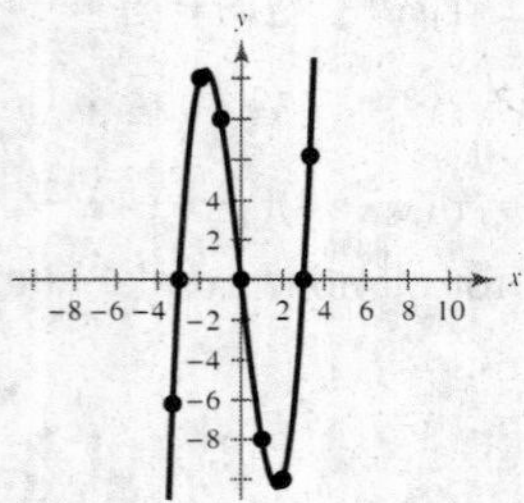

70. (a) The degree of g is even and the leading coefficient is 1. The graph rises to the left and rises to the right.

(b) $g(x) = x^4 - 4x^2 = x^2(x^2 - 4)$

$= x^2(x - 2)(x + 2)$

Zeros: $0, 2, -2$: $(0, 0)$, $(\pm 2, 0)$

(c) and (d)

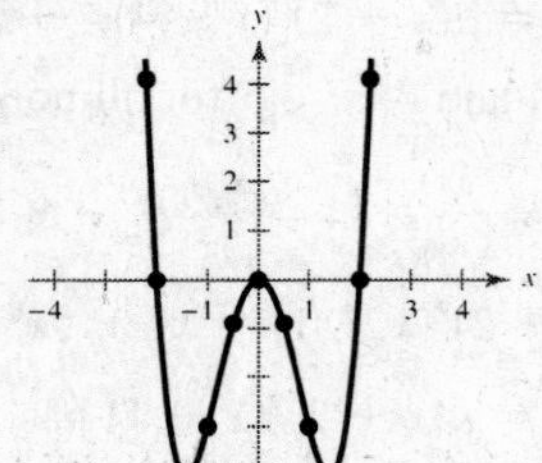

71. (a) The degree of f is odd and the leading coefficient is 1. The graph falls to the left and rises to the right.

(b) $f(x) = x^3 - 3x^2 = x^2(x - 3)$

Zeros: 0, 3

(c) and (d)

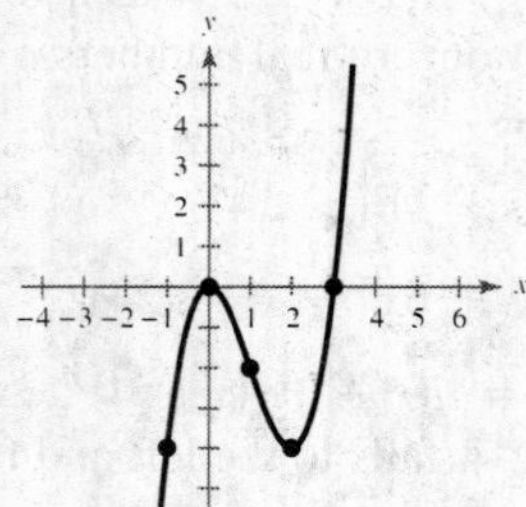

72. (a) The degree of f is odd and the leading coefficient is 3. The graph falls to the left and rises to the right.

(b) $f(x) = 3x^3 - 24x^2 = 3x^2(x - 8)$

Zeros: 0, 8

(c) and (d)

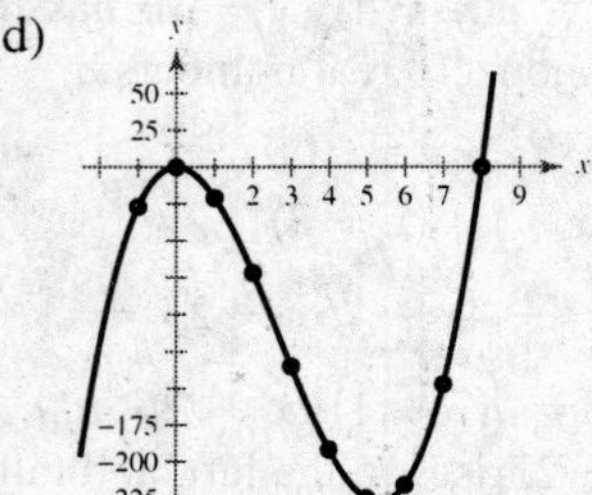

73. (a) The degree of f is even and the leading coefficient is -1. The graph falls to the left and falls to the right.

(b) $f(x) = -x^4 + 9x^2 - 20 = -(x^2 - 4)(x^2 - 5)$

Zeros: $\pm 2, \pm\sqrt{5}$: $(\pm 2, 0), (\pm\sqrt{5}, 0)$

(c) and (d)

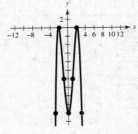

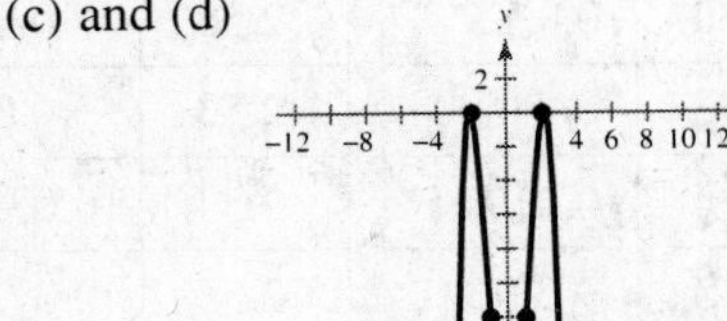

74. (a) The degree is even and the leading coefficient is -1. The graph falls to the left and falls to the right.

(b) $f(x) = -x^6 + 7x^3 + 8 = -(x^3 + 1)(x^3 - 8)$

Zeros: $-1, 2$: $(-1, 0), (2, 0)$

(c) and (d)

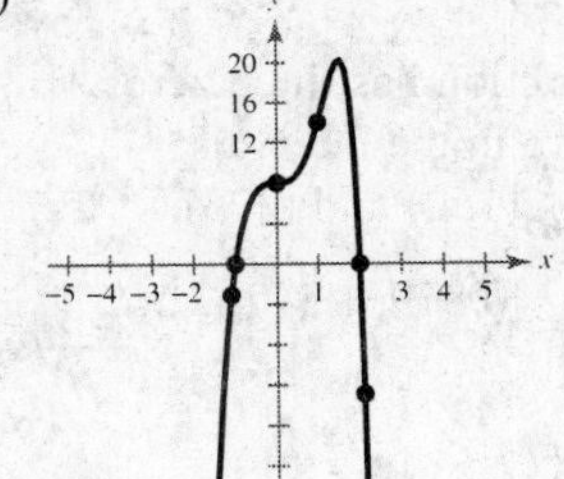

75. (a) The degree is odd and the leading coefficient is 1. The graph falls to the left and rises to the right.

(b) $x^3 + 3x^2 - 9x - 27 = x^2(x + 3) - 9(x + 3)$

$= (x^2 - 9)(x + 3)$

$= (x - 3)(x + 3)^2$

Zeros: $3, -3$: $(3, 0), (-3, 0)$

(c) and (d)

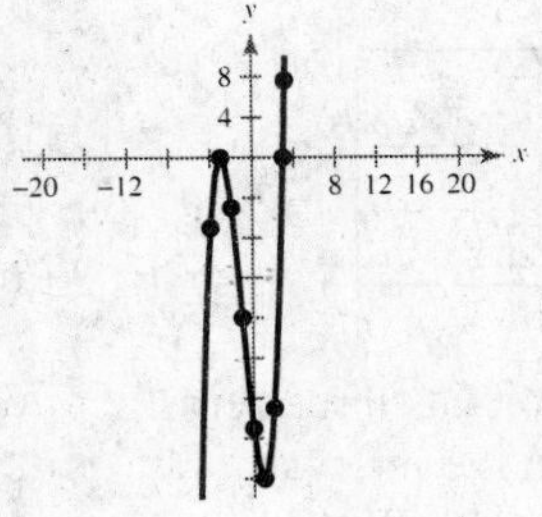

76. (a) The degree is odd and the leading coefficient is 1. The graph falls to the left and rises to the right.

(b) $x^5 - 4x^3 + 8x^2 - 32 = x^3(x^2 - 4) + 8(x^2 - 4)$

$= (x^3 + 8)(x^2 - 4)$

$= (x + 2)(x^2 - 2x + 4)(x - 2)(x + 2)$

Zeros: $-2, 2$: $(\pm 2, 0)$

(c) and (d)

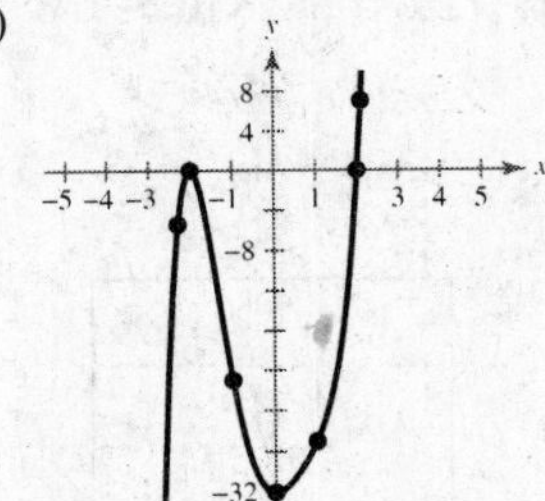

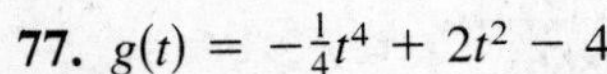

77. $g(t) = -\frac{1}{4}t^4 + 2t^2 - 4$

(a) Falls to left and falls to right; $\left(-\frac{1}{4} < 0\right)$

(b) $g(t) = -\frac{1}{4}(t^4 - 8t^2 + 16) = -\frac{1}{4}(t^2 - 4)^2$

$t = -2, -2, 2, 2 \Longrightarrow (-2, 0), (2, 0)$; zeros

(c) and (d)

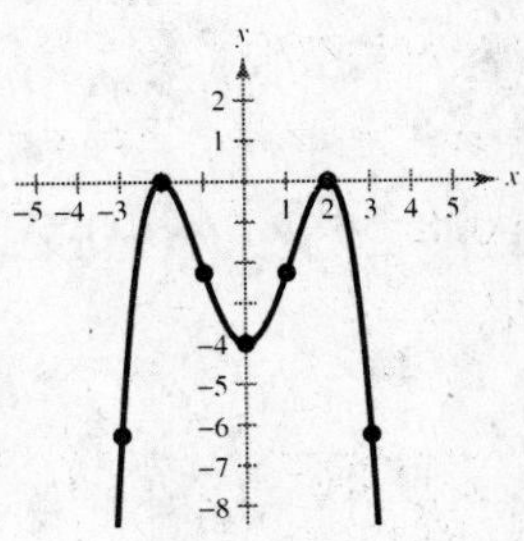

78. $g(x) = \frac{1}{10}(x^4 - 4x^3 - 2x^2 + 12x + 9)$

(a) Rises to right and rises to left; $\left(\frac{1}{10} > 0\right)$

(b) $g(x) = \frac{1}{10}(x + 1)^2(x - 3)^2$

Zeros: $(-1, 0), (3, 0)$

(c) and (d)

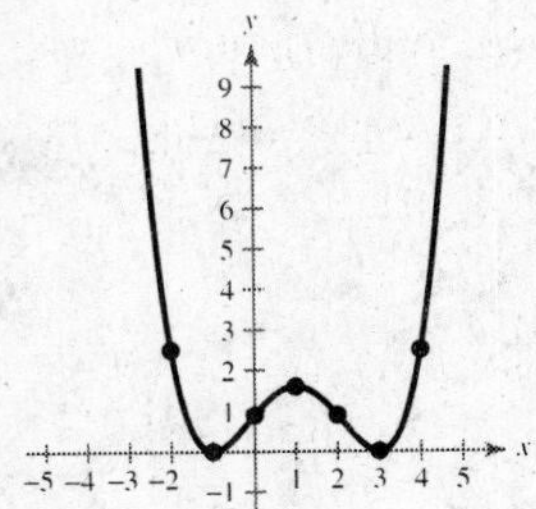

79. $f(x) = x^3 - 3x^2 + 3$

(a)

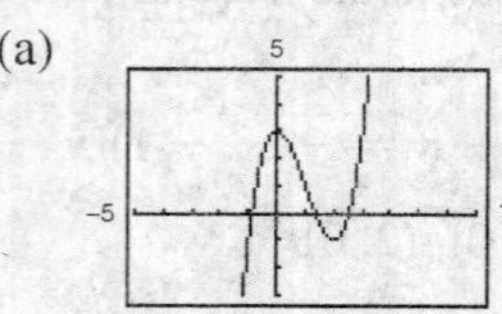

The function has three zeros. They are in the intervals $(-1, 0)$, $(1, 2)$ and $(2, 3)$.

(b) Zeros: -0.879, 1.347, 2.532

(c)

x	y_1
−0.9	−0.159
−0.89	−0.0813
−0.88	−0.0047
−0.87	0.0708
−0.86	0.14514
−0.85	0.21838
−0.84	0.2905

x	y_1
1.3	0.127
1.31	0.09979
1.32	0.07277
1.33	0.04594
1.34	0.0193
1.35	−0.0071
1.36	−0.0333

x	y_1
2.5	−0.125
2.51	−0.087
2.52	−0.0482
2.53	−0.0084
2.54	0.03226
2.55	0.07388
2.56	0.11642

80. $f(x) = -2x^3 - 6x^2 + 3$

(a)

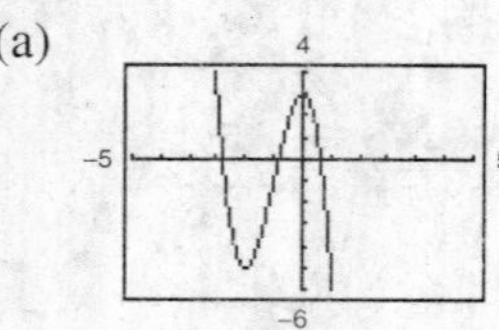

The function has three zeros. They are in the intervals $(-3, -2)$, $(-1, 0)$, and $(0, 1)$..

(b) Zeros: -2.810, -0.832, 0.642

(c)

x	y_1
−2.83	0.277
−2.82	0.137
−2.81	≈ 0
−2.80	−0.136
−2.79	−0.269

x	y_1
−0.86	−0.166
−0.85	−0.107
−0.84	−0.048
−0.83	0.010
−0.82	0.068

x	y_1
0.62	0.217
0.63	0.119
0.64	0.018
0.65	−0.084
0.66	−0.189

81. $g(x) = 3x^4 + 4x^3 - 3$

(a)

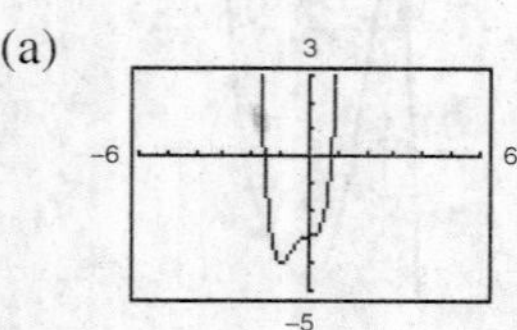

The function has two zeros. They are in the intervals $(-2, -1)$ and $(0, 1)$.

(b) Zeros: -1.585, 0.779

(c)

x	y_1
−1.6	0.2768
−1.59	0.09515
−1.58	−0.0812
−1.57	−0.2524
−1.56	−0.4184
−1.55	−0.5795
−1.54	−0.7356

x	y_1
0.75	−0.3633
0.76	−0.2432
0.77	−0.1193
0.78	0.00866
0.79	0.14066
0.80	0.2768
0.81	0.41717

82. $h(x) = x^4 - 10x^2 + 2$

(a)

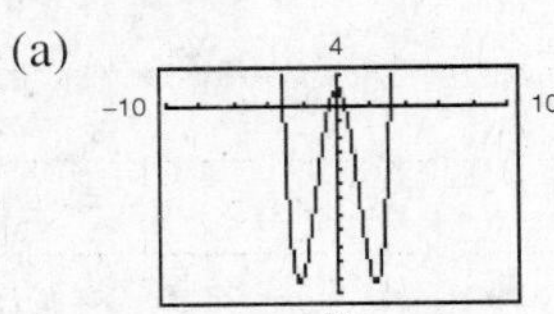

The function has four zeros. They are in the intervals $(0, 1)$, $(3, 4)$, $(-1, 0)$ and $(-4, -3)$.

(b) Notice that h is even. Hence, the zeros come in symmetric pairs. Zeros: ± 0.452, ± 3.130

(c) Because the function is even, we only need to verify the positive zeros.

x	y_1
0.42	0.26712
0.43	0.18519
0.44	0.10148
0.45	0.01601
0.46	-0.0712
0.47	-0.1602
0.48	-0.2509

x	y_1
3.09	-2.315
3.10	-1.748
3.11	-1.171
3.12	-0.5855
3.13	0.01025
3.14	0.61571
3.15	1.231

83.

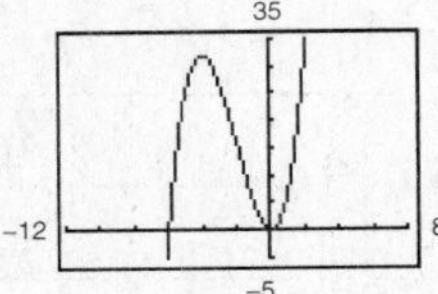

$f(x) = x^2(x + 6)$

No symmetry

Two x-intercepts

84. $h(x) = x^3(x - 4)^2$

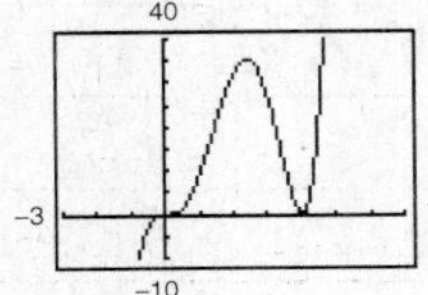

No symmetry

Two x-intercepts $(0, 0)$, $(4, 0)$

85.

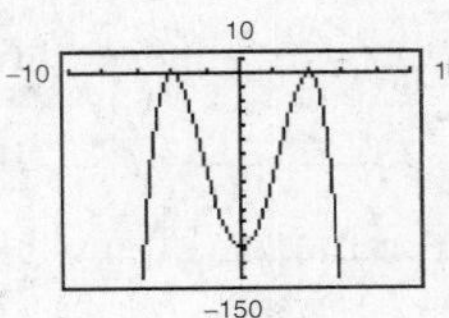

$g(t) = -\frac{1}{2}(t - 4)^2(t + 4)^2$

Symmetric about the y-axis

Two x-intercepts

86. $g(x) = \frac{1}{8}(x + 1)^2(x - 3)^3$

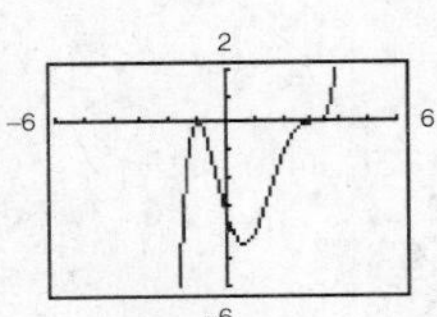

No symmetry.

Two x-intercepts $(-1, 0)$, $(3, 0)$

87.

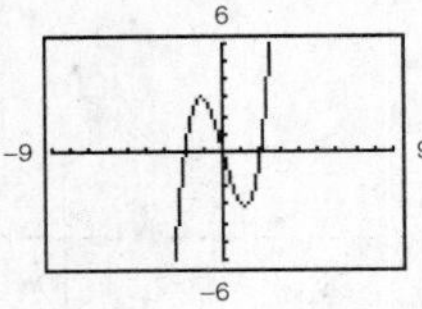

$f(x) = x^3 - 4x$

$= x(x + 2)(x - 2)$

Symmetric to origin

Three x-intercepts

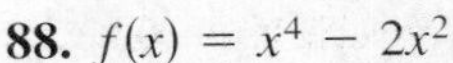

88. $f(x) = x^4 - 2x^2$

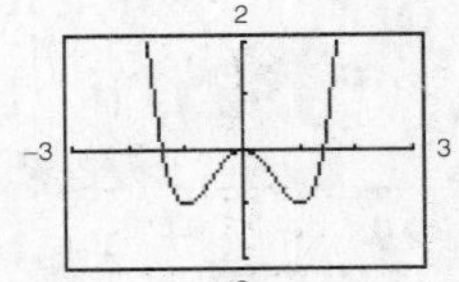

Symmetric with respect to y-axis

Three x-intercepts $(0, 0)$, $(\pm\sqrt{2}, 0)$

89.

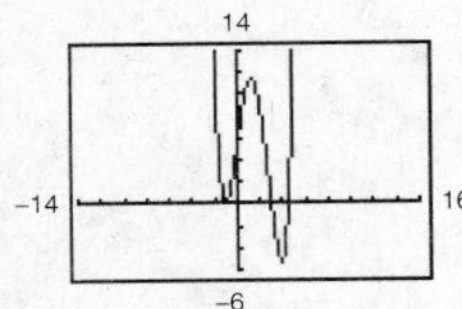

$g(x) = \frac{1}{5}(x + 1)^2(x - 3)(2x - 9)$

Three x-intercepts

No symmetry

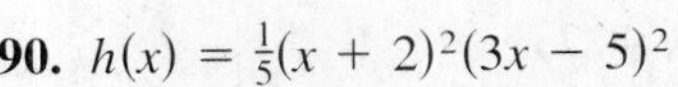

90. $h(x) = \frac{1}{5}(x + 2)^2(3x - 5)^2$

No symmetry; two x-intercepts

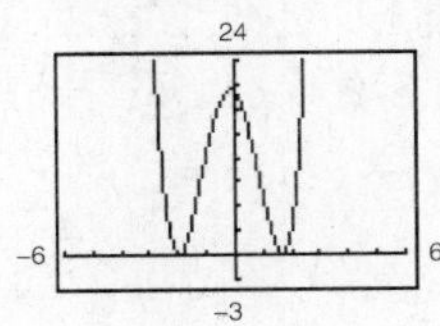

91. (a) Volume = length × width × height

Because the box is made from a square, length = width.

Thus:

Volume = $(\text{length})^2 \times \text{height} = (36 - 2x)^2 x$

(b) Domain: $0 < 36 - 2x < 36$

$-36 < -2x < 0$

$18 > x > 0$

(c)

Height, x	Length and Width	Volume, V
1	$36 - 2(1)$	$1[36 - 2(1)]^2 = 1156$
2	$36 - 2(2)$	$2[36 - 2(2)]^2 = 2048$
3	$36 - 2(3)$	$3[36 - 2(3)]^2 = 2700$
4	$36 - 2(4)$	$4[36 - 2(4)]^2 = 3136$
5	$36 - 2(5)$	$5[36 - 2(5)]^2 = 3380$
6	$36 - 2(6)$	$6[36 - 2(6)]^2 = 3456$
7	$36 - 2(7)$	$7[36 - 2(7)]^2 = 3388$

Maximum volume 3456 for $x = 6$

(d) 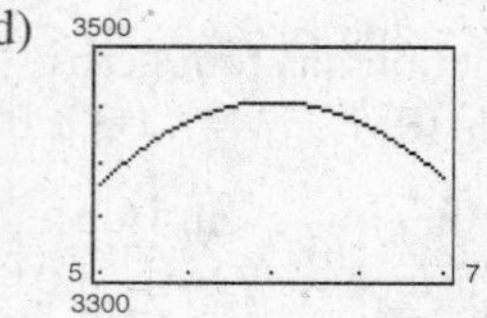

$x = 6$ when $V(x)$ is maximum.

92. (a) $V(x) = \text{length} \times \text{width} \times \text{height}$

$= (24 - 2x)(24 - 4x)x$

$= 8x(12 - x)(6 - x)$

(b) Domain: $0 < x < 6$

(c) 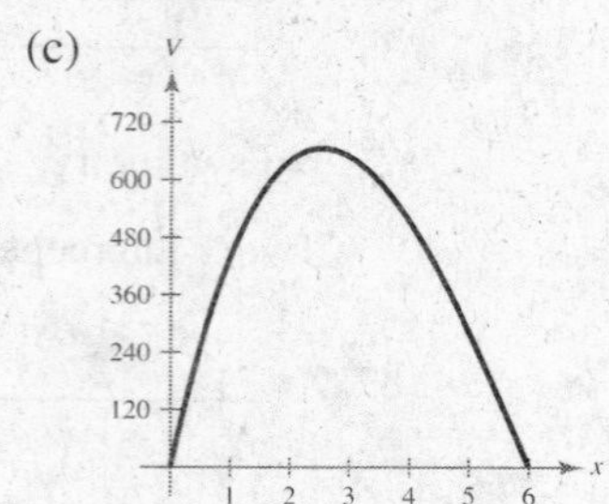

Maximum occurs at $x \approx 2.54$.

93. The point of diminishing returns (where the graph changes from curving upward to curving downward) occurs when $x = 200$. The point is (200, 160) which corresponds to spending $2,000,000 on advertising to obtain a revenue of $160 million.

94. 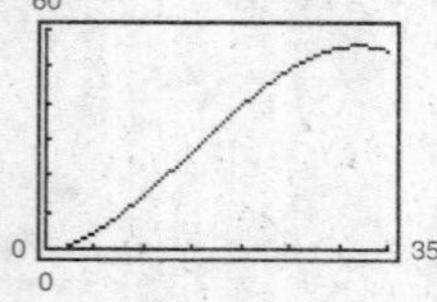

Point of Diminishing Returns: (15.2, 27.3)
15.2 years

95. 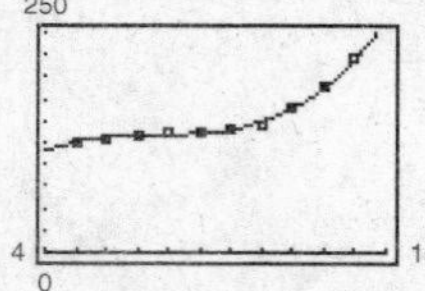

The model is a good fit.

96.
200
4 15
0

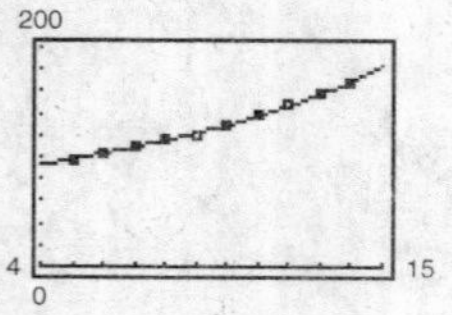

97. For 2010, $t = 20$, and

$y_1 \approx \$730.2$ thousand

$y_2 \approx \$285.0$ thousand.

Answers will vary.

98. Answers will vary.

99. True. $f(x) = x^6$ has only one zero, 0.

100. True. The degree is odd and the leading coefficient is -1.

101. False. The graph touches at $x = 1$, but does not cross the x-axis there.

102. False. The graph crosses the x-axis at $x = -3$ and $x = 0$.

103. True. The exponent of $(x + 2)$ is odd (3).

104. False. The graph rises to the left, and rises to the right.

105. The zeros are 0, 1, 1, and the graph rises to the right. Matches (b).

106. The zeros are 0, 0, 2, 2, and the graph falls to the right. Matches (e).

107. The zeros are 1, 1, -2, -2, and the graph rises to the right. Matches (a).

108. $(f + g)(-4) = f(-4) + g(-4)$
$$= -59 + 128 = 69$$

109. $(g - f)(3) = g(3) - f(3) = 8(3)^2 - [14(3) - 3]$
$$= 72 - 39 = 33$$

110. $(f \circ g)\left(-\frac{4}{7}\right) = f\left(-\frac{4}{7}\right)g\left(-\frac{4}{7}\right) = (-11)\left(\frac{8 \cdot 16}{49}\right) = -\frac{1408}{49} \approx -28.7347$

111. $\left(\frac{f}{g}\right)(-1.5) = \frac{f(-1.5)}{g(-1.5)} = \frac{-24}{18} = -\frac{4}{3}$

112. $(f \circ g)(-1) = f(g(-1)) = f(8) = 109$

113. $(g \circ f)(0) = g(f(0)) = g(-3) = 8(-3)^2 = 72$

114. $3(x - 5) < 4x - 7$
$$3x - 15 < 4x - 7$$
$$-8 < x$$

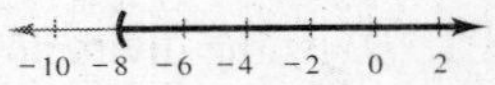

115.
$$2x^2 - x \geq 1$$
$$2x^2 - x - 1 \geq 0$$
$$(2x + 1)(x - 1) \geq 0$$
$[2x + 1 \geq 0 \text{ and } x - 1 \geq 0]$ or $[2x + 1 \leq 0 \text{ and } x - 1 \leq 0]$

$[x \geq -\frac{1}{2} \text{ and } x \geq 1]$ or $[x \leq -\frac{1}{2} \text{ and } x \leq 1]$

$x \geq 1$ or $x \leq -\frac{1}{2}$

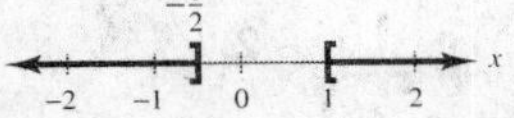

116.
$$\frac{5x - 2}{x - 7} \leq 4$$
$$\frac{5x - 2}{x - 7} - 4 \leq 0$$
$$\frac{5x - 2 - 4(x - 7)}{x - 7} \leq 0$$
$$\frac{x + 26}{x - 7} \leq 0$$
$[x + 26 \geq 0 \text{ and } x - 7 < 0]$ or $[x + 26 \leq 0 \text{ and } x - 7 > 0]$

$[x \geq -26 \text{ and } x < 7]$ or $[x \leq -26 \text{ and } x > 7]$

$-26 \leq x < 7$ impossible

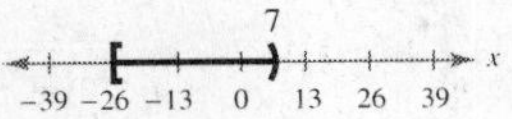

117. $|x + 8| - 1 \ge 15$

$|x + 8| \ge 16$

$x + 8 \ge 16$ or $x + 8 \le -16$

$x \ge 8$ or $x \le -24$

-32 -24 -16 -8 0 8 16 x

Section 2.3 Real Zeros of Polynomial Functions

You should know the following basic techniques and principles of polynomial division.

- The Division Algorithm (Long Division of Polynomials)
- Synthetic Division
- $f(k)$ is equal to the remainder of $f(x)$ divided by $(x - k)$.
- $f(k) = 0$ if and only if $(x - k)$ is a factor of $f(x)$.
- The Rational Zero Test
- The Upper and Lower Bound Rule

Vocabulary Check

1. $f(x)$is the dividend, $d(x)$ is the divisor, $q(x)$ is the quotient, and $r(x)$ is the remainder.

2. improper, proper **3.** synthetic division **4.** Rational Zero

5. Descartes's Rule, Signs **6.** Remainder Theorem **7.** upper bound, lower bound

1.
$$\begin{array}{r} 2x + 4 \\ x + 3 \overline{) 2x^2 + 10x + 12} \\ \underline{2x^2 + 6x} \\ 4x + 12 \\ \underline{4x + 12} \\ 0 \end{array}$$

$$\frac{2x^2 + 10x + 12}{x + 3} = 2x + 4, x \neq -3$$

2.
$$\begin{array}{r} 5x + 3 \\ x - 4 \overline{) 5x^2 - 17x - 12} \\ \underline{5x^2 - 20x} \\ 3x - 12 \\ \underline{3x - 12} \\ 0 \end{array}$$

$$\frac{5x^2 - 17x - 12}{x - 4} = 5x + 3, x \neq 4$$

3.
$$\begin{array}{r} x^3 + 3x^2 \qquad - 1 \\ x + 2 \overline{) x^4 + 5x^3 + 6x^2 - x - 2} \\ \underline{x^4 + 2x^3} \\ 3x^3 + 6x^2 \\ \underline{3x^3 + 6x^2} \\ -x - 2 \\ \underline{-x - 2} \\ 0 \end{array}$$

$$\frac{x^4 + 5x^3 + 6x^2 - x - 2}{x + 2} = x^3 + 3x^2 - 1, x \neq -2$$

4.
$$\begin{array}{r} x^2 - x - 20 \\ x - 3 \overline{) x^3 - 4x^2 - 17x + 6} \\ \underline{x^3 - 3x^2} \\ -x^2 - 17x \\ \underline{-x^2 + 3x} \\ -20x + 6 \\ \underline{-20x + 60} \\ -54 \end{array}$$

$$\frac{x^3 - 4x^2 - 17x + 6}{x - 3} = x^2 - x - 20 - \frac{54}{x - 3}$$

5.

$$\begin{array}{r}
x^2 - 3x + 1 \\
4x + 5 \overline{\smash{)}\, 4x^3 - 7x^2 - 11x + 5} \\
\underline{4x^3 + 5x^2} \qquad\qquad \\
-12x^2 - 11x \qquad \\
\underline{-12x^2 - 15x} \qquad \\
4x + 5 \\
\underline{4x + 5} \\
0
\end{array}$$

$$\frac{4x^3 - 7x^2 - 11x + 5}{4x + 5} = x^2 - 3x + 1, \quad x \neq -\frac{5}{4}$$

6.

$$\begin{array}{r}
x^2 \qquad - 25 \\
2x - 3 \overline{\smash{)}\, 2x^3 - 3x^2 - 50x + 75} \\
\underline{2x^3 - 3x^2} \qquad\qquad \\
-50x + 75 \\
\underline{-50x + 75} \\
0
\end{array}$$

$$\frac{2x^3 - 3x^2 - 50x + 75}{2x - 3} = x^2 - 25, \; x \neq \frac{3}{2}$$

7.

$$\begin{array}{r}
7x^2 - 14x + 28 \\
x + 2 \overline{\smash{)}\, 7x^3 + 0x^2 + 0x + 3} \\
\underline{7x^3 + 14x^2} \qquad\qquad \\
-14x^2 \qquad\qquad \\
\underline{-14x^2 - 28x} \qquad \\
28x + 3 \\
\underline{28x + 56} \\
-53
\end{array}$$

$$\frac{7x^3 + 3}{x + 2} = 7x^2 - 14x + 28 - \frac{53}{x + 2}$$

8.

$$\begin{array}{r}
4x^3 - 2x^2 + x - \tfrac{1}{2} \\
2x + 1 \overline{\smash{)}\, 8x^4 + 0x^3 + 0x^2 + 0x - 5} \\
\underline{8x^4 + 4x^3} \qquad\qquad\qquad \\
-4x^3 \qquad\qquad\qquad \\
\underline{-4x^3 - 2x^2} \qquad\qquad \\
2x^2 \qquad\qquad \\
\underline{2x^2 + x} \qquad \\
-x - 5 \\
\underline{-x - \tfrac{1}{2}} \\
-\tfrac{9}{2}
\end{array}$$

$$\frac{8x^4 - 5}{2x + 1} = 4x^3 - 2x^2 + x - \frac{1}{2} - \frac{9/2}{2x + 1}$$

9.

$$\begin{array}{r}
3x + 5 \\
2x^2 + 0x + 1 \overline{\smash{)}\, 6x^3 + 10x^2 + x + 8} \\
\underline{6x^3 + 0x^2 + 3x} \qquad \\
10x^2 - 2x + 8 \\
\underline{10x^2 + 0x + 5} \\
-2x + 3
\end{array}$$

$$\frac{6x^3 + 10x^2 + x + 8}{2x^2 + 1} = 3x + 5 - \frac{2x - 3}{2x^2 + 1}$$

10.

$$\begin{array}{r}
x^2 + 2x + 4 \\
x^2 - 2x + 3 \overline{\smash{)}\, x^4 + 0x^3 + 3x^2 + 0x + 1} \\
\underline{x^4 - 2x^3 + 3x^2} \qquad\qquad \\
2x^3 \qquad + 0x \qquad \\
\underline{2x^3 - 4x^2 + 6x} \qquad \\
4x^2 - 6x + 1 \\
\underline{4x^2 - 8x + 12} \\
2x - 11
\end{array}$$

$$\frac{x^4 + 3x^2 + 1}{x^2 - 2x + 3} = x^2 + 2x + 4 + \frac{2x - 11}{x^2 - 2x + 3}$$

11.

$$\begin{array}{r}
x \qquad\qquad \\
x^2 + 1 \overline{\smash{)}\, x^3 + 0x^2 + 0x - 9} \\
\underline{x^3 \qquad + x} \qquad \\
-x - 9
\end{array}$$

$$\frac{x^3 - 9}{x^2 + 1} = x - \frac{x + 9}{x^2 + 1}$$

12.

$$\begin{array}{r}
x^2 \qquad\qquad\qquad \\
x^3 - 1 \overline{\smash{)}\, x^5 + 0x^4 + 0x^3 + 0x^2 + 0x + 7} \\
\underline{x^5 \qquad\qquad - x^2 \qquad\qquad} \\
x^2 + 7
\end{array}$$

$$\frac{x^5 + 7}{x^3 - 1} = x^2 + \frac{x^2 + 7}{x^3 - 1}$$

13.

$$\begin{array}{r} 2x \\ x^2 - 2x + 1 \overline{) 2x^3 - 4x^2 - 15x + 5} \\ \underline{2x^3 - 4x^2 + 2x} \\ -17x + 5 \end{array}$$

$$\frac{2x^3 - 4x^2 - 15x + 5}{(x - 1)^2} = 2x - \frac{17x - 5}{(x - 1)^2}$$

14. $(x - 1)^3 = x^3 - 3x^2 + 3x - 1$

$$\begin{array}{r} x + 3 \\ x^3 - 3x^2 + 3x - 1 \overline{) x^4} \\ \underline{x^4 - 3x^3 + 3x^2 - x} \\ 3x^3 - 3x^2 + x \\ \underline{3x^3 - 9x^2 + 9x - 3} \\ 6x^2 - 8x + 3 \end{array}$$

$$\frac{x^4}{(x - 1)^3} = x + 3 + \frac{6x^2 - 8x + 3}{(x - 1)^3}$$

15.

$$\begin{array}{r|rrrr} 5 & 3 & -17 & 15 & -25 \\ & & 15 & -10 & 25 \\ \hline & 3 & -2 & 5 & 0 \end{array}$$

$$\frac{3x^3 - 17x^2 + 15x - 25}{x - 5} = 3x^2 - 2x + 5,\ x \neq 5$$

16.

$$\begin{array}{r|rrrr} -3 & 5 & 18 & 7 & -6 \\ & & -15 & -9 & 6 \\ \hline & 5 & 3 & -2 & 0 \end{array}$$

$$\frac{5x^3 + 18x^2 + 7x - 6}{x + 3} = 5x^2 + 3x - 2, x \neq -3$$

17.

$$\begin{array}{r|rrrr} 3 & 6 & 7 & -1 & 26 \\ & & 18 & 75 & 222 \\ \hline & 6 & 25 & 74 & 248 \end{array}$$

$$\frac{6x^3 + 7x^2 - x + 26}{x - 3} = 6x^2 + 25x + 74 + \frac{248}{x - 3}$$

18.

$$\begin{array}{r|rrrr} -6 & 2 & 14 & -20 & 7 \\ & & -12 & -12 & 192 \\ \hline & 2 & 2 & -32 & 199 \end{array}$$

$$\frac{2x^3 + 14x^2 - 20x + 7}{x + 6} = 2x^2 + 2x - 32 + \frac{199}{x + 6}$$

19.

$$\begin{array}{r|rrrr} 2 & 9 & -18 & -16 & 32 \\ & & 18 & 0 & -32 \\ \hline & 9 & 0 & -16 & 0 \end{array}$$

$$\frac{9x^3 - 18x^2 - 16x + 32}{x - 2} = 9x^2 - 16,\ x \neq 2$$

20.

$$\begin{array}{r|rrrr} -2 & 5 & 0 & 6 & 8 \\ & & -10 & 20 & -52 \\ \hline & 5 & -10 & 26 & -44 \end{array}$$

$$\frac{5x^3 + 6x + 8}{x + 2} = 5x^2 - 10x + 26 - \frac{44}{x + 2}$$

21.

$$\begin{array}{r|rrrr} -8 & 1 & 0 & 0 & 512 \\ & & -8 & 64 & -512 \\ \hline & 1 & -8 & 64 & 0 \end{array}$$

$$\frac{x^3 + 512}{x + 8} = x^2 - 8x + 64,\ x \neq -8$$

22.

$$\begin{array}{r|rrrr} 9 & 1 & 0 & 0 & -729 \\ & & 9 & 81 & 729 \\ \hline & 1 & 9 & 81 & 0 \end{array}$$

$$\frac{x^3 - 729}{x - 9} = x^2 + 9x + 81, x \neq 9$$

23.

$$\begin{array}{r|rrrr} -\frac{1}{2} & 4 & 16 & -23 & -15 \\ & & -2 & -7 & 15 \\ \hline & 4 & 14 & -30 & 0 \end{array}$$

$$\frac{4x^3 + 16x^2 - 23x - 15}{x + \frac{1}{2}} = 4x^2 + 14x - 30, x \neq -\frac{1}{2}$$

24.

$$\begin{array}{r|rrrr} \frac{3}{2} & 3 & -4 & 0 & 5 \\ & & \frac{9}{2} & \frac{3}{4} & \frac{9}{8} \\ \hline & 3 & \frac{1}{2} & \frac{3}{4} & \frac{49}{8} \end{array}$$

$$\frac{3x^3 - 4x^2 + 5}{x - \frac{3}{2}} = 3x^2 + \frac{1}{2}x + \frac{3}{4} + \frac{49}{8x - 12}$$

25. $y_2 = x - 2 + \dfrac{4}{x+2}$

$= \dfrac{(x-2)(x+2)+4}{x+2}$

$= \dfrac{x^2 - 4 + 4}{x+2}$

$= \dfrac{x^2}{x+2}$

$= y_1$

26. $y_2 = x - 1 + \dfrac{2}{x+3}$

$= \dfrac{(x-1)(x+3)+2}{x+3}$

$= \dfrac{x^2 + 2x - 3 + 2}{x+3}$

$= \dfrac{x^2 + 2x - 1}{x+3}$

$= y_1$

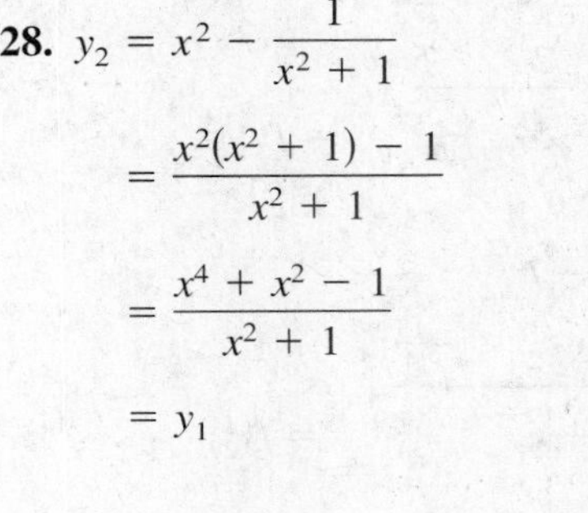

27. $y_2 = x^2 - 8 + \dfrac{39}{x^2+5}$

$= \dfrac{(x^2-8)(x^2+5)+39}{x^2+5}$

$= \dfrac{x^4 - 8x^2 + 5x^2 - 40 + 39}{x^2+5}$

$= \dfrac{x^4 - 3x^2 - 1}{x^2+5}$

$= y_1$

28. $y_2 = x^2 - \dfrac{1}{x^2+1}$

$= \dfrac{x^2(x^2+1) - 1}{x^2+1}$

$= \dfrac{x^4 + x^2 - 1}{x^2+1}$

$= y_1$

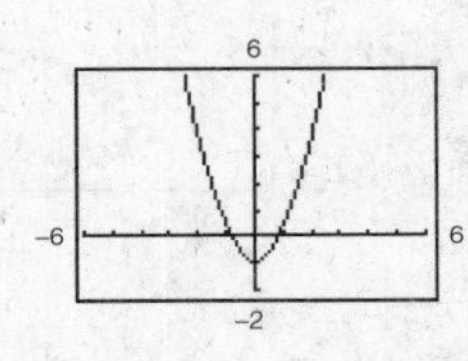

29. $f(x) = x^3 - x^2 - 14x + 11, \quad k = 4$

$$\begin{array}{r|rrrr} 4 & 1 & -1 & -14 & 11 \\ & & 4 & 12 & -8 \\ \hline & 1 & 3 & -2 & 3 \end{array}$$

$f(x) = (x-4)(x^2 + 3x - 2) + 3$

$f(4) = (0)(26) + 3 = 3$

30. $f(x) = 15x^4 + 10x^3 - 6x^2 + 14, \quad k = -\frac{2}{3}$

$$\begin{array}{r|rrrrr} -\frac{2}{3} & 15 & 10 & -6 & 0 & 14 \\ & & -10 & 0 & 4 & -\frac{8}{3} \\ \hline & 15 & 0 & -6 & 4 & \frac{34}{3} \end{array}$$

$f(x) = \left(x + \frac{2}{3}\right)(15x^3 - 6x + 4) + \frac{34}{3}$

$f\left(-\frac{2}{3}\right) = \frac{34}{3}$

31.
$$\begin{array}{r|rrrr} \sqrt{2} & 1 & 3 & -2 & -14 \\ & & \sqrt{2} & 2 + 3\sqrt{2} & 6 \\ \hline & 1 & 3 + \sqrt{2} & 3\sqrt{2} & -8 \end{array}$$

$f(x) = \left(x - \sqrt{2}\right)\left(x^2 + \left(3 + \sqrt{2}\right)x + 3\sqrt{2}\right) - 8$

$f\left(\sqrt{2}\right) = 0\left(4 + 6\sqrt{2}\right) - 8 = -8$

32.
$$\begin{array}{r|rrrr} -\sqrt{5} & 1 & 2 & -5 & -4 \\ & & -\sqrt{5} & 5 - 2\sqrt{5} & 10 \\ \hline & 1 & 2 - \sqrt{5} & -2\sqrt{5} & 6 \end{array}$$

$f(x) = \left(x + \sqrt{5}\right)\left(x^2 + \left(2 - \sqrt{5}\right)x - 2\sqrt{5}\right) + 6$

$f\left(-\sqrt{5}\right) = 6$

33.
$$\begin{array}{r|rrrr} 1-\sqrt{3} & 4 & -6 & -12 & -4 \\ & & 4-4\sqrt{3} & 10-2\sqrt{3} & 4 \\ \hline & 4 & -2-4\sqrt{3} & -2-2\sqrt{3} & 0 \end{array}$$

$f(x) = \left(x - 1 + \sqrt{3}\right)\left[4x^2 - \left(2 + 4\sqrt{3}\right)x - \left(2 + 2\sqrt{3}\right)\right]$

$f\left(1 - \sqrt{3}\right) = 0$

34.
$$\begin{array}{r|rrrr} 2+\sqrt{2} & -3 & 8 & 10 & -8 \\ & & -6-3\sqrt{2} & -2-4\sqrt{2} & 8 \\ \hline & -3 & 2-3\sqrt{2} & 8-4\sqrt{2} & 0 \end{array}$$

$f(x) = \left(x - \left(2 + \sqrt{2}\right)\right)\left(-3x^2 + \left(2 - 3\sqrt{2}\right)x + 8 - 4\sqrt{2}\right)$

$f\left(2 + \sqrt{2}\right) = 0$

35. $f(x) = 2x^3 - 7x + 3$

(a)
$$\begin{array}{r|rrrr} 1 & 2 & 0 & -7 & 3 \\ & & 2 & 2 & -5 \\ \hline & 2 & 2 & -5 & -2 \end{array} = f(1)$$

(b)
$$\begin{array}{r|rrrr} -2 & 2 & 0 & -7 & 3 \\ & & -4 & 8 & -2 \\ \hline & 2 & -4 & 1 & 1 \end{array} = f(-2)$$

(c)
$$\begin{array}{r|rrrr} \frac{1}{2} & 2 & 0 & -7 & 3 \\ & & 1 & \frac{1}{2} & -\frac{13}{4} \\ \hline & 2 & 1 & -\frac{13}{2} & -\frac{1}{4} \end{array} = f\left(\tfrac{1}{2}\right)$$

(d)
$$\begin{array}{r|rrrr} 2 & 2 & 0 & -7 & 3 \\ & & 4 & 8 & 2 \\ \hline & 2 & 4 & 1 & 5 \end{array} = f(2)$$

36. $g(x) = 2x^6 + 3x^4 - x^2 + 3$

(a)
$$\begin{array}{r|rrrrrrr} 2 & 2 & 0 & 3 & 0 & -1 & 0 & 3 \\ & & 4 & 8 & 22 & 44 & 86 & 172 \\ \hline & 2 & 4 & 11 & 22 & 43 & 86 & 175 \end{array} = g(2)$$

(b)
$$\begin{array}{r|rrrrrrr} 1 & 2 & 0 & 3 & 0 & -1 & 0 & 3 \\ & & 2 & 2 & 5 & 5 & 4 & 4 \\ \hline & 2 & 2 & 5 & 5 & 4 & 4 & 7 \end{array} = g(1)$$

(c)
$$\begin{array}{r|rrrrrrr} 3 & 2 & 0 & 3 & 0 & -1 & 0 & 3 \\ & & 6 & 18 & 63 & 189 & 564 & 1692 \\ \hline & 2 & 6 & 21 & 63 & 188 & 564 & 1695 \end{array} = g(3)$$

(d)
$$\begin{array}{r|rrrrrrr} -1 & 2 & 0 & 3 & 0 & -1 & 0 & 3 \\ & & -2 & 2 & -5 & 5 & -4 & 4 \\ \hline & 2 & -2 & 5 & -5 & 4 & -4 & 7 \end{array} = g(-1)$$

37. $h(x) = x^3 - 5x^2 - 7x + 4$

(a)
$$\begin{array}{r|rrrr} 3 & 1 & -5 & -7 & 4 \\ & & 3 & -6 & -39 \\ \hline & 1 & -2 & -13 & -35 \end{array} = h(3)$$

(b)
$$\begin{array}{r|rrrr} 2 & 1 & -5 & -7 & 4 \\ & & 2 & -6 & -26 \\ \hline & 1 & -3 & -13 & -22 \end{array} = h(2)$$

(c)
$$\begin{array}{r|rrrr} -2 & 1 & -5 & -7 & 4 \\ & & -2 & 14 & -14 \\ \hline & 1 & -7 & 7 & -10 \end{array} = h(-2)$$

(d)
$$\begin{array}{r|rrrr} -5 & 1 & -5 & -7 & 4 \\ & & -5 & 50 & -215 \\ \hline & 1 & -10 & 43 & -211 \end{array} = h(-5)$$

38. $f(x) = 4x^4 - 16x^3 + 7x^2 + 20$

(a)
$$\begin{array}{r|rrrrr} 1 & 4 & -16 & 7 & 0 & 20 \\ & & 4 & -12 & -5 & -5 \\ \hline & 4 & -12 & -5 & -5 & 15 \end{array} = f(1)$$

(b)
$$\begin{array}{r|rrrrr} -2 & 4 & -16 & 7 & 0 & 20 \\ & & -8 & 48 & -110 & 220 \\ \hline & 4 & -24 & 55 & -110 & 240 \end{array} = f(-2)$$

(c)
$$\begin{array}{r|rrrrr} 5 & 4 & -16 & 7 & 0 & 20 \\ & & 20 & 20 & 135 & 675 \\ \hline & 4 & 4 & 27 & 135 & 695 \end{array} = f(5)$$

(d)
$$\begin{array}{r|rrrrr} -10 & 4 & -16 & 7 & 0 & 20 \\ & & -40 & 560 & -5670 & 56{,}700 \\ \hline & 4 & -56 & 567 & -5670 & 56{,}720 \end{array} = f(-10)$$

39.
$$\begin{array}{r|rrrr} 2 & 1 & 0 & -7 & 6 \\ & & 2 & 4 & -6 \\ \hline & 1 & 2 & -3 & 0 \end{array}$$

$x^3 - 7x + 6 = (x - 2)(x^2 + 2x - 3)$

$= (x - 2)(x + 3)(x - 1)$

Zeros: $2, -3, 1$

40.
$$\begin{array}{r|rrrr} -4 & 1 & 0 & -28 & -48 \\ & & -4 & 16 & 48 \\ \hline & 1 & -4 & -12 & 0 \end{array}$$

$x^3 - 28x - 48 = (x + 4)(x^2 - 4x - 12)$

$= (x + 4)(x - 6)(x + 2)$

Zeros: $-4, -2, 6$

41.
$$\begin{array}{r|rrrr} \frac{1}{2} & 2 & -15 & 27 & -10 \\ & & 1 & -7 & 10 \\ \hline & 2 & -14 & 20 & 0 \end{array}$$

$2x^3 - 15x^2 + 27x - 10$

$= \left(x - \frac{1}{2}\right)(2x^2 - 14x + 20)$

$= (2x - 1)(x - 2)(x - 5)$

Zeros: $\frac{1}{2}, 2, 5$

42.
$$\begin{array}{r|rrrr} \frac{2}{3} & 48 & -80 & 41 & -6 \\ & & 32 & -32 & 6 \\ \hline & 48 & -48 & 9 & 0 \end{array}$$

$48x^3 - 80x^2 + 41x - 6 = \left(x - \frac{2}{3}\right)(48x^2 - 48x + 9)$

$= (3x - 2)(4x - 3)(4x - 1)$

Zeros: $\frac{2}{3}, \frac{3}{4}, \frac{1}{4}$

43. (a)
$$\begin{array}{r|rrrr} -2 & 2 & 1 & -5 & 2 \\ & & -4 & 6 & -2 \\ \hline & 2 & -3 & 1 & 0 \end{array}$$

(b) $2x^2 - 3x + 1 = (2x - 1)(x - 1)$

Remaining factors: $(2x - 1)$, $(x - 1)$

(c) $f(x) = (x + 2)(2x - 1)(x - 1)$

(d) Real zeros: $-2, \frac{1}{2}, 1$

(e)

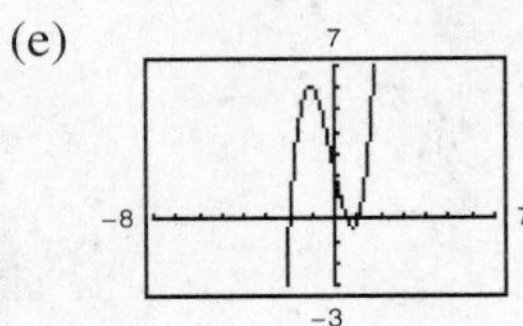

44. (a)
$$\begin{array}{r|rrrr} -3 & 3 & 2 & -19 & 6 \\ & & -9 & 21 & -6 \\ \hline & 3 & -7 & 2 & 0 \end{array}$$

(b) $3x^2 - 7x + 2 = (3x - 1)(x - 2)$

Remaining factors: $(3x - 1)$, $(x - 2)$

(c) $f(x) = (x + 3)(3x - 1)(x - 2)$

(d) Real zeros: $-3, \frac{1}{3}, 2$

(e)

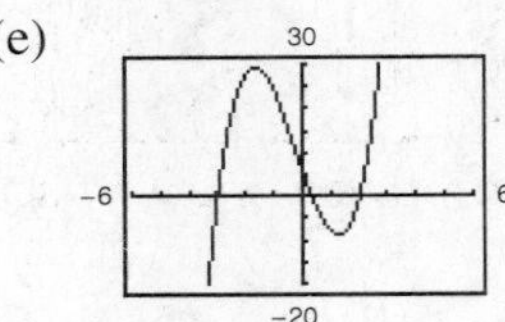

45. (a) $\begin{array}{r|rrrrr} 5 & 1 & -4 & -15 & 58 & -40 \\ & & 5 & 5 & -50 & 40 \\ \hline & 1 & 1 & -10 & 8 & 0 \end{array}$

$\begin{array}{r|rrrr} -4 & 1 & 1 & -10 & 8 \\ & & -4 & 12 & -8 \\ \hline & 1 & -3 & 2 & 0 \end{array}$

(b) $x^2 - 3x + 2 = (x - 2)(x - 1)$

Remaining factors: $(x - 2)$, $(x - 1)$

(c) $f(x) = (x - 5)(x + 4)(x - 2)(x - 1)$

(d) Real zeros: $5, -4, 2, 1$

(e)

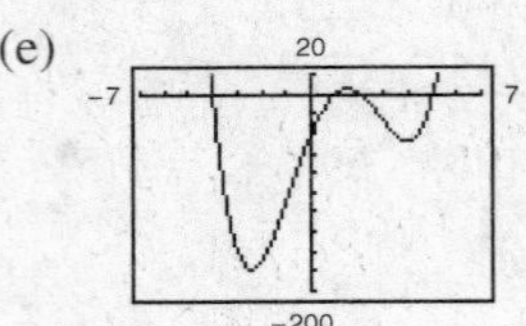

46. (a) $\begin{array}{r|rrrrr} -2 & 8 & -14 & -71 & -10 & 24 \\ & & -16 & 60 & 22 & -24 \\ \hline & 8 & -30 & -11 & 12 & 0 \end{array}$

$\begin{array}{r|rrrr} 4 & 8 & -30 & -11 & 12 \\ & & 32 & 8 & -12 \\ \hline & 8 & 2 & -3 & 0 \end{array}$

(b) $8x^2 + 2x - 3 = (4x + 3)(2x - 1)$

Remaining factors: $(4x + 3)$, $(2x - 1)$

(c) $f(x) = (x + 2)(x - 4)(4x + 3)(2x - 1)$

(d) Real zeros: $-2, 4, -\frac{3}{4}, \frac{1}{2}$

(e)

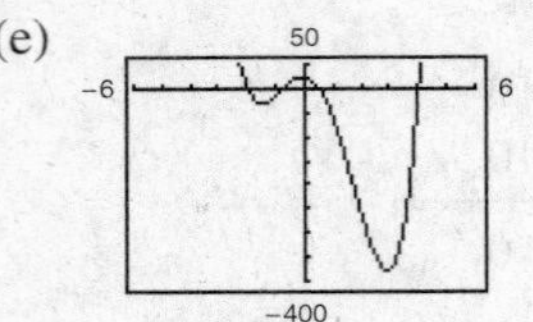

47. (a) $\begin{array}{r|rrrr} -\frac{1}{2} & 6 & 41 & -9 & -14 \\ & & -3 & -19 & 14 \\ \hline & 6 & 38 & -28 & 0 \end{array}$

(b) $6x^2 + 38x - 28 = (3x - 2)(2x + 14)$

Remaining factors: $(3x - 2)$, $(x + 7)$

(c) $f(x) = (2x + 1)(3x - 2)(x + 7)$

(d) Real zeros: $-\frac{1}{2}, \frac{2}{3}, -7$

(e)

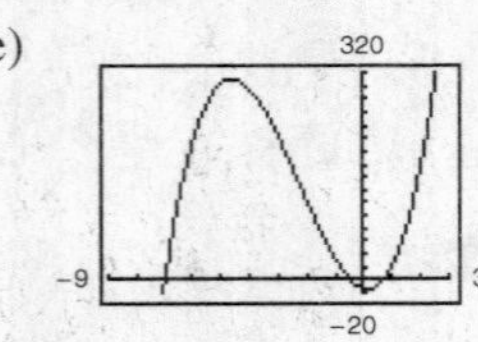

48. (a) $\begin{array}{r|rrrr} \frac{1}{2} & 2 & -1 & -10 & 5 \\ & & 1 & 0 & -5 \\ \hline & 2 & 0 & -10 & 0 \end{array}$

(b) $2x^2 - 10 = 2(x - \sqrt{5})(x + \sqrt{5})$

Remaining factors: $(x - \sqrt{5})$, $(x + \sqrt{5})$

(c) $f(x) = (2x - 1)(x + \sqrt{5})(x - \sqrt{5})$

(d) Real zeros: $\frac{1}{2}$, $\pm\sqrt{5}$

(e)

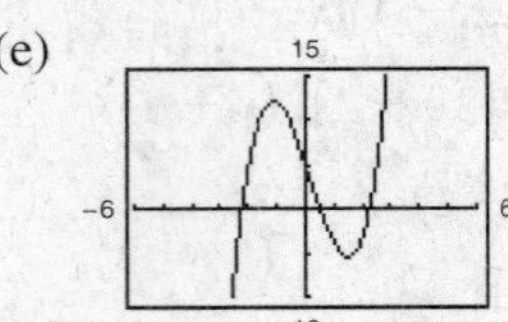

49. $f(x) = x^3 + 3x^2 - x - 3$

$p =$ factor of -3

$q =$ factor of 1

Possible rational zeros: $\pm 1, \pm 3$

$f(x) = x^2(x + 3) - (x + 3) = (x + 3)(x^2 - 1)$

Rational zeros: $\pm 1, -3$

50. $f(x) = x^3 - 4x^2 - 4x + 16$

$p =$ factor of 16

$q =$ factor of 1

Possible rational zeros: $\pm 1, \pm 2, \pm 4, \pm 8, \pm 16$

$f(x) = x^2(x - 4) - 4(x - 4) = (x - 4)(x^2 - 4)$

Rational zeros: $4, \pm 2$

51. $f(x) = 2x^4 - 17x^3 + 35x^2 + 9x - 45$

$p =$ factor of -45

$q =$ factor of 2

Possible rational zeros: $\pm 1, \pm 3, \pm 5, \pm 9, \pm 15, \pm 45,$
$\pm\frac{1}{2}, \pm\frac{3}{2}, \pm\frac{5}{2}, \pm\frac{9}{2}, \pm\frac{15}{2}, \pm\frac{45}{2}$

Using synthetic division, -1, 3, and 5 are zeros.

$f(x) = (x + 1)(x - 3)(x - 5)(2x - 3)$

Rational zeros: $-1, 3, 5, \frac{3}{2}$

52. $f(x) = 4x^5 - 8x^4 - 5x^3 + 10x^2 + x - 2$

$p =$ factor of -2

$q =$ factor of 4

Possible rational zeros: $\pm 2, \pm 1, \pm\frac{1}{2}, \pm\frac{1}{4}$

Using synthetic division, -1, 1 and 2 are zeros.

$f(x) = (x + 1)(x - 1)(x - 2)(2x - 1)(2x + 1)$

Rational zeros: $\pm 1, \pm\frac{1}{2}, 2$

53. $z^4 - z^3 - 2z - 4 = 0$

Possible rational zeros: $\pm 1, \ \pm 2, \ \pm 4$

$$\begin{array}{r|rrrrr} -1 & 1 & -1 & 0 & -2 & -4 \\ & & -1 & 2 & -2 & 4 \\ \hline & 1 & -2 & 2 & -4 & 0 \end{array} \qquad \begin{array}{r|rrrr} 2 & 1 & -2 & 2 & -4 \\ & & 2 & 0 & 4 \\ \hline & 1 & 0 & 2 & 0 \end{array}$$

$z^4 - z^3 - 2z - 4 = (z + 1)(z - 2)(z^2 + 2) = 0$

The only real zeros are -1 and 2. You can verify this by graphing the function $f(z) = z^4 - z^3 - 2z - 4$.

54. $x^4 - x^3 - 29x^2 - x - 30 = 0$

Using a graphing utility and synthetic division, $x = 6$ and $x = -5$ are rational zeros. Hence, $(x - 6)(x + 5)(x^2 + 1) = 0 \implies x = -5, 6.$

55. $2y^4 + 7y^3 - 26y^2 + 23y - 6 = 0$

Using a graphing utility and synthetic division, $1/2$, 1, and -6 are rational zeros. Hence,

$(y + 6)(y - 1)^2(2y - 1) = 0 \implies y = -6, 1, \frac{1}{2}.$

56. $x^5 - x^4 - 3x^3 + 5x^2 - 2x = 0$

$x(x^4 - x^3 - 3x^2 + 5x - 2) = 0$

$$\begin{array}{r|rrrrr} 1 & 1 & -1 & -3 & 5 & -2 \\ & & 1 & 0 & -3 & 2 \\ \hline & 1 & 0 & -3 & 2 & 0 \end{array} \qquad \begin{array}{r|rrrr} -2 & 1 & 0 & -3 & 2 \\ & & -2 & 4 & -2 \\ \hline & 1 & -2 & 1 & 0 \end{array}$$

$x(x - 1)(x + 2)(x^2 - 2x + 1) = 0$

$x(x - 1)(x + 2)(x - 1)(x - 1) = 0$

The real zeros are $-2, 0, 1$.

57. $4x^4 - 55x^2 - 45x + 36 = 0$

Using a graphing utility and synthetic division, $4, -3, \frac{1}{2}, -\frac{3}{2}$ are rational zeros. Hence, $(x - 4)(x + 3)(2x - 1)(2x + 3) = 0 \implies$

$x = 4, -3, \frac{1}{2}, -\frac{3}{2}.$

58. $4x^4 - 43x^2 - 9x + 90 = 0$

Using a graphing utility and synthetic division, $-\frac{5}{2}$, $-2, \frac{3}{2}$, and 3 are rational zeros. Hence,

$(2x + 5)(x + 2)(2x - 3)(x - 3) = 0 \implies$

$x = -\frac{5}{2}, -2, \frac{3}{2}, 3.$

59. $4x^5 + 12x^4 - 11x^3 - 42x^2 + 7x + 30 = 0$

Using a graphing utility and synthetic division, 1, -1, -2, $\frac{3}{2}$, and $-\frac{5}{2}$ are rational zeros. Hence, $(x - 1)(x + 1)(x + 2)(2x - 3)(2x + 5) = 0 \Longrightarrow$ $x = 1, -1, -2, \frac{3}{2}, -\frac{5}{2}$.

60. $4x^5 + 8x^4 - 15x^3 - 23x^2 + 11x + 15 = 0$

Using a graphing utility and synthetic division, 1, -1, -1, $\frac{3}{2}$, and $-\frac{5}{2}$ are rational zeros. Hence, $(x - 1)(x + 1)^2(2x - 3)(2x + 5) = 0 \Longrightarrow$ $x = 1, -1, -1, \frac{3}{2}, -\frac{5}{2}$.

61. $h(t) = t^3 - 2t^2 - 7t + 2$

(a) Zeros: -2, 3.732, 0.268

(b)
$$\begin{array}{r|rrrr} -2 & 1 & -2 & -7 & 2 \\ & & -2 & 8 & -2 \\ \hline & 1 & -4 & 1 & 0 \end{array}$$
$t = -2$ is a zero.

(c) $h(t) = (t + 2)(t^2 - 4t + 1)$

$= (t + 2)\left[t - \left(\sqrt{3} + 2\right)\right]\left[t + \left(\sqrt{3} - 2\right)\right]$

62. $f(s) = s^3 - 12s^2 + 40s - 24$

(a) Zeros: 6, 5.236, 0.764

(b)
$$\begin{array}{r|rrrr} 6 & 1 & -12 & 40 & -24 \\ & & 6 & -36 & 24 \\ \hline & 1 & -6 & 4 & 0 \end{array}$$

$f(s) = (s - 6)(s^2 - 6s + 4)$

$= (s - 6)\left(s - 3 - \sqrt{5}\right)\left(s - 3 + \sqrt{5}\right)$

63. $h(x) = x^5 - 7x^4 + 10x^3 + 14x^2 - 24x$

(a) $h(x) = x(x^4 - 7x^3 + 10x^2 + 14x - 24)$

From the calculator we have $x = 0, 3, 4$ and $x \approx \pm 1.414$.

(b)
$$\begin{array}{r|rrrrr} 3 & 1 & -7 & 10 & 14 & -24 \\ & & 3 & -12 & -6 & 24 \\ \hline & 1 & -4 & -2 & 8 & 0 \end{array}$$
$$\begin{array}{r|rrrr} 4 & 1 & -4 & -2 & 8 \\ & & 4 & 0 & -8 \\ \hline & 1 & 0 & -2 & 0 \end{array}$$

(c) $h(x) = x(x - 3)(x - 4)(x^2 - 2)$

$= x(x - 3)(x - 4)\left(x - \sqrt{2}\right)\left(x + \sqrt{2}\right)$

The exact roots are $x = 0,\ 3,\ 4,\ \pm\sqrt{2}$.

64. $g(x) = 6x^4 - 11x^3 - 51x^2 + 99x - 27$

(a) $x = \pm 3.0, 1.5, 0.333$

(b)
$$\begin{array}{r|rrrrr} 3 & 6 & -11 & -51 & 99 & -27 \\ & & 18 & 21 & -90 & 27 \\ \hline & 6 & 7 & -30 & 9 & 0 \end{array}$$
$$\begin{array}{r|rrrr} -3 & 6 & 7 & -30 & 9 \\ & & -18 & 33 & -9 \\ \hline & 6 & -11 & 3 & 0 \end{array}$$

$g(x) = (x - 3)(x + 3)(6x^2 - 11x + 3)$

$= (x - 3)(x + 3)(3x - 1)(2x - 3)$

65. $f(x) = 2x^4 - x^3 + 6x^2 - x + 5$

4 variations in sign $\Longrightarrow$ 4, 2 or 0 positive real zeros

$f(-x) = 2x^4 + x^3 + 6x^2 + x + 5$

0 variations in sign $\Longrightarrow$ 0 negative real zeros

66. $f(x) = 3x^4 + 5x^3 - 6x^2 + 8x - 3$

3 sign changes $\Longrightarrow$ 3 or 1 positive zeros

$f(-x) = 3x^4 - 5x^3 - 6x^2 - 8x - 3$

1 sign change $\Longrightarrow$ 1 negative zero

67. $g(x) = 4x^3 - 5x + 8$

2 variations in sign $\Longrightarrow$ 2 or 0 positive real zeros

$g(-x) = -4x^3 + 5x + 8$

1 variation in sign $\Longrightarrow$ 1 negative real zero

68. $g(x) = 2x^3 - 4x^2 - 5$

1 sign change $\Longrightarrow$ 1 positive zero

$g(-x) = -2x^3 - 4x^2 - 5$

No sign change $\Longrightarrow$ no negative zeros

69. $f(x) = x^3 + x^2 - 4x - 4$

(a) $f(x)$ has 1 variation in sign $\Rightarrow$ 1 positive real zero.

$f(-x) = -x^3 + x^2 + 4x - 4$ has 2 variations in sign $\Rightarrow$ 2 or 0 negative real zeros.

(b) Possible rational zeros: $\pm 1, \pm 2, \pm 4$

(c)

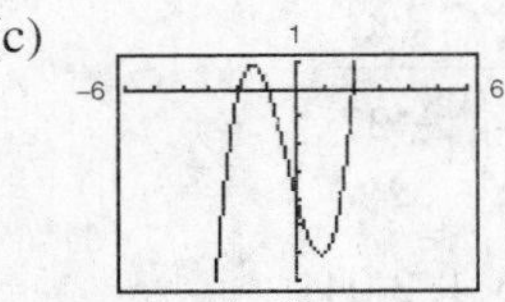

(d) Real zeros: $-2, -1, 2$

70. (a) $f(x) = -3x^3 + 20x^2 - 36x + 16$

3 sign changes $\Rightarrow$ 3 or 1 positive zeros

$f(-x) = 3x^3 + 20x^2 + 36x + 16$

0 sign changes $\Rightarrow$ 0 negative zeros

(b) $\pm\frac{1}{3}, \pm\frac{2}{3}, \pm\frac{4}{3}, \pm\frac{8}{3}, \pm\frac{16}{3}; \pm 1, \pm 2, \pm 4, \pm 8, \pm 16$

(c)

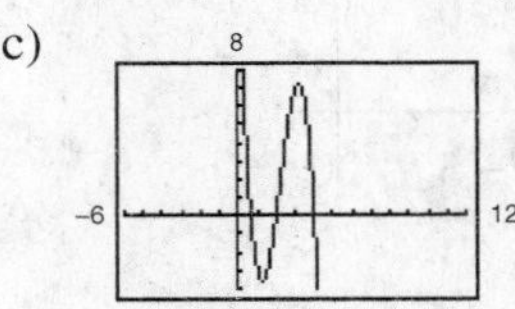

(d) Zeros: $\frac{2}{3}, 2, 4$

71. $f(x) = -2x^4 + 13x^3 - 21x^2 + 2x + 8$

(a) $f(x)$ has 3 variations in sign $\Rightarrow$ 3 or 1 positive real zeros.

$f(-x) = -2x^4 - 13x^3 - 21x^2 - 2x + 8$ has 1 variation in sign $\Rightarrow$ 1 negative real zero.

(b) Possible rational zeros: $\pm\frac{1}{2}, \pm 1, \pm 2, \pm 4, \pm 8$

(c)

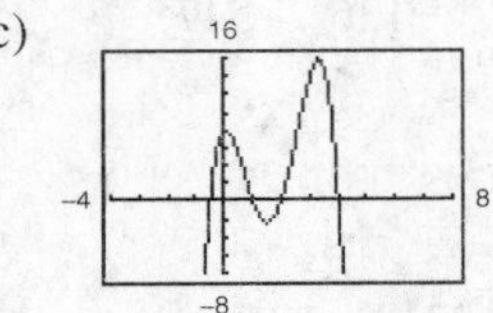

(d) Real zeros: $-\frac{1}{2}, 1, 2, 4$

72. (a) $f(x) = 4x^4 - 17x^2 + 4$

2 sign changes $\Rightarrow$ 0 or 2 positive zeros

$f(-x) = 4x^4 - 17x^2 + 4$

2 sign changes $\Rightarrow$ 0 or 2 negative zeros

(b) $\pm\frac{1}{4}, \pm\frac{1}{2}, \pm 1, \pm 2, \pm 4$

(c)

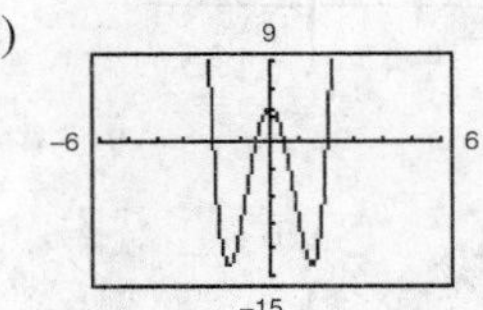

(d) Zeros: $\pm 2, \pm\frac{1}{2}$

73. $f(x) = 32x^3 - 52x^2 + 17x + 3$

(a) $f(x)$ has 2 variations in sign $\Rightarrow$ 2 or 0 positive real zeros.

$f(-x) = -32x^3 - 52x^2 - 17x + 3$ has 1 variation in sign $\Rightarrow$ 1 negative real zero.

(b) Possible rational zeros: $\pm\frac{1}{32}, \pm\frac{1}{16}, \pm\frac{1}{8}, \pm\frac{1}{4}$,

$\pm\frac{1}{2}, \pm 1, \pm\frac{3}{32}, \pm\frac{3}{16}, \pm\frac{3}{8}, \pm\frac{3}{4}, \pm\frac{3}{2}, \pm 3$

(c)

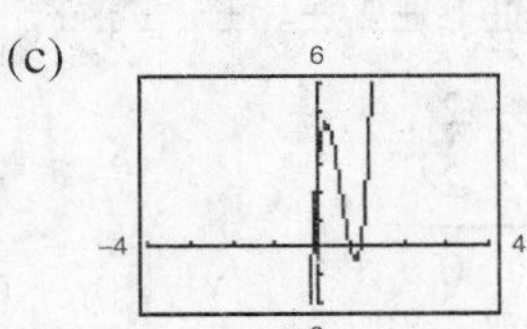

(d) Real zeros: $1, \dfrac{3}{4}, -\dfrac{1}{8}$

74. (a) $f(x) = 4x^3 + 7x^2 - 11x - 18$

1 sign change $\Rightarrow$ 1 positive zero

$f(-x) = -4x^3 + 7x^2 + 11x - 18$

2 sign changes $\Rightarrow$ 0 or 2 negative zeros

(b) $\pm 1, \pm 2, \pm 3, \pm 6, \pm 9, \pm 18, \pm\frac{1}{2}, \pm\frac{3}{2}, \pm\frac{9}{2}, \pm\frac{1}{4}$

$\pm\frac{3}{4}, \pm\frac{9}{4}$

(c)

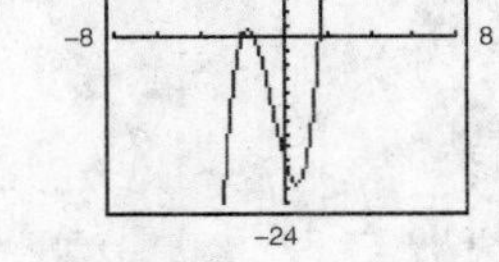

(d) Zeros: $-2, \dfrac{1}{8} \pm \dfrac{\sqrt{145}}{8}$

75. $f(x) = x^4 - 4x^3 + 15$

$$\begin{array}{r|rrrrr} 4 & 1 & -4 & 0 & 0 & 15 \\ & & 4 & 0 & 0 & 0 \\ \hline & 1 & 0 & 0 & 0 & 15 \end{array}$$

4 is an upper bound.

$$\begin{array}{r|rrrrr} -1 & 1 & -4 & 0 & 0 & 15 \\ & & -1 & 5 & -5 & 5 \\ \hline & 1 & -5 & 5 & -5 & 20 \end{array}$$

-1 is a lower bound.

Real zeros: 1.937, 3.705

76. $f(x) = 2x^3 - 3x^2 - 12x + 8$

$$\begin{array}{r|rrrr} 4 & 2 & -3 & -12 & 8 \\ & & 8 & 20 & 32 \\ \hline & 2 & 5 & 8 & 40 \end{array}$$

4 is an upper bound.

$$\begin{array}{r|rrrr} -3 & 2 & -3 & -12 & 8 \\ & & -6 & 27 & -45 \\ \hline & 2 & -9 & 15 & -37 \end{array}$$

-3 is a lower bound.

Real zeros: -2.152, 0.611, 3.041

77. $f(x) = x^4 - 4x^3 + 16x - 16$

$$\begin{array}{r|rrrrr} 5 & 1 & -4 & 0 & 16 & -16 \\ & & 25 & 105 & 525 & 2705 \\ \hline & 5 & 21 & 105 & 541 & 2689 \end{array}$$

5 is an upper bound.

$$\begin{array}{r|rrrrr} -3 & 1 & -4 & 0 & 16 & -16 \\ & & -3 & 21 & -63 & 141 \\ \hline & 1 & -7 & 21 & -47 & 125 \end{array}$$

-3 is a lower bound.

Real zeros: -2, 2

78. $f(x) = 2x^4 - 8x + 3$

$$\begin{array}{r|rrrrr} 3 & 2 & 0 & 0 & -8 & 3 \\ & & 6 & 18 & 54 & 138 \\ \hline & 2 & 6 & 18 & 46 & 141 \end{array}$$

3 is an upper bound.

$$\begin{array}{r|rrrrr} -4 & 2 & 0 & 0 & -8 & 3 \\ & & -8 & 32 & -128 & 544 \\ \hline & 2 & -8 & 32 & -136 & 547 \end{array}$$

-4 is a lower bound.

Real zeros: 0.380, 1.435

79. $P(x) = x^4 - \frac{25}{4}x^2 + 9$

$= \frac{1}{4}(4x^4 - 25x^2 + 36)$

$= \frac{1}{4}(4x^2 - 9)(x^2 - 4)$

$= \frac{1}{4}(2x + 3)(2x - 3)(x + 2)(x - 2)$

The rational zeros are $\pm\frac{3}{2}$ and ± 2.

80. $f(x) = \frac{1}{2}(2x^3 - 3x^2 - 23x + 12)$

Possible rational zeros: $\pm 1, \pm 2, \pm 3, \pm 4, \pm 6, \pm 12, \pm\frac{1}{2}, \pm\frac{3}{2}$

$$\begin{array}{r|rrrr} 4 & 2 & -3 & -23 & 12 \\ & & 8 & 20 & -12 \\ \hline & 2 & 5 & -3 & 0 \end{array}$$

$f(x) = \frac{1}{2}(x - 4)(2x^2 + 5x - 3)$

$= \frac{1}{2}(x - 4)(2x - 1)(x + 3)$

Rational zeros: $-3, \frac{1}{2}, 4$

81. $f(x) = x^3 - \frac{1}{4}x^2 - x + \frac{1}{4}$

$= \frac{1}{4}(4x^3 - x^2 - 4x + 1)$

$= \frac{1}{4}[x^2(4x - 1) - 1(4x - 1)]$

$= \frac{1}{4}(4x - 1)(x^2 - 1)$

$= \frac{1}{4}(4x - 1)(x + 1)(x - 1)$

The rational zeros are $\frac{1}{4}$ and ± 1.

82. $f(z) = \frac{1}{6}(6z^3 + 11z^2 - 3z - 2)$

Possible rational zeros: $\pm 1, \pm 2, \pm\frac{1}{2}, \pm\frac{1}{3}, \pm\frac{2}{3}, \pm\frac{1}{6}$

$$\begin{array}{r|rrrr} -2 & 6 & 11 & -3 & -2 \\ & & -12 & 2 & 2 \\ \hline & 6 & -1 & -1 & 0 \end{array}$$

$f(x) = \frac{1}{6}(z + 2)(6z^2 - z - 1)$

$= \frac{1}{6}(z + 2)(3z + 1)(2z - 1)$

Rational zeros: $-2, -\frac{1}{3}, \frac{1}{2}$

83. $f(x) = x^3 - 1$

$= (x - 1)(x^2 + x + 1)$

Rational zeros: 1 $(x = 1)$

Irrational zeros: 0

Matches (d).

84. $f(x) = x^3 - 2$

$= \left(x - \sqrt[3]{2}\right)\left(x^2 + \sqrt[3]{2}x + \sqrt[3]{4}\right)$

Rational zeros: 0

Irrational zeros: 1, $\left(x = \sqrt[3]{2}\right)$

Matches (a).

85. $f(x) = x^3 - x = x(x + 1)(x - 1)$

Rational zeros: 3 $(x = 0, \pm 1)$

Irrational zeros: 0

Matches (b).

86. $f(x) = x^3 - 2x$

$= x(x^2 - 2)$

$= x\left(x + \sqrt{2}\right)\left(x - \sqrt{2}\right)$

Rational zeros: 1, $(x = 0)$

Irrational zeros: 2, $\left(x = \pm\sqrt{2}\right)$

Matches (c).

87. $y = 2x^4 - 9x^3 + 5x^2 + 3x - 1$

Using the graph and synthetic division, $-1/2$ is a zero:

$$\begin{array}{r|rrrrr} -\frac{1}{2} & 2 & -9 & 5 & 3 & -1 \\ & & -1 & 5 & -5 & 1 \\ \hline & 2 & -10 & 10 & -2 & 0 \end{array}$$

$y = \left(x + \frac{1}{2}\right)(2x^3 - 10x^2 + 10x - 2)$

$x = 1$ is a zero of the cubic, so

$y = \left(2x + 1\right)(x - 1)(x^2 - 4x + 1).$

For the quadratic term, use the Quadratic Formula.

$$x = \frac{4 \pm \sqrt{16 - 4}}{2} = 2 \pm \sqrt{3}$$

The real zeros are $-\frac{1}{2}, 1, 2 \pm \sqrt{3}$.

88. $y = x^4 - 5x^3 - 7x^2 + 13x - 2$

Using the graph and synthetic division, 1 and -2 are zeros:

$y = (x - 1)(x + 2)(x^2 - 6x + 1)$

Using the Quadratic Formula:

$$x = \frac{6 \pm \sqrt{36 - 4}}{2} = 3 \pm 2\sqrt{2}$$

The real zeros are $1, -2, 3 \pm 2\sqrt{2}$.

89. $y = -2x^4 + 17x^3 - 3x^2 - 25x - 3$

Using the graph and synthetic division, -1 and $3/2$ are zeros:

$y = -(x + 1)(2x - 3)(x^2 - 8x - 1)$

Using the Quadratic Formula:

$$x = \frac{8 \pm \sqrt{64 + 4}}{2} = 4 \pm \sqrt{17}$$

The real zeros are $-1, 3/2, 4 \pm \sqrt{17}$.

90. $y = -x^4 + 5x^3 - 10x - 4$

Using the graph and synthetic division, 2 and -1 are zeros:

$y = -(x - 2)(x + 1)(x^2 - 4x - 2)$

Using the Quadratic Formula:

$$x = \frac{4 \pm \sqrt{16 + 8}}{2} = 2 \pm \sqrt{6}$$

The real zeros are $2, -1, 2 \pm \sqrt{6}$.

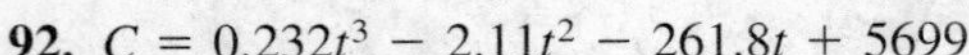

91. (a) $P(t) = 0.0058t^3 + 0.500t^2 + 1.38t + 4.6$

(b)

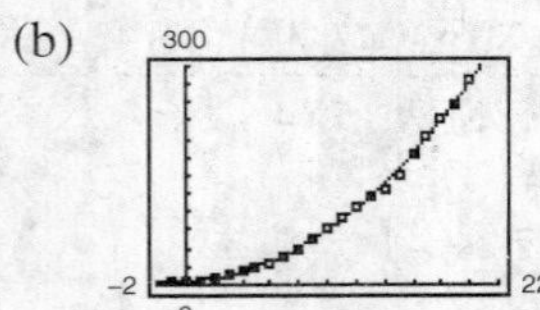

(c) The model fits the data well.

(d) For 2010, $t = 21$ and:

21	0.0058	0.5	1.38	4.6
		0.1218	13.0578	303.1938
	0.0058	0.6218	14.4378	307.7938

Hence, the population will be about 307.8 million, which seems reasonable.

92. $C = 0.232t^3 - 2.11t^2 - 261.8t + 5699$

(a)

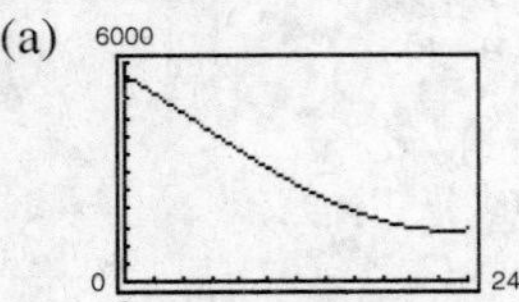

(b) For 1980, $t = 0$ and $C = 5699$ mines.

For 1990, $t = 10$ and:

10	0.232	−2.11	−261.8	5699
		2.32	2.1	−2597
	0.232	0.21	−259.7	3102

3102 mines in 1990

(c) Answers will vary.

93. (a) Combined length and width:

$4x + y = 120 \Rightarrow y = 120 - 4x$

$$\text{Volume} = l \cdot w \cdot h = x^2y = x^2(120 - 4x) = 4x^2(30 - x)$$

(b)

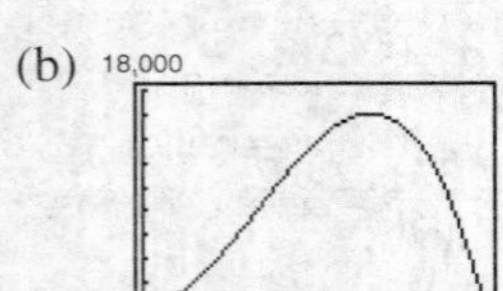

Dimensions with maximum volume: $20 \times 20 \times 40$

(c) $13{,}500 = 4x^2(30 - x)$

$4x^3 - 120x^2 + 13{,}500 = 0$

$x^3 - 30x^2 + 3375 = 0$

15	1	−30	0	3375
		15	−225	−3375
	1	−15	−225	0

$(x - 15)(x^2 - 15x - 225) = 0$

Using the Quadratic Formula, $x = 15$ or $\dfrac{15 \pm 15\sqrt{5}}{2}$.

The value of $\dfrac{15 - 15\sqrt{5}}{2}$ is not possible because it is negative.

94. $y = -5.05x^3 + 3857x - 38{,}411.25,\ 13 \le x \le 18$

(a)

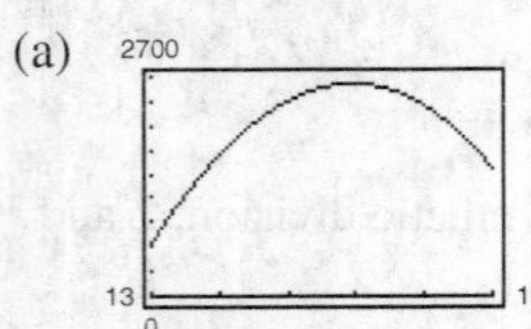

(b) The second air-fuel ratio of 16.89 can be obtained by finding the second point where the curves y and $y_1 = 2400$ intersect.

(c) Solve $-5.05x^3 + 3857x - 38{,}411.25 = 2400$ or $-5.05x^3 + 3857x - 40{,}811.25 = 0$.

By synthetic division:

15	−5.05	0	3857	−40,811.25
		−75.75	−1136.25	40,811.25
	−5.05	−75.75	2720.75	0

(d) The positive zero of the quadratic $-5.05x^2 - 75.75x + 2720.75$ can be found using the Quadratic Formula.

$$x = \frac{75.75 - \sqrt{(-75.75)^2 - 4(-5.05)(2720.75)}}{2(-5.05)} \approx 16.89$$

95. False, $-\frac{4}{7}$ is a zero of f.

96. $\frac{1}{2}$

	6	1	−92	45	184	4	−48
		3	2	−45	0	92	48
	6	4	−90	0	184	96	0

True

97. The zeros are 1, 1, and −2. The graph falls to the right.

$y = a(x - 1)^2(x + 2)\ \ a < 0$

Since $f(0) = -4$, $a = -2$.

$y = -2(x - 1)^2(x + 2) = -2x^3 + 6x - 4$

98. The zeros are 1, −1, and −2. The graph rises to the right.

$y = a(x - 1)(x + 1)(x + 2), a > 0$

Since $f(0) = -4$, $a = 2$.

$y = 2(x - 1)(x + 1)(x + 2) = 2x^3 + 4x^2 - 2x - 4$

99. $f(x) = -(x + 1)(x - 1)(x + 2)(x - 2)$

100. $f(x) = 2(x + 2)(x - 1)(x - 2)$

101.

4	1	$-k$	$2k$	-8
		4	$16 - 4k$	$64 - 8k$
	1	$4 - k$	$16 - 2k$	$56 - 8k$

Hence, $56 - 8k = 0 \Rightarrow k = 7$.

102. Use synthetic division:

3	1	$-k$	$2k$	-12
		3	$9 - 3k$	$27 - 3k$
	1	$3 - k$	$9 - k$	$15 - 3k$

Since the remainder $15 - 3k$ should be 0, $k = 5$.

103. (a) $\dfrac{x^2 - 1}{x - 1} = x + 1, \quad x \neq 1$

(b) $\dfrac{x^3 - 1}{x - 1} = x^2 + x + 1, \quad x \neq 1$

(c) $\dfrac{x^4 - 1}{x - 1} = x^3 + x^2 + x + 1, \quad x \neq 1$

In general,

$$\frac{x^n - 1}{x - 1} = x^{n-1} + x^{n-2} + \cdots + x + 1, \quad x \neq 1.$$

104. You can check polynomial division by multiplying the quotient by the divisor and adding the remainder. This should yield the original dividend if the multiplication was performed correctly.

105.
$$9x^2 - 25 = 0$$
$$(3x + 5)(3x - 5) = 0$$
$$x = -\frac{5}{3}, \frac{5}{3}$$

106.
$$16x^2 - 21 = 0$$
$$x^2 = \frac{21}{16}$$
$$x = \pm\frac{\sqrt{21}}{4}$$

107.
$$2x^2 + 6x + 3 = 0$$
$$x = \frac{-6 \pm \sqrt{6^2 - 4(2)(3)}}{2(2)}$$
$$= \frac{-6 \pm \sqrt{12}}{4}$$
$$= \frac{-3 \pm \sqrt{3}}{2}$$
$$x = -\frac{3}{2} + \frac{\sqrt{3}}{2}, \quad -\frac{3}{2} - \frac{\sqrt{3}}{2}$$

108.
$$8x^2 - 22x + 15 = 0$$
$$(4x - 5)(2x - 3) = 0$$
$$x = \frac{5}{4}, \frac{3}{2}$$

109. $f(x) = (x - 0)(x + 12) = x^2 + 12x$

[Answer not unique]

110. $f(x) = (x - 1)(x + 3)(x - 8)$

$= x^3 - 6x^2 - 19x + 24$

[Answer not unique]

111. $f(x) = (x - 0)(x + 1)(x - 2)(x - 5)$

$= (x^2 + x)(x^2 - 7x + 10)$

$= x^4 - 6x^3 + 3x^2 + 10x$

[Answer not unique]

112. $f(x) = \left[x - \left(2 + \sqrt{3}\right)\right]\left[x - \left(2 - \sqrt{3}\right)\right]$

$= \left[(x - 2) - \sqrt{3}\right]\left[(x - 2) + \sqrt{3}\right]$

$= (x - 2)^2 - 3$

$= x^2 - 4x + 4 - 3$

$= x^2 - 4x + 1$

[Answer not unique]

Section 2.4 Complex Numbers

- You should know how to work with complex numbers.
- Operations on complex numbers
  (a) Addition: $(a + bi) + (c + di) = (a + c) + (b + d)i$
  (b) Subtraction: $(a + bi) - (c + di) = (a - c) + (b - d)i$
  (c) Multiplication: $(a + bi)(c + di) = (ac - bd) + (ad + bc)i$
  (d) Division: $\dfrac{a + bi}{c + di} = \dfrac{a + bi}{c + di} \cdot \dfrac{c - di}{c - di} = \dfrac{ac + bd}{c^2 + d^2} + \dfrac{bc - ad}{c^2 + d^2}i$
- The complex conjugate of $a + bi$ is $a - bi$:
  $(a + bi)(a - bi) = a^2 + b^2$
- The additive inverse of $a + bi$ is $-a - bi$.
- The multiplicative inverse of $a + bi$ is
  $\dfrac{a - bi}{a^2 + b^2}.$
- $\sqrt{-a} = \sqrt{a}\, i$ for $a > 0$.

Vocabulary Check

1. (a) ii (b) iii (c) i

2. $\sqrt{-1}, -1$

3. complex, $a + bi$

4. real, imaginary

5. Mandelbrot Set

1. $a + bi = -9 + 4i$

$a = -9$

$b = 4$

2. $a + bi = 12 + 5i$

$a = 12$

$b = 5$

3. $(a - 1) + (b + 3)i = 5 + 8i$

$a - 1 = 5 \Rightarrow a = 6$

$b + 3 = 8 \Rightarrow b = 5$

4. $(a + 6) + 2bi = 6 - 5i$

$2b = -5$

$b = -\frac{5}{2}$

$a + 6 = 6$

$a = 0$

5. $5 + \sqrt{-16} = 5 + \sqrt{16(-1)}$

$= 5 + 4i$

6. $2 - \sqrt{-9} = 2 - \sqrt{9(-1)}$

$= 2 - 3i$

7. $-6 = -6 + 0i$

8. $8 = 8 + 0i$

9. $-5i + i^2 = -5i - 1 = -1 - 5i$

10. $-3i^2 + i = -3(-1) + i$

$= 3 + i$

11. $\left(\sqrt{-75}\right)^2 = -75$

12. $\left(\sqrt{-4}\right)^2 - 7 = -4 - 7$

$= -11$

13. $\sqrt{-0.09} = \sqrt{0.09}\,i = 0.3i$

14. $\sqrt{-0.0004} = 0.02i$

15. $(4 + i) - (7 - 2i) = (4 - 7) + (1 + 2)i$

$= -3 + 3i$

16. $(11 - 2i) - (-3 + 6i) = (11 + 3) + (-2 - 6)i$

$= 14 - 8i$

17. $\left(-1 + \sqrt{-8}\right) + \left(8 - \sqrt{-50}\right) = 7 + 2\sqrt{2}i - 5\sqrt{2}i = 7 - 3\sqrt{2}i$

18. $\left(7 + \sqrt{-18}\right) + \left(3 + \sqrt{-32}\right) = \left(7 + 3\sqrt{2}i\right) + \left(3 + 4\sqrt{2}i\right) = (7 + 3) + \left(3\sqrt{2} + 4\sqrt{2}\right)i = 10 + 7\sqrt{2}i$

19. $13i - (14 - 7i) = 13i - 14 + 7i = -14 + 20i$

20. $22 + (-5 + 8i) - 10i = (22 - 5) + (8 - 10)i = 17 - 2i$

21. $\left(\frac{3}{2} + \frac{5}{2}i\right) + \left(\frac{5}{3} + \frac{11}{3}i\right) = \left(\frac{3}{2} + \frac{5}{3}\right) + \left(\frac{5}{2} + \frac{11}{3}\right)i$

$= \frac{9 + 10}{6} + \frac{15 + 22}{6}i$

$= \frac{19}{6} + \frac{37}{6}i$

22. $\left(\frac{3}{4} + \frac{7}{5}i\right) - \left(\frac{5}{6} - \frac{1}{6}i\right) = \left(\frac{3}{4} - \frac{5}{6}\right) + \left(\frac{7}{5} + \frac{1}{6}\right)i$

$= -\frac{1}{12} + \frac{47}{30}i$

23. $(1.6 + 3.2i) + (-5.8 + 4.3i) = -4.2 + 7.5i$

24. $-(-3.7 - 12.8i) - \left(6.1 - \sqrt{-24.5}\right) = 3.7 + 12.8i - 6.1 + \sqrt{\frac{49}{2}}i$

$= -2.4 + \left(12.8 + \frac{7\sqrt{2}}{2}\right)i$

$\approx -2.4 + 17.75i$

25. $\sqrt{-6} \cdot \sqrt{-2} = \left(\sqrt{6}i\right)\left(\sqrt{2}i\right)$

$= \sqrt{12}i^2 = \left(2\sqrt{3}\right)(-1) = -2\sqrt{3}$

26. $\sqrt{-5} \cdot \sqrt{-10} = \left(\sqrt{5}i\right)\left(\sqrt{10}i\right)$

$= \sqrt{50}i^2 = 5\sqrt{2}(-1) = -5\sqrt{2}$

27. $\left(\sqrt{-10}\right)^2 = \left(\sqrt{10}i\right)^2 = 10i^2 = -10$

28. $\left(\sqrt{-75}\right)^2 = \left(\sqrt{75}i\right)^2 = 75i^2 = -75$

29. $(1 + i)(3 - 2i) = 3 - 2i + 3i - 2i^2$
$= 3 + i + 2$
$= 5 + i$

30. $(6 - 2i)(2 - 3i) = 12 - 18i - 4i + 6i^2$
$= 12 - 22i - 6$
$= 6 - 22i$

31. $4i(8 + 5i) = 32i + 20i^2$
$= 32i + 20(-1)$
$= -20 + 32i$

32. $-3i(6 - i) = -18i - 3 = -3 - 18i$

33. $(\sqrt{14} + \sqrt{10}\,i)(\sqrt{14} - \sqrt{10}\,i) = 14 - 10i^2 = 14 + 10 = 24$

34. $(3 + \sqrt{-5})(7 - \sqrt{-10}) = (3 + \sqrt{5}i)(7 - \sqrt{10}i)$
$= 21 - 3\sqrt{10}i + 7\sqrt{5}i - \sqrt{50}i^2$
$= 21 + \sqrt{50} + 7\sqrt{5}i - 3\sqrt{10}i$
$= (21 + 5\sqrt{2}) + (7\sqrt{5} - 3\sqrt{10})i$

35. $(4 + 5i)^2 - (4 - 5i)^2 = [(4 + 5i) + (4 - 5i)][(4 + 5i) - (4 - 5i)] = 8(10i) = 80i$

36. $(1 - 2i)^2 - (1 + 2i)^2 = 1 - 4i + 4i^2 - (1 + 4i + 4i^2)$
$= 1 - 4i + 4i^2 - 1 - 4i - 4i^2$
$= -8i$

37. $4 - 3i$ is the complex conjugate of $4 + 3i$.
$(4 + 3i)(4 - 3i) = 16 + 9 = 25$

38. The conjugate of $7 - 5i$ is $7 + 5i$.
$(7 - 5i)(7 + 5i) = 49 + 25 = 74$

39. $-6 + \sqrt{5}i$ is the complex conjugate of $-6 - \sqrt{5}i$.
$(-6 - \sqrt{5}i)(-6 + \sqrt{5}i) = 36 + 5 = 41$

40. The conjugate of $-3 + \sqrt{2}i$ is $-3 - \sqrt{2}i$.
$(-3 + \sqrt{2}i)(-3 - \sqrt{2}i) = 9 + 2 = 11$

41. $-\sqrt{20}i$ is the complex conjugate of $\sqrt{-20} = \sqrt{20}i$.
$(\sqrt{20}i)(-\sqrt{20}i) = 20$

42. The conjugate of $\sqrt{-13} = \sqrt{13}i$ is $-\sqrt{13}i$.
$\sqrt{-13}(-\sqrt{13}i) = (\sqrt{13}i)(-\sqrt{13}i) = 13$

43. $3 + \sqrt{2}i$ is the complex conjugate of $3 - \sqrt{-2} = 3 - \sqrt{2}i$.
$(3 - \sqrt{2}i)(3 + \sqrt{2}i) = 9 + 2 = 11$

44. The conjugate of $1 + \sqrt{-8} = 1 + 2\sqrt{2}i$ is $1 - 2\sqrt{2}i$.
$(1 + 2\sqrt{2}i)(1 - 2\sqrt{2}i) = 1 + 8 = 9$

45. $\dfrac{6}{i} = \dfrac{6}{i} \cdot \dfrac{-i}{-i} = \dfrac{-6i}{-i^2} = \dfrac{-6i}{1} = -6i$

46. $\dfrac{-5}{2i} \cdot \dfrac{i}{i} = \dfrac{-5i}{-2} = \dfrac{5}{2}i$

47. $\dfrac{2}{4 - 5i} = \dfrac{2}{4 - 5i} \cdot \dfrac{4 + 5i}{4 + 5i} = \dfrac{8 + 10i}{16 + 25} = \dfrac{8}{41} + \dfrac{10}{41}i$

48. $\dfrac{3}{1 - i} \cdot \dfrac{1 + i}{1 + i} = \dfrac{3 + 3i}{1 - i^2} = \dfrac{3 + 3i}{2} = \dfrac{3}{2} + \dfrac{3}{2}i$

49. $\dfrac{2+i}{2-i} = \dfrac{2+i}{2-i} \cdot \dfrac{2+i}{2+i}$

$= \dfrac{4+4i+i^2}{4+1}$

$= \dfrac{3+4i}{5} = \dfrac{3}{5} + \dfrac{4}{5}i$

50. $\dfrac{8-7i}{1-2i} \cdot \dfrac{1+2i}{1+2i} = \dfrac{8+16i-7i-14i^2}{1-4i^2}$

$= \dfrac{22+9i}{5} = \dfrac{22}{5} + \dfrac{9}{5}i$

51. $\dfrac{i}{(4-5i)^2} = \dfrac{i}{16-25-40i}$

$= \dfrac{i}{-9-40i} \cdot \dfrac{-9+40i}{-9+40i}$

$= \dfrac{-40-9i}{81+40^2}$

$= \dfrac{-40}{1681} - \dfrac{9}{1681}i$

52. $\dfrac{5i}{(2+3i)^2} = \dfrac{5i}{-5+12i} \cdot \dfrac{-5-12i}{-5-12i}$

$= \dfrac{-25i+60}{25+144}$

$= \dfrac{60}{169} - \dfrac{25}{169}i$

53. $\dfrac{2}{1+i} - \dfrac{3}{1-i} = \dfrac{2(1-i)-3(1+i)}{(1+i)(1-i)}$

$= \dfrac{2-2i-3-3i}{1+1}$

$= \dfrac{-1-5i}{2}$

$= -\dfrac{1}{2} - \dfrac{5}{2}i$

54. $\dfrac{2i}{2+i} + \dfrac{5}{2-i} = \dfrac{2i(2-i)}{(2+i)(2-i)} + \dfrac{5(2+i)}{(2+i)(2-i)}$

$= \dfrac{4i-2i^2+10+5i}{4-i^2}$

$= \dfrac{12+9i}{5}$

$= \dfrac{12}{5} + \dfrac{9}{5}i$

55. $\dfrac{i}{3-2i} + \dfrac{2i}{3+8i} = \dfrac{3i+8i^2+6i-4i^2}{(3-2i)(3+8i)}$

$= \dfrac{-4+9i}{9+18i+16}$

$= \dfrac{-4+9i}{25+18i} \cdot \dfrac{25-18i}{25-18i}$

$= \dfrac{-100+72i+225i+162}{25^2+18^2}$

$= \dfrac{62+297i}{949}$

$= \dfrac{62}{949} + \dfrac{297}{949}i$

56. $\dfrac{1+i}{i} - \dfrac{3}{4-i} = \dfrac{1+i}{i} \cdot \dfrac{-i}{-i} - \dfrac{3}{4-i} \cdot \dfrac{4+i}{4+i}$

$= \dfrac{-i+1}{1} - \dfrac{12+3i}{16+1}$

$= \dfrac{5}{17} - \dfrac{20}{17}i$

57. $-6i^3 + i^2 = -6i^2 i + i^2 = -6(-1)i + (-1) = 6i - 1 = -1 + 6i$

58. $4i^2 - 2i^3 = -4 + 2i$

59. $\left(\sqrt{-75}\right)^3 = \left(5\sqrt{3}i\right)^3 = 5^3\left(\sqrt{3}\right)^3 i^3 = 125\left(3\sqrt{3}\right)(-i)$

$= -375\sqrt{3}i$

60. $\left(\sqrt{-2}\right)^6 = \left(\sqrt{2}i\right)^6 = 8i^6 = 8i^4 i^2 = -8$

61. $\dfrac{1}{i^3} = \dfrac{1}{i^3} \cdot \dfrac{i}{i} = \dfrac{i}{i^4} = \dfrac{i}{1} = i$

62. $\dfrac{1}{(2i)^3} = \dfrac{1}{8i^3} = \dfrac{1}{-8i} \cdot \dfrac{8i}{8i} = \dfrac{8i}{-64i^2} = \dfrac{1}{8}i$

63. $(2)^3 = 8$

$$\left(-1+\sqrt{3}i\right)^3 = (-1)^3 + 3(-1)^2\left(\sqrt{3}i\right) + 3(-1)\left(\sqrt{3}i\right)^2 + \left(\sqrt{3}i\right)^3$$
$$= -1 + 3\sqrt{3}i - 9i^2 + 3\sqrt{3}i^3$$
$$= -1 + 3\sqrt{3}i + 9 - 3\sqrt{3}i$$
$$= 8$$
$$\left(-1-\sqrt{3}i\right)^3 = (-1)^3 + 3(-1)^2\left(-\sqrt{3}i\right) + 3(-1)\left(-\sqrt{3}i\right)^2 + \left(-\sqrt{3}i\right)^3$$
$$= -1 - 3\sqrt{3}i - 9i^2 - 3\sqrt{3}i^3$$
$$= -1 - 3\sqrt{3}i + 9 + 3\sqrt{3}i$$
$$= 8$$

The three numbers are cube roots of 8.

64. (a) $2^4 = 16$ (b) $(-2)^4 = 16$

(c) $(2i)^4 = 2^4 i^4 = 16(1) = 16$ (d) $(-2i)^4 = (-2)^4 i^4 = 16(1) = 16$

65. $4 + 3i$ **66.** $-1 - 2i$ **67.** $5i$

68. -3 **69.** 2 **70.** $-4i$

71. $4 - 5i$ **72.** $-7 + 2i$ **73.** $3i$

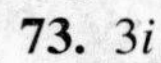

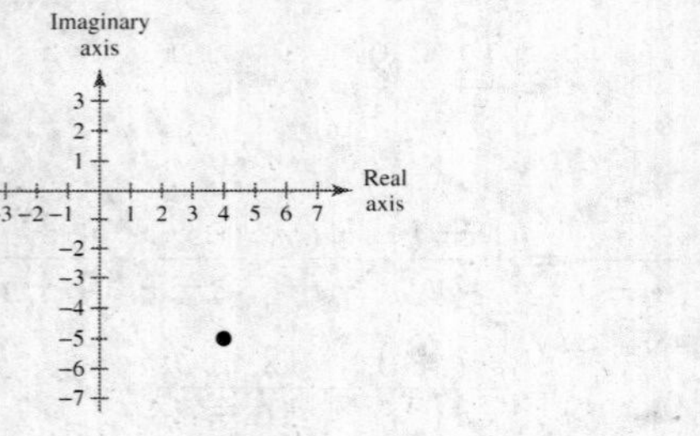

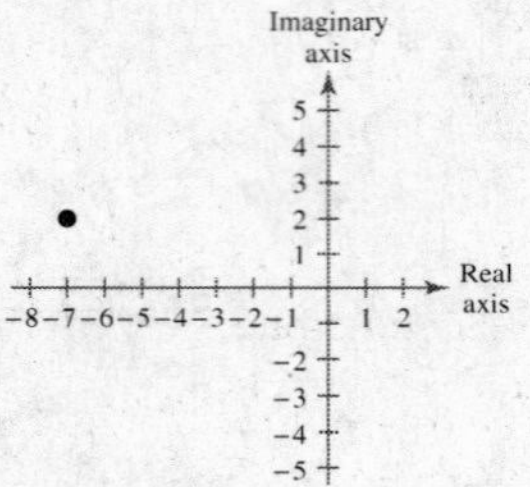

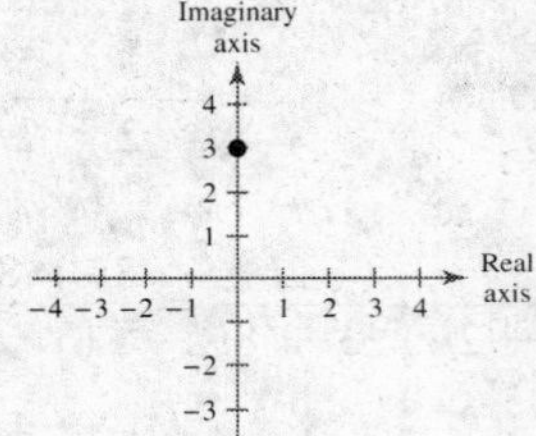

74. $-5i$ **75.** 1 **76.** -6

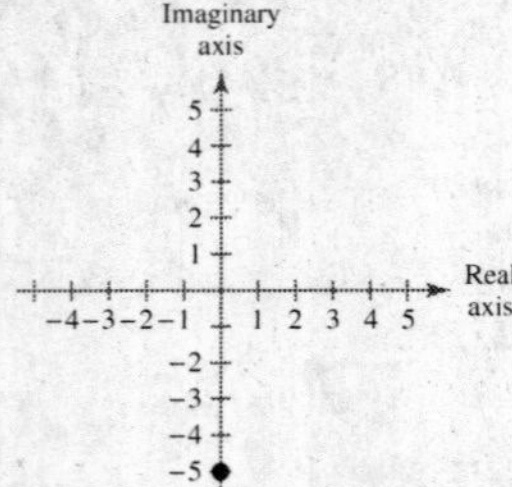

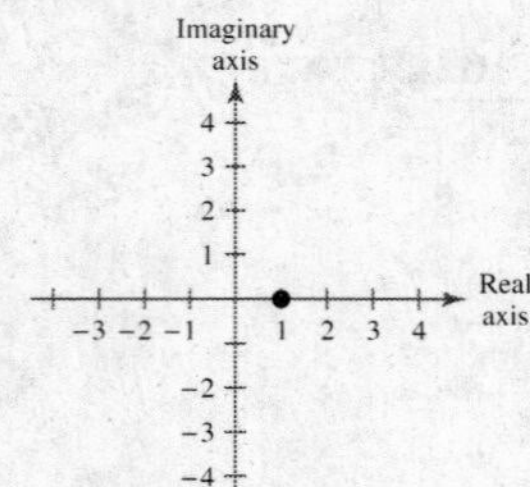

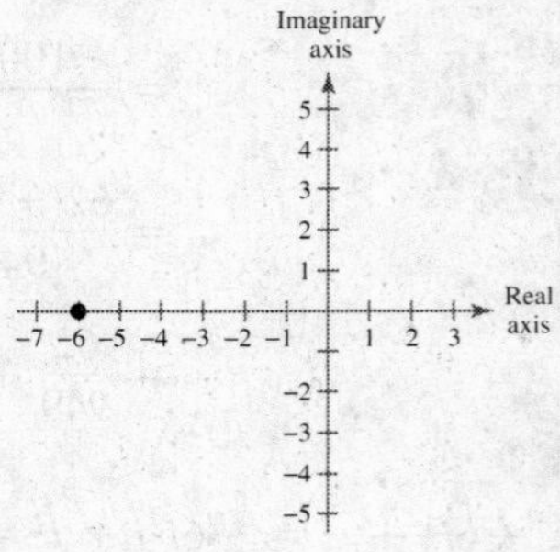

77. The complex number $\frac{1}{2}i$, is in the Mandelbrot Set since for $c = \frac{1}{2}i$, the corresponding Mandelbrot sequence is

$$\frac{1}{2}i,\ -\frac{1}{4}+\frac{1}{2}i,\ -\frac{3}{16}+\frac{1}{4}i,\ -\frac{7}{256}+\frac{13}{32}i,\ -\frac{10{,}767}{65{,}536}+\frac{1957}{4096}i,\ -\frac{864{,}513{,}055}{4{,}294{,}967{,}296}+\frac{46{,}037{,}845}{134{,}217{,}728}i$$

which is bounded. Or in decimal form

$0.5i,\ -0.25 + 0.5i,\ -0.1875 + 0.25i,\ -0.02734 + 0.40625i,\ -0.164291 + 0.477783i,\ -0.201285 + 0.343009i.$

78. 2

$2^2 + 2 = 6$

$6^2 + 2 = 38$

$38^2 + 2 = 1446$

$1446^2 + 2 = 2{,}090{,}918$

4.4×10^{12}

Not bounded. $c = 2$ is not in the Mandelbrot Set.

79. $z_1 = 5 + 2i$

$z_2 = 3 - 4i$

$$\frac{1}{z} = \frac{1}{z_1} + \frac{1}{z_2} = \frac{1}{5 + 2i} + \frac{1}{3 - 4i}$$

$$= \frac{(3 - 4i) + (5 + 2i)}{(5 + 2i)(3 - 4i)}$$

$$= \frac{8 - 2i}{23 - 14i}$$

$$z = \frac{23 - 14i}{8 - 2i}\left(\frac{8 + 2i}{8 + 2i}\right)$$

$$= \frac{212 - 66i}{68} \approx 3.118 - 0.971i$$

80. $z_1 = 16i + 9$

$z_2 = 20 - 10i$

$$\frac{1}{z} = \frac{1}{z_1} + \frac{1}{z_2} = \frac{1}{9 + 16i} + \frac{1}{20 - 10i}$$

$$= \frac{(20 - 10i) + (9 + 16i)}{(9 + 16i)(20 - 10i)}$$

$$= \frac{29 + 6i}{340 + 230i}$$

$$z = \frac{340 + 230i}{29 + 6i}\left(\frac{29 - 6i}{29 - 6i}\right) = \frac{11240 + 4630i}{877} \approx 12.816 + 5.279i$$

81. False. A real number $a + 0i = a$ is equal to its conjugate.

82. False. $i^{44} + i^{150} - i^{74} - i^{109} + i^{61} = 1 - 1 + 1 - i + i = 1$

83. False. For example, $(1 + 2i) + (1 - 2i) = 2$, which is not an imaginary number.

84. False. For example, $(i)(i) = -1$, which is not an imaginary number.

85. True. Let $z_1 = a_1 + b_1 i$ and $z_2 = a_2 + b_2 i$. Then

$$\overline{z_1 z_2} = \overline{(a_1 + b_1 i)(a_2 + b_2 i)}$$

$$= \overline{(a_1 a_2 - b_1 b_2) + (a_1 b_2 + b_1 a_2)i}$$

$$= (a_1 a_2 - b_1 b_2) - (a_1 b_2 + b_1 a_2)i$$

$$= (a_1 - b_1 i)(a_2 - b_2 i)$$

$$= \overline{a_1 + b_1 i}\ \overline{a_2 + b_2 i}$$

$$= \overline{z_1}\ \overline{z_2}.$$

86. True. Let $z_1 = a_1 + b_1 i$ and $z_2 = a_2 + b_2 i$. Then

$$\overline{z_1 + z_2} = \overline{(a_1 + b_1 i) + (a_2 + b_2 i)}$$

$$= \overline{(a_1 + a_2) + (b_1 + b_2)i}$$

$$= (a_1 + a_2) - (b_1 + b_2)i$$

$$= (a_1 - b_1 i) + (a_2 - b_2 i)$$

$$= \overline{a_1 + b_1 i} + \overline{a_2 + b_2 i}$$

$$= \overline{z_1} + \overline{z_2}.$$

87. $(4x - 5)(4x + 5) = 16x^2 - 20x + 20x - 25$
$= 16x^2 - 25$

88. $(x + 2)^3 = x^3 + 3x^2 2 + 3x(2)^2 + 2^3$
$= x^3 + 6x^2 + 12x + 8$

89. $\left(3x - \frac{1}{2}\right)(x + 4) = 3x^2 - \frac{1}{2}x + 12x - 2$
$= 3x^2 + \frac{23}{2}x - 2$

90. $(2x - 5)^2 = 4x^2 - 20x + 25$

Section 2.5 The Fundamental Theorem of Algebra

- You should know that if f is a polynomial of degree $n > 0$, then f has at least one zero in the complex number system. (Fundamental Theorem of Algebra)
- You should know that if $a + bi$ is a complex zero of a polynomial f, with real coefficients, then $a - bi$ is also a complex zero of f.
- You should know the difference between a factor that is irreducible over the rationals (such as $x^2 - 7$) and a factor that is irreducible over the reals (such as $x^2 + 9$).

Vocabulary Check

1. Fundamental Theorem, Algebra
2. Linear Factorization Theorem
3. irreducible, reals
4. complex conjugate

1. $f(x) = x^2(x + 3)$

The three zeros are $x = 0$, $x = 0$ and $x = -3$.

2. $g(x) = (x - 2)(x + 4)^3$

Zeros: $2, -4, -4, -4$

3. $f(x) = (x + 9)(x + 4i)(x - 4i)$

Zeros: $-9, \pm 4i$

4. $h(t) = (t - 3)(t - 2)(t - 3i)(t + 3i)$

The four zeros are $t = 3, 2, 3i, -3i$.

5. $f(x) = x^3 - 4x^2 + x - 4 = x^2(x - 4) + 1(x - 4) = (x - 4)(x^2 + 1)$

Zeros: $4, \pm i$

The only real zero of $f(x)$ is $x = 4$. This corresponds to the x-intercept of $(4, 0)$ on the graph.

6. $f(x) = x^3 - 4x^2 - 4x + 16$
$= x^2(x - 4) - 4(x - 4)$
$= (x^2 - 4)(x - 4)$
$= (x + 2)(x - 2)(x - 4)$

The zeros are $x = 2, -2$, and 4. This corresponds to the x-intercepts of $(-2, 0)$, $(2, 0)$, and $(4, 0)$ on the graph.

7. $f(x) = x^4 + 4x^2 + 4 = (x^2 + 2)^2$

Zeros: $\pm\sqrt{2}i, \pm\sqrt{2}i$

$f(x)$ has no real zeros and the graph of $f(x)$ has no x-intercepts.

8. $f(x) = x^4 - 3x^2 - 4$
$= (x^2 - 4)(x^2 + 1)$
$= (x + 2)(x - 2)(x^2 + 1)$

Zeros: $\pm 2, \pm i$

The only real zeros are $x = -2, 2$. This corresponds to the x-intercepts of $(-2, 0)$ and $(2, 0)$ on the graph.

9. $h(x) = x^2 - 4x + 1$

h has no rational zeros. By the Quadratic Formula, the zeros are

$$x = \frac{4 \pm \sqrt{16 - 4}}{2} = 2 \pm \sqrt{3}.$$

$$h(x) = \left[x - \left(2 + \sqrt{3}\right)\right]\left[x - \left(2 - \sqrt{3}\right)\right]$$
$$= \left(x - 2 - \sqrt{3}\right)\left(x - 2 + \sqrt{3}\right)$$

10. $g(x) = x^2 + 10x + 23$

Zeros: $x = \dfrac{-10 \pm \sqrt{8}}{2} = -5 \pm \sqrt{2}$

$$g(x) = \left(x + 5 + \sqrt{2}\right)\left(x + 5 - \sqrt{2}\right)$$

11. $f(x) = x^2 - 12x + 26$

f has no rational zeros. By the Quadratic Formula, the zeros are

$$x = \frac{12 \pm \sqrt{(-12)^2 - 4(26)}}{2} = 6 \pm \sqrt{10}.$$

$$f(x) = \left[x - \left(6 + \sqrt{10}\right)\right]\left[x - \left(6 - \sqrt{10}\right)\right]$$
$$= \left(x - 6 - \sqrt{10}\right)\left(x - 6 + \sqrt{10}\right)$$

12. $f(x) = x^2 + 6x - 2$

f has no rational zeros. By the Quadratic Formula, the zeros are

$$x = \frac{-6 \pm \sqrt{6^2 - 4(-2)}}{2} = -3 \pm \sqrt{11}.$$

$$f(x) = \left(x - \left(-3 + \sqrt{11}\right)\right)\left(x - \left(-3 - \sqrt{11}\right)\right)$$
$$= \left(x + 3 - \sqrt{11}\right)\left(x + 3 + \sqrt{11}\right)$$

13. $f(x) = x^2 + 25$
$= (x + 5i)(x - 5i)$

The zeros of $f(x)$ are $x = \pm 5i$.

14. $f(x) = x^2 + 36$

Zeros: $\pm 6i$

$f(x) = (x + 6i)(x - 6i)$

15. $f(x) = 16x^4 - 81$
$= (4x^2 - 9)(4x^2 + 9)$
$= (2x - 3)(2x + 3)(2x + 3i)(2x - 3i)$

Zeros: $\pm\frac{3}{2}, \pm\frac{3}{2}i$

16. $f(y) = 81y^4 - 625$
$= (9y^2 + 25)(9y^2 - 25)$
$= (3y + 5i)(3y - 5i)(3y + 5)(3y - 5)$

Zeros: $\pm\frac{5}{3}, \pm\frac{5}{3}i$

17. $f(z) = z^2 - z + 56$

$$z = \frac{1 \pm \sqrt{1 - 4(56)}}{2}$$
$$= \frac{1 \pm \sqrt{-223}}{2}$$
$$= \frac{1}{2} \pm \frac{\sqrt{223}}{2}i$$

$$f(z) = \left(z - \frac{1}{2} + \frac{\sqrt{223}i}{2}\right)\left(z - \frac{1}{2} - \frac{\sqrt{223}i}{2}\right)$$

18. $h(x) = x^2 - 4x - 3$

$$x = \frac{4 \pm \sqrt{16 + 12}}{2} = 2 \pm \sqrt{7}$$

Zeros: $2 \pm \sqrt{7}$

$$h(x) = \left(x - 2 + \sqrt{7}\right)\left(x - 2 - \sqrt{7}\right)$$

19. $f(x) = x^4 + 10x^2 + 9$

$= (x^2 + 1)(x^2 + 9)$

$= (x + i)(x - i)(x + 3i)(x - 3i)$

The zeros of $f(x)$ are $x = \pm i$ and $x = \pm 3i$.

20. $f(x) = x^4 + 29x^2 + 100$

$= (x^2 + 25)(x^2 + 4)$

Zeros: $x = \pm 2i, \pm 5i$

$f(x) = (x + 2i)(x - 2i)(x + 5i)(x - 5i)$

21. $f(x) = 3x^3 - 5x^2 + 48x - 80$

Using synthetic division, $\frac{5}{3}$ is a zero:

$$\begin{array}{r|rrrr} \frac{5}{3} & 3 & -5 & 48 & -80 \\ & & 5 & 0 & 80 \\ \hline & 3 & 0 & 48 & 0 \end{array}$$

$f(x) = \left(x - \frac{5}{3}\right)(3x^2 + 48)$

$= (3x - 5)(x^2 + 16)$

$= (3x - 5)(x + 4i)(x - 4i)$

The zeros are $\frac{5}{3}, 4i, -4i$.

22. $f(x) = 3x^3 - 2x^2 + 75x - 50$

Using synthetic division, $\frac{2}{3}$ is a zero:

$$\begin{array}{r|rrrr} \frac{2}{3} & 3 & -2 & 75 & -50 \\ & & 2 & 0 & 50 \\ \hline & 3 & 0 & 75 & 0 \end{array}$$

$f(x) = \left(x - \frac{2}{3}\right)(3x^3 + 75)$

$= (3x - 2)(x^2 + 25)$

$= (3x - 2)(x + 5i)(x - 5i)$

The zeros are $\frac{2}{3}, 5i, -5i$.

23. $f(t) = t^3 - 3t^2 - 15t + 125$

Possible rational zeros: $\pm 1, \pm 5, \pm 25, \pm 125$

$$\begin{array}{r|rrrr} -5 & 1 & -3 & -15 & 125 \\ & & -5 & 40 & -125 \\ \hline & 1 & -8 & 25 & 0 \end{array}$$

By the Quadratic Formula, the zeros of $t^2 - 8t + 25$ are

$$t = \frac{8 \pm \sqrt{64 - 100}}{2} = 4 \pm 3i.$$

The zeros of $f(t)$ are $t = -5$ and $t = 4 \pm 3i$.

$f(t) = [t - (-5)][t - (4 + 3i)][t - (4 - 3i)]$

$= (t + 5)(t - 4 - 3i)(t - 4 + 3i)$

24. $f(x) = x^3 + 11x^2 + 39x + 29$

$$\begin{array}{r|rrrr} -1 & 1 & 11 & 39 & 29 \\ & & -1 & -10 & -29 \\ \hline & 1 & 10 & 29 & 0 \end{array}$$

Zeros: $x = -1, \dfrac{-10 \pm \sqrt{16}i}{2} = -5 \pm 2i$

$f(x) = (x + 1)(x + 5 + 2i)(x + 5 - 2i)$

25. $f(x) = 5x^3 - 9x^2 + 28x + 6$

Possible rational zeros: $\pm 6, \pm \frac{6}{5}, \pm 3, \pm \frac{3}{5}, \pm 2, \pm \frac{2}{5}, \pm 1, \pm \frac{1}{5}$

$$\begin{array}{r|rrrr} -\frac{1}{5} & 5 & -9 & 28 & 6 \\ & & -1 & 2 & -6 \\ \hline & 5 & -10 & 30 & 0 \end{array}$$

By the Quadratic Formula, the zeros of $5x^2 - 10x + 30$ are those of $x^2 - 2x + 6$:

$$x = \frac{2 \pm \sqrt{4 - 4(6)}}{2} = 1 \pm \sqrt{5}i$$

Zeros: $-\frac{1}{5}, 1 \pm \sqrt{5}i$

$f(x) = 5\left(x + \frac{1}{5}\right)\left(x - \left(1 + \sqrt{5}i\right)\right)\left(x - \left(1 - \sqrt{5}i\right)\right) = (5x + 1)\left(x - 1 - \sqrt{5}i\right)\left(x - 1 + \sqrt{5}i\right)$

26. $f(s) = 3s^3 - 4s^2 + 8s + 8$

$= (3s + 2)(s^2 - 2s + 4)$

Factoring the quadratic,

$$s = \frac{2 \pm \sqrt{4 - 16}}{2} = 1 \pm \sqrt{3}i.$$

Zeros: $-\frac{2}{3}, 1 \pm \sqrt{3}i$

$f(s) = (3s + 2)(s - 1 + \sqrt{3}i)(s - 1 - \sqrt{3}i)$

27. $g(x) = x^4 - 4x^3 + 8x^2 - 16x + 16$

Possible rational zeros: $\pm 1, \pm 2, \pm 4, \pm 8, \pm 16$

$$\begin{array}{r|rrrrr} 2 & 1 & -4 & 8 & -16 & 16 \\ & & 2 & -4 & 8 & -16 \\ \hline 2 & 1 & -2 & 4 & -8 & 0 \\ & & 2 & 0 & 8 & \\ \hline & 1 & 0 & 4 & 0 & \end{array}$$

$g(x) = (x - 2)(x - 2)(x^2 + 4)$

$= (x - 2)^2(x + 2i)(x - 2i)$

The zeros of g are 2, 2, and $\pm 2i$.

28. $h(x) = x^4 + 6x^3 + 10x^2 + 6x + 9$

$$\begin{array}{r|rrrrr} -3 & 1 & 6 & 10 & 6 & 9 \\ & & -3 & -9 & -3 & -9 \\ \hline -3 & 1 & 3 & 1 & 3 & 0 \\ & & -3 & 0 & -3 & \\ \hline & 1 & 0 & 1 & 0 & \end{array}$$

Zeros: $x = -3, \pm i$

$h(x) = (x + 3)^2(x + i)(x - i)$

29. (a) $f(x) = x^2 - 14x + 46$.

By the Quadratic Formula,

$$x = \frac{14 \pm \sqrt{(-14)^2 - 4(46)}}{2} = 7 \pm \sqrt{3}.$$

The zeros are $7 + \sqrt{3}$ and $7 - \sqrt{3}$.

(b) $f(x) = [x - (7 + \sqrt{3})][x - (7 - \sqrt{3})]$

$= (x - 7 - \sqrt{3})(x - 7 + \sqrt{3})$

(c) x-intercepts: $(7 + \sqrt{3}, 0)$ and $(7 - \sqrt{3}, 0)$

(d)

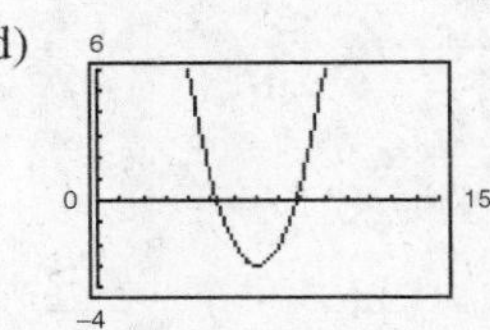

30. (a) $f(x) = x^2 - 12x + 34$

By the Quadratic Formula,

$$x = \frac{12 \pm \sqrt{(-12)^2 - 4(34)}}{2} = 6 \pm \sqrt{2}.$$

The zeros are $6 + \sqrt{2}$ and $6 - \sqrt{2}$.

(b) $f(x) = (x - (6 + \sqrt{2}))(x - (6 - \sqrt{2}))$

$= (x - 6 - \sqrt{2})(x - 6 + \sqrt{2})$

(c) x-intercepts: $(6 + \sqrt{2}, 0)(6 - \sqrt{2}, 0)$

(d)

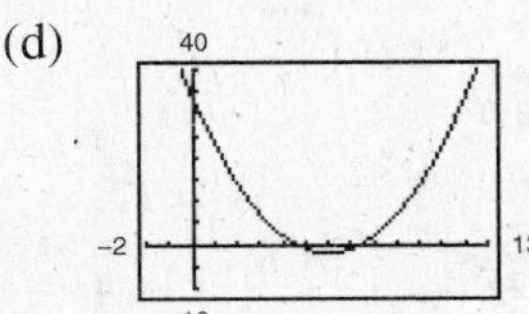

31. (a) $f(x) = 2x^3 - 3x^2 + 8x - 12$

$= (2x - 3)(x^2 + 4)$

The zeros are $\frac{3}{2}, \pm 2i$.

(b) $f(x) = (2x - 3)(x + 2i)(x - 2i)$

(c) x-intercept: $\left(\frac{3}{2}, 0\right)$

(d)

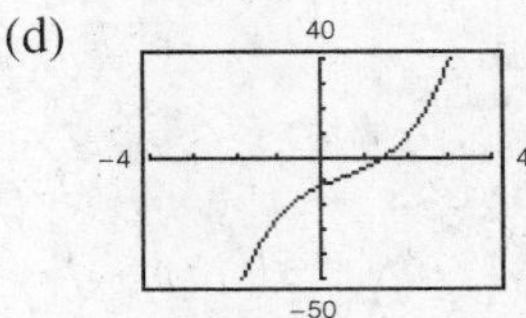

32. (a) $f(x) = 2x^3 - 5x^2 + 18x - 45$

$= (2x - 5)(x^2 + 9)$

The zeros are $\frac{5}{2}, \pm 3i$.

(b) $f(x) = (2x - 5)(x + 3i)(x - 3i)$

(c) x-intercept: $\left(\frac{5}{2}, 0\right)$

(d)

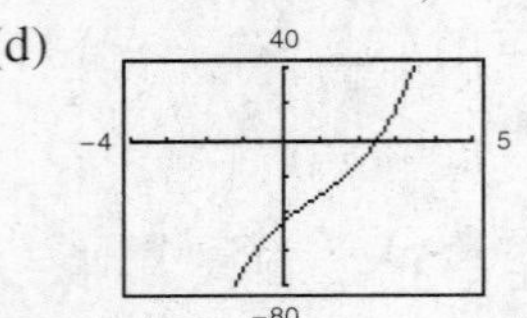

33. (a) $f(x) = x^3 - 11x + 150$

$= (x + 6)(x^2 - 6x + 25)$

Use the Quadratic Formula to find the zeros of $x^2 - 6x + 25$.

$$x = \frac{6 \pm \sqrt{(-6)^2 - 4(25)}}{2} = 3 \pm 4i.$$

The zeros are -6, $3 + 4i$, and $3 - 4i$.

(b) $f(x) = (x + 6)(x - 3 + 4i)(x - 3 - 4i)$

(c) x-intercept: $(-6, 0)$

(d)

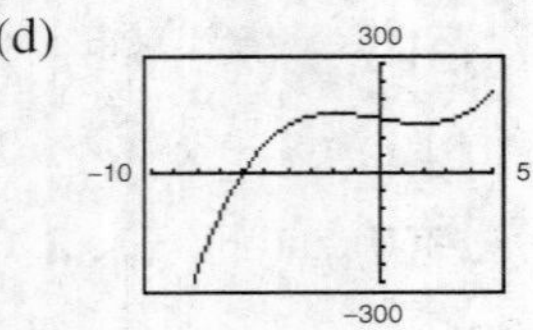

34. (a) $f(x) = x^3 + 10x^2 + 33x + 34$

$= (x + 2)(x^2 + 8x + 17)$

Use the Quadratic Formula to find the zeros of $x^2 + 8x + 17$.

$$x = \frac{-8 \pm \sqrt{8^2 - 4(17)}}{2}$$

$$= \frac{-8 \pm \sqrt{-4}}{2} = -4 + i$$

The zeros are -2, $-4 + i$, and $-4 - i$.

(b) $f(x) = (x + 2)(x + 4 + i)(x + 4 - i)$

(c) x-intercept: $(-2, 0)$

(d)

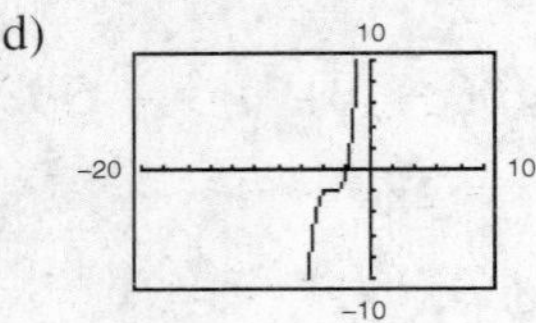

35. (a) $f(x) = x^4 + 25x^2 + 144$

$= (x^2 + 9)(x^2 + 16)$

The zeros are $\pm 3i, \pm 4i$.

(b) $f(x) = (x^2 + 9)(x^2 + 16)$

$= (x + 3i)(x - 3i)(x + 4i)(x - 4i)$

(c) No x-intercepts

(d)

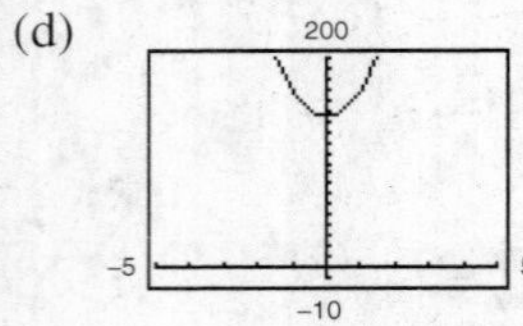

36. (a) $f(x) = x^4 - 8x^3 + 17x^2 - 8x + 16$

$= (x^2 + 1)(x^2 - 8x + 16)$

$= (x^2 + 1)(x - 4)^2$

The zeros are $i, -i$, 4 and 4.

(b) $f(x) = (x^2 + 1)(x - 4)^2$

(c) x-intercept: $(4, 0)$

(d)

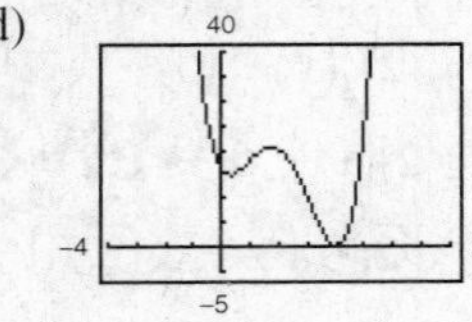

37. $f(x) = (x - 2)(x - i)(x + i)$

$= (x - 2)(x^2 + 1)$

$= (x^3 - 2x^2 + x - 2)$

Note that $f(x) = a(x^3 - 2x^2 + x - 2)$, where a is any nonzero real number, has zeros $2, \pm i$.

38. $f(x) = (x - 3)(x - 4i)(x + 4i)$

$= (x - 3)(x^2 + 16)$

$= x^3 - 3x^2 + 16x - 48$

Note that $f(x) = a(x^3 - 3x^2 + 16x - 48)$, where a is any nonzero real number, has zeros $3, \pm 4i$.

39. $f(x) = (x - 2)^2(x - 4 - i)(x - 4 + i)$

$= (x - 2)^2(x - 8x + 16 + 1)$

$= (x^2 - 4x + 4)(x^2 - 8x + 17)$

$= x^4 - 12x^3 + 53x^2 - 100x + 68$

Note that $f(x) = a(x^4 - 12x^3 + 53x^2 - 100x + 68)$, where a is any nonzero real number, has zeros 2, 2, $4 \pm i$.

40. Because $2 + 5i$ is a zero, so is $2 - 5i$.

$f(x) = (x + 1)^2(x - 2 - 5i)(x - 2 + 5i)$

$= (x + 1)^2(x^2 - 4x + 4 + 25)$

$= (x^2 + 2x + 1)(x^2 - 4x + 29)$

$= x^4 - 2x^3 + 22x^2 + 54x + 29$

Note that $f(x) = a(x^4 - 2x^3 + 22x^2 + 54x + 29)$, where a is any nonzero real number, has zeros -1, -1, $2 \pm 5i$.

41. Because $1 + \sqrt{2}i$ is a zero, so is $1 - \sqrt{2}i$.

$f(x) = (x - 0)(x + 5)(x - 1 - \sqrt{2}i)(x - 1 + \sqrt{2}i)$

$= (x^2 + 5x)(x^2 - 2x + 1 + 2)$

$= (x^2 + 5x)(x^2 - 2x + 3)$

$= x^4 + 3x^3 - 7x^2 + 15x$

Note that $f(x) = a(x^4 + 3x^3 - 7x^2 + 15x)$, where a is any nonzero real number, has zeros 0, -5, $1 \pm \sqrt{2}i$.

42. Because $1 + \sqrt{2}i$ is a zero, so is $1 \pm \sqrt{2}i$.

$f(x) = (x - 0)(x - 4)(x - 1 - \sqrt{2}i)(x - 1 + \sqrt{2}i)$

$= (x^2 - 4x)(x^2 - 2x + 1 + 2)$

$= x^4 - 6x^3 + 11x^2 - 12x$

Note that $f(x) = a(x^4 - 6x^3 + 11x^2 - 12x)$, where a is any nonzero real number, has zeros 0, 4, $1 \pm \sqrt{2}i$.

43. (a) $f(x) = a(x - 1)(x + 2)(x - 2i)(x + 2i)$

$= a(x - 1)(x + 2)(x^2 + 4)$

$f(-1) = 10 = a(-2)(1)(5) \Rightarrow a = -1$

$f(x) = -(x - 1)(x + 2)(x - 2i)(x + 2i)$

(b) $f(x) = -(x - 1)(x + 2)(x^2 + 4)$

$= -(x^2 + x - 2)(x^2 + 4)$

$= -x^4 - x^3 - 2x^2 - 4x + 8$

44. (a) $f(x) = a(x + 1)(- 2)(x - i)(x + i)$

$= a(x + 1)(x - 2)(x^2 + 1)$

$f(1) = 8 = a(2)(-1)(2) \Rightarrow a = -2$

$f(x) = -2(x + 1)(x - 2)(x - i)(x + i)$

(b) $f(x) = -2(x^2 - x - 2)(x^2 + 1)$

$= -2x^4 + 2x^3 + 2x^2 + 2x + 4$

45. (a) $f(x) = a(x + 1)(x - 2 - \sqrt{5}i)(x - 2 + \sqrt{5}i)$

$= a(x + 1)(x^2 - 4x + 4 + 5)$

$= a(x + 1)(x^2 - 4x + 9)$

$f(-2) = 42 = a(-1)(4 + 8 + 9) \Rightarrow a = -2$

$f(x) = -2(x + 1)(x - 2 - \sqrt{5}i)(x - 2 + \sqrt{5}i)$

(b) $f(x) = -2(x + 1)(x^2 - 4x + 9)$

$= -2x^3 + 6x^2 - 10x - 18$

46. (a) $f(x) = a(x + 2)(x - 2 - 2\sqrt{2}i)(x - 2 + 2\sqrt{2}i)$

$= a(x + 2)(x^2 - 4x + 4 + 8)$

$= a(x + 2)(x^2 - 4x + 12)$

$f(-1) = -34 = a(1)(17) \Rightarrow a = -2$

$f(x) = -2(x + 2)(x - 2 - 2\sqrt{2}i)(x - 2 + 2\sqrt{2}i)$

(b) $f(x) = -2(x + 2)(x^2 - 4x + 12)$

$= -2x^3 + 4x^2 - 8x - 48$

47. $f(x) = x^4 - 6x^2 - 7$

(a) $f(x) = (x^2 - 7)(x^2 + 1)$

(b) $f(x) = (x - \sqrt{7})(x + \sqrt{7})(x^2 + 1)$

(c) $f(x) = (x - \sqrt{7})(x + \sqrt{7})(x + i)(x - i)$

48. $f(x) = x^4 + 6x^2 - 27$

(a) $f(x) = (x^2 + 9)(x^2 - 3)$

(b) $f(x) = (x^2 + 9)(x + \sqrt{3})(x - \sqrt{3})$

(c) $f(x) = (x + 3i)(x - 3i)(x + \sqrt{3})(x - \sqrt{3})$

49. $f(x) = x^4 - 2x^3 - 3x^2 + 12x - 18$

(a) $f(x) = (x^2 - 6)(x^2 - 2x + 3)$

(b) $f(x) = (x + \sqrt{6})(x - \sqrt{6})(x^2 - 2x + 3)$

(c) $f(x) = (x + \sqrt{6})(x - \sqrt{6})(x - 1 - \sqrt{2}i)(x - 1 + \sqrt{2}i)$

50. $f(x) = x^4 - 3x^3 - x^2 - 12x - 20$

(a) $f(x) = (x^2 + 4)(x^2 - 3x - 5)$

(b) $f(x) = (x^2 + 4)\left(x - \dfrac{3 + \sqrt{29}}{2}\right)\left(x - \dfrac{3 - \sqrt{29}}{2}\right)$

(c) $f(x) = (x + 2i)(x - 2i)\left(x - \dfrac{3 + \sqrt{29}}{2}\right)\left(x - \dfrac{3 - \sqrt{29}}{2}\right)$

51. $f(x) = 2x^3 + 3x^2 + 50x + 75$

Since $5i$ is a zero, so is $-5i$.

$$\begin{array}{r|rrrr} 5i & 2 & 3 & 50 & 75 \\ & & 10i & -50 + 15i & -75 \\ \hline & 2 & 3 + 10i & 15i & 0 \end{array}$$

$$\begin{array}{r|rrr} -5i & 2 & 3 + 10i & 15i \\ & & -10i & -15i \\ \hline & 2 & 3 & 0 \end{array}$$

The zero of $2x + 3$ is $x = -\frac{3}{2}$. The zeros of f are $x = -\frac{3}{2}$ and $x = \pm 5i$.

Alternate Solution

Since $x = \pm 5i$ are zeros of $f(x)$, $(x + 5i)(x - 5i) = x^2 + 25$ is a factor of $f(x)$. By long division we have:

$$\begin{array}{r} 2x + 3 \\ x^2 + 0x + 25 \overline{) 2x^3 + 3x^2 + 50x + 75} \\ \underline{2x^3 + 0x^2 + 50x} \\ 3x^2 + 0x + 75 \\ \underline{3x^2 + 0x + 75} \\ 0 \end{array}$$

Thus, $f(x) = (x^2 + 25)(2x + 3)$ and the zeros of f are $x = \pm 5i$ and $x = -\frac{3}{2}$.

52. $f(x) = x^3 + x^2 + 9x + 9$

Since $3i$ is a zero, so is $-3i$.

$$\begin{array}{r|rrrr} 3i & 1 & 1 & 9 & 9 \\ & & 3i & -9 + 3i & -9 \\ \hline & 1 & 1 + 3i & 3i & 0 \end{array}$$

$$\begin{array}{r|rrr} -3i & 1 & 1 + 3i & 3i \\ & & -3i & -3i \\ \hline & 1 & 1 & 0 \end{array}$$

The zeros of f are $3i$, $-3i$ and -1.

53. $g(x) = x^3 - 7x^2 - x + 87$. Since $5 + 2i$ is a zero, so is $5 - 2i$.

$$\begin{array}{r|rrrr} 5 + 2i & 1 & -7 & -1 & 87 \\ & & 5 + 2i & -14 + 6i & -87 \\ \hline & 1 & -2 + 2i & -15 + 6i & 0 \end{array}$$

$$\begin{array}{r|rrr} 5 - 2i & 1 & -2 + 2i & -15 + 6i \\ & & 5 - 2i & 15 - 6i \\ \hline & 1 & 3 & 0 \end{array}$$

The zero of $x + 3$ is $x = -3$.

The zeros of f are -3, $5 \pm 2i$.

54. $g(x) = 4x^3 + 23x^2 + 34x - 10$

Since $-3 + i$ is a zero, so is $-3 - i$.

$$\begin{array}{r|rrrr} -3+i & 4 & 23 & 34 & -10 \\ & & -12+4i & -37-i & 10 \\ \hline & 4 & 11+4i & -3-i & 0 \end{array}$$

$$\begin{array}{r|rrr} -3-i & 4 & 11+4i & -3-i \\ & & -12-4i & 3+i \\ \hline & 4 & -1 & 0 \end{array}$$

The zero of $4x - 1$ is $x = \frac{1}{4}$. The zeros of $g(x)$ are $x = -3 \pm i$ and $x = \frac{1}{4}$.

Alternate Solution

Since $-3 \pm i$ are zeros of $g(x)$,

$$\begin{aligned}[x - (-3 + i)][x - (-3 - i)] &= [(x - 3) - i][(x + 3) + i] \\ &= (x + 3)^2 - i^2 = x^2 + 6x + 10\end{aligned}$$

is a factor of $g(x)$. By long division we have:

$$\begin{array}{r} 4x - 1 \\ x^2 + 6x + 10 \overline{)\, 4x^3 + 23x^2 + 34x - 10} \\ \underline{4x^3 + 24x^2 + 40x} \\ -x^2 - 6x - 10 \\ \underline{-x^2 - 6x - 10} \\ 0 \end{array}$$

Thus, $g(x) = (x^2 + 6x + 10)(4x - 1)$ and the zeros of g are $x = -3 \pm i$ and $x = \frac{1}{4}$.

55. $h(x) = 3x^3 - 4x^2 + 8x + 8$. Since $1 - \sqrt{3}i$ is a zero, so is $1 + \sqrt{3}i$.

$$\begin{array}{r|rrrr} 1-\sqrt{3}i & 3 & -4 & 8 & 8 \\ & & 3-3\sqrt{3}i & -10-2\sqrt{3}i & -8 \\ \hline & 3 & -1-3\sqrt{3}i & -2-2\sqrt{3}i & 0 \end{array}$$

$$\begin{array}{r|rrr} 1+\sqrt{3}i & 3 & -1-3\sqrt{3}i & -2-2\sqrt{3}i \\ & & 3+3\sqrt{3}i & 2+2\sqrt{3}i \\ \hline & 3 & 2 & 0 \end{array}$$

The zero of $3x + 2$ is $x = -\frac{2}{3}$. The zeros of h are $x = -\frac{2}{3}, 1 \pm \sqrt{3}i$.

56. $f(x) = x^3 + 4x^2 + 14x + 20$

Since $-1 - 3i$ is a zero, so is $-1 + 3i$.

$$\begin{array}{r|rrrr} -1-3i & 1 & 4 & 14 & 20 \\ & & -1-3i & -12-6i & -20 \\ \hline & 1 & 3-3i & 2-6i & 0 \end{array}$$

$$\begin{array}{r|rrr} -1+3i & 1 & 3-3i & 2-6i \\ & & -1+3i & -2+6i \\ \hline & 1 & 2 & 0 \end{array}$$

The zero of $x + 2$ is $x = -2$. The zeros of f are $x = -2, -1 \pm 3i$.

57. $h(x) = 8x^3 - 14x^2 + 18x - 9$. Since $\frac{1}{2}(1 - \sqrt{5}i)$ is a zero, so is $\frac{1}{2}(1 + \sqrt{5}i)$.

$$\begin{array}{r|cccc} \frac{1}{2}(1-\sqrt{5}i) & 8 & -14 & 18 & -9 \\ & & 4-4\sqrt{5}i & -15+3\sqrt{5}i & 9 \\ \hline & 8 & -10-4\sqrt{5}i & 3+3\sqrt{5}i & 0 \end{array}$$

$$\begin{array}{r|ccc} \frac{1}{2}(1+\sqrt{5}i) & 8 & -10-4\sqrt{5}i & 3+3\sqrt{5}i \\ & & 4+4\sqrt{5}i & -3-3\sqrt{5}i \\ \hline & 8 & -6 & 0 \end{array}$$

The zero of $8x - 6$ is $x = \frac{3}{4}$. The zeros of h are $x = \frac{3}{4}, \frac{1}{2}(1 \pm \sqrt{5}i)$.

58. $f(x) = 25x^3 - 55x^2 - 54x - 18$

Since $\frac{1}{5}(-2 + \sqrt{2}i) = \frac{-2 + \sqrt{2}i}{5}$ is a zero, so is $\frac{-2 - \sqrt{2}i}{5}$.

$$\begin{array}{r|cccc} \frac{-2+\sqrt{2}i}{5} & 25 & -55 & -54 & -18 \\ & & -10+5\sqrt{2}i & 24-15\sqrt{2}i & 18 \\ \hline \frac{-2-\sqrt{2}i}{5} & 25 & -65+5\sqrt{2}i & -30-15\sqrt{2}i & 0 \\ & & -10-5\sqrt{2}i & 30+15\sqrt{2}i & \\ \hline & 25 & -75 & 0 & \end{array}$$

The zero of $25x - 75$ is $x = 3$. The zeros of f are $x = 3, \frac{-2 \pm \sqrt{2}i}{5}$.

59. $f(x) = x^4 + 3x^3 - 5x^2 - 21x + 22$

(a) The root feature yields the real roots 1 and 2, and the complex roots $-3 \pm 1.414i$.

(b) By synthetic division:

$$\begin{array}{r|rrrrr} 1 & 1 & 3 & -5 & -21 & 22 \\ & & 1 & 4 & -1 & -22 \\ \hline & 1 & 4 & -1 & -22 & 0 \end{array}$$

$$\begin{array}{r|rrrr} 2 & 1 & 4 & -1 & -22 \\ & & 2 & 12 & 22 \\ \hline & 1 & 6 & 11 & 0 \end{array}$$

The complex roots of $x^2 + 6x + 11$ are $x = \frac{-6 \pm \sqrt{6^2 - 4(11)}}{2} = -3 \pm \sqrt{2}i$.

60. $f(x) = x^3 + 4x^2 + 14x + 20$

(a) Zeros: $-2, -1 \pm 3i$

(b) $x = -2$

$$\begin{array}{r|rrrr} -2 & 1 & 4 & 14 & 20 \\ & & -2 & -4 & -20 \\ \hline & 1 & 2 & 10 & 0 \end{array}$$

$x^2 + 2x + 10$ has zeros $-1 \pm 3i$.

61. $h(x) = 8x^3 - 14x^2 + 18x - 9$

(a) The root feature yields the real root 0.75, and the complex roots $0.5 \pm 1.118i$.

(b) By synthetic division:

$$\begin{array}{r|rrrr} \frac{3}{4} & 8 & -14 & 18 & -9 \\ & & 6 & -6 & 9 \\ \hline & 8 & -8 & 12 & 0 \end{array}$$

The complex roots of $8x^2 - 8x + 12$ are

$$x = \frac{8 \pm \sqrt{64 - 4(8)(12)}}{2(8)} = \frac{1}{2} \pm \frac{\sqrt{5}}{2}i.$$

62. $f(x) = 25x^3 - 55x^2 - 54x - 18$

(a) Zeros: $3, -0.4 \pm 0.2828i$

(b)
$$\begin{array}{r|rrrr} 3 & 25 & -55 & -54 & -18 \\ & & 75 & 60 & 18 \\ \hline & 25 & 20 & 6 & 0 \end{array}$$

$25x^2 + 20x + 6$ has zeros $\dfrac{-2 \pm \sqrt{2}i}{5}$.

63. $-16t^2 + 48t = 64, \quad 0 \le t \le 3$

$-16t^2 + 48t - 64 = 0$

$$t = \frac{-48 \pm \sqrt{1792}i}{-32}$$

Since the roots are imaginary, the ball never will reach a height of 64 feet. You can verify this graphically by observing that $y_1 = -16t^2 + 48t$ and $y_2 = 64$ do not intersect.

64. No. Setting $P = R - C = xp - C = x(140 - 0.0001x) - (80x + 150{,}000) = 9{,}000{,}000$ yields a quadratic with no real roots.

$-0.0001x^2 + 60x - 9{,}150{,}000 = 0$

65. False, a third degree polynomial must have at least one real zero.

66. True. The complex conjugate of the zero $4 + 3i$ is also a zero.

67. $f(x) = x^4 - 4x^2 + k$

(a) f has two real zeros each of multiplicity 2 for $k = 4$: $f(x) = x^4 - 4x^2 + 4 = (x^2 - 2)^2$.

(b) f has two real zeros and two complex zeros if $k < 0$.

68. Answers will vary.

69. $f(x) = x^2 - 7x - 8 = \left(x^2 - 7x + \frac{49}{4}\right) - 8 - \frac{49}{4}$

$= \left(x - \frac{7}{2}\right)^2 - \frac{81}{4}$

Vertex: $\left(\frac{7}{2}, -\frac{81}{4}\right)$

$f(x) = (x - 8)(x + 1)$

Intercepts: $(8, 0), (-1, 0), (0, -8)$

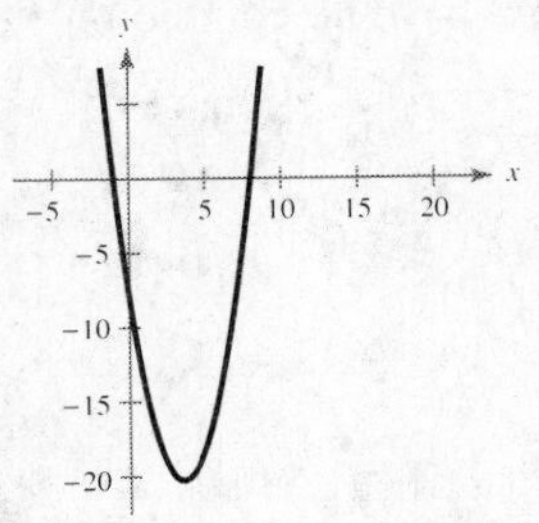

70. $f(x) = -x^2 + x + 6$

$= -\left(x^2 - x + \frac{1}{4}\right) + 6 + \frac{1}{4}$

$= -\left(x - \frac{1}{2}\right)^2 + \frac{25}{4}$

Vertex: $\left(\frac{1}{2}, \frac{25}{4}\right)$

$f(x) = -(x^2 - x - 6) = -(x - 3)(x + 2)$

Intercepts: $(3, 0), (-2, 0), (0, 6)$

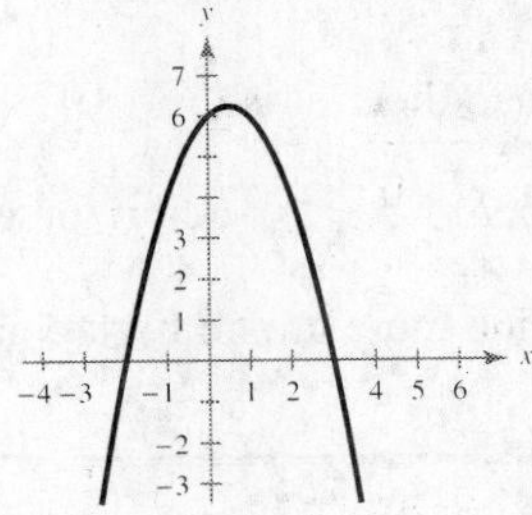

71. $f(x) = 6x^2 + 5x - 6 = (3x - 2)(2x + 3)$

Intercepts: $\left(\frac{2}{3}, 0\right), \left(-\frac{3}{2}, 0\right), (0, -6)$

$f(x) = 6x^2 + 5x - 6$

$= 6\left(x^2 + \frac{5}{6}x + \frac{25}{144}\right) - 6 - \frac{25}{24}$

$= 6\left(x + \frac{5}{12}\right)^2 - \frac{169}{24}$

Vertex: $\left(-\frac{5}{12}, -\frac{169}{24}\right)$

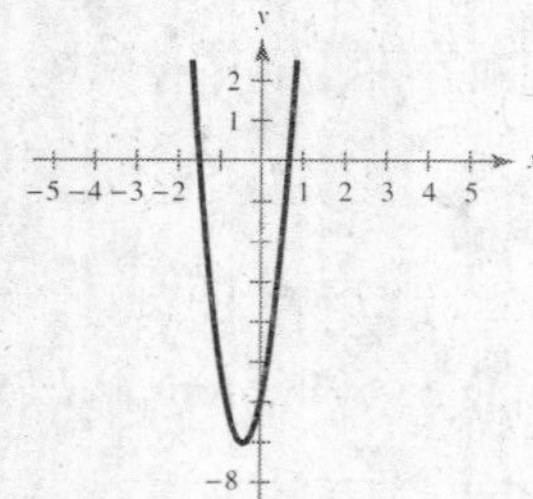

72. $f(x) = 4x^2 + 2x - 12$

$= 4\left(x^2 + \frac{1}{2}x + \frac{1}{16}\right) - 12 - \frac{1}{4}$

$= 4\left(x + \frac{1}{4}\right)^2 - \frac{49}{4}$

Vertex: $\left(-\frac{1}{4}, -\frac{49}{4}\right)$

$f(x) = (2x - 3)(2x + 4)$

Intercepts: $\left(\frac{3}{2}, 0\right), (-2, 0), (0, -12)$

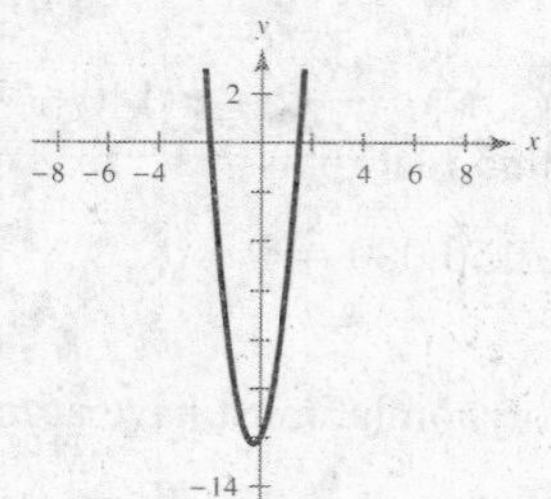

Section 2.6 Rational Functions and Asymptotes

- You should know the following basic facts about rational functions.
  (a) A function of the form $f(x) = P(x)/Q(x)$, $Q(x) \neq 0$, where $P(x)$ and $Q(x)$ are polynomials, is called a rational function.
  (b) The domain of a rational function is the set of all real numbers except those which make the denominator zero.
  (c) If $f(x) = P(x)/Q(x)$ is in reduced form, and a is a value such that $Q(a) = 0$, then the line $x = a$ is a vertical asymptote of the graph of f. $f(x) \to \infty$ or $f(x) \to -\infty$ as $x \to a$.
  (d) The line $y = b$ is a horizontal asymptote of the graph of f if $f(x) \longrightarrow b$ as $x \longrightarrow \infty$ or $x \longrightarrow -\infty$.
  (e) Let $f(x) = \dfrac{P(x)}{Q(x)} = \dfrac{a_nx^n + a_{n-1}x^{n-1} + \cdots + a_1x + a_0}{b_mx^m + b_{m-1}x^{m-1} + \cdots + b_1x + b_0}$ where $P(x)$ and $Q(x)$ have no common factors.
  1. If $n < m$, then the x-axis $(y = 0)$ is a horizontal asymptote.
  2. If $n = m$, then $y = \dfrac{a_n}{b_m}$ is a horizontal asymptote.
  3. If $n > m$, then there are no horizontal asymptotes.

Vocabulary Check

1. rational functions **2.** vertical asymptote **3.** horizontal asymptote

1. $f(x) = \dfrac{1}{x - 1}$

(a) Domain: all $x \neq 1$

(b)

x	$f(x)$
0.5	−2
0.9	−10
0.99	−100
0.999	−1000

x	$f(x)$
1.5	2
1.1	10
1.01	100
1.001	1000

x	$f(x)$
5	0.25
10	$0.\overline{1}$
100	$0.\overline{01}$
1000	$0.\overline{001}$

x	$f(x)$
−5	$-0.\overline{16}$
−10	$-0.\overline{09}$
−100	$-0.\overline{0099}$
−1000	$-0.\overline{00099}$

(c) f approaches $-\infty$ from the left of 1 and ∞ from the right of 1.

2. $f(x) = \dfrac{5x}{x - 1}$

(a) Domain: all $x \neq 1$

(b)

x	$f(x)$
0.5	−5
0.9	−45
0.99	−495
0.999	−4995

x	$f(x)$
1.5	15
1.1	55
1.01	505
1.001	5005

x	$f(x)$
5	6.25
10	$5.\overline{55}$
100	$5.\overline{05}$
1000	$5.\overline{005}$

x	$f(x)$
−5	$4.\overline{16}$
−10	$4.\overline{54}$
−100	$4.95\overline{0495}$
−1000	4.995

(c) f approaches $-\infty$ from the left of 1 and ∞ from the right of 1.

3. $f(x) = \dfrac{3x}{|x - 1|}$

(a) Domain: all $x \neq 1$

(b)

x	$f(x)$
0.5	3
0.9	27
0.99	297
0.999	2997

x	$f(x)$
1.5	9
1.1	33
1.01	303
1.001	3003

x	$f(x)$
5	3.75
10	$3.\overline{33}$
100	$3.\overline{03}$
1000	$3.\overline{003}$

x	$f(x)$
−5	−2.5
−10	−2.727
−100	−2.970
−1000	−2.997

(c) f approaches ∞ from both the left and the right of 1.

4. $f(x) = \dfrac{3}{|x - 1|}$

(a) Domain: all $x \neq 1$

(b)

x	$f(x)$
0.5	6
0.9	30
0.99	300
0.999	3000

x	$f(x)$
1.5	6
1.1	30
1.01	300
1.001	3000

x	$f(x)$
5	0.75
10	$0.\overline{33}$
100	$0.\overline{03}$
1000	$0.\overline{003}$

x	$f(x)$
−5	0.5
−10	$0.\overline{27}$
−100	0.0297
−1000	0.003

(c) f approaches ∞ from both the left and the right of 1.

5. $f(x) = \dfrac{3x^2}{x^2 - 1}$

(a) Domain: all $x \neq \pm 1$

(b)

x	$f(x)$
0.5	-1
0.9	-12.79
0.99	-147.8
0.999	-1498

x	$f(x)$
1.5	5.4
1.1	17.29
1.01	152.3
1.001	1502.3

x	$f(x)$
5	3.125
10	$3.\overline{03}$
100	$3.\overline{0003}$
1000	3

x	$f(x)$
-5	3.125
-10	$3.\overline{03}$
-100	$3.\overline{0003}$
-1000	3

(c) f approaches $-\infty$ from the left of 1, and ∞ from the right of 1. f approaches ∞ from the left of -1, and $-\infty$ from the right of -1.

6. $f(x) = \dfrac{4x}{x^2 - 1}$

(a) Domain: all $x \neq \pm 1$

(b)

x	$f(x)$
0.5	$-2.\overline{66}$
0.9	-18.95
0.99	-199
0.999	-1999

x	$f(x)$
1.5	4.8
1.1	20.95
1.01	201
1.001	2001

x	$f(x)$
5	$-0.8\overline{33}$
10	$0.\overline{40}$
100	0.04
1000	0.004

x	$f(x)$
-5	$-0.8\overline{33}$
-10	$-0.\overline{40}$
-100	-0.04
-1000	-0.004

(c) f approaches $-\infty$ from the left of 1, and ∞ from the right of 1. f approaches $-\infty$ from the left of -1, and ∞ from the right of -1.

7. $f(x) = \dfrac{2}{x + 2}$

Vertical asymptote: $x = -2$

Horizontal asymptote: $y = 0$

Matches graph (a).

8. $f(x) = \dfrac{1}{x - 3}$

Vertical asymptote: $x = 3$

Horizontal asymptote: $y = 0$

Matches graph (d).

9. $f(x) = \dfrac{4x + 1}{x}$

Vertical asymptote: $x = 0$

Horizontal asymptote: $y = 4$

Matches graph (c).

10. $f(x) = \dfrac{1 - x}{x}$

Vertical asymptote: $x = 0$

Horizontal asymptote: $y = -1$

Matches graph (e).

11. $f(x) = \dfrac{x - 2}{x - 4}$

Vertical asymptote: $x = 4$

Horizontal asymptote: $y = 1$

Matches graph (b).

12. $f(x) = -\dfrac{x + 2}{x + 4}$

Vertical asymptote: $x = -4$

Horizontal asymptote: $y = -1$

Matches graph (f).

13. $f(x) = \dfrac{1}{x^2}$

(a) Vertical asymptote: $x = 0$

Horizontal asymptote: $y = 0$

(b) Holes: none

14. $f(x) = \dfrac{3}{(x - 2)^3}$

(a) Vertical asymptote: $x = 2$

Horizontal asymptote: $y = 0$

(b) Holes: none

15. $f(x) = \dfrac{x(2 + x)}{2x - x^2} = \dfrac{2 + x}{2 - x}, \; x \neq 0$

(a) Vertical asymptote: $x = 2$

Horizontal asymptote: $y = -1$

(b) Hole at $x = 0$: $(0, 1)$

16. $f(x) = \dfrac{x^2 + 2x + 1}{2x^2 - x - 3} = \dfrac{(x + 1)^2}{(x + 1)(2x - 3)} = \dfrac{x + 1}{2x - 3},$

$x \neq -1$

(a) Vertical asymptote: $x = \dfrac{3}{2}$

Horizontal asymptote: $y = \dfrac{1}{2}$

(b) Hole at $x = -1$: $(-1, 0)$

17. $f(x) = \dfrac{x^2 - 25}{x^2 + 5x}$

$= \dfrac{(x - 5)(x + 5)}{x(x + 5)}$

$= \dfrac{x - 5}{x}, \; x \neq -5$

(a) Vertical asymptote: $x = 0$

Horizontal asymptote: $y = 1$

(b) Hole at $x = -5$: $(-5, 2)$

18. $f(x) = \dfrac{-(5x^2 + 14x - 3)}{2x^2 + 7x + 3}$

$= \dfrac{-(x + 3)(5x - 1)}{(x + 3)(2x + 1)}$

$= -\dfrac{5x - 1}{2x + 1}, \; x \neq -3$

(a) Vertical asymptote: $x = -\dfrac{1}{2}$

Horizontal asymptote: $y = -\dfrac{5}{2}$

(b) Hole at $x = -3$: $\left(-3, -\dfrac{16}{5}\right)$

19. $f(x) = \dfrac{3x^2 + x - 5}{x^2 + 1}$

(a) Domain: all real numbers

(b) Vertical asymptote: none

Horizontal asymptote: $y = 3$

(c)

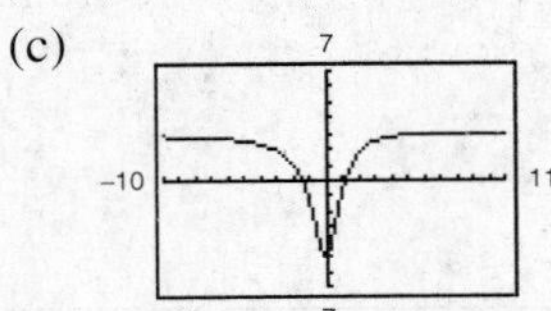

20. $f(x) = \dfrac{3x^2 + 1}{x^2 + x + 9}$

(a) Domain: All real numbers. The denominator has no real zeros. [Try the Quadratic Formula on the denominator.]

(b) Vertical asymptote: none

Horizontal asymptote: $y = 3$

[degree $p(x)$ = degree $q(x)$]

(c)

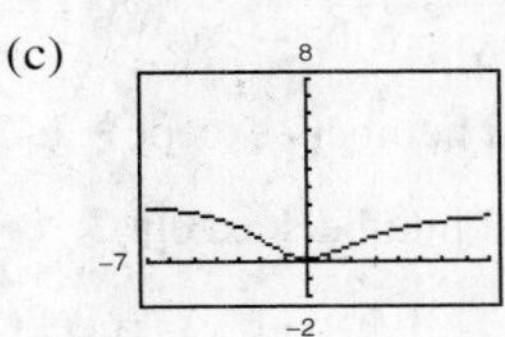

21. $f(x) = \dfrac{x - 3}{|x|}$

(a) Domain: all real numbers except $x = 0$

(b) Vertical asymptote: $x = 0$

Horizontal asymptote:

$y = 1$ to the right

$y = -1$ (to the left)

(c)

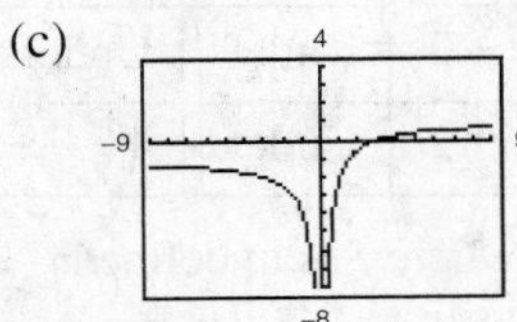

22. $f(x) = \dfrac{x + 1}{|x| + 1}$

(a) Domain: all x

(b) No vertical asymptotes.

Horizontal asymptotes $y = \pm 1$

(c)

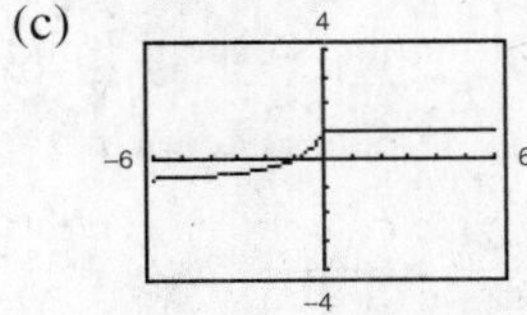

23. $f(x) = \dfrac{x^2 - 16}{x - 4}$, $g(x) = x + 4$

(a) Domain of f: all real numbers except 4

Domain of g: all real numbers

(b) $f(x) = \dfrac{(x - 4)(x + 4)}{x - 4} = x + 4,\ x \neq 4$

f has no vertical asymptotes.

(c) Hole at $x = 4$

(d)

x	1	2	3	4	5	6	7
$f(x)$	5	6	7	Undef.	9	10	11
$g(x)$	5	6	7	8	9	20	11

(e) f and g differ at $x = 4$, where f is undefined.

24. $f(x) = \dfrac{x^2 - 9}{x - 3}$, $g(x) = x + 3$

(a) Domain of f: all real numbers except 3

Domain of g: all real numbers

(b) $f(x) = \dfrac{(x - 3)(x + 3)}{x - 3} = x + 3,\ x \neq 3$

f has no vertical asymptotes.

(c) Hole at $x = 3$

(d)

x	0	1	2	3	4	5	6
$f(x)$	3	4	5	Undef.	7	8	9
$g(x)$	3	4	5	6	7	8	9

(e) f and g differ at $x = 3$, where f is undefined.

25. $f(x) = \dfrac{x^2 - 1}{x^2 - 2x - 3} = \dfrac{(x - 1)(x + 1)}{(x + 1)(x - 3)}$, $g(x) = \dfrac{x - 1}{x - 3}$

(a) Domain of f: all real numbers except -1, 3

Domain of g: all real numbers except 3

(b) $f(x) = \dfrac{(x - 1)(x + 1)}{(x + 1)(x - 3)} = \dfrac{x - 1}{x - 3},\ x \neq -1$

f has a vertical asymptote at $x = 3$.

(c) The graph has a hole at $x = -1$.

(d)

x	-2	-1	0	1	2	3	4
$f(x)$	$\frac{3}{5}$	Undef.	$\frac{1}{3}$	0	-1	Undef.	3
$g(x)$	$\frac{3}{5}$	$\frac{1}{2}$	$\frac{1}{3}$	0	-1	Undef.	3

(e) f and g differ at $x = -1$, where f is undefined.

26. $f(x) = \dfrac{x^2 - 4}{x^2 - 3x + 2} = \dfrac{(x + 2)(x - 2)}{(x - 2)(x - 1)}$, $g(x) = \dfrac{x + 2}{x - 1}$

(a) Domain of f: all real numbers except 1 and 2

Domain of g: all real numbers except 1

(b) $f(x) = \dfrac{(x + 2)(x - 2)}{(x - 2)(x - 1)} = \dfrac{x + 2}{x - 1},\ x \neq 2$

f has a vertical asymptote at $x = 1$.

(c) The graph has a hole at $x = 2$.

(d)

x	-3	-2	-1	0	1	2	3
$f(x)$	$\frac{1}{4}$	0	$-\frac{1}{2}$	-2	Undef.	Undef.	3
$g(x)$	$\frac{1}{4}$	0	$-\frac{1}{2}$	-2	Undef.	4	3

(e) f and g differ at $x = 2$, where f is undefined.

27. $f(x) = 4 - \dfrac{1}{x}$

(a) As $x \to \pm\infty, f(x) \to 4$

(b) As $x \to \infty, f(x) \to 4$ but is less than 4.

(c) As $x \to -\infty, f(x) \to 4$ but is greater than 4.

28. $f(x) = 2 + \dfrac{1}{x - 3}$

(a) As $x \to \pm\infty, f(x) \to 2$.

(b) As $x \to \infty, f(x) \to 2$ but is greater than 2.

(c) As $x \to -\infty, f(x) \to 2$ but is less than 2.

29. $f(x) = \dfrac{2x - 1}{x - 3}$

(a) As $x \to \pm\infty, f(x) \to 2$.

(b) As $x \to \infty, f(x) \to 2$ but is greater than 2.

(c) As $x \to -\infty, f(x) \to 2$ but is less than 2.

30. $f(x) = \dfrac{2x - 1}{x^2 + 1}$

(a) As $x \to \pm\infty, f(x) \to 0$.

(b) As $x \to \infty, f(x) \to 0$ but is greater than 0.

(c) As $x \to -\infty, f(x) \to 0$ but is less than 0.

31. $g(x) = \dfrac{x^2 - 4}{x + 3} = \dfrac{(x - 2)(x + 2)}{x + 3}$

The zeros of g are the zeros of the numerator: $x = \pm 2$

32. $g(x) = \dfrac{x^3 - 8}{x^2 + 4}$

The zero of g corresponds to the zero of the numerator and is $x = 2$.

33. $f(x) = 1 - \dfrac{2}{x - 5} = \dfrac{x - 7}{x - 5}$

The zero of f corresponds to the zero of the numerator and is $x = 7$.

34. $h(x) = 5 + \dfrac{3}{x^2 + 1}$

There are no real zeros.

35. $g(x) = \dfrac{x^2 - 2x - 3}{x^2 + 1} = \dfrac{(x - 3)(x + 1)}{x^2 + 1} = 0$

Zeros: $x = -1, 3$

36. $g(x) = \dfrac{x^2 - 5x + 6}{x^2 + 4} = \dfrac{(x - 3)(x - 2)}{x^2 + 4} = 0$

Zeros: $x = 2, 3$

37. $f(x) = \dfrac{2x^2 - 5x + 2}{2x^2 - 7x + 3} = \dfrac{(2x - 1)(x - 2)}{(2x - 1)(x - 3)} = \dfrac{x - 2}{x - 3}, \; x \neq \dfrac{1}{2}$

Zero: $x = 2$ $\left(x = \dfrac{1}{2} \text{ is not in the domain.}\right)$

38. $f(x) = \dfrac{2x^2 + 3x - 2}{x^2 + x - 2} = \dfrac{(x + 2)(2x - 1)}{(x + 2)(x + 1)} = \dfrac{2x - 1}{x + 1}, \; x = -2$

Zero: $x = \dfrac{1}{2}$ ($x = -2$ is not in the domain.)

39. $C = \dfrac{255p}{100 - p}, \; 0 \le p < 100$

(a) $C(10) = \dfrac{255(10)}{100 - 10} \approx 28.33$ million dollars

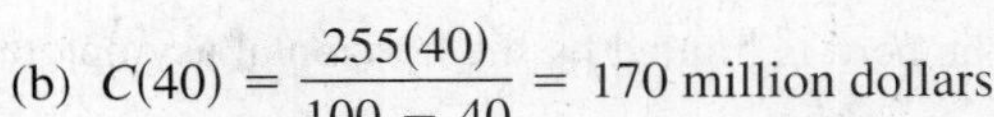

(b) $C(40) = \dfrac{255(40)}{100 - 40} = 170$ million dollars

(c) $C(75) = \dfrac{255(75)}{100 - 75} = 765$ million dollars

(d)

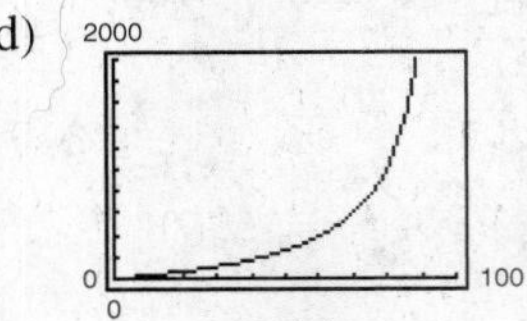

(e) $C \to \infty$ as $x \to 100$. No, it would not be possible to remove 100% of the pollutants.

40. (a) $C = \dfrac{25{,}000(15)}{100 - 15} \approx 4411.76$

The cost would be $4411.76.

(b) $C = \dfrac{25{,}000(50)}{100 - 50} = 25{,}000$

The cost would be $25,000.

(c) $C = \dfrac{25{,}000(90)}{100 - 90} = 225{,}000$

The cost would be $225,000.

(d)

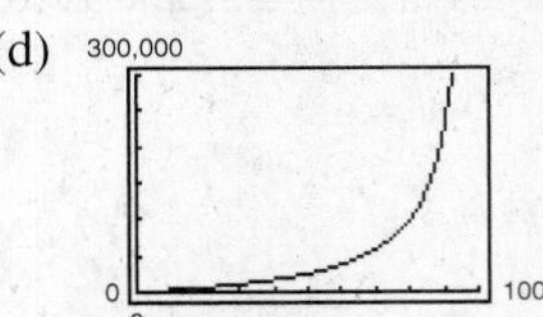

(e) No. The model is undefined for $p = 100$.

41. (a) Use data $\left(16, \frac{1}{3}\right), \left(32, \frac{1}{4.7}\right), \left(44, \frac{1}{9.8}\right),$

$\left(50, \frac{1}{19.7}\right), \left(60, \frac{1}{39.4}\right).$

$$\frac{1}{y} = -0.007x + 0.445$$

$$y = \frac{1}{0.445 - 0.007x}$$

(b)

x	16	32	44	50	60
y	3.0	4.5	7.3	10.5	40

(Answers will vary.)

(c) No, the function is negative for $x = 70$.

42. (a)

M	200	400	600	800	1000	1200	1400	1600	1800	2000
t	0.472	0.596	0.710	0.817	0.916	1.009	1.096	1.178	1.255	1.328

The greater the mass, the more time required per oscillation. The model is a good fit to the actual data.

(b) You can find M corresponding to $t = 1.056$ by finding the point of intersection of

$$t = \frac{38M + 16{,}965}{10(M + 500)} \text{ and } t = 1.056.$$

If you do this, you obtain $M \approx 1306$ grams.

43. $N = \dfrac{20(5 + 3t)}{1 + 0.04t}, \quad 0 \le t$

(a)

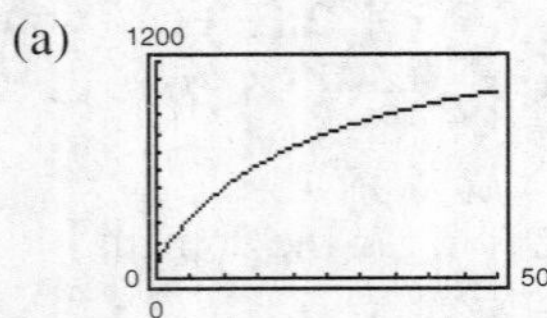

(b) $N(5) \approx 333$ deer

$N(10) = 500$ deer

$N(25) = 800$ deer

(c) The herd is limited by the horizontal asymptote:

$$N = \frac{60}{0.04} = 1500 \text{ deer}$$

44. (a)

The model is a good fit.

(b) For 2010, $t = 20$ and $D \approx \$366.8$ billion.

For 2015, $t = 25$ and $D \approx \$332.3$ billion.

For 2020, $t = 30$ and $D \approx \$319.1$ billion.

Answers will vary.

(c) Horizontal asymptote

$$y = \frac{1.493}{0.0051} \approx 292.7$$

As time passes, the national defense outlays approach \$292.7 billion.

45. False. A rational function can have at most n vertical asymptotes, where n is the degree of the denominator.

46. False. For example, $f(x) = \dfrac{1}{x^2 + 1}$ has no vertical asymptote.

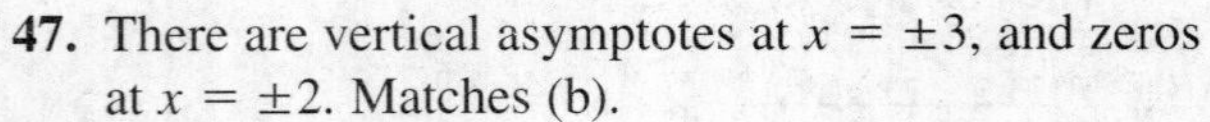

47. There are vertical asymptotes at $x = \pm 3$, and zeros at $x = \pm 2$. Matches (b).

48. There are vertical asymptotes at $x = \pm 1$, and $x = 0$ is a zero. Matches (c).

49. $f(x) = \dfrac{x - 1}{x^3 - 8}$

50. $f(x) = \dfrac{x - 2}{(x + 1)^2}$

51. $f(x) = \dfrac{2(x + 3)(x - 3)}{(x + 2)(x - 1)} = \dfrac{2x^2 - 18}{x^2 + x - 2}$

52. $f(x) = \dfrac{-2(x + 2)(x - 3)}{(x + 1)(x - 2)} = \dfrac{-2x^2 + 2x + 12}{x^2 - x - 2}$

53. $y - 2 = \dfrac{-1 - 2}{0 - 3}(x - 3) = 1(x - 3)$

$y = x - 1$

$y - x + 1 = 0$

54. $y - 1 = \dfrac{1 + 5}{-6 - 4}(x + 6)$

$-10y + 10 = 6x + 36$

$3x + 5y + 13 = 0$

55. $y - 7 = \dfrac{10 - 7}{3 - 2}(x - 2) = 3(x - 2)$

$y = 3x + 1$

$3x - y + 1 = 0$

56. $y - 0 = \dfrac{4 - 0}{-9 - 0}(x - 0)$

$-9y = 4x$

$4x + 9y = 0$

57.

$$\begin{array}{r}
x + 9 \\
x - 4 \,\overline{\smash{)}\, x^2 + 5x + 6} \\
\underline{x^2 - 4x } \\
9x + 6 \\
\underline{9x - 36} \\
42
\end{array}$$

$$\frac{x^2 + 5x + 6}{x - 4} = x + 9 + \frac{42}{x - 4}$$

58.

$$\begin{array}{r|rrr}
3 & 1 & -10 & 15 \\
 & & 3 & -21 \\
\hline
 & 1 & -7 & -6
\end{array}$$

$$\frac{x^2 - 10x + 15}{x - 3} = x - 7 + \frac{-6}{x - 3}$$

59.

$$\begin{array}{r}
2x^2 - 9 \\
x^2 + 5 \,\overline{\smash{)}\, 2x^4 + 0x^3 + x^2 + 0x - 11} \\
\underline{2x^4 + 10x^2 } \\
-9x^2 - 11 \\
\underline{-9x^2 - 45} \\
34
\end{array}$$

$$\frac{2x^4 + x^2 - 11}{x^2 + 5} = 2x^2 - 9 + \frac{34}{x^2 + 5}$$

60.

$$\begin{array}{r}
2x^4 - 3x^3 + 6x^2 - 9x + \frac{27}{2} \\
2x + 3 \,\overline{\smash{)}\, 4x^5 + 0x^4 + 3x^3 + 0x^2 + 0x - 10} \\
\underline{4x^5 + 6x^4} \\
-6x^4 + 3x^3 \\
\underline{-6x^4 - 9x^3} \\
12x^3 \\
\underline{12x^3 + 18x^2} \\
-18x^2 \\
\underline{-18x^2 - 27x} \\
27x - 10 \\
\underline{27x + \frac{81}{2}} \\
-\frac{101}{2}
\end{array}$$

$$\frac{4x^5 + 3x^3 - 10}{2x + 3} = 2x^4 - 3x^3 + 6x^2 - 9x + \frac{27}{2} - \frac{101}{4x + 6}$$

Section 2.7 Graphs of Rational Functions

- You should be able to graph $f(x) = \dfrac{p(x)}{q(x)}$.
  - (a) Find the x- and y-intercepts.
  - (b) Find any vertical or horizontal asymptotes.
  - (c) Plot additional points.
  - (d) If the degree of the numerator is one more than the degree of the denominator, use long division to find the slant asymptote.

Vocabulary Check

1. slant, asymptote
2. vertical

1. $g(x) = \dfrac{2}{x} + 1$

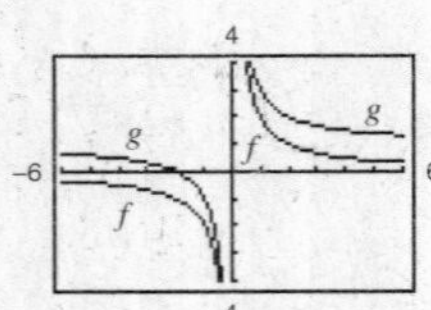

Vertical shift one unit upward

2.

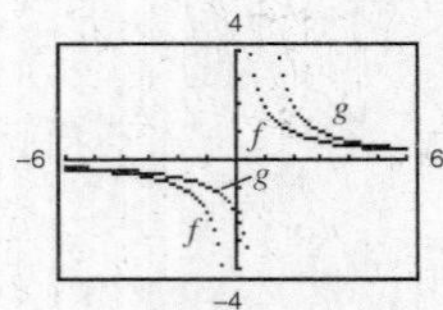

Horizontal shift one unit to the right

3. $g(x) = -\dfrac{2}{x}$

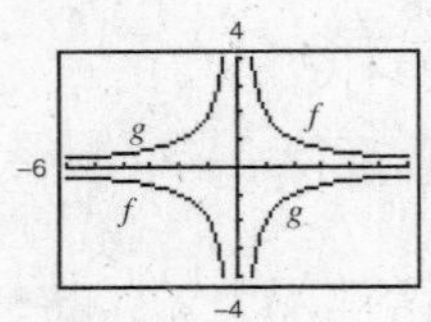

Reflection in the x-axis

4.

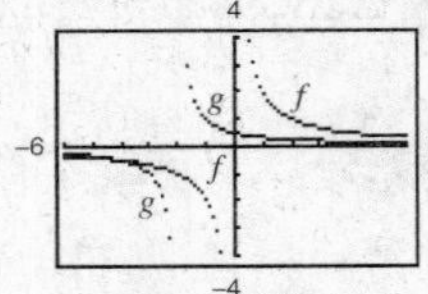

Horizontal shift two units to the left, and vertical shrink

5. $g(x) = \dfrac{2}{x^2} - 2$

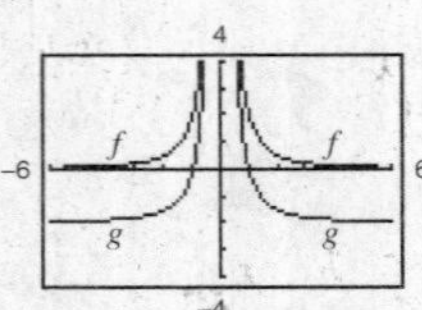

Vertical shift two units downward

6.

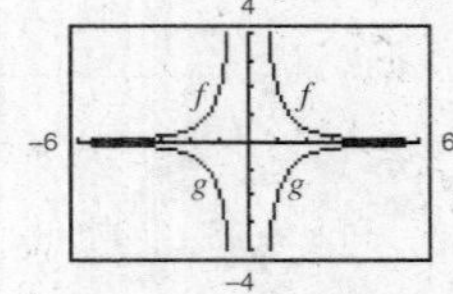

Reflection in the x-axis

7. $g(x) = \dfrac{2}{(x-2)^2}$

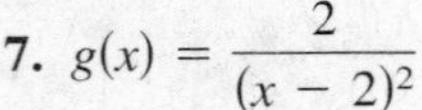

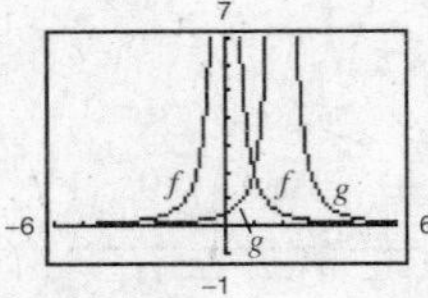

Horizontal shift two units to the right

8.

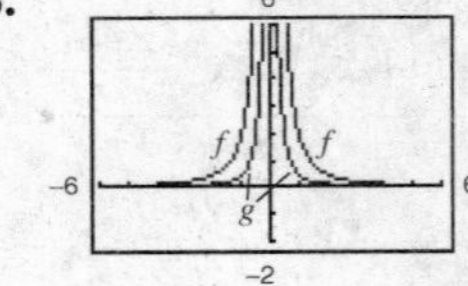

Each y-value is multiplied by $\frac{1}{4}$.

Vertical shrink

9. $f(x) = \dfrac{1}{x+2}$

y-intercept: $\left(0, \dfrac{1}{2}\right)$

Vertical asymptote: $x = -2$

Horizontal asymptote: $y = 0$

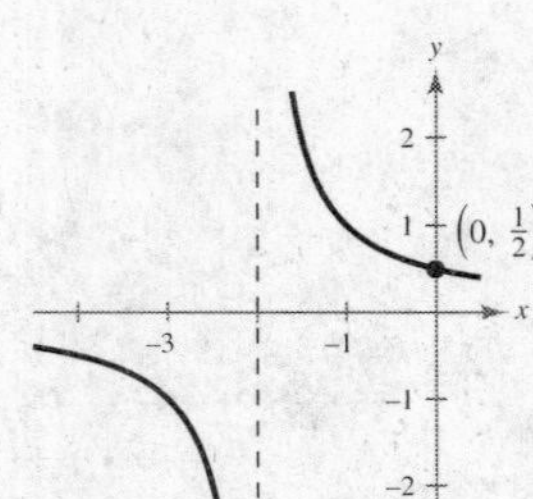

x	-4	-3	-1	0	1
y	$-\frac{1}{2}$	-1	1	$\frac{1}{2}$	$\frac{1}{3}$

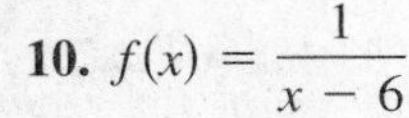

10. $f(x) = \dfrac{1}{x - 6}$

y-intercept: $\left(0, -\dfrac{1}{6}\right)$

Vertical asymptote: $x = 6$

Horizontal asymptote: $y = 0$

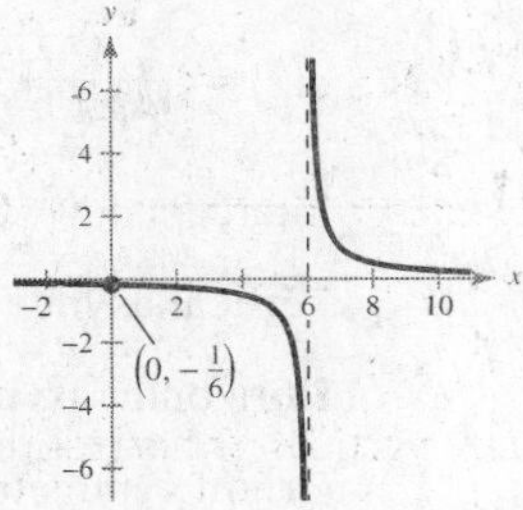

x	-1	0	2	4	8	10
y	$-\frac{1}{7}$	$-\frac{1}{6}$	$-\frac{1}{4}$	$-\frac{1}{2}$	$\frac{1}{2}$	$\frac{1}{4}$

11. $C(x) = \dfrac{5 + 2x}{1 + x} = \dfrac{2x + 5}{x + 1}$

x-intercept: $\left(-\dfrac{5}{2}, 0\right)$

y-intercept: $(0, 5)$

Vertical asymptote: $x = -1$

Horizontal asymptote: $y = 2$

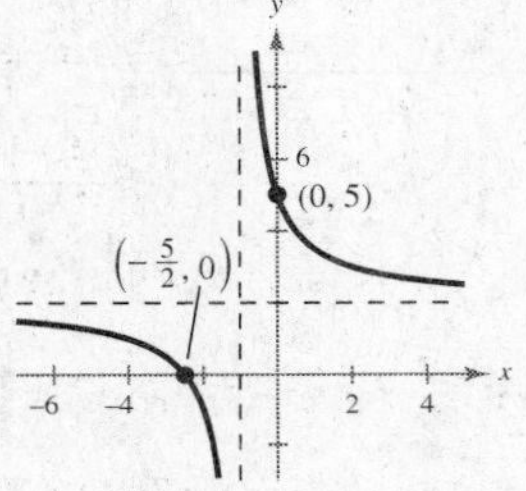

x	-4	-3	-2	0	1	2
$C(x)$	1	$\frac{1}{2}$	-1	5	$\frac{7}{2}$	3

12. $P(x) = \dfrac{1 - 3x}{1 - x} = \dfrac{3x - 1}{x - 1}$

x-intercept: $\left(\dfrac{1}{3}, 0\right)$

y-intercept: $(0, 1)$

Vertical asymptote: $x = 1$

Horizontal asymptote: $y = 3$

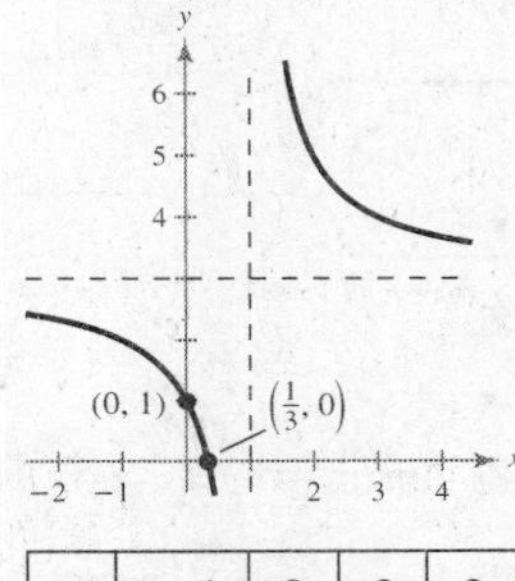

x	-1	0	2	3
y	2	1	5	4

13. $f(t) = \dfrac{1 - 2t}{t} = -\dfrac{2t - 1}{t}$

t-intercept: $\left(\dfrac{1}{2}, 0\right)$

Vertical asymptote: $t = 0$

Horizontal asymptote: $y = -2$

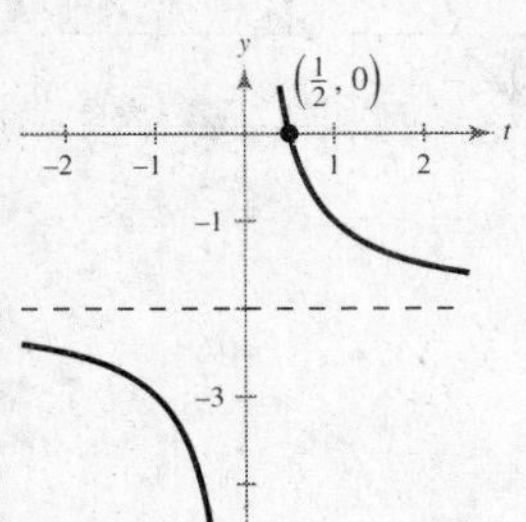

x	-2	-1	$\frac{1}{2}$	1	2
y	$-\frac{5}{2}$	-3	0	-1	$-\frac{3}{2}$

14. $g(x) = \dfrac{1}{x + 2} + 2 = \dfrac{2x + 5}{x + 2}$

y-intercept: $\left(0, \dfrac{5}{2}\right)$

x-intercept: $\left(-\dfrac{5}{2}, 0\right)$

Vertical asymptote: $x = -2$

Horizontal asymptote: $y = 2$

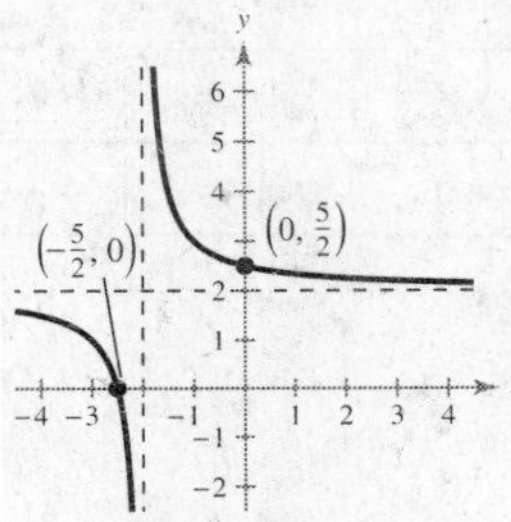

x	-4	$-\frac{5}{2}$	-1	0	2
y	$\frac{3}{2}$	0	3	$\frac{5}{2}$	$\frac{9}{4}$

15. $f(x) = \dfrac{x^2}{x^2 - 4}$

Intercept: $(0, 0)$

Vertical asymptotes: $x = 2,\ x = -2$

Horizontal asymptote: $y = 1$

y-axis symmetry

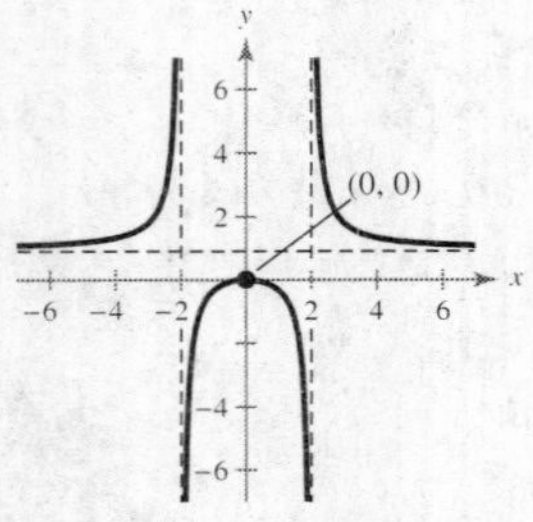

x	-4	-1	0	-1	4
y	$\frac{4}{3}$	$-\frac{1}{3}$	0	$-\frac{1}{3}$	$\frac{4}{3}$

16. $g(x) = \dfrac{x}{x^2 - 9}$

Intercepts: $(0, 0)$

Vertical asymptotes: $x = \pm 3$

Horizontal asymptote: $y = 0$

Origin symmetry

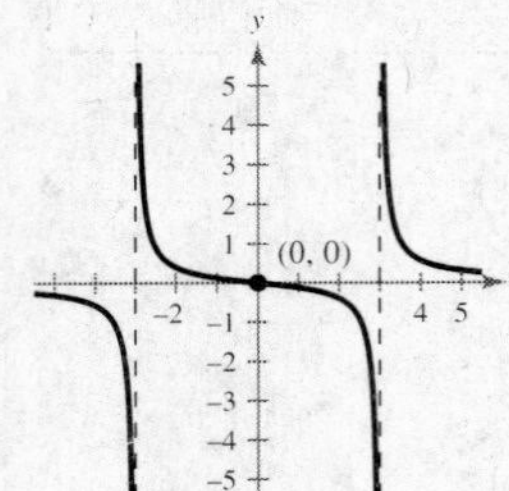

x	-5	-4	-2	0	2	4	5
y	$-\frac{5}{16}$	$-\frac{4}{7}$	$\frac{2}{5}$	0	$-\frac{2}{5}$	$\frac{4}{7}$	$\frac{5}{16}$

17. $f(x) = \dfrac{x}{x^2 - 1} = \dfrac{x}{(x + 1)(x - 1)}$

Intercept: $(0, 0)$

Vertical asymptotes: $x = 1$ and $x = -1$

Horizontal asymptote: $y = 0$

Origin symmetry

x	-3	-2	$-\frac{1}{2}$	0	$\frac{1}{2}$	2	3	4
y	$-\frac{3}{8}$	$-\frac{2}{3}$	$\frac{2}{3}$	0	$-\frac{2}{3}$	$\frac{2}{3}$	$\frac{3}{8}$	$\frac{4}{15}$

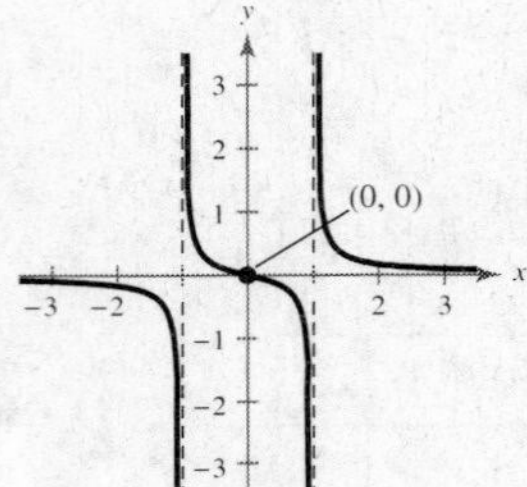

18. $f(x) = -\dfrac{1}{(x - 2)^2}$

y-intercept: $\left(0, -\dfrac{1}{4}\right)$

Vertical asymptote: $x = 2$

Horizontal asymptote: $y = 0$

x	0	$\frac{1}{2}$	1	$\frac{3}{2}$	$\frac{5}{2}$	3	$\frac{7}{2}$	4
y	$-\frac{1}{4}$	$-\frac{4}{9}$	-1	-4	-4	-1	$-\frac{4}{9}$	$-\frac{1}{4}$

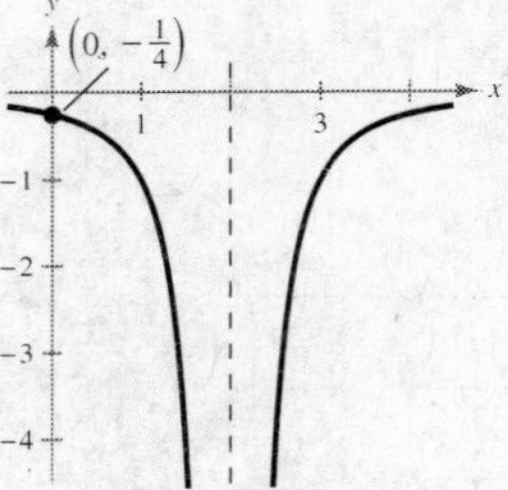

19. $g(x) = \dfrac{4(x + 1)}{x(x - 4)}$

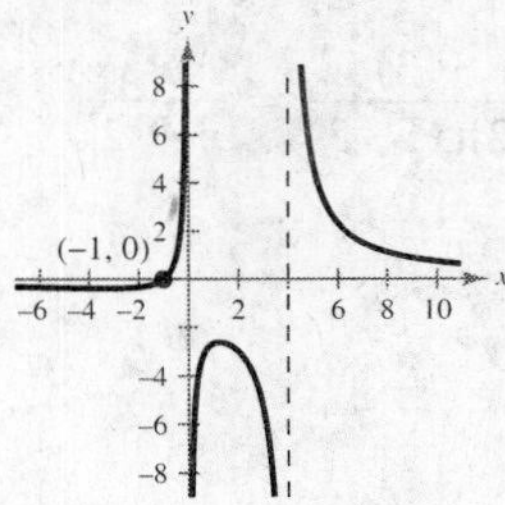

Intercept: $(-1, 0)$

Vertical asymptotes: $x = 0$ and $x = 4$

Horizontal asymptote: $y = 0$

x	-2	-1	1	2	3	5	6
y	$-\frac{1}{3}$	0	$-\frac{8}{3}$	-3	$-\frac{16}{3}$	$\frac{24}{5}$	$\frac{7}{3}$

20. $h(x) = \dfrac{2}{x^2(x - 3)}$

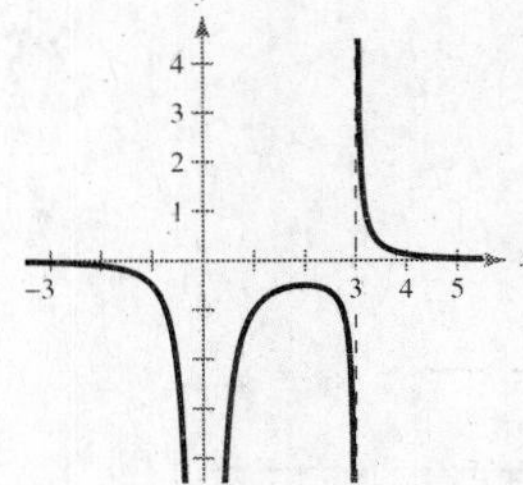

Vertical asymptotes: $x = 0, x = 3$

Horizontal asymptote: $y = 0$

x	-2	0	1	2	3	4
y	$-\frac{1}{10}$	Undef.	-1	$-\frac{1}{2}$	Undef.	$\frac{1}{8}$

21. $f(x) = \dfrac{3x}{x^2 - x - 2} = \dfrac{3x}{(x + 1)(x - 2)}$

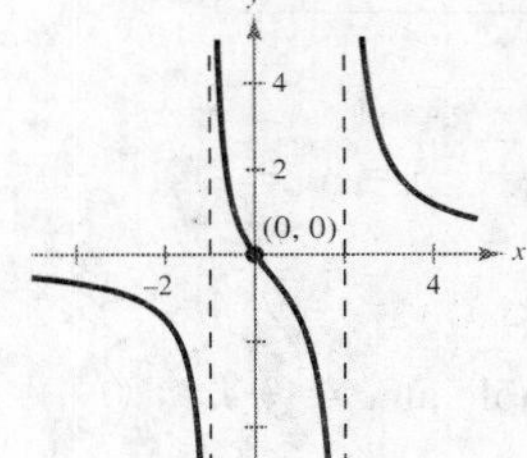

Intercept: $(0, 0)$

Vertical asymptotes: $x = -1, 2$

Horizontal asymptote: $y = 0$

x	-3	0	1	3	4
y	$-\frac{9}{10}$	0	$-\frac{3}{2}$	$\frac{9}{4}$	$\frac{6}{5}$

22. $f(x) = \dfrac{2x}{x^2 + x - 2} = \dfrac{2x}{(x + 2)(x - 1)}$

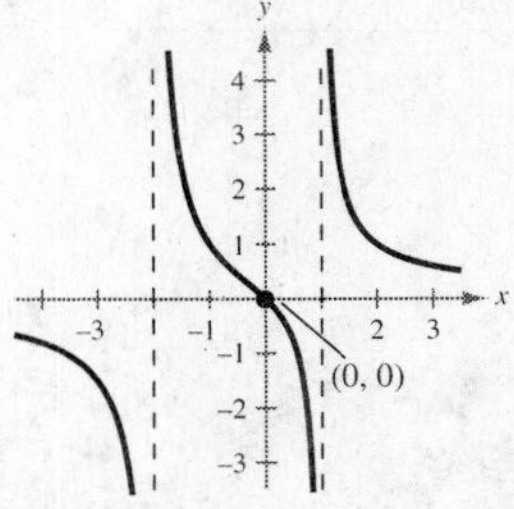

Intercept: $(0, 0)$

Vertical asymptotes: $x = -2, 1$

Horizontal asymptote: $y = 0$

x	-4	-3	-1	0	$\frac{1}{2}$	2	3
y	$-\frac{4}{5}$	$-\frac{3}{2}$	1	0	$-\frac{4}{5}$	1	$\frac{3}{5}$

23. $f(x) = \dfrac{x^2 + 3x}{x^2 + x - 6} = \dfrac{x(x + 3)}{(x - 2)(x + 3)} = \dfrac{x}{x - 2}$, $x \neq -3$

Intercept: $(0, 0)$

Vertical asymptote: $x = 2$

(There is a hole at $x = -3$.)

Horizontal asymptote: $y = 1$

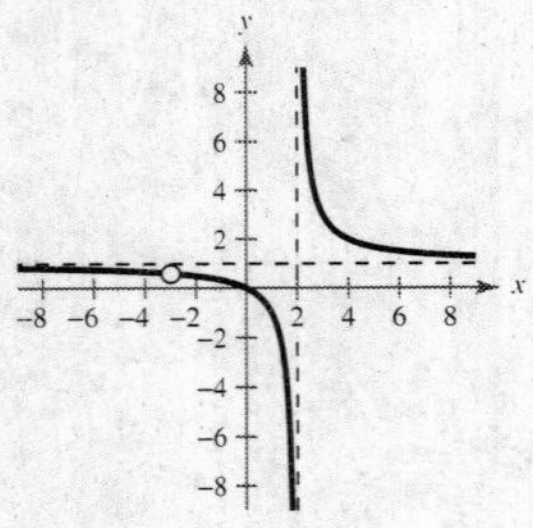

x	-2	-1	0	1	2	3
y	$\frac{1}{2}$	$\frac{1}{3}$	0	-1	Undef.	3

24. $g(x) = \dfrac{5(x + 4)}{x^2 + x - 12} = \dfrac{5(x + 4)}{(x + 4)(x - 3)} = \dfrac{5}{x - 3}$, $x \neq -4$

Vertical asymptote: $x = 3$

Horizontal asymptote: $y = 0$

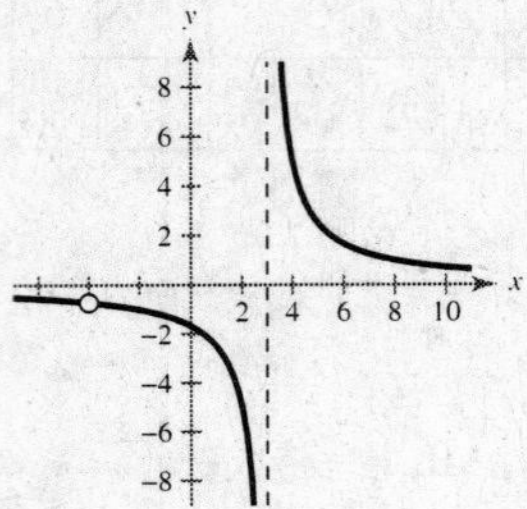

Hole at $x = -4$

x	-4	0	1	3	4
y	Undef.	$-\frac{5}{3}$	$-\frac{5}{2}$	Undef.	5

25. $f(x) = \dfrac{x^2 - 1}{x + 1} = \dfrac{(x + 1)(x - 1)}{x + 1} = x - 1$, $x \neq -1$

The graph is a line, with a hole at $x = -1$.

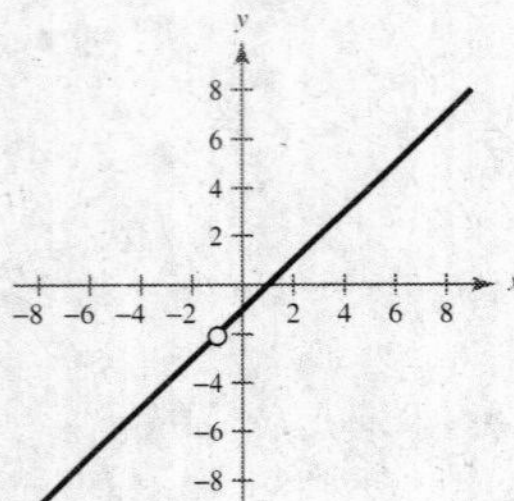

26. $f(x) = \dfrac{x^2 - 16}{x - 4} = x + 4, x \neq 4$

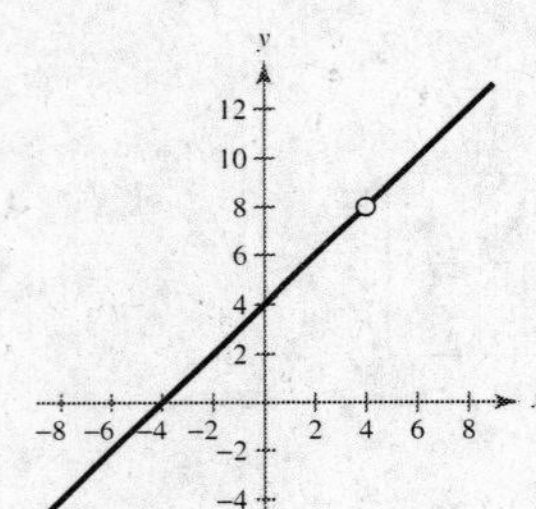

Hole at $x = 4$

27. $f(x) = \dfrac{2 + x}{1 - x} = -\dfrac{x + 2}{x - 1}$

Vertical asymptote: $x = 1$

Horizontal asymptote: $y = -1$

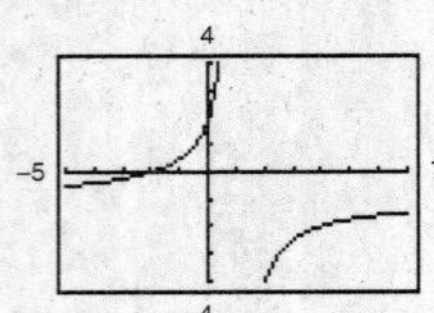

Domain: $x \neq 1$ or $(-\infty, 1) \cup (1, \infty)$

28. $f(x) = \dfrac{3 - x}{2 - x} = \dfrac{x - 3}{x - 2}$

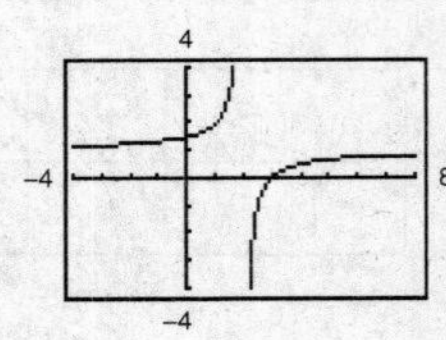

x-intercept: $(3, 0)$

y-intercept: $\left(0, \dfrac{3}{2}\right)$

Vertical asymptote: $x = 2$

Horizontal asymptote: $y = 1$

Domain: all $x \neq 2$

29. $f(t) = \dfrac{3t + 1}{t}$

Vertical asymptote: $t = 0$

Horizontal asymptote: $y = 3$

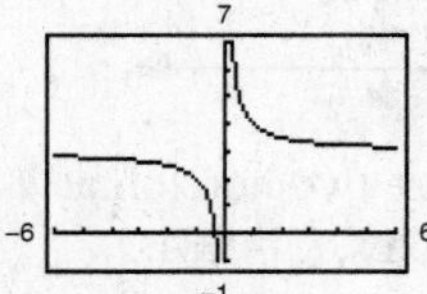

Domain: $t \neq 0$ or $(-\infty, 0) \cup (0, \infty)$

30. $h(x) = \dfrac{x - 2}{x - 3}$

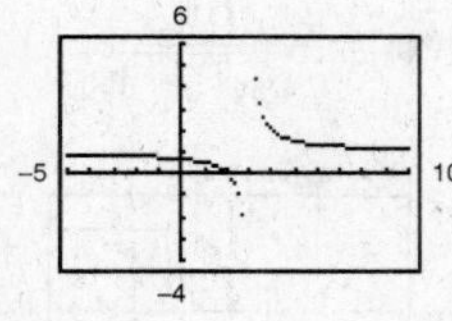

x-intercept: $(2, 0)$

y-intercept: $\left(0, \dfrac{2}{3}\right)$

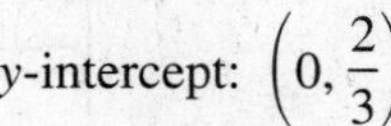

Vertical asymptote: $x = 3$

Horizontal asymptote: $y = 1$

Domain: all $x \neq 3$

31. $h(t) = \dfrac{4}{t^2 + 1}$

Domain: all real numbers OR $(-\infty, \infty)$

Horizontal asymptote: $y = 0$

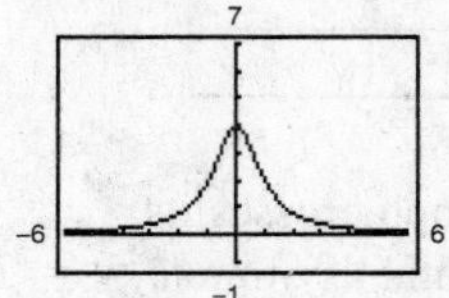

32. $g(x) = -\dfrac{x}{(x - 2)^2}$

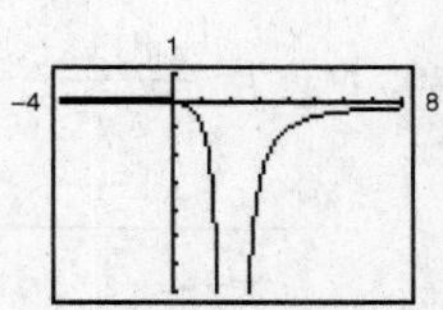

Domain: all real numbers except 2 or $(-\infty, 2) \cup (2, \infty)$

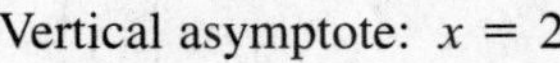

Vertical asymptote: $x = 2$

Horizontal asymptote: $y = 0$

33. $f(x) = \dfrac{x + 1}{x^2 - x - 6} = \dfrac{x + 1}{(x - 3)(x + 2)}$

Domain: all real numbers except $x = 3, -2$

Vertical asymptotes: $x = 3,\ x = -2$

Horizontal asymptote: $y = 0$

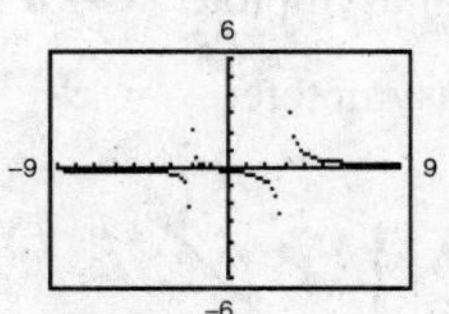

34. $f(x) = \dfrac{x + 4}{x^2 + x - 6}$

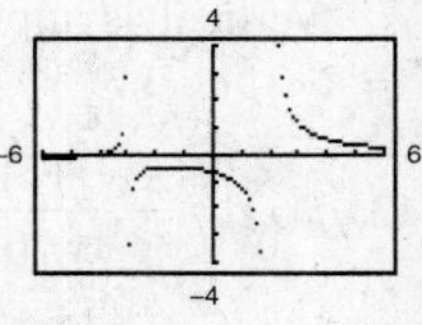

Domain: all real numbers except -3 and 2 or $(-\infty, -3) \cup (-3, 2) \cup (2, \infty)$

Vertical asymptotes: $x = -3, x = 2$

Horizontal asymptote: $y = 0$

35. $f(x) = \dfrac{20x}{x^2 + 1} - \dfrac{1}{x} = \dfrac{19x^2 - 1}{x(x^2 + 1)}$

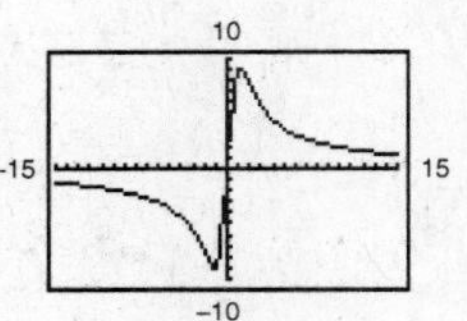

Domain: all real numbers except 0, OR $(-\infty, 0) \cup (0, \infty)$

Vertical asymptote: $x = 0$

Horizontal asymptote: $y = 0$

36. $f(x) = 5\left(\dfrac{1}{x - 4} - \dfrac{1}{x + 2}\right) = \dfrac{30}{(x - 4)(x + 2)}$

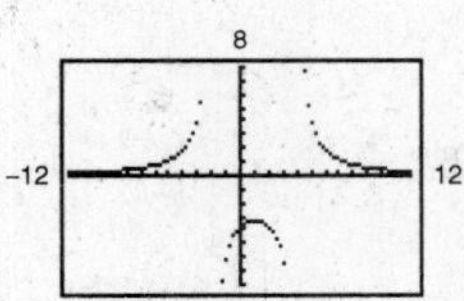

Domain: all real numbers except -2 and 4

Vertical asymptotes: $x = -2, x = 4$

Horizontal asymptote: $y = 0$

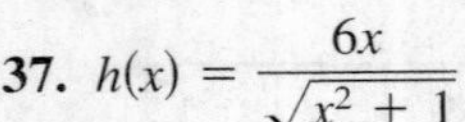

37. $h(x) = \dfrac{6x}{\sqrt{x^2 + 1}}$

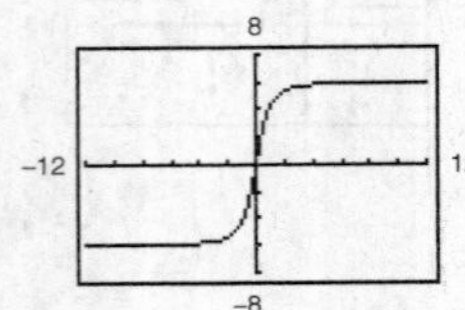

There are two horizontal asymptotes, $y = \pm 6$.

38. $f(x) = \dfrac{-x}{\sqrt{9 + x^2}}$

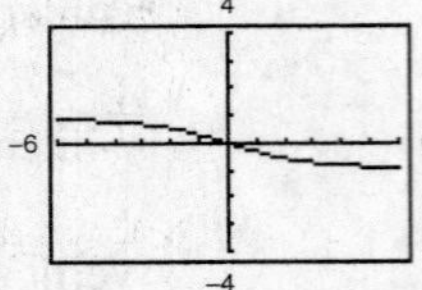

There are two horizontal asymptotes, $y = \pm 1$.

39. $g(x) = \dfrac{4|x - 2|}{x + 1}$

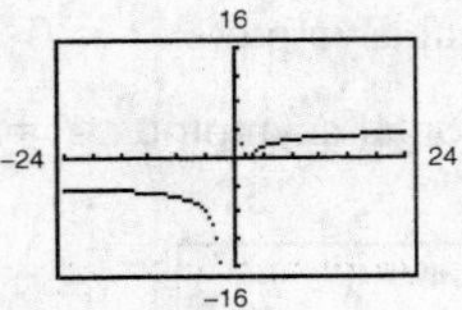

There are two horizontal asymptotes, $y = \pm 4$.

One vertical asymptote: $x = -1$

40. $f(x) = \dfrac{-8|3 + x|}{x - 2} = \dfrac{8|3 + x|}{2 - x}$

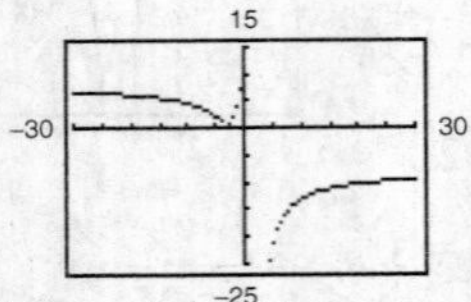

There are two horizontal asymptotes, $y = -8$ and $y = 8$.

Vertical asymptote: $x = 2$

41. $f(x) = \dfrac{4(x - 1)^2}{x^2 - 4x + 5}$

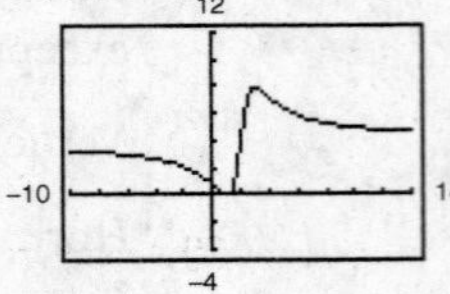

The graph crosses its horizontal asymptote, $y = 4$.

42. $g(x) = \dfrac{3x^4 - 5x + 3}{x^4 + 1}$

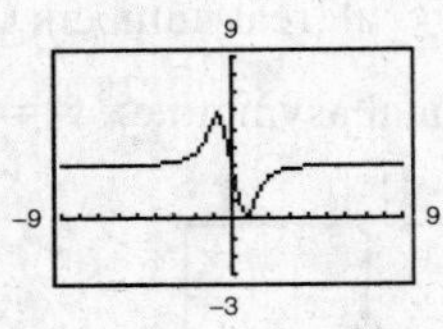

The graph crosses its horizontal asymptote, $y = 3$.

43. $f(x) = \dfrac{2x^2 + 1}{x} = 2x + \dfrac{1}{x}$

Vertical asymptote: $x = 0$

Slant asymptote: $y = 2x$

Origin symmetry

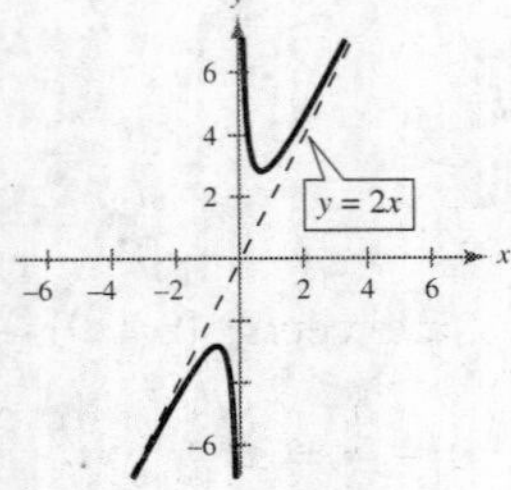

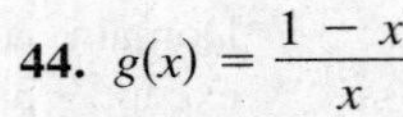

44. $g(x) = \dfrac{1 - x^2}{x}$

Intercepts: $(1, 0), (-1, 0)$

Vertical asymptote: $x = 0$

Slant asymptote: $y = -x$

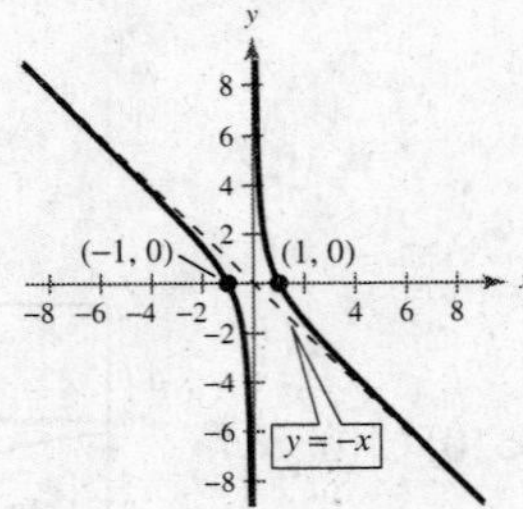

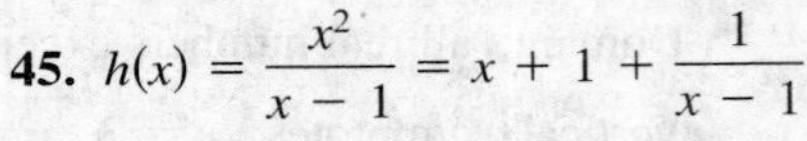

45. $h(x) = \dfrac{x^2}{x - 1} = x + 1 + \dfrac{1}{x - 1}$

Intercept: $(0, 0)$

Vertical asymptote: $x = 1$

Slant asymptote: $y = x + 1$

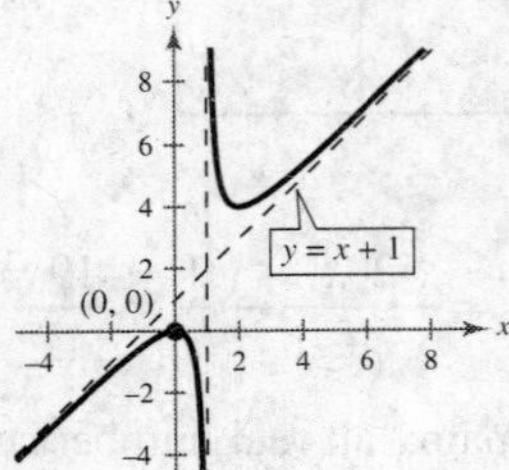

46. $f(x) = \dfrac{x^3}{x^2 - 1} = x + \dfrac{x}{x^2 - 1}$

Intercept: $(0, 0)$

Vertical asymptotes: $x = \pm 1$

Slant asymptote: $y = x$

Origin symmetry

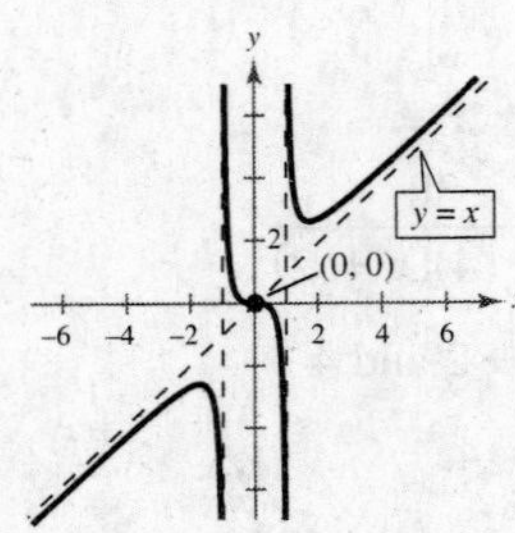

47. $g(x) = \dfrac{x^3}{2x^2 - 8} = \dfrac{1}{2}x + \dfrac{4x}{2x^2 - 8}$

Intercept: $(0, 0)$

Vertical asymptotes: $x = \pm 2$

Slant asymptote: $y = \dfrac{1}{2}x$

Origin symmetry

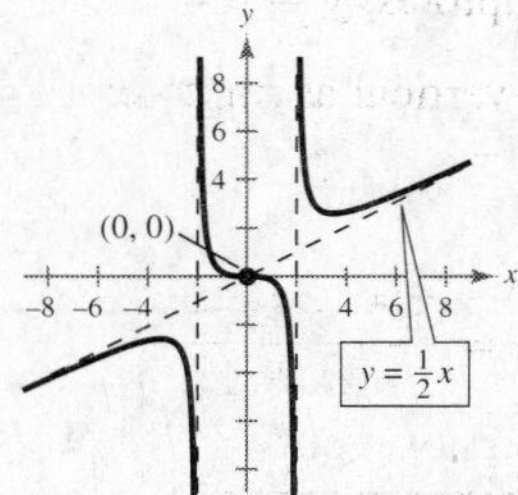

48. $f(x) = \dfrac{x^2 - 1}{x^2 + 4}$

No vertical asymptotes

Horizontal asymptote: $y = 1$

Intercepts: $(\pm 1, 0), \left(0, -\dfrac{1}{4}\right)$

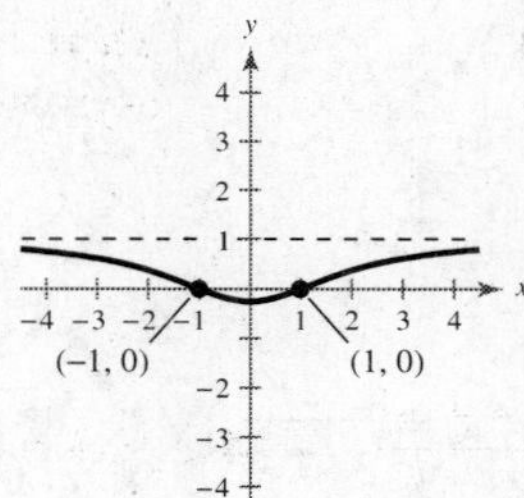

49. $f(x) = \dfrac{x^3 + 2x^2 + 4}{2x^2 + 1} = \dfrac{x}{2} + 1 + \dfrac{3 - \frac{x}{2}}{2x^2 + 1}$

Intercepts: $(-2.594, 0), (0, 4)$

Slant asymptote: $y = \dfrac{x}{2} + 1$

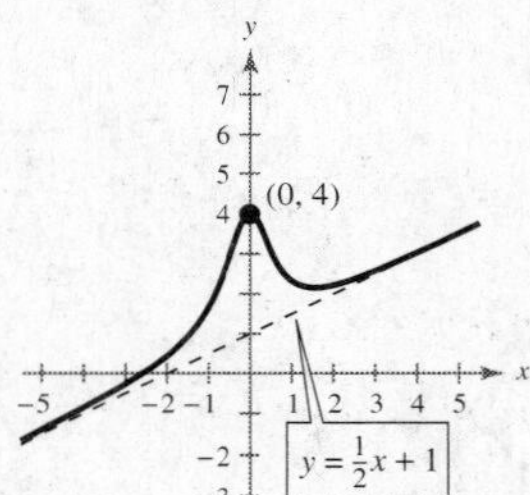

50. $f(x) = \dfrac{2x^2 - 5x + 5}{x - 2} = 2x - 1 + \dfrac{3}{x - 2}$

y-intercept: $\left(0, -\dfrac{5}{2}\right)$

Vertical asymptote: $x = 2$

Slant asymptote: $y = 2x - 1$

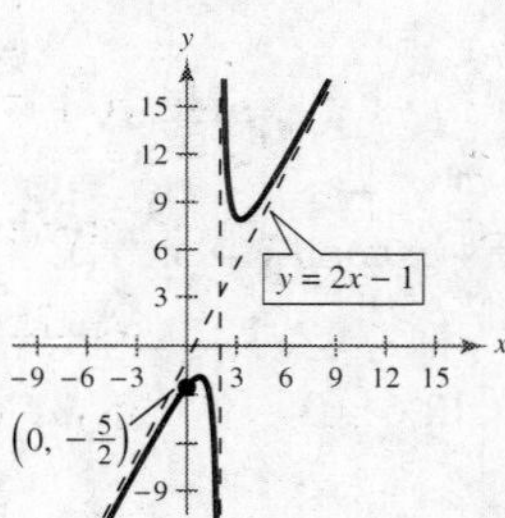

51. $y = \dfrac{x + 1}{x - 3}$

(a) x-intercept: $(-1, 0)$

(b) $0 = \dfrac{x + 1}{x - 3}$

$0 = x + 1$

$-1 = x$

52. $y = \dfrac{2x}{x - 3}$

(a) x-intercept: $(0, 0)$

(b) $0 = \dfrac{2x}{x - 3}$

$0 = 2x$

$0 = x$

53. $y = \dfrac{1}{x} - x$

(a) x-intercepts: $(\pm 1, 0)$

(b) $0 = \dfrac{1}{x} - x$

$x = \dfrac{1}{x}$

$x^2 = 1$

$x = \pm 1$

54. $y = x - 3 + \frac{2}{x}$

(a) x-intercepts: $(1, 0), (2, 0)$

(b) $0 = x - 3 + \frac{2}{x}$

$0 = x^2 - 3x + 2$

$0 = (x - 1)(x - 2)$

$x = 1, 2$

55. $y = \frac{2x^2 + x}{x + 1} = 2x - 1 + \frac{1}{x + 1}$

Domain: all real numbers except $x = -1$

Vertical asymptote: $x = -1$

Slant asymptote: $y = 2x - 1$

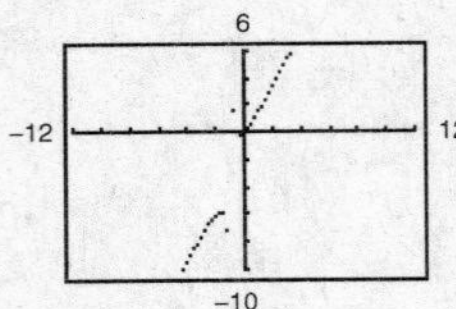

56. $y = \frac{x^2 + 5x + 8}{x + 3} = x + 2 + \frac{2}{x + 3}$

Domain: all $x \neq -3$

Vertical asymptote: $x = -3$

Slant asymptote: $y = x + 2$

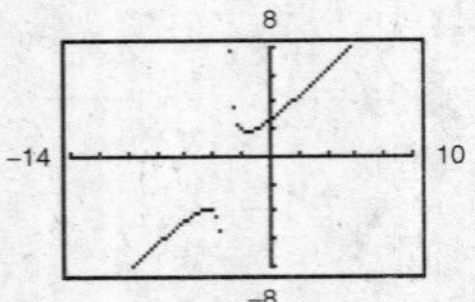

57. $y = \frac{1 + 3x^2 - x^3}{x^2} = \frac{1}{x^2} + 3 - x = -x + 3 + \frac{1}{x^2}$

Domain: all real numbers except 0 or $(-\infty, 0) \cup (0, \infty)$

Vertical asymptote: $x = 0$

Slant asymptote: $y = -x + 3$

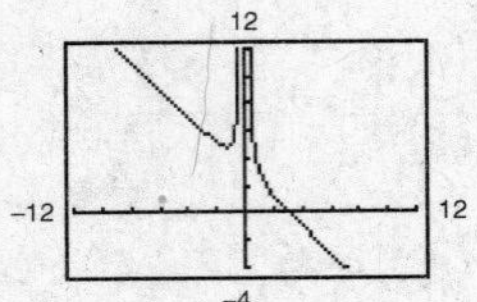

58. $y = \frac{12 - 2x - x^2}{2(4 + x)} = -\frac{1}{2}x + 1 + \frac{2}{4 + x}$

Domain: all real numbers except -4 or $(-\infty, -4) \cup (-4, \infty)$

x-intercepts: $(-4.61, 0), (2.61, 0)$

y-intercept: $\left(0, \frac{3}{2}\right)$

Vertical asymptote: $x = -4$

Slant asymptote: $y = -\frac{1}{2}x + 1$

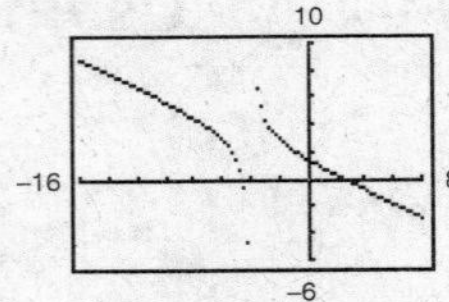

59. $f(x) = \frac{x^2 - 5x + 4}{x^2 - 4} = \frac{(x - 4)(x - 1)}{(x - 2)(x + 2)}$

Vertical asymptotes: $x = 2, x = -2$

Horizontal asymptote: $y = 1$

No slant asymptotes, no holes

60. $f(x) = \frac{x^2 - 2x - 8}{x^2 - 9} = \frac{(x - 4)(x + 2)}{(x - 3)(x + 3)}$

Vertical asymptotes: $x = 3, x = -3$

Horizontal asymptote: $y = 1$

No slant asymptotes, no holes

61. $f(x) = \dfrac{2x^2 - 5x + 2}{2x^2 - x - 6} = \dfrac{(2x - 1)(x - 2)}{(2x + 3)(x - 2)} = \dfrac{2x - 1}{2x + 3},$

$x \neq 2$

Vertical asymptote: $x = -\dfrac{3}{2}$

Horizontal asymptote: $y = 1$

No slant asymptotes

Hole at $x = 2, \left(2, \dfrac{3}{7}\right)$

62. $f(x) = \dfrac{3x^2 - 8x + 4}{2x^2 - 3x - 2} = \dfrac{(3x - 2)(x - 2)}{(2x + 1)(x - 2)} = \dfrac{3x - 2}{2x + 1},$

$x \neq 2$

Vertical asymptote: $x = -\dfrac{1}{2}$

Horizontal asymptote: $y = \dfrac{3}{2}$

No slant asymptotes

Hole at $x = 2, \left(2, \dfrac{4}{5}\right)$

63. $f(x) = \dfrac{2x^3 - x^2 - 2x + 1}{x^2 + 3x + 2}$

$= \dfrac{(x - 1)(x + 1)(2x - 1)}{(x + 1)(x + 2)}$

$= \dfrac{(x - 1)(2x - 1)}{x + 2}, \ x \neq -1$

Long division gives

$f(x) = \dfrac{2x^2 - 3x + 1}{x + 2} = 2x - 7 + \dfrac{15}{x + 2}.$

Vertical asymptote: $x = -2$

No horizontal asymptote

Slant asymptote: $y = 2x - 7$

Hole at $x = -1, (-1, 6)$

64. $f(x) = \dfrac{2x^3 + x^2 - 8x - 4}{x^2 - 3x + 2}$

$= \dfrac{(x - 2)(x + 2)(2x + 1)}{(x - 2)(x - 1)}$

$= \dfrac{(x + 2)(2x + 1)}{x - 1}, \ x \neq 2$

Long division gives $f(x) = 2x + 7 + \dfrac{9}{x - 1}.$

Vertical asymptote: $x = 1$

No horizontal asymptote

Slant asymptote: $y = 2x + 7$

Hole at $x = 2, (2, 20)$

65. $y = \dfrac{1}{x + 5} + \dfrac{4}{x}$

(a)

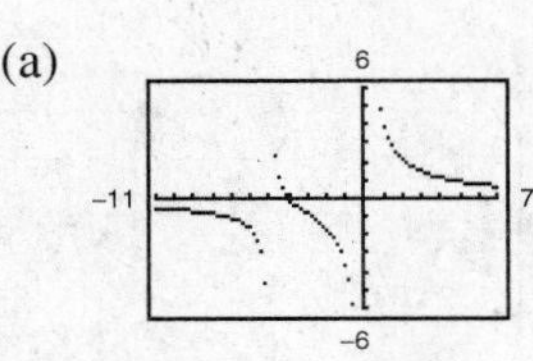

x-intercept: $(-4, 0)$

(b)

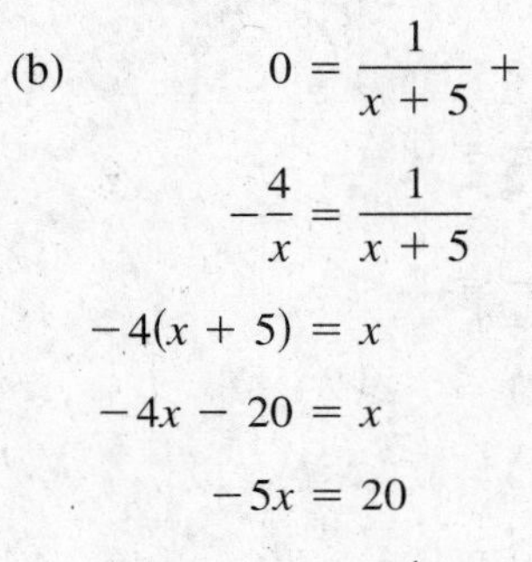

$0 = \dfrac{1}{x + 5} + \dfrac{4}{x}$

$-\dfrac{4}{x} = \dfrac{1}{x + 5}$

$-4(x + 5) = x$

$-4x - 20 = x$

$-5x = 20$

$x = -4$

66. $y = \dfrac{2}{x + 1} - \dfrac{3}{x}$

(a)

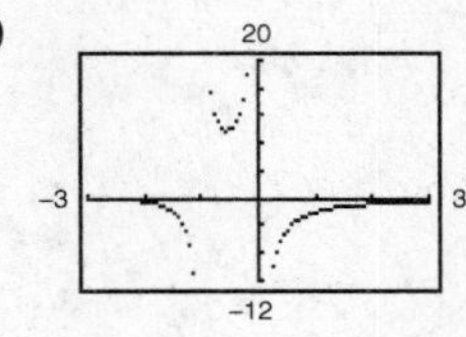

x-intercept: $(-3, 0)$

(b) $\dfrac{2}{x + 1} - \dfrac{3}{x} = 0$

$\dfrac{2}{x + 1} = \dfrac{3}{x}$

$2x = 3x + 3$

$-3 = x$

67. $y = \dfrac{1}{x + 2} + \dfrac{2}{x + 4}$

(a)

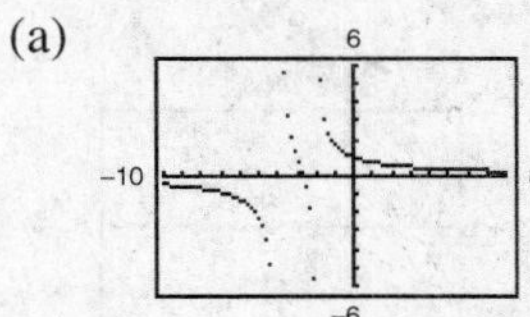

x-intercept: $\left(-\dfrac{8}{3}, 0\right)$

(b) $\dfrac{1}{x + 2} + \dfrac{2}{x + 4} = 0$

$\dfrac{1}{x + 2} = \dfrac{-2}{x + 4}$

$x + 4 = -2x - 4$

$3x = -8$

$x = -\dfrac{8}{3}$

68. $y = \dfrac{2}{x+2} - \dfrac{3}{x-1}$

(a)

(b) $\dfrac{2}{x+2} = \dfrac{3}{x-1}$

$2x - 2 = 3x + 6$

$-8 = x$

x-intercept: $(-8, 0)$

69. $y = x - \dfrac{6}{x-1}$

(a)

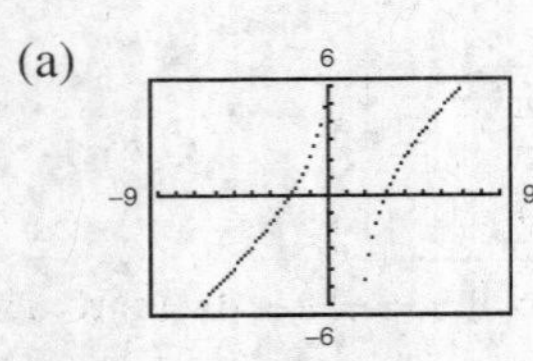

x-intercept: $(-2, 0), (3, 0)$

(b) $0 = x - \dfrac{6}{x-1}$

$\dfrac{6}{x-1} = x$

$6 = x(x-1)$

$0 = x^2 - x - 6$

$0 = (x+2)(x-3)$

$x = -2, \quad x = 3$

70. $y = x - \dfrac{9}{x}$

(a)

x-intercepts: $(-3, 0), (3, 0)$

(b) $0 = x - \dfrac{9}{x}$

$\dfrac{9}{x} = x$

$9 = x^2$

$\pm 3 = x$

71. $y = x + 2 - \dfrac{1}{x+1}$

(a)

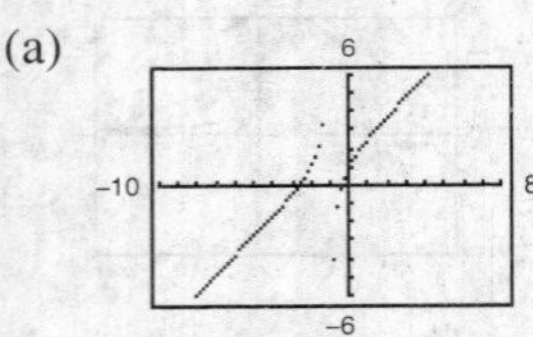

x-intercepts: $(-2.618, 0), (-0.382, 0)$

(b) $x + 2 = \dfrac{1}{x+2}$

$x^2 + 3x + 2 = 1$

$x^2 + 3x + 1 = 0$

$x = \dfrac{-3 \pm \sqrt{9-4}}{2}$

$= \dfrac{-3}{2} \pm \dfrac{\sqrt{5}}{2}$

$\approx -2.618, -0.382$

72. $y = 2x - 1 + \dfrac{1}{x-2}$

(a)

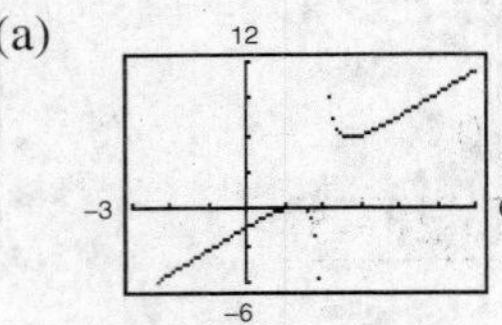

x-intercepts: $(1, 0), \left(\dfrac{3}{2}, 0\right)$

(b) $2x - 1 + \dfrac{1}{x-2} = 0$

$\dfrac{1}{x-2} = 1 - 2x$

$1 = -2x^2 + 5x - 2$

$2x^2 - 5x + 3 = 0$

$(x-1)(2x-3) = 0$

$x = 1, \dfrac{3}{2}$

73. $y = x + 1 + \dfrac{2}{x - 1}$

(a)

No x-intercepts

(b) $x + 1 + \dfrac{2}{x - 1} = 0$

$$\frac{2}{x - 1} = -x - 1$$

$$2 = -x^2 + 1$$

$$x^2 + 1 = 0$$

No real zeros

74. $y = x + 2 + \dfrac{2}{x + 2}$

(a)

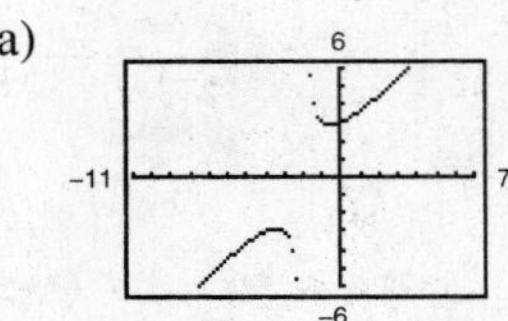

No x-intercept

(b) $x + 2 + \dfrac{2}{x + 2} = 0$

$$\frac{2}{x + 2} = -x - 2$$

$$2 = -x^2 - 4x - 4$$

$$x^2 + 4x + 6 = 0$$

Because $b^2 - 4ac = 16 - 24 < 0$, there are no real zeros.

75. $y = x + 3 - \dfrac{2}{2x - 1}$

(a)

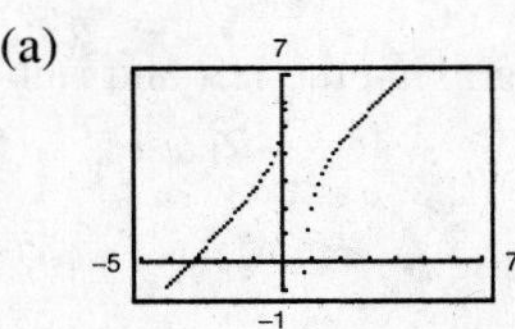

x-intercepts: $(0.766, 0), (-3.266, 0)$

(b) $x + 3 - \dfrac{2}{2x - 1} = 0$

$$x + 3 = \frac{2}{2x - 1}$$

$$2x^2 + 5x - 3 = 2$$

$$2x^2 + 5x - 5 = 0$$

$$x = \frac{-5 \pm \sqrt{25 - 4(2)(-5)}}{4}$$

$$= \frac{-5 \pm \sqrt{65}}{4}$$

$$\approx 0.766, -3.266$$

76. $y = x - 1 - \dfrac{2}{2x - 3}$

(a)

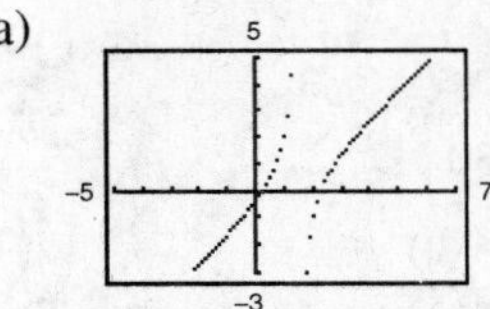

x-intercepts: $(0.219, 0), (2.281, 0)$

(b) $x - 1 - \dfrac{2}{2x - 3} = 0$

$$x - 1 = \frac{2}{2x - 3}$$

$$2x^2 - 5x + 3 = 2$$

$$2x^2 - 5x + 1 = 0$$

$$x = \frac{5 \pm \sqrt{25 - 8}}{4}$$

$$= \frac{5 \pm \sqrt{17}}{4} \approx 0.219, 2.281$$

77. (a) $0.25(50) + 0.75(x) = C(50 + x)$

$$\frac{12.5 + 0.75x}{50 + x} = C$$

$$\frac{50 + 3x}{200 + 4x} = C$$

$$C = \frac{3x + 50}{4(x + 50)}$$

(b) Domain: $x \geq 0$ and $x \leq 1000 - 50 = 950$

Thus, $0 \leq x \leq 950$.

(c)

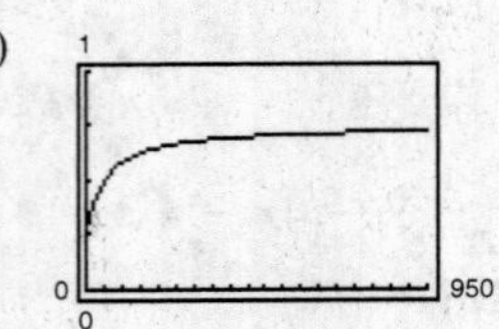

As the tank fills, the rate that the concentration is increasing slows down. It approaches the horizontal asymptote $C = \frac{3}{4} = 0.75$. When the tank is full ($x = 950$), the concentration is $C = 0.725$.

78. (a) Area $= xy = 500$

$$y = \frac{500}{x}$$

(b) Domain: $x > 0$

(c)

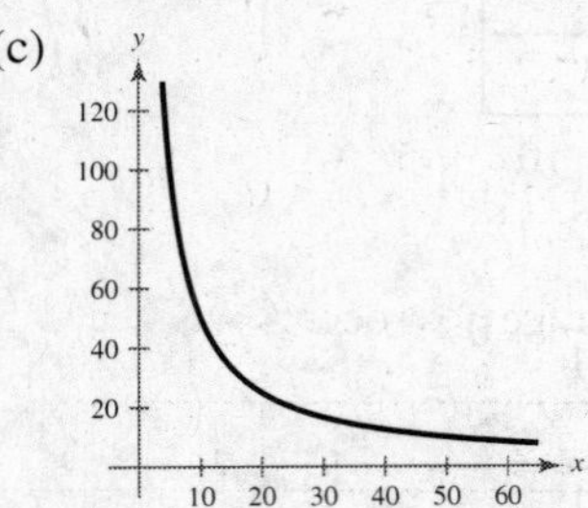

For $x = 30$, $y = \frac{500}{30} = 16\frac{2}{3}$ meters.

79. (a) $A = xy$ and

$(x - 2)(y - 4) = 30$

$$y - 4 = \frac{30}{x - 2}$$

$$y = 4 + \frac{30}{x - 2} = \frac{4x + 22}{x - 2}$$

Thus, $A = xy = x\left(\frac{4x + 22}{x - 2}\right) = \frac{2x(2x + 11)}{x - 2}$.

(b) Domain: Since the margins on the left and right are each 1 inch, $x > 2$, or $(2, \infty)$.

(c)

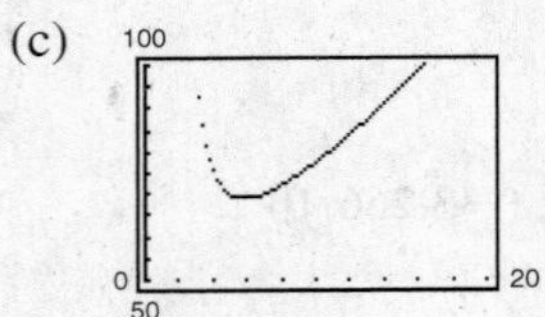

The area is minimum when $x \approx 5.87$ in. and $y \approx 11.75$ in.

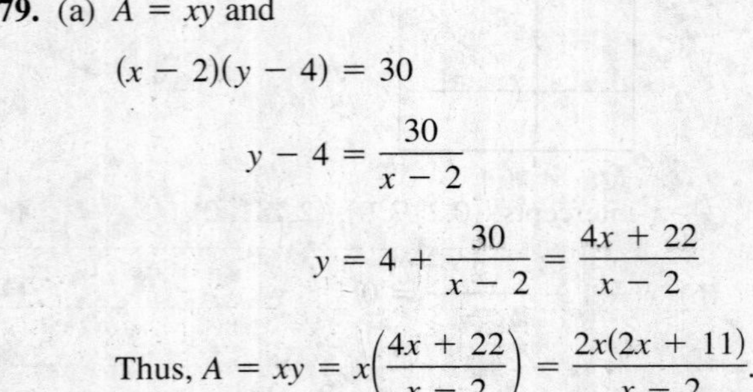

80. (a) The line passes through the points $(a, 0)$ and $(3, 2)$ and has a slope of

$$m = \frac{2 - 0}{3 - a} = \frac{2}{3 - a}.$$

$y - 0 = \frac{2}{3 - a}(x - a)$ by the point-slope form

$$y = \frac{2(x - a)}{3 - a} = \frac{-2(a - x)}{-1(a - 3)}$$

$$= \frac{2(a - x)}{a - 3},\ 0 \leq x \leq a$$

(b) The area of a triangle is $A = \frac{1}{2}bh$.

$b = a$

$h = y$ when $x = 0$, so $h = \frac{2(a - 0)}{a - 3} = \frac{2a}{a - 3}$.

$$A = \frac{1}{2}a\left(\frac{2a}{a - 3}\right) = \frac{a^2}{a - 3}$$

(c) $A = \frac{a^2}{a - 3} = a + 3 + \frac{9}{a - 3}$

Vertical asymptote: $a = 3$

Slant asymptote: $A = a + 3$

A is a minimum when $a = 6$ and $A = 12$.

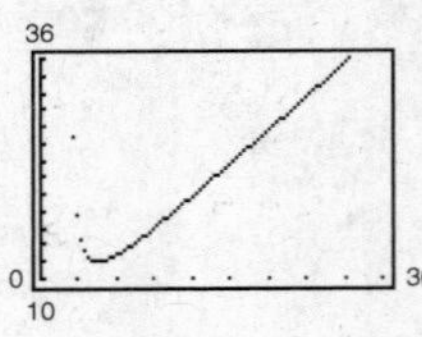

81. $C = 100\left(\dfrac{200}{x^2} + \dfrac{x}{x + 30}\right), \ 1 \le x$

The minimum occurs when $x \approx 40.4 \approx 40$.

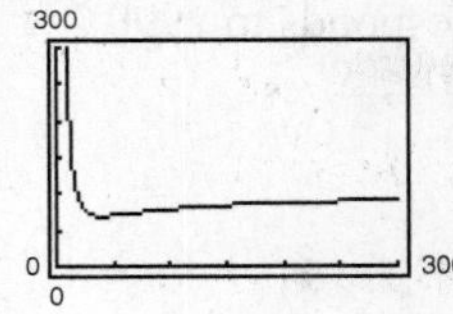

82. $\overline{C} = \dfrac{C}{x} = \dfrac{0.2x^2 + 10x + 5}{x}, x > 0$

The minimum average cost occurs when $x = 5$.

x	0.5	1	2	3	4	5	6	7
$\overline{C}$	20.1	15.2	12.9	12.3	12.05	12	≈ 12.0	12.1

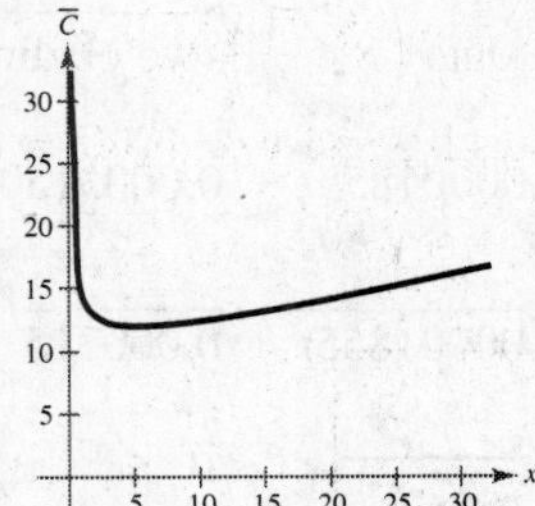

83. $C = \dfrac{3t^2 + t}{t^3 + 50}, \ 0 \le t$

(a) The horizontal asymptote is the t-axis, or $C = 0$. This indicates that the chemical eventually dissipates.

(b) The maximum occurs when $t \approx 4.5$.

(c) Graph C together with $y = 0.345$. The graphs intersect at $t \approx 2.65$ and $t \approx 8.32$. $C < 0.345$ when $0 \le t < 2.65$ hours and when $t > 8.32$ hours.

84. (a) Rate $\times$ Time $=$ Distance or $\dfrac{\text{Distance}}{\text{Rate}} = \text{Time}$

$$\frac{100}{x} + \frac{100}{y} = \frac{200}{50} = 4$$

$$\frac{25}{x} + \frac{25}{y} = 1$$

$$25y + 25x = xy$$

$$25x = xy - 25y$$

$$25x = y(x - 25)$$

$$y = \frac{25x}{x - 25}$$

(b) Vertical asymptote: $x = 25$

Horizontal asymptote: $y = 25$

(c)

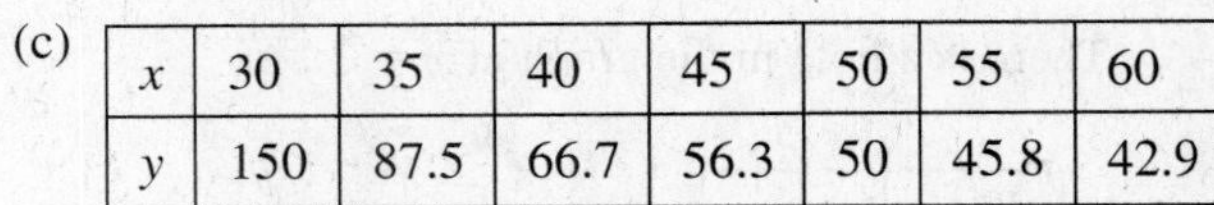

x	30	35	40	45	50	55	60
y	150	87.5	66.7	56.3	50	45.8	42.9

The results in the table are unexpected. You would expect the average speed for the round trip to be the average of the average speeds for the two parts of the trip.

(d)

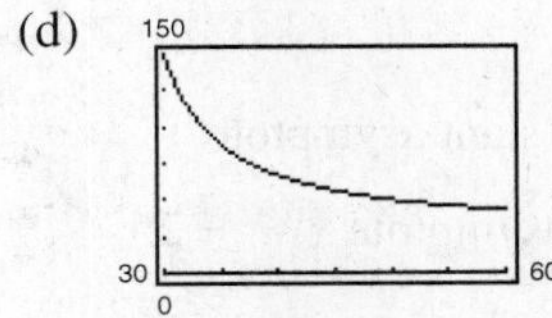

(e) No, it is not possible to average 20 miles per hour in one direction and still average 50 miles per hour on the round trip. At 20 miles per hour you would use more time in one direction than is required for the round trip at an average speed of 50 miles per hour.

85. (a) $y_1 = 583.8t + 2414$ ($t = 0$ corresponds to 1990)

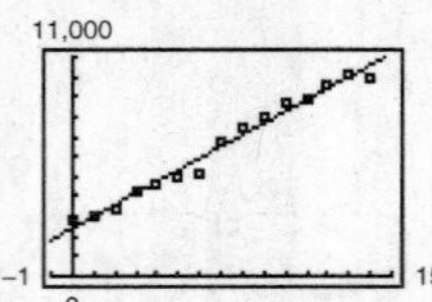

(b) Using the data $\left(t, \dfrac{1}{A}\right)$, we obtain:

$y_2 = -0.00001855t + 0.0003150$

$y_3 = \dfrac{1}{-0.00001855t + 0.000315} = \dfrac{1}{A}$

(c)

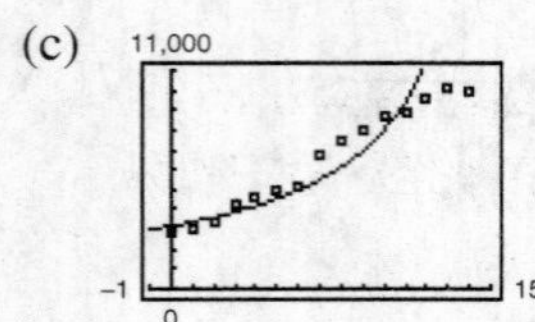

86. (a) Domain: $t \geq 0$

(b) At $t = 0$, $P = 10$.

(c) $P(25) \approx 22$ elk

$P(50) \approx 24$ elk

$P(100) \approx 25$ elk

(d) Yes, the horizontal aymptote $y = \dfrac{2.7}{0.1} \approx 27$ is the limit.

87. False, you will have to lift your pencil to cross the vertical asymptote.

88. False. $f(x) = \dfrac{x}{x^3 + 1}$ crosses its horizontal asymptote $y = 0$ at $x = 0$.

89. $h(x) = \dfrac{6 - 2x}{3 - x} = \dfrac{2(3 - x)}{3 - x} = 2, \quad x \neq 3$

Since $h(x)$ is not reduced and $(3 - x)$ is a factor of both the numerator and the denominator, $x = 3$ is not a horizontal asymptote.

There is a hole in the graph at $x = 3$.

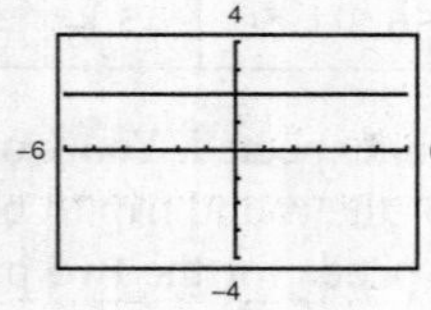

90. $g(x) = \dfrac{x^2 + x - 2}{x - 1}$

$= \dfrac{(x + 2)(x - 1)}{x - 1} = x + 2, x \neq 1$

Since $g(x)$ is not reduced $(x - 1)$ is a factor of both the numerator and the denominator, $x = 1$ is not a horizontal asymptote.

There is a hole at $x = 1$.

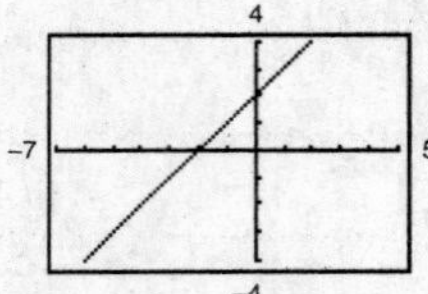

91. $y = x + 1 + \dfrac{a}{x + 2}$ has a slant asymptote $y = x + 1$ and a vertical asymptote $x = -2$.

$0 = 2 + 1 + \dfrac{a}{2 + 2}$

$0 = 3 + \dfrac{a}{4}$

$\dfrac{a}{4} = -3$

$a = -12$

Hence, $y = x + 1 - \dfrac{12}{x + 2} = \dfrac{x^2 + 3x - 10}{x + 2}$.

92. $y = x - 2 + \dfrac{a}{x + 4}$ has slant asymptote $y = x - 2$ and vertical asymptote at $x = -4$. We determine a so that y has a zero at $x = 3$:

$0 = 3 - 2 + \dfrac{a}{3 + 4} = 1 + \dfrac{a}{7} \Rightarrow a = -7$

Hence, $y = x - 2 + \dfrac{-7}{x + 4} = \dfrac{x^2 + 2x - 15}{x + 4}$.

93. $\left(\dfrac{x}{8}\right)^{-3} = \left(\dfrac{8}{x}\right)^3 = \dfrac{512}{x^3}$

94. $(4x^2)^{-2} = \dfrac{1}{(4x^2)^2} = \dfrac{1}{16x^4}$

95. $\dfrac{3^{7/6}}{3^{1/6}} = 3^{6/6} = 3$

96. $\dfrac{x^{-2} \cdot x^{1/2}}{x^{-1} \cdot x^{5/2}} = \dfrac{x \cdot x^{1/2}}{x^2 \cdot x^{5/2}} = \dfrac{x^{3/2}}{x^{9/2}}$

$= \dfrac{1}{x^3}$

97.

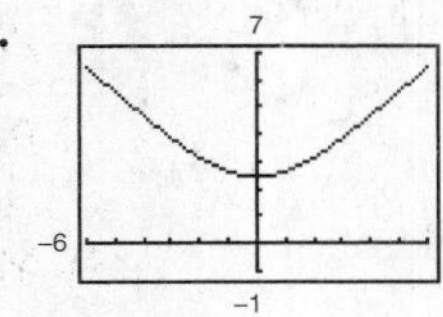

Domain: all x

Range: $y \geq \sqrt{6}$

98.

Semicircle

Domain: $-11 \leq x \leq 11$

Range: $0 \leq y \leq 11$

99.

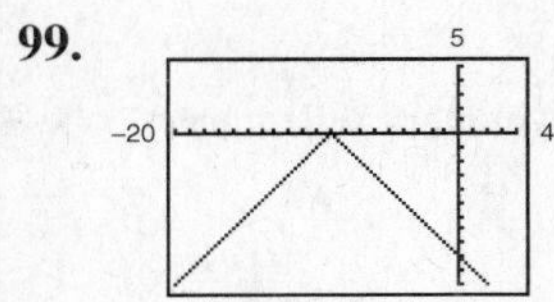

Domain: all x

Range: $y \leq 0$

100.

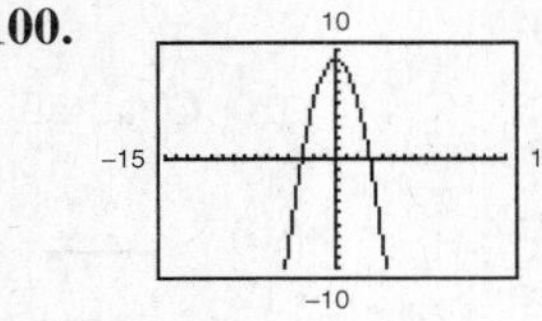

Parabola

Domain: all x

Range: $y \leq 9$

101. Answers will vary. (Make a Decision)

Section 2.8 Quadratic Models

You should know how to

- Construct and classify scatter plots.
- Fit a quadratic model to data.
- Choose an appropriate model given a set of data.

Vocabulary Check

1. linear

2. quadratic

1. A quadratic model is better.

2. Linear

3. A linear model is better.

4. Neither

5. Neither linear nor quadratic

6. Quadratic

7. (a)

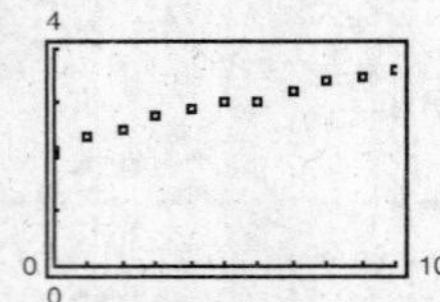

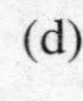

(b) Linear model is better.

(c) $y = 0.14x + 2.2$, linear

$[y = -0.00478x^2 + 0.1887x + 2.1692$, quadratic$]$

(d)

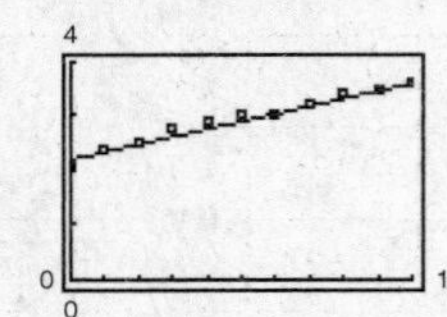

(e)

x	0	1	2	3	4	5	6	7	8	9	10
y	2.1	2.4	2.5	2.8	2.9	3.0	3.0	3.2	3.4	3.5	3.6
Model	2.2	2.4	2.5	2.7	2.8	2.9	3.1	3.2	3.4	3.5	3.6

8. (a)

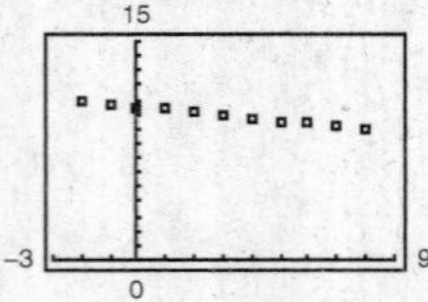

(b) Quadratic model is better. Answers will vary.

(c) $y = -0.19x + 10.5$, linear

$y = 0.006x^2 - 0.23x + 10.5$, quadratic

(d)

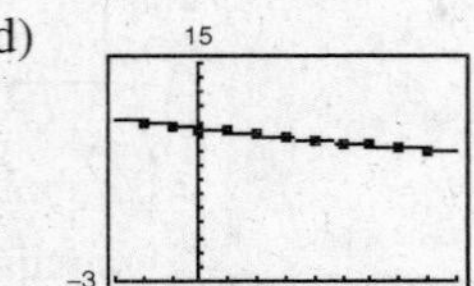

(e)

x	-2	-1	0	1	2	3	4	5	6	7	8
y	11	10.7	10.4	10.3	10.1	9.9	9.6	9.4	9.4	9.2	9.0
Model	11	10.7	10.4	10.3	10.1	9.9	9.7	9.5	9.3	9.2	9.0

9. (a)

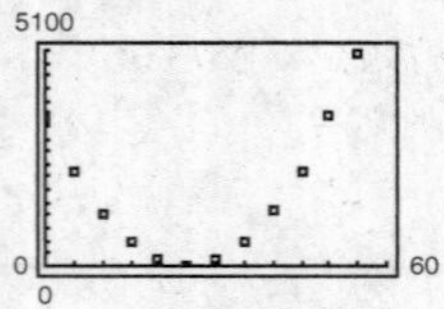

(b) Quadratic model is better.

(c) $y = 5.55x^2 - 277.5x + 3478$

(d)

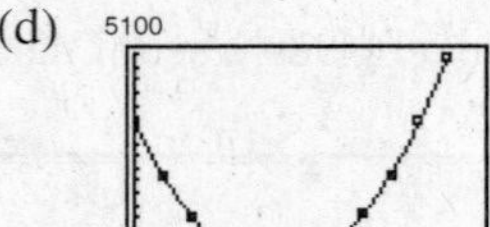

(e)

x	0	5	10	15	20	25	30	35	40	45	50	55
y	3480	2235	1250	565	150	12	145	575	1275	2225	3500	5010
Model	3478	2229	1258	564	148	9	148	564	1258	2229	3478	5004

10. (a)

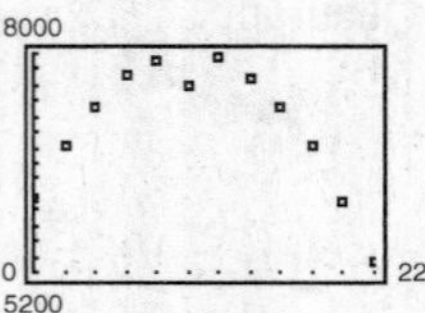

(b) Quadratic

(d)

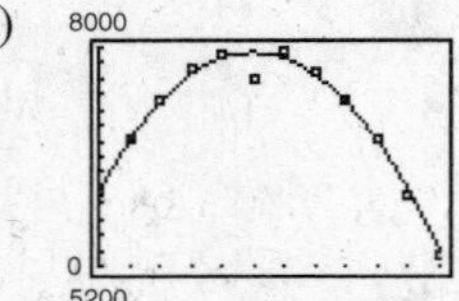

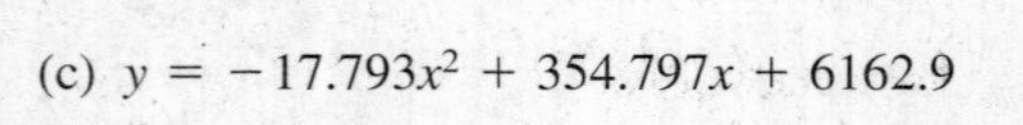

(c) $y = -17.793x^2 + 354.797x + 6162.9$

—CONTINUED—

10. —CONTINUED—

(e)

x	0	2	4	6	8	10	12	14	16	18	20	22
y	6140	6815	7335	7710	7915	7590	7975	7700	7325	6820	6125	5325
Model	6163	6801	7297	7651	7863	7932	7858	7643	7285	6784	6142	5357

(Answers will vary.)

11. (a) $y = 2.48x + 1.1$, linear

$y = 0.071x^2 + 1.69x + 2.7$, quadratic

(b) 0.98995 for linear model

0.99519 for quadratic model

(c) Quadratic fits better.

12. (a) $y = 2.10x$, linear model

$y = 0.006x^2 + 2.04x$, quadratic model

(b) 0.99978 for the linear model

0.99984 for the quadratic model

(c) The quadratic model is slightly better.

13. (a) $y = -0.89x + 5.3$, linear

$y = 0.001x^2 - 0.90x + 5.3$, quadratic

(b) 0.99982 for the linear model

0.99987 for the quadratic model

(c) The quadratic model is slightly better.

14. (a) $y = -8.6x + 612$

$y = 0.08x^2 - 9.0x + 595$

(b) 0.98235, linear

0.99653, quadratic

(c) Quadratic is better.

15. (a)

(b) $P = 0.1322t^2 - 1.901t + 6.87$

(c)

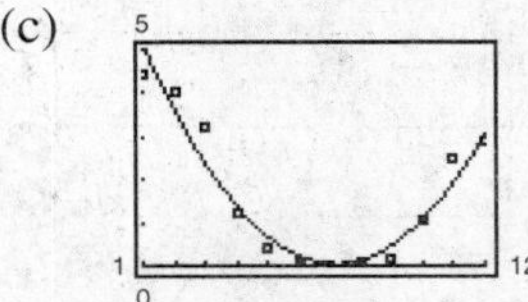

(d) The model's minimum is $H \approx 0.03$ at $t = 7.2$. This corresponds to July.

16. (a)

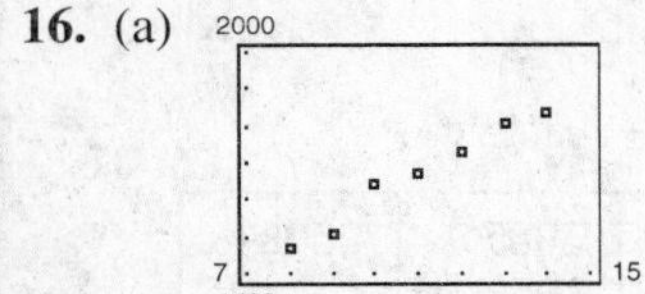

(b) $S = -3.07t^2 + 131.9t + 597$

$(t = 8 \leftrightarrow 1998)$

(c)

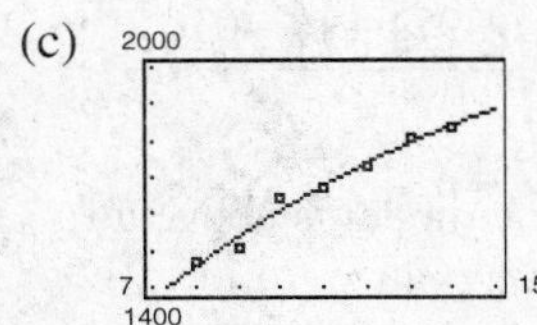

(d) Using a graphics utility, $S > 2000$ when $t \approx 19.4$, or 2009.

(e) No, because the coefficient of t^2 is negative. The graph turns downward as time increases. Answers will vary.

17. (a)

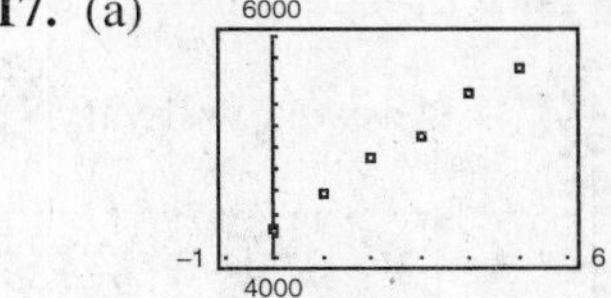

(b) $y = -2.630t^2 + 301.74t + 4270.2$

(c)

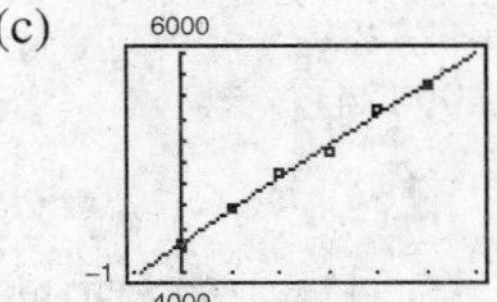

(d) According to the model, $y > 10{,}000$ when $t \approx 24$, or 2024.

(e) Answers will vary.

18. (a)

(b) $S = 117.1t + 4727$, linear model (0.98921)

(c) 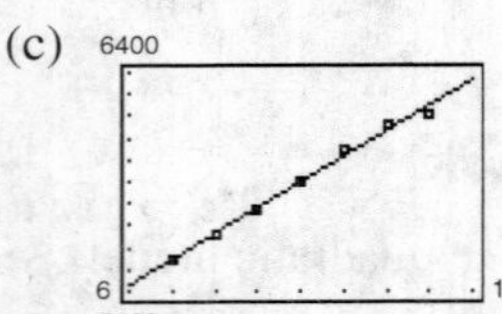

(d) $S_2 = -3.26t^2 + 182.3t + 4413$ (0.99151)

(e) 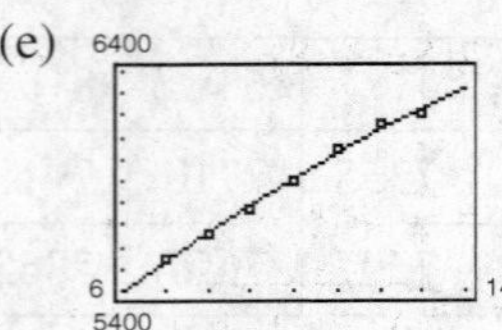

(f) Answers will vary.

(g) $S_1 > 7000$ for $t > 19.4$, or 2009.

S_2 is never greater than 7000.

19. (a)

(b) 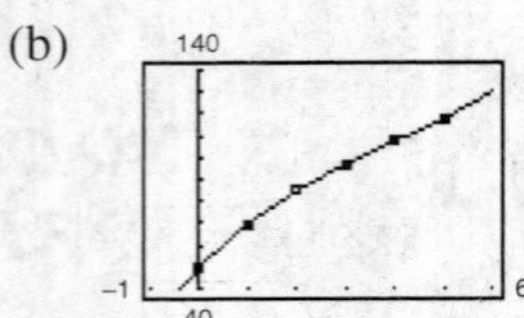

(c) $y = -1.1357t^2 + 18.999t + 50.32$, quadratic model, (0.99859)

(d) 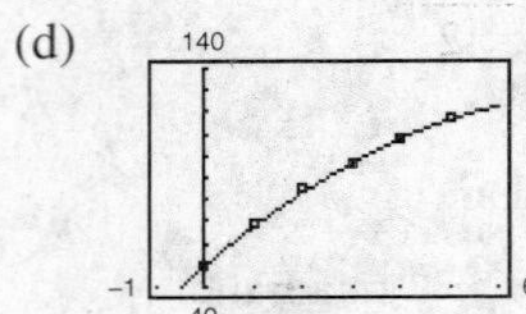

(e) The cubic model is a better fit.

(f)

Year	2006 ($t = 6$)	2007 ($t = 7$)	2008 ($t = 8$)
A^*	127.76	140.15	154.29
Cubic	129.91	145.13	164.96
Quadratic	123.40	127.64	129.60

20. (a)

(b) 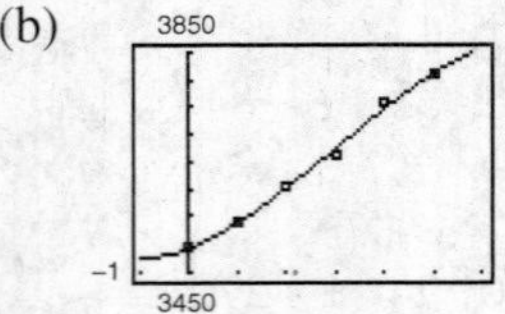

Answers will vary.

(c) $y = 2.36t^2 + 53.7t + 3489$ quadratic model, (0.99474)

(d) Answers will vary.

(e) Cubic model is better.

(f)

Year	2006 ($t = 6$)	2007 ($t = 7$)	2008 ($t = 8$)
A^*	3890	3949	4059
Cubic	3858	3878	3862
Quadratic	3896	3981	4070

21. True

22. True

23. The model is above all data points.

24. (a) $(f \circ g)(x) = f(x^2 + 3) = 2(x^2 + 3) - 1 = 2x^2 + 5$

(b) $(g \circ f)(x) = g(2x - 1) = (2x - 1)^2 + 3 = 4x^2 - 4x + 4$

25. (a) $f(g(x)) = f(2x^2 - 1) = 5(2x^2 - 1) + 8 = 10x^2 + 3$

(b) $g(f(x)) = g(5x + 8) = 2(5x + 8)^2 - 1 = 50x^2 + 160x + 127$

26. (a) $(f \circ g)(x) = f\left(\sqrt[3]{x + 1}\right) = x + 1 - 1 = x$

(b) $(g \circ f)(x) = g(x^3 - 1) = \sqrt[3]{x^3 - 1 + 1} = x$

27. (a) $f(g(x)) = f(x^3 - 5) = \sqrt[3]{x^3 - 5 + 5} = x$

(b) $g(f(x)) = g\left(\sqrt[3]{x + 5}\right) = \left[\sqrt[3]{x + 5}\right]^3 - 5 = x$

28. f is one-to-one.

$$y = 2x + 5$$
$$x = 2y + 5$$
$$2y = x - 5$$
$$y = \frac{(x - 5)}{2} \Longrightarrow f^{-1}(x) = \frac{x - 5}{2}$$

29. f is one-to-one.

$$y = \frac{x - 4}{5}$$
$$x = \frac{y - 4}{5}$$
$$5x + 4 = y \Longrightarrow f^{-1}(x) = 5x + 4$$

30. f is one-to-one on $[0, \infty)$.

$$y = x^2 + 5, \quad x \geq 0$$
$$x = y^2 + 5, \quad y \geq 0$$
$$y^2 = x - 5$$
$$y = \sqrt{x - 5} \Longrightarrow f^{-1}(x) = \sqrt{x - 5}, \; x \geq 5$$

31. f is one-to-one.

$$y = 2x^2 - 3, \quad x \geq 0$$
$$x = 2y^2 - 3, \quad y \geq 0$$
$$y^2 = \frac{(x + 3)}{2}$$
$$y = \sqrt{\frac{x + 3}{2}} \Longrightarrow f^{-1}(x) = \sqrt{\frac{x + 3}{2}}$$
$$= \frac{\sqrt{2x + 6}}{2}, \quad x \geq -3$$

32.

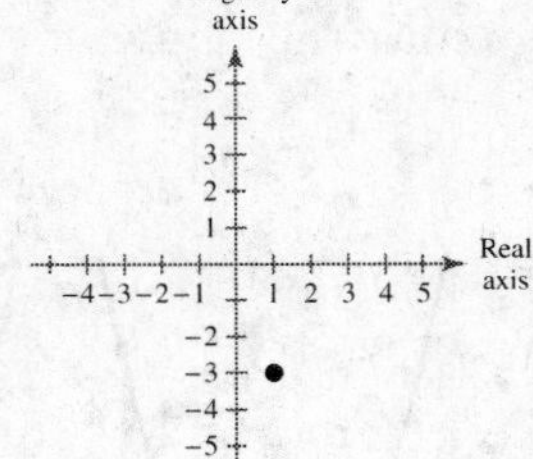

33.

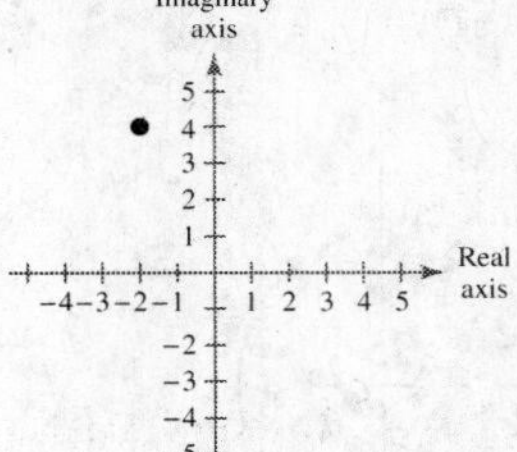

34.

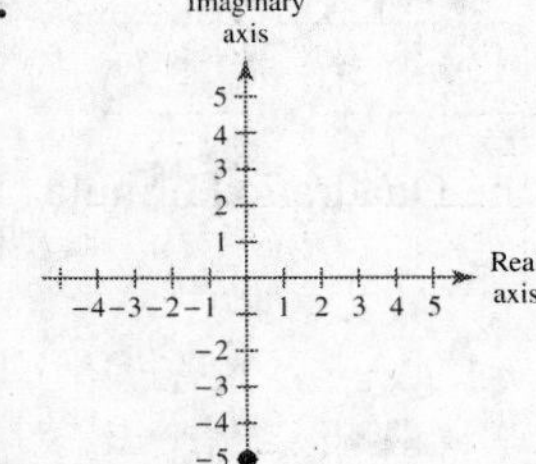

35.

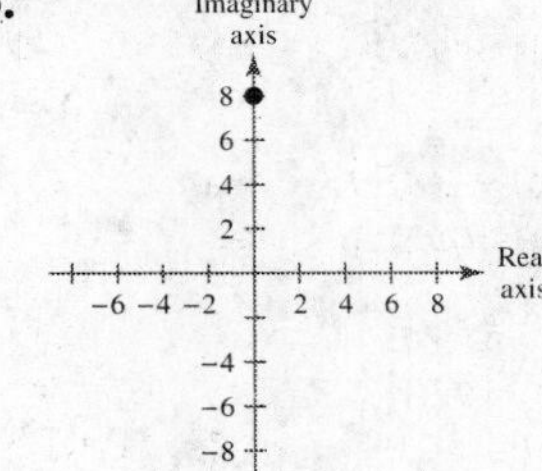

Review Exercises for Chapter 2

1.

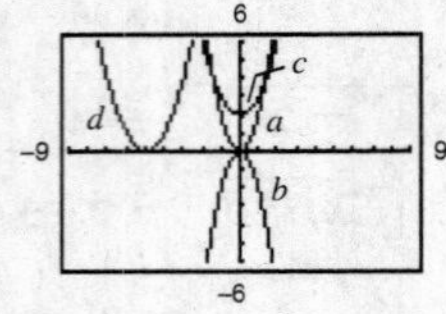

(a) $y = 2x^2$ is a vertical stretch.

(b) $y = -2x^2$ is a vertical stretch and reflection in the x-axis.

(c) $y = x^2 + 2$ is a vertical shift two units upward.

(d) $y = (x + 5)^2$ is a horizontal shift five units to the left.

2.

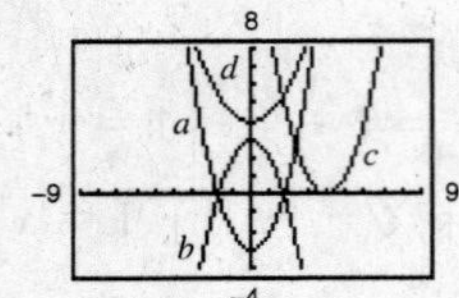

(a) Vertical shift three units downward

(b) Reflection in the x-axis and vertical shift three units upward

(c) Horizontal shift four units to the right

(d) Vertical shrink followed by vertical shift four units upward

3. $f(x) = \left(x + \frac{3}{2}\right)^2 + 1$

Vertex: $\left(-\frac{3}{2}, 1\right)$

y-intercept: $\left(0, \frac{13}{4}\right)$

No x-intercepts

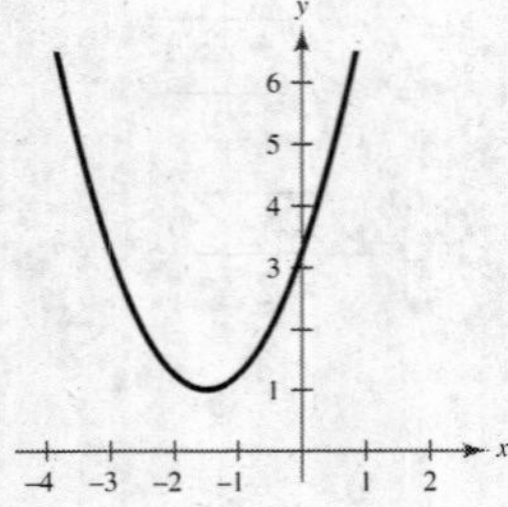

4. $f(x) = (x - 4)^2 - 4$

Vertex: $(4, -4)$

y-intercept: $(0, 12)$

x-intercepts: $(2, 0), (6, 0)$

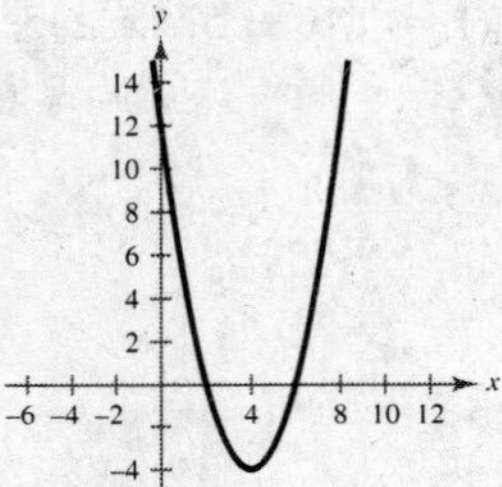

5. $f(x) = \dfrac{1}{3}(x^2 + 5x - 4)$

$$= \frac{1}{3}\left(x^2 + 5x + \frac{25}{4} - \frac{25}{4} - 4\right)$$

$$= \frac{1}{3}\left[\left(x + \frac{5}{2}\right)^2 - \frac{41}{4}\right]$$

$$= \frac{1}{3}\left(x + \frac{5}{2}\right)^2 - \frac{41}{12}$$

Vertex: $\left(-\dfrac{5}{2}, -\dfrac{41}{12}\right)$

y-intercept: $\left(0, -\dfrac{4}{3}\right)$

x-intercepts: $0 = \dfrac{1}{3}(x^2 + 5x - 4)$

$$0 = x^2 + 5x - 4$$

$$x = \frac{-5 \pm \sqrt{41}}{2} \quad \text{Use the Quadratic Formula.}$$

$$\left(\frac{-5 \pm \sqrt{41}}{2}, 0\right)$$

6. 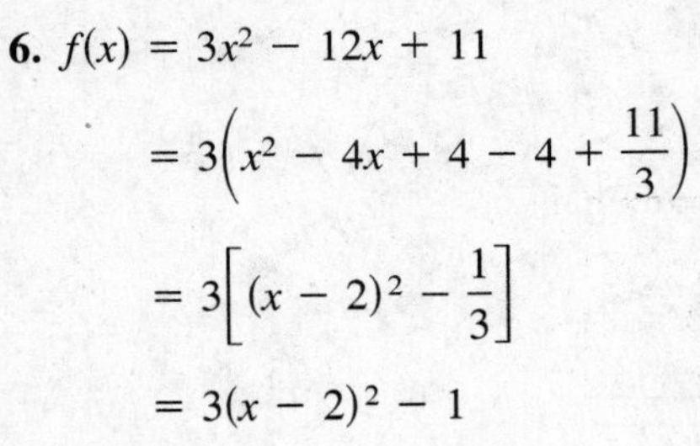

$$f(x) = 3x^2 - 12x + 11$$
$$= 3\left(x^2 - 4x + 4 - 4 + \frac{11}{3}\right)$$
$$= 3\left[(x-2)^2 - \frac{1}{3}\right]$$
$$= 3(x-2)^2 - 1$$

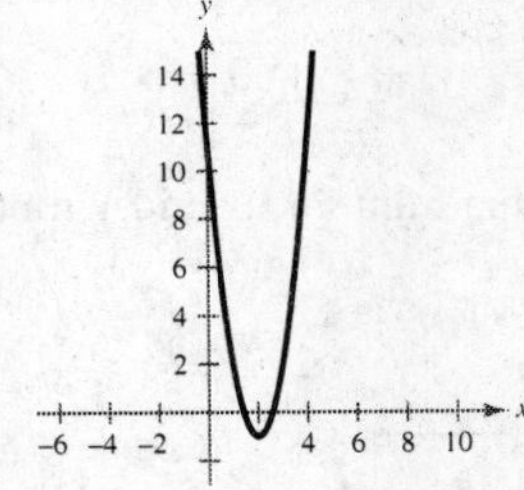

Vertex: $(2, -1)$

y-intercept: $(0, 11)$

x-intercepts: $x = \dfrac{12 \pm \sqrt{12}}{6} = 2 \pm \dfrac{1}{3}\sqrt{3}$

$\left(2 + \frac{1}{3}\sqrt{3}, 0\right), \left(2 - \frac{1}{3}\sqrt{3}, 0\right)$

7. $f(x) = 3 - x^2 - 4x$

$$= 3 - (x^2 + 4x + 4) + 4$$
$$= 7 - (x+2)^2$$

Vertex: $(-2, 7)$

Intercepts: $(0, 3), \left(-2 \pm \sqrt{7}, 0\right)$

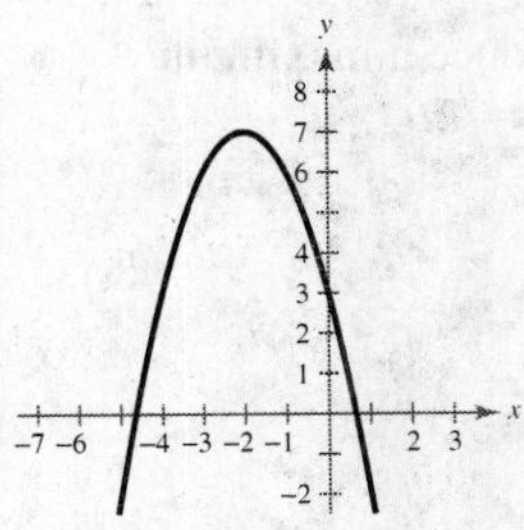

8. $f(x) = 3\left(x^2 + \frac{23}{3}x + \frac{529}{36}\right) + 30 - \frac{529}{12}$

$$= 3\left(x + \tfrac{23}{6}\right)^2 - \tfrac{169}{12}$$

Vertex: $\left(-\frac{23}{6}, -\frac{169}{12}\right)$

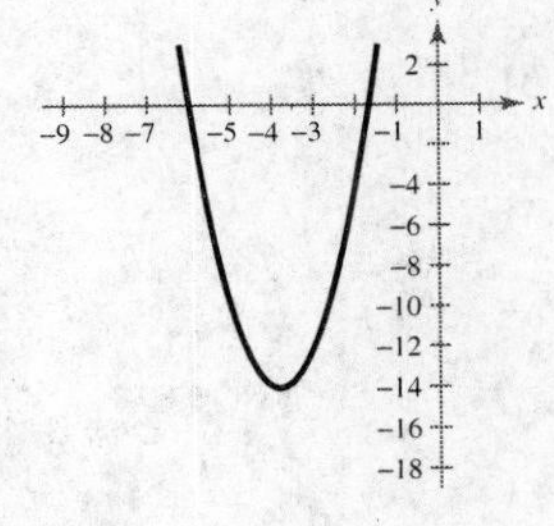

$3\left(x + \frac{23}{6}\right)^2 = \frac{169}{12}$

$x + \frac{23}{6} = \pm\sqrt{\frac{169}{36}} = \pm\frac{13}{6}$

$x = -6, -\frac{5}{3}$

Intercepts: $(-6, 0), \left(-\frac{5}{3}, 0\right), (0, 30)$

9. Vertex: $(1, -4) \Rightarrow f(x) = a(x-1)^2 - 4$

Point: $(2, -3) \Rightarrow -3 = a(2-1)^2 - 4$

$1 = a$

Thus, $f(x) = (x-1)^2 - 4$.

10. 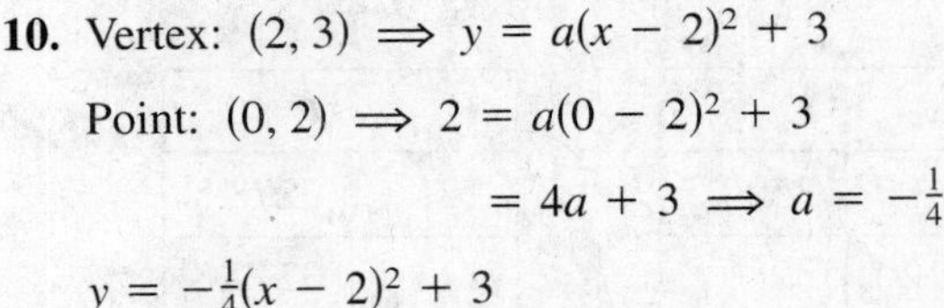

Vertex: $(2, 3) \Rightarrow y = a(x-2)^2 + 3$

Point: $(0, 2) \Rightarrow 2 = a(0-2)^2 + 3$

$= 4a + 3 \Rightarrow a = -\frac{1}{4}$

$y = -\frac{1}{4}(x-2)^2 + 3$

11. Vertex: $(-2, -2) \Rightarrow f(x) = a(x+2)^2 - 2$

Point: $(-1, 0) \Rightarrow 0 = a(-1+2)^2 - 2$

$a = 2$

Thus, $f(x) = 2(x+2)^2 - 2$.

12. Vertex: $\left(-\frac{1}{4}, \frac{3}{2}\right) \Rightarrow y = a\left(x + \frac{1}{4}\right)^2 + \frac{3}{2}$

Point: $(-2, 0) \Rightarrow 0 = a\left(-2 + \frac{1}{4}\right)^2 + \frac{3}{2}$

$= \frac{49}{16}a + \frac{3}{2} \Rightarrow a = -\frac{24}{49}$

$y = -\frac{24}{49}\left(x + \frac{1}{4}\right)^2 + \frac{3}{2}$

13. (a) $A = xy = x\left(\frac{8-x}{2}\right)$, since $x + 2y - 8 = 0 \Rightarrow y = \frac{8-x}{2}$.

Since the figure is in the first quadrant and x and y must be positive, the domain of

$A = x\left(\frac{8-x}{2}\right)$ is $0 < x < 8$.

(b)

x	y	Area
1	$4 - \frac{1}{2}(1)$	$(1)\left[4 - \frac{1}{2}(1)\right] = \frac{7}{2}$
2	$4 - \frac{1}{2}(2)$	$(2)\left[4 - \frac{1}{2}(2)\right] = 6$
3	$4 - \frac{1}{2}(3)$	$(3)\left[4 - \frac{1}{2}(3)\right] = \frac{15}{2}$
4	$4 - \frac{1}{2}(4)$	$(4)\left[4 - \frac{1}{2}(4)\right] = 8$
5	$4 - \frac{1}{2}(5)$	$(5)\left[4 - \frac{1}{2}(5)\right] = \frac{15}{2}$
6	$4 - \frac{1}{2}(6)$	$(6)\left[4 - \frac{1}{2}(6)\right] = 6$

The dimensions that will produce a maximum area seem to be $x = 4$ and $y = 2$.

(c) 9 0 0 8

The maximum area of 8 occurs at the vertex when $x = 4$ and $y = \frac{8-4}{2} = 2$.

(d)
$$\begin{aligned} A &= x\left(\frac{8-x}{2}\right) \\ &= \frac{1}{2}(8x - x^2) \\ &= -\frac{1}{2}(x^2 - 8x) \\ &= -\frac{1}{2}(x^2 - 8x + 16 - 16) \\ &= -\frac{1}{2}[(x-4)^2 - 16] \\ &= -\frac{1}{2}(x-4)^2 + 8 \end{aligned}$$

The maximum area of 8 occurs when $x = 4$ and $y = \frac{8-4}{2} = 2$.

(e) The answers are the same.

14. $C = 10{,}000 - 110x + 0.45x^2$

x	C
100	3500
120	3280
124	3279.2
130	3305

x	C
121	3278.5
122	3277.8
122.5	3277.8
123	3278.1

The minimum is 122 units.

15. 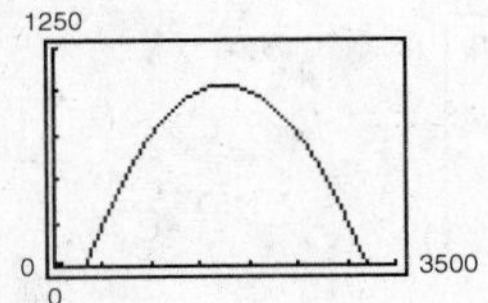

$6x + 4y = 1500$ Total amount of fencing

$A = 3xy$ Area enclosed

Because $y = \frac{1}{4}(1500 - 6x)$,

$$A = 3x\left(\frac{1}{4}\right)(1500 - 6x)$$

$$= -\frac{9}{2}x^2 + 1125x.$$

The vertex is at $x = \frac{-b}{2a} = \frac{-1125}{2(-9/2)} = 125$. Thus $x = 125$ feet, $y = \frac{1}{4}(1500 - 6(125)) = 187.5$ and the dimensions are 375 feet by 187.5 feet.

16. (a)

$P = 1.75x - (0.0005x^2 + 500)$

(b) The maximum is $(1750, 1031.25)$.

To maximize profit, sell 1750 songs.

(c) $P = -0.0005x^2 + 1.75x - 500$ opens downward. The vertex is at

$$x = \frac{-b}{2a} = \frac{-1.75}{-0.001} = 1750.$$

(d) The maximum profit is $P(1750) = \$1031.25$.

17. (a)

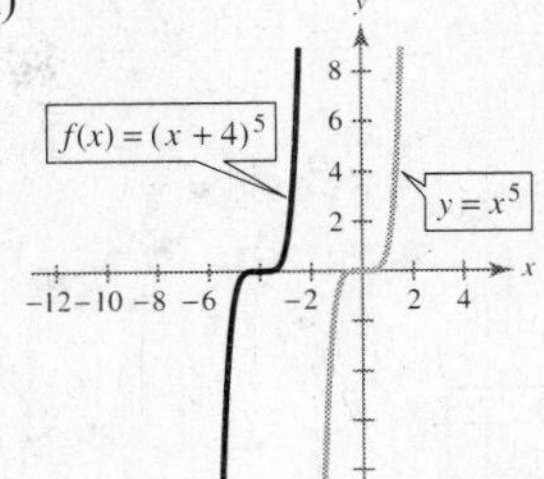

(b)

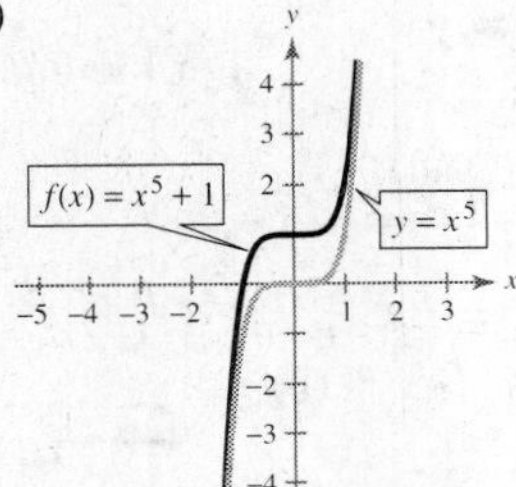

(c)

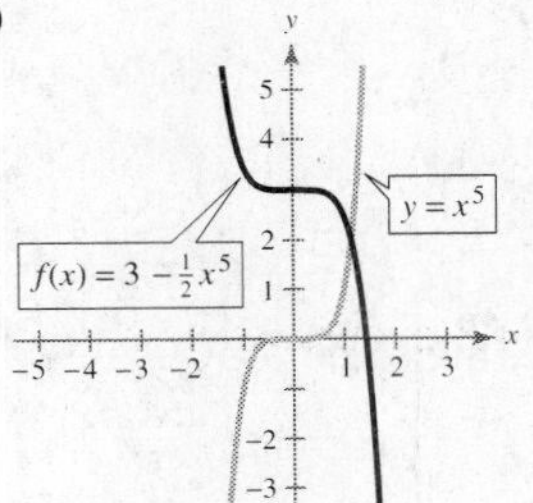

(d)

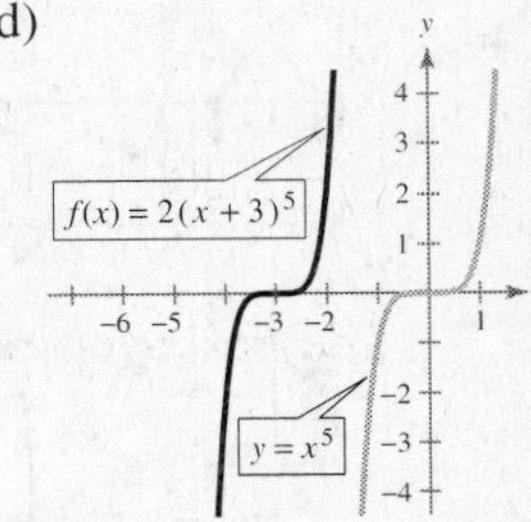

18. (a)

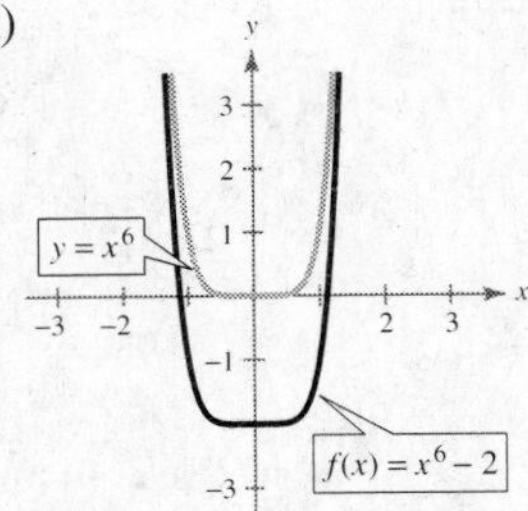

(b)

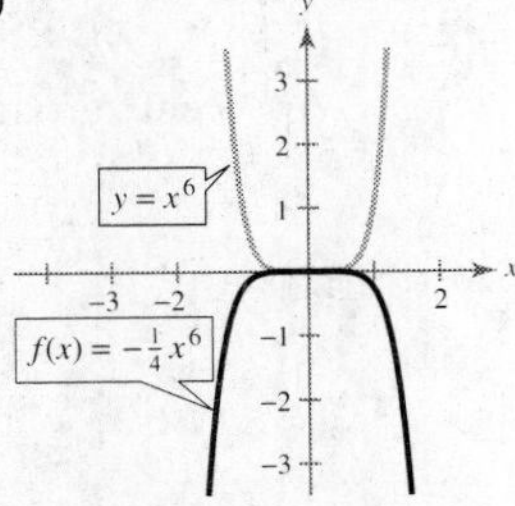

(c)

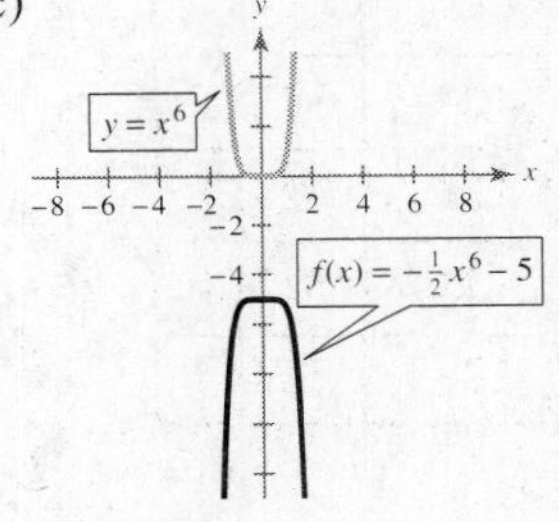

(d)

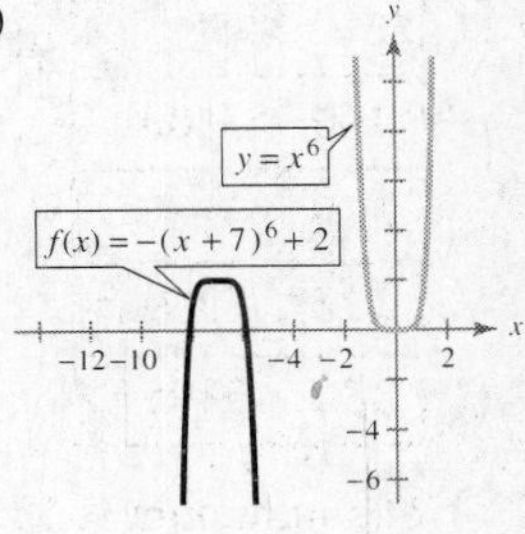

19. $f(x) = \frac{1}{2}x^3 - 2x + 1;\ g(x) = \frac{1}{2}x^3$

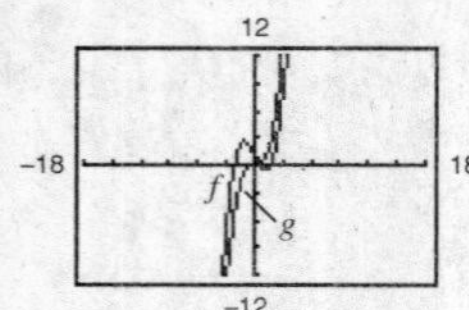

20. $f(x) = -x^4 + 2x^3;\ g(x) = -x^4$

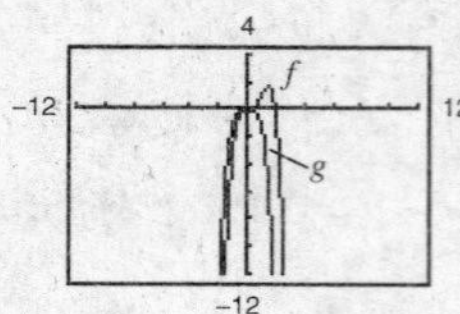

21. $f(x) = -x^2 + 6x + 9$

The degree is even and the leading coefficient is negative. The graph falls to the left and right.

22. $f(x) = \frac{1}{2}x^3 + 2x$

The degree is odd and the leading coefficient is positive. The graph falls to the left and rises to the right.

23. $f(x) = \frac{3}{4}(x^4 + 3x^2 + 2)$

The degree is even and the leading coefficient is positive. The graph rises to the left and right.

24. $h(x) = -x^5 - 7x^2 + 10x$

The degree is odd and the leading coefficient is negative. The graph rises to the left and falls to the right.

25. (a) $x^4 - x^3 - 2x^2 = x^2(x^2 - x - 2)$

$= x^2(x - 2)(x + 1) = 0$

Zeros: $x = -1, 0, 2$

(b)

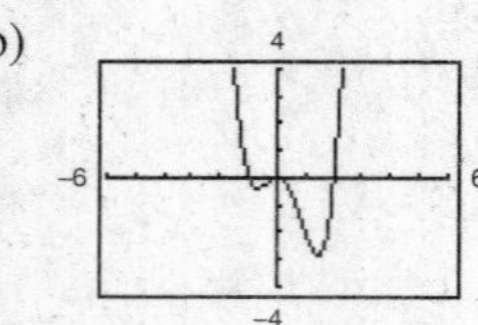

(c) Zeros: $x = -1, 0, 2$; the same

26. (a) $-2x^3 - x^2 + x = -x(2x^2 + x - 1)$

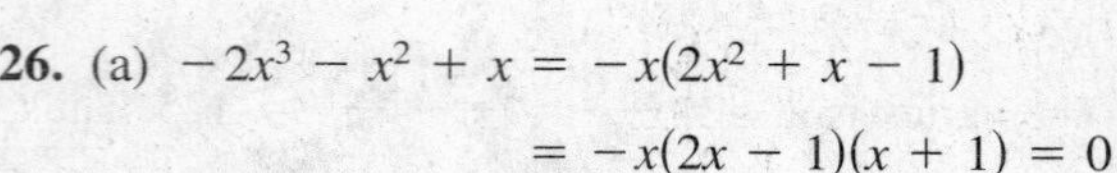

$= -x(2x - 1)(x + 1) = 0$

Zeros: $x = -1, 0, \frac{1}{2}$

(b)

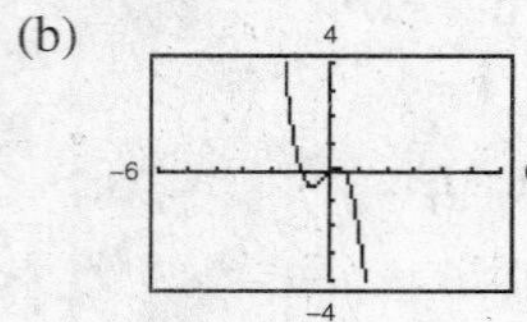

(c) Zeros: $-1, 0, 0.5$; the same

27. (a) $t^3 - 3t = t(t^2 - 3) = t(t + \sqrt{3})(t - \sqrt{3}) = 0$

Zeros: $t = 0, \pm\sqrt{3}$

(b)

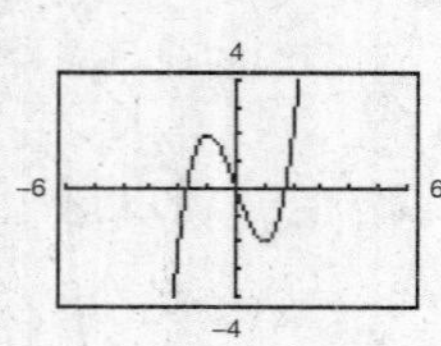

(c) Zeros: $t = 0, \pm 1.732$, the same

28. (a) $-(x + 6)^3 - 8 = 0$

$x^3 + 18x^2 + 108x + 224 = 0$

$(x + 8)(x^2 + 10x + 28)$

For the quadratic, $x = \dfrac{-10 \pm \sqrt{100 - 112}}{2}$

$= -5 \pm \sqrt{3}i.$

Zeros: $-8, -5 \pm \sqrt{3}i$

(b)

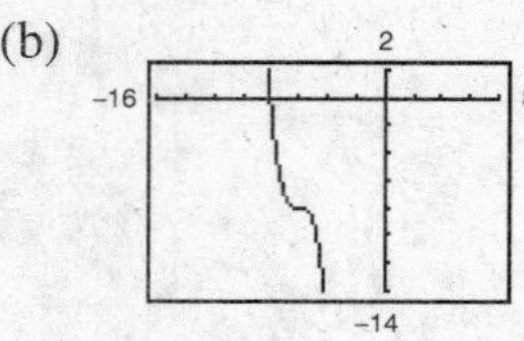

(c) Real zero: $x = -8$

29. (a) $x(x + 3)^2 = 0$

Zeros: $x = 0, -3$

(b)

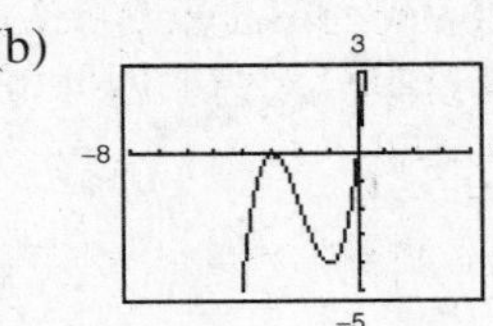

(c) Zeros: $x = -3, 0$, the same

30. (a) $t^4 - 4t^2 = 0$

$t^2(t^2 - 4) = 0$

$t^2(t + 2)(t - 2) = 0$

Zeros: $t = 0, \pm 2$

(b)

(c) Zeros: $t = 0, \pm 2$, the same

31. $f(x) = (x + 2)(x - 1)^2(x - 5)$

$= x^4 - 5x^3 - 3x^2 + 17x - 10$

32. $f(x) = (x + 3)x(x - 1)(x - 4)$

$= x^4 - 2x^3 - 11x^2 + 12x$

33. $f(x) = (x - 3)(x - 2 + \sqrt{3})(x - 2 - \sqrt{3})$

$= x^3 - 7x^2 + 13x - 3$

34. $f(x) = (x + 7)(x - 4 + \sqrt{6})(x - 4 - \sqrt{6})$

$= x^3 - x^2 - 46x + 70$

35. (a) Degree is even and leading coefficient is $1 > 0$. Rises to the left and rises to the right.

(b) $x^4 - 2x^3 - 12x^2 + 18x + 27 = (x - 3)^2(x + 1)(x + 3)$

Zeros: $\pm 3, -1$

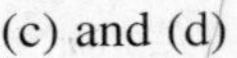

(c) and (d)

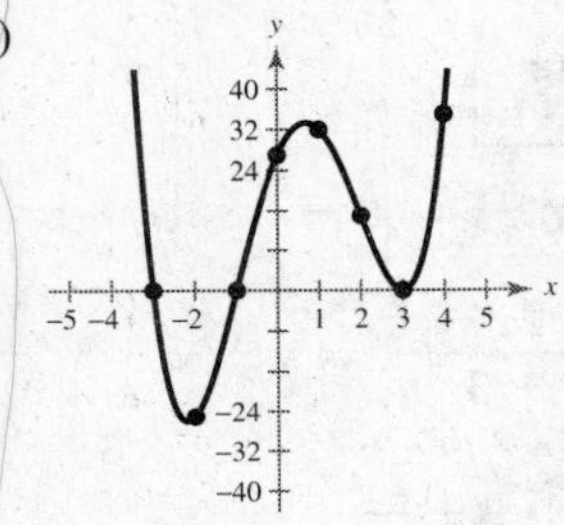

36. (a) Degree is odd and leading coefficient is $-3 < 0$. Rises to the left and falls to the right.

(b) $-3x^3 - 2x^2 + 27x + 18 = -(x - 3)(x + 3)(3x + 2)$

Zeros: $x = \pm 3, -\frac{2}{3}$

(c) and (d)

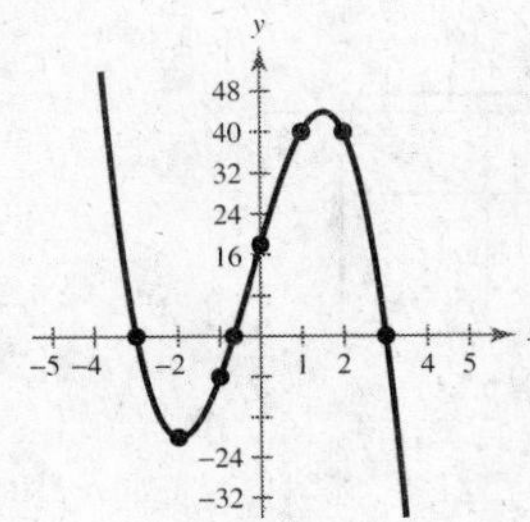

37. $f(x) = x^3 + 2x^2 - x - 1$

(a) $f(-3) < 0,\ f(-2) > 0 \Rightarrow$ zero in $[-3, -2]$

$f(-1) > 0,\ f(0) < 0 \Rightarrow$ zero in $[-1, 0]$

$f(0) < 0,\ f(1) > 0 \Rightarrow$ zero in $[0, 1]$

(b) Zeros: $-2.247, -0.555, 0.802$

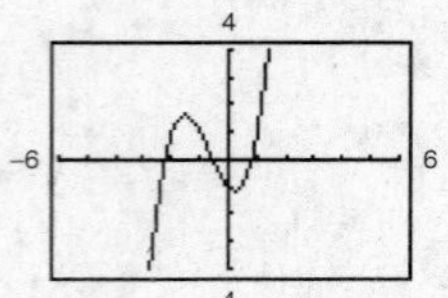

38. (a) $f(x) = 0.24x^3 - 2.6x - 1.4$

$f(-3) < 0, f(-2) > 0 \Rightarrow$ zero in $[-3, -2]$

$f(-1) > 0, f(0) < 0 \Rightarrow$ zero in $[-1, 0]$

$f(3) < 0, f(4) > 0 \Rightarrow$ zero in $[3, 4]$

(b) Zeros: $-2.979, -0.554, 3.533$

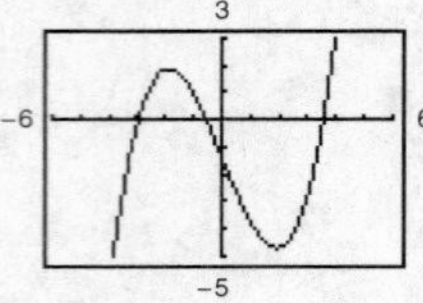

39. $f(x) = x^4 - 6x^2 - 4$

(a) $f(-3) > 0,\ f(-2) < 0 \Rightarrow$ zero in $[-3, -2]$

$f(2) < 0,\ f(3) > 0 \Rightarrow$ zero in $[2, 3]$

(b) Zeros: ± 2.570

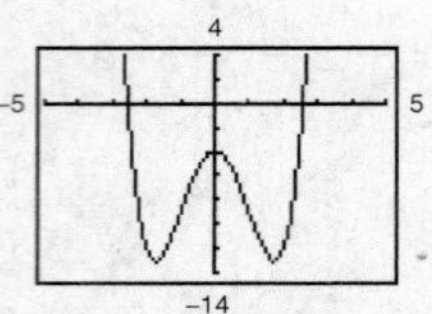

40. $f(x) = 2x^4 + \frac{7}{2}x^3 - 2$

(a) $f(-2) > 0, f(-1) < 0 \Rightarrow$ zero in $[-2, -1]$

$f(0) < 0, f(1) > 0 \Rightarrow$ zero in $[0, 1]$

(b) Zeros: $-1.897, 0.738$

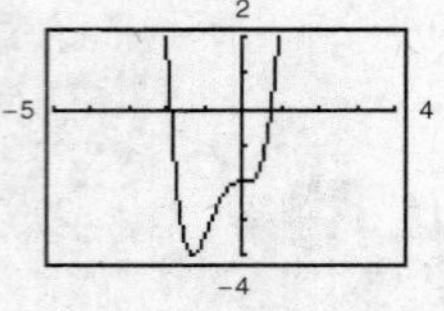

41. $y_1 = \dfrac{x^2}{x - 2}$

$$y_2 = x + 2 + \frac{4}{x - 2}$$

$$= \frac{(x + 2)(x - 2)}{x - 2} + \frac{4}{x - 2}$$

$$= \frac{x^2 - 4}{x - 2} + \frac{4}{x - 2}$$

$$= \frac{x^2}{x - 2} = y_1$$

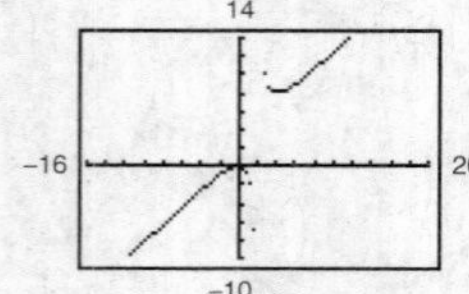

42. $y_1 = \dfrac{x^2 + 2x - 1}{x + 3},\ y_2 = x - 1 + \dfrac{2}{x + 3}$

$$y_2 = x - 1 + \frac{2}{x + 3}$$

$$= \frac{(x - 1)(x + 3) + 2}{x + 3}$$

$$= \frac{x^2 + 2x - 1}{x + 3} = y_1$$

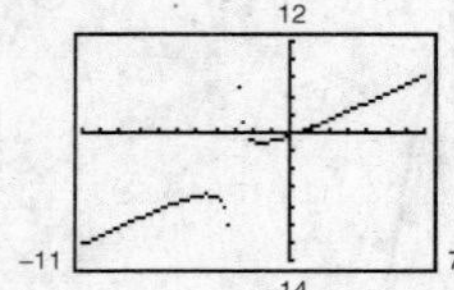

43. $y_1 = \dfrac{x^4 + 1}{x^2 + 2}$

$$y_2 = x^2 - 2 + \frac{5}{x^2 + 2}$$

$$= \frac{x^2(x^2 + 2)}{x^2 + 2} - \frac{2(x^2 + 2)}{x^2 + 2} + \frac{5}{x^2 + 2}$$

$$= \frac{x^4 + 2x^2 - 2x^2 - 4 + 5}{x^2 + 2}$$

$$= \frac{x^4 + 1}{x^2 + 2} = y_1$$

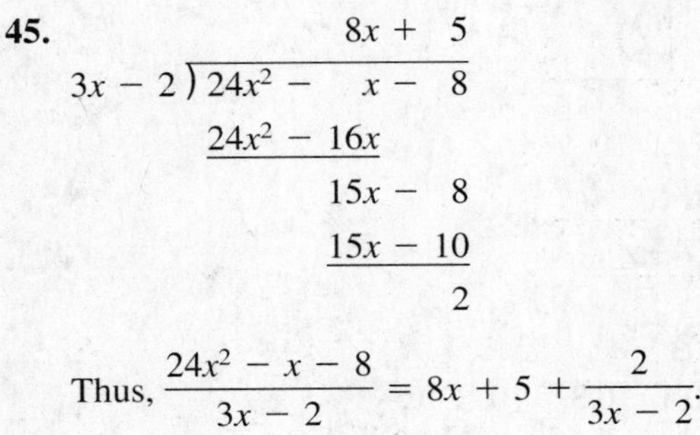

44. $y_1 = \dfrac{x^4 + x^2 - 1}{x^2 + 1}$

$$y_2 = x^2 - \frac{1}{x^2 + 1}$$

$$= \frac{x^2(x^2 + 1) - 1}{x^2 + 1}$$

$$= \frac{x^4 + x^2 - 1}{x^2 + 1} = y_1$$

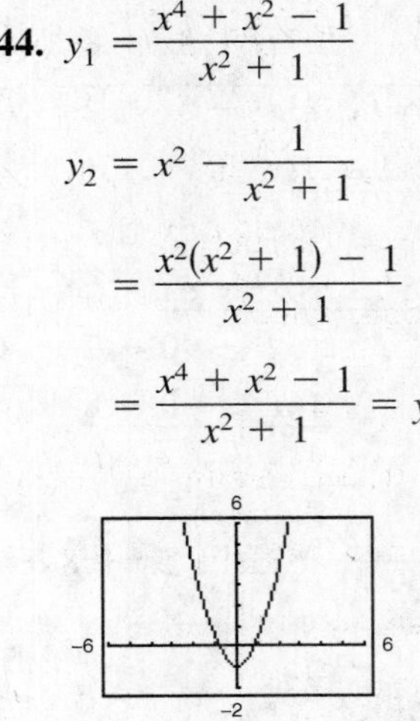

45.

$$\begin{array}{r} 8x + 5 \\ 3x - 2\,\overline{)\,24x^2 - x - 8} \\ \underline{24x^2 - 16x} \\ 15x - 8 \\ \underline{15x - 10} \\ 2 \end{array}$$

Thus, $\dfrac{24x^2 - x - 8}{3x - 2} = 8x + 5 + \dfrac{2}{3x - 2}$.

46.

$$\begin{array}{r} \frac{4}{3}x + \frac{8}{9} \\ 3x - 2\,\overline{)\,4x^2 + 0x + 7} \\ \underline{4x^2 - \frac{8}{3}x} \\ \frac{8}{3}x + 7 \\ \underline{\frac{8}{3}x - \frac{16}{9}} \\ \frac{79}{9} \end{array}$$

$$\frac{4x^2 + 7}{3x - 2} = \frac{4}{3}x + \frac{8}{9} + \frac{\frac{79}{9}}{3x - 2} = \frac{4}{3}x + \frac{8}{9} + \frac{79}{27x - 18}$$

47.

$$\begin{array}{r} x^2 - 2 \\ x^2 - 1\,\overline{)\,x^4 - 3x^2 + 2} \\ \underline{x^4 - x^2} \\ -2x^2 + 2 \\ \underline{-2x^2 + 2} \\ 0 \end{array}$$

Thus, $\dfrac{x^4 - 3x^2 + 2}{x^2 - 1} = x^2 - 2, (x \neq \pm 1)$.

48.

$$\begin{array}{r} 3x^2 + 4 \\ x^2 - 1\,\overline{)\,3x^4 + x^2 - 1} \\ \underline{3x^4 - 3x^2} \\ 4x^2 - 1 \\ \underline{4x^2 - 4} \\ 3 \end{array}$$

Thus, $\dfrac{3x^4 + x^2 - 1}{x^2 - 1} = 3x^2 + 4 + \dfrac{3}{x^2 - 1}$.

49.

$$\begin{array}{r} 5x + 2 \\ x^2 - 3x + 1\,\overline{)\,5x^3 - 13x^2 - x + 2} \\ \underline{5x^3 - 15x^2 + 5x} \\ 2x^2 - 6x + 2 \\ \underline{2x^2 - 6x + 2} \\ 0 \end{array}$$

Thus, $\dfrac{5x^3 - 13x^2 - x + 2}{x^2 - 3x + 1} = 5x + 2$,

$x \neq \dfrac{1}{2}(3 \pm \sqrt{5})$.

50.

$$\begin{array}{r} x^2 - x + 1 \\ x^2 + 2x\,\overline{)\,x^4 + x^3 - x^2 + 2x} \\ \underline{x^4 + 2x^3} \\ -x^3 - x^2 \\ \underline{-x^3 - 2x^2} \\ x^2 + 2x \\ \underline{x^2 + 2x} \\ 0 \end{array}$$

Thus,
$\dfrac{x^4 + x^3 - x^2 + 2x}{x^2 + 2x} = x^2 - x + 1, (x \neq 0, -2)$.

51.
$$\begin{array}{r} 3x^2+5x+8 \\ 2x^2+0x-1\,\overline{)\,6x^4+10x^3+13x^2-5x+2} \\ \underline{6x^4+0x^3-3x^2} \\ 10x^3+16x^2-5x \\ \underline{10x^3+0x^2-5x} \\ 16x^2-0+2 \\ \underline{16x^2+0-8} \\ 10 \end{array}$$

$$\frac{6x^4+10x^3+13x^2-5x+2}{2x^2-1}=3x^2+5x+8+\frac{10}{2x^2-1}$$

52.
$$\begin{array}{r} x^2-3x+2 \\ x^2+2\,\overline{)\,x^4-3x^3+4x^2-6x+3} \\ \underline{x^4+2x^2} \\ -3x^3+2x^2-6x \\ \underline{-3x^3-6x} \\ 2x^2+3 \\ \underline{2x^2+4} \\ -1 \end{array}$$

$$\frac{x^4-3x^3+4x^2-6x+3}{x^2+2}=x^2-3x+2+\frac{-1}{x^2+2}$$

53.
$$\begin{array}{r|rrrrr} -2 & 0.25 & -4 & 0 & 0 & 0 \\ & & -\frac{1}{2} & 9 & -18 & 36 \\ \hline & \frac{1}{4} & -\frac{9}{2} & 9 & -18 & 36 \end{array}$$

Hence,

$$\frac{0.25x^4-4x^3}{x+2}=\frac{1}{4}x^3-\frac{9}{2}x^2+9x-18+\frac{36}{x+2}.$$

54.
$$\begin{array}{r|rrrr} 5 & 0.1 & 0.3 & 0 & -0.5 \\ & & 0.5 & 4 & 20 \\ \hline & 0.1 & 0.8 & 4 & 19.5 \end{array}$$

$$\frac{0.1x^3+0.3x^2-0.5}{x-5}=0.1x^2+0.8x+4+\frac{19.5}{x-5}$$

55.
$$\begin{array}{r|rrrrr} \frac{2}{3} & 6 & -4 & -27 & 18 & 0 \\ & & 4 & 0 & -18 & 0 \\ \hline & 6 & 0 & -27 & 0 & 0 \end{array}$$

Thus,

$$\frac{6x^4-4x^3-27x^2+18x}{x-(2/3)}=6x^3-27x,\ x\neq\frac{2}{3}.$$

56.
$$\begin{array}{r|rrrr} \frac{1}{2} & 2 & 2 & -1 & 2 \\ & & 1 & \frac{3}{2} & \frac{1}{4} \\ \hline & 2 & 3 & \frac{1}{2} & \frac{9}{4} \end{array}$$

$$\frac{2x^3+2x^2-x+2}{x-(1/2)}=2x^2+3x+\frac{1}{2}+\frac{9/4}{x-(1/2)}$$

57.
$$\begin{array}{r|rrrr} 4 & 3 & -10 & 12 & -22 \\ & & 12 & 8 & 80 \\ \hline & 3 & 2 & 20 & 58 \end{array}$$

Thus,

$$\frac{3x^3-10x^2+12x-22}{x-4}=3x^2+2x+20+\frac{58}{x-4}.$$

58.
$$\begin{array}{r|rrrr} 1 & 2 & 6 & -14 & 9 \\ & & 2 & 8 & -6 \\ \hline & 2 & 8 & -6 & 3 \end{array}$$

$$\frac{2x^3+6x^2-14x+9}{x-1}=2x^2+8x-6+\frac{3}{x-1}$$

59. (a)
$$\begin{array}{r|rrrrr} -3 & 1 & 10 & -24 & 20 & 44 \\ & & -3 & -21 & 135 & -465 \\ \hline & 1 & 7 & -45 & 155 & -421 = f(-3) \end{array}$$

(b)
$$\begin{array}{r|rrrrr} -2 & 1 & 10 & -24 & 20 & 44 \\ & & -2 & -16 & 80 & -200 \\ \hline & 1 & 8 & -40 & 100 & -156 = f(-2) \end{array}$$

60. $g(t) = 2t^5 - 5t^4 - 8t + 20$

(a)
$$\begin{array}{r|rrrrrr} -4 & 2 & -5 & 0 & 0 & -8 & 20 \\ & & -8 & 52 & -208 & 832 & -3296 \\ \hline & 2 & -13 & 52 & -208 & 824 & -3276 = g(-4) \end{array}$$

(b)
$$\begin{array}{r|cccccc} \sqrt{2} & 2 & -5 & 0 & 0 & -8 & 20 \\ & & 2\sqrt{2} & 4 - 5\sqrt{2} & 4\sqrt{2} - 10 & 8 - 10\sqrt{2} & -20 \\ \hline & 2 & 2\sqrt{2} - 5 & 4 - 5\sqrt{2} & 4\sqrt{2} - 10 & -10\sqrt{2} & 0 \end{array} = g(\sqrt{2})$$

61. $f(x) = x^3 + 4x^2 - 25x - 28$

(a)
$$\begin{array}{r|rrrr} 4 & 1 & 4 & -25 & -28 \\ & & 4 & 32 & 28 \\ \hline & 1 & 8 & 7 & 0 \end{array}$$

$(x - 4)$ is a factor.

(b) $x^2 + 8x + 7 = (x + 1)(x + 7)$

Remaining factors: $(x + 1)$, $(x + 7)$

(c) $f(x) = (x - 4)(x + 1)(x + 7)$

(d) Zeros: $4, -1, -7$

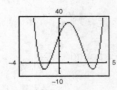

62. (a) $f(x) = 2x^3 + 11x^2 - 21x - 90$

$$\begin{array}{r|rrrr} -6 & 2 & 11 & -21 & -90 \\ & & -12 & 6 & 90 \\ \hline & 2 & -1 & -15 & 0 \end{array}$$

(b) Remaining factors of $2x^2 - x - 15$ are $(2x + 5)$, $(x - 3)$.

(c) $f(x) = (x + 6)(2x + 5)(x - 3)$

(d) Zeros: $-6, -\frac{5}{2}, 3$

63. $f(x) = x^4 - 4x^3 - 7x^2 + 22x + 24$

(a)
$$\begin{array}{r|rrrrr} -2 & 1 & -4 & -7 & 22 & 24 \\ & & -2 & 12 & -10 & -24 \\ \hline & 1 & -6 & 5 & 12 & 0 \end{array}$$

$(x + 2)$ is a factor.

$$\begin{array}{r|rrrr} 3 & 1 & -6 & 5 & 12 \\ & & 3 & -9 & -12 \\ \hline & 1 & -3 & -4 & 0 \end{array}$$

$(x - 3)$ is a factor.

(b) $x^2 - 3x - 4 = (x - 4)(x + 1)$

Remaining factors: $(x - 4)$, $(x + 1)$

(c) $f(x) = (x + 2)(x - 3)(x - 4)(x + 1)$

(d) Zeros: $-2, 3, 4, -1$

64. (a) $f(x) = x^4 - 11x^3 + 41x^2 - 61x + 30$

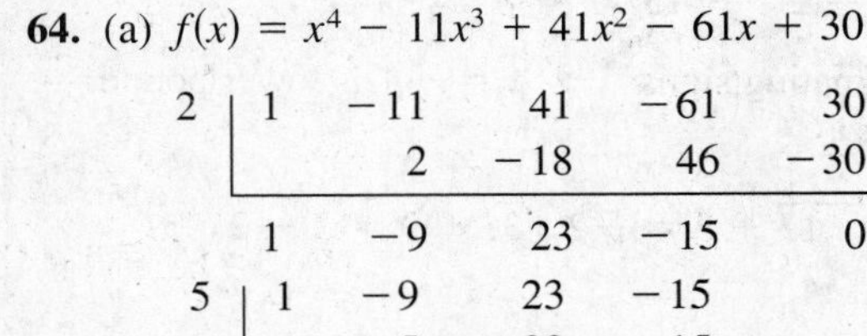

$$\begin{array}{r|rrrrr} 2 & 1 & -11 & 41 & -61 & 30 \\ & & 2 & -18 & 46 & -30 \\ \hline & 1 & -9 & 23 & -15 & 0 \end{array}$$

$$\begin{array}{r|rrrr} 5 & 1 & -9 & 23 & -15 \\ & & 5 & -20 & 15 \\ \hline & 1 & -4 & 3 & 0 \end{array}$$

(b) Remaining factors of $x^2 - 4x + 3$ are $(x - 3)$, $(x - 1)$.

(c) $f(x) = (x - 2)(x - 5)(x - 3)(x - 1)$

(d) Zeros: $1, 2, 3, 5$

65. $f(x) = 4x^3 - 11x^2 + 10x - 3$

Possible rational zeros: $\pm 3, \pm\frac{3}{2}, \pm\frac{3}{4}, \pm 1, \pm\frac{1}{2}, \pm\frac{1}{4}$

Zeros: $1, 1, \frac{3}{4}$

66. $f(x) = 10x^3 + 21x^2 - x - 6$

Possible rational zeros:
$\pm 1, \pm 2, \pm 3, \pm 6, \pm\frac{1}{5}, \pm\frac{1}{10}, \pm\frac{1}{2}, \pm\frac{3}{10}, \pm\frac{2}{5}, \pm\frac{3}{5}, \pm\frac{6}{5}, \pm\frac{3}{2}$

Actual rational zeros: $-2, \frac{1}{2}, -\frac{3}{5}$

67. $f(x) = 6x^3 - 5x^2 + 24x - 20$
$= (6x - 5)(x^2 + 4)$

Real zero: $\frac{5}{6}$

68. $f(x) = x^3 - 1.3x^3 - 1.7x + 0.6$
$= \frac{1}{10}(x - 2)(x + 1)(10x - 3)$

Zeros: $-1, 2, \frac{3}{10}$

69. $f(x) = 6x^4 - 25x^3 + 14x^2 + 27x - 18$

Possible rational zeros: $\pm 1, \pm 2, \pm 3, \pm 6, \pm 9, \pm 18, \pm\frac{1}{2}, \pm\frac{3}{2}, \pm\frac{9}{2}, \pm\frac{1}{3}, \pm\frac{2}{3}, \pm\frac{1}{6}$

Use a graphing utility to see that $x = -1$ and $x = 3$ are probably zeros.

$$\begin{array}{r|rrrrr} -1 & 6 & -25 & 14 & 27 & -18 \\ & & -6 & 31 & -45 & 18 \\ \hline & 6 & -31 & 45 & -18 & 0 \end{array} \qquad \begin{array}{r|rrrr} 3 & 6 & -31 & 45 & -18 \\ & & 18 & -39 & 18 \\ \hline & 6 & -13 & 6 & 0 \end{array}$$

$$6x^4 - 25x^3 + 14x^2 + 27x - 18 = (x + 1)(x - 3)(6x^2 - 13x + 6)$$
$$= (x + 1)(x - 3)(3x - 2)(2x - 3)$$

Thus, the zeros of f are $x = -1$, $x = 3$, $x = \frac{2}{3}$, and $x = \frac{3}{2}$.

70. $f(x) = 5x^4 + 126x^2 + 25$
$= (5x^2 + 1)(x^2 + 25)$

No real zeros

71. $g(x) = 5x^3 - 6x + 9$ has two variations in sign $\Rightarrow$ 0 or 2 positive real zeros.

$g(-x) = -5x^3 + 6x + 9$ has one variation in sign $\Rightarrow$ 1 negative real zero.

72. $f(x) = 2x^5 - 3x^2 + 2x - 1$ has three variations in sign $\Rightarrow$ 1 or 3 positive real zeros.

$f(-x) = -2x^5 - 3x^2 - 2x - 1$ has no variations in sign $\Rightarrow$ 0 negative real zeros.

73.
$$\begin{array}{r|rrrr} 1 & 4 & -3 & 4 & -3 \\ & & 4 & 1 & 5 \\ \hline & 4 & 1 & 5 & 2 \end{array}$$

All entries positive; $x = 1$ is upper bound.

$$\begin{array}{r|rrrr} -\frac{1}{4} & 4 & -3 & 4 & -3 \\ & & -1 & 1 & -\frac{5}{4} \\ \hline & 4 & -4 & 5 & -\frac{17}{4} \end{array}$$

Alternating signs; $x = -\frac{1}{4}$ is lower bound.

74.
$$\begin{array}{r|rrrr} 8 & 2 & -5 & -14 & 8 \\ & & 16 & 88 & 592 \\ \hline & 2 & 11 & 74 & 600 \end{array}$$

All positive $\Rightarrow x = 8$ is upper bound.

$$\begin{array}{r|rrrr} -4 & 2 & -5 & -14 & 8 \\ & & -8 & 52 & -152 \\ \hline & 2 & -13 & 38 & -144 \end{array}$$

Alternating signs $\Rightarrow x = -4$ is lower bound.

75. $6 + \sqrt{-25} = 6 + 5i$

76. $-\sqrt{-12} + 3 = -2\sqrt{3}i + 3 = 3 - 2\sqrt{3}i$

77. $-2i^2 + 7i = 2 + 7i$

78. $-i^2 - 4i = 1 - 4i$

79. $(7 + 5i) + (-4 + 2i) = (7 - 4) + (5i + 2i)$
$= 3 + 7i$

80. $\left(\frac{\sqrt{2}}{2} - \frac{\sqrt{2}}{2}i\right) - \left(\frac{\sqrt{2}}{2} + \frac{\sqrt{2}}{2}i\right) = -\sqrt{2}\,i$

81. $5i(13 - 8i) = 65i - 40i^2 = 40 + 65i$

82. $(1 + 6i)(5 - 2i) = 5 - 2i + 30i + 12 = 17 + 28i$

83. $\left(\sqrt{-16} + 3\right)\left(\sqrt{-25} - 2\right) = (4i + 3)(5i - 2)$
$= -20 - 8i + 15i - 6$
$= -26 + 7i$

84. $\left(5 - \sqrt{-4}\right)\left(5 + \sqrt{-4}\right) = (5 - 2i)(5 + 2i)$
$= 25 + 4$
$= 29$

85. $\sqrt{-9} + 3 + \sqrt{-36} = 3i + 3 + 6i$
$= 3 + 9i$

86. $7 - \sqrt{-81} + \sqrt{-49} = 7 - 9i + 7i$
$= 7 - 2i$

87. $(10 - 8i)(2 - 3i) = 20 - 30i - 16i + 24i^2$
$= -4 - 46i$

88. $i(6 + i)(3 - 2i) = i(18 + 3i - 12i + 2)$
$= i(20 - 9i) = 9 + 20i$

89. $(3 + 7i)^2 + (3 - 7i)^2 = (9 + 42i - 49) + (9 - 42i - 49)$
$= -80$

90. $(4 - i)^2 - (4 + i)^2 = (16 - 8i - 1) - (16 + 8i - 1)$
$= -16i$

91. $\frac{6 + i}{i} = \frac{6 + i}{i} \cdot \frac{-i}{-i} = \frac{-6i - i^2}{-i^2}$
$= \frac{-6i + 1}{1} = 1 - 6i$

92. $\frac{4}{-3i} = \frac{-4}{3i} \cdot \frac{-i}{-i} = \frac{4i}{3} = \frac{4}{3}i$

93. $\frac{3 + 2i}{5 + i} \cdot \frac{5 - i}{5 - i} = \frac{15 + 10i - 3i + 2}{25 + 1}$
$= \frac{17}{26} + \frac{7}{26}i$

94. $\frac{1 - 7i}{2 + 3i} \cdot \frac{2 - 3i}{2 - 3i} = \frac{2 - 21 - 17i}{4 + 9}$
$= \frac{-19}{13} + \frac{-17}{13}i$

95. $-3 - 2i$

96. $2 - i$

97. $2 - 5i$

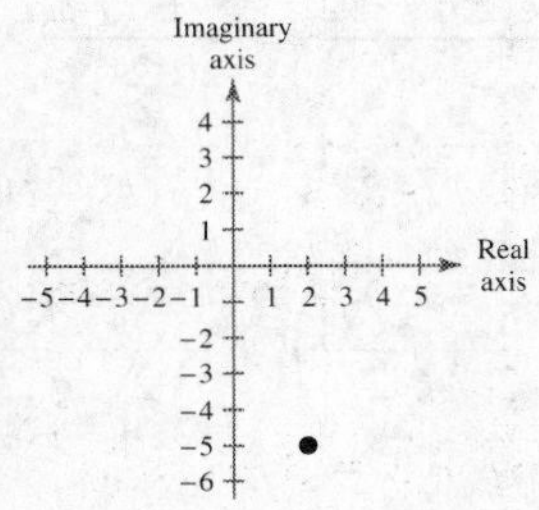

98. $-1 + 4i$

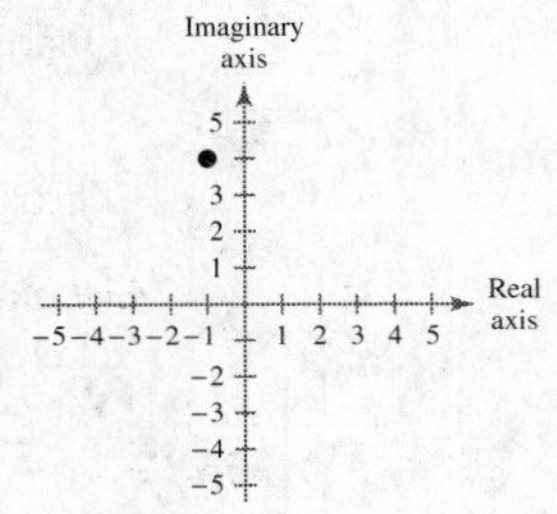

99. $-6i$

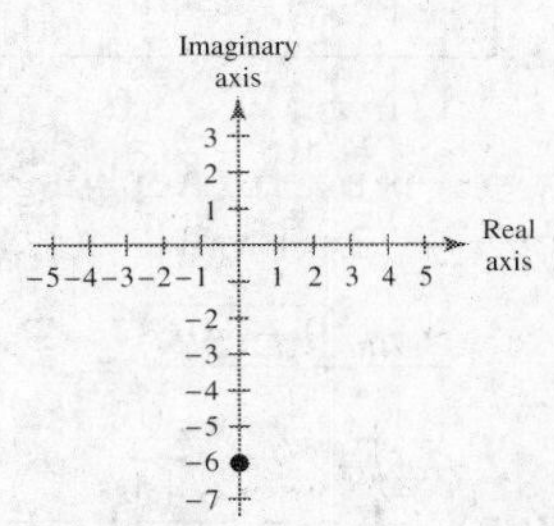

100. $7i$

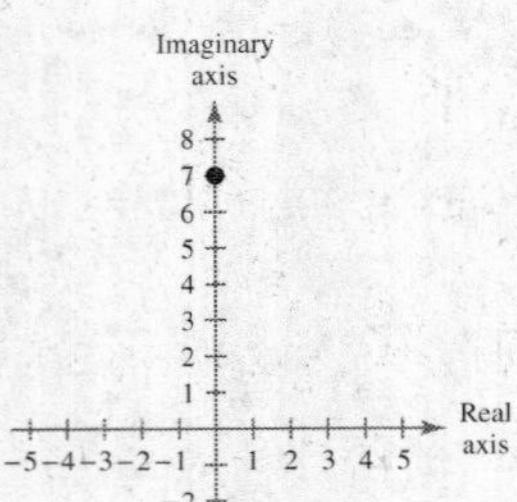

101. 3

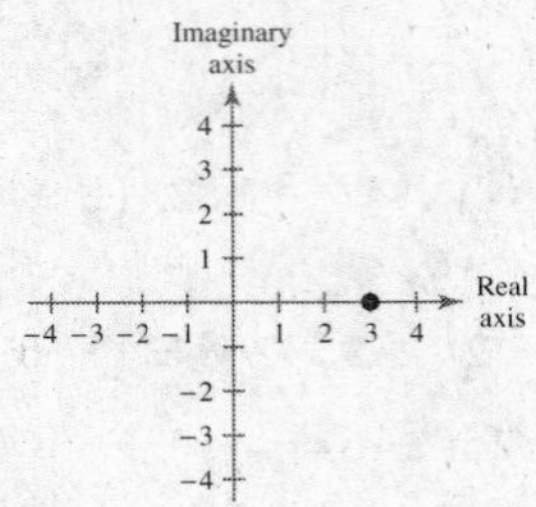

102. -2

103. $f(x) = 3x(x - 2)^2$

Zeros: $0, 2, 2$

104. $f(x) = (x - 4)(x + 9)^2$

Zeros: $4, -9, -9$

105. $f(x) = 2x^4 - 5x^3 + 10x - 12$

$$\begin{array}{r|rrrrr} 2 & 2 & -5 & 0 & 10 & -12 \\ & & 4 & -2 & -4 & 12 \\ \hline & 2 & -1 & -2 & 6 & 0 \end{array}$$

$x = 2$ is a zero.

$$\begin{array}{r|rrrr} -\frac{3}{2} & 2 & -1 & -2 & 6 \\ & & -3 & 6 & -6 \\ \hline & 2 & -4 & 4 & 0 \end{array}$$

$x = -\dfrac{3}{2}$ is a zero.

$$f(x) = (x - 2)\left(x + \frac{3}{2}\right)(2x^2 - 4x + 4)$$

$$= (x - 2)(2x + 3)(x^2 - 2x + 2)$$

By the Quadratic Formula, applied to $x^2 - 2x + 2$,

$$x = \frac{2 \pm \sqrt{4 - 4(2)}}{2} = 1 \pm i.$$

Zeros: $2, -\dfrac{3}{2}, 1 \pm i$

$$f(x) = (x - 2)(2x + 3)(x - 1 + i)(x - 1 - i)$$

106. $g(x) = 3x^4 - 4x^3 + 7x^2 + 10x - 4$

$$= (x + 1)(3x - 1)(x^2 - 2x + 4)$$

Quadratic: $x = \dfrac{2 \pm \sqrt{4 - 16}}{2} = 1 \pm \sqrt{3}i$

Zeros: $-1, \dfrac{1}{3}, 1 \pm \sqrt{3}i$

$$g(x) = (x + 1)(3x - 1)\left(x - 1 + \sqrt{3}i\right)\left(x - 1 - \sqrt{3}i\right)$$

107. $h(x) = x^3 - 7x^2 + 18x - 24$

$$\begin{array}{r|rrrr} 4 & 1 & -7 & 18 & -24 \\ & & 4 & -12 & 24 \\ \hline & 1 & -3 & 6 & 0 \end{array}$$

$x = 4$ is a zero. Applying the Quadratic Formula on $x^2 - 3x + 6$,

$$x = \frac{3 \pm \sqrt{9 - 4(6)}}{2} = \frac{3}{2} \pm \frac{\sqrt{15}}{2}i.$$

Zeros: $4, \dfrac{3}{2} + \dfrac{\sqrt{15}}{2}i, \dfrac{3}{2} - \dfrac{\sqrt{15}}{2}i$

$$h(x) = (x - 4)\left(x - \frac{3 + \sqrt{15}i}{2}\right)\left(x - \frac{3 - \sqrt{15}i}{2}\right)$$

108. $f(x) = 2x^3 - 5x^2 - 9x + 40$

$$= (2x + 5)(x^2 - 5x + 8)$$

Quadratic: $x = \dfrac{5 \pm \sqrt{25 - 32}}{2} = \dfrac{5 \pm \sqrt{7}i}{2}$

Zeros: $-\dfrac{5}{2}, \dfrac{5}{2} \pm \dfrac{\sqrt{7}}{2}i$

$$f(x) = (2x + 5)\left(x - \frac{5}{2} + \frac{\sqrt{7}}{2}i\right)\left(x - \frac{5}{2} - \frac{\sqrt{7}}{2}i\right)$$

109. $f(x) = x^5 + x^4 + 5x^3 + 5x^2$

$= x^2(x^3 + x^2 + 5x + 5)$

$= x^2[x^2(x + 1) + 5(x + 1)]$

$= x^2(x + 1)(x^2 + 5)$

$= x^2(x + 1)(x + \sqrt{5}i)(x - \sqrt{5}i)$

Zeros: $0, 0, -1, \pm\sqrt{5}i$

110. $f(x) = x^5 - 5x^3 + 4x$

$= x(x^4 - 5x^2 + 4)$

$= x(x^2 - 4)(x^2 - 1)$

$f(x) = x(x - 2)(x + 2)(x - 1)(x + 1)$

Zeros: $0, \pm 1, \pm 2$

111. $f(x) = x^3 - 4x^2 + 6x - 4$

(a) $x^3 - 4x^2 + 6x - 4 = (x - 2)(x^2 - 2x + 2)$

By the Quadratic Formula, for $x^2 - 2x + 2$,

$$x = \frac{2 \pm \sqrt{(-2)^2 - 4(2)}}{2} = 1 \pm i.$$

Zeros: $2, 1 + i, 1 - i$

(b) $f(x) = (x - 2)(x - 1 - i)(x - 1 + i)$

(c) x-intercept: $(2, 0)$

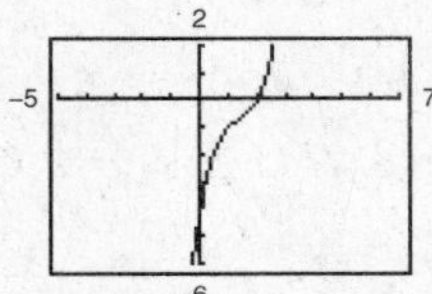

112. (a) $f(x) = x^3 - 5x^2 - 7x + 51$

$= (x + 3)(x^2 - 8x + 17)$

$$x = \frac{8 \pm \sqrt{(-8)^2 - 4(17)}}{2} = \frac{8 \pm \sqrt{-4}}{2}$$

$= 4 \pm i$

Zeros: $-3, 4 + i, 4 - i$

(b) $f(x) = (x + 3)(x - 4 - i)(x - 4 + i)$

(c) x-intercept: $(-3, 0)$

113. (a) $f(x) = -3x^3 - 19x^2 - 4x + 12$

$$\begin{array}{r|rrrr} -1 & -3 & -19 & -4 & 12 \\ & & 3 & 16 & -12 \\ \hline & -3 & -16 & 12 & 0 \end{array}$$

(b) $f(x) = -(x + 1)(3x^2 + 16x - 12)$

$= -(x + 1)(3x - 2)(x + 6)$

(c) x-intercepts: $(-1, 0), (-6, 0), \left(\frac{2}{3}, 0\right)$

114. (a) $f(x) = 2x^3 - 9x^2 + 22x - 30$

$= (2x - 5)(x^2 - 2x + 6)$

$$x = \frac{2 \pm \sqrt{(-2)^2 - 4(6)}}{2} = 1 \pm \sqrt{5}i$$

Zeros: $\frac{5}{2}, 1 + \sqrt{5}i, 1 - \sqrt{5}i$

(b) $f(x) = (2x - 5)(x - 1 - \sqrt{5}i)(x - 1 + \sqrt{5}i)$

(c) x-intercept: $\left(\frac{5}{2}, 0\right)$

115. $f(x) = x^4 + 34x^2 + 225$

(a) $x^4 + 34x^2 + 225 = (x^2 + 9)(x^2 + 25)$

Zeros: $\pm 3i, \pm 5i$

(b) $(x + 3i)(x - 3i)(x + 5i)(x - 5i)$

(c) No x-intercepts

(d)

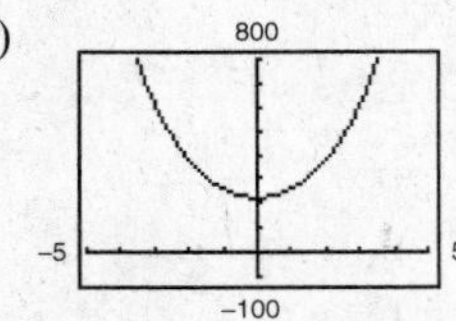

116. (a), (b)

$f(x) = x^4 + 10x^3 + 26x^2 + 10x + 25$

$= (x^2 + 1)(x^2 + 10x + 25)$

$= (x^2 + 1)(x + 5)^2 = (x + i)(x - i)(x + 5)^2$

Zeros: $\pm i, -5, -5$

(c) x-intercept: $(-5, 0)$

117. Since $5i$ is a zero, so is $-5i$.

$$\begin{aligned} f(x) &= (x-4)(x+2)(x-5i)(x+5i) \\ &= (x^2-2x-8)(x^2+25) \\ &= x^4-2x^3+17x^2-50x-200 \end{aligned}$$

118. Since $2i$ is a zero, so is $-2i$.

$$\begin{aligned} f(x) &= (x-2)(x+2)(x-2i)(x+2i) \\ &= (x^2-4)(x^2+4) \\ &= x^4-16 \end{aligned}$$

119. $$\begin{aligned} f(x) &= (x-1)(x+4)(x+3-5i)(x+3+5i) \\ &= (x^2+3x-4)((x+3)^2+25) \\ &= (x^2+3x-4)(x^2+6x+34) \\ &= x^4+9x^3+48x^2+78x-136 \end{aligned}$$

120. $$\begin{aligned} f(x) &= (x+4)(x+4)\left(x-1-\sqrt{3}i\right)\left(x-1+\sqrt{3}i\right) \\ &= (x^2+8x+16)((x-1)^2+3) \\ &= (x^2+8x+16)(x^2-2x+4) \\ &= x^4+6x^3+4x^2+64 \end{aligned}$$

121. $f(x) = x^4-2x^3+8x^2-18x-9$

(a) $f(x) = (x^2+9)(x^2-2x-1)$

For the quadratic x^2-2x-1, $x = \dfrac{2 \pm \sqrt{(-2)^2-4(-1)}}{2} = 1 \pm \sqrt{2}$.

(b) $f(x) = (x^2+9)\left(x-1+\sqrt{2}\right)\left(x-1-\sqrt{2}\right)$

(c) $f(x) = (x+3i)(x-3i)\left(x-1+\sqrt{2}\right)\left(x-1-\sqrt{2}\right)$

122. $f(x) = x^4-4x^3+3x^2+8x-16$

(a) $f(x) = (x^2-x-4)(x^2-3x+4)$

(b) $x = \dfrac{1 \pm \sqrt{(-1)^2-4(-4)}}{2} = \dfrac{1}{2} \pm \dfrac{\sqrt{17}}{2}$

$$f(x) = \left(x-\frac{1}{2}-\frac{\sqrt{17}}{2}\right)\left(x-\frac{1}{2}+\frac{\sqrt{17}}{2}\right)(x^2-3x+4)$$

(c) $x = \dfrac{3 \pm \sqrt{(-3)^2-4(4)}}{2} = \dfrac{3}{2} \pm \dfrac{\sqrt{7}}{2}i$

$$f(x) = \left(x-\frac{1}{2}-\frac{\sqrt{17}}{2}\right)\left(x-\frac{1}{2}+\frac{\sqrt{17}}{2}\right)\left(x-\frac{3}{2}+\frac{\sqrt{7}}{2}i\right)\left(x-\frac{3}{2}-\frac{\sqrt{7}}{2}i\right)$$

123. Zeros: $-2i, 2i$

$(x+2i)(x-2i) = x^2+4$ is a factor.

$f(x) = (x^2+4)(x+3)$

Zeros: $\pm 2i, -3$

124. Zeros: $2+\sqrt{5}i, 2-\sqrt{5}i$

$\left(x-2-\sqrt{5}i\right)\left(x-2+\sqrt{5}i\right) = (x-2)^2+5 = x^2-4x+9$ is a factor.

$f(x) = (x^2-4x+9)(2x+1)$

Zeros: $x = -\frac{1}{2}, 2 \pm \sqrt{5}i$

125. (a) Domain: all $x \neq -3$

(b) Horizontal asymptote: $y = -1$

Vertical asymptote: $x = -3$

126. (a) Domain: all $x \neq 8$

(b) Horizontal asymptote: $y = 4$

Vertical asymptote: $x = 8$

127. $f(x) = \dfrac{2}{x^2 - 3x - 18} = \dfrac{2}{(x - 6)(x + 3)}$

(a) Domain: all $x \neq 6, \ -3$

(b) Horizontal asymptote: $y = 0$

Vertical asymptotes: $x = 6, \ x = -3$

128. The denominator $x^2 + x + 3$ has no zeros.

Domain: all x

Horizontal asymptote: $y = 2$

Vertical asymptotes: none

129. $f(x) = \dfrac{7 + x}{7 - x}$

(a) Domain: all $x \neq 7$

(b) Horizontal asymptote: $y = -1$

Vertical asymptote: $x = 7$

130. $f(x) = \dfrac{6x}{x^2 - 1} = \dfrac{6x}{(x + 1)(x - 1)}$

(a) Domain: all $x \neq \pm 1$

(b) Horizontal asymptote: $y = 0$

Vertical asymptotes: $x = \pm 1$

131. $f(x) = \dfrac{4x^2}{2x^2 - 3}$

(a) Domain: all $x \neq \pm\sqrt{\dfrac{3}{2}} = \pm\dfrac{\sqrt{6}}{2}$

(b) Horizontal asymptote: $y = 2$

Vertical asymptotes: $x = \pm\sqrt{\dfrac{3}{2}} = \pm\dfrac{\sqrt{6}}{2}$

132. $f(x) = \dfrac{3x^2 - 11x - 4}{x^2 + 2}$

(a) Domain: all x

(b) Horizontal asymptote: $y = 3$

No vertical asymptote

133. $f(x) = \dfrac{2x - 10}{x^2 - 2x - 15} = \dfrac{2(x - 5)}{(x - 5)(x + 3)} = \dfrac{2}{x + 3}$, $x \neq 5$

(a) Domain: all $x \neq 5, -3$

(b) Vertical asymptote: $x = -3$

(There is a hole at $x = 5$.)

Horizontal asymptote: $y = 0$

134. $f(x) = \dfrac{x^3 - 4x^2}{x^2 + 3x + 2} = \dfrac{x^2(x - 4)}{(x + 2)(x + 1)}$

(a) Domain: all $x \neq -1, -2$

(b) Vertical asymptote: $x = -2, x = -1$

No horizontal asymptotes

135. $f(x) = \dfrac{x - 2}{|x| + 2}$

(a) Domain: all real numbers

(b) No vertical asymptotes

Horizontal asymptotes: $y = 1, y = -1$

136. $f(x) = \dfrac{2x}{|2x - 1|}$

(a) Domain: all $x \neq \dfrac{1}{2}$

(b) Vertical asymptote: $x = \dfrac{1}{2}$

Horizontal asymptotes: $y = 1$ (to the right)
$y = -1$ (to the left)

137. $C = \dfrac{528p}{100 - p}, \quad 0 \le p < 100$

(a) When $p = 25$, $C = \dfrac{528(25)}{100 - 25} = 176$ million.

When $p = 50$, $C = \dfrac{528(50)}{100 - 50} = 528$ million.

When $p = 75$, $C = \dfrac{528(75)}{100 - 75} = 1584$ million.

(b)

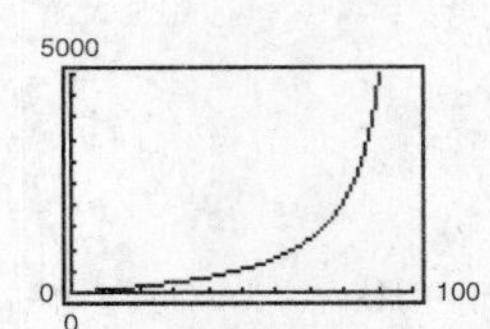

(c) No. As $p \to 100$, C tends to infinity.

138. $y = \dfrac{1.568x - 0.001}{6.360x + 1}, x > 0$

The moth will be satiated at the horizontal asymptote, $y = \dfrac{1.568}{6.360} \approx 0.247$ mg.

139. $f(x) = \dfrac{x^2 - 5x + 4}{x^2 - 1}$

$= \dfrac{(x - 4)(x - 1)}{(x - 1)(x + 1)}$

$= \dfrac{x - 4}{x + 1}, \quad x \neq 1$

Vertical asymptotes: $x = -1$

Horizontal asymptote: $y = 1$

No slant asymptotes

Hole at $x = 1$: $\left(1, -\dfrac{3}{2}\right)$

140. $f(x) = \dfrac{x^2 - 3x - 8}{x^2 - 4}$

$= \dfrac{x^2 - 3x - 8}{(x - 2)(x + 2)}$

Vertical asymptotes: $x = \pm 2$

Horizontal asymptote: $y = 1$

No slant asymptotes

Holes: none

141. $f(x) = \dfrac{2x^2 - 7x + 3}{2x^2 - 3x - 9}$

$= \dfrac{(x - 3)(2x - 1)}{(x - 3)(2x + 3)}$

$= \dfrac{2x - 1}{2x + 3}, x \neq 3$

Vertical asymptote: $x = -\dfrac{3}{2}$

Horizontal asymptote: $y = 1$

No slant asymptotes

Hole at $x = 3$: $\left(3, \dfrac{5}{9}\right)$

142. $f(x) = \dfrac{3x^2 + 13x - 10}{2x^2 + 11x + 5}$

$= \dfrac{(x + 5)(3x - 2)}{(x + 5)(2x + 1)}$

$= \dfrac{3x - 2}{2x + 1}, \quad x \neq -5$

Vertical asymptote: $x = -\dfrac{1}{2}$

Horizontal asymptote: $y = \dfrac{3}{2}$

No slant asymptotes

Hole at $x = -5$: $\left(-5, \dfrac{17}{9}\right)$

143. $f(x) = \dfrac{3x^3 - x^2 - 12x + 4}{x^2 + 3x + 2}$

$= \dfrac{(x - 2)(x + 2)(3x - 1)}{(x + 1)(x + 2)}$

$= \dfrac{(x - 2)(3x - 1)}{x + 1}, \quad x \neq -2$

$= 3x - 10 + \dfrac{12}{x + 1}, \quad x \neq -2$

Vertical asymptote: $x = -1$

No horizontal asymptotes

Slant asymptote: $y = 3x - 10$

Hole at $x = -2$: $(-2, -28)$

144. $f(x) = \dfrac{2x^3 + 3x^2 - 2x - 3}{x^2 - 3x + 2}$

$= \dfrac{(x - 1)(x + 1)(2x + 3)}{(x - 1)(x - 2)}$

$= \dfrac{(x + 1)(2x + 3)}{x - 2}, \quad x \neq 1$

$= 2x + 9 + \dfrac{21}{x - 2}, \quad x \neq 1$

Vertical asymptote: $x = 2$

No horizontal asymptotes

Slant asymptote: $y = 2x + 9$

Hole at $x = 1$: $(1, -10)$

145. $f(x) = \dfrac{2x - 1}{x - 5}$

Intercepts: $\left(0, \frac{1}{5}\right), \left(\frac{1}{2}, 0\right)$

Vertical asymptote: $x = 5$

Horizontal asymptote: $y = 2$

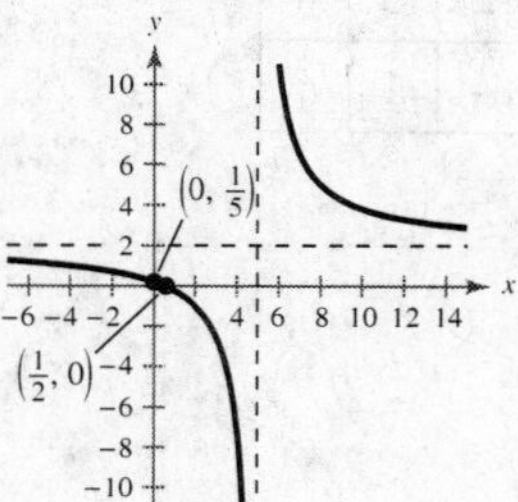

146. $f(x) = \dfrac{x - 3}{x - 2}$

x-intercept: $(3, 0)$

y-intercept: $\left(0, \frac{3}{2}\right)$

Vertical asymptote: $x = 2$

Horizontal asymptote: $y = 1$

x	-1	0	1	3	4	5
y	$\frac{4}{3}$	$\frac{3}{2}$	2	0	$\frac{1}{2}$	$\frac{2}{3}$

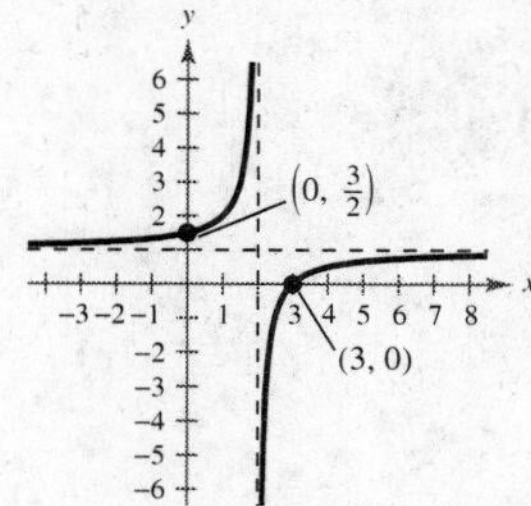

147. $f(x) = \dfrac{2x}{x^2 + 4}$

Intercept: $(0, 0)$

Origin symmetry

Horizontal asymptote: $y = 0$

x	-2	-1	0	1	2
y	$-\frac{1}{2}$	$-\frac{2}{5}$	0	$\frac{2}{5}$	$\frac{1}{2}$

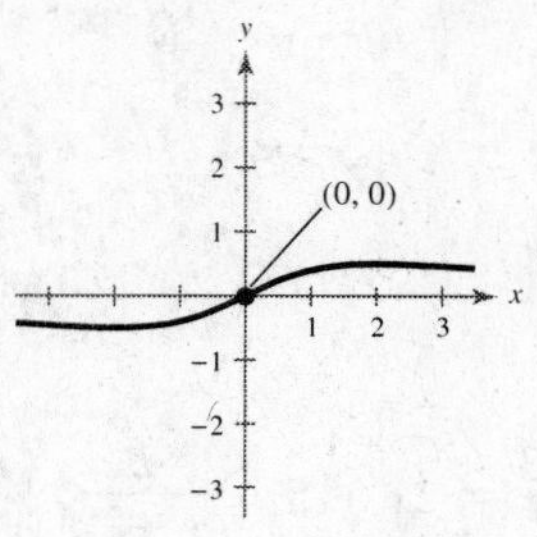

148. $f(x) = \dfrac{2x^2}{x^2 - 4}$

Intercept: $(0, 0)$

y-axis symmetry

Vertical asymptotes: $x = 2$, $x = -2$

Horizontal asymptote: $y = 2$

x	± 5	± 4	± 3	± 1	0
y	$\frac{50}{21}$	$\frac{8}{3}$	$\frac{18}{5}$	$-\frac{2}{3}$	0

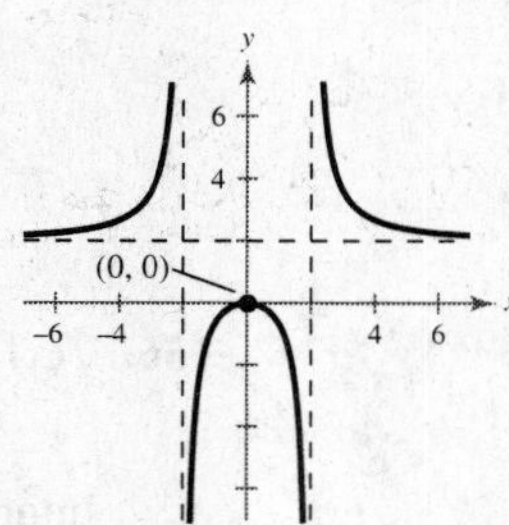

149. $f(x) = \dfrac{x^2}{x^2 + 1}$

Intercept: $(0, 0)$

y-axis symmetry

Horizontal asymptote: $y = 1$

x	± 3	± 2	± 1	0
y	$\frac{9}{10}$	$\frac{4}{5}$	$\frac{1}{2}$	0

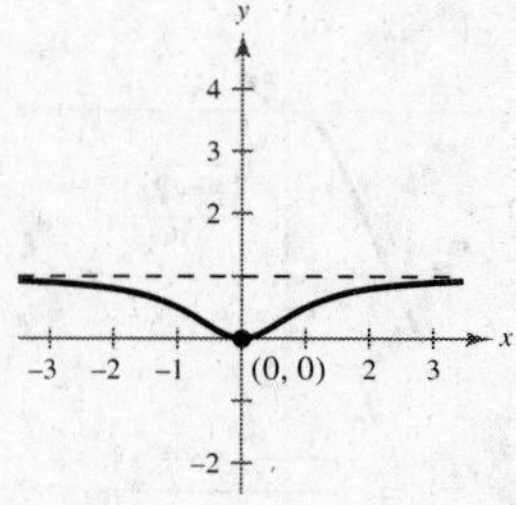

150. $f(x) = \dfrac{5x}{x^2 + 1}$

Intercept: $(0, 0)$

Symmetry: origin

Horizontal asymptote: $y = 0$

No vertical asymptotes

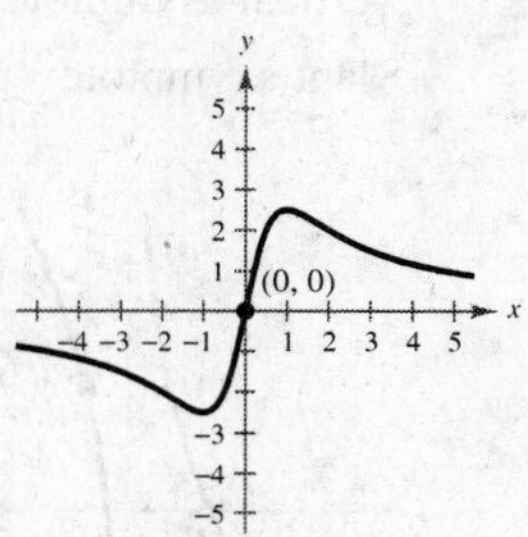

151. $f(x) = \dfrac{2}{(x + 1)^2}$

Intercept: $(0, 2)$

Horizontal asymptote: $y = 0$

Vertical asymptote: $x = -1$

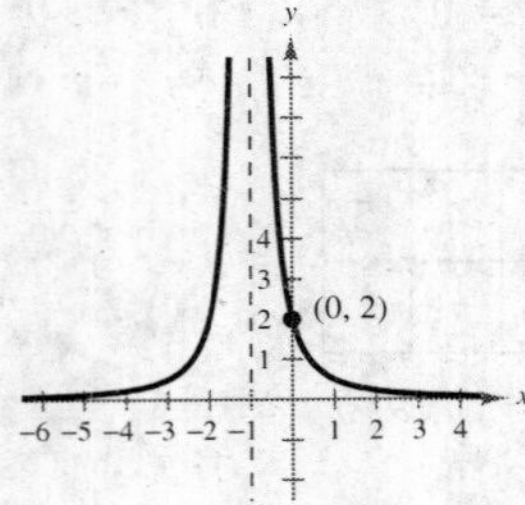

152. $h(x) = \dfrac{4}{(x - 1)^2}$

y-intercept: $(0, 4)$

Vertical asymptote: $x = 1$

Horizontal asymptote: $y = 0$

x	-2	-1	0	2	3	4
y	$\frac{4}{9}$	1	4	4	1	$\frac{4}{9}$

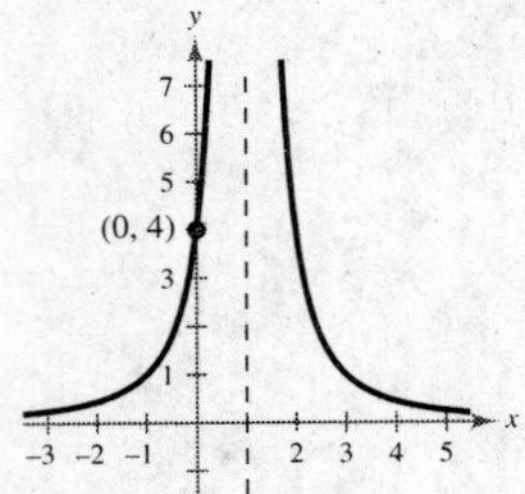

153. $f(x) = \dfrac{2x^3}{x^2 + 1} = 2x - \dfrac{2x}{x^2 + 1}$

Intercept: $(0, 0)$

Origin symmetry

Slant asymptote: $y = 2x$

x	-2	-1	0	1	2
y	$-\frac{16}{5}$	-1	0	1	$\frac{16}{5}$

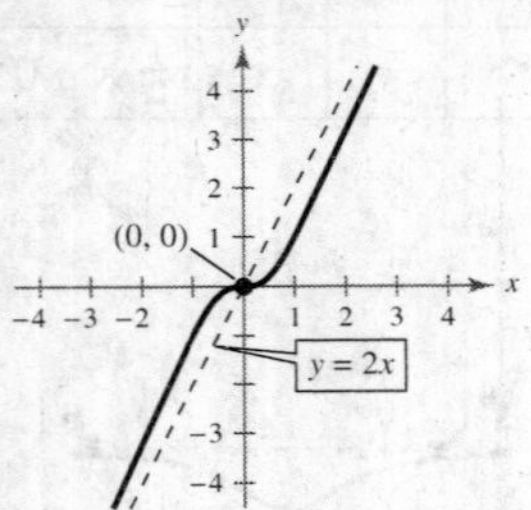

154. $f(x) = \dfrac{x^3}{3x^2 - 6} = \dfrac{1}{3}x + \dfrac{2x}{3x^2 - 6} = \dfrac{1}{3}\left[x + \dfrac{2x}{x^2 - 2}\right]$

Intercepts: $(0, 0)$

Vertical asymptotes: $x = \pm\sqrt{2}$

Slant asymptote: $y = \dfrac{1}{3}x$

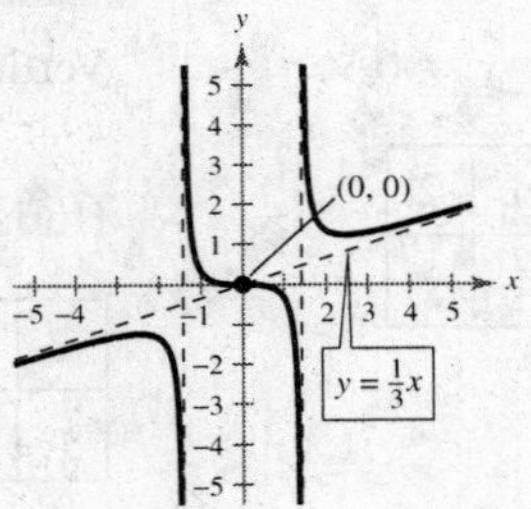

155. $f(x) = \dfrac{x^2 - x + 1}{x - 3} = x + 2 + \dfrac{7}{x - 3}$

Intercept: $\left(0, -\dfrac{1}{3}\right)$

Vertical asymptote: $x = 3$

Slant asymptote: $y = x + 2$

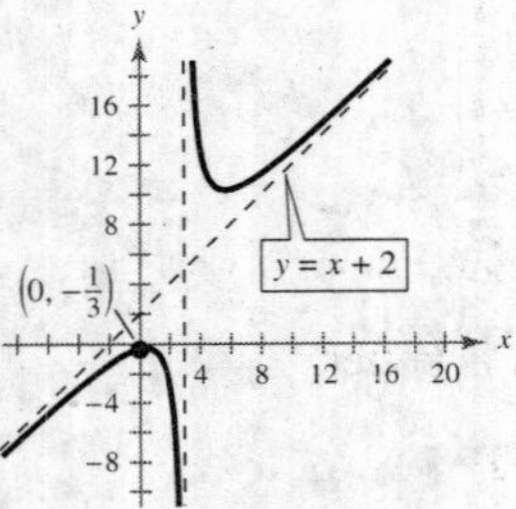

156. $f(x) = \dfrac{2x^2 + 7x + 3}{x + 1} = 2x + 5 - \dfrac{2}{x + 1}$

Intercepts: $(0, 3), (-3, 0), \left(-\dfrac{1}{2}, 0\right)$

Vertical asymptote: $x = -1$

Slant asymptote: $y = 2x + 5$

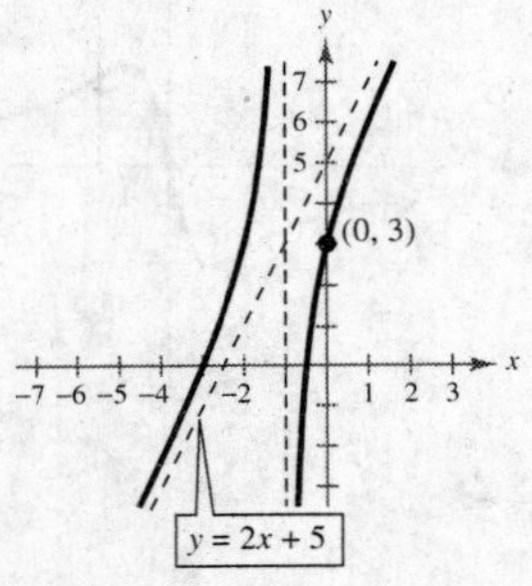

157. $N = \dfrac{20(4 + 3t)}{1 + 0.05t}, \quad t \geq 0$

(a) 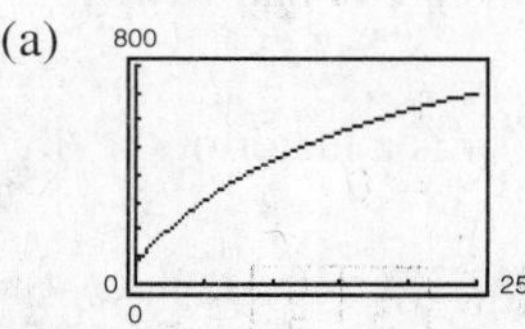

(b) $N(5) = 304{,}000$ fish

$N(10) \approx 453{,}333$ fish

$N(25) \approx 702{,}222$ fish

(c) The limit is

$\dfrac{60}{0.05} = 1{,}200{,}000$ fish, the horizontal asymptote.

158. (a) 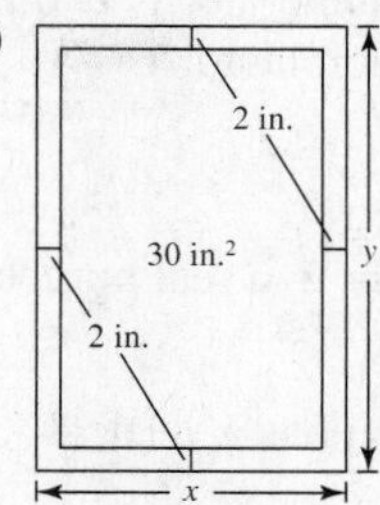

(b) $(x - 4)(y - 4) = 30 \Rightarrow y = 4 + \dfrac{30}{x - 4}$

$$\text{Area} = A = xy = x\left[4 + \frac{30}{x - 4}\right]$$
$$= x\left[\frac{4x - 16 + 30}{x - 4}\right]$$
$$= \frac{2x(2x + 7)}{x - 4}$$

(c) Domain: $x > 4$

(d) 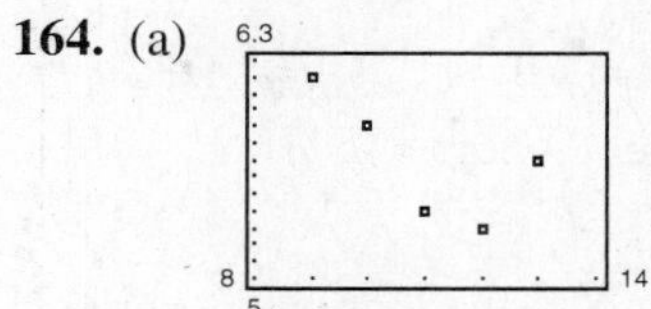

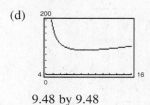

9.48 by 9.48

159. Quadratic model

160. Neither

161. Linear model

162. Quadratic

163. (a) 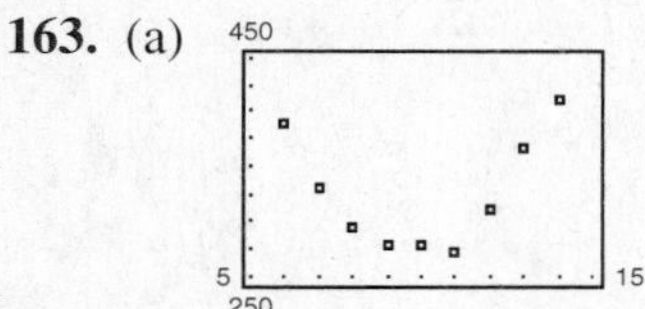

(b) $y = 8.03t^2 - 157.1t + 1041$; 0.98348

(c) 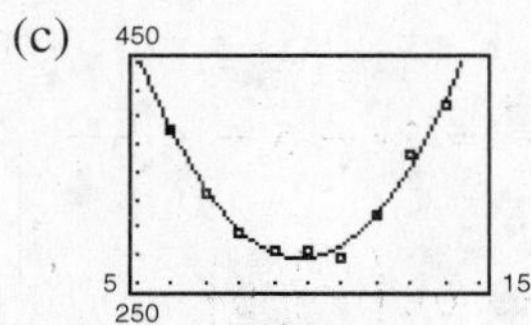

Yes, the model is a good fit.

(d) From the model, $y \geq 500$ when $t \approx 15.1$, or 2005.

(e) Answers will vary.

164. (a) 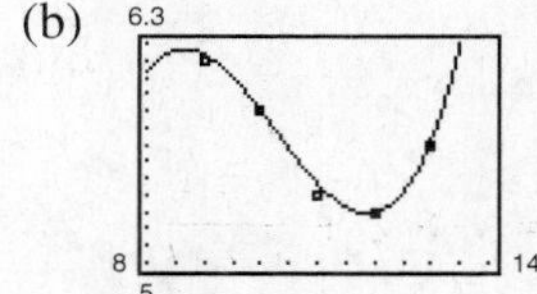

(b) 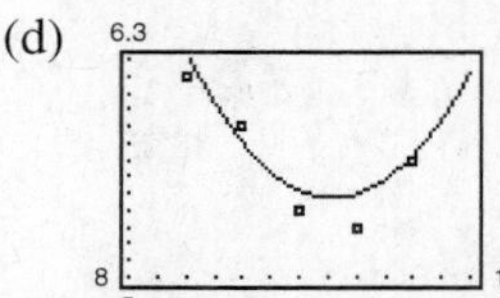

Yes, the model is an excellent fit.

(c) $y = 0.129t^2 - 2.99t + 22.8$

(d)

The quadratic model is not a good fit.

(e) The cubic model is better.

(f) Answers will vary.

165. False. The degree of the numerator is two more than the degree of the denominator.

166. False. A fourth degree polynomial with real coefficients can have at most four zeros. Since $-8i$ and $4i$ are zeros, so are $8i$ and $-4i$.

167. False. $(1 + i) + (1 - i) = 2$, a real number

168. It means that the divisor is a factor of the dividend.

169. Not every rational function has a vertical asymptote. For example,

$$y = \frac{x}{x^2 + 1}.$$

170. $\sqrt{-6}\sqrt{-6} \neq \sqrt{(-6)(-6)}$

In fact, $\sqrt{-6}\sqrt{-6} = \sqrt{6}i\,\sqrt{6}i = -6.$

171. The error is $\sqrt{-4} \neq 4i$. In fact,

$-i\left(\sqrt{-4} - 1\right) = -i(2i - 1) = 2 + i.$

172. (a) $i^{40} = (i^4)^{10} = 1^{10} = 1$

(b) $i^{25} = i(i^{24}) = i(1) = i$

(c) $i^{50} = i^2(i^{48}) = (-1)(1) = -1$

(d) $i^{67} = i^3(i^{64}) = -i(1) = -i$

Chapter 2 Practice Test

1. Sketch the graph of $f(x) = x^2 - 6x + 5$ by hand and identify the vertex and the intercepts.

2. Find the number of units x that produce a minimum cost C if $C = 0.01x^2 - 90x + 15{,}000$.

3. Find the quadratic function that has a maximum at $(1, 7)$ and passes through the point $(2, 5)$.

4. Find two quadratic functions that have x-intercepts $(2, 0)$ and $\left(\frac{4}{3}, 0\right)$.

5. Use the leading Coefficient Test to determine the right-hand and left-hand behavior of the graph of the polynomial function $f(x) = -3x^5 + 2x^3 - 17$.

6. Find all the real zeros of $f(x) = x^5 - 5x^3 + 4x$. Verify your answer with a graphing utility.

7. Find a polynomial function with 0, 3, and -2 as zeros.

8. Sketch $f(x) = x^3 - 12x$ by hand.

9. Divide $3x^4 - 7x^2 + 2x - 10$ by $x - 3$ using long division.

10. Divide $x^3 - 11$ by $x^2 + 2x - 1$.

11. Use synthetic division to divide $3x^5 + 13x^4 + 12x - 1$ by $x + 5$.

12. Use synthetic division to find $f(-6)$ when $f(x) = 7x^3 + 40x^2 - 12x + 15$.

13. Find the real zeros of $f(x) = x^3 - 19x - 30$.

14. Find the real zeros of $f(x) = x^4 + x^3 - 8x^2 - 9x - 9$.

15. List all possible rational zeros of the function $f(x) = 6x^3 - 5x^2 + 4x - 15$.

16. Find the rational zeros of the polynomial $f(x) = x^3 - \frac{20}{3}x^2 + 9x - \frac{10}{3}$.

17. Write $f(x) = x^4 + x^3 + 3x^2 + 5x - 10$ as a product of linear factors.

18. Write $\dfrac{2}{1 + i}$ in standard form.

19. Write $\dfrac{3 + i}{2} - \dfrac{i + 1}{4}$ in standard form.

20. Find a polynomial with real coefficients that has 2, $3 + i$, and $3 - 2i$ as zeros.

21. Use synthetic division to show that $3i$ is a zero of $f(x) = x^3 + 4x^2 + 9x + 36$.

22. Find a mathematical model for the statement, "z varies directly as the square of x and inversely as the square root of y".

23. Sketch the graph of $f(x) = \dfrac{x - 1}{2x}$ and label all intercepts and asymptotes.

24. Sketch the graph of $f(x) = \dfrac{3x^2 - 4}{x}$ and label all intercepts and asymptotes.

25. Find all the asymptotes of $f(x) = \dfrac{8x^2 - 9}{x^2 + 1}$.

26. Find all the asymptotes of $f(x) = \dfrac{4x^2 - 2x + 7}{x - 1}$.

27. Sketch the graph of $f(x) = \dfrac{x - 5}{(x - 5)^2}$.

CHAPTER 3
Exponential and Logarithmic Functions

Section 3.1 Exponential Functions and Their Graphs **193**

Section 3.2 Logarithmic Functions and Their Graphs **205**

Section 3.3 Properties of Logarithms **214**

Section 3.4 Solving Exponential and Logarithmic Equations **225**

Section 3.5 Exponential and Logarithmic Models **241**

Section 3.6 Nonlinear Models **250**

Review Exercises **256**

Practice Test **270**

CHAPTER 3
Exponential and Logarithmic Functions

Section 3.1 Exponential Functions and Their Graphs

- You should know that a function of the form $y = a^x$, where $a > 0$, $a \neq 1$, is called an exponential function with base a.
- You should be able to graph exponential functions.
- You should be familiar with the number e and the natural exponential function $f(x) = e^x$.
- You should know formulas for compound interest.

  (a) For n compoundings per year: $A = P\left(1 + \frac{r}{n}\right)^{nt}$.

  (b) For continuous compoundings: $A = Pe^{rt}$.

Vocabulary Check

1. algebraic
2. transcendental
3. natural exponential, natural
4. $A = P\left(1 + \frac{r}{n}\right)^{nt}$
5. $A = Pe^{rt}$

1. $(3.4)^{6.8} \approx 4112.033$

2. $1.2^{1/3} \approx 1.063$

3. $5^{-\pi} \approx 0.006$

4. $8.6^{-3(-\sqrt{2})} = 8.6^{3\sqrt{2}} \approx 9220.217$

5. $g(x) = 5^x$

x	-2	-1	0	1	2
y	$\frac{1}{25}$	$\frac{1}{5}$	1	5	25

Asymptote: $y = 0$

Intercept: $(0, 1)$

Increasing

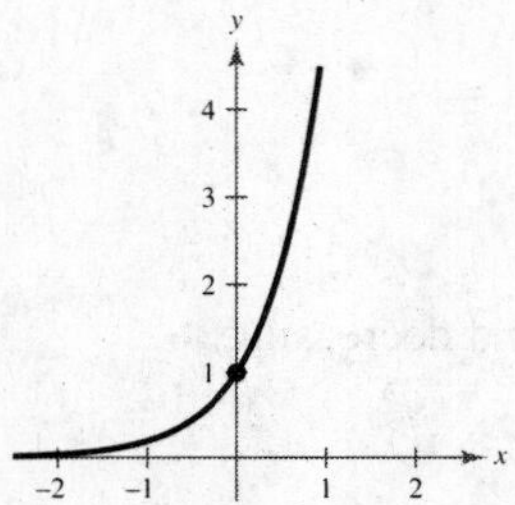

6. $f(x) = \left(\frac{3}{2}\right)^x$

x	-2	-1	0	1	2
y	$\frac{4}{9}$	$\frac{2}{3}$	1	$\frac{3}{2}$	$\frac{9}{4}$

Asymptote: $y = 0$

Intercept: $(0, 1)$

Increasing

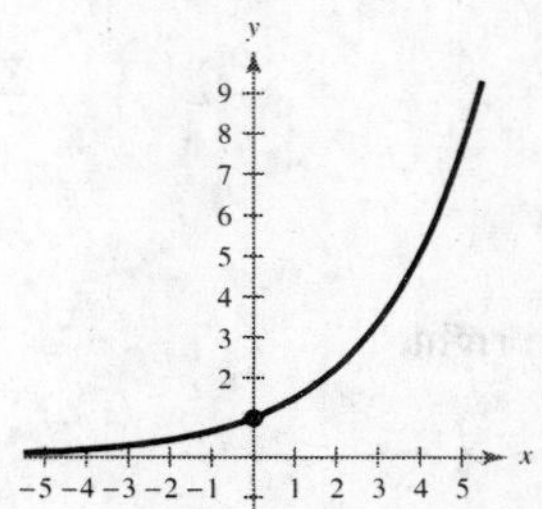

7. $f(x) = \left(\frac{1}{5}\right)^x = 5^{-x}$

x	-2	-1	0	1	2
y	25	5	1	$\frac{1}{5}$	$\frac{1}{25}$

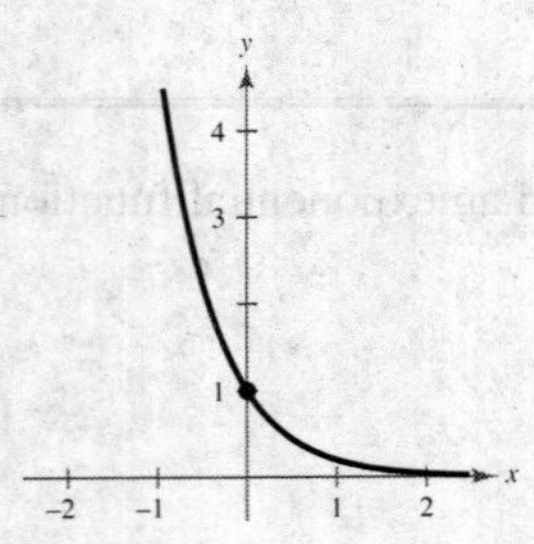

Asymptote: $y = 0$

Intercept: $(0, 1)$

Decreasing

8. $h(x) = \left(\frac{3}{2}\right)^{-x}$

x	-2	-1	0	1	2
y	$\frac{9}{4}$	$\frac{3}{2}$	1	$\frac{2}{3}$	$\frac{4}{9}$

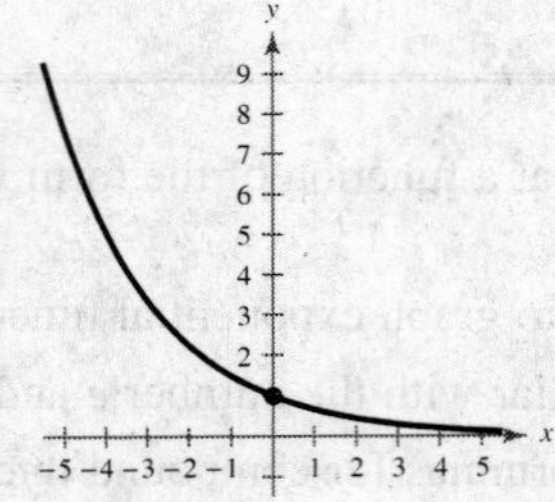

Asymptote: $y = 0$

Intercept: $(0, 1)$

Decreasing

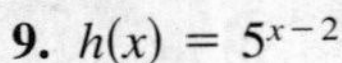

9. $h(x) = 5^{x-2}$

x	-1	0	1	2	3
y	$\frac{1}{125}$	$\frac{1}{25}$	$\frac{1}{5}$	1	5

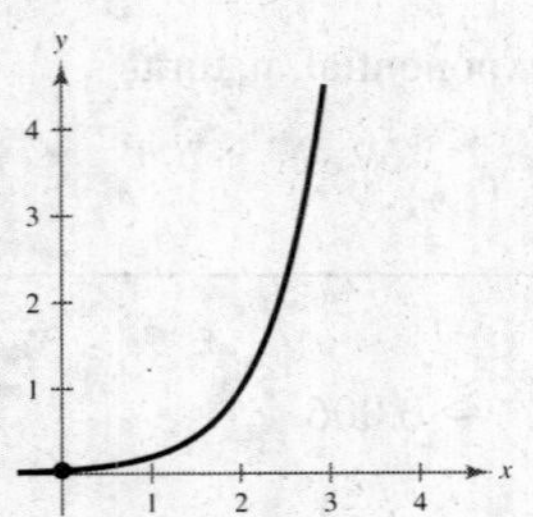

Asymptote: $y = 0$

Intercept: $\left(0, \frac{1}{25}\right)$

Increasing

10. $g(x) = \left(\frac{3}{2}\right)^{x+2}$

x	-4	-3	-2	-1	0
y	$\frac{4}{9}$	$\frac{2}{3}$	1	$\frac{3}{2}$	$\frac{9}{4}$

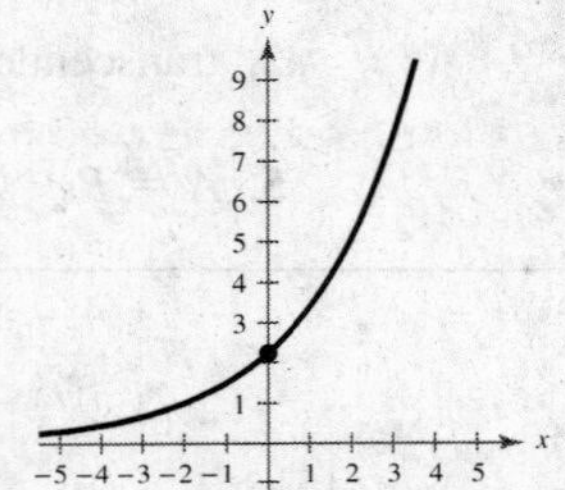

Asymptote: $y = 0$

Intercept: $\left(0, \frac{9}{4}\right)$

Increasing

11. $g(x) = 5^{-x} - 3$

x	-1	0	1	2
y	2	-2	$-2\frac{4}{5}$	$-2\frac{24}{25}$

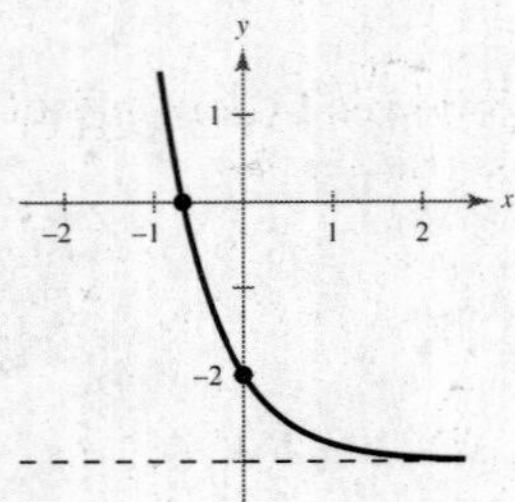

Asymptote: $y = -3$

Intercepts:

$(0, -2), (-0.683, 0)$

Decreasing

12. $f(x) = \left(\frac{3}{2}\right)^{-x} + 2$

x	-2	-1	0	1	2
y	$\frac{17}{4}$	$\frac{7}{2}$	3	$\frac{8}{3}$	$\frac{22}{9}$

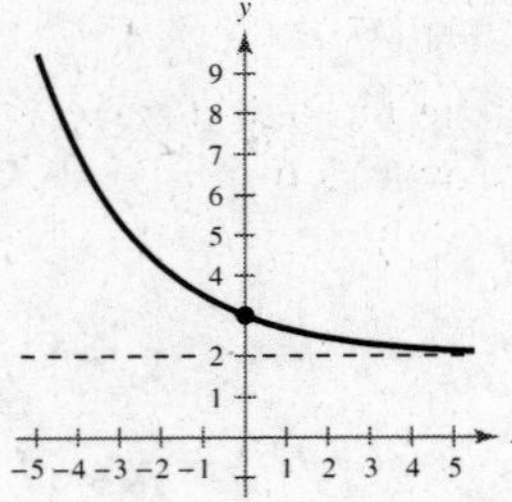

Asymptote: $y = 2$

Intercept: $(0, 3)$

Decreasing

13. $f(x) = 2^{x-2}$ rises to the right.

Asymptote: $y = 0$

Intercept: $\left(0, \frac{1}{4}\right)$

Matches graph (d).

14. $f(x) = 2^{-x}$ is positive and decreasing.

Matches graph (a).

15. $f(x) = 2^x - 4$ rises to the right.

Asymptote: $y = -4$

Intercept: $(0, -3)$

Matches graph (c).

16. $f(x) = 2^x + 1$ is increasing and has $(0, 2)$ intercept.

Matches graph (b).

17. $f(x) = 3^x$

$g(x) = 3^{x-5} = f(x - 5)$

Horizontal shift five units to the right

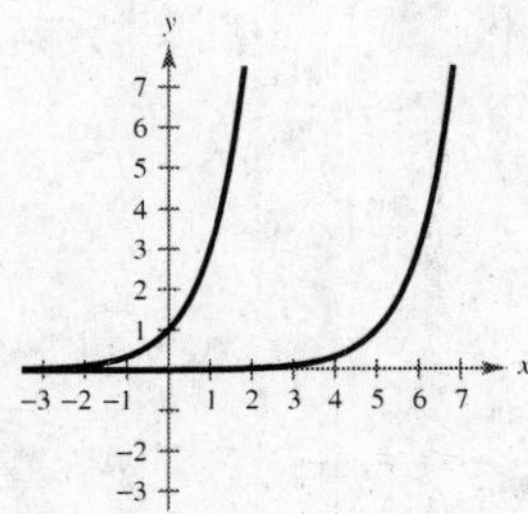

18. $f(x) = -2^x$

$g(x) = 5 - 2^x = 5 + f(x)$

Vertical shift five units upward

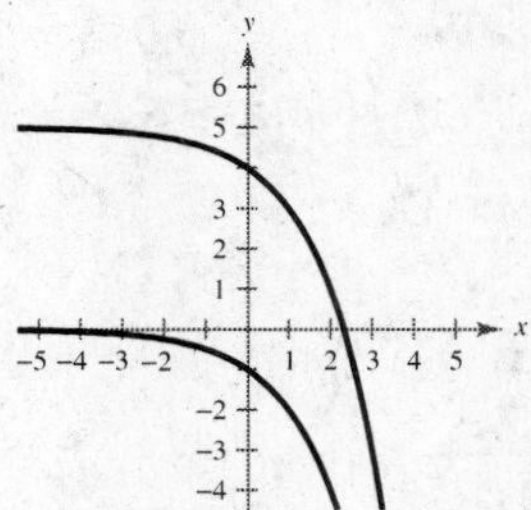

19. $f(x) = \left(\frac{3}{5}\right)^x$

$g(x) = -\left(\frac{3}{5}\right)^{x+4} = -f(x + 4)$

Horizontal shift four units to the left, followed by reflection in x-axis

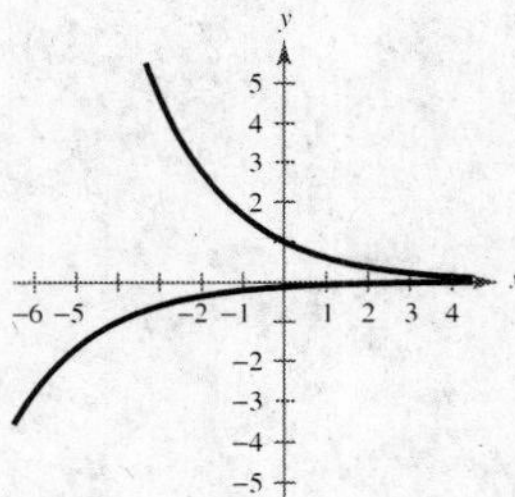

20. $f(x) = 0.3^x$

$g(x) = -0.3^x + 5 = -f(x) + 5$

Reflection in x-axis followed by vertical shift five units upward

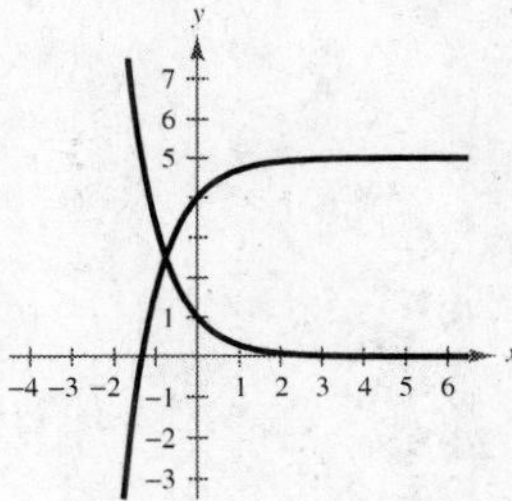

21. $f(x) = 4^x$

$g(x) = 4^{x-2} - 3 = f(x - 2) - 3$

Horizontal shift two units to the right followed by vertical shift three units downward

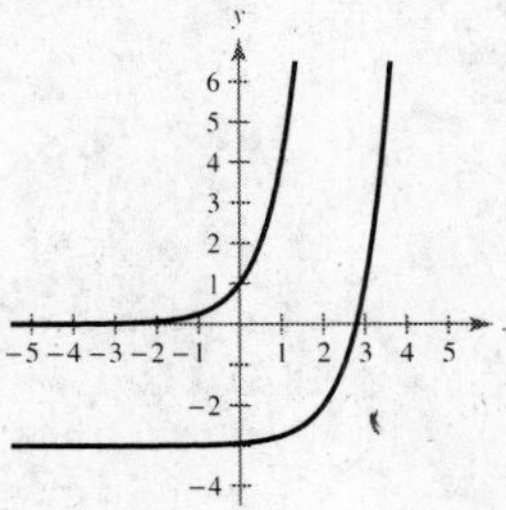

22. $f(x) = \left(\frac{1}{2}\right)^x$

$g(x) = \left(\frac{1}{2}\right)^{-(x+4)}$

Reflection in the y-axis followed by left shift of four units

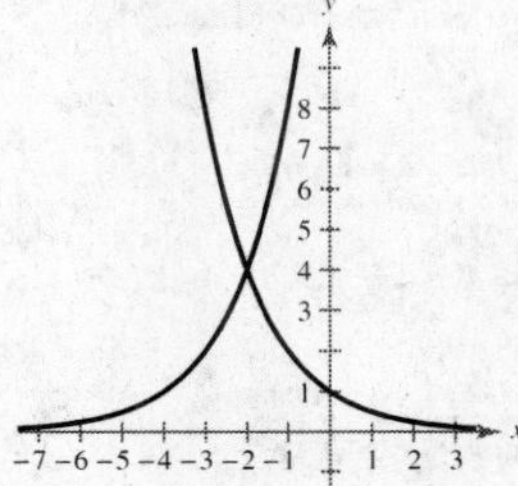

23. $e^{9.2} \approx 9897.129$

24. $e^{-(-3/4)} = e^{3/4}$

≈ 2.117

25. $50e^{4(0.02)} \approx 54.164$

26. $-5.5e^{-200} = 7.611 \times 10^{-87} \approx 0$

27. $f(x) = \left(\frac{5}{2}\right)^x$

x	-2	-1	0	1	2
$f(x)$	0.16	0.4	1	2.5	6.25

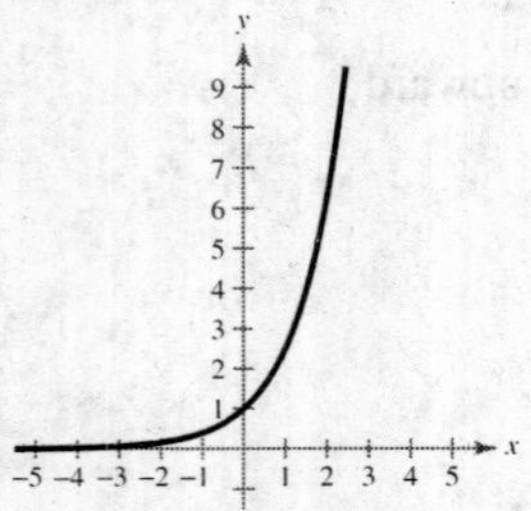

Asymptote: $y = 0$

28. $f(x) = \left(\frac{5}{2}\right)^{-x}$

x	-2	-1	0	1	2
$f(x)$	6.25	2.5	1	0.4	0.16

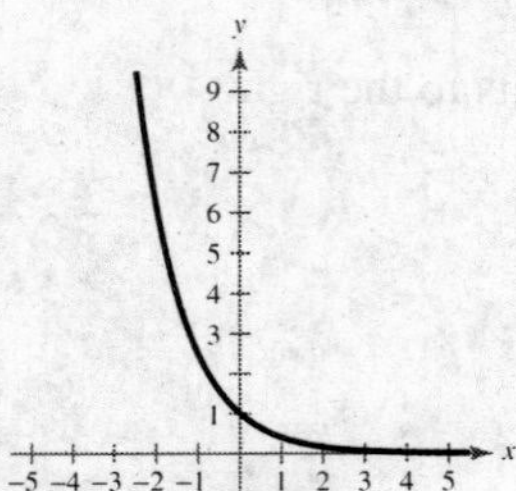

Asymptote: $y = 0$

29. $f(x) = 6^x$

x	-2	-1	0	1	2
$f(x)$	0.03	0.17	1	6	36

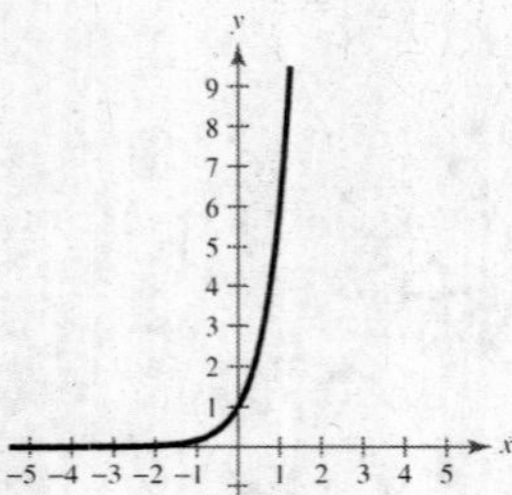

Asymptote: $y = 0$

30. $f(x) = 2^{x-1}$

x	-1	0	1	2	3
$f(x)$	0.25	0.5	1	2	4

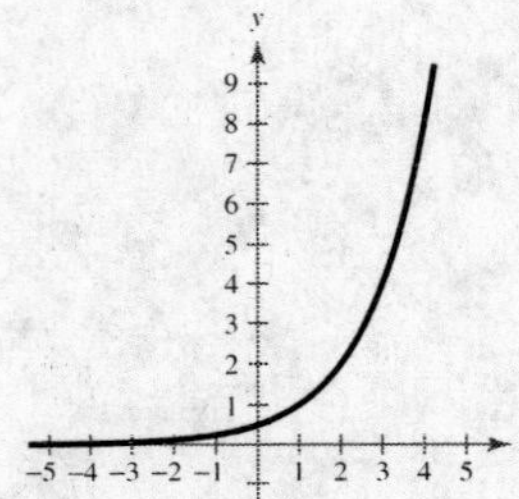

Asymptote: $y = 0$

31. $f(x) = 3^{x+2}$

x	-3	-2	-1	0	1
$f(x)$	0.33	1	3	9	27

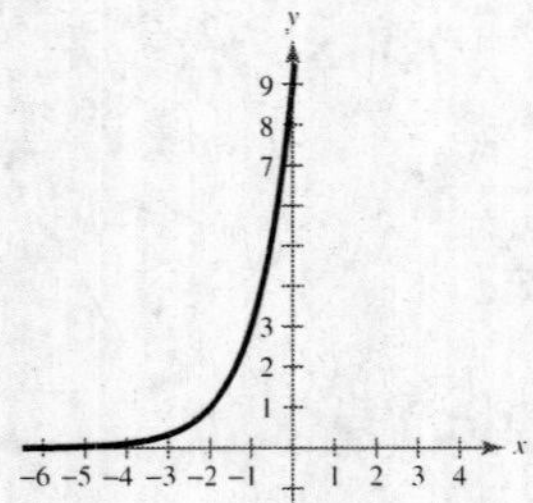

Asymptote: $y = 0$

32. $f(x) = 4^{x-3} + 3$

x	0	1	2	3	4	5
$f(x)$	3.016	3.063	3.25	4	7	19

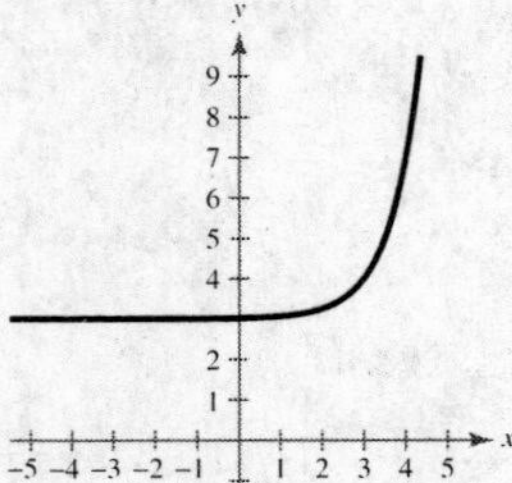

Asymptote: $y = 3$

33. $y = 2^{-x^2}$

x	-2	-1	0	1	2
y	0.06	0.5	1	0.5	0.06

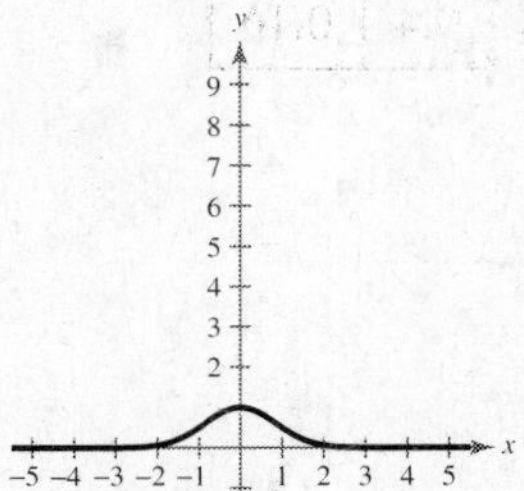

Asymptote: $y = 0$

34. $y = 3^{-|x|}$

x	-2	-1	0	1	2
y	0.11	0.33	1	0.33	0.11

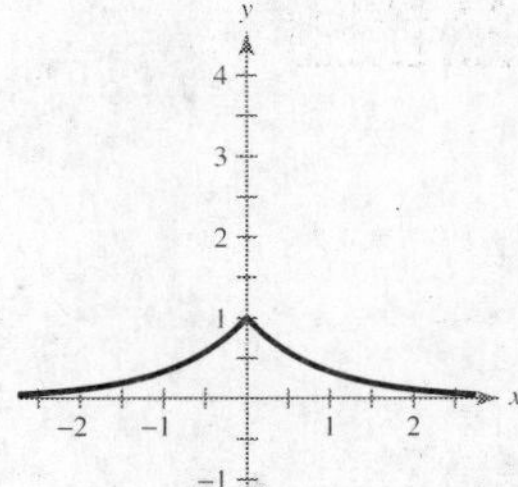

Asymptote: $y = 0$

35. $y = 3^{x-2} + 1$

x	-1	0	1	2	3	4
y	1.04	1.11	1.33	2	4	10

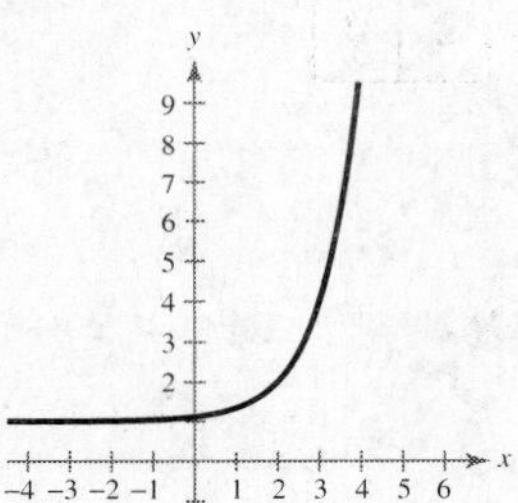

Asymptote: $y = 1$

36. $y = 4^{x+1} - 2$

x	-2	-1	0	1	2
y	-1.75	-1	2	14	62

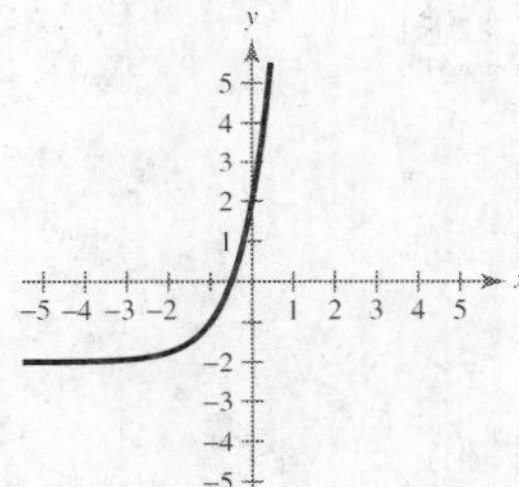

Asymptote: $y = -2$

37. $f(x) = e^{-x}$

x	-2	-1	0	1	2
$f(x)$	7.39	2.72	1	0.37	0.14

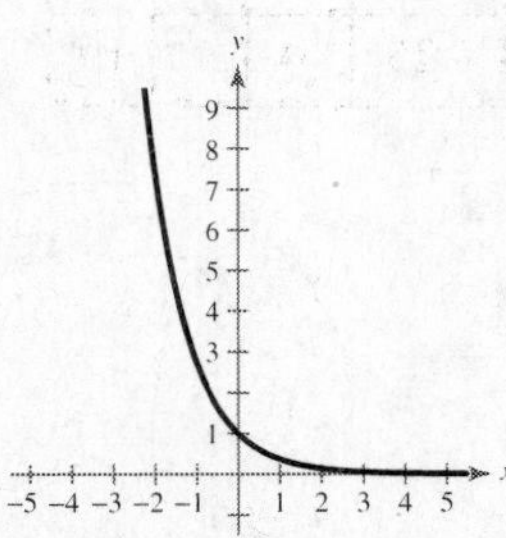

Asymptote: $y = 0$

38. $s(t) = 3e^{-0.2t}$

t	-1	0	1	2	3	4
$s(t)$	3.66	3	2.46	2.011	1.65	1.35

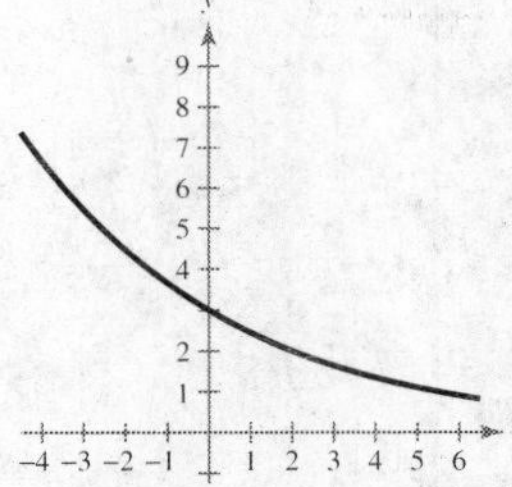

Asymptote: $y = 0$

39. $f(x) = 3e^{x+4}$

x	-6	-5	-4	-3	-2
$f(x)$	0.41	1.10	3	8.15	22.17

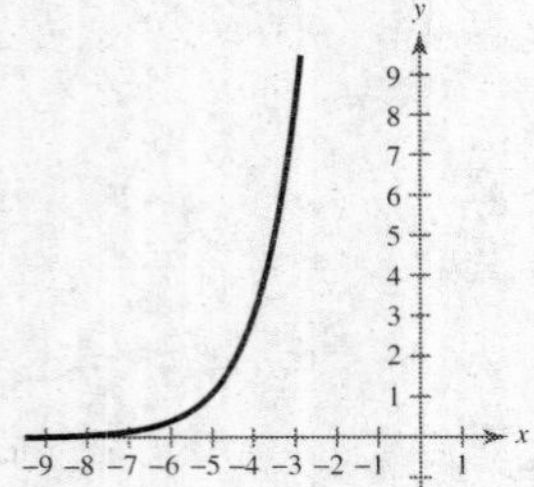

Asymptote: $y = 0$

40. $f(x) = 2e^{-0.5x}$

x	-2	-1	0	1	2
$f(x)$	5.44	3.30	2	1.21	0.74

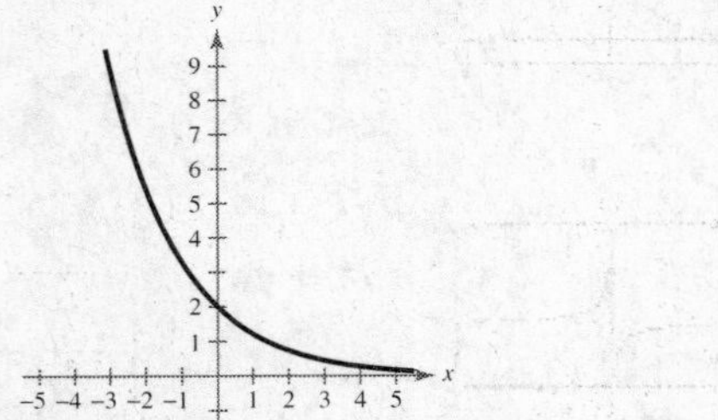

Asymptote: $y = 0$

41. $f(x) = 2 + e^{x-5}$

x	3	4	5	6	7
$f(x)$	2.14	2.37	3	4.72	9.39

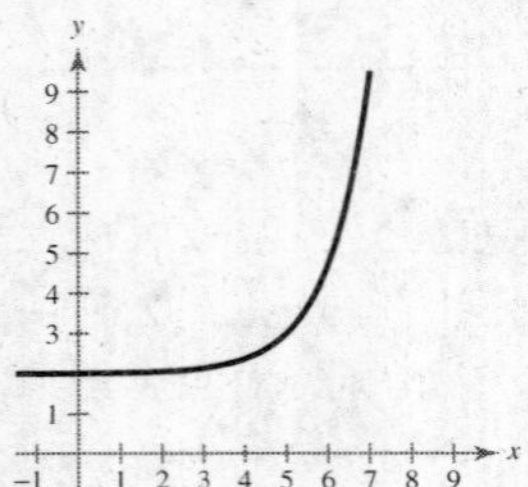

Asymptote: $y = 2$

42. $g(x) = 2 - e^{-x}$

x	-2	-1	0	1	2
$g(x)$	-5.39	-0.72	1	1.63	1.86

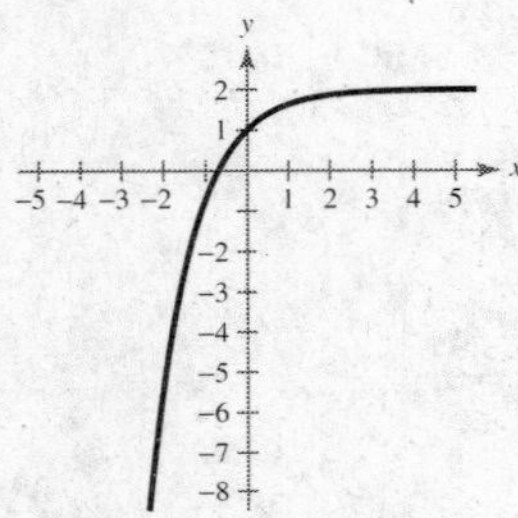

Asymptote: $y = 2$

43. $s(t) = 2e^{0.12t}$

t	-2	-1	0	1	2
$s(t)$	1.57	1.77	2	2.26	2.54

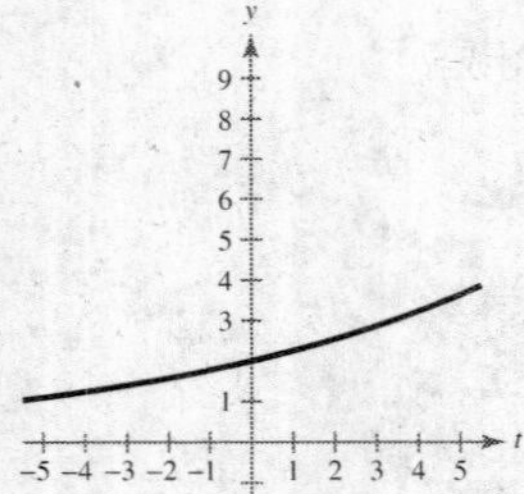

Asymptote: $y = 0$

44. $g(x) = 1 + e^{-x}$

x	-2	-1	0	1	2
$g(x)$	8.39	3.72	2	1.37	1.14

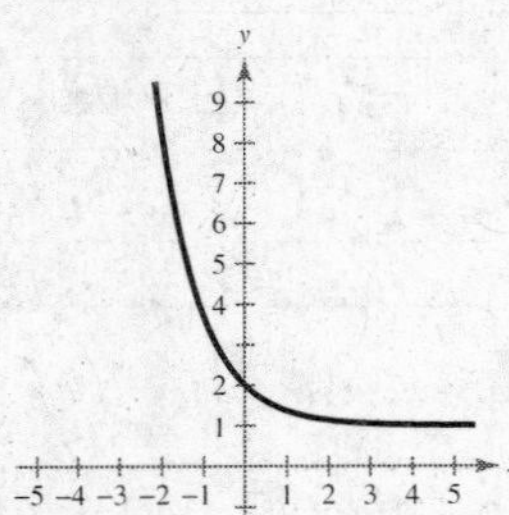

Asymptote: $y = 1$

45. $f(x) = \dfrac{8}{1 + e^{-0.5x}}$

(a)

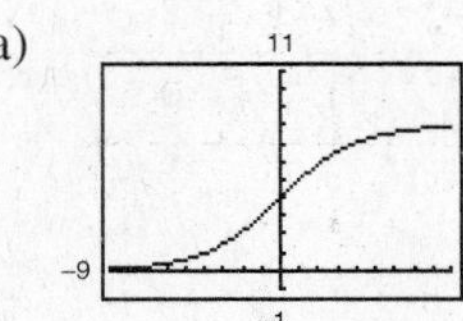

(b)

x	-30	-20	-10	0	10	20	30
$f(x)$	≈ 0	≈ 0	0.05	4	7.95	≈ 8	≈ 8

Horizontal asymptotes: $y = 0$, $y = 8$

46. (a)

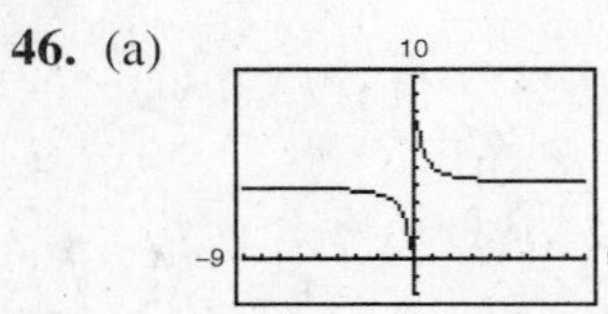

(b)

x	-15	-2	-1	-0.2	-0.1
$f(x)$	3.93	3.5	3.0	0.61	0.05

x	0	0.01	0.2	1	5
$f(x)$	undef.	8	7.4	5.0	4.2

Horizontal asymptote: $y = 4$

Vertical asymptote: $x = 0$

47. $f(x) = \dfrac{-6}{2 - e^{0.2x}}$

(a)

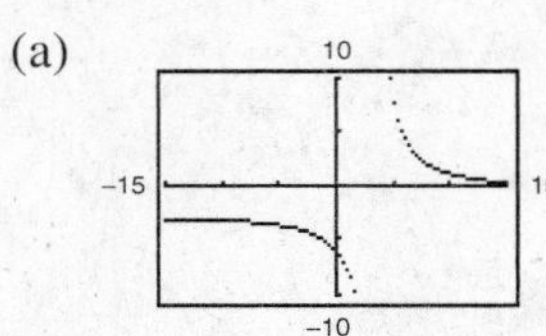

(b)

x	-20	-10	0	3	3.4	3.46
$f(x)$	-3.03	-3.22	-6	-34	-230	-2617

x	3.47	4	5	10	20
$f(x)$	3516	26.6	8.4	1.11	0.11

Horizontal asymptotes: $y = -3$, $y = 0$

Vertical asymptote: $x \approx 3.47$

48. (a)

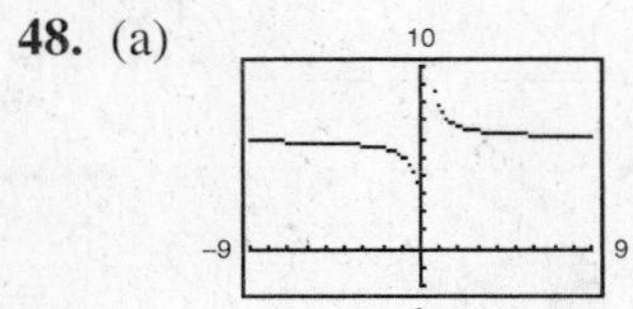

(b)

x	-15	-10	-1	-0.1	-0.01
$f(x)$	5.9	5.9	5.1	3.2	3

x	$\dfrac{0.2}{\ln 2}$	0.289	1	4	10
$f(x)$	undef.	2715	7.7	6.3	6.1

Asymptotes: $y = 6$

$$x = \frac{0.2}{\ln 2} \approx 0.2885$$

49.

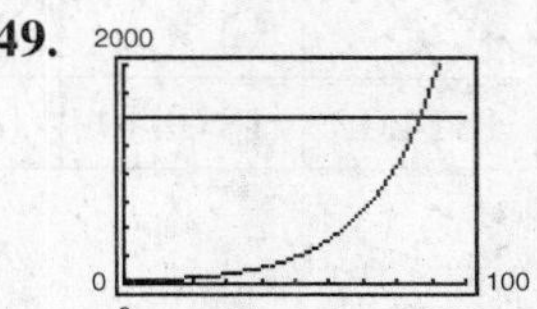

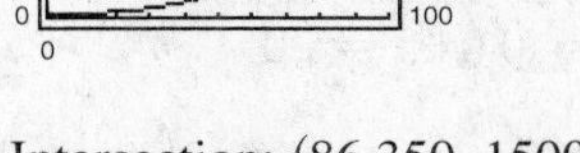

Intersection: (86.350, 1500)

50.

Intersection: (482.831, 12,500)

51. $f(x) = x^2e^{-x}$

(a)

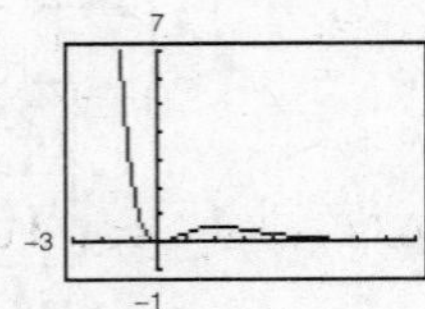

(b) Decreasing: $(-\infty, 0), (2, \infty)$

Increasing: $(0, 2)$

(c) Relative maximum: $(2, 4e^{-2}) \approx (2, 0.541)$

Relative minimum: $(0, 0)$

52. $f(x) = 2x^2e^{x+1}$

(a)

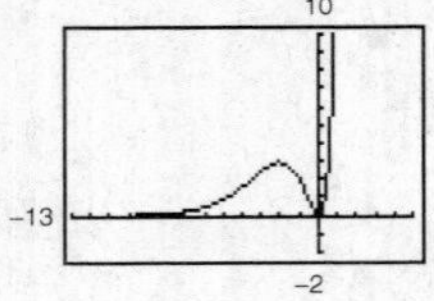

(b) Increasing on $(-\infty, -2)$ and $(0, \infty)$

Decreasing on $(-2, 0)$

(c) Relative maximum: $(-2, 2.943)$

Relative minimum: $(0, 0)$

53. $P = 2500, r = 2.5\% = 0.025, t = 10$

Compounded n times per year: $A = P\left(1 + \frac{r}{n}\right)^{nt} = 2500\left(1 + \frac{0.025}{n}\right)^{10n}$

Compounded continuously: $A = Pe^{rt} = 2500e^{(0.025)(10)}$

n	1	2	4	12	365	Continuous
A	3200.21	3205.09	3207.57	3209.23	3210.04	3210.06

54. $P = 1000, r = 6\% = 0.06, t = 10$

n	1	2	4	12	365	Continuous
A	1790.85	1806.11	1814.02	1819.40	1822.03	1822.12

55. $P = 2500, r = 4\% = 0.04, t = 20$

Compounded n times per year: $A = P\left(1 + \frac{r}{n}\right)^{nt} = 2500\left(1 + \frac{0.04}{n}\right)^{20n}$

Compounded continuously: $A = Pe^{rt} = 2500e^{(0.04)(20)}$

n	1	2	4	12	365	Continuous
A	5477.81	5520.10	5541.79	5556.46	5563.61	5563.85

56. $P = 1000, r = 3\% = 0.03, t = 40$

n	1	2	4	12	365	Continuous
A	3262.04	3290.66	3305.28	3315.15	3319.95	3320.12

57. $P = 12{,}000,\ r = 4\% = 0.04$

$A = Pe^{rt} = 12000e^{0.04t}$

t	1	10	20	30	40	50
A	12,489.73	17,901.90	26,706.49	39,841.40	59,436.39	88,668.67

58. $P = 12{,}000,\ r = 6\% = 0.06$, compounded continuously: $A = Pe^{rt} = 12{,}000e^{(0.06)t}$

t	1	10	20	30	40	50
A	12,742.04	21,865.43	39,841.40	75,595.77	132,278.12	241,026.44

59. $P = 12{,}000,\ r = 3.5\% = 0.035$

$A = Pe^{rt} = 12{,}000e^{0.035t}$

t	1	10	20	30	40	50
A	12,427.44	17,028.81	24,165.03	34,291.81	48,662.40	69,055.23

60. $P = 12{,}000,\ r = 2.5\% = 0.025$, compounded continuously: $A = Pe^{rt} = 12{,}000e^{0.025t}$

t	1	10	20	30	40	50
A	12,303.78	15,408.31	19,784.66	25,404.00	32,619.38	41,884.12

61. $A = 25\left[\dfrac{(1 + 0.12/12)^{48} - 1}{0.12/12}\right]$

$= 25\left[\dfrac{1.01^{48} - 1}{0.01}\right]$

$= \$1530.57$

62. $A = 100\left[\dfrac{(1 + 0.09/12)^{60} - 1}{0.09/12}\right]$

$= \$7542.41$

63. $A = 200\left[\dfrac{(1 + 0.06/12)^{72} - 1}{0.06/12}\right]$

$= \$17{,}281.77$

64. $A = 75\left[\dfrac{(1 + 0.03/12)^{24} - 1}{0.03/12}\right]$

$= \$1852.71$

65. $p = 5000\left(1 - \dfrac{4}{4 + e^{-0.002x}}\right)$

(a) 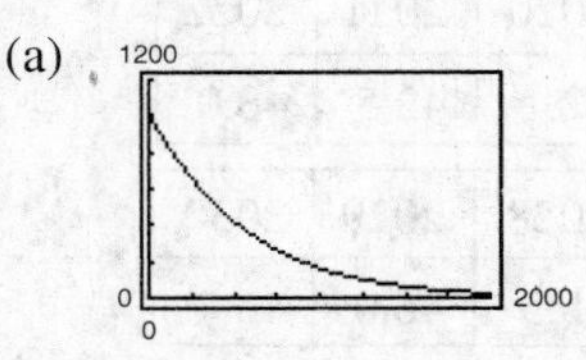

(b) If $x = 500$, $p \approx \$421.12$.

(c) For $x = 600$, $p \approx \$350.13$.

x	100	200	300	400	500	600	700
p	849.53	717.64	603.25	504.94	421.12	350.13	290.35

66. (a) $y_1 = 500(1 + 0.07)^x$

$y_2 = 500\left(1 + \frac{0.07}{4}\right)^{4x}$

$y_3 = 500e^{0.07x}$

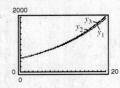

(b) y_3 has the highest return.

After 20 years,

$y_2 - y_1 = 2003.20 - 1934.84 = \$68.36$

$y_3 - y_2 = 2027.60 - 2003.20 = \$24.40$

$y_3 - y_1 = 2027.60 - 1934.84 = \$92.76$

67. $Q = 25\left(\frac{1}{2}\right)^{t/1599}$

(a) When $t = 0$,

$Q = 25\left(\frac{1}{2}\right)^{0/1599} = 25(1) = 25$ grams.

(b) When $t = 1000$,

$Q = 25\left(\frac{1}{2}\right)^{1000/1599} \approx 16.21$ grams.

(c)

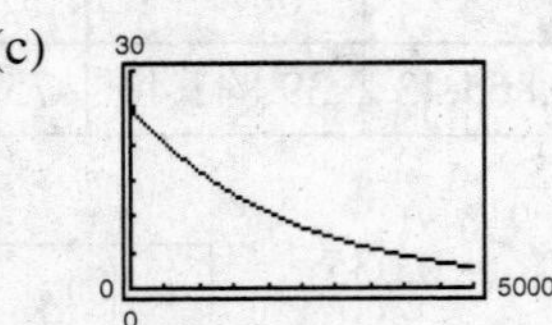

(d) Never. The graph has a horizontal asymptote $Q = 0$.

68. $Q = 10\left(\frac{1}{2}\right)^{t/5715}$

(a) When $t = 0$, $Q = 10$.

(b) When $t = 2000$,

$Q = 10\left(\frac{1}{2}\right)^{2000/5715} \approx 7.85$ grams.

(c)

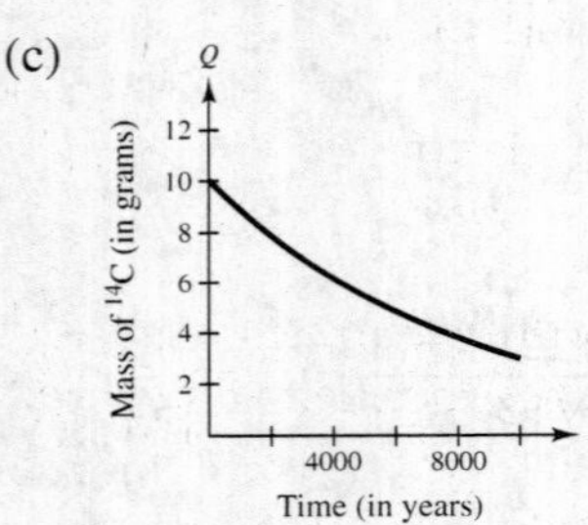

69. $P(t) = 100e^{0.2197t}$

(a)

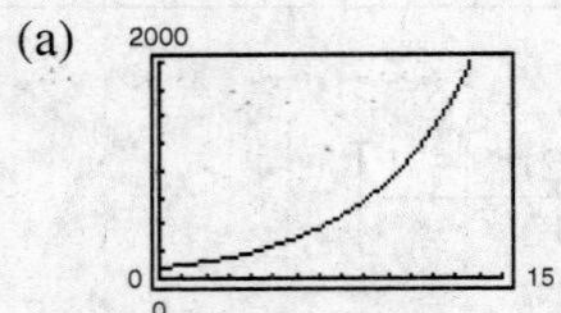

(b) $P(0) = 100$

$P(5) \approx 300$

$P(10) \approx 900$

(c) $P(0) = 100e^{0.2197(0)} = 100$

$P(5) = 100e^{0.2197(5)} = 299.966 \approx 300$

$P(10) = 100e^{0.2197(10)} = 899.798 \approx 900$

70. (a)

(b)

Year	2015	2016	2017	2018	2019	2020	2021	2022
P	40.1	40.5	40.9	41.3	41.7	42.1	42.5	43.0

Year	2023	2024	2025	2026	2027	2028	2029	2030
P	43.4	43.8	44.2	44.7	45.1	45.5	46.0	46.4

(c) $P = 34.706e^{0.0097t} = 50$

$e^{0.0097t} = 1.441$

$0.0097t = \ln(1.441)$

$t \approx 38$, or 2038

(Answers will vary.)

71. $C(t) = P(1.04)^t$

(a) 

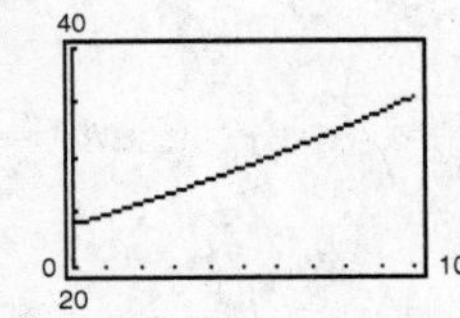

(b) $C(10) \approx 35.45$

(c) $C(10) = 23.95(1.04)^{10} \approx 35.45$

72. (a)

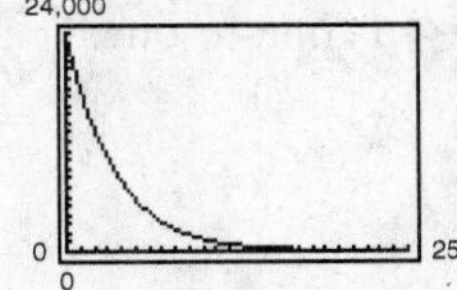

(b)

t	1	2	3	4	5
V	17,978	13,483	10,112	7584	5688

t	6	7	8	9	10
V	4266	3200	2400	1800	1350

(c) According to the model, $V(t) \to 0$ as t increases. However, $V \neq 0$.

73. True. $f(x) = 1^x$ is not an exponential function.

74. False. e is an irrational number.

75. The graph decreases for all x and has positive y-intercept. Matches (d).

76. $y_1 = e^x$

$y_2 = x^2$

$y_3 = x^3$

$y_4 = \sqrt{x}$

$y_5 = |x|$

(a) $y_1 = e^x$ increases at the fastest rate.

(b) For any positive integer n, $e^x > x^n$ for x sufficiently large. That is, e^x grows faster than x^n.

(c) A quantity is growing exponentially if its growth rate is of the form $y = ce^{rx}$. This is a faster rate than any polynomial growth rate.

77. $f(x) = \left(1 + \dfrac{0.5}{x}\right)^x$ and $g(x) = e^{0.5} \approx 1.6487$

(Horizontal line)

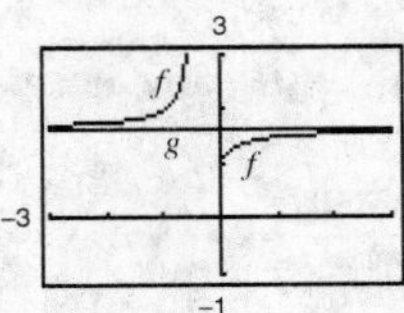

As $x \to \infty, f(x) \to g(x)$.

78. $y = 3^x$ (c) and $y = 2^{-x}$ (d) are exponential functions because the exponents are variable.

79. $e^{\pi} \approx 23.14,\ \pi^e \approx 22.46$

$e^{\pi} > \pi^e$

80. $2^{10} = 1024,\ 10^2 = 100$

$2^{10} > 10^2$

81. $5^{-3} = 0.008,\ 3^{-5} \approx 0.0041$

$5^{-3} > 3^{-5}$

82. $4^{1/2} = 2,\ \left(\frac{1}{2}\right)^4 = \frac{1}{16}$

$4^{1/2} > \left(\frac{1}{2}\right)^4$

83. f has an inverse because f is one-to-one.

$$y = 5x - 7$$
$$x = 5y - 7$$
$$x + 7 = 5y$$
$$f^{-1}(x) = \frac{1}{5}(x + 7)$$

84. f is one-to-one, so it has an inverse.

$$f(x) = -\frac{2}{3}x + \frac{5}{2}$$
$$y = -\frac{2}{3}x + \frac{5}{2}$$
$$x = -\frac{2}{3}y + \frac{5}{2}$$
$$x - \frac{5}{2} = -\frac{2}{3}y$$
$$-\frac{3}{2}\left(x - \frac{5}{2}\right) = y$$
$$f^{-1}(x) = -\frac{3}{2}x + \frac{15}{4}$$

85. f has an inverse because f is one-to-one.

$$y = \sqrt[3]{x + 8}$$
$$x = \sqrt[3]{y + 8}$$
$$x^3 = y + 8$$
$$x^3 - 8 = y$$
$$f^{-1}(x) = x^3 - 8$$

86. f is not one-to-one, so it does not have an inverse.

87. $f(x) = \dfrac{2x}{x - 7}$

Vertical asymptote: $x = 7$

Horizontal asymptote: $y = 2$

Intercept: $(0, 0)$

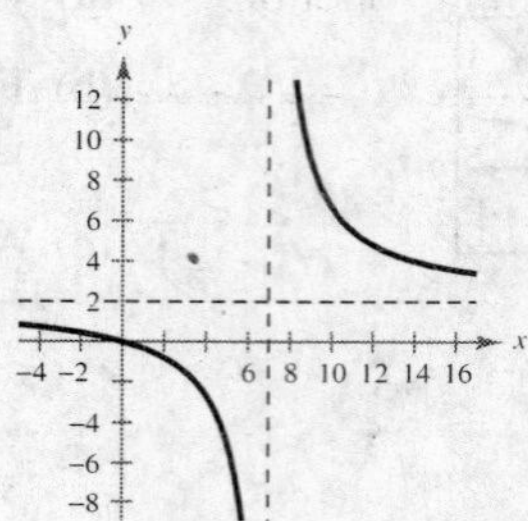

88. $f(x) = \dfrac{x^2 + 3}{x + 1} = x - 1 + \dfrac{4}{x + 1}$

Slant asymptote: $y = x - 1$

Vertical asymptote: $x = -1$

Intercept: $(0, 3)$

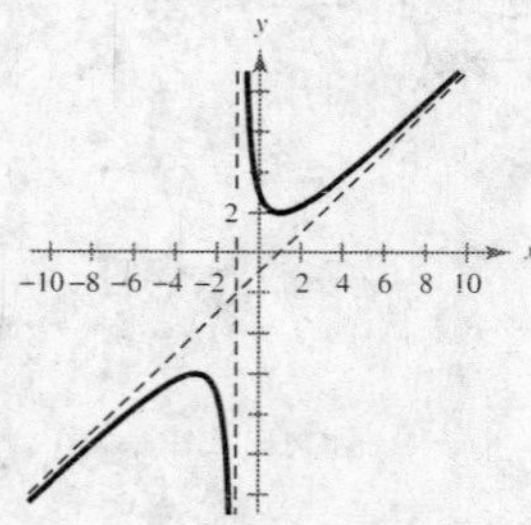

89. Answers will vary.

Section 3.2 Logarithmic Functions and Their Graphs

- You should know that a function of the form $y = \log_a x$, where $a > 0$, $a \neq 1$, and $x > 0$, is called a logarithm of x to base a.
- You should be able to convert from logarithmic form to exponential form and vice versa.

  $y = \log_a x \Leftrightarrow a^y = x$
- You should know the following properties of logarithms.

  (a) $\log_a 1 = 0$ since $a^0 = 1$.
  (c) $\log_a a^x = x$ since $a^x = a^x$.
  (b) $\log_a a = 1$ since $a^1 = a$.
  (d) If $\log_a x = \log_a y$, then $x = y$.
- You should know the definition of the natural logarithmic function.

  $\log_e x = \ln x, x > 0$
- You should know the properties of the natural logarithmic function.

  (a) $\ln 1 = 0$ since $e^0 = 1$.
  (c) $\ln e^x = x$ since $e^x = e^x$.
  (b) $\ln e = 1$ since $e^1 = e$.
  (d) If $\ln x = \ln y$, then $x = y$.
- You should be able to graph logarithmic functions.

Vocabulary Check

1. logarithmic function
2. 10
3. natural logarithmic
4. $a^{\log_a x} = x$
5. $x = y$

1. $\log_4 64 = 3 \Rightarrow 4^3 = 64$

2. $\log_3 81 = 4 \Rightarrow 3^4 = 81$

3. $\log_7 \frac{1}{49} = -2 \Rightarrow 7^{-2} = \frac{1}{49}$

4. $\log_{10} \frac{1}{1000} = -3 \Rightarrow 10^{-3} = \frac{1}{1000}$

5. $\log_{32} 4 = \frac{2}{5} \Rightarrow 32^{2/5} = 4$

6. $\log_{16} 8 = \frac{3}{4} \Rightarrow 16^{3/4} = 8$

7. $\ln 1 = 0 \Rightarrow e^0 = 1$

8. $\ln 4 = 1.3862\ldots \Rightarrow e^{1.3862\ldots} = 4$

9. $\ln e = 1 \Rightarrow e^1 = e$

10. $\ln e^3 = 3 \Rightarrow e^3 = e^3$

11. $\ln \sqrt{e} = \frac{1}{2} \Rightarrow e^{1/2} = \sqrt{e}$

12. $\ln \frac{1}{e^2} = -2 \Rightarrow e^{-2} = \frac{1}{e^2}$

13. $5^3 = 125 \Rightarrow \log_5 125 = 3$

14. $8^2 = 64 \Rightarrow \log_8 64 = 2$

15. $81^{1/4} = 3 \Rightarrow \log_{81} 3 = \frac{1}{4}$

16. $9^{3/2} = 27 \Rightarrow \log_9 27 = \frac{3}{2}$

17. $6^{-2} = \frac{1}{36} \Rightarrow \log_6 \frac{1}{36} = -2$

18. $10^{-3} = 0.001 \Rightarrow \log_{10} 0.001 = -3$

19. $e^3 = 20.0855\ldots \Rightarrow \ln 20.0855\ldots = 3$

20. $e^4 \approx 54.5981\ldots \Rightarrow \ln 54.5981\ldots = 4$

21. $e^{1.3} = 3.6692\ldots \Rightarrow \ln 3.6692\ldots = 1.3$

22. $e^{2.5} = 12.1824\ldots \Rightarrow \ln 12.1824\ldots = 2.5$

23. $\sqrt[3]{e} = 1.3956\ldots \Rightarrow \ln(1.3956\ldots) = \frac{1}{3}$

24. $\dfrac{1}{e^4} = e^{-4} = 0.0183\ldots \Rightarrow \ln 0.0183\ldots = -4$

25. $\log_2 16 = \log_2 2^4 = 4$

26. $\log_{16}\left(\dfrac{1}{4}\right) = -\dfrac{1}{2}$

because $16^{-1/2} = \dfrac{1}{16^{1/2}} = \dfrac{1}{4}.$

27. $g\left(\dfrac{1}{1000}\right) = \log_{10}\left(\dfrac{1}{1000}\right)$

$= \log_{10}(10^{-3})$

$= -3$

28. $g(10{,}000) = \log_{10}(10{,}000)$

$= \log_{10}(10^4)$

$= 4$

29. $\log_{10} 345 \approx 2.538$

30. $\log_{10}\left(\frac{4}{5}\right) \approx -0.097$

31. $6 \log_{10} 14.8 \approx 7.022$

32. $1.9 \log_{10}(4.3) \approx 1.204$

33. $\log_7 x = \log_7 9$

$x = 9$

34. $x = \log_5 5 = 1$

35. $\log_6 6^2 = x$

$2 \log_6 6 = x$

$2 = x$

36. $\log_2 2^{-1} = x$

$-1 = x$

37. $\log_8 x = \log_8 10^{-1}$

$x = 10^{-1} = \frac{1}{10}$

38. $x = \log_4(4^3)$

$= 3$

39. $\log_4 4^{3x} = (3x) \log_4 4 = 3x$

40. $6^{\log_6 36} = 36$

41. $3 \log_2\left(\frac{1}{2}\right) = 3 \log_2(2^{-1})$

$= 3(-1) = -3$

42. $\frac{1}{4} \log_4 16 = \frac{1}{4} \log_4 4^2 = \frac{1}{4}(2) = \frac{1}{2}$

43. $f(x) = 3^x$ and $g(x) = \log_3 x$ are inverses of each other.

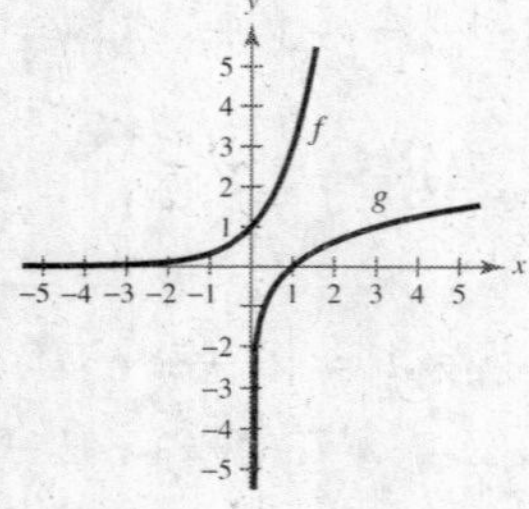

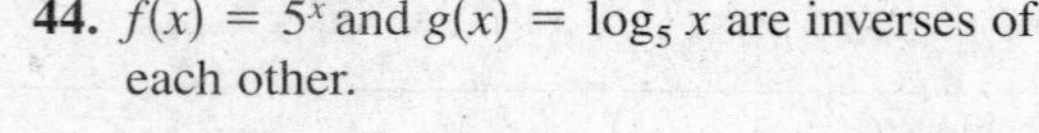

44. $f(x) = 5^x$ and $g(x) = \log_5 x$ are inverses of each other.

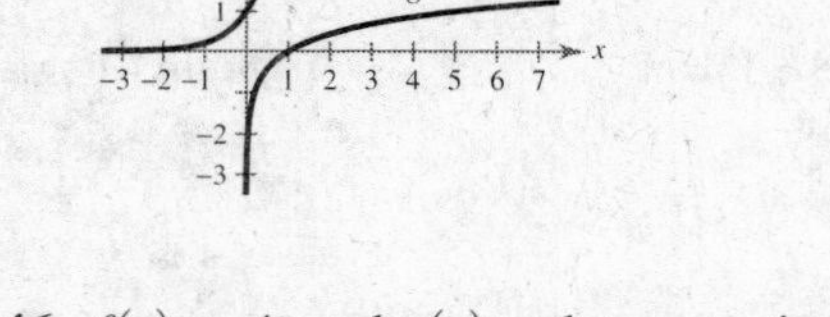

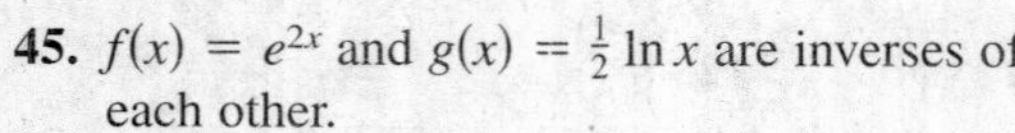

45. $f(x) = e^{2x}$ and $g(x) = \frac{1}{2} \ln x$ are inverses of each other.

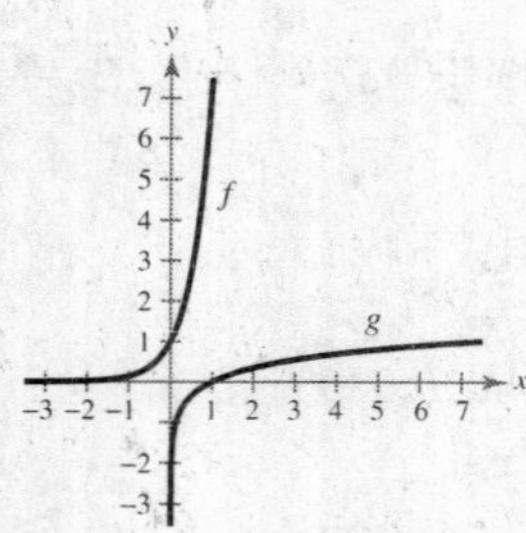

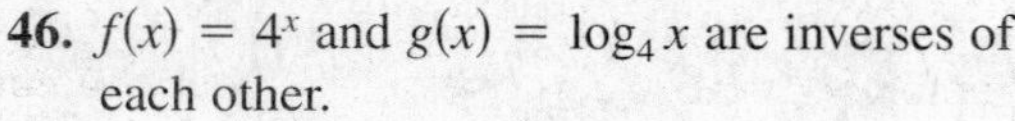

46. $f(x) = 4^x$ and $g(x) = \log_4 x$ are inverses of each other.

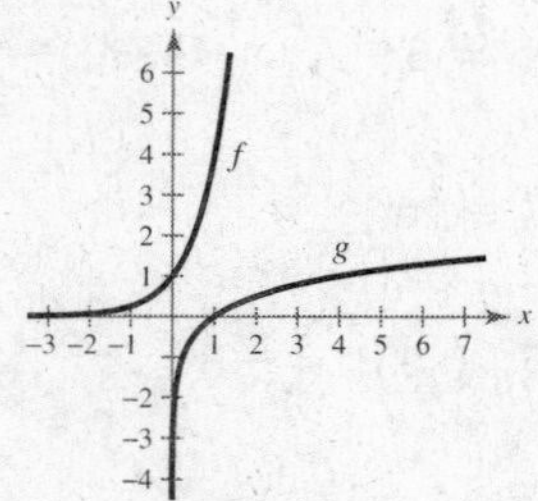

47. $y = \log_2(x + 2)$

Domain: $x + 2 > 0 \Rightarrow x > -2$

Vertical asymptote: $x = -2$

$\log_2(x + 2) = 0$

$x + 2 = 1$

$x = -1$

x-intercept: $(-1, 0)$

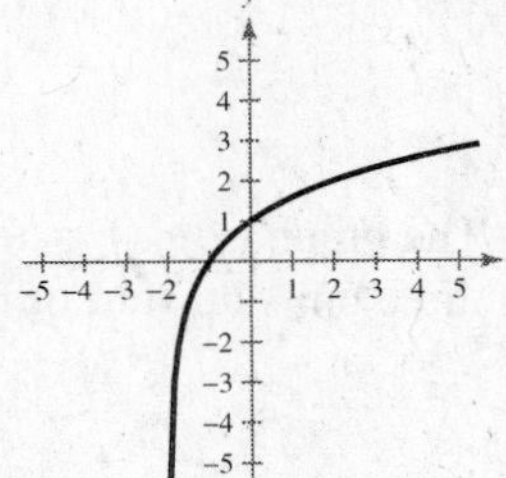

48. $y = \log_2(x - 1)$

Domain: $x - 1 > 0 \Rightarrow x > 1$

Vertical asymptote: $x = 1$

$\log_2(x - 1) = 0$

$x - 1 = 1$

$x = 2$

x-intercept: $(2, 0)$

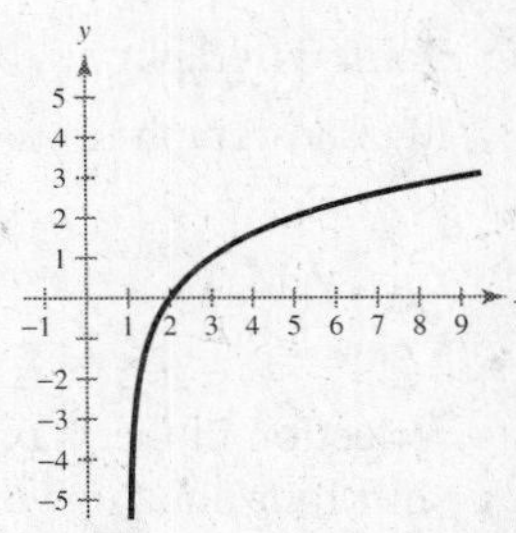

49. $y = 1 + \log_2 x$

Domain: $x > 0$

Vertical asymptote: $x = 0$

$1 + \log_2 x = 0$

$\log_2 x = -1$

$x = 2^{-1} = \frac{1}{2}$

x-intercept: $\left(\frac{1}{2}, 0\right)$

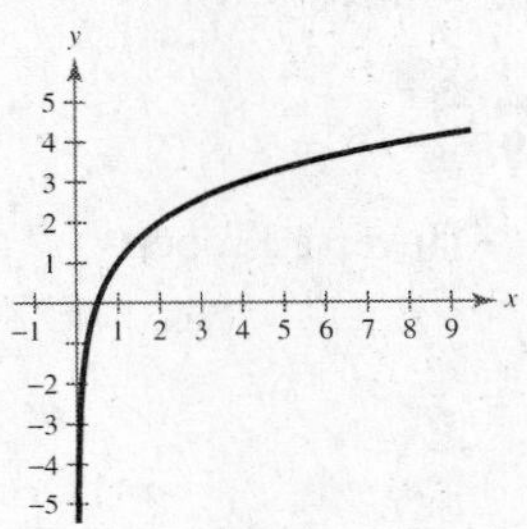

50. $y = 2 - \log_2 x$

Domain: $x > 0$

Vertical asymptote: $x = 0$

$2 - \log_2 x = 0$

$\log_2 x = 2$

$x = 2^2 = 4$

x-intercept: $(4, 0)$

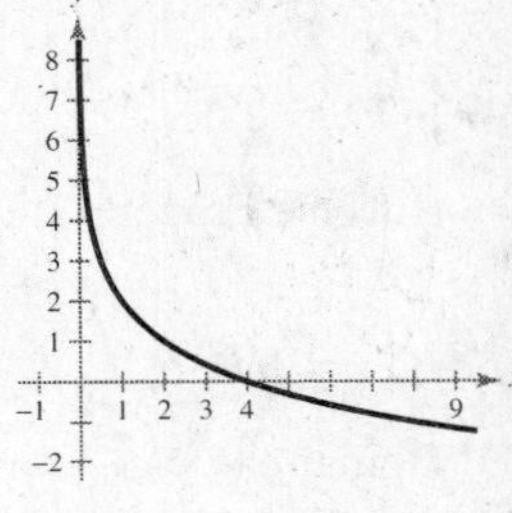

51. $y = 1 + \log_2(x - 2)$

Domain: $x - 2 > 0 \Rightarrow x > 2$

Vertical asymptote: $x = 2$

$1 + \log_2(x - 2) = 0$

$\log_2(x - 2) = -1$

$x - 2 = 2^{-1} = \frac{1}{2}$

$x = \frac{5}{2}$

x-intercept: $\left(\frac{5}{2}, 0\right)$

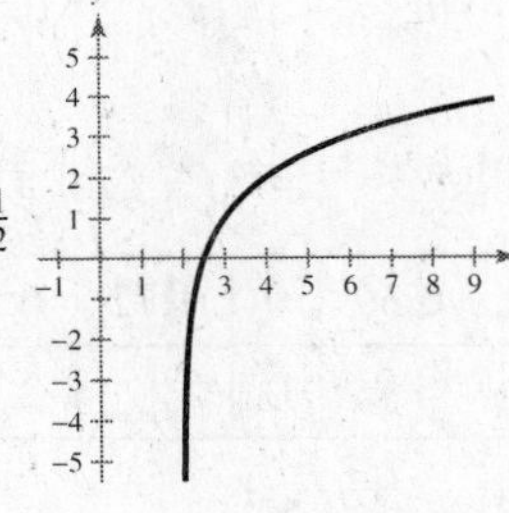

52. $y = 2 + \log_2(x + 1)$

Domain: $x + 1 > 0 \Rightarrow x > -1$

Vertical asymptote: $x = -1$

$2 + \log_2(x + 1) = 0$

$\log_2(x + 1) = -2$

$x + 1 = 2^{-2} = \frac{1}{4}$

$x = -\frac{3}{4}$

x-intercept: $\left(-\frac{3}{4}, 0\right)$

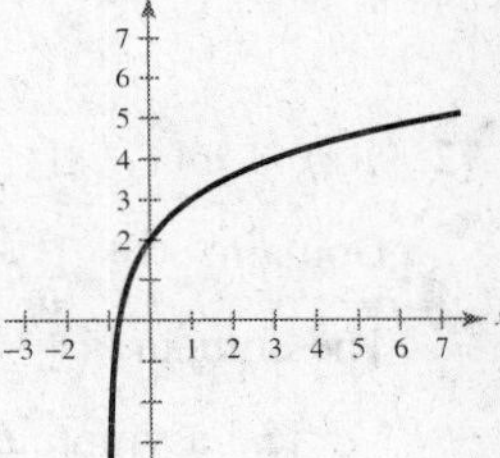

53. $f(x) = \log_3 x + 2$

Asymptote: $x = 0$

Point on graph: $(1, 2)$

Matches graph (b).

54. $f(x) = -\log_3 x$

Asymptote: $x = 0$

Point on graph: $(1, 0)$

Matches graph (c).

55. $f(x) = -\log_3(x + 2)$

Asymptote: $x = -2$

Point on graph: $(-1, 0)$

Matches graph (d).

56. $f(x) = \log_3(1 - x)$

Asymptote: $x = 1$

Domain: $1 - x > 0 \Rightarrow x < 1$

Point on graph: $(0, 0)$

Matches graph (a).

57. $f(x) = \log_{10} x$

$g(x) = -\log_{10} x$ is a reflection in the x-axis of the graph of f.

58. The graph of $g(x) = \log_{10}(x + 7)$ is a horizontal shift 7 units to the left of the graph of $f(x) = \log_{10} x$.

59. $f(x) = \log_2 x$

$g(x) = 4 - \log_2 x$ is obtained from f by a reflection in the x-axis followed by a vertical shift four units upward.

60. The graph of $g(x) = \log_2 x + 3$ is a vertical shift three units upward of the graph of $f(x) = \log_2 x$.

61. Horizontal shift three units to the left and a vertical shift two units downward

62. Horizontal shift one unit to the right and a vertical shift four units upward

63. $\ln\sqrt{42} \approx 1.869$

64. $\ln 18.31 \approx 2.907$

65. $-\ln\left(\frac{1}{2}\right) \approx 0.693$

66. $3\ln(0.75) \approx -0.863$

67. $\ln e^2 = 2$

(Inverse Property)

68. $-\ln e = -1$

69. $e^{\ln 1.8} = 1.8$

(Inverse Property)

70. $7\ln e^0 = 7\ln 1$

$= 7(0) = 0$

71. $f(x) = \ln(x - 1)$

Domain: $x > 1$

Vertical asymptote: $x = 1$

x-intercept: $(2, 0)$

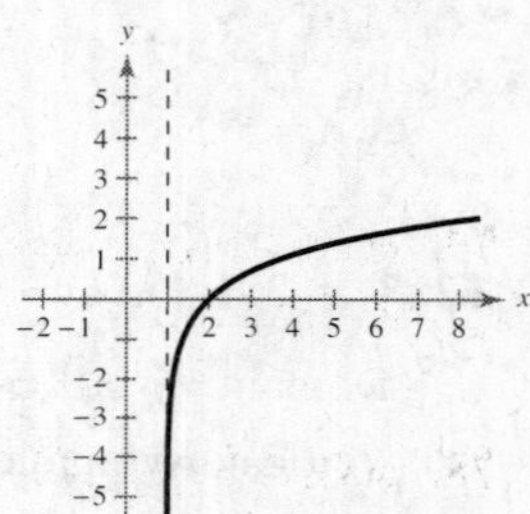

72. $h(x) = \ln(x + 1)$

Domain: $x + 1 > 0 \Rightarrow x > -1$

The domain is $(-1, \infty)$.

Vertical asymptote: $x + 1 = 0 \Rightarrow x = -1$

x-intercept: $\ln(x + 1) = 0$

$$e^0 = x + 1$$
$$1 = x + 1$$
$$0 = x$$

The x-intercept is $(0, 0)$.

$y = \ln(x + 1) \Rightarrow e^y - 1 = x$

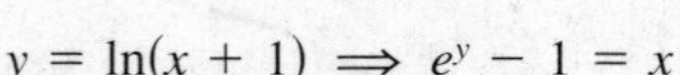

x	-0.39	0	1.72	6.39	19.09
y	$-\frac{1}{2}$	0	1	2	3

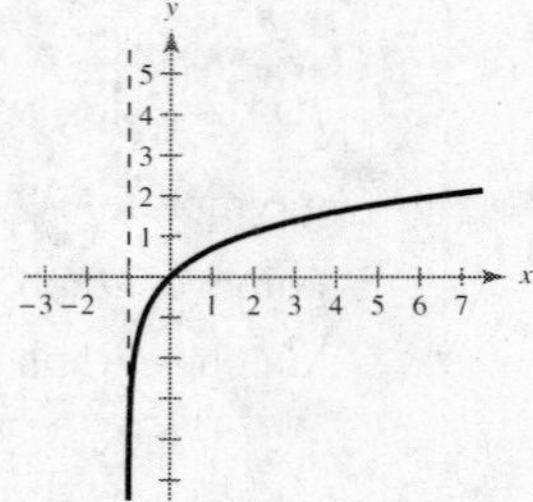

73. $g(x) = \ln(-x)$

Domain: $-x > 0 \Rightarrow x < 0$

The domain is $(-\infty, 0)$.

Vertical asymptote: $-x = 0 \Rightarrow x = 0$

x-intercept: $0 = \ln(-x)$

$e^0 = -x$

$-1 = x$

The x-intercept is $(-1, 0)$.

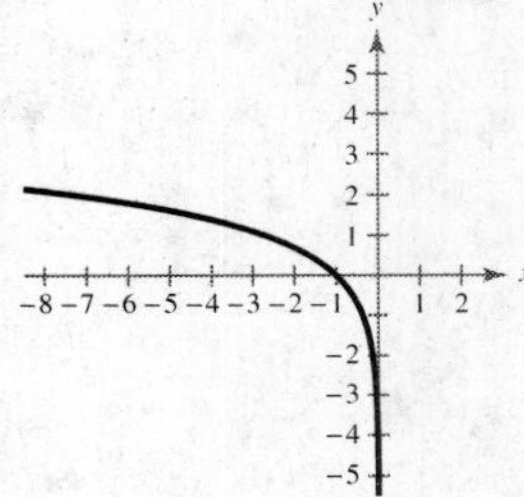

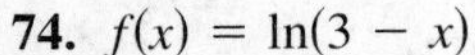

74. $f(x) = \ln(3 - x)$

Domain: $3 - x > 0 \Rightarrow x < 3$

The domain is $(-\infty, 3)$.

Vertical asymptote: $3 - x = 0 \Rightarrow x = 3$

x-intercept: $\ln(3 - x) = 0$

$e^0 = 3 - x$

$1 = 3 - x$

$2 = x$

The x-intercept is $(2, 0)$.

$y = \ln(3 - x) \Rightarrow x = 3 - e^y$

x	2.95	2.86	2.63	2	0.28
y	-3	-2	-1	0	1

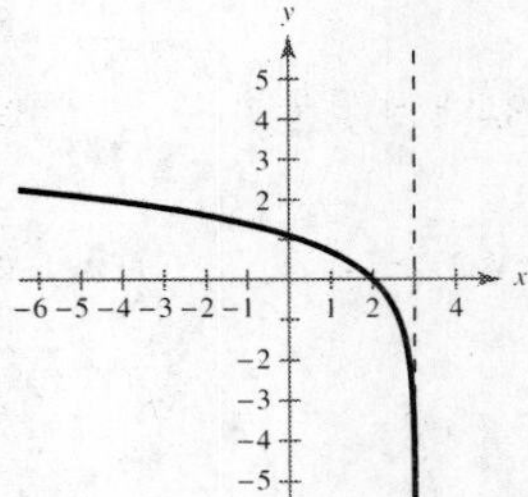

75. $g(x) = \ln(x + 3)$ is a horizontal shift three units to the left.

76. $g(x) = \ln(x - 4)$ is a horizontal shift four units to the right.

77. $g(x) = \ln x - 5$ is a vertical shift five units downward.

78. $g(x) = \ln x + 4$ is a vertical shift four units upward.

79. $g(x) = \ln(x - 1) + 2$ is a horizontal shift one unit to the right and a vertical shift two units upward.

80. $g(x) = \ln(x + 2) - 5$ is a horizontal shift two units to the left and a vertical shift five units downward.

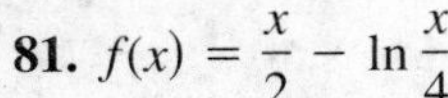

81. $f(x) = \dfrac{x}{2} - \ln \dfrac{x}{4}$

(a)

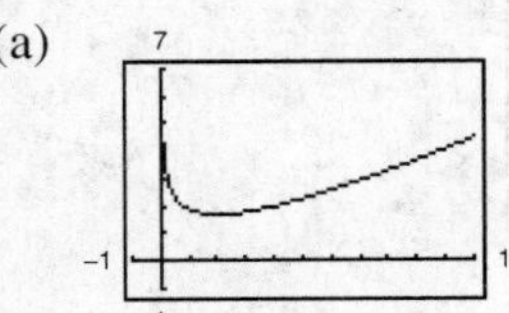

(b) Domain: $(0, \infty)$

(c) Increasing on $(2, \infty)$

Decreasing on $(0, 2)$

(d) Relative minimum: $(2, 1.693)$

82. $g(x) = \dfrac{12 \ln x}{x}$

(a)

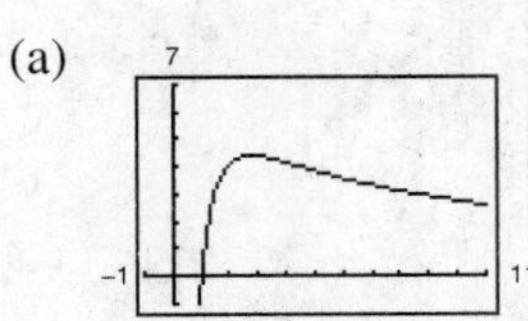

(b) Domain: $(0, \infty)$

(c) Increasing on $(0, 2.72)$

Decreasing on $(2.72, \infty)$

(d) Relative maximum: $(2.72, 4.41)$

83. $h(x) = 4x \ln x$

(a)

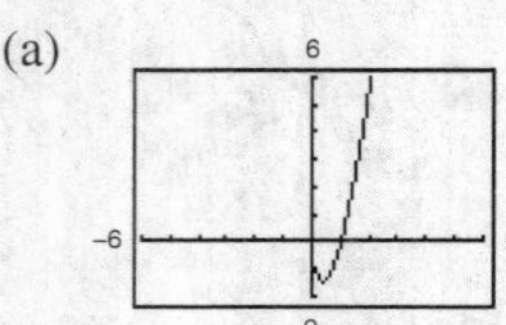

(b) Domain: $(0, \infty)$

(c) Increasing on $(0.368, \infty)$

Decreasing on $(0, 0.368)$

(d) Relative minimum: $(0.368, -1.472)$

84. $f(x) = \dfrac{x}{\ln x}$

(a)

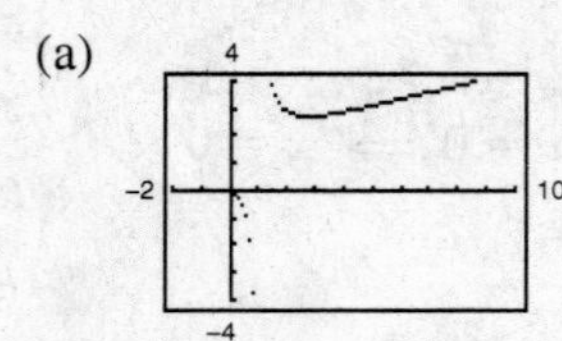

(b) Domain: $(0, 1)$ $(1, \infty)$

(c) Increasing on $(2.72, \infty)$

Decreasing on $(0, 1)$ $(1, 2.72)$

(d) Relative minimum: $(2.72, 2.72)$

85. $f(x) = \ln\left(\dfrac{x + 2}{x - 1}\right)$

(a)

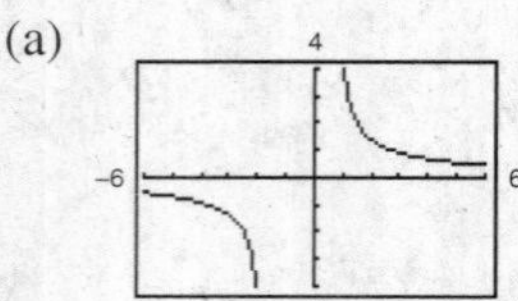

(b) $\dfrac{x + 2}{x - 1} > 0$; Critical numbers: $1, -2$

Test intervals: $(-\infty, -2), (-2, 1), (1, \infty)$

Testing these three intervals, we see that the domain is $(-\infty, -2) \cup (1, \infty)$.

(c) The graph is decreasing on $(-\infty, -2)$ and decreasing on $(1, \infty)$.

(d) There are no relative maximum or minimum values.

86. $f(x) = \ln\left(\dfrac{2x}{x + 2}\right)$

(a)

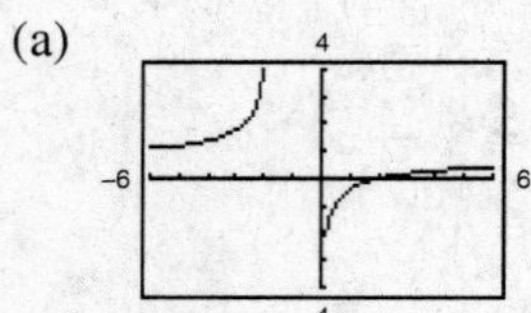

(b) $\dfrac{2x}{x + 2} > 0$; Critical numbers: $0, -2$

Test intervals: $(-\infty, -2), (-2, 0), (0, \infty)$

Testing these three intervals, we see that the domain is $(-\infty, -2) \cup (0, \infty)$.

(c) The graph is increasing on $(-\infty, -2)$ and increasing on $(0, \infty)$.

(d) There are no relative maximum or minimum values.

87. $f(x) = \ln\left(\dfrac{x^2}{10}\right)$

(a)

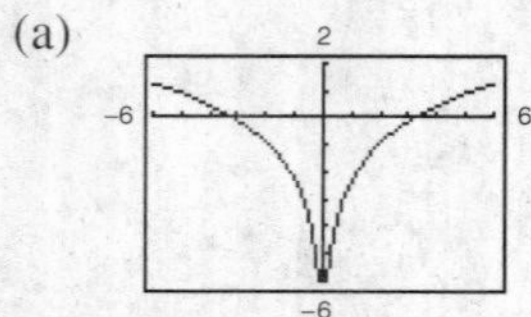

(b) $\dfrac{x^2}{10} > 0 \implies x \neq 0$; Domain: all $x \neq 0$

(c) The graph is increasing on $(0, \infty)$ and decreasing on $(-\infty, 0)$.

(d) There are no relative maximum or relative minimum values.

88. $f(x) = \ln\left(\dfrac{x}{x^2 + 1}\right)$

(a)

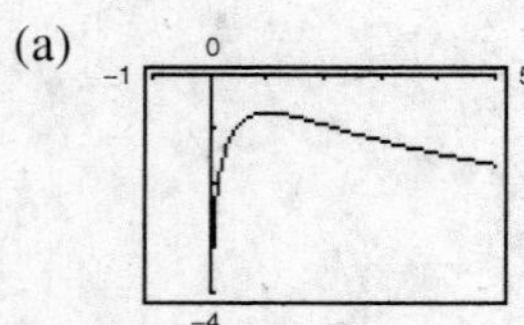

(b) Domain: $x > 0$

(c) The graph is increasing on $(0, 1)$ and decreasing on $(1, \infty)$.

(d) Relative maximum: $(1, -0.693)$

89. $f(x) = \sqrt{\ln x}$

(a)

(b) $\ln x \geq 0 \implies x \geq 1$; Domain: $x \geq 1$

(c) The graph is increasing on $(1, \infty)$.

(d) There are no relative maximum or relative minimum values.

90. $f(x) = (\ln x)^2$

(a)

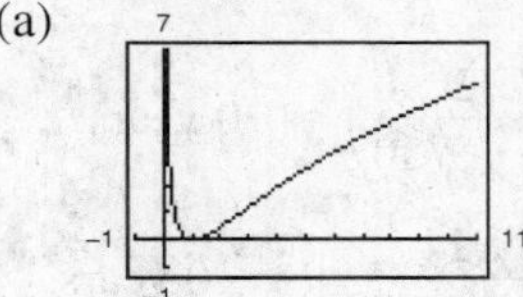

(b) Domain: $x > 0$

(c) The graph is decreasing on $(0, 1)$ and increasing on $(1, \infty)$.

(d) Relative minimum: $(1, 0)$

91. $f(t) = 80 - 17 \log_{10}(t + 1), \quad 0 \leq t \leq 12$

(a) $f(0) = 80 - 17 \log_{10}(0 + 1) = 80$

(b) $f(4) = 80 - 17 \log_{10}(4 + 1) \approx 68.1$

(c) $f(10) = 80 - 17 \log_{10}(10 + 1) \approx 62.3$

(d)

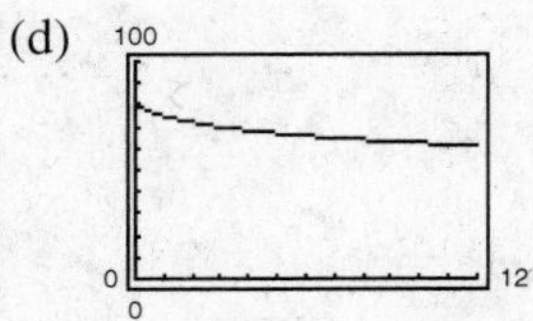

92. (a)

The model is a good fit.

(b) $T > 300°\text{F}$ when $p > 67.3$ pounds per square inch

[The graph of T and $y = 300$ intersect at $p = 67.3$.]

(c) $T(74) = 306.48°\text{F}$

93. $t = \dfrac{\ln K}{0.055}$

(a)

K	1	2	4	6	8	10	12
t	0	12.6	25.2	32.6	37.8	41.9	45.2

As the amount increases, the time increases, but at a lesser rate.

(b)

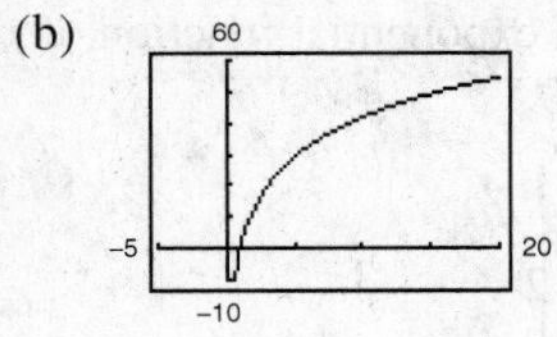

94. (a)

r	0.005	0.010	0.015
t	138.6 yr	69.3 yr	46.2 yr

r	0.020	0.025	0.030
t	34.7 yr	27.7 yr	23.1 yr

The doubling time decreases as r increases.

(b)

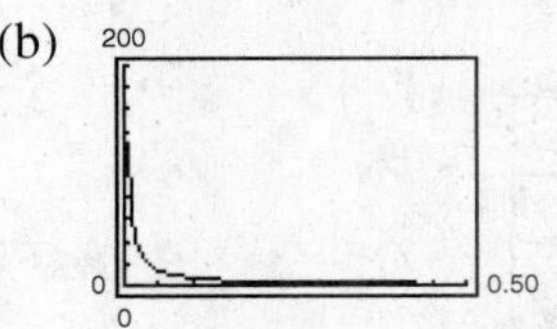

95. $\beta = 10 \log_{10}\left(\dfrac{I}{10^{-12}}\right)$

(a) $I = 1$: $\beta = 10 \log_{10}\left(\dfrac{1}{10^{-12}}\right) = 10 \cdot \log_{10}(10^{12}) = 10(12) = 120$ decibels

(b) $I = 10^{-2}$: $\beta = 10 \log_{10}\left(\dfrac{10^{-2}}{10^{-12}}\right) = 10 \log_{10}(10^{10}) = 10(10) = 100$ decibels

(c) No, this is a logarithmic scale.

96. $t = 16.625 \ln\left(\frac{x}{x - 750}\right), x > 750$

(a) $16.625 \ln\left(\frac{897.72}{897.72 - 750}\right) \approx 30$ years

$16.625 \ln\left(\frac{1659.24}{1659.24 - 750}\right) \approx 10$ years

(b) $(897.72)(30)(12) = 323{,}179.20$

$(1659.24)(10)(12) = 199{,}108.80$

Interest for 30-year loan is
$323{,}179.20 - 150{,}000 = 173{,}179.20$.

Interest for 10-year loan is
$199{,}108.80 - 150{,}000 = 49{,}108.80$.

97. $y = 80.4 - 11 \ln x$

$y(300) = 80.4 - 11 \ln 300 \approx 17.66 \text{ ft}^3/\text{min}$

98. $y = 80.4 - 11 \ln x,\ 100 \le x \le 1500$

(a) $\frac{450 \text{ cubic ft per minute}}{30 \text{ children}} = 15$ cubic feet per minute per child

(b) From the graph, for $y = 15$ you get $x \approx 382$ cubic feet.

(c) If ceiling height is 30, then 382 square feet of floor space is needed.

99. False. You would reflect $y = 6^x$ in the line $y = x$.

100. True. $\log_3(27) = \log_3 3^3 = 3$

101. $5 = \log_b 32$

$b^5 = 32 = 2^5$

$b = 2$

102. $4 = \log_b 81$

$b^4 = 81 = 3^4$

$b = 3$

103. $2 = \log_b\left(\frac{1}{16}\right)$

$b^2 = \frac{1}{16} = \left(\frac{1}{4}\right)^2$

$b = \frac{1}{4}$

104. $3 = \log_b\left(\frac{1}{27}\right)$

$b^3 = \frac{1}{27} = \left(\frac{1}{3}\right)^3$

$b = \frac{1}{3}$

105. The vertical asymptote is to the right of the y-axis, and the graph increases. Matches (b).

106. The vertical asymptote is to the left of the y-axis.

Matches (b).

107. $f(x) = \log_a x$ is the inverse of $g(x) = a^x$, where $a > 0, a \neq 1$.

108. (a) $f(x) = \ln x,\ g(x) = \sqrt{x}$

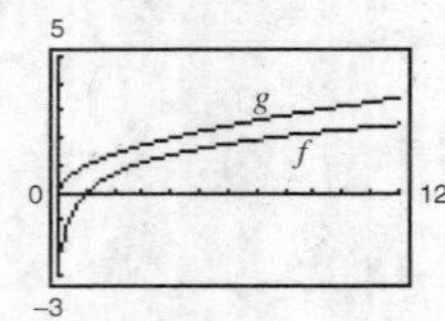

(b) $f(x) = \ln x,\ g(x) = \sqrt[4]{x}$

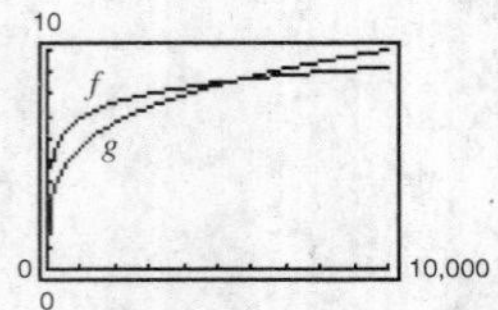

The rate of growth of the natural logarithmic function is slower than $g(x) = x^{1/n}$ for any n.

109. (a) False, y is not an exponential function of x. (y can never be 0.)

(b) True, y could be $\log_2 x$.

(c) True, x could be 2^y.

(d) False, y is not linear. (The points are not collinear.)

110. (a)

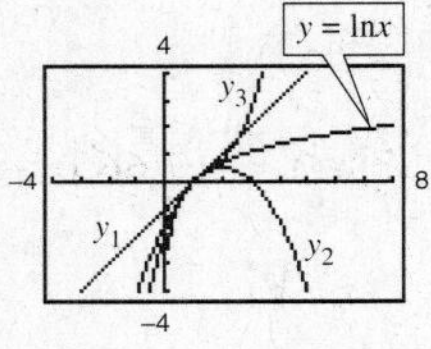

(b) Pattern is $(x - 1) - \frac{1}{2}(x - 1)^2 + \frac{1}{3}(x - 1)^3 - \frac{1}{4}(x - 1)^4 + \cdots$.

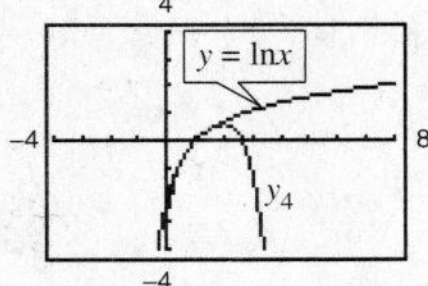

As you use more terms, the graph better approximates the graph of ln x on the interval $(0, 2)$.

111. $f(x) = \dfrac{\ln x}{x}$

(a)

x	1	5	10	10^2	10^4	10^6
$f(x)$	0	0.322	0.230	0.046	0.00092	0.0000138

(b) As x increases without bound, $f(x)$ approaches 0.

(c)

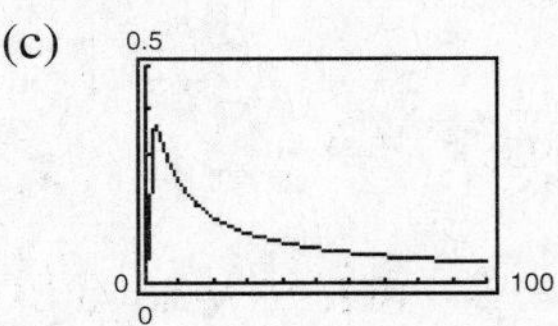

112.
$$f(t) = 75 - 6\ln(t + 1)$$
$$60 = 75 - 6\ln(t + 1)$$
$$\ln(t + 1) = \tfrac{15}{6} = \tfrac{5}{2}$$
$$t = e^{5/2} - 1 \approx 11.18$$

Or, you could graph $f(t)$ and $y = 60$ together in the same viewing window, and determine their point of intersection.

113. $x^2 + 2x - 3 = (x + 3)(x - 1)$

114. $2x^2 + 3x - 5 = (2x + 5)(x - 1)$

115. $12x^2 + 5x - 3 = (4x + 3)(3x - 1)$

116. $16x^2 + 16x + 7$

$$x = \frac{-16 \pm \sqrt{256 - 448}}{32}$$
$$= -\frac{1}{2} \pm \frac{\sqrt{3}}{4}i$$
$$\left(x + \frac{1}{2} - \frac{\sqrt{3}}{4}i\right)\left(x + \frac{1}{2} + \frac{\sqrt{3}}{4}i\right)$$

117. $16x^2 - 25 = (4x + 5)(4x - 5)$

118. $36x^2 - 49 = (6x - 7)(6x + 7)$

119. $2x^3 + x^2 - 45x = x(2x^2 + x - 45)$
$= x(2x - 9)(x + 5)$

120. $3x^3 - 5x^2 - 12x = x(3x^2 - 5x - 12)$
$= x(3x + 4)(x - 3)$

121. $(f + g)(2) = f(2) + g(2) = [3(2) + 2] + [2^3 - 1] = 8 + 7 = 15$

122. $(f - g)(-1) = (-1) - (-2) = 1$

123. $(fg)(6) = f(6)g(6) = [3(6) + 2][6^3 - 1] = [20][215] = 4300$

124. $\left(\frac{f}{g}\right)(0) = \frac{2}{-1} = -2$

125. $5x - 7 = x + 4$

The graphs of $y = 5x - 7$ and $y_2 = x + 4$ intersect when $x = 2.75$ or $\frac{11}{4}$.

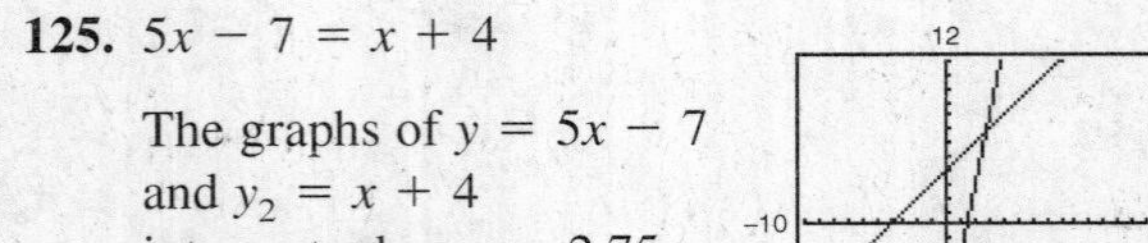

126. $y = -2x + 3$ and $y = 8x$ intersect at $x = 0.3$

127. $\sqrt{3x - 2} = 9$

The graphs of $y_1 = \sqrt{3x - 2}$ and $y_2 = 9$ intersect when $x \approx 27.667$ or $\frac{83}{3}$.

128. $y = \sqrt{x - 11}$ and $y = x + 2$ do not intersect.

No solution

Section 3.3 Properties of Logarithms

- You should know the following properties of logarithms.

  (a) $\log_a x = \dfrac{\log_b x}{\log_b a}$

  (b) $\log_a(uv) = \log_a u + \log_a v$ $\qquad \ln(uv) = \ln u + \ln v$

  (c) $\log_a(u/v) = \log_a u - \log_a v$ $\qquad \ln(u/v) = \ln u - \ln v$

  (d) $\log_a u^n = n \log_a u$ $\qquad \ln u^n = n \ln u$

- You should be able to rewrite logarithmic expressions using these properties.

Vocabulary Check

1. change-of-base **2.** $\dfrac{\ln x}{\ln a}$ **3.** $\log_a u^n$ **4.** $\ln u + \ln v$

1. (a) $\log_5 x = \dfrac{\log_{10} x}{\log_{10} 5}$

(b) $\log_5 x = \dfrac{\ln x}{\ln 5}$

2. (a) $\log_3 x = \dfrac{\log_{10} x}{\log_{10} 3}$

(b) $\log_3 x = \dfrac{\ln x}{\ln 3}$

3. (a) $\log_{1/5} x = \dfrac{\log_{10} x}{\log_{10} 1/5} = \dfrac{\log_{10} x}{-\log_{10} 5}$

(b) $\log_{1/5} x = \dfrac{\ln x}{\ln 1/5} = \dfrac{\ln x}{-\ln 5}$

4. (a) $\log_{1/3} x = \dfrac{\log_{10} x}{\log_{10}(1/3)} = \dfrac{-\log_{10} x}{\log_{10} 3}$

(b) $\log_{1/3} x = \dfrac{\ln x}{\ln(1/3)} = \dfrac{-\ln x}{\ln 3}$

5. (a) $\log_a\left(\dfrac{3}{10}\right) = \dfrac{\log_{10}(3/10)}{\log_{10} a}$

(b) $\log_a\left(\dfrac{3}{10}\right) = \dfrac{\ln(3/10)}{\ln a}$

6. (a) $\log_a\left(\dfrac{3}{4}\right) = \dfrac{\log_{10}(3/4)}{\log_{10} a}$

(b) $\log_a\left(\dfrac{3}{4}\right) = \dfrac{\ln(3/4)}{\ln a}$

7. (a) $\log_{2.6} x = \dfrac{\log_{10} x}{\log_{10} 2.6}$

(b) $\log_{2.6} x = \dfrac{\ln x}{\ln 2.6}$

8. (a) $\log_{7.1} x = \dfrac{\log_{10} x}{\log_{10} 7.1}$

(b) $\log_{7.1} x = \dfrac{\ln x}{\ln 7.1}$

9. $\log_3 7 = \dfrac{\ln 7}{\ln 3} \approx 1.771$

10. $\log_7 4 = \dfrac{\ln 4}{\ln 7} \approx 0.712$

11. $\log_{1/2} 4 = \dfrac{\ln 4}{\ln (1/2)} = -2$

12. $\log_{1/8} 64 = \dfrac{\ln 64}{\ln(1/8)}$

$= \dfrac{\ln 8^2}{-\ln 8} = -2$

13. $\log_9(0.8) = \dfrac{\ln(0.8)}{\ln 9} \approx -0.102$

14. $\log_3(0.015) = \dfrac{\ln(0.015)}{\ln 3}$

≈ -3.823

15. $\log_{15} 1460 = \dfrac{\ln 1460}{\ln 15} \approx 2.691$

16. $\log_{20} 135 = \dfrac{\ln 135}{\ln 20} \approx 1.637$

17. $\ln 20 = \ln(4 \cdot 5)$

$= \ln 4 + \ln 5$

18. $\ln 500 = \ln(5^3 \cdot 4)$

$= \ln 5^3 + \ln 4$

$= 3 \ln 5 + \ln 4$

19. $\ln \frac{5}{64} = \ln 5 - \ln 64$

$= \ln 5 - \ln 4^3$

$= \ln 5 - 3 \ln 4$

20. $\ln \frac{2}{5} = \ln 2 - \ln 5$

$= \ln 4^{1/2} - \ln 5$

$= \frac{1}{2} \ln 4 - \ln 5$

21. $\log_b 25 = \log_b 5^2$

$= 2 \log_b 5$

$\approx 2(0.8271) \approx 1.6542$

22. $\log_b 30 = \log_b(2 \cdot 3 \cdot 5)$

$= \log_b 2 + \log_b 3 + \log_b 5$

$\approx 0.3562 + 0.5646 + 0.8271 \approx 1.7479$

23. $\log_b \sqrt{3} = \frac{1}{2} \log_b 3$

$\approx \frac{1}{2}(0.5646)$

≈ 0.2823

24. $\log_b\left(\frac{25}{9}\right) = \log_b 5^2 - \log_b 3^2$

$= 2 \log_b 5 - 2 \log_b 3$

$\approx 2(0.8271) - 2(0.5646) \approx 0.5250$

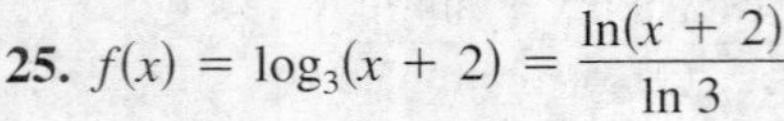

25. $f(x) = \log_3(x + 2) = \dfrac{\ln(x + 2)}{\ln 3}$

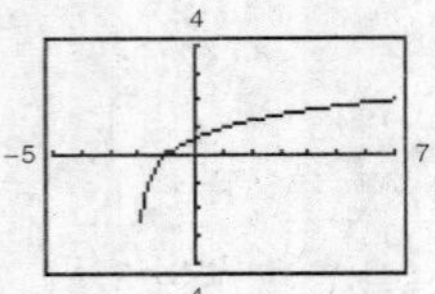

26. $f(x) = \log_2(x - 1) = \dfrac{\ln(x - 1)}{\ln 2}$

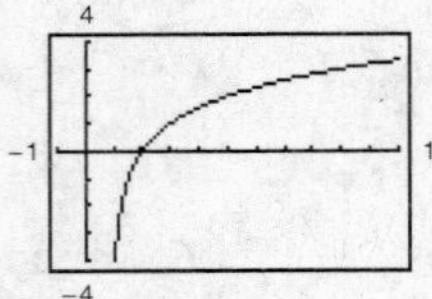

27. $f(x) = \log_{1/2}(x - 2) = \dfrac{\ln(x - 2)}{\ln(1/2)} = \dfrac{\ln(x - 2)}{-\ln 2}$

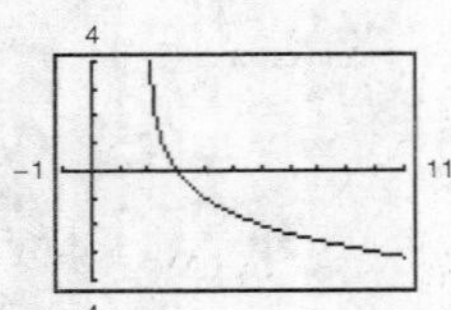

28. $f(x) = \log_{1/3}(x + 1) = \dfrac{\ln(x + 1)}{\ln(1/3)} = \dfrac{\ln(x + 1)}{-\ln 3}$

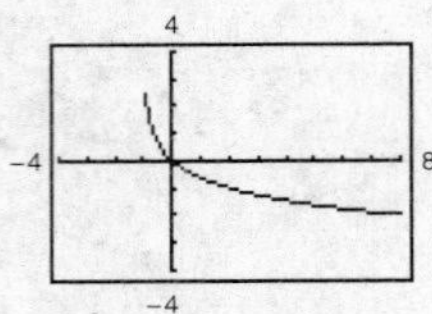

29. $f(x) = \log_{1/4}(x^2) = \dfrac{\ln x^2}{\ln(1/4)} = \dfrac{\ln x^2}{-\ln 4}$

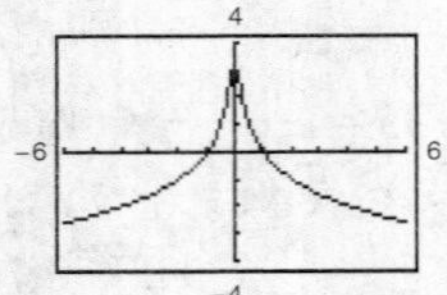

30. $f(x) = \log_{1/2}\left(\dfrac{x}{2}\right) = \dfrac{\ln(x/2)}{\ln(1/2)} = \dfrac{\ln(x/2)}{-\ln 2}$

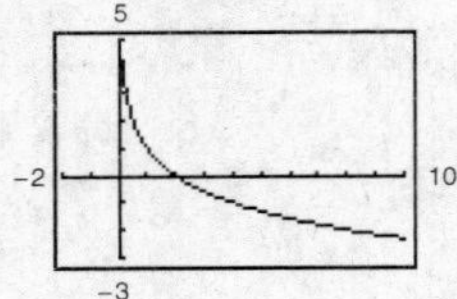

31. $\log_4 8 = \log_4 2^3 = 3 \log_4 2$

$= 3 \log_4 4^{1/2} = 3\left(\frac{1}{2}\right) \log_4 4$

$= \frac{3}{2}$

32. $\log_2(4^2 \cdot 3^4) = \log_2 4^2 + \log_2 3^4$

$= 2 \log_2 4 + 4 \log_2 3$

$= 2 \log_2 2^2 + 4 \log_2 3$

$= 4 \log_2 2 + 4 \log_2 3$

$= 4 + 4 \log_2 3$

33. $\ln(5e^6) = \ln 5 + \ln e^6 = \ln 5 + 6 = 6 + \ln 5$

34. $\ln \dfrac{6}{e^2} = \ln 6 - \ln e^2$

$= \ln 6 - 2 \ln e = \ln 6 - 2$

35. $\log_5 \frac{1}{250} = \log_5 1 - \log_5 250 = 0 - \log_5(125 \cdot 2)$

$= -\log_5(5^3 \cdot 2) = -[\log_5 5^3 + \log_5 2]$

$= -[3 \log_5 5 + \log_5 2] = -3 - \log_5 2$

36. $-\ln 24 = -\ln(2^3 \cdot 3)$

$= -\ln 2^3 - \ln 3$

$= -3 \ln 2 - \ln 3$

$= -(3 \ln 2 + \ln 3)$

37. $\log_{10} 5x = \log_{10} 5 + \log_{10} x$

38. $\log_{10} 10z = \log_{10} 10 + \log_{10} z = 1 + \log_{10} z$

39. $\log_{10} \dfrac{5}{x} = \log_{10} 5 - \log_{10} x$

40. $\log_{10} \dfrac{y}{2} = \log_{10} y - \log_{10} 2$

41. $\log_8 x^4 = 4 \log_8 x$

42. $\log_6 z^{-3} = -3\log_6 z$

43. $\ln\sqrt{z} = \ln z^{1/2} = \frac{1}{2}\ln z$

44. $\ln\sqrt[3]{t} = \ln t^{1/3} = \frac{1}{3}\ln t$

45. $\ln xyz = \ln x + \ln y + \ln z$

46. $\ln\frac{xy}{z} = \ln x + \ln y - \ln z$

47. $\log_3(a^2bc^3) = \log_3 a^2 + \log_3 b + \log_3 c^3$
$= 2\log_3 a + \log_3 b + 3\log_3 c$

48. $\log_5(x^3y^3z) = \log_5 x^3 + \log_5 y^3 + \log_5 z$
$= 3\log_5 x + 3\log_5 y + \log_5 z$

49. $\ln(a^2\sqrt{a-1}) = \ln a^2 + \ln(a-1)^{1/2}$
$= 2\ln a + \frac{1}{2}\ln(a-1),\ a > 1$

50. $\ln[z(z-1)^2] = \ln z + \ln(z-1)^2$
$= \ln z + 2\ln(z-1)$

51. $\ln\sqrt[3]{\frac{x}{y}} = \frac{1}{3}\ln\frac{x}{y}$
$= \frac{1}{3}[\ln x - \ln y]$
$= \frac{1}{3}\ln x - \frac{1}{3}\ln y$

52. $\ln\sqrt{\frac{x^2}{y^3}} = \ln\left(\frac{x^2}{y^3}\right)^{1/2} = \frac{1}{2}\ln\left(\frac{x^2}{y^3}\right)$
$= \frac{1}{2}(\ln x^2 - \ln y^3)$
$= \frac{1}{2}(2\ln x - 3\ln y)$
$= \ln x - \frac{3}{2}\ln y$

53. $\ln\left(\frac{x^2-1}{x^3}\right) = \ln(x^2-1) - \ln x^3$
$= \ln[(x-1)(x+1)] - 3\ln x$
$= \ln(x-1) + \ln(x+1) - 3\ln x,\ x > 1$

54. $\ln\left(\frac{x}{\sqrt{x^2+1}}\right) = \ln x - \ln\sqrt{x^2+1}$
$= \ln x - \ln(x^2+1)^{1/2}$
$= \ln x - \frac{1}{2}\ln(x^2+1)$

55. $\ln\left(\frac{x^4\sqrt{y}}{z^5}\right) = \ln x^4\sqrt{y} - \ln z^5$
$= \ln x^4 + \ln\sqrt{y} - \ln z^5$
$= 4\ln x + \frac{1}{2}\ln y - 5\ln z$

56. $\log_b\frac{\sqrt{x}y^4}{z^4} = \log_b\sqrt{x}y^4 - \log_b z^4$
$= \log_b x^{1/2} + \log_b y^4 - \log_b z^4$
$= \frac{1}{2}\log_b x + 4\log_b y - 4\log_b z$

57. $y_1 = \ln[x^3(x+4)]$
$y_2 = 3\ln x + \ln(x+4)$

(a)

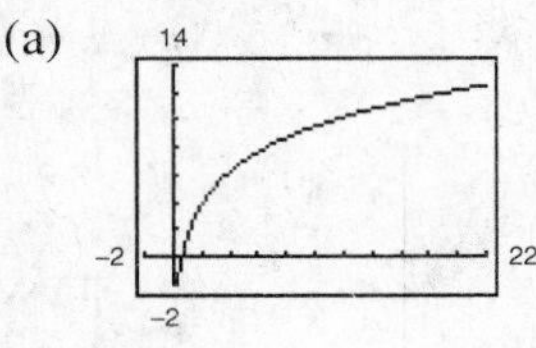

(b)

x	0.5	1	1.5	2	3	10
y_1	−0.5754	1.6094	2.9211	3.8712	5.2417	9.5468
y_2	−0.5754	1.6094	2.9211	3.8712	5.2417	9.5468

(c) The graphs and table suggest that $y_1 = y_2$ for $x > 0$. In fact,

$y_1 = \ln[x^3(x+4)] = \ln x^3 + \ln(x+4)$
$= 3\ln x + \ln(x+4) = y_2.$

58. $y_1 = \ln\left(\dfrac{\sqrt{x}}{x-2}\right)$, $y_2 = \dfrac{1}{2}\ln x - \ln(x-2)$

(a)

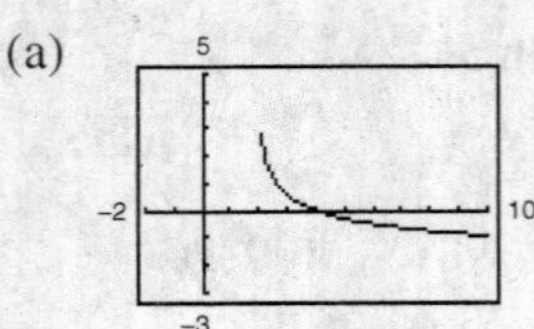

(b)

x	3	4	5	6	10	20
y_1	0.5493	0	−0.2939	−0.4904	−0.9281	−1.393
y_2	0.5493	0	−0.2939	−0.4904	−0.9281	−1.393

(c) The graphs and table suggest that $y_1 = y_2$.

In fact,

$$y_1 = \ln\left(\frac{\sqrt{x}}{x-2}\right) = \ln x^{1/2} - \ln(x-2) = \frac{1}{2}\ln x - \ln(x-2) = y_2.$$

59. $\ln x + \ln 4 = \ln 4x$

60. $\ln y + \ln z = \ln yz$

61. $\log_4 z - \log_4 y = \log_4 \dfrac{z}{y}$

62. $\log_5 8 - \log_5 t = \log_5 \dfrac{8}{t}$

63. $2\log_2(x+3) = \log_2(x+3)^2$

64. $\dfrac{5}{2}\log_7(z-4) = \log_7(z-4)^{5/2}$

65. $\frac{1}{2}\ln(x^2+4) = \ln(x^2+4)^{1/2}$
$= \ln\sqrt{x^2+4}$

66. $2\ln x + \ln(x+1) = \ln x^2 + \ln(x+1)$
$= \ln(x^2(x+1))$
$= \ln(x^3 + x^2)$

67. $\ln x - 3\ln(x+1) = \ln x - \ln(x+1)^3$
$= \ln \dfrac{x}{(x+1)^3}$

68. $\ln x - 2\ln(x+2) = \ln x - \ln(x+2)^2$
$= \ln \dfrac{x}{(x+2)^2}$

69. $\ln(x-2) - \ln(x+2) = \ln\left(\dfrac{x-2}{x+2}\right)$

70. $3\ln x + 2\ln y - 4\ln z = \ln x^3 + \ln y^2 - \ln z^4$
$= \ln x^3y^2 - \ln z^4$
$= \ln \dfrac{x^3y^2}{z^4}$

71. $\ln x - 2[\ln(x+2) + \ln(x-2)] = \ln x - 2\ln[(x+2)(x-2)]$
$= \ln x - 2\ln(x^2-4)$
$= \ln x - \ln(x^2-4)^2$
$= \ln \dfrac{x}{(x^2-4)^2}$

72. $4[\ln z + \ln(z+5)] - 2\ln(z-5) = 4[\ln z(x+5)] - \ln(z-5)^2$
$= \ln[z(z+5)]^4 - \ln(z-5)^2$
$= \ln \dfrac{z^4(z+5)^4}{(z-5)^2}$

73. $\frac{1}{3}[2\ln(x+3) + \ln x - \ln(x^2-1)] = \frac{1}{3}[\ln(x+3)^2 + \ln x - \ln(x^2-1)]$

$$= \frac{1}{3}[\ln[x(x+3)^2] - \ln(x^2-1)]$$

$$= \frac{1}{3}\ln\frac{x(x+3)^2}{x^2-1}$$

$$= \ln\sqrt[3]{\frac{x(x+3)^2}{x^2-1}}$$

74. $2[\ln x - \ln(x+1) - \ln(x-1)] = 2\left[\ln\frac{x}{x+1} - \ln(x-1)\right]$

$$= 2\left[\ln\frac{x}{(x+1)(x-1)}\right]$$

$$= 2\left[\ln\frac{x}{x^2-1}\right]$$

$$= \ln\left(\frac{x}{x^2-1}\right)^2$$

75. $\frac{1}{3}[\ln y + 2\ln(y+4)] - \ln(y-1) = \frac{1}{3}[\ln y + \ln(y+4)^2] - \ln(y-1)$

$$= \frac{1}{3}\ln[y(y+4)^2] - \ln(y-1)$$

$$= \ln\sqrt[3]{y(y+4)^2} - \ln(y-1)$$

$$= \ln\frac{\sqrt[3]{y(y+4)^2}}{y-1}$$

76. $\frac{1}{2}[\ln(x+1) + 2\ln(x-1)] + 3\ln x = \frac{1}{2}[\ln(x+1) + \ln(x-1)^2] + \ln x^3$

$$= \frac{1}{2}[\ln(x+1)(x-1)^2] + \ln x^3$$

$$= \ln[(x+1)(x-1)^2]^{1/2} + \ln x^3$$

$$= \ln[(x+1)^{1/2}(x-1)] + \ln x^3$$

$$= \ln\left[x^3(x-1)\sqrt{x+1}\right]$$

77. $y_1 = 2[\ln 8 - \ln(x^2+1)]$

$y_2 = \ln\left[\frac{64}{(x^2+1)^2}\right]$

(a)

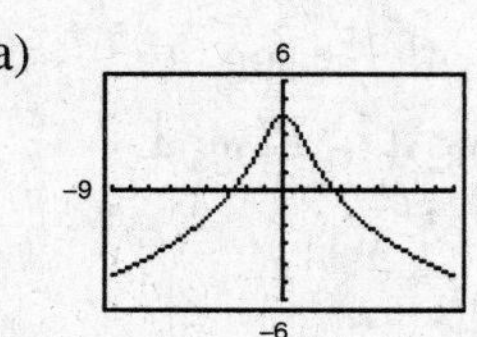

(b)

x	-8	-4	-2	0	2	4	8
y_1	-4.1899	-1.5075	0.9400	4.1589	0.9400	-1.5075	-4.1899
y_2	-4.1899	-1.5075	0.9400	4.1589	0.9400	-1.5075	-4.1899

(c) The graphs and table suggest that $y_1 = y_2$. In fact,

$$y_1 = 2[\ln 8 - \ln(x^2+1)]$$

$$= 2\ln\frac{8}{x^2+1} = \ln\frac{64}{(x^2+1)^2} = y_2.$$

78. $y_1 = \ln x + \frac{1}{2}\ln(x+1),\ y_2 = \ln\left(x\sqrt{x+1}\right),\ x > 0$

(a) 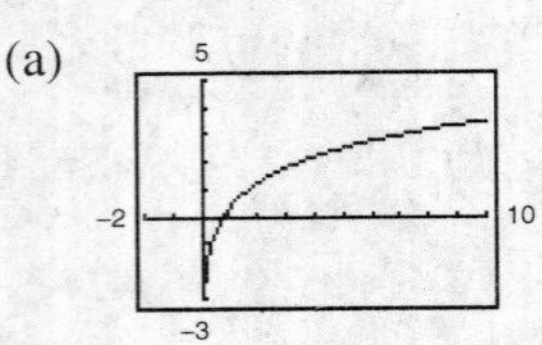

(b)

x	0	1	2	5	10
y_1	ERROR	0.34657	1.2425	2.5053	3.5015
y_2	ERROR	0.34657	1.2425	2.5053	3.5015

(c) The graphs and table suggest that $y_1 = y_2$.

In fact,

$$y_1 = \ln x + \tfrac{1}{2}\ln(x+1) = \ln x + \ln(x+1)^{1/2} = \ln\left[x\sqrt{x+1}\right] = y_2.$$

79. $y_1 = \ln x^2$

$y_2 = 2 \ln x$

(a) 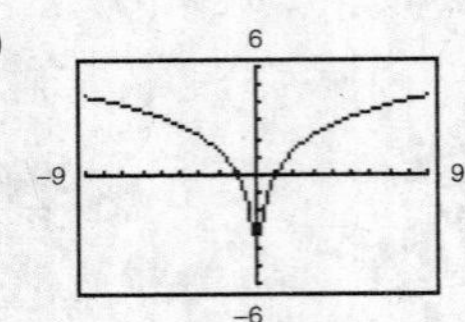

(The domain of y_2 is $x > 0$.)

(b)

x	-8	-4	1	2	4
y_1	4.1589	2.7726	0	1.3863	2.7726
y_2	undefined	undefined	0	1.3863	2.7726

(c) The graphs and table suggest that $y_1 = y_2$ for $x > 0$. The functions are not equivalent because the domains are different.

80. $y_1 = \frac{1}{4}\ln[x^4(x^2+1)],\ y_2 = \ln x + \frac{1}{4}\ln(x^2+1)$

(a) 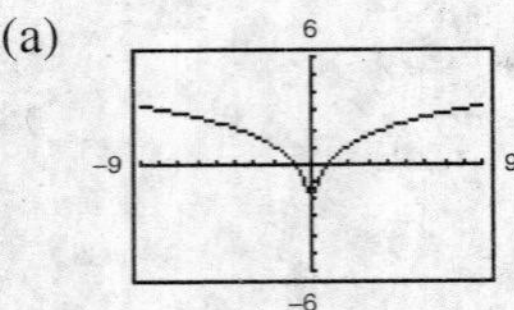

(b)

x	-10	-1	0	1	5	10
y_1	3.4564	0.17329	ERROR	0.17329	2.4240	3.4564
y_2	ERROR	ERROR	ERROR	0.17329	2.4240	3.4564

(c) No, the expressions are not equivalent. The domain of y_1 is all $x \neq 0$, whereas the domain of y_2 is $x > 0$.

81. $\log_3 9 = 2 \log_3 3 = 2$

82. $\log_6 \sqrt[3]{6} = \log_6 6^{1/3} = \frac{1}{3}\log_6 6 = \frac{1}{3}(1) = \frac{1}{3}$

83. $\log_4 16^{3.4} = 3.4 \log_4(4^2) = 6.8 \log_4 4 = 6.8$

84. $\log_5 \frac{1}{125} = \log_5 5^{-3} = -3 \log_5 5 = -3(1) = -3$

85. $\log_2(-4)$ is undefined. -4 is not in the domain of $f(x) = \log_2 x$.

86. $\log_4(-16)$ is undefined because -16 is not in the domain of $\log_4 x$.

87. $\log_5 75 - \log_5 3 = \log_5 \frac{75}{3} = \log_5 25 = \log_5 5^2 = 2$

88. $\log_4 2 + \log_4 32 = \log_4 4^{1/2} + \log_4 4^{5/2}$

$= \frac{1}{2}\log_4 4 + \frac{5}{2}\log_4 4$

$= \frac{1}{2}(1) + \frac{5}{2}(1)$

$= 3$

89. $\ln e^3 - \ln e^7 = 3 - 7 = -4$

90. $\ln e^6 - 2 \ln e^5 = 6 \ln e - 10 \ln e = 6 - 10 = -4$

91. $2 \ln e^4 = 2(4) \ln e = 8$

92. $\ln e^{4.5} = 4.5 \ln e = 4.5$

93. $\ln\left(\frac{1}{\sqrt{e}}\right) = \ln(1) - \ln e^{1/2} = 0 - \frac{1}{2}\ln e = -\frac{1}{2}$

94. $\ln \sqrt[5]{e^3} = \ln e^{3/5} = \frac{3}{5}\ln e = \frac{3}{5}$

95. (a) $\beta = 10 \cdot \log_{10}\left(\frac{I}{10^{-12}}\right) = 10[\log_{10} \text{I} - \log_{10} 10^{-12}]$

$= 10[\log_{10} \text{I} - (-12)\log_{10} 10]$

$= 10[\log_{10} \text{I} + 12] = 120 + 10 \cdot \log_{10} \text{I}$

(b)

I	10^{-4}	10^{-6}	10^{-8}	10^{-10}	10^{-12}	10^{-14}
β	80	60	40	20	0	-20

(c) $\beta(10^{-4}) = 120 + 10 \cdot \log_{10} 10^{-4} = 120 - 40 = 80$

$\beta(10^{-6}) = 120 + 10 \cdot \log_{10} 10^{-6} = 120 - 60 = 60$

$\beta(10^{-8}) = 120 + 10 \cdot \log_{10} 10^{-8} = 120 - 80 = 40$

$\beta(10^{-10}) = 120 + 10 \cdot \log_{10} 10^{-10} = 120 - 100 = 20$

$\beta(10^{-12}) = 120 + 10 \cdot \log_{10} 10^{-12} = 120 - 120 = 0$

$\beta(10^{-14}) = 120 + 10 \cdot \log_{10} 10^{-14} = 120 - 140 = -20$

96. $f(t) = 90 - 15\log_{10}(t + 1), 0 \le t \le 12$

(a)

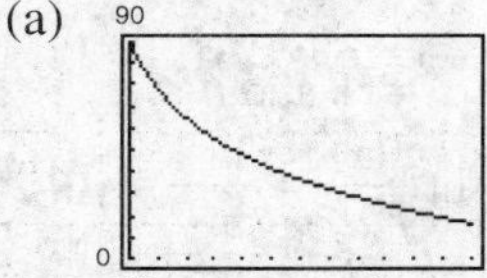

(b) When $t = 0, f(0) = 90$.

(c) $f(6) \approx 77$

(d) $f(12) \approx 73$

(e) $f(t) = 75$ when $t = 9$ months.

97. (a)

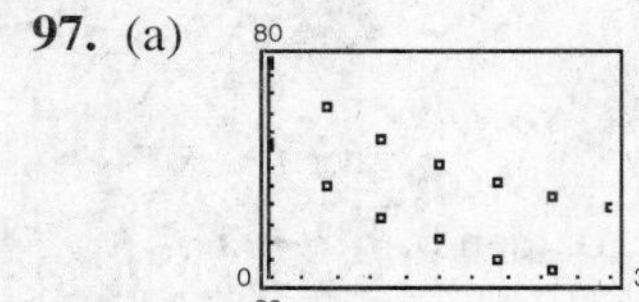

(b) $T - 21 = 54.4(0.964)^t$

$T = 21 + 54.4(0.964)^t$

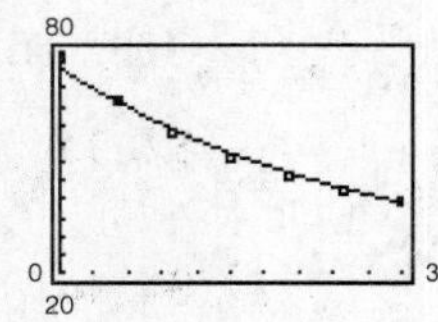

The data $(t, T - 21)$ fits the model

$T - 21 = 54.4(0.964)^t$.

The model

$T = 21 + 54.4(0.964)^t$

fits the original data.

—CONTINUED—

97. —CONTINUED—

(c) $\ln(T - 21) = -0.0372t + 3.9971$, linear model

$$T - 21 = e^{-0.0372t + 3.9971}$$

$$T = 21 + 54.4e^{-0.0372t}$$

$$= 21 + 54.4(0.964)^t$$

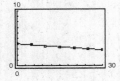

(d)

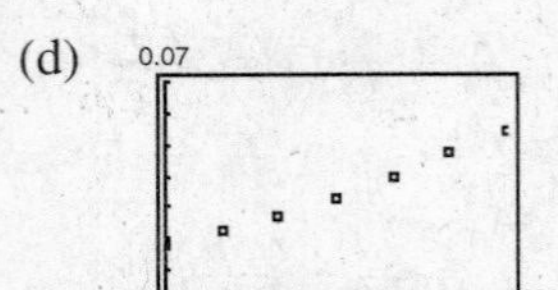

$$\frac{1}{T - 21} = 0.00121t + 0.01615, \text{ linear model}$$

$$T - 21 = \frac{1}{0.00121t + 0.01615}$$

$$T = 21 + \frac{1}{0.00121t + 0.01615}$$

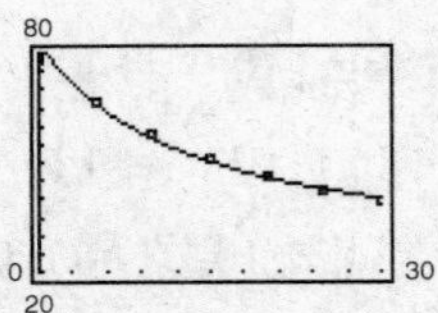

98. If $y = ab^x$, then $\ln y = \ln(ab^x) = \ln a + x \ln b$, which is linear. If $y = \dfrac{1}{cx + d}$, then $\dfrac{1}{y} = cx + d$.

99. True

100. False. For example, let $x = 2$ and $a = 1$. Then $f(x - a) = \ln(2 - 1) = 0$, but $f(x) - f(a) = \ln(2) - \ln 1 = \ln 2$.

101. False. For example, let $x = 1$ and $a = 2$. Then $f\left(\dfrac{x}{a}\right) = \ln\left(\dfrac{1}{2}\right)$. But $\dfrac{f(x)}{f(a)} = \dfrac{\ln 1}{\ln 2} = 0$.

102. False. For example, let $x = 1$ and $a = 1$. Then $f(x + a) = \ln(1 + 1) = \ln 2$, but $f(x)f(a) = (\ln 1)(\ln 1) = 0$.

103. False. $\sqrt{\ln x} \neq \frac{1}{2} \ln x$

In fact, $\ln x^{1/2} = \frac{1}{2} \ln x$.

104. False. For example, let $n = 2$ and $x = e$. Then $[f(x)]^n = [\ln e]^2 = 1$, but $nf(x) = 2 \ln e = 2$.

105. True. In fact, if $\ln x < 0$, then $0 < x < 1$.

106. False. For example, let $x = \sqrt{e}$. Then $f(x) = \ln \sqrt{e} = \frac{1}{2} \ln e = \frac{1}{2} > 0$, but $\sqrt{e} < e$.

107. Let $y = \log_a x$ and $z = \log_{a/b} x$, then $a^y = x = \left(\dfrac{a}{b}\right)^z$ and

$$\left(\frac{1}{b}\right)^z = a^{y-z}$$

$$\frac{1}{b} = a^{(y-z)/z}$$

$$\log_a\left(\frac{1}{b}\right) = \frac{y - z}{z} = \frac{y}{z} - 1 \Rightarrow 1 + \log_a\left(\frac{1}{b}\right) = \frac{\log_a x}{\log_{a/b} x}.$$

108. $f(x) = \ln \dfrac{x}{2}$

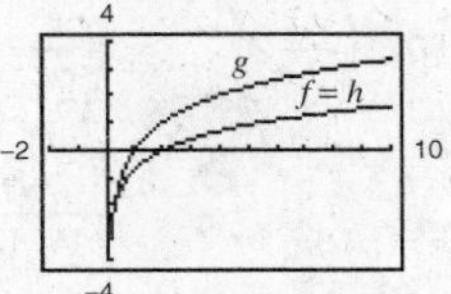

$g(x) = \dfrac{\ln x}{\ln 2}$

$h(x) = \ln x - \ln 2$

$f(x) = h(x)$ by Property 2.

109. $f(x) = \log_2 x = \dfrac{\ln x}{\ln 2}$

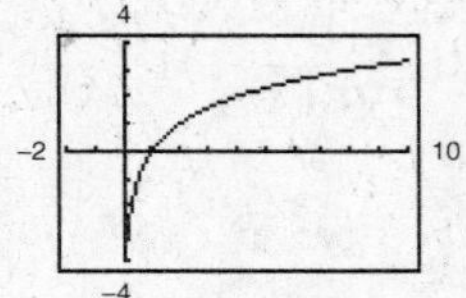

110. $f(x) = \log_4 x = \dfrac{\ln x}{\ln 4}$

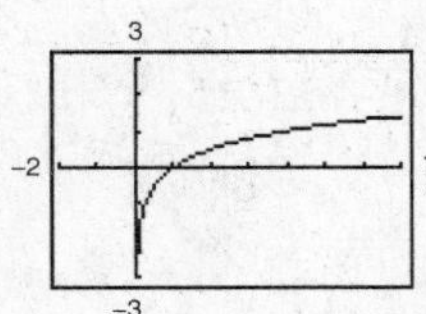

111. $f(x) = \log_3 \sqrt{x} = \dfrac{1}{2} \dfrac{\ln x}{\ln 3}$

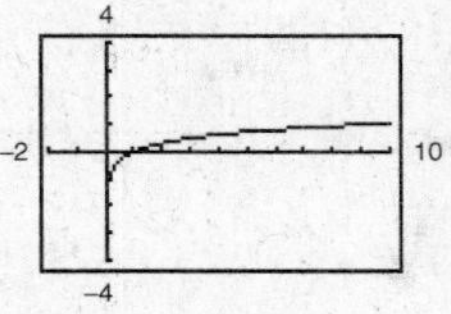

112. $f(x) = \log_2 \sqrt[3]{x} = \dfrac{1}{3} \dfrac{\ln x}{\ln 2}$

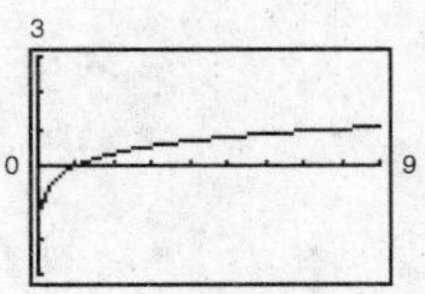

113. $f(x) = \log_5\left(\dfrac{x}{3}\right) = \dfrac{\ln(x/3)}{\ln 5}$

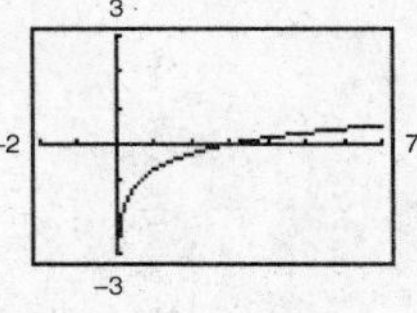

114. $f(x) = \log_3 \dfrac{x}{5} = \dfrac{\ln x - \ln 5}{\ln 3}$

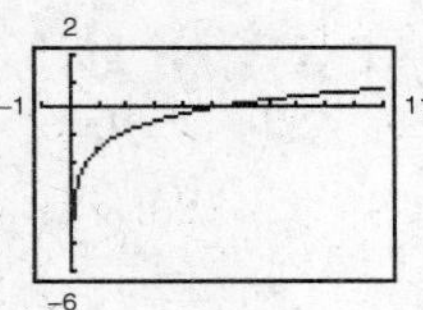

115. $\ln 1 = 0$, $\ln 2 \approx 0.6931$, $\ln 3 \approx 1.0986$, $\ln 5 \approx 1.6094$

$\ln 2 \approx 0.6931$

$\ln 3 \approx 1.0986$

$\ln 4 = \ln 2 + \ln 2 \approx 0.6931 + 0.6931 = 1.3862$

$\ln 5 \approx 1.6094$

$\ln 6 = \ln 2 + \ln 3 \approx 0.6931 + 1.0986 = 1.7917$

$\ln 8 = \ln 2^3 = 3 \ln 2 \approx 3(0.6931) = 2.0793$

$\ln 9 = \ln 3^2 = 2 \ln 3 \approx 2(1.0986) = 2.1972$

$\ln 10 = \ln 5 + \ln 2 \approx 1.6094 + 0.6931 = 2.3025$

$\ln 12 = \ln 2^2 + \ln 3 = 2 \ln 2 + \ln 3 \approx 2(0.6931) + 1.0986 = 2.4848$

$\ln 15 = \ln 5 + \ln 3 \approx 1.6094 + 1.0986 = 2.7080$

$\ln 16 = \ln 2^4 = 4 \ln 2 \approx 4(0.6931) = 2.7724$

$\ln 18 = \ln 3^2 + \ln 2 = 2 \ln 3 + \ln 2 \approx 2(1.0986) + 0.6931 = 2.8903$

$\ln 20 = \ln 5 + \ln 2^2 = \ln 5 + 2 \ln 2 \approx 1.6094 + 2(0.6931) = 2.9956$

116. $\dfrac{24xy^{-2}}{16x^{-3}y} = \dfrac{24xx^3}{16yy^2} = \dfrac{3x^4}{2y^3}$

117. $\left(\dfrac{2x^2}{3y}\right)^{-3} = \left(\dfrac{3y}{2x^2}\right)^3$

$= \dfrac{(3y)^3}{(2x^2)^3}$

$= \dfrac{27y^3}{8x^6}$

118. $(18x^3y^4)^{-3}(18x^3y^4)^3 = \dfrac{(18x^3y^4)^3}{(18x^3y^4)^3} = 1 \text{ if } x \neq 0, y \neq 0$

119. $xy(x^{-1} + y^{-1})^{-1} = \dfrac{xy}{x^{-1} + y^{-1}}$

$= \dfrac{xy}{\dfrac{1}{x} + \dfrac{1}{y}}$

$= \dfrac{xy}{\dfrac{y + x}{xy}}$

$= \dfrac{(xy)^2}{x + y}, x \neq 0, y \neq 0$

120. $x^2 - 6x + 2 = 0$

$x = \dfrac{6 \pm \sqrt{36 - 4(2)}}{2} = 3 \pm \sqrt{7}$

121. $2x^3 + 20x^2 + 50x = 0$

$2x(x^2 + 10x + 25) = 0$

$2x(x + 5)^2 = 0$

$x = 0, -5, -5$

122. $x^4 - 19x^2 + 48 = 0$

$(x^2 - 16)(x^2 - 3) = 0$

$(x - 4)(x + 4)(x - \sqrt{3})(x + \sqrt{3}) = 0$

$x = \pm 4, \pm\sqrt{3}$

123. $9x^4 - 37x^2 + 4 = 0$

$(x^2 - 4)(9x^2 - 1) = 0$

$(x - 2)(x + 2)(3x - 1)(3x + 1) = 0$

$x = \pm 2, \pm\frac{1}{3}$

124. $x^3 - 6x^2 - 4x + 24 = 0$

$x^2(x - 6) - 4(x - 6) = 0$

$(x^2 - 4)(x - 6) = 0$

$(x - 2)(x + 2)(x - 6) = 0$

$x = 2, -2, 6$

125. $9x^4 - 226x^2 + 25 = 0$

$(x^2 - 25)(9x^2 - 1) = 0$

$(x - 5)(x + 5)(3x + 1)(3x - 1) = 0$

$x = \pm 5, \pm\frac{1}{3}$

Section 3.4 Solving Exponential and Logarithmic Equations

- To solve an exponential equation, isolate the exponential expression, then take the logarithm of both sides. Then solve for the variable.
  1. $\log_a a^x = x$
  2. $\ln e^x = x$
- To solve a logarithmic equation, rewrite it in exponential form. Then solve for the variable.
  1. $a^{\log_a x} = x$
  2. $e^{\ln x} = x$
- If $a > 0$ and $a \neq 1$ we have the following:
  1. $\log_a x = \log_a y \Rightarrow x = y$
  2. $a^x = a^y \Rightarrow x = y$
- Use your graphing utility to approximate solutions.

Vocabulary Check

1. solve

2. (a) $x = y$ (b) $x = y$ (c) x (d) x

3. extraneous

1. $4^{2x-7} = 64$

(a) $x = 5$

$4^{2(5)-7} = 4^3 = 64$

Yes, $x = 5$ is a solution.

(b) $x = 2$

$4^{2(2)-7} = 4^{-3} = \frac{1}{64} \neq 64$

No, $x = 2$ is not a solution.

2. $2^{3x+1} = 32$

(a) $x = -1$

$2^{3(-1)+1} = 2^{-2} = \frac{1}{4}$

No, $x = -1$ is not a solution.

(b) $x = 2$

$2^{3(2)+1} = 2^7 = 128$

No, $x = 2$ is not a solution.

3. $3e^{x+2} = 75$

(a) $x = -2 + e^{25}$

$3e^{(-2+e^{25})+2} = 3e^{e^{25}} \neq 75$

No, $x = -2 + e^{25}$ is not a solution.

(b) $x = -2 + \ln 25$

$3e^{(-2+\ln 25)+2} = 3e^{\ln 25} = 3(25) = 75$

Yes, $x = -2 + \ln 25$ is a solution.

(c) $x \approx 1.2189$

$3e^{1.2189+2} = 3e^{3.2189} \approx 75$

Yes, $x \approx 1.2189$ is a solution.

4. $4e^{x-1} = 60$

(a) $x = 1 + \ln 15$

$4e^{(1+\ln 15)-1} = 4e^{\ln 15} = 4(15) = 60$

Yes

(b) $x \approx 3.7081$

$4e^{3.7081-1} = 4e^{2.7081} \approx 60$

Yes

(c) $x = \ln 16$

$4e^{\ln 16 - 1} \approx 23.5 \neq 60$

No

5. $\log_4(3x) = 3$

$4^3 = 3x$

$x = \frac{64}{3} \approx 21.333$

(a) $x = 21.3560$ is an approximate solution.

(b) No, $x = -4$ is not a solution.

(c) Yes, $x = \frac{64}{3}$ is a solution.

6. $\log_6\left(\frac{5}{3}x\right) = 2 \Leftrightarrow \frac{\ln\left(\frac{5}{3}x\right)}{\ln 6} = 2$

(a) $x \approx 20.2882;\ \frac{\ln\left(\frac{5}{3} \cdot 20.2882\right)}{\ln 6} = 1.965 \neq 2$; No

(b) $x = \frac{108}{5};\ \log_6\left(\frac{5}{3} \cdot \frac{108}{5}\right) = \log_6(36) = 2$; Yes

(c) $x = 7.2;\ \frac{\ln\left(\frac{5}{3}(7.2)\right)}{\ln 6} \approx 1.3869 \neq 2$; No

7. $\ln(x - 1) = 3.8$

(a) $x = 1 + e^{3.8}$

$\ln(1 + e^{3.8} - 1) = \ln e^{3.8} = 3.8$

Yes, $x = 1 + e^{3.8}$ is a solution.

(b) $x \approx 45.7012$

$\ln(45.7012 - 1) = \ln(44.7012) \approx 3.8$

Yes, $x \approx 45.7012$ is a solution.

(c) $x = 1 + \ln 3.8$

$\ln(1 + \ln 3.8 - 1) = \ln(\ln 3.8) \approx 0.289$

No, $x = 1 + \ln 3.8$ is not a solution.

8. $\ln(2 + x) = 2.5$

(a) $x = e^{2.5} - 2;\ \ln(2 + e^{2.5} - 2) = \ln e^{2.5} = 2.5$; Yes

(b) $x \approx \frac{4073}{400};\ \ln\left(2 + \frac{4073}{400}\right) \approx 2.5$; Yes

(c) $x = \frac{1}{2};\ \ln\left(2 + \frac{1}{2}\right) \approx 0.9163 \neq 2.5$; No

9.

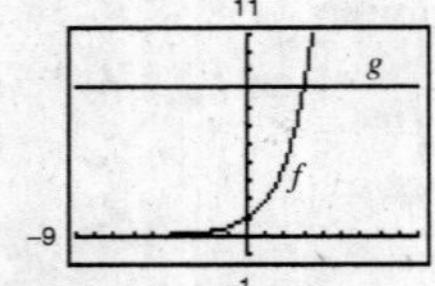

Point of intersection: (3, 8)

Algebraically: $2^x = 8$

$2^x = 2^3$

$x = 3 \Rightarrow y = 8 \Rightarrow (3, 8)$

10. $f(x) = g(x)$

$27^x = 9$

$27^x = 27^{2/3}$

$x = \frac{2}{3}$

Point of intersection: $\left(\frac{2}{3}, 9\right)$

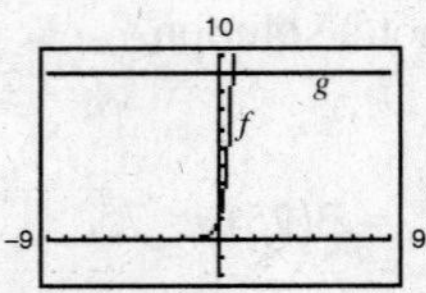

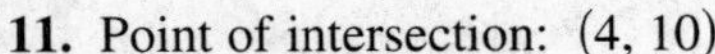

11. Point of intersection: $(4, 10)$

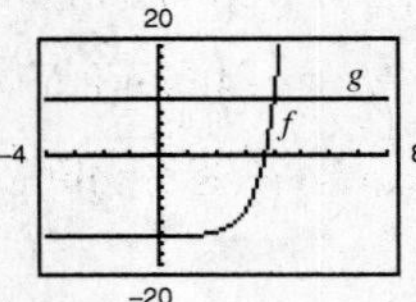

Algebraically: $5^{x-2} - 15 = 10$

$$5^{x-2} = 25 = 5^2$$

$$x - 2 = 2$$

$$x = 4$$

$(4, 10)$

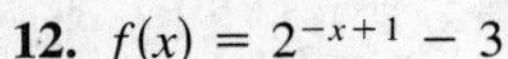

12. $f(x) = 2^{-x+1} - 3$

$g(x) = 13$

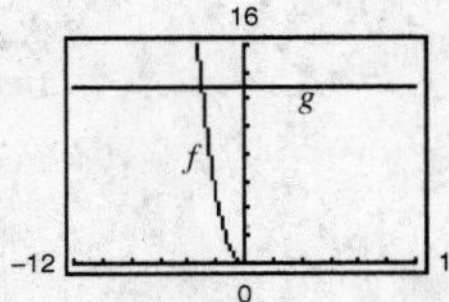

Point of intersection: $(-3, 13)$

$2^{-x+1} - 3 = 13$

$$2^{-x+1} = 16 = 2^4$$

$$-x + 1 = 4$$

$$x = -3 \Rightarrow (-3, 13)$$

13.

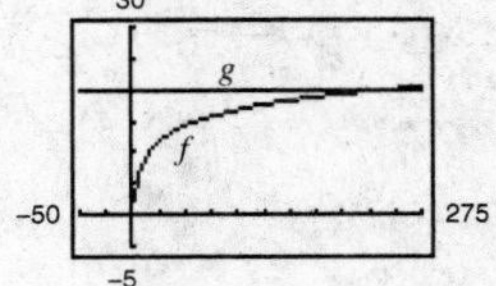

Point of intersection: $(243, 20)$

Algebraically: $4 \log_3 x = 20$

$$\log_3 x = 5$$

$$x = 3^5 = 243$$

$(243, 20)$

14. $f(x) = 3 \log_5 x = 3 \cdot \dfrac{\ln x}{\ln 5}$

$g(x) = 6$

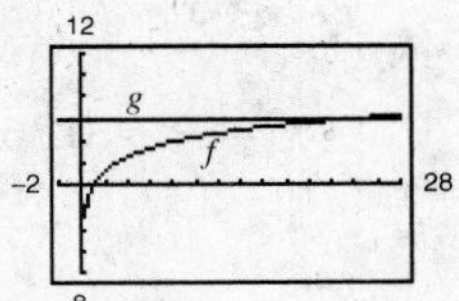

Point of intersection: $(25, 6)$

$3 \log_5 x = 6$

$$\log_5 x = 2$$

$$x = 5^2 = 25 \Rightarrow (25, 6)$$

15.

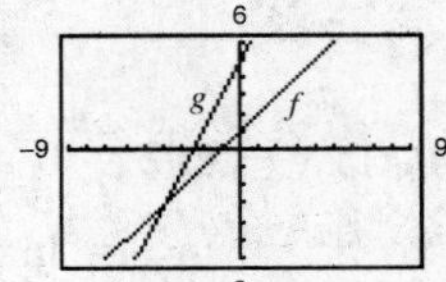

Point of intersection: $(-4, -3)$

Algebraically: $\ln e^{x+1} = 2x + 5$

$$x + 1 = 2x + 5$$

$$-4 = x$$

$(-4, -3)$

16. $f(x) = \ln e^{x-2} = x - 2$

$g(x) = 3x + 2$

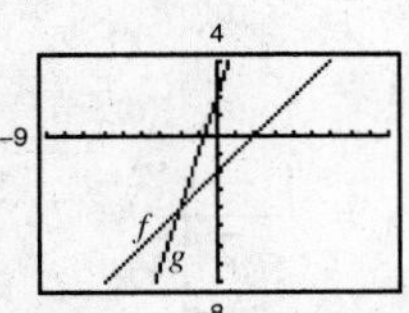

Point of intersection: $(-2, -4)$

$x - 2 = 3x + 2$

$$-4 = 2x$$

$$x = -2 \Rightarrow (-2, -4)$$

17. $4^x = 16$

$4^x = 4^2$

$x = 2$

18. $3^x = 243$

$3^x = 3^5$

$x = 5$

19. $5^x = \dfrac{1}{625}$

$5^x = \dfrac{1}{5^4} = 5^{-4}$

$x = -4$

20. $7^x = \dfrac{1}{49}$

$7^x = 7^{-2}$

$x = -2$

21. $\left(\frac{1}{8}\right)^x = 64$

$8^{-x} = 8^2$

$-x = 2$

$x = -2$

22. $\left(\frac{1}{2}\right)^x = 32$

$\left(\frac{1}{2}\right)^x = \left(\frac{1}{2}\right)^{-5}$

$x = -5$

23. $\left(\frac{2}{3}\right)^x = \frac{81}{16}$

$\left(\frac{3}{2}\right)^{-x} = \left(\frac{3}{2}\right)^4$

$-x = 4$

$x = -4$

24. $\left(\frac{3}{4}\right)^x = \frac{27}{64}$

$\left(\frac{3}{4}\right)^x = \left(\frac{3}{4}\right)^3$

$x = 3$

25. $6(10^x) = 216$

$10^x = 36$

$\log_{10} 10^x = \log_{10} 36$

$x = \log_{10} 36 \approx 1.5563$

26. $5(8^x) = 325$

$8^x = 65$

$x = \log_8 65$

$= \dfrac{\ln 65}{\ln 8} \approx 2.0075$

27. $2^{x+3} = 256$

$2^x \cdot 2^3 = 256$

$2^x = 32$

$x = 5$

Alternate solution:

$2^{x+3} = 2^8$

$x + 3 = 8$

$x = 5$

28. $3^{x-1} = \frac{1}{81}$

$3^{x-1} = 3^{-4}$

$x - 1 = -4$

$x = -3$

29. $\ln x - \ln 5 = 0$

$\ln x = \ln 5$

$x = 5$

30. $\ln x - \ln 2 = 0$

$\ln x = \ln 2$

$x = 2$

31. $\ln x = -7$

$x = e^{-7}$

32. $\ln x = -1$

$e^{-1} = x$

$x = \dfrac{1}{e} \approx 0.368$

33. $\log_x 625 = 4$

$x^4 = 625$

$x^4 = 5^4$

$x = 5$

34. $\log_x 25 = 2$

$x^2 = 25$

$x = 5$

35. $\log_{10} x = -1$

$x = 10^{-1}$

$x = \frac{1}{10}$

36. $\log_{10} x = -\dfrac{1}{2}$

$x = 10^{-1/2} = \dfrac{1}{\sqrt{10}}$

≈ 0.316

37. $\ln(2x - 1) = 5$

$2x - 1 = e^5$

$x = \dfrac{1 + e^5}{2} \approx 74.707$

38. $\ln(3x + 5) = 8$

$e^8 = 3x + 5$

$x = \dfrac{1}{3}(e^8 - 5)$

≈ 991.986

39. $\ln e^{x^2} = x^2 \ln e^x = x^2$

40. $\ln e^{2x-1} = 2x - 1$

41. $e^{\ln(5x+2)} = 5x + 2$

42. $e^{\ln x^2} = x^2$

43. $-1 + \ln e^{2x} = -1 + 2x = 2x - 1$

44. $-8 + e^{\ln x^3} = -8 + x^3 = x^3 - 8$

45.
$$8^{3x} = 360$$
$$\ln 8^{3x} = \ln 360$$
$$3x \ln 8 = \ln 360$$
$$3x = \frac{\ln 360}{\ln 8}$$
$$x = \frac{1}{3}\frac{\ln 360}{\ln 8}$$
$$x \approx 0.944$$

46.
$$6^{5x} = 3000$$
$$\ln 6^{5x} = \ln 3000$$
$$(5x)\ln 6 = \ln 3000$$
$$5x = \frac{\ln 3000}{\ln 6}$$
$$x = \frac{\ln 3000}{5 \ln 6} \approx 0.894$$

47.
$$5^{-t/2} = 0.20 = \frac{1}{5}$$
$$-\frac{t}{2}\ln 5 = \ln\left(\frac{1}{5}\right)$$
$$-\frac{t}{2}\ln 5 = -\ln 5$$
$$\frac{t}{2} = 1$$
$$t = 2$$

48.
$$4^{-3t} = 0.10$$
$$\ln 4^{-3t} = \ln 0.10$$
$$(-3t)\ln 4 = \ln 0.10$$
$$-3t = \frac{\ln 0.10}{\ln 4}$$
$$t = -\frac{\ln 0.10}{3 \ln 4} \approx 0.554$$

49.
$$5(2^{3-x}) - 13 = 100$$
$$5(2^{3-x}) = 113$$
$$2^{3-x} = \frac{113}{5}$$
$$\ln 2^{3-x} = \ln\left(\frac{113}{5}\right)$$
$$3 - x = \frac{\ln(113/5)}{\ln 2}$$
$$x = 3 - \frac{\ln(113/5)}{\ln 2}$$
$$x \approx -1.498$$

50.
$$6(8^{-2-x}) + 15 = 2601$$
$$6(8^{-2-x}) = 2586$$
$$8^{-2-x} = 431$$
$$(-2 - x)\ln 8 = \ln 431$$
$$-2 - x = \frac{\ln 431}{\ln 8}$$
$$x = -2 - \frac{\ln 431}{\ln 8}$$
$$x \approx -4.917$$

51.
$$\left(1 + \frac{0.10}{12}\right)^{12t} = 2$$
$$\left(\frac{12.1}{12}\right)^{12t} = 2$$
$$(12t)\ln\left(\frac{12.1}{12}\right) = \ln 2$$
$$t = \frac{1}{12}\frac{\ln 2}{\ln(12.1/12)}$$
$$t \approx 6.960$$

52.
$$\left(16 + \frac{0.878}{26}\right)^{3t} = 30$$
$$3t \ln\left(16 + \frac{0.878}{26}\right) = \ln 30$$
$$t = \frac{\ln 30}{3 \ln\left(16 + \frac{0.878}{26}\right)}$$
$$\approx \frac{3.4012}{8.3241} \approx 0.409$$

53.
$$5000\left[\frac{(1 + 0.005)^x}{0.005}\right] = 250{,}000$$
$$5000(1.005)^x = 1250$$
$$1.005^x = 0.25$$
$$x \ln(1.005) = \ln 0.25$$
$$x = \frac{\ln 0.25}{\ln(1.005)}$$
$$x \approx -277.951$$

54.
$$250\left[\frac{(1 + 0.01)^x}{0.01}\right] = 150{,}000$$
$$250(1.01)^x = 1500$$
$$1.01^x = 6$$
$$x \ln 1.01 = \ln 6$$
$$x = \frac{\ln 6}{\ln 1.01}$$
$$x \approx 180.070$$

55. $2e^{5x} = 18$

$e^{5x} = 9$

$5x = \ln 9$

$x = \frac{1}{5}\ln 9$

$x \approx 0.439$

56. $4e^{2x} = 40$

$e^{2x} = 10$

$2x = \ln 10$

$x = \frac{1}{2}\ln 10 \approx 1.151$

57. $500e^{-x} = 300$

$e^{-x} = \frac{3}{5}$

$-x = \ln\frac{3}{5}$

$x = -\ln\frac{3}{5} = \ln\frac{5}{3} \approx 0.511$

58. $1000e^{-4x} = 75$

$e^{-4x} = \frac{3}{40}$

$\ln e^{-4x} = \ln\frac{3}{40}$

$-4x = \ln\frac{3}{40}$

$x = -\frac{1}{4}\ln\frac{3}{40} \approx 0.648$

59. $7 - 2e^x = 5$

$-2e^x = -2$

$e^x = 1$

$x = \ln 1 = 0$

60. $-14 + 3e^x = 11$

$3e^x = 25$

$e^x = \frac{25}{3}$

$\ln e^x = \ln\frac{25}{3}$

$x = \ln\frac{25}{3} \approx 2.120$

61. $e^{2x} - 4e^x - 5 = 0$

$(e^x - 5)(e^x + 1) = 0$

$e^x = 5$ or $e^x = -1$

$x = \ln 5 \approx 1.609$

($e^x = -1$ is impossible.)

62. $e^{2x} - 5e^x + 6 = 0$

$(e^x - 2)(e^x - 3) = 0$

$e^x = 2$ or $e^x = 3$

$x = \ln 2 \approx 0.693$ or

$x = \ln 3 \approx 1.099$

63. $250e^{0.02x} = 10{,}000$

$e^{0.02x} = 40$

$0.02x = \ln 40$

$x = \dfrac{\ln 40}{0.02}$

$x \approx 184.444$

64. $100e^{0.005x} = 125{,}000$

$e^{0.005x} = 1250$

$0.005x = \ln 1250$

$x = \dfrac{\ln 1250}{0.005}$

$x \approx 1426.180$

65. $e^x = e^{x^2-2}$

$x = x^2 - 2$

$x^2 - x - 2 = 0$

$(x - 2)(x + 1) = 0$

$x = 2, -1$

66. $e^{2x} = e^{x^2-8}$

$2x = x^2 - 8$

$x^2 - 2x - 8 = 0$

$(x - 4)(x + 2) = 0$

$x = 4, -2$

67. $e^{x^2-3x} = e^{x-2}$

$x^2 - 3x = x - 2$

$x^2 - 4x + 2 = 0$

$x = \dfrac{4 \pm \sqrt{16-8}}{2}$

$x = 2 \pm \sqrt{2}$

$x \approx 3.414, 0.586$

68. $e^{-x^2} = e^{x^2-2x}$

$-x^2 = x^2 - 2x$

$2x^2 - 2x = 0$

$2x(x - 1) = 0$

$x = 0, 1$

69. $\dfrac{400}{1 + e^{-x}} = 350$

$1 + e^{-x} = \dfrac{400}{350} = \dfrac{8}{7}$

$e^{-x} = \dfrac{1}{7}$

$-x = \ln\left(\dfrac{1}{7}\right) = -\ln 7$

$x = \ln 7 \approx 1.946$

70. $\dfrac{525}{1+e^{-x}} = 275$

$$1 + e^{-x} = \frac{525}{275}$$

$$e^{-x} = \frac{525}{275} - 1 = \frac{250}{275} = \frac{10}{11}$$

$$-x = \ln\frac{10}{11}$$

$$x = -\ln\frac{10}{11} = \ln\frac{11}{10} \approx 0.095$$

71. $\dfrac{40}{1-5e^{-0.01x}} = 200$

$$1 - 5e^{-0.01x} = \frac{40}{200} = \frac{1}{5}$$

$$5e^{-0.01x} = \frac{4}{5}$$

$$e^{-0.01x} = \frac{4}{25}$$

$$-0.01x = \ln\left(\frac{4}{25}\right)$$

$$x = \frac{\ln(4/25)}{-0.01}$$

$$x \approx 183.258$$

72. $\dfrac{50}{1-2e^{-0.001x}} = 1000$

$$1 - 2e^{-0.001x} = \frac{50}{1000} = 0.05$$

$$2e^{-0.001x} = 0.95$$

$$e^{-0.001x} = 0.475$$

$$-0.001x = \ln 0.475$$

$$x = \frac{\ln 0.475}{-0.001}$$

$$x \approx 744.440$$

73. $e^{3x} = 12$

x	0.6	0.7	0.8	0.9	1.0
$f(x)$	6.05	8.17	11.02	14.88	20.09

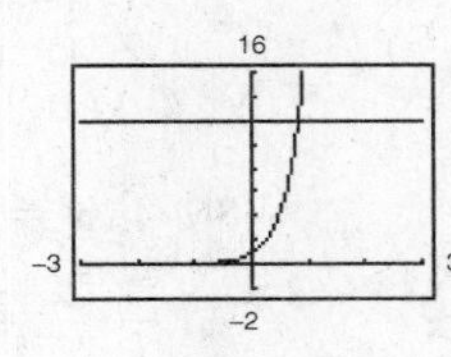

$x \approx 0.828$

74. $e^{2x} = 50$

x	1.6	1.7	1.8	1.9	2.0
e^{2x}	24.53	29.96	36.60	44.70	54.60

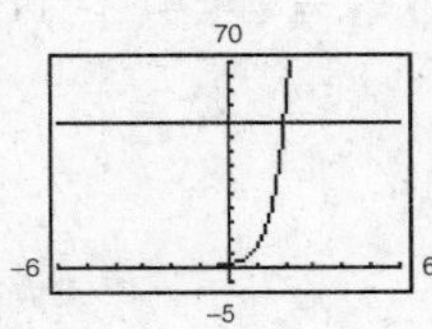

$x \approx 1.956$

75. $20(100 - e^{x/2}) = 500$

x	5	6	7	8	9
$f(x)$	1756	1598	1338	908	200

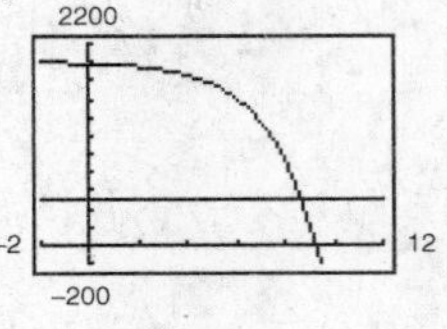

$x \approx 8.635$

76. $\dfrac{400}{1+e^{-x}} = 350$

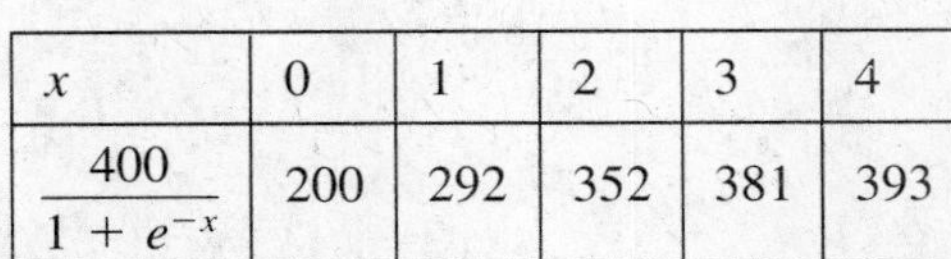

x	0	1	2	3	4
$\dfrac{400}{1+e^{-x}}$	200	292	352	381	393

$x \approx 1.946$

77. $\left(1 + \frac{0.065}{365}\right)^{365t} = 4 \Rightarrow t = 21.330$

78. $\left(4 - \frac{2.471}{40}\right)^{9t} = 21$

$3.938225^{9t} = 21$

The zero of $y = 3.938225^{9t} - 21$ is $t \approx 0.247$.

79. $\frac{3000}{2 + e^{2x}} = 2$

The zero of $y = \frac{3000}{2 + e^{2x}} - 2$ is $x \approx 3.656$.

80. $\frac{119}{e^{6x} - 14} = 7$

The zero of $y = \frac{119}{e^{6x} - 14} - 7$ is $x \approx 0.572$.

81. $g(x) = 6e^{1-x} - 25$

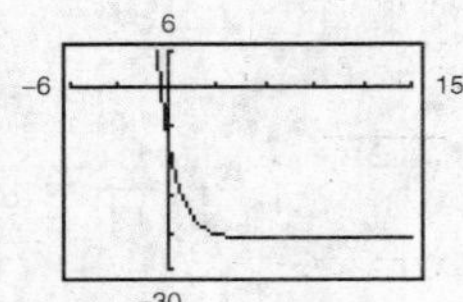

Zero at $x = -0.427$

82. $f(x) = 3e^{3x/2} - 962$

The zero is $x \approx 3.847$.

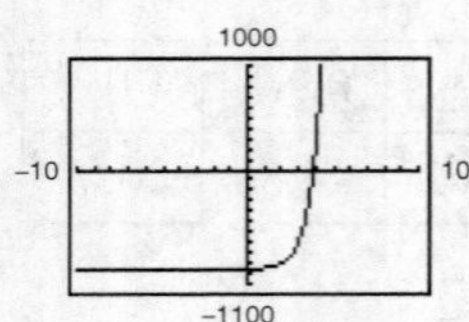

83. $g(t) = e^{0.09t} - 3$

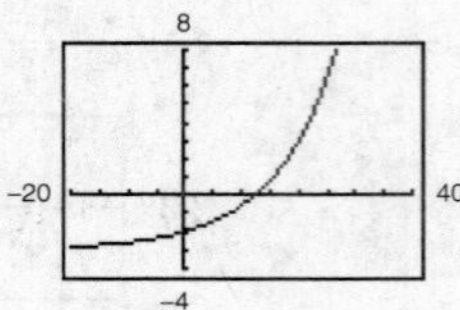

Zero at $t = 12.207$

84. $h(t) = e^{0.125t} - 8$

The zero is $t \approx 16.636$.

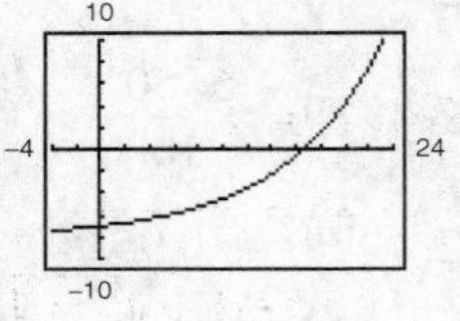

85. $\ln x = -3$

$x = e^{-3} \approx 0.050$

86. $\ln x = -2$

$x = e^{-2} = \frac{1}{e^2} \approx 0.135$

87. $\ln 4x = 2.1$

$4x = e^{2.1}$

$x = \frac{1}{4}e^{2.1} \approx 2.042$

88. $\ln 2x = 1.5$

$e^{1.5} = 2x$

$x = \frac{1}{2}e^{1.5} \approx 2.241$

89. $-2 + 2 \ln 3x = 17$

$2 \ln 3x = 19$

$\ln 3x = \frac{19}{2}$

$3x = e^{19/2}$

$x = \frac{1}{3}e^{19/2}$

$x \approx 4453.242$

90. $3 + 2 \ln x = 10$

$2 \ln x = 7$

$\ln x = \frac{7}{2} = 3.5$

$x = e^{3.5} \approx 33.115$

91. $\log_5(3x + 2) = \log_5(6 - x)$

$3x + 2 = 6 - x$

$4x = 4$

$x = 1$

92. $\log_9(4 + x) = \log_9(2x - 1)$

$4 + x = 2x - 1$

$x = 5$

93. $\log_{10}(z - 3) = 2$

$z - 3 = 10^2$

$z = 10^2 + 3$

$= 103$

94. $\log_{10} x^2 = 6$

$x^2 = 10^6$

$x = \pm\sqrt{10^6} = \pm 1000$

95. $7 \log_4(0.6x) = 12$

$\log_4(0.6x) = \frac{12}{7}$

$4^{12/7} = 0.6x = \frac{3}{5}x$

$x = \frac{5}{3} 4^{12/7}$

≈ 17.945

96. $4 \log_{10}(x - 6) = 11$

$\log_{10}(x - 6) = \frac{11}{4}$

$10^{11/4} = x - 6$

$x = 6 + 10^{11/4}$

≈ 568.341

97. $\ln\sqrt{x + 2} = 1$

$\sqrt{x + 2} = e^1$

$x + 2 = e^2$

$x = e^2 - 2 \approx 5.389$

98. $\ln\sqrt{x - 8} = 5$

$\frac{1}{2}\ln(x - 8) = 5$

$\ln(x - 8) = 10$

$e^{10} = x - 8$

$x = 8 + e^{10}$

$\approx 22{,}034.466$

99. $\ln(x + 1)^2 = 2$

$e^{\ln(x+1)^2} = e^2$

$(x + 1)^2 = e^2$

$x + 1 = e$ or $x + 1 = -e$

$x = e - 1 \approx 1.718$

or

$x = -e - 1 \approx -3.718$

100. $\ln(x^2 + 1) = 8$

$e^8 = x^2 + 1$

$x = \pm\sqrt{e^8 - 1} = \pm 54.589$

101. $\log_4 x - \log_4(x - 1) = \dfrac{1}{2}$

$\log_4\left(\dfrac{x}{x - 1}\right) = \dfrac{1}{2}$

$4^{\log_4(x/x-1)} = 4^{1/2}$

$\dfrac{x}{x - 1} = 2$

$x = 2(x - 1)$

$x = 2x - 2$

$2 = x$

102. $\log_3 x + \log_3(x - 8) = 2$

$\log_3[x(x - 8)] = 2$

$3^2 = x(x - 8) = x^2 - 8x$

$x^2 - 8x - 9 = 0$

$(x - 9)(x + 1) = 0$

$x = 9$

($x = -1$ is extraneous.)

103. $\ln(x + 5) = \ln(x - 1) - \ln(x + 1)$

$\ln(x + 5) = \ln\left(\dfrac{x - 1}{x + 1}\right)$

$x + 5 = \dfrac{x - 1}{x + 1}$

$(x + 5)(x + 1) = x - 1$

$x^2 + 6x + 5 = x - 1$

$x^2 + 5x + 6 = 0$

$(x + 2)(x + 3) = 0$

$x = -2$ or $x = -3$

Both of these solutions are extraneous, so the equation has no solution.

104. $\ln(x + 1) - \ln(x - 2) = \ln x, \ (x > 2)$

$$\ln\left(\frac{x+1}{x-2}\right) = \ln x$$

$$\frac{x+1}{x-2} = x$$

$$x + 1 = x(x - 2) = x^2 - 2x$$

$$x^2 - 3x - 1 = 0$$

$$x = \frac{3 \pm \sqrt{9+4}}{2} = \frac{3 \pm \sqrt{13}}{2}$$

Taking the positive solution, $x = \dfrac{3 + \sqrt{13}}{2} \approx 3.303$.

105. $\log_{10} 8x - \log_{10}(1 + \sqrt{x}) = 2$

$$\log_{10} \frac{8x}{1 + \sqrt{x}} = 2$$

$$\frac{8x}{1 + \sqrt{x}} = 10^2$$

$$8x = 100 + 100\sqrt{x}$$

$$8x - 100\sqrt{x} - 100 = 0$$

$$2x - 25\sqrt{x} - 25 = 0$$

$$\sqrt{x} = \frac{25 \pm \sqrt{25^2 - 4(2)(-25)}}{4}$$

$$= \frac{25 \pm 5\sqrt{33}}{4}$$

Choosing the positive value, we have $\sqrt{x} \approx 13.431$ and $x \approx 180.384$.

106. $\log_{10} 4x - \log_{10}(12 + \sqrt{x}) = 2, (x > 0)$

$$\log_{10} \frac{4x}{12 + \sqrt{x}} = 2$$

$$\frac{4x}{12 + \sqrt{x}} = 10^2 = 100$$

$$4x = 1200 + 100\sqrt{x}$$

$$x - 25\sqrt{x} - 300 = 0, \text{ Quadratic in } \sqrt{x}$$

$$\sqrt{x} = \frac{25 \pm \sqrt{(-25)^2 - 4(-300)}}{2} = \frac{25 \pm \sqrt{1825}}{2}$$

Taking the positive root and squaring, $x \approx 1146.5$.

107. $\ln 2x = 2.4$

x	2	3	4	5	6
$f(x)$	1.39	1.79	2.08	2.30	2.48

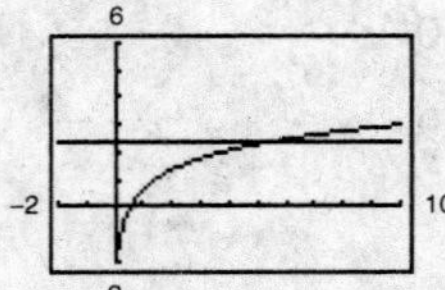

$x \approx 5.512$

108.

x	4	5	6	7	8
$f(x)$	8.99	9.66	10.20	10.67	11.07

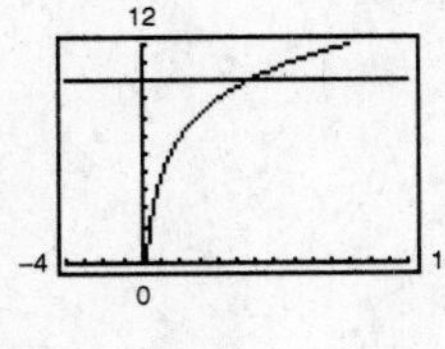

$x \approx 5.606$

109. $6 \log_3(0.5x) = 11$

x	12	13	14	15	16
$f(x)$	9.79	10.22	10.63	11.00	11.36

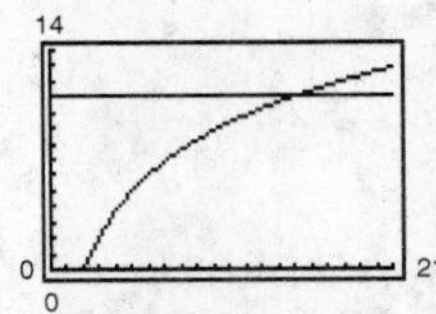

$x \approx 14.988$

110.

x	150	155	160	165	170
$f(x)$	10.85	10.92	10.99	11.06	11.13

$x \approx 160.489$

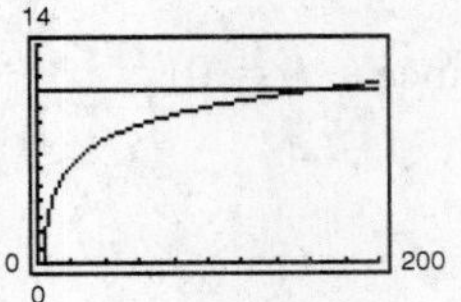

111. $\log_{10} x = x^3 - 3$

Graphing $y = \log_{10} x - x^3 + 3$, you obtain two zeros, $x \approx 1.469$ and $x \approx 0.001$.

112. Solving $y = \log_{10} x^2 - 4 = 0$, $x = \pm 100$.

113. $\ln x + \ln(x - 2) = 1$

Graphing $y = \ln x + \ln(x - 2) - 1$, you obtain one zero, $x \approx 2.928$.

114. $\ln x + \ln(x + 1) = 2$

Graphing $y = \ln x + \ln(x + 1) - 2$, you obtain one zero, $x \approx 2.264$.

115. $\ln(x - 3) + \ln(x + 3) = 1$

Graphing $y = \ln(x - 3) + \ln(x + 3) - 1$, you obtain $x \approx 3.423$.

116. $\ln x + \ln(x^2 + 4) = 10$

Solving $y = \ln x + \ln(x^2 + 4) - 10 = 0$, $x = 27.984$.

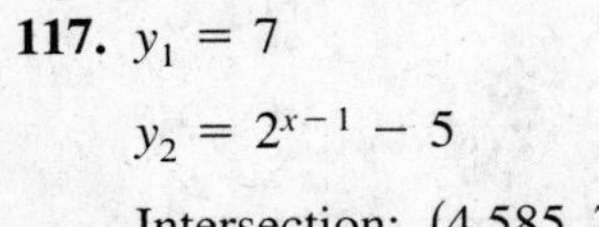

117. $y_1 = 7$

$y_2 = 2^{x-1} - 5$

Intersection: $(4.585, 7)$

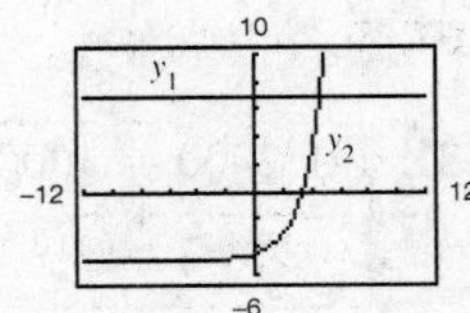

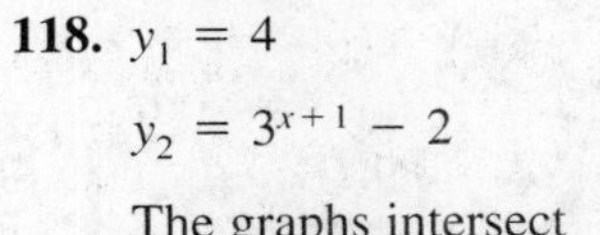

118. $y_1 = 4$

$y_2 = 3^{x+1} - 2$

The graphs intersect at $(x, y) \approx (0.631, 4)$.

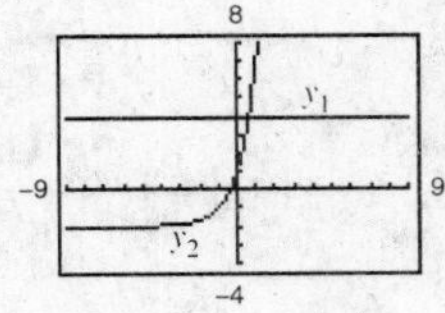

119. $y_1 = 80$

$y_2 = 4e^{-0.2x}$

Intersection: $(-14.979, 80)$

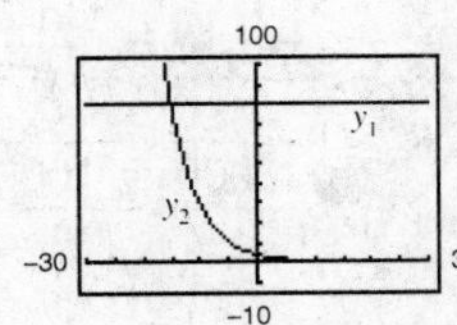

120. $y_1 = 500$

$y_2 = 1500e^{-x/2}$

From the graph, we have $(x, y) \approx (2.197, 500)$.

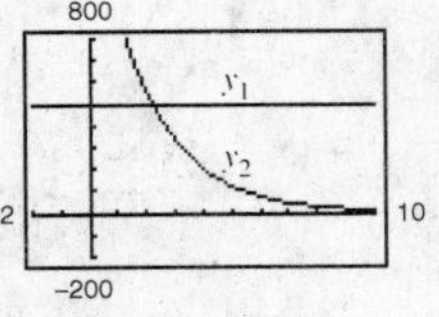

121. $y_1 = 3.25$

$y_2 = \frac{1}{2} \ln(x + 2)$

Intersection: $(663.142, 3.25)$

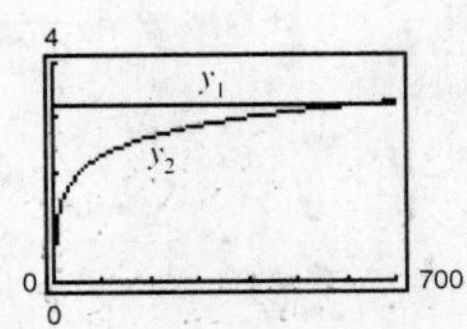

122. $y_1 = 1.05$

$y_2 = \ln\sqrt{x-2} = \frac{1}{2}\ln(x-2)$

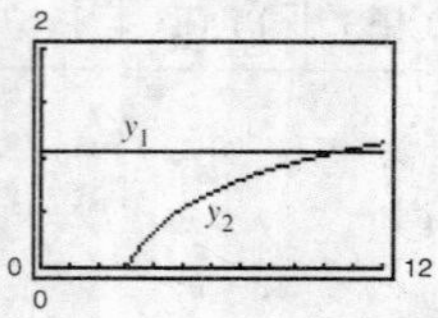

The graphs intersect at (10.166, 1.05).

123. $2x^2e^{2x} + 2xe^{2x} = 0$

$(2x^2 + 2x)e^{2x} = 0$

$2x^2 + 2x = 0 \quad (\text{since } e^{2x} \neq 0)$

$2x(x+1) = 0$

$x = 0, -1$

124. $-x^2e^{-x} + 2xe^{-x} = 0$

$(-x^2 + 2x)e^{-x} = 0$

$-x^2 + 2x = 0 \quad (\text{since } e^{-x} \neq 0)$

$-x(x-2) = 0$

$x = 0, 2$

125. $-xe^{-x} + e^{-x} = 0$

$(-x+1)e^{-x} = 0$

$-x + 1 = 0 \quad (\text{since } e^{-x} \neq 0)$

$x = 1$

126. $e^{-2x} - 2xe^{-2x} = 0$

$(1 - 2x)e^{-2x} = 0$

$1 - 2x = 0 \quad (\text{since } e^{-2x} \neq 0)$

$x = \frac{1}{2}$

127. $2x\ln x + x = 0$

$x(2\ln x + 1) = 0$

$2\ln x + 1 = 0 \quad (\text{since } x > 0)$

$\ln x = -\frac{1}{2}$

$x = e^{-1/2} \approx 0.607$

128. $\dfrac{1 - \ln x}{x^2} = 0$

$1 - \ln x = 0 \quad (x > 0)$

$\ln x = 1$

$x = e \approx 2.718$

129. $\dfrac{1 + \ln x}{2} = 0$

$1 + \ln x = 0$

$\ln x = -1$

$x = e^{-1} = \dfrac{1}{e} \approx 0.368$

130. $2x\ln\left(\dfrac{1}{x}\right) - x = 0$

$x\left(2\ln\left(\dfrac{1}{x}\right) - 1\right) = 0$

$2\ln\left(\dfrac{1}{x}\right) - 1 = 0 \quad (\text{since } x > 0)$

$\ln\left(\dfrac{1}{x}\right) = \dfrac{1}{2}$

$\dfrac{1}{x} = e^{1/2}$

$x = e^{-1/2} \approx 0.607$

131. (a) $2000 = 1000e^{0.075t}$

$2 = e^{0.075t}$

$\ln 2 = 0.075t$

$t = \dfrac{\ln 2}{0.075} \approx 9.24 \text{ years}$

(b) $3000 = 1000e^{0.075t}$

$3 = e^{0.075t}$

$\ln 3 = 0.075t$

$t = \dfrac{\ln 3}{0.075} \approx 14.65 \text{ years}$

132. (a) $2000 = 1000e^{0.06t}$

$$2 = e^{0.06t}$$

$$\ln 2 = 0.06t$$

$$t = \frac{\ln 2}{0.06} \approx 11.55 \text{ years}$$

(b) $3000 = 1000e^{0.06t}$

$$3 = e^{0.06t}$$

$$\ln 3 = 0.06t$$

$$t = \frac{\ln 3}{0.06} \approx 18.31 \text{ years}$$

133. (a) $2000 = 1000e^{0.025t}$

$$2 = e^{0.025t}$$

$$\ln 2 = 0.025t$$

$$t = \frac{\ln 2}{0.025} \approx 27.73 \text{ years}$$

(b) $3000 = 1000e^{0.025t}$

$$3 = e^{0.025t}$$

$$\ln 3 = 0.025t$$

$$t = \frac{\ln 3}{0.025} \approx 43.94 \text{ years}$$

134. (a) $2000 = 1000e^{0.0375t}$

$$2 = e^{0.0375t}$$

$$\ln 2 = 0.0375t$$

$$t = \frac{\ln 2}{0.0375} \approx 18.48 \text{ years}$$

(b) $3000 = 1000e^{0.0375t}$

$$3 = e^{0.0375t}$$

$$\ln 3 = 0.0375t$$

$$t = \frac{\ln 3}{0.0375} \approx 29.30 \text{ years}$$

135. $p = 500 - 0.5(e^{0.004x})$

(a) $p = 350$

$$350 = 500 - 0.5(e^{0.004x})$$

$$300 = e^{0.004x}$$

$$0.004x = \ln 300$$

$$x \approx 1426 \text{ units}$$

(b) $p = 300$

$$300 = 500 - 0.5(e^{0.004x})$$

$$400 = e^{0.004x}$$

$$0.004x = \ln 400$$

$$x \approx 1498 \text{ units}$$

136. $p = 5000\left(1 - \frac{4}{4 + e^{-0.002x}}\right)$

(a) When $p = \$600$:

$$600 = 5000\left(1 - \frac{4}{4 + e^{-0.002x}}\right)$$

$$0.12 = 1 - \frac{4}{4 + e^{-0.002x}}$$

$$\frac{4}{4 + e^{-0.002x}} = 0.88$$

$$4 = 3.52 + 0.88e^{-0.002x}$$

$$0.48 = 0.88e^{-0.002x}$$

$$\frac{6}{11} = e^{-0.002x}$$

$$\ln\frac{6}{11} = \ln e^{-0.002x}$$

$$\ln\frac{6}{11} = -0.002x$$

$$x = \frac{\ln(6/11)}{-0.002} \approx 303 \text{ units}$$

(b) When $p = \$400$:

$$400 = 5000\left(1 - \frac{4}{4 + e^{-0.002x}}\right)$$

$$0.08 = 1 - \frac{4}{4 + e^{-0.002x}}$$

$$\frac{4}{4 + e^{-0.002x}} = 0.92$$

$$4 = 3.68 + 0.92e^{-0.002x}$$

$$0.32 = 0.92e^{-0.002x}$$

$$\frac{8}{23} = e^{-0.002x}$$

$$\ln\frac{8}{23} = \ln e^{-0.002x}$$

$$x = \frac{\ln(8/23)}{-0.002} \approx 528 \text{ units}$$

137. $7247 - 596.5 \ln t = 5800$

$$-596.5 \ln t = -1447$$

$$\ln t \approx 2.4258$$

$$t \approx 11.3, \text{ or } 2001$$

138. $V = 6.7e^{-48.1/t},\ t > 0$

(a)

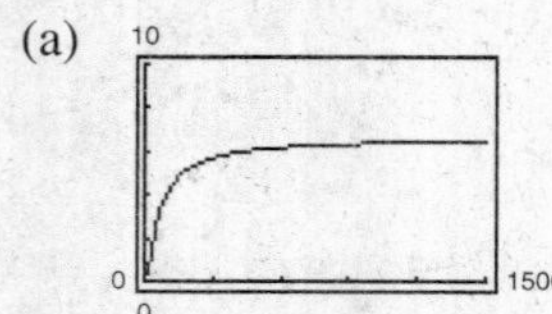

(b) As $t \to \infty$, $V \to 6.7$.

Horizontal asymptote: $y = 6.7$

The yield will approach 6.7 million cubic feet per acre.

(c)

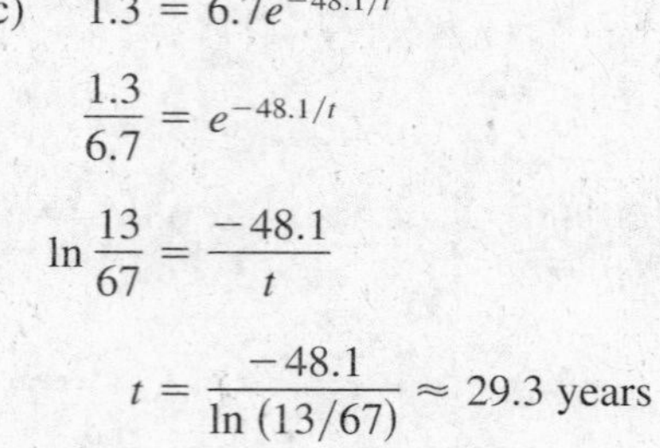

$$1.3 = 6.7e^{-48.1/t}$$

$$\frac{1.3}{6.7} = e^{-48.1/t}$$

$$\ln \frac{13}{67} = \frac{-48.1}{t}$$

$$t = \frac{-48.1}{\ln(13/67)} \approx 29.3 \text{ years}$$

139. (a)

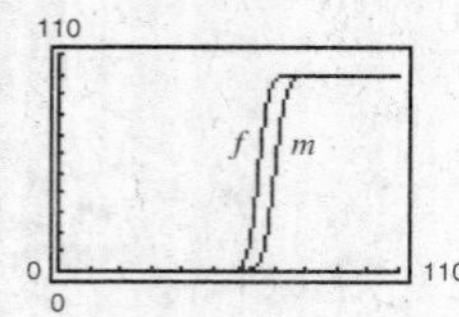

(b) From the graph we see horizontal asymptotes at $y = 0$ and $y = 100$. These represent the lower and upper percent bounds.

(c) Males: $50 = \dfrac{100}{1 + e^{-0.6114(x-69.71)}}$

$$1 + e^{-0.6114(x-69.71)} = 2$$

$$e^{-0.6114(x-69.71)} = 1$$

$$-0.6114(x - 69.71) = \ln 1$$

$$-0.6114(x - 69.71) = 0$$

$$x = 69.71 \text{ inches}$$

Females: $50 = \dfrac{100}{1 + e^{-0.66607(x-64.51)}}$

$$1 + e^{-0.66607(x-64.51)} = 2$$

$$e^{-0.66607(x-64.51)} = 1$$

$$-0.66607(x - 64.51) = \ln 1$$

$$-0.66607(x - 64.51) = 0$$

$$x = 64.51 \text{ inches}$$

140. $P = \dfrac{0.83}{1 + e^{-0.2n}}$

(a)

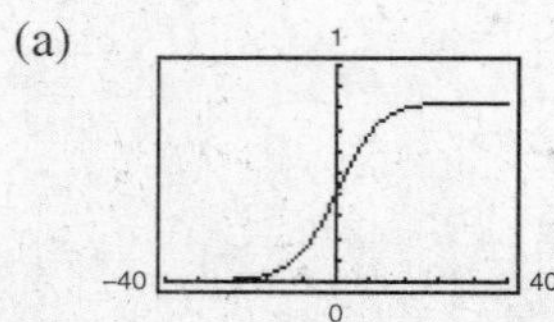

(b) Horizontal asymptotes: $y = 0$, $y = 0.83$
The upper asymptote, $y = 0.83$, indicates that the proportion of correct responses will approach 0.83 as the number of trials increases.

(c) When $P = 60\%$ or $P = 0.60$:

$$0.60 = \frac{0.83}{1 + e^{-0.2n}}$$

$$1 + e^{-0.2n} = \frac{0.83}{0.60}$$

$$e^{-0.2n} = \frac{0.83}{0.60} - 1$$

$$\ln e^{-0.2n} = \ln\left(\frac{0.83}{0.60} - 1\right)$$

$$-0.2n = \ln\left(\frac{0.83}{0.60} - 1\right)$$

$$n = -\frac{\ln\left(\frac{0.83}{0.60} - 1\right)}{0.2} \approx 5 \text{ trials}$$

141. $T = 20[1 + 7(2^{-h})]$

(a)

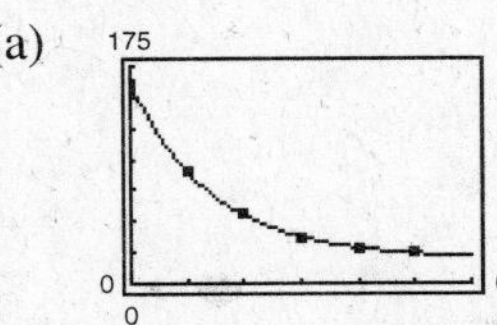

(b) We see a horizontal asymptote at $y = 20$. This represents the room temperature.

(c)
$$100 = 20[1 + 7(2^{-h})]$$
$$5 = 1 + 7(2^{-h})$$
$$4 = 7(2^{-h})$$
$$\frac{4}{7} = 2^{-h}$$
$$\ln\left(\frac{4}{7}\right) = \ln 2^{-h}$$
$$\ln\left(\frac{4}{7}\right) = -h \ln 2$$
$$\frac{\ln(4/7)}{-\ln 2} = h$$
$$h \approx 0.81 \text{ hour}$$

142. (a)
$$13{,}387 - 2190.5 \ln t = 7250$$
$$2190.5 \ln t = 6137$$
$$\ln t = 2.8016$$
$$t \approx 16.5, \text{ or } 2006$$

(b)

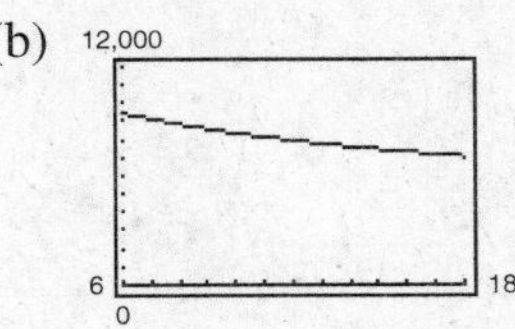

(c) Let $y_1 = 13{,}387 - 2190.5 \ln t$ and $y_2 = 7250$. The graphs of y_1 and y_2 intersect at $t \approx 16.5$.

143. False. The equation $e^x = 0$ has no solutions.

144. False. A logarithmic equation can have any number of extraneous solutions. For example $\ln(2x - 1) + \ln(x + 2) = \ln(x^2 - x - 5)$ has two extraneous solutions, $x = -1$ and $x = -3$.

145. Answers will vary.

146. $f(x) = \log_a x$, $g(x) = a^x$, $a > 1$.

(a) $a = 1.2$

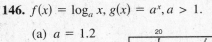

The curves intersect twice: $(1.258, 1.258)$ and $(14.767, 14.767)$

(b) If $f(x) = \log_a x = a^x = g(x)$ intersect exactly once, then

$x = \log_a x = a^x \Rightarrow a = x^{1/x}$.

The graphs of $y = x^{1/x}$ and $y = a$ intersect once for $a = e^{1/e} \approx 1.445$. Then

$\log_a x = x \Rightarrow (e^{1/e})^x = x \Rightarrow e^{x/e} = x \Rightarrow x = e$.

For $a = e^{1/e}$, the curves intersect once at (e, e).

(c) For $1 < a < e^{1/e}$ the curves intersect twice. For $a > e^{1/e}$, the curves do not intersect.

147. Yes. The doubling time is given by

$$2P = Pe^{rt}$$
$$2 = e^{rt}$$
$$\ln 2 = rt$$
$$t = \frac{\ln 2}{r}.$$

The time to quadruple is given by

$$4P = Pe^{rt}$$
$$4 = e^{rt}$$
$$\ln 4 = rt$$
$$t = \frac{\ln 4}{r} = \frac{\ln 2^2}{r} = \frac{2 \ln 2}{r} = 2\left[\frac{\ln 2}{r}\right]$$

which is twice as long.

148. To find the length of time it takes for an investment P to double to $2P$, solve

$$2P = Pe^{rt}$$
$$2 = e^{rt}$$
$$\ln 2 = rt$$
$$\frac{\ln 2}{r} = t.$$

Thus, you can see that the time is not dependent on the size of the investment, but rather the interest rate.

149. $f(x) = 3x^3 - 4$

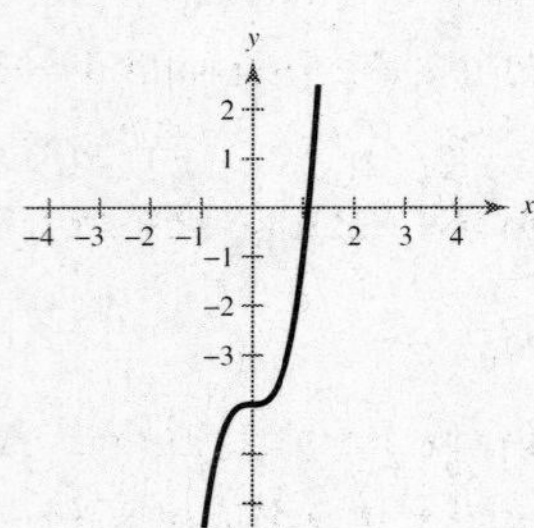

150. $f(x) = -(x + 1)^3 + 2$

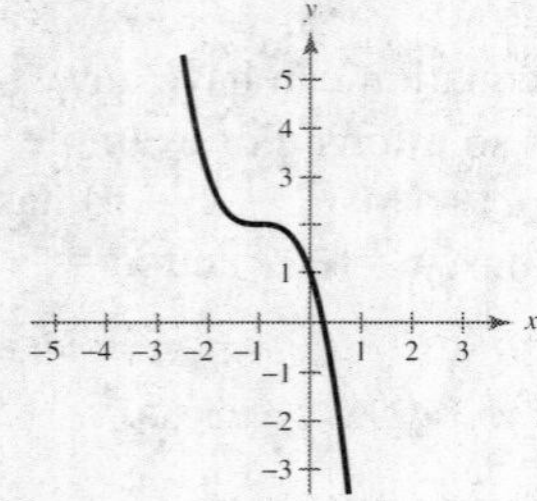

151. $f(x) = |x| + 9$

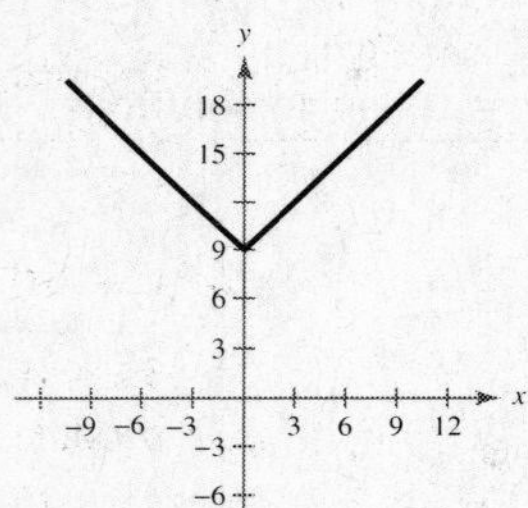

152. $f(x) = |x + 2| - 8$

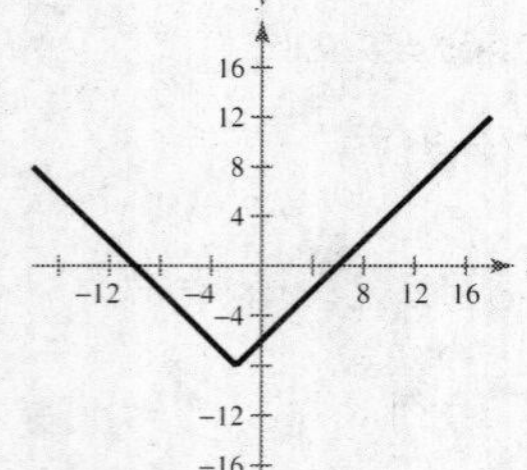

153. $f(x) = \begin{cases} 2x, & x < 0 \\ -x^2 + 4, & x \geq 0 \end{cases}$

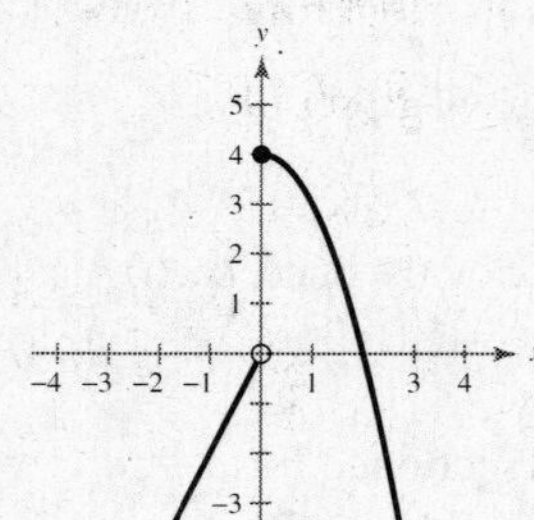

154. $f(x) = \begin{cases} x - 9, & x \leq -1 \\ x^2 + 1, & x > -1 \end{cases}$

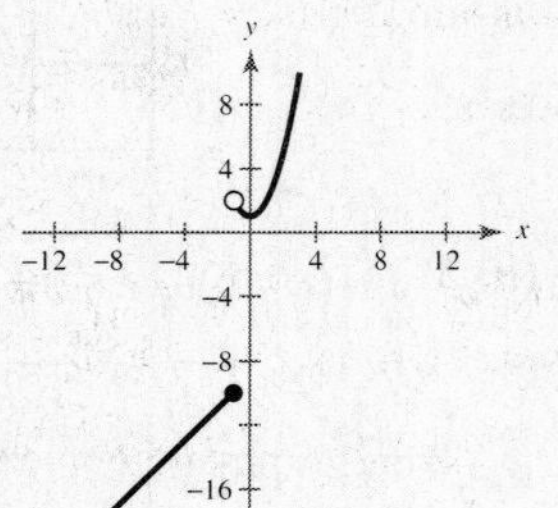

Section 3.5 Exponential and Logarithmic Models

- You should be able to solve compound interest problems.
  1. $A = P\left(1 + \frac{r}{n}\right)^{nt}$
  2. $A = Pe^{rt}$
- You should be able to solve growth and decay problems.
  (a) Exponential growth if $b > 0$ and $y = ae^{bx}$.
  (b) Exponential decay if $b > 0$ and $y = ae^{-bx}$.
- You should be able to use the Gaussian model
  $y = ae^{-(x-b)^2/c}$.
- You should be able to use the logistics growth model
  $y = \dfrac{a}{1 + be^{-(x-c)/d}}$.
- You should be able to use the logarithmic models
  $y = \ln(ax + b)$ and $y = \log_{10}(ax + b)$.

Vocabulary Check

1. (a) iv (b) i (c) vi (d) iii (e) vii (f) ii (g) v

2. Normally

3. Sigmoidal

4. Bell-shaped, mean

1. $y = 2e^{x/4}$

This is an exponential growth model.

Matches graph (c).

2. $y = 6e^{-x/4}$

This is an exponential decay model.

Matches graph (e).

3. $y = 6 + \log_{10}(x + 2)$

This is a logarithmic model, and contains $(-1, 6)$.

Matches graph (b).

4. $y = 3e^{-(x-2)^2/5}$

Gaussian model

Matches (a).

5. $y = \ln(x + 1)$

This is a logarithmic model.

Matches graph (d).

6. $y = \dfrac{4}{1 + e^{-2x}}$

Logistics model

Matches (f).

7. Since $A = 10{,}000e^{0.035t}$, the time to double is given by

$$20{,}000 = 10{,}000e^{0.035t}$$
$$2 = e^{0.035t}$$
$$\ln 2 = 0.035t$$
$$t = \frac{\ln 2}{0.035} \approx 19.8 \text{ years.}$$

Amount after 10 years:

$$A = 10{,}000e^{0.035(10)} \approx \$14{,}190.68$$

8. Since $A = 2000e^{0.015t}$, the time to double is given by

$$4000 = 2000e^{0.015t}$$
$$2 = e^{0.015t}$$
$$\ln 2 = 0.015t$$
$$t = \frac{\ln 2}{0.015} \approx 46.2 \text{ years.}$$

Amount after 10 years:

$$A = 2000e^{0.015(10)} \approx \$2323.67$$

9. Since $A = 7500e^{rt}$ and $A = 15{,}000$ when $t = 21$, we have the following.

$$15{,}000 = 7500e^{21r}$$
$$2 = e^{21r}$$
$$\ln 2 = 21r$$
$$r = \frac{\ln 2}{21} \approx 0.033 = 3.3\%$$

Amount after 10 years:

$$A = 7500e^{0.033(10)} \approx \$10{,}432.26$$

10. Since $A = 1000e^{rt}$ and $A = 2000$ when $t = 12$, we have the following.

$$2000 = 1000e^{12r}$$
$$2 = e^{12r}$$
$$\ln 2 = 12r$$
$$r = \frac{\ln 2}{12} \approx 0.058 = 5.8\%$$

Amount after 10 years:

$$A = 1000e^{0.058(10)} \approx \$1786.04$$

11. Since $A = 5000e^{rt}$ and $A = 5665.74$ when $t = 10$, we have the following.

$$5665.74 = 5000e^{10r}$$
$$\frac{5665.74}{5000} = e^{10r}$$
$$\ln\left(\frac{5665.74}{5000}\right) = 10r$$
$$r = \frac{1}{10}\ln\left(\frac{5665.74}{5000}\right)$$
$$\approx 0.0125 = 1.25\%$$

The time to double is given by

$$10{,}000 = 5000e^{0.0125t}$$
$$2 = e^{0.0125t}$$
$$\ln 2 = 0.0125t$$
$$t = \frac{\ln 2}{0.0125} \approx 55.5 \text{ years.}$$

12. Since $A = 300e^{rt}$ and $A = 385.21$ when $t = 10$, we have the following.

$$385.21 = 300e^{10r}$$
$$\frac{385.21}{300} = e^{10r}$$
$$\ln\left(\frac{385.21}{300}\right) = 10r$$
$$r = \frac{1}{10}\ln\left(\frac{385.21}{300}\right)$$
$$\approx 0.025 = 2.5\%$$

The time to double is given by

$$600 = 300e^{0.025t}$$
$$2 = e^{0.025t}$$
$$\ln 2 = 0.025t$$
$$t = \frac{\ln 2}{0.025} \approx 27.7 \text{ years.}$$

13. Since $A = Pe^{0.045t}$ and $A = 100{,}000$ when $t = 10$, we have the following.

$$100{,}000 = Pe^{0.045(10)}$$
$$\frac{100{,}000}{e^{0.45}} = P \approx 63{,}762.82$$

The time to double is given by

$$127{,}525.64 = 63{,}762.82e^{0.045t}$$
$$2 = e^{0.045t}$$
$$\ln 2 = 0.045t$$
$$t = \frac{\ln 2}{0.045} \approx 15.4 \text{ years.}$$

14. Since $A = Pe^{0.02t}$ and $A = 2500$ when $t = 10$, we have the following.

$$2500 = Pe^{0.02(10)}$$
$$\frac{2500}{e^{0.02}} = P \approx \$2046.83$$

The time to double is given by

$$4093.66 = 2046.83e^{0.02t}$$
$$2 = e^{0.02t}$$
$$\ln 2 = 0.02t$$
$$t = \frac{\ln 2}{0.02} \approx 34.7 \text{ years.}$$

15. $3P = Pe^{rt}$

$3 = e^{rt}$

$\ln 3 = rt$

$\frac{\ln 3}{r} = t$

r	2%	4%	6%	8%	10%	12%
$t = \frac{\ln 3}{r}$	54.93	27.47	18.31	13.73	10.99	9.16

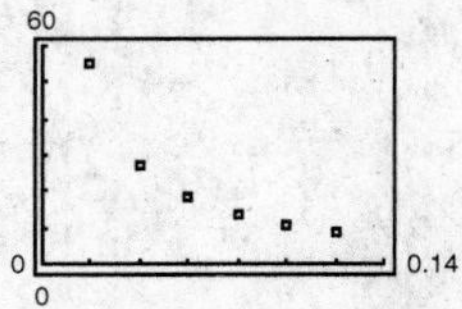

16. $3P = P(1 + r)^t$

$3 = (1 + r)^t$

$\ln 3 = \ln(1 + r)^t$

$\ln 3 = t \ln(1 + r)$

$\frac{\ln 3}{\ln(1 + r)} = t$

r	2%	4%	6%	8%	10%	12%
$t = \frac{\ln 3}{\ln(1 + r)}$	55.48	28.01	18.85	14.27	11.53	9.69

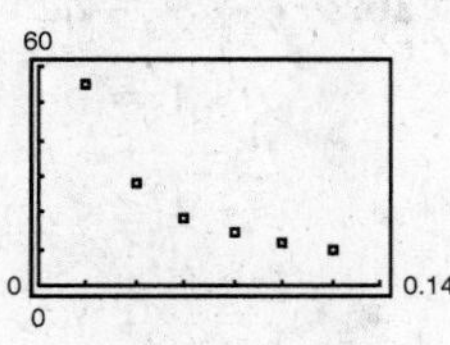

17.

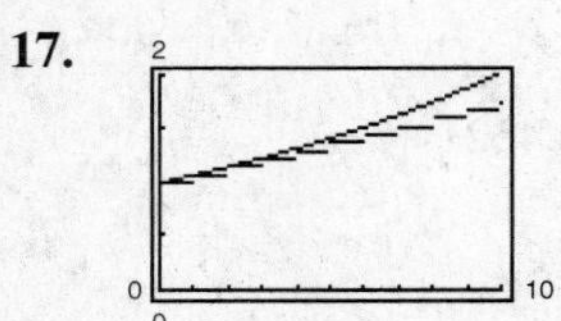

Continuous compounding results in faster growth.

$A = 1 + 0.075[\![t]\!]$

and $A = e^{0.07t}$

18.

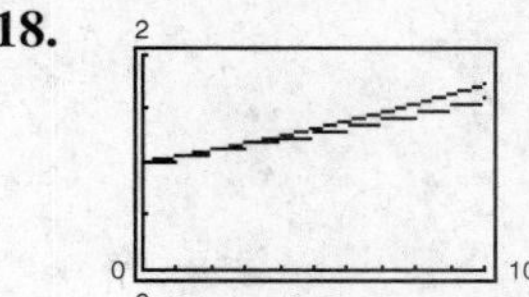

$A = 1 + 0.06[\![t]\!]$

$A = \left(1 + \frac{0.055}{365}\right)^{[\![365t]\!]}$

From the graph, $5\frac{1}{2}\%$ compounded daily grows faster than 6% simple interest.

19. $\frac{1}{2}C = Ce^{k(1599)}$

$\frac{1}{2} = e^{1599k}$

$k = \frac{\ln(1/2)}{1599}$

$y = Ce^{kt}$

$= 10e^{[\ln(1/2)/1599]1000}$

≈ 6.48 g

20. $\frac{1}{2}C = Ce^{k(1599)}$

$\frac{1}{2} = e^{1599k}$

$k = \frac{\ln(1/2)}{1599}$

$y = Ce^{kt}$

$1.5 = Ce^{[\ln(1/2)/1599]1000}$

$1.5 \approx C(0.64824)$

$C \approx 2.31$ g

21. $\frac{1}{2}C = Ce^{k(5715)}$

$\frac{1}{2} = e^{5715k}$

$k = \frac{\ln(1/2)}{5715}$

$y = Ce^{kt}$

$= 3e^{[\ln(1/2)/5715]1000}$

≈ 2.66 g

22. $\frac{1}{2}C = Ce^{k(24,100)}$

$\frac{1}{2} = e^{24,100k}$

$k = \frac{\ln(1/2)}{24,100}$

$0.4 = Ce^{[\ln(1/2)/24,100]1000}$

$\approx C(0.97165)$

$C \approx 0.41$ g

23. $y = ae^{bx}$

$1 = ae^{b(0)} \implies 1 = a$

$10 = e^{b(3)}$

$\ln 10 = 3b$

$\frac{\ln 10}{3} = b \implies b \approx 0.7675$

Thus, $y = e^{0.7675x}$.

24. $y = ae^{bx}$

$\frac{1}{2} = ae^{b(0)} \implies a = \frac{1}{2}$

$5 = \frac{1}{2}e^{b(4)}$

$10 = e^{4b}$

$\ln 10 = 4b$

$b = \frac{\ln 10}{4} \approx 0.5756$

Thus, $y = \frac{1}{2}e^{0.5756x}$.

25. $(0, 4) \implies a = 4$

$(5, 1) \implies 1 = 4e^{b(5)} \implies b = \frac{1}{5}\ln\left(\frac{1}{4}\right)$

$= -\frac{1}{5}\ln 4 \approx -0.2773$

$y = 4e^{-0.2773x}$

26. $y = ae^{bx}$

$1 = ae^{b(0)} \implies 1 = a$

$\frac{1}{4} = e^{b(3)}$

$\ln\left(\frac{1}{4}\right) = 3b$

$\frac{\ln(1/4)}{3} = b \implies b \approx -0.4621$

Thus, $y = e^{-0.4621x}$.

27. (a) Australia: (0, 19.2), (10, 20.9)

$a = 19.2$ and $20.9 = 19.2e^{b(10)} \implies b = 0.008484$

$y = 19.2e^{0.008484t}$

For 2030, $y \approx 24.8$ million.

Canada: (0, 31.3), (10, 34.3)

$a = 31.3$ and $34.3 = 31.3e^{b(10)} \implies b = 0.009153$

$y = 31.3e^{0.009153t}$

For 2030, $y \approx 41.2$ million.

Philippines: (0, 79.7), (10, 95.9)

$a = 79.7$ and $95.9 = 79.7e^{b(10)} \implies b = 0.0185$

$y = 79.7e^{0.0185t}$

For 2030, $y \approx 138.8$ million.

South Africa: (0, 44.1), (10, 43.3)

$a = 44.1$ and $43.3 = 44.1e^{b(10)} \implies b = -0.00183$

$y = 44.1e^{-0.00183t}$

For 2030, $y \approx 41.7$ million.

—CONTINUED—

27. (a) **—CONTINUED—**

Turkey: (0, 65.7), (10, 73.3)

$a = 65.7$ and $73.3 = 65.7e^{b(10)} \Rightarrow b = 0.01095$

$y = 65.7e^{0.01095t}$

For 2030, $y \approx 91.2$ million.

(b) The constant b gives the growth rates.

(c) The constant b is negative for South Africa.

28. $P = 372.55e^{-0.01052t}$

(a) Decreasing because the exponent is negative.

(b) For 1990, $t = 0$ and $P \approx 372{,}550$ people.

For 2000, $t = 10$ and $P \approx 335{,}349$ people.

For 2004, $t = 14$ and $P \approx 321{,}530$ people.

(c) $300 = 372.55e^{-0.01052t} \Rightarrow t \approx 20.6$, or 2010

29. (a) $180 = 134.0e^{k(10)}$

$$10k = \ln \frac{180}{134.0}$$

$$k \approx 0.0295$$

(b) For 2010, $t = 20$ and

$P = 134.0e^{0.0295(20)} \approx 241{,}734$ people.

30. $P = 258.0e^{kt}$

(a) $478 = 258.0e^{k(10)}$

$$10k = \ln\left(\frac{478}{258}\right)$$

$$k \approx 0.0617$$

(b) For 2010, $t = 20$ and

$P = 258e^{0.0617(20)} \approx 886{,}215$ people.

31.

$$y = Ce^{kt}$$

$$\frac{1}{2}C = Ce^{(1599)k}$$

$$\ln\left(\frac{1}{2}\right) = 1599k$$

$$k = \frac{\ln(1/2)}{1599}$$

When $t = 100$, we have

$y = Ce^{[(\ln(1/2) \cdot 100)/1599]} \approx 0.958C$, or 95.8%.

32.

$$y = Ce^{kt}$$

$$\frac{1}{2}C = Ce^{5715k}$$

$$\ln\left(\frac{1}{2}\right) = 5715k$$

$$k = \frac{\ln(1/2)}{5715}$$

The ancient charcoal has only 15% as much radioactive carbon.

$$0.15C = Ce^{[(\ln(1/2)/5715)t]}$$

$$\ln 0.15 = \frac{\ln(1/2)}{5715}t$$

$$t \approx 15{,}642 \text{ years}$$

33. (a) $V = mt + b$, $V(0) = 30{,}788 \Rightarrow b = 30{,}788$

$V(2) = 24{,}000 \Rightarrow 24{,}000 = 2m + 30{,}788$

$\Rightarrow m = -3394$

$V(t) = -3394t + 30{,}788$

(b) $V = ae^{kt}$, $V(0) = 30{,}788 \Rightarrow b = 30{,}788$

$V(2) = 24{,}000 \Rightarrow 24{,}000 = 30{,}788e^{2k}$

$$\Rightarrow k = \frac{1}{2}\ln\left(\frac{24{,}000}{30{,}788}\right) \approx -0.1245$$

$V = 30{,}788e^{-0.1245t}$

(c)

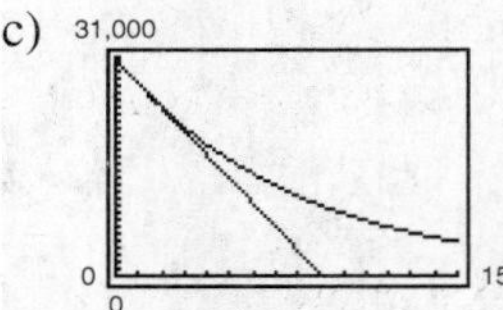

(d) The exponential model depreciates faster in the first year.

(e) Answers will vary.

34. Let $t = 0$ correspond to 2005.

(a) $V = mt + b$, $V(0) = 1150 \Rightarrow b = 1150$

$V(2) = 550 \Rightarrow 550 = m(2) + 1150 \Rightarrow m = -300$

$V(t) = -300t + 1150$

(b) $V = ae^{kt}$, $V(0) = 1150 \Rightarrow a = 1150$

$V(2) = 550 \Rightarrow 550 = 1150e^{2k}$

$\Rightarrow k = \frac{1}{2}\ln\left(\frac{55}{115}\right) \approx -0.3688$

$V(t) = 1150e^{-0.3688t}$

(c) 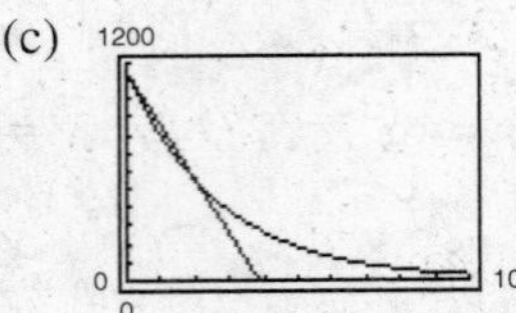

(d) The exponential model depreciates faster in the first year.

(e) Answers will vary.

35. $S(t) = 100(1 - e^{kt})$

(a) $15 = 100(1 - e^{k(1)})$

$-85 = -100e^k$

$k = \ln 0.85$

$k \approx -0.1625$

$S(t) = 100(1 - e^{-0.1625t})$

(b) 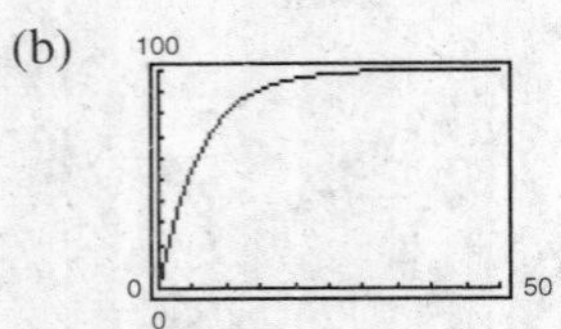

(c) $S(5) = 100(1 - e^{-0.1625(5)})$

$\approx 55.625 = 55{,}625$ units

36. $S = 10(1 - e^{kx})$

$x = 5$ (in hundreds)

$S = 2.5$ (in thousands)

(a) $2.5 = 10(1 - e^{k(5)})$

$0.25 = 1 - e^{5k}$

$e^{5k} = 0.75$

$5k = \ln 0.75$

$k \approx -0.0575$

$S = 10(1 - e^{-0.0575x})$

(b) When $x = 7$, $S = 10(1 - e^{-0.0575(7)}) \approx 3.314$ which corresponds to 3314 units.

37. $y = 0.0266e^{-(x-100)^2/450}$, $70 \le x \le 115$

(a) 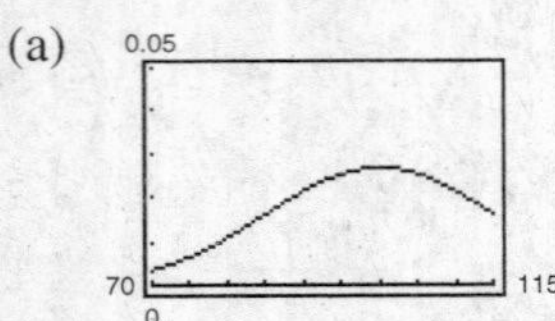

(b) Maximum point is $x = 100$, the average IQ score.

38. $y = 0.7979e^{-(x-5.4)^2/0.5}$

(a) 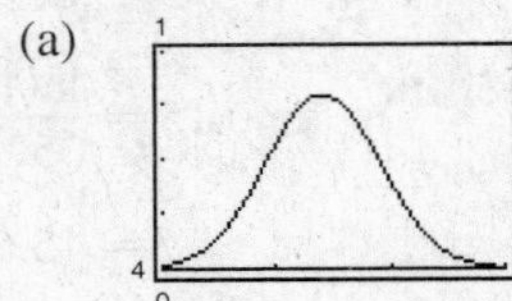

(b) About 5.4 hours

39. $p(t) = \dfrac{1000}{1 + 9e^{-0.1656t}}$

(a) $p(5) = \dfrac{1000}{1 + 9e^{-0.1656(5)}} \approx 203$ animals

(b)
$$500 = \frac{1000}{1 + 9e^{-0.1656t}}$$
$$1 + 9e^{-0.1656t} = 2$$
$$9e^{-0.1656t} = 1$$
$$e^{-0.1656t} = \frac{1}{9}$$
$$t = \frac{-\ln(1/9)}{0.1656} \approx 13 \text{ months}$$

(c)

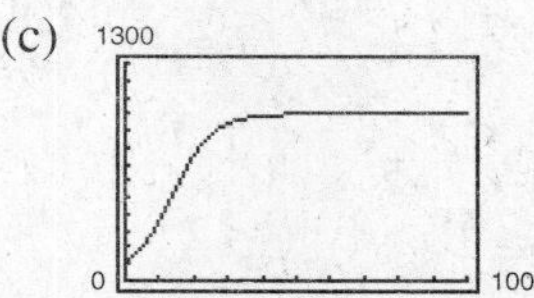

The horizontal asymptotes are $p = 0$ and $p = 1000$. The population will approach 1000 as time increases.

40. $y = \dfrac{663}{1 + 72e^{-0.547t}}, \ 0 \le t \le 18$

(a)

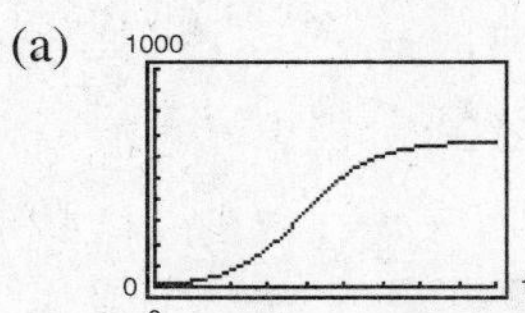

(b) For $t = 19$, $y \approx 662$.

For $t = 30$, $y \approx 663$.

(c) As $t \to \infty$, $y \to \dfrac{663}{1} = 663$, limiting value.

(d) Answers will vary.

41. $R = \log_{10}\left(\dfrac{I}{I_0}\right) = \log_{10}(I) \Longrightarrow I = 10^R$

(a) $I = 10^{6.1} \approx 1{,}258{,}925$

(b) $I = 10^{7.6} \approx 39{,}810{,}717$

(c) $I = 10^{9.0} \approx 1{,}000{,}000{,}000$

42. $R = \log_{10}\left(\dfrac{I}{I_0}\right) = \log_{10}(I)$

(a) $R = \log_{10}(39{,}811{,}000) \approx 7.6$

(b) $R = \log_{10}(12{,}589{,}000) \approx 7.1$

(c) $R = \log_{10}(251{,}200) \approx 5.4$

43. $\beta(I) = 10\log_{10}(I/I_0)$, where $I_0 = 10^{-12}$ watt per square meter.

(a) $\beta(10^{-10}) = 10 \cdot \log_{10}\left(\dfrac{10^{-10}}{10^{-12}}\right) = 10\log_{10} 10^2 = 20$ decibels

(b) $\beta(10^{-5}) = 10 \cdot \log_{10}\left(\dfrac{10^{-5}}{10^{-12}}\right) = 10\log_{10} 10^7 = 70$ decibels

(c) $\beta(10^{0}) = 10 \cdot \log_{10}\left(\dfrac{10^{0}}{10^{-12}}\right) = 10\log_{10} 10^{12} = 120$ decibels

44. $\beta = 10\log_{10}\left(\dfrac{I}{I_0}\right) = 10\log_{10}\left(\dfrac{I}{10^{-12}}\right)$

(a) $\beta(10^{-4}) = 10\log_{10}\left(\dfrac{10^{-4}}{10^{-12}}\right) = 10\log_{10}(10^8) = 80$ decibels

(b) $\beta(10^{-3}) = 90$ decibels

(c) $\beta(10^{-2}) = 100$ decibels

45. $\beta = 10 \log_{10}\left(\frac{I}{I_0}\right)$

$10^{\beta/10} = \frac{I}{I_0}$

$I = I_0 10^{\beta/10}$

$\% \text{ decrease} = \frac{I_0 10^{8.8} - I_0 10^{7.2}}{I_0 10^{8.8}} \times 100$

$= 97.5\%$

46. $\beta = 10 \log_{10}\left(\frac{I}{I_0}\right)$

$10^{\beta/10} = \frac{I}{I_0}$

$I = I_0 10^{\beta/10}$

$\% \text{ decrease} = \frac{I_0 10^{9.3} - I_0 10^{8.0}}{I_0 10^{9.3}} \times 100 \approx 95\%$

47. $\text{pH} = -\log_{10}[\text{H}^+] = -\log_{10}[2.3 \times 10^{-5}] \approx 4.64$

48. $5.8 = -\log_{10}[\text{H}^+]$

$10^{-5.8} = [\text{H}^+]$

$[\text{H}^+] \approx 1.58 \times 10^{-6}$ moles per liter

49. $\text{pH} = -\log_{10}[\text{H}^+]$

$-\text{pH} = \log_{10}[\text{H}^+]$

$10^{-\text{pH}} = [\text{H}^+]$

$\frac{\text{Hydrogen ion concentration of grape}}{\text{Hydrogen ion concentration of milk of magnesia}}$

$= \frac{10^{-3.5}}{10^{-10.5}} = 10^7$

50. $\text{pH} - 1 = -\log_{10}[\text{H}^+]$

$-(\text{pH} - 1) = \log_{10}[\text{H}^+]$

$10^{-(\text{pH}-1)} = [\text{H}^+]$

$10^{-\text{pH}+1} = [\text{H}^+]$

$10^{-\text{pH}} \cdot 10 = [\text{H}^+]$

The hydrogen ion concentration is increased by a factor of 10.

51. (a) $P = 120{,}000,\ r = 0.075,\ M = 839.06$

$u = M - \left(M - \frac{Pr}{12}\right)\left(1 + \frac{r}{12}\right)^{12t}$

$= 839.06 - (839.06 - 750)(1 + 0.00625)^{12t}$

$v = (839.06 - 750)(1.00625)^{12t}$

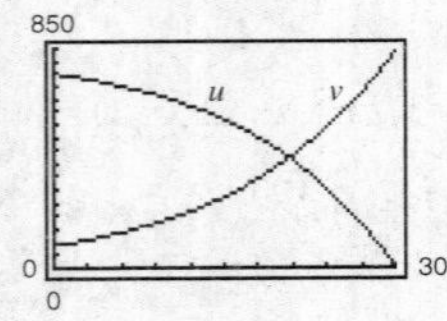

(b) In the early years, the majority of the monthly payment goes toward interest. The interest and principle are equal when $t \approx 20.729 \approx 21$ years.

(c) $P = 120{,}000,\ r = 0.075,\ M = 966.71$

$u = 966.71 - (966.71 - 750)(1.00625)^{12t}$

$v = (966.71 - 750)(1.00625)^{12t}$

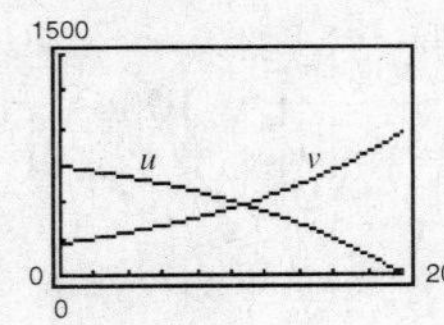

$u = v$ when $t \approx 10.73$ years.

52. $u = 120{,}000\left[\frac{0.075t}{1 - \left(\frac{1}{1 + 0.075/12}\right)^{12t}} - 1\right]$

(a) 120,000 0 20 0

(b) From the graph, when $u = 120{,}000$, $t \approx 21.2$ years. Yes, a mortgage of approximately 37.6 years will result in about $240,000 of interest.

53. $t = -10 \ln\left(\dfrac{T - 70}{98.6 - 70}\right)$

At 9:00 A.M. we have
$t = -10 \ln [(85.7 - 70)/(98.6 - 70)] \approx 6$ hours.

Thus, we can conclude that the person died 6 hours before 9 A.M., or 3:00 A.M.

54. $t = -5.05 \ln\left(\dfrac{T - 40}{0 - 40}\right)$ ($t = 0$ is 11 A.M.)

$$7 = -5.05 \ln\left(\frac{T - 40}{0 - 40}\right)$$

$$\frac{-7}{5.05} = \ln\left(\frac{T - 40}{-40}\right)$$

$$\left(\frac{T - 40}{-40}\right) = e^{-7/5.05}$$

$$T = 40 - 40e^{-7/5.05} \approx 29.998 \approx 30 < 32$$

Hence, the steaks do not thaw out in time.

55. False. The domain could be all real numbers.

56. False. See Example 5, page 380.

57. True. For the Gaussian model, $y > 0$.

58. True. See page 379.

59. $4x - 3y - 9 = 0 \implies y = \frac{1}{3}(4x - 9)$

Slope: $\frac{4}{3}$

Matches (a).

Intercepts: $(0, -3)$, $\left(\frac{9}{4}, 0\right)$

60. Line with intercepts (5, 0) and (0, 2).

Matches (b).

61. $y = 25 - 2.25x$

Slope: -2.25

Matches (d).

Intercepts: $(0, 25)$, $\left(\frac{100}{9}, 0\right)$

62. Line with intercepts (2, 0) and (0, 4).

Matches (c).

63. $f(x) = 2x^3 - 3x^2 + x - 1$

The graph falls to the left and rises to the right.

64. $f(x) = -4x^4 - x^2 + 5$

Falls to the left and falls to right

65. $g(x) = -1.6x^5 + 4x^2 - 2$

The graph rises to the left and falls to the right.

66. $g(x) = 7x^6 + 9.1x^5 - 3.2x^4 + 25x^3$

Rises to left and rises to right

67.
$$\begin{array}{r|rrrr} 4 & 2 & -8 & 3 & -9 \\ & & 8 & 0 & 12 \\ \hline & 2 & 0 & 3 & 3 \end{array}$$

$$\frac{2x^3 - 8x^2 + 3x - 9}{x - 4} = 2x^2 + 3 + \frac{3}{x - 4}$$

68.
$$\begin{array}{r|rrrrr} -5 & 1 & 0 & 0 & -3 & 1 \\ & & -5 & 25 & -125 & 640 \\ \hline & 1 & -5 & 25 & -128 & 641 \end{array}$$

$$\frac{x^4 - 3x + 1}{x + 5} = x^3 - 5x^2 + 25x - 128 + \frac{641}{x + 5}$$

69. Answers will vary.

Section 3.6 Nonlinear Models

- You should be able to use a graphing utility to find nonlinear models, including:
  (a) Quadratic models
  (b) Exponential models
  (c) Power models
  (d) Logarithmic models
  (e) Logistic models
- You should be able to use a scatter plot to determine which model is best.
- You should be able to determine the sum of squared differences for a model.

Vocabulary Check

1. $y = ax + b$ **2.** quadratic **3.** $y = ax^b$

4. sum, squared differences **5.** $y = ab^x, ae^{cx}$

1. Logarithmic model **2.** Linear model **3.** Quadratic model **4.** Exponential model

5. Exponential model **6.** Logistic model **7.** Quadratic model **8.** Linear model

9.

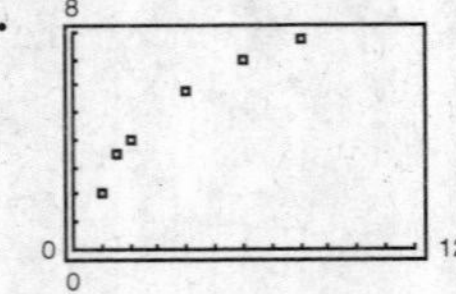

Logarithmic model

10.

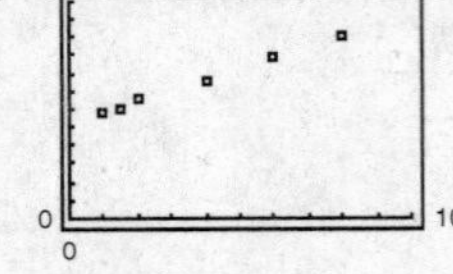

Linear model

11.

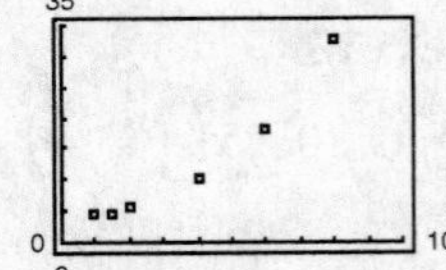

Exponential model

12.

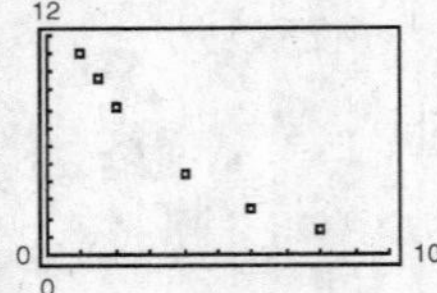

Exponential model

13.

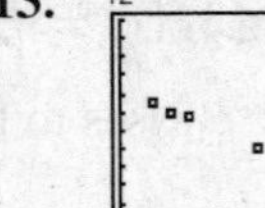

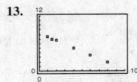

Linear model

14.

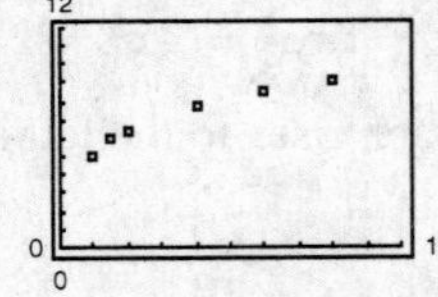

Logarithmic model

15. $y = 4.752(1.2607)^x$

Coefficient of determination: 0.96773

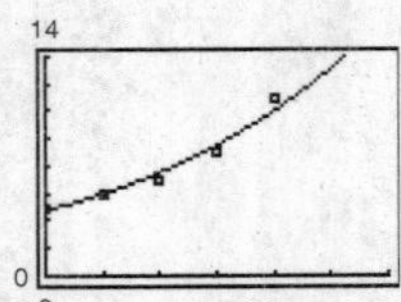

16. $y = 3.964(1.4084)^x$

Coefficient of determination: 0.99495

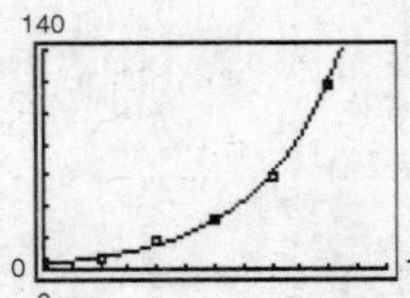

17. $y = 8.463(0.7775)^x$

Coefficient of determination: 0.86639

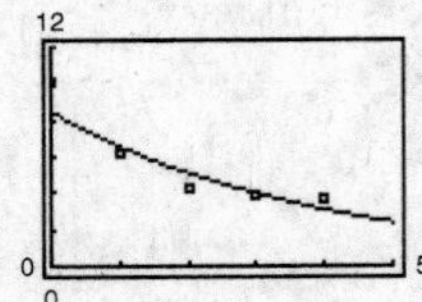

18. $y = 87.262(0.9438)^x$

Coefficient of determination: 0.85030

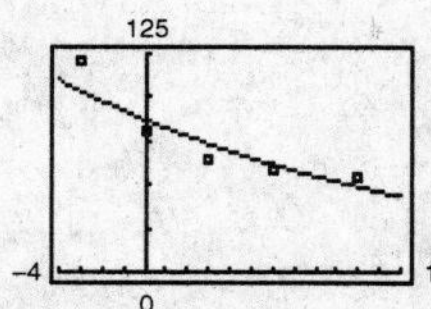

19. $y = 2.083 + 1.257 \ln x$

Coefficient of determination: 0.98672

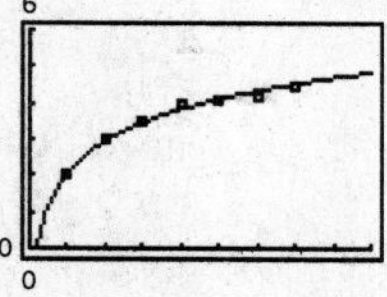

20. $y = 9.027 + 2.537 \ln x$

Coefficient of determination: 0.96884

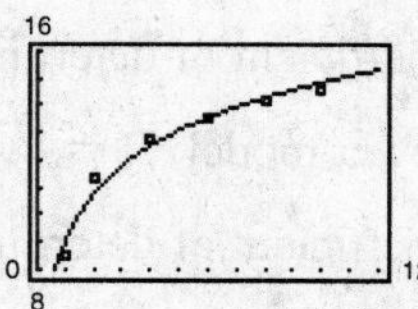

21. $y = 9.826 - 4.097 \ln x$

Coefficient of determination: 0.93704

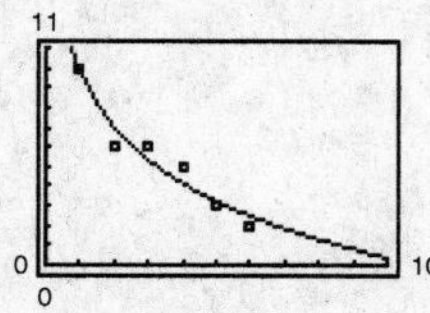

22. $y = 20.076 - 5.027 \ln x$

Coefficient of determination: 0.99977

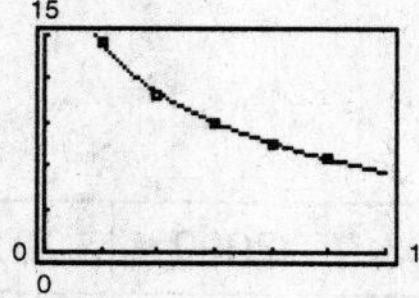

23. $y = 1.985x^{0.760}$

Coefficient of determination: 0.99686

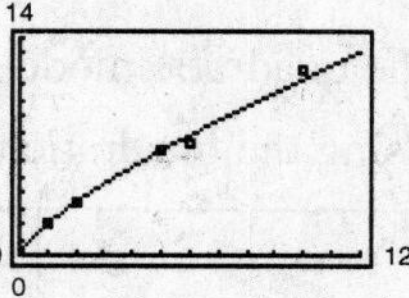

24. $y = 3.397x^{1.650}$

Coefficient of determination: 0.99788

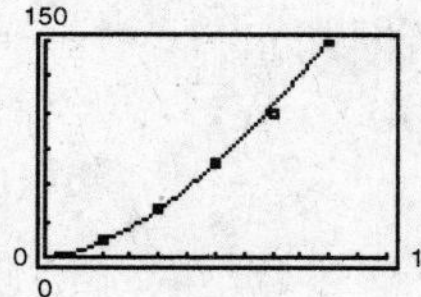

25. $y = 16.103x^{-3.174}$

Coefficient of determination: 0.88161

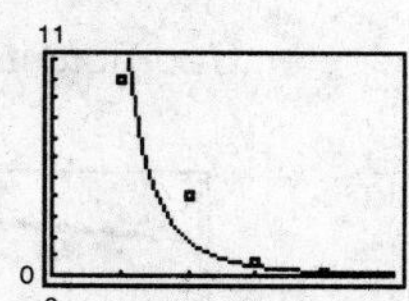

26. $y = 525.428x^{-0.226}$

Coefficient of determination: 0.99549

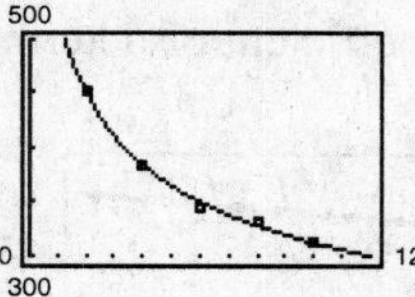

27. (a) Quadratic model: $R = 0.031t^2 + 1.13t + 97.1$

Exponential model: $R = 94.435(1.0174)^t$

Power model: $R = 77.837t^{0.1918}$

(b)

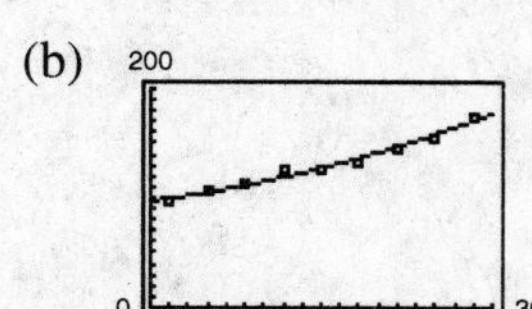

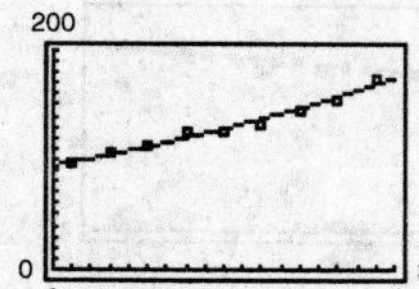

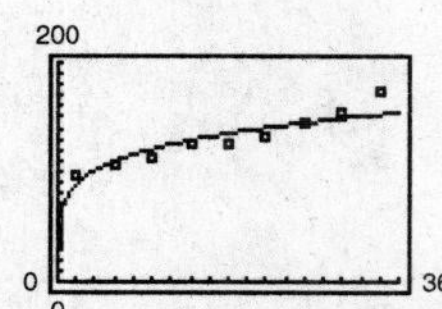

(c) The exponential model fits best. Answers will vary.

(d) For 2008, $t = 38$ and $R \approx 181.9$ million.

For 2012, $t = 42$ and $R \approx 194.9$ million.

Answers will vary.

28. (a) Quadratic model: $R = -0.0136t^2 + 0.396t + 1.01$

Coefficient of determination: 0.97730

Exponential model: $R = 2.296(1.0425)^t$

Coefficient of determination: 0.90739

Power model: $R = 1.480t^{0.3791}$

Coefficient of determination: 0.96052

(b)

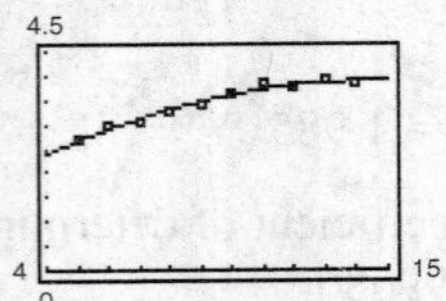

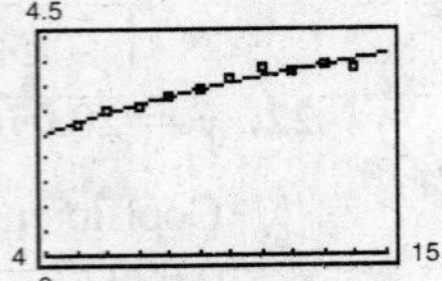

(c) The quadratic model fits best.

(d) Using the quadratic model:

Year	2005	2006	2007	2008	2009	2010
Price	3.89	3.86	3.81	3.73	3.62	3.49

Answers will vary.

29. (a) Linear model: $P = 3.11t + 250.9$

Coefficient of determination: 0.99942

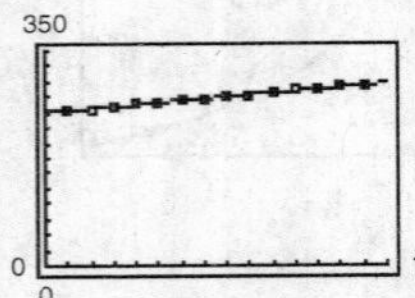

(b) Power model: $P = 246.52t^{0.0587}$

Coefficient of determination: 0.90955

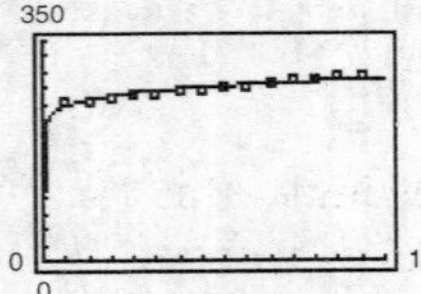

(c) Exponential model: $P = 251.57(1.0114)^t$

Coefficient of determination: 0.99811

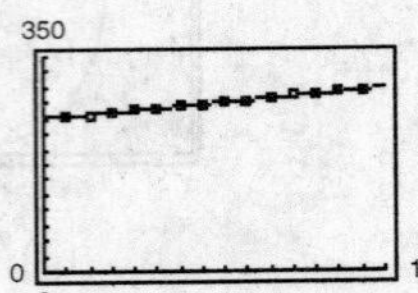

(d) Quadratic model: $P = -0.020t^2 + 3.41t + 250.1$

Coefficient of determination: 0.99994

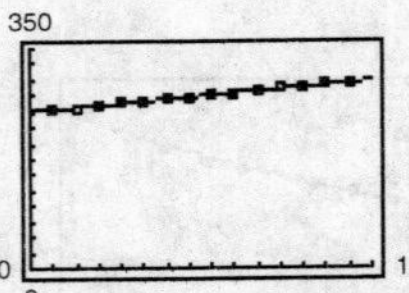

(e) The quadratic model is best because its coefficient of determination is closest to 1.

—CONTINUED—

29. —CONTINUED—

(f) Linear model:

Year	2005	2006	2007	2008	2009	2010
Population (in millions)	297.6	300.7	303.8	306.9	310.0	313.1

Power model:

Year	2005	2006	2007	2008	2009	2010
Population (in millions)	289.0	290.1	291.1	292.1	293.0	293.9

Exponential model:

Year	2005	2006	2007	2008	2009	2010
Population (in millions)	298.2	301.6	305.0	308.5	312.0	315.6

Quadratic model:

Year	2005	2006	2007	2008	2009	2010
Population (in millions)	296.8	299.5	302.3	305.0	307.7	310.3

(g) and (h) Answers will vary.

30. (a) $h = 0$ is not in the domain of the logarithmic function.

(b) $h = 0.863 - 6.447 \ln p$

(c)

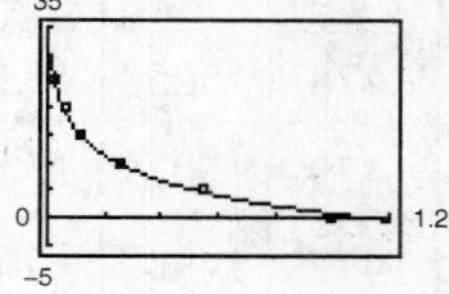

(d) For $p = 0.75$, $h \approx 2.71$ km.

(e) For $h = 13$, $p \approx 0.15$ atmospheres.

31. (a) $T = -1.239t + 73.02$

No, the data does not appear linear.

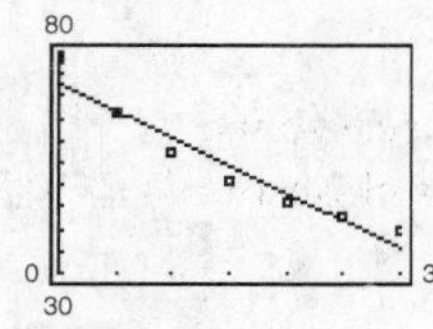

(b) $T = 0.034t^2 - 2.26t + 77.3$

Yes, the data appears quadratic. But, for $t = 60$, the graph is increasing, which is incorrect.

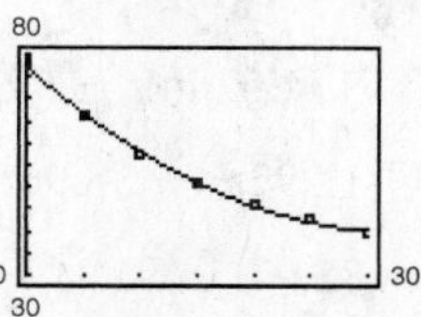

(c) Subtracting 21 from the T-values, the exponential model is $y = 54.438(0.9635)^t$. Adding back 21, $T = 54.438(0.9635)^t + 21$.

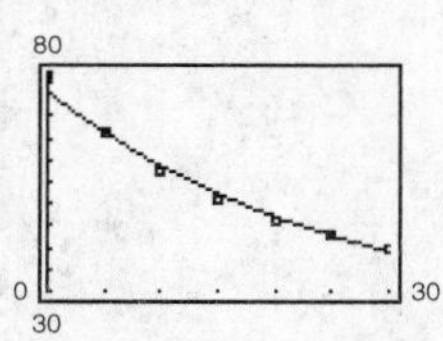

(d) Answers will vary.

32. (a)

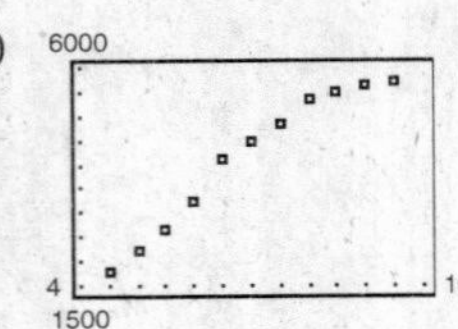

(b)

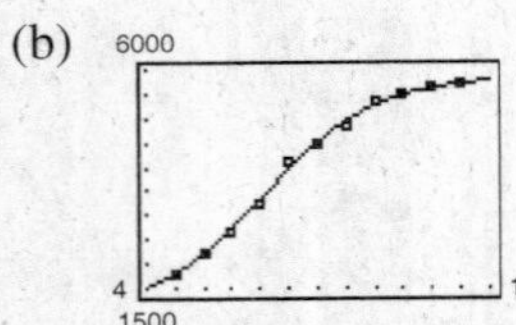

This model is a good fit.

(c) $S = 1018.4 + \dfrac{4827.2}{1 + e^{-(t-8.1391)/1.9372}}$

Using a graphing utility, $t \approx 15.7$ or 2005.

33. (a) $P = \dfrac{162.4}{1 + 0.34e^{0.5609x}}$

(b)

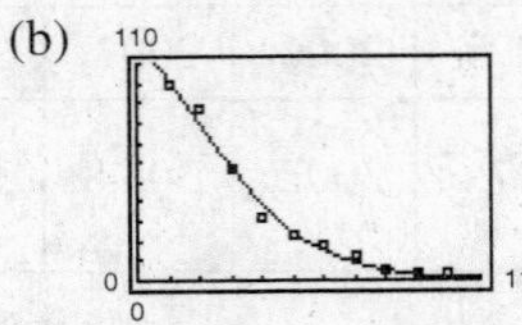

The model is a good fit.

34. (a)

(b) Linear model: $y = 18.5x + 1365$

Quadratic model: $-2.10x^2 + 54.2x + 1230$

Cubic model: $y = -0.071x^3 - 0.30x^2 + 39.9x + 1265$

Power model: $y = 1239.7 \cdot x^{0.0985}$

Exponential model: $y = 1370.4(1.012)^x$

(c)

Year	1994	1995	1996	1997	1998	1999	2000	2001	2002	2003
Linear	1439	1458	1476	1495	1513	1532	1550	1569	1587	1606
Quadratic	1413	1449	1480	1507	1529	1548	1562	1572	1578	1580
Cubic	1415	1448	1478	1505	1529	1548	1563	1573	1578	1577
Power	1421	1453	1479	1502	1522	1539	1555	1570	1584	1596
Exponential	1437	1455	1472	1490	1508	1526	1544	1563	1581	1600

Answers will vary.

(d) For 2015, $x = 25$ and $y \approx 1273$ million metric tons.

35. (a) Linear model: $y = 15.71t + 51.0$

Logarithmic model: $y = 134.67 \ln t - 97.5$

Quadratic model: $y = -1.292t^2 + 38.96t - 45.0$

Exponential model: $y = 85.97(1.091)^t$

Power model: $y = 37.27t^{0.7506}$

—CONTINUED—

35. —CONTINUED—

(b)

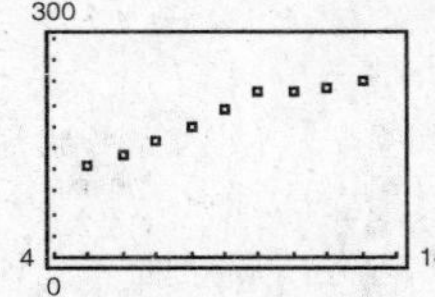

Linear model:

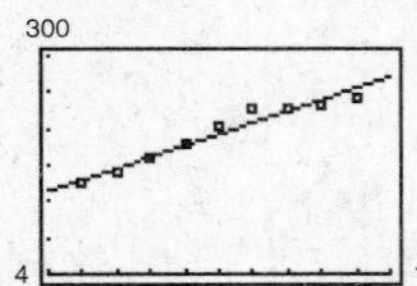

Logarithmic model:

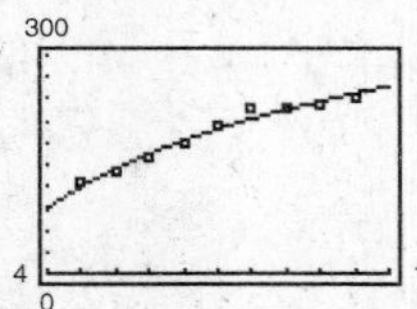

Quadratic model:

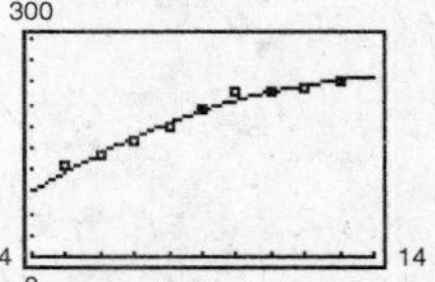

Exponential model:

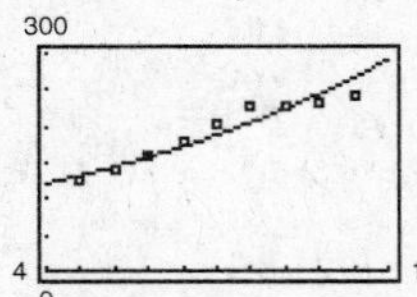

Power model:

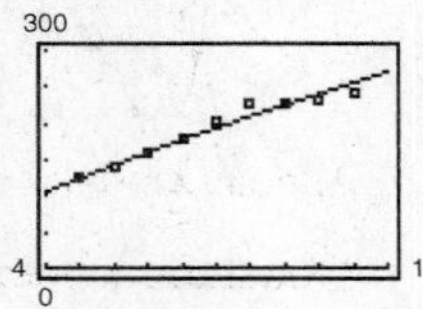

(c) Linear: 803.9

Logarithmic: 411.7

Quadratic: 289.8 (Best)

Exponential: 1611.4

Power: 667.1

(d) Linear: 0.9485

Logarithmic: 0.9736

Quadratic: 0.9814 (Best)

Exponential: 0.9274

Power: 0.9720

(e) Quadratic model is best.

36. Answers will vary.

37. True

38. False. Write b as $b = e^{\ln b}$. Then,
$y = ab^x = ae^{(\ln b)x} = ae^{cx}$.

39. $2x + 5y = 10$

$$5y = -2x + 10$$

$$y = -\frac{2}{5}x + 2$$

Slope: $-\frac{2}{5}$

y-intercept: $(0, 2)$

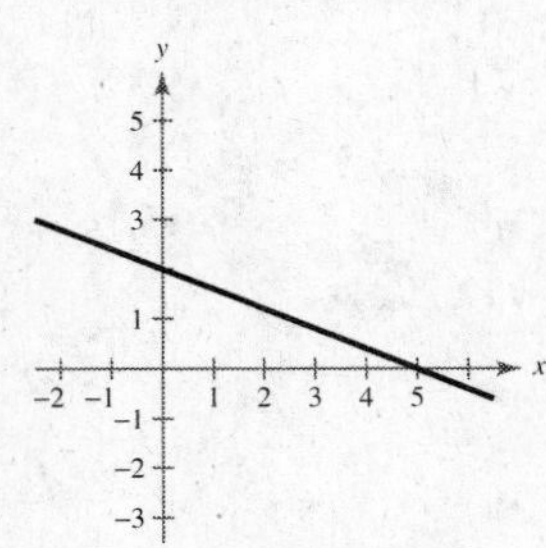

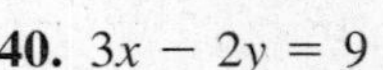
40. $3x - 2y = 9$

$$y = \frac{3}{2}x - \frac{9}{2}$$

Slope: $\frac{3}{2}$

y-intercept: $\left(0, -\frac{9}{2}\right)$

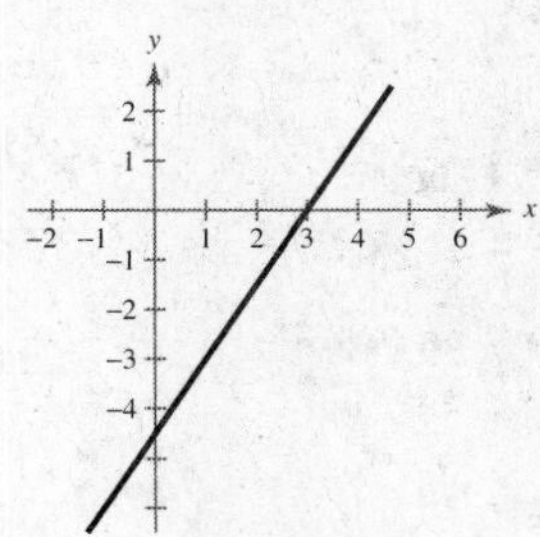

41. $1.2x + 3.5y = 10.5$

$$35y = -12x + 105$$
$$y = -\frac{12}{35}x + \frac{105}{35}$$
$$= -\frac{12}{35}x + 3$$

Slope: $-\frac{12}{35}$

y-intercept: $(0, 3)$

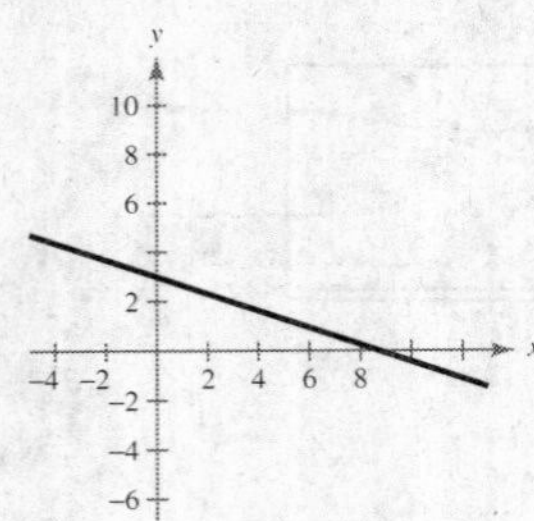

42. $0.4x - 2.5y = 12.0$

$$25y = 4x - 120$$
$$y = \frac{4}{25}x - \frac{24}{5}$$

Slope: $\frac{4}{25} = 0.16$

y-intercept: $\left(0, -\frac{24}{5}\right) = (0, -4.8)$

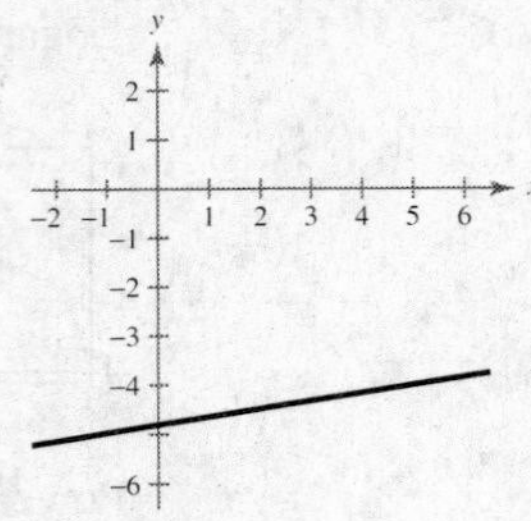

Review Exercises for Chapter 3

1. $(1.45)^{2\pi} \approx 10.3254$

2. $7^{-\sqrt{11}} \approx 0.002$

3. $60^{2(-1.1)} = 60^{-2.2}$
$\approx 0.0001225 \approx 0.0$

4. $25^{-3(3/2)} \approx 5.12 \times 10^{-7} \approx 0$

5. $e^8 \approx 2980.958$

6. $5e^{\sqrt{5}} \approx 46.7823$

7. $e^{-(-2.1)} \approx e^{2.1} \approx 8.1662$

8. $-4e^{(-3/5)} \approx -2.1952$

9. $f(x) = 4^x$

Intercept: $(0, 1)$

Horizontal asymptote: x-axis

Increasing on: $(-\infty, \infty)$

Matches graph (c).

10. $f(x) = 4^{-x}$

Intercept: $(0,1)$

Horizontal asymptote: x-axis

Decreasing on: $(-\infty, \infty)$

Matches graph (d).

11. $f(x) = -4^x$

Intercept: $(0, -1)$

Horizontal asymptote: x-axis

Decreasing on: $(-\infty, \infty)$

Matches graph (b).

12. $f(x) = 4^x + 1$

Intercept: $(0, 2)$

Horizontal asymptote: $y = 1$

Increasing on: $(-\infty, \infty)$

Matches graph (a).

13. $f(x) = 6^x$

Intercept: $(0, 1)$

Horizontal asymptote: x-axis

Increasing on: $(-\infty, \infty)$

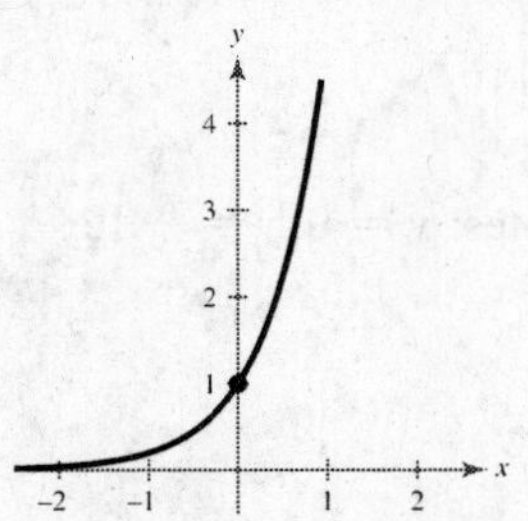

14. $f(x) = 0.3^{x+1} = \left(\frac{3}{10}\right)^{x+1}$

Horizontal asymptote: $y = 0$

Intercept: $(0, 0.3)$

Decreasing on $(-\infty, \infty)$

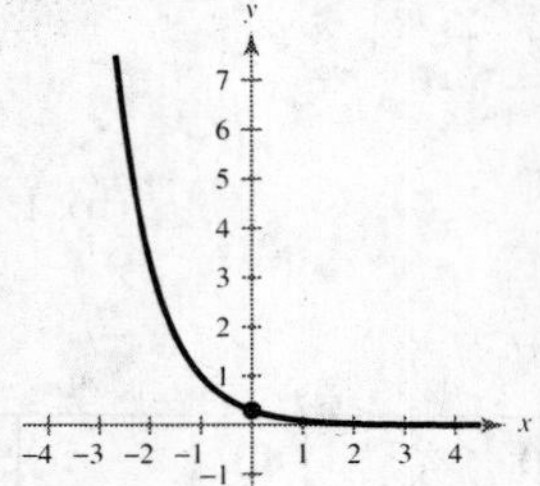

15. $g(x) = 1 + 6^{-x}$

Intercept: $(0, 2)$

Horizontal asymptote: $y = 1$

Decreasing on: $(-\infty, \infty)$

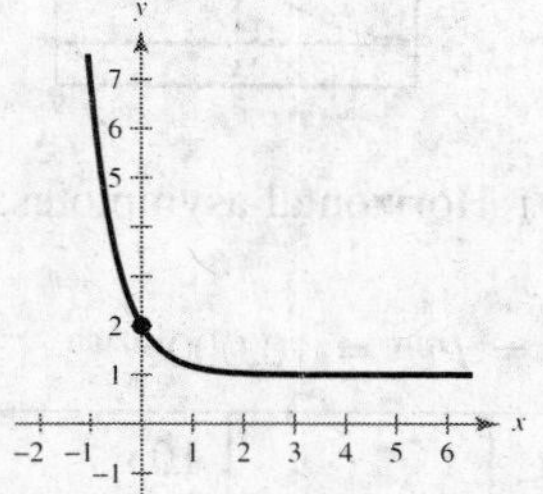

16. $g(x) = 0.3^{-x}$

x	-2	-1	0	1	2
y	0.09	0.3	1	$3\frac{1}{3}$	$11\frac{1}{9}$

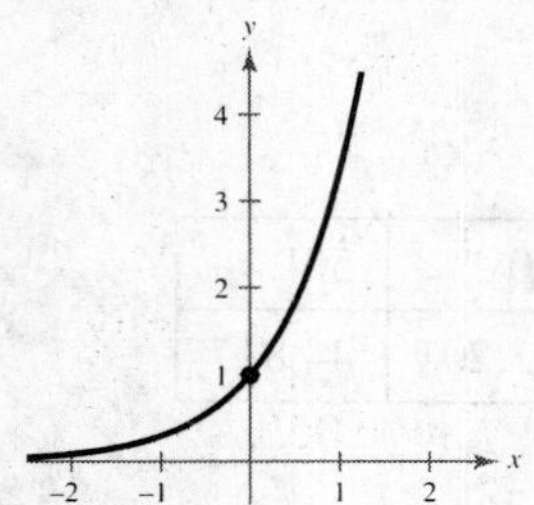

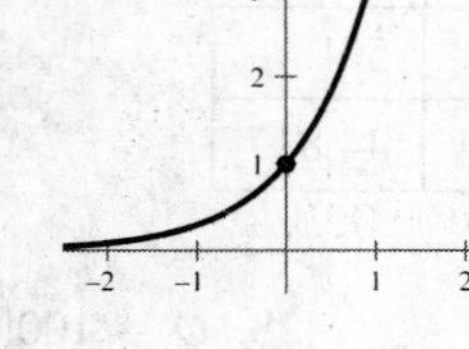

17.

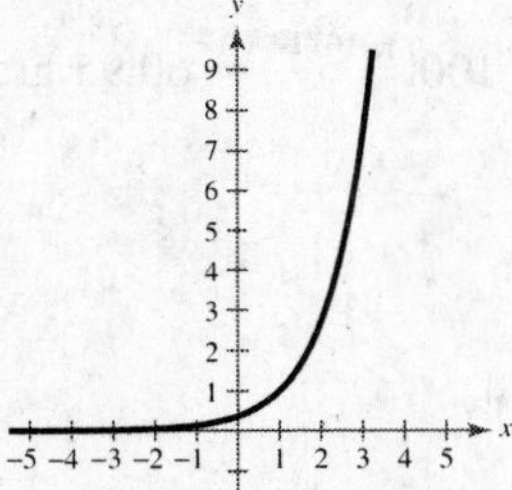

$h(x) = e^{x-1}$

Horizontal asymptote: $y = 0$

18.

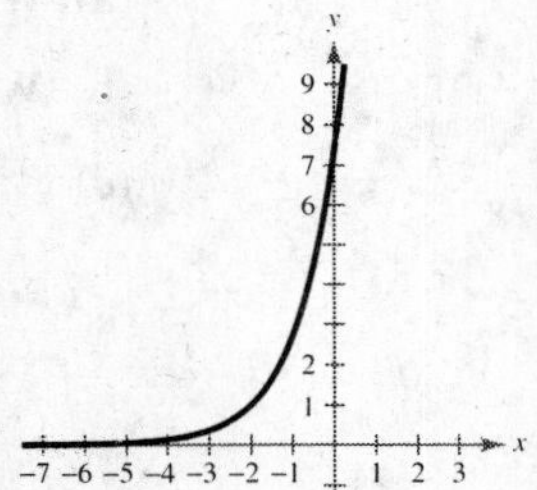

$f(x) = e^{x+2}$

Horizontal asymptote: $y = 0$

19.

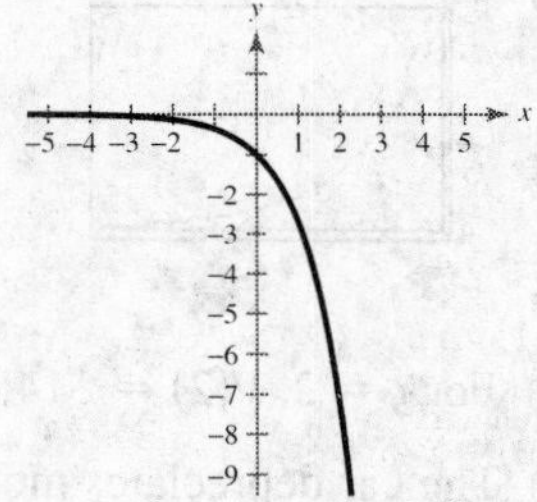

$h(x) = -e^x$

Horizontal asymptote: $y = 0$

20.

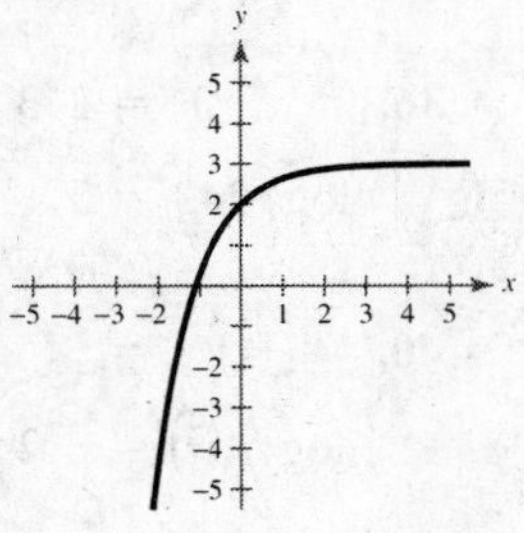

$f(x) = 3 - e^{-x}$

Horizontal asymptote: $y = 3$

21.

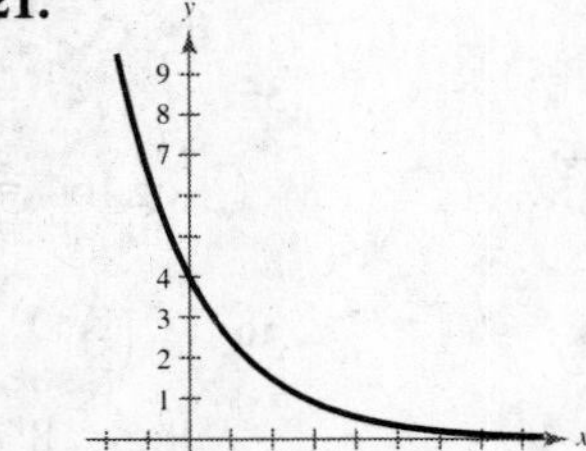

$f(x) = 4e^{-0.5x}$

Horizontal asymptote: $y = 0$

22.

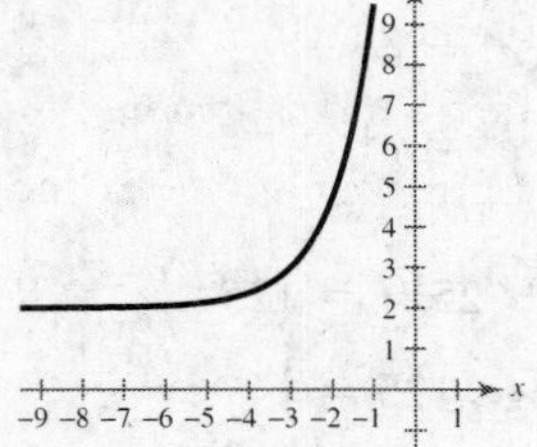

$f(x) = 2 + e^{x+3}$

Horizontal asymptote: $y = 2$

23. $f(x) = \dfrac{10}{1 + 2e^{-0.05x}}$

(a) 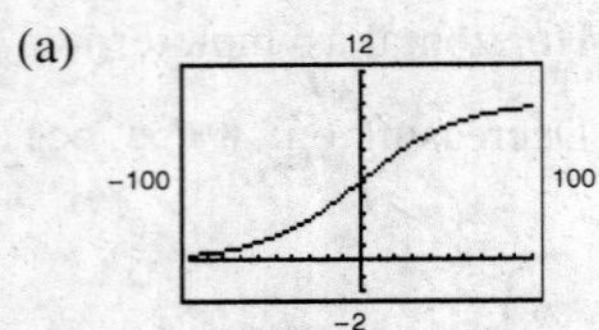

(b) Horizontal asymptotes: $y = 0, y = 10$

24. $f(x) = \dfrac{-12}{1 + 4^{-x}}$

(a) 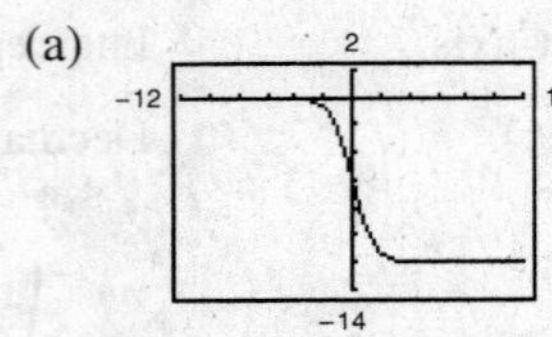

(b) Horizontal asymptotes: $y = 0, y = -12$

25. $A = Pe^{rt} = 10{,}000e^{0.08t}$

t	1	10	20	30	40	50
A	10,832.87	22,255.41	49,530.32	110,231.76	245,325.30	545,981.50

26. $r = 3\% = 0.03, A = 10{,}000e^{0.03t}$

t	1	10	20	30	40	50
A	10,305	13,499	18,221	24,596	33,201	44,817

27. $V(t) = 26{,}000\left(\frac{3}{4}\right)^t$

(a) 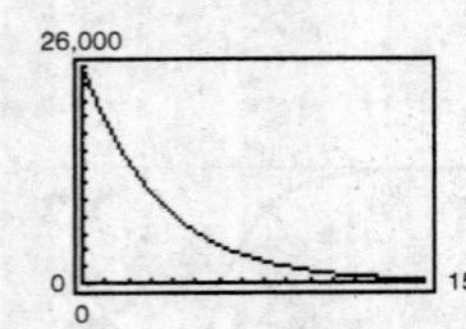

(b) For $t = 2$, $V(2) = \$14{,}625$.

(c) The car depreciates most rapidly at the beginning, which is realistic.

28. $Q = 100\left(\frac{1}{2}\right)^{t/14}$

(a) When $t = 0$, $Q = 100$ grams.

(b) When $t = 10$, $Q = 100\left(\frac{1}{2}\right)^{10/14} \approx 60.95$ grams.

(c) 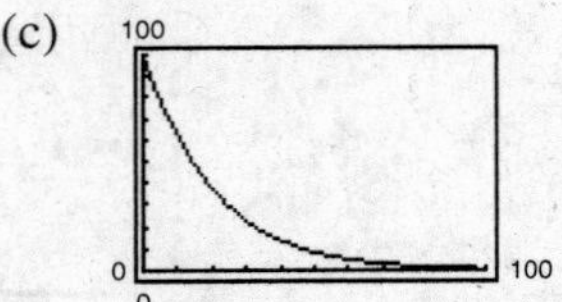

29. $\log_5 125 = 3$

$5^3 = 125$

30. $\log_6 36 = 2$

$6^2 = 36$

31. $\log_{64} 2 = \frac{1}{6}$

$64^{1/6} = 2$

32. $\log_{10}\left(\frac{1}{100}\right) = -2$

$10^{-2} = \frac{1}{100}$

33. $\ln e^4 = 4$

$e^4 = e^4$

34. $\ln\sqrt{e^3} = \frac{3}{2}$

$e^{3/2} = \sqrt{e^3}$

35. $4^3 = 64$

$\log_4 64 = 3$

36. $3^5 = 243$

$\log_3 243 = 5$

37. $25^{3/2} = 125$

$\log_{25} 125 = \frac{3}{2}$

38. $12^{-1} = \frac{1}{12}$

$\log_{12}\left(\frac{1}{12}\right) = -1$

39. $\left(\frac{1}{2}\right)^{-3} = 8$

$\log_{1/2} 8 = -3$

40. $\left(\frac{2}{3}\right)^{-2} = \frac{9}{4}$

$\log_{2/3}\left(\frac{9}{4}\right) = -2$

41. $e^7 = 1096.6331\ldots$

$\ln 1096.6331\ldots = 7$

42. $e^{-3} = 0.0497\ldots$

$\ln 0.0497\ldots = -3$

43. $\log_6 216 = \log_6 6^3$

$= 3\log_6 6$

$= 3$

44. $\log_7 1 = 0$

45. $\log_4\left(\frac{1}{4}\right) = \log_4(4^{-1})$
$= -\log_4 4$
$= -1$

46. $\log_{10} 0.001 = \log_{10} 10^{-3}$
$= -3$

47. $g(x) = -\log_2 x + 5 = 5 - \dfrac{\ln x}{\ln 2}$

Domain: $x > 0$
Vertical asymptote: $x = 0$
x-intercept: $(32, 0)$

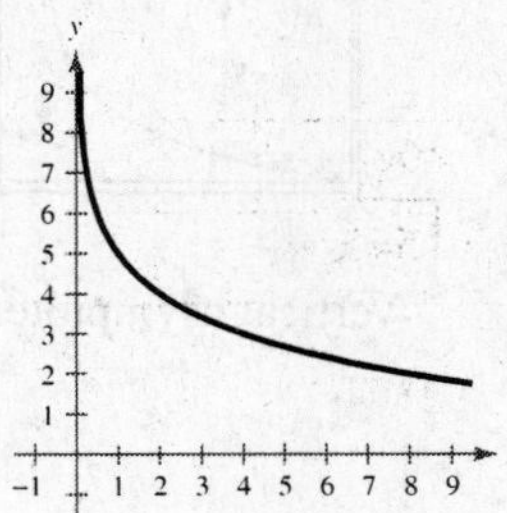

48. $g(x) = \log_5(x - 3)$

Vertical asymptote: $x = 3$
Intercept: $(4, 0)$
Domain: $x > 3$

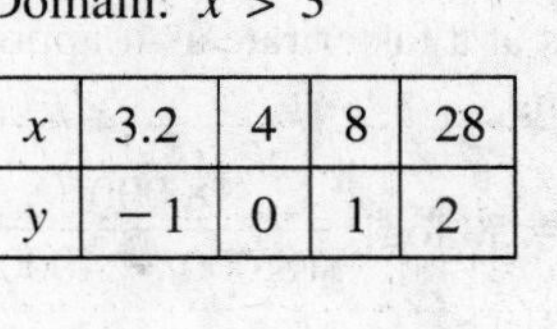

x	3.2	4	8	28
y	-1	0	1	2

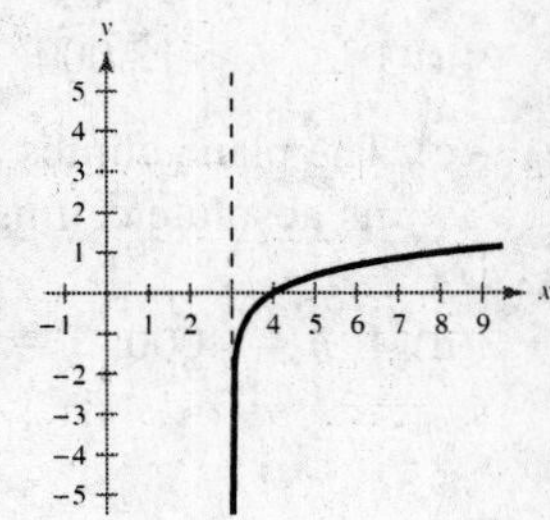

49. $f(x) = \log_2(x - 1) + 6 = 6 + \dfrac{\ln(x - 1)}{\ln(2)}$

Domain: $x > 1$
Vertical asymptote: $x = 1$
x-intercept: $(1.016, 0)$

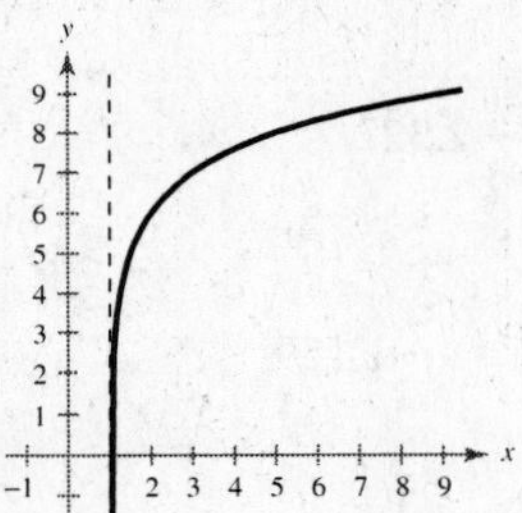

50. $f(x) = \log_5(x + 2) - 3$

Vertical asymptote: $x = -2$
Intercept: $(123, 0)$
Domain: $x > -2$

x	-1.8	-1	3	23
y	-4	-3	-2	-1

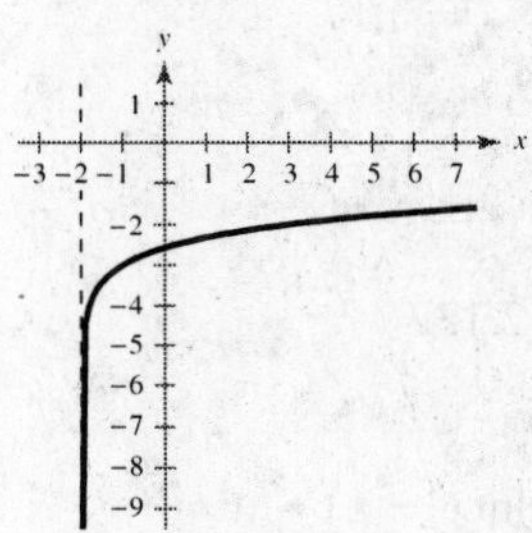

51. $\ln(21.5) \approx 3.068$

52. $\ln(0.98) \approx -0.020$

53. $\ln\sqrt{6} \approx 0.896$

54. $\ln\left(\frac{2}{5}\right) \approx -0.916$

55. $\log_5 3 = \log_5 x$
$3 = x$

56. $\log_2 8 = x$
$2^x = 8$
$x = 3$

57. $\log_9 x = \log_9 3^{-2}$
$x = 3^{-2} = \frac{1}{9}$

58. $\log_4 4^3 = x$
$4^x = 4^3$
$x = 3$

59. $f(x) = \ln x + 3$

Domain: $(0, \infty)$
Vertical asymptote: $x = 0$
x-intercept: $(0.05, 0)$

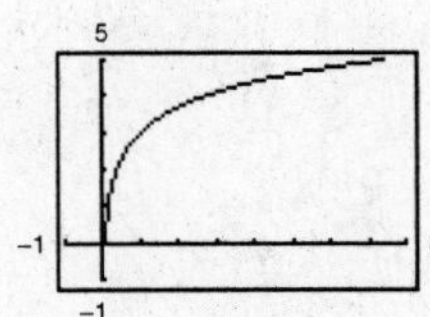

60. $f(x) = \ln(x - 3)$

Domain: $(3, \infty)$
Vertical asymptote: $x = 3$
Intercept: $(4, 0)$

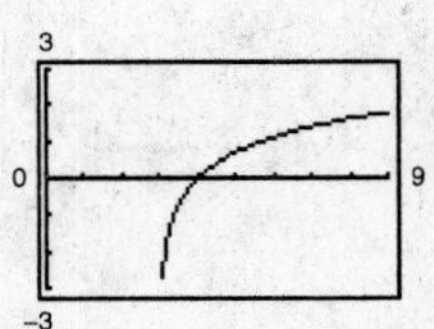

61. $h(x) = \frac{1}{2} \ln x$

Domain: $x > 0$

Vertical asymptote: $x = 0$

x-intercept: $(1, 0)$

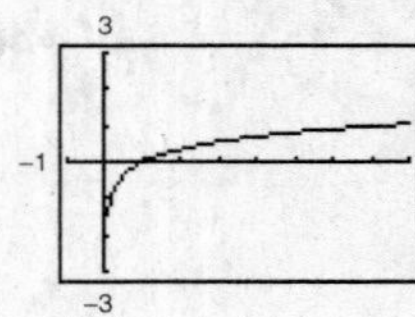

62. $f(x) = \frac{1}{4} \ln x$

Domain: $(0, \infty)$

Vertical asymptote: $x = 0$

Intercept: $(1, 0)$

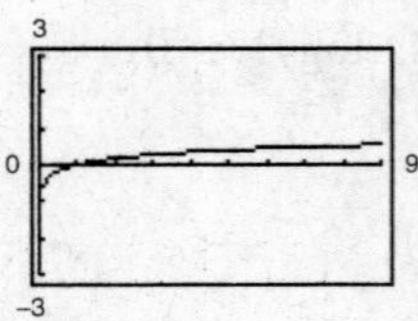

63. $t = 50 \log_{10} \dfrac{18{,}000}{18{,}000 - h}$

(a) $0 \le h < 18{,}000$

(b)

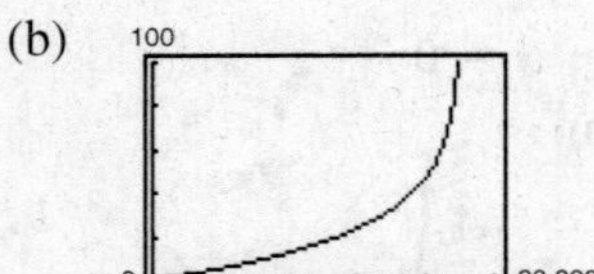

Vertical asymptote: $h = 18{,}000$

(c) The plane climbs at a faster rate as it approaches its absolute ceiling.

(d) If $h = 4000$, $t = 50 \log_{10} \dfrac{18{,}000}{18{,}000 - 4000} \approx 5.46$ minutes.

64. $t = 12.542 \ln\left(\dfrac{x}{x - 1000}\right)$, $x > 1000$

(a) For $x = 1254.68$, $t \approx 20$ years.

(b) For $x = 1254.68$, $t = 20$, the total amount paid is $(1254.68)(20)(12) = \$301{,}123.20$.

The interest is $301{,}123.20 - 150{,}000.00 = \$151{,}123.20$.

65. $\log_4 9 = \dfrac{\log_{10} 9}{\log_{10} 4} \approx 1.585$

$\log_4 9 = \dfrac{\ln 9}{\ln 4} \approx 1.585$

66. $\log_{1/2} 5 = \dfrac{\log_{10} 5}{\log_{10}(1/2)} \approx -2.322$

$\log_{1/2} 5 = \dfrac{\ln 5}{\ln(1/2)} \approx -2.322$

67. $\log_{12} 200 = \dfrac{\log_{10} 200}{\log_{10} 12} \approx 2.132$

$\log_{12} 200 = \dfrac{\ln 200}{\ln 12} \approx 2.132$

68. $\log_3 0.28 = \dfrac{\log_{10} 0.28}{\log_{10} 3} \approx -1.159$

$\log_3 0.28 = \dfrac{\ln 0.28}{\ln 3} \approx -1.159$

69. $f(x) = \log_2(x - 1) = \dfrac{\ln(x - 1)}{\ln 2}$

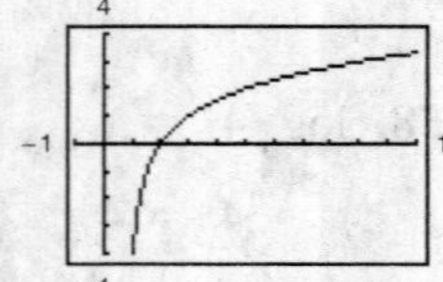

70. $f(x) = 2 - \log_3 x = 2 - \dfrac{\ln x}{\ln 3}$

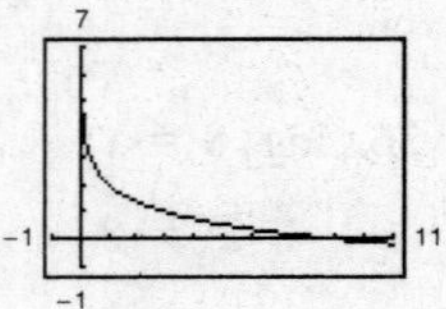

71. $f(x) = -\log_{1/2}(x+2) = -\dfrac{\ln(x+2)}{\ln(1/2)} = \dfrac{\ln(x+2)}{\ln 2}$

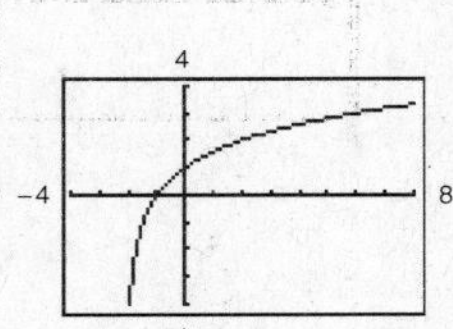

72. $f(x) = \log_{1/3}(x-1) + 1$

$= \dfrac{\ln(x-1)}{\ln(1/3)} + 1 = -\dfrac{\ln(x-1)}{\ln 3} + 1$

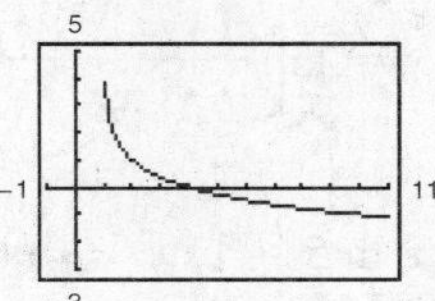

73. $\log_b 9 = \log_b 3^2$
$= 2\log_b 3$
$= 2(0.5646)$
$= 1.1292$

74. $\log_b\left(\frac{4}{9}\right) = \log_b 2^2 - \log_b 3^2$
$= 2\log_b 2 - 2\log_b 3$
$= 2(0.3562) - 2(0.5646)$
$= -0.4168$

75. $\log_b \sqrt{5} = \log_b 5^{1/2}$
$= \frac{1}{2}\log_b 5$
$= \frac{1}{2}(0.8271)$
$= 0.41355$

76. $\log_b 50 = \log_b[2 \cdot 5^2]$
$= \log_b 2 + 2\log_b 5$
$= 0.3562 + 2(0.8271)$
$= 2.0104$

77. $\ln(5e^{-2}) = \ln 5 + \ln e^{-2}$
$= \ln 5 - 2\ln e$
$= \ln 5 - 2$

78. $\ln\sqrt{e^5} = \ln e^{5/2}$
$= \frac{5}{2}\ln e = \frac{5}{2}$

79. $\log_{10} 200 = \log_{10}(2 \cdot 100)$
$= \log_{10} 2 + \log_{10} 10^2$
$= \log_{10} 2 + 2$

80. $\log_{10} 0.002 = \log_{10}(2 \cdot 10^{-3})$
$= \log_{10} 2 + \log_{10} 10^{-3}$
$= \log_{10} 2 - 3$

81. $\log_5 5x^2 = \log_5 5 + \log_5 x^2 = 1 + 2\log_5 x$

82. $\log_4(3xy^2) = \log_4 3 + \log_4 x + 2\log_4 y$

83. $\log_{10}\dfrac{5\sqrt{y}}{x^2} = \log_{10} 5\sqrt{y} - \log_{10} x^2$
$= \log_{10} 5 + \log_{10}\sqrt{y} - \log_{10} x^2$
$= \log_{10} 5 + \dfrac{1}{2}\log_{10} y - 2\log_{10} x$

84. $\ln\dfrac{\sqrt{x}}{4} = \ln x^{1/2} - \ln 4 = \dfrac{1}{2}\ln x - \ln 4$
$= \dfrac{1}{2}\ln x - 2\ln 2$

85. $\ln\left(\dfrac{x+3}{xy}\right) = \ln(x+3) - \ln(xy)$
$= \ln(x+3) - \ln x - \ln y$

86. $\ln\dfrac{xy^5}{\sqrt{z}} = \ln x + \ln y^5 - \ln z^{1/2}$
$= \ln x + 5\ln y - \dfrac{1}{2}\ln z$

87. $\log_2 5 + \log_2 x = \log_2 5x$

88. $\log_6 y - 2\log_6 z = \log_6 y - \log_6 z^2$
$= \log_6 \dfrac{y}{z^2}$

89. $\dfrac{1}{2}\ln(2x-1) - 2\ln(x+1) = \ln\sqrt{2x-1} - \ln(x+1)^2$
$= \ln\dfrac{\sqrt{2x-1}}{(x+1)^2}$

90. $5\ln(x-2) - \ln(x+2) - 3\ln(x) = \ln(x-2)^5 - \ln(x+2) - \ln(x)^3$

$$= \ln\left(\frac{(x-2)^5}{(x+2)x^3}\right)$$

91. $\ln 3 + \frac{1}{3}\ln(4-x^2) - \ln x = \ln\left[\frac{3(4-x^2)^{1/3}}{x}\right] = \ln\left[\frac{3\sqrt[3]{4-x^2}}{x}\right]$

92. $3[\ln x - 2\ln(x^2+1)] + 2\ln 5 = \ln x^3 - \ln(x^2+1)^6 + \ln 5^2$

$$= \ln \frac{25x^3}{(x^2+1)^6}$$

93. $s = 25 - \dfrac{13\ln(h/12)}{\ln 3}$

(a)

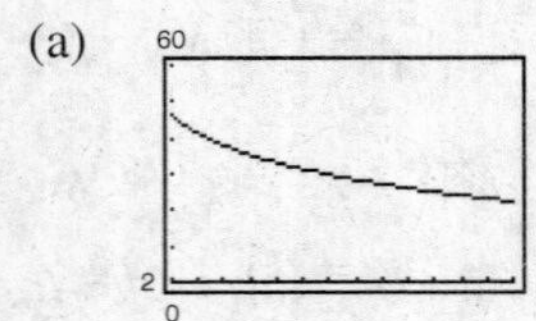

(b)

h	4	6	8	10	12	14
s	38	33.2	29.8	27.2	25	23.2

(c) As the depth increases, the number of miles of roads cleared decreases.

94.
$$f(t) = 85 - 14\log_{10}(t+1)$$
$$71 = 85 - 14\log_{10}(t+1)$$
$$\log_{10}(t+1) = 1$$
$$t = 9 \text{ months}$$

95. $8^x = 512 = 8^3 \implies x = 3$

96. $3^x = 729 = 3^6 \implies x = 6$

97. $6^x = \frac{1}{216} = \frac{1}{6^3} = 6^{-3} \implies x = -3$

98. $6^{x-2} = 1296 = 6^4 \implies x - 2 = 4 \implies x = 6$

99.
$$2^{x+1} = \frac{1}{16}$$
$$2^{x+1} = 2^{-4}$$
$$x + 1 = -4$$
$$x = -5$$

100.
$$4^{x/2} = 64$$
$$4^{x/2} = 4^3$$
$$\frac{x}{2} = 3$$
$$x = 6$$

101. $\log_7 x = 4 \implies x = 7^4 = 2401$

102. $\log_x 243 = 5 \implies x^5 = 243 = 3^5 \implies x = 3$

103.
$$\log_2(x-1) = 3$$
$$2^3 = x - 1$$
$$x = 9$$

104.
$$\log_5(2x+1) = 2$$
$$5^2 = 2x + 1$$
$$2x = 24$$
$$x = 12$$

105.
$$\ln x = 4$$
$$x = e^4 \approx 54.598$$

106. $\ln x = -3$

$x = e^{-3} \approx 0.0498$

107. $\ln(x - 1) = 2$

$e^2 = x - 1$

$x = 1 + e^2$

108. $\ln(2x + 1) = -4$

$e^{-4} = 2x + 1$

$x = \dfrac{e^{-4} - 1}{2}$

$= \dfrac{1 - e^4}{2e^4}$

109. $3e^{-5x} = 132$

$e^{-5x} = 44$

$-5x = \ln 44$

$x = -\dfrac{\ln 44}{5} \approx -0.757$

110. $14e^{3x+2} = 560$

$e^{3x+2} = 40$

$\ln e^{3x+2} = \ln 40$

$3x + 2 = \ln 40$

$x = \dfrac{(\ln 40) - 2}{3} \approx 0.563$

111. $2^x + 13 = 35$

$2^x = 22$

$x \ln 2 = \ln 22$

$x = \dfrac{\ln 22}{\ln 2} \approx 4.459$

112. $6^x - 28 = -8$

$6^x = 20$

$x \ln 6 = \ln 20$

$x = \dfrac{\ln 20}{\ln 6} \approx 1.672$

113. $-4(5^x) = -68$

$5^x = 17$

$x \ln 5 = \ln 17$

$x = \dfrac{\ln 17}{\ln 5} \approx 1.760$

114. $2(12^x) = 190$

$12^x = 95$

$x \ln 12 = \ln 95$

$x = \dfrac{\ln 95}{\ln 12} \approx 1.833$

115. $2e^{x-3} - 1 = 4$

$2e^{x-3} = 5$

$e^{x-3} = \dfrac{5}{2}$

$x - 3 = \ln\left(\dfrac{5}{2}\right)$

$x = 3 + \ln\left(\dfrac{5}{2}\right) \approx 3.916$

116. $-e^{x/2} + 1 = \dfrac{1}{2}$

$e^{x/2} = \dfrac{1}{2}$

$\dfrac{x}{2} = \ln\left(\dfrac{1}{2}\right) = -\ln 2$

$x = -2 \ln 2$

$= -\ln 4 \approx -1.386$

117. $e^{2x} - 7e^x + 10 = 0$

$(e^x - 5)(e^x - 2) = 0$

$e^x = 5 \Rightarrow x = \ln 5 \approx 1.609$

$e^x = 2 \Rightarrow x = \ln 2 \approx 0.693$

118. $e^{2x} - 6e^x + 8 = 0$

$(e^x - 4)(e^x - 2) = 0$

$e^x = 4$ or $e^x = 2$

$x = \ln 4$ or $x = \ln 2$

$x \approx 1.386$ $\quad x \approx 0.693$

119. $\ln 3x = 8.2$

$3x = e^{8.2}$

$x = \dfrac{e^{8.2}}{3} \approx 1213.650$

120. $\ln 5x = 7.2$

$5x = e^{7.2}$

$x = \dfrac{1}{5}e^{7.2} \approx 267.886$

121. $\ln x - \ln 3 = 2$

$\ln \dfrac{x}{3} = 2$

$\dfrac{x}{3} = e^2$

$x = 3e^2 \approx 22.167$

122. $\ln x - \ln 5 = 4$

$\ln\left(\dfrac{x}{5}\right) = 4$

$e^4 = \dfrac{x}{5}$

$x = 5e^4 \approx 272.991$

123. $\ln\sqrt{x + 1} = 2$

$\dfrac{1}{2}\ln(x + 1) = 2$

$\ln(x + 1) = 4$

$x + 1 = e^4$

$x = e^4 - 1$

≈ 53.598

124. $\ln\sqrt{x+8} = 3$

$\frac{1}{2}\ln(x+8) = 3$

$\ln(x+8) = 6$

$x + 8 = e^6$

$x = e^6 - 8 \approx 395.429$

125. $\log_4(x-1) = \log_4(x-2) - \log_4(x+2)$

$\log_4(x-1) = \log_4\left(\frac{x-2}{x+2}\right)$

$x - 1 = \frac{x-2}{x+2}$

$(x-1)(x+2) = x - 2$

$x^2 + x - 2 = x - 2$

$x^2 = 0$

$x = 0$ (extraneous)

No solution

126. $\log_5(x+2) - \log_5(x) = \log_5(x+5)$

$\log_5\left(\frac{x+2}{x}\right) = \log_5(x+5)$

$\frac{x+2}{x} = x + 5$

$x + 2 = x^2 + 5x$

$x^2 + 4x - 2 = 0$

$x = \frac{-4 \pm \sqrt{16 - 4(-2)}}{2} = -2 \pm \sqrt{6}$

$x = -2 + \sqrt{6} \approx 0.449$

(Other zero is extraneous.)

127. $\log_{10}(1-x) = -1$

$10^{-1} = 1 - x$

$x = 1 - 10^{-1} = 0.9$

128. $\log_{10}(-x-4) = 2$

$-x - 4 = 10^2 = 100$

$-x = 104$

$x = -104$

129. $xe^x + e^x = 0$

$(x+1)e^x = 0$

$x + 1 = 0$ (since $e^x \neq 0$)

$x = -1$

130. $2xe^{2x} + e^{2x} = 0$

$(2x+1)e^{2x} = 0$

$2x + 1 = 0$ (since $e^{2x} \neq 0$)

$x = -\frac{1}{2}$

131. $x \ln x + x = 0$

$x(\ln x + 1) = 0$

$\ln x + 1 = 0$ (since $x > 0$)

$\ln x = -1$

$x = e^{-1} = \frac{1}{e} \approx 0.368$

132. $\frac{1 - \ln x}{x^2} = 0$

$1 - \ln x = 0$ (since $x > 0$)

$\ln x = 1$

$x = e \approx 2.718$

133. $3(7550) = 7550e^{0.0725t}$

$3 = e^{0.0725t}$

$\ln 3 = 0.0725t$

$t = \frac{\ln 3}{0.0725} \approx 15.2$ years

134. $p = 500 - 0.5e^{0.004x}$

(a)
$$p = 450$$
$$450 = 500 - 0.5e^{0.004x}$$
$$0.5e^{0.004x} = 50$$
$$e^{0.004x} = 100$$
$$0.004x = \ln 100$$
$$x \approx 1151 \text{ units}$$

(b)
$$p = 400$$
$$400 = 500 - 0.5e^{0.004x}$$
$$0.5e^{0.004x} = 100$$
$$e^{0.004x} = 200$$
$$0.004x = \ln 200$$
$$x \approx 1325 \text{ units}$$

135. $y = 3e^{-2x/3}$

Decreasing exponential

Matches graph (e).

136. $y = 4e^{2x/3}$

Intercept: $(0, 4)$

Increasing

Matches (b).

137. $y = \ln(x + 3)$

Logarithmic function shifted to left

Matches graph (f).

138. $y = 7 - \log(x + 3)$

Vertical asymptote: $x = -3$

Decreasing

Matches (d).

139. $y = 2e^{-(x+4)^2/3}$

Gaussian model

Matches graph (a).

140. $y = \dfrac{6}{1 + 2e^{-2x}}$

Logistic model

Matches (c).

141.
$$y = ae^{bx}$$
$$2 = ae^{b(0)} \implies a = 2$$
$$3 = 2e^{b(4)}$$
$$1.5 = e^{4b}$$
$$\ln 1.5 = 4b \implies b \approx 0.1014$$

Thus, $y = 2e^{0.1014x}$.

142. $y = ae^{bx}$

$2 = ae^{b(0)} \implies a = 2$

$1 = 2e^{b(5)} \implies \frac{1}{2} = e^{5b} \implies 5b = \ln\frac{1}{2} \implies b = \frac{1}{5}\ln\frac{1}{2} = -\frac{1}{5}\ln 2 \approx -0.1386$

$y = 2e^{-0.1386x}$

143.
$$y = ae^{bx}$$
$$\frac{1}{2} = ae^{b(0)} \implies a = \frac{1}{2}$$
$$5 = \frac{1}{2}e^{b(5)}$$
$$10 = e^{5b}$$
$$\ln 10 = 5b \implies b \approx 0.4605$$

Thus, $y = \frac{1}{2}e^{0.4605x}$.

144.
$$y = ae^{bx}$$
$$4 = ae^{b(0)} = a \implies a = 4$$
$$\frac{1}{2} = 4e^{b(5)}$$
$$\frac{1}{8} = e^{5b}$$
$$\ln\frac{1}{8} = 5b \implies b = -\frac{\ln 8}{5} \approx -0.4159$$
$$\implies y = 4e^{-0.4159x}$$

145. $P = 361e^{kt}$

$t = 0$ corresponds to 2000.

$(-20, 215)$:

$$215 = 361e^{k(-20)}$$

$$\frac{215}{361} = e^{-20k}$$

$$-20k = \ln\left(\frac{215}{361}\right)$$

$$k = -\frac{1}{20}\ln\left(\frac{215}{361}\right) = \frac{1}{20}\ln\left(\frac{361}{215}\right) \approx 0.02591$$

$$P = 361e^{0.02591t}$$

For 2020, $P(20) = 361e^{0.02591(20)} \approx 606.1$ or 606,100 population in 2020.

146. $\frac{1}{2}P = Pe^{k(245,500)}$

$$\ln\left(\frac{1}{2}\right) = 245,500k \implies k = \frac{-\ln 2}{245,500} \approx -2.8234 \times 10^{-6}$$

After 5000 years,

$A = e^{k(5000)} \approx 0.98598$ or 98.6% remains.

147. (a) $20,000 = 10,000e^{r(12)}$

$$2 = e^{12r}$$

$$\ln 2 = 12r$$

$$r = \frac{\ln 2}{12} \approx 0.0578 \text{ or } 5.78\%$$

(b) $10,000e^{0.0578(1)} \approx \$10,595.03$

148. (a)

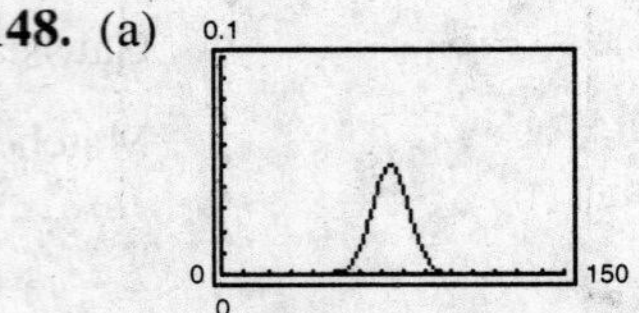

$y = 0.0499e^{-(x-74)^2/128}$

(b) The average score corresponds to the maximum, 74.

149. (a)

$$50 = \frac{158}{1 + 5.4e^{-0.12t}}$$

$$1 + 5.4e^{-0.12t} = \frac{158}{50}$$

$$5.4e^{-0.12t} = \frac{108}{50}$$

$$e^{-0.12t} = \frac{108}{50(5.4)}$$

$$-0.12t = \ln\frac{108}{270}$$

$$t = \frac{\ln(108/270)}{-0.12} \approx 7.6 \text{ weeks}$$

(b) Similarly:

$$75 = \frac{158}{1 + 5.4e^{-0.12t}}$$

$$1 + 5.4e^{-0.12t} = \frac{158}{75}$$

$$e^{-0.12t} = 0.20494$$

$$-0.12t = \ln(0.20494)$$

$$t \approx 13.2 \text{ weeks}$$

150. $R = \log_{10}\left(\frac{I}{I_0}\right) = \log_{10}(I) \implies I = 10^R$

(a) $I = 10^{8.4} \approx 251,188,643$

(b) $I = 10^{6.85} \approx 7,079,458$

(c) $I = 10^{9.1} \approx 1,258,925,412$

151. Logistic model

152. Linear model

153. Logarithmic model

154. Quadratic model (or exponential)

155. (a) Linear model: $y = 297.8t + 739$; 0.97653

Quadratic model: $y = 11.79t^2 + 38.5t + 2118$; 0.98112

Exponential model: $y = 1751.5(1.077)^t$; 0.98225

Logarithmic model: $y = 3169.8 \ln t - 3532$; 0.95779

Power model: $y = 598.1t^{0.7950}$; 0.97118

(b)

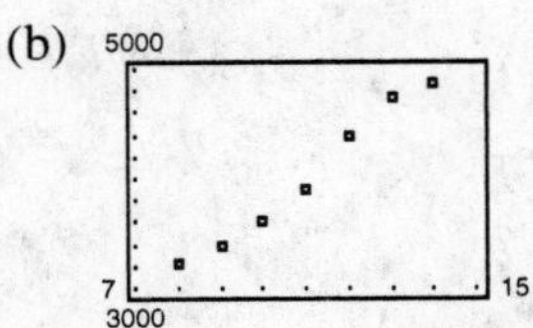

Linear model:

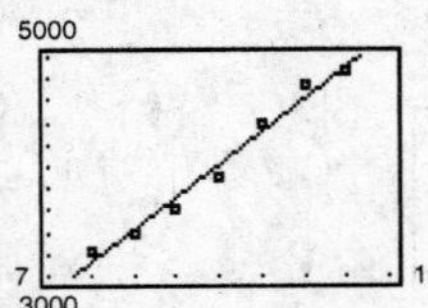

Quadratic model:

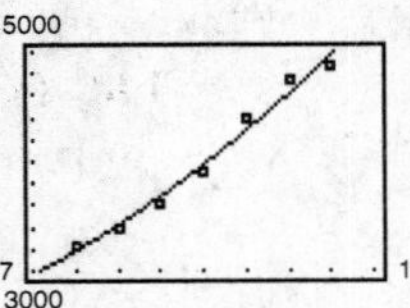

Exponential model:

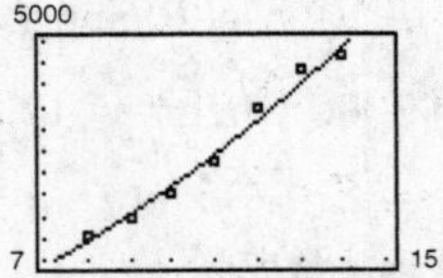

Logarithmic model:

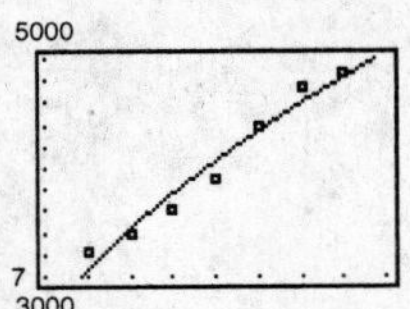

Power model:

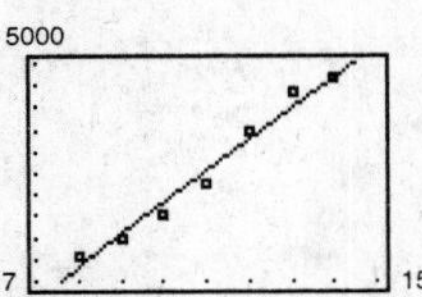

(c) The exponential model is best because its coefficient of determination is closest to 1. Answers will vary.

(d) For 2010, $t = 20$ and $y \approx \$7722$ million.

(e) $y = 5250$ when $t \approx 14.8$, or 2004.

156. (a) Linear model: $y = 82.9t + 1825$; 0.96953

Quadratic model: $y = -3.35t^2 + 133.2t + 1691$; 0.98982

Exponential model: $y = 1865(1.0354)^t$; 0.95481

Logarithmic model: $y = 1663 + 435.5 \ln t$; 0.91664

Power model: $y = 1733t^{0.1862}$; 0.93412

—CONTINUED—

156. —CONTINUED—

(b) Linear model:

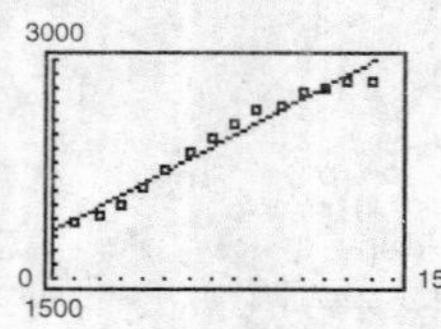

Quadratic model:

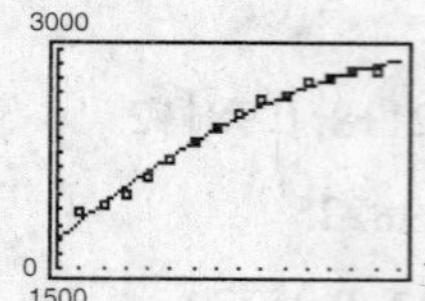

Exponential model:

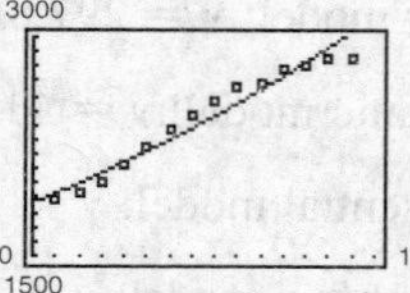

Logarithmic model:

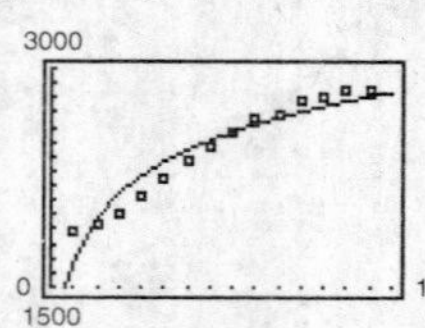

Power model:

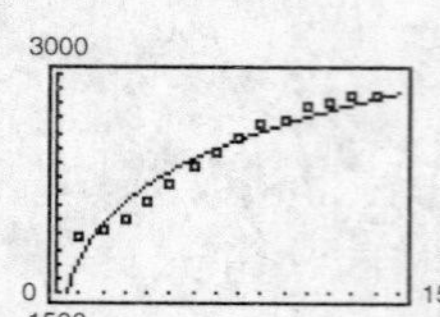

(c) The quadratic model is best because its coefficient of determination is closest to 1.

(d) For 2010, $t = 20$ and $y \approx 3015$ thousand.

(e) $y = 3000$ when $t \approx 17.8$, or 2007.

157. (a) $P = \dfrac{9999.887}{1 + 19.0e^{-0.2x}}$

(b)

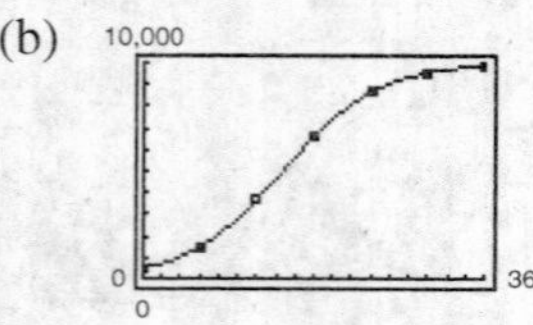

(c) The model is a good fit.

(d) The limiting size is $\dfrac{9999.887}{1 + 0} \approx 10{,}000$ fish.

158. $P = 56.8e^{0.001603t}$

(a)

Year	1990	1991	1992	1993	1994	1995
P	56.8	56.9	57	57.1	57.2	57.3

Year	1996	1997	1998	1999	2000	2001
P	57.3	57.4	57.5	57.6	57.7	57.8

Year	2002	2003	2004	2005
P	57.9	58.0	58.1	58.2

(b) $\text{Slope} = \dfrac{58.2 - 56.8}{15 - 0} \approx 0.09$

$y - 56.8 = 0.09(t - 0)$

$y = 0.09t + 56.8$, Linear model

(c) Slope is 0.09. The population increases by 90,000 people each year.

(d)

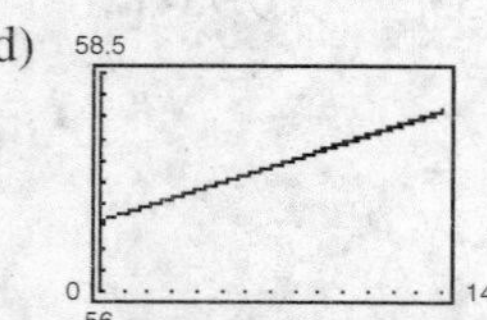

Answers will vary.

159. True; by the Inverse Properties, $\log_b b^{2x} = 2x$.

160. $e^{x-1} = e^x \cdot e^{-1} = \dfrac{e^x}{e}$

True (by Properties of exponents).

161. False; $\ln x + \ln y = \ln(xy) \neq \ln(x + y)$

162. $\ln(x + y) = \ln(x \cdot y)$

False

$\ln(x \cdot y) = \ln x + \ln y \neq \ln(x + y)$

163. False. The domain of $f(x) = \ln(x)$ is $x > 0$.

164. True. $\ln\left(\dfrac{x}{y}\right) = \ln x - \ln y$

165. Since $1 < \sqrt{2} < 2$, $2^1 < 2^{\sqrt{2}} < 2^2 \Rightarrow 2 < 2^{\sqrt{2}} < 4$.

166. (a)

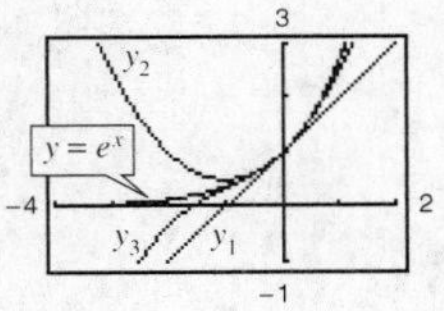

(b) Pattern $\displaystyle\sum_{i=0}^{n} \frac{x^i}{i!}$

$$y_4 = 1 + x + \frac{x^2}{2!} + \frac{x^3}{3!} + \frac{x^4}{4!}$$

The graph of y_4 closely approximates $y = e^x$ near $(0, 1)$.

Chapter 3 Practice Test

1. Solve for x: $x^{3/5} = 8$

2. Solve for x: $3^{x-1} = \frac{1}{81}$

3. Graph $f(x) = 2^{-x}$ by hand.

4. Graph $g(x) = e^x + 1$ by hand.

5. If \$5000 is invested at 9% interest, find the amount after three years if the interest is compounded
   (a) monthly. (b) quarterly. (c) continuously.

6. Write the equation in logarithmic form: $7^{-2} = \frac{1}{49}$

7. Solve for x: $x - 4 = \log_2 \frac{1}{64}$

8. Given $\log_b 2 = 0.3562$ and $\log_b 5 = 0.8271$, evaluate $\log_b \sqrt[4]{8/25}$.

9. Write $5 \ln x - \frac{1}{2} \ln y + 6 \ln z$ as a single logarithm.

10. Using your calculator and the change of base formula, evaluate $\log_9 28$.

11. Use your calculator to solve for N: $\log_{10} N = 0.6646$

12. Graph $y = \log_4 x$ by hand.

13. Determine the domain of $f(x) = \log_3(x^2 - 9)$.

14. Graph $y = \ln(x - 2)$ by hand.

15. True or false: $\dfrac{\ln x}{\ln y} = \ln(x - y)$

16. Solve for x: $5^x = 41$

17. Solve for x: $x - x^2 = \log_5 \frac{1}{25}$

18. Solve for x: $\log_2 x + \log_2(x - 3) = 2$

19. Solve for x: $\dfrac{e^x + e^{-x}}{3} = 4$

20. Six thousand dollars is deposited into a fund at an annual percentage rate of 13%. Find the time required for the investment to double if the interest is compounded continuously.

21. Use a graphing utility to find the points of intersection of the graphs of $y = \ln(3x)$ and $y = e^x - 4$.

22. Use a graphing utility to find the power model $y = ax^b$ for the data (1, 1), (2, 5), (3, 8), and (4, 17).

CHAPTER 4
Trigonometric Functions

Section 4.1 Radian and Degree Measure **272**

Section 4.2 Trigonometric Functions: The Unit Circle **281**

Section 4.3 Right Triangle Trigonometry **289**

Section 4.4 Trigonometric Functions of Any Angle **300**

Section 4.5 Graphs of Sine and Cosine Functions **317**

Section 4.6 Graphs of Other Trigonometric Functions **329**

Section 4.7 Inverse Trigonometric Functions **339**

Section 4.8 Applications and Models **350**

Review Exercises **360**

Practice Test **377**

CHAPTER 4
Trigonometric Functions

Section 4.1 Radian and Degree Measure

You should know the following basic facts about angles, their measurement, and their applications.

- Types of Angles:
  - (a) Acute: Measure between 0° and 90°.
  - (b) Right: Measure 90°.
  - (c) Obtuse: Measure between 90° and 180°.
  - (d) Straight: Measure 180°.
- α and β are complementary if $\alpha + \beta = 90°$. They are supplementary if $\alpha + \beta = 180°$.
- Two angles in standard position that have the same terminal side are called coterminal angles.
- To convert degrees to radians, use $1° = \pi/180$ radians.
- To convert radians to degrees, use 1 radian $= (180/\pi)°$.
- $1' =$ one minute $= 1/60$ of $1°$
- $1'' =$ one second $= 1/60$ of $1' = 1/3600$ of $1°$
- The length of a circular arc is $s = r\theta$ where θ is measured in radians.
- Speed $=$ distance/time
- Angular speed $= \theta/t = s/rt$

Vocabulary Check

1. Trigonometry **2.** angle **3.** standard position **4.** coterminal

5. radian **6.** complementary **7.** supplementary **8.** degree

9. linear **10.** angular

1. The angle shown is approximately 2 radians.

2. 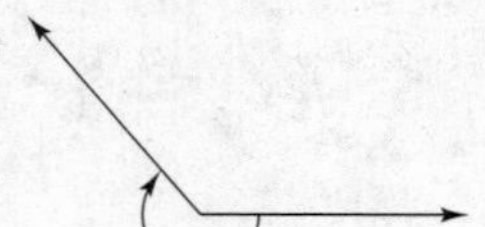

The angle shown is approximately -4 radians.

3. (a) Since $\frac{3\pi}{2} < \frac{7\pi}{4} < 2\pi$, $\frac{7\pi}{4}$ lies in Quadrant IV.

(b) Since $\frac{5\pi}{2} < \frac{11\pi}{4} < 3\pi$, $\frac{11\pi}{4}$ lies in Quadrant II.

4. (a) Since $-\frac{\pi}{2} < -\frac{5\pi}{12} < 0$, $\frac{5\pi}{2}$ lies in Quadrant IV.

(b) Since $-\frac{3\pi}{2} < -\frac{13\pi}{9} < -\pi$, $\frac{13\pi}{9}$ lies in Quadrant II.

5. (a) Since $-\frac{\pi}{2} < -1 < 0$; -1 lies in Quadrant IV.

(b) Since $-\pi < -2 < -\frac{\pi}{2}$; -2 lies in Quadrant III.

6. (a) Since $\pi < 3.5 < \frac{3\pi}{2}$, 3.5 lies in Quadrant III.

(b) Since $\frac{\pi}{2} < 2.25 < \pi$, 2.25 lies in Quadrant II.

7. (a) $\frac{13\pi}{4}$

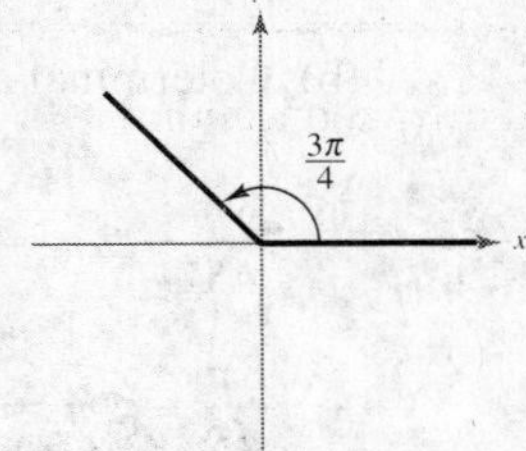

(b) $\frac{4\pi}{3}$

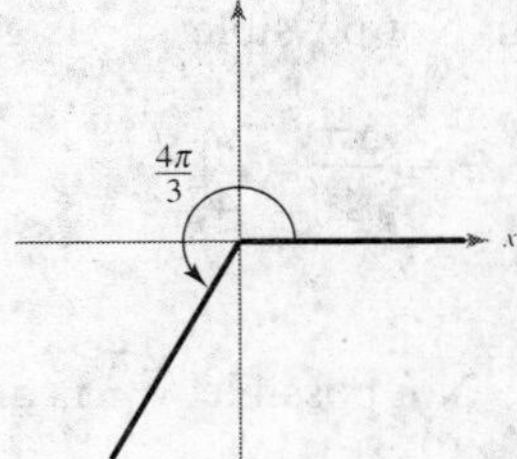

8. (a) $-\frac{7\pi}{4}$

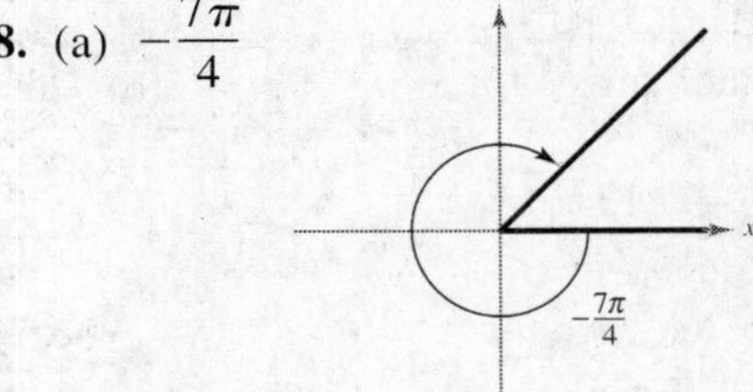

(b) $-\frac{5\pi}{2}$

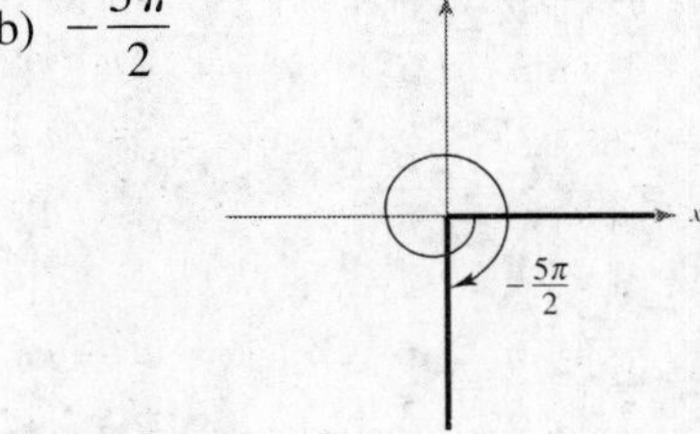

9. (a) $\frac{11\pi}{6}$

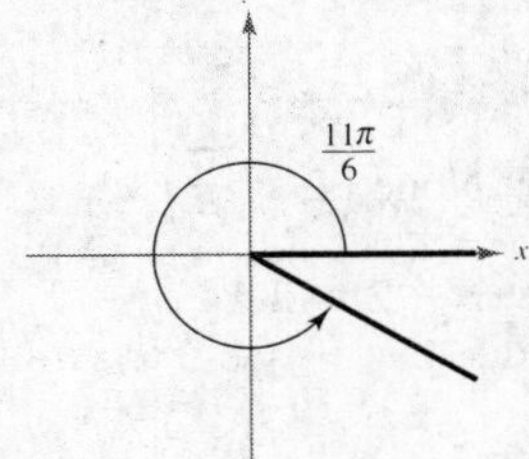

(b) $\frac{2\pi}{3}$

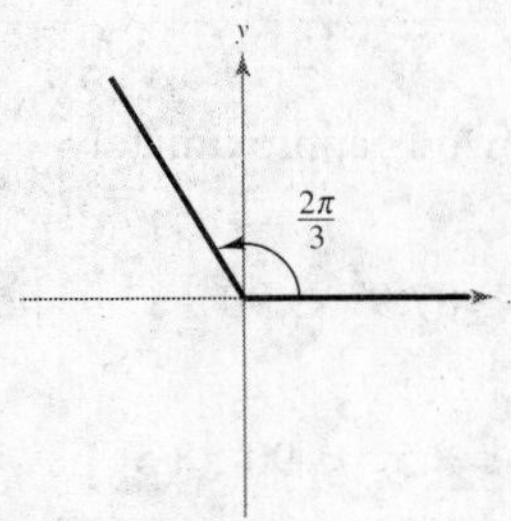

10. (a) 4

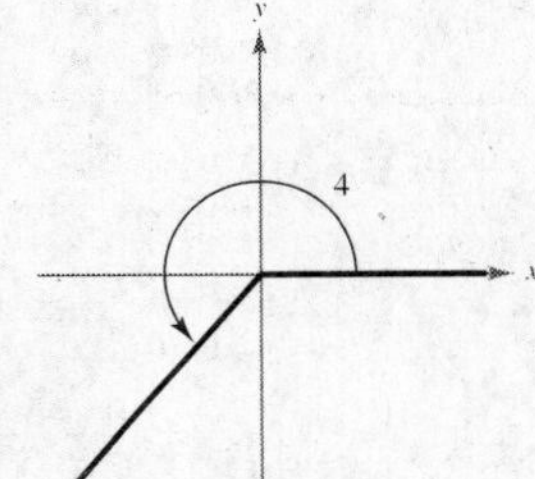

(b) -3

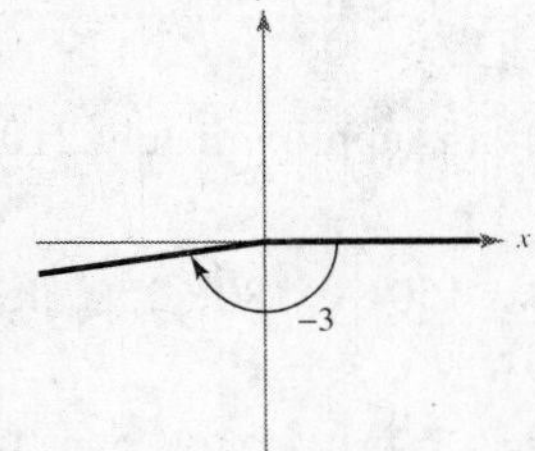

11. (a) Coterminal angles for $\frac{\pi}{6}$:

$$\frac{\pi}{6} + 2\pi = \frac{13\pi}{6}$$

$$\frac{\pi}{6} - 2\pi = -\frac{11\pi}{6}$$

(b) Coterminal angles for $\frac{2\pi}{3}$:

$$\frac{2\pi}{3} + 2\pi = \frac{8\pi}{3}$$

$$\frac{2\pi}{3} - 2\pi = -\frac{4\pi}{3}$$

12. (a) Coterminal angles for $\frac{7\pi}{6}$:

$\frac{7\pi}{6} + 2\pi = \frac{19\pi}{6}$

$\frac{7\pi}{6} - 2\pi = -\frac{5\pi}{6}$

(b) Coterminal angles for $\frac{5\pi}{4}$:

$\frac{5\pi}{4} + 2\pi = \frac{13\pi}{4}$

$\frac{5\pi}{4} - 2\pi = -\frac{3\pi}{4}$

13. (a) Coterminal angles for $-\frac{9\pi}{4}$:

$-\frac{9\pi}{4} + 2\pi = -\frac{\pi}{4}$

$-\frac{9\pi}{4} + 4\pi = \frac{7\pi}{4}$

(b) Coterminal angles for $-\frac{2\pi}{15}$:

$-\frac{2\pi}{15} + 2\pi = \frac{28\pi}{15}$

$-\frac{2\pi}{15} - 2\pi = -\frac{32\pi}{15}$

14. (a) Coterminal angles for $\frac{7\pi}{8}$:

$\frac{7\pi}{8} + 2\pi = \frac{23\pi}{8}$

$\frac{7\pi}{8} - 2\pi = -\frac{9\pi}{8}$

(b) Coterminal angles for $\frac{8\pi}{45}$:

$\frac{8\pi}{45} + 2\pi = \frac{98\pi}{45}$

$\frac{8\pi}{45} - 2\pi = -\frac{82\pi}{45}$

15. Complement: $\frac{\pi}{2} - \frac{\pi}{3} = \frac{\pi}{6}$

Supplement: $\pi - \frac{\pi}{3} = \frac{2\pi}{3}$

16. Complement: Not possible; $\frac{3\pi}{4}$ is greater than $\frac{\pi}{2}$.

Supplement: $\pi - \frac{3\pi}{4} = \frac{\pi}{4}$

17. Complement: $\frac{\pi}{2} - \frac{\pi}{6} = \frac{\pi}{3}$

Supplement: $\pi - \frac{\pi}{6} = \frac{5\pi}{6}$

18. Complement: Not possible; $\frac{2\pi}{3}$ is greater than $\frac{\pi}{2}$.

Supplement: $\pi - \frac{2\pi}{3} = \frac{\pi}{3}$

19. Complement: $\frac{\pi}{2} - 1 \approx 0.57$

Supplement: $\pi - 1 \approx 2.14$

20. Complement: None $\left(2 > \frac{\pi}{2}\right)$

Supplement: $\pi - 2 \approx 1.14$

21.

The angle shown is approximately 210°.

22.

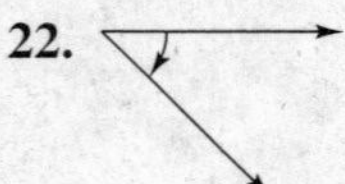

The angle shown is approximately $-45°$.

23. (a) Since $90° < 150° < 180°$, 150° lies in Quadrant II.

(b) Since $270° < 282° < 360°$, 282° lies in Quadrant IV.

24. (a) Since $0° < 87.9° < 90°$, 87.9° lies in Quadrant I.

(b) Since $0° < 8.5° < 90°$, 8.5° lies in Quadrant I.

25. (a) Since $-180° < -132° 50' < -90°$, $-132° 50'$ lies in Quadrant III.

(b) Since $-360° < -336° 30' < -270°$, $-336° 30'$ lies in Quadrant I.

26. (a) Since $-270° < -245.25° < -180°$, $-245.25°$ lies in Quadrant II.

(b) Since $-90° < -12.35° < -0°$, $-12.35°$ lies in Quadrant IV.

27. (a) $30°$

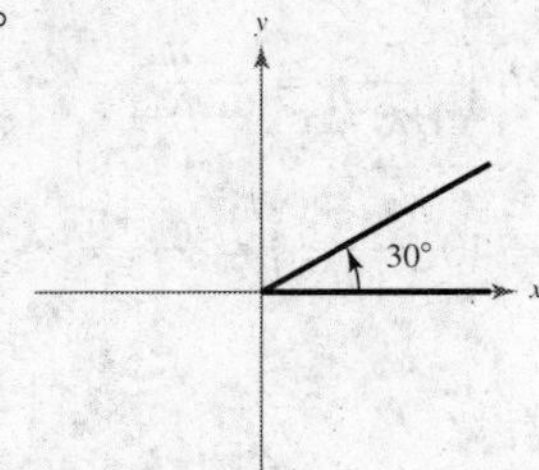

(b) $150°$

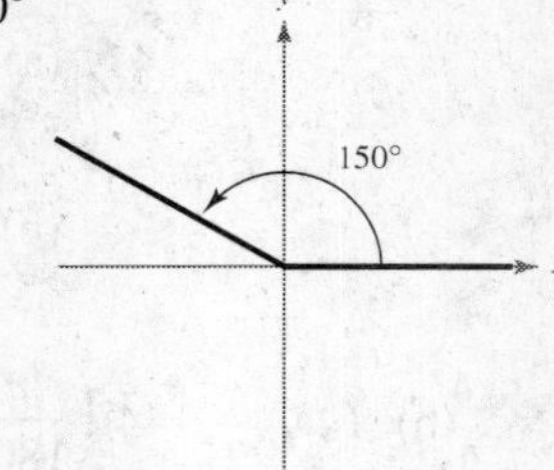

28. (a) $-270°$

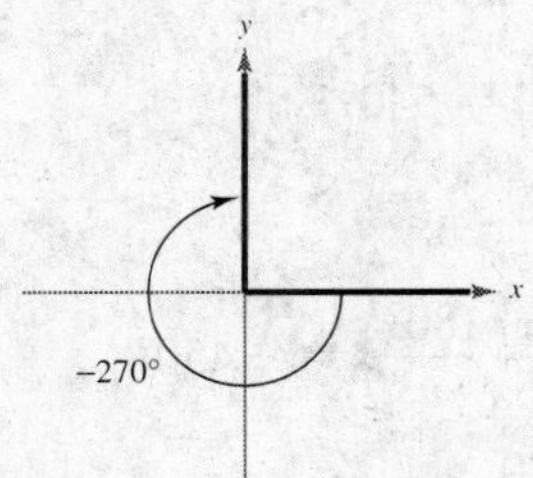

(b) $-120°$

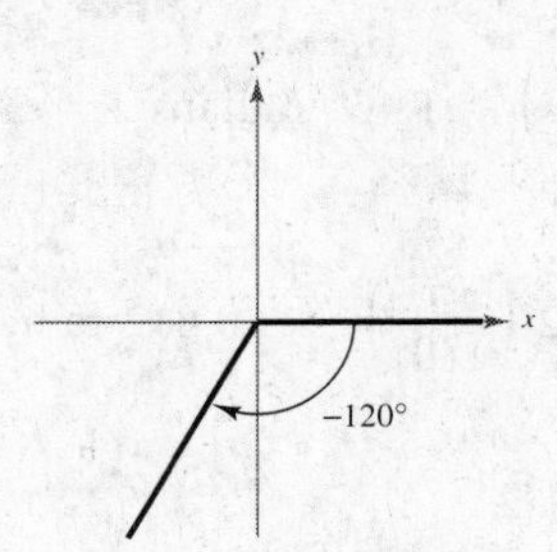

29. (a) $405°$

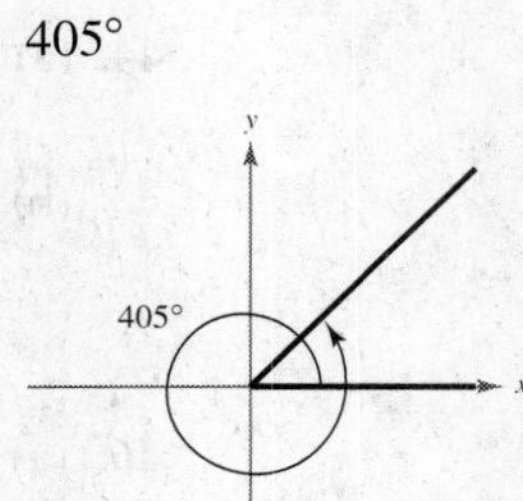

(b) $780°$

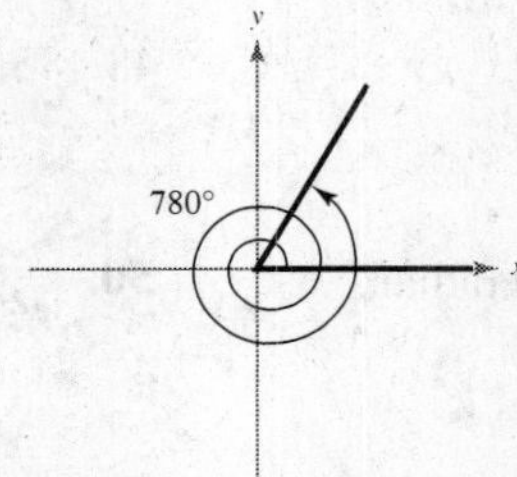

30. (a) $-450°$

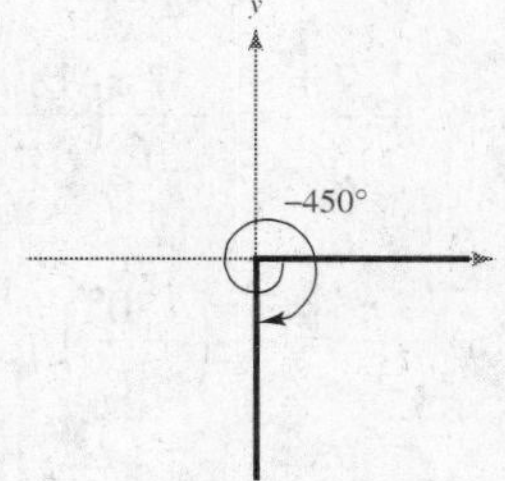

(b) $-600°$

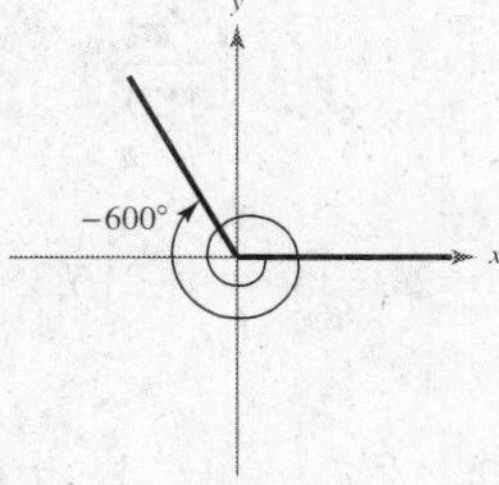

31. (a) Coterminal angles for $52°$:

$52° + 360° = 412°$

$52° - 360° = -308°$

(b) Coterminal angles for $-36°$:

$-36° + 360° = 324°$

$-36° - 360° = -396°$

32. (a) Coterminal angles for $114°$:

$114° + 360° = 474°$

$114° - 360° = -246°$

(b) Coterminal angles for $-390°$:

$-390° + 720° = 330°$

$-390° + 360° = -30°$

33. (a) Coterminal angles for $300°$:

$300° + 360° = 660°$

$300° - 360° = -60°$

(b) Coterminal angles for $230°$:

$230° + 360° = 590°$

$230° - 360° = -130°$

34. (a) Coterminal angles for $-445°$:

$-445° + 720° = 275°$

$-445° + 360° = -85°$

(b) Coterminal angles for $-740°$:

$-740° + 1080° = 340°$

$-740° + 720° = -20°$

35. Complement: $90° - 24° = 66°$

Supplement: $180° - 24° = 156°$

36. Complement: Not possible

Supplement: $180° - 129° = 51°$

37. Complement: $90° - 87° = 3°$

Supplement: $180° - 87° = 93°$

38. Complement: Not possible

Supplement: $180° - 167° = 13°$

39. (a) $30° = 30°\left(\frac{\pi}{180°}\right) = \frac{\pi}{6}$

(b) $150° = 150°\left(\frac{\pi}{180°}\right) = \frac{5\pi}{6}$

40. (a) $315° = 315°\left(\frac{\pi}{180°}\right) = \frac{7\pi}{4}$

(b) $120° = 120°\left(\frac{\pi}{180°}\right) = \frac{2\pi}{3}$

41. (a) $-20° = -20°\left(\frac{\pi}{180°}\right) = -\frac{\pi}{9}$

(b) $-240° = -240°\left(\frac{\pi}{180°}\right) = -\frac{4\pi}{3}$

42. (a) $-270° = -270°\left(\frac{\pi}{180°}\right) = -\frac{3\pi}{2}$ (b) $144° = 144°\left(\frac{\pi}{180°}\right) = \frac{4\pi}{5}$

43. (a) $\frac{3\pi}{2} = \frac{3\pi}{2}\left(\frac{180°}{\pi}\right) = 270°$

(b) $-\frac{7\pi}{6} = -\frac{7\pi}{6}\left(\frac{180°}{\pi}\right) = -210°$

44. (a) $-4\pi = -4\pi\left(\frac{180°}{\pi}\right) = -720°$

(b) $3\pi = 3\pi\left(\frac{180°}{\pi}\right) = 540°$

45. (a) $\frac{7\pi}{3} = \frac{7\pi}{3}\left(\frac{180°}{\pi}\right) = 420°$

(b) $-\frac{13\pi}{60} = -\frac{13\pi}{60}\left(\frac{180°}{\pi}\right) = -39°$

46. (a) $-\frac{15\pi}{6} = -\frac{15\pi}{6}\left(\frac{180°}{\pi}\right) = -450°$

(b) $\frac{28\pi}{15} = \frac{28\pi}{15}\left(\frac{180°}{\pi}\right) = 336°$

47. $115° = 115\left(\frac{\pi}{180°}\right) \approx 2.007$ radians

48. $83.7° = 83.7°\left(\frac{\pi}{180°}\right) \approx 1.461$ radians

49. $-216.35° = -216.35\left(\frac{\pi}{180°}\right) \approx -3.776$ radians

50. $-46.52° = -46.52°\left(\frac{\pi}{180°}\right) \approx -0.812$ radians

51. $-0.78° = -0.78\left(\frac{\pi}{180°}\right) \approx -0.014$ radians

52. $395° = 395°\left(\frac{\pi}{180°}\right) \approx 6.894$ radians

53. $\frac{\pi}{7} = \frac{\pi}{7}\left(\frac{180°}{\pi}\right) \approx 25.714°$

54. $\frac{8\pi}{13} = \frac{8\pi}{13}\left(\frac{180°}{\pi}\right) \approx 110.769°$

55. $6.5\pi = 6.5\pi\left(\frac{180°}{\pi}\right) = 1170°$

56. $-4.2\pi = -4.2\pi\left(\frac{180°}{\pi}\right) = -756°$

57. $-2 = -2\left(\frac{180°}{\pi}\right) \approx -114.592°$

58. $-0.48 = -0.48\left(\frac{180°}{\pi}\right) \approx -27.502°$

59. $64°\,45' = 64° + \left(\frac{45}{60}\right)^{\circ} = 64.75°$

60. $-124°\,30' = -124.5°$

61. $85°\,18'\,30'' = 85° + \left(\frac{18}{60}\right)^{\circ} + \left(\frac{30}{3600}\right)^{\circ} \approx 85.308°$

62. $-408°\,16'\,25'' \approx -408.274°$

63. $-125°\,36'' = -125° - \left(\frac{36}{3600}\right)^{\circ} = -125.01°$

64. $330°\,25'' \approx 330.007°$

65. $280.6° = 280° + 0.6(60)' = 280°\,36'$

66. $-115.8° = -115°\,48'$

67. $-345.12° = -345°\,7'\,12''$

68. $310.75° = 310°\,45'$

69. $-0.355 = -0.355\left(\dfrac{180°}{\pi}\right)$

$\approx -20.34° = -20°\,20'\,24''$

70. $0.7865 = 0.7865\left(\dfrac{180°}{\pi}\right)$

$\approx 45.0631°$

$= 45° + (0.0631)(60')$

$= 45° + 3' + 0.786(60'')$

$\approx 45°\,3'\,47''$

71. $s = r\theta$

$6 = 5\theta$

$\theta = \frac{6}{5}$ radians

72. $s = r\theta$

$31 = 12\theta$

$\theta = \frac{31}{12} = 2\frac{7}{12}$ radians

73. $s = r\theta$

$32 = 7\theta$

$\theta = \frac{32}{7} = 4\frac{4}{7}$ radians

74. $s = r\theta$

$60 = 75\theta$

$\theta = \frac{60}{75} = \frac{4}{5}$ radians

Because the angle represented is clockwise, this angle is $-\frac{4}{5}$ radians.

75. The angles in radians are:

$0° = 0$

$30° = \dfrac{\pi}{6}$

$45° = \dfrac{\pi}{4}$

$60° = \dfrac{\pi}{3}$

$90° = \dfrac{\pi}{2}$

$135° = \dfrac{3\pi}{4}$

$180° = \pi$

$210° = \dfrac{7\pi}{6}$

$270° = \dfrac{3\pi}{2}$

$330° = \dfrac{11\pi}{6}$

76. The angles in degrees are:

$\dfrac{\pi}{6} = 30°$

$\dfrac{\pi}{4} = 45°$

$\dfrac{\pi}{3} = 60°$

$\dfrac{2\pi}{3} = 120°$

$\dfrac{5\pi}{6} = 150°$

$\dfrac{5\pi}{4} = 225°$

$\dfrac{4\pi}{3} = 240°$

$\dfrac{5\pi}{3} = 300°$

$\dfrac{7\pi}{4} = 315°$

$\pi = 180°$

77. $s = r\theta$

$8 = 15\theta$

$\theta = \dfrac{8}{15}$ radians

78. $\theta = \dfrac{s}{r} = \dfrac{10}{22} = \dfrac{5}{11}$ radian

79. $s = r\theta$

$35 = 14.5\theta$

$\theta = \dfrac{70}{29} \approx 2.414$ radians

80. $r = 80$ kilometers, $s = 160$ kilometers

$\theta = \dfrac{s}{r} = \dfrac{160}{80} = 2$ radians

81. $s = r\theta$, θ in radians

$s = 14(180)\left(\dfrac{\pi}{180}\right) = 14\pi \approx 43.982$ inches

82. $r = 9$ feet, $\theta = 60° = \dfrac{\pi}{3}$

$s = r\theta = 9\left(\dfrac{\pi}{3}\right) = 3\pi$ feet

83. $s = r\theta$, θ in radians

$s = 27\left(\dfrac{2\pi}{3}\right) = 18\pi$ meters ≈ 56.55 meters

84. $r = 12$ centimeters, $\theta = \dfrac{3\pi}{4}$

$s = r\theta = 12\left(\dfrac{3\pi}{4}\right) = 9\pi$ centimeters ≈ 28.27 cm

85. $r = \dfrac{s}{\theta} = \dfrac{36}{\pi/2} = \dfrac{72}{\pi}$ feet ≈ 22.92 feet

86. $r = \dfrac{s}{\theta} = \dfrac{3}{4\pi/3} = \dfrac{9}{4\pi}$ meters ≈ 0.72 meter

87. $r = \dfrac{s}{\theta} = \dfrac{82}{135°(\pi/180°)} = \dfrac{328}{3\pi}$ miles ≈ 34.80 miles

88. $r = \dfrac{s}{\theta} = \dfrac{8}{330°(\pi/180°)} = \dfrac{48}{11\pi}$ inches ≈ 1.39 inches

89. $\theta = 42°\,7'\,33'' - 25°\,46'\,32''$

$= 16°\,21'\,1'' \approx 0.28537$ radian

$s = r\theta = 4000(0.28537) \approx 1141.48$ miles

90. $r = 4000$ miles

$\theta = 31°\,46' + 26°\,8' = 57°\,54' \approx 1.0105$ rad

$s = r\theta = 4000(1.0105) \approx 4042.0$ miles

91. $\theta = \dfrac{s}{r} = \dfrac{450}{6378} \approx 0.07056$ radian $\approx 4.04°$

$\approx 4°\,2'\,33.02''$

92. $r = 6378$, $s = 400$

$\theta = \dfrac{s}{r} = \dfrac{400}{6378} \approx 0.0627$ rad $\approx 3.59°$

93. $\theta = \dfrac{s}{r} = \dfrac{2.5}{6} = \dfrac{25}{60} = \dfrac{5}{12}$ radian $\approx 23.87°$

94. $\theta = \dfrac{s}{r} = \dfrac{24}{5} = 4.8$ rad $\approx 275.02°$

95. (a) single axel: $1\frac{1}{2}$ revolutions $= 360° + 180° = 540°$

$= 2\pi + \pi = 3\pi$ radians

(b) double axel: $2\frac{1}{2}$ revolutions $= 720° + 180° = 900°$

$= 4\pi + \pi = 5\pi$ radians

(c) triple axel: $3\frac{1}{2}$ revolutions $= 1260° = 7\pi$ radians

96. Linear speed $= \dfrac{s}{t} = \dfrac{r\theta}{t} = \dfrac{(6400 + 1250)2\pi}{110} \approx 436.967$ km/min

97. (a) $\dfrac{\text{Revolutions}}{\text{Second}} = \dfrac{2400}{60} = 40$ rev/sec

Angular speed $= (2\pi)(40) = 80\pi$ rad/sec

(b) Radius of saw blade $= \dfrac{7.5}{2} = 3.75$ in.

Radius in feet $= \dfrac{3.75}{12} = 0.3125$ ft

Speed $= \dfrac{s}{t} = \dfrac{r\theta}{t} = r\dfrac{\theta}{t} = r(\text{angular speed})$

$= 0.3125(80\pi) = 78.54$ ft/sec

98. (a) $\dfrac{\text{Revolutions}}{\text{Second}} = \dfrac{4800}{60} = 80$ rev/sec

Angular speed $= (2\pi)(80) = 160\pi$ rad/sec

(b) Radius of saw blade $= \dfrac{7.25}{2} = 3.625$ in.

Radius in feet $= \dfrac{3.625}{12} \approx 0.3021$ ft

Speed $= \dfrac{s}{t} = \dfrac{r\theta}{t} = r\dfrac{\theta}{t} = r(\text{angular speed})$

$= 0.3021(160\pi) \approx 151.84$ ft/sec

99. (a) $\dfrac{\text{Revolutions}}{\text{Hour}} = \dfrac{480}{(1/60)} = 28{,}800 \text{ rev/hr}$

Angular speed $= 2\pi(28{,}800) = 57{,}600\pi$ rad/hr

Radius of wheel $= \dfrac{25/2}{(12 \text{ in./ft})(5280 \text{ ft/mi})} = \dfrac{5}{25{,}344}$ miles

Speed $= \dfrac{s}{t} = \dfrac{r\theta}{t} = r\dfrac{\theta}{t} = r(\text{angular speed})$

$= \dfrac{5}{25{,}344} \cdot 57{,}600\pi = \dfrac{125\pi}{11} \approx 35.70$ miles/hr

(b) Let $x =$ spin balance machine rate.

$70 = r(\text{angular speed}) = r\left(2\pi \cdot \dfrac{x}{(1/60)}\right) = \dfrac{5}{25{,}344}120\pi x \Longrightarrow x \approx 941.18$ rev/min

100. (a) $200 \le \dfrac{\text{revolutions}}{\text{minute}} \le 500$

$2\pi(200) \le \text{angular speed} \le 2\pi(500)$

$400\pi \text{ rad/min} \le \text{angular speed} \le 1000\pi \text{ rad/min}$

(b) Speed $= \dfrac{s}{t} = \dfrac{r\theta}{t} = r\dfrac{\theta}{t} = r(\text{angular speed}) = 6(\text{angular speed})$

$6(400\pi) \le \text{linear speed} \le 6(1000\pi)$

For the outermost track, 6000π cm/min

101. False, 1 radian $= \left(\dfrac{180}{\pi}\right)^\circ \approx 57.3^\circ$, so one radian is much larger than one degree.

102. No, -1260° is coterminal with 180°.

103. True: $\dfrac{2\pi}{3} + \dfrac{\pi}{4} + \dfrac{\pi}{12} = \dfrac{8\pi + 3\pi + \pi}{12} = \pi = 180^\circ$

104. (a) An angle is in standard position when the origin is the vertex and the initial side coincides with the positive x-axis.

(b) A negative angle is generated by a clockwise rotation.

(c) Angles that have the same initial and terminal sides are coterminal angles.

(d) An obtuse angle is between 90° and 180°.

105. If θ is constant, the length of the arc is proportional to the radius ($s = r\theta$), and hence increasing.

106. Let A be the area of a circular sector of radius r and central angle θ. Then

$$\frac{A}{\pi r^2} = \frac{\theta}{2\pi} \Longrightarrow A = \frac{1}{2}r^2\theta.$$

107. $A = \dfrac{1}{2}r^2\theta = \dfrac{1}{2}(10)^2 \cdot \dfrac{\pi}{3} = \dfrac{50}{3}\pi$ square meters

108. Because $s = r\theta$, $\theta = \dfrac{12}{15}$.

Hence, $A = \dfrac{1}{2}r^2\theta = \dfrac{1}{2}15^2\left(\dfrac{12}{15}\right) = 90 \text{ ft}^2$.

109. $A = \frac{1}{2}r^2\theta, s = r\theta$

(a) $\theta = 0.8 \implies A = \frac{1}{2}r^2(0.8) = 0.4r^2$ Domain: $r > 0$

$s = r\theta = r(0.8)$ Domain: $r > 0$

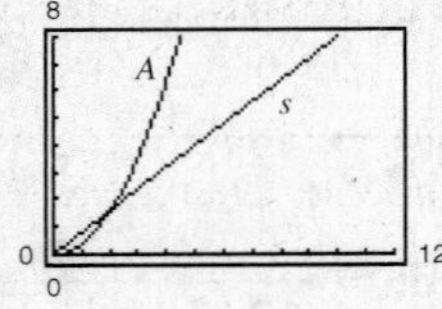

The area function changes more rapidly for $r > 1$ because it is quadratic and the arc length function is linear.

(b) $r = 10 \implies A = \frac{1}{2}(10^2)\theta = 50\theta$ Domain: $0 < \theta < 2\pi$

$s = r\theta = 10\theta$ Domain: $0 < \theta < 2\pi$

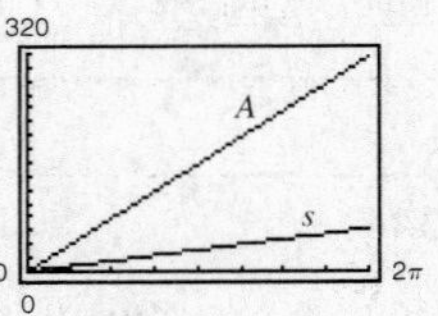

110. If a fan of greater diameter is installed, the angular speed does not change.

111. Answers will vary.

112. Answers will vary.

113.

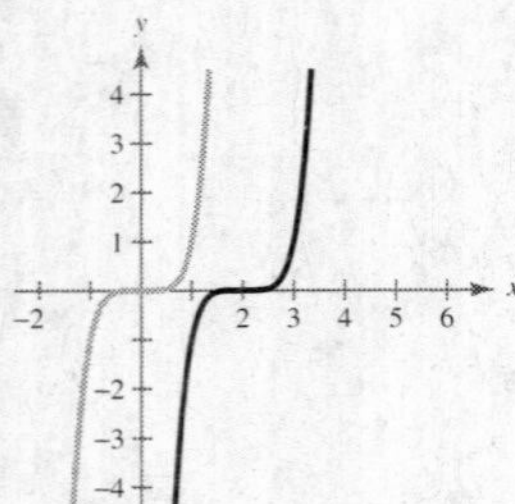

114.

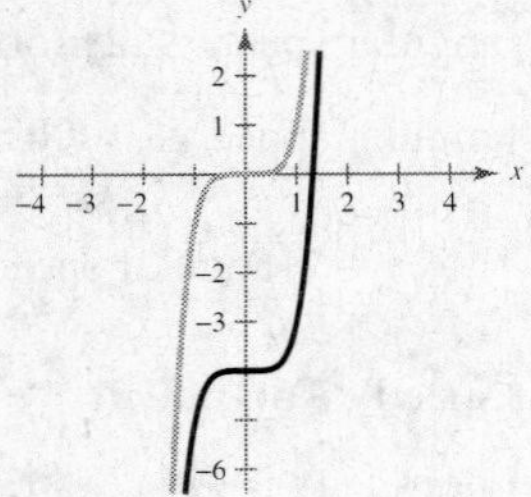

115.

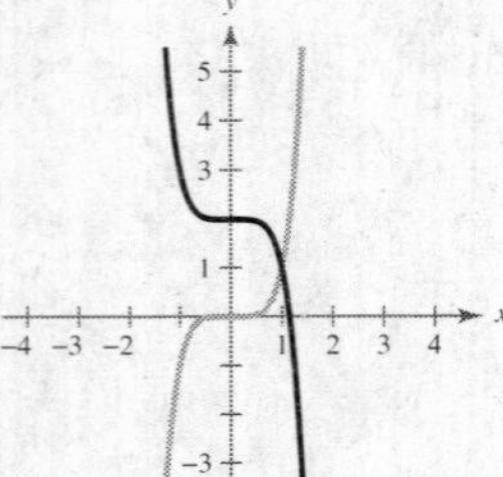

116.

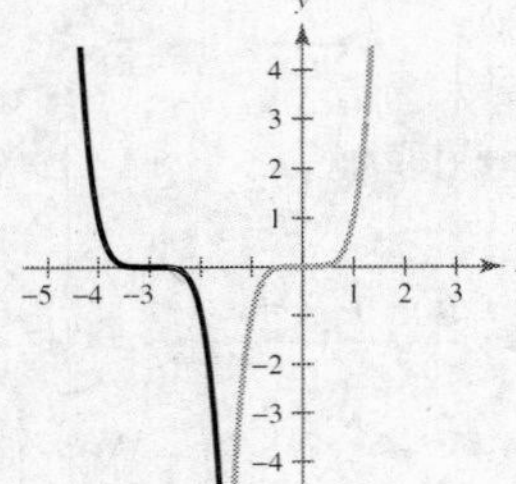

117.

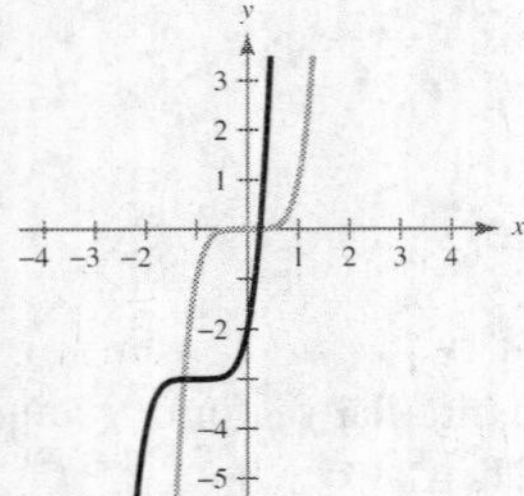

118.

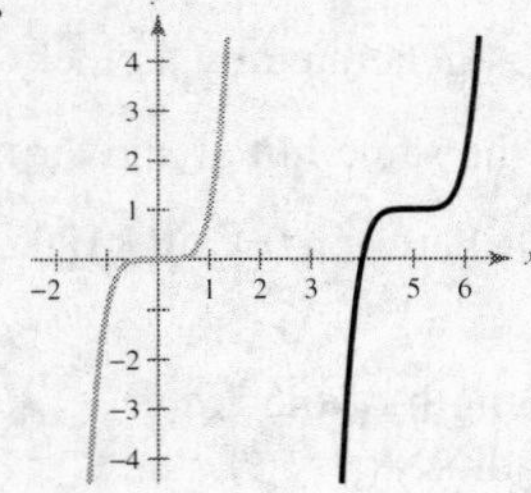

Section 4.2 Trigonometric Functions: The Unit Circle

- You should know how to evaluate trigonometric functions using the unit circle.
- You should know the definition of a *periodic* function.
- You should be able to recognize even and odd trigonometric functions.
- You should be able to evaluate trigonometric functions with a calculator in both radian and degree mode.

Vocabulary Check

1. unit circle **2.** periodic **3.** odd, even

1. $\sin\theta = y = \frac{15}{17}$

$\cos\theta = x = -\frac{8}{17}$

$\tan\theta = \frac{y}{x} = -\frac{15}{8}$

$\cot\theta = \frac{x}{y} = -\frac{8}{15}$

$\sec\theta = \frac{1}{x} = -\frac{17}{8}$

$\csc\theta = \frac{1}{y} = \frac{17}{15}$

2. $(x, y) = \left(\frac{12}{13}, \frac{5}{13}\right)$

$\sin\theta = y = \frac{5}{13}$

$\cos\theta = x = \frac{12}{13}$

$\tan\theta = \frac{y}{x} = \frac{5/13}{12/13} = \frac{5}{12}$

$\csc\theta = \frac{1}{y} = \frac{1}{5/13} = \frac{13}{5}$

$\sec\theta = \frac{1}{x} = \frac{1}{12/13} = \frac{13}{12}$

$\cot\theta = \frac{x}{y} = \frac{12/13}{5/13} = \frac{12}{5}$

3. $\sin\theta = y = -\frac{5}{13}$

$\cos\theta = x = \frac{12}{13}$

$\tan\theta = \frac{y}{x} = -\frac{5}{12}$

$\cot\theta = \frac{x}{y} = -\frac{12}{5}$

$\sec\theta = \frac{1}{x} = \frac{13}{12}$

$\csc\theta = \frac{1}{y} = -\frac{13}{5}$

4. $(x, y) = \left(-\frac{4}{5}, -\frac{3}{5}\right)$

$\sin\theta = y = -\frac{3}{5}$

$\cos\theta = x = -\frac{4}{5}$

$\tan\theta = \frac{y}{x} = \frac{-3/5}{-4/5} = \frac{3}{4}$

$\csc\theta = \frac{1}{y} = \frac{1}{-3/5} = -\frac{5}{3}$

$\sec\theta = \frac{1}{x} = \frac{1}{-4/5} = -\frac{5}{4}$

$\cot\theta = \frac{x}{y} = \frac{-4/5}{-3/5} = \frac{4}{3}$

5. $t = \frac{\pi}{4}$ corresponds to $\left(\frac{\sqrt{2}}{2}, \frac{\sqrt{2}}{2}\right)$.

6. $t = \frac{\pi}{3} \Rightarrow \left(\frac{1}{2}, \frac{\sqrt{3}}{2}\right)$

7. $t = \frac{7\pi}{6}$ corresponds to $\left(-\frac{\sqrt{3}}{2}, -\frac{1}{2}\right)$.

8. $t = \frac{5\pi}{4} \Rightarrow \left(-\frac{\sqrt{2}}{2}, -\frac{\sqrt{2}}{2}\right)$

9. $t = \frac{2\pi}{3}$ corresponds to $\left(-\frac{1}{2}, \frac{\sqrt{3}}{2}\right)$.

10. $t = \frac{5\pi}{3}$ corresponds to $\left(\frac{1}{2}, -\frac{\sqrt{3}}{2}\right)$.

11. $t = \frac{3\pi}{2}$ corresponds to $(0, -1)$.

12. $t = \pi \Rightarrow (-1, 0)$

13. $t = -\frac{7\pi}{4}$ corresponds to $\left(\frac{\sqrt{2}}{2}, \frac{\sqrt{2}}{2}\right)$.

14. $t = -\frac{4\pi}{3}$ corresponds to $\left(-\frac{1}{2}, \frac{\sqrt{3}}{2}\right)$.

15. $t = -\frac{3\pi}{2}$ corresponds to $(0, 1)$.

16. $t = -2\pi$ corresponds to $(1, 0)$.

17. $t = \frac{\pi}{4}$ corresponds to $\left(\frac{\sqrt{2}}{2}, \frac{\sqrt{2}}{2}\right)$.

$\sin t = y = \frac{\sqrt{2}}{2}$

$\cos t = x = \frac{\sqrt{2}}{2}$

$\tan t = \frac{y}{x} = 1$

18. $t = \frac{\pi}{3}$ corresponds to $\left(\frac{1}{2}, \frac{\sqrt{3}}{2}\right)$.

$\sin \frac{\pi}{3} = y = \frac{\sqrt{3}}{2}$

$\cos \frac{\pi}{3} = x = \frac{1}{2}$

$\tan \frac{\pi}{3} = \frac{y}{x} = \frac{\sqrt{3}/2}{1/2} = \sqrt{3}$

19. $t = \frac{7\pi}{6}$ corresponds to $\left(-\frac{\sqrt{3}}{2}, -\frac{1}{2}\right)$.

$\sin t = y = -\frac{1}{2}$

$\cos t = x = -\frac{\sqrt{3}}{2}$

$\tan t = \frac{y}{x} = \frac{1}{\sqrt{3}} = \frac{\sqrt{3}}{3}$

20. $t = -\frac{5\pi}{4}$ corresponds to $\left(-\frac{\sqrt{2}}{2}, \frac{\sqrt{2}}{2}\right)$.

$\sin t = y = \frac{\sqrt{2}}{2}$

$\cos t = x = -\frac{\sqrt{2}}{2}$

$\tan t = \frac{y}{x} = -1$

21. $t = \frac{2\pi}{3}$ corresponds to $\left(-\frac{1}{2}, \frac{\sqrt{3}}{2}\right)$.

$\sin t = y = \frac{\sqrt{3}}{2}$

$\cos t = x = -\frac{1}{2}$

$\tan t = \frac{y}{x} = -\sqrt{3}$

22. $t = \frac{5\pi}{3}$ corresponds to $\left(\frac{1}{2}, -\frac{\sqrt{3}}{2}\right)$.

$\sin t = y = -\frac{\sqrt{3}}{2}$

$\cos t = x = \frac{1}{2}$

$\tan t = \frac{y}{x} = -\sqrt{3}$

23. $t = -\frac{5\pi}{3}$ corresponds to $\left(\frac{1}{2}, \frac{\sqrt{3}}{2}\right)$.

$\sin t = y = \frac{\sqrt{3}}{2}$

$\cos t = x = \frac{1}{2}$

$\tan t = \frac{y}{x} = \sqrt{3}$

24. $t = \frac{11\pi}{6}$ corresponds to $\left(\frac{\sqrt{3}}{2}, -\frac{1}{2}\right)$.

$\sin t = y = -\frac{1}{2}$

$\cos t = x = \frac{\sqrt{3}}{2}$

$\tan t = \frac{y}{x} = -\frac{\sqrt{3}}{3}$

25. $t = -\frac{\pi}{6}$ corresponds to $\left(\frac{\sqrt{3}}{2}, -\frac{1}{2}\right)$.

$\sin t = y = -\frac{1}{2}$

$\cos t = x = \frac{\sqrt{3}}{2}$

$\tan t = \frac{y}{x} = -\frac{\sqrt{3}}{3}$

26. $t = -\frac{3\pi}{4}$ corresponds to $\left(-\frac{\sqrt{2}}{2}, -\frac{\sqrt{2}}{2}\right)$.

$\sin\left(-\frac{3\pi}{4}\right) = y = -\frac{\sqrt{2}}{2}$

$\cos\left(-\frac{3\pi}{4}\right) = x = -\frac{\sqrt{2}}{2}$

$\tan\left(-\frac{3\pi}{4}\right) = \frac{y}{x} = 1$

27. $t = -\frac{7\pi}{4}$ corresponds to $\left(\frac{\sqrt{2}}{2}, \frac{\sqrt{2}}{2}\right)$.

$\sin t = y = \frac{\sqrt{2}}{2}$

$\cos t = x = \frac{\sqrt{2}}{2}$

$\tan t = \frac{y}{x} = 1$

28. $t = -\frac{4\pi}{3}$ corresponds to $\left(-\frac{1}{2}, \frac{\sqrt{3}}{2}\right)$.

$\sin t = y = \frac{\sqrt{3}}{2}$

$\cos t = x = -\frac{1}{2}$

$\tan t = \frac{y}{x} = -\sqrt{3}$

29. $t = -\frac{3\pi}{2}$ corresponds to $(0, 1)$.

$\sin t = y = 1$

$\cos t = x = 0$

$\tan t = \frac{y}{x}$ is undefined.

30. $t = -2\pi$ corresponds to $(1, 0)$.

$\sin(-2\pi) = y = 0$

$\cos(-2\pi) = x = 1$

$\tan(-2\pi) = \frac{y}{x} = \frac{0}{1} = 0$

31. $t = \frac{3\pi}{4}$ corresponds to $\left(-\frac{\sqrt{2}}{2}, \frac{\sqrt{2}}{2}\right)$.

$\sin t = y = \frac{\sqrt{2}}{2}$ $\qquad$ $\csc t = \frac{1}{y} = \sqrt{2}$

$\cos t = x = -\frac{\sqrt{2}}{2}$ $\qquad$ $\sec t = \frac{1}{x} = -\sqrt{2}$

$\tan t = \frac{y}{x} = -1$ $\qquad$ $\cot t = \frac{x}{y} = -1$

32. $t = \frac{5\pi}{6}$ corresponds to $\left(-\frac{\sqrt{3}}{2}, \frac{1}{2}\right)$.

$\sin t = y = \frac{1}{2}$

$\cos t = x = -\frac{\sqrt{3}}{2}$

$\tan t = \frac{y}{x} = -\frac{1}{\sqrt{3}} = -\frac{\sqrt{3}}{3}$

$\csc t = \frac{1}{y} = 2$

$\sec t = \frac{1}{x} = -\frac{2}{\sqrt{3}} = -\frac{2\sqrt{3}}{3}$

$\cot t = \frac{x}{y} = -\sqrt{3}$

33. $t = \frac{\pi}{2}$ corresponds to $(0, 1)$.

$\sin t = y = 1$ $\qquad \csc t = \frac{1}{y} = 1$

$\cos t = x = 0$ $\qquad \sec t = \frac{1}{x}$ is undefined.

$\tan t = \frac{y}{x}$ is undefined. $\qquad \cot t = \frac{x}{y} = 0$

34. $t = \frac{3\pi}{2}$ corresponds to $(0, -1)$.

$\sin \frac{3\pi}{2} = y = -1$

$\cos \frac{3\pi}{2} = x = 0$

$\tan \frac{3\pi}{2} = \frac{y}{x} = \frac{-1}{0} \Rightarrow$ undefined

$\csc \frac{3\pi}{2} = \frac{1}{y} = \frac{1}{-1} = -1$

$\sec \frac{3\pi}{2} = \frac{1}{x} = \frac{1}{0} \Rightarrow$ undefined

$\cot \frac{3\pi}{2} = \frac{x}{y} = \frac{0}{-1} = 0$

35. $t = -\frac{2\pi}{3}$ corresponds to $\left(-\frac{1}{2}, -\frac{\sqrt{3}}{2}\right)$.

$\sin t = y = -\frac{\sqrt{3}}{2}$ $\qquad \csc t = -\frac{2\sqrt{3}}{3}$

$\cos t = x = -\frac{1}{2}$ $\qquad \sec \theta = -2$

$\tan t = \frac{y}{x} = \sqrt{3}$ $\qquad \cot \theta = \frac{\sqrt{3}}{3}$

36. $t = -\frac{7\pi}{4}$ corresponds to $\left(\frac{\sqrt{2}}{2}, \frac{\sqrt{2}}{2}\right)$.

$\sin\left(-\frac{7\pi}{4}\right) = y = \frac{\sqrt{2}}{2}$ $\qquad \csc\left(-\frac{7\pi}{4}\right) = \frac{1}{y} = \sqrt{2}$

$\cos\left(-\frac{7\pi}{4}\right) = x = \frac{\sqrt{2}}{2}$ $\qquad \sec\left(-\frac{7\pi}{4}\right) = \frac{1}{x} = \sqrt{2}$

$\tan\left(-\frac{7\pi}{4}\right) = \frac{y}{x} = 1$ $\qquad \cot\left(-\frac{7\pi}{4}\right) = \frac{x}{y} = 1$

37. $\sin 5\pi = \sin \pi = 0$

38. Because $7\pi = 6\pi + \pi$:

$\cos 7\pi = \cos(6\pi + \pi) = \cos \pi = -1$

39. $\cos \frac{8\pi}{3} = \cos \frac{2\pi}{3} = -\frac{1}{2}$

40. Because $\frac{9\pi}{4} = 2\pi + \frac{\pi}{4}$:

$\sin \frac{9\pi}{4} = \sin\left(2\pi + \frac{\pi}{4}\right) = \sin \frac{\pi}{4} = \frac{\sqrt{2}}{2}$

41. $\cos\left(-\frac{13\pi}{6}\right) = \cos\left(-\frac{\pi}{6}\right) = \cos\left(\frac{11\pi}{6}\right) = \frac{\sqrt{3}}{2}$

42. Because $-\frac{19\pi}{6} = -4\pi + \frac{5\pi}{6}$:

$\sin\left(-\frac{19\pi}{6}\right) = \sin\left(-4\pi + \frac{5\pi}{6}\right)$

$= \sin\left(\frac{5\pi}{6}\right) = \frac{1}{2}$

43. $\sin\left(-\frac{9\pi}{4}\right) = \sin\left(-\frac{\pi}{4}\right) = -\frac{\sqrt{2}}{2}$

44. Because $-\frac{8\pi}{3} = -4\pi + \frac{4\pi}{3}$:

$\cos\left(-\frac{8\pi}{3}\right) = \cos\left(-4\pi + \frac{4\pi}{3}\right)$

$= \cos \frac{4\pi}{3} = -\frac{1}{2}$

45. $\sin t = \frac{1}{3}$

(a) $\sin(-t) = -\sin t = -\frac{1}{3}$

(b) $\csc(-t) = -\csc t = -3$

46. $\cos t = -\frac{3}{4}$

(a) $\cos(-t) = \cos t = -\frac{3}{4}$

(b) $\sec(-t) = \frac{1}{\cos(-t)} = \frac{1}{\cos t} = -\frac{4}{3}$

47. $\cos(-t) = -\frac{1}{5}$

(a) $\cos t = \cos(-t) = -\frac{1}{5}$

(b) $\sec(-t) = \frac{1}{\cos(-t)} = -5$

48. $\sin(-t) = \frac{3}{8}$

(a) $\sin t = -\sin(-t) = -\frac{3}{8}$

(b) $\csc t = \frac{1}{\sin(t)} = \frac{1}{-\sin(-t)} = -\frac{8}{3}$

49. $\sin t = \frac{4}{5}$

(a) $\sin(\pi - t) = \sin t = \frac{4}{5}$

(b) $\sin(t + \pi) = -\sin t = -\frac{4}{5}$

50. $\cos t = \frac{4}{5}$

(a) $\cos(\pi - t) = -\cos t = -\frac{4}{5}$

(b) $\cos(t + \pi) = -\cos t = -\frac{4}{5}$

51. $\sin \frac{7\pi}{9} \approx 0.6428$

52. $\tan \frac{2\pi}{5} \approx 3.0777$

53. $\cos \frac{11\pi}{5} \approx 0.8090$

54. $\sin \frac{11\pi}{9} \approx -0.6428$

55. $\csc 1.3 \approx 1.0378$

56. $\cot 3.7 = \frac{1}{\tan 3.7} \approx 1.6007$

57. $\cos(-1.7) \approx -0.1288$

58. $\cos(-2.5) \approx -0.8011$

59. $\csc 0.8 = \frac{1}{\sin 0.8} \approx 1.3940$

60. $\sec 1.8 = \frac{1}{\cos 1.8} \approx -4.4014$

61. $\sec 22.8 = \frac{1}{\cos 22.8} \approx -1.4486$

62. $\sin(-13.4) \approx -0.7404$

63. $\cot 2.5 = \frac{1}{\tan 2.5} \approx -1.3386$

64. $\tan 1.75 \approx -5.5204$

65. $\csc(-1.5) = \frac{1}{\sin(-1.5)} \approx -1.0025$

66. $\tan(-2.25) \approx 1.2386$

67. $\sec(-4.5) = \frac{1}{\cos(-4.5)} \approx -4.7439$

68. $\csc(-5.2) = \frac{1}{\sin(-5.2)} \approx 1.1319$

69. (a) $\sin 5 \approx -1$

(b) $\cos 2 \approx -0.4$

70. (a) $\sin 0.75 = y \approx 0.7$

(b) $\cos 2.5 = x \approx -0.8$

71. (a) $\sin t = 0.25$

$t \approx 0.25$ or 2.89

(b) $\cos t = -0.25$

$t \approx 1.82$ or 4.46

72. (a) $\sin t = -0.75$

$t \approx 4.0$ or $t \approx 5.4$

(b) $\cos t = 0.75$

$t \approx 0.72$ or $t \approx 5.56$

73. $I = 5e^{-2t} \sin t$

$I(0.7) = 5e^{-1.4} \sin 0.7$

≈ 0.79 amperes

74. At $t = 1.4$,

$I \approx 5e^{-2(1.4)} \sin 1.4 \approx 0.30$ amperes.

75. $y(t) = \frac{1}{4}\cos 6t$

(a) $y(0) = \frac{1}{4}\cos 0 = 0.2500$ ft

(b) $y\left(\frac{1}{4}\right) = \frac{1}{4}\cos \frac{3}{2} \approx 0.0177$ ft

(c) $y\left(\frac{1}{2}\right) = \frac{1}{4}\cos 3 \approx -0.2475$ ft

76. $y(t) = \frac{1}{4}e^{-t}\cos 6t$

(a) $y(0) = \frac{1}{4}e^{-0}\cos(0) = \frac{1}{4}$ foot

(b)

t	0.50	1.02	1.54	2.07	2.59
y	−0.15	0.09	−0.05	0.03	−0.02

(c) The maximum displacements are decreasing because of friction, which is modeled by the e^{-t} term.

(d) $\frac{1}{4}e^{-t}\cos 6t = 0$

$\cos 6t = 0$

$6t = \frac{\pi}{2}, \frac{3\pi}{2}$

$t = \frac{\pi}{12}, \frac{\pi}{4}$

77. False. $\sin\left(\frac{-4\pi}{3}\right) = \frac{\sqrt{3}}{2} > 0$

78. True

79. False. 0 corresponds to $(1, 0)$.

80. True

81. (a) The points have y-axis symmetry.

(b) $\sin t_1 = \sin(\pi - t_1)$ since they have the same y-value.

(c) $-\cos t_1 = \cos(\pi - t_1)$ since the x-values have opposite signs.

82. (a) The points (x_1, y_1) and (x_2, y_2) are symmetric about the origin.

(b) Because of the symmetry of the points, you can make the conjecture that $\sin(t_1 + \pi) = -\sin t_1$.

(c) Because of the symmetry of the points, you can make the conjecture that $\cos(t_1 + \pi) = -\cos t_1$.

83. $\cos 1.5 \approx 0.0707$, $2\cos 0.75 \approx 1.4634$

Thus, $\cos 2t \neq 2\cos t$.

84. $\sin(0.25) + \sin(0.75) \approx 0.2474 + 0.6816 = 0.9290$

$$\sin 1 \approx 0.8415$$

Therefore, $\sin t_1 + \sin t_2 \neq \sin(t_1 + t_2)$.

85. $\cos\theta = x = \cos(-\theta)$

$$\sec\theta = \frac{1}{\cos\theta} = \frac{1}{\cos(-\theta)} = \sec(-\theta)$$

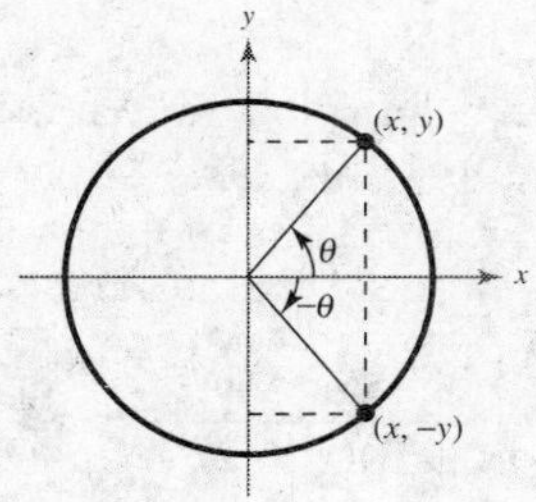

86. $\sin\theta = y = -\sin(-\theta)$

$$\csc\theta = \frac{1}{y} = -\csc(-\theta)$$

$$\tan\theta = \frac{y}{x} = -\tan(-\theta)$$

$$\cot\theta = \frac{x}{y} = -\cot(-\theta)$$

87. $h(t) = f(t)g(t)$ is odd.

$h(-t) = f(-t)g(-t) = -f(t)g(t) = -h(t)$

88. $f(t) = \sin t$ and $g(t) = \tan t$

Both f and g are odd functions.

$$h(t) = f(t)g(t) = \sin t \tan t$$
$$h(-t) = \sin(-t)\tan(-t)$$
$$= (-\sin t)(-\tan t)$$
$$= \sin t \tan t = h(t)$$

The function $h(t) = f(t)g(t)$ is even.

89. $f(x) = \frac{1}{2}(3x - 2)$

$y = \frac{1}{2}(3x - 2)$

$x = \frac{1}{2}(3y - 2)$

$2x = 3y - 2$

$2x + 2 = 3y$

$\frac{2}{3}(x + 1) = y$

$f^{-1}(x) = \frac{2}{3}(x + 1)$

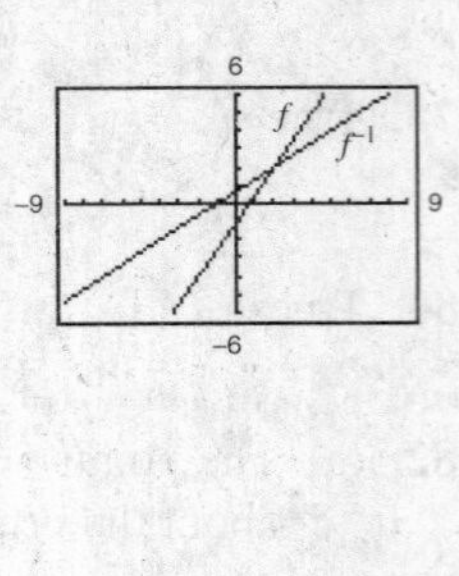

90. $f(x) = \frac{1}{4}x^3 + 1$

$y = \frac{1}{4}x^3 + 1$

$x = \frac{1}{4}y^3 + 1$

$x - 1 = \frac{1}{4}y^3$

$4(x - 1) = y^3$

$y = \sqrt[3]{4(x - 1)}$

$f^{-1}(x) = \sqrt[3]{4(x - 1)}$

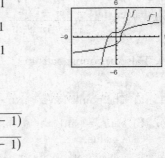

91. $f(x) = \sqrt{x^2 - 4},\ x \geq 2,\ y \geq 0$

$y = \sqrt{x^2 - 4}$

$x = \sqrt{y^2 - 4}$

$x^2 = y^2 - 4$

$x^2 + 4 = y^2$

$\sqrt{x^2 + 4} = y,\ x \geq 0$

$f^{-1}(x) = \sqrt{x^2 + 4},\ x \geq 0$

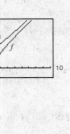

92. $f(x) = \dfrac{2x}{x + 1},\ x > -1$

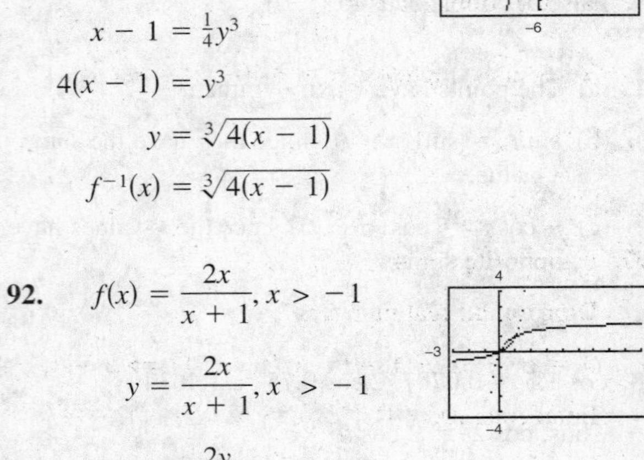

$y = \dfrac{2x}{x + 1},\ x > -1$

$x = \dfrac{2y}{y + 1}$

$xy + x = 2y$

$x = 2y - xy$

$x = y(2 - x)$

$\dfrac{x}{2 - x} = y,\ x < 2$

$f^{-1}(x) = \dfrac{x}{2 - x},\ x < 2$

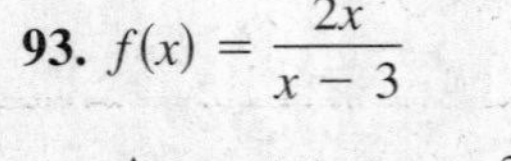

93. $f(x) = \dfrac{2x}{x - 3}$

Asymptotes: $x = 3,\ y = 2$

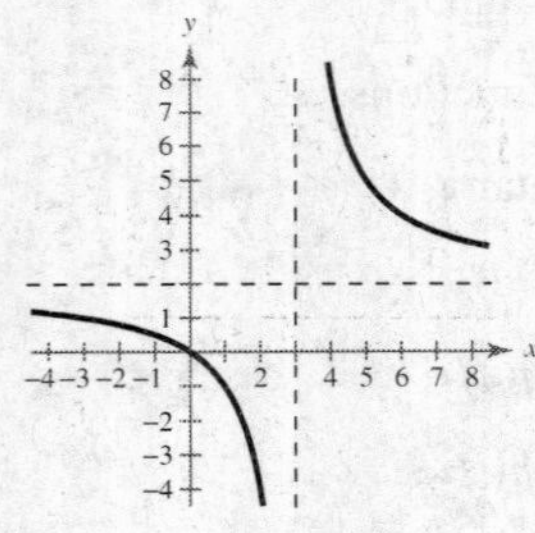

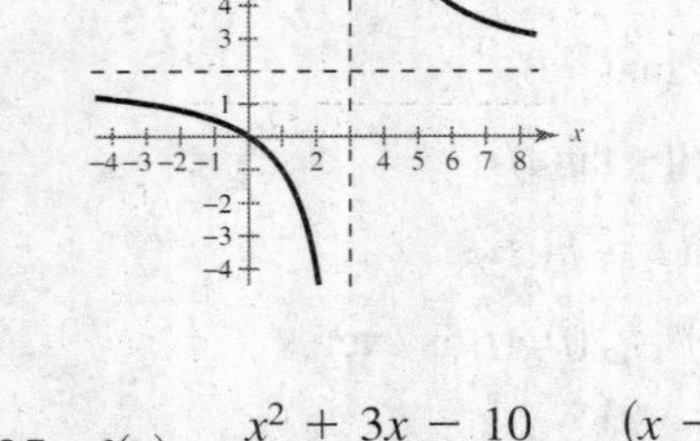

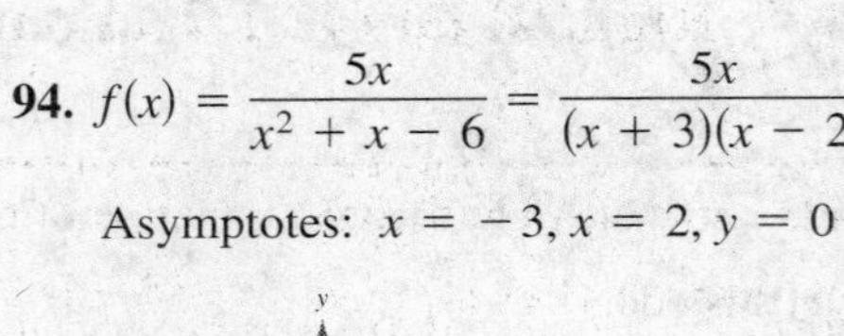

94. $f(x) = \dfrac{5x}{x^2 + x - 6} = \dfrac{5x}{(x + 3)(x - 2)}$

Asymptotes: $x = -3,\ x = 2,\ y = 0$

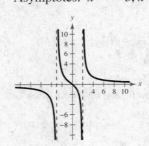

95. $f(x) = \dfrac{x^2 + 3x - 10}{2x^2 - 8} = \dfrac{(x - 2)(x + 5)}{2(x - 2)(x + 2)}$

$= \dfrac{x + 5}{2(x + 2)},\quad x \neq 2$

Asymptotes: $x = -2,\ y = \dfrac{1}{2}$

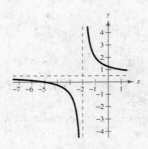

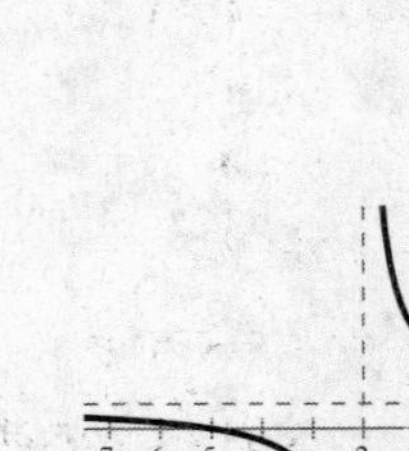

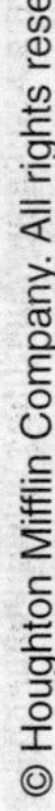

96. $f(x) = \dfrac{x^3 - 6x^2 + x - 1}{2x^2 - 5x - 8} = \dfrac{x}{2} - \dfrac{7}{4} - \dfrac{15(x + 4)}{4(2x^2 - 5x - 8)}$

Slant asymptote: $y = \dfrac{x}{2} - \dfrac{7}{4}$

Vertical asymptotes: $x \approx 3.608, x \approx -1.108$

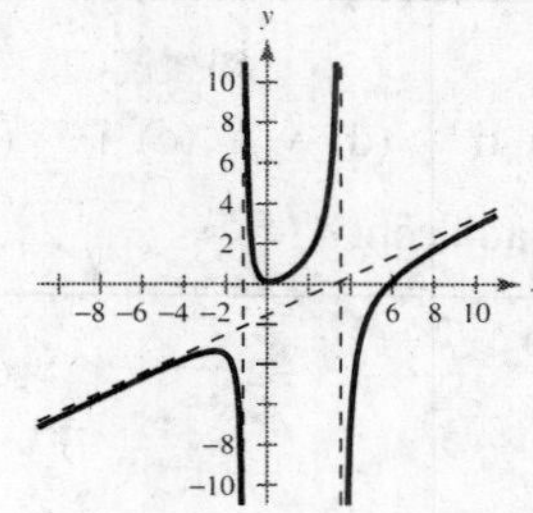

97. $y = x^2 + 3x - 4$

Domain: all real numbers

$0 = x^2 + 3x - 4 = (x + 4)(x - 1) \Longrightarrow x = 1, -4$

Intercepts: $(0, -4), (1, 0), (-4, 0)$

No asymptotes

98. $y = \ln x^4$

Domain: all $x \neq 0$

$\ln x^4 = 0 \Longrightarrow x^4 = 1 \Longrightarrow x = \pm 1$

Intercepts: $(1, 0), (-1, 0)$

Asymptote: $x = 0$

99. $f(x) = 3^{x+1} + 2$

Domain: all real numbers

Intercept: $(0, 5)$

Asymptote: $y = 2$

100. $f(x) = \dfrac{x - 7}{(x^2 + 4x + 4)} = \dfrac{x - 7}{(x + 2)^2}$

Domain: all real numbers $x \neq -2$

Intercepts: $(7, 0), \left(0, -\dfrac{7}{4}\right)$

Asymptotes: $x = -2, y = 0$

Section 4.3 Right Triangle Trigonometry

■ You should know the right triangle definition of trigonometric functions.

(a) $\sin \theta = \dfrac{\text{opp}}{\text{hyp}}$ (b) $\cos \theta = \dfrac{\text{adj}}{\text{hyp}}$ (c) $\tan \theta = \dfrac{\text{opp}}{\text{adj}}$

(d) $\csc \theta = \dfrac{\text{hyp}}{\text{opp}}$ (e) $\sec \theta = \dfrac{\text{hyp}}{\text{adj}}$ (f) $\cot \theta = \dfrac{\text{adj}}{\text{opp}}$

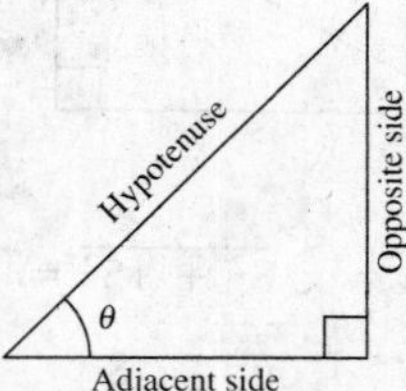

■ You should know the following identities.

(a) $\sin \theta = \dfrac{1}{\csc \theta}$ (b) $\csc \theta = \dfrac{1}{\sin \theta}$ (c) $\cos \theta = \dfrac{1}{\sec \theta}$

(d) $\sec \theta = \dfrac{1}{\cos \theta}$ (e) $\tan \theta = \dfrac{1}{\cot \theta}$ (f) $\cot \theta = \dfrac{1}{\tan \theta}$

(g) $\tan \theta = \dfrac{\sin \theta}{\cos \theta}$ (h) $\cot \theta = \dfrac{\cos \theta}{\sin \theta}$ (i) $\sin^2 \theta + \cos^2 \theta = 1$

(j) $1 + \tan^2 \theta = \sec^2 \theta$ (k) $1 + \cot^2 \theta = \csc^2 \theta$

■ You should know that two acute angles α and β are complementary if $\alpha + \beta = 90°$, and cofunctions of complementary angles are equal.

■ You should know the trigonometric function values of 30°, 45°, and 60°, or be able to construct triangles from which you can determine them.

Vocabulary Check

1. (a) iii (b) vi (c) ii (d) v (e) i (f) iv

2. hypotenuse, opposite, adjacent

3. elevation, depression

1.

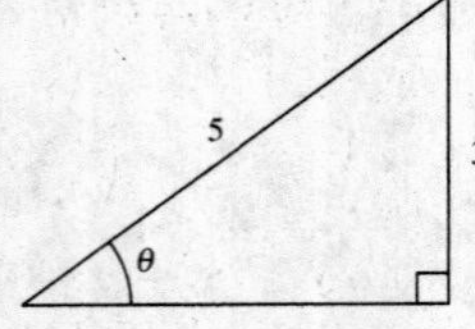

$\text{adj} = \sqrt{5^2 - 3^2} = \sqrt{16} = 4$

$\sin\theta = \dfrac{\text{opp}}{\text{hyp}} = \dfrac{3}{5}$

$\cos\theta = \dfrac{\text{adj}}{\text{hyp}} = \dfrac{4}{5}$

$\tan\theta = \dfrac{\text{opp}}{\text{adj}} = \dfrac{3}{4}$

$\csc\theta = \dfrac{\text{hyp}}{\text{opp}} = \dfrac{5}{3}$

$\sec\theta = \dfrac{\text{hyp}}{\text{adj}} = \dfrac{5}{4}$

$\cot\theta = \dfrac{\text{adj}}{\text{opp}} = \dfrac{4}{3}$

2.

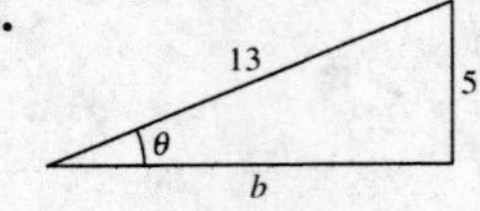

$b = \sqrt{13^2 - 5^2} = \sqrt{169 - 25} = 12$

$\sin\theta = \dfrac{\text{opp}}{\text{hyp}} = \dfrac{5}{13}$

$\cos\theta = \dfrac{\text{adj}}{\text{hyp}} = \dfrac{12}{13}$

$\tan\theta = \dfrac{\text{opp}}{\text{adj}} = \dfrac{5}{12}$

$\csc\theta = \dfrac{\text{hyp}}{\text{opp}} = \dfrac{13}{5}$

$\sec\theta = \dfrac{\text{hyp}}{\text{adj}} = \dfrac{13}{12}$

$\cot\theta = \dfrac{\text{adj}}{\text{opp}} = \dfrac{12}{5}$

3.

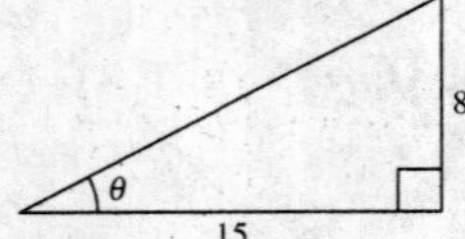

$\text{hyp} = \sqrt{8^2 + 15^2} = 17$

$\sin\theta = \dfrac{\text{opp}}{\text{hyp}} = \dfrac{8}{17}$

$\cos\theta = \dfrac{\text{adj}}{\text{hyp}} = \dfrac{15}{17}$

$\tan\theta = \dfrac{\text{opp}}{\text{adj}} = \dfrac{8}{15}$

$\csc\theta = \dfrac{\text{hyp}}{\text{opp}} = \dfrac{17}{8}$

$\sec\theta = \dfrac{\text{hyp}}{\text{adj}} = \dfrac{17}{15}$

$\cot\theta = \dfrac{\text{adj}}{\text{opp}} = \dfrac{15}{8}$

4.

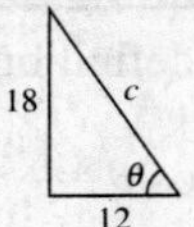

$C = \sqrt{18^2 + 12^2} = \sqrt{468} = 6\sqrt{13}$

$\sin\theta = \dfrac{18}{6\sqrt{13}} = \dfrac{3\sqrt{13}}{13}$

$\cos\theta = \dfrac{12}{6\sqrt{13}} = \dfrac{2\sqrt{13}}{13}$

$\tan\theta = \dfrac{18}{12} = \dfrac{3}{2}$

$\csc\theta = \dfrac{\sqrt{13}}{3}$

$\sec\theta = \dfrac{\sqrt{13}}{2}$

$\cot\theta = \dfrac{2}{3}$

5. $\text{opp} = \sqrt{10^2 - 8^2} = 6$

$\sin\theta = \dfrac{\text{opp}}{\text{hyp}} = \dfrac{6}{10} = \dfrac{3}{5}$

$\cos\theta = \dfrac{\text{adj}}{\text{hyp}} = \dfrac{8}{10} = \dfrac{4}{5}$

$\tan\theta = \dfrac{\text{opp}}{\text{adj}} = \dfrac{6}{8} = \dfrac{3}{4}$

$\csc\theta = \dfrac{\text{hyp}}{\text{opp}} = \dfrac{10}{6} = \dfrac{5}{3}$

$\sec\theta = \dfrac{\text{hyp}}{\text{adj}} = \dfrac{10}{8} = \dfrac{5}{4}$

$\cot\theta = \dfrac{\text{adj}}{\text{opp}} = \dfrac{8}{6} = \dfrac{4}{3}$

10

8

θ

$\text{opp} = \sqrt{2.5^2 - 2^2} = 1.5$

2.5

2

θ

$\sin\theta = \dfrac{\text{opp}}{\text{hyp}} = \dfrac{1.5}{2.5} = \dfrac{3}{5}$

$\cos\theta = \dfrac{\text{adj}}{\text{hyp}} = \dfrac{2}{2.5} = \dfrac{4}{5}$

$\tan\theta = \dfrac{\text{opp}}{\text{adj}} = \dfrac{1.5}{2} = \dfrac{3}{4}$

$\csc\theta = \dfrac{\text{hyp}}{\text{opp}} = \dfrac{2.5}{1.5} = \dfrac{5}{3}$

$\sec\theta = \dfrac{\text{hyp}}{\text{adj}} = \dfrac{2.5}{2} = \dfrac{5}{4}$

$\cot\theta = \dfrac{\text{adj}}{\text{opp}} = \dfrac{2}{1.5} = \dfrac{4}{3}$

The function values are the same since the triangles are similar and the corresponding sides are proportional.

6. $\text{adj} = \sqrt{15^2 - 8^2} = \sqrt{161}$

$\sin\theta = \dfrac{\text{opp}}{\text{hyp}} = \dfrac{8}{15}$

$\cos\theta = \dfrac{\text{adj}}{\text{hyp}} = \dfrac{\sqrt{161}}{15}$

$\tan\theta = \dfrac{\text{opp}}{\text{adj}} = \dfrac{8}{\sqrt{161}} = \dfrac{8\sqrt{161}}{161}$

$\csc\theta = \dfrac{\text{hyp}}{\text{opp}} = \dfrac{15}{8}$

$\sec\theta = \dfrac{\text{hyp}}{\text{adj}} = \dfrac{15}{\sqrt{161}} = \dfrac{15\sqrt{161}}{161}$

$\cot\theta = \dfrac{\text{adj}}{\text{opp}} = \dfrac{\sqrt{161}}{8}$

15

8

θ

$\text{adj} = \sqrt{7.5^2 - 4^2} = \dfrac{\sqrt{161}}{2}$

7.5

4

θ

$\sin\theta = \dfrac{\text{opp}}{\text{hyp}} = \dfrac{4}{7.5} = \dfrac{8}{15}$

$\cos\theta = \dfrac{\text{adj}}{\text{hyp}} = \dfrac{\sqrt{161}}{2 \cdot 7.5} = \dfrac{\sqrt{161}}{15}$

$\tan\theta = \dfrac{\text{opp}}{\text{adj}} = \dfrac{4}{\left(\sqrt{161}/2\right)} = \dfrac{8}{\sqrt{161}} = \dfrac{8\sqrt{161}}{161}$

$\csc\theta = \dfrac{\text{hyp}}{\text{opp}} = \dfrac{7.5}{4} = \dfrac{15}{8}$

$\sec\theta = \dfrac{\text{hyp}}{\text{adj}} = \dfrac{7.5}{\left(\sqrt{161}/2\right)} = \dfrac{15}{\sqrt{161}} = \dfrac{15\sqrt{161}}{161}$

$\cot\theta = \dfrac{\text{adj}}{\text{opp}} = \dfrac{\sqrt{161}}{2 \cdot 4} = \dfrac{\sqrt{161}}{8}$

The function values are the same because the triangles are similar, and corresponding sides are proportional.

7. adj $= \sqrt{3^2 - 1^2} = \sqrt{8} = 2\sqrt{2}$

$\sin\theta = \dfrac{\text{opp}}{\text{hyp}} = \dfrac{1}{3}$

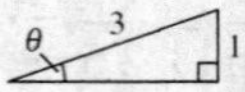

$\cos\theta = \dfrac{\text{adj}}{\text{hyp}} = \dfrac{2\sqrt{2}}{3}$

$\tan\theta = \dfrac{\text{opp}}{\text{adj}} = \dfrac{1}{2\sqrt{2}} = \dfrac{\sqrt{2}}{4}$

$\csc\theta = \dfrac{\text{hyp}}{\text{opp}} = 3$

$\sec\theta = \dfrac{\text{hyp}}{\text{adj}} = \dfrac{3}{2\sqrt{2}} = \dfrac{3\sqrt{2}}{4}$

$\cot\theta = \dfrac{\text{adj}}{\text{opp}} = 2\sqrt{2}$

adj $= \sqrt{6^2 - 2^2} = \sqrt{32} = 4\sqrt{2}$

$\sin\theta = \dfrac{\text{opp}}{\text{hyp}} = \dfrac{2}{6} = \dfrac{1}{3}$

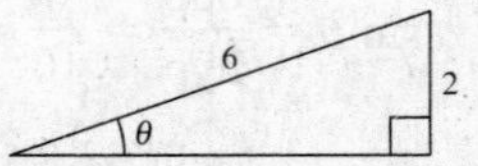

$\cos\theta = \dfrac{\text{adj}}{\text{hyp}} = \dfrac{4\sqrt{2}}{6} = \dfrac{2\sqrt{2}}{3}$

$\tan\theta = \dfrac{\text{opp}}{\text{adj}} = \dfrac{2}{4\sqrt{2}} = \dfrac{1}{2\sqrt{2}} = \dfrac{\sqrt{2}}{4}$

$\csc\theta = \dfrac{\text{hyp}}{\text{opp}} = \dfrac{6}{2} = 3$

$\sec\theta = \dfrac{\text{hyp}}{\text{adj}} = \dfrac{6}{4\sqrt{2}} = \dfrac{3}{2\sqrt{2}} = \dfrac{3\sqrt{2}}{4}$

$\cot\theta = \dfrac{\text{adj}}{\text{opp}} = \dfrac{4\sqrt{2}}{2} = 2\sqrt{2}$

The function values are the same since the triangles are similar and the corresponding sides are proportional.

8. hyp $= \sqrt{1^2 + 2^2} = \sqrt{5}$

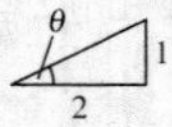

$\sin\theta = \dfrac{\text{opp}}{\text{hyp}} = \dfrac{1}{\sqrt{5}} = \dfrac{\sqrt{5}}{5}$

$\cos\theta = \dfrac{\text{adj}}{\text{hyp}} = \dfrac{2}{\sqrt{5}} = \dfrac{2\sqrt{5}}{5}$

$\tan\theta = \dfrac{\text{opp}}{\text{adj}} = \dfrac{1}{2}$

$\csc\theta = \dfrac{\text{hyp}}{\text{opp}} = \dfrac{\sqrt{5}}{1} = \sqrt{5}$

$\sec\theta = \dfrac{\text{hyp}}{\text{adj}} = \dfrac{\sqrt{5}}{2}$

$\cot\theta = \dfrac{\text{adj}}{\text{opp}} = \dfrac{2}{1} = 2$

hyp $= \sqrt{3^2 + 6^2} = 3\sqrt{5}$

$\sin\theta = \dfrac{3}{3\sqrt{5}} = \dfrac{1}{\sqrt{5}} = \dfrac{\sqrt{5}}{5}$

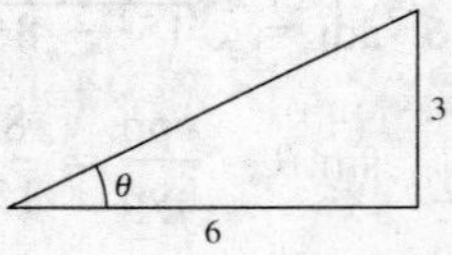

$\cos\theta = \dfrac{6}{3\sqrt{5}} = \dfrac{2}{\sqrt{5}} = \dfrac{2\sqrt{5}}{5}$

$\tan\theta = \dfrac{3}{6} = \dfrac{1}{2}$

$\csc\theta = \dfrac{3\sqrt{5}}{3} = \sqrt{5}$

$\sec\theta = \dfrac{3\sqrt{5}}{6} = \dfrac{\sqrt{5}}{2}$

$\cot\theta = \dfrac{6}{3} = 2$

The function values are the same because the triangles are similar, and corresponding sides are proportional.

9. Given: $\sin\theta = \dfrac{5}{6} = \dfrac{\text{opp}}{\text{hyp}}$

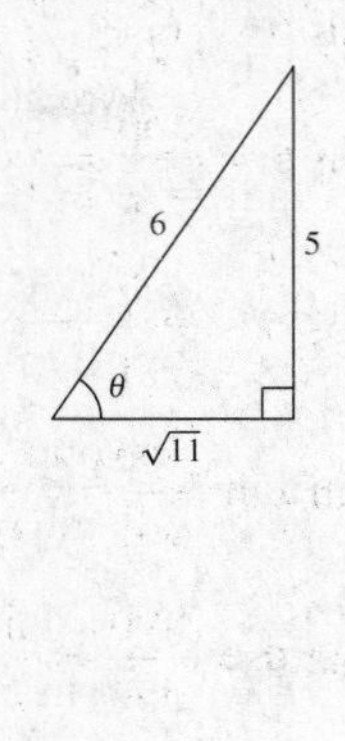

$$5^2 + (\text{adj})^2 = 6^2$$

$$\text{adj} = \sqrt{11}$$

$$\cos\theta = \frac{\text{adj}}{\text{hyp}} = \frac{\sqrt{11}}{6}$$

$$\tan\theta = \frac{\text{opp}}{\text{adj}} = \frac{5}{\sqrt{11}} = \frac{5\sqrt{11}}{11}$$

$$\cot\theta = \frac{\text{adj}}{\text{opp}} = \frac{\sqrt{11}}{5}$$

$$\sec\theta = \frac{\text{hyp}}{\text{adj}} = \frac{6}{\sqrt{11}} = \frac{6\sqrt{11}}{11}$$

$$\csc\theta = \frac{\text{hyp}}{\text{opp}} = \frac{6}{5}$$

10. $\text{hyp} = \sqrt{5^2 + 1^2} = \sqrt{26}$

$$\sin\theta = \frac{\text{opp}}{\text{hyp}} = \frac{1}{\sqrt{26}} = \frac{\sqrt{26}}{26}$$

$$\cos\theta = \frac{\text{adj}}{\text{hyp}} = \frac{5}{\sqrt{26}} = \frac{5\sqrt{26}}{26}$$

$$\tan\theta = \frac{\text{opp}}{\text{adj}} = \frac{1}{5}$$

$$\csc\theta = \frac{\text{hyp}}{\text{opp}} = \frac{\sqrt{26}}{1} = \sqrt{26}$$

$$\sec\theta = \frac{\text{hyp}}{\text{adj}} = \frac{\sqrt{26}}{5}$$

11. Given: $\sec\theta = 4 = \dfrac{4}{1} = \dfrac{\text{hyp}}{\text{adj}}$

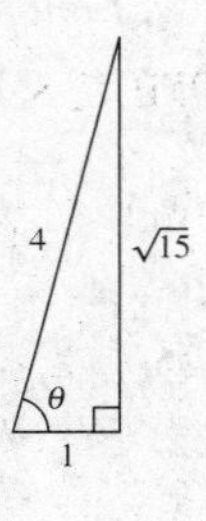

$$(\text{opp})^2 + 1^2 = 4^2$$

$$\text{opp} = \sqrt{15}$$

$$\sin\theta = \frac{\sqrt{15}}{4}$$

$$\cos\theta = \frac{1}{4}$$

$$\tan\theta = \sqrt{15}$$

$$\cot\theta = \frac{1}{\sqrt{15}} = \frac{\sqrt{15}}{15}$$

$$\csc\theta = \frac{4}{\sqrt{15}} = \frac{4\sqrt{15}}{15}$$

12. $\text{opp} = \sqrt{7^2 - 3^2} = \sqrt{40} = 2\sqrt{10}$

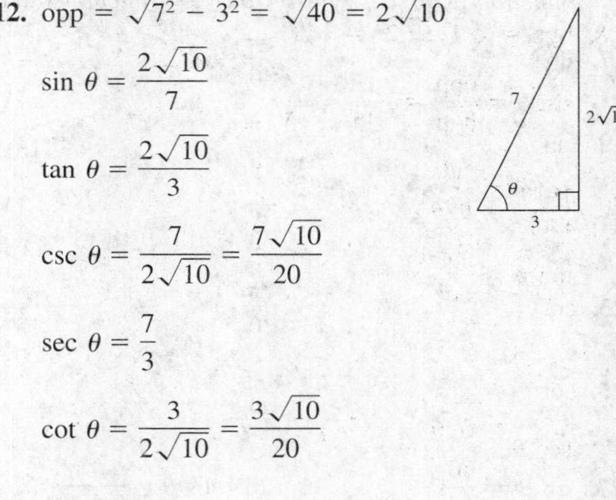

$$\sin\theta = \frac{2\sqrt{10}}{7}$$

$$\tan\theta = \frac{2\sqrt{10}}{3}$$

$$\csc\theta = \frac{7}{2\sqrt{10}} = \frac{7\sqrt{10}}{20}$$

$$\sec\theta = \frac{7}{3}$$

$$\cot\theta = \frac{3}{2\sqrt{10}} = \frac{3\sqrt{10}}{20}$$

13. Given: $\tan\theta = 3 = \dfrac{3}{1} = \dfrac{\text{opp}}{\text{adj}}$

$$3^2 + 1^2 = (\text{hyp})^2$$

$$\text{hyp} = \sqrt{10}$$

$$\sin\theta = \frac{3\sqrt{10}}{10}$$

$$\cos\theta = \frac{\sqrt{10}}{10}$$

$$\sec\theta = \sqrt{10}$$

$$\cot\theta = \frac{1}{3}$$

$$\csc\theta = \frac{\sqrt{10}}{3}$$

14. $\text{adj} = \sqrt{17^2 - 4^2} = \sqrt{273}$

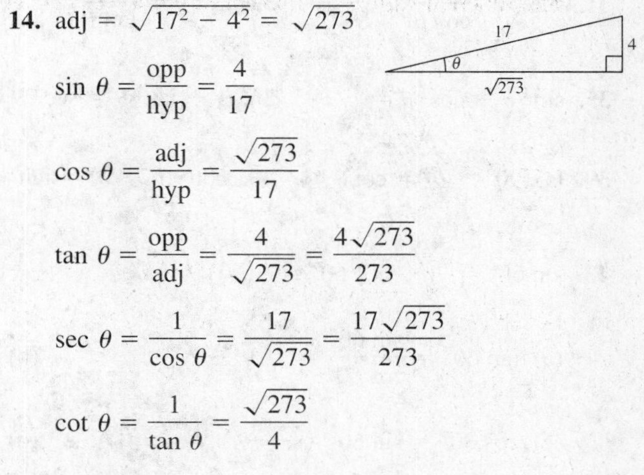

$$\sin\theta = \frac{\text{opp}}{\text{hyp}} = \frac{4}{17}$$

$$\cos\theta = \frac{\text{adj}}{\text{hyp}} = \frac{\sqrt{273}}{17}$$

$$\tan\theta = \frac{\text{opp}}{\text{adj}} = \frac{4}{\sqrt{273}} = \frac{4\sqrt{273}}{273}$$

$$\sec\theta = \frac{1}{\cos\theta} = \frac{17}{\sqrt{273}} = \frac{17\sqrt{273}}{273}$$

$$\cot\theta = \frac{1}{\tan\theta} = \frac{\sqrt{273}}{4}$$

15. Given: $\cot\theta = \dfrac{9}{4} = \dfrac{\text{adj}}{\text{opp}}$

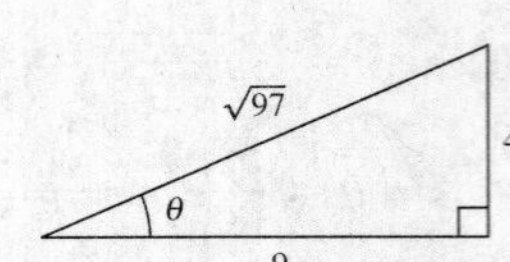

$4^2 + 9^2 = (\text{hyp})^2$

$\text{hyp} = \sqrt{97}$

$\sin\theta = \dfrac{4}{\sqrt{97}} = \dfrac{4\sqrt{97}}{97}$

$\cos\theta = \dfrac{9}{\sqrt{97}} = \dfrac{9\sqrt{97}}{97}$

$\tan\theta = \dfrac{4}{9}$

$\sec\theta = \dfrac{\sqrt{97}}{9}$

$\csc\theta = \dfrac{\sqrt{97}}{4}$

16. $\sin\theta = \dfrac{3}{8}$

$\text{adj} = \sqrt{8^2 - 3^2} = \sqrt{55}$

$\cos\theta = \dfrac{\text{adj}}{\text{hyp}} = \dfrac{\sqrt{55}}{8}$

$\tan\theta = \dfrac{\text{opp}}{\text{adj}} = \dfrac{3}{\sqrt{55}} = \dfrac{3\sqrt{55}}{55}$

$\csc\theta = \dfrac{1}{\sin\theta} = \dfrac{8}{3}$

$\sec\theta = \dfrac{1}{\cos\theta} = \dfrac{8}{\sqrt{55}} = \dfrac{8\sqrt{55}}{55}$

$\cot\theta = \dfrac{1}{\tan\theta} = \dfrac{\sqrt{55}}{3}$

	Function	*θ (deg)*	*θ (rad)*	*Function Value*
17.	sin	30°	$\frac{\pi}{6}$	$\frac{1}{2}$
18.	cos	45°	$\frac{\pi}{4}$	$\frac{\sqrt{2}}{2}$
19.	tan	60°	$\frac{\pi}{3}$	$\sqrt{3}$
20.	sec	45°	$\frac{\pi}{4}$	$\sqrt{2}$
21.	cot	60°	$\frac{\pi}{3}$	$\frac{\sqrt{3}}{3}$
22.	csc	45°	$\frac{\pi}{4}$	$\sqrt{2}$
23.	cos	30°	$\frac{\pi}{6}$	$\frac{\sqrt{3}}{2}$
24.	sin	45°	$\frac{\pi}{4}$	$\frac{\sqrt{2}}{2}$
25.	cot	45°	$\frac{\pi}{4}$	1
26.	tan	30°	$\frac{\pi}{6}$	$\frac{1}{\sqrt{3}}$

27. $\sin\theta = \dfrac{1}{\csc\theta}$ **28.** $\cos\theta = \dfrac{1}{\sec\theta}$ **29.** $\tan\theta = \dfrac{1}{\cot\theta}$ **30.** $\csc\theta = \dfrac{1}{\sin\theta}$

31. $\sec\theta = \dfrac{1}{\cos\theta}$ **32.** $\cot\theta = \dfrac{1}{\tan\theta}$ **33.** $\tan\theta = \dfrac{\sin\theta}{\cos\theta}$ **34.** $\cot\theta = \dfrac{\cos\theta}{\sin\theta}$

35. $\sin^2\theta + \cos^2\theta = 1$ **36.** $1 + \tan^2\theta = \sec^2\theta$ **37.** $\sin(90° - \theta) = \cos\theta$ **38.** $\cos(90° - \theta) = \sin\theta$

39. $\tan(90° - \theta) = \cot\theta$ **40.** $\cot(90° - \theta) = \tan\theta$ **41.** $\sec(90° - \theta) = \csc\theta$ **42.** $\csc(90° - \theta) = \sec\theta$

43. $\sin 60° = \dfrac{\sqrt{3}}{2}, \ \cos 60° = \dfrac{1}{2}$

(a) $\tan 60° = \dfrac{\sin 60°}{\cos 60°} = \sqrt{3}$

(b) $\sin 30° = \cos 60° = \dfrac{1}{2}$

(c) $\cos 30° = \sin 60° = \dfrac{\sqrt{3}}{2}$

(d) $\cot 60° = \dfrac{\cos 60°}{\sin 60°} = \dfrac{1}{\sqrt{3}} = \dfrac{\sqrt{3}}{3}$

44. $\sin 30° = \frac{1}{2}, \tan 30° = \frac{\sqrt{3}}{3}$

(a) $\csc 30° = \frac{1}{\sin 30°} = 2$

(b) $\cot 60° = \tan(90° - 60°) = \tan 30° = \frac{\sqrt{3}}{3}$

(c) $\cos 30° = \frac{\sin 30°}{\tan 30°} = \frac{(1/2)}{(\sqrt{3}/3)} = \frac{3}{2\sqrt{3}} = \frac{\sqrt{3}}{2}$

(d) $\cot 30° = \frac{1}{\tan 30°} = \frac{3}{\sqrt{3}} = \frac{3\sqrt{3}}{3} = \sqrt{3}$

45. $\csc \theta = 3,\ \sec \theta = \frac{3\sqrt{2}}{4}$

(a) $\sin \theta = \frac{1}{\csc \theta} = \frac{1}{3}$

(b) $\cos \theta = \frac{1}{\sec \theta} = \frac{2\sqrt{2}}{3}$

(c) $\tan \theta = \frac{\sin \theta}{\cos \theta} = \frac{1/3}{(2\sqrt{2})/3} = \frac{\sqrt{2}}{4}$

(d) $\sec(90° - \theta) = \csc \theta = 3$

46. $\sec \theta = 5, \tan \theta = 2\sqrt{6}$

(a) $\cos \theta = \frac{1}{\sec \theta} = \frac{1}{5}$

(b) $\cot \theta = \frac{1}{\tan \theta} = \frac{1}{2\sqrt{6}} = \frac{\sqrt{6}}{12}$

(c) $\cot(90° - \theta) = \tan \theta = 2\sqrt{6}$

(d) $\sin \theta = \tan \theta \cos \theta = (2\sqrt{6})\left(\frac{1}{5}\right) = \frac{2\sqrt{6}}{5}$

47. $\cos \alpha = \frac{1}{4}$

(a) $\sec \alpha = \frac{1}{\cos \alpha} = 4$

(b) $\sin^2 \alpha + \cos^2 \alpha = 1$

$$\sin^2 \alpha + \left(\frac{1}{4}\right)^2 = 1$$

$$\sin^2 \alpha = \frac{15}{16}$$

$$\sin \alpha = \frac{\sqrt{15}}{4}$$

(c) $\cot \alpha = \frac{\cos \alpha}{\sin \alpha}$

$$= \frac{1/4}{\sqrt{15}/4}$$

$$= \frac{1}{\sqrt{15}} = \frac{\sqrt{15}}{15}$$

(d) $\sin(90° - \alpha) = \cos \alpha = \frac{1}{4}$

48. $\tan \beta = 5$ (β lies in Quadrant I or III.)

(a) $\cot \beta = \frac{1}{\tan \beta} = \frac{1}{5}$

(b) $\sec^2 \beta = 1 + \tan^2 \beta \Longrightarrow \cos \beta = \frac{1}{\sqrt{1 + \tan^2 \beta}} = \frac{1}{\sqrt{1 + 25}} = \frac{1}{\sqrt{26}} = \frac{\sqrt{26}}{26}$

(c) $\tan(90° - \beta) = \cot \beta = \frac{1}{5}$

(d) $\csc \beta = \sqrt{1 + \cot^2 \beta} = \sqrt{1 + \frac{1}{25}} = \frac{\sqrt{26}}{5}$

49. $\tan \theta \cot \theta = \tan \theta\left(\frac{1}{\tan \theta}\right) = 1$

50. $\csc \theta \tan \theta = \frac{1}{\sin \theta} \cdot \frac{\sin \theta}{\cos \theta} = \frac{1}{\cos \theta} = \sec \theta$

51. $\tan \theta \cos \theta = \left(\frac{\sin \theta}{\cos \theta}\right) \cos \theta = \sin \theta$

52. $\cot \theta \sin \theta = \frac{\cos \theta}{\sin \theta} \sin \theta = \cos \theta$

53. $(1 + \cos\theta)(1 - \cos\theta) = 1 - \cos^2\theta$
$= (\sin^2\theta + \cos^2\theta) - \cos^2\theta$
$= \sin^2\theta$

54. $(\csc\theta + \cot\theta)(\csc\theta - \cot\theta) = \csc^2\theta - \cot^2\theta$
$= 1$

55. $\dfrac{\sin\theta}{\cos\theta} + \dfrac{\cos\theta}{\sin\theta} = \dfrac{\sin^2\theta + \cos^2\theta}{\sin\theta\cos\theta}$
$= \dfrac{1}{\sin\theta\cos\theta}$
$= \dfrac{1}{\sin\theta}\cdot\dfrac{1}{\cos\theta} = \csc\theta\sec\theta$

56. $\dfrac{\tan\theta + \cot\theta}{\tan\theta} = \dfrac{\tan\theta}{\tan\theta} + \dfrac{\cot\theta}{\tan\theta}$
$= 1 + \dfrac{\cot\theta}{(1/\cot\theta)}$
$= 1 + \cot^2\theta = \csc^2\theta$

57. (a) $\sin 41° \approx 0.6561$
(b) $\cos 87° \approx 0.0523$

58. (a) $\tan 18.5° \approx 0.3346$
(b) $\cot 71.5° = \dfrac{1}{\tan 71.5°} \approx 0.3346$

59. (a) $\sec 42°\,12' = \sec 42.2° = \dfrac{1}{\cos 42.2°} \approx 1.3499$
(b) $\csc 48°\,7' = \dfrac{1}{\sin\left(48 + \frac{7}{60}\right)°} \approx 1.3432$

60. (a) $\cos(8°\,50'\,25'') = \cos\left(8 + \dfrac{50}{60} + \dfrac{25}{3600}\right)$
$\approx \cos(8.840278) \approx 0.9881$
(b) $\sec(8°\,50'\,25'') = \dfrac{1}{\cos(8°\,50'\,25'')} \approx 1.0120$

61. Make sure that your calculator is in radian mode.
(a) $\cot\dfrac{\pi}{16} = \dfrac{1}{\tan(\pi/16)} \approx 5.0273$
(b) $\tan\dfrac{\pi}{8} \approx 0.4142$

62. (a) $\sec(1.54) = \dfrac{1}{\cos(1.54)} \approx 32.4765$
(b) $\cos(1.25) \approx 0.3153$

63. (a) $\sin\theta = \dfrac{1}{2} \implies \theta = 30° = \dfrac{\pi}{6}$
(b) $\csc\theta = 2 \implies \theta = 30° = \dfrac{\pi}{6}$

64. (a) $\cos\theta = \dfrac{\sqrt{2}}{2} \implies \theta = 45° = \dfrac{\pi}{4}$
(b) $\tan\theta = 1 \implies \theta = 45° = \dfrac{\pi}{4}$

65. (a) $\sec\theta = 2 \implies \theta = 60° = \dfrac{\pi}{3}$
(b) $\cot\theta = 1 \implies \theta = 45° = \dfrac{\pi}{4}$

66. (a) $\tan\theta = \sqrt{3} \implies \theta = 60° = \dfrac{\pi}{3}$
(b) $\cos\theta = \dfrac{1}{2} \implies \theta = 60° = \dfrac{\pi}{3}$

67. (a) $\csc\theta = \dfrac{2\sqrt{3}}{3} \implies \theta = 60° = \dfrac{\pi}{3}$
(b) $\sin\theta = \dfrac{\sqrt{2}}{2} \implies \theta = 45° = \dfrac{\pi}{4}$

68. (a) $\cot\theta = \dfrac{\sqrt{3}}{3}$
$\tan\theta = \dfrac{3}{\sqrt{3}} = \sqrt{3} \implies \theta = 60° = \dfrac{\pi}{3}$
(b) $\sec\theta = \sqrt{2}$
$\cos\theta = \dfrac{1}{\sqrt{2}} = \dfrac{\sqrt{2}}{2} \implies \theta = 45° = \dfrac{\pi}{4}$

69. $\tan 30° = \dfrac{y}{105} \implies y = 105 \tan 30° = 105 \cdot \dfrac{\sqrt{3}}{3} = 35\sqrt{3}$

$\cos 30° = \dfrac{105}{r} \implies r = \dfrac{105}{\cos 30°} = \dfrac{105}{\sqrt{3}/2} = \dfrac{210}{\sqrt{3}} = 70\sqrt{3}$

70. $\cos 30° = \dfrac{x}{15} \implies x = 15 \cos 30° = 15 \cdot \dfrac{\sqrt{3}}{2} = \dfrac{15\sqrt{3}}{2}$

$\sin 30° = \dfrac{y}{15} \implies y = 15 \sin 30° = 15\left(\dfrac{1}{2}\right) = \dfrac{15}{2}$

71. $\cos 60° = \dfrac{x}{16} \implies x = 16 \cos 60° = 16\left(\dfrac{1}{2}\right) = 8$

$\sin 60° = \dfrac{y}{16} \implies y = 16 \sin 60° = 16\left(\dfrac{\sqrt{3}}{2}\right) = 8\sqrt{3}$

72. $\cot 60° = \dfrac{x}{38} \implies x = 38 \cot 60° = 38 \cdot \dfrac{1}{\sqrt{3}} = \dfrac{38\sqrt{3}}{3}$

$\sin 60° = \dfrac{38}{r} \implies r = \dfrac{38}{\sin 60°} = \dfrac{38}{\sqrt{3}/2} = \dfrac{76\sqrt{3}}{3}$

73. $\tan 45° = \dfrac{20}{x} \implies 1 = \dfrac{20}{x} \implies x = 20$

$r^2 = 20^2 + 20^2 \implies r = 20\sqrt{2}$

74. $\tan 45° = \dfrac{y}{10} \implies 1 = \dfrac{y}{10} \implies y = 10$

$r^2 = 10^2 + 10^2 \implies r = 10\sqrt{2}$

75. $\tan 45° = \dfrac{2\sqrt{5}}{x} \implies 1 = \dfrac{2\sqrt{5}}{x} \implies x = 2\sqrt{5}$

$r^2 = (2\sqrt{5})^2 + (2\sqrt{5})^2 = 20 + 20 = 40 \implies r = 2\sqrt{10}$

76. $\tan 45° = \dfrac{y}{4\sqrt{6}} \implies 1 = \dfrac{y}{4\sqrt{6}} \implies y = 4\sqrt{6}$

$r^2 = (4\sqrt{6})^2 + (4\sqrt{6})^2 = 96 + 96 = 192 \implies r = 8\sqrt{3}$

77. (a)

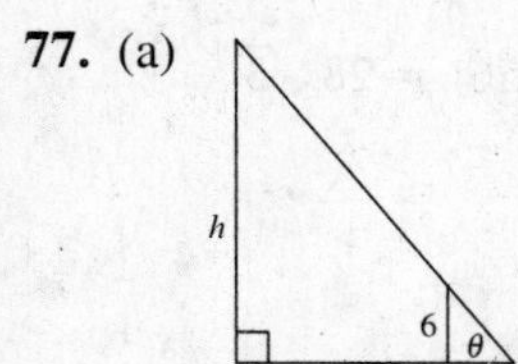

(b) $\tan \theta = \dfrac{6}{5}$ and $\tan \theta = \dfrac{h}{21}$. Thus, $\dfrac{6}{5} = \dfrac{h}{21}$.

(c) $h = \dfrac{6(21)}{5} = 25.2$ feet

78. (a)

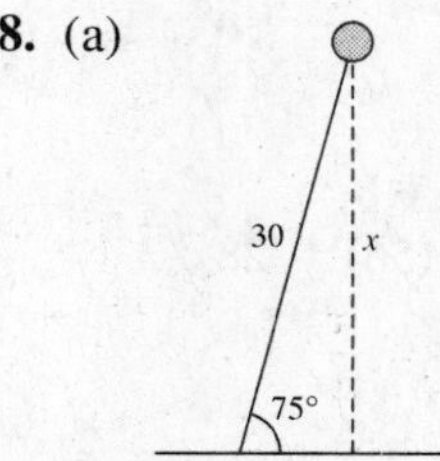

(b) $\sin 75° = \dfrac{x}{30}$

(c) $x = 30 \sin 75° \approx 28.98$ meters

79. $\tan \theta = \dfrac{\text{opp}}{\text{adj}}$

$\tan 58° = \dfrac{w}{100}$

$w = 100 \tan 58° \approx 160$ feet

80. $\cot 9° = \dfrac{c}{h}$

$\cot 3.5° = \dfrac{13 + c}{h}$

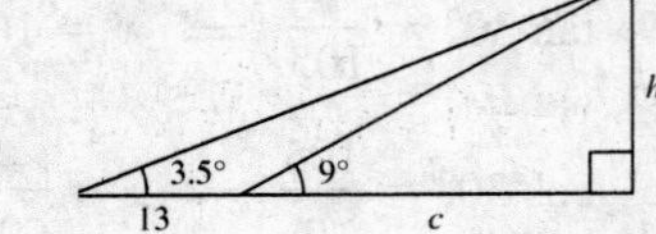

not drawn to scale

Subtracting, $\dfrac{13}{h} = \cot 3.5° - \cot 9°$

$h = \dfrac{13}{\cot 3.5° - \cot 9°}$

$\approx \dfrac{13}{16.3499 - 6.3138} \approx 1.295 \approx 1.3$ miles.

81. (a) $\tan \theta = \dfrac{50}{50} = 1 \Longrightarrow \theta = 45°$

(b) $L^2 = 50^2 + 50^2 = 2 \cdot 50^2 \quad \Longrightarrow \quad L = 50\sqrt{2}$ feet

(c) $\dfrac{50\sqrt{2}}{6} = \dfrac{25\sqrt{2}}{3}$ ft/sec rate down the zip line

$\dfrac{50}{6} = \dfrac{25}{3}$ ft/sec vertical rate

82. (a) $\sin 35.4° = \dfrac{x}{896.5}$

$x = 896.5 \sin 35.4° \approx 519.3$ feet

(b) $1693.5 - 519.3 = 1174.2$ feet above sea level

(c) $\dfrac{896.5}{300}$ minutes to reach top

Vertical rate $= \dfrac{519.3}{(896.5/300)}$

≈ 173.8 feet per minute

83.

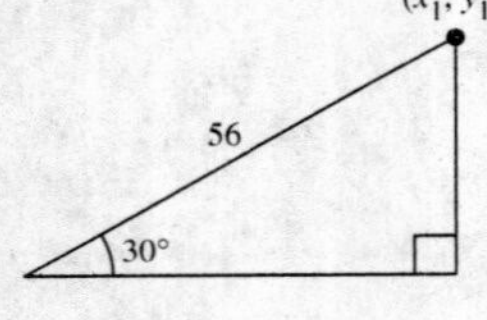

$\sin 30° = \dfrac{y_1}{56}$

$y_1 = (\sin 30°)(56) = \left(\dfrac{1}{2}\right)(56) = 28$

$\cos 30° = \dfrac{x_1}{56}$

$x_1 = \cos 30°(56) = \dfrac{\sqrt{3}}{2}(56) = 28\sqrt{3}$

$(x_1, y_1) = (28\sqrt{3}, 28)$

(x_2, y_2)

56

60°

$\sin 60° = \dfrac{y_2}{56}$

$y_2 = \sin 60°(56) = \left(\dfrac{\sqrt{3}}{2}\right)(56) = 28\sqrt{3}$

$\cos 60° = \dfrac{x_2}{56}$

$x_2 = (\cos 60°)(56) = \left(\dfrac{1}{2}\right)(56) = 28$

$(x_2, y_2) = (28, 28\sqrt{3})$

84. $x \approx 9.397,\ y \approx 3.420$

$\sin 20° = \dfrac{y}{10} \approx 0.34 \qquad \cos 20° = \dfrac{x}{10} \approx 0.94$

$\tan 20° = \dfrac{y}{x} \approx 0.36 \qquad \cot 20° = \dfrac{x}{y} \approx 2.75$

$\sec 20° = \dfrac{10}{x} \approx 1.06 \qquad \csc 20° = \dfrac{10}{y} \approx 2.92$

85. True

$\sin 60° \csc 60° = \sin 60° \dfrac{1}{\sin 60°} = 1$

86. False

$\sin 45° + \cos 45° = \dfrac{\sqrt{2}}{2} + \dfrac{\sqrt{2}}{2} = \sqrt{2} \neq 1$

87. True

$1 + \cot^2 \theta = \csc^2 \theta$ for all θ

88. No. $\tan^2 \theta + 1 = \sec^2 \theta$, so you can find $\pm \sec \theta$.

89. (a)

θ	0°	20°	40°	60°	80°
$\sin \theta$	0	0.3420	0.6428	0.8660	0.9848
$\cos \theta$	1	0.9397	0.7660	0.5000	0.1736
$\tan \theta$	0	0.3640	0.8391	1.7321	5.6713

(b) Sine and tangent are increasing, cosine is decreasing.

(c) In each case, $\tan \theta = \dfrac{\sin \theta}{\cos \theta}$.

90.

θ	0°	20°	40°	60°	80°
$\cos \theta$	1	0.9397	0.7660	0.5000	0.1736
$\sin(90° - \theta)$	1	0.9397	0.7660	0.5000	0.1736

$\cos \theta = \sin(90° - \theta)$

θ and $90° - \theta$ are complementary angles.

91.

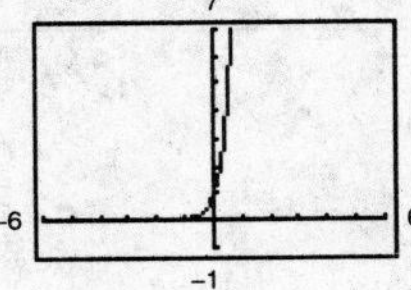

92.

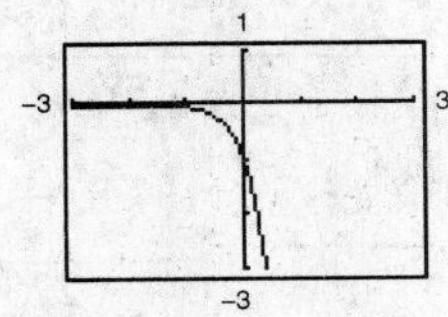

93.

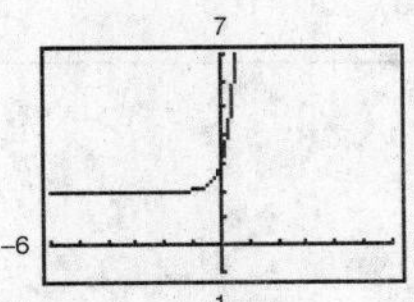

94.

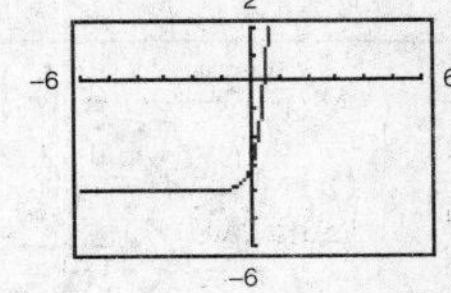

95.

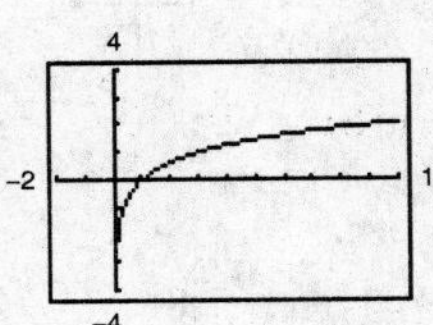

96.

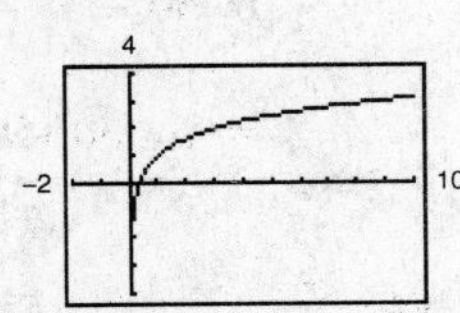

97.

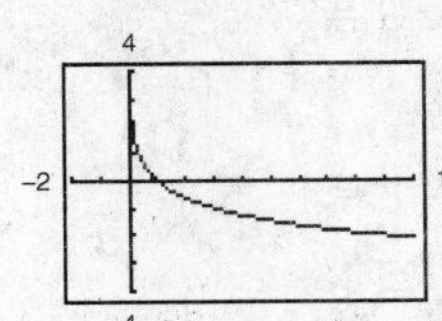

98.

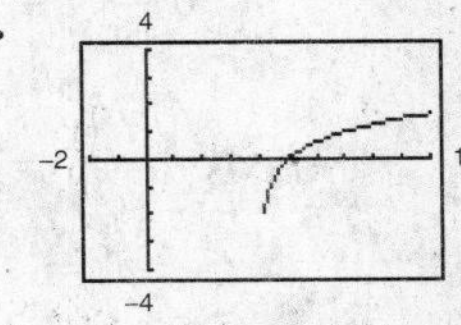

Section 4.4 Trigonometric Functions of Any Angle

- Know the Definitions of Trigonometric Functions of Any Angle.

  If θ is in standard position, (x, y) a point on the terminal side and $r = \sqrt{x^2 + y^2} \neq 0$, then:

  $\sin\theta = \dfrac{y}{r}$ $\qquad \csc\theta = \dfrac{r}{y},\ y \neq 0$

  $\cos\theta = \dfrac{x}{r}$ $\qquad \sec\theta = \dfrac{r}{x},\ x \neq 0$

  $\tan\theta = \dfrac{y}{x},\ x \neq 0$ $\qquad \cot\theta = \dfrac{x}{y},\ y \neq 0$
- You should know the signs of the trigonometric functions in each quadrant.
- You should know the trigonometric function values of the quadrant angles $0, \dfrac{\pi}{2}, \pi$, and $\dfrac{3\pi}{2}$.
- You should be able to find reference angles.
- You should be able to evaluate trigonometric functions of any angle. (Use reference angles.)
- You should know that the period of sine and cosine is 2π.
- You should know which trigonometric functions are odd and even.

  Even: $\cos x$ and $\sec x$

  Odd: $\sin x$, $\tan x$, $\cot x$, $\csc x$

Vocabulary Check

1. $\dfrac{y}{r}$
2. $\csc\theta$
3. $\dfrac{y}{x}$
4. $\dfrac{r}{x}$
5. $\cos\theta$
6. $\cot\theta$
7. reference

1. (a) $(x, y) = (4, 3)$

$r = \sqrt{16 + 9} = 5$

$\sin\theta = \dfrac{y}{r} = \dfrac{3}{5}$ $\qquad \csc\theta = \dfrac{r}{y} = \dfrac{5}{3}$

$\cos\theta = \dfrac{x}{r} = \dfrac{4}{5}$ $\qquad \sec\theta = \dfrac{r}{x} = \dfrac{5}{4}$

$\tan\theta = \dfrac{y}{x} = \dfrac{3}{4}$ $\qquad \cot\theta = \dfrac{x}{y} = \dfrac{4}{3}$

(b) $(x, y) = (-8, -15)$

$r = \sqrt{64 + 225} = 17$

$\sin\theta = \dfrac{y}{r} = -\dfrac{15}{17}$ $\qquad \csc\theta = \dfrac{r}{y} = -\dfrac{17}{15}$

$\cos\theta = \dfrac{x}{r} = -\dfrac{8}{17}$ $\qquad \sec\theta = \dfrac{r}{x} = -\dfrac{17}{8}$

$\tan\theta = \dfrac{y}{x} = \dfrac{15}{8}$ $\qquad \cot\theta = \dfrac{x}{y} = \dfrac{8}{15}$

2. (a) $x = 12, y = -5$

$r = \sqrt{12^2 + (-5)^2} = 13$

$\sin\theta = \frac{y}{r} = \frac{-5}{13} = -\frac{5}{13}$

$\cos\theta = \frac{x}{r} = \frac{12}{13}$

$\tan\theta = \frac{y}{x} = \frac{-5}{12} = -\frac{5}{12}$

$\csc\theta = \frac{r}{y} = \frac{13}{-5} = -\frac{13}{5}$

$\sec\theta = \frac{r}{x} = \frac{13}{12}$

$\cot\theta = \frac{x}{y} = \frac{12}{-5} = -\frac{12}{5}$

(b) $x = -1, y = 1$

$r = \sqrt{(-1)^2 + 1^2} = \sqrt{2}$

$\sin\theta = \frac{y}{r} = \frac{1}{\sqrt{2}} = \frac{\sqrt{2}}{2}$

$\cos\theta = \frac{x}{r} = \frac{-1}{\sqrt{2}} = -\frac{\sqrt{2}}{2}$

$\tan\theta = \frac{y}{x} = \frac{1}{-1} = -1$

$\csc\theta = \frac{r}{y} = \frac{\sqrt{2}}{1} = \sqrt{2}$

$\sec\theta = \frac{r}{x} = \frac{\sqrt{2}}{-1} = -\sqrt{2}$

$\cot\theta = \frac{x}{y} = \frac{-1}{1} = -1$

3. (a) $(x, y) = \left(-\sqrt{3}, -1\right)$

$r = \sqrt{3 + 1} = 2$

$\sin\theta = \frac{y}{r} = -\frac{1}{2}$ $\qquad \csc\theta = \frac{r}{y} = -2$

$\cos\theta = \frac{x}{r} = \frac{-\sqrt{3}}{2}$ $\qquad \sec\theta = \frac{r}{x} = \frac{-2\sqrt{3}}{3}$

$\tan\theta = \frac{y}{x} = \frac{\sqrt{3}}{3}$ $\qquad \cot\theta = \frac{x}{y} = \sqrt{3}$

(b) $(x, y) = (-2, 2)$

$r = \sqrt{4 + 4} = 2\sqrt{2}$

$\sin\theta = \frac{y}{r} = \frac{\sqrt{2}}{2}$ $\qquad \csc\theta = \frac{r}{y} = \sqrt{2}$

$\cos\theta = \frac{x}{r} = -\frac{\sqrt{2}}{2}$ $\qquad \sec\theta = \frac{r}{x} = -\sqrt{2}$

$\tan\theta = \frac{y}{x} = -1$ $\qquad \cot\theta = \frac{x}{y} = -1$

4. (a) $x = 3, y = 1$

$r = \sqrt{3^2 + 1^2} = \sqrt{10}$

$\sin\theta = \frac{y}{r} = \frac{1}{\sqrt{10}} = \frac{\sqrt{10}}{10}$

$\cos\theta = \frac{x}{r} = \frac{3}{\sqrt{10}} = \frac{3\sqrt{10}}{10}$

$\tan\theta = \frac{y}{x} = \frac{1}{3}$

$\csc\theta = \frac{r}{y} = \frac{\sqrt{10}}{1} = \sqrt{10}$

$\sec\theta = \frac{r}{x} = \frac{\sqrt{10}}{3}$

$\cot\theta = \frac{x}{y} = \frac{3}{1} = 3$

(b) $x = 2, y = -4$

$r = \sqrt{2^2 + (-4)^2} = 2\sqrt{5}$

$\sin\theta = \frac{y}{r} = \frac{-4}{2\sqrt{5}} = -\frac{2\sqrt{5}}{5}$

$\cos\theta = \frac{x}{r} = \frac{2}{2\sqrt{5}} = \frac{\sqrt{5}}{5}$

$\tan\theta = \frac{y}{x} = \frac{-4}{2} = -2$

$\csc\theta = \frac{r}{y} = \frac{2\sqrt{5}}{-4} = -\frac{\sqrt{5}}{2}$

$\sec\theta = \frac{r}{x} = \frac{2\sqrt{5}}{2} = \sqrt{5}$

$\cot\theta = \frac{x}{y} = \frac{2}{-4} = -\frac{1}{2}$

5. $(x, y) = (7, 24)$

$r = \sqrt{49 + 576} = 25$

$\sin\theta = \frac{y}{r} = \frac{24}{25}$ $\quad \csc\theta = \frac{r}{y} = \frac{25}{24}$

$\cos\theta = \frac{x}{r} = \frac{7}{25}$ $\quad \sec\theta = \frac{r}{x} = \frac{25}{7}$

$\tan\theta = \frac{y}{x} = \frac{24}{7}$ $\quad \cot\theta = \frac{x}{y} = \frac{7}{24}$

6. $x = 8, y = 15,$

$r = \sqrt{8^2 + 15^2} = 17$

$\sin\theta = \frac{y}{r} = \frac{15}{17}$ $\quad \cos\theta = \frac{x}{r} = \frac{8}{17}$

$\tan\theta = \frac{y}{x} = \frac{15}{8}$ $\quad \csc\theta = \frac{r}{y} = \frac{17}{15}$

$\sec\theta = \frac{r}{x} = \frac{17}{8}$ $\quad \cot\theta = \frac{x}{y} = \frac{8}{15}$

7. $(x, y) = (5, -12)$

$r = \sqrt{5^2 + (-12)^2} = \sqrt{25 + 144} = \sqrt{169} = 13$

$\sin\theta = \frac{y}{r} = -\frac{12}{13}$

$\cos\theta = \frac{x}{r} = \frac{5}{13}$

$\tan\theta = \frac{y}{x} = -\frac{12}{5}$

$\csc\theta = \frac{r}{y} = -\frac{13}{12}$

$\sec\theta = \frac{r}{x} = \frac{13}{5}$

$\cot\theta = \frac{x}{y} = -\frac{5}{12}$

8. $x = -24, y = 10$

$r = \sqrt{(-24)^2 + (10)^2} = 26$

$\sin\theta = \frac{y}{r} = \frac{10}{26} = \frac{5}{13}$

$\cos\theta = \frac{x}{r} = \frac{-24}{26} = \frac{-12}{13}$

$\tan\theta = \frac{y}{x} = \frac{10}{-24} = -\frac{5}{12}$

$\csc\theta = \frac{r}{y} = \frac{13}{5}$

$\sec\theta = \frac{r}{x} = -\frac{13}{12}$

$\cot\theta = \frac{x}{y} = -\frac{12}{5}$

9. $(x, y) = (-4, 10)$

$r = \sqrt{16 + 100} = 2\sqrt{29}$

$\sin\theta = \frac{y}{r} = \frac{5\sqrt{29}}{29}$

$\cos\theta = \frac{x}{r} = -\frac{2\sqrt{29}}{29}$

$\tan\theta = \frac{y}{x} = -\frac{5}{2}$

$\csc\theta = \frac{r}{y} = \frac{\sqrt{29}}{5}$

$\sec\theta = \frac{r}{x} = -\frac{\sqrt{29}}{2}$

$\cot\theta = \frac{x}{y} = -\frac{2}{5}$

10. $x = -5, y = -6$

$r = \sqrt{(-5)^2 - + (-6)^2} = \sqrt{61}$

$\sin\theta = \frac{y}{r} = \frac{-6}{\sqrt{61}} = \frac{-6\sqrt{61}}{61}$

$\cos\theta = \frac{x}{r} = \frac{-5}{\sqrt{61}} = \frac{-5\sqrt{61}}{61}$

$\tan\theta = \frac{y}{x} = \frac{-6}{-5} = \frac{6}{5}$

$\csc\theta = \frac{r}{y} = -\frac{\sqrt{61}}{6}$

$\sec\theta = \frac{r}{x} = -\frac{\sqrt{61}}{5}$

$\cot\theta = \frac{x}{y} = \frac{5}{6}$

11. $(x, y) = (-10, 8)$

$r = \sqrt{(-10)^2 + 8^2} = \sqrt{164} = 2\sqrt{41}$

$\sin\theta = \frac{y}{r} = \frac{8}{2\sqrt{41}} = \frac{4\sqrt{41}}{41}$

$\cos\theta = \frac{x}{r} = \frac{-10}{2\sqrt{41}} = -\frac{5\sqrt{41}}{41}$

$\tan\theta = \frac{y}{x} = \frac{8}{-10} = -\frac{4}{5}$

$\csc\theta = \frac{r}{y} = \frac{\sqrt{41}}{4}$

$\sec\theta = \frac{r}{x} = -\frac{-\sqrt{41}}{5}$

$\cot\theta = \frac{x}{y} = -\frac{5}{4}$

12. $x = 3, y = -9$

$r = \sqrt{3^2 + (-9)^2} = \sqrt{90} = 3\sqrt{10}$

$\sin\theta = \frac{y}{r} = \frac{-9}{3\sqrt{10}} = \frac{-3\sqrt{10}}{10}$

$\cos\theta = \frac{x}{r} = \frac{3}{3\sqrt{10}} = \frac{\sqrt{10}}{10}$

$\tan\theta = \frac{y}{x} = \frac{-9}{3} = -3$

$\csc\theta = \frac{r}{y} = -\frac{\sqrt{10}}{3}$

$\sec\theta = \frac{r}{x} = \sqrt{10}$

$\cot\theta = \frac{x}{y} = -\frac{1}{3}$

13. $\sin\theta < 0 \implies \theta$ lies in Quadrant III or Quadrant IV.

$\cos\theta < 0 \implies \theta$ lies in Quadrant II or Quadrant III.

$\sin\theta < 0$ *and* $\cos\theta < 0 \implies \theta$ lies in Quadrant III.

14. $\sec\theta > 0$ and $\cot\theta < 0$

$\frac{r}{x} > 0$ and $\frac{x}{y} < 0$

Quadrant IV

15. $\cot\theta > 0 \implies \theta$ lies in Quadrant I or Quadrant III.

$\cos\theta > 0 \implies \theta$ lies in Quadrant I or Quadrant IV.

$\cot\theta > 0$ and $\cos\theta > 0 \implies \theta$ lies in Quadrant I.

16. $\tan\theta > 0$ and $\csc\theta < 0$

$\frac{y}{x} > 0$ and $\frac{r}{y} < 0$

Quadrant III

17. $\sin\theta = \frac{y}{r} = \frac{3}{5} \implies x^2 = 25 - 9 = 16$

θ in Quadrant II $\implies x = -4$

$\sin\theta = \frac{y}{r} = \frac{3}{5}$ $\qquad \csc\theta = \frac{r}{y} = \frac{5}{3}$

$\cos\theta = \frac{x}{r} = -\frac{4}{5}$ $\qquad \sec\theta = \frac{r}{x} = -\frac{5}{4}$

$\tan\theta = \frac{y}{x} = -\frac{3}{4}$ $\qquad \cot\theta = \frac{x}{y} = -\frac{4}{3}$

18. $\cos\theta = \frac{x}{r} = \frac{-4}{5} \implies |y| = 3$

θ in Quadrant III $\implies y = -3$

$\sin\theta = \frac{y}{r} = -\frac{3}{5}$ $\qquad \csc\theta = -\frac{5}{3}$

$\cos\theta = \frac{x}{r} = -\frac{4}{5}$ $\qquad \sec\theta = -\frac{5}{4}$

$\tan\theta = \frac{y}{x} = \frac{3}{4}$ $\qquad \cot\theta = \frac{4}{3}$

19. $\sin\theta < 0 \Rightarrow y < 0$

$\tan\theta = \frac{y}{x} = \frac{-15}{8} \Rightarrow r = 17$

$\sin\theta = \frac{y}{r} = -\frac{15}{17}$ $\csc\theta = \frac{r}{y} = -\frac{17}{15}$

$\cos\theta = \frac{x}{r} = \frac{8}{17}$ $\sec\theta = \frac{r}{x} = \frac{17}{8}$

$\cot\theta = \frac{x}{y} = -\frac{8}{15}$

20. $\csc\theta = \frac{r}{y} = \frac{4}{1} \Rightarrow x = \pm\sqrt{15}$

$\cot\theta < 0 \Rightarrow x = -\sqrt{15}$

$\sin\theta = \frac{y}{r} = \frac{1}{4}$ $\csc\theta = 4$

$\cos\theta = \frac{x}{r} = -\frac{\sqrt{15}}{4}$ $\sec\theta = -\frac{4\sqrt{15}}{15}$

$\tan\theta = \frac{y}{x} = -\frac{\sqrt{15}}{15}$ $\cot\theta = -\sqrt{15}$

21. $\sec\theta = \frac{r}{x} = \frac{2}{-1} \Rightarrow y^2 = 4 - 1 = 3$

$\sin\theta \geq 0 \Rightarrow y = \sqrt{3}$

$\sin\theta = \frac{y}{r} = \frac{\sqrt{3}}{2}$ $\csc\theta = \frac{r}{y} = \frac{2\sqrt{3}}{3}$

$\cos\theta = \frac{x}{r} = -\frac{1}{2}$ $\sec\theta = \frac{r}{x} = -2$

$\tan\theta = \frac{y}{x} = -\sqrt{3}$ $\cot\theta = \frac{x}{y} = -\frac{\sqrt{3}}{3}$

22. $\sin\theta = 0$ and $\frac{\pi}{2} \leq \theta \leq \frac{3\pi}{2} \Rightarrow \theta = \pi$

$\cos\theta = \cos\pi = -1$

$\tan\theta = \frac{\sin\theta}{\cos\theta} = 0$

$\csc\theta$ is undefined.

$\sec\theta = -1$

$\cot\theta$ is undefined.

23. $\cot\theta$ is undefined $\Rightarrow \theta = n\pi$.

$\frac{\pi}{2} \leq \theta \leq \frac{3\pi}{2} \Rightarrow \theta = \pi, y = 0, x = -r$

$\sin\theta = \frac{y}{r} = 0$ $\csc\theta = \frac{r}{y}$ is undefined.

$\cos\theta = \frac{x}{r} = \frac{-r}{r} = -1$ $\sec\theta = \frac{r}{x} = -1$

$\tan\theta = \frac{y}{x} = \frac{0}{x} = 0$ $\cot\theta$ is undefined.

24. $\tan\theta$ is undefined and $\pi \leq \theta \leq 2\pi \Rightarrow \theta = \frac{3\pi}{2}$.

$\sin\theta = -1$

$\cos\theta = 0$

$\tan\theta$ is undefined.

$\csc\theta = -1$

$\sec\theta$ is undefined.

$\cot\theta = 0$

25. To find a point on the terminal side of θ, use any point on the line $y = -x$ that lies in Quadrant II. $(-1, 1)$ is one such point.

$x = -1, y = 1, r = \sqrt{2}$

$\sin\theta = \frac{1}{\sqrt{2}} = \frac{\sqrt{2}}{2}$ $\csc\theta = \sqrt{2}$

$\cos\theta = -\frac{1}{\sqrt{2}} = -\frac{\sqrt{2}}{2}$ $\sec\theta = -\sqrt{2}$

$\tan\theta = -1$ $\cot\theta = -1$

26. $\left(-x, -\frac{1}{3}x\right)$ Quadrant III, $x > 0$

$$r = \sqrt{x^2 + \frac{1}{9}x^2} = \frac{\sqrt{10}x}{3}$$

$$\sin \theta = \frac{y}{r} = \frac{(-x/3)}{(\sqrt{10}x)/3} = -\frac{\sqrt{10}}{10}$$

$$\cos \theta = \frac{x}{r} = \frac{-x}{(\sqrt{10}x)/3} = -\frac{3\sqrt{10}}{10}$$

$$\tan \theta = \frac{y}{x} = \frac{(-1/3)x}{-x} = \frac{1}{3}$$

$$\csc \theta = \frac{r}{y} = \frac{(\sqrt{10}x)/3}{(-1/3)x} = -\sqrt{10}$$

$$\sec \theta = \frac{r}{x} = \frac{(\sqrt{10}x)/3}{-x} = -\frac{\sqrt{10}}{3}$$

$$\cot \theta = \frac{x}{y} = \frac{-x}{(-1/3)x} = 3$$

27. To find a point on the terminal side of θ, use any point on the line $y = 2x$ that lies in Quadrant III. $(-1, -2)$ is one such point.

$x = -1, y = -2, r = \sqrt{5}$

$$\sin \theta = -\frac{2}{\sqrt{5}} = -\frac{2\sqrt{5}}{5}$$

$$\cos \theta = -\frac{1}{\sqrt{5}} = -\frac{\sqrt{5}}{5}$$

$$\tan \theta = \frac{-2}{-1} = 2$$

$$\csc \theta = \frac{\sqrt{5}}{-2} = -\frac{\sqrt{5}}{2}$$

$$\sec \theta = \frac{\sqrt{5}}{-1} = -\sqrt{5}$$

$$\cot \theta = \frac{-1}{-2} = \frac{1}{2}$$

28. $4x + 3y = 0 \implies y = -\frac{4}{3}x$

$\left(x, -\frac{4}{3}x\right)$ Quadrant IV, $x > 0$

$$r = \sqrt{x^2 + \frac{16}{9}x^2} = \frac{5}{3}x$$

$$\sin \theta = \frac{y}{r} = \frac{(-4/3)x}{(5/3)x} = -\frac{4}{5} \qquad \csc \theta = -\frac{5}{4}$$

$$\cos \theta = \frac{x}{r} = \frac{x}{(5/3)x} = \frac{3}{5} \qquad \sec \theta = \frac{5}{3}$$

$$\tan \theta = \frac{y}{x} = \frac{(-4/3)x}{x} = -\frac{4}{3} \qquad \cot \theta = -\frac{3}{4}$$

29. $(x, y) = (-1, 0)$

$$\sec \pi = \frac{r}{x} = \frac{1}{-1} = -1$$

30. $\tan \frac{\pi}{2} = \frac{y}{x} = \frac{1}{0} \implies$ undefined

since $\frac{\pi}{2}$ corresponds to $(0, 1)$.

31. $(x, y) = (0, -1)$

$$\cot\left(\frac{3\pi}{2}\right) = \frac{x}{y} = \frac{0}{-1} = 0$$

32. $\csc 0 = \frac{r}{y} = \frac{1}{0} \implies$ undefined

33. $(x, y) = (1, 0)$

$$\sec 0 = \frac{r}{x} = \frac{1}{1} = 1$$

34. $\csc \frac{3\pi}{2} = \frac{1}{\sin \frac{3\pi}{2}} = \frac{1}{-1} = -1$

35. $(x, y) = (-1, 0)$

$$\cot \pi = \frac{x}{y} = -\frac{1}{0} \implies \text{undefined}$$

36. $\csc \frac{\pi}{2} = \frac{1}{\sin \frac{\pi}{2}} = \frac{1}{1} = 1$

37. $\theta = 120°$

$\theta' = 180° - 120° = 60°$

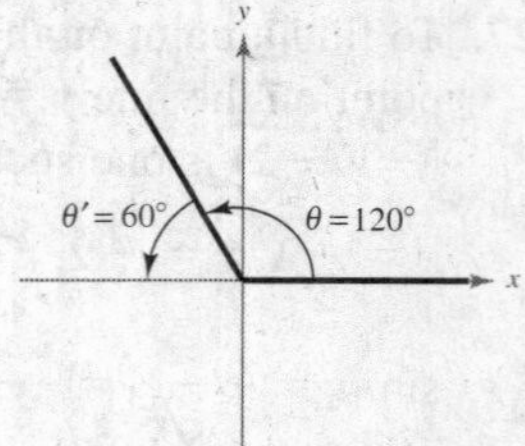

38. $\theta' = 225° - 180° = 45°$

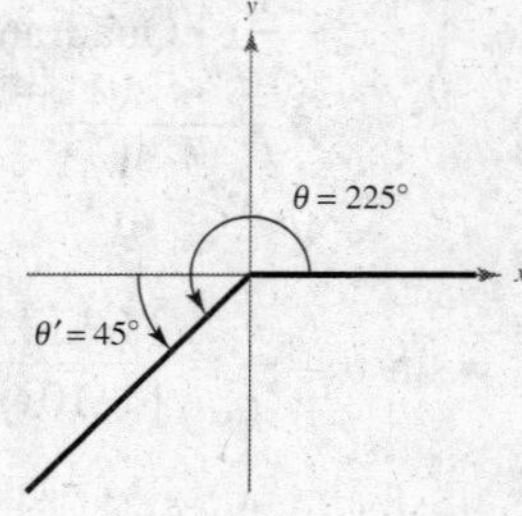

39. $\theta = -135°$ is coterminal with 225°.

$\theta' = 225° - 180° = 45°$

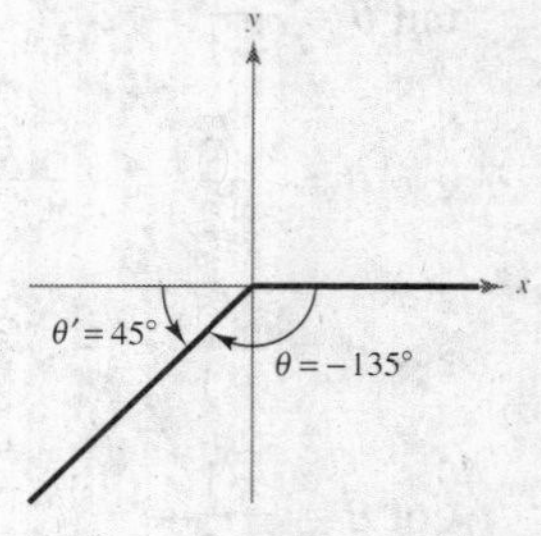

40. $\theta' = -330° + 360° = 30°$

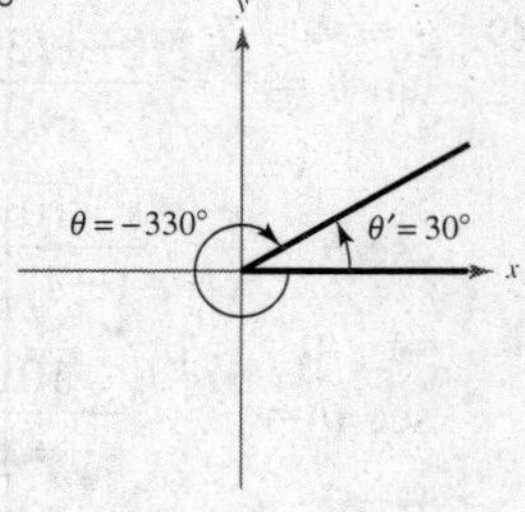

41. $\theta = \dfrac{5\pi}{3}, \theta' = 2\pi - \dfrac{5\pi}{3} = \dfrac{\pi}{3}$

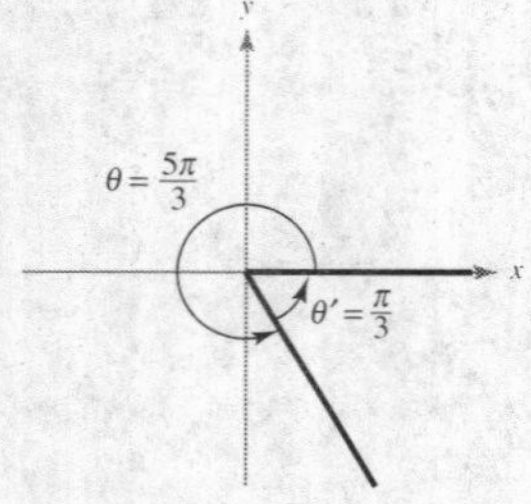

42. $\theta' = \pi - \dfrac{3\pi}{4} = \dfrac{\pi}{4}$

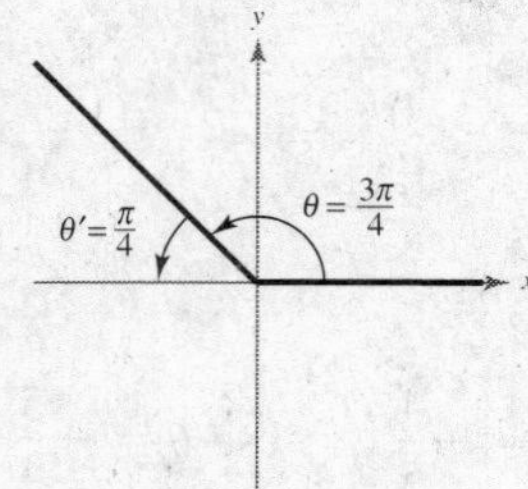

43. $\theta = -\dfrac{5\pi}{6}$ is coterminal with $\dfrac{7\pi}{6}$.

$\theta' = \dfrac{7\pi}{6} - \pi = \dfrac{\pi}{6}$

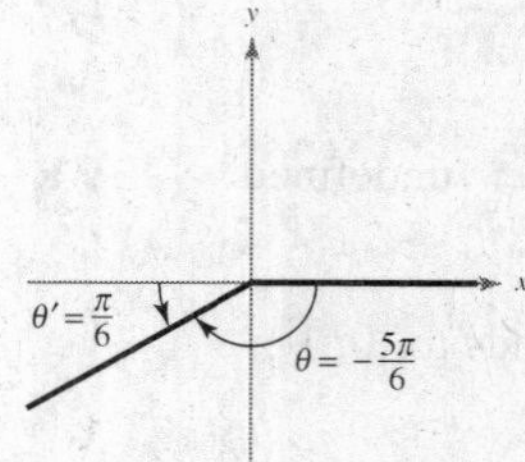

44. $\theta' = \dfrac{-2\pi}{3} + \pi = \dfrac{\pi}{3}$

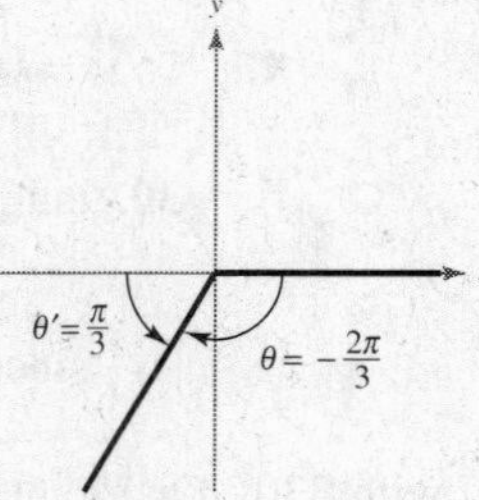

45. $\theta = 208°$

$\theta' = 208° - 180° = 28°$

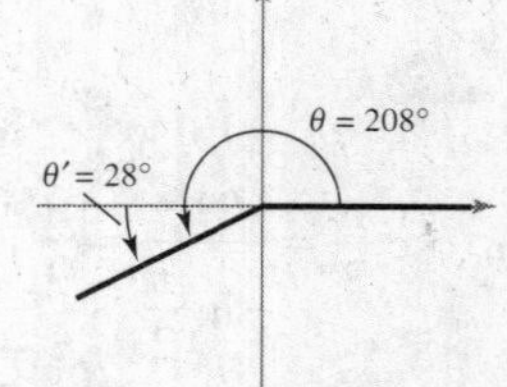

46. $\theta = 322°$

$\theta' = 360° - 322° = 38°$

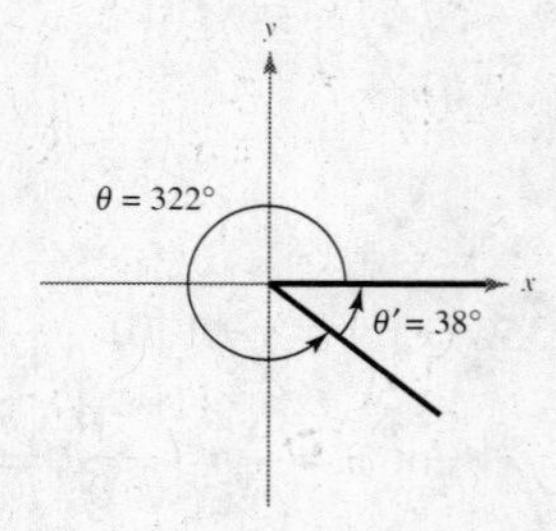

47. $\theta = -292°$

$\theta' = 360° - 292° = 68°$

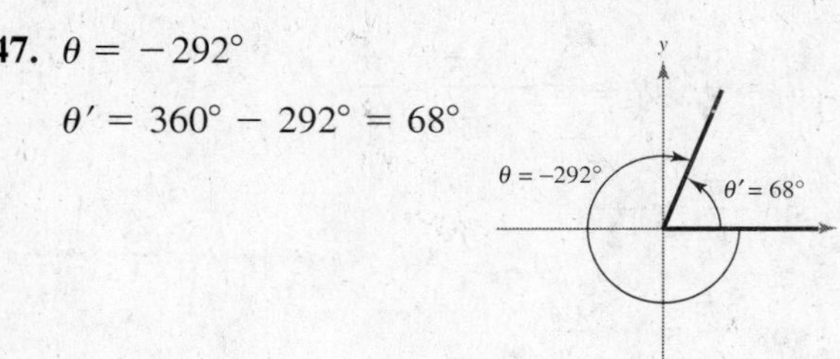

48. $\theta = -165°$ lies in Quadrant III.

Reference angle:
$180° - 165° = 15°$

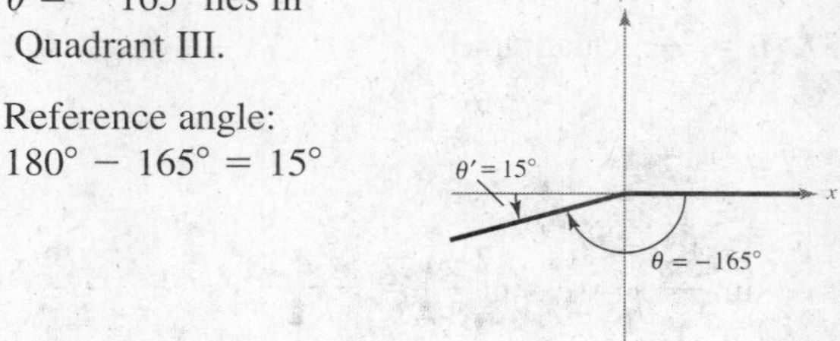

49. $\theta = \dfrac{11\pi}{5}$ is coterminal with $\dfrac{\pi}{5}$.

$\theta' = \dfrac{\pi}{5}$

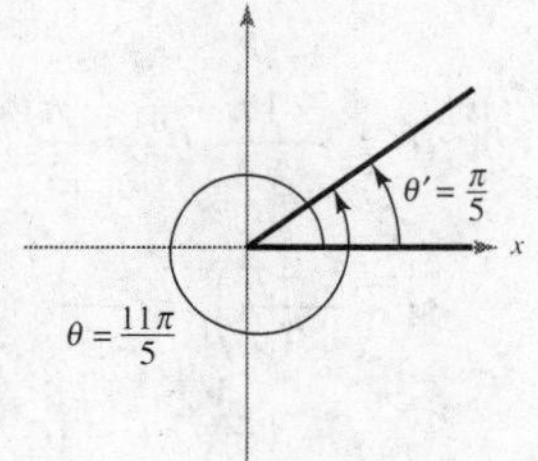

50. $\theta' = \dfrac{17\pi}{7} - \dfrac{14\pi}{7} = \dfrac{3\pi}{7}$

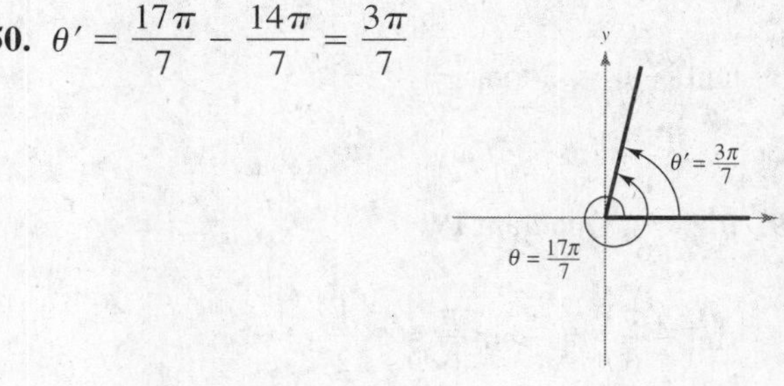

51. $\theta = -1.8$ lies in Quadrant III.

Reference angle: $\pi - 1.8 \approx 1.342$

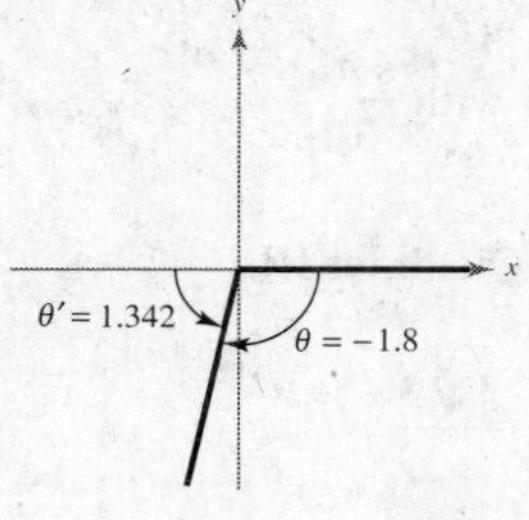

52. θ lies in Quadrant IV.

Reference angle: $4.5 - \pi \approx 1.358$

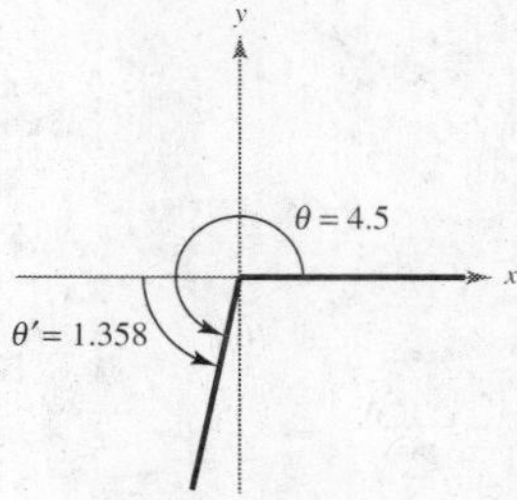

53. $\theta' = 45°$, Quadrant III

$\sin 225° = -\sin 45° = -\dfrac{\sqrt{2}}{2}$

$\cos 225° = -\cos 45° = -\dfrac{\sqrt{2}}{2}$

$\tan 225° = \tan 45° = 1$

54. $\theta = 300°$, $\theta' = 360° - 300° = 60°$, Quadrant IV

$\sin 300° = -\sin 60° = -\dfrac{\sqrt{3}}{2}$

$\cos 300° = \cos 60° = \dfrac{1}{2}$

$\tan 300° = -\tan 60° = -\sqrt{3}$

55. $\theta = -750°$ is coterminal with 330°, Quadrant IV.

$\theta' = 360° - 330° = 30°$

$\sin(-750°) = -\sin 30° = -\dfrac{1}{2}$

$\cos(-750°) = \cos 30° = \dfrac{\sqrt{3}}{2}$

$\tan(-750°) = -\tan 30° = -\dfrac{\sqrt{3}}{3}$

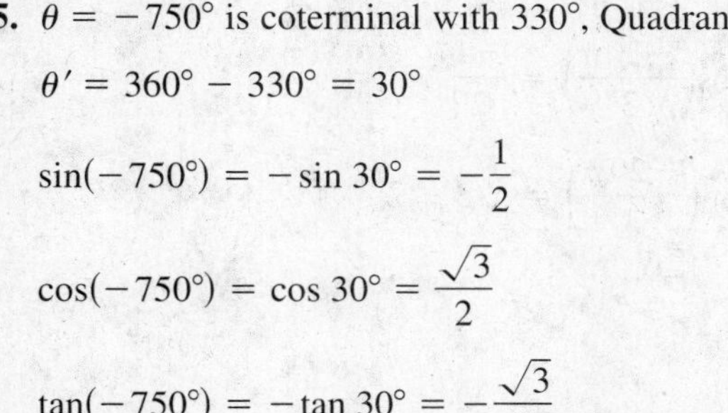

56. $\theta = -495°$, $\theta' = 45°$, Quadrant III

$\sin(-495°) = -\sin 45° = -\dfrac{\sqrt{2}}{2}$

$\cos(-495°) = -\cos 45° = -\dfrac{\sqrt{2}}{2}$

$\tan(-495°) = \tan 45° = 1$

57. $\theta = \frac{5\pi}{3}$, Quadrant IV

$\theta' = 2\pi - \frac{5\pi}{3} = \frac{\pi}{3}$

$\sin\left(\frac{5\pi}{3}\right) = -\sin\left(\frac{\pi}{3}\right) = -\frac{\sqrt{3}}{2}$

$\cos\left(\frac{5\pi}{3}\right) = \cos\left(\frac{\pi}{3}\right) = \frac{1}{2}$

$\tan\left(\frac{5\pi}{3}\right) = -\tan\left(\frac{\pi}{3}\right) = -\sqrt{3}$

58. $\theta = \frac{3\pi}{4}$, $\theta' = \pi - \frac{3\pi}{4} = \frac{\pi}{4}$

$\sin \frac{3\pi}{4} = \frac{\sqrt{2}}{2}$

$\cos \frac{3\pi}{4} = -\frac{\sqrt{2}}{2}$

$\tan \frac{3\pi}{4} = -1$

59. $\theta' = \frac{\pi}{6}$, Quadrant IV

$\sin\left(-\frac{\pi}{6}\right) = -\sin \frac{\pi}{6} = -\frac{1}{2}$

$\cos\left(-\frac{\pi}{6}\right) = \cos \frac{\pi}{6} = \frac{\sqrt{3}}{2}$

$\tan\left(-\frac{\pi}{6}\right) = -\tan \frac{\pi}{6} = -\frac{\sqrt{3}}{3}$

60. $\theta = \frac{-4\pi}{3}$, $\theta' = \frac{\pi}{3}$

$\sin\left(\frac{-4\pi}{3}\right) = \frac{\sqrt{3}}{2}$

$\cos\left(\frac{-4\pi}{3}\right) = \frac{-1}{2}$

$\tan\left(\frac{-4\pi}{3}\right) = -\sqrt{3}$

61. $\theta' = \frac{\pi}{4}$, Quadrant II

$\sin \frac{11\pi}{4} = \sin \frac{\pi}{4} = \frac{\sqrt{2}}{2}$

$\cos \frac{11\pi}{4} = -\cos \frac{\pi}{4} = -\frac{\sqrt{2}}{2}$

$\tan \frac{11\pi}{4} = -\tan \frac{\pi}{4} = -1$

62. $\theta = \frac{10\pi}{3}$ is coterminal with $\frac{4\pi}{3}$.

$\theta' = \frac{4\pi}{3} - \pi = \frac{\pi}{3}$ in Quadrant III.

$\sin \frac{10\pi}{3} = -\sin \frac{\pi}{3} = -\frac{\sqrt{3}}{2}$

$\cos \frac{10\pi}{3} = -\cos \frac{\pi}{3} = -\frac{1}{2}$

$\tan \frac{10\pi}{3} = \tan \frac{\pi}{3} = \sqrt{3}$

63. $\theta = -\frac{17\pi}{6}$ is coterminal with $\frac{7\pi}{6}$.

$\theta' = \frac{7\pi}{6} - \pi = \frac{\pi}{6}$, Quadrant III

$\sin\left(-\frac{17\pi}{6}\right) = -\sin\left(\frac{\pi}{6}\right) = -\frac{1}{2}$

$\cos\left(-\frac{17\pi}{6}\right) = -\cos\left(\frac{\pi}{6}\right) = -\frac{\sqrt{3}}{2}$

$\tan\left(-\frac{17\pi}{6}\right) = \tan\left(\frac{\pi}{6}\right) = \frac{\sqrt{3}}{3}$

64. $\theta = \frac{-20\pi}{3}$, $\theta' = \frac{\pi}{3}$

$\sin\left(\frac{-20\pi}{3}\right) = \frac{-\sqrt{3}}{2}$

$\cos\left(\frac{-20\pi}{3}\right) = \frac{-1}{2}$

$\tan\left(\frac{-20\pi}{3}\right) = \sqrt{3}$

65. $\sin\theta = -\frac{3}{5}$

$\sin^2\theta + \cos^2\theta = 1$

$\cos^2\theta = 1 - \sin^2\theta$

$\cos^2\theta = 1 - \left(-\frac{3}{5}\right)^2$

$\cos^2\theta = 1 - \frac{9}{25}$

$\cos^2\theta = \frac{16}{25}$

$\cos\theta > 0$ in Quadrant IV.

$\cos\theta = \frac{4}{5}$

66. $\cot\theta = -3$

$1 + \cot^2\theta = \csc^2\theta$

$1 + (-3)^2 = \csc^2\theta$

$10 = \csc^2\theta$

$\csc\theta > 0$ in Quadrant II.

$\sqrt{10} = \csc\theta$

$\csc\theta = \frac{1}{\sin\theta}$

$\sin\theta = \frac{1}{\csc\theta} = \frac{1}{\sqrt{10}} = \frac{\sqrt{10}}{10}$

67. $\csc\theta = -2$

$1 + \cot^2\theta = \csc^2\theta$

$\cot^2\theta = \csc^2\theta - 1$

$\cot^2\theta = (-2)^2 - 1$

$\cot^2\theta = 3$

$\cot\theta < 0$ in Quadrant IV.

$\cot\theta = -\sqrt{3}$

68. $\cos\theta = \frac{5}{8}$

$\cos\theta = \frac{1}{\sec\theta} \Rightarrow \sec\theta = \frac{1}{\cos\theta}$

$\sec\theta = \frac{1}{5/8} = \frac{8}{5}$

69. $\sec\theta = -\frac{9}{4}$

$1 + \tan^2\theta = \sec^2\theta$

$\tan^2\theta = \sec^2\theta - 1$

$\tan^2\theta = \left(-\frac{9}{4}\right)^2 - 1$

$\tan^2\theta = \frac{65}{16}$

$\tan\theta > 0$ in Quadrant III.

$\tan\theta = \frac{\sqrt{65}}{4}$

70. $\tan\theta = -\frac{5}{4} \Rightarrow \cot\theta = -\frac{4}{5}$

$1 + \cot^2\theta = \csc^2\theta$

$1 + \frac{16}{25} = \csc^2\theta$

$\csc\theta = \pm\frac{\sqrt{41}}{5}$

Quadrant IV $\Rightarrow \csc\theta = -\frac{\sqrt{41}}{5}$

71. $\sin\theta = \frac{2}{5}$ and $\cos\theta < 0 \Longrightarrow \theta$ is in Quadrant II.

$$\cos\theta = -\sqrt{1-\sin^2\theta} = -\sqrt{1-\frac{4}{25}} = -\frac{\sqrt{21}}{5}$$

$$\tan\theta = \frac{\sin\theta}{\cos\theta} = \frac{2/5}{-\sqrt{21}/5} = \frac{-2}{\sqrt{21}} = \frac{-2\sqrt{21}}{21}$$

$$\csc\theta = \frac{1}{\sin\theta} = \frac{5}{2}$$

$$\sec\theta = \frac{1}{\cos\theta} = \frac{-5}{\sqrt{21}} = \frac{-5\sqrt{21}}{21}$$

$$\cot\theta = \frac{1}{\tan\theta} = \frac{-\sqrt{21}}{2}$$

72. $\cos\theta = -\frac{3}{7}$ and $\sin\theta < 0 \Longrightarrow \theta$ is in Quadrant III.

$$\sin\theta = -\sqrt{1-\cos^2\theta} = -\sqrt{1-\frac{9}{49}} = \frac{-\sqrt{40}}{7} = \frac{-2\sqrt{10}}{7}$$

$$\tan\theta = \frac{\sin\theta}{\cos\theta} = \frac{-2\sqrt{10}/7}{-3/7} = \frac{2\sqrt{10}}{3}$$

$$\cot\theta = \frac{1}{\tan\theta} = \frac{3}{2\sqrt{10}} = \frac{3\sqrt{10}}{20}$$

$$\csc\theta = \frac{1}{\sin\theta} = \frac{-7}{2\sqrt{10}} = \frac{-7\sqrt{10}}{20}$$

$$\sec\theta = \frac{1}{\cos\theta} = -\frac{7}{3}$$

73. $\tan\theta = -4$ and $\cos\theta < 0 \Longrightarrow \theta$ is in Quadrant II.

$$\sec\theta = -\sqrt{1+\tan^2\theta} = -\sqrt{1+16} = -\sqrt{17}$$

$$\cos\theta = \frac{1}{\sec\theta} = \frac{-1}{\sqrt{17}} = \frac{-\sqrt{17}}{17}$$

$$\sin\theta = \tan\theta\cos\theta = (-4)\left(-\frac{\sqrt{17}}{17}\right) = \frac{4\sqrt{17}}{17}$$

$$\csc\theta = \frac{1}{\sin\theta} = \frac{17}{4\sqrt{17}} = \frac{\sqrt{17}}{4}$$

$$\cot\theta = \frac{1}{\tan\theta} = -\frac{1}{4}$$

74. $\cot\theta = -5$ and $\sin\theta > 0 \Longrightarrow \theta$ is in Quadrant II.

$$\tan\theta = \frac{1}{\cot\theta} = \frac{-1}{5}$$

$$\sec\theta = -\sqrt{1+\tan^2\theta} = -\sqrt{1+\frac{1}{25}} = \frac{-\sqrt{26}}{5}$$

$$\cos\theta = \frac{1}{\sec\theta} = \frac{-5}{\sqrt{26}} = \frac{-5\sqrt{26}}{26}$$

$$\sin\theta = \tan\theta\cos\theta = \left(-\frac{1}{5}\right)\left(\frac{-5\sqrt{26}}{26}\right) = \frac{\sqrt{26}}{26}$$

$$\csc\theta = \frac{1}{\sin\theta} = \frac{26}{\sqrt{26}} = \sqrt{26}$$

75. $\csc\theta = -\frac{3}{2}$ and $\tan\theta < 0 \Rightarrow \theta$ is in Quadrant IV.

$\sin\theta = \frac{1}{\csc\theta} = -\frac{2}{3}$

$\cos\theta = \sqrt{1-\sin^2\theta} = \sqrt{1-\frac{4}{9}} = \frac{\sqrt{5}}{3}$

$\sec\theta = \frac{1}{\cos\theta} = \frac{3}{\sqrt{5}} = \frac{3\sqrt{5}}{5}$

$\tan\theta = \frac{\sin\theta}{\cos\theta} = \frac{-2/3}{\sqrt{5}/3} = \frac{-2}{\sqrt{5}} = \frac{-2\sqrt{5}}{5}$

$\cot\theta = \frac{1}{\tan\theta} = \frac{-\sqrt{5}}{2}$

76. $\sec\theta = -\frac{4}{3}$ and $\cot\theta > 0 \Rightarrow \theta$ is in Quadrant III.

$\cos\theta = \frac{1}{\sec\theta} = -\frac{3}{4}$

$\sin\theta = -\sqrt{1-\cos^2\theta} = -\sqrt{1-\frac{9}{16}} = -\frac{\sqrt{7}}{4}$

$\csc\theta = \frac{1}{\sin\theta} = -\frac{4}{\sqrt{7}} = \frac{-4\sqrt{7}}{7}$

$\tan\theta = \frac{\sin\theta}{\cos\theta} = \frac{-\sqrt{7}/4}{-3/4} = \frac{\sqrt{7}}{3}$

$\cot\theta = \frac{1}{\tan\theta} = \frac{3}{\sqrt{7}} = \frac{3\sqrt{7}}{7}$

77. $\sin 10° \approx 0.1736$

78. $\sec 235° = \frac{1}{\cos 235°} \approx -1.7434$

79. $\tan 245° \approx 2.1445$

80. $\csc 320° = \frac{1}{\sin 320°} = -1.5557$

81. $\cos(-110°) \approx -0.3420$

82. $\cot(-220°) = \frac{1}{\tan(-220°)} \approx -1.1918$

83. $\sec(-280°) = \frac{1}{\cos(-280°)} \approx 5.7588$

84. $\csc 0.33 = \frac{1}{\sin 0.33} \approx 3.0860$

85. $\tan\left(\frac{2\pi}{9}\right) \approx 0.8391$

86. $\tan\frac{11\pi}{9} \approx 0.8391$

87. $\csc\left(-\frac{8\pi}{9}\right) = \frac{1}{\sin\left(-\frac{8\pi}{9}\right)} \approx -2.9238$

88. $\cos\left(\frac{-15\pi}{14}\right) \approx -0.9749$

89. (a) $\sin\theta = \frac{1}{2} \Rightarrow$ reference angle is 30° or $\frac{\pi}{6}$ and θ is in Quadrant I or Quadrant II.

Values in degrees: 30°, 150°

Values in radian: $\frac{\pi}{6}, \frac{5\pi}{6}$

(b) $\sin\theta = -\frac{1}{2} \Rightarrow$ reference angle is 30° or $\frac{\pi}{6}$ and θ is in Quadrant III or Quadrant IV.

Values in degrees: 210°, 330°

Values in radians: $\frac{7\pi}{6}, \frac{11\pi}{6}$

90. (a) $\cos\theta = \frac{\sqrt{2}}{2} \Rightarrow$ reference angle is 45° or $\frac{\pi}{4}$ and θ is in Quadrant I or IV.

Values in degrees: 45°, 315°

Values in radians: $\frac{\pi}{4}, \frac{7\pi}{4}$

(b) $\cos\theta = -\frac{\sqrt{2}}{2} \Rightarrow$ reference angle is 45° or $\frac{\pi}{4}$ and θ is in Quadrant II or III.

Values in degrees: 135°, 225°

Values in radians: $\frac{3\pi}{4}, \frac{5\pi}{4}$

91. (a) $\csc \theta = \dfrac{2\sqrt{3}}{3} \Rightarrow$ reference angle is 60° or $\dfrac{\pi}{3}$ and θ is in Quadrant I or Quadrant II.

Values in degrees: 60°, 120°

Values in radians: $\dfrac{\pi}{3}, \dfrac{2\pi}{3}$

(b) $\cot \theta = -1 \Rightarrow$ reference angle is 45° or $\dfrac{\pi}{4}$ and θ is in Quadrant II or Quadrant IV.

Values in degrees: 135°, 315°

Values in radians: $\dfrac{3\pi}{4}, \dfrac{7\pi}{4}$

92. (a) $\csc \theta = -\sqrt{2} \Rightarrow \sin \theta = \dfrac{-1}{\sqrt{2}}$

Reference angle is 45° or $\dfrac{\pi}{4}$.

Values in degrees: 225°, 315°

Values in radians: $\dfrac{5\pi}{4}, \dfrac{7\pi}{4}$

(b) $\csc \theta = 2 \Rightarrow \sin \theta = \dfrac{1}{2}$

Reference angle is $\dfrac{\pi}{6}$ or 30°.

Values in degrees: 30°, 150°

Values in radians: $\dfrac{\pi}{6}, \dfrac{5\pi}{6}$

93. (a) $\sec \theta = -\dfrac{2\sqrt{3}}{3} \Rightarrow$ reference angle is $\dfrac{\pi}{6}$ or 30°, and θ is in Quadrant II or Quadrant III.

Values in degrees: 150°, 210°

Values in radians: $\dfrac{5\pi}{6}, \dfrac{7\pi}{6}$

(b) $\cos \theta = -\dfrac{1}{2} \Rightarrow$ reference angle is $\dfrac{\pi}{3}$ or 60°, and θ is in Quadrant II or Quadrant III.

Values in degrees: 120°, 240°

Values in radians: $\dfrac{2\pi}{3}, \dfrac{4\pi}{3}$

94. (a) $\cot \theta = -\sqrt{3} \Rightarrow \dfrac{\cos \theta}{\sin \theta} = -\sqrt{3}$

Reference angle is $\dfrac{\pi}{6}$ or 30°.

Values in degrees: 150°, 330°

Values in radians: $\dfrac{5\pi}{6}, \dfrac{11\pi}{6}$

(b) Values in degrees: 45° or 315°

Values in radians: $\dfrac{\pi}{4}$ or $\dfrac{7\pi}{4}$

95. (a) $f(\theta) + g(\theta) = \sin 30° + \cos 30° = \dfrac{1}{2} + \dfrac{\sqrt{3}}{2} = \dfrac{1 + \sqrt{3}}{2}$

(b) $\cos 30° - \sin 30° = \dfrac{\sqrt{3} - 1}{2}$

(c) $[\cos 30°]^2 = \left(\dfrac{\sqrt{3}}{2}\right)^2 = \dfrac{3}{4}$

(d) $\sin 30° \cos 30° = \left(\dfrac{1}{2}\right)\left(\dfrac{\sqrt{3}}{2}\right) = \dfrac{\sqrt{3}}{4}$

(e) $2 \sin 30° = 2\left(\dfrac{1}{2}\right) = 1$

(f) $\cos(-30°) = \cos 30° = \dfrac{\sqrt{3}}{2}$

96. (a) $f(\theta) + g(\theta) = \sin 60° + \cos 60° = \dfrac{\sqrt{3}}{2} + \dfrac{1}{2} = \dfrac{\sqrt{3} + 1}{2}$

(b) $\cos 60° - \sin 60° = \dfrac{1}{2} - \dfrac{\sqrt{3}}{2} = \dfrac{1 - \sqrt{3}}{2}$

(c) $[\cos 60°]^2 = \left(\dfrac{1}{2}\right)^2 = \dfrac{1}{4}$

(d) $\sin 60° \cos 60° = \left(\dfrac{\sqrt{3}}{2}\right)\left(\dfrac{1}{2}\right) = \dfrac{\sqrt{3}}{4}$

(e) $2 \sin 60° = 2\dfrac{\sqrt{3}}{2} = \sqrt{3}$

(f) $\cos(-60°) = \cos 60° = \dfrac{1}{2}$

97. (a) $f(\theta) + g(\theta) = \sin 315° + \cos 315° = -\frac{\sqrt{2}}{2} + \frac{\sqrt{2}}{2} = 0$

(b) $\cos 315° - \sin 315° = \frac{\sqrt{2}}{2} - \left(\frac{-\sqrt{2}}{2}\right) = \sqrt{2}$

(c) $[\cos 315°]^2 = \left(\frac{\sqrt{2}}{2}\right)^2 = \frac{1}{2}$

(d) $\sin 315° \cos 315° = \left(\frac{-\sqrt{2}}{2}\right)\left(\frac{\sqrt{2}}{2}\right) = -\frac{1}{2}$

(e) $2 \sin 315° = 2\left(\frac{-\sqrt{2}}{2}\right) = -\sqrt{2}$

(f) $\cos(-315°) = \cos(315°) = \frac{\sqrt{2}}{2}$

98. (a) $f(\theta) + g(\theta) = \sin 225° + \cos 225° = -\frac{\sqrt{2}}{2} - \frac{\sqrt{2}}{2} = -\sqrt{2}$

(b) $\cos 225° - \sin 225° = \frac{-\sqrt{2}}{2} - \left(\frac{-\sqrt{2}}{2}\right) = 0$

(c) $[\cos 225°]^2 = \left(\frac{-\sqrt{2}}{2}\right)^2 = \frac{1}{2}$

(d) $\sin 225° \cos 225° = \left(\frac{-\sqrt{2}}{2}\right)\left(\frac{-\sqrt{2}}{2}\right) = \frac{1}{2}$

(e) $2 \sin 225° = 2\left(\frac{-\sqrt{2}}{2}\right) = -\sqrt{2}$

(f) $\cos(-225°) = \cos(225°) = -\frac{\sqrt{2}}{2}$

99. (a) $f(\theta) + g(\theta) = \sin 150° + \cos 150° = \frac{1}{2} + \frac{-\sqrt{3}}{2} = \frac{1 - \sqrt{3}}{2}$

(b) $\cos 150° - \sin 150° = \frac{-\sqrt{3}}{2} - \frac{1}{2} = \frac{-1 - \sqrt{3}}{2}$

(c) $[\cos 150°]^2 = \left(\frac{-\sqrt{3}}{2}\right)^2 = \frac{3}{4}$

(d) $\sin 150° \cos 150° = \frac{1}{2} \cdot \frac{-\sqrt{3}}{2} = \frac{-\sqrt{3}}{4}$

(e) $2 \sin 150° = 2\left(\frac{1}{2}\right) = 1$

(f) $\cos(-150°) = \cos(150°) = \frac{-\sqrt{3}}{2}$

100. (a) $f(\theta) + g(\theta) = \sin 300° + \cos 300° = \frac{-\sqrt{3}}{2} + \frac{1}{2} = \frac{1 - \sqrt{3}}{2}$

(b) $\cos 300° - \sin 300° = \frac{1}{2} - \left(\frac{-\sqrt{3}}{2}\right) = \frac{1 + \sqrt{3}}{2}$

(c) $[\cos 300°]^2 = \left(\frac{1}{2}\right)^2 = \frac{1}{4}$

(d) $\sin 300° \cos 300° = \left(\frac{-\sqrt{3}}{2}\right)\left(\frac{1}{2}\right) = \frac{-\sqrt{3}}{4}$

(e) $2 \sin 300° = 2\left(\frac{-\sqrt{3}}{2}\right) = -\sqrt{3}$

(f) $\cos(-300°) = \cos(300°) = \frac{1}{2}$

101. (a) $f(\theta) + g(\theta) = \sin \frac{7\pi}{6} + \cos \frac{7\pi}{6} = -\frac{1}{2} - \frac{\sqrt{3}}{2} = \frac{-1 - \sqrt{3}}{2}$

(b) $\cos \frac{7\pi}{6} - \sin \frac{7\pi}{6} = \frac{-\sqrt{3}}{2} - \left(-\frac{1}{2}\right) = \frac{1 - \sqrt{3}}{2}$

(c) $\left[\cos \frac{7\pi}{6}\right]^2 = \left(\frac{-\sqrt{3}}{2}\right)^2 = \frac{3}{4}$

(d) $\sin \frac{7\pi}{6} \cos \frac{7\pi}{6} = \left(-\frac{1}{2}\right)\left(-\frac{\sqrt{3}}{2}\right) = \frac{\sqrt{3}}{4}$

(e) $2 \sin \frac{7\pi}{6} = 2\left(-\frac{1}{2}\right) = -1$

(f) $\cos\left(\frac{-7\pi}{6}\right) = \cos\left(\frac{7\pi}{6}\right) = \frac{-\sqrt{3}}{2}$

102. (a) $f(\theta) + g(\theta) = \sin\frac{5\pi}{6} + \cos\frac{5\pi}{6} = \frac{1}{2} + \frac{-\sqrt{3}}{2} = \frac{1-\sqrt{3}}{2}$

(b) $\cos\frac{5\pi}{6} - \sin\frac{5\pi}{6} = \frac{-\sqrt{3}}{2} - \frac{1}{2} = \frac{-1-\sqrt{3}}{2}$

(c) $\left[\cos\frac{5\pi}{6}\right]^2 = \left(\frac{-\sqrt{3}}{2}\right)^2 = \frac{3}{4}$

(d) $\sin\frac{5\pi}{6}\cos\frac{5\pi}{6} = \left(\frac{1}{2}\right)\left(\frac{-\sqrt{3}}{2}\right) = \frac{-\sqrt{3}}{4}$

(e) $2\sin\frac{5\pi}{6} = 2\left(\frac{1}{2}\right) = 1$

(f) $\cos\left(\frac{-5\pi}{6}\right) = \cos\left(\frac{5\pi}{6}\right) = \frac{-\sqrt{3}}{2}$

103. (a) $f(\theta) + g(\theta) = \sin\frac{4\pi}{3} + \cos\frac{4\pi}{3} = \frac{-\sqrt{3}}{2} - \frac{1}{2} = \frac{-1-\sqrt{3}}{2}$

(b) $\cos\frac{4\pi}{3} - \sin\frac{4\pi}{3} = -\frac{1}{2} - \left(\frac{-\sqrt{3}}{2}\right) = \frac{\sqrt{3}-1}{2}$

(c) $\left[\cos\frac{4\pi}{3}\right]^2 = \left(-\frac{1}{2}\right)^2 = \frac{1}{4}$

(d) $\sin\frac{4\pi}{3}\cos\frac{4\pi}{3} = \left(\frac{-\sqrt{3}}{2}\right)\left(-\frac{1}{2}\right) = \frac{\sqrt{3}}{4}$

(e) $2\sin\frac{4\pi}{3} = 2\left(\frac{-\sqrt{3}}{2}\right) = -\sqrt{3}$

(f) $\cos\left(\frac{-4\pi}{3}\right) = \cos\left(\frac{4\pi}{3}\right) = -\frac{1}{2}$

104. (a) $f(\theta) + g(\theta) = \sin\frac{5\pi}{3} + \cos\frac{5\pi}{3} = \frac{-\sqrt{3}}{2} + \frac{1}{2} = \frac{1-\sqrt{3}}{2}$

(b) $\cos\frac{5\pi}{3} - \sin\frac{5\pi}{3} = \frac{1}{2} - \left(\frac{-\sqrt{3}}{2}\right) = \frac{1+\sqrt{3}}{2}$

(c) $\left[\cos\frac{5\pi}{3}\right]^2 = \left(\frac{1}{2}\right)^2 = \frac{1}{4}$

(d) $\sin\frac{5\pi}{3}\cos\frac{5\pi}{3} = \left(\frac{-\sqrt{3}}{2}\right)\left(\frac{1}{2}\right) = \frac{-\sqrt{3}}{4}$

(e) $2\sin\frac{5\pi}{3} = 2\left(\frac{-\sqrt{3}}{2}\right) = -\sqrt{3}$

(f) $\cos\left(\frac{-5\pi}{3}\right) = \cos\left(\frac{5\pi}{3}\right) = \frac{1}{2}$

105. (a) $f(\theta) + g(\theta) = \sin 270° + \cos 270° = -1 + 0 = -1$

(b) $\cos 270° - \sin 270° = 0 - (-1) = 1$

(c) $[\cos 270°]^2 = 0^2 = 0$

(d) $\sin 270° \cos 270° = (-1)(0) = 0$

(e) $2\sin 270° = 2(-1) = -2$

(f) $\cos(-270°) = \cos(270°) = 0$

106. (a) $f(\theta) + g(\theta) = \sin 180° + \cos 180° = 0 - 1 = -1$

(b) $\cos 180° - \sin 180° = -1 - 0 = -1$

(c) $[\cos 180°]^2 = (-1)^2 = 1$

(d) $\sin 180° \cos 180° = 0(-1) = 0$

(e) $2\sin 180° = 2(0) = 0$

(f) $\cos(-180°) = \cos(180°) = -1$

107. (a) $f(\theta) + g(\theta) = \sin\frac{7\pi}{2} + \cos\frac{7\pi}{2} = -1 + 0 = -1$

(b) $\cos\frac{7\pi}{2} - \sin\frac{7\pi}{2} = 0 - (-1) = 1$

(c) $\left[\cos\frac{7\pi}{2}\right]^2 = 0^2 = 0$

(d) $\sin\frac{7\pi}{2}\cos\frac{7\pi}{2} = (-1)(0) = 0$

(e) $2\sin\frac{7\pi}{2} = 2(-1) = -2$

(f) $\cos\left(\frac{-7\pi}{2}\right) = \cos\left(\frac{7\pi}{2}\right) = 0$

108. (a) $f(\theta) + g(\theta) = \sin\frac{5\pi}{2} + \cos\frac{5\pi}{2} = 1 + 0 = 1$

(b) $\cos\frac{5\pi}{2} - \sin\frac{5\pi}{2} = 0 - 1 = -1$

(c) $\left[\cos\frac{5\pi}{2}\right]^2 = 0^2 = 0$

(d) $\sin\frac{5\pi}{2}\cos\frac{5\pi}{2} = (1)(0) = 0$

(e) $2\sin\frac{5\pi}{2} = 2(1) = 2$

(f) $\cos\left(\frac{-5\pi}{2}\right) = \cos\left(\frac{5\pi}{2}\right) = 0$

109. $T = 49.5 + 20.5\cos\left(\frac{\pi t}{6} - \frac{7\pi}{6}\right)$

(a) January: $t = 1 \Rightarrow T = 49.5 + 20.5\cos\left(\frac{\pi(1)}{6} - \frac{7\pi}{6}\right) = 29°$

(b) July: $t = 7 \Rightarrow T = 70°$

(c) December: $t = 12 \Rightarrow T \approx 31.75°$

110. $S = 23.1 + 0.442t + 4.3\sin\left(\frac{\pi t}{6}\right)$, $t = 1 \leftrightarrow$ Jan. 2004

(a) $S(1) = 23.1 + 0.442(1) + 4.3\sin\left(\frac{\pi}{6}\right) \approx 25.7$ thousand

(b) $S(14) \approx 33.0$ thousand

(c) $S(5) \approx 27.5$ thousand

(d) $S(6) \approx 25.8$ thousand

Answers will vary.

111. $\sin\theta = \frac{6}{d} \Rightarrow d = \frac{6}{\sin\theta}$

(a) $\theta = 30°$

$$d = \frac{6}{\sin 30°} = \frac{6}{(1/2)} = 12 \text{ miles}$$

(b) $\theta = 90°$

$$d = \frac{6}{\sin 90°} = \frac{6}{1} = 6 \text{ miles}$$

(c) $\theta = 120°$

$$d = \frac{6}{\sin 120°} \approx 6.9 \text{ miles}$$

112. As θ increases from 0° to 90°, x decreases from 12 cm to 0 cm and y increases from 0 cm to 12 cm. Therefore, $\sin\theta = y/12$ increases from 0 to 1, and $\cos\theta = x/12$ decreases from 1 to 0. Thus, $\tan\theta = y/x$ begins at 0 and increases without bound. When $\theta = 90°$, the tangent is undefined.

113. True. The reference angle for $\theta = 151°$ is $\theta' = 180° - 151° = 29°$, and sine is positive in Quadrants I and II.

114. False. $-\cot\left(\frac{3\pi}{4}\right) = -(-1) = 1$ and

$\cot\left(-\frac{\pi}{4}\right) = -1$

115. (a)

θ	0°	20°	40°	60°	80°
$\sin\theta$	0	0.3420	0.6428	0.8660	0.9848
$\sin(180° - \theta)$	0	0.3420	0.6428	0.8660	0.9848

(b) It appears that $\sin\theta = \sin(180° - \theta)$.

116.

Function	$\sin x$	$\cos x$	$\tan x$
Domain	$(-\infty, \infty)$	$(-\infty, \infty)$	All reals except $\frac{\pi}{2} + n\pi$
Range	$[-1, 1]$	$[-1, 1]$	$(-\infty, \infty)$
Evenness	No	Yes	No
Oddness	Yes	No	Yes
Period	2π	2π	π
Zeros	$n\pi$	$\frac{\pi}{2} + n\pi$	$n\pi$

Function	$\csc x$	$\sec x$	$\cot x$
Domain	All reals except $n\pi$	All reals except $\frac{\pi}{2} + n\pi$	All reals except $n\pi$
Range	$(-\infty, -1] \cup [1, \infty)$	$(-\infty, -1] \cup [1, \infty)$	$(-\infty, \infty)$
Evenness	No	Yes	No
Oddness	Yes	No	Yes
Period	2π	2π	π
Zeros	None	None	$\frac{\pi}{2} + n\pi$

Patterns and conclusions may vary.

117. $3x - 7 = 14$

$3x = 21$

$x = 7$

118. $44 - 9x = 61$

$9x = -17$

$x = -\frac{17}{9} \approx -1.889$

119. $x^2 - 2x - 5 = 0$

$$x = \frac{2 \pm \sqrt{4 + 20}}{2} = 1 \pm \sqrt{6}$$

$x \approx 3.449,\ x \approx -1.449$

120. $2x^2 + x - 4 = 0$

$$x = \frac{-1 \pm \sqrt{1 + 4(4)(2)}}{4} = \frac{-1 \pm \sqrt{33}}{4}$$

$x \approx 1.186,\ -1.686$

121. $\dfrac{3}{x-1} = \dfrac{x+2}{9}$

$27 = (x-1)(x+2)$

$x^2 + x - 29 = 0$

$x = \dfrac{-1 \pm \sqrt{1 + 4(29)}}{2} = \dfrac{-1 \pm \sqrt{117}}{2}$

$x \approx -5.908, 4.908$

122. $\dfrac{5}{x} = \dfrac{x+4}{2x}$

$10x = x^2 + 4x$

$x^2 - 6x = 0$

$x(x-6) = 0$

$x = 6 \quad (x = 0 \text{ extraneous})$

123. $4^{3-x} = 726$

$3 - x = \log_4 726$

$x = 3 - \log_4 726 = 3 - \dfrac{\ln 726}{\ln 4} \approx -1.752$

124. $\dfrac{4500}{4 + e^{2x}} = 50$

$90 = 4 + e^{2x}$

$86 = e^{2x}$

$2x = \ln 86$

$x = \dfrac{1}{2}\ln 86 \approx 2.227$

125. $\ln x = -6$

$x = e^{-6} \approx 0.002479 \approx 0.002$

126. $\ln\sqrt{x+10} = \frac{1}{2}\ln(x+10) = 1 \implies \ln(x+10) = 2 \implies x + 10 = e^2 \implies x = e^2 - 10 \approx -2.611$

Section 4.5 Graphs of Sine and Cosine Functions

- You should be able to graph $y = a\sin(bx - c)$ and $y = a\cos(bx - c)$.
- Amplitude: $|a|$
- Period: $\dfrac{2\pi}{|b|}$
- Shift: Solve $bx - c = 0$ and $bx - c = 2\pi$.
- Key increments: $\dfrac{1}{4}$ (period)

Vocabulary Check

1. amplitude **2.** one cycle **3.** $\dfrac{2\pi}{b}$ **4.** phase shift

1. $f(x) = \sin x$

(a) x-intercepts: $(-2\pi, 0), (-\pi, 0), (0, 0), (\pi, 0), (2\pi, 0)$

(b) y-intercept: $(0, 0)$

(c) Increasing on: $\left(-2\pi, -\frac{3\pi}{2}\right), \left(-\frac{\pi}{2}, \frac{\pi}{2}\right), \left(\frac{3\pi}{2}, 2\pi\right)$

Decreasing on: $\left(-\frac{3\pi}{2}, -\frac{\pi}{2}\right), \left(\frac{\pi}{2}, \frac{3\pi}{2}\right)$

(d) Relative maxima: $\left(-\frac{3\pi}{2}, 1\right), \left(\frac{\pi}{2}, 1\right)$

Relative minima: $\left(-\frac{\pi}{2}, -1\right), \left(\frac{3\pi}{2}, -1\right)$

2. $f(x) = \cos x$

(a) x-intercepts: $\left(-\frac{3\pi}{2}, 0\right), \left(-\frac{\pi}{2}, 0\right), \left(\frac{\pi}{2}, 0\right), \left(\frac{3\pi}{2}, 0\right)$

(b) y-intercept: $(0, 1)$

(c) Increasing on: $(-\pi, 0), (\pi, 2\pi)$

Decreasing on: $(-2\pi, -\pi), (0, \pi)$

(d) Relative maxima: $(-2\pi, 1), (0, 1), (2\pi, 1)$

Relative minima: $(-\pi, -1), (\pi, -1)$

3. $y = 3 \sin 2x$

Period: $\frac{2\pi}{2} = \pi$

Amplitude: $|3| = 3$

Xmin = -2π
Xmax = 2π
Xscl = $\pi/2$
Ymin = -4
Ymax = 4
Yscl = 1

4. $y = 2 \cos 3x$

Period: $\frac{2\pi}{b} = \frac{2\pi}{3}$

Amplitude: $|a| = 2$

Xmin = $-\pi$
Xmax = π
Xscl = $\pi/4$
Ymin = -3
Ymax = 3
Yscl = 1

5. $y = \frac{5}{2} \cos \frac{x}{2}$

Period: $\frac{2\pi}{1/2} = 4\pi$

Amplitude: $\left|\frac{5}{2}\right| = \frac{5}{2}$

Xmin = -4π
Xmax = 4π
Xscl = π
Ymin = -3
Ymax = 3
Yscl = 1

6. $y = -3 \sin \frac{x}{3}$

Period: $\frac{2\pi}{b} = \frac{2\pi}{(1/3)} = 6\pi$

Amplitude: $|a| = |-3| = 3$

Xmin = -6π
Xmax = 6π
Xscl = π
Ymin = -4
Ymax = 4
Yscl = 1

7. $y = \frac{2}{3} \sin \pi x$

Period: $\frac{2\pi}{\pi} = 2$

Amplitude: $\left|\frac{2}{3}\right| = \frac{2}{3}$

8. $y = \frac{3}{2} \cos \frac{\pi x}{2}$

Period: $\frac{2\pi}{b} = \frac{2\pi}{(\pi/2)} = 4$

Amplitude: $|a| = \frac{3}{2}$

9. $y = -2 \sin x$

Period: $\dfrac{2\pi}{1} = 2\pi$

Amplitude: $|-2| = 2$

10. $y = -\cos \dfrac{2x}{5}$

Period: $\dfrac{2\pi}{b} = \dfrac{2\pi}{2/5} = 5\pi$

Amplitude: $|a| = |-1| = 1$

11. $y = \dfrac{1}{4} \cos \dfrac{2x}{3}$

Period: $\dfrac{2\pi}{2/3} = 3\pi$

Amplitude: $\left|\dfrac{1}{4}\right| = \dfrac{1}{4}$

12. $y = \dfrac{5}{2} \cos \dfrac{x}{4}$

Period: $\dfrac{2\pi}{b} = \dfrac{2\pi}{1/4} = 8\pi$

Amplitude: $|a| = \dfrac{5}{2}$

13. $y = \dfrac{1}{3} \sin 4\pi x$

Period: $\dfrac{2\pi}{4\pi} = \dfrac{1}{2}$

Amplitude: $\left|\dfrac{1}{3}\right| = \dfrac{1}{3}$

14. $y = \dfrac{3}{4} \cos \dfrac{\pi x}{12}$

Period: $\dfrac{2\pi}{b} = \dfrac{2\pi}{\pi/12} = 24$

Amplitude: $|a| = \dfrac{3}{4}$

15. $f(x) = \sin x$

$g(x) = \sin(x - \pi)$

The graph of g is a horizontal shift to the right π units of the graph of f (a phase shift).

16. $f(x) = \cos x$, $g(x) = \cos(x + \pi)$

g is a horizontal shift of f π units to the left.

17. $f(x) = \cos 2x$

$g(x) = -\cos 2x$

The graph of g is a reflection in the x-axis of the graph of f.

18. $f(x) = \sin 3x$, $g(x) = \sin(-3x)$

g is a reflection of f about the y-axis. (or, about the x-axis)

19. $f(x) = \cos x$

$g(x) = -5 \cos x$

The graph of g has five times the amplitude of f, and reflected in the x-axis.

20. $f(x) = \sin x$, $g(x) = -\frac{1}{2} \sin x$

The amplitude of g is one-half that of f. g is a reflection of f in the x-axis.

21. $f(x) = \sin 2x$

$g(x) = 5 + \sin 2x$

The graph of g is a vertical shift upward of five units of the graph of f.

22. $f(x) = \cos 4x$, $g(x) = -6 + \cos 4x$

g is a vertical shift of f six units downward.

23. The graph of g has twice the amplitude as the graph of f. The period is the same.

24. The period of g is one-half the period of f.

25. The graph of g is a horizontal shift π units to the right of the graph of f.

26. Shift the graph of f two units upward to obtain the graph of g.

27. $f(x) = \sin x$

Period: 2π

Amplitude: 1

$g(x) = -4 \sin x$

Period: 2π

Amplitude: $|-4| = 4$

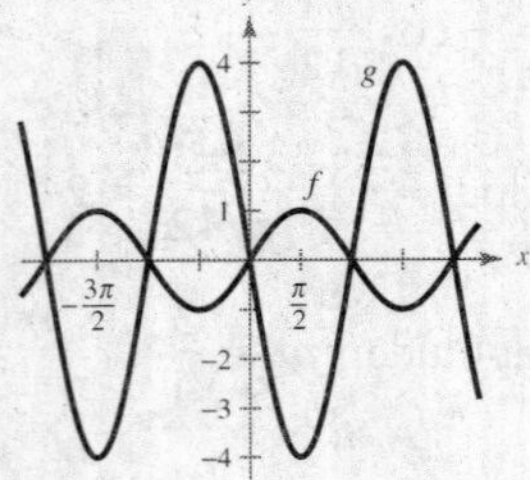

28. $f(x) = \sin x$

$g(x) = \sin \dfrac{x}{3}$

x	0	$\frac{\pi}{2}$	π	$\frac{3\pi}{2}$	2π
$\sin x$	0	1	0	-1	0
$\sin \frac{x}{3}$	0	$\frac{1}{2}$	$\frac{\sqrt{3}}{2}$	1	$\frac{\sqrt{3}}{2}$

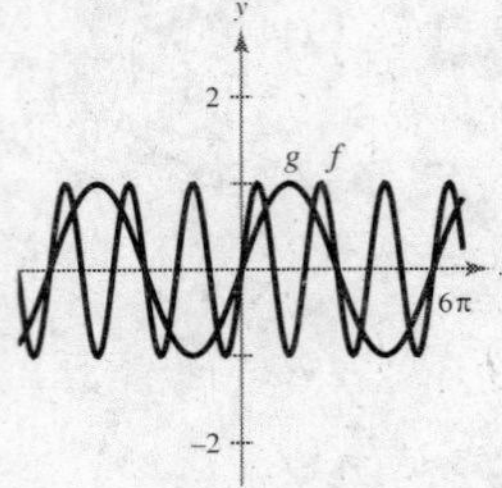

29. $f(x) = \cos x$

Period: 2π

Amplitude: 1

$g(x) = 4 + \cos x$ is a vertical shift of the graph of $f(x)$ four units upward.

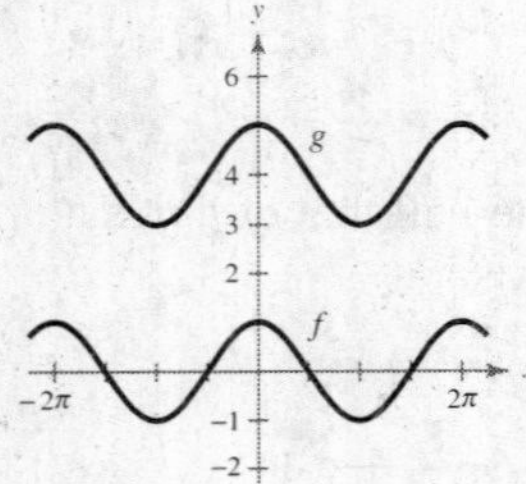

30. $f(x) = 2 \cos 2x$

$g(x) = -\cos 4x$

x	0	$\frac{\pi}{4}$	$\frac{\pi}{2}$	$\frac{3\pi}{4}$	π
$2 \cos 2x$	2	0	-2	0	2
$-\cos 4x$	-1	1	-1	1	-1

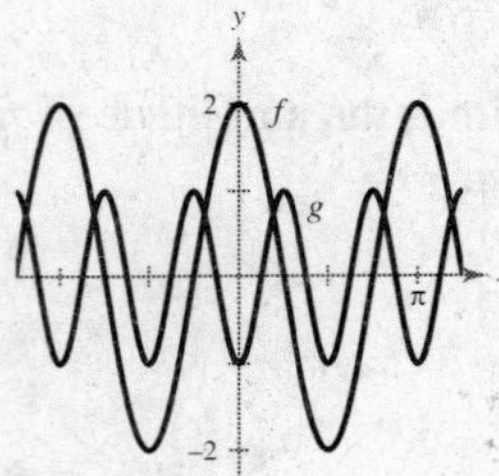

31. $f(x) = -\dfrac{1}{2} \sin \dfrac{x}{2}$

Period: 4π

Amplitude: $\dfrac{1}{2}$

$g(x) = 3 - \dfrac{1}{2} \sin \dfrac{x}{2}$ is the graph of $f(x)$ shifted vertically three units upward.

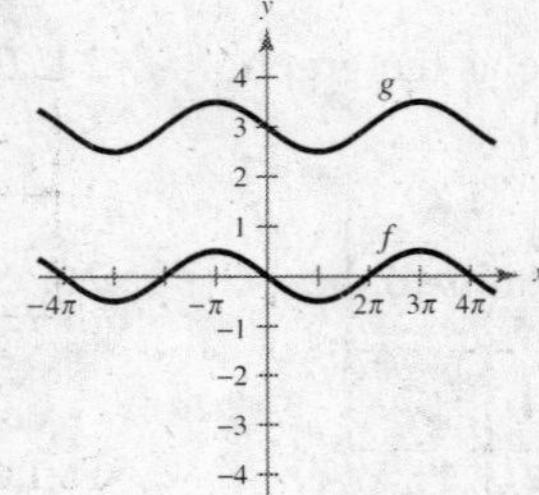

32. $f(x) = 4 \sin \pi x$

$g(x) = 4 \sin \pi x - 2$

x	0	$\frac{1}{2}$	1	$\frac{3}{2}$	2
$f(x)$	0	4	0	-4	0
$g(x)$	-2	2	-2	-6	-2

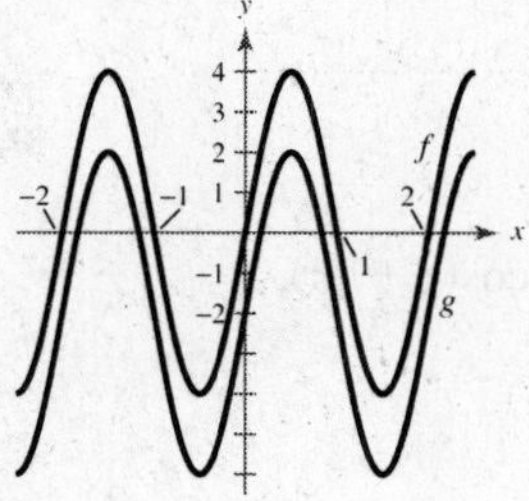

33. $f(x) = 2 \cos x$

Period: 2π

Amplitude: 2

$g(x) = 2 \cos(x + \pi)$ is the graph of $f(x)$ shifted π units to the left.

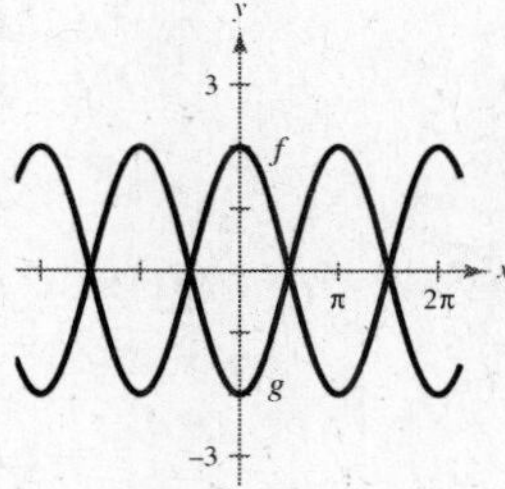

34. $f(x) = -\cos x$

$g(x) = -\cos\left(x - \frac{\pi}{2}\right)$

x	0	$\frac{\pi}{2}$	π	$\frac{3\pi}{2}$	2π
$-\cos x$	-1	0	1	0	-1
$-\cos\left(x - \frac{\pi}{2}\right)$	0	-1	0	1	0

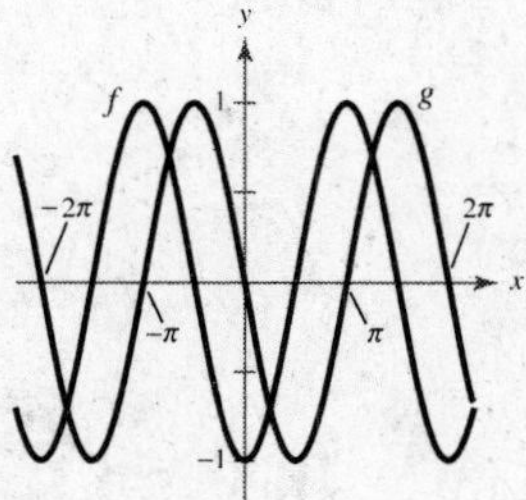

35. $f(x) = \sin x,\ g(x) = \cos\left(x - \frac{\pi}{2}\right)$

$\sin x = \cos\left(x - \frac{\pi}{2}\right)$

Period: 2π

Amplitude: 1

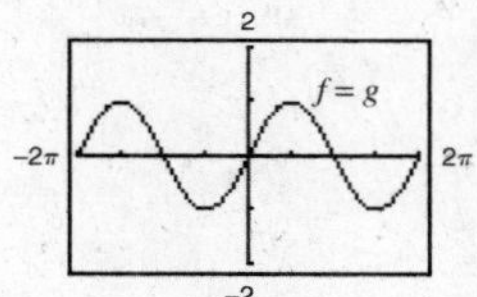

36. $f(x) = \sin x,\ g(x) = -\cos\left(x + \frac{\pi}{2}\right)$

x	0	$\frac{\pi}{2}$	π	$\frac{3\pi}{2}$	2π
$\sin x$	0	1	0	-1	0
$-\cos\left(x + \frac{\pi}{2}\right)$	0	1	0	-1	0

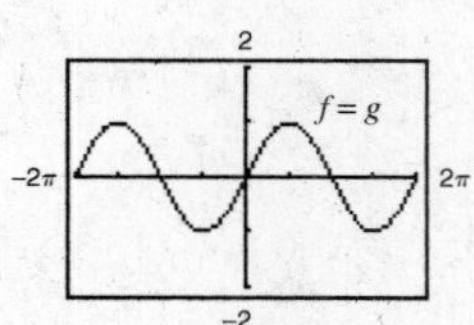

Conjecture: $\sin x = -\cos\left(x + \frac{\pi}{2}\right)$

37. $f(x) = \cos x$

$g(x) = -\sin\left(x - \frac{\pi}{2}\right) = \sin\left(\frac{\pi}{2} - x\right) = \cos x$

Thus, $f(x) = g(x)$.

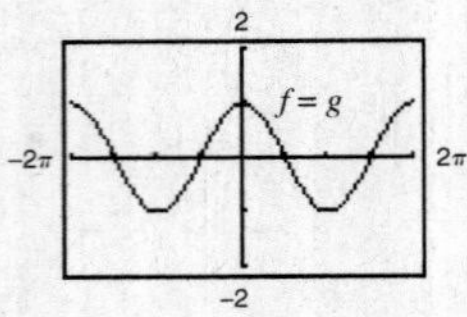

38. $f(x) = \cos x$, $g(x) = -\cos(x - \pi)$

x	0	$\frac{\pi}{2}$	π	$\frac{3\pi}{2}$	2π
$\cos x$	1	0	-1	0	1
$-\cos(x - \pi)$	1	0	-1	0	1

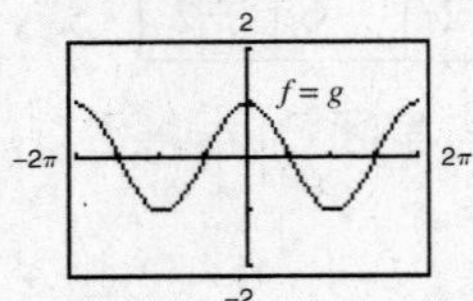

Conjecture: $\cos x = -\cos(x - \pi)$

39. $y = 3 \sin x$

Period: 2π

Amplitude: 3

Key points: $(0, 0)$, $\left(\frac{\pi}{2}, 3\right)$, $(\pi, 0)$, $\left(\frac{3\pi}{2}, -3\right)$, $(2\pi, 0)$

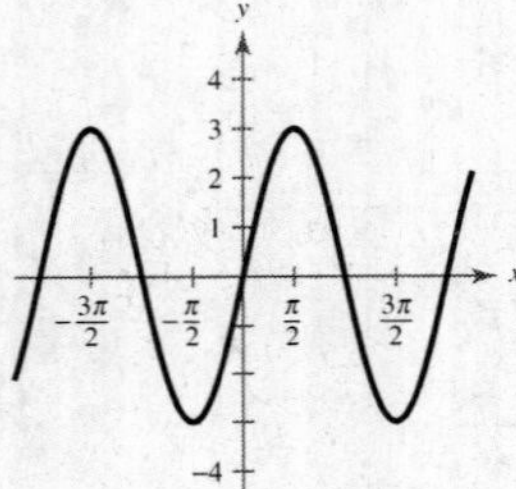

40. $y = \frac{1}{4} \cos x$

Period: 2π

Amplitude: $\frac{1}{4}$

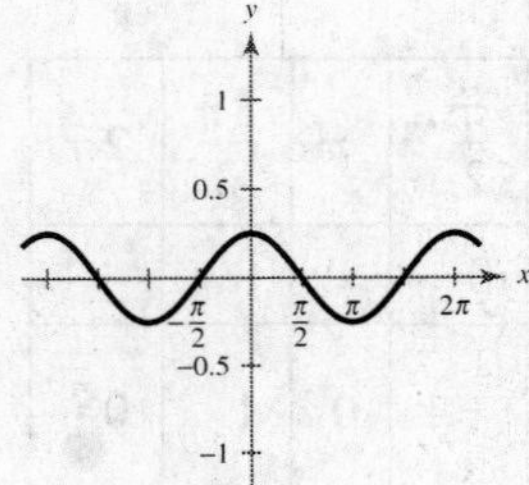

41. $y = \cos \frac{x}{2}$

Period: 4π

Amplitude: 1

Key points: $(0, 1)$, $(\pi, 0)$, $(2\pi, -1)$, $(3\pi, 0)$, $(4\pi, 1)$

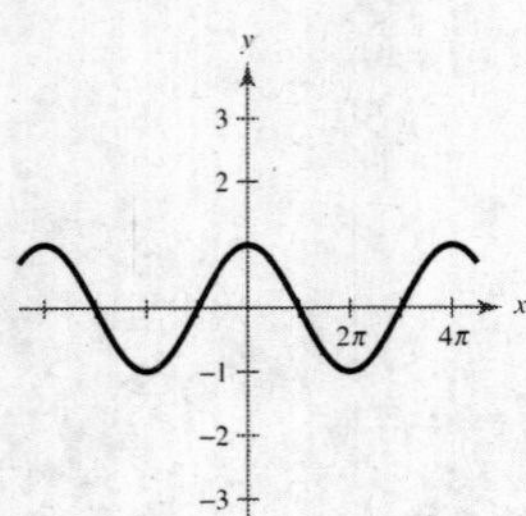

42. $y = \sin 4x$

Period: $\frac{2\pi}{4} = \frac{\pi}{2}$

Amplitude: 1

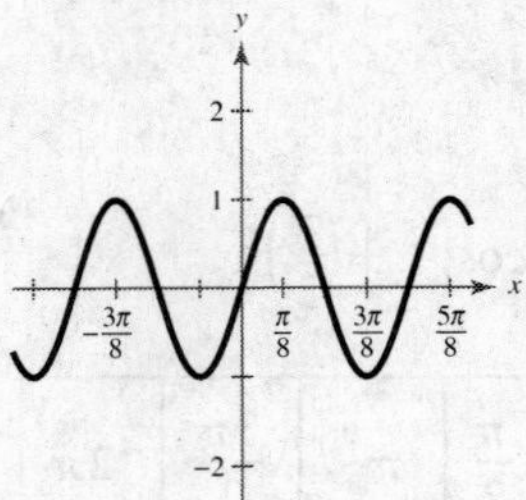

43. $y = \sin\left(x - \frac{\pi}{4}\right)$; $a = 1,\ b = 1,\ c = \frac{\pi}{4}$

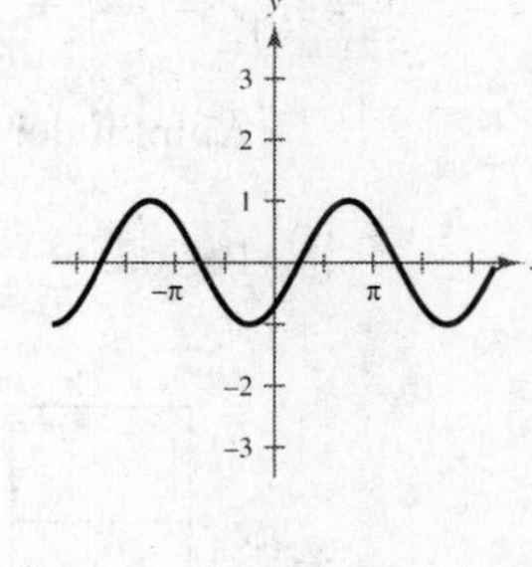

Period: 2π

Amplitude: 1

Shift: Set $x - \frac{\pi}{4} = 0$ and $x - \frac{\pi}{4} = 2\pi$

$$x = \frac{\pi}{4} \qquad x = \frac{9\pi}{4}$$

Key points: $\left(\frac{\pi}{4}, 0\right), \left(\frac{3\pi}{4}, 1\right), \left(\frac{5\pi}{4}, 0\right), \left(\frac{7\pi}{4}, -1\right), \left(\frac{9\pi}{4}, 0\right)$

44. $y = \sin(x - \pi)$

Horizontal shift π units to the right

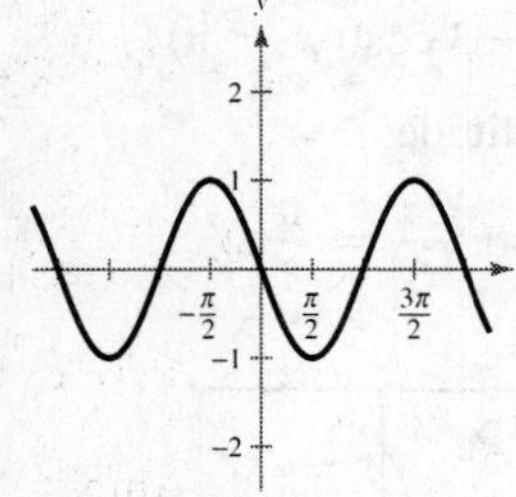

45. $y = -8\cos(x + \pi)$

Period: 2π

Amplitude: 8

Key points: $(-\pi, -8), \left(-\frac{\pi}{2}, 0\right), (0, 8), \left(\frac{\pi}{2}, 0\right), (\pi, -8)$

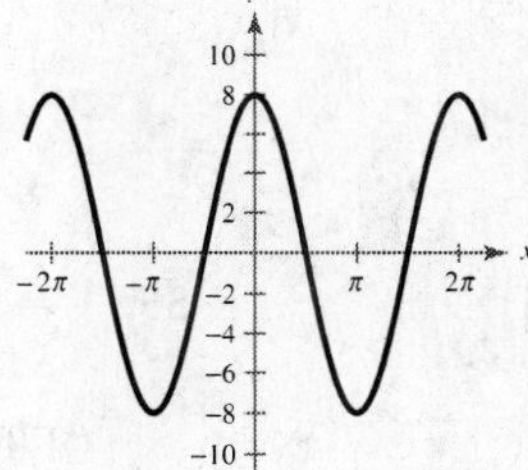

46. $y = 3\cos\left(x + \frac{\pi}{2}\right)$

Amplitude: 3

Horizontal shift $\frac{\pi}{2}$ units to the left

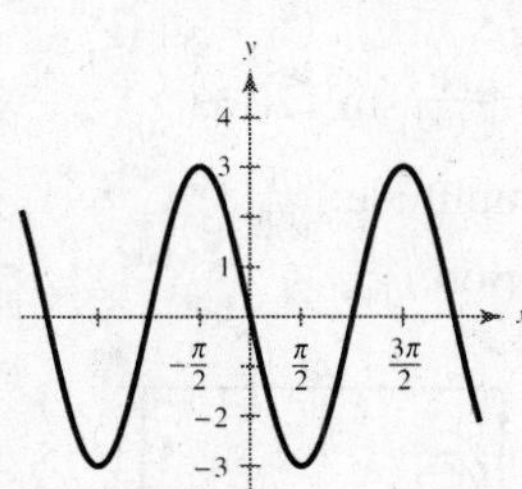

Note: $3\cos\left(x + \frac{\pi}{2}\right) = -3\sin x$

47. $y = -2\sin\frac{2\pi x}{3}$

Amplitude: 2

Period: $\frac{2\pi}{2\pi/3} = 3$

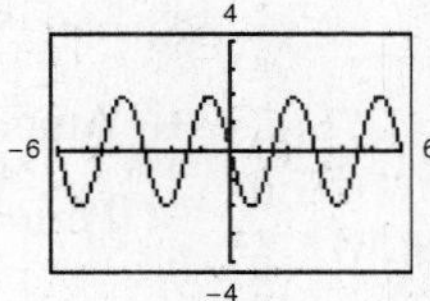

48. $y = -10\cos\dfrac{\pi x}{6}$

Amplitude: 10

Period: $\dfrac{2\pi}{\pi/6} = 12$

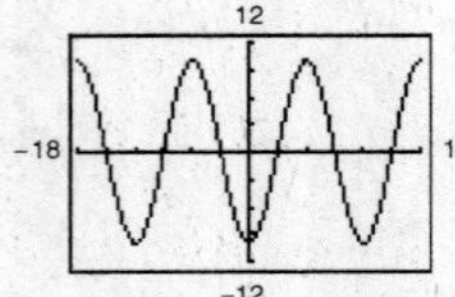

49. $y = -4 + 5\cos\dfrac{\pi t}{12}$

Amplitude: 5

Period: $\dfrac{2\pi}{\pi/12} = 24$

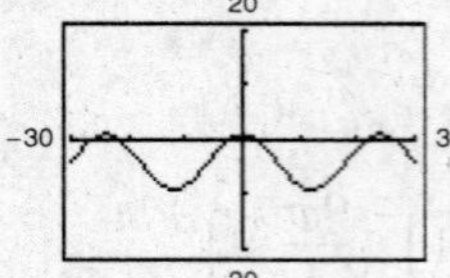

50. $y = 2 - 2\sin\dfrac{2\pi x}{3}$

Amplitude: 2

Period: $\dfrac{2\pi}{2\pi/3} = 3$

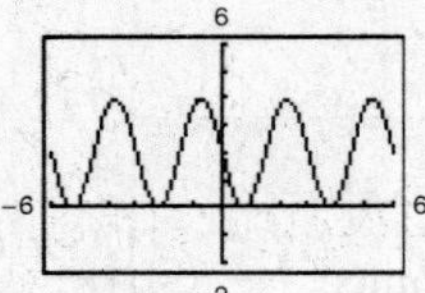

51. $y = \dfrac{2}{3}\cos\left(\dfrac{x}{2} - \dfrac{\pi}{4}\right)$

Amplitude: $\dfrac{2}{3}$

Period: $\dfrac{2\pi}{1/2} = 4\pi$

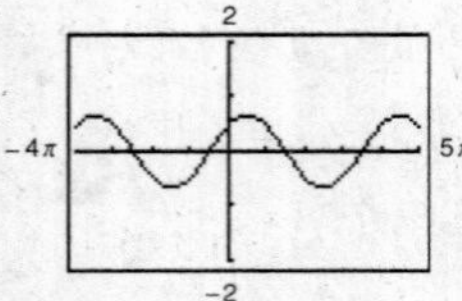

52. $y = -3\cos(6x + \pi)$

Amplitude: 3

Period: $\dfrac{2\pi}{6} = \dfrac{\pi}{3}$

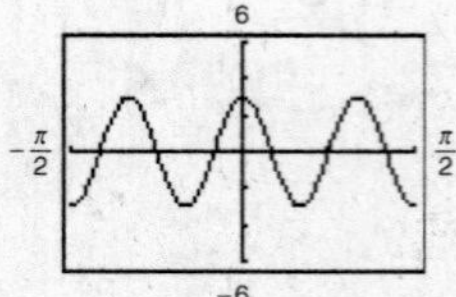

53. $y = -2\sin(4x + \pi)$

Amplitude: 2

Period: $\dfrac{\pi}{2}$

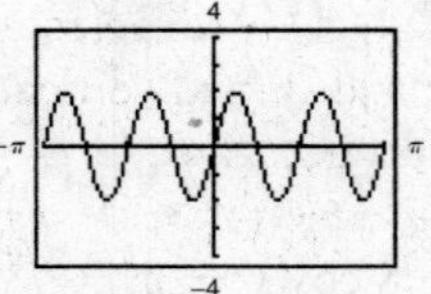

54. $y = -4\sin\left(\dfrac{2}{3}x - \dfrac{\pi}{3}\right)$

Amplitude: 4

Period: 3π

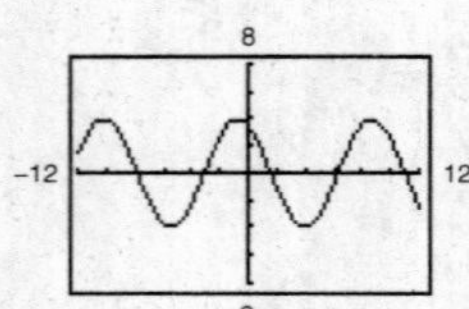

55. $y = \cos\left(2\pi x - \dfrac{\pi}{2}\right) + 1$

Amplitude: 1

Period: 1

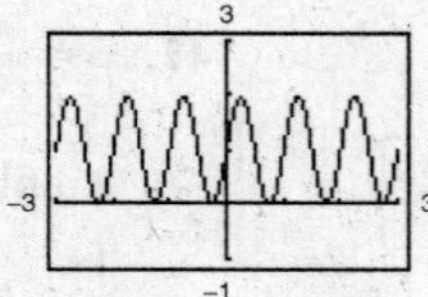

56. $y = 3\cos\left(\dfrac{\pi x}{2} + \dfrac{\pi}{2}\right) - 3$

Amplitude: 3

Period: 4

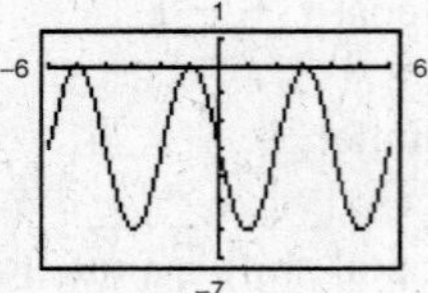

57. $y = 5\sin(\pi - 2x) + 10$

Amplitude: 5

Period: π

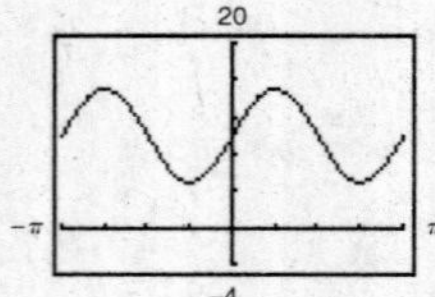

58. $y = 5\cos(\pi - 2x) + 6$

Amplitude: 5

Period: π

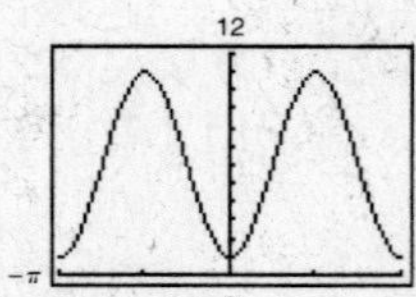

59. $y = \frac{1}{100}\sin 120\pi t$

Amplitude: $\frac{1}{100}$

Period: $\frac{1}{60}$

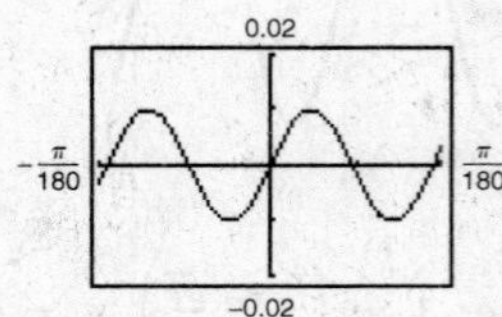

60. $y = \frac{-1}{100}\cos(50\pi t)$

Amplitude: $\frac{1}{100}$

Period: $\frac{1}{25}$

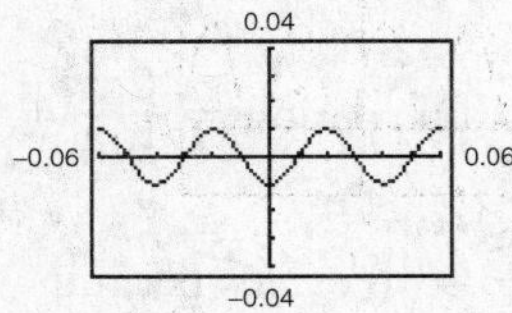

61. $f(x) = a\cos x + d$

Amplitude: $\frac{1}{2}[8 - 0] = 4$

Since $f(x)$ is the graph of $g(x) = 4\cos x$ reflected about the x-axis and shifted vertically four units upward, we have $a = -4$ and $d = 4$. Thus,

$$f(x) = -4\cos x + 4$$
$$= 4 - 4\cos x.$$

62. $f(x) = a\cos x + d$

Amplitude: $\frac{-2 - (-4)}{2} = 1$

Reflected in the x-axis:

$a = -1$

$-4 = -1\cos 0 + d$

$d = -3$

$y = -3 - \cos x$

63. $f(x) = a\cos x + d$

Amplitude: $\frac{1}{2}[7 - (-5)] = 6$

Graph of f is the graph of $g(x) = 6\cos x$ reflected about the x-axis and shifted vertically one unit upward. Thus, $f(x) = -6\cos x + 1$.

64. $y = a\cos x + d$

Amplitude: $\frac{1}{2}$

Period: 2π

Reflected in x-axis, $a = -\frac{1}{2}$

$d = -4$

$y = -4 - \frac{1}{2}\cos x$

65. $f(x) = a\sin(bx - c)$

Amplitude: $|a| = 3$

Since the graph is reflected about the x-axis, we have $a = -3$.

Period: $\frac{2\pi}{b} = \pi \Rightarrow b = 2$

Phase shift: $c = 0$

Thus, $f(x) = -3\sin 2x$.

66. $y = a\sin(bx - c)$

Amplitude: $2 \Rightarrow a = 2$

Period: 4π

$\frac{2\pi}{b} = 4\pi \Rightarrow b = \frac{1}{2}$

Phase shift: $c = 0$

$y = 2\sin\left(\frac{x}{2}\right)$

67. $f(x) = a\sin(bx - c)$

Amplitude: $a = 1$

Period: $2\pi \Rightarrow b = 1$

Phase shift: $bx - c = 0$ when $x = \frac{\pi}{4}$.

$$(1)\left(\frac{\pi}{4}\right) - c = 0 \Rightarrow c = \frac{\pi}{4}$$

Thus, $f(x) = \sin\left(x - \frac{\pi}{4}\right)$.

68. $y = a\sin(bx - c)$

Amplitude: $2 \Rightarrow a = 2$

Period: 4

$\frac{2\pi}{b} = 4 \Rightarrow b = \frac{\pi}{2}$

Phase shift: $\frac{c}{b} = -1 \Rightarrow c = -\frac{\pi}{2}$

$y = 2\sin\left(\frac{\pi x}{2} + \frac{\pi}{2}\right)$

69. $y_1 = \sin x$

$y_2 = -\frac{1}{2}$

In the interval $[-2\pi, 2\pi]$, $\sin x = -\frac{1}{2}$ when

$x = -\frac{5\pi}{6}, -\frac{\pi}{6}, \frac{7\pi}{6}, \frac{11\pi}{6}$.

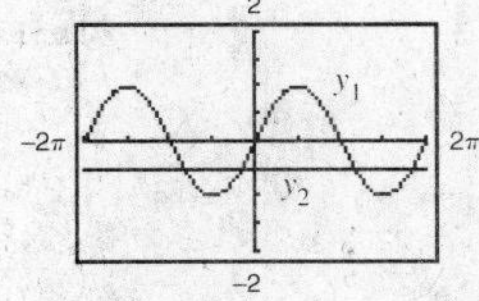

70. $y_1 = \cos x$

$y_2 = -1$

$y_1 = y_2$ when $x = \pi, -\pi$.

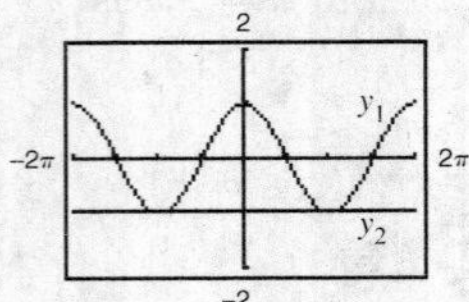

71. 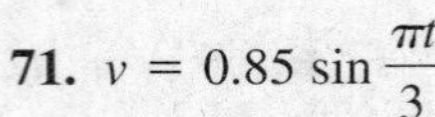 $v = 0.85 \sin \dfrac{\pi t}{3}$

(a)

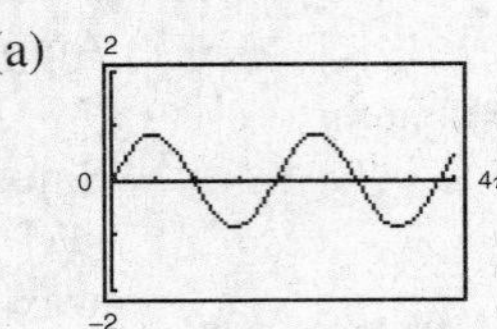

(b) Time for one cycle $=$ one period $= \dfrac{2\pi}{\pi/3} = 6$ sec

(c) Cycles per min $= \dfrac{60}{6} = 10$ cycles per min

(d) The period would change.

72. $S = 74.50 + 43.75 \cos \dfrac{\pi t}{6}$

(a)

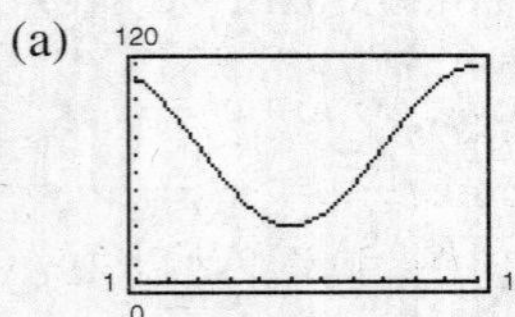

(b) Maximum sales: December ($t = 12$)

Minimum sales: June ($t = 6$)

73. $h = 25 \sin \dfrac{\pi}{15}(t - 75) + 30$

(a)

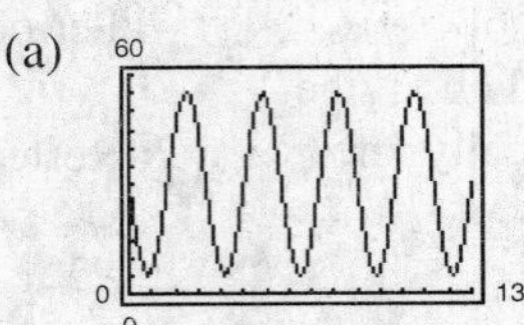

(b) Minimum: $30 - 25 = 5$ feet

Maximum: $30 + 25 = 55$ feet

74. $P = 100 - 20 \cos \dfrac{8\pi}{3}t$

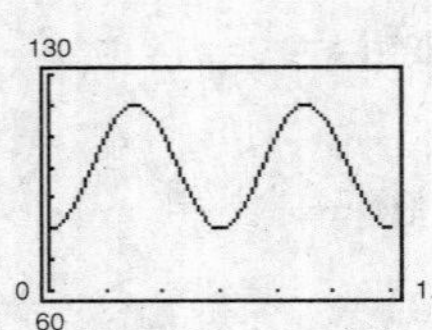

Period: $\dfrac{2\pi}{(8\pi/3)} = \dfrac{3}{4}$

$\dfrac{1 \text{ heartbeat}}{(3/4)} \Rightarrow \dfrac{4}{3}$ heartbeats/second $= 80$ heartbeats/minute

75. $C = 30.3 + 21.6 \sin\left(\dfrac{2\pi t}{365} + 10.9\right)$

(a) Period: $\dfrac{2\pi}{b} = \dfrac{2\pi}{(2\pi/365)} = 365$ days

This is to be expected: 365 days $=$ 1 year

(b) The constant 30.3 gallons is the average daily fuel consumption.

(c)

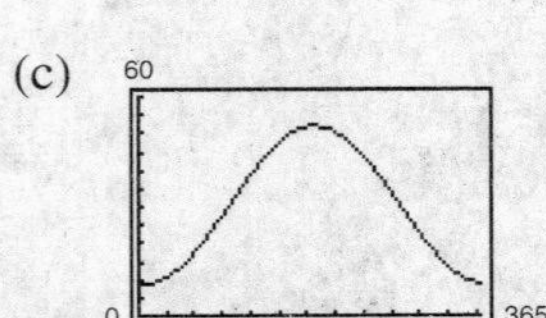

Consumption exceeds 40 gallons/day when $124 \le x \le 252$. (Graph C together with $y = 40$.) (Beginning of May through part of September)

76. (a) Yes, y is a function of t because for each value of t there corresponds one and only one value of y.

(b) The period is approximately $2(0.375 - 0.125) = 0.5$ seconds.

The amplitude is approximately $\frac{1}{2}(2.35 - 1.65) = 0.35$ centimeters.

(c) One model is $y = 0.35 \sin 4\pi t + 2$.

(d)

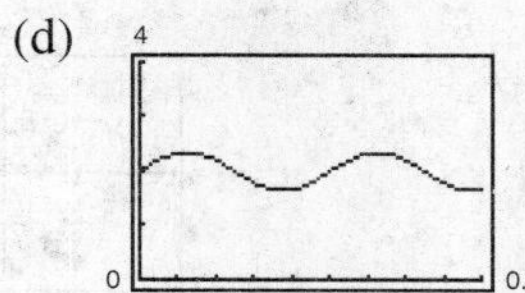

77. (a)

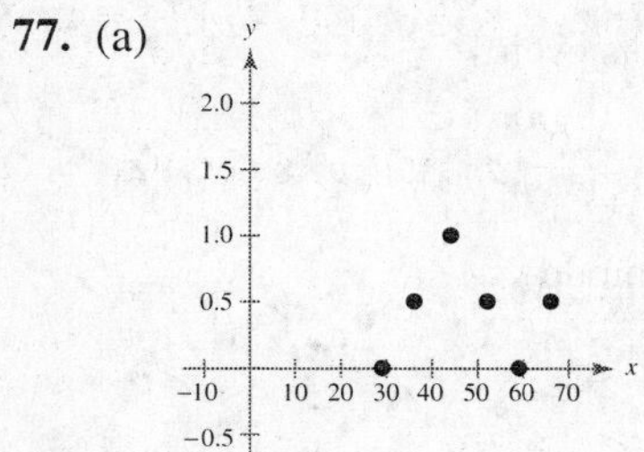

(b) $y = 0.506 \sin(0.209x - 1.336) + 0.526$

(c)

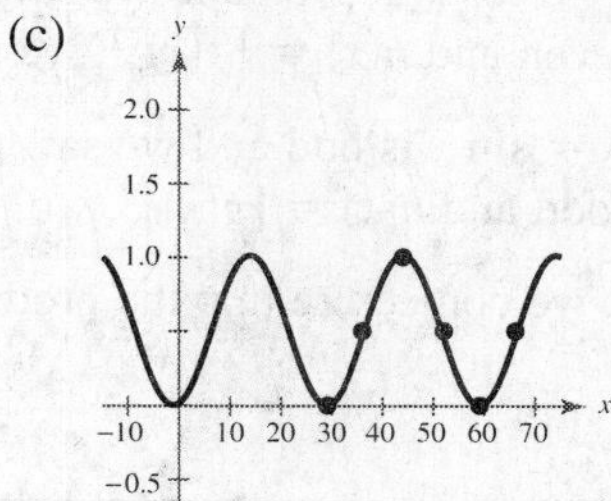

The model is a good fit.

(d) The period is $\dfrac{2\pi}{0.209} \approx 30.06$.

(e) June 29, 2007 is day 545. Using the model, $y \approx 0.2709$ or 27.09%.

78. (a) $A(t) = 19.73 \sin(0.472t - 1.74) + 70.2$

(b)

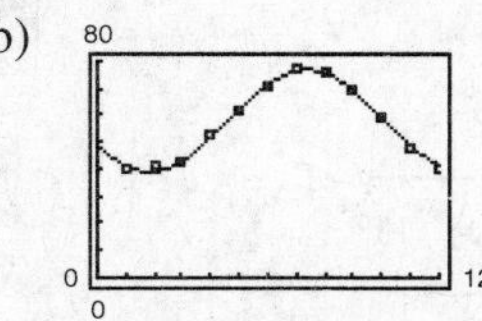

The model somewhat fits the data.

(c)

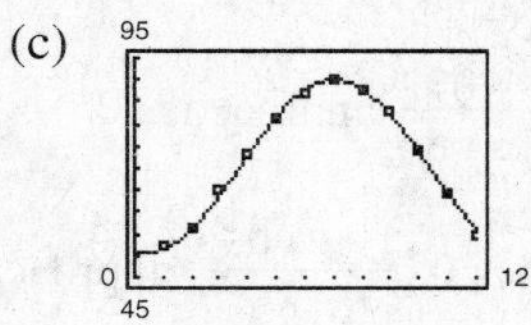

The model is a good fit.

(d) Nantucket: 58°

Athens: 70.2°

The constant term (d) gives the average daily high temperature.

(e) Period for $N(t) = \dfrac{2\pi}{(2\pi/11)} = 11$

Period for $A(t) = \dfrac{2\pi}{0.472} \approx 13$

You would expect the period to be 12 (1 year).

(f) Athens has greater variability. This is given by the amplitude.

79. True. The period is $\dfrac{2\pi}{3/10} = \dfrac{20\pi}{3}$.

80. False. The amplitude is $\dfrac{1}{2}$ that of $y = \cos x$.

81. True

82. Answers will vary.

83. The graph passes through $(0, 0)$ and has period π. Matches (e).

84. The amplitude is 4 and the period 2π. Since $(0, -4)$ is on the graph, matches (a).

85. The period is 4π and the amplitude is 1. Since $(0, 1)$ and $(\pi, 0)$ are on the graph, matches (c).

86. The period is π. Since $(0, -1)$ is on the graph, matches (d).

87. (a) $h(x) = \cos^2 x$ is even. (b) $h(x) = \sin^2 x$ is even. (c) $h(x) = \sin x \cos x$ is odd.

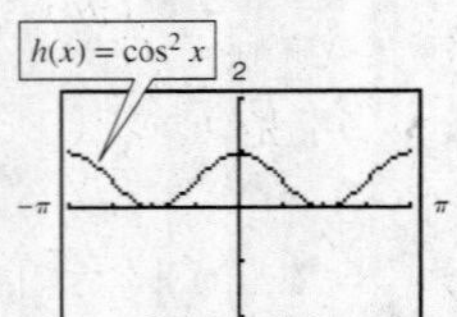

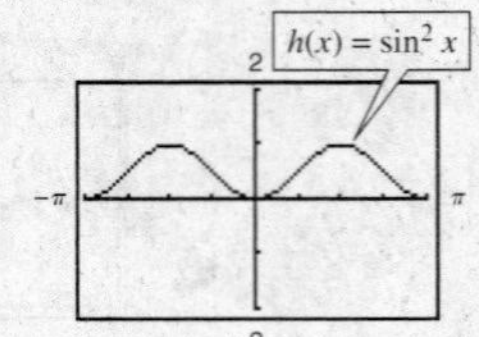

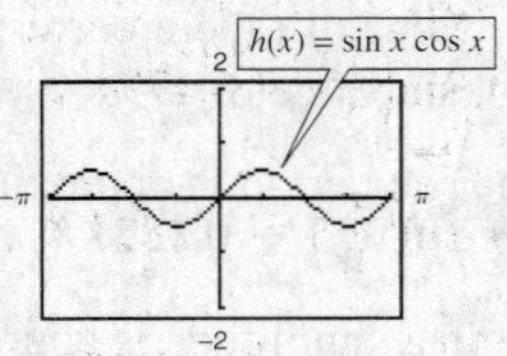

88. (a) In Exercise 87, $f(x) = \cos x$ is even and we saw that $h(x) = \cos^2 x$ is even. Therefore, for $f(x)$ even and $h(x) = [f(x)]^2$, we make the conjecture that $h(x)$ is even.

(b) In Exercise 87, $g(x) = \sin x$ is odd and we saw that $h(x) = \sin^2 x$ is even. Therefore, for $g(x)$ odd and $h(x) = [g(x)]^2$, we make the conjecture that $h(x)$ is even.

(c) From part (c) of 87, we conjecture that the product of an even function and an odd function is odd.

89. (a)

x	-1	-0.1	-0.01	-0.001
$\dfrac{\sin x}{x}$	0.8415	0.9983	1.0	1.0

x	0	0.001	0.01	0.1	1
$\dfrac{\sin x}{x}$	Undef.	1.0	1.0	0.9983	0.8415

(b)

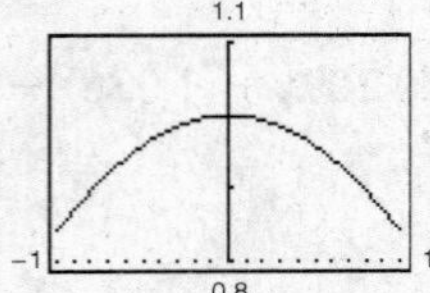

As $x \to 0$, $f(x) = \dfrac{\sin x}{x}$ approaches 1.

(c) As x approaches 0, $\dfrac{\sin x}{x}$ approaches 1.

90. (a)

x	-1	-0.1	-0.01	-0.001
$\dfrac{1 - \cos x}{x}$	-0.4597	-0.05	-0.005	-0.0005

x	0	0.001	0.01	0.1	1
$\dfrac{1 - \cos x}{x}$	Undef.	0.0005	0.005	0.05	0.4597

(b)

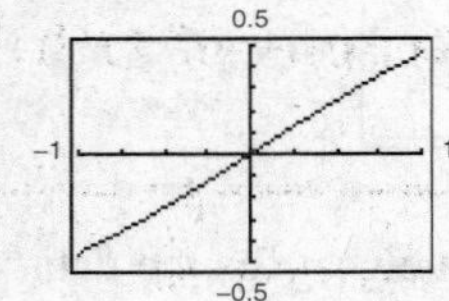

As $x \to 0$, $\dfrac{1 - \cos x}{x}$ approaches 0.

(c) As x approaches 0, $\dfrac{1 - \cos x}{x}$ approaches 0.

91. (a)

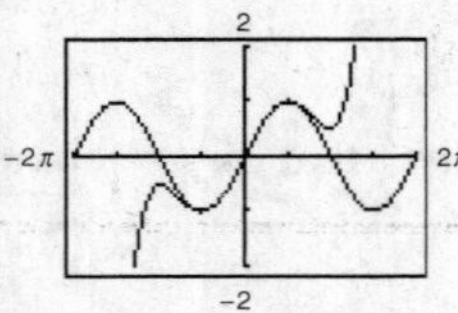

(b)

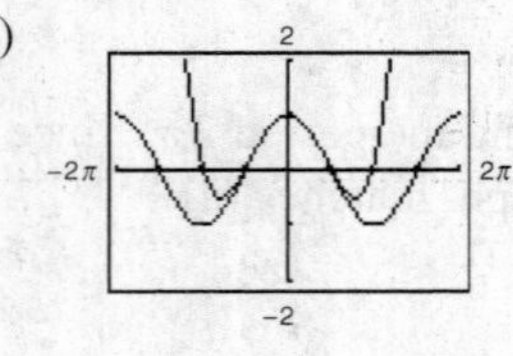

(c) Next term for sine approximation: $-\dfrac{x^7}{7!}$

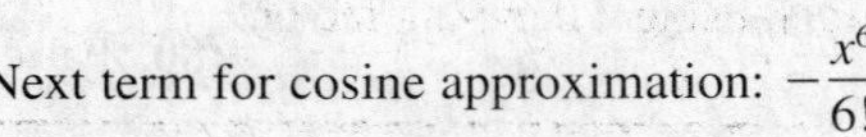

Next term for cosine approximation: $-\dfrac{x^6}{6!}$

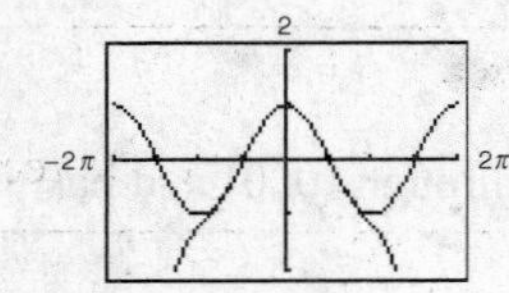

92. (a) $\sin(1) \approx 0.8415$ (d) $\cos(-1) \approx 0.5403$

(b) $\sin\left(\frac{1}{2}\right) \approx 0.4794$ (e) $\cos\left(-\frac{\pi}{4}\right) \approx 0.7071$

(c) $\sin\left(\frac{\pi}{8}\right) \approx 0.3827$ (f) $\cos\left(-\frac{1}{2}\right) \approx 0.8776$

In all cases, the approximations are very accurate.

93.

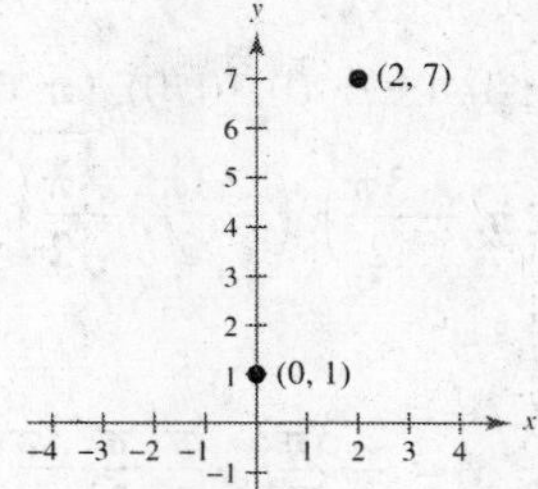

$$\text{Slope} = \frac{7-1}{2-0} = 3$$

94.

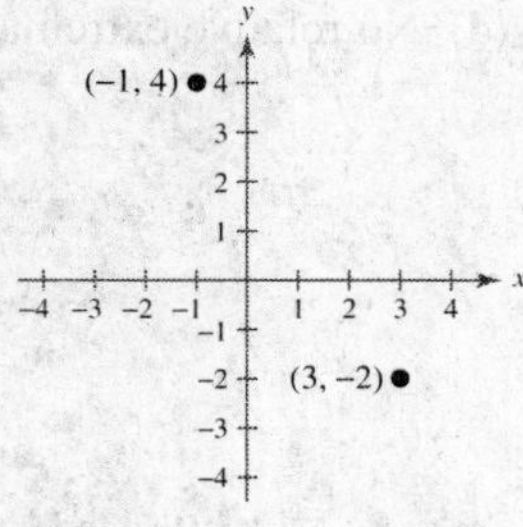

$$m = \frac{-2-4}{3+1} = \frac{-6}{4} = \frac{-3}{2}$$

95. $8.5 = 8.5\left(\frac{180°}{\pi}\right) \approx 487.014°$

96. $-0.48 = -0.48\left(\frac{180°}{\pi}\right) \approx -27.502°$

97. Answers will vary. (Make a Decision)

Section 4.6   Graphs of Other Trigonometric Functions

- You should be able to graph:

  $y = a\tan(bx - c)$ $y = a\cot(bx - c)$

  $y = a\sec(bx - c)$ $y = a\csc(bx - c)$

- When graphing $y = a\sec(bx - c)$ or $y = a\csc(bx - c)$ you should know to first graph $y = a\cos(bx - c)$ or $y = a\sin(bx - c)$ since
  (a) The intercepts of sine and cosine are vertical asymptotes of cosecant and secant.
  (b) The maximums of sine and cosine are local minimums of cosecant and secant.
  (c) The minimums of sine and cosine are local maximums of cosecant and secant.
- You should be able to graph using a damping factor.

Vocabulary Check

1. vertical   **2.** reciprocal   **3.** damping

1. $f(x) = \tan x$

(a) x-intercepts: $(-2\pi, 0), (-\pi, 0), (0, 0), (\pi, 0), (2\pi, 0)$

(b) y-intercept: $(0, 0)$

(c) Increasing on: $\left(-2\pi, -\frac{3\pi}{2}\right), \left(-\frac{3\pi}{2}, -\frac{\pi}{2}\right), \left(-\frac{\pi}{2}, \frac{\pi}{2}\right), \left(\frac{\pi}{2}, \frac{3\pi}{2}\right), \left(\frac{3\pi}{2}, 2\pi\right)$

Never decreasing

(d) No relative extrema

(e) Vertical asymptotes: $x = -\frac{3\pi}{2}, -\frac{\pi}{2}, \frac{\pi}{2}, \frac{3\pi}{2}$

2. $f(x) = \cot x$

(a) x-intercepts: $\left(-\frac{3\pi}{2}, 0\right), \left(-\frac{\pi}{2}, 0\right), \left(\frac{\pi}{2}, 0\right), \left(\frac{3\pi}{2}, 0\right)$

(b) No y-intercepts

(c) Decreasing on: $(-2\pi, -\pi), (-\pi, 0), (0, \pi), (\pi, 2\pi)$

Never increasing

(d) No relative extrema

(e) Vertical asymptotes: $x = -2\pi, -\pi, 0, \pi, 2\pi$

3. $f(x) = \sec x$

(a) No x-intercepts

(b) y-intercept: $(0, 1)$

(c) Increasing on intervals:

$\left(-2\pi, -\frac{3\pi}{2}\right), \left(-\frac{3\pi}{2}, -\pi\right), \left(0, \frac{\pi}{2}\right), \left(\frac{\pi}{2}, \pi\right)$

Decreasing on intervals:

$\left(-\pi, -\frac{\pi}{2}\right), \left(-\frac{\pi}{2}, 0\right), \left(\pi, \frac{3\pi}{2}\right), \left(\frac{3\pi}{2}, 2\pi\right)$

(d) Relative minima: $(-2\pi, 1), (0, 1), (2\pi, 1)$,

Relative maxima: $(-\pi, -1), (\pi, -1)$

(e) Vertical asymptotes: $x = -\frac{3\pi}{2}, -\frac{\pi}{2}, \frac{\pi}{2}, \frac{3\pi}{2}$

4. $f(x) = \csc x$

(a) No x-intercepts

(b) No y-intercepts

(c) Increasing on intervals:

$\left(-\frac{3\pi}{2}, -\pi\right), \left(-\pi, -\frac{\pi}{2}\right), \left(\frac{\pi}{2}, \pi\right), \left(\pi, \frac{3\pi}{2}\right)$

Decreasing on intervals:

$\left(-2\pi, -\frac{3\pi}{2}\right), \left(-\frac{\pi}{2}, 0\right), \left(0, \frac{\pi}{2}\right), \left(\frac{3\pi}{2}, 2\pi\right)$

(d) Relative minima: $\left(-\frac{3\pi}{2}, 1\right), \left(\frac{\pi}{2}, 1\right)$

Relative maxima: $\left(-\frac{\pi}{2}, -1\right), \left(\frac{3\pi}{2}, -1\right)$

(e) Vertical asymptotes: $x = \pm\pi, \pm 2\pi$

5. $y = \frac{1}{2}\tan x$

Period: π

Two consecutive asymptotes: $x = -\frac{\pi}{2}$ and $x = \frac{\pi}{2}$

x	$-\frac{\pi}{4}$	0	$\frac{\pi}{4}$
y	$-\frac{1}{2}$	0	$\frac{1}{2}$

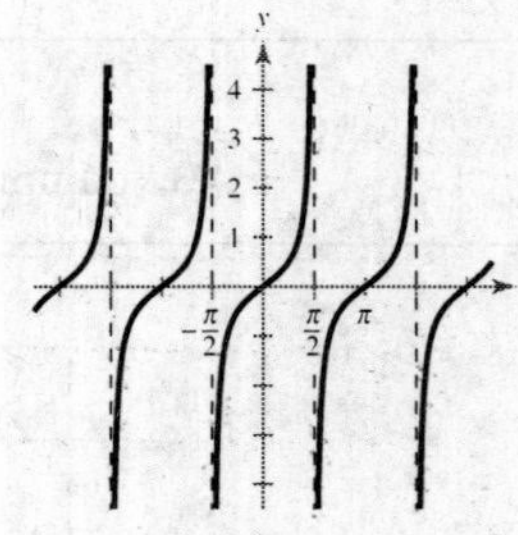

6. $y = \frac{1}{4}\tan x$

Period: π

Asymptotes: $x = \pm\frac{\pi}{2}$

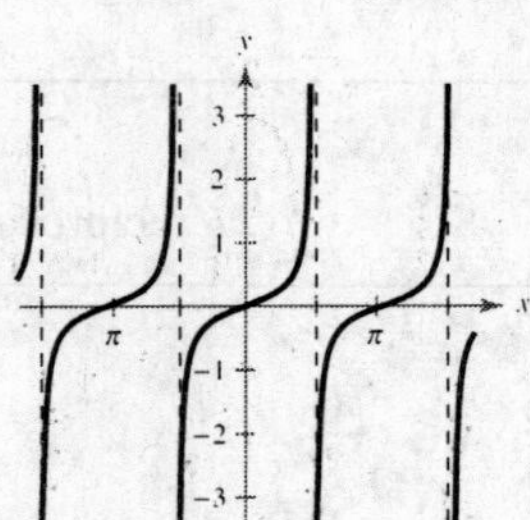

7. $y = -2 \tan 2x$

Period: $\frac{\pi}{2}$

Two consecutive asymptotes:

$2x = -\frac{\pi}{2} \Rightarrow x = -\frac{\pi}{4}$

$2x = \frac{\pi}{2} \Rightarrow x = \frac{\pi}{4}$

x	$-\frac{\pi}{8}$	0	$\frac{\pi}{8}$
y	2	0	-2

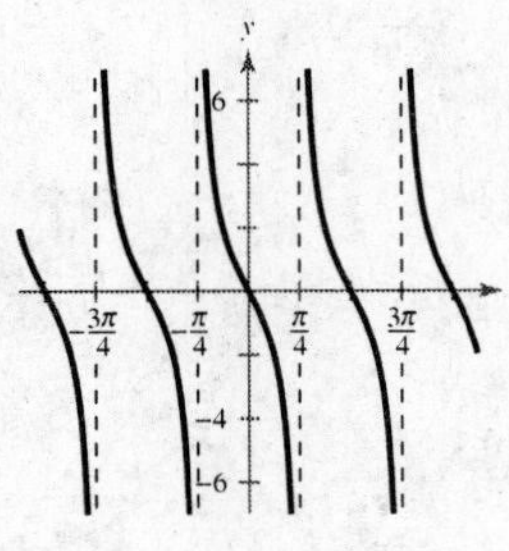

8. $y = -3 \tan 4x$

Period: $\frac{\pi}{4}$

Asymptotes:

$4x = \frac{-\pi}{2} \Rightarrow x = \frac{-\pi}{8}$

$4x = \frac{\pi}{2} \Rightarrow x = \frac{\pi}{8}$

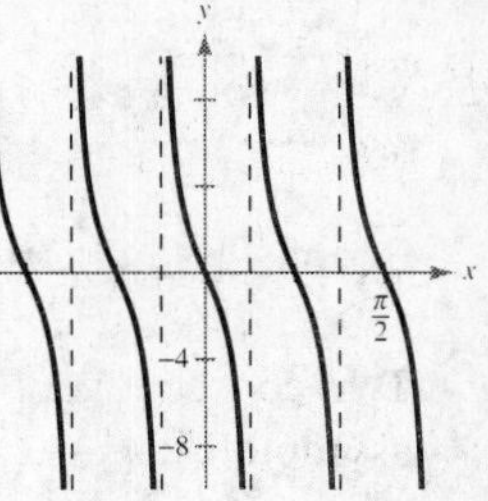

9. $y = -\frac{1}{2} \sec x$

Graph $y = -\frac{1}{2} \cos x$ first.

Period: 2π

One cycle: 0 to 2π

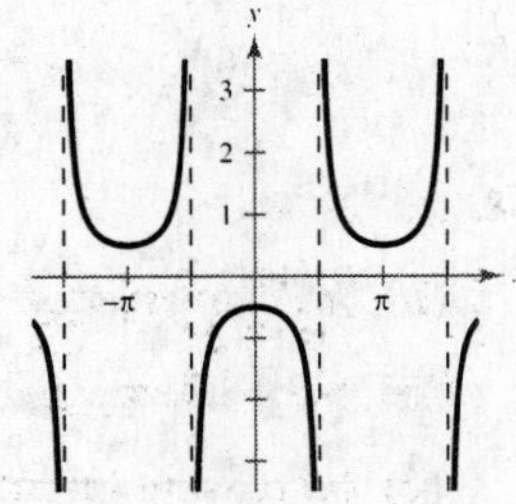

10. $y = \frac{1}{4} \sec x$

Period: 2π

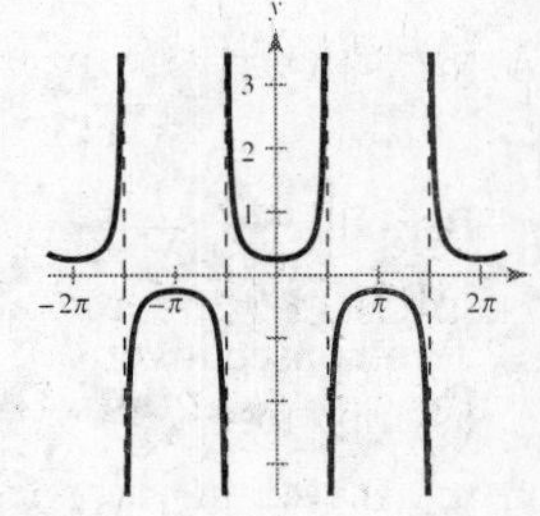

11. $y = \sec \pi x - 3$

Period: 2

Shift graph of $\sec \pi x$ down three units.

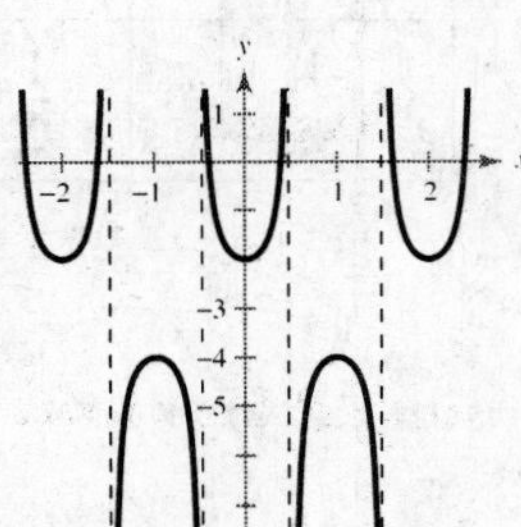

12. $y = -2 \sec 4x + 2$

Period: $\frac{2\pi}{4} = \frac{\pi}{2}$

Asymptotes:

$x = -\frac{\pi}{8}, x = \frac{\pi}{8}$

x	$-\frac{\pi}{16}$	0	$\frac{\pi}{16}$
y	-0.828	0	-0.828

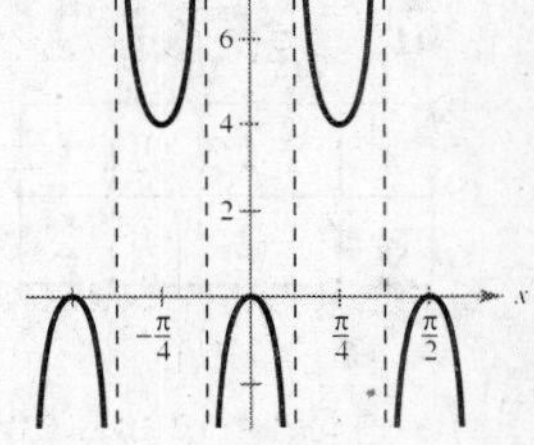

13. $y = 3 \csc \frac{x}{2}$

Graph $y = 3 \sin \frac{x}{2}$ first.

Period: $\frac{2\pi}{1/2} = 4\pi$

One cycle: 0 to 4π

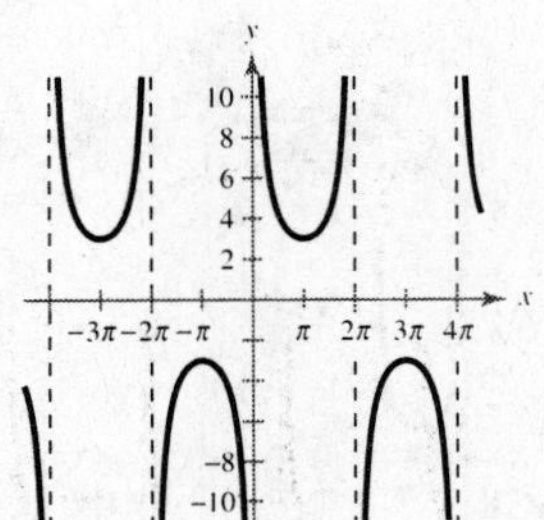

14. $y = -\csc \frac{x}{3}$

Period: $\frac{2\pi}{(1/3)} = 6\pi$

Asymptotes:

$x = 0, x = 3\pi$

x	π	2π	4π
y	-1.155	-1.155	1.155

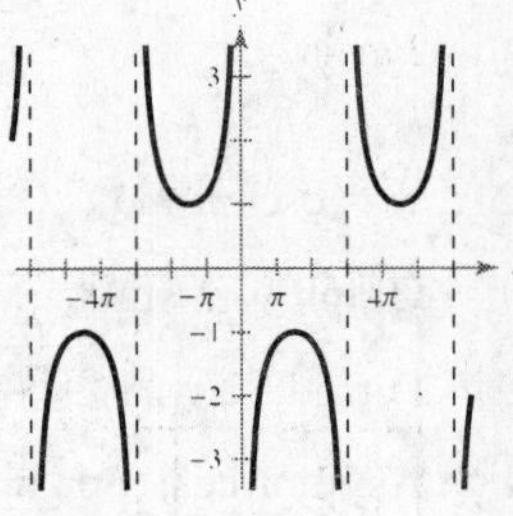

15. $y = \frac{1}{2}\cot\frac{x}{2}$

Period: $\frac{\pi}{1/2} = 2\pi$

Two consecutive asymptotes:

$\frac{x}{2} = 0 \Rightarrow x = 0$

$\frac{x}{2} = \pi \Rightarrow x = 2\pi$

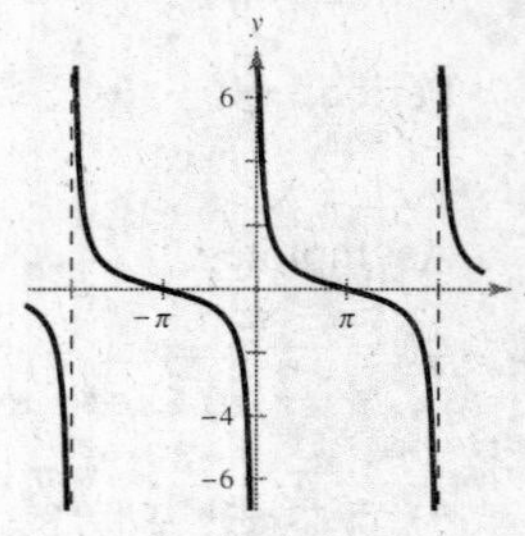

x	$\frac{\pi}{2}$	π	$\frac{3\pi}{2}$
y	$\frac{1}{2}$	0	$-\frac{1}{2}$

16. $y = 3\cot\pi x$

Period: $\frac{\pi}{\pi} = 1$

Asymptotes: $x = 0, x = 1$

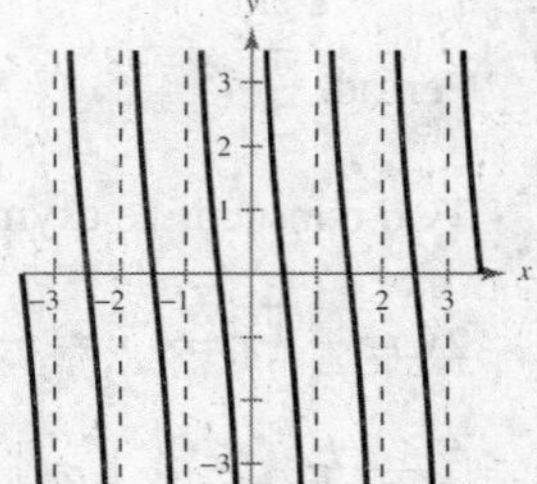

17. $y = 2\tan\frac{\pi x}{4}$

Period: $\frac{\pi}{\pi/4} = 4$

Two consecutive asymptotes:

$\frac{\pi x}{4} = -\frac{\pi}{2} \Rightarrow x = -2$

$\frac{\pi x}{4} = \frac{\pi}{2} \Rightarrow x = 2$

x	-1	0	1
y	-2	0	2

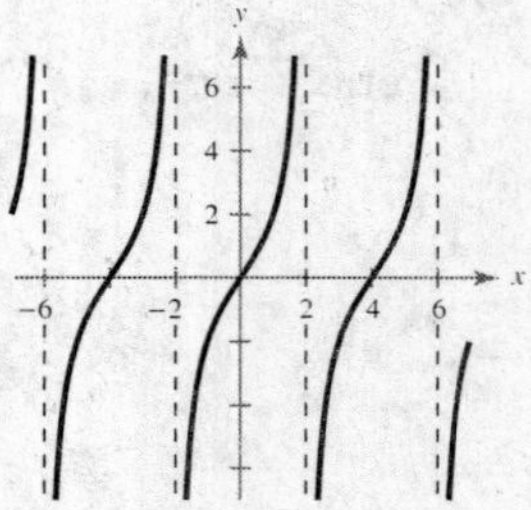

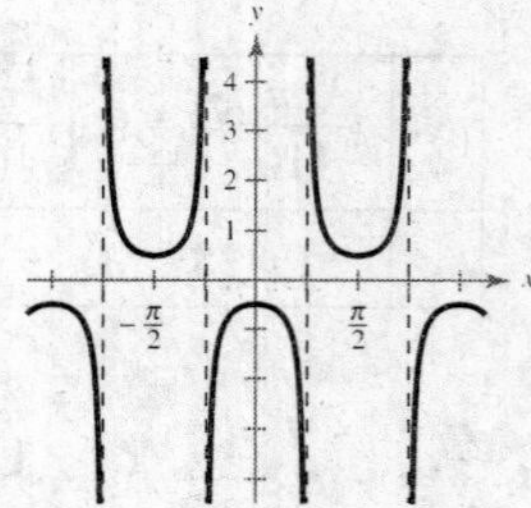

18. $y = -\frac{1}{2}\tan\pi x$

Period: 1

Asymptotes: $x = -\frac{1}{2}, x = \frac{1}{2}$

x	$-\frac{1}{4}$	0	$\frac{1}{4}$
y	$\frac{1}{2}$	0	$-\frac{1}{2}$

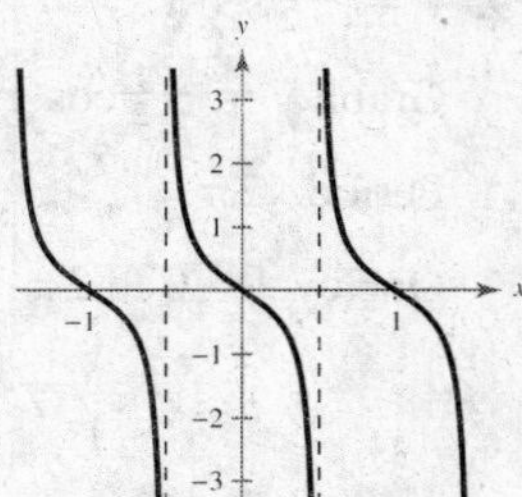

19. $y = \frac{1}{2}\sec(2x - \pi)$

Period: $\frac{2\pi}{2} = \pi$

Asymptotes: $x = \pm\frac{\pi}{4}$

20. $y = -\sec(x + \pi)$

Period: 2π

Asymptotes: $x = \pm\frac{\pi}{2}$

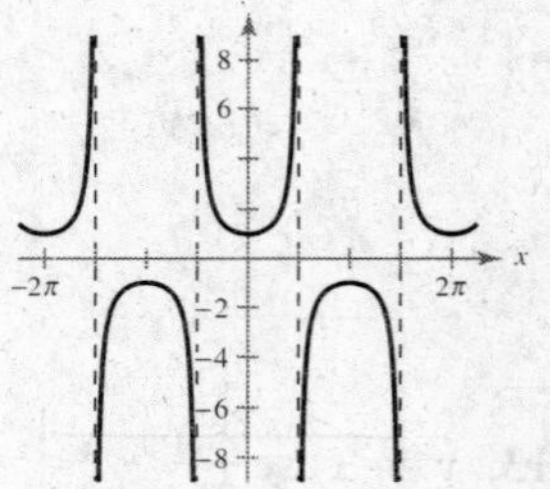

21. $y = \csc(\pi - x)$

Graph $y = \sin(\pi - x)$ first.

Period: 2π

Asymptotes: Set $\pi - x = 0$ and $\pi - x = 2\pi$

$x = \pi \qquad x = -\pi$

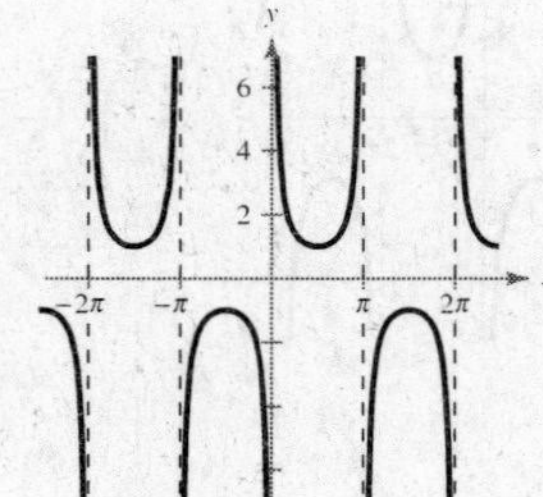

22. $y = \csc(2x - \pi)$

Period: $\frac{2\pi}{2} = \pi$

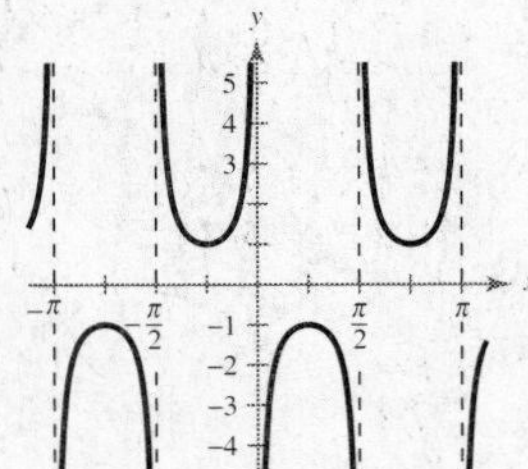

23. $y = 2\cot\left(x - \frac{\pi}{2}\right)$

Period: π

Two consecutive asymptotes:

$x - \frac{\pi}{2} = 0 \Rightarrow x = \frac{\pi}{2}$

$x - \frac{\pi}{2} = \pi \Rightarrow x = \frac{3\pi}{2}$

x	$\frac{3\pi}{4}$	π	$\frac{5\pi}{4}$
y	2	0	-2

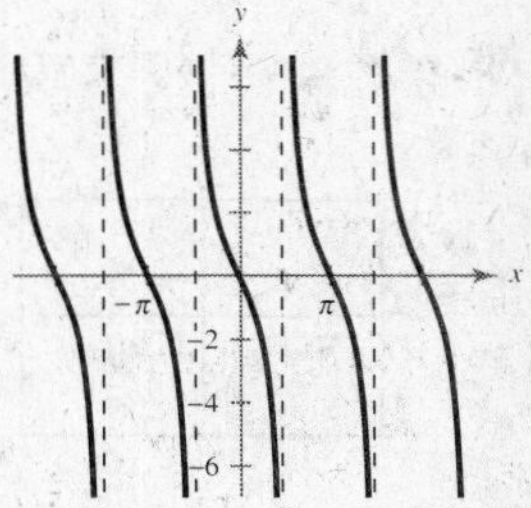

24. $y = \frac{1}{4}\cot(x + \pi)$

Period: π

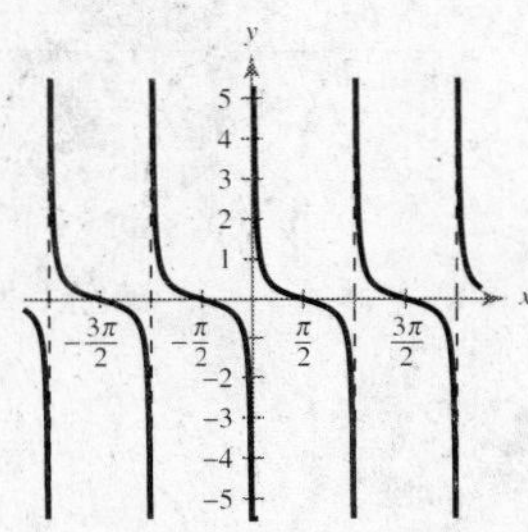

25. $y = 2\csc 3x = \frac{2}{\sin(3x)}$

Period: $\frac{2\pi}{3}$

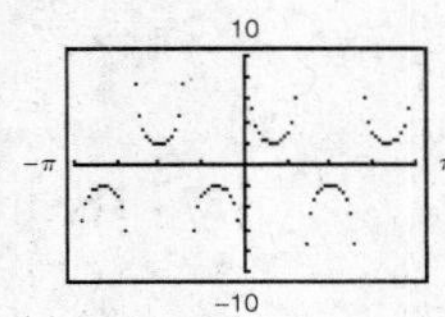

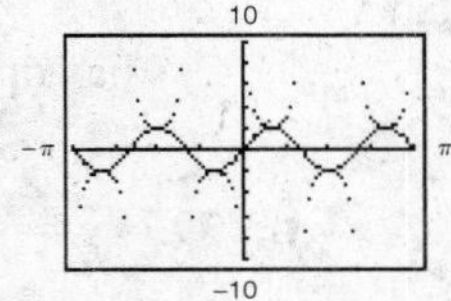

26. $y = -\csc(4x - \pi)$

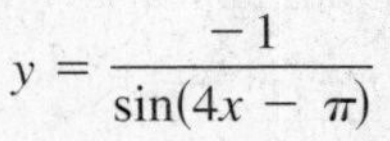

$y = \frac{-1}{\sin(4x - \pi)}$

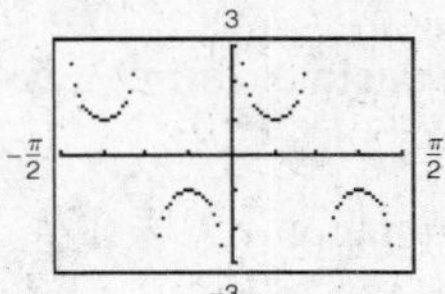

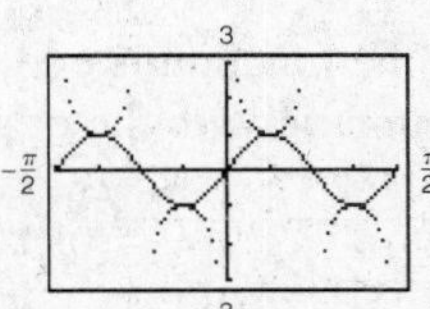

27. $y = -2\sec 4x$

$= \frac{-2}{\cos 4x}$

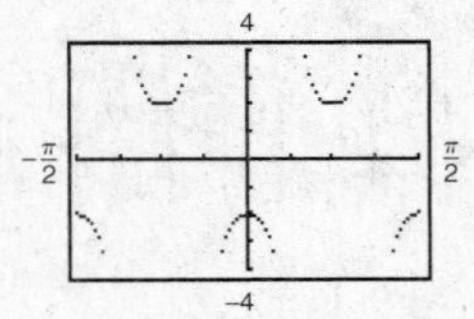

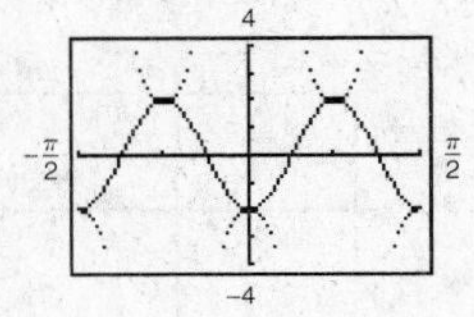

28. $y = \frac{1}{4}\sec \pi x = \frac{1}{4\cos \pi x}$

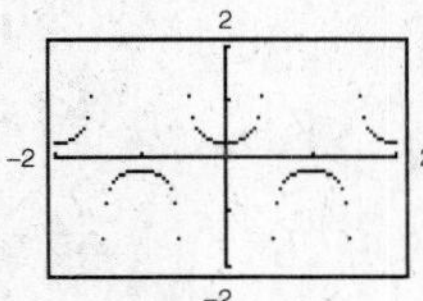

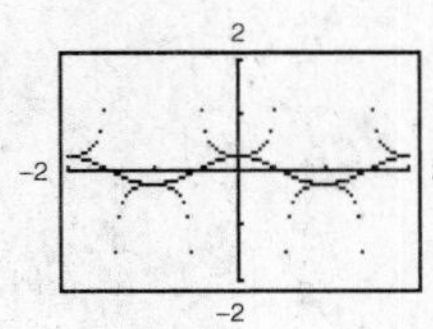

29. $y = \frac{1}{3}\sec\left(\frac{\pi x}{2} + \frac{\pi}{2}\right)$

$= \frac{1}{3\cos\left(\frac{\pi x}{2} + \frac{\pi}{2}\right)}$

Period: 4

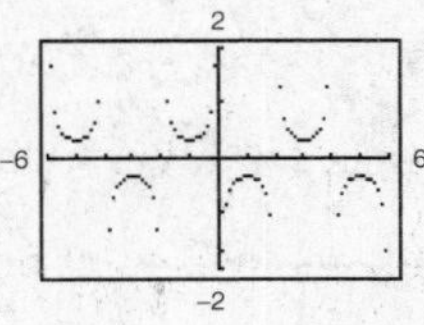

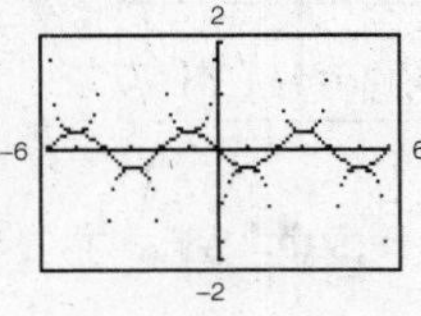

30. $y = \frac{1}{2}\csc(2x - \pi)$

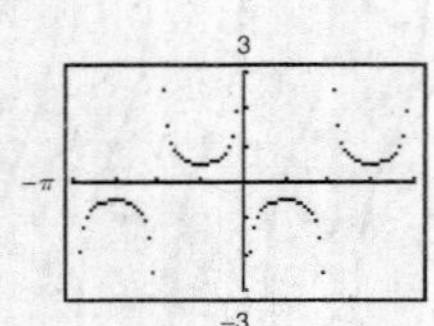
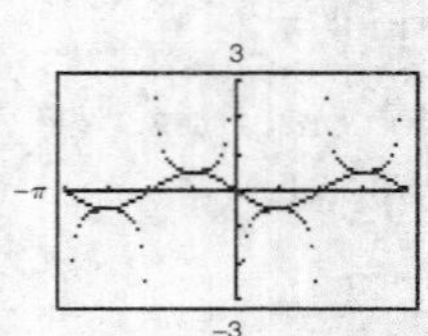

31. $\tan x = 1$

$x = -\frac{7\pi}{4}, -\frac{3\pi}{4}, \frac{\pi}{4}, \frac{5\pi}{4}$

32. $\cot x = -\sqrt{3}$

The solutions appear to be:

$x = -\frac{7\pi}{6}, -\frac{\pi}{6}, \frac{5\pi}{6}, \frac{11\pi}{6}$

(or in decimal form: $-3.665, -0.524, 2.618, 5.760$)

33. $\sec x = -2$

$x = \pm\frac{2\pi}{3}, \pm\frac{4\pi}{3}$

34. $\csc x = \sqrt{2}$

The solutions appear to be:

$-\frac{7\pi}{4}, -\frac{5\pi}{4}, \frac{\pi}{4}, \frac{3\pi}{4}$

(or in decimal form: $-5.498, -3.927, 0.785, 2.356$)

35. The graph of $f(x) = \sec x$ has y-axis symmetry. Thus, the function is even.

36. $f(x) = \tan x$

$\tan(-x) = -\tan x$

Thus, the function is odd and the graph of $y = \tan x$ is symmetric with the origin.

37. The function

$f(x) = \csc 2x = \frac{1}{\sin 2x}$

has origin symmetry. Thus, the function is odd.

38. $f(x) = \cot 2x$

$f(-x) = \cot(-2x)$

$= \frac{\cos(-2x)}{\sin(-2x)} = -\frac{\cos(2x)}{\sin(2x)} = -f(x)$

Odd

39. $y_1 = \sin x \csc x$ and $y_2 = 1$

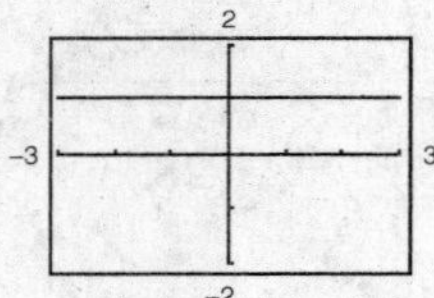

Not equivalent because y_1 is not defined at 0.

$\sin x \csc x = \sin x\left(\frac{1}{\sin x}\right) = 1, \quad \sin x \neq 0$

40. $y_1 = \sin x \sec x$, $y_2 = \tan x$

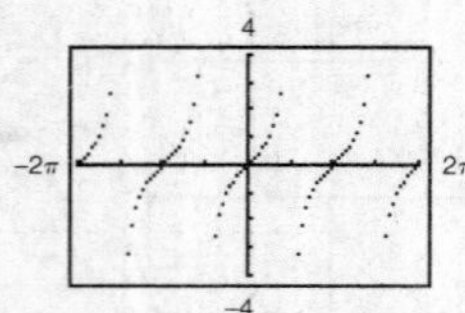

It appears that $y_1 = y_2$.

$\sin x \sec x = \sin x \frac{1}{\cos x} = \frac{\sin x}{\cos x} = \tan x$

41. $y_1 = \frac{\cos x}{\sin x}$ and $y_2 = \cot x = \frac{1}{\tan x}$

Equivalent

$\cot x = \frac{\cos x}{\sin x}$

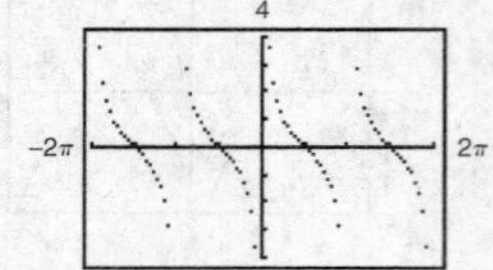

42. $y_1 = \sec^2 x - 1, y_2 = \tan^2 x$

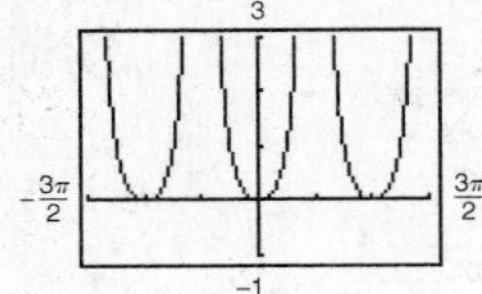

It appears that $y_1 = y_2$.

$1 + \tan^2 x = \sec^2 x$

$\tan^2 x = \sec^2 x - 1$

43. $f(x) = x \cos x$

As $x \to 0, f(x) \to 0$.

Odd function

$f\left(\frac{3\pi}{2}\right) = 0$

Matches graph (d).

44. $f(x) = |x \sin x|$

Matches graph (a) as $x \to 0$, $f(x) \to 0$, and $f(x) \ge 0$ for all x.

45. $g(x) = |x| \sin x$

As $x \to 0, g(x) \to 0$.

Odd function

$g(2\pi) = 0$

Matches graph (b).

46. $g(x) = |x| \cos x$

Even function

Matches graph (c) as $x \to 0, g(x) \to 0$.

47. $f(x) = \sin x + \cos\left(x + \frac{\pi}{2}\right), g(x) = 0$

$f(x) = g(x)$

The graph is the line $y = 0$.

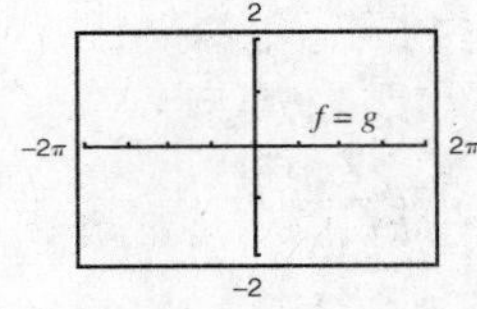

48. $f(x) = \sin x - \cos\left(x + \frac{\pi}{2}\right)$

$g(x) = 2 \sin x$

It appears that $f(x) = g(x)$. That is,

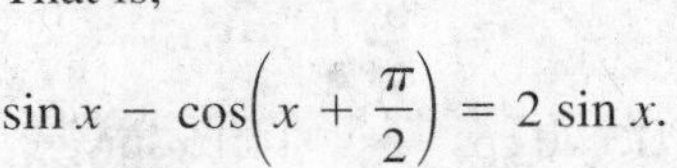

$\sin x - \cos\left(x + \frac{\pi}{2}\right) = 2 \sin x.$

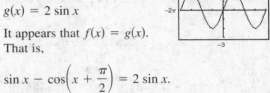

49. $f(x) = \sin^2 x, g(x) = \frac{1}{2}(1 - \cos 2x)$

$f(x) = g(x)$

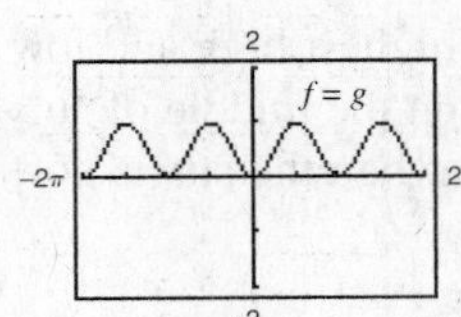

50. $f(x) = \cos^2 \frac{\pi x}{2}$

$g(x) = \frac{1}{2}(1 + \cos \pi x)$

It appears that $f(x) = g(x)$. That is, that

$\cos^2 \frac{\pi x}{2} = \frac{1}{2}(1 + \cos \pi x).$

51. $f(x) = e^{-x} \cos x$

Damping factor: e^{-x}

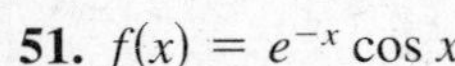

$x \to \infty, f(x) \to 0$

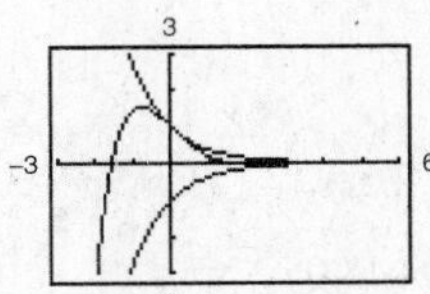

52. $f(x) = e^{-2x} \sin x$

Damping factor: e^{-2x}

$f(x) \to 0$ as $x \to \infty$

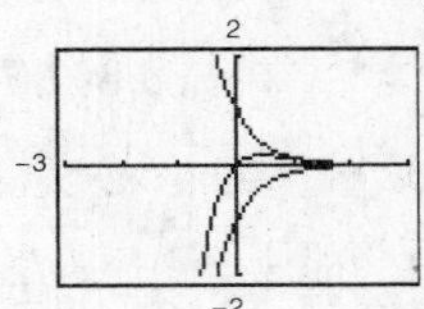

53. $h(x) = e^{-x^2/4} \cos x$

Damping factor: $e^{-x^2/4}$

$h \to 0$ as $x \to \infty$

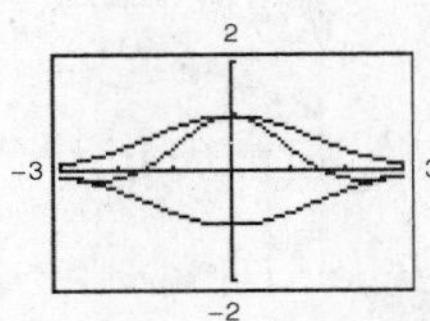

54. $g(x) = e^{-x^2/2} \sin x$

Damping factor: $y = e^{-x^2/2}$

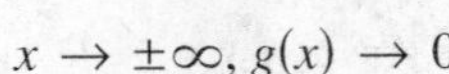

$-e^{-x^2/2} \le g(x) \le e^{-x^2/2}$

$x \to \pm\infty, g(x) \to 0$

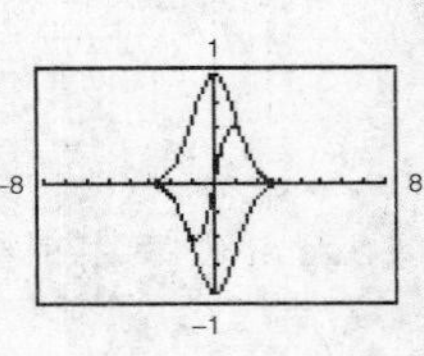

55. (a) As $x \to \frac{\pi^+}{2}, f(x) \to -\infty$.

(b) As $x \to \frac{\pi^-}{2}, f(x) \to \infty$.

(c) As $x \to -\frac{\pi^+}{2}, f(x) \to -\infty$.

(d) As $x \to -\frac{\pi^-}{2}, f(x) \to \infty$.

56. $f(x) = \sec x$

(a) As $x \to \frac{\pi^+}{2}, f(x) \to -\infty$.

(b) As $x \to \frac{\pi^-}{2}, f(x) \to \infty$.

(c) As $x \to -\frac{\pi^+}{2}, f(x) \to \infty$.

(d) As $x \to -\frac{\pi^-}{2}, f(x) \to -\infty$.

57. $f(x) = \cot x$

(a) As $x \to 0^+, f(x) \to \infty$.

(b) As $x \to 0^-, f(x) \to -\infty$.

(c) As $x \to \pi^+, f(x) \to \infty$.

(d) As $x \to \pi^-, f(x) \to -\infty$.

58. $f(x) = \csc x$

(a) As $x \to 0^+, f(x) \to \infty$.

(b) As $x \to 0^-, f(x) \to -\infty$.

(c) As $x \to \pi^+, f(x) \to -\infty$.

(d) As $x \to \pi^-, f(x) \to \infty$.

59. As the predator population increases, the number of prey decreases. When the number of prey is small, the number of predators decreases.

60. $H(t) = 54.33 - 20.38 \cos \frac{\pi t}{6} - 15.69 \sin \frac{\pi t}{6}$

$L(t) = 39.36 - 15.70 \cos \frac{\pi t}{6} - 14.16 \sin \frac{\pi t}{6}$

(a)

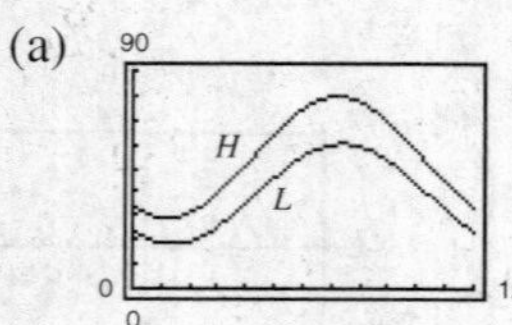

Period of $\cos \frac{\pi t}{6}$: $\frac{2\pi}{(\pi/6)} = 12$

Period of $\sin \frac{\pi t}{6}$: $\frac{2\pi}{(\pi/6)} = 12$

Period of $H(t)$: 12

Period of $L(t)$: 12

(b) From the graph, it appears that the greatest difference between high and low temperatures occurs in summer. The smallest difference occurs in winter.

(c) The highest high and low temperatures appear to occur around the middle of July, roughly one month after the time when the sun is northernmost in the sky.

61. $\tan x = \frac{5}{d}$

$d = \frac{5}{\tan x} = 5 \cot x$

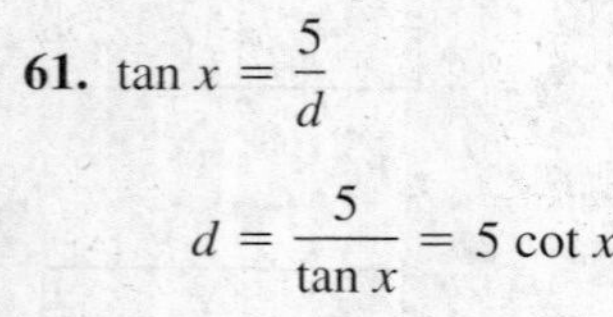

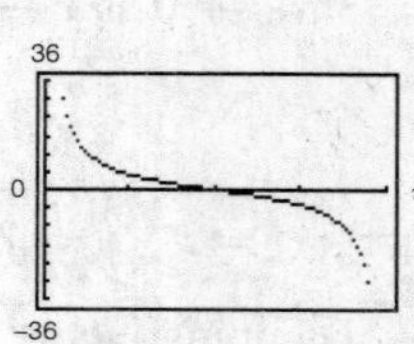

62. $\cos x = \frac{36}{d}$

$d = \frac{36}{\cos x} = 36 \sec x$

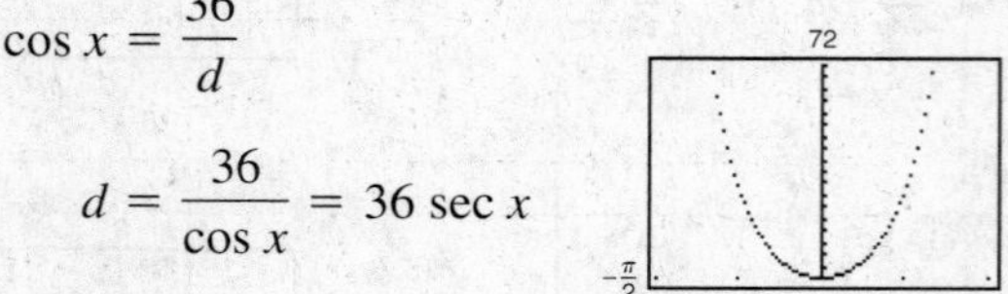

63. (a)

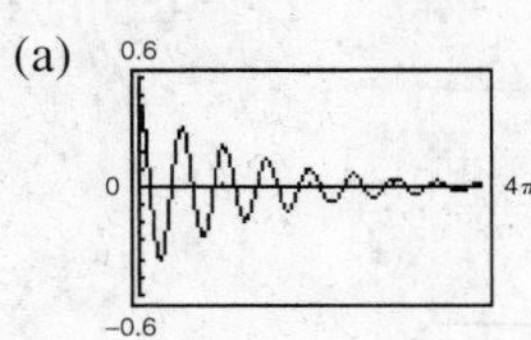

(b) The displacement function is not periodic, but damped. It approaches 0 as t increases.

64. (a) $\frac{1700}{2} = 850$ rev/min

(b) The direction of the saw is reversed.

(c) $L = 60\left[\left(\frac{\pi}{2} + \phi\right) + \cot\phi\right],\ 0 < \phi < \frac{\pi}{2}$

(d)

ϕ	0.3	0.6	0.9	1.2	1.5
L	306.2	217.9	195.9	189.6	188.5

(e) Straight line lengths change faster.

(f)

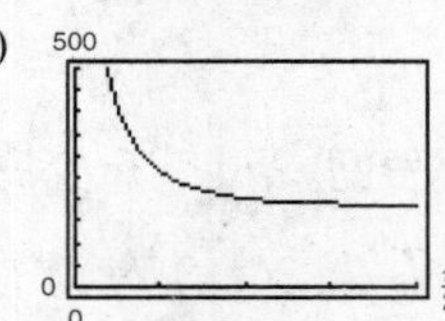

65. True. $-\frac{3\pi}{2} + \pi = -\frac{\pi}{2}$ and $x = -\frac{\pi}{2}$ is a vertical asymptote for the tangent function.

66. True. For $x \to -\infty$, $2^x \to 0$.

67. $f(x) = 2\sin x,\ g(x) = \frac{1}{2}\csc x$

(a)

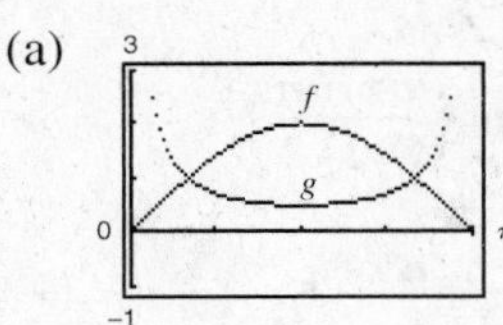

(b) $f(x) > g(x)$ for $\frac{\pi}{6} < x < \frac{5\pi}{6}$

(c) As $x \to \pi$, $2\sin x \to 0$ and $\frac{1}{2}\csc x \to \infty$, since $g(x)$ is the reciprocal of $f(x)$.

68. (a)

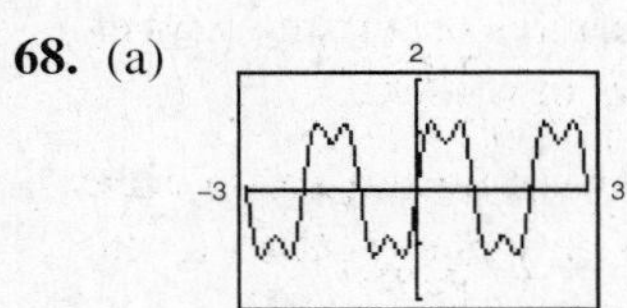

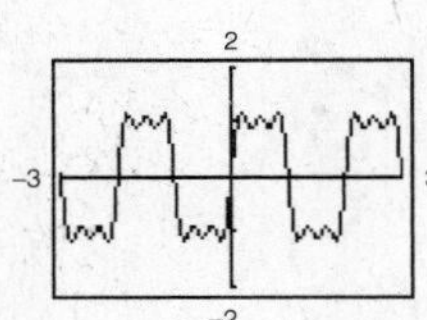

(b) $y_3 = \frac{4}{\pi}\left(\sin \pi x + \frac{1}{3}\sin 3\pi x + \frac{1}{5}\sin 5\pi x + \frac{1}{7}\sin 7\pi x\right)$

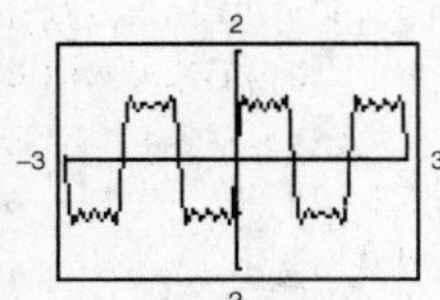

(c) $y_4 = y_3 + \frac{4}{\pi}\left(\frac{1}{9}\sin 9\pi x\right)$

69. (a)

x	-1	-0.1	-0.01	-0.001
$\frac{\tan x}{x}$	1.5574	1.0033	1.0	1.0

x	0	0.001	0.01	0.1	1
$\frac{\tan x}{x}$	Undef.	1.0	1.0	1.0033	1.5574

(b)

As $x \to 0$, $f(x) = \frac{\tan x}{x} \to 1$.

(c) The ratio approaches 1 as x approaches 0.

70. (a)

x	-1	-0.1	-0.01	-0.001	0	0.001	0.01	0.1	1
$\dfrac{\tan 3x}{3x}$	-0.0475	1.0311	1.0003	1.0	Undef.	1.0	1.0003	1.0311	-0.0475

(b)

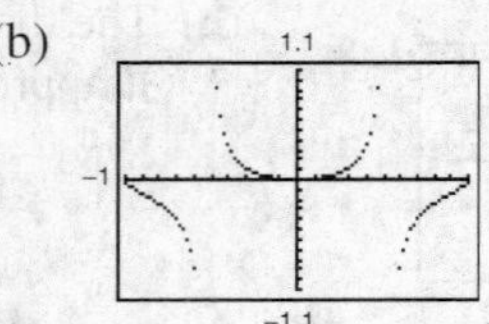

As $x \to 0, f(x) = \dfrac{\tan 3x}{3x} \to 1.$

(c) The ratio approaches 1 as x approaches 0.

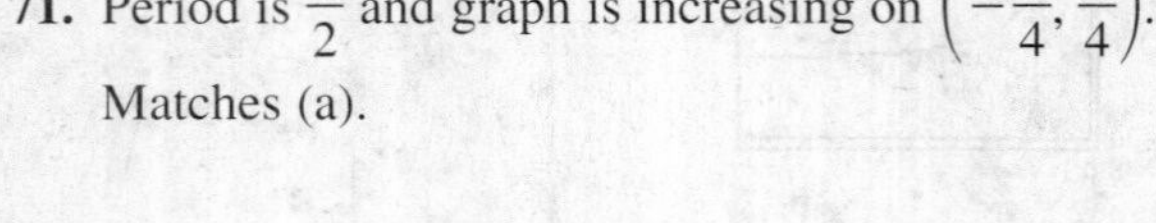

71. Period is $\dfrac{\pi}{2}$ and graph is increasing on $\left(-\dfrac{\pi}{4}, \dfrac{\pi}{4}\right)$.

Matches (a).

72. Period is $\dfrac{\pi}{2}$ and $\left(\dfrac{\pi}{8}, 1\right)$ is on the graph.

Matches (b).

73.

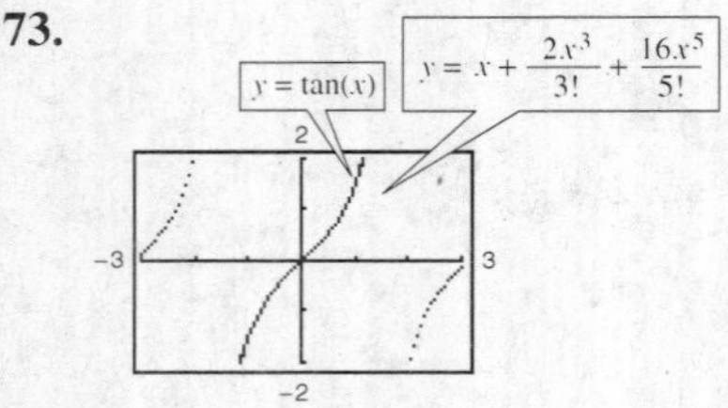

The graphs of $y_1 = \tan x$ and $y_2 = x + \dfrac{2x^3}{3!} + \dfrac{16x^5}{5!}$ are similar on the interval $\left(-\dfrac{\pi}{2}, \dfrac{\pi}{2}\right)$.

74.

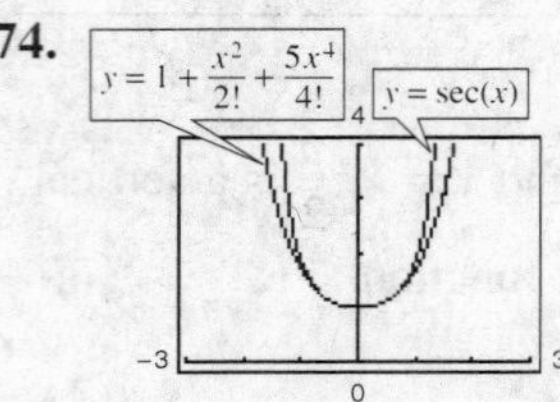

The graphs of $y_1 = \sec x$ and $y_2 = 1 + \dfrac{x^2}{2!} + \dfrac{5x^4}{4!}$ are similar on the interval $\left(-\dfrac{\pi}{2}, \dfrac{\pi}{2}\right)$.

75. Distributive Property

76. $7\left(\frac{1}{7}\right) = 1$

Multiplicative Inverse Property

77. Additive Identity Property

78. $(a + b) + 10 = a + (b + 10)$

Associative Property of Addition

79. Not one-to-one

80. Not one-to-one

81. $y = \sqrt{3x - 14},\ x \ge \frac{14}{3},\ y \ge 0$

$x = \sqrt{3y - 14},\ y \ge \frac{14}{3},\ x \ge 0$

$x^2 = 3y - 14$

$y = \frac{1}{3}(x^2 + 14)$

$f^{-1}(x) = \frac{1}{3}(x^2 + 14),\ x \ge 0$

82. One-to-one

$y = (x - 5)^{1/3}$

$x = (y - 5)^{1/3}$

$x^3 = y - 5$

$f^{-1}(x) = x^3 + 5$

Section 4.7 Inverse Trigonometric Functions

- You should know the definitions, domains, and ranges of $y = \arcsin x$, $y = \arccos x$, and $y = \arctan x$.

Function	Domain	Range
$y = \arcsin x \Rightarrow x = \sin y$	$-1 \le x \le 1$	$-\frac{\pi}{2} \le y \le \frac{\pi}{2}$
$y = \arccos x \Rightarrow x = \cos y$	$-1 \le x \le 1$	$0 \le y \le \pi$
$y = \arctan x \Rightarrow x = \tan y$	$-\infty < x < \infty$	$-\frac{\pi}{2} < y < \frac{\pi}{2}$

- You should know the inverse properties of the inverse trigonometric functions.

$\sin(\arcsin x) = x, \; -1 \le x \le 1$ and $\arcsin(\sin y) = y, \; -\frac{\pi}{2} \le y \le \frac{\pi}{2}$

$\cos(\arccos x) = x, \; -1 \le x \le 1$ and $\arccos(\cos y) = y, \; 0 \le y \le \pi$

$\tan(\arctan x) = x$ and $\arctan(\tan y) = y, \; -\frac{\pi}{2} < y < \frac{\pi}{2}$

- You should be able to use the triangle technique to convert trigonometric functions or inverse trigonometric functions into algebraic expressions.

Vocabulary Check

1. $y = \sin^{-1} x, -1 \le x \le 1$

2. $y = \arccos x, 0 \le y \le \pi$

3. $y = \tan^{-1} x, -\infty < x < \infty, -\frac{\pi}{2} < y < \frac{\pi}{2}$

1. (a) $\arcsin \frac{1}{2} = \frac{\pi}{6}$ (b) $\arcsin 0 = 0$

2. (a) $y = \arccos \frac{1}{2} \Rightarrow \cos y = \frac{1}{2}$ for $0 \le y \le \pi \Rightarrow y = \frac{\pi}{3}$

(b) $y = \arccos 0 \Rightarrow \cos y = 0$ for $0 \le y \le \pi \Rightarrow y = \frac{\pi}{2}$

3. (a) $\arcsin 1 = \frac{\pi}{2}$ because $\sin \frac{\pi}{2} = 1$ and $-\frac{\pi}{2} \le \frac{\pi}{2} \le \frac{\pi}{2}$.

(b) $\arccos 1 = 0$ because $\cos 0 = 1$ and $0 \le 1 \le \pi$.

4. (a) $\arctan 1 = \frac{\pi}{4}$ because $\tan \frac{\pi}{4} = 1$ and $-\frac{\pi}{2} < \frac{\pi}{4} < \frac{\pi}{2}$.

(b) $\arctan 0 = 0$ because $\tan 0 = 0$ and $-\frac{\pi}{2} < 0 < \frac{\pi}{2}$.

5. (a) $\arctan \dfrac{\sqrt{3}}{3} = \dfrac{\pi}{6}$

(b) $\arctan(-1) = -\dfrac{\pi}{4}$

6. (a) $\arccos\left(-\dfrac{\sqrt{2}}{2}\right) = \dfrac{3\pi}{4}$

(b) $\arcsin\left(-\dfrac{\sqrt{2}}{2}\right) = -\dfrac{\pi}{4}$

7. (a) $y = \arctan(-\sqrt{3}) \Rightarrow \tan y = -\sqrt{3}$ for $-\dfrac{\pi}{2} < y < \dfrac{\pi}{2} \Rightarrow y = -\dfrac{\pi}{3}$

(b) $y = \arctan \sqrt{3} \Rightarrow \tan y = \sqrt{3} \Rightarrow y = \dfrac{\pi}{3}$

8. (a) $y = \arccos\left(-\dfrac{1}{2}\right) \Rightarrow \cos y = -\dfrac{1}{2}$ for $0 \le y \le \pi \Rightarrow y = \dfrac{2\pi}{3}$

(b) $y = \arcsin \dfrac{\sqrt{2}}{2} \Rightarrow \sin y = \dfrac{\sqrt{2}}{2}$ for $-\dfrac{\pi}{2} \le y \le \dfrac{\pi}{2} \Rightarrow y = \dfrac{\pi}{4}$

9. (a) $y = \sin^{-1} \dfrac{\sqrt{3}}{2} \Rightarrow \sin y = \dfrac{\sqrt{3}}{2}$ for $-\dfrac{\pi}{2} \le y \le \dfrac{\pi}{2} \Rightarrow y = \dfrac{\pi}{3}$

(b) $y = \tan^{-1}\left(\dfrac{-\sqrt{3}}{3}\right) \Rightarrow \tan y = \dfrac{-\sqrt{3}}{3} \Rightarrow y = -\dfrac{\pi}{6}$

10. (a)

x	-1.0	-0.8	-0.6	-0.4	-0.2
y	-1.5708	-0.9273	-0.6435	-0.4115	-0.2014

x	0	0.2	0.4	0.6	0.8	1
y	0	0.2014	0.4115	0.6435	0.9273	1.5708

(b)

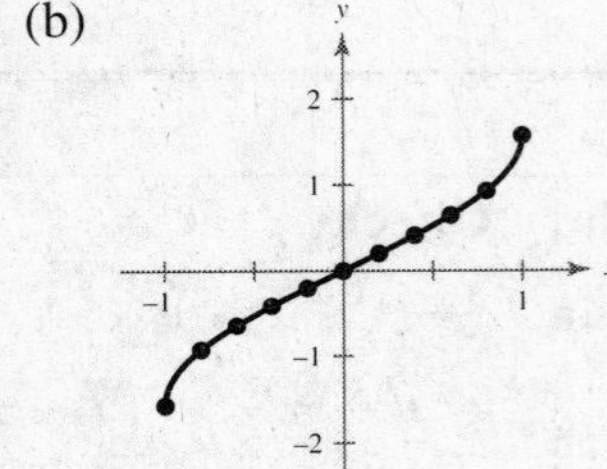

(c)

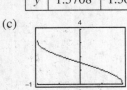

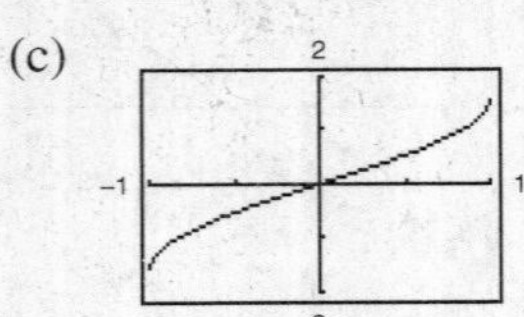

(d) (0, 0), symmetric to the origin

11. $y = \arccos x$

(a)

x	-1	-0.8	-0.6	-0.4	-0.2
y	3.1416	2.4981	2.2143	1.9823	1.7722

x	0	0.2	0.4	0.6	0.8	1.0
y	1.5708	1.3694	1.1593	0.9273	0.6435	0

(b)

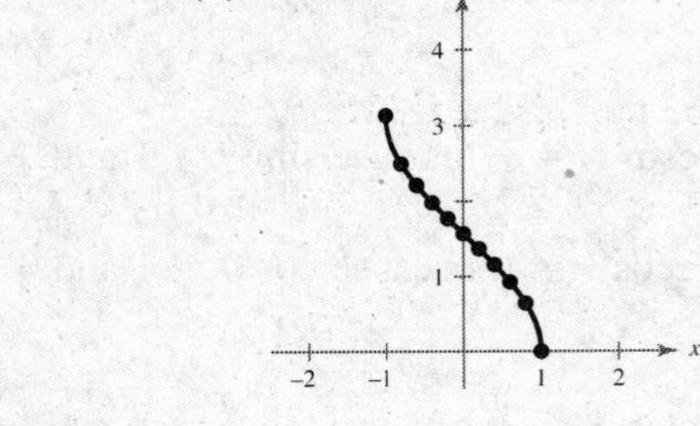

(c)

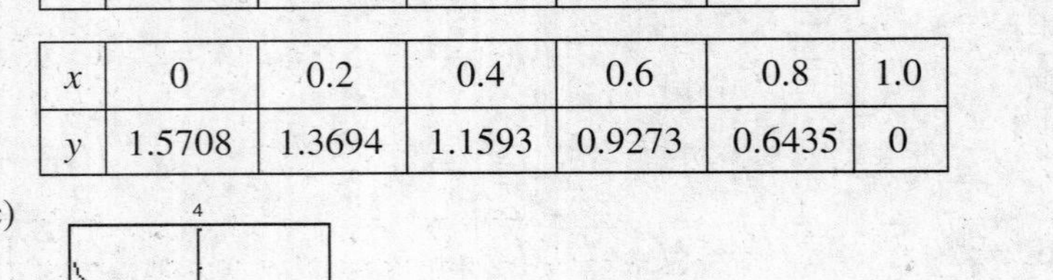

(d) Intercepts: $\left(0, \dfrac{\pi}{2}\right)$, (1, 0), no symmetry

12. (a)

x	-10	-8	-6	-4	-2
y	-1.4711	-1.4464	-1.4056	-1.3258	-1.1071

x	0	2	4	6	8	10
y	0	1.1071	1.3258	1.4056	1.4464	1.4711

(b)

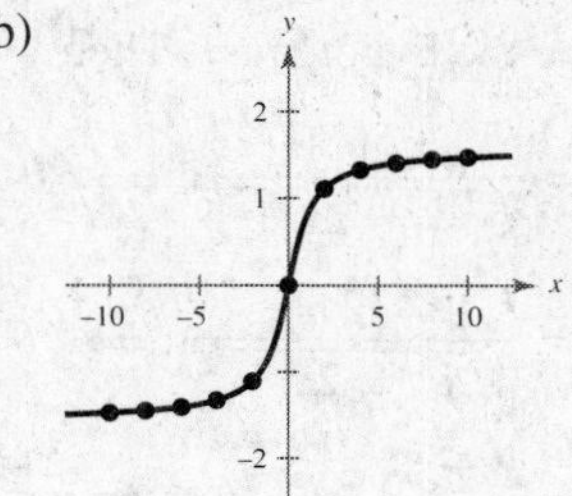

(c)

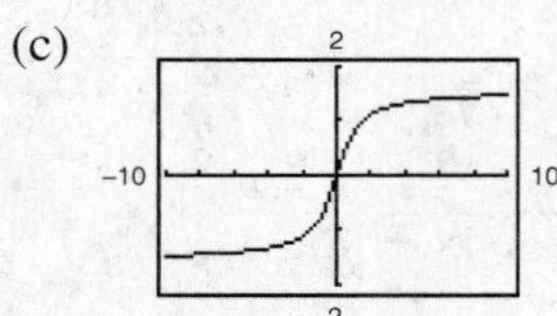

(d) Horizontal asymptotes: $y = \pm\dfrac{\pi}{2}$

13. $y = \arctan x \leftrightarrow \tan y = x$

$\left(-\sqrt{3}, -\dfrac{\pi}{3}\right), \left(-\dfrac{\sqrt{3}}{3}, -\dfrac{\pi}{6}\right), \left(1, \dfrac{\pi}{4}\right)$

14. $y = \arccos x$

$x = -1 \implies y = \pi, \quad (\cos \pi = -1)$

$x = -\dfrac{1}{2} \implies y = \dfrac{2\pi}{3}, \left(\cos \dfrac{2\pi}{3} = -\dfrac{1}{2}\right)$

$y = \dfrac{\pi}{6} \implies x = \dfrac{\sqrt{3}}{2}, \left(\cos \dfrac{\pi}{6} = \dfrac{\sqrt{3}}{2}\right)$

15. $\cos^{-1}(0.75) \approx 0.72$

16. $\sin^{-1} 0.56 \approx 0.59$

17. $\arcsin(-0.75) \approx -0.85$

18. $\arccos(-0.7) \approx 2.35$

19. $\arctan(-6) \approx -1.41$

20. $\tan^{-1} 5.9 \approx 1.40$

21. $\tan \theta = \dfrac{x}{8}$

$\theta = \arctan \dfrac{x}{8}$

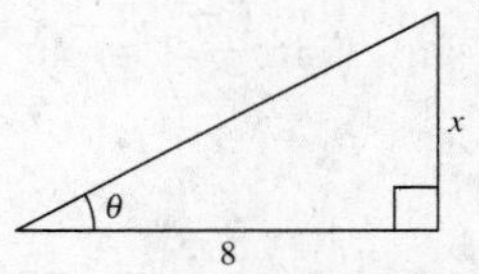

22. $\cos \theta = \dfrac{4}{x}$

$\theta = \arccos \dfrac{4}{x}$

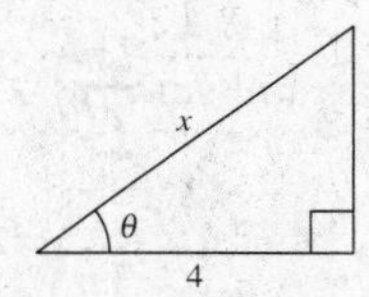

23. $\sin \theta = \dfrac{x+2}{5}$

$\theta = \arcsin\left(\dfrac{x+2}{5}\right)$

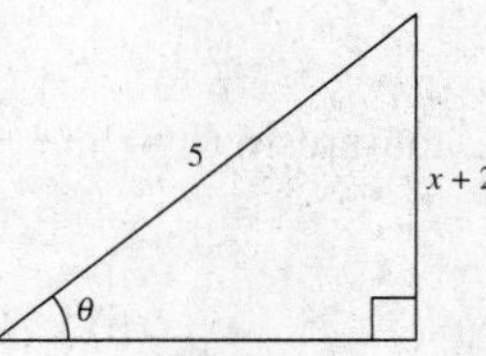

24. $\tan \theta = \dfrac{x+1}{10}$

$\theta = \arctan\left(\dfrac{x+1}{10}\right)$

25. Let y be the third side. Then

$y^2 = 2^2 - x^2 = 4 - x^2 \implies y = \sqrt{4 - x^2}$

$\sin \theta = \dfrac{x}{2} \implies \theta = \arcsin \dfrac{x}{2}$

$\cos \theta = \dfrac{\sqrt{4 - x^2}}{2} \implies \theta = \arccos \dfrac{\sqrt{4 - x^2}}{2}$

$\tan \theta = \dfrac{x}{\sqrt{4 - x^2}} \implies \theta = \arctan \dfrac{x}{\sqrt{4 - x^2}}$

26. Let y be the third side. Then

$y^2 = 3^2 - x^2 = 9 - x^2 \implies y = \sqrt{9 - x^2}.$

$\sin \theta = \dfrac{x}{3} \implies \theta = \arcsin \dfrac{x}{3}$

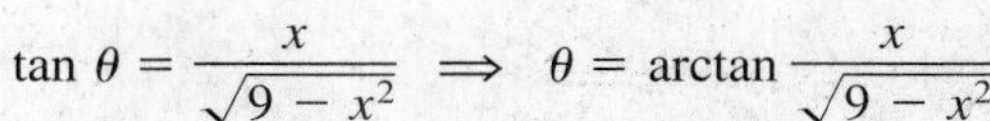

$\cos \theta = \dfrac{\sqrt{9 - x^2}}{3} \implies \theta = \arccos \dfrac{\sqrt{9 - x^2}}{3}$

$\tan \theta = \dfrac{x}{\sqrt{9 - x^2}} \implies \theta = \arctan \dfrac{x}{\sqrt{9 - x^2}}$

27. Let y be the hypotenuse. Then $y^2 = (x + 1)^2 + 2^2 = x^2 + 2x + 5 \implies y = \sqrt{x^2 + 2x + 5}$.

$$\sin\theta = \frac{x+1}{\sqrt{x^2+2x+5}} \implies \theta = \arcsin\frac{x+1}{\sqrt{x^2+2x+5}}$$

$$\cos\theta = \frac{2}{\sqrt{x^2+2x+5}} \implies \theta = \arccos\frac{2}{\sqrt{x^2+2x+5}}$$

$$\tan\theta = \frac{x+1}{2} \implies \theta = \arctan\frac{x+1}{2}$$

28. Let y be the hypotenuse. Then $y^2 = (x + 2)^2 + 3^2 = x^2 + 4x + 13 \implies y = \sqrt{x^2 + 4x + 13}$.

$$\sin\theta = \frac{x+2}{\sqrt{x^2+4x+13}} \implies \theta = \arcsin\frac{x+2}{\sqrt{x^2+4x+13}}$$

$$\cos\theta = \frac{3}{\sqrt{x^2+4x+13}} \implies \theta = \arccos\frac{3}{\sqrt{x^2+4x+13}}$$

$$\tan\theta = \frac{x+2}{3} \implies \theta = \arctan\frac{x+2}{3}$$

29. $\sin(\arcsin 0.7) = 0.7$

30. $\tan(\arctan 35) = 35$

31. $\cos[\arccos(-0.3)] = -0.3$

32. $\sin(\arcsin(-0.1)) = -0.1$

33. $\arcsin(\sin 3\pi) = \arcsin(0) = 0$

Note: 3π is not in the range of the arcsine function.

34. $\arccos\left(\cos\frac{7\pi}{2}\right) = \arccos(0) = \frac{\pi}{2}$

35. $\arctan\left(\tan\frac{11\pi}{6}\right) = \arctan\left(-\frac{\sqrt{3}}{3}\right) = -\frac{\pi}{6}$

36. $\arcsin\left(\sin\frac{7\pi}{4}\right) = \arcsin\left(-\frac{\sqrt{2}}{2}\right) = -\frac{\pi}{4}$

37. $\sin^{-1}\left(\sin\frac{5\pi}{2}\right) = \sin^{-1} 1 = \frac{\pi}{2}$

38. $\cos^{-1}\left(\cos\frac{3\pi}{2}\right) = \cos^{-1} 0 = \frac{\pi}{2}$

39. $\sin^{-1}\left(\tan\frac{5\pi}{4}\right) = \sin^{-1} 1 = \frac{\pi}{2}$

40. $\cos^{-1}\left(\tan\frac{3\pi}{4}\right) = \cos^{-1}(-1) = \pi$

41. $\tan(\arcsin 0) = \tan 0 = 0$

42. $\cos(\arctan(-1)) = \cos\left(-\frac{\pi}{4}\right) = \frac{\sqrt{2}}{2}$

43. $\sin(\arctan 1) = \sin\left(\frac{\pi}{4}\right) = \frac{\sqrt{2}}{2}$

44. $\sin(\arctan(-1)) = \sin\left(-\frac{\pi}{4}\right) = -\frac{\sqrt{2}}{2}$

45. $\arcsin\left[\cos\left(-\frac{\pi}{6}\right)\right] = \arcsin\left(\frac{\sqrt{3}}{2}\right) = \frac{\pi}{3}$

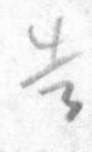

46. $\arccos\left[\sin\left(-\frac{\pi}{6}\right)\right] = \arccos\left(-\frac{1}{2}\right) = \frac{2\pi}{3}$

47. Let $y = \arctan\frac{4}{3}$. Then

$\tan y = \frac{4}{3}, 0 < y < \frac{\pi}{2}$, and

$\sin y = \frac{4}{5}$.

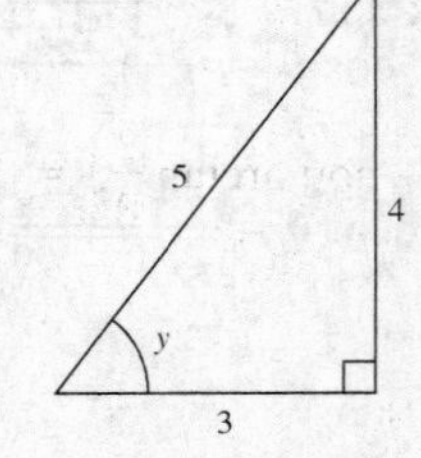

48. Let $u = \arcsin \frac{3}{5}$,

$\sin u = \frac{3}{5}, 0 < u < \frac{\pi}{2}.$

$$\sec\left(\arcsin \frac{3}{5}\right) = \sec u$$

$$= \frac{\text{hyp}}{\text{adj}} = \frac{5}{4}$$

49. Let $y = \arcsin \frac{24}{25}$. Then

$\sin y = \frac{24}{25}$, and $\cos y = \frac{7}{25}$.

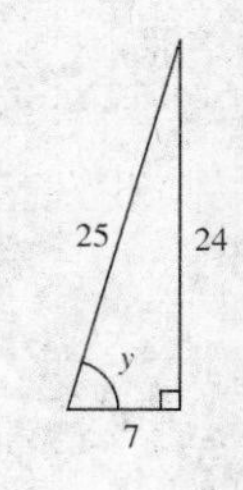

50. Let $u = \arctan\left(-\frac{12}{5}\right)$,

$\tan u = -\frac{12}{5}, -\frac{\pi}{2} < u < 0.$

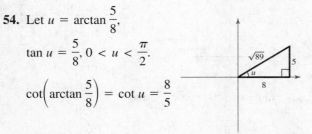

$$\csc\left[\arctan\left(-\frac{12}{5}\right)\right] = \csc u = \frac{\text{hyp}}{\text{opp}} = -\frac{13}{12}$$

51. Let $y = \arctan\left(-\frac{3}{5}\right)$. Then,

$\tan y = -\frac{3}{5},\ -\frac{\pi}{2} < y < 0$ and $\sec y = \frac{\sqrt{34}}{5}$.

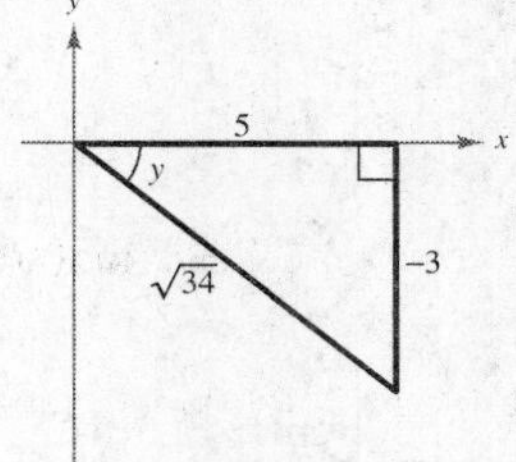

52. Let $u = \arcsin\left(-\frac{3}{4}\right)$,

$\sin u = -\frac{3}{4}, -\frac{\pi}{2} < u < 0.$

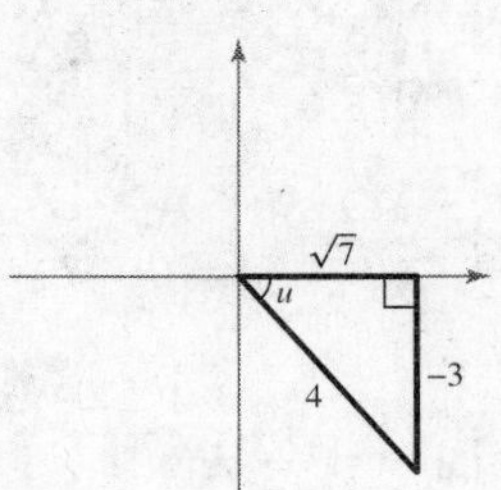

$$\tan\left(\arcsin\left(-\frac{3}{4}\right)\right) = \tan u = \frac{-3}{\sqrt{7}} = \frac{-3\sqrt{7}}{7}$$

53. Let $y = \arccos\left(-\frac{2}{3}\right)$. Then,

$\cos y = -\frac{2}{3},\ \frac{\pi}{2} < y < \pi$ and $\sin y = \frac{\sqrt{5}}{3}$.

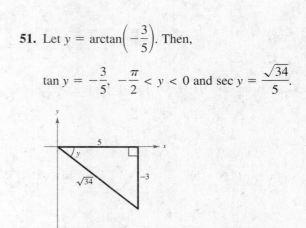

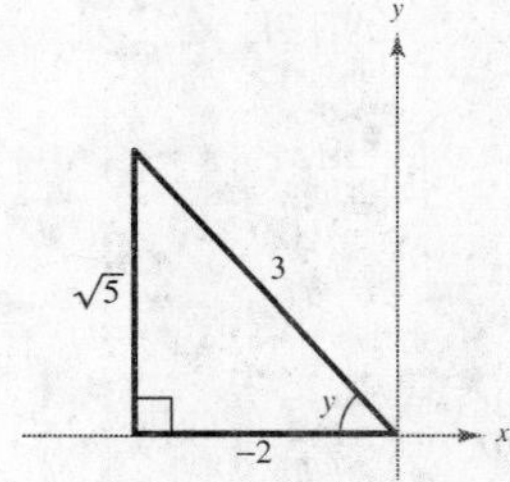

54. Let $u = \arctan \frac{5}{8}$,

$\tan u = \frac{5}{8}, 0 < u < \frac{\pi}{2}.$

$$\cot\left(\arctan \frac{5}{8}\right) = \cot u = \frac{8}{5}$$

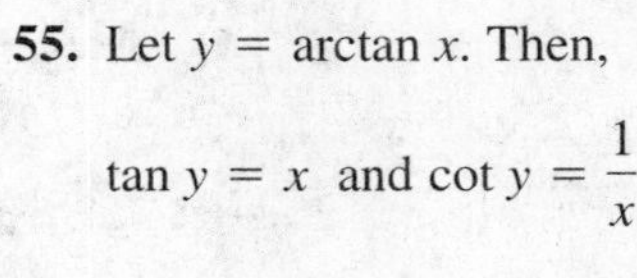

55. Let $y = \arctan x$. Then,

$\tan y = x$ and $\cot y = \frac{1}{x}$.

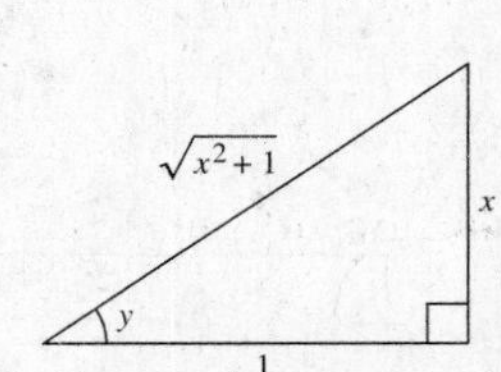

56. Let $u = \arctan x$, $\tan u = x = \dfrac{x}{1}$.

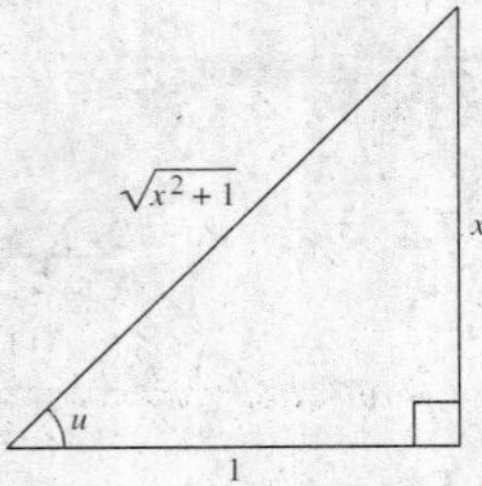

$$\sin(\arctan x) = \sin u = \frac{\text{opp}}{\text{hyp}} = \frac{x}{\sqrt{x^2+1}}$$

57. Let $y = \arccos(x+2)$, $\cos y = x + 2$.

Opposite side: $\sqrt{1-(x+2)^2}$

$$\sin y = \frac{\sqrt{1-(x+2)^2}}{1} = \sqrt{-x^2-4x-3}$$

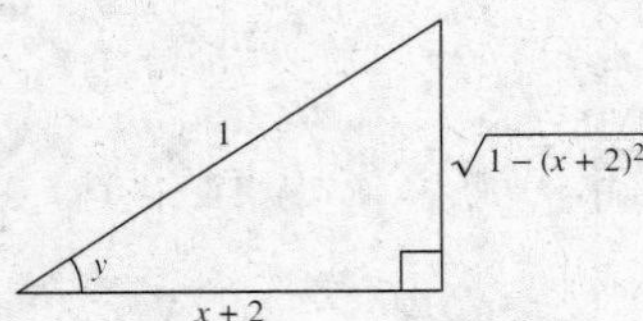

58. Let $u = \arcsin(x-1)$, $\sin u = x - 1 = \dfrac{x-1}{1}$.

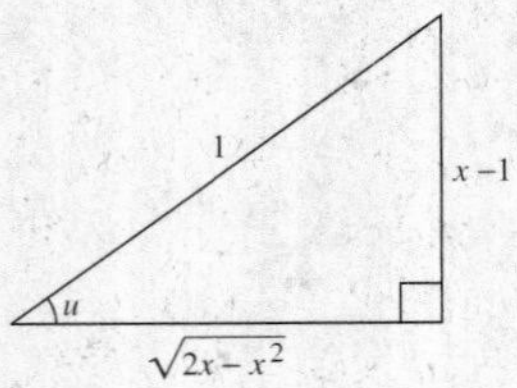

$$\sec[\arcsin(x-1)] = \sec u = \frac{\text{hyp}}{\text{adj}} = \frac{1}{\sqrt{2x-x^2}}$$

59. Let $y = \arccos \dfrac{x}{5}$. Then $\cos y = \dfrac{x}{5}$, and

$$\tan y = \frac{\sqrt{25-x^2}}{x}.$$

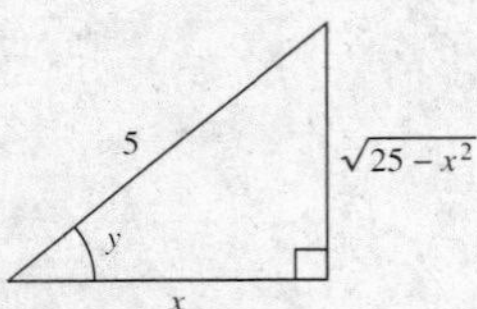

60. Let $u = \arctan \dfrac{4}{x}$, $\tan u = \dfrac{4}{x}$.

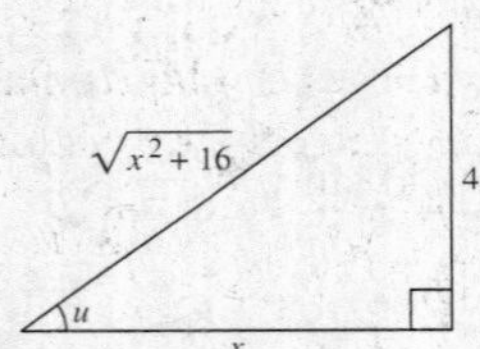

$$\cot\left(\arctan \frac{4}{x}\right) = \cot u = \frac{\text{adj}}{\text{opp}} = \frac{x}{4}$$

61. Let $y = \arctan \dfrac{x}{\sqrt{7}}$. Then $\tan y = \dfrac{x}{\sqrt{7}}$ and

$$\csc y = \frac{\sqrt{7+x^2}}{x}.$$

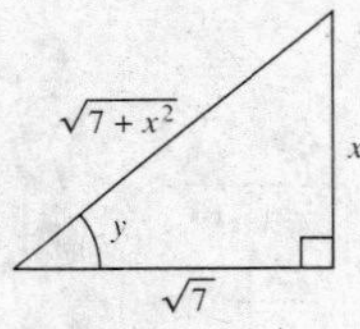

62. Let $u = \arcsin \dfrac{x-h}{r}$, $\sin u = \dfrac{x-h}{r}$.

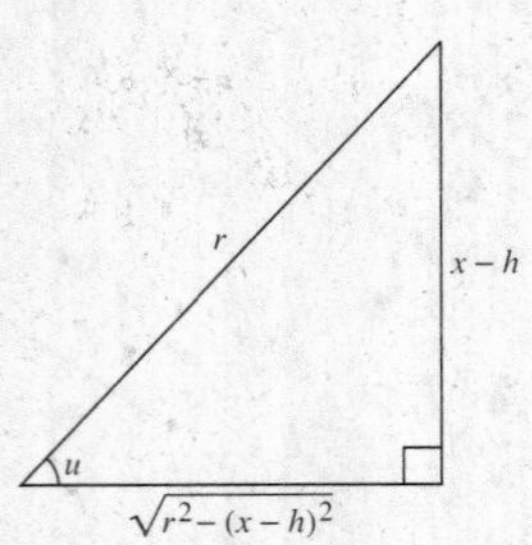

$$\cos\left(\arcsin \frac{x-h}{r}\right) = \cos u = \frac{\sqrt{r^2-(x-h)^2}}{r}$$

63. Let $y = \arctan \dfrac{14}{x}$. Then $\tan y = \dfrac{14}{x}$ and

$$\sin y = \frac{14}{\sqrt{196+x^2}}. \text{ Thus, } y = \arcsin\left(\frac{14}{\sqrt{196+x^2}}\right).$$

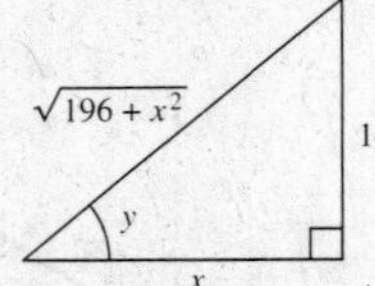

64. If $\arcsin \dfrac{\sqrt{36 - x^2}}{6} = u$, then $\sin u = \dfrac{\sqrt{36 - x^2}}{6}$.

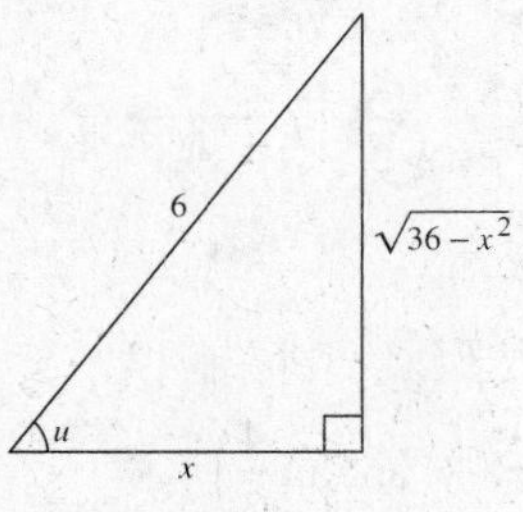

$$\arcsin \frac{\sqrt{36 - x^2}}{6} = \arccos \frac{x}{6}$$

65. Let $y = \arccos \dfrac{3}{\sqrt{x^2 - 2x + 10}}$. Then,

$$\cos y = \frac{3}{\sqrt{x^2 - 2x + 10}} = \frac{3}{\sqrt{(x - 1)^2 + 9}}$$

and $\sin y = \dfrac{|x - 1|}{\sqrt{(x - 1)^2 + 9}}$. Thus,

$$y = \arcsin \frac{|x - 1|}{\sqrt{(x - 1)^2 + 9}} = \arcsin \frac{|x - 1|}{\sqrt{x^2 - 2x + 10}}.$$

66. If $\arccos \dfrac{x - 2}{2} = u$, $2 < x < 4$ then $\cos u = \dfrac{x - 2}{2}$.

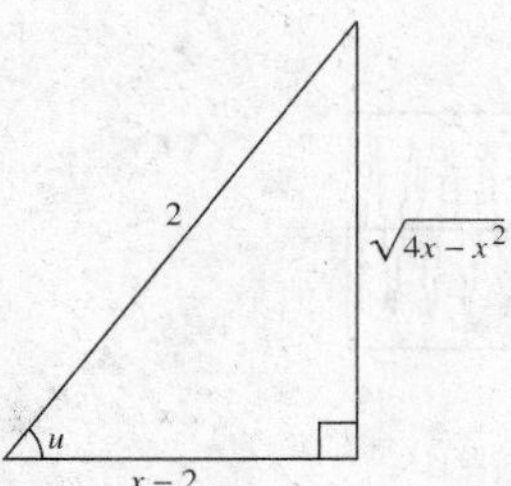

$$\arccos \frac{x - 2}{2} = \arctan \frac{\sqrt{4x - x^2}}{x - 2}, \text{ since } 2 < x < 4$$

67. $y = 2 \arccos x$

Domain: $-1 \le x \le 1$

Range: $0 \le y \le 2\pi$

Vertical stretch of $f(x) = \arccos x$

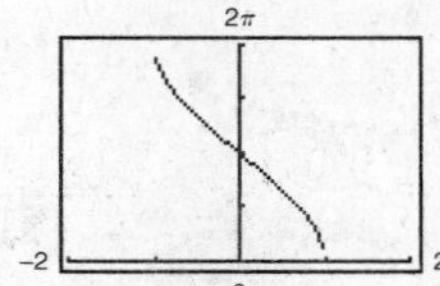

68. $y = \arcsin \dfrac{x}{2}$

Domain: $-2 \le x \le 2$

Range: $-\dfrac{\pi}{2} \le y \le \dfrac{\pi}{2}$

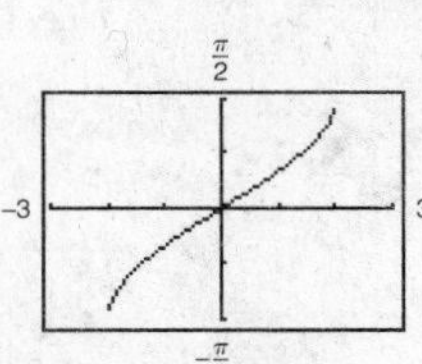

69. The graph of $f(x) = \arcsin(x - 2)$ is a horizontal translation of the graph of $y = \arcsin x$ by two units.

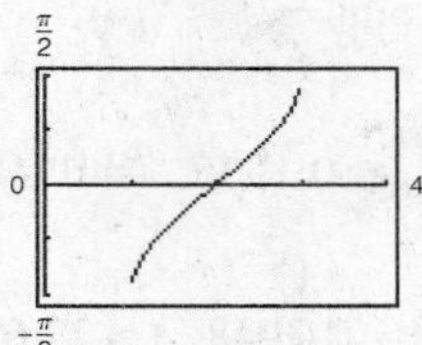

70. $g(t) = \arccos(t + 2)$

Domain: $-3 \le t \le -1$

This is the graph of $y = \arccos t$ shifted two units to the left.

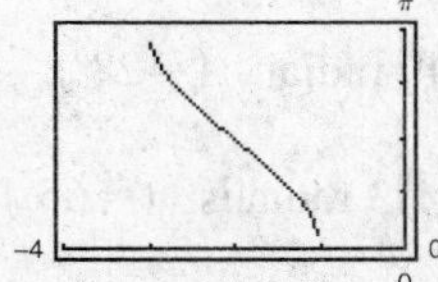

71. $f(x) = \arctan 2x$

Domain: all real numbers

Range: $-\dfrac{\pi}{2} < y < \dfrac{\pi}{2}$

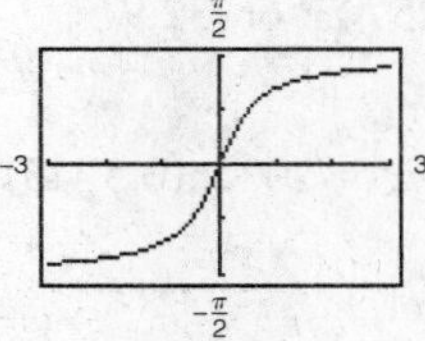

72. $f(x) = \arccos \frac{x}{4}$

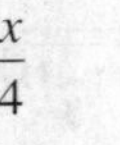

Domain: $[-4, 4]$

Range: $[0, \pi]$

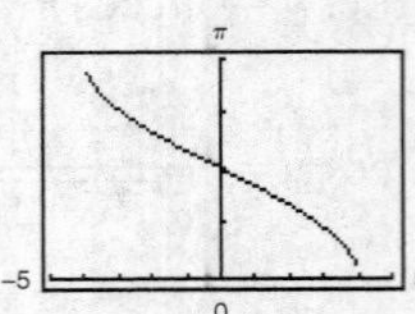

73. $f(t) = 3 \cos 2t + 3 \sin 2t$

$= \sqrt{3^2 + 3^2} \sin\left(2t + \arctan \frac{3}{3}\right)$

$= 3\sqrt{2} \sin(2t + \arctan 1)$

$= 3\sqrt{2} \sin\left(2t + \frac{\pi}{4}\right)$

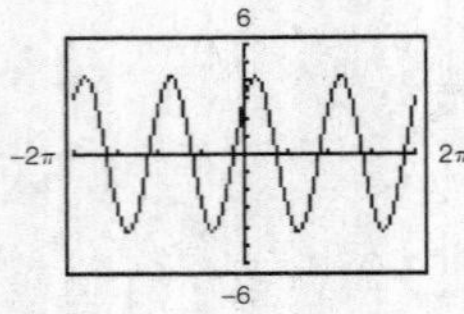

The graphs are the same.

74. $f(t) = 4 \cos \pi t + 3 \sin \pi t$

$= \sqrt{4^2 + 3^2} \sin\left(\pi t + \arctan \frac{4}{3}\right)$

$= 5 \sin\left(\pi t + \arctan \frac{4}{3}\right)$

The graph suggests that

$A \cos \omega t + B \sin \omega t = \sqrt{A^2 + B^2} \sin\left(\omega t + \arctan \frac{A}{B}\right)$

is true.

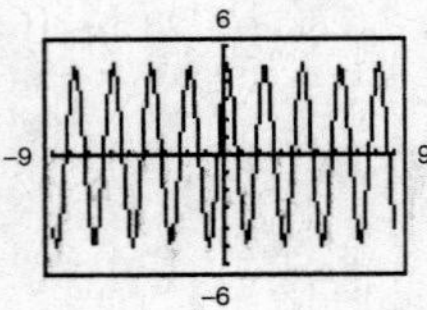

75. As $x \to 1^-$, $\arcsin x \to \frac{\pi}{2}$.

76. As $x \to 1^-$, $\arccos x \to 0$.

77. As $x \to \infty$, $\arctan x \to \frac{\pi}{2}$.

78. As $x \to -1^+$, $\arcsin x \to -\frac{\pi}{2}$.

79. As $x \to -1^+$, $\arccos x \to \pi$.

80. As $x \to -\infty$, $\arctan x \to -\frac{\pi}{2}$.

81. (a) $\sin \theta = \frac{10}{s} \implies \theta = \arcsin\left(\frac{10}{s}\right)$

(b) $s = 52$: $\theta = \arcsin\left(\frac{10}{52}\right) \approx 0.1935$, $(\approx 11.1°)$

$s = 26$: $\theta = \arcsin\left(\frac{10}{26}\right) \approx 0.3948$, $(\approx 22.6°)$

82. (a)

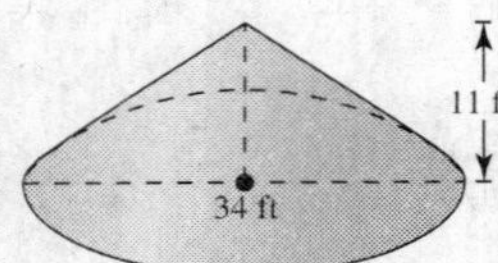

(b) $\tan \theta = \frac{11}{17} \implies \theta \approx 0.5743$ or $32.9°$

(c) $\tan(0.5743) = \frac{h}{20} \implies h = 20 \tan(0.5743)$

≈ 12.94 feet

83. (a) $\tan \theta = \frac{s}{750}$

$\theta = \arctan\left(\frac{s}{750}\right)$

(b) When $s = 400$,

$\theta = \arctan\left(\frac{400}{750}\right) \approx 0.49$ radian, $(\approx 28°)$.

When $s = 1600$, $\theta \approx 1.13$ radians, $(\approx 65°)$.

84. $\beta = \arctan \dfrac{3x}{x^2 + 4}, x > 0$

(a) 1.5 / 0 / 6 / −0.5

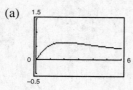

(b) β is maximum when $x = 2$ feet.

(c) The graph has a horizontal asymptote at $\beta = 0$. As the camera moves further from the picture, the angle subtended by the camera approaches 0.

85. (a) $\tan \theta = \dfrac{6}{x}$

$$\theta = \arctan\left(\frac{6}{x}\right)$$

(b) When $x = 10$,

$$\theta = \arctan\left(\frac{6}{10}\right) \approx 0.54 \text{ radian, } (\approx 31°).$$

When $x = 3$,

$$\theta = \arctan\left(\frac{6}{3}\right) \approx 1.11 \text{ radians, } (\approx 63°).$$

86. (a) $\tan \theta = \dfrac{x}{20}$

$$\theta = \arctan \frac{x}{20}$$

(b) When $x = 5$,

$$\theta = \arctan \frac{5}{20} \approx 14.0°, (0.24 \text{ rad}).$$

When $x = 12$,

$$\theta = \arctan \frac{12}{20} \approx 31.0°, (0.54 \text{ rad}).$$

87. False. $\arcsin \dfrac{1}{2} = \dfrac{\pi}{6}$

88. False. $\tan x = \dfrac{\sin x}{\cos x}$

89. $y = \text{arccot}\, x$ if and only if $\cot y = x$, $-\infty < x < \infty$ and $0 < y < \pi$.

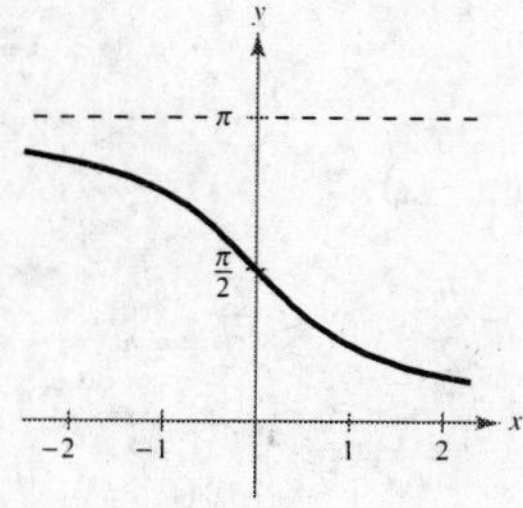

90. $y = \text{arcsec}\, x$ if and only if $\sec y = x$ where $x \le -1 \cup x \ge 1$ and $0 \le y < \pi/2$ and $\pi/2 < y \le \pi$. The domain of $y = \text{arcsec}\, x$ is $(-\infty, -1] \cup [1, \infty)$ and the range is $[0, \pi/2) \cup (\pi/2, \pi]$.

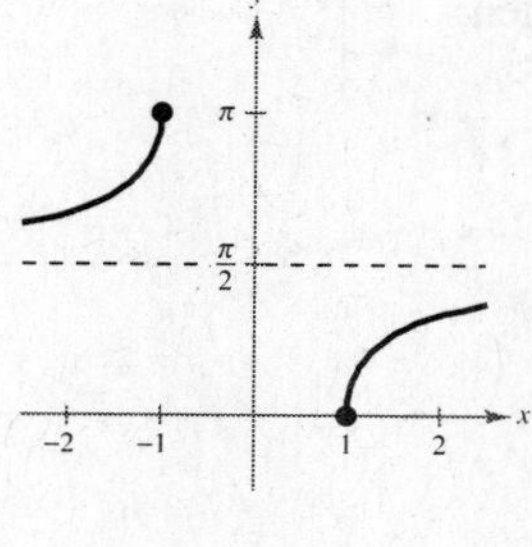

91. $y = \text{arccsc}\, x$ if and only if $\csc y = x$.

Domain: $(-\infty, -1] \cup [1, \infty)$

Range: $\left[-\dfrac{\pi}{2}, 0\right) \cup \left(0, \dfrac{\pi}{2}\right]$

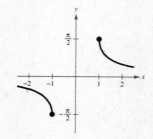

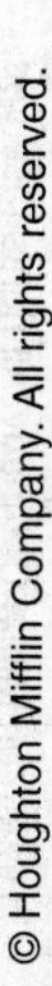

92. (a) $y = \operatorname{arccot} x$ if and only if $x = \cot y$, $-\infty < x < \infty$ and $0 < y < \pi$.

Thus, $\frac{1}{x} = \tan y$ and $y = \arctan\left(\frac{1}{x}\right)$.

Hence, graph $y = \begin{cases} \pi + \arctan(1/x), & x < 0 \\ \pi/2, & x = 0. \\ \arctan(1/x), & x > 0 \end{cases}$

(b) $y = \operatorname{arcsec} x$ if and only if $x = \sec y$, $x \le -1$ or $x \ge 1$, and $0 \le y < \frac{\pi}{2}$ or $\frac{\pi}{2} < y < \pi$.

Thus, $\frac{1}{x} = \cos y$ and $y = \arccos\left(\frac{1}{x}\right)$. Hence graph $y = \arccos\frac{1}{x}$, $x \in (-\infty, -1] \cup [1, \infty)$.

(c) $y = \operatorname{arccsc} x$ if and only if $x = \csc y$, $x \le -1$ or $x \ge 1$, and $-\frac{\pi}{2} \le y < 0$ or $0 < y \le \frac{\pi}{2}$.

Thus, $\frac{1}{x} = \sin y$ and $y = \arcsin\left(\frac{1}{x}\right)$. Hence, graph $y = \arcsin\left(\frac{1}{x}\right)$, $x \in (-\infty, -1] \cup [1, \infty)$.

93. $y = \operatorname{arcsec}\sqrt{2} \implies \sec y = \sqrt{2}$ and $0 \le y < \frac{\pi}{2} \cup \frac{\pi}{2} < y \le \pi \implies y = \frac{\pi}{4}$

94. $y = \operatorname{arcsec} 1 \implies \sec y = 1$ and $0 \le y < \frac{\pi}{2} \cup \frac{\pi}{2} < y \le \pi \implies y = 0$

95. $y = \operatorname{arccot}(-\sqrt{3}) \implies \cot y = -\sqrt{3}$ and $0 < y < \pi \implies y = \frac{5\pi}{6}$

96. $y = \operatorname{arccsc} 2 \implies \csc y = 2$ and $-\frac{\pi}{2} \le y < 0 \cup 0 < y \le \frac{\pi}{2} \implies y = \frac{\pi}{6}$

97. Let $y = \arcsin(-x)$. Then,

$$\begin{aligned} \sin y &= -x \\ -\sin y &= x \\ \sin(-y) &= x \\ -y &= \arcsin x \\ y &= -\arcsin x. \end{aligned}$$

Therefore, $\arcsin(-x) = -\arcsin x$.

98.

$$\begin{aligned} y &= \arctan(-x) \\ \tan y &= -x, \ -\frac{\pi}{2} < y < \frac{\pi}{2} \\ -\tan y &= x \\ \tan(-y) &= x, \ -\frac{\pi}{2} < -y < \frac{\pi}{2} \\ \arctan(\tan(-y)) &= \arctan x \\ -y &= \arctan x \\ y &= -\arctan x \end{aligned}$$

99. $\arcsin x + \arccos x = \frac{\pi}{2}$

Let $\alpha = \arcsin x \implies \sin \alpha = x$.

Let $\beta = \arccos x \implies \cos \beta = x$.

Hence, $\sin a = \cos \beta \implies a$ and β are complementary angles $\implies a + \beta = \frac{\pi}{2} \implies \arcsin x + \arccos x = \frac{\pi}{2}$.

100. Area $=$ arctan b $-$ arctan a

(a) $a = 0, b = 1$

Area $= \arctan 1 - \arctan 0$

$= \frac{\pi}{4} - 0 = \frac{\pi}{4} \approx 0.785$

(b) $a = -1, b = 1$

Area $= \arctan 1 - \arctan(-1)$

$= \frac{\pi}{4} - \left(-\frac{\pi}{4}\right) = \frac{\pi}{2} \approx 1.571$

(c) $a = 0, b = 3$

Area $= \arctan 3 - \arctan 0$

$\approx 1.25 - 0 = 1.25$

$= 1.25$

(d) $a = -1, b = 3$

Area $= \arctan 3 - \arctan(-1)$

$\approx 1.25 - \left(-\frac{\pi}{4}\right) \approx 2.03$

101. $\frac{4}{4\sqrt{2}} = \frac{1}{\sqrt{2}} = \frac{\sqrt{2}}{2}$

102. $\frac{2}{\sqrt{3}} = \frac{2\sqrt{3}}{\sqrt{3}\sqrt{3}} = \frac{2\sqrt{3}}{3}$

103. $\frac{2\sqrt{3}}{6} = \frac{\sqrt{3}}{3}$

104. $\frac{5\sqrt{5}}{2\sqrt{10}} = \frac{5\sqrt{5}}{2\sqrt{2}\sqrt{5}} = \frac{5}{2\sqrt{2}} = \frac{5\sqrt{2}}{4}$

105. $\sin\theta = \frac{5}{6}$

Adjacent side: $\sqrt{6^2 - 5^2} = \sqrt{11}$

$\cos\theta = \frac{\sqrt{11}}{6}$

$\tan\theta = \frac{5}{\sqrt{11}} = \frac{5\sqrt{11}}{11}$

$\csc\theta = \frac{6}{5}$

$\sec\theta = \frac{6}{\sqrt{11}} = \frac{6\sqrt{11}}{11}$

$\cot\theta = \frac{\sqrt{11}}{5}$

106. $\tan\theta = 2, 0 < \theta < \frac{\pi}{2}$

$\sin\theta = \frac{2}{\sqrt{5}} = \frac{2\sqrt{5}}{5}$

$\cos\theta = \frac{\sqrt{5}}{5}$

$\csc\theta = \frac{\sqrt{5}}{2}$

$\sec\theta = \sqrt{5}$

$\cot\theta = \frac{1}{2}$

107. $\sin\theta = \frac{3}{4}$

Adjacent side: $\sqrt{16 - 9} = \sqrt{7}$

$\cos\theta = \frac{\sqrt{7}}{4}$

$\tan\theta = \frac{3}{\sqrt{7}} = \frac{3\sqrt{7}}{7}$

$\csc\theta = \frac{4}{3}$

$\sec\theta = \frac{4}{\sqrt{7}} = \frac{4\sqrt{7}}{7}$

$\cot\theta = \frac{\sqrt{7}}{3}$

108. $\sec\theta = 3, 0 < \theta < \frac{\pi}{2}$

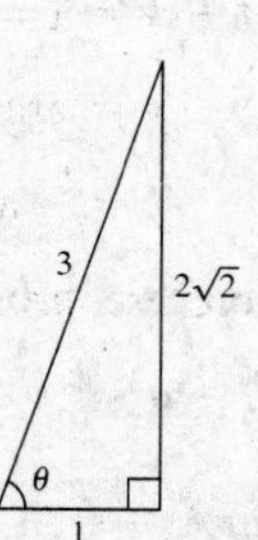

$\sin\theta = \frac{2\sqrt{2}}{3}$

$\cos\theta = \frac{1}{3}$

$\tan\theta = 2\sqrt{2}$

$\csc\theta = \frac{3}{2\sqrt{2}} = \frac{3\sqrt{2}}{4}$

$\cot\theta = \frac{1}{2\sqrt{2}} = \frac{\sqrt{2}}{4}$

Section 4.8 Applications and Models

- You should be able to solve right triangles.
- You should be able to solve right triangle applications.
- You should be able to solve applications of simple harmonic motion: $d = a \sin wt$ or $d = a \cos wt$.

Vocabulary Check

1. elevation, depression **2.** bearing **3.** harmonic motion

1. Given: $A = 30°, b = 10$

$B = 90° - 30° = 60°$

$\tan A = \dfrac{a}{b} \implies a = b \tan A = 10 \tan 30° \approx 5.77$

$\cos A = \dfrac{b}{c} \implies c = \dfrac{b}{\cos A} = \dfrac{10}{\cos 30°} \approx 11.55$

2. Given: $B = 60°, c = 15$

$A = 90° - 60° = 30°$

$\sin B = \dfrac{b}{c} \implies b = c \sin B = 15 \sin 60° = \dfrac{15\sqrt{3}}{2} \approx 12.99$

$\cos B = \dfrac{a}{c} \implies a = c \cos B = 15 \cos 60° = \dfrac{15}{2} = 7.50$

3. Given: $B = 71°, b = 14$

$\tan B = \dfrac{b}{a} \implies a = \dfrac{b}{\tan B} = \dfrac{14}{\tan 71°} \approx 4.82$

$\sin B = \dfrac{b}{c} \implies c = \dfrac{b}{\sin B} = \dfrac{14}{\sin 71°} \approx 14.81$

$A = 90° - 71° = 19°$

4. Given: $A = 7.4°, a = 20.5$

$B = 90° - 7.4° = 82.6°$

$\tan A = \dfrac{a}{b} \implies b = \dfrac{a}{\tan A} = \dfrac{20.5}{\tan 7.4°} \approx 157.84$

$\sin A = \dfrac{a}{c} \implies c = \dfrac{a}{\sin A} = \dfrac{20.5}{\sin 7.4°} \approx 159.17$

5. Given: $a = 6, b = 12$

$c^2 = a^2 + b^2 \implies c = \sqrt{36 + 144} \approx 13.42$

$\tan A = \dfrac{a}{b} = \dfrac{6}{12} = \dfrac{1}{2} \implies A = \arctan \dfrac{1}{2} \approx 26.57°$

$B = 90° - 26.57° = 63.43°$

6. Given: $a = 25, c = 45$

$b = \sqrt{c^2 - a^2} = \sqrt{1400} = 10\sqrt{14} \approx 37.42$

$\sin A = \dfrac{a}{c} \implies A = \arcsin\left(\dfrac{25}{45}\right) \approx 33.75°$

$\cos B = \dfrac{a}{c} \implies B = \arccos\left(\dfrac{25}{45}\right) \approx 56.25°$

7. Given: $b = 16, c = 54$

$a = \sqrt{c^2 - b^2} = \sqrt{2660} \approx 51.58$

$\cos A = \frac{b}{c} = \frac{16}{54} \Rightarrow A = \arccos\left(\frac{16}{54}\right) \approx 72.76°$

$B = 90° - 72.76° = 17.24°$

8. Given: $b = 1.32, c = 18.9$

$a = \sqrt{c^2 - b^2} = \sqrt{355.4676} \approx 18.85$

$\cos A = \frac{b}{c} = \frac{1.32}{18.9} \Rightarrow A = \arccos\left(\frac{1.32}{18.9}\right) \approx 86.00°$

$\sin B = \frac{b}{c} \Rightarrow B = \arcsin\left(\frac{1.32}{18.9}\right) \approx 4.00°$

9. $A = 12° 15', c = 430.5$

$B = 90° - 12° 15' = 77° 45'$

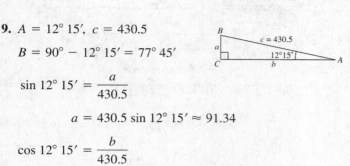

$\sin 12° 15' = \frac{a}{430.5}$

$a = 430.5 \sin 12° 15' \approx 91.34$

$\cos 12° 15' = \frac{b}{430.5}$

$b = 430.5 \cos 12° 15' \approx 420.70$

10. Given: $B = 65° 12', a = 145.5$

$A = 90° - 65° 12' = 24° 48'$

$\cos B = \frac{a}{c} \Rightarrow c = \frac{a}{\cos B} = \frac{145.5}{\cos(65° 12')} \approx 346.88$

$\tan B = \frac{b}{a} \Rightarrow b = a \tan B = 145.5 \tan(65° 12') \approx 314.89$

11. $\tan \theta = \frac{h}{b/2}$

$h = \frac{1}{2} b \tan \theta$

$h = \frac{1}{2}(8) \tan 52° \approx 5.12$ in.

12. $\tan \theta = \frac{h}{b/2}$

$h = \frac{1}{2} b \tan \theta$

$h = \frac{1}{2}(12) \tan 18° \approx 1.95$ meters

13. $\tan \theta = \frac{h}{b/2}$

$h = \frac{1}{2} b \tan \theta$

$h = \frac{1}{2}(18.5) \tan 41.6° \approx 8.21$ ft

14. $\tan \theta = \frac{h}{b/2}$

$h = \frac{1}{2} b \tan \theta$

$h = \frac{1}{2}(3.26) \tan 72.94° \approx 5.31$ cm

15. (a)

(b) $\tan \theta = \frac{60}{L}$

$L = \frac{60}{\tan \theta}$

$= 60 \cot \theta$

(c)

θ	10°	20°	30°	40°	50°
L	340	165	104	72	50

(d) No, the shadow lengths do not increase in equal increments. The cotangent function is not linear.

16. (a)

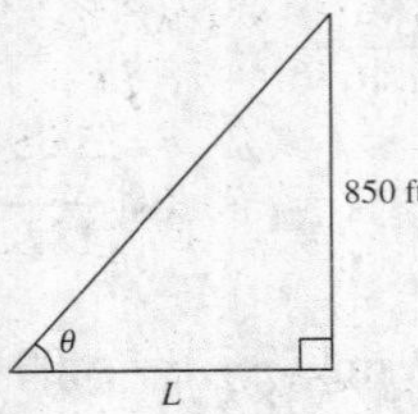

(b) $\tan\theta = \dfrac{850}{L}$

$L = \dfrac{850}{\tan\theta}$

$= 850\cot\theta$

(c)

θ	10°	20°	30°	40°	50°
L	4821	2335	1472	1013	713

(d) No, the cotangent function is not a linear function.

17. $\sin 80° = \dfrac{h}{20}$

$h = 20\sin 80°$

≈ 19.70 feet

18. $\tan(13°) = \dfrac{h}{58.2}$

$h = 58.2\tan(13°) \approx 13.44$ meters

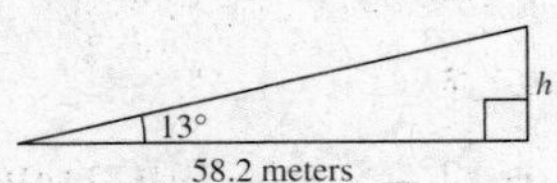

19. $\sin 50° = \dfrac{h}{100}$

$h = 100\sin 50°$

≈ 76.6 feet

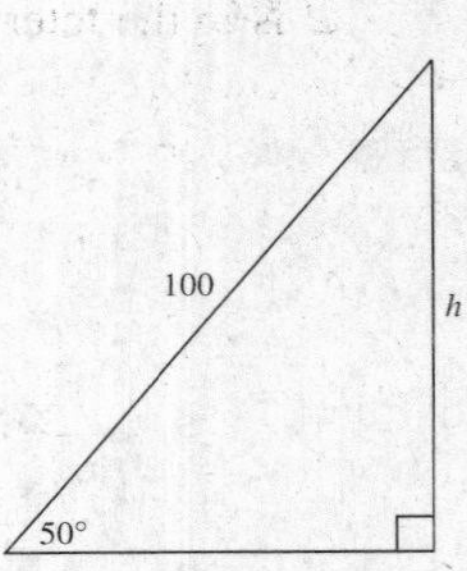

20. $\sin 31.5° = \dfrac{x}{4000}$

$x = 4000\sin 31.5°$

≈ 2089.99 feet

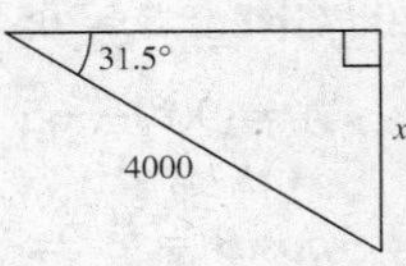

21. (a)

(b) Let the height of the church $= x$ and the height of the church and steeple $= y$. Then:

$\tan 35° = \dfrac{x}{50}$ and $\tan 47°\,40' = \dfrac{y}{50}$

$x = 50\tan 35°$ and $y = 50\tan 47°\,40'$

$h = y - x = 50(\tan 47°\,40' - \tan 35°)$

(c) $h \approx 19.9$ feet

22. $\tan 28° = \dfrac{a}{100} \implies a = 100\tan 28°$

$\tan 39.75° = \dfrac{a+s}{100}$

$a + s = 100\tan 39.75°$

$s = 100\tan 39.75° - a$

$= 100\tan 39.75° - 100\tan 28°$

≈ 30 feet

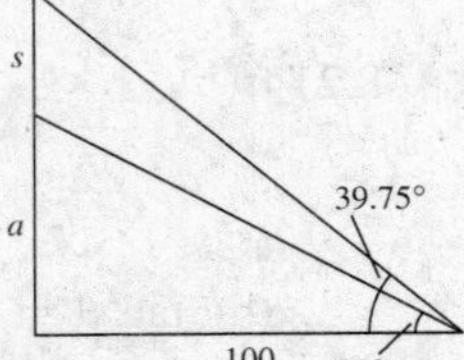

23. (a) $l^2 = 100^2 + (20 - 3 + h)^2$

$l = \sqrt{100^2 + (17 + h)^2}$

$= \sqrt{h^2 + 34h + 10,289}$

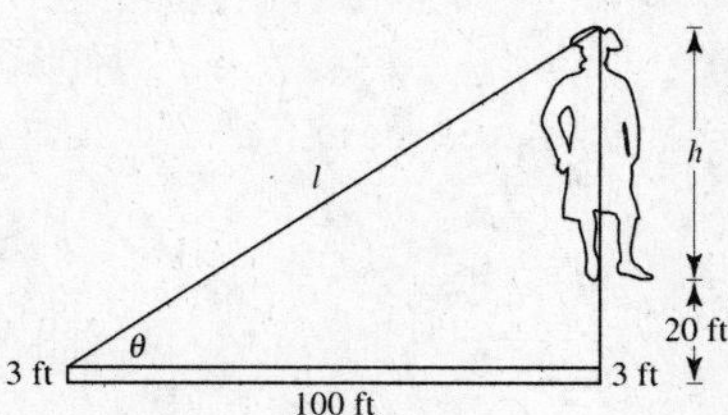

(b) $\cos\theta = \dfrac{100}{l} \implies \theta = \arccos\left(\dfrac{100}{l}\right)$

(c) If $\theta = 35°$, then $l = \dfrac{100}{\cos 35°} \approx 122.077$. Then

$(17 + h)^2 + 100^2 = l^2$

$(17 + h)^2 = l^2 - 100^2 \approx 4902.906$

$17 + h \approx 70.02$

$h \approx 53.02$ feet

≈ 53 feet, $\dfrac{1}{4}$ inch.

24. (a) $\sin 60° = \dfrac{h}{30} \implies h = 30\sin 60°$

$= 15\sqrt{3} \approx 25.98$ ft

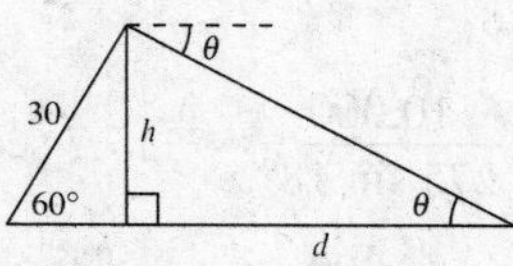

(b) $\tan\theta = \dfrac{h}{d} = \dfrac{15\sqrt{3}}{d} \approx \dfrac{25.98}{d}$

(c) $25° \le \theta \le 30°$

$\tan 25° \le \tan\theta \le \tan 30°$

$\tan 25° \le \dfrac{h}{d} \le \tan 30°$

$\dfrac{h}{\tan 25°} \ge d \ge \dfrac{h}{\tan 30°}$

$55.72 \ge d \ge 45.00$

d is in the interval $(45.0, 55.72)$.

25. $\tan\theta = \dfrac{75}{95}$

$\theta = \arctan\dfrac{15}{19} \approx 38.29°$

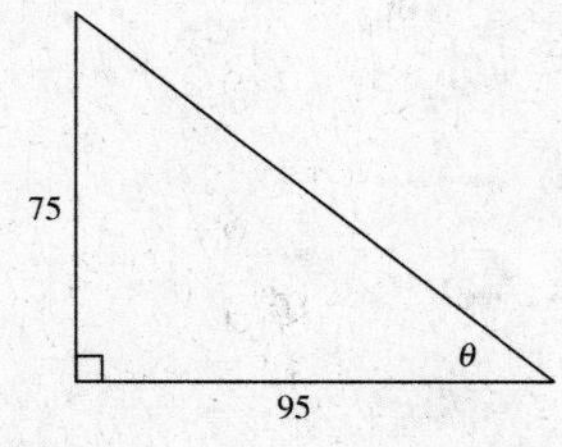

26. (a)

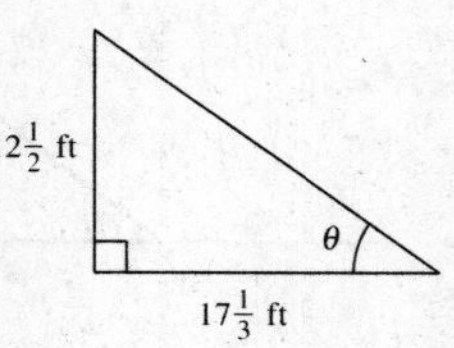

(b) $\tan\theta = \dfrac{12\frac{1}{2}}{17\frac{1}{3}}$

(c) $\theta = \arctan\dfrac{12\frac{1}{2}}{17\frac{1}{3}} \approx 35.8°$

27. $\sin\alpha = \dfrac{4000}{16,500} \implies \alpha \approx 14.03°$

$\theta \approx 90° - \alpha \approx 75.97°$

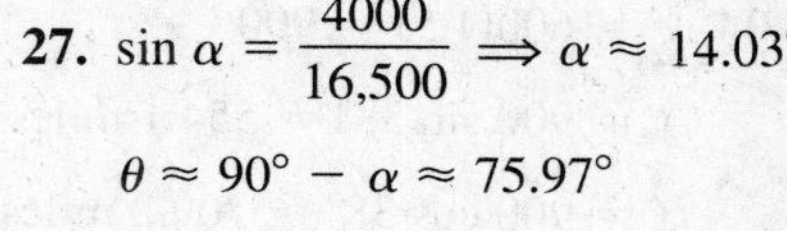

28. $\tan\theta = \dfrac{250}{2.5(5280)}$

$\theta = \arctan\left(\dfrac{250}{2.5(5280)}\right) \approx 1.09°$

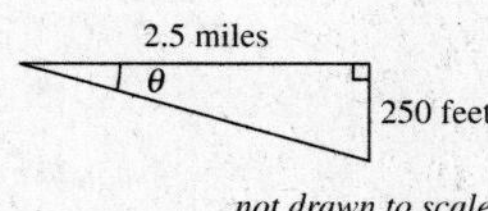

29. Since the airplane speed is

$\left(275\,\dfrac{\text{ft}}{\text{sec}}\right)\left(60\,\dfrac{\text{sec}}{\text{min}}\right) = 16,500\,\dfrac{\text{ft}}{\text{min}}$,

after one minute its distance travelled is 16,500 feet.

$\sin 18° = \dfrac{a}{16,500}$

$a = 16,500 \sin 18°$

≈ 5099 ft

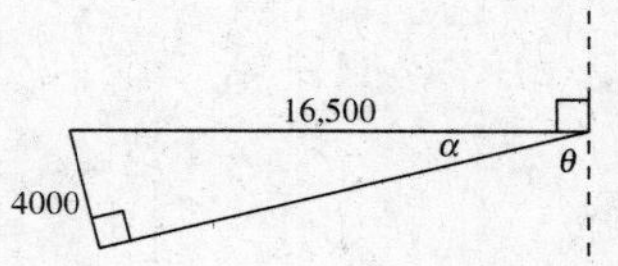

30. $\sin 18° = \dfrac{h}{275(s)}$

$s = \dfrac{h}{275 \sin 18°}$

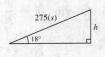

If $h = 10{,}000$, $s = \dfrac{10{,}000}{275 \sin 18°} \approx 117.7$ seconds.

If $h = 16{,}000$, $s = \dfrac{16{,}000}{275 \sin 18°} \approx 188.3$ seconds.

31. $\sin 9.5° = \dfrac{x}{4}$

$x = 4 \sin 9.5°$

≈ 0.66 mile

32. $\sin(25.2°) = \dfrac{1808}{L}$

$\Rightarrow L = \dfrac{1808}{\sin(25.2°)} \approx 4246.3$ feet

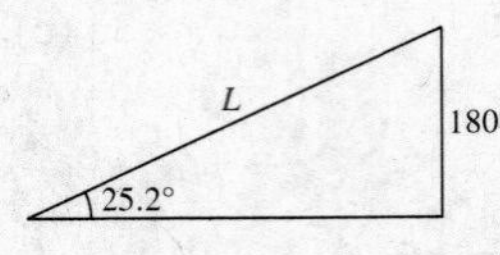

33. $90° - 29° = 61°$

$(20)(6) = 120$ nautical miles

$\sin 61° = \dfrac{a}{120} \Rightarrow a = 120 \sin 61° \approx 104.95$ nautical miles

$\cos 61° = \dfrac{b}{120} \Rightarrow b = 120 \cos 61° \approx 58.18$ nautical miles

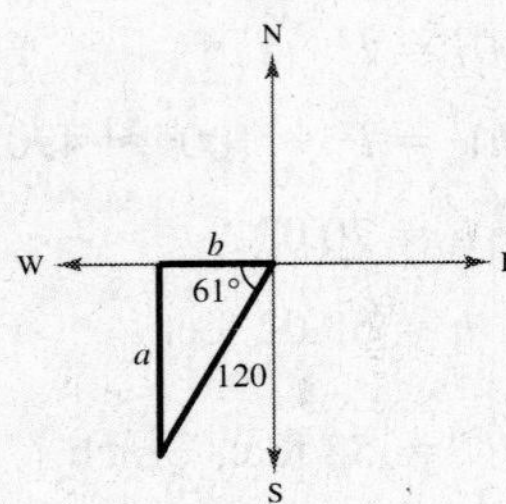

34. $c = 600(1.5) = 900$

$y = 900 \sin 38° \approx 554.1$ miles

$x = 900 \cos 38° \approx 709.2$ miles

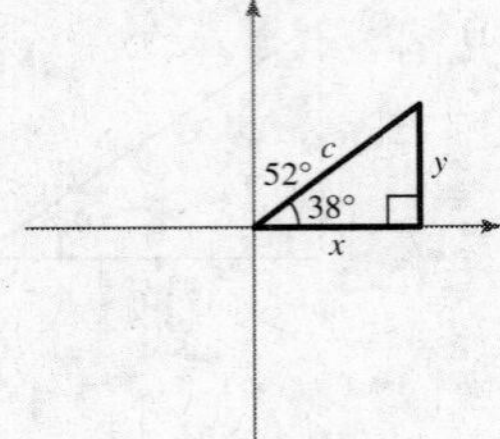

35. $\theta = 32°$, $\phi = 68°$ *Note: ABC* forms a right triangle.

(a) $\alpha = 90° - 32° = 58°$

Bearing from A to C: N 58° E

(b) $\beta = \theta = 32°$

$\gamma = 90° - \phi = 22°$

$C = \beta + \gamma = 54°$

$\tan C = \dfrac{d}{50} \Rightarrow \tan 54° = \dfrac{d}{50} \Rightarrow d \approx 68.82$ m

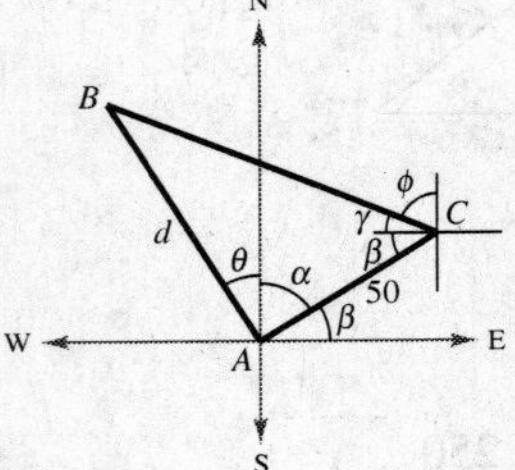

36. $\tan 14° = \dfrac{d}{x} \implies x = d \cot 14°$

$$\tan 34° = \frac{d}{y} \implies \frac{d}{30 - x} = \frac{d}{30 - d \cot 14°}$$

$$\cot 34° = \frac{30 - d \cot 14°}{d}$$

$$d \cot 34° = 30 - d \cot 14°$$

$$d = \frac{30}{\cot 34° + \cot 14°} \approx 5.46 \text{ kilometers}$$

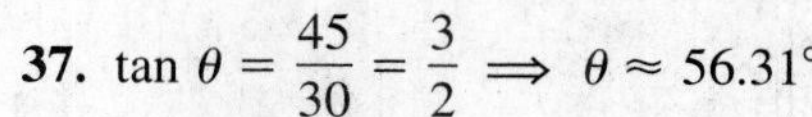

37. $\tan \theta = \dfrac{45}{30} = \dfrac{3}{2} \implies \theta \approx 56.31°$

Bearing: N 56.31° W

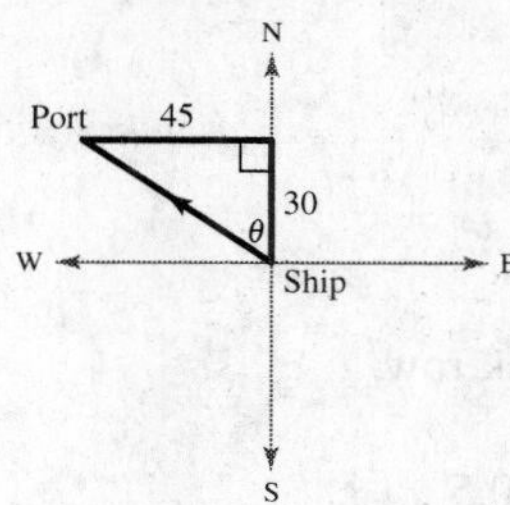

38. $\tan \theta = \dfrac{85}{160} \implies \theta \approx 27.98°$

Bearing: S 27.98° W

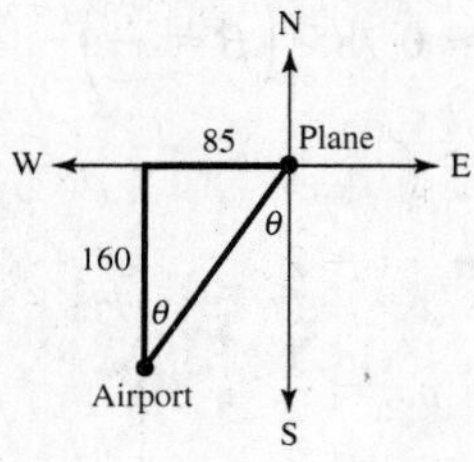

39. $\tan 6.5° = \dfrac{350}{d} \implies d \approx 3071.91$ ft

$\tan 4° = \dfrac{350}{D} \implies D \approx 5005.23$ ft

Distance between ships: $D - d \approx 1933.3$ ft

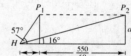

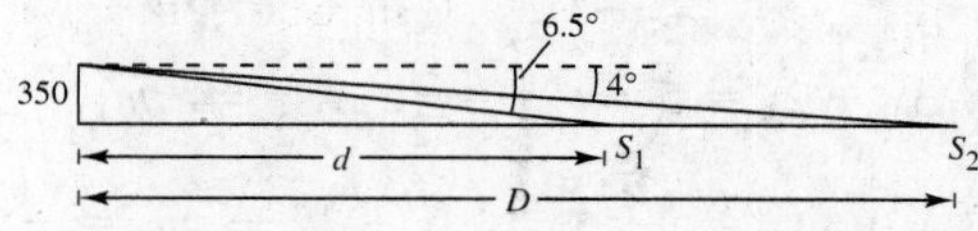

40.

$$\cot 55° = \frac{d}{10} \implies d \approx 7 \text{ kilometers}$$

$$\cot 28° = \frac{D}{10} \implies D \approx 18.8 \text{ kilometers}$$

Distance between towns:

$$D - d = 18.8 - 7 = 11.8 \text{ kilometers}$$

41. $\tan 57° = \dfrac{a}{x} \implies x = a \cot 57°$

$$\tan 16° = \frac{a}{x + (55/6)}$$

$$\tan 16° = \frac{a}{a \cot 57° + (55/6)}$$

$$\cot 16° = \frac{a \cot 57° + (55/6)}{a}$$

$$a \cot 16° - a \cot 57° = \frac{55}{6}$$

$$\implies a \approx 3.23 \text{ miles} \approx 17{,}054 \text{ feet}$$

42. $\tan 2.5° = \dfrac{h}{x}, \tan 10° = \dfrac{h}{x - 18}$

$$x = \frac{h}{\tan 2.5°}, x = \frac{h}{\tan 10°} + 18$$

$$\frac{h}{\tan 2.5°} = \frac{h}{\tan 10°} + 18 = \frac{h + 18 \tan 10°}{\tan 10°}$$

$$h \tan 10° = h \tan 2.5° + 18(\tan 10°)(\tan 2.5°)$$

$$h = \frac{18(\tan 10°)(\tan 2.5°)}{\tan 10° - \tan 2.5°} \approx 1.04 \text{ miles} \approx 5515 \text{ feet}$$

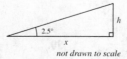

43. (a)

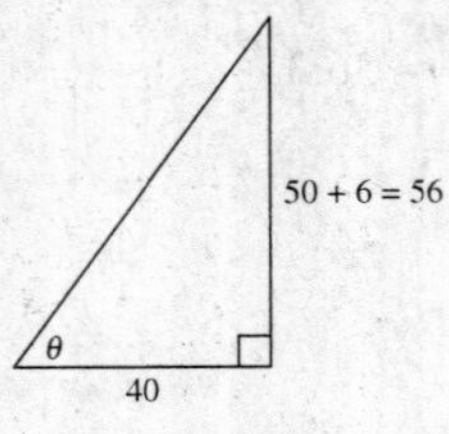

$\theta = \arctan \dfrac{56}{40} \approx 54.5°$

Similarly for the back row,

$\theta = \arctan \dfrac{56}{150} \approx 20.5°.$

(b) For 45°, you need to be 56 feet away since

$\arctan \dfrac{56}{56} = 45°.$

44. (a) Using the two triangles with acute angle β,

$\cos \beta = \dfrac{3}{L_1}$ and $\sin \beta = \dfrac{3}{L_2}.$

Hence, $L = L_1 + L_2 = 3 \sec \beta + 3 \csc \beta.$

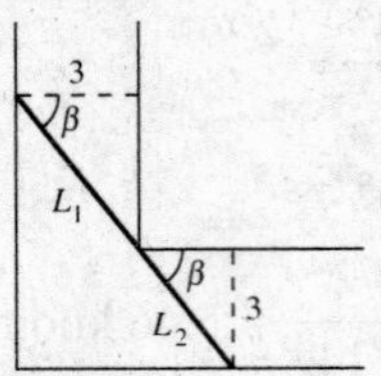

(b)

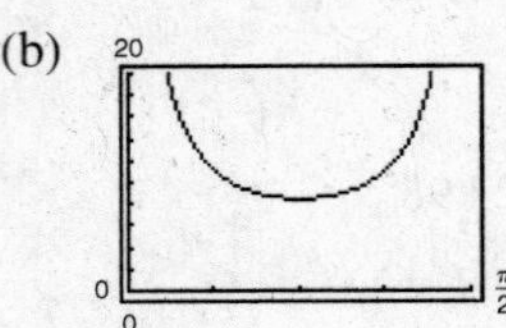

(c) The least value is $\beta \approx 0.785. \left(\beta = \dfrac{\pi}{4}\right)$

45. L_1: $3x - 2y = 5 \Rightarrow y = \dfrac{3}{2}x - \dfrac{5}{2} \Rightarrow m_1 = \dfrac{3}{2}$

L_2: $x + y = 1 \Rightarrow y = -x + 1 \Rightarrow m_2 = -1$

$\tan \alpha = \left|\dfrac{-1 - (3/2)}{1 + (-1)(3/2)}\right| = \left|\dfrac{-5/2}{-1/2}\right| = 5$

$\alpha = \arctan 5 \approx 78.7°$

46. $L_1 = 2x + y = 8 \Rightarrow m_1 = -2$

$L_2 = x - 5y = -4 \Rightarrow m_2 = \dfrac{1}{5}$

$\tan \alpha = \left|\dfrac{m_2 - m_1}{1 + m_2 m_1}\right|$

$\alpha = \arctan\left|\dfrac{m_2 - m_1}{1 + m_2 m_1}\right|$

$= \arctan\left|\dfrac{\frac{1}{5} - (-2)}{1 + \frac{1}{5}(-2)}\right| = \arctan\left(3\tfrac{2}{3}\right) \approx 74.7°$

47. The diagonal of the base has a length of $\sqrt{a^2 + a^2} = \sqrt{2}a$. Now, we have:

$\tan \theta = \dfrac{a}{\sqrt{2}a} = \dfrac{1}{\sqrt{2}}$

$\theta = \arctan \dfrac{1}{\sqrt{2}} \approx 35.3°$

48. $\tan \theta = \dfrac{a\sqrt{2}}{a} = \sqrt{2}$

$\theta = \arctan \sqrt{2} \approx 54.7°$

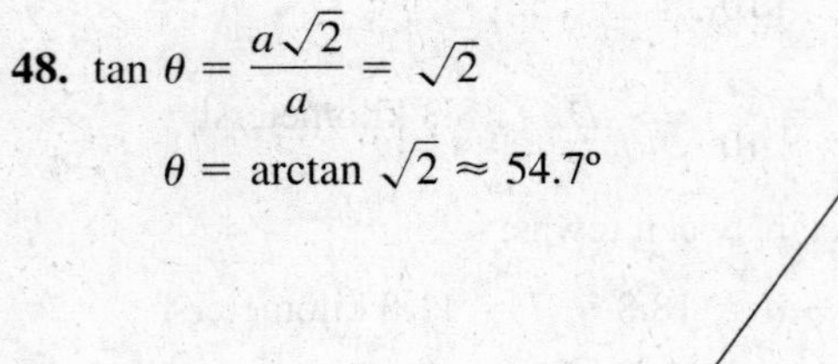

49. $\cos 30° = \dfrac{b}{r}$

$b = \cos 30° r$

$b = \dfrac{\sqrt{3}r}{2}$

$y = 2b$

$= 2\left(\dfrac{\sqrt{3}r}{2}\right) = \sqrt{3}r$

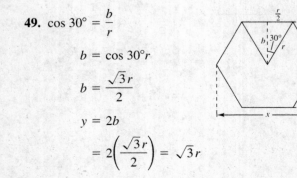

50. $c = \dfrac{35}{2} = 17.5$

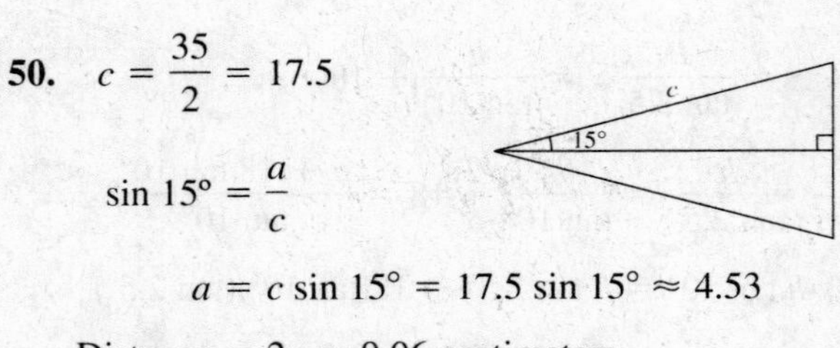

$\sin 15° = \dfrac{a}{c}$

$a = c \sin 15° = 17.5 \sin 15° \approx 4.53$

Distance $= 2a \approx 9.06$ centimeters

51. $d = 0$ when $t = 0, a = 8$, period $= 2$

Use $d = a \sin \omega t$ since $d = 0$ when $t = 0$.

$$\frac{2\pi}{\omega} = 2 \Rightarrow \omega = \pi$$

Thus, $d = 8 \sin \pi t$.

52. Displacement at $t = 0$ is $0 \Rightarrow d = a \sin \omega t$.

Amplitude: $|a| = 3$

Period: $\frac{2\pi}{\omega} = 6 \Rightarrow \omega = \frac{\pi}{3}$

$$d = 3 \sin\left(\frac{\pi t}{3}\right)$$

53. $d = 3$ when $t = 0, a = 3$, period $= 1.5$

Use $d = a \cos \omega t$ since $d = 3$ when $t = 0$.

$$\frac{2\pi}{\omega} = 1.5 \Rightarrow \omega = \frac{4}{3}\pi$$

Thus, $d = 3 \cos\left(\frac{4}{3}\pi t\right)$.

54. Displacement at $t = 0$ is $2 \Rightarrow d = a \cos \omega t$

Amplitude: $|a| = 2$

Period: $\frac{2\pi}{\omega} = 10 \Rightarrow \omega = \frac{\pi}{5}$

$$d = 2 \cos\left(\frac{\pi t}{5}\right)$$

55. $d = 4 \cos 8\pi t$

(a) Maximum displacement $=$ amplitude $= 4$

(b) Frequency $= \frac{\omega}{2\pi} = \frac{8\pi}{2\pi}$

$= 4$ cycles per unit of time

(c) $d = 4 \cos(8\pi(5)) = 4$

(d) $8\pi t = \frac{\pi}{2} \Rightarrow t = \frac{1}{16}$

56. $d = \frac{1}{2} \cos 20\pi t$

(a) Maximum displacement: $|a| = \left|\frac{1}{2}\right| = \frac{1}{2}$

(b) Frequency: $\frac{\omega}{2\pi} = \frac{20\pi}{2\pi} = 10$

(c) When $t = 5$, $d = \frac{1}{2} \cos[20\pi(5)] = \frac{1}{2}$.

(d) Least positive value for t for which $d = 0$:

$$\frac{1}{2} \cos 20\pi t = 0$$

$$\cos 20\pi t = 0$$

$$20\pi t = \frac{\pi}{2}$$

$$t = \frac{\pi}{2} \cdot \frac{1}{20\pi} = \frac{1}{40}$$

57. $d = \frac{1}{16} \sin 140\pi t$

(a) Maximum displacement $=$ amplitude $= \frac{1}{16}$

(b) Frequency $= \frac{\omega}{2\pi} = \frac{140\pi}{2\pi}$

$= 70$ cycles per unit of time

(c) $d = 0$

(d) $140\pi t = \pi \Rightarrow t = \frac{1}{140}$

58. $d = \frac{1}{64}\sin 792\pi t$

(a) Maximum displacement: $|a| = \left|\frac{1}{64}\right| = \frac{1}{64}$

(b) Frequency: $\frac{\omega}{2\pi} = \frac{792\pi}{2\pi} = 396$

(c) When $t = 5$, $d = \frac{1}{64}\sin[792\pi(5)] = 0$.

(d) Least positive value for t for which $d = 0$:

$$\frac{1}{64}\sin 792\pi t = 0$$

$$\sin 792\pi t = 0$$

$$792\pi t = \pi$$

$$t = \frac{\pi}{792\pi} = \frac{1}{792}$$

59. $d = a \sin \omega t$

$$\text{Period} = \frac{2\pi}{\omega} = \frac{1}{\text{frequency}}$$

$$\frac{2\pi}{\omega} = \frac{1}{264}$$

$$\omega = 2\pi(264) = 528\pi$$

60. At $t = 0$, buoy is at its high point $\Rightarrow$ $d = a\cos\omega t$.

Distance from high to low $= 2|a| = 3.5$

$$|a| = \frac{7}{4}$$

Returns to high point every 10 seconds:

$$\text{Period} = \frac{2\pi}{\omega} = 10 \Rightarrow \omega = \frac{\pi}{5}$$

$$d = \frac{7}{4}\cos\frac{\pi t}{5}$$

61. $y = \frac{1}{4}\cos 16t,\ t > 0$

(a)

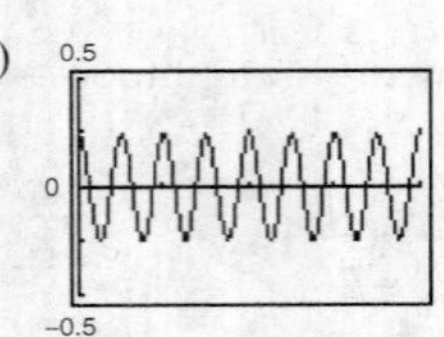

(b) Period: $\frac{2\pi}{16} = \frac{\pi}{8}$ seconds

(c) $\frac{1}{4}\cos 16t = 0$ when

$$16t = \frac{\pi}{2} \Rightarrow t = \frac{\pi}{32} \text{ seconds.}$$

62. (a)

θ	L_1	L_2	$L_1 + L_2$
0.1	$\frac{2}{\sin 0.1}$	$\frac{3}{\cos 0.1}$	23.0
0.2	$\frac{2}{\sin 0.2}$	$\frac{3}{\cos 0.2}$	13.1
0.3	$\frac{2}{\sin 0.3}$	$\frac{3}{\cos 0.3}$	9.9
0.4	$\frac{2}{\sin 0.4}$	$\frac{3}{\cos 0.4}$	8.4

(b)

0.5	$\frac{2}{\sin 0.5}$	$\frac{3}{\cos 0.5}$	7.6
0.6	$\frac{2}{\sin 0.6}$	$\frac{3}{\cos 0.6}$	7.2
0.7	$\frac{2}{\sin 0.7}$	$\frac{3}{\cos 0.7}$	7.0
0.8	$\frac{2}{\sin 0.8}$	$\frac{3}{\cos 0.8}$	7.1

The minimum length of the elevator is 7.0 meters.

(c) $L = L_1 + L_2 = \frac{2}{\sin\theta} + \frac{3}{\cos\theta}$

(d)

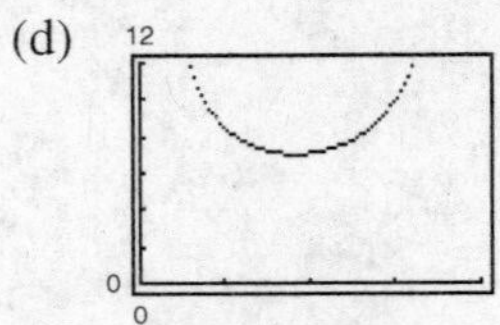

From the graph, it appears that the minimum length is 7.0 meters, which agrees with the estimate of part (b).

63. (a), (b)

Base 1	Base 2	Altitude	Area
8	$8 + 16\cos 10°$	$8\sin 10°$	22.1
8	$8 + 16\cos 20°$	$8\sin 20°$	42.5
8	$8 + 16\cos 30°$	$8\sin 30°$	59.7
8	$8 + 16\cos 40°$	$8\sin 40°$	72.7
8	$8 + 16\cos 50°$	$8\sin 50°$	80.5
8	$8 + 16\cos 60°$	$8\sin 60°$	83.1
8	$8 + 16\cos 70°$	$8\sin 70°$	80.7

Maximum $\approx$ 83.1 square feet

(c) $A = \frac{1}{2}(b_1 + b_2)h$

$= \frac{1}{2}[8 + 8 + 16\cos\theta]8\sin\theta$

$= 64(1 + \cos\theta)\sin\theta$

(d) Maximum area is approximately 83.1 square feet for $\theta = 60°$.

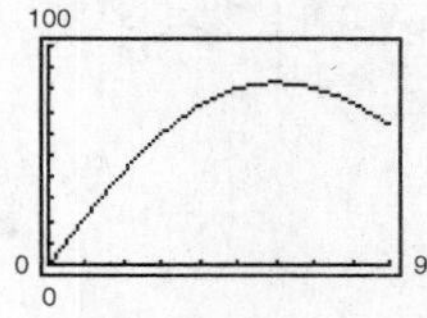

64. (a)

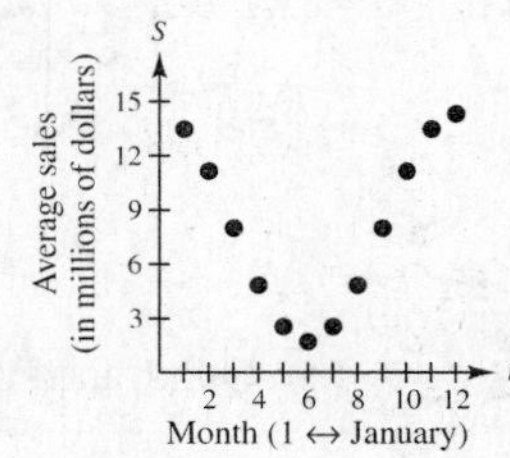

(b) $a = \frac{1}{2}(14.30 - 1.70) = 6.3$

$\frac{2\pi}{b} = 12 \Rightarrow b = \frac{\pi}{6}$

Shift: $d = 14.3 - 6.3 = 8$

$S = d + a\cos bt$

$S = 8 + 6.3\cos\left(\frac{\pi t}{6}\right)$

The model is a good fit.

(c) Period: $\frac{2\pi}{\pi/6} = 12$

This corresponds to the 12 months in a year. Since the sales of outerwear is seasonal, this is reasonable.

(d) The amplitude represents the maximum displacement from the average sale of 8 million dollars. Sales are greatest in December (cold weather + holidays) and least in June.

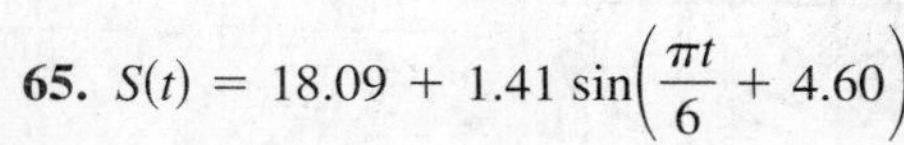

65. $S(t) = 18.09 + 1.41\sin\left(\frac{\pi t}{6} + 4.60\right)$

(a)

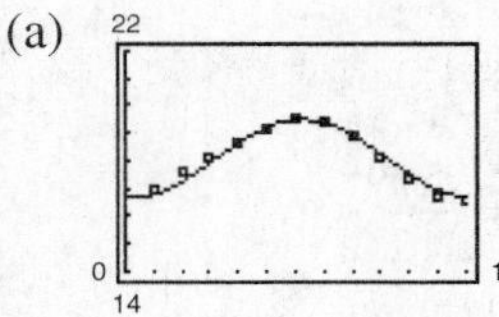

(b) The period is $\frac{2\pi}{(\pi/6)} = 12$ months, which is 1 year.

(c) The amplitude is 1.41. This gives the maximum change in time from the average time (18.09) of sunset.

66. False

It means 24 degrees east of north.

67. False. The other acute angle is $90° - 48.1° = 41.9°$. Then

$$\tan(41.9°) = \frac{\text{opp}}{\text{adj}}$$

$$= \frac{a}{22.56} \Rightarrow a = 22.56 \cdot \tan(41.9°).$$

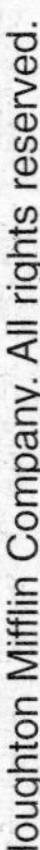

68. False

69.
$$y - 2 = 4(x + 1)$$
$$4x - y + 6 = 0$$

70.
$$y - 0 = -\tfrac{1}{2}\left(x - \tfrac{1}{3}\right)$$
$$2y = -x + \tfrac{1}{3}$$
$$3x + 6y - 1 = 0$$

71. $\text{Slope} = \dfrac{6 - 2}{-2 - 3} = -\dfrac{4}{5}$
$$y - 2 = -\frac{4}{5}(x - 3)$$
$$5y - 10 = -4x + 12$$
$$4x + 5y - 22 = 0$$

72. $m = \dfrac{1/3 + 2/3}{-1/2 - 1/4} = \dfrac{1}{-3/4} = -\dfrac{4}{3}$
$$y + \frac{2}{3} = -\frac{4}{3}\left(x - \frac{1}{4}\right)$$
$$3y + 2 = -4x + 1$$
$$4x + 3y + 1 = 0$$

73. Domain: $(-\infty, \infty)$

74. Domain: $(-\infty, \infty)$

75. Domain: $(-\infty, \infty)$

76. Domain: $7 - x \geq 0$ or $x \leq 7$

Review Exercises for Chapter 4

1. 40° or 0.7 radian

2. 250° or 4.4 radians

3. (a)

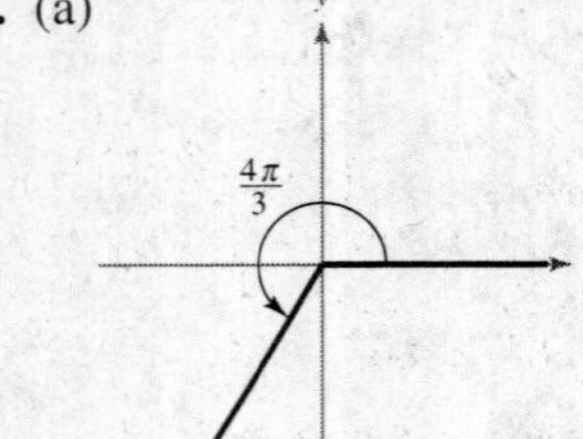

(b) Quadrant III

(c) $\dfrac{4\pi}{3} + 2\pi = \dfrac{10\pi}{3}$

$\dfrac{4\pi}{3} - 2\pi = -\dfrac{2\pi}{3}$

4. (a)

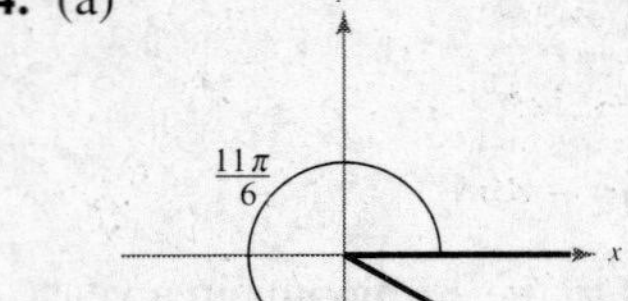

(b) Quadrant IV

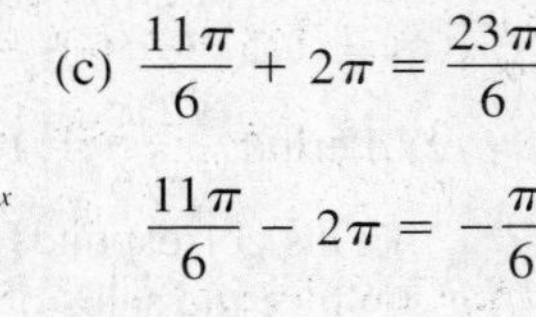

(c) $\dfrac{11\pi}{6} + 2\pi = \dfrac{23\pi}{6}$

$\dfrac{11\pi}{6} - 2\pi = -\dfrac{\pi}{6}$

5. (a)

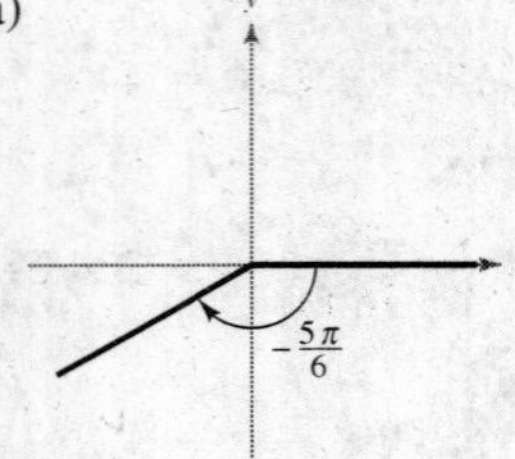

(b) Quadrant III

(c) $-\dfrac{5\pi}{6} + 2\pi = \dfrac{7\pi}{6}$

$-\dfrac{5\pi}{6} - 2\pi = -\dfrac{17\pi}{6}$

6. (a)

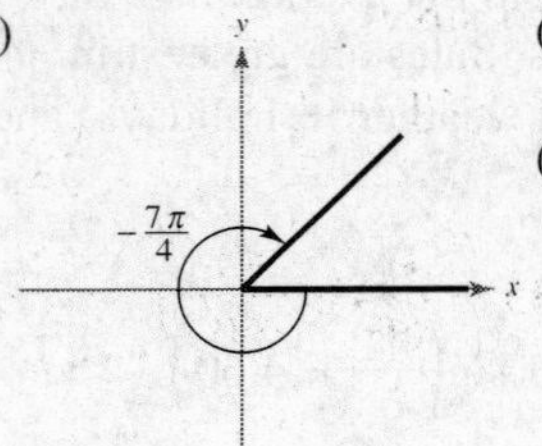

(b) Quadrant I

(c) $-\dfrac{7\pi}{4} + 2\pi = \dfrac{\pi}{4}$

$-\dfrac{7\pi}{4} - 2\pi = -\dfrac{15\pi}{4}$

7. Complement: $\dfrac{\pi}{2} - \dfrac{\pi}{8} = \dfrac{3\pi}{8}$

Supplement: $\pi - \dfrac{\pi}{8} = \dfrac{7\pi}{8}$

8. Complement: $\dfrac{\pi}{2} - \dfrac{\pi}{12} = \dfrac{5\pi}{12}$

Supplement: $\pi - \dfrac{\pi}{12} = \dfrac{11\pi}{12}$

9. Complement: $\dfrac{\pi}{2} - \dfrac{3\pi}{10} = \dfrac{\pi}{5}$

Supplement: $\pi - \dfrac{3\pi}{10} = \dfrac{7\pi}{10}$

10. Complement: $\dfrac{\pi}{2} - \dfrac{2\pi}{21} = \dfrac{17\pi}{42}$

Supplement: $\pi - \dfrac{2\pi}{21} = \dfrac{19\pi}{21}$

11. (a)

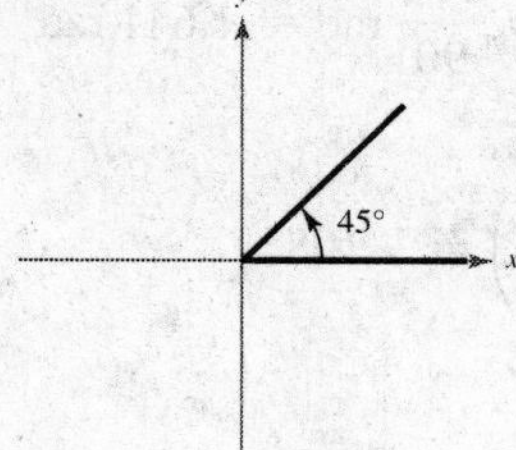

(b) Quadrant I

(c) $45° + 360° = 405°$

$45° - 360° = -315°$

12. (a)

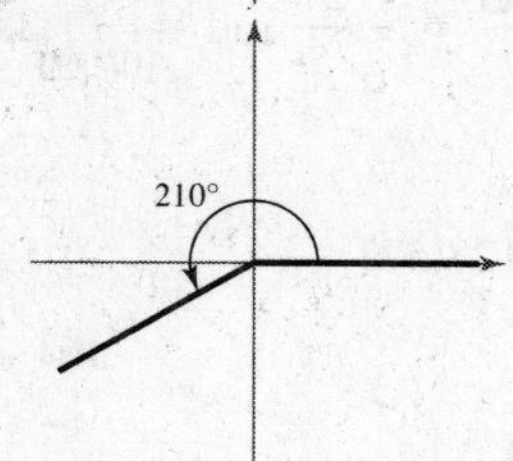

(b) Quadrant III

(c) $210° + 360° = 570°$

$210° - 360° = -150°$

13. (a)

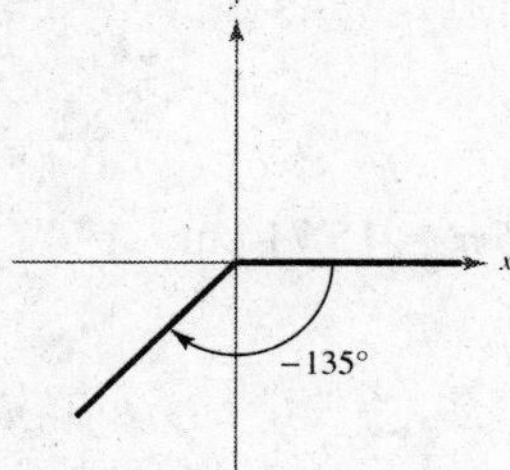

(b) Quadrant III

(c) $-135° + 360° = 225°$

$-135° - 360° = -495°$

14. (a)

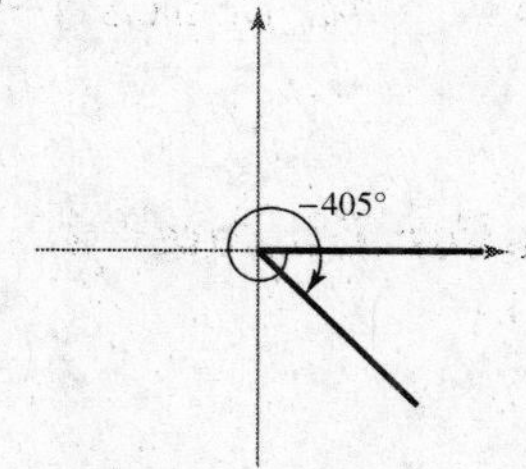

(b) Quadrant IV

(c) $-405° + 720° = 315°$

$-405° + 360° = -45°$

15. Complement of 5°: $90° - 5° = 85°$

Supplement of 5°: $180° - 5° = 175°$

16. Complement of 84°: $90° - 84° = 6°$

Supplement of 84°: $180° - 84° = 96°$

17. Complement: not possible

Supplement: $180° - 171° = 9°$

18. Complement of 136°: not possible

Supplement of 136°: $180° - 136° = 44°$

19. $135° \, 16' 45'' = \left(135 + \dfrac{16}{60} + \dfrac{45}{3600}\right)^{\circ} \approx 135.279°$

20. $-234° \, 40'' = -\left(234° + \dfrac{40°}{3600}\right) \approx -234.011°$

21. $5° \, 22' \, 53'' = \left(5 + \dfrac{22}{60} + \dfrac{53}{3600}\right)^{\circ} \approx 5.381°$

22. $280° \, 8' 50'' = 280° + \dfrac{8°}{60} + \dfrac{50°}{3600}$

$\approx 280° + 0.13° + 0.01° = 280.147°$

23. $135.29° = 135° + (0.29)(60)' = 135° \, 17' 24''$

24. $25.8° = 25° \, 48'$

25. $-85.36° = -[85 + 0.36(60')] = -85° \, 21' 36''$

26. $-327.93° = -327° \, 55' 48''$

27. $415° = 415° \cdot \dfrac{\pi \text{ rad}}{180°} = \dfrac{83\pi}{36} \text{ rad} \approx 7.243 \text{ rad}$

28. $-355° = -355° \cdot \dfrac{\pi \text{ rad}}{180°}$

$= -\dfrac{71\pi}{36} \text{ rad} \approx -6.196 \text{ rad}$

29. $-72° = -72° \cdot \dfrac{\pi \text{ rad}}{180°} = -\dfrac{2\pi}{5} \text{ rad} \approx -1.257 \text{ rad}$

30. $94° = 94° \cdot \dfrac{\pi \text{ rad}}{180°} = \dfrac{47\pi}{90} \text{ rad} \approx 1.641 \text{ rad}$

31. $\dfrac{5\pi}{7} = \dfrac{5\pi}{7}\left(\dfrac{180°}{\pi}\right) \approx 128.571°$

32. $-\dfrac{3\pi}{5} = -\dfrac{3\pi}{5}\left(\dfrac{180°}{\pi}\right) = -108°$

33. $-3.5 = -3.5\left(\dfrac{180°}{\pi}\right) \approx -200.535°$

34. $1.55 = 1.55\left(\dfrac{180°}{\pi}\right) \approx 88.808°$

35. $s = r\theta$

$25 = 12\theta$

$\theta = \dfrac{25}{12} \approx 2.083$

36. $s = r\theta \implies \theta = \dfrac{s}{r} = \dfrac{245}{60} = 4.08\overline{3} = \dfrac{49}{12}$ radians

37. $s = r\theta$

$s = 20(138°)\dfrac{\pi}{180°}$

$s \approx 48.171$ m

38. $s = r\theta = (15)\dfrac{\pi}{3} = 5\pi \approx 15.71$ cm

39. In one revolution, the arc length traveled is $s = 2\pi r = 2\pi(6) = 12\pi$ cm. The time required for one revolution is

$t = \dfrac{1}{500}$ minutes $= \dfrac{1}{500}(60) = \dfrac{3}{25}$ seconds.

Linear speed $= \dfrac{s}{t} = \dfrac{12\pi}{3/25} = 100\pi$ cm/sec

40. (a) 28 miles per hour $= \dfrac{28(5280)}{60} = 2464$ ft/min

Circumference of wheel: $C = \pi\left(2\dfrac{1}{3}\right) = \dfrac{7}{3}\pi$

Number of revolutions per minute:

$\dfrac{2464}{(7/3)\pi} = \dfrac{7392}{7\pi} \approx 336.1$ rev/min

(b) $\dfrac{\theta}{t} = \dfrac{7392}{7\pi}(2\pi) = \dfrac{14{,}724}{7} \approx 2112$ rad/min

41. $t = \dfrac{7\pi}{4}$ corresponds to $\left(\dfrac{\sqrt{2}}{2}, -\dfrac{\sqrt{2}}{2}\right)$.

42. $\cos\dfrac{3\pi}{4} = -\dfrac{\sqrt{2}}{2}$, $\sin\dfrac{3\pi}{4} = \dfrac{\sqrt{2}}{2}$

$(x, y) = \left(-\dfrac{\sqrt{2}}{2}, \dfrac{\sqrt{2}}{2}\right)$

43. $\cos\dfrac{5\pi}{6} = -\dfrac{\sqrt{3}}{2}$

$\sin\dfrac{5\pi}{6} = \dfrac{1}{2}$

$(x, y) = \left(-\dfrac{\sqrt{3}}{2}, \dfrac{1}{2}\right)$

44. $t = \dfrac{4\pi}{3}$ corresponds to $\left(-\dfrac{1}{2}, -\dfrac{\sqrt{3}}{2}\right)$.

45. $t = -\dfrac{2\pi}{3}$ corresponds to $\left(-\dfrac{1}{2}, -\dfrac{\sqrt{3}}{2}\right)$.

46. $t = -\dfrac{7\pi}{6}$ corresponds to $\left(-\dfrac{\sqrt{3}}{2}, \dfrac{1}{2}\right)$.

47. $t = -\frac{5\pi}{4}$ corresponds to $\left(-\frac{\sqrt{2}}{2}, \frac{\sqrt{2}}{2}\right)$.

48. $t = -\frac{5\pi}{6}$ corresponds to $\left(-\frac{\sqrt{3}}{2}, -\frac{1}{2}\right)$.

49. $\sin\frac{7\pi}{6} = -\frac{1}{2}$ $\qquad \cot\frac{7\pi}{6} = \sqrt{3}$

$\cos\frac{7\pi}{6} = -\frac{\sqrt{3}}{2}$ $\qquad \sec\frac{7\pi}{6} = -\frac{2}{\sqrt{3}} = -\frac{2\sqrt{3}}{3}$

$\tan\frac{7\pi}{6} = \frac{1}{\sqrt{3}} = \frac{\sqrt{3}}{3}$ $\qquad \csc\frac{7\pi}{6} = -2$

50. $\sin\frac{\pi}{4} = \frac{\sqrt{2}}{2} = \cos\frac{\pi}{4}$

$\tan\frac{\pi}{4} = 1 = \cot\frac{\pi}{4}$

$\sec\frac{\pi}{4} = \sqrt{2} = \csc\frac{\pi}{4}$

51. $t = 2\pi$ corresponds to $(1, 0)$.

$\sin 2\pi = y = 0$ $\qquad \cot 2\pi = \frac{x}{y}$, undefined

$\cos 2\pi = x = 1$ $\qquad \sec 2\pi = \frac{1}{x} = 1$

$\tan 2\pi = \frac{y}{x} = 0$ $\qquad \csc 2\pi = \frac{1}{y}$, undefined

52. $t = -\pi$ corresponds to $(-1, 0)$.

$\sin(-\pi) = y = 0$ $\qquad \cot(-\pi) = \frac{x}{y}$, undefined

$\cos(-\pi) = x = -1$ $\qquad \sec(-\pi) = \frac{1}{x} = -1$

$\tan(-\pi) = \frac{y}{x} = 0$ $\qquad \csc(-\pi) = \frac{1}{y}$, undefined

53. $t = -\frac{11\pi}{6}$ corresponds to $\left(\frac{\sqrt{3}}{2}, \frac{1}{2}\right)$.

$\sin\left(-\frac{11\pi}{6}\right) = y = \frac{1}{2}$

$\cos\left(-\frac{11\pi}{6}\right) = x = \frac{\sqrt{3}}{2}$

$\tan\left(-\frac{11\pi}{6}\right) = \frac{y}{x} = \frac{\sqrt{3}}{3}$

$\cot\left(-\frac{11\pi}{6}\right) = \frac{x}{y} = \sqrt{3}$

$\sec\left(-\frac{11\pi}{6}\right) = \frac{1}{x} = \frac{2\sqrt{3}}{3}$

$\csc\left(-\frac{11\pi}{6}\right) = \frac{1}{y} = 2$

54. $t = -\frac{5\pi}{6}$ corresponds to $\left(-\frac{\sqrt{3}}{2}, -\frac{1}{2}\right)$.

$\sin\left(-\frac{5\pi}{6}\right) = y = -\frac{1}{2}$

$\cos\left(-\frac{5\pi}{6}\right) = x = -\frac{\sqrt{3}}{2}$

$\tan\left(-\frac{5\pi}{6}\right) = \frac{y}{x} = \frac{\sqrt{3}}{3}$

$\cot\left(-\frac{5\pi}{6}\right) = \frac{x}{y} = \sqrt{3}$

$\sec\left(-\frac{5\pi}{6}\right) = \frac{1}{x} = -\frac{2\sqrt{3}}{3}$

$\csc\left(-\frac{5\pi}{6}\right) = \frac{1}{y} = -2$

55. $t = -\frac{\pi}{2}$ corresponds to $(0, -1)$.

$\sin\left(-\frac{\pi}{2}\right) = y = -1$ $\qquad \cot\left(-\frac{\pi}{2}\right) = \frac{x}{y} = 0$

$\cos\left(-\frac{\pi}{2}\right) = x = 0$ $\qquad \sec\left(-\frac{\pi}{2}\right) = \frac{1}{x}$, undefined

$\tan\left(-\frac{\pi}{2}\right) = \frac{y}{x}$, undefined $\qquad \csc\left(-\frac{\pi}{2}\right) = \frac{1}{y} = -1$

56. $t = -\dfrac{\pi}{4}$ corresponds to $\left(\dfrac{\sqrt{2}}{2}, -\dfrac{\sqrt{2}}{2}\right)$.

$\sin\left(-\dfrac{\pi}{4}\right) = y = -\dfrac{\sqrt{2}}{2}$ $\quad$ $\cot\left(-\dfrac{\pi}{4}\right) = \dfrac{x}{y} = -1$

$\cos\left(-\dfrac{\pi}{4}\right) = x = \dfrac{\sqrt{2}}{2}$ $\quad$ $\sec\left(-\dfrac{\pi}{4}\right) = \dfrac{1}{x} = \sqrt{2}$

$\tan\left(-\dfrac{\pi}{4}\right) = \dfrac{y}{x} = -1$ $\quad$ $\csc\left(-\dfrac{\pi}{4}\right) = \dfrac{1}{y} = -\sqrt{2}$

57. $\sin\left(\dfrac{11\pi}{4}\right) = \sin\left(\dfrac{3\pi}{4}\right) = \dfrac{\sqrt{2}}{2}$

58. $\cos 4\pi = \cos 0 = 1$

59. $\sin\left(-\dfrac{17\pi}{6}\right) = \sin\left(\dfrac{7\pi}{6}\right) = -\dfrac{1}{2}$

60. $\cos\left(-\dfrac{13\pi}{3}\right) = \cos\dfrac{5\pi}{3} = \dfrac{1}{2}$

61. $\sin t = \dfrac{3}{5}$

(a) $\sin(-t) = -\sin t = -\dfrac{3}{5}$

(b) $\csc(-t) = \dfrac{1}{\sin(-t)} = -\dfrac{5}{3}$

62. $\cos t = \dfrac{5}{13}$

(a) $\cos(-t) = \cos t = \dfrac{5}{13}$

(b) $\sec(-t) = \dfrac{1}{\cos(-t)} = \dfrac{13}{5}$

63. $\sin(-t) = -\dfrac{2}{3}$

(a) $\sin t = -\sin(-t) = -\left(-\dfrac{2}{3}\right) = \dfrac{2}{3}$

(b) $\csc t = \dfrac{1}{\sin t} = \dfrac{3}{2}$

64. $\cos(-t) = \dfrac{5}{8}$

(a) $\cos t = \cos(-t) = \dfrac{5}{8}$

(b) $\sec(-t) = \dfrac{1}{\cos(-t)} = \dfrac{8}{5}$

65. $\cot 2.3 = \dfrac{1}{\tan 2.3} \approx -0.8935$

66. $\sec 4.5 = \dfrac{1}{\cos 4.5} \approx -4.7439$

67. $\cos\dfrac{5\pi}{3} = \dfrac{1}{2}$

68. $\tan\left(-\dfrac{11\pi}{6}\right) \approx 0.5774$

69. The opposite side is $\sqrt{9^2 - 4^2} = \sqrt{81 - 16} = \sqrt{65}$.

$\sin\theta = \dfrac{\text{opp}}{\text{hyp}} = \dfrac{\sqrt{65}}{9}$ $\quad$ $\csc\theta = \dfrac{1}{\sin\theta} = \dfrac{9}{\sqrt{65}} = \dfrac{9\sqrt{65}}{65}$

$\cos\theta = \dfrac{\text{adj}}{\text{hyp}} = \dfrac{4}{9}$ $\quad$ $\sec\theta = \dfrac{1}{\cos\theta} = \dfrac{9}{4}$

$\tan\theta = \dfrac{\text{opp}}{\text{adj}} = \dfrac{\sqrt{65}}{4}$ $\quad$ $\cot\theta = \dfrac{1}{\tan\theta} = \dfrac{4}{\sqrt{65}} = \dfrac{4\sqrt{65}}{65}$

70. $\sin\theta = \dfrac{15}{3\sqrt{41}} = \dfrac{5\sqrt{41}}{41}$

$\cos\theta = \dfrac{12}{3\sqrt{41}} = \dfrac{4\sqrt{41}}{41}$

$\tan\theta = \dfrac{15}{12} = \dfrac{5}{4}$

$\csc\theta = \dfrac{41}{5\sqrt{41}} = \dfrac{\sqrt{41}}{5}$

$\sec\theta = \dfrac{41}{4\sqrt{41}} = \dfrac{\sqrt{41}}{4}$

$\cot\theta = \dfrac{4}{5}$

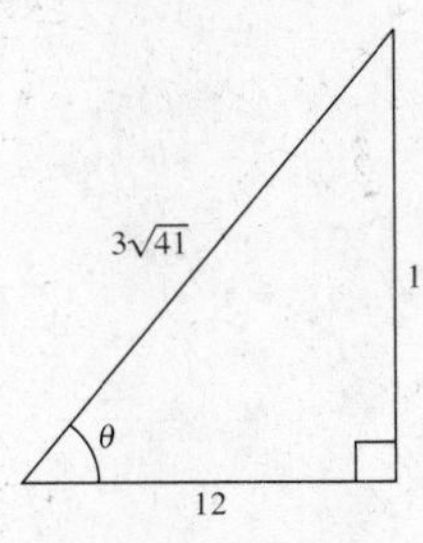

71. The hypotenuse is $\sqrt{12^2 + 10^2} = \sqrt{244} = 2\sqrt{61}$.

$\sin\theta = \dfrac{\text{opp}}{\text{hyp}} = \dfrac{10}{2\sqrt{61}} = \dfrac{5}{\sqrt{61}} = \dfrac{5\sqrt{61}}{61}$

$\cos\theta = \dfrac{\text{adj}}{\text{hyp}} = \dfrac{12}{2\sqrt{61}} = \dfrac{6}{\sqrt{61}} = \dfrac{6\sqrt{61}}{61}$

$\tan\theta = \dfrac{\text{opp}}{\text{adj}} = \dfrac{10}{12} = \dfrac{5}{6}$

$\csc\theta = \dfrac{1}{\sin\theta} = \dfrac{\sqrt{61}}{5}$

$\sec\theta = \dfrac{1}{\cos\theta} = \dfrac{\sqrt{61}}{6}$

$\cot\theta = \dfrac{1}{\tan\theta} = \dfrac{6}{5}$

72. $\sin\theta = \dfrac{2}{10} = \dfrac{1}{5}$ $\qquad \csc\theta = 5$

$\cos\theta = \dfrac{4\sqrt{6}}{10} = \dfrac{2\sqrt{6}}{5}$ $\qquad \sec\theta = \dfrac{5}{2\sqrt{6}} = \dfrac{5\sqrt{6}}{12}$

$\tan\theta = \dfrac{2}{4\sqrt{6}} = \dfrac{\sqrt{6}}{12}$ $\qquad \cot\theta = \dfrac{12}{\sqrt{6}} = 2\sqrt{6}$

10, 2, θ, $\sqrt{96} = 4\sqrt{6}$

73. $\csc\theta\tan\theta = \dfrac{1}{\sin\theta}\cdot\dfrac{\sin\theta}{\cos\theta} = \dfrac{1}{\cos\theta} = \sec\theta$

74. $\dfrac{\cot\theta + \tan\theta}{\cot\theta} = 1 + \dfrac{\tan\theta}{\cot\theta} = 1 + \tan^2\theta = \sec^2\theta$

75. (a) $\cos 84° \approx 0.1045$

(b) $\sin 6° \approx 0.1045$

76. (a) $\csc(52°\ 12') = \dfrac{1}{\sin(52°\ 12')} = \dfrac{1}{\sin 52.2°} \approx 1.2656$

(b) $\sec(54°\ 7') = \dfrac{1}{\cos(54°\ 7')} = \dfrac{1}{\cos(54.1167°)} \approx 1.7061$

77. (a) $\cos\dfrac{\pi}{4} \approx 0.7071$

(b) $\sec\dfrac{\pi}{4} \approx 1.4142$

78. (a) $\tan\left(\dfrac{3\pi}{20}\right) \approx 0.5095$

(b) $\cot\left(\dfrac{3\pi}{20}\right) = \dfrac{1}{\tan(3\pi/20)}$

≈ 1.9626

79. $\tan 62° = \dfrac{\omega}{125}$

$x = 125 \tan 62°$

≈ 235 feet

80. (a)

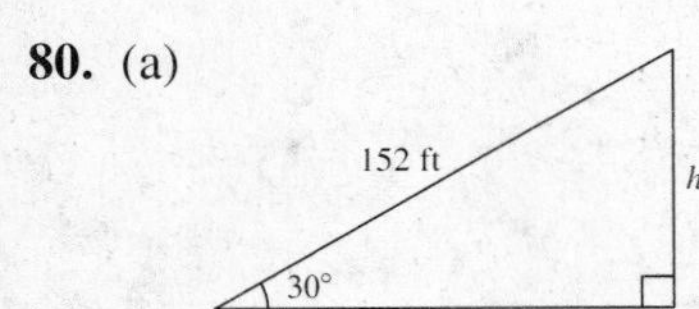

(b) $\sin 30° = \dfrac{h}{152} \Rightarrow h = 152 \sin 30°$

(c) $h = 152\left(\dfrac{1}{2}\right) = 76$ feet

81. $x = 12, y = 16, r = \sqrt{144 + 256} = \sqrt{400} = 20$

$\sin\theta = \frac{y}{r} = \frac{4}{5}$ $\qquad \csc\theta = \frac{r}{y} = \frac{5}{4}$

$\cos\theta = \frac{x}{r} = \frac{3}{5}$ $\qquad \sec\theta = \frac{r}{x} = \frac{5}{3}$

$\tan\theta = \frac{y}{x} = \frac{4}{3}$ $\qquad \cot\theta = \frac{x}{y} = \frac{3}{4}$

82. $x = 2, y = 10, r = \sqrt{4 + 100} = \sqrt{104} = 2\sqrt{26}$

$\sin\theta = \frac{y}{r} = \frac{10}{2\sqrt{26}} = \frac{5\sqrt{26}}{26}$

$\cos\theta = \frac{x}{r} = \frac{2}{2\sqrt{26}} = \frac{\sqrt{26}}{26}$

$\tan\theta = \frac{y}{x} = \frac{10}{2} = 5$

$\csc\theta = \frac{r}{y} = \frac{\sqrt{26}}{5}$

$\sec\theta = \frac{r}{x} = \sqrt{26}$

$\cot\theta = \frac{x}{y} = \frac{1}{5}$

83. $x = -7,\ y = 2,\ r = \sqrt{49 + 4} = \sqrt{53}$

$\sin\theta = \frac{y}{r} = \frac{2}{\sqrt{53}} = \frac{2\sqrt{53}}{53}$

$\cos\theta = \frac{x}{r} = -\frac{7}{\sqrt{53}} = -\frac{7\sqrt{53}}{53}$

$\tan\theta = \frac{y}{x} = -\frac{2}{7}$

$\csc\theta = \frac{\sqrt{53}}{2}$

$\sec\theta = -\frac{\sqrt{53}}{7}$

$\cot\theta = -\frac{7}{2}$

84. $x = 3, y = -4, r = \sqrt{3^2 + (-4)^2} = 5$

$\sin\theta = \frac{y}{r} = -\frac{4}{5}$

$\cos\theta = \frac{x}{r} = \frac{3}{5}$

$\tan\theta = \frac{y}{x} = -\frac{4}{3}$

$\csc\theta = \frac{x}{y} = -\frac{5}{4}$

$\sec\theta = \frac{r}{x} = \frac{5}{3}$

$\cot\theta = \frac{r}{y} = -\frac{3}{4}$

85. $x = \frac{2}{3}$ and $y = \frac{5}{8}$, $r = \sqrt{\left(\frac{2}{3}\right)^2 + \left(\frac{5}{8}\right)^2} = \frac{\sqrt{481}}{24}$

$\sin\theta = \frac{y}{r} = \frac{5/8}{\sqrt{481}/24} = \frac{15\sqrt{481}}{481}$

$\cos\theta = \frac{x}{r} = \frac{2/3}{\sqrt{481}/24} = \frac{16\sqrt{481}}{481}$

$\tan\theta = \frac{y}{x} = \frac{5/8}{2/3} = \frac{15}{16}$

$\csc\theta = \frac{r}{y} = \frac{\sqrt{481}}{15}$

$\sec\theta = \frac{r}{x} = \frac{\sqrt{481}}{16}$

$\cot\theta = \frac{x}{y} = \frac{16}{15}$

86. $x = -\frac{10}{3}, y = -\frac{2}{3}, r = \sqrt{\left(-\frac{10}{3}\right)^2 + \left(-\frac{2}{3}\right)^2} = \frac{2\sqrt{26}}{3}$

$\sin\theta = \frac{y}{r} = \frac{-2/3}{2\sqrt{26}/3} = \frac{-1}{\sqrt{26}} = \frac{-\sqrt{26}}{26}$ $\qquad$ $\csc\theta = \frac{r}{y} = -\sqrt{26}$

$\cos\theta = \frac{x}{r} = \frac{-10/3}{2\sqrt{26}/3} = \frac{-5}{\sqrt{26}} = \frac{-5\sqrt{26}}{26}$ $\qquad$ $\sec\theta = \frac{r}{x} = -\frac{\sqrt{26}}{5}$

$\tan\theta = \frac{y}{x} = \frac{-2/3}{-10/3} = \frac{1}{5}$ $\qquad$ $\cot\theta = \frac{x}{y} = 5$

87. $\sec\theta = \frac{6}{5}$, $\tan\theta < 0 \Rightarrow \theta$ is in Quadrant IV.

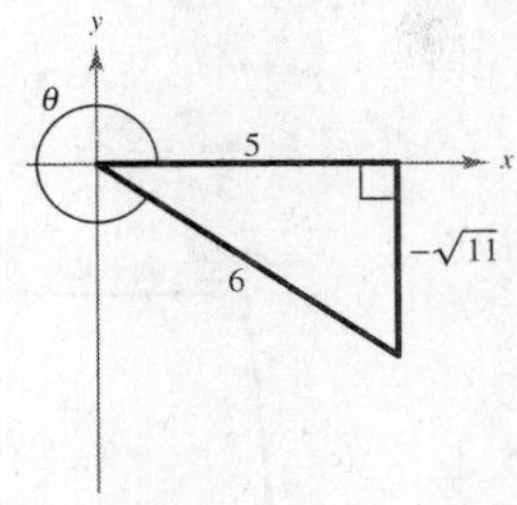

$r = 6, x = 5, y = -\sqrt{36 - 25} = -\sqrt{11}$

$\sin\theta = \frac{y}{r} = -\frac{\sqrt{11}}{6}$ $\qquad$ $\csc\theta = -\frac{6\sqrt{11}}{11}$

$\cos\theta = \frac{x}{r} = \frac{5}{6}$ $\qquad$ $\sec\theta = \frac{6}{5}$

$\tan\theta = \frac{y}{x} = -\frac{\sqrt{11}}{5}$ $\qquad$ $\cot\theta = -\frac{5\sqrt{11}}{11}$

88. $\tan\theta = \frac{y}{x} = -\frac{12}{5} \Rightarrow r = 13, \sin\theta > 0 \Rightarrow y = 12, x = -5$

$\sin\theta = \frac{y}{r} = \frac{12}{13}$ $\qquad$ $\csc\theta = \frac{r}{y} = \frac{13}{12}$

$\cos\theta = \frac{x}{r} = -\frac{5}{13}$ $\qquad$ $\sec\theta = \frac{r}{x} = \frac{13}{-5} = -\frac{13}{5}$

$\cot\theta = \frac{x}{y} = -\frac{5}{12}$

89. $\sin\theta = \frac{3}{8}$, $\cos\theta < 0 \Rightarrow \theta$ is in Quadrant II.

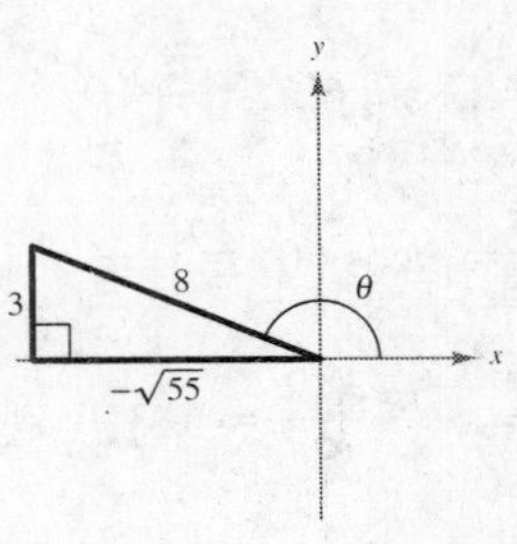

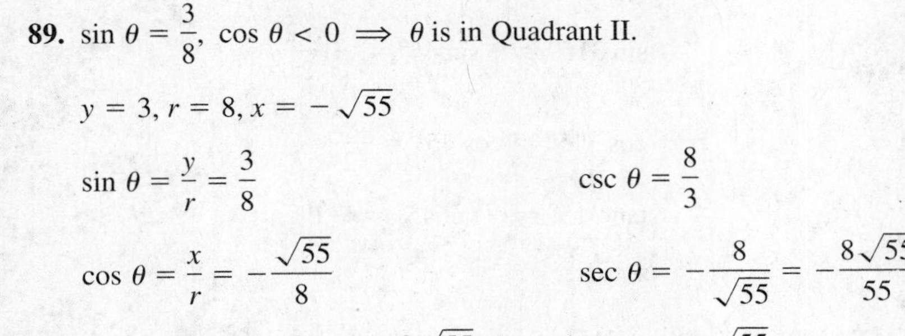

$y = 3, r = 8, x = -\sqrt{55}$

$\sin\theta = \frac{y}{r} = \frac{3}{8}$ $\qquad$ $\csc\theta = \frac{8}{3}$

$\cos\theta = \frac{x}{r} = -\frac{\sqrt{55}}{8}$ $\qquad$ $\sec\theta = -\frac{8}{\sqrt{55}} = -\frac{8\sqrt{55}}{55}$

$\tan\theta = \frac{y}{x} = -\frac{3}{\sqrt{55}} = -\frac{3\sqrt{55}}{55}$ $\qquad$ $\cot\theta = -\frac{\sqrt{55}}{3}$

90. $\cos\theta = \dfrac{x}{r} = \dfrac{-2}{5} \implies y = \pm\sqrt{21},\ \sin\theta > 0 \implies y = \sqrt{21}$

$\sin\theta = \dfrac{y}{r} = \dfrac{\sqrt{21}}{5}$ $\qquad$ $\sec\theta = \dfrac{r}{x} = \dfrac{5}{-2} = -\dfrac{5}{2}$

$\tan\theta = \dfrac{y}{x} = -\dfrac{\sqrt{21}}{2}$ $\qquad$ $\cot\theta = \dfrac{x}{y} = \dfrac{-2}{\sqrt{21}} = -\dfrac{2\sqrt{21}}{21}$

$\csc\theta = \dfrac{r}{y} = \dfrac{5}{\sqrt{21}} = \dfrac{5\sqrt{21}}{21}$

91. Reference angle:

$264° - 180° = 84°$

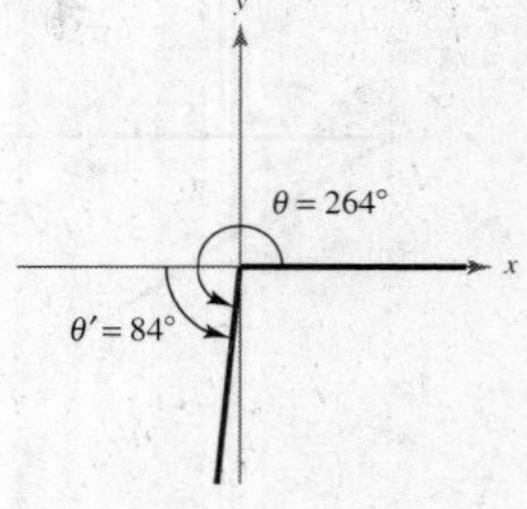

92. 635° is coterminal with 275°.

Reference angle:

$360° - 275° = 85°$

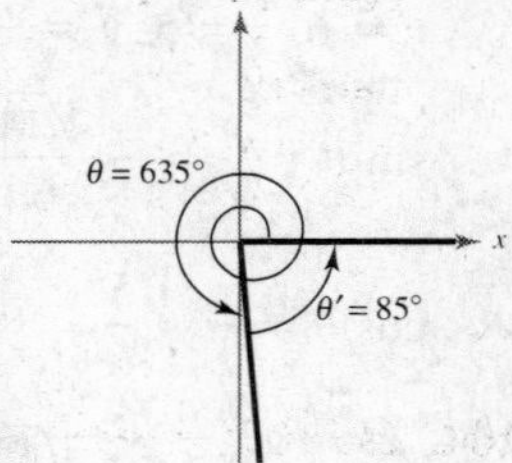

93. Coterminal angle:

$2\pi - \dfrac{6\pi}{5} = \dfrac{4\pi}{5}$

Reference angle:

$\pi - \dfrac{4\pi}{5} = \dfrac{\pi}{5}$

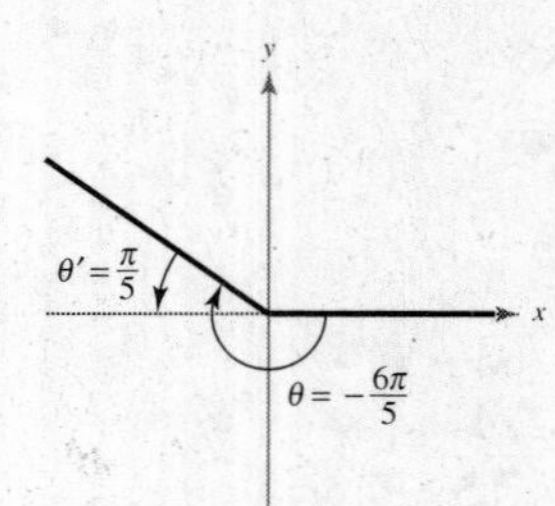

94. $\dfrac{17\pi}{3}$ is coterminal with $\dfrac{5\pi}{3}$.

Reference angle:

$2\pi - \dfrac{5\pi}{3} = \dfrac{\pi}{3}$

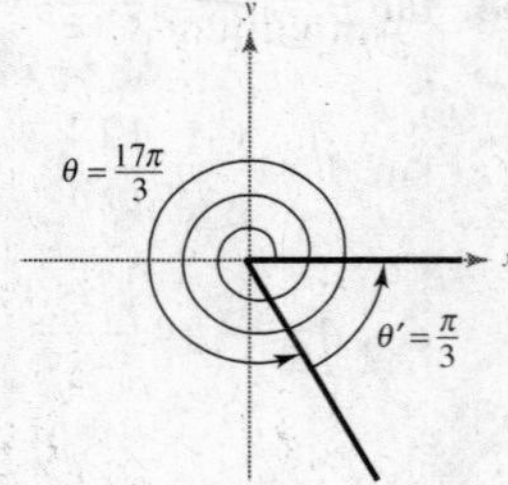

95. 240° is in Quadrant III with reference angle 60°.

$\sin 240° = -\sin 60° = -\dfrac{\sqrt{3}}{2}$

$\cos 240° = -\cos 60° = -\dfrac{1}{2}$

$\tan 240° = \dfrac{-\sqrt{3}/2}{-1/2} = \sqrt{3}$

96. 315° is in Quadrant IV with reference angle 45°.

$\sin 315° = -\sin 45° = -\dfrac{\sqrt{2}}{2}$

$\cos 315° = \cos 45° = \dfrac{\sqrt{2}}{2}$

$\tan 315° = -\tan 45° = -1$

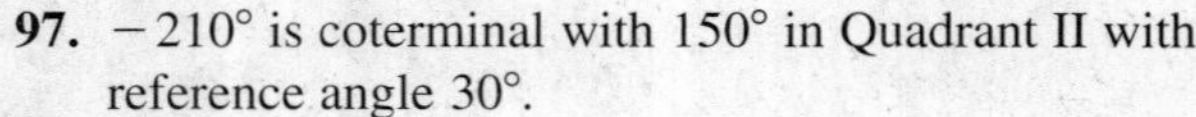

97. $-210°$ is coterminal with 150° in Quadrant II with reference angle 30°.

$\sin(-210°) = \sin(30°) = \dfrac{1}{2}$

$\cos(-210°) = -\cos(30°) = -\dfrac{\sqrt{3}}{2}$

$\tan(-210°) = \dfrac{1/2}{-\sqrt{3}/2} = -\dfrac{1}{\sqrt{3}} = -\dfrac{\sqrt{3}}{3}$

98. $-315°$ is coterminal with 45° in Quadrant I.

$\sin(-315°) = \dfrac{\sqrt{2}}{2}$

$\cos(-315°) = \dfrac{\sqrt{2}}{2}$

$\tan(-315°) = 1$

99. $-9\pi/4$ is coterminal with $7\pi/4$ in Quadrant IV with reference angle $\pi/4$.

$$\sin\left(-\frac{9\pi}{4}\right) = -\sin\left(\frac{\pi}{4}\right) = -\frac{\sqrt{2}}{2}$$

$$\cos\left(-\frac{9\pi}{4}\right) = \cos\left(\frac{\pi}{4}\right) = \frac{\sqrt{2}}{2}$$

$$\tan\left(-\frac{9\pi}{4}\right) = \frac{-\sqrt{2}/2}{\sqrt{2}/2} = -1$$

100. $11\pi/6$ is in Quadrant IV.

$$\sin\left(\frac{11\pi}{6}\right) = -\frac{1}{2}$$

$$\cos\left(\frac{11\pi}{6}\right) = \frac{\sqrt{3}}{2}$$

$$\tan\left(\frac{11\pi}{6}\right) = -\frac{\sqrt{3}}{3}$$

101. $\sin(4\pi) = \sin(0) = 0$

$\cos(4\pi) = 1$

$\tan(4\pi) = 0$

102. $\sin\left(\frac{7\pi}{3}\right) = \sin\left(\frac{\pi}{3}\right) = \frac{\sqrt{3}}{2}$

$\cos\left(\frac{7\pi}{3}\right) = \frac{1}{2}$

$\tan\left(\frac{7\pi}{3}\right) = \sqrt{3}$

103. $\tan 33° \approx 0.6494$

104. $\csc 105° = \frac{1}{\sin 105°} \approx 1.0353$

105. $\sec \frac{12\pi}{5} = \frac{1}{\cos(12\pi/5)} \approx 3.2361$

106. $\sin\left(-\frac{\pi}{9}\right) \approx -0.3420$

107. $f(x) = 3 \sin x$

Amplitude: 3

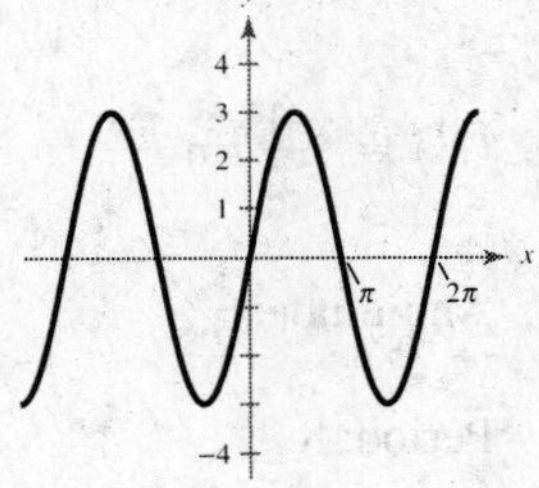

108. $f(x) = 2 \cos x$

Amplitude: 2

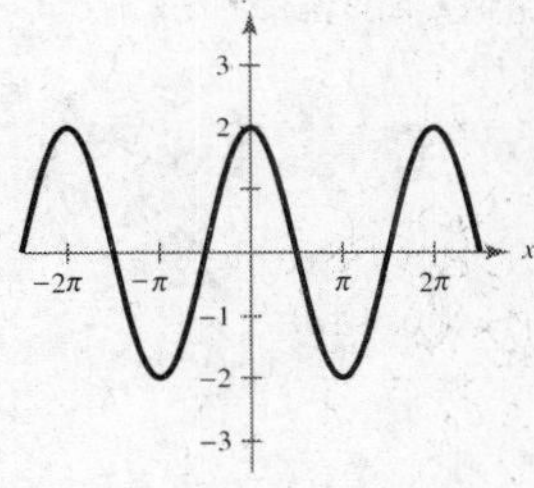

109. $f(x) = \frac{1}{4} \cos x$

Amplitude: $\frac{1}{4}$

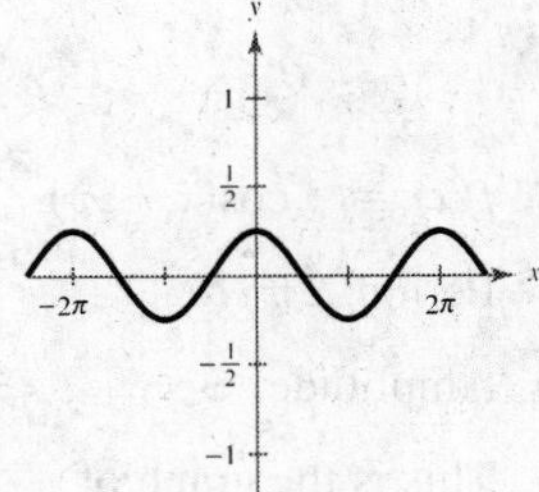

110. $f(x) = \frac{7}{2} \sin x$

Amplitude: $\frac{7}{2}$

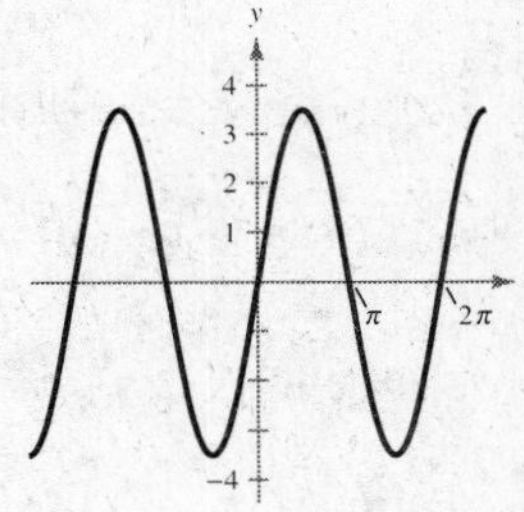

111. Period: $\frac{2\pi}{\pi} = 2$

Amplitude: 5

112. Period: $\frac{2\pi}{(1/2)} = 4\pi$

Amplitude: $\frac{3}{2}$

113. Period: $\frac{2\pi}{2} = \pi$

Amplitude: 3.4

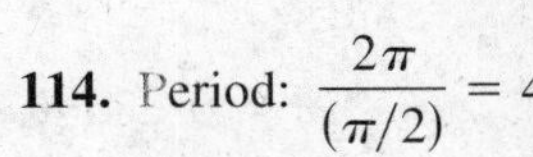

114. Period: $\frac{2\pi}{(\pi/2)} = 4$

Amplitude: 4

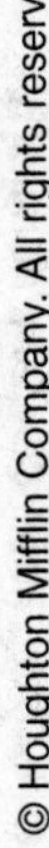

115. $y = 3 \cos 2\pi x$

Amplitude: 3

Period: $\dfrac{2\pi}{2\pi} = 1$

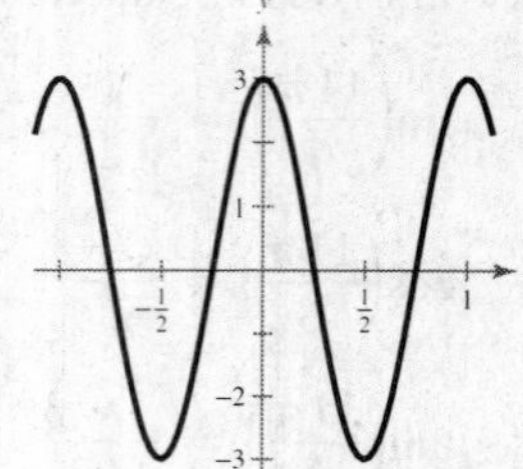

116. $y = -2 \sin \pi x$

Period: $\dfrac{2\pi}{\pi} = 2$

Amplitude: $|-2| = 2$

Reflected in x-axis

x	$-\frac{1}{2}$	0	$\frac{1}{2}$
y	2	0	-2

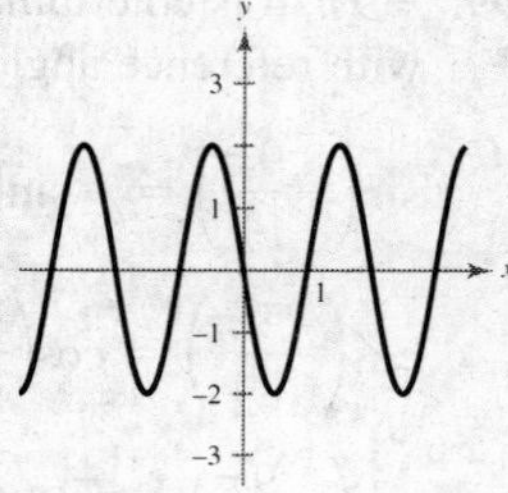

117. $f(x) = 5 \sin \dfrac{2x}{5}$

Amplitude: 5

Period: $\dfrac{2\pi}{2/5} = 5\pi$

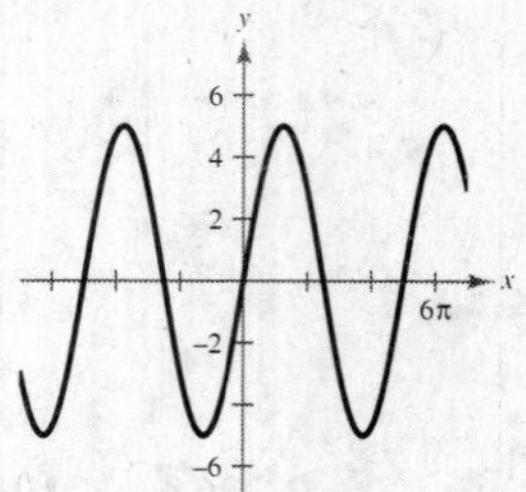

118. $f(x) = 8 \cos\left(-\dfrac{x}{4}\right)$

Period: $\dfrac{2\pi}{(1/4)} = 8\pi$

Amplitude: 8

Reflected in y-axis

x	-4π	-2π	0	2π	4π
y	-8	0	8	0	-8

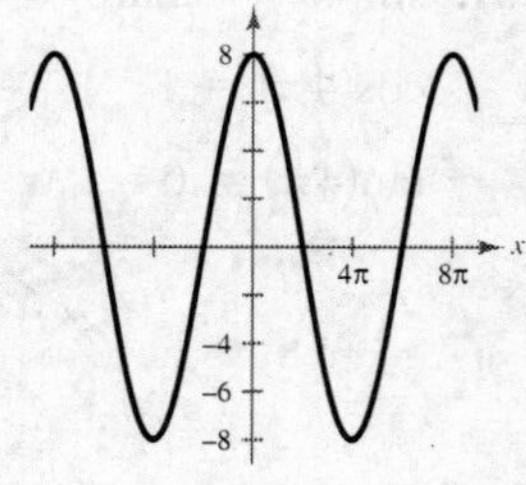

119. $f(x) = -\dfrac{5}{2} \cos\left(\dfrac{x}{4}\right)$

Amplitude: $\dfrac{5}{2}$

Period: $\dfrac{2\pi}{1/4} = 8\pi$

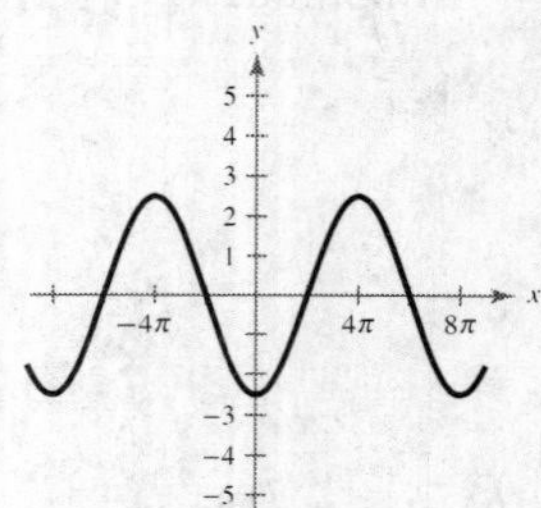

120. $f(x) = -\dfrac{1}{2} \sin \dfrac{\pi x}{4}$

Amplitude: $\dfrac{1}{2}$

Period: 8

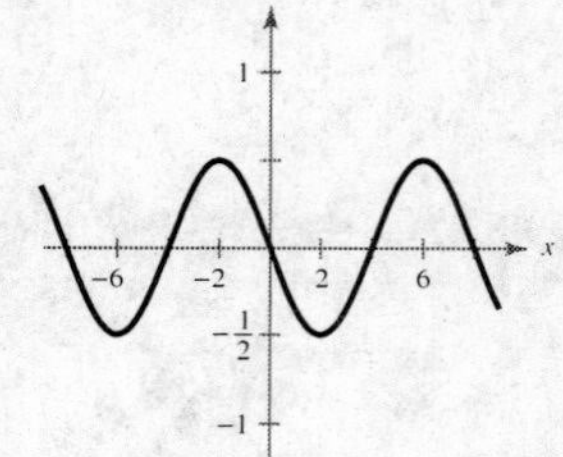

121. $f(x) = \dfrac{5}{2} \sin(x - \pi)$

Amplitude: $\dfrac{5}{2}$

Period: 2π

Shift:

$x - \pi = 0$ and $x - \pi = 2\pi$

$x = \pi \qquad\qquad x = 3\pi$

122. $f(x) = 3 \cos(x + \pi)$

Period: 2π

Amplitude: 3

This is the graph of $y = 3 \cos x$ shifted to the left π units.

x	$-\pi$	$-\frac{\pi}{2}$	0	$\frac{\pi}{2}$	π
$f(x)$	3	0	-3	0	3

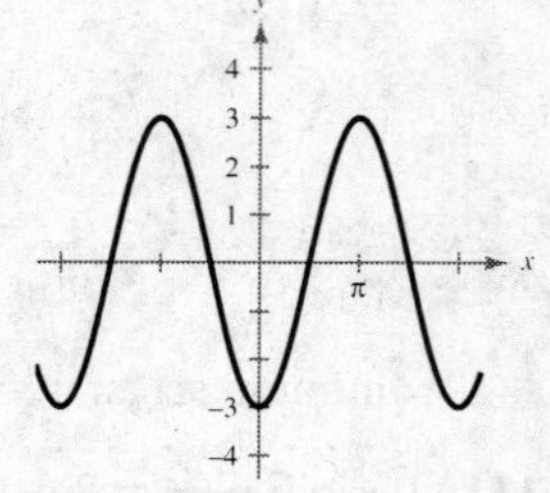

123. $f(x) = 2 - \cos \dfrac{\pi x}{2}$

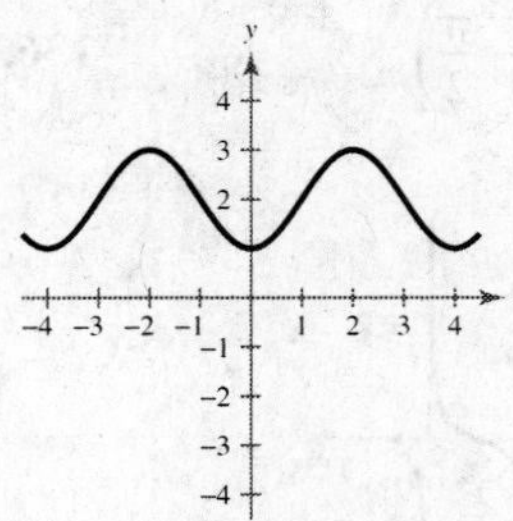

124. $f(x) = \dfrac{1}{2} \sin \pi x - 3$

Amplitude: $\dfrac{1}{2}$

Period: 2

Vertical shift downward three units

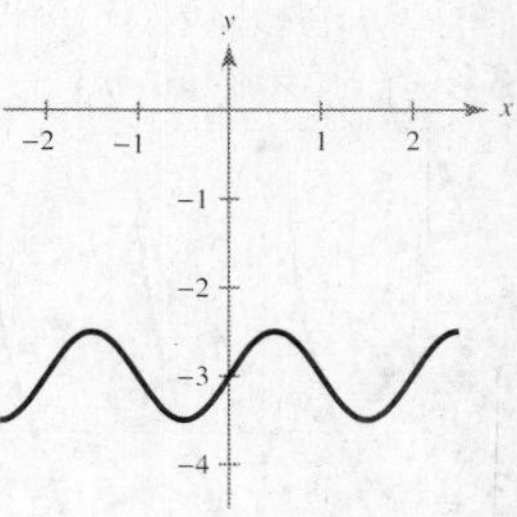

125. $f(x) = -3 \cos\left(\dfrac{x}{2} - \dfrac{\pi}{4}\right)$

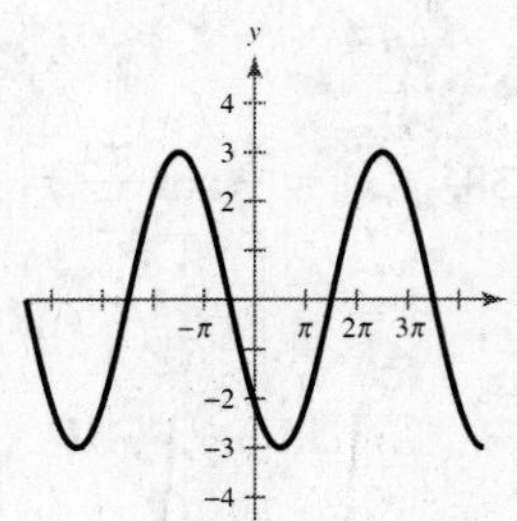

126. $f(x) = 4 - 2\cos(4x + \pi)$

Amplitude: 2

Period: $\dfrac{\pi}{2}$

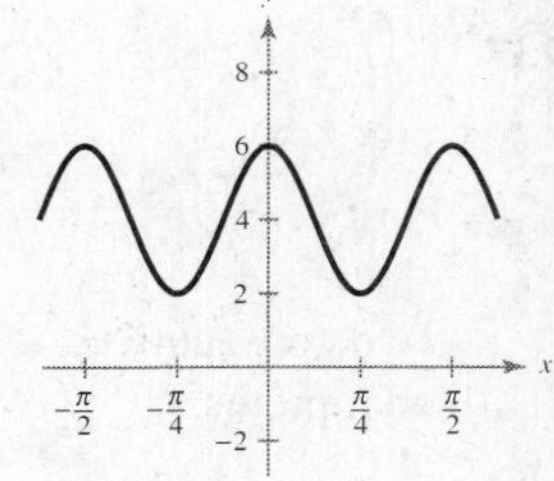

127. $f(x) = -2\cos\left(x - \dfrac{\pi}{4}\right)$

128. $f(x) = a\cos(bx - c)$

Amplitude: 3

Period: $\pi \implies f(x) = 3\cos(2x)$

129. $f(x) = -4\cos\left(2x - \dfrac{\pi}{2}\right)$

130. $f(x) = a\cos(bx - c)$

Amplitude: $\dfrac{1}{2}$

Period: $2 \implies f(x) = \dfrac{1}{2}\cos \pi x$

131. $S = 48.4 - 6.1 \cos \dfrac{\pi t}{6}$

Maximum sales: $t = 6$ (June)

Minimum sales: $t = 12$ (December)

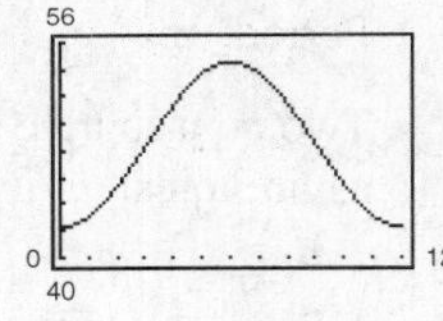

132. $S = 56.25 + 9.50 \sin \dfrac{\pi t}{6}$

Maximum sales: $t = 3$ (March)

Minimum sales: $t = 9$ (September)

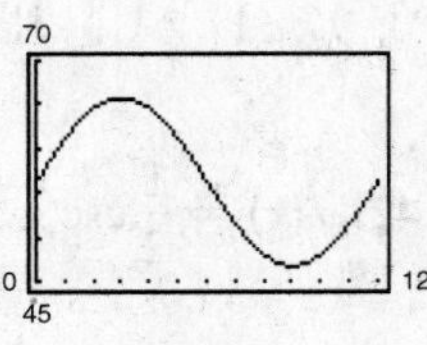

133. $f(x) = -\tan \dfrac{\pi x}{4}$

Period: $\dfrac{\pi}{(\pi/4)} = 4$

Asymptotes: $x = -2, x = 2$

Reflected in x-axis

x	-1	0	1
y	1	0	-1

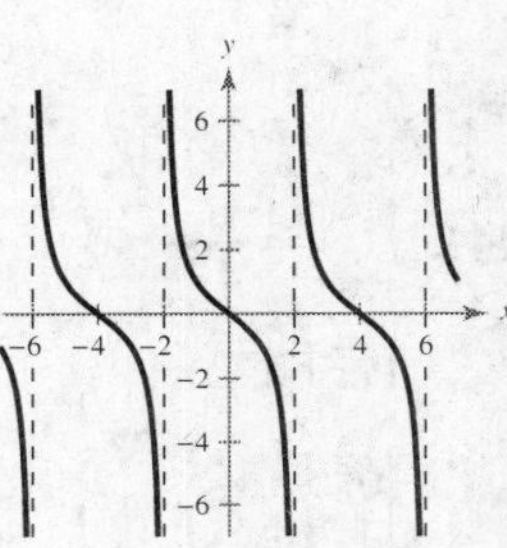

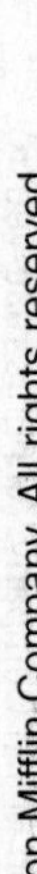

134. $f(x) = 4 \tan \pi x$

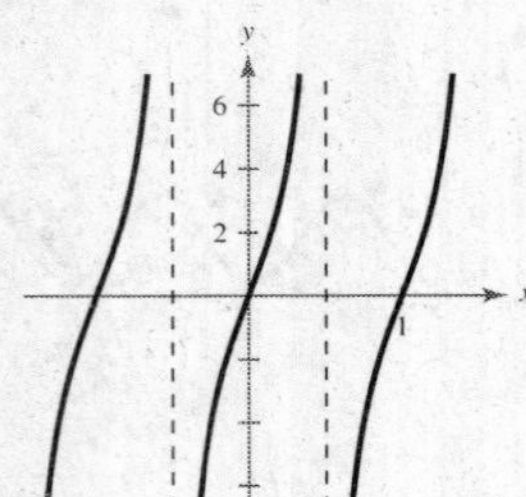

135. $f(x) = \frac{1}{4} \tan\left(x - \frac{\pi}{2}\right)$

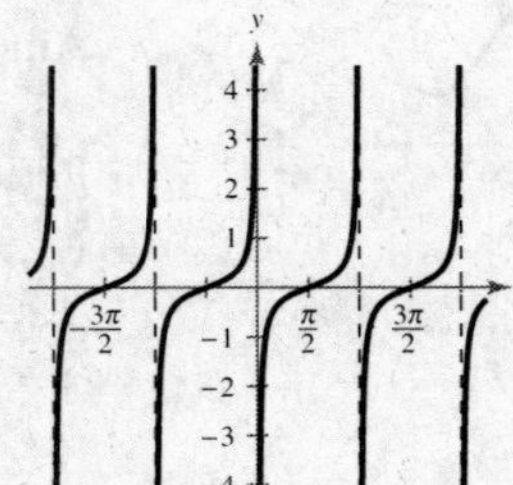

136. $f(x) = 2 + 2 \tan \frac{x}{3}$

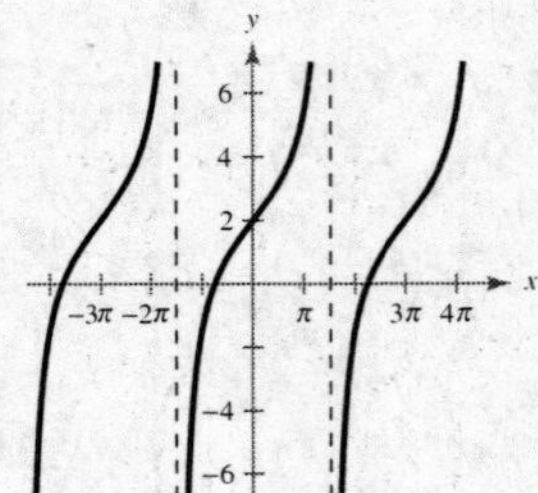

137. $f(x) = 3 \cot \frac{x}{2}$

Period: $\frac{\pi}{1/2} = 2\pi$

Two consecutive asymptotes:

$\frac{x}{2} = 0 \Rightarrow x = 0$

$\frac{x}{2} = \pi \Rightarrow x = 2\pi$

138. $f(x) = \frac{1}{2} \cot \frac{\pi x}{2} = \frac{1}{2 \tan \frac{\pi x}{2}}$

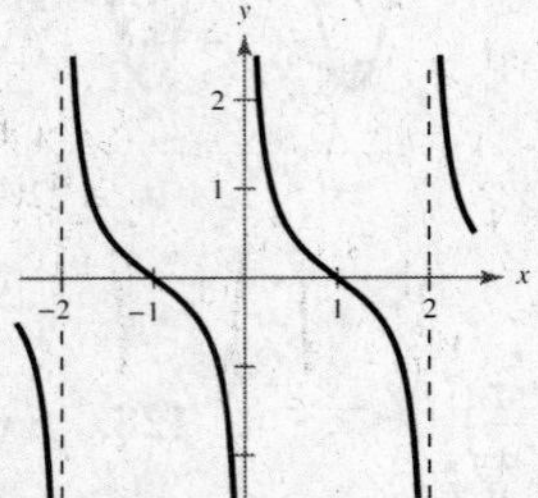

139. $f(x) = \frac{1}{2} \cot\left(x - \frac{\pi}{2}\right)$

Period: π

Two consecutive asymptotes:

$x - \frac{\pi}{2} = 0 \Rightarrow x = \frac{\pi}{2}$

$x - \frac{\pi}{2} = \pi \Rightarrow x = \frac{3\pi}{2}$

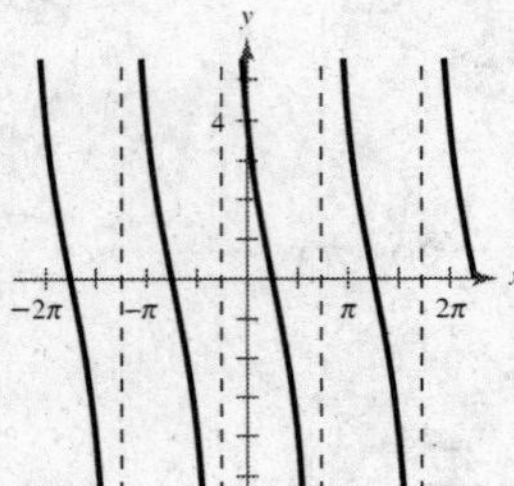

140. $f(x) = 4 \cot\left(x + \frac{\pi}{4}\right) = \frac{4}{\tan\left(x + \frac{\pi}{4}\right)}$

141. $f(x) = \frac{1}{4} \sec x$

Period: 2π

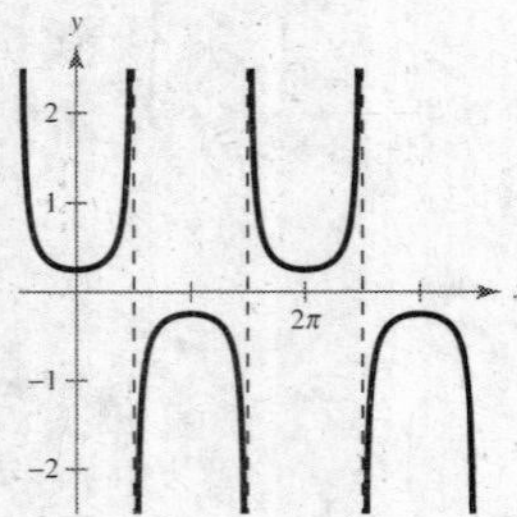

142. $f(x) = \frac{1}{2} \csc x = \frac{1}{2 \sin x}$

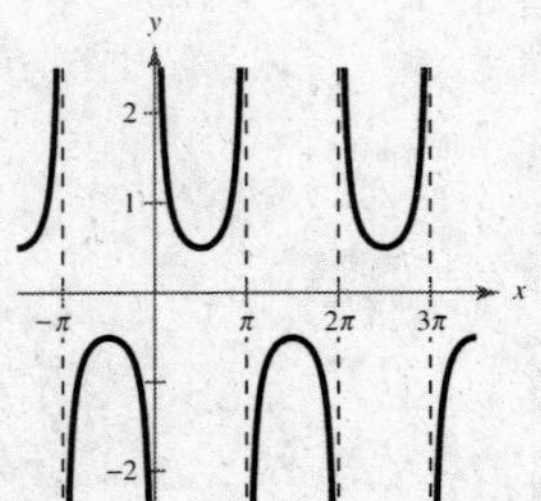

143. $f(x) = \frac{1}{4}\csc 2x$

Period: π

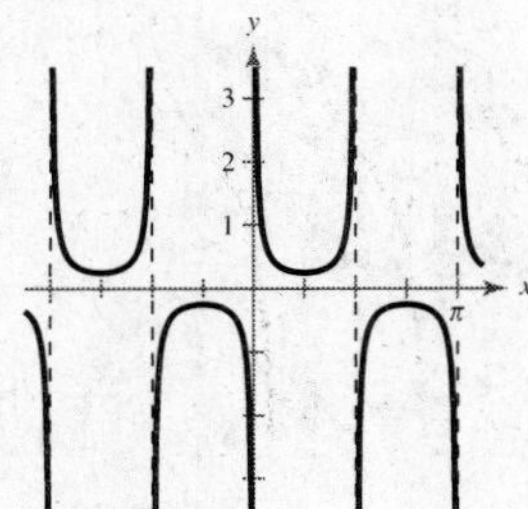

144. $f(x) = \frac{1}{2}\sec 2\pi x = \frac{1}{2\cos 2\pi x}$

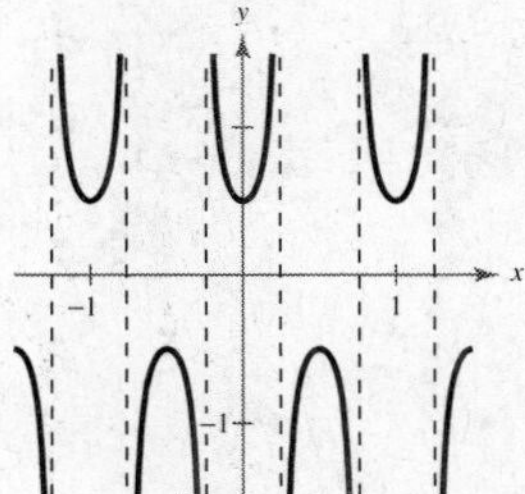

145. $f(x) = \sec\left(x - \frac{\pi}{4}\right)$

Secant function shifted $\frac{\pi}{4}$ to right

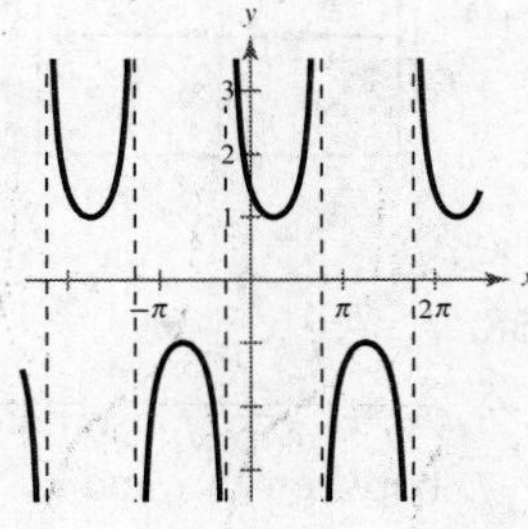

146. $f(x) = \frac{1}{2}\csc(2x + \pi) = \frac{1}{2\sin(2x + \pi)}$

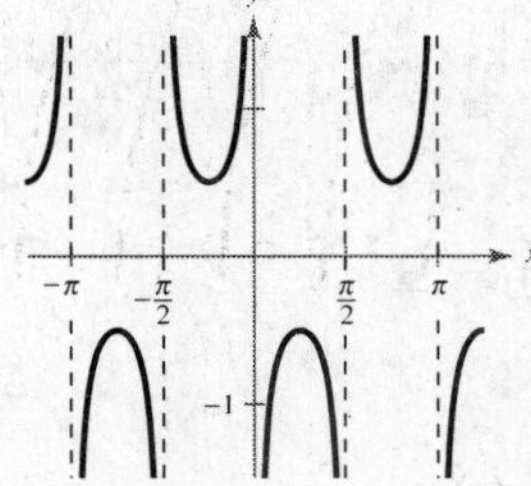

147. $f(x) = \frac{1}{4}\tan\frac{\pi x}{2}$

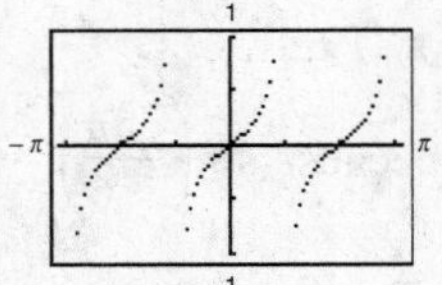

148. $f(x) = \tan\left(x + \frac{\pi}{4}\right)$

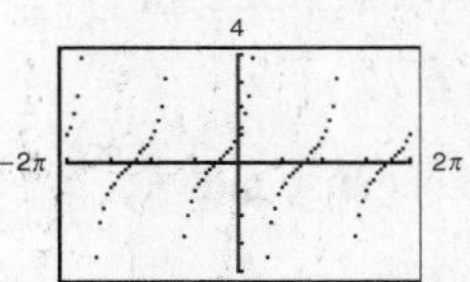

149. $f(x) = 4\cot(2x - \pi) = \frac{4}{\tan(2x - \pi)}$

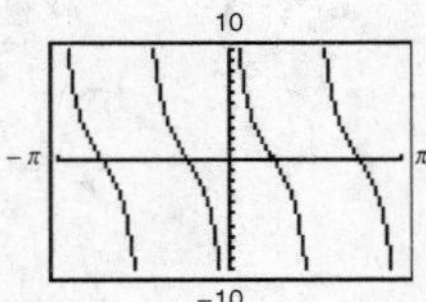

150. $f(x) = -2\cot(4x + \pi) = -\frac{2}{\tan(4x + \pi)}$

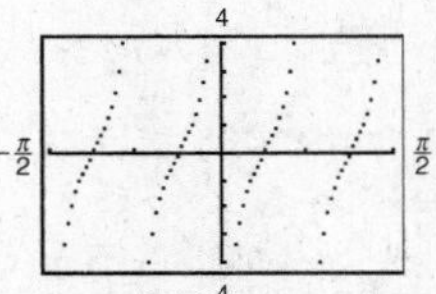

151. $f(x) = 2\sec(x - \pi) = \frac{2}{\cos(x - \pi)}$

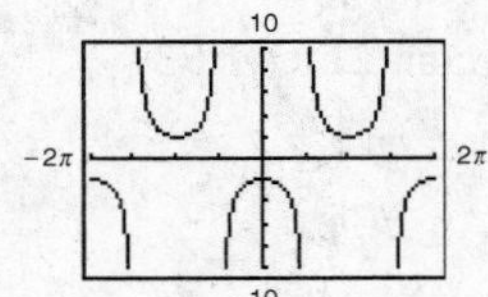

152. $f(x) = -2\csc(x - \pi) = \frac{-2}{\sin(x - \pi)}$

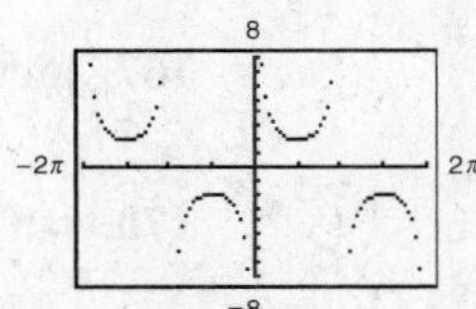

153. $f(x) = \csc\left(3x - \dfrac{\pi}{2}\right) = \dfrac{1}{\sin(3x - (\pi/2))}$

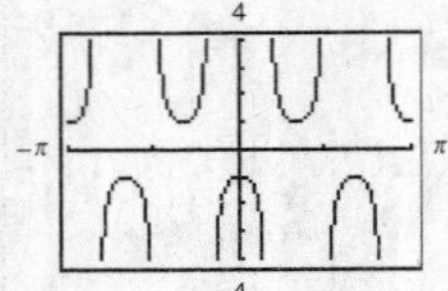

154. $f(x) = 3\csc\left(2x + \dfrac{\pi}{4}\right) = \dfrac{3}{\sin(2x + (\pi/4))}$

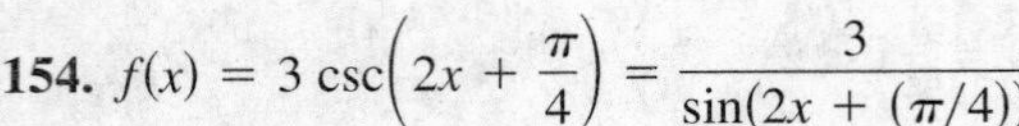

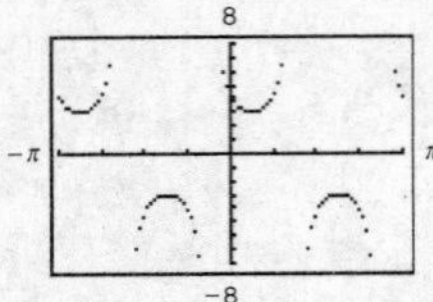

155. $f(x) = e^x \sin 2x$

Damping factor: $y = e^x$

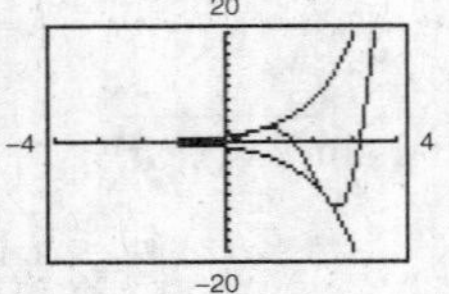

156. $f(x) = e^x \cos x$

Damping factor: e^x

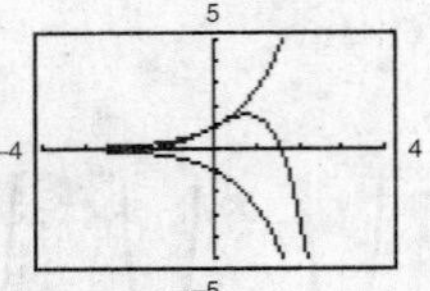

157. $f(x) = 2x \cos x$

Damping factor: $g(x) = 2x$

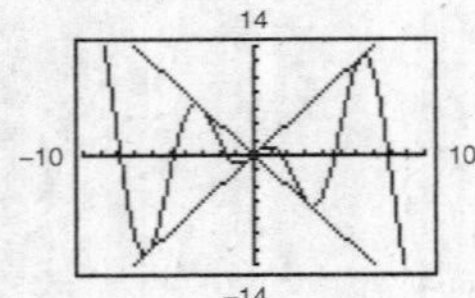

As $x \to \infty$, f oscillates between $2x$ and $-2x$.

158. $f(x) = x \sin \pi x$

As $x \to \infty$, f oscillates between $-x$ and x.

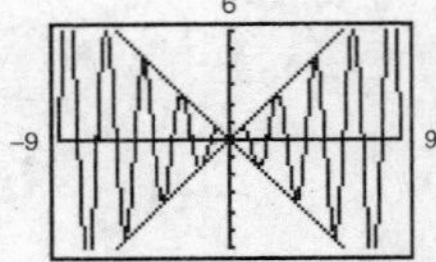

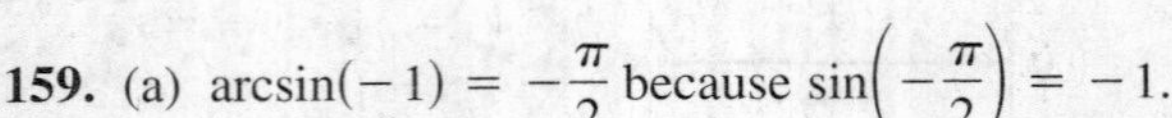

159. (a) $\arcsin(-1) = -\dfrac{\pi}{2}$ because $\sin\left(-\dfrac{\pi}{2}\right) = -1$.

(b) arcsin 4 does not exist because the domain of arcsin is $[-1, 1]$.

160. (a) $\arcsin\left(-\dfrac{1}{2}\right) = -\dfrac{\pi}{6}$ because $\sin\left(-\dfrac{\pi}{6}\right) = -\dfrac{1}{2}$.

(b) $\arcsin\left(-\dfrac{\sqrt{3}}{2}\right) = -\dfrac{\pi}{3}$ because $\sin\left(-\dfrac{\pi}{3}\right) = -\dfrac{\sqrt{3}}{2}$.

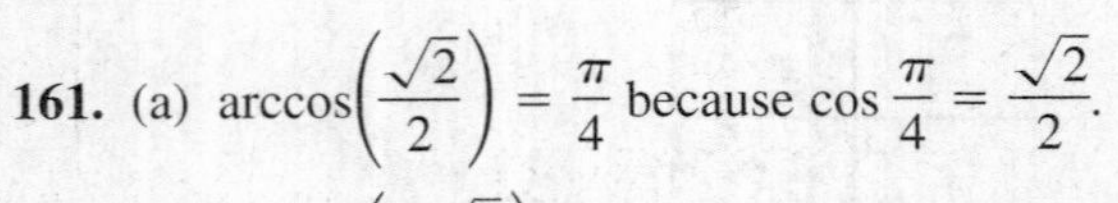

161. (a) $\arccos\left(\dfrac{\sqrt{2}}{2}\right) = \dfrac{\pi}{4}$ because $\cos\dfrac{\pi}{4} = \dfrac{\sqrt{2}}{2}$.

(b) $\arccos\left(-\dfrac{\sqrt{3}}{2}\right) = \dfrac{5\pi}{6}$ because $\cos\dfrac{5\pi}{6} = -\dfrac{\sqrt{3}}{2}$.

162. (a) $\arctan(-\sqrt{3}) = -\dfrac{\pi}{3}$

(b) $\arctan(1) = \dfrac{\pi}{4}$

163. $\arccos(0.42) \approx 1.14$

164. $\arcsin 0.63 \approx 0.68$

165. $\sin^{-1}(-0.94) \approx -1.22$

166. $\cos^{-1}(-0.12) \approx 1.69$

167. $\arctan(-12) \approx -1.49$

168. $\arctan 21 \approx 1.52$

169. $\tan^{-1}(0.81) \approx 0.68$

170. $\tan^{-1} 6.4 \approx 1.42$

171. $\sin\theta = \dfrac{x+3}{16} \Rightarrow \theta = \arcsin\left(\dfrac{x+3}{16}\right)$

172. $\tan\theta = \dfrac{x+1}{20} \Rightarrow \theta = \arctan\left(\dfrac{x+1}{20}\right)$

173. Let $y = \arcsin(x - 1)$. Then,

$$\sin y = (x - 1) = \frac{x - 1}{1} \text{ and}$$

$$\sec y = \frac{1}{\sqrt{-x^2 + 2x}}$$

$$= \frac{\sqrt{-x^2 + 2x}}{-x^2 + 2x}.$$

174. Let $u = \arccos \frac{x}{2}$, $\cos u = \frac{x}{2}$.

$$\tan\left(\arccos \frac{x}{2}\right) = \tan u$$

$$= \frac{\sqrt{4 - x^2}}{x}$$

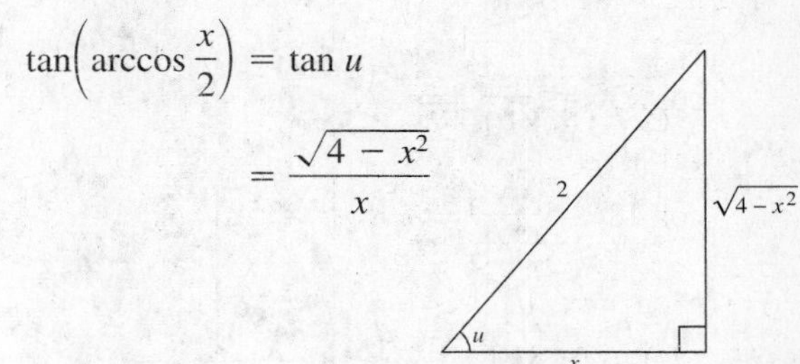

175. Let $y = \arccos \frac{x^2}{4 - x^2}$. Then $\cos y = \frac{x^2}{4 - x^2}$ and

$$\sin y = \frac{\sqrt{(4 - x^2)^2 - (x^2)^2}}{4 - x^2}.$$

$$= \frac{\sqrt{16 - 8x^2}}{4 - x^2}$$

$$= \frac{2\sqrt{4 - 2x^2}}{4 - x^2}.$$

176. Let $u = \arcsin 10x$, $\sin u = 10x$.

$$\csc(\arcsin 10x) = \csc u$$

$$= \frac{\text{hyp}}{\text{opp}} = \frac{1}{10x}$$

177. $\sin(1° \, 10') = \frac{a}{3.5}$

$$a = 3.5 \sin(1° \, 10') = 3.5 \sin\left(\frac{7°}{6}\right) \approx 0.0713 \text{ or } 71 \text{ meters}$$

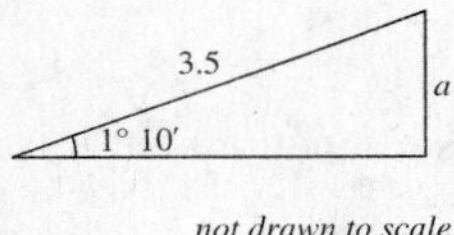

178. $\tan \theta = \frac{12}{100}$

$$\theta = \arctan\left(\frac{12}{100}\right) \approx 0.1194 \text{ or } 6.84°$$

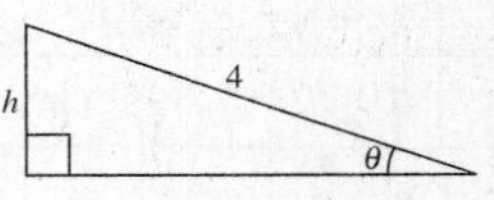

$$\sin(\theta) = \frac{h}{4}$$

$$h = 4 \sin(0.1194) \approx 0.48 \text{ miles or } 2534 \text{ feet (answer depends on angle } \theta \text{ accuracy)}$$

179. $\tan 14° = \frac{y}{37{,}000} \Longrightarrow y = 37{,}000 \tan 14° \approx 9225.1$ feet

$\tan 58° = \frac{x + y}{37{,}000} \Longrightarrow x + y = 37{,}000 \tan 58° \approx 59{,}212.4$ feet

$$x = 59{,}212.4 - 9225.1 \approx 49{,}987.2 \text{ feet}$$

The towns are approximately 50,000 feet apart or 9.47 miles.

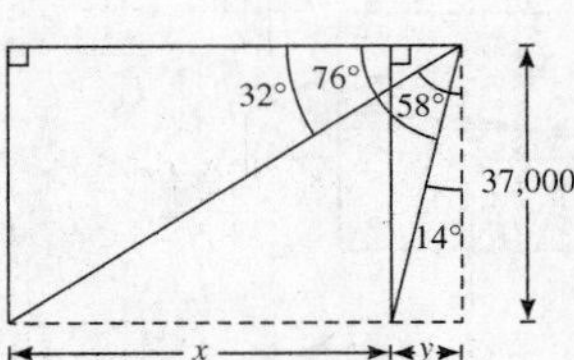

180. $\sin 48° = \frac{d_1}{650} \Rightarrow d_1 \approx 483$, $\cos 25° = \frac{d_2}{810} \Rightarrow d_2 \approx 734$ $\Big\}$ $d_1 + d_2 = 1217$

$\cos 48° = \frac{d_3}{650} \Rightarrow d_3 \approx 435$, $\sin 25° = \frac{d_4}{810} \Rightarrow d_4 \approx 342$ $\Big\}$ $d_3 - d_4 \approx 93$

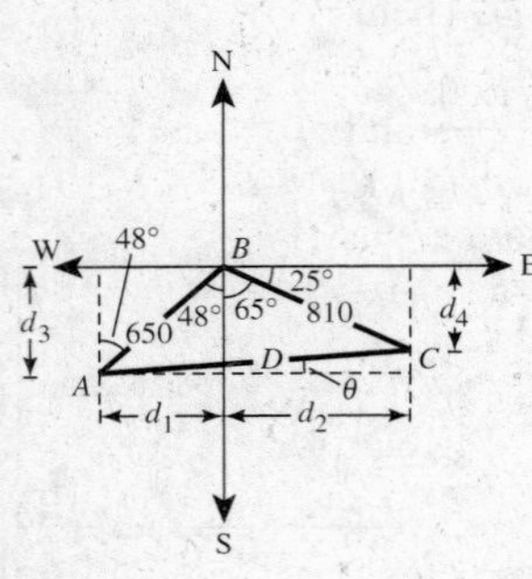

$$\tan \theta \approx \frac{93}{1217} \Rightarrow \theta \approx 4.4°$$

$$\sec 4.4° \approx \frac{D}{1217} \Rightarrow D \approx 1217 \sec 4.4° \approx 1221$$

The distance is 1221 miles and the bearing is N 85.6 E.

181. Use cosine model with amplitude 3 feet.

Period: 15 seconds

$$y = 3 \cos\left(\frac{2\pi}{15}t\right)$$

182. Use a cosine model with amplitude $\frac{1.5}{2} = 0.75$.

Period: 3 seconds

$$y = 0.75 \cos\left(\frac{2\pi}{3}t\right)$$

183. False. $y = \sin \theta$ is a function, but it is not one-to-one.

184. False. The sine and cosine functions are useful for modeling simple harmonic motion.

185. $\tan \theta = \frac{0.672s^2}{3000}$

(a)

s	10	20	30	40	50	60
θ	1.28°	5.12°	11.40°	19.72°	29.25°	38.88°

(b) θ increases at an increasing rate. The function is not linear.

186. (a)

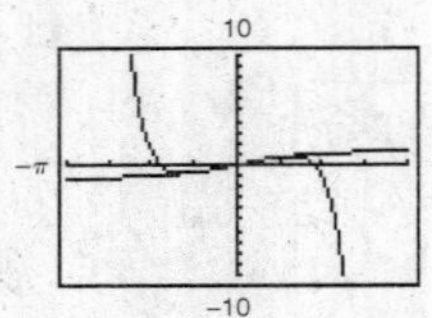

(b) Next term: $\frac{x^9}{9}$

$$\arctan x \approx x - \frac{x^3}{3} + \frac{x^5}{5} - \frac{x^7}{7} + \frac{x^9}{9}$$

The accuracy of the approximation increases as more terms are added.

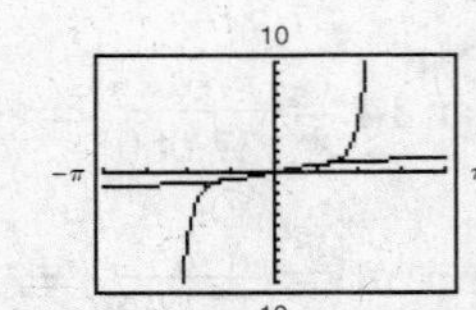

Chapter 4 Practice Test

1. Express 350° in radian measure.

2. Express $(5\pi)/9$ in degree measure.

3. Convert 135° 14′ 12″ to decimal form.

4. Convert −22.569° to D° M′ S″ form.

5. If $\cos\theta = \frac{2}{3}$, use the trigonometric identities to find $\tan\theta$.

6. Find θ given $\sin\theta = 0.9063$.

7. Solve for x in the figure below.

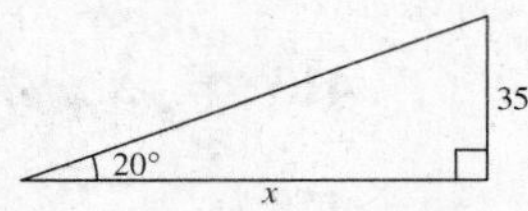

8. Find the magnitude of the reference angle for $\theta = (6\pi)/5$.

9. Evaluate csc 3.92.

10. Find $\sec\theta$ given that θ lies in Quadrant III and $\tan\theta = 6$.

11. Graph $y = 3\sin\dfrac{x}{2}$.

12. Graph $y = -2\cos(x - \pi)$.

13. Graph $y = \tan 2x$.

14. Graph $y = -\csc\left(x + \dfrac{\pi}{4}\right)$.

15. Graph $y = 2x + \sin x$, using a graphing calculator.

16. Graph $y = 3x\cos x$, using a graphing calculator.

17. Evaluate arcsin 1.

18. Evaluate $\arctan(-3)$.

19. Evaluate $\sin\left(\arccos\dfrac{4}{\sqrt{35}}\right)$.

20. Write an algebraic expression for $\cos\left(\arcsin\dfrac{x}{4}\right)$.

For Exercises 21–23, solve the right triangle.

21. $A = 40°$, $c = 12$

22. $B = 6.84°$, $a = 21.3$

23. $a = 5$, $b = 9$

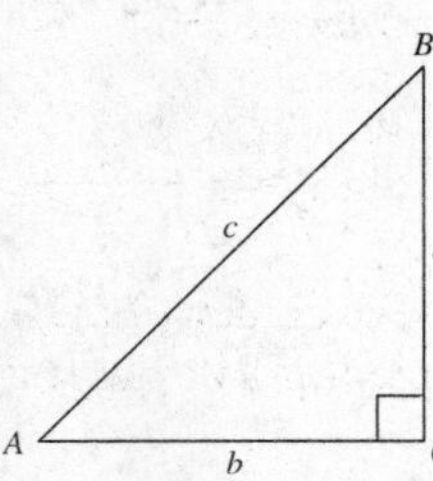

24. A 20-foot ladder leans against the side of a barn. Find the height of the top of the ladder if the angle of elevation of the ladder is 67°.

25. An observer in a lighthouse 250 feet above sea level spots a ship off the shore. If the angle of depression to the ship is 5°, how far out is the ship?

CHAPTER 5
Analytic Trigonometry

Section 5.1 Using Fundamental Identities **379**

Section 5.2 Verifying Trigonometric Identities **391**

Section 5.3 Solving Trigonometric Equations **401**

Section 5.4 Sum and Difference Formulas **413**

Section 5.5 Multiple-Angle and Product-to-Sum Formulas **428**

Review Exercises **450**

Practice Test **464**

CHAPTER 5
Analytic Trigonometry

Section 5.1 Using Fundamental Identities

- You should know the fundamental trigonometric identities.

  (a) Reciprocal Identities

  $$\sin u = \frac{1}{\csc u} \qquad \csc u = \frac{1}{\sin u}$$

  $$\cos u = \frac{1}{\sec u} \qquad \sec u = \frac{1}{\cos u}$$

  $$\tan u = \frac{1}{\cot u} = \frac{\sin u}{\cos u} \qquad \cot u = \frac{1}{\tan u} = \frac{\cos u}{\sin u}$$

  (b) Pythagorean Identities

  $$\sin^2 u + \cos^2 u = 1$$
  $$1 + \tan^2 u = \sec^2 u$$
  $$1 + \cot^2 u = \csc^2 u$$

  (c) Cofunction Identities

  $$\sin\left(\frac{\pi}{2} - u\right) = \cos u \qquad \cos\left(\frac{\pi}{2} - u\right) = \sin u$$

  $$\tan\left(\frac{\pi}{2} - u\right) = \cot u \qquad \cot\left(\frac{\pi}{2} - u\right) = \tan u$$

  $$\sec\left(\frac{\pi}{2} - u\right) = \csc u \qquad \csc\left(\frac{\pi}{2} - u\right) = \sec u$$

  (d) Negative Angle Identities

  $$\sin(-x) = -\sin x \qquad \csc(-x) = -\csc x$$
  $$\cos(-x) = \cos x \qquad \sec(-x) = \sec x$$
  $$\tan(-x) = -\tan x \qquad \cot(-x) = -\cot x$$

- You should be able to use these fundamental identities to find function values.
- You should be able to convert trigonometric expressions to equivalent forms by using the fundamental identities.
- You should be able to check your answers with a graphing utility.

Vocabulary Check

1. $\sec u$ **2.** $\tan u$ **3.** $\cot u$ **4.** $\csc u$

5. $\tan^2 u$ **6.** $\csc^2 u$ **7.** $\sin u$ **8.** $\sec u$

9. $-\tan u$ **10.** $\cos u$

1. $\sin x = \frac{1}{2}, \cos x = \frac{\sqrt{3}}{2}$, x is in Quadrant I.

$\tan x = \frac{1/2}{\sqrt{3}/2} = \frac{1}{\sqrt{3}} = \frac{\sqrt{3}}{3}$

$\cot x = \sqrt{3}$

$\csc x = 2$

$\sec x = \frac{2}{\sqrt{3}} = \frac{2\sqrt{3}}{3}$

2. $\csc \theta = 2, \tan \theta = \frac{\sqrt{3}}{3}$, θ is in Quadrant I.

$\sin \theta = \frac{1}{2}$

$\cot \theta = \frac{3}{\sqrt{3}} = \sqrt{3}$

$\cos \theta = \cot \theta \sin \theta = \frac{\sqrt{3}}{2}$

$\sec \theta = \frac{2}{\sqrt{3}} = \frac{2\sqrt{3}}{3}$

3. $\sec \theta = \sqrt{2}, \sin \theta = -\frac{\sqrt{2}}{2} \Rightarrow \theta$ is in Quadrant IV.

$\cos \theta = \frac{1}{\sec \theta} = \frac{1}{\sqrt{2}} = \frac{\sqrt{2}}{2}$

$\tan \theta = \frac{\sin \theta}{\cos \theta} = \frac{-\sqrt{2}/2}{\sqrt{2}/2} = -1$

$\cot \theta = \frac{1}{\tan \theta} = -1$

$\csc \theta = -\sqrt{2}$

4. $\tan x = \frac{\sqrt{3}}{3}, \cos x = -\frac{\sqrt{3}}{2}$, x is in Quadrant III.

$\sin x = -\sqrt{1 - \left(-\frac{\sqrt{3}}{2}\right)^2} = -\sqrt{\frac{1}{4}} = -\frac{1}{2}$

$\csc x = \frac{1}{\sin x} = -2$

$\sec x = \frac{1}{\cos x} = -\frac{2}{\sqrt{3}} = -\frac{2\sqrt{3}}{3}$

$\cot x = \frac{1}{\tan x} = \frac{3}{\sqrt{3}} = \sqrt{3}$

5. $\tan x = \frac{7}{24}, \sec x = \frac{-25}{24} \Rightarrow x$ is in Quadrant III.

$\cot x = \frac{24}{7}$

$\cos x = -\frac{24}{25}$

$\sin x = -\sqrt{1 - \cos^2 x} = -\frac{7}{25}$

$\csc x = \frac{1}{\sin x} = -\frac{25}{7}$

6. $\cot \phi = -5, \sin \phi = \frac{\sqrt{26}}{26}$, ϕ is in Quadrant II

$\cos \phi = \cot \phi \cdot \sin \phi = \frac{-5\sqrt{26}}{26}$

$\tan \phi = \frac{1}{\cot \phi} = -\frac{1}{5}$

$\csc \phi = \frac{1}{\sin \phi} = \frac{26}{\sqrt{26}} = \sqrt{26}$

$\sec \phi = \frac{1}{\cos \phi} = \frac{-26}{5\sqrt{26}} = \frac{-\sqrt{26}}{5}$

7. $\sec \phi = -\frac{17}{15}, \sin \phi = \frac{8}{17}$, ϕ is in Quadrant II.

$\cos \phi = -\frac{15}{17}$

$\csc \phi = \frac{17}{8}$

$\tan \phi = \frac{8/17}{-15/17} = -\frac{8}{15}$

$\cot \phi = -\frac{15}{8}$

8. $\cos\left(\frac{\pi}{2} - x\right) = \frac{3}{5}, \cos x = \frac{4}{5},$ x is in Quadrant I.

$$\sin x = \sqrt{1 - \left(\frac{4}{5}\right)^2} = \frac{3}{5}$$

$$\tan x = \frac{\sin x}{\cos x} = \frac{3}{5} \cdot \frac{5}{4} = \frac{3}{4}$$

$$\csc x = \frac{1}{\sin x} = \frac{5}{3}$$

$$\sec x = \frac{1}{\cos x} = \frac{5}{4}$$

$$\cot x = \frac{1}{\tan x} = \frac{4}{3}$$

9. $\sin(-x) = -\sin x = -\frac{2}{3} \Rightarrow \sin x = \frac{2}{3}$

$\sin x = \frac{2}{3}, \tan x = -\frac{2\sqrt{5}}{5} \Rightarrow$ x is in Quadrant II.

$$\cos x = -\sqrt{1 - \sin^2 x} = -\sqrt{1 - \frac{4}{9}} = -\frac{\sqrt{5}}{3}$$

$$\cot x = \frac{1}{\tan x} = -\frac{\sqrt{5}}{2}$$

$$\sec x = \frac{1}{\cos x} = -\frac{3\sqrt{5}}{5}$$

$$\csc x = \frac{1}{\sin x} = \frac{3}{2}$$

10. $\csc x = 5, \cos x > 0,$ x is in Quadrant I.

$$\sin x = \frac{1}{\csc x} = \frac{1}{5}$$

$$\cos x = \frac{2\sqrt{6}}{5}$$

$$\tan x = \frac{\sin x}{\cos x} = \frac{1}{5} \cdot \frac{5}{2\sqrt{6}} = \frac{\sqrt{6}}{12}$$

$$\sec x = \frac{1}{\cos x} = \frac{5}{2\sqrt{6}} = \frac{5\sqrt{6}}{12}$$

$$\cot x = \frac{1}{\tan x} = 2\sqrt{6}$$

11. $\tan\theta = 2, \sin\theta < 0 \Rightarrow \theta$ is in Quadrant III.

$$\sec\theta = -\sqrt{\tan^2\theta + 1} = -\sqrt{5}$$

$$\cos\theta = \frac{1}{-\sqrt{5}} = -\frac{\sqrt{5}}{5}$$

$$\cot\theta = \frac{1}{2}$$

$$\sin\theta = -\sqrt{1 - \cos^2\theta}$$

$$= -\sqrt{1 - \frac{1}{5}} = -\sqrt{\frac{4}{5}} = \frac{-2}{\sqrt{5}} = \frac{-2\sqrt{5}}{5}$$

$$\csc\theta = -\frac{\sqrt{5}}{2}$$

12. $\sec\theta = -3, \tan\theta < 0, \theta$ is in Quadrant II.

$$\cos\theta = -\frac{1}{3}$$

$$\tan^2\theta = \sec^2\theta - 1 = 9 - 1 = 8 \Rightarrow \tan\theta = -\sqrt{8} = -2\sqrt{2}$$

$$\cot\theta = \frac{1}{-2\sqrt{2}} = \frac{-\sqrt{2}}{4}$$

$$\sin\theta = \tan\theta\cos\theta = \left(-2\sqrt{2}\right)\left(-\frac{1}{3}\right) = \frac{2\sqrt{2}}{3}$$

$$\csc\theta = \frac{3}{2\sqrt{2}} = \frac{3\sqrt{2}}{4}$$

13. $\csc\theta$ is undefined and $\cos\theta < 0 \Rightarrow \theta = \pi.$

$\sin\theta = 0$

$\cos\theta = -1$

$\tan\theta = 0$

$\cot\theta$ is undefined.

$\sec\theta = -1$

14. $\tan\theta$ is undefined, $\sin\theta > 0$.

$\theta = \dfrac{\pi}{2}$

$\tan\theta = \dfrac{\sin\theta}{\cos\theta}$ is undefined $\Rightarrow \cos\theta = 0.$

$\sin\theta = \sqrt{1 - 0^2} = 1$

$\csc\theta = \dfrac{1}{\sin\theta} = 1$

$\sec\theta = \dfrac{1}{\cos\theta}$ is undefined.

$\cot\theta = \dfrac{\cos\theta}{\sin\theta} = \dfrac{0}{1} = 0$

15. $\sec x \cos x = \dfrac{1}{\cos x} \cdot \cos x = 1$

Matches (d).

16. $\tan x \csc x = \dfrac{\sin x}{\cos x}\dfrac{1}{\sin x} = \dfrac{1}{\cos x} = \sec x$

Matches (a).

17. $\cot^2 x - \csc^2 x = \cot^2 x - (1 + \cot^2 x) = -1$

Matches (b).

18. $(1 - \cos^2 x)\csc x = \sin^2 x\left(\dfrac{1}{\sin x}\right) = \sin x$

Matches (f).

19. $\dfrac{\sin(-x)}{\cos(-x)} = \dfrac{-\sin x}{\cos x} = -\tan x$

Matches (e).

20. $\dfrac{\sin[(\pi/2) - x]}{\cos[(\pi/2) - x]} = \dfrac{\cos x}{\sin x} = \cot x$

Matches (c).

21. $\sin x \sec x = \sin x\left(\dfrac{1}{\cos x}\right) = \tan x$

Matches (b).

22. $\cos^2 x(\sec^2 x - 1) = \cos^2 x \tan^2 x = \sin^2 x$

Matches (c).

23. $\sec^4 x - \tan^4 x = (\sec^2 x + \tan^2 x)(\sec^2 x - \tan^2 x)$

$= (\sec^2 x + \tan^2 x)(1)$

$= \sec^2 x + \tan^2 x$

Matches (f).

24. $\cot x \sec x = \dfrac{\cos x}{\sin x} \cdot \dfrac{1}{\cos x} = \dfrac{1}{\sin x}$

$= \csc x$

Matches (a).

25. $\dfrac{\sec^2 x - 1}{\sin^2 x} = \dfrac{\tan^2 x}{\sin^2 x} = \dfrac{\sin^2 x}{\cos^2 x} \cdot \dfrac{1}{\sin^2 x} = \sec^2 x$

Matches (e).

26. $\dfrac{\cos^2[(\pi/2) - x]}{\cos x} = \dfrac{\sin^2 x}{\cos x} = \dfrac{\sin x}{\cos x}\sin x$

$= \tan x \sin x$

Matches (d).

27. $\cot x \sin x = \dfrac{\cos x}{\sin x}\sin x = \cos x$

28. $\cos\beta\tan\beta = \cos\beta\left(\dfrac{\sin\beta}{\cos\beta}\right) = \sin\beta$

29. $\sin\phi(\csc\phi - \sin\phi) = \sin\phi\csc\phi - \sin^2\phi$

$= \sin\phi \cdot \dfrac{1}{\sin\phi} - \sin^2\phi$

$= 1 - \sin^2\phi$

$= \cos^2\phi$

30. $\sec^2 x(1 - \sin^2 x) = \sec^2 x - \sec^2 x \sin^2 x$

$= \sec^2 x - \dfrac{1}{\cos^2 x} \cdot \sin^2 x$

$= \sec^2 x - \dfrac{\sin^2 x}{\cos^2 x}$

$= \sec^2 x - \tan^2 x = 1$

31. $\dfrac{\csc x}{\cot x} = \dfrac{1}{\sin x} \cdot \dfrac{\sin x}{\cos x} = \dfrac{1}{\cos x} = \sec x$

32. $\dfrac{\sec \theta}{\csc \theta} = \dfrac{1}{\cos \theta} \sin \theta = \tan \theta$

33. $\sec \alpha \dfrac{\sin \alpha}{\tan \alpha} = \dfrac{1}{\cos \alpha}(\sin \alpha) \cot \alpha$

$= \dfrac{1}{\cos \alpha}(\sin \alpha)\left(\dfrac{\cos \alpha}{\sin \alpha}\right) = 1$

34. $\dfrac{\tan^2 \theta}{\sec^2 \theta} = \dfrac{\sin^2 \theta}{\cos^2 \theta} \cdot \dfrac{1}{\sec^2 \theta}$

$= \dfrac{\sin^2 \theta}{\cos^2 \theta} \cdot \dfrac{1}{\dfrac{1}{\cos^2 \theta}} = \dfrac{\sin^2 \theta \cos^2 \theta}{\cos^2 \theta} = \sin^2 \theta$

35. $\sin\left(\dfrac{\pi}{2} - x\right) \csc x = \cos x \cdot \dfrac{1}{\sin x} = \cot x$

36. $\cot\left(\dfrac{\pi}{2} - x\right) \cos x = \tan x \cos x$

$= \dfrac{\sin x}{\cos x} \cdot \cos x = \sin x$

37. $\dfrac{\cos^2 y}{1 - \sin y} = \dfrac{1 - \sin^2 y}{1 - \sin y}$

$= \dfrac{(1 + \sin y)(1 - \sin y)}{1 - \sin y}$

$= 1 + \sin y$

38. $\dfrac{1}{\cot^2 x + 1} = \dfrac{1}{\csc^2 x} = \sin^2 x$

39. $\sin \theta + \cos \theta \cot \theta = \sin \theta + \cos \theta \dfrac{\cos \theta}{\sin \theta}$

$= \dfrac{\sin^2 \theta + \cos^2 \theta}{\sin \theta}$

$= \dfrac{1}{\sin \theta} = \csc \theta$

40. $(\sec \theta - \tan \theta)(\csc \theta + 1) = \dfrac{1}{\cos \theta}(1 - \sin \theta)\left(\dfrac{1}{\sin \theta} + 1\right)$

$= \dfrac{1}{\cos \theta}(1 - \sin \theta)(1 + \sin \theta) \dfrac{1}{\sin \theta}$

$= \dfrac{1}{\cos \theta \cdot \sin \theta}(1 - \sin^2 \theta)$

$= \dfrac{1}{\cos \theta \sin \theta} \cos^2 \theta = \cot \theta$

41. $\dfrac{\cos \theta}{1 - \sin \theta} = \dfrac{\cos \theta}{1 - \sin \theta} \cdot \dfrac{1 + \sin \theta}{1 + \sin \theta}$

$= \dfrac{\cos \theta(1 + \sin \theta)}{1 - \sin^2 \theta}$

$= \dfrac{\cos \theta(1 + \sin \theta)}{\cos^2 \theta}$

$= \dfrac{1 + \sin \theta}{\cos \theta} = \sec \theta + \tan \theta$

42. $\dfrac{1 + \csc \theta}{\cot \theta + \cos \theta} = \dfrac{1 + \csc \theta}{\cos \theta(\csc \theta + 1)}$

$= \dfrac{1}{\cos \theta} = \sec \theta$

43. $\dfrac{1+\cos\theta}{\sin\theta}+\dfrac{\sin\theta}{1+\cos\theta}=\dfrac{1+2\cos\theta+\cos^2\theta+\sin^2\theta}{\sin\theta(1+\cos\theta)}$

$=\dfrac{2+2\cos\theta}{\sin\theta(1+\cos\theta)}$

$=\dfrac{2(1+\cos\theta)}{\sin\theta(1+\cos\theta)}$

$=\dfrac{2}{\sin\theta}=2\csc\theta$

44. $\dfrac{\sin\theta+\cos\theta}{\sin\theta}-\dfrac{\cos\theta-\sin\theta}{\cos\theta}=1+\cot\theta-1+\tan\theta$

$=\cot\theta+\tan\theta$

$=\dfrac{\cos\theta}{\sin\theta}+\dfrac{\sin\theta}{\cos\theta}$

$=\dfrac{\cos^2\theta+\sin^2\theta}{\sin\theta\cos\theta}$

$=\dfrac{1}{\sin\theta\cos\theta}=\sec\theta\csc\theta$

45. $\csc\theta\tan\theta=\dfrac{1}{\sin\theta}\cdot\dfrac{\sin\theta}{\cos\theta}=\dfrac{1}{\cos\theta}=\sec\theta$

46. $\sin\theta\csc\theta-\sin^2\theta=1-\sin^2\theta=\cos^2\theta$

47. $1-\dfrac{\sin^2\theta}{1-\cos\theta}=\dfrac{1-\cos\theta-\sin^2\theta}{1-\cos\theta}$

$=\dfrac{\cos^2\theta-\cos\theta}{1-\cos\theta}$

$=\dfrac{\cos\theta(\cos\theta-1)}{1-\cos\theta}$

$=-\cos\theta$

48. $\dfrac{\tan\theta}{1+\sec\theta}+\dfrac{1+\sec\theta}{\tan\theta}=\dfrac{\tan^2\theta+1+2\sec\theta+\sec^2\theta}{(1+\sec\theta)\tan\theta}$

$=\dfrac{2\sec^2\theta+2\sec\theta}{(1+\sec\theta)\tan\theta}$

$=\dfrac{2\sec\theta(\sec\theta+1)}{(1+\sec\theta)\tan\theta}$

$=\dfrac{2\sec\theta}{\tan\theta}=2\csc\theta$

49. $\dfrac{\cot(-\theta)}{\csc\theta}=\dfrac{\cos(-\theta)}{\sin(-\theta)}\sin\theta$

$=\dfrac{\cos\theta}{-\sin\theta}\sin\theta=-\cos\theta$

50. $\dfrac{\csc\left(\dfrac{\pi}{2}-\theta\right)}{\tan(-\theta)}=\dfrac{\sec\theta}{-\tan\theta}=-\csc\theta$

51. $\cot^2 x - \cot^2 x \cos^2 x = \cot^2 x(1 - \cos^2 x)$

$= \dfrac{\cos^2 x}{\sin^2 x}\sin^2 x = \cos^2 x$

52. $\sec^2 x \tan^2 x + \sec^2 x = \sec^2 x(\tan^2 x + 1)$

$= \sec^2 x(\sec^2 x) = \sec^4 x$

53. $\dfrac{\cos^2 x - 4}{\cos x - 2} = \dfrac{(\cos x + 2)(\cos x - 2)}{\cos x - 2} = \cos x + 2$

54. $\dfrac{\csc^2 x - 1}{\csc x - 1} = \dfrac{(\csc x - 1)(\csc x + 1)}{\csc x - 1} = \csc x + 1$

55. $\tan^4 x + 2\tan^2 x + 1 = (\tan^2 x + 1)^2$

$= (\sec^2 x)^2 = \sec^4 x$

56. $1 - 2\sin^2 x + \sin^4 x = (1 - \sin^2 x)^2$

$= (\cos^2 x)^2 = \cos^4 x$

57. $\sin^4 x - \cos^4 x = (\sin^2 x + \cos^2 x)(\sin^2 x - \cos^2 x)$

$= (1)(\sin^2 x - \cos^2 x) = \sin^2 x - \cos^2 x$

58. $\sec^4 x - \tan^4 x = (\sec^2 x + \tan^2 x)(\sec^2 x - \tan^2 x) = \sec^2 x + \tan^2 x$

59. $\csc^3 x - \csc^2 x - \csc x + 1 = \csc^2 x(\csc x - 1) - (\csc x - 1)$

$= (\csc^2 x - 1)(\csc x - 1)$

$= \cot^2 x(\csc x - 1)$

60. $\sec^3 x - \sec^2 x - \sec x + 1 = \sec^2 x(\sec x - 1) - (\sec x - 1)$

$= (\sec^2 x - 1)(\sec x - 1)$

$= \tan^2 x(\sec x - 1)$

61. $(\sin x + \cos x)^2 = \sin^2 x + 2\sin x\cos x + \cos^2 x$

$= (\sin^2 x + \cos^2 x) + 2\sin x\cos x$

$= 1 + 2\sin x\cos x$

62. $(\tan x + \sec x)(\tan x - \sec x) = \tan^2 x - \sec^2 x$

$= -1$

63. $(\csc x + 1)(\csc x - 1) = \csc^2 x - 1 = \cot^2 x$

64. $(5 - 5\sin x)(5 + 5\sin x) = 25 - 25\sin^2 x$

$= 25(1 - \sin^2 x)$

$= 25\cos^2 x$

65. $\dfrac{1}{1 + \cos x} + \dfrac{1}{1 - \cos x} = \dfrac{1 - \cos x + 1 + \cos x}{(1 + \cos x)(1 - \cos x)}$

$= \dfrac{2}{1 - \cos^2 x}$

$= \dfrac{2}{\sin^2 x}$

$= 2\csc^2 x$

66. $\dfrac{1}{\sec x + 1} - \dfrac{1}{\sec x - 1} = \dfrac{\sec x - 1 - (\sec x + 1)}{(\sec x + 1)(\sec x - 1)}$

$= \dfrac{\sec x - 1 - \sec x - 1}{\sec^2 x - 1}$

$= \dfrac{-2}{\tan^2 x}$

$= -2\left(\dfrac{1}{\tan^2 x}\right)$

$= -2\cot^2 x$

67. $\tan x - \dfrac{\sec^2 x}{\tan x} = \dfrac{\tan^2 x - \sec^2 x}{\tan x} = \dfrac{-1}{\tan x} = -\cot x$

68. $\dfrac{\cos x}{1 + \sin x} + \dfrac{1 + \sin x}{\cos x} = \dfrac{\cos^2 x + 1 + 2\sin x + \sin^2 x}{\cos x(1 + \sin x)}$

$= \dfrac{2 + 2\sin x}{\cos x(1 + \sin x)}$

$= \dfrac{2}{\cos x} = 2\sec x$

69. $\dfrac{\sin^2 y}{1 - \cos y} = \dfrac{1 - \cos^2 y}{1 - \cos y}$

$= \dfrac{(1 + \cos y)(1 - \cos y)}{1 - \cos y}$

$= 1 + \cos y$

70. $\dfrac{5}{\tan x + \sec x} \cdot \dfrac{\tan x - \sec x}{\tan x - \sec x} = \dfrac{5(\tan x - \sec x)}{\tan^2 x - \sec^2 x}$

$= \dfrac{5(\tan x - \sec x)}{-1}$

$= 5(\sec x - \tan x)$

71. $\dfrac{3}{\sec x - \tan x} \cdot \dfrac{\sec x + \tan x}{\sec x + \tan x} = \dfrac{3(\sec x + \tan x)}{\sec^2 x - \tan^2 x}$

$= \dfrac{3(\sec x + \tan x)}{1}$

$= 3(\sec x + \tan x)$

72. $\dfrac{\tan^2 x}{\csc x + 1} \cdot \dfrac{\csc x - 1}{\csc x - 1} = \dfrac{\tan^2 x(\csc x - 1)}{\csc^2 x - 1}$

$= \dfrac{\tan^2 x(\csc x - 1)}{\cot^2 x}$

$= \tan^2 x(\csc x - 1)\tan^2 x$

$= \tan^4 x(\csc x - 1)$

73. $y_1 = \cos\left(\dfrac{\pi}{2} - x\right),\ y_2 = \sin x$

x	0.2	0.4	0.6	0.8	1.0	1.2	1.4
y_1	0.1987	0.3894	0.5646	0.7174	0.8415	0.9320	0.9854
y_2	0.1987	0.3894	0.5646	0.7174	0.8415	0.9320	0.9854

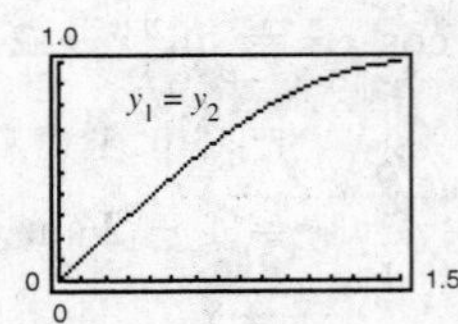

Conjecture: $y_1 = y_2$

74. $y_1 = \cos x + \sin x \tan x,\ y_2 = \sec x$

x	0.2	0.4	0.6	0.8	1.0	1.2	1.4
y_1	1.0203	1.0857	1.2116	1.4353	1.8508	2.7597	5.8835
y_2	1.0203	1.0857	1.2116	1.4353	1.8508	2.7597	5.8835

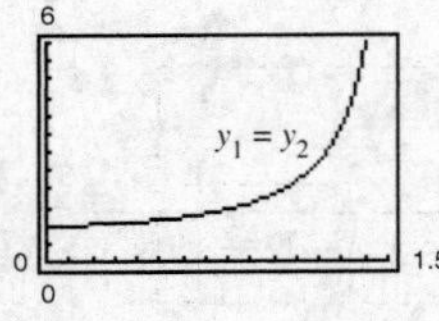

Conjecture: $y_1 = y_2$

75. $y_1 = \dfrac{\cos x}{1 - \sin x},\ y_2 = \dfrac{1 + \sin x}{\cos x}$

x	0.2	0.4	0.6	0.8	1.0	1.2	1.4
y_1	1.2230	1.5085	1.8958	2.4650	3.4082	5.3319	11.6814
y_2	1.2230	1.5085	1.8958	2.4650	3.4082	5.3319	11.6814

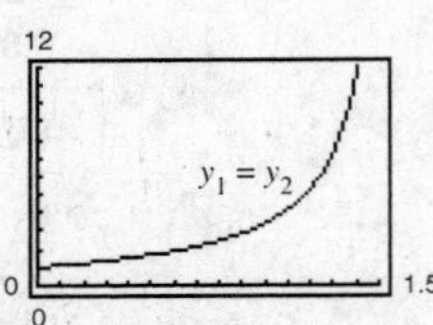

Conjecture: $y_1 = y_2$

76. $y_1 = \sec^4 x - \sec^2 x, y_2 = \tan^2 x + \tan^4 x$

x	0.2	0.4	0.6	0.8	1.0	1.2	1.4
y_1	0.0428	0.2107	0.6871	2.1841	8.3087	50.3869	1163.6143
y_2	0.0428	0.2107	0.6871	2.1841	8.3087	50.3869	1163.6143

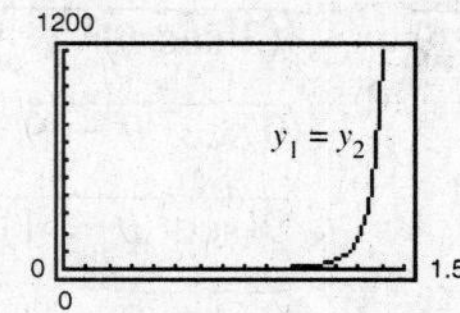

Conjecture: $y_1 = y_2$

77. $y_1 = \cos x \cot x + \sin x = \csc x$

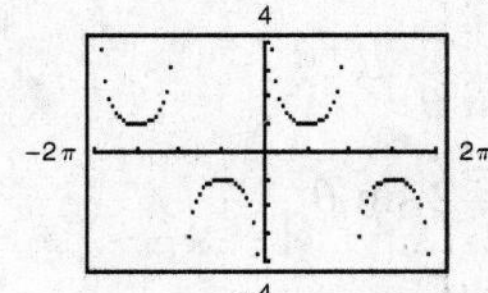

78. $\sin x(\cot x + \tan x) = \sec x$

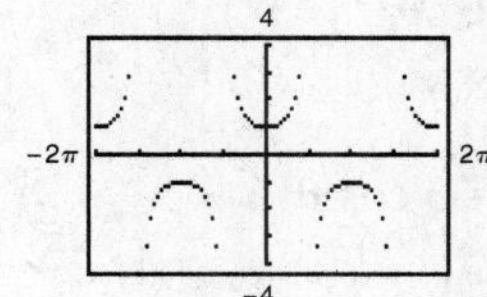

79. $y_1 = \sec x - \dfrac{\cos x}{1 + \sin x} = \tan x$

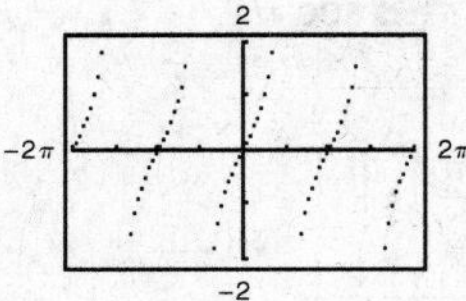

80. $y_1 = \dfrac{1}{2}\left(\dfrac{1 + \sin \theta}{\cos \theta} + \dfrac{\cos \theta}{1 + \sin \theta}\right)$

y_1 and $y_2 = \sin \theta$

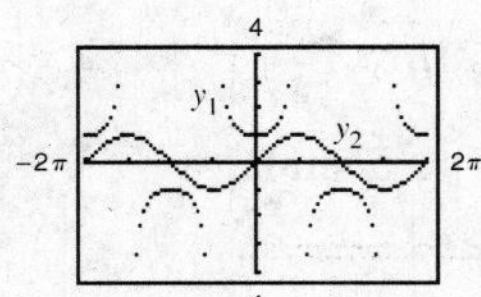

y_1 and $y_2 = \cos \theta$

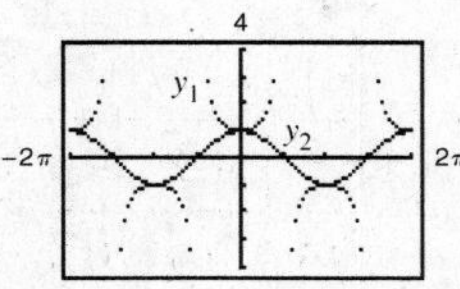

y_1 and $y_2 = \tan \theta$

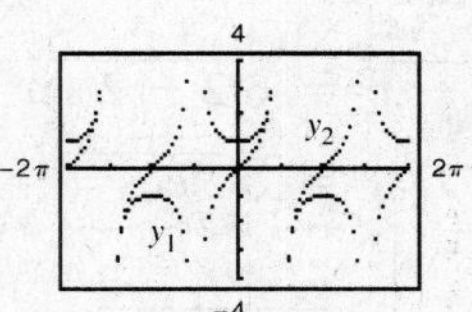

y_1 and $y_2 = \dfrac{1}{\sin \theta} = \csc \theta$

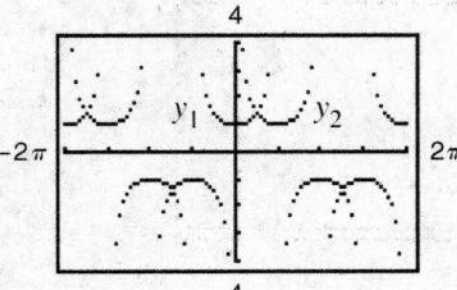

y_1 and $y_2 = \dfrac{1}{\cos \theta} = \sec \theta$

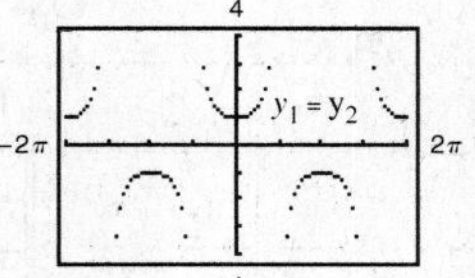

y_1 and $y_2 = \dfrac{1}{\tan \theta} = \cot \theta$

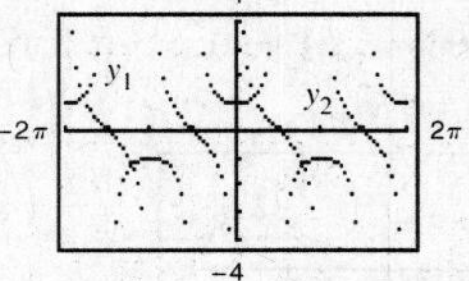

It appears that $\dfrac{1}{2}\left(\dfrac{1 + \sin \theta}{\cos \theta} + \dfrac{\cos \theta}{1 + \sin \theta}\right) = \sec \theta.$

81. $\sqrt{25 - x^2} = \sqrt{25 - (5 \sin \theta)^2}, \; x = 5 \sin \theta$

$= \sqrt{25 - 25 \sin^2 \theta}$

$= \sqrt{25(1 - \sin^2 \theta)}$

$= \sqrt{25 \cos^2 \theta}$

$= 5 \cos \theta$

82. Let $x = 2 \cos \theta$.

$\sqrt{64 - 16x^2} = \sqrt{64 - 16(4 \cos^2 \theta)}$

$= 8\sqrt{1 - \cos^2 \theta}$

$= 8 \sin \theta$

83. $\sqrt{x^2 - 9} = \sqrt{(3 \sec \theta)^2 - 9},\ x = 3 \sec \theta$

$= \sqrt{9 \sec^2 \theta - 9}$

$= \sqrt{9(\sec^2 \theta - 1)}$

$= \sqrt{9 \tan^2 \theta}$

$= 3 \tan \theta$

84. Let $x = 10 \tan \theta$.

$\sqrt{x^2 + 100} = \sqrt{(10 \tan \theta)^2 + 100}$

$= \sqrt{100(\tan^2 \theta + 1)}$

$= \sqrt{100 \sec^2 \theta}$

$= 10 \sec \theta$

85. $x = 3 \sin \theta, 0 < \theta < \dfrac{\pi}{2}$

$\sqrt{9 - x^2} = \sqrt{9 - 9 \sin^2 \theta}$

$= \sqrt{9 \cos^2 \theta} = 3 \cos \theta$

86. $x = 2 \cos \theta, 0 < \theta < \dfrac{\pi}{2}$

$\sqrt{4 - x^2} = \sqrt{4 - 4 \cos^2 \theta}$

$= \sqrt{4 \sin^2 \theta} = 2 \sin \theta$

87. $2x = 3 \tan \theta,\ 0 < \theta < \dfrac{\pi}{2}$

$\sqrt{4x^2 + 9} = \sqrt{9 \tan^2 \theta + 9}$

$= \sqrt{9 \sec^2 \theta} = 3 \sec \theta$

88. $3x = 2 \tan \theta,\ 0 < \theta < \dfrac{\pi}{2}$

$\sqrt{9x^2 + 4} = \sqrt{4 \tan^2 \theta + 4}$

$= \sqrt{4 \sec^2 \theta} = 2 \sec \theta$

89. $4x = 3 \sec \theta,\ 0 < \theta < \dfrac{\pi}{2}$

$\sqrt{16x^2 - 9} = \sqrt{9 \sec^2 \theta - 9}$

$= \sqrt{9 \tan^2 \theta} = 3 \tan \theta$

90. $3x = 5 \sec \theta,\ 0 < \theta < \dfrac{\pi}{2}$

$\sqrt{9x^2 - 25} = \sqrt{25 \sec^2 \theta - 25}$

$= \sqrt{25 \tan^2 \theta} = 5 \tan \theta$

91. $x = \sqrt{2} \sin \theta, 0 < \theta < \dfrac{\pi}{2}$

$\sqrt{2 - x^2} = \sqrt{2 - 2 \sin^2 \theta}$

$= \sqrt{2 \cos^2 \theta} = \sqrt{2} \cos \theta$

92. $x = \sqrt{5} \cos \theta,\ 0 < \theta < \dfrac{\pi}{2}$

$\sqrt{5 - x^2} = \sqrt{5 - 5 \cos^2 \theta}$

$= \sqrt{5 \sin^2 \theta} = \sqrt{5} \sin \theta$

93. $\sin \theta = \sqrt{1 - \cos^2 \theta}$

Let $y_1 = \sin x$ and $y_2 = \sqrt{1 - \cos^2 x}, 0 \le x < 2\pi$.

$y_1 = y_2$ for $0 \le x \le \pi$, so we have

$\sin \theta = \sqrt{1 - \cos^2 \theta}$ for $0 \le \theta \le \pi$.

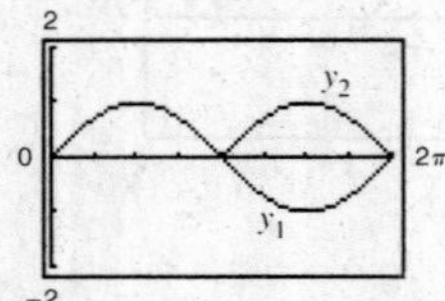

94. $\cos \theta = -\sqrt{1 - \sin^2 \theta}$

Let $y_1 = \cos \theta$ and $y_2 = -\sqrt{1 - \sin^2 \theta}$.

$y_1 = y_2$ for $\dfrac{\pi}{2} \le \theta \le \dfrac{3\pi}{2}$.

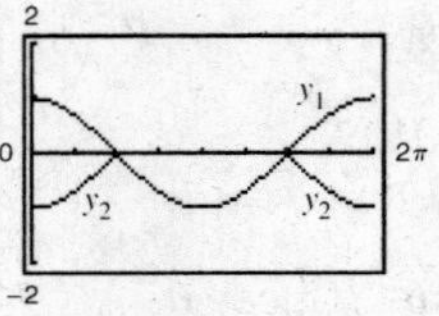

95. $\sec \theta = \sqrt{1 + \tan^2 \theta}$

Let $y_1 = \dfrac{1}{\cos x}$ and $y_2 = \sqrt{1 + \tan^2 x}, 0 \le x < 2\pi$.

$y_1 = y_2$ for $0 \le x < \dfrac{\pi}{2}$ and $\dfrac{3\pi}{2} < x < 2\pi$, so we

have $\sec \theta = \sqrt{1 + \tan^2 \theta}$ for $0 \le \theta < \dfrac{\pi}{2}$ and $\dfrac{3\pi}{2} < \theta < 2\pi$.

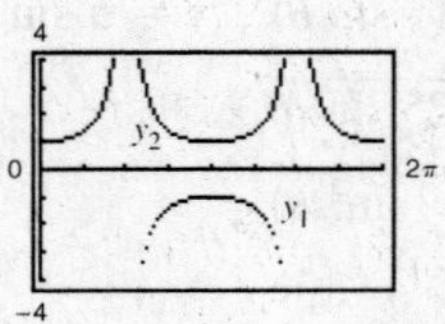

96. $\tan\theta = \sqrt{\sec^2\theta - 1}$

$0 \le \theta < \frac{\pi}{2},\ \pi \le \theta < \frac{3\pi}{2}$

97. $\ln|\cos\theta| - \ln|\sin\theta| = \ln\frac{|\cos\theta|}{|\sin\theta|} = \ln|\cot\theta|$

98. $\ln|\csc\theta| + \ln|\tan\theta| = \ln|\csc\theta \cdot \tan\theta|$

$= \ln|\sec\theta|$

99. $\ln(1 + \sin x) - \ln|\sec x| = \ln\left|\frac{1 + \sin x}{\sec x}\right|$

$= \ln|\cos x(1 + \sin x)|$

100. $\ln|\cot t| + \ln(1 + \tan^2 t) = \ln\left[|\cot t|(1 + \tan^2 t)\right]$

$= \ln\frac{(1 + \tan^2 t)}{|\tan t|}$

$= \ln\left|\frac{1}{\tan t} + \frac{\tan^2 t}{\tan t}\right|$

$= \ln|\cot t + \tan t|$

101. Let $\theta = \frac{7\pi}{6}$. Then

$\cos\theta = \cos\frac{7\pi}{6} = -\frac{\sqrt{3}}{2} \ne \sqrt{1 - \sin^2\theta} = \frac{\sqrt{3}}{2}.$

102. Let $\theta = \frac{2\pi}{3}$. Then

$\tan\theta = \tan\frac{2\pi}{3} = -\sqrt{3} \ne \sqrt{\sec^2\theta - 1} = \sqrt{3}.$

103. Let $\theta = \frac{5\pi}{3}$. Then

$\sin\theta = \sin\frac{5\pi}{3} = -\frac{\sqrt{3}}{2} \ne \sqrt{1 - \cos^2\theta} = \frac{\sqrt{3}}{2}.$

104. Let $\theta = \pi$. Then

$\sec\theta = \sec\pi = -1 \ne \sqrt{1 + \tan^2\theta} = 1.$

105. Let $\theta = \frac{7\pi}{4}$. Then

$\csc\theta = \csc\frac{7\pi}{4} = -\sqrt{2} \ne \sqrt{1 + \cot^2\theta} = \sqrt{2}.$

106. Let $\theta = \frac{3\pi}{4}$. Then

$\cot\theta = \cot\frac{3\pi}{4} = -1 \ne \sqrt{\csc^2\theta - 1} = 1.$

107. (a) $\csc^2 132° - \cot^2 132° \approx 1.8107 - 0.8107 = 1$

(b) $\csc^2\frac{2\pi}{7} - \cot^2\frac{2\pi}{7} \approx 1.6360 - 0.6360 = 1$

108. $\tan^2\theta + 1 = \sec^2\theta$

(a) $\theta = 346°$

$(\tan 346°)^2 + 1 \approx 1.0622$

$(\sec 346°)^2 = \left(\frac{1}{\cos 346°}\right)^2 \approx 1.0622$

(b) $\theta = 3.1$

$(\tan 3.1)^2 + 1 \approx 1.00173$

$(\sec 3.1)^2 = \left(\frac{1}{\cos 3.1}\right)^2 \approx 1.00173$

109. $\cos\left(\frac{\pi}{2} - \theta\right) = \sin\theta$

(a) $\theta = 80°$

$\cos(90° - 80°) = \sin 80°$

$0.9848 = 0.9848$

(b) $\theta = 0.8$

$\cos\left(\frac{\pi}{2} - 0.8\right) = \sin 0.8$

$0.7174 = 0.7174$

110. $\sin(-\theta) = -\sin\theta$

(a) $\theta = 250°$

$\sin(-250°) \approx 0.9397$

$-(\sin 250°) \approx 0.9397$

(b) $\theta = \frac{1}{2}$

$\sin\left(-\frac{1}{2}\right) \approx -0.4794$

$-\left(\sin\frac{1}{2}\right) \approx -0.4794$

111. $\csc x \cot x - \cos x = \frac{1}{\sin x} \cdot \frac{\cos x}{\sin x} - \cos x$

$= \cos x(\csc^2 x - 1)$

$= \cos x \cdot \cot^2 x$

112. $\sec x \tan x - \sin x = \frac{1}{\cos x}\frac{\sin x}{\cos x} - \sin x$

$= \sin x[\sec^2 x - 1]$

$= \sin x \cdot \tan^2 x$

113. True for all $\theta \neq n\pi$

$\sin\theta \cdot \csc\theta = \sin\theta\left(\frac{1}{\sin\theta}\right) = 1$

114. False

$\cos 0 \sec\frac{\pi}{4} \neq 1$

115. As $x \rightarrow \frac{\pi}{2}^-$, $\sin x \rightarrow 1$ and $\csc x \rightarrow 1$.

116. As $x \rightarrow 0^+$,

$\cos x \rightarrow 1$ and $\sec x = \frac{1}{\cos x} \rightarrow 1$.

117. As $x \rightarrow \frac{\pi}{2}^-$, $\tan x \rightarrow \infty$ and $\cot x \rightarrow 0$.

118. As $x \rightarrow \pi^+$,

$\sin x \rightarrow 0$ and $\csc x = \frac{1}{\sin x} \rightarrow -\infty$.

119. $\sin\theta$

$\cos\theta = \pm\sqrt{1 - \sin^2\theta}$

$\tan\theta = \frac{\sin\theta}{\cos\theta} = \pm\frac{\sin\theta}{\sqrt{1 - \sin^2\theta}}$

$\csc\theta = \frac{1}{\sin\theta}$

$\sec\theta = \frac{\pm 1}{\sqrt{1 - \sin^2\theta}}$

$\cot\theta = \pm\frac{\sqrt{1 - \sin^2\theta}}{\sin\theta}$

The sign + or − depends on the choice of θ.

120. $\cos\theta$

$\sin\theta = \pm\sqrt{1 - \cos^2\theta}$

$\tan\theta = \frac{\sin\theta}{\cos\theta} = \pm\frac{\sqrt{1 - \cos^2\theta}}{\cos\theta}$

$\csc\theta = \frac{1}{\sin\theta} = \pm\frac{1}{\sqrt{1 - \cos^2\theta}}$

$\sec\theta = \frac{1}{\cos\theta}$

$\cot\theta = \frac{1}{\tan\theta} = \pm\frac{\cos\theta}{\sqrt{1 - \cos^2\theta}}$

The sign + or − depends on the choice of θ.

121. $\sin\theta = \dfrac{\text{opp}}{\text{hyp}}, \cos\theta = \dfrac{\text{adj}}{\text{hyp}}$

From the Pythagorean Theorem,

$(\text{opp})^2 + (\text{adj})^2 = (\text{hyp})^2$

$\sin^2\theta + \cos^2\theta = 1.$

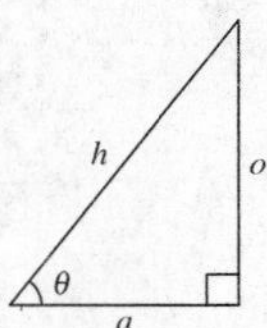

122. $\sin^2\theta + \cos^2\theta = 1$

$\dfrac{\sin^2\theta}{\sin^2\theta} + \dfrac{\cos^2\theta}{\sin^2\theta} = \dfrac{1}{\sin^2\theta}$

$1 + \cot^2\theta = \csc^2\theta$

$\sin^2\theta + \cos^2\theta = 1$

$\dfrac{\sin^2\theta}{\cos^2\theta} + \dfrac{\cos^2\theta}{\cos^2\theta} = \dfrac{1}{\cos^2\theta}$

$\tan^2\theta + 1 = \sec^2\theta$

123. $f(x) = \dfrac{1}{2}\sin\pi x$

Period: $\dfrac{2\pi}{\pi} = 2$

Amplitude: $\dfrac{1}{2}$

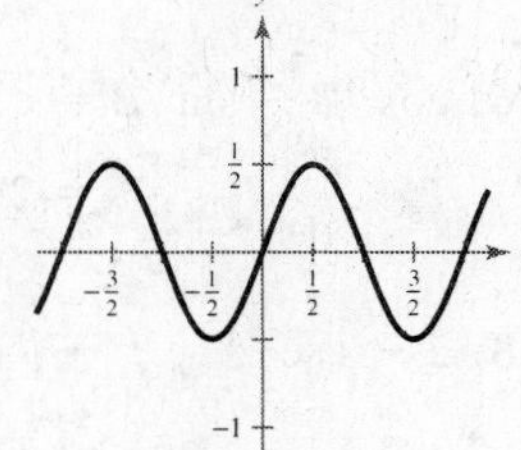

124. $f(x) = -2\tan\dfrac{\pi x}{2}$

Period: $\dfrac{\pi}{\pi/2} = 2$

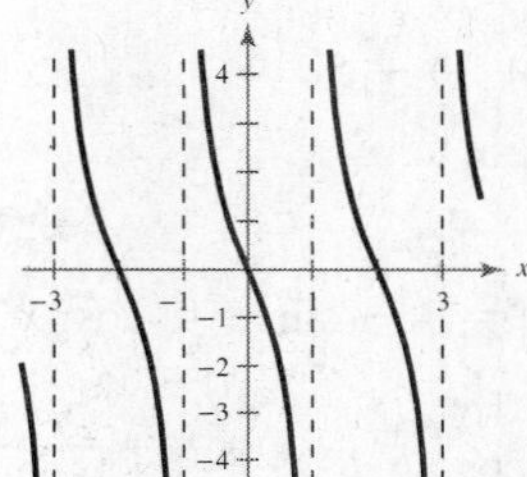

125. $f(x) = \dfrac{1}{2}\cot\left(x + \dfrac{\pi}{4}\right)$

Period: π

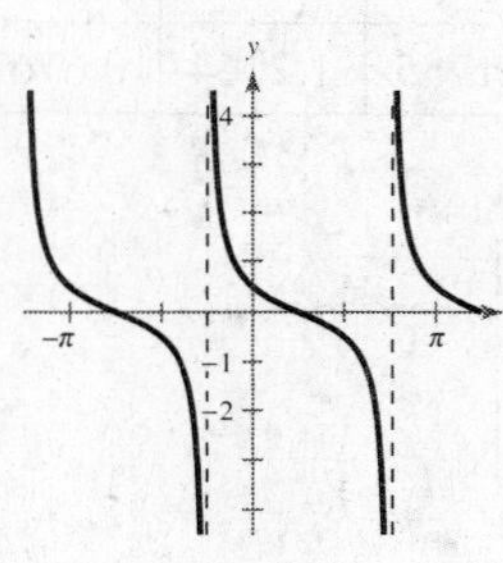

126. $f(x) = \dfrac{3}{2}\cos(x - \pi) + 3$

Amplitude: $\dfrac{3}{2}$

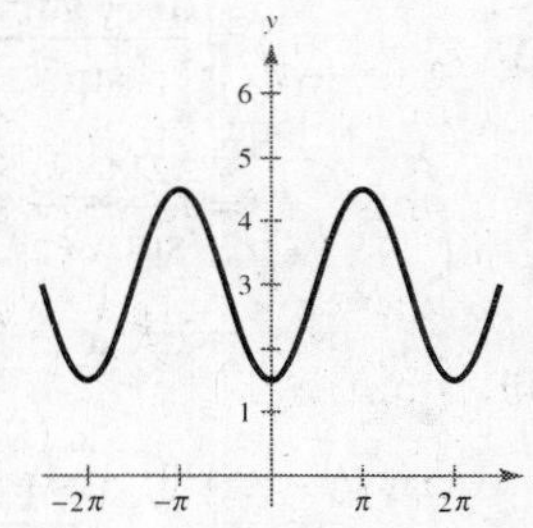

Section 5.2 Verifying Trigonometric Identities

- You should know the difference between an expression, a conditional equation, and an identity.
- You should be able to solve trigonometric identities, using the following techniques.
  - (a) Work with *one* side at a time. Do not "cross" the equal sign.
  - (b) Use algebraic techniques such as combining fractions, factoring expressions, rationalizing denominators, and squaring binomials.
  - (c) Use the fundamental identities.
  - (d) Convert all the terms into sines and cosines.

Vocabulary Check

1. conditional
2. identity
3. $\cot u$
4. $\sin u$
5. $\tan u$
6. $\cos u$
7. $\cos^2 u$
8. $\cot u$
9. $-\sin u$
10. $\sec u$

1. $\sin t \csc t = \sin t\left(\dfrac{1}{\sin t}\right) = 1$

2. $\sec y \cos y = \dfrac{1}{\cos y} \cos y = 1$

3. $\dfrac{\csc^2 x}{\cot x} = \dfrac{1}{\sin^2 x} \cdot \dfrac{\sin x}{\cos x} = \dfrac{1}{\sin x \cdot \cos x}$

$= \csc x \cdot \sec x$

4. $\dfrac{\sin^2 t}{\tan^2 t} = \dfrac{\sin^2 t}{\dfrac{\sin^2 t}{\cos^2 t}} = \cos^2 t$

5. $\cos^2 \beta - \sin^2 \beta = (1 - \sin^2 \beta) - \sin^2 \beta$

$= 1 - 2\sin^2 \beta$

6. $\cos^2 \beta - \sin^2 \beta = \cos^2 \beta - (1 - \cos^2 \beta)$

$= 2\cos^2 \beta - 1$

7. $\tan^2 \theta + 6 = (\tan^2 \theta + 1) + 5$

$= \sec^2 \theta + 5$

8. $2 - \csc^2 z = 2 - (\cot^2 z + 1) = 1 - \cot^2 z$

9. $(1 + \sin x)(1 - \sin x) = 1 - \sin^2 x = \cos^2 x$

10. $\tan^2 y(\csc^2 y - 1) = \tan^2 y \cot^2 y = 1$

11. $\dfrac{1}{\sec x \tan x} = \cos x \cdot \dfrac{\cos x}{\sin x}$

$= \dfrac{\cos^2 x}{\sin x}$

$= \dfrac{1 - \sin^2 x}{\sin x}$

$= \dfrac{1}{\sin x} - \sin x$

$= \csc x - \sin x$

x	0.2	0.4	0.6	0.8	1.0	1.2	1.4
y_1	4.8348	2.1785	1.2064	0.6767	0.3469	0.1409	0.0293
y_2	4.8348	2.1785	1.2064	0.6767	0.3469	0.1409	0.0293

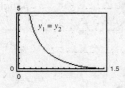

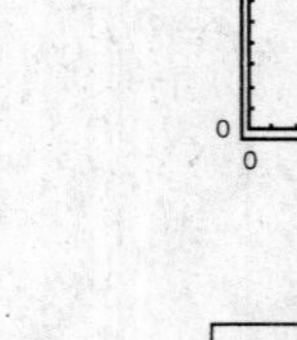

12. $y_1 = \dfrac{\csc x - 1}{1 - \sin x} = \dfrac{\dfrac{1}{\sin x} - 1}{1 - \sin x}$

$= \dfrac{1 - \sin x}{\sin x} \cdot \dfrac{1}{1 - \sin x}$

$= \dfrac{1}{\sin x}$

$= \csc x = y_2$

x	0.2	0.4	0.6	0.8	1.0	1.2	1.4
y_1	5.0335	2.5679	1.7710	1.3940	1.1884	1.0729	1.0148
y_2	5.0335	2.5679	1.7710	1.3940	1.1884	1.0729	1.0148

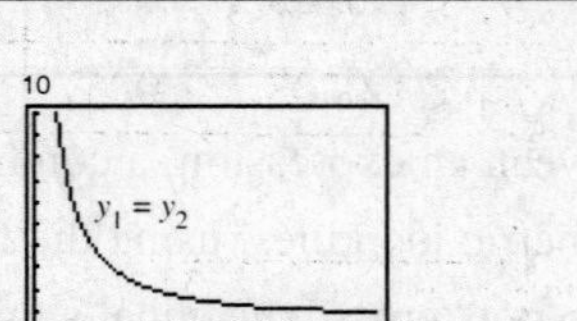

13. $\csc x - \sin x = \dfrac{1}{\sin x} - \sin x$

$= \dfrac{1 - \sin^2 x}{\sin x}$

$= \dfrac{\cos^2 x}{\sin x}$

$= \cos x \cdot \dfrac{\cos x}{\sin x}$

$= \cos x \cdot \cot x$

x	0.2	0.4	0.6	0.8	1.0	1.2	1.4
y_1	4.8348	2.1785	1.2064	0.6767	0.3469	0.1409	0.0293
y_2	4.8348	2.1785	1.2064	0.6767	0.3469	0.1409	0.0293

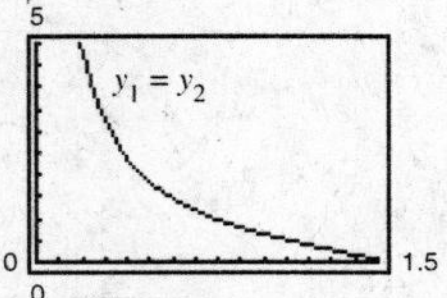

14. $y_1 = \sec x - \cos x = \dfrac{1}{\cos x} - \cos x$

$= \dfrac{1 - \cos^2 x}{\cos x}$

$= \dfrac{\sin^2 x}{\cos x}$

$= \sin x\left(\dfrac{\sin x}{\cos x}\right)$

$= \sin x \tan x$

$= y_2$

x	0.2	0.4	0.6	0.8	1.0	1.2	1.4
y_1	0.0403	0.1646	0.3863	0.7386	1.3105	2.3973	5.7135
y_2	0.0403	0.1646	0.3863	0.7386	1.3105	2.3973	5.7135

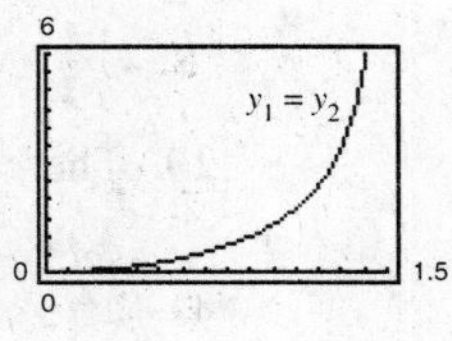

15. $\sin x + \cos x \cot x = \sin x + \cos x \dfrac{\cos x}{\sin x}$

$= \dfrac{\sin^2 x + \cos^2 x}{\sin x}$

$= \dfrac{1}{\sin x}$

$= \csc x$

x	0.2	0.4	0.6	0.8	1.0	1.2	1.4
y_1	5.0335	2.5679	1.7710	1.3940	1.1884	1.0729	1.0148
y_2	5.0335	2.5679	1.7710	1.3940	1.1884	1.0729	1.0148

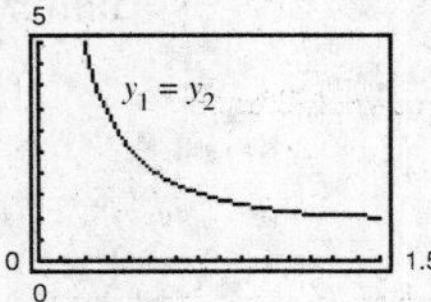

16. $y_1 = \cos x + \sin x \tan x$

$= \cos x + \dfrac{\sin^2 x}{\cos x}$

$= \dfrac{\cos^2 x + \sin^2 x}{\cos x}$

$= \dfrac{1}{\cos x}$

$= \sec x = y_2$

x	0.2	0.4	0.6	0.8	1.0	1.2	1.4
y_1	1.0203	1.0857	1.2116	1.4353	1.8508	2.7597	5.8835
y_2	1.0203	1.0857	1.2116	1.4353	1.8508	2.7597	5.8835

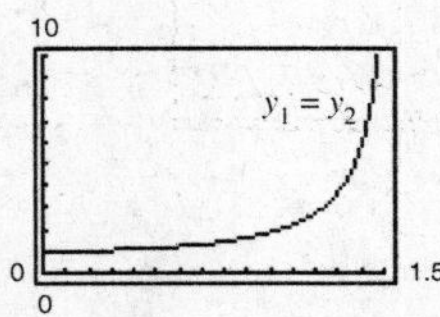

17. $\dfrac{1}{\tan x} + \dfrac{1}{\cot x} = \dfrac{\cot x + \tan x}{\tan x \cdot \cot x}$

$= \cot x + \tan x$

x	0.2	0.4	0.6	0.8	1.0	1.2	1.4
y_1	5.1359	2.7880	2.1458	2.0009	2.1995	2.9609	5.9704
y_2	5.1359	2.7880	2.1458	2.0009	2.1995	2.9609	5.9704

18. $y_1 = \dfrac{1}{\sin x} - \dfrac{1}{\csc x}$

$= \csc x - \sin x = y_2$

x	0.2	0.4	0.6	0.8	1.0	1.2	1.4
y_1	4.8348	2.1785	1.2064	0.6767	0.3469	0.1409	0.0293
y_2	4.8348	2.1785	1.2064	0.6767	0.3469	0.1409	0.0293

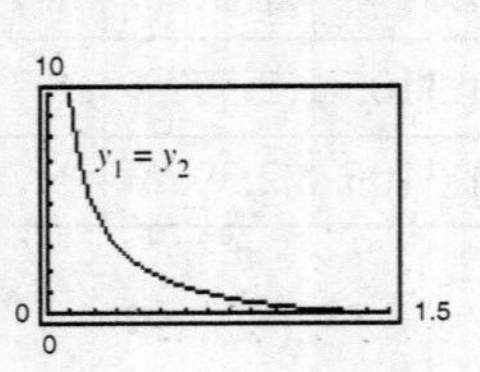

19. The error is in line 1: $\cot(-x) \neq \cot x$.

20. There are two errors in line 1:

$\sec(-\theta) = \sec \theta$ and $\sin(-\theta) = -\sin \theta$.

21. $\sin^{1/2} x \cos x - \sin^{5/2} x \cos x = \sin^{1/2} x \cos x(1 - \sin^2 x) = \sin^{1/2} x \cos x \cdot \cos^2 x = \cos^3 x\sqrt{\sin x}$

22. $\sec^6 x(\sec x \tan x) - \sec^4 x(\sec x \tan x) = \sec^4 x(\sec x \tan x)(\sec^2 x - 1)$

$= \sec^4 x(\sec x \tan x) \tan^2 x$

$= \sec^5 x \tan^3 x$

23. $\cot\left(\dfrac{\pi}{2} - x\right) \csc x = \tan x \csc x$

$= \dfrac{\sin x}{\cos x} \cdot \dfrac{1}{\sin x}$

$= \dfrac{1}{\cos x} = \sec x$

24. $\dfrac{\sec(\pi/2 - x)}{\tan(\pi/2 - x)} = \dfrac{\csc x}{\cot x}$

$= \dfrac{1}{\sin x} \cdot \dfrac{\sin x}{\cos x}$

$= \dfrac{1}{\cos x} = \sec x$

25. $\dfrac{\csc(-x)}{\sec(-x)} = \dfrac{1/\sin(-x)}{1/\cos(-x)}$

$= \dfrac{\cos(-x)}{\sin(-x)}$

$= \dfrac{\cos x}{-\sin x}$

$= -\cot x$

26. $(1 + \sin y)[1 + \sin(-y)] = (1 + \sin y)(1 - \sin y)$

$= 1 - \sin^2 y$

$= \cos^2 y$

27. $$\frac{\cos(-\theta)}{1+\sin(-\theta)} = \frac{\cos\theta}{1-\sin\theta}\cdot\frac{1+\sin\theta}{1+\sin\theta}$$
$$= \frac{\cos\theta(1+\sin\theta)}{1-\sin^2\theta}$$
$$= \frac{\cos\theta(1+\sin\theta)}{\cos^2\theta}$$
$$= \frac{1+\sin\theta}{\cos\theta}$$
$$= \frac{1}{\cos\theta} + \frac{\sin\theta}{\cos\theta}$$
$$= \sec\theta + \tan\theta$$

28. $$\frac{1+\csc(-\theta)}{\cos(-\theta)+\cot(-\theta)} = \frac{1-\csc\theta}{\cos\theta-\cot\theta}$$
$$= \frac{1-\csc\theta}{\cos\theta\left(1-\dfrac{1}{\sin\theta}\right)}$$
$$= \frac{1-\csc\theta}{\cos\theta(1-\csc\theta)}$$
$$= \frac{1}{\cos\theta}$$
$$= \sec\theta$$

29. $$\frac{\sin x\cos y+\cos x\sin y}{\cos x\cos y-\sin x\sin y} = \frac{\dfrac{\sin x\cos y}{\cos x\cos y}+\dfrac{\cos x\sin y}{\cos x\cos y}}{\dfrac{\cos x\cos y}{\cos x\cos y}-\dfrac{\sin x\sin y}{\cos x\cos y}} = \frac{\tan x+\tan y}{1-\tan x\tan y}$$

30. $$\frac{\tan x+\tan y}{1-\tan x\tan y} = \frac{\dfrac{1}{\cot x}+\dfrac{1}{\cot y}}{1-\dfrac{1}{\cot x}\cdot\dfrac{1}{\cot y}}\cdot\frac{\cot x\cot y}{\cot x\cot y} = \frac{\cot y+\cot x}{\cot x\cot y-1}$$

31. $$\frac{\cos x-\cos y}{\sin x+\sin y}+\frac{\sin x-\sin y}{\cos x+\cos y} = \frac{(\cos x+\cos y)(\cos x-\cos y)+(\sin x+\sin y)(\sin x-\sin y)}{(\sin x+\sin y)(\cos x+\cos y)}$$
$$= \frac{\cos^2 x-\cos^2 y+\sin^2 x-\sin^2 y}{(\sin x+\sin y)(\cos x+\cos y)}$$
$$= \frac{1-1}{(\sin x+\sin y)(\cos x+\cos y)}$$
$$= 0$$

32. $$\frac{\tan x+\cot y}{\tan x\cot y} = \frac{1}{\cot y}+\frac{1}{\tan x} = \tan y+\cot x$$

33. $$\sqrt{\frac{1+\sin\theta}{1-\sin\theta}} = \sqrt{\frac{1+\sin\theta}{1-\sin\theta}\cdot\frac{1+\sin\theta}{1+\sin\theta}}$$
$$= \sqrt{\frac{(1+\sin\theta)^2}{1-\sin^2\theta}}$$
$$= \sqrt{\frac{(1+\sin\theta)^2}{\cos^2\theta}}$$
$$= \frac{1+\sin\theta}{|\cos\theta|}$$

Note: Check your answer with a graphing utility. What happens if you leave off the absolute value?

34. $$\sqrt{\frac{1-\cos\theta}{1+\cos\theta}} = \sqrt{\frac{1-\cos\theta}{1+\cos\theta}\cdot\frac{1-\cos\theta}{1-\cos\theta}}$$
$$= \sqrt{\frac{(1-\cos\theta)^2}{1-\cos^2\theta}}$$
$$= \sqrt{\frac{(1-\cos\theta)^2}{\sin^2\theta}}$$
$$= \frac{1-\cos\theta}{|\sin\theta|}$$

35. $\sin^2\left(\frac{\pi}{2} - x\right) + \sin^2 x = \cos^2 x + \sin^2 x = 1$

36. $\sec^2 y - \cot^2\left(\frac{\pi}{2} - y\right) = \sec^2 y - \tan^2 y = 1$

37. $\sin x \csc\left(\frac{\pi}{2} - x\right) = \sin x \sec x$

$$= \sin x\left(\frac{1}{\cos x}\right)$$

$$= \tan x$$

38. $\sec^2\left(\frac{\pi}{2} - x\right) - 1 = \csc^2 x - 1 = \cot^2 x$

39. $2\sec^2 x - 2\sec^2 x \sin^2 x - \sin^2 x - \cos^2 x = 2\sec^2 x(1 - \sin^2 x) - (\sin^2 x + \cos^2 x)$

$$= 2\sec^2 x(\cos^2 x) - 1$$

$$= 2 \cdot \frac{1}{\cos^2 x} \cdot \cos^2 x - 1$$

$$= 2 - 1 = 1$$

40. $\csc x(\csc x - \sin x) + \frac{\sin x - \cos x}{\sin x} + \cot x = \csc^2 x - \csc x \sin x + 1 - \frac{\cos x}{\sin x} + \cot x$

$$= \csc^2 x - 1 + 1 - \cot x + \cot x$$

$$= \csc^2 x$$

41. $\frac{\cot x \tan x}{\sin x} = \frac{1}{\sin x} = \csc x$

42. $\frac{1 + \csc\theta}{\sec\theta} - \cot\theta = \cos\theta\left(1 + \frac{1}{\sin\theta}\right) - \frac{\cos\theta}{\sin\theta}$

$$= \frac{\cos\theta}{\sin\theta}(\sin\theta + 1 - 1)$$

$$= \cos\theta$$

43. $\csc^4 x - 2\csc^2 x + 1 = (\csc^2 x - 1)^2$

$$= (\cot^2 x)^2 = \cot^4 x$$

44. $\sin x(1 - 2\cos^2 x + \cos^4 x) = \sin x(1 - \cos^2 x)^2$

$$= \sin x(\sin^2 x)^2$$

$$= \sin^5 x$$

45. $\sec^4\theta - \tan^4\theta = (\sec^2\theta + \tan^2\theta)(\sec^2\theta - \tan^2\theta)$

$$= (1 + \tan^2\theta + \tan^2\theta)(1)$$

$$= 1 + 2\tan^2\theta$$

46. $\csc^4\theta - \cot^4\theta = (\csc^2\theta - \cot^2\theta)(\csc^2\theta + \cot^2\theta)$

$$= \csc^2\theta + \cot^2\theta$$

$$= \csc^2\theta + (\csc^2\theta - 1)$$

$$= 2\csc^2\theta - 1$$

47. $\frac{\sin\beta}{1 - \cos\beta} \cdot \frac{1 + \cos\beta}{1 + \cos\beta} = \frac{\sin\beta(1 + \cos\beta)}{1 - \cos^2\beta}$

$$= \frac{\sin\beta(1 + \cos\beta)}{\sin^2\beta}$$

$$= \frac{1 + \cos\beta}{\sin\beta}$$

48. $\frac{\cot\alpha}{\csc\alpha - 1} \cdot \frac{\csc\alpha + 1}{\csc\alpha + 1} = \frac{\cot\alpha(\csc\alpha + 1)}{\csc^2\alpha - 1}$

$$= \frac{\cot\alpha(\csc\alpha + 1)}{\cot^2\alpha}$$

$$= \frac{\csc\alpha + 1}{\cot\alpha}$$

49. $\dfrac{\tan^3 \alpha - 1}{\tan \alpha - 1} = \dfrac{(\tan \alpha - 1)(\tan^2 \alpha + \tan \alpha + 1)}{\tan \alpha - 1} = \tan^2 \alpha + \tan \alpha + 1$

50. $\dfrac{\sin^3 \beta + \cos^3 \beta}{\sin \beta + \cos \beta} = \dfrac{(\sin \beta + \cos \beta)(\sin^2 \beta - \sin \beta \cos \beta + \cos^2 \beta)}{\sin \beta + \cos \beta}$

$= \sin^2 \beta + \cos^2 \beta - \sin \beta \cos \beta$

$= 1 - \sin \beta \cos \beta$

51. It appears that $y_1 = 1$. Analytically,

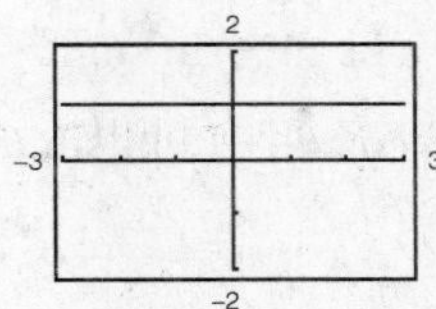

$\dfrac{1}{\cot x + 1} + \dfrac{1}{\tan x + 1} = \dfrac{\tan x + 1 + \cot x + 1}{(\cot x + 1)(\tan x + 1)}$

$= \dfrac{\tan x + \cot x + 2}{\cot x \tan x + \cot x + \tan x + 1}$

$= \dfrac{\tan x + \cot x + 2}{\tan x + \cot x + 2}$

$= 1.$

52. The function appears to be $y = \cos x$. Analytically,

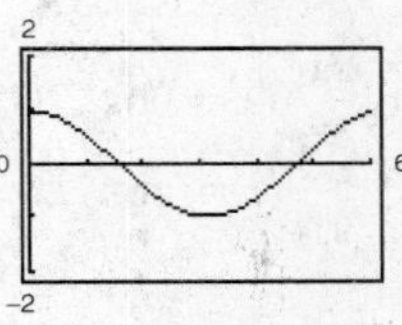

$y = \dfrac{\cos x}{1 - \tan x} + \dfrac{\sin x \cdot \cos x}{\sin x - \cos x}$

$= \dfrac{\cos x}{1 - (\sin x/\cos x)} + \dfrac{\sin x \cos x}{\sin x - \cos x}$

$= \dfrac{\cos^2 x}{\cos x - \sin x} - \dfrac{\sin x \cos x}{\cos x - \sin x}$

$= \dfrac{\cos x(\cos x - \sin x)}{\cos x - \sin x} = \cos x.$

53. It appears that $y_1 = \sin x$. Analytically,

$\dfrac{1}{\sin x} - \dfrac{\cos^2 x}{\sin x} = \dfrac{1 - \cos^2 x}{\sin x} = \dfrac{\sin^2 x}{\sin x} = \sin x.$

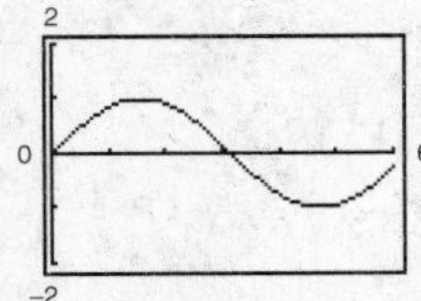

54. The function appears to be $y = \csc t$. Analytically,

$y = \sin t + \dfrac{\cot^2 t}{\csc t}$

$= \dfrac{1 + \cot^2 t}{\csc t}$

$= \dfrac{\csc^2 t}{\csc t} = \csc t.$

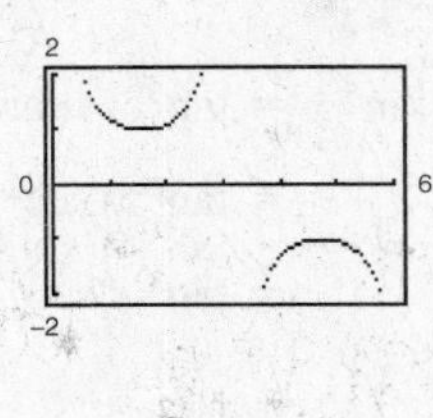

55. $\ln|\cot \theta| = \ln\left|\dfrac{\cos \theta}{\sin \theta}\right|$

$= \ln \dfrac{|\cos \theta|}{|\sin \theta|}$

$= \ln|\cos \theta| - \ln|\sin \theta|$

56. $\ln|\sec \theta| = \ln\left|\dfrac{1}{\cos \theta}\right|$

$= \ln|\cos \theta|^{-1}$

$= -\ln|\cos \theta|$

57. $-\ln(1+\cos\theta) = \ln(1+\cos\theta)^{-1}$

$$= \ln\left[\frac{1}{1+\cos\theta}\cdot\frac{1-\cos\theta}{1-\cos\theta}\right]$$

$$= \ln\frac{1-\cos\theta}{1-\cos^2\theta}$$

$$= \ln\frac{1-\cos\theta}{\sin^2\theta}$$

$$= \ln(1-\cos\theta) - \ln\sin^2\theta$$

$$= \ln(1-\cos\theta) - 2\ln|\sin\theta|$$

58. $-\ln|\csc\theta + \cot\theta| = -\ln\left|\frac{1}{\sin\theta} + \frac{\cos\theta}{\sin\theta}\right|$

$$= \ln\left|\frac{1+\cos\theta}{\sin\theta}\right|^{-1}$$

$$= \ln\left|\frac{\sin\theta}{1+\cos\theta}\right|$$

$$= \ln\left|\frac{\sin\theta}{1+\cos\theta}\cdot\frac{1-\cos\theta}{1-\cos\theta}\right|$$

$$= \ln\left|\frac{\sin\theta(1-\cos\theta)}{1-\cos^2\theta}\right|$$

$$= \ln\left|\frac{\sin\theta(1-\cos\theta)}{\sin^2\theta}\right|$$

$$= \ln\left|\frac{1-\cos\theta}{\sin\theta}\right|$$

$$= \ln|\csc\theta - \cot\theta|$$

59. $\sin^2 35° + \sin^2 55° = \cos^2(90° - 35°) + \sin^2 55°$

$$= \cos^2 55° + \sin^2 55° = 1$$

60. $\cos^2 14° + \cos^2 76° = \sin^2(90° - 14°) + \cos^2 76°$

$$= \sin^2 76° + \cos^2 76° = 1$$

61. $\cos^2 20° + \cos^2 52° + \cos^2 38° + \cos^2 70° = \cos^2 20° + \cos^2 52° + \sin^2(90° - 38°) + \sin^2(90° - 70°)$

$$= \cos^2 20° + \cos^2 52° + \sin^2 52° + \sin^2 20°$$

$$= (\cos^2 20° + \sin^2 20°) + (\cos^2 52° + \sin^2 52°)$$

$$= 1 + 1 = 2$$

62. $\sin^2 18° + \sin^2 40° + \sin^2 50° + \sin^2 72° = (\sin^2 18° + \sin^2 72°) + (\sin^2 40° + \sin^2 50°)$

$$= (\sin^2 18° + \cos^2 18°) + (\sin^2 40° + \cos^2 40°)$$

$$= 1 + 1 = 2$$

63. $\tan^5 x = \tan^3 x \cdot \tan^2 x$

$$= \tan^3 x(\sec^2 x - 1)$$

$$= \tan^3 x \sec^2 x - \tan^3 x$$

64. $\sec^4 x \tan^2 x = \sec^2 x(1 + \tan^2 x)\tan^2 x$

$$= (\tan^2 x + \tan^4 x)\sec^2 x$$

65. $(\sin^2 x - \sin^4 x)\cos x = \sin^2 x(1 - \sin^2 x)\cos x = \sin^2 x \cdot \cos^2 x \cdot \cos x = \cos^3 x \sin^2 x$

66. $1 - 2\cos^2 x + 2\cos^4 x = [1 - 2\cos^2 x + \cos^4 x] + \cos^4 x = (1 - \cos^2 x)^2 + \cos^4 x = \sin^4 x + \cos^4 x$

67. Let $\theta = \sin^{-1} x \Rightarrow \sin\theta = x = \frac{x}{1}$.

From the diagram,

$$\tan(\sin^{-1} x) = \tan\theta = \frac{x}{\sqrt{1-x^2}}.$$

1, x, θ, $\sqrt{1-x^2}$

68. Let $\theta = \sin^{-1} x \Rightarrow \sin\theta = x = \frac{x}{1}$.

From the diagram,

$$\cos(\sin^{-1} x) = \cos\theta = \sqrt{1-x^2}.$$

1, x, θ, $\sqrt{1-x^2}$

69. Let $\theta = \sin^{-1}\frac{x-1}{4} \Rightarrow \sin\theta = \frac{x-1}{4}$.

From the diagram,

$$\tan\left(\sin^{-1}\frac{x-1}{4}\right) = \tan\theta = \frac{x-1}{\sqrt{16-(x-1)^2}}.$$

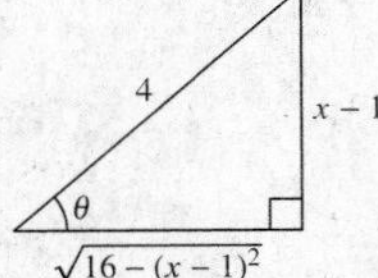

70. Let $\theta = \cos^{-1}\frac{x+1}{2} \Rightarrow \cos\theta = \frac{x+1}{2}$.

From the diagram,

$$\tan\left(\cos^{-1}\frac{x+1}{2}\right) = \tan\theta = \frac{\sqrt{4-(x+1)^2}}{x+1}.$$

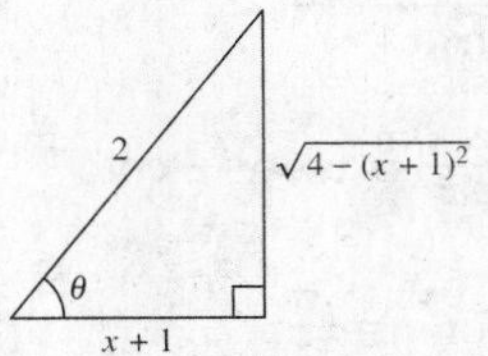

71. $\mu W\cos\theta = W\sin\theta$

$$\mu = \frac{W\sin\theta}{W\cos\theta} = \frac{\sin\theta}{\cos\theta} = \tan\theta,\ W \neq 0$$

72. $s = \frac{h\sin(90° - \theta)}{\sin\theta} = h\frac{\cos\theta}{\sin\theta} = h\cot\theta$

73. True

74. True. Cosine and secant are even.

75. False. Just because the equation is true for one value of θ, you cannot conclude that the equation is an identity. For example,

$$\sin^2\frac{\pi}{4} + \cos^2\frac{\pi}{4} = 1 \neq 1 + \tan^2\frac{\pi}{4}.$$

76. False. For example, $\sin(1^2) \neq \sin^2(1)$.

77. (a) $$\frac{\sin x}{1+\cos x} = \frac{\sin x}{1+\cos x}\cdot\frac{1-\cos x}{1-\cos x}$$
$$= \frac{\sin x(1-\cos x)}{1-\cos^2 x}$$
$$= \frac{\sin x(1-\cos x)}{\sin^2 x}$$
$$= \frac{1-\cos x}{\sin x}$$

(b) Not true for $x = 0$ because $(1-\cos x)/\sin x$ is not defined for $x = 0$.

78. (a) $$\frac{\tan x}{\sec x - \cos x} = \frac{\tan x}{\frac{1}{\cos x} - \cos x}$$
$$= \frac{\frac{\sin x}{\cos x}\cos x}{1-\cos^2 x}$$
$$= \frac{\sin x}{\sin^2 x}$$
$$= \frac{1}{\sin x}\cdot\frac{1/\cos x}{1/\cos x}$$
$$= \frac{\sec x}{\tan x}$$

(b) Not true for $x = \pi$ because $\sec x/\tan x$ is not defined for $x = \pi$.

79. (a) $\dfrac{\sin x}{1 + \cos x} = \dfrac{\sin x}{1 + \cos x} \cdot \dfrac{1 - \cos x}{1 - \cos x}$

$= \dfrac{\sin x(1 - \cos x)}{1 - \cos^2 x}$

$= \dfrac{\sin x(1 - \cos x)}{\sin^2 x}$

$= \dfrac{1 - \cos x}{\sin x} = \csc x - \cot x$

(b) The identity is true for $x = \dfrac{\pi}{2}$:

$\dfrac{\sin(\pi/2)}{1 + \cos(\pi/2)} = \dfrac{1}{1 + 0}$

$= 1 = \csc \dfrac{\pi}{2} - \cot \dfrac{\pi}{2}$

80. (a) $\dfrac{\cot x - 1}{\cot x + 1} = \dfrac{\cot x - 1}{\cot x + 1} \cdot \dfrac{\tan x}{\tan x}$

$= \dfrac{1 - \tan x}{1 + \tan x}$

(b) The identity is true for $x = \dfrac{\pi}{4}$:

$\dfrac{\cot(\pi/4) - 1}{\cot(\pi/4) + 1} = \dfrac{1 - 1}{1 + 1} = 0$

$\dfrac{1 - \tan(\pi/4)}{1 + \tan(\pi/4)} = \dfrac{1 - 1}{1 + 1} = 0$

81. $\sqrt{a^2 - u^2} = \sqrt{a^2 - a^2 \sin^2 \theta}$

$= \sqrt{a^2(1 - \sin^2 \theta)}$

$= \sqrt{a^2 \cos^2 \theta}$

$= a \cos \theta$

82. $\sqrt{a^2 - u^2} = \sqrt{a^2 - a^2 \cos^2 \theta}$

$= \sqrt{a^2(1 - \cos^2 \theta)}$

$= \sqrt{a^2 \sin^2 \theta}$

$= a \sin \theta$

83. $\sqrt{a^2 + u^2} = \sqrt{a^2 + a^2 \tan^2 \theta}$

$= \sqrt{a^2(1 + \tan^2 \theta)}$

$= \sqrt{a^2 \sec^2 \theta}$

$= a \sec \theta$

84. $\sqrt{u^2 - a^2} = \sqrt{a^2 \sec^2 \theta - a^2}$

$= \sqrt{a^2(\sec^2 \theta - 1)}$

$= \sqrt{a^2 \tan^2 \theta}$

$= a \tan \theta$

85. $\sqrt{\tan^2 x} = |\tan x|$

Let $x = \dfrac{3\pi}{4}$. Then, $\sqrt{\tan^2 x} = \sqrt{(-1)^2} = 1 \neq \tan\left(\dfrac{3\pi}{4}\right) = -1$.

86. $\sin \theta = \sqrt{1 - \cos^2 \theta}$.

True identity is $\sin \theta = \pm\sqrt{1 - \cos^2 \theta}$.

For example, $\sin \theta \neq \sqrt{1 - \cos^2 \theta}$ for $\theta = \dfrac{3\pi}{2}$:

$\sin\left(\dfrac{3\pi}{2}\right) = -1 \neq \sqrt{1 - 0} = 1$

87. When n is even, $\cos\left[\dfrac{(2n + 1)\pi}{2}\right] = \cos \dfrac{\pi}{2} = 0$.

When n is odd, $\cos\left[\dfrac{(2n + 1)\pi}{2}\right] = \cos \dfrac{3\pi}{2} = 0$.

Thus, $\cos\left[\dfrac{(2n + 1)\pi}{2}\right] = 0$ for all n.

88. $\sin\left[\dfrac{(12n + 1)\pi}{6}\right] = \sin\left[\dfrac{1}{6}(12n\pi + \pi)\right]$

$= \sin\left(2n\pi + \dfrac{\pi}{6}\right) = \sin \dfrac{\pi}{6} = \dfrac{1}{2}$

Thus, $\sin\left[\dfrac{(12n + 1)\pi}{6}\right] = \dfrac{1}{2}$ for all integers n.

89. $(x - 1)(x - 8i)(x + 8i) = (x - 1)(x^2 + 64)$

$= x^3 - x^2 + 64x - 64$

Answers will vary.

90. $(x - i)(x + i)(x - 4i)(x + 4i) = (x^2 + 1)(x^2 + 16) = x^4 + 17x^2 + 16$

91. $(x - 4)(x - 6 - i)(x - 6 + i) = (x - 4)((x - 6)^2 + 1)$

$= (x - 4)(x^2 - 12x + 37)$

$= x^3 - 16x^2 + 85x - 148$

Answers will vary.

92. $x^2(x - 2)(x - (1 - i))(x - (1 + i)) = (x^3 - 2x^2)((x - 1)^2 + 1)$

$= (x^3 - 2x^2)(x^2 - 2x + 2)$

$= x^5 - 4x^4 + 6x^3 - 4x^2$

93. $f(x) = 2^x + 3$

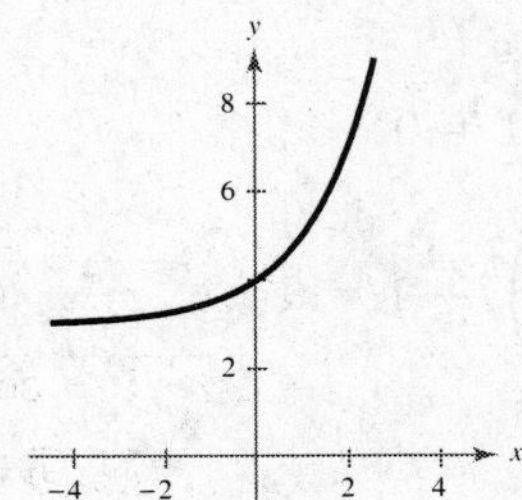

94. $f(x) = -2^{x-3}$

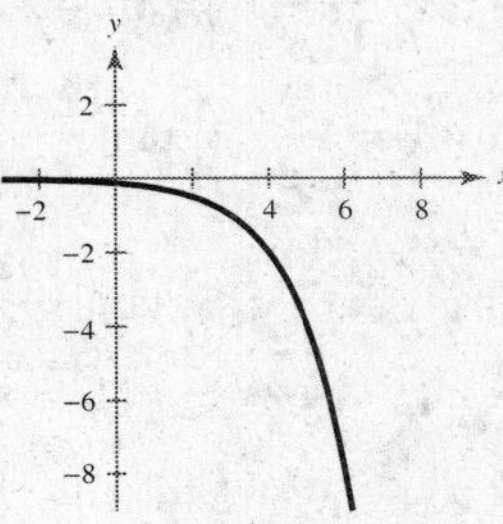

95. $f(x) = 2^{-x} + 1$

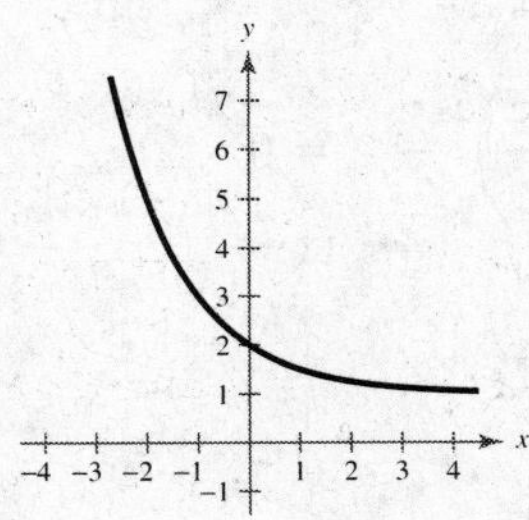

96. $f(x) = 2^{x-1} + 3$

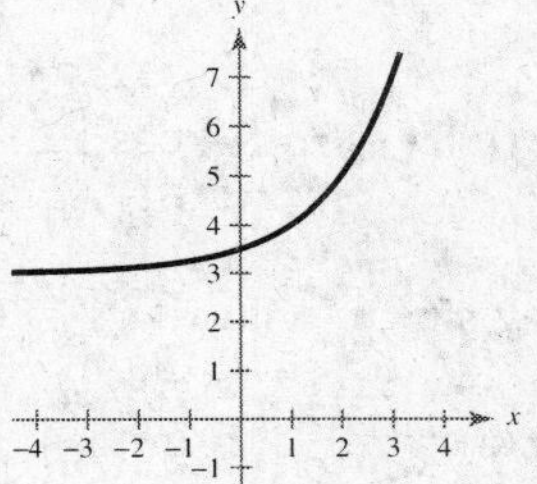

97. $\csc \theta > 0$ and $\tan \theta < 0 \Rightarrow$ Quadrant II

98. Quadrant III

99. $\sec \theta > 0$ and $\sin \theta < 0 \Rightarrow$ Quadrant IV

100. Quadrant III

Section 5.3 Solving Trigonometric Equations

- You should be able to identify and solve trigonometric equations.
- A trigonometric equation is a conditional equation. It is true for a specific set of values.
- To solve trigonometric equations, use algebraic techniques such as collecting like terms, taking square roots, factoring, squaring, converting to quadratic form, using formulas, and using inverse functions. Study the examples in this section.
- Use your graphing utility to calculate solutions and verify results.

Vocabulary Check

1. general
2. quadratic
3. extraneous

1. $2\cos x - 1 = 0$

(a) $x = \frac{\pi}{3}$: $2\cos\frac{\pi}{3} - 1 = 2\left(\frac{1}{2}\right) - 1 = 0$

(b) $x = \frac{5\pi}{3}$: $2\cos\frac{5\pi}{3} - 1 = 2\left(\frac{1}{2}\right) - 1 = 0$

2. $\sec x - 2 = 0$

(a) $x = \frac{\pi}{3}$: $\sec\left(\frac{\pi}{3}\right) - 2 = \frac{1}{\cos(\pi/3)} - 2$

$= 2 - 2 = 0$

(b) $x = \frac{5\pi}{3}$: $\sec\left(\frac{5\pi}{3}\right) - 2 = 2 - 2 = 0$

3. $3\tan^2 2x - 1 = 0$

(a) $x = \frac{\pi}{12}$: $3\left[\tan\left(\frac{2\pi}{12}\right)\right]^2 - 1 = 3\tan^2\frac{\pi}{6} - 1 = 3\left(\frac{1}{\sqrt{3}}\right)^2 - 1 = 0$

(b) $x = \frac{5\pi}{12}$: $3\left[\tan\left(\frac{10\pi}{12}\right)\right]^2 - 1 = 3\tan^2\frac{5\pi}{6} - 1 = 3\left(-\frac{1}{\sqrt{3}}\right)^2 - 1 = 0$

4. $4\cos^2 2x - 2 = 0$

(a) $x = \frac{\pi}{8}$: $4\cos^2\left(2 \cdot \frac{\pi}{8}\right) - 2 = 4\cos^2\left(\frac{\pi}{4}\right) - 2 = 4\left(\frac{\sqrt{2}}{2}\right)^2 - 2 = 0$

(b) $x = \frac{7\pi}{8}$: $4\cos^2\left(2 \cdot \frac{7\pi}{8}\right) - 2 = 4\cos^2\left(\frac{7\pi}{4}\right) - 2 = 4\left(\frac{\sqrt{2}}{2}\right)^2 - 2 = 0$

5. $2\sin^2 x - \sin x - 1 = 0$

(a) $x = \frac{\pi}{2}$: $2\sin^2\left(\frac{\pi}{2}\right) - \sin\left(\frac{\pi}{2}\right) - 1 = 2 - 1 - 1 = 0$

(b) $x = \frac{7\pi}{6}$: $2\sin^2\left(\frac{7\pi}{6}\right) - \sin\left(\frac{7\pi}{6}\right) - 1 = 2\left(\frac{1}{4}\right) - \left(-\frac{1}{2}\right) - 1 = 0$

6. $\sec^4 x - 3\sec^2 x - 4 = 0$

(a) $x = \frac{2\pi}{3}$: $\sec\frac{2\pi}{3} = -2$ and $\sec^4 x - 3\sec^2 x - 4 = (-2)^4 - 3(-2)^2 - 4 = 0$

(b) $x = \frac{5\pi}{3}$: $\sec\frac{5\pi}{3} = 2$ and $\sec^4 x - 3\sec^2 x - 4 = 2^4 - 3(2)^2 - 4 = 0$

7. $\sin x = \frac{1}{2}$

$x = 30°, 150°$

8. $\cos x = \frac{\sqrt{3}}{2}$

$x = 30°, 330°$

9. $\cos x = -\frac{1}{2}$

$x = 120°, 240°$

10. $\sin x = -\frac{\sqrt{2}}{2}$

$x = 225°, 315°$

11. $\tan x = 1$

$x = 45°, 225°$

12. $\tan x = -\sqrt{3}$

$x = 120°, 300°$

13. $\cos x = -\frac{\sqrt{3}}{2}$

$x = \frac{5\pi}{6}, \frac{7\pi}{6}$

14. $\sin x = -\frac{1}{2}$

$x = \frac{7\pi}{6}, \frac{11\pi}{6}$

15. $\cot x = -1$

$x = \frac{3\pi}{4}, \frac{7\pi}{4}$

16. $\sin x = \frac{\sqrt{3}}{2}$

$x = \frac{\pi}{3}, \frac{2\pi}{3}$

17. $\tan x = -\frac{\sqrt{3}}{3}$

$x = \frac{5\pi}{6}, \frac{11\pi}{6}$

18. $\cos x = \frac{\sqrt{2}}{2}$

$x = \frac{\pi}{4}, \frac{7\pi}{4}$

19. $\csc x = -2 \Rightarrow \sin x = -\frac{1}{2}$

$x = \frac{7\pi}{6}, \frac{11\pi}{6}$

20. $\sec x = \sqrt{2} \Rightarrow \cos x = \frac{\sqrt{2}}{2}$

$x = \frac{\pi}{4}, \frac{7\pi}{4}$

21. $\cot x = \sqrt{3} \Rightarrow \tan x = \frac{\sqrt{3}}{3}$

$x = \frac{\pi}{6}, \frac{7\pi}{6}$

22. $\sec x = 2 \Rightarrow \cos x = \frac{1}{2}$

$x = \frac{\pi}{3}, \frac{5\pi}{3}$

23. $\tan x = -1$

$x = \frac{3\pi}{4}, \frac{7\pi}{4}$

24. $\csc x = -\sqrt{2} \Rightarrow \sin x = -\frac{\sqrt{2}}{2}$

$x = \frac{5\pi}{4}, \frac{7\pi}{4}$

25. $2\cos x + 1 = 0$

$$2\cos x = -1$$
$$\cos x = -\frac{1}{2}$$
$$x = \frac{2\pi}{3} + 2n\pi$$
$$\text{or } x = \frac{4\pi}{3} + 2n\pi$$

26. $\sqrt{2}\sin x + 1 = 0$

$$\sin x = -\frac{1}{\sqrt{2}}$$
$$x = \frac{5\pi}{4} + 2n\pi$$
$$x = \frac{7\pi}{4} + 2n\pi$$

27. $\sqrt{3}\sec x - 2 = 0$

$$\sqrt{3}\sec x = 2$$
$$\sec x = \frac{2}{\sqrt{3}}$$
$$\cos x = \frac{\sqrt{3}}{2}$$
$$x = \frac{\pi}{6} + 2n\pi$$
$$\text{or } x = \frac{11\pi}{6} + 2n\pi$$

28. $\cot x + 1 = 0$

$$\cot x = -1$$
$$x = \frac{3\pi}{4} + n\pi$$

29. $3\csc^2 x - 4 = 0$

$$\csc^2 x = \frac{4}{3}$$
$$\csc x = \pm\frac{2}{\sqrt{3}}$$
$$\sin x = \pm\frac{\sqrt{3}}{2}$$
$$x = \frac{\pi}{3} + n\pi \text{ or } x = \frac{2\pi}{3} + n\pi$$

30. $3\cot^2 x - 1 = 0$

$$\cot^2 x = \frac{1}{3}$$
$$\cot x = \pm\frac{\sqrt{3}}{3}$$
$$x = \frac{\pi}{3} + n\pi$$
$$x = \frac{2\pi}{3} + n\pi$$

31. $4\cos^2 x - 1 = 0$

$$\cos^2 x = \frac{1}{4}$$
$$\cos x = \pm\frac{1}{2}$$
$$x = \frac{\pi}{3} + n\pi \text{ or } x = \frac{2\pi}{3} + n\pi$$

32. $\cos x(\cos x - 1) = 0$

$\cos x = 0$ or $\cos x = 1$

$x = \dfrac{\pi}{2} + n\pi$ or $x = 2n\pi$

33.

$$\sin^2 x = 3\cos^2 x$$
$$\sin^2 x - 3(1 - \sin^2 x) = 0$$
$$4\sin^2 x = 3$$
$$\sin x = \pm\frac{\sqrt{3}}{2}$$
$$x = \frac{\pi}{3} + n\pi$$
$$\text{or } x = \frac{2\pi}{3} + n\pi$$

34. $(3\tan^2 x - 1)(\tan^2 x - 3) = 0$

$\tan^2 x = \dfrac{1}{3}$ or $\tan^2 x = 3$

$\tan x = \pm\dfrac{1}{\sqrt{3}}$ or $\tan x = \pm\sqrt{3}$

$x = \dfrac{\pi}{6} + n\pi$ $\quad x = \dfrac{\pi}{3} + n\pi$

$x = \dfrac{5\pi}{6} + n\pi$ $\quad x = \dfrac{2\pi}{3} + n\pi$

35. $\tan x + \sqrt{3} = 0$

$$\tan x = -\sqrt{3}$$
$$x = \frac{2\pi}{3}, \frac{5\pi}{3}$$

36. $2\sin x + 1 = 0$

$$\sin x = -\frac{1}{2}$$
$$x = \frac{7\pi}{6}, \frac{11\pi}{6}$$

37. $\csc^2 x - 2 = 0$

$$\csc^2 x = 2$$
$$\csc x = \pm\sqrt{2}$$
$$\sin x = \pm\frac{1}{\sqrt{2}}$$
$$x = \frac{\pi}{4}, \frac{3\pi}{4}, \frac{5\pi}{4}, \frac{7\pi}{4}$$

38. $\tan^2 x - 1 = 0$

$$\tan^2 x = 1$$
$$\tan x = \pm 1$$
$$x = \frac{\pi}{4}, \frac{3\pi}{4}, \frac{5\pi}{4}, \frac{7\pi}{4}$$

39. $3\tan^3 x - \tan x = 0$

$\tan x(3\tan^2 x - 1) = 0$

$\tan x = 0$ or $3\tan^2 x - 1 = 0$

$x = 0, \pi$ $\quad \tan x = \pm\dfrac{\sqrt{3}}{3}$

$$x = \frac{\pi}{6}, \frac{5\pi}{6}, \frac{7\pi}{6}, \frac{11\pi}{6}$$

40.

$$2\sin^2 x = 2 + \cos x$$
$$2 - 2\cos^2 x = 2 + \cos x$$
$$2\cos^2 x + \cos x = 0$$
$$\cos x(2\cos x + 1) = 0$$

$\cos x = 0$ or $2\cos x + 1 = 0$

$x = \dfrac{\pi}{2}, \dfrac{3\pi}{2}$ $\quad 2\cos x = -1$

$$\cos x = -\frac{1}{2}$$
$$x = \frac{2\pi}{3}, \frac{4\pi}{3}$$

41. $\sec^2 x - \sec x - 2 = 0$

$(\sec x - 2)(\sec x + 1) = 0$

$\sec x - 2 = 0$ or $\sec x + 1 = 0$

$\sec x = 2$ $\quad \sec x = -1$

$x = \dfrac{\pi}{3}, \dfrac{5\pi}{3}$ $\quad x = \pi$

42. $\sec x \csc x = 2 \csc x$

$\sec x \csc x - 2 \csc x = 0$

$\csc x(\sec x - 2) = 0$

$\csc x = 0$ or $\sec x - 2 = 0$

No solution $\quad \sec x = 2$

$x = \frac{\pi}{3}, \frac{5\pi}{3}$

43. $2 \sin x + \csc x = 0$

$2 \sin x + \frac{1}{\sin x} = 0$

$2 \sin^2 x + 1 = 0$

Since $2 \sin^2 x + 1 > 0$, there are no solutions.

44. $\sec x + \tan x = 1$

$(\sec x + \tan x)(\sec x - \tan x) = \sec x - \tan x$

$\sec^2 x - \tan^2 x = \sec x - \tan x$

$1 = \sec x - \tan x$

Hence, $\sec x + \tan x = \sec x - \tan x \Rightarrow \tan x = 0$.

$\sec x = 1, \tan x = 0 \Rightarrow x = 0$

45. $\cos x + \sin x \tan x = 2$

$\cos x + \frac{\sin^2 x}{\cos x} = 2$

$\frac{\cos^2 x + \sin^2 x}{\cos x} = 2$

$\frac{1}{\cos x} = 2$

$\cos x = \frac{1}{2}$

$x = \frac{\pi}{3}, \frac{5\pi}{3}$

46. $\sin^2 x + \cos x + 1 = 0$

$(1 - \cos^2 x) + \cos x + 1 = 0$

$\cos^2 x - \cos x - 2 = 0$

$(\cos x - 2)(\cos x + 1) = 0$

$\cos x = 2$, Impossible

$\cos x + 1 = 0 \Rightarrow x = \pi$

47. $\sec^2 x + \tan x = 3$

$(1 + \tan^2 x) + \tan x = 3$

$\tan^2 x + \tan x - 2 = 0$

$(\tan x + 2)(\tan x - 1) = 0$

$\tan x = -2$ or $\tan x = 1$

$x \approx 2.0344, 5.1760 \quad x = \frac{\pi}{4}, \frac{5\pi}{4}$

48. $2 \cos^2 x + \cos x - 1 = (2 \cos x - 1)(\cos x + 1) = 0$

$2 \cos x = 1$ or $\cos x = -1$

$\cos x = \frac{1}{2}$

$x = \frac{\pi}{3}, \frac{5\pi}{3} \quad x = \pi$

49. $2 \sin^2 x + 3 \sin x + 1 = 0$

$y = 2 \sin^2 x + 3 \sin x + 1$

$x \approx 3.6652, 5.7596, 4.7124$

50. $2 \sec^2 x + \tan^2 x - 3 = 0$

$y = \frac{2}{\cos^2 x} + \tan^2 x - 3$

$x \approx 0.5236, 2.6180, 3.6652, 5.7596$

51. $y = 4\sin^2 x - 2\cos x - 1$

$x \approx 0.8614, 5.4218$

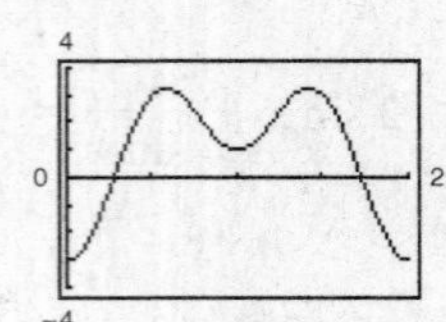

52. $y = \dfrac{1}{\sin^2 x} - \dfrac{3}{\sin x} - 4$

$x \approx 0.2527, 2.8889, 4.7124$

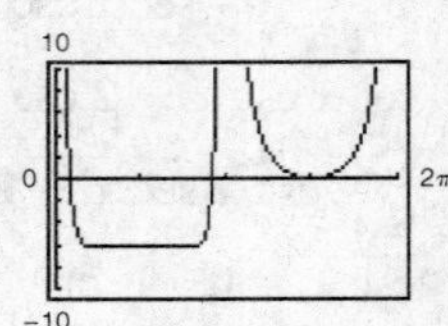

53. $y = \csc x + \cot x - 1 = \dfrac{1}{\sin x} + \dfrac{\cos x}{\sin x} - 1$

$x \approx 1.5708, \quad \left(\dfrac{\pi}{2}\right)$

54. $y = 4\sin x - \cos x + 2$

$x \approx 3.8930, 6.0217$

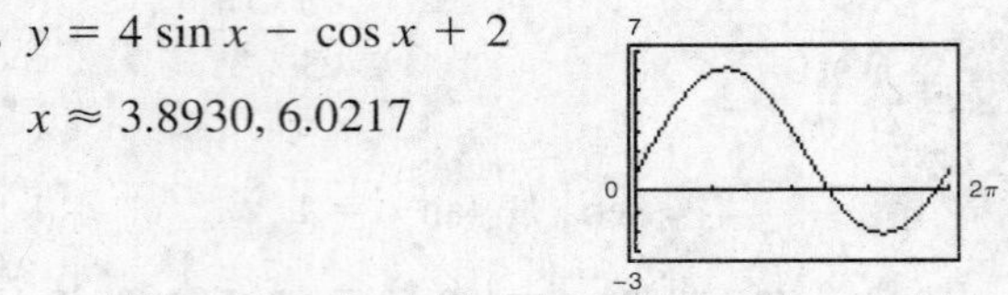

55. $\dfrac{\cos x \cot x}{1 - \sin x} = 3$

Graph $y = \dfrac{\cos x}{(1 - \sin x)\tan x} - 3$.

The solutions are approximately $x \approx 0.5236, x \approx 2.6180$.

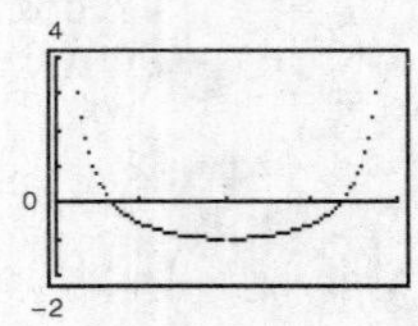

56. $\dfrac{1 + \sin x}{\cos x} + \dfrac{\cos x}{1 + \sin x} - 4 = 0$

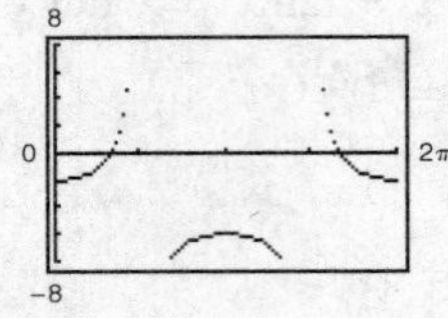

$x \approx 1.0472, 5.2360$

57. (a)

(b) $\sin 2x = x^2 - 2x$

(c) Points of intersection: $(0, 0)$, $(1.7757, -0.3984)$

58. (a)

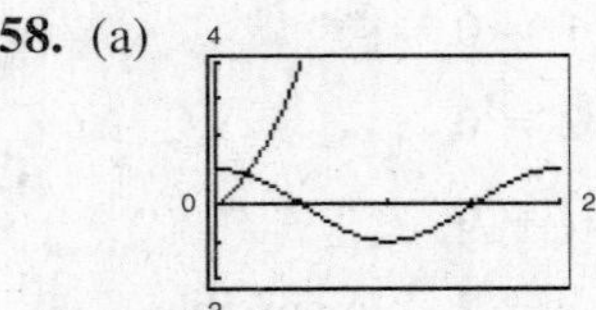

(b) $\cos x = x + x^2$

(c) Points of intersection:

$(-1.2512, 0.3142)$ (outside interval),

$(0.5500, 0.8525)$

59. (a)

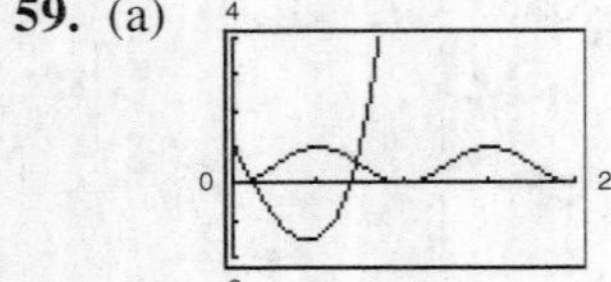

(b) $\sin^2 x = e^x - 4x$

(c) Points of intersection:

$(0.3194, 0.0986)$, $(2.2680, 0.5878)$

60. (a)

(b) $\cos^2 x = e^{-x} + x - 1$

(c) Points of intersection:

$(0.9510, 0.3374)$, and

$(-0.8266, -0.4589)$ (outside interval)

61. $\cos \frac{x}{4} = 0$

$\frac{x}{4} = \frac{\pi}{2} + 2n\pi$ or $\frac{x}{4} = \frac{3\pi}{2} + 2n\pi$

$x = 2\pi + 8n\pi$ or $x = 6\pi + 8n\pi$

Combining, $x = 2\pi + 4n\pi$.

62. $\sin \frac{x}{2} = 0$

$\frac{x}{2} = n\pi$

$x = 2n\pi$

63. $\sin 4x = 1$

$4x = \frac{\pi}{2} + 2n\pi$

$x = \frac{\pi}{8} + \frac{n\pi}{2}$

64. $\cos 2x = -1$

$2x = \pi + 2n\pi$

$x = \frac{\pi}{2} + n\pi$

65. $\sin 2x = -\frac{\sqrt{3}}{2}$

$2x = \frac{4\pi}{3} + 2n\pi$ or $2x = \frac{5\pi}{3} + 2n\pi$

$x = \frac{2\pi}{3} + n\pi$ $\quad x = \frac{5\pi}{6} + n\pi$

66. $\sec 4x = 2$

$4x = \frac{\pi}{3} + 2n\pi$ or $4x = \frac{5\pi}{3} + 2n\pi$

$x = \frac{\pi}{12} + \frac{n\pi}{2}$ $\quad x = \frac{5\pi}{12} + \frac{n\pi}{2}$

67. $2 \sin^2 2x = 1$

$\sin^2 2x = \frac{1}{2}$

$\sin 2x = \pm\frac{\sqrt{2}}{2}$

$2x = \frac{\pi}{4} + \frac{n\pi}{2}$

$x = \frac{\pi}{8} + \frac{n\pi}{4}$

68. $\tan^2 3x = 3$

$\tan 3x = \pm\sqrt{3}$

$3x = \frac{\pi}{3} + n\pi$ or $3x = \frac{2\pi}{3} + n\pi$

$x = \frac{\pi}{9} + \frac{n\pi}{3}$ or $x = \frac{2\pi}{9} + \frac{n\pi}{3}$

69. $\tan 3x(\tan x - 1) = 0$

$\tan 3x = 0$ or $\tan x - 1 = 0$

$3x = n\pi$ or $x = \frac{\pi}{4} + n\pi$

$x = \frac{n\pi}{3}$ $\quad x = \frac{\pi}{4} + n\pi$

70. $\cos 2x(2 \cos x + 1) = 0$

$\cos 2x = 0$ or $2 \cos x + 1 = 0$

$2x = \frac{\pi}{2} + n\pi$ $\quad \cos x = -\frac{1}{2}$

$x = \frac{\pi}{4} + \frac{n\pi}{2}$ $\quad x = \frac{2\pi}{3} + 2n\pi$

$x = \frac{4\pi}{3} + 2n\pi$

71. $\cos\dfrac{x}{2} = \dfrac{\sqrt{2}}{2}$

$\dfrac{x}{2} = \dfrac{\pi}{4} + 2n\pi$ or $\dfrac{x}{2} = \dfrac{7\pi}{4} + 2n\pi$

$x = \dfrac{\pi}{2} + 4n\pi$ $\quad x = \dfrac{7\pi}{2} + 4n\pi$

72. $\tan\dfrac{x}{3} = 1$

$\dfrac{x}{3} = \dfrac{\pi}{4} + n\pi$

$x = \dfrac{3\pi}{4} + 3n\pi$

73. $y = \sin\dfrac{\pi x}{2} + 1$

From the graph in the textbook we see that the curve has x-intercepts at $x = -1$ and at $x = 3$.

74. $y = \sin \pi x + \cos \pi x$

From the graph in the textbook, we see that the curve has x-intercepts at $x = -0.25, 0.75, 1.75$, and 2.75.

75. $y = \tan^2\left(\dfrac{\pi x}{6}\right) - 3$

From the graph in the textbook, we see that the curve has x-intercepts at $x = \pm 2$.

76. $y = \sec^4\left(\dfrac{\pi x}{8}\right) - 4$

From the graph in the textbook, we see that the curve has x-intercepts at $x = -2, 2$.

77. $2\cos x - \sin x = 0$

Graph $y_1 = 2\cos x - \sin x$ and estimate the zeros.

$x \approx 1.1071, 4.2487$

78. $y = 2\sin x + \cos x$

$x \approx 2.6779, 5.8195$

79. $x\tan x - 1 = 0$

Graph $y_1 = x\tan x - 1$ and estimate the zeros.

$x \approx 0.8603, 3.4256$

80. $2x\sin x - 2 = 0$

$y = 2x\sin x - 2$

$x \approx 1.1142, 2.7726$

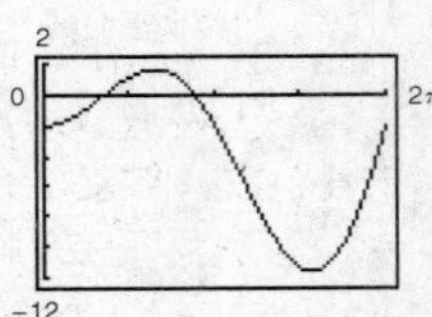

81. $\sec^2 x + 0.5\tan x - 1 = 0$

Graph $y_1 = \dfrac{1}{(\cos x)^2} + 0.5\tan x - 1$.

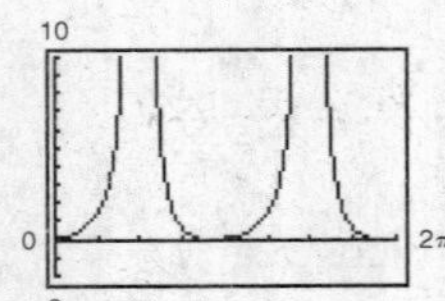

$x = 0, x \approx 2.6779, 3.1416, 5.8195$

82. $\csc^2 x + 0.5\cot x - 5 = 0$

$y_1 = \left(\dfrac{1}{\sin x}\right)^2 + \dfrac{1}{2\tan x} - 5$

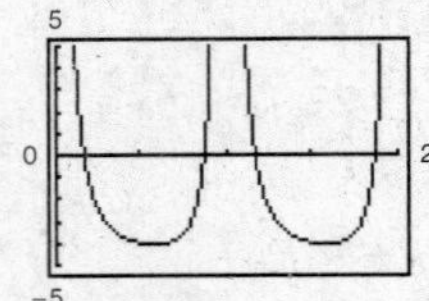

$x \approx 0.5153, 2.7259, 3.6569, 5.8675$

83. $12\sin^2 x - 13\sin x + 3 = 0$

Graph $y_1 = 12\sin^2 x - 13\sin x + 3$.

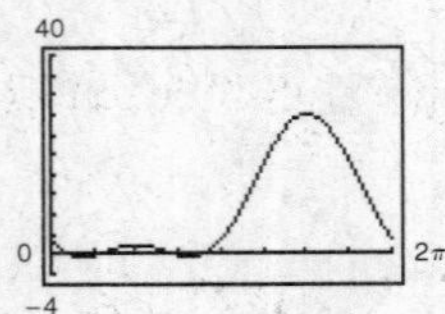

$x \approx 0.3398, 0.8481, 2.2935, 2.8018$

84. $3\tan^2 x + 4\tan x - 4 = 0$

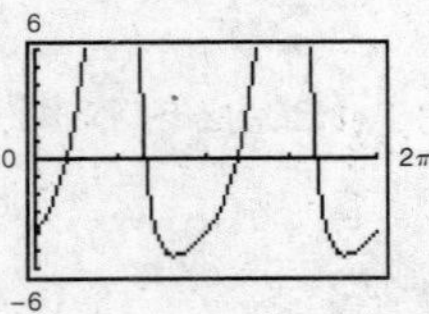

$x \approx 0.5880, 2.0344, 3.7296, 5.1760$

85. $3\tan^2 x + 5\tan x - 4 = 0, \quad \left[-\frac{\pi}{2}, \frac{\pi}{2}\right]$

$x \approx -1.154, 0.534$

86. $y = \cos^2 x - 2\cos x - 1 = 0, \ [0, \pi]$

$x \approx 1.998$

87. $4\cos^2 x - 2\sin x + 1 = 0, \quad \left[-\frac{\pi}{2}, \frac{\pi}{2}\right]$

$x \approx 1.110$

88. $y = 2\sec^2 x + \tan x - 6 = 0, \quad \left[-\frac{\pi}{2}, \frac{\pi}{2}\right]$

$x \approx -1.035, 0.870$

89. $f(x) = \sin 2x$

(a) 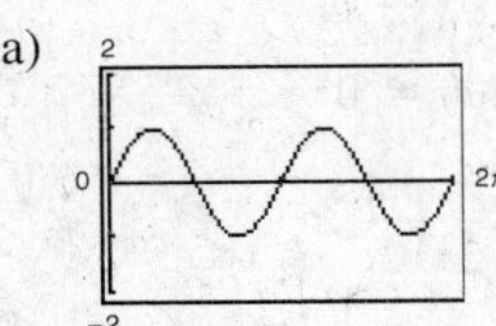

Maxima: (0.7854, 1), (3.9270, 1)

Minima: (2.3562, −1), (5.4978, −1)

(b) $2\cos 2x = 0$

$\cos 2x = 0$

$2x = \frac{\pi}{2} + n\pi$

$x = \frac{\pi}{4} + \frac{n\pi}{2}$

The zeros are 0.7854, 2.3562, 3.9270, and 5.4978.

90. $f(x) = \cos 2x$

(a) 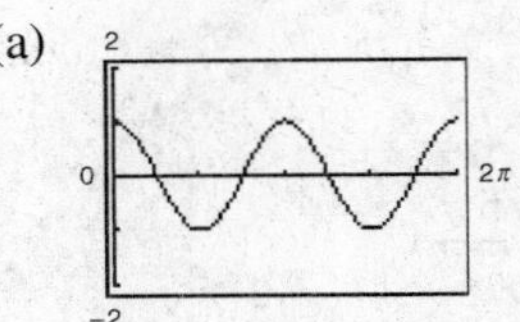

Maxima: (0, 1), (3.1416, 1), (6.2832, 1)

Minima: (1.5708, −1), (4.7124, −1)

(b) $-2\sin 2x = 0$

$\sin 2x = 0$

$2x = n\pi$

$x = \frac{n\pi}{2}$

The zeros are 0, 1.5708, 3.1416, 4.7124, and 6.2832.

91. $f(x) = \sin^2 x + \cos x$

(a) 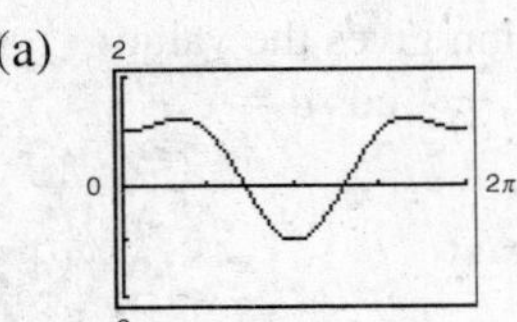

Maxima: (1.0472, 1.25), (5.2360, 1.25)

Minima: (3.1416, −1)

(b) $2\sin x\cos x - \sin x = 0$

$\sin x(2\cos x - 1) = 0$

$\sin x = 0 \Rightarrow x = n\pi$

$\cos x = \frac{1}{2} \Rightarrow x = \frac{\pi}{3} + 2n\pi, \frac{5\pi}{3} + 2n\pi$

The zeros are 1.0472, 3.1416, and 5.2360.

92. $f(x) = \cos^2 x - \sin x$

(a) 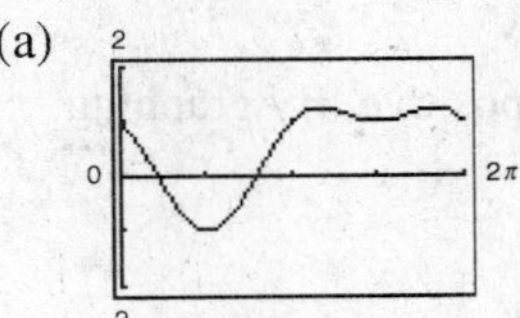

Maxima: (3.6652, 1.25), (5.7596, 1.25)

Minima: (1.5708, −1)

(b) $-2\sin x\cos x - \cos x = 0$

$\cos x(2\sin x + 1) = 0$

$\cos x = 0 \Rightarrow x = \frac{\pi}{2} + n\pi$

$\sin x = -\frac{1}{2} \Rightarrow x = \frac{7\pi}{6} + 2n\pi, \frac{11\pi}{6} + 2n\pi$

The zeros are 1.5708, 3.6652, 5.7596, and 4.7124.

93. (a) $f(x) = \sin x + \cos x$

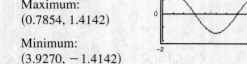

Maximum:
$(0.7854, 1.4142)$

Minimum:
$(3.9270, -1.4142)$

(b) $\cos x - \sin x = 0$

$$\cos x = \sin x$$

$$1 = \frac{\sin x}{\cos x}$$

$$\tan x = 1$$

$$x = \frac{\pi}{4}, \frac{5\pi}{4}$$

$$f\left(\frac{\pi}{4}\right) = \sin\frac{\pi}{4} + \cos\frac{\pi}{4} = \frac{\sqrt{2}}{2} + \frac{\sqrt{2}}{2} = \sqrt{2}$$

$$f\left(\frac{5\pi}{4}\right) = \sin\frac{5\pi}{4} + \cos\frac{5\pi}{4}$$

$$= -\sin\frac{\pi}{4} + \left(-\cos\frac{\pi}{4}\right)$$

$$= -\frac{\sqrt{2}}{2} - \frac{\sqrt{2}}{2} = -\sqrt{2}$$

Therefore, the maximum point in the interval $[0, 2\pi)$ is $(\pi/4, \sqrt{2})$ and the minimum point is $(5\pi/4, -\sqrt{2})$.

94. $y = 2\sin x + \cos 2x$

(a)

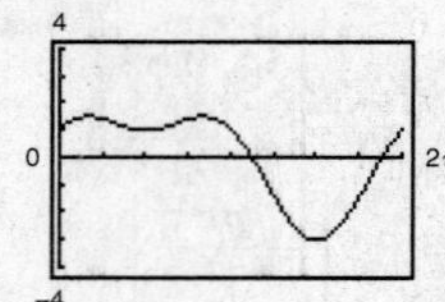

Maximum: $(0.5236, 1.5)$, $(2.6180, 1.5)$

Minimum: $(4.7124, -3.0)$

(b) $2\cos x - 4\sin x\cos x = 0$

$$2\cos x(1 - 2\sin x) = 0$$

$$\cos x = 0 \Rightarrow x = \frac{\pi}{2}, \frac{3\pi}{2}$$

$$1 - 2\sin x = 0 \Rightarrow \sin x = \frac{1}{2} \Rightarrow x = \frac{\pi}{6}, \frac{5\pi}{6}$$

The zeros are 0.5236, 2.618, 4.712 and 1.571. The first three correspond to the values in (a).

95. $f(x) = \tan\dfrac{\pi x}{4}$

$\tan 0 = 0$, but 0 is not positive. By graphing

$$y = \tan\frac{\pi x}{4} - x,$$

you see that the smallest positive fixed point is $x = 1$.

96. Graph $y = \cos x$ and $y = x$ on the same set of axes. Their point of intersection gives the value of c such that $f(c) = c \Rightarrow \cos c = c$.

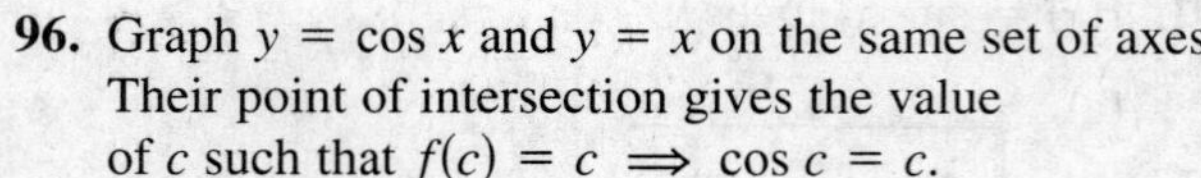

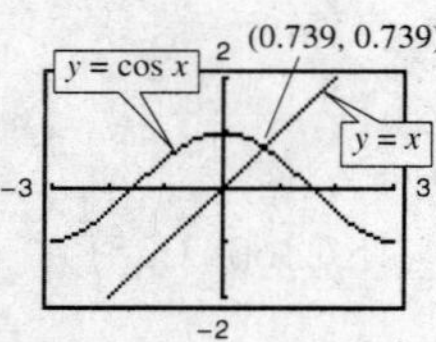

$c \approx 0.739$

97. $f(x) = \cos\dfrac{1}{x}$

(a) The domain of $f(x)$ is all real numbers except 0.

(b) The graph has y-axis symmetry and a horizontal asymptote at $y = 1$.

(c) As $x \to 0$, $f(x)$ oscillates between -1 and 1.

(d) There are an infinite number of solutions in the interval $[-1, 1]$.

$$\frac{1}{x} = \frac{\pi}{2} + n\pi = \frac{\pi + 2n\pi}{2} \Rightarrow x = \frac{2}{\pi(2n + 1)}$$

(e) The greatest solution appears to occur at $x \approx 0.6366$.

98. $f(x) = \dfrac{\sin x}{x}$

(a) Domain: all real numbers except $x = 0$.

(b) The graph has y-axis symmetry.

Horizontal asymptote: $y = 0$

(c) As $x \to 0, f(x) \to 1$.

(d) $\sin x/x = 0$ has four solutions in the interval $[-8, 8]$.

$$(\sin x)\left(\frac{1}{x}\right) = 0$$

$$\sin x = 0$$

$$x = -2\pi, -\pi, \pi, 2\pi$$

99. $S = 74.50 - 43.75 \cos \dfrac{\pi t}{6}$

t	1	2	3	4	5	6	7	8	9	10	11	12
S	36.6	52.6	74.5	96.4	112.4	118.3	112.4	96.4	74.5	52.6	36.6	30.8

$S > 100$ for $t = 5, 6, 7$ (May, June, July)

100. $D = 31 \sin\left(\dfrac{2\pi}{365}t - 1.4\right)$

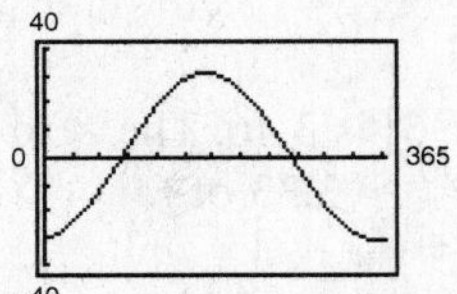

$D > 20°$ for $123 \le t \le 223$ days

101.
$$y = \frac{1}{12}(\cos 8t - 3 \sin 8t)$$

$$\frac{1}{12}(\cos 8t - 3 \sin 8t) = 0$$

$$\cos 8t = 3 \sin 8t$$

$$\frac{1}{3} = \tan 8t$$

$$8t = 0.32175 + n\pi$$

$$t = 0.04 + \frac{n\pi}{8}$$

In the interval $0 \le t \le 1$, $t = 0.04, 0.43$, and 0.83 second.

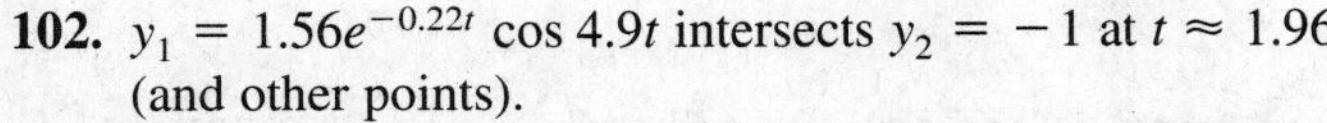

102. $y_1 = 1.56e^{-0.22t} \cos 4.9t$ intersects $y_2 = -1$ at $t \approx 1.96$ (and other points).

The displacement does not exceed one foot from equilibrium after $t = 1.96$ seconds.

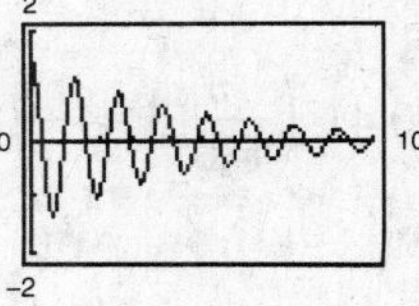

103.
$$r = \frac{1}{32}v_0^2 \sin 2\theta$$

$$300 = \frac{1}{32}(100)^2 \sin 2\theta$$

$\sin 2\theta = 0.96$

$2\theta \approx 1.287$ or $2\theta \approx \pi - 1.287 \approx 1.855$

$\theta \approx 0.6435 \approx 37°$ or $\theta \approx 0.9275 \approx 53°$

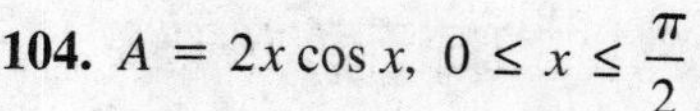

104. $A = 2x \cos x,\ 0 \le x \le \dfrac{\pi}{2}$

(a)

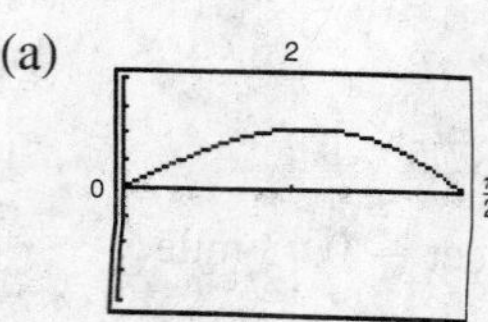

The maximum area of $A \approx 1.12$ occurs when $x \approx 0.86$.

(b) $A \ge 1$ for $0.6 < x < 1.1$

105. (a)

Unemployment rate

Year ($0 \leftrightarrow 1990$)

(b) Models 1 and 2 are both good fits, but model 1 seems better.

(c) The constant term 5.45 gives the average unemployment rate, 5.45%.

(d) The length is approximately one period

$$\frac{2\pi}{0.47} \approx 13.37 \text{ years.}$$

(e) $r = 1.24 \sin(0.47t + 0.40) + 5.45 = 5.0$

Using a graphing utility, $t \approx 19.99 \approx 20$, or 2010.

106. $f(x) = 3 \sin(0.6x - 2)$

(a) Zero: $\sin(0.6x - 2) = 0$

$$0.6x - 2 = 0$$

$$0.6x = 2$$

$$x = \frac{2}{0.6} = \frac{10}{3}$$

(b) $g(x) = -0.45x^2 + 5.52x - 13.70$

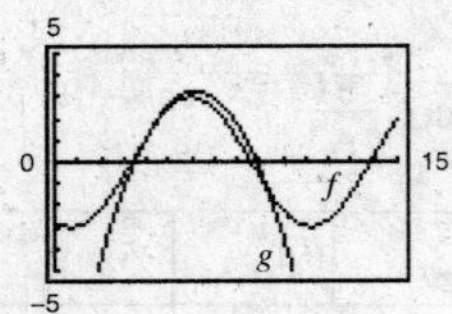

For $3.5 \le x \le 6$ the approximation appears to be good. Answers will vary.

(c) $-0.45x^2 + 5.52x - 13.70 = 0$

$$x = \frac{-5.52 \pm \sqrt{(5.52)^2 - 4(-0.45)(-13.70)}}{2(-0.45)}$$

$$x \approx 3.46, 8.81$$

The zero of g on $[0, 6]$ is 3.46. The zero is close to the zero $\frac{10}{3} \approx 3.33$ of f.

107. False. $\sin x - x = 0$ has one solution, $x = 0$.

108. False. There might not be periodicity, as in the equation $\sin(x^2) = 0$.

109. False. The equation has no solution because $-1 \le \sin x \le 1$.

110. Answers will vary.

111. $124° = 124°\left(\frac{\pi}{180°}\right) \approx 2.164$ radians

112. $486° = 486°\left(\frac{\pi}{180°}\right) \approx 8.482$ radians

113. $-0.41° = -0.41°\left(\frac{\pi}{180°}\right) \approx -0.007$ radian

114. $-210.55° = -210.55°\left(\frac{\pi}{180°}\right) \approx -3.675$ radians

115. $\tan 30° = \frac{14}{x} \implies x = \frac{14}{\tan 30°} = \frac{14}{\sqrt{3}/3} \approx 24.249$

116. $\sin 70° = \frac{x}{10} \implies x = 10 \cdot \sin 70° \approx 9.397 \approx 9.4$

117. $\tan 87.5° = \frac{x}{100}$

$$x = 100 \tan 87.5°$$

$$\approx 2290.4 \text{ feet} \approx 0.43 \text{ mile}$$

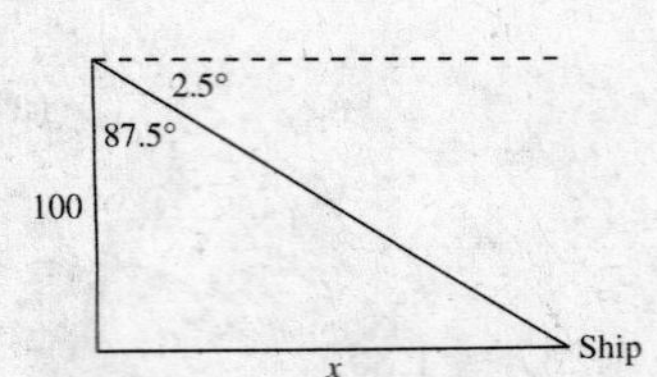

118. Answers will vary.

Section 5.4 Sum and Difference Formulas

- You should memorize the sum and difference formulas.

$$\sin(u \pm v) = \sin u \cos v \pm \cos u \sin v$$

$$\cos(u \pm v) = \cos u \cos v \mp \sin u \sin v$$

$$\tan(u \pm v) = \frac{\tan u \pm \tan v}{1 \mp \tan u \tan v}$$

- You should be able to use these formulas to find the values of the trigonometric functions of angles whose sums or differences are special angles.
- You should be able to use these formulas to solve trigonometric equations.

Vocabulary Check

1. $\sin u \cos v - \cos u \sin v$

2. $\cos u \cos v - \sin u \sin v$

3. $\dfrac{\tan u + \tan v}{1 - \tan u \tan v}$

4. $\sin u \cos v + \cos u \sin v$

5. $\cos u \cos v + \sin u \sin v$

6. $\dfrac{\tan u - \tan v}{1 + \tan u \tan v}$

1. (a) $\cos(240° - 0°) = \cos(240°) = -\frac{1}{2}$

(b) $\cos(240°) - \cos 0° = -\frac{1}{2} - 1 = -\frac{3}{2}$

2. (a) $\sin(405° + 120°) = \sin 405° \cos 120° + \cos 405° \sin 120°$

$$= \frac{\sqrt{2}}{2}\left(-\frac{1}{2}\right) + \frac{\sqrt{2}}{2}\left(\frac{\sqrt{3}}{2}\right) = \frac{\sqrt{6} - \sqrt{2}}{4}$$

(b) $\sin 405° + \sin 120° = \dfrac{\sqrt{2}}{2} + \dfrac{\sqrt{3}}{2} = \dfrac{\sqrt{2} + \sqrt{3}}{2}$

3. (a) $\cos\left(\dfrac{\pi}{4} + \dfrac{\pi}{3}\right) = \cos\dfrac{\pi}{4}\cos\dfrac{\pi}{3} - \sin\dfrac{\pi}{4}\sin\dfrac{\pi}{3}$

$$= \frac{\sqrt{2}}{2}\left(\frac{1}{2}\right) - \frac{\sqrt{2}}{2}\left(\frac{\sqrt{3}}{2}\right)$$

$$= \frac{\sqrt{2} - \sqrt{6}}{4}$$

(b) $\cos\dfrac{\pi}{4} + \cos\dfrac{\pi}{3} = \dfrac{\sqrt{2}}{2} + \dfrac{1}{2} = \dfrac{\sqrt{2} + 1}{2}$

4. (a) $\sin\left(\dfrac{2\pi}{3} + \dfrac{5\pi}{6}\right) = \sin\left(\dfrac{9\pi}{6}\right) = -1$

(b) $\sin\dfrac{2\pi}{3} + \sin\dfrac{5\pi}{6} = \dfrac{\sqrt{3}}{2} + \dfrac{1}{2} = \dfrac{\sqrt{3} + 1}{2}$

5. (a) $\sin(315° - 60°) = \sin 315° \cos 60° - \cos 315° \sin 60° = -\dfrac{\sqrt{2}}{2} \cdot \dfrac{1}{2} - \dfrac{\sqrt{2}}{2} \cdot \dfrac{\sqrt{3}}{2} = \dfrac{-\sqrt{2} - \sqrt{6}}{4}$

(b) $\sin 315° - \sin 60° = -\dfrac{\sqrt{2}}{2} - \dfrac{\sqrt{3}}{2} = -\dfrac{\sqrt{2} + \sqrt{3}}{2}$

6. (a) $\sin\left(\dfrac{7\pi}{6} - \dfrac{\pi}{3}\right) = \sin\left(\dfrac{5\pi}{6}\right) = \sin\dfrac{\pi}{6} = \dfrac{1}{2}$

(b) $\sin\dfrac{7\pi}{6} - \sin\dfrac{\pi}{3} = -\dfrac{1}{2} - \dfrac{\sqrt{3}}{2} = \dfrac{-1 - \sqrt{3}}{2}$

7. $\sin 105° = \sin(60° + 45°)$

$= \sin 60° \cos 45° + \sin 45° \cos 60°$

$= \frac{\sqrt{3}}{2} \cdot \frac{\sqrt{2}}{2} + \frac{\sqrt{2}}{2} \cdot \frac{1}{2}$

$= \frac{\sqrt{2}}{4}(\sqrt{3} + 1)$

$\cos 105° = \cos(60° + 45°)$

$= \cos 60° \cos 45° - \sin 60° \sin 45°$

$= \frac{1}{2} \cdot \frac{\sqrt{2}}{2} - \frac{\sqrt{3}}{2} \cdot \frac{\sqrt{2}}{2}$

$= \frac{\sqrt{2}}{4}(1 - \sqrt{3})$

$\tan 105° = \tan(60° + 45°)$

$= \frac{\tan 60° + \tan 45°}{1 - \tan 60° \tan 45°}$

$= \frac{\sqrt{3} + 1}{1 - \sqrt{3}} = \frac{\sqrt{3} + 1}{1 - \sqrt{3}} \cdot \frac{1 + \sqrt{3}}{1 + \sqrt{3}}$

$= \frac{4 + 2\sqrt{3}}{-2} = -2 - \sqrt{3}$

8. $165° = 135° + 30°$

$\sin 165° = \sin(135° + 30°)$

$= \sin 135° \cos 30° + \sin 30° \cos 135°$

$= \sin 45° \cos 30° - \sin 30° \cos 45°$

$= \frac{\sqrt{2}}{2} \cdot \frac{\sqrt{3}}{2} - \frac{1}{2} \cdot \frac{\sqrt{2}}{2} = \frac{\sqrt{2}}{4}(\sqrt{3} - 1)$

$\cos 165° = \cos(135° + 30°)$

$= \cos 135° \cos 30° - \sin 135° \sin 30°$

$= -\cos 45° \cos 30° - \sin 45° \sin 30°$

$= -\frac{\sqrt{2}}{2} \cdot \frac{\sqrt{3}}{2} - \frac{\sqrt{2}}{2} \cdot \frac{1}{2}$

$= -\frac{\sqrt{2}}{4}(\sqrt{3} + 1)$

$\tan 165° = \tan(135° + 30°)$

$= \frac{\tan 135° + \tan 30°}{1 - \tan 135° \tan 30°}$

$= \frac{-\tan 45° + \tan 30°}{1 + \tan 45° \tan 30°}$

$= \frac{-1 + (\sqrt{3}/3)}{1 + (\sqrt{3}/3)} = -2 + \sqrt{3}$

9. $\sin 195° = \sin(225° - 30°)$

$= \sin 225° \cos 30° - \sin 30° \cos 225°$

$= -\sin 45° \cos 30° + \sin 30° \cos 45°$

$= -\frac{\sqrt{2}}{2} \cdot \frac{\sqrt{3}}{2} + \frac{1}{2} \cdot \frac{\sqrt{2}}{2} = \frac{\sqrt{2}}{4}(1 - \sqrt{3})$

$\cos 195° = \cos(225° - 30°)$

$= \cos 225° \cos 30° + \sin 225° \sin 30°$

$= -\cos 45° \cos 30° - \sin 45° \sin 30°$

$= -\frac{\sqrt{2}}{2} \cdot \frac{\sqrt{3}}{2} - \frac{\sqrt{2}}{2} \cdot \frac{1}{2} = -\frac{\sqrt{2}}{4}(\sqrt{3} + 1)$

$\tan 195° = \tan(225° - 30°)$

$= \frac{\tan 225° - \tan 30°}{1 + \tan 225° \tan 30°}$

$= \frac{\tan 45° - \tan 30°}{1 + \tan 45° \tan 30°}$

$= \frac{1 - (\sqrt{3}/3)}{1 + (\sqrt{3}/3)} = \frac{3 - \sqrt{3}}{3 + \sqrt{3}} \cdot \frac{3 - \sqrt{3}}{3 - \sqrt{3}}$

$= \frac{12 - 6\sqrt{3}}{6} = 2 - \sqrt{3}$

10. $255° = 300° - 45°$

$\sin 255° = \sin(300° - 45°)$

$= \sin 300° \cos 45° - \cos 300° \cos 45°$

$= \left(-\frac{\sqrt{3}}{2}\right)\frac{\sqrt{2}}{2} - \frac{1}{2}\left(\frac{\sqrt{2}}{2}\right) = \frac{-\sqrt{6} - \sqrt{2}}{4}$

$\cos 255° = \cos(300° - 45°)$

$= \cos 300° \cos 45° + \sin 300° \sin 45°$

$= \frac{1}{2}\left(\frac{\sqrt{2}}{2}\right) + \left(-\frac{\sqrt{3}}{2}\right)\frac{\sqrt{2}}{2} = \frac{-\sqrt{6} + \sqrt{2}}{4}$

$\tan 255° = \tan(300° - 45°)$

$= \frac{\tan 300° - \tan 45°}{1 + \tan 300° \tan 45°}$

$= \frac{-\sqrt{3} - 1}{1 + (-\sqrt{3})(1)}$

$= \frac{1 + \sqrt{3}}{\sqrt{3} - 1}$

$= \frac{1 + \sqrt{3}}{\sqrt{3} - 1} \cdot \frac{\sqrt{3} + 1}{\sqrt{3} + 1}$

$= \frac{4 + 2\sqrt{3}}{2} = 2 + \sqrt{3}$

11. $\sin\frac{11\pi}{12} = \sin\left(\frac{3\pi}{4} + \frac{\pi}{6}\right)$

$= \sin\frac{3\pi}{4}\cos\frac{\pi}{6} + \sin\frac{\pi}{6}\cos\frac{3\pi}{4}$

$= \frac{\sqrt{2}}{2}\cdot\frac{\sqrt{3}}{2} + \frac{1}{2}\left(-\frac{\sqrt{2}}{2}\right) = \frac{\sqrt{2}}{4}(\sqrt{3} - 1)$

$\cos\frac{11\pi}{12} = \cos\left(\frac{3\pi}{4} + \frac{\pi}{6}\right)$

$= \cos\frac{3\pi}{4}\cos\frac{\pi}{6} - \sin\frac{3\pi}{4}\sin\frac{\pi}{6}$

$= -\frac{\sqrt{2}}{2}\cdot\frac{\sqrt{3}}{2} - \frac{\sqrt{2}}{2}\cdot\frac{1}{2}$

$= -\frac{\sqrt{2}}{4}(\sqrt{3} + 1)$

$\tan\frac{11\pi}{12} = \tan\left(\frac{3\pi}{4} + \frac{\pi}{6}\right)$

$= \frac{\tan(3\pi/4) + \tan(\pi/6)}{1 - \tan(3\pi/4)\tan(\pi/6)}$

$= \frac{-1 + (\sqrt{3}/3)}{1 - (-1)(\sqrt{3}/3)}$

$= \frac{-3 + \sqrt{3}}{3 + \sqrt{3}}\cdot\frac{3 - \sqrt{3}}{3 - \sqrt{3}}$

$= \frac{-12 + 6\sqrt{3}}{6} = -2 + \sqrt{3}$

12. $\frac{17\pi}{12} = \frac{7\pi}{6} + \frac{\pi}{4}$

$\sin\frac{17\pi}{12} = \sin\left(\frac{7\pi}{6} + \frac{\pi}{4}\right)$

$= \sin\frac{7\pi}{6}\cos\frac{\pi}{4} + \cos\frac{7\pi}{6}\sin\frac{\pi}{4}$

$= \left(-\frac{1}{2}\right)\left(\frac{\sqrt{2}}{2}\right) + \left(-\frac{\sqrt{3}}{2}\right)\frac{\sqrt{2}}{2}$

$= \frac{-\sqrt{6} - \sqrt{2}}{4}$

$\cos\frac{17\pi}{12} = \cos\left(\frac{7\pi}{6} + \frac{\pi}{4}\right)$

$= \cos\frac{7\pi}{6}\cos\frac{\pi}{4} - \sin\frac{7\pi}{6}\sin\frac{\pi}{4}$

$= \left(-\frac{\sqrt{3}}{2}\right)\frac{\sqrt{2}}{2} - \left(-\frac{1}{2}\right)\frac{\sqrt{2}}{2}$

$= \frac{\sqrt{2} - \sqrt{6}}{4}$

$\tan\frac{17\pi}{12} = \tan\left(\frac{7\pi}{6} + \frac{\pi}{4}\right)$

$= \frac{\tan\frac{7\pi}{6} + \tan\frac{\pi}{4}}{1 - \tan\frac{7\pi}{6}\tan\frac{\pi}{4}} = \frac{\frac{\sqrt{3}}{3} + 1}{1 - \frac{\sqrt{3}}{3}(1)}$

$= \frac{\sqrt{3} + 3}{3 - \sqrt{3}} = 2 + \sqrt{3}$

13. $-\frac{\pi}{12} = \frac{\pi}{6} - \frac{\pi}{4}$

$\sin\left(-\frac{\pi}{12}\right) = \sin\left(\frac{\pi}{6} - \frac{\pi}{4}\right)$

$= \sin\frac{\pi}{6}\cos\frac{\pi}{4} - \sin\frac{\pi}{4}\cos\frac{\pi}{6}$

$= \frac{1}{2}\cdot\frac{\sqrt{2}}{2} - \frac{\sqrt{2}}{2}\cdot\frac{\sqrt{3}}{2} = \frac{\sqrt{2}}{4}(1 - \sqrt{3})$

$\cos\left(-\frac{\pi}{12}\right) = \cos\left(\frac{\pi}{6} - \frac{\pi}{4}\right)$

$= \cos\frac{\pi}{6}\cos\frac{\pi}{4} + \sin\frac{\pi}{6}\sin\frac{\pi}{4}$

$= \frac{\sqrt{3}}{2}\cdot\frac{\sqrt{2}}{2} + \frac{1}{2}\cdot\frac{\sqrt{2}}{2} = \frac{\sqrt{2}}{4}(\sqrt{3} + 1)$

$\tan\left(-\frac{\pi}{12}\right) = \tan\left(\frac{\pi}{6} - \frac{\pi}{4}\right)$

$= \frac{\tan(\pi/6) - \tan(\pi/4)}{1 + \tan(\pi/6)\tan(\pi/4)}$

$= \frac{(\sqrt{3}/3) - 1}{1 + (\sqrt{3}/3)} = \frac{\sqrt{3} - 3}{\sqrt{3} + 3}\cdot\frac{\sqrt{3} - 3}{\sqrt{3} - 3}$

$= \frac{12 - 6\sqrt{3}}{-6} = -2 + \sqrt{3}$

14. $-\dfrac{19\pi}{12} = \dfrac{2\pi}{3} - \dfrac{9\pi}{4}$

$$\sin\left(-\frac{19\pi}{12}\right) = \sin\left(\frac{2\pi}{3} - \frac{9\pi}{4}\right)$$

$$= \sin\frac{2\pi}{3}\cos\frac{9\pi}{4} - \cos\frac{2\pi}{3}\sin\frac{9\pi}{4}$$

$$= \frac{\sqrt{3}}{2}\frac{\sqrt{2}}{2} - \left(-\frac{1}{2}\right)\frac{\sqrt{2}}{2} = \frac{\sqrt{6} + \sqrt{2}}{4}$$

$$\cos\left(-\frac{19\pi}{12}\right) = \cos\left(\frac{2\pi}{3} - \frac{9\pi}{4}\right)$$

$$= \cos\frac{2\pi}{3}\cos\frac{9\pi}{4} + \sin\frac{2\pi}{3}\sin\frac{9\pi}{4}$$

$$= \left(-\frac{1}{2}\right)\frac{\sqrt{2}}{2} + \frac{\sqrt{3}}{2}\frac{\sqrt{2}}{2} = \frac{\sqrt{6} - \sqrt{2}}{4}$$

$$\tan\left(-\frac{19\pi}{12}\right) = \tan\left(\frac{2\pi}{3} - \frac{9\pi}{4}\right) = \frac{\tan\frac{2\pi}{3} - \tan\frac{9\pi}{4}}{1 + \tan\frac{2\pi}{3}\tan\frac{9\pi}{4}}$$

$$= \frac{-\sqrt{3} - 1}{1 + (-\sqrt{3})(1)}$$

$$= \frac{\sqrt{3} + 1}{\sqrt{3} - 1}$$

$$= 2 + \sqrt{3}$$

15. $\sin 75° = \sin(30° + 45°)$

$$= \sin 30° \cos 45° + \sin 45° \cos 30°$$

$$= \frac{1}{2} \cdot \frac{\sqrt{2}}{2} + \frac{\sqrt{2}}{2} \cdot \frac{\sqrt{3}}{2} = \frac{\sqrt{2}}{4}(1 + \sqrt{3})$$

$$\cos 75° = \cos(30° + 45°)$$

$$= \cos 30° \cos 45° - \sin 30° \sin 45°$$

$$= \frac{\sqrt{3}}{2} \cdot \frac{\sqrt{2}}{2} - \frac{1}{2} \cdot \frac{\sqrt{2}}{2} = \frac{\sqrt{2}}{4}(\sqrt{3} - 1)$$

$$\tan 75° = \tan(30° + 45°)$$

$$= \frac{\tan 30° + \tan 45°}{1 - \tan 30° \tan 45°}$$

$$= \frac{(\sqrt{3}/3) + 1}{1 - (\sqrt{3}/3)} = \frac{\sqrt{3} + 3}{3 - \sqrt{3}} \cdot \frac{3 + \sqrt{3}}{3 + \sqrt{3}}$$

$$= \frac{6\sqrt{3} + 12}{6} = \sqrt{3} + 2$$

16. $15° = 45° - 30°$

$$\sin 15° = \sin(45° - 30°) = \sin 45° \cos 30° - \cos 45° \sin 30°$$

$$= \left(\frac{\sqrt{2}}{2}\right)\left(\frac{\sqrt{3}}{2}\right) - \left(\frac{\sqrt{2}}{2}\right)\left(\frac{1}{2}\right) = \frac{\sqrt{2}(\sqrt{3} - 1)}{4} = \frac{\sqrt{2}}{4}(\sqrt{3} - 1)$$

$$\cos 15° = \cos(45° - 30°) = \cos 45° \cos 30° + \sin 45° \sin 30°$$

$$= \left(\frac{\sqrt{2}}{2}\right)\left(\frac{\sqrt{3}}{2}\right) + \left(\frac{\sqrt{2}}{2}\right)\left(\frac{1}{2}\right) = \frac{\sqrt{2}(\sqrt{3} + 1)}{4} = \frac{\sqrt{2}}{4}(\sqrt{3} + 1)$$

$$\tan 15° = \tan(45° - 30°) = \frac{\tan 45° - \tan 30°}{1 + \tan 45° \tan 30°}$$

$$= \frac{1 - \frac{\sqrt{3}}{3}}{1 + (1)\left(\frac{\sqrt{3}}{3}\right)} = \frac{\frac{3 - \sqrt{3}}{3}}{\frac{3 + \sqrt{3}}{3}} = \frac{3 - \sqrt{3}}{3 + \sqrt{3}} \cdot \frac{3 - \sqrt{3}}{3 - \sqrt{3}}$$

$$= \frac{12 - 6\sqrt{3}}{6} = 2 - \sqrt{3}$$

17. $-225°$ is coterminal with $135°$, and lies in Quadrant II.

$$\sin(-225°) = \frac{\sqrt{2}}{2}$$

$$\cos(-225°) = -\frac{\sqrt{2}}{2}$$

$$\tan(-225°) = -1$$

18. $-165° = -135° - 30°$

(a) $\sin(-165°) = \sin(-135° - 30°)$

$$= \sin(-135°)\cos 30° - \cos(-135°)\sin 30°$$

$$= \left(-\frac{\sqrt{2}}{2}\right)\frac{\sqrt{3}}{2} - \left(-\frac{\sqrt{2}}{2}\right)\frac{1}{2} = \frac{\sqrt{2} - \sqrt{6}}{4}$$

(b) $\cos(-165°) = \cos(-135° - 30°)$

$$= \cos(-135°)\cos 30° + \sin(-135°)\sin 30°$$

$$= \left(-\frac{\sqrt{2}}{2}\right)\frac{\sqrt{3}}{2} + \left(-\frac{\sqrt{2}}{2}\right)\frac{1}{2} = \frac{-\sqrt{6} - \sqrt{2}}{4}$$

(c) $\tan(-165°) = \tan(-135° - 30°)$

$$= \frac{\tan(-135°) - \tan 30°}{1 + \tan(-135°)\tan 30°}$$

$$= \frac{1 - \sqrt{3}/3}{1 + 1\left(\sqrt{3}/3\right)}$$

$$= \frac{3 - \sqrt{3}}{3 + \sqrt{3}} = \frac{3 - \sqrt{3}}{3 + \sqrt{3}} \cdot \frac{3 - \sqrt{3}}{3 - \sqrt{3}}$$

$$= \frac{12 - 6\sqrt{3}}{6} = 2 - \sqrt{3}$$

19. $\frac{13\pi}{12} = \frac{3\pi}{4} + \frac{\pi}{3}$

$$\sin\frac{13\pi}{12} = \sin\left(\frac{3\pi}{4} + \frac{\pi}{3}\right) = \sin\frac{3\pi}{4}\cos\frac{\pi}{3} + \sin\frac{\pi}{3}\cos\frac{3\pi}{4}$$

$$= \frac{\sqrt{2}}{2}\cdot\frac{1}{2} + \frac{\sqrt{3}}{2}\left(-\frac{\sqrt{2}}{2}\right) = \frac{\sqrt{2} - \sqrt{6}}{4}$$

$$\cos\frac{13\pi}{12} = \cos\left(\frac{3\pi}{4} + \frac{\pi}{3}\right) = \cos\frac{3\pi}{4}\cos\frac{\pi}{3} - \sin\frac{3\pi}{4}\sin\frac{\pi}{3}$$

$$= \left(-\frac{\sqrt{2}}{2}\right)\left(\frac{1}{2}\right) - \left(\frac{\sqrt{2}}{2}\right)\left(\frac{\sqrt{3}}{2}\right) = -\frac{\sqrt{6} + \sqrt{2}}{4}$$

$$\tan\frac{13\pi}{12} = \tan\left(\frac{3\pi}{4} + \frac{\pi}{3}\right) = \frac{\tan(3\pi/4) + \tan(\pi/3)}{1 - \tan(3\pi/4)\tan(\pi/3)}$$

$$= \frac{(-1) + \sqrt{3}}{1 - (-1)\sqrt{3}} = \frac{\sqrt{3} - 1}{\sqrt{3} + 1} = 2 - \sqrt{3}$$

20. $\frac{5\pi}{12} = \frac{\pi}{4} + \frac{\pi}{6}$

$$\sin\left(\frac{5\pi}{12}\right) = \sin\left(\frac{\pi}{4} + \frac{\pi}{6}\right) = \sin\frac{\pi}{4}\cos\frac{\pi}{6} + \sin\frac{\pi}{6}\cos\frac{\pi}{4}$$
$$= \frac{\sqrt{2}}{2}\frac{\sqrt{3}}{2} + \frac{1}{2}\frac{\sqrt{2}}{2} = \frac{\sqrt{6} + \sqrt{2}}{4}$$

$$\cos\left(\frac{5\pi}{12}\right) = \cos\left(\frac{\pi}{4} + \frac{\pi}{6}\right) = \cos\frac{\pi}{4}\cos\frac{\pi}{6} - \sin\frac{\pi}{4}\sin\frac{\pi}{6}$$
$$= \frac{\sqrt{2}}{2}\frac{\sqrt{3}}{2} - \frac{\sqrt{2}}{2}\frac{1}{2} = \frac{\sqrt{6} - \sqrt{2}}{4}$$

$$\tan\left(\frac{5\pi}{12}\right) = \frac{\sin(5\pi/12)}{\cos(5\pi/12)} = \frac{\sqrt{6} + \sqrt{2}}{\sqrt{6} - \sqrt{2}} = 2 + \sqrt{3}$$

21. $-\frac{7\pi}{12} = \frac{\pi}{6} - \frac{3\pi}{4}$

$$\sin\left(-\frac{7\pi}{12}\right) = \sin\left(\frac{\pi}{6} - \frac{3\pi}{4}\right) = \sin\frac{\pi}{6}\cos\frac{3\pi}{4} - \sin\frac{3\pi}{4}\cos\frac{\pi}{6}$$
$$= \frac{1}{2}\left(-\frac{\sqrt{2}}{2}\right) - \frac{\sqrt{2}}{2}\left(\frac{\sqrt{3}}{2}\right) = -\frac{\sqrt{2} + \sqrt{6}}{4}$$

$$\cos\left(-\frac{7\pi}{12}\right) = \cos\left(\frac{\pi}{6} - \frac{3\pi}{4}\right) = \cos\frac{\pi}{6}\cos\frac{3\pi}{4} + \sin\frac{\pi}{6}\sin\frac{3\pi}{4}$$
$$= \frac{\sqrt{3}}{2}\left(-\frac{\sqrt{2}}{2}\right) + \frac{1}{2}\cdot\frac{\sqrt{2}}{2} = \frac{\sqrt{2} - \sqrt{6}}{4}$$

$$\tan\left(-\frac{7\pi}{12}\right) = \tan\left(\frac{\pi}{6} - \frac{3\pi}{4}\right) = \frac{\tan(\pi/6) - \tan(3\pi/4)}{1 + \tan(\pi/6)\tan(3\pi/4)}$$
$$= \frac{\left(\sqrt{3}/3\right) - (-1)}{1 + \left(\sqrt{3}/3\right)(-1)} = \frac{3 + \sqrt{3}}{3 - \sqrt{3}} = 2 + \sqrt{3}$$

22. $\frac{-13\pi}{12} = \frac{-3\pi}{4} - \frac{\pi}{3}$

$$\sin\left(\frac{-13\pi}{12}\right) = \sin\left(\frac{-3\pi}{4} - \frac{\pi}{3}\right) = \sin\left(\frac{-3\pi}{4}\right)\cos\frac{\pi}{3} - \cos\left(\frac{-3\pi}{4}\right)\sin\frac{\pi}{3}$$
$$= \frac{-\sqrt{2}}{2}\left(\frac{1}{2}\right) - \left(\frac{-\sqrt{2}}{2}\right)\frac{\sqrt{3}}{2} = \frac{\sqrt{6} - \sqrt{2}}{4}$$

$$\cos\left(\frac{-13\pi}{12}\right) = \cos\left(\frac{-3\pi}{4} - \frac{\pi}{3}\right) = \cos\left(\frac{-3\pi}{4}\right)\cos\frac{\pi}{3} + \sin\left(\frac{-3\pi}{4}\right)\sin\frac{\pi}{3}$$
$$= \frac{-\sqrt{2}}{2}\left(\frac{1}{2}\right) + \left(\frac{-\sqrt{2}}{2}\right)\frac{\sqrt{3}}{2} = -\frac{\sqrt{6} + \sqrt{2}}{4}$$

$$\tan\left(\frac{-13\pi}{12}\right) = \frac{\sin\left(\frac{-13\pi}{12}\right)}{\cos\left(\frac{-13\pi}{12}\right)} = \frac{\sqrt{2} - \sqrt{6}}{\sqrt{2} + \sqrt{6}} = \sqrt{3} - 2$$

23. $\cos 60° \cos 20° - \sin 60° \sin 20° = \cos(60° + 20°) = \cos 80°$

24. $\sin 110° \cos 80° + \cos 110° \sin 80° = \sin(110° + 80°) = \sin(190°)$

25. $\dfrac{\tan 325° - \tan 86°}{1 + \tan 325° \tan 86°} = \tan(325° - 86°) = \tan 239°$

26. $\dfrac{\tan 154° - \tan 49°}{1 + \tan 154° \tan 49°} = \tan(154° - 49°) = \tan 105°$

27. $\sin 3.5 \cos 1.2 - \cos 3.5 \sin 1.2 = \sin(3.5 - 1.2) = \sin 2.3$

28. $\cos 0.96 \cos 0.42 + \sin 0.96 \sin 0.42 = \cos(0.96 - 0.42) = \cos(0.54)$

29. $\cos\dfrac{\pi}{9}\cos\dfrac{\pi}{7} - \sin\dfrac{\pi}{9}\sin\dfrac{\pi}{7} = \cos\left(\dfrac{\pi}{9} + \dfrac{\pi}{7}\right) = \cos\left(\dfrac{16\pi}{63}\right)$

30. $\sin\dfrac{4\pi}{9}\cos\dfrac{\pi}{8} + \cos\dfrac{4\pi}{9}\sin\dfrac{\pi}{8} = \sin\left(\dfrac{4\pi}{9} + \dfrac{\pi}{8}\right) = \sin\left(\dfrac{41\pi}{72}\right)$

31. $y_1 = \sin\left(\dfrac{\pi}{6} + x\right)$

$= \sin\dfrac{\pi}{6}\cos x + \sin x \cdot \cos\dfrac{\pi}{6}$

$= \dfrac{1}{2}\cos x + \dfrac{\sqrt{3}}{2}\sin x$

$= \dfrac{1}{2}(\cos x + \sqrt{3}\sin x) = y_2$

x	0.2	0.4	0.6	0.8	1.0	1.2	1.4
y_1	0.6621	0.7978	0.9017	0.9696	0.9989	0.9883	0.9384
y_2	0.6621	0.7978	0.9017	0.9696	0.9989	0.9883	0.9384

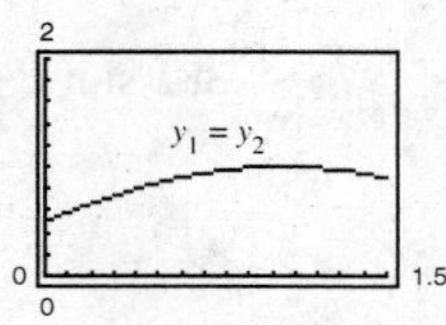

32.

x	0.2	0.4	0.6	0.8	1.0	1.2	1.4
y_1	−0.8335	−0.9266	−0.9829	−0.9999	−0.9771	−0.9153	−0.8170
y_2	−0.8335	−0.9266	−0.9829	−0.9999	−0.9771	−0.9153	−0.8170

$y_1 = \cos\left(\dfrac{5\pi}{4} - x\right) = \cos\dfrac{5\pi}{4}\cos x + \sin\dfrac{5\pi}{4}\sin x$

$= -\dfrac{\sqrt{2}}{2}\cos x - \dfrac{\sqrt{2}}{2}\sin x$

$= -\dfrac{\sqrt{2}}{2}(\cos x + \sin x) = y_2$

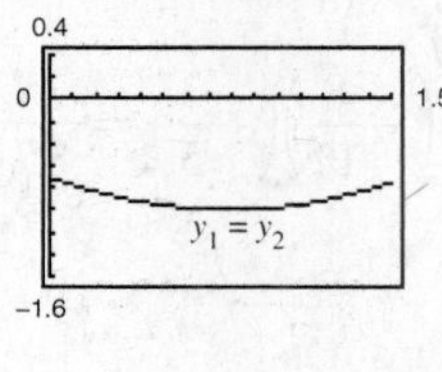

33. $y_1 = \cos(x + \pi)\cos(x - \pi)$

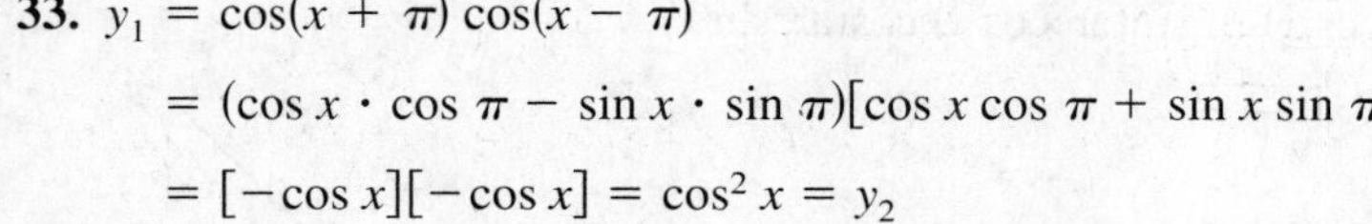

$= (\cos x \cdot \cos \pi - \sin x \cdot \sin \pi)[\cos x \cos \pi + \sin x \sin \pi]$

$= [-\cos x][-\cos x] = \cos^2 x = y_2$

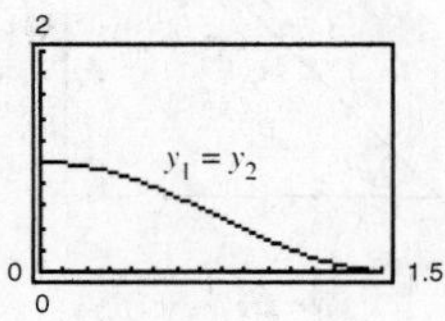

x	0.2	0.4	0.6	0.8	1.0	1.2	1.4
y_1	0.9605	0.8484	0.6812	0.4854	0.2919	0.1313	0.0289
y_2	0.9605	0.8484	0.6812	0.4854	0.2919	0.1313	0.0289

34. $y_1 = \sin(x + \pi)\sin(x - \pi)$

$= [\sin x \cos \pi + \sin \pi \cos \pi][\sin x \cos \pi - \sin \pi \cos x] = [-\sin x][-\sin x] = \sin^2 x = y_2$

x	0.2	0.4	0.6	0.8	1.0	1.2	1.4
y_1	0.0395	0.1516	0.3188	0.5146	0.7081	0.8687	0.9711
y_2	0.0395	0.1516	0.3188	0.5146	0.7081	0.8687	0.9711

For Exercises 35–38,

$\sin u = \frac{5}{13}$ **and** u **in Quadrant II** $\Rightarrow$ $\cos u = -\frac{12}{13}$

$\cos v = -\frac{3}{5}$ **and** v **in Quadrant II** $\Rightarrow$ $\sin v = \frac{4}{5}$

$\tan u = -\frac{5}{12}$ **and** $\tan v = -\frac{4}{3}$**.**

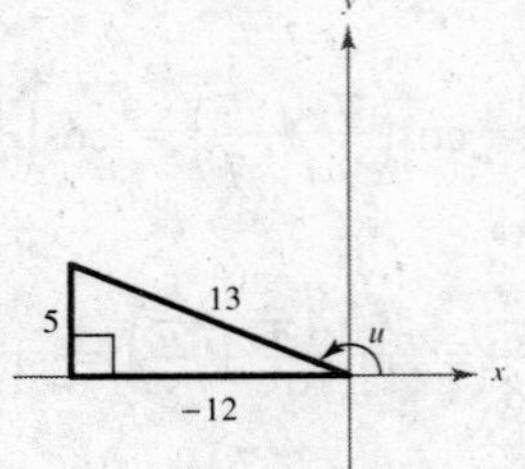

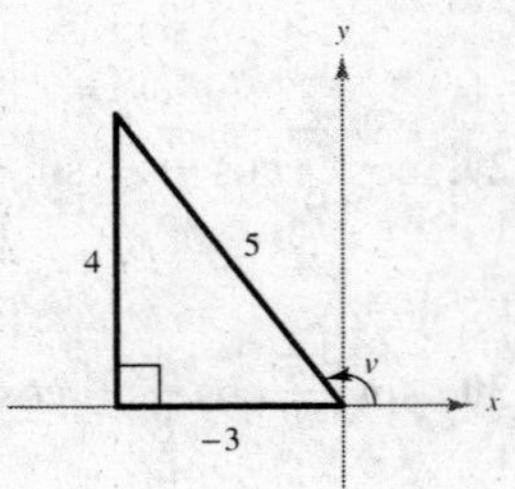

35. $\sin(u + v) = \sin u \cos v + \sin v \cos u$

$$= \frac{5}{13}\left(\frac{-3}{5}\right) + \frac{4}{5}\left(\frac{-12}{13}\right) = -\frac{63}{65}$$

36. $\cos(v - u) = \cos v \cos u + \sin v \sin u$

$$= \left(\frac{-3}{5}\right)\left(\frac{-12}{13}\right) + \left(\frac{4}{5}\right)\left(\frac{5}{13}\right) = \frac{56}{65}$$

37. $\tan(u + v) = \dfrac{\tan u + \tan v}{1 - \tan u \tan v}$

$$= \frac{(-5/12) - (4/3)}{1 - (-5/12)(-4/3)}$$

$$= \frac{-63/36}{16/36} = -\frac{63}{16}$$

38. $\sin(u - v) = \sin u \cos v - \sin v \cos u$

$$= \frac{5}{13}\left(\frac{-3}{5}\right) - \left(\frac{4}{5}\right)\left(\frac{-12}{13}\right)$$

$$= \frac{33}{65}$$

For Exercises 39–42, $\sin u = -\frac{8}{17}$, $\cos u = -\frac{15}{17}$, $\sin v = -\frac{3}{5}$, $\cos v = -\frac{4}{5}$, $\tan u = \frac{8}{15}$, $\tan v = \frac{3}{4}$**.**

39. $\cos(u + v) = \cos u \cos v - \sin u \sin v$

$$= \left(-\frac{15}{17}\right)\left(-\frac{4}{5}\right) - \left(-\frac{8}{17}\right)\left(-\frac{3}{5}\right) = \frac{36}{85}$$

40. $\tan(u + v) = \dfrac{\tan u + \tan v}{1 - \tan u \tan v}$

$$= \frac{(8/15) + (3/4)}{1 - (8/15)(3/4)} = \frac{32 + 45}{60 - 24} = \frac{77}{36}$$

41. $\sin(v - u) = \sin v \cos u - \cos v \sin u$

$$= \left(-\tfrac{3}{5}\right)\left(-\tfrac{15}{17}\right) - \left(-\tfrac{4}{5}\right)\left(-\tfrac{8}{17}\right) = \tfrac{13}{85}$$

42. $\cos(u - v) = \cos u \cos v + \sin u \sin v$

$$= \left(-\tfrac{15}{17}\right)\left(-\tfrac{4}{5}\right) + \left(-\tfrac{8}{17}\right)\left(-\tfrac{3}{5}\right) = \tfrac{84}{85}$$

43. $\sin(\arcsin x + \arccos x) = \sin(\arcsin x)\cos(\arccos x) + \sin(\arccos x)\cos(\arcsin x)$

$= x \cdot x + \sqrt{1 - x^2} \cdot \sqrt{1 - x^2}$

$= x^2 + 1 - x^2$

$= 1$

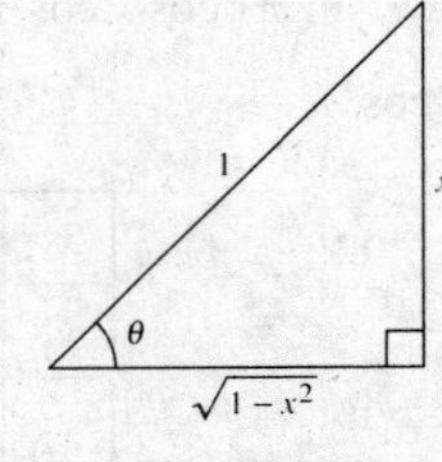

$\theta = \arcsin x$

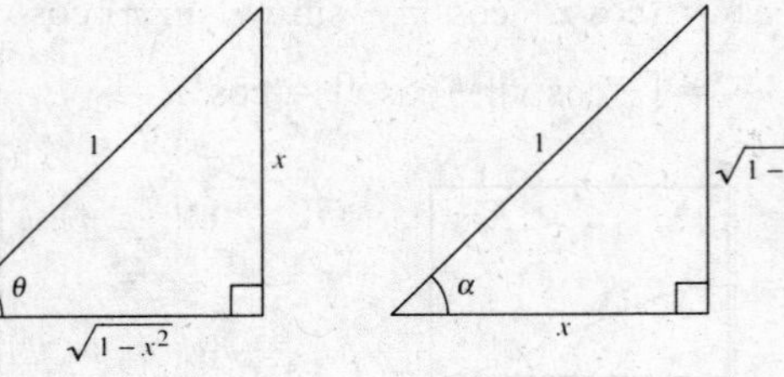

$\alpha = \arccos x$

44. Let: $u = \arccos x$ and $v = \arcsin x$

$\cos u = x$ $\sin v = x$

$$\begin{aligned}\cos(\arccos x - \arcsin x) &= \cos(\arccos x)\cos(\arcsin x) + \sin(\arccos x)\sin(\arcsin x)\\ &= x\sqrt{1-x^2} + \sqrt{1-x^2}\,x\\ &= 2x\sqrt{1-x^2}\end{aligned}$$

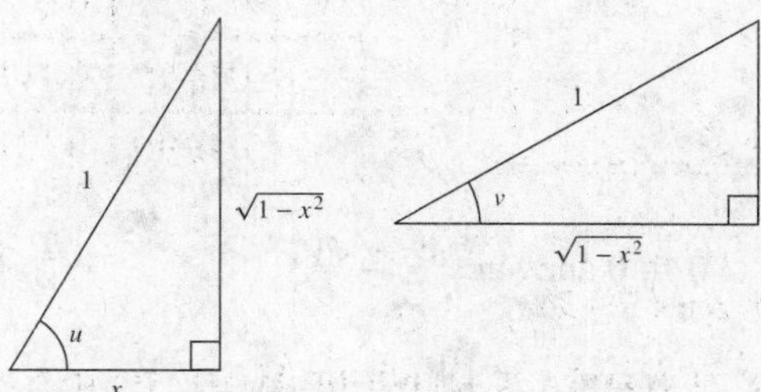

45. Let: $u = \arctan 2x$ and $v = \arccos x$

$\tan u = 2x$ $\cos v = x$

$$\begin{aligned}\sin(\arctan 2x - \arccos x) &= \sin(u - v)\\ &= \sin u \cos v - \cos u \sin v\\ &= \frac{2x}{\sqrt{4x^2+1}}(x) - \frac{1}{\sqrt{4x^2+1}}\left(\sqrt{1-x^2}\right)\\ &= \frac{2x^2 - \sqrt{1-x^2}}{\sqrt{4x^2+1}}\end{aligned}$$

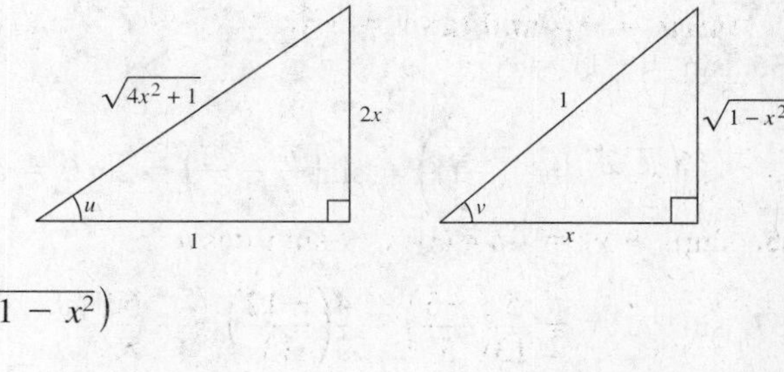

46. Let: $u = \arcsin x$ and $v = \arctan 2x$

$\sin u = x$ $\tan v = 2x$

$$\begin{aligned}\cos(\arcsin x - \arctan 2x) &= \cos(\arcsin x)\cos(\arctan 2x) + \sin(\arcsin x)\sin(\arctan 2x)\\ &= \sqrt{1-x^2}\frac{1}{\sqrt{4x^2+1}} + x\frac{2x}{\sqrt{4x^2+1}}\\ &= \frac{2x^2 + \sqrt{1-x^2}}{\sqrt{4x^2+1}}\end{aligned}$$

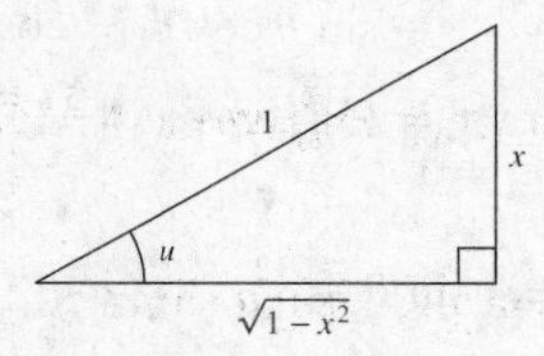

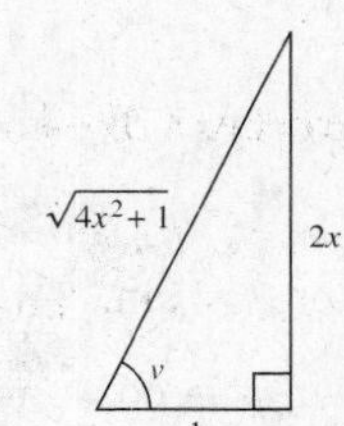

47. $\sin^{-1} 1 = \frac{\pi}{2}$ because $\sin \frac{\pi}{2} = 1$.

$\cos^{-1} 1 = 0$ because $\cos 0 = 1$.

$\sin(\sin^{-1} 1 + \cos^{-1} 1) = \sin\left(\frac{\pi}{2} + 0\right) = 1$

48. $\sin^{-1}(-1) = -\frac{\pi}{2}$ and $\cos^{-1} 0 = \frac{\pi}{2}$

$$\begin{aligned}\cos(\sin^{-1}(-1) + \cos^{-1} 0) &= \cos\left(-\frac{\pi}{2} + \frac{\pi}{2}\right)\\ &= \cos 0 = 1\end{aligned}$$

49. $\sin^{-1} 1 = \frac{\pi}{2}$ and $\cos^{-1}(-1) = \pi$

$$\begin{aligned}\sin(\sin^{-1} 1 - \cos^{-1}(-1)) &= \sin\left(\frac{\pi}{2} - \pi\right)\\ &= \sin\left(-\frac{\pi}{2}\right) = -1\end{aligned}$$

50. $\cos^{-1}(-1) = \pi$ and $\cos^{-1} 1 = 0$

$\cos(\cos^{-1}(-1) - \cos^{-1} 1) = \cos(\pi - 0) = -1$

51. $\sin^{-1}\frac{1}{2} = \frac{\pi}{6}$ and $\cos^{-1}\frac{1}{2} = \frac{\pi}{3}$

$$\sin\left(\sin^{-1}\frac{1}{2} - \cos^{-1}\frac{1}{2}\right) = \sin\left(\frac{\pi}{6} - \frac{\pi}{3}\right) = \sin\left(-\frac{\pi}{6}\right) = -\frac{1}{2}$$

52. $\cos^{-1}\left(-\frac{1}{2}\right) = \frac{2\pi}{3}$ and $\sin^{-1} 1 = \frac{\pi}{2}$

$$\cos\left(\cos^{-1}\left(-\frac{1}{2}\right) + \sin^{-1} 1\right) = \cos\left(\frac{2\pi}{3} + \frac{\pi}{2}\right) = \cos\frac{7\pi}{6} = -\frac{\sqrt{3}}{2}$$

53. $\sin^{-1} 0 = 0$ and $\sin^{-1}\frac{1}{2} = \frac{\pi}{6}$

$$\tan\left(\sin^{-1} 0 + \sin^{-1}\frac{1}{2}\right) = \tan\left(0 + \frac{\pi}{6}\right) = \frac{\sqrt{3}}{3}$$

54. $\cos^{-1}\frac{\sqrt{2}}{2} = \frac{\pi}{4}$ and $\sin^{-1} 0 = 0$

$$\tan\left(\cos^{-1}\frac{\sqrt{2}}{2} - \sin^{-1} 0\right) = \tan\left(\frac{\pi}{4} - 0\right) = 1$$

55. $\sin^{-1}(-1) = -\frac{\pi}{2}$

$$\sin\left(\frac{\pi}{2} + \sin^{-1}(-1)\right) = \sin\left(\frac{\pi}{2} - \frac{\pi}{2}\right) = \sin 0 = 0$$

56. $\cos^{-1}(-1) = \pi$

$$\sin(\cos^{-1}(-1) + \pi) = \sin(\pi + \pi) = \sin 2\pi = 0$$

57. $\sin^{-1} 1 = \frac{\pi}{2}$

$$\cos(\pi + \sin^{-1} 1) = \cos\left(\pi + \frac{\pi}{2}\right) = \cos\frac{3\pi}{2} = 0$$

58. $\cos^{-1}(-1) = \pi$

$$\cos(\pi - \cos^{-1}(-1)) = \cos(\pi - \pi) = \cos 0 = 1$$

59. Let $\theta = \cos^{-1}\frac{3}{5} \Rightarrow \cos\theta = \frac{3}{5}$.

Let $\phi = \sin^{-1}\frac{5}{13} \Rightarrow \sin\phi = \frac{5}{13}$.

$$\begin{aligned}\sin\left(\cos^{-1}\tfrac{3}{5} - \sin^{-1}\tfrac{5}{13}\right) &= \sin(\theta - \phi)\\ &= \sin\theta\cos\phi - \cos\theta\sin\phi\\ &= \left(\tfrac{4}{5}\right)\left(\tfrac{12}{13}\right) - \left(\tfrac{3}{5}\right)\left(\tfrac{5}{13}\right) = \tfrac{33}{65}\end{aligned}$$

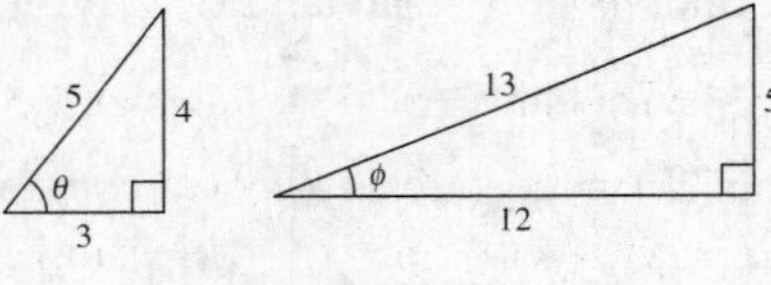

60. Let $\theta = \sin^{-1}\frac{12}{13} \Rightarrow \sin\theta = \frac{12}{13}$.

Let $\phi = \cos^{-1}\frac{8}{17} \Rightarrow \cos\phi = \frac{8}{17}$.

$$\begin{aligned}\cos\left(\sin^{-1}\tfrac{12}{13} + \cos^{-1}\tfrac{8}{17}\right) &= \cos(\theta + \phi)\\ &= \cos\theta\cos\phi - \sin\theta\sin\phi\\ &= \left(\tfrac{5}{13}\right)\left(\tfrac{8}{17}\right) - \left(\tfrac{12}{13}\right)\left(\tfrac{15}{17}\right) = -\tfrac{140}{221}\end{aligned}$$

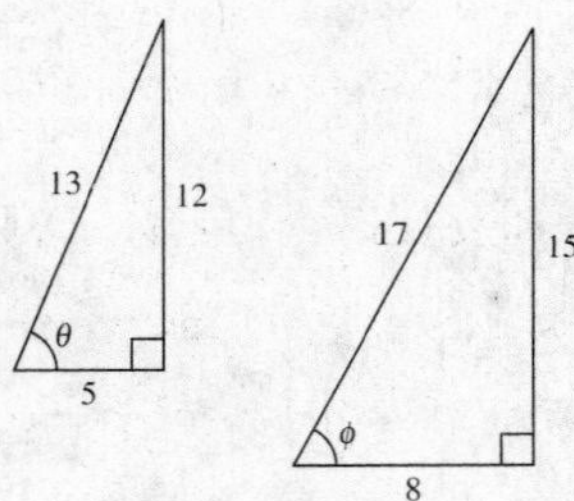

61. Let $\theta = \tan^{-1}\frac{3}{4} \Rightarrow \tan\theta = \frac{3}{4}$.

Let $\phi = \sin^{-1}\frac{3}{5} \Rightarrow \sin\phi = \frac{3}{5}$.

$$\begin{aligned}\sin\left(\tan^{-1}\tfrac{3}{4} + \sin^{-1}\tfrac{3}{5}\right) &= \sin(\theta + \phi)\\ &= \sin\theta\cos\phi + \sin\phi\cos\theta\\ &= \tfrac{3}{5}\left(\tfrac{4}{5}\right) + \tfrac{3}{5}\left(\tfrac{4}{5}\right) = \tfrac{24}{25}\end{aligned}$$

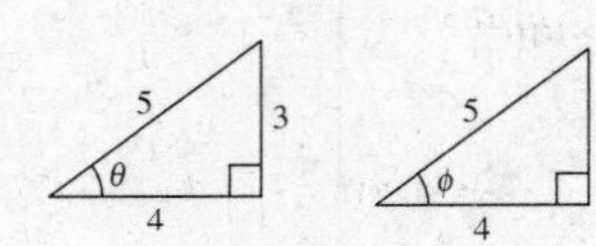

Note: $\theta = \phi$

62. Let $\theta = \sin^{-1}\frac{4}{5} \Rightarrow \sin\theta = \frac{4}{5}$.

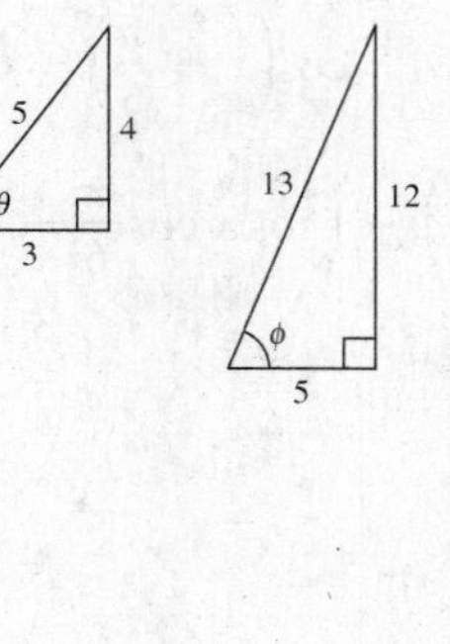

Let $\phi = \cos^{-1}\frac{5}{13} \Rightarrow \cos\phi = \frac{5}{13}$.

$$\tan\left(\sin^{-1}\frac{4}{5} - \cos^{-1}\frac{5}{13}\right) = \tan(\theta - \phi)$$

$$= \frac{\tan\theta - \tan\phi}{1 + \tan\theta\tan\phi}$$

$$= \frac{(4/3) - (12/5)}{1 + (4/3)\cdot(12/5)} = \frac{-16}{63}$$

63. $\sin\left(\frac{\pi}{2} + x\right) = \sin\frac{\pi}{2}\cos x + \sin x\cos\frac{\pi}{2}$

$= (1)\cos x + 0 = \cos x$

64. $\sin(3\pi - x) = \sin 3\pi\cos x - \cos 3\pi\sin x$

$= (0)\cos x - (-1)\sin x = \sin x$

65. $\tan(x + \pi) - \tan(\pi - x) = \dfrac{\tan x + \tan\pi}{1 - \tan x\cdot\tan\pi} - \dfrac{\tan\pi - \tan x}{1 + \tan\pi\tan x}$

$= \dfrac{\tan x}{1} - \left(-\dfrac{\tan x}{1}\right) = 2\tan x$

66. $\tan\left(\frac{\pi}{4} - \theta\right) = \dfrac{\tan(\pi/4) - \tan\theta}{1 + \tan(\pi/4)\tan\theta} = \dfrac{1 - \tan\theta}{1 + \tan\theta}$

67. $\sin(x + y) + \sin(x - y) = \sin x\cos y + \sin y\cos x + \sin x\cos y - \sin y\cos x = 2\sin x\cos y$

68. $\cos(x + y) + \cos(x - y) = \cos x\cos y - \sin x\sin y + \cos x\cos y + \sin x\sin y = 2\cos x\cos y$

69. $\cos(x + y)\cos(x - y) = [\cos x\cos y - \sin x\sin y][\cos x\cos y + \sin x\sin y]$

$= \cos^2 x\cos^2 y - \sin^2 x\sin^2 y = \cos^2 x(1 - \sin^2 y) - \sin^2 x\sin^2 y$

$= \cos^2 x - \sin^2 y(\cos^2 x + \sin^2 x) = \cos^2 x - \sin^2 y$

70. $\sin(x + y)\sin(x - y) = [\sin x\cos y + \cos x\sin y][\sin x\cos y - \cos x\sin y]$

$= \sin^2 x\cos^2 y - \cos^2 x\sin^2 y = \sin^2 x(1 - \sin^2 y) - \cos^2 x\sin^2 y$

$= \sin^2 x - \sin^2 y(\sin^2 x + \cos^2 x) = \sin^2 x - \sin^2 y$

71. $$\sin\left(x + \frac{\pi}{3}\right) + \sin\left(x - \frac{\pi}{3}\right) = 1$$

$$\sin x\cos\frac{\pi}{3} + \cos x\sin\frac{\pi}{3} + \sin x\cos\frac{\pi}{3} - \cos x\sin\frac{\pi}{3} = 1$$

$$2\sin x(0.5) = 1$$

$$\sin x = 1$$

$$x = \frac{\pi}{2}$$

72.

$$\cos\left(x+\frac{\pi}{6}\right)-\cos\left(x-\frac{\pi}{6}\right)=1$$

$$\left(\cos x\cos\frac{\pi}{6}-\sin x\sin\frac{\pi}{6}\right)-\left(\cos x\cos\frac{\pi}{6}+\sin x\sin\frac{\pi}{6}\right)=1$$

$$-2\sin x\sin\frac{\pi}{6}=1$$

$$-2\sin x\left(\frac{1}{2}\right)=1$$

$$\sin x=-1$$

$$x=\frac{3\pi}{2}$$

73.

$$\tan(x+\pi)+2\sin(x+\pi)=0$$

$$\frac{\tan x+\tan\pi}{1-\tan x\tan\pi}+2(\sin x\cos\pi+\cos x\sin\pi)=0$$

$$\frac{\tan x+0}{1-\tan x(0)}+2[\sin x(-1)+\cos x(0)]=0$$

$$\frac{\tan x}{1}-2\sin x=0$$

$$\frac{\sin x}{\cos x}=2\sin x$$

$$\sin x=2\sin x\cos x$$

$$\sin x(1-2\cos x)=0$$

$$\sin x=0 \quad\text{or}\quad \cos x=\frac{1}{2}$$

$$x=0,\pi \qquad x=\frac{\pi}{3},\frac{5\pi}{3}$$

74.

$$2\sin\left(x+\frac{\pi}{2}\right)+3\tan(\pi-x)=0$$

$$2\left[\sin x\cos\frac{\pi}{2}+\cos x\sin\frac{\pi}{2}\right]+3\tan(-x)=0$$

$$2\cos x-3\frac{\sin x}{\cos x}=0$$

$$2\cos^2 x-3\sin x=0$$

$$2(1-\sin^2 x)-3\sin x=0$$

$$2\sin^2 x+3\sin x-2=0$$

$$(2\sin x-1)(\sin x+2)\implies \sin x=\frac{1}{2}\implies x=\frac{\pi}{6},\frac{5\pi}{6}$$

75. Graph $y_1 = \cos\left(x + \frac{\pi}{4}\right) + \cos\left(x - \frac{\pi}{4}\right)$ and $y_2 = 1$.

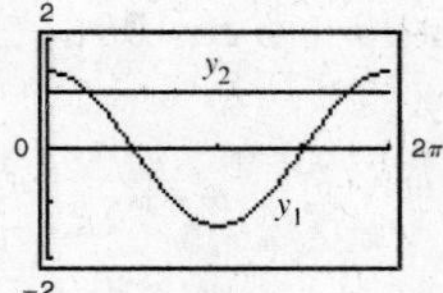

$x \approx 0.7854, 5.4978$

76. $\sin\left(x + \frac{\pi}{2}\right) - \cos\left(x + \frac{3\pi}{2}\right) = 0$

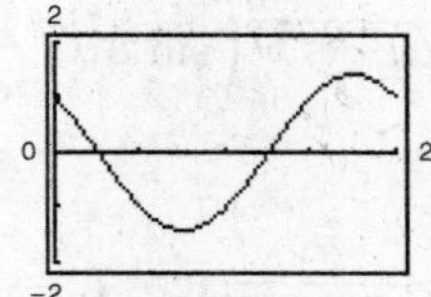

$x \approx 0.7854, 3.9270$

77. $\tan(x + \pi) - \cos\left(x + \frac{\pi}{2}\right) = 0$

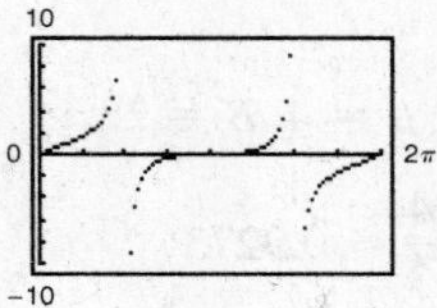

Answers: 0.0, 3.1416 $(x = 0, \pi)$

78. $\tan(\pi - x) + 2\cos\left(x + \frac{3\pi}{2}\right) = 0$

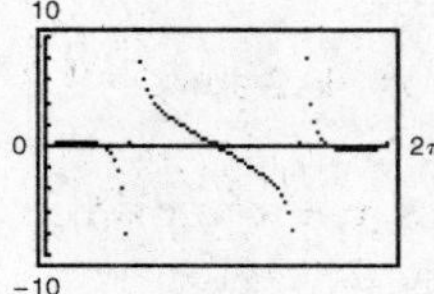

$x = 0, 1.0472, 3.1416, 5.2360$

79. $y_1 + y_2 = A\cos 2\pi\left(\frac{t}{T} - \frac{x}{\lambda}\right) + A\cos 2\pi\left(\frac{t}{T} + \frac{x}{\lambda}\right)$

$$= A\left[\cos\left(\frac{2\pi t}{T}\right)\cos\left(\frac{2\pi x}{\lambda}\right) + \sin\left(\frac{2\pi t}{T}\right)\sin\left(\frac{2\pi x}{\lambda}\right)\right] + A\left[\cos\left(\frac{2\pi t}{T}\right)\cos\left(\frac{2\pi x}{\lambda}\right) - \sin\left(\frac{2\pi t}{T}\right)\sin\left(\frac{2\pi x}{\lambda}\right)\right]$$

$$= 2A\cos\left(\frac{2\pi t}{T}\right)\cos\left(\frac{2\pi x}{\lambda}\right)$$

80. $y = \frac{1}{3}\sin 2t + \frac{1}{4}\cos 2t$

(a)

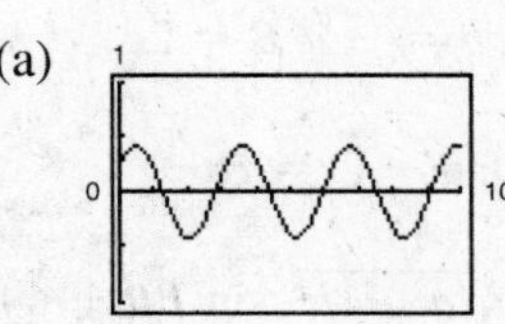

(b) $a = \frac{1}{3},\ b = \frac{1}{4},\ B = 2$

$C = \arctan\frac{b}{a} = \arctan\frac{3}{4} \approx 0.6435$

$y \approx \sqrt{\left(\frac{1}{3}\right)^2 + \left(\frac{1}{4}\right)^2}\sin(2t + 0.6435) = \frac{5}{12}\sin(2t + 0.6435)$

(c) Amplitude: $\frac{5}{12}$

(d) Frequency: $\frac{1}{\text{period}} = \frac{B}{2\pi} = \frac{2}{2\pi} = \frac{1}{\pi}$

81. False. See page 380.

82. True. $\sin\left(x - \frac{11\pi}{2}\right) = \sin x\cos\frac{11\pi}{2} - \cos x\sin\frac{11\pi}{2} = 0 - \cos x(-1) = \cos x$

83. $\cos(n\pi + \theta) = \cos n\pi\cos\theta - \sin n\pi\sin\theta$

$= (-1)^n(\cos\theta) - (0)(\sin\theta)$

$= (-1)^n(\cos\theta)$, where n is an integer.

84. $\sin(n\pi + \theta) = \sin n\pi\cos\theta + \sin\theta\cos n\pi$

$= (0)(\cos\theta) + (\sin\theta)(-1)^n$

$= (-1)^n(\sin\theta)$, where n is an integer.

85. $C = \arctan \frac{b}{a} \Rightarrow \tan C = \frac{b}{a} \Rightarrow \sin C = \frac{b}{\sqrt{a^2 + b^2}}, \cos C = \frac{a}{\sqrt{a^2 + b^2}}$

$$\sqrt{a^2 + b^2}\sin(B\theta + C) = \sqrt{a^2 + b^2}\left(\sin B\theta \cdot \frac{a}{\sqrt{a^2 + b^2}} + \frac{b}{\sqrt{a^2 + b^2}} \cdot \cos B\theta\right) = a \sin B\theta + b \cos B\theta$$

86. $C = \arctan \frac{a}{b} \Rightarrow \sin C = \frac{a}{\sqrt{a^2 + b^2}}, \cos C = \frac{b}{\sqrt{a^2 + b^2}}$

$$\sqrt{a^2 + b^2}\cos(B\theta - C) = \sqrt{a^2 + b^2}\left(\cos B\theta \cdot \frac{b}{\sqrt{a^2 + b^2}} + \sin B\theta \cdot \frac{a}{\sqrt{a^2 + b^2}}\right)$$
$$= b \cos B\theta + a \sin B\theta$$
$$= a \sin B\theta + b \cos B\theta$$

87. $\sin \theta + \cos \theta$

$a = 1,\ b = 1,\ B = 1$

(a) $C = \arctan \frac{b}{a} = \arctan 1 = \frac{\pi}{4}$

$$\sin \theta + \cos \theta = \sqrt{a^2 + b^2}\sin(B\theta + C)$$
$$= \sqrt{2}\sin\left(\theta + \frac{\pi}{4}\right)$$

(b) $C = \arctan \frac{a}{b} = \arctan 1 = \frac{\pi}{4}$

$$\sin \theta + \cos \theta = \sqrt{a^2 + b^2}\cos(B\theta - C)$$
$$= \sqrt{2}\cos\left(\theta - \frac{\pi}{4}\right)$$

88. $3 \sin 2\theta + 4 \cos 2\theta;\ a = 3, b = 4, B = 2$

(a) $C = \arctan \frac{b}{a} = \arctan \frac{4}{3} \approx 0.9273$

$$3 \sin 2\theta + 4 \cos 2\theta = \sqrt{a^2 + b^2}\sin(B\theta + C)$$
$$\approx 5 \sin(2\theta + 0.9273)$$

(b) $C = \arctan \frac{a}{b} = \arctan \frac{3}{4} \approx 0.6435$

$$3 \sin 2\theta + 4 \cos 2\theta = \sqrt{a^2 + b^2}\cos(B\theta - C)$$
$$\approx 5 \cos(2\theta - 0.6435)$$

89. $12 \sin 3\theta + 5 \cos 3\theta;\ a = 12,\ b = 5,\ B = 3$

(a) $C = \arctan \frac{b}{a} = \arctan \frac{5}{12} \approx 0.3948$

$$12 \sin 3\theta + 5 \cos 3\theta = \sqrt{a^2 + b^2}\sin(B\theta + C)$$
$$\approx 13 \sin(3\theta + 0.3948)$$

(b) $C = \arctan \frac{a}{b} = \arctan \frac{12}{5} \approx 1.1760$

$$12 \sin 3\theta + 5 \cos 3\theta = \sqrt{a^2 + b^2}\cos(B\theta - C)$$
$$\approx 13 \cos(3\theta - 1.1760)$$

90. $\sin 2\theta - \cos 2\theta;\ a = 1, b = -1, B = 2$

(a) $C = \arctan \frac{b}{a} = \arctan(-1) = -\frac{\pi}{4}$

$$\sin 2\theta - \cos 2\theta = \sqrt{a^2 + b^2}\sin(B\theta + C)$$
$$= \sqrt{2}\sin\left(2\theta - \frac{\pi}{4}\right)$$

(b) Because $b > 0$ in the formula, we write the given expression as

$-(-\sin 2\theta + \cos 2\theta);\ a = -1, b = 1, B = 2,$

$C = \arctan\left(\frac{a}{b}\right) = \arctan(-1) = -\frac{\pi}{4}.$

Hence,

$$-(-\sin 2\theta + \cos 2\theta) = -\sqrt{a^2 + b^2}\cos(B\theta - C)$$
$$= -\sqrt{2}\cos\left(2\theta + \frac{\pi}{4}\right).$$

91. $C = \arctan \dfrac{b}{a} = \dfrac{\pi}{2} \implies a = 0$

$\sqrt{a^2 + b^2} = 2 \implies b = 2$

$B = 1$

$2 \sin\left(\theta + \dfrac{\pi}{2}\right) = (0)(\sin \theta) + (2)(\cos \theta) = 2 \cos \theta$

92. $C = -\dfrac{\pi}{4} = \arctan\left(\dfrac{a}{b}\right) \implies \dfrac{a}{b} = -1$

$\implies a = -1, b = 1$

$\sqrt{a^2 + b^2} = \sqrt{2}$

Hence, $B = 1$ and

$$\begin{aligned} 5 \cos\left(\theta + \frac{\pi}{4}\right) &= \frac{5}{\sqrt{2}}\sqrt{2} \cos\left[\theta - \left(-\frac{\pi}{4}\right)\right] \\ &= \frac{5}{\sqrt{2}}[-\sin \theta + \cos \theta] \\ &= -\frac{5}{\sqrt{2}} \sin \theta + \frac{5}{\sqrt{2}} \cos \theta \\ &= -\frac{5\sqrt{2}}{2} \sin \theta + \frac{5\sqrt{2}}{2} \cos \theta. \end{aligned}$$

93. $$\begin{aligned} \frac{\sin(x + h) - \sin x}{h} &= \frac{\sin x \cos h + \cos x \sin h - \sin x}{h} \\ &= \frac{\sin x(\cos h - 1) + \cos x \sin h}{h} \\ &= \frac{\cos x \sin h}{h} - \frac{\sin x(1 - \cos h)}{h} \end{aligned}$$

94. (a) Domains of f and g are all real numbers, $h \neq 0$.

(b)

h	0.01	0.02	0.05	0.1	0.2	0.5
$f(h)$	0.4957	0.4913	0.4781	0.4559	0.4104	0.2674
$g(h)$	0.4957	0.4913	0.4781	0.4559	0.4104	0.2674

(c)

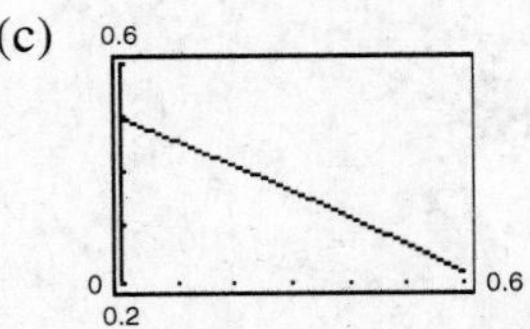

(d) As $h \to 0, f \to \frac{1}{2}$ and $g \to \frac{1}{2}$. In fact, $f = g$.

95. From the figure, it appears that $u + v = w$. Assume that u, v, and w are all in Quadrant I. From the figure:

$\tan u = \dfrac{s}{3s} = \dfrac{1}{3}$

$\tan v = \dfrac{s}{2s} = \dfrac{1}{2}$

$\tan w = \dfrac{s}{s} = 1$

$$\tan(u + v) = \frac{\tan u + \tan v}{1 - \tan u \tan v} = \frac{(1/3) + (1/2)}{1 - (1/3)(1/2)} = \frac{5/6}{1 - (1/6)} = 1 = \tan w.$$

Thus, $\tan(u + v) = \tan w$. Because u, v, and w are all in Quadrant I, we have

$$\begin{aligned} \arctan[\tan(u + v)] &= \arctan[\tan w] \\ u + v &= w. \end{aligned}$$

96. (a) $\sin(u + v + w) = \sin u \cos(v + w) + \cos u \sin(v + w)$

$= \sin u[\cos v \cos w - \sin v \sin w] + \cos u[\sin v \cos w + \sin w \cos v]$

$= \sin u \cos v \cos w - \sin u \sin v \sin w + \cos u \sin v \cos w + \cos u \sin w \cos v$

(b) $$\tan(u + v + w) = \frac{\tan(u + v) + \tan w}{1 - \tan(u + v)\tan w} = \frac{\left[\dfrac{\tan u + \tan v}{1 - \tan u \tan v}\right] + \tan w}{1 - \left[\dfrac{\tan u + \tan v}{1 - \tan u \tan v}\right]\tan w}$$

$$= \frac{\tan u + \tan v + \tan w(1 - \text{an } u \tan v)}{(1 - \tan u \tan v) - (\tan u + \tan v)\tan w} = \frac{\tan u + \tan v + \tan w - \tan u \tan v \tan w}{1 - \tan u \tan v - \tan u \tan w - \tan v \tan w}$$

97. $x = 0$: $y = -\frac{1}{2}(0 - 10) + 14 = 5 + 14 = 19$

y-intercept: $(0, 19)$

$y = 0$: $0 = -\frac{1}{2}(x - 10) + 14$

$= -\frac{1}{2}x + 19 \Rightarrow x = 38$

x-intercept: $(38, 0)$

98. $y = 0$: $x^2 - 3x - 40 = (x - 8)(x + 5) = 0$

x-intercepts: $(8, 0), (-5, 0)$

$x = 0 \Rightarrow y = -40$

y-intercept: $(0, -40)$

99. $x = 0$: $|2(0) - 9| - 5 = 9 - 5 = 4$

y-intercept: $(0, 4)$

$y = 0$: $|2x - 9| = 5 \Rightarrow x = 7, 2$

x-intercepts: $(2, 0), (7, 0)$

100. $y = 0$: $2x\sqrt{x + 7} = 0 \Rightarrow x = 0, -7$

x-intercepts: $(0, 0), (-7, 0)$

$x = 0 \Rightarrow y = 0$

y-intercept: $(0, 0)$

101. $\arccos\left(\frac{\sqrt{3}}{2}\right) = \frac{\pi}{6}$ because $\cos\frac{\pi}{6} = \frac{\sqrt{3}}{2}$.

102. $\arctan(-\sqrt{3}) = -\frac{\pi}{3}$ because $\tan\left(-\frac{\pi}{3}\right) = -\sqrt{3}$.

103. $\arcsin 1 = \frac{\pi}{2}$ because $\sin\frac{\pi}{2} = 1$.

104. $\arctan 0 = 0$

Section 5.5 Multiple-Angle and Product-to-Sum Formulas

- You should know the following double-angle formulas.

(a) $\sin 2u = 2 \sin u \cos u$

(b) $\cos 2u = \cos^2 u - \sin^2 u$
$= 2\cos^2 u - 1$
$= 1 - 2\sin^2 u$

(c) $\tan 2u = \dfrac{2 \tan u}{1 - \tan^2 u}$

- You should be able to reduce the power of a trigonometric function.

(a) $\sin^2 u = \dfrac{1 - \cos 2u}{2}$ (b) $\cos^2 u = \dfrac{1 + \cos 2u}{2}$ (c) $\tan^2 u = \dfrac{1 - \cos 2u}{1 + \cos 2u}$

- You should be able to use the half-angle formulas.

(a) $\sin\dfrac{u}{2} = \pm\sqrt{\dfrac{1 - \cos u}{2}}$ (b) $\cos\dfrac{u}{2} = \pm\sqrt{\dfrac{1 + \cos u}{2}}$ (c) $\tan\dfrac{u}{2} = \dfrac{1 - \cos u}{\sin u} = \dfrac{\sin u}{1 + \cos u}$

—CONTINUED—

—CONTINUED—

- You should be able to use the product-sum formulas.

(a) $\sin u \sin v = \frac{1}{2}[\cos(u - v) - \cos(u + v)]$

(b) $\cos u \cos v = \frac{1}{2}[\cos(u - v) + \cos(u + v)]$

(c) $\sin u \cos v = \frac{1}{2}[\sin(u + v) + \sin(u - v)]$

(d) $\cos u \sin v = \frac{1}{2}[\sin(u + v) - \sin(u - v)]$

- You should be able to use the sum-product formulas.

(a) $\sin x + \sin y = 2 \sin\left(\frac{x + y}{2}\right) \cos\left(\frac{x - y}{2}\right)$

(b) $\sin x - \sin y = 2 \cos\left(\frac{x + y}{2}\right) \sin\left(\frac{x - y}{2}\right)$

(c) $\cos x + \cos y = 2 \cos\left(\frac{x + y}{2}\right) \cos\left(\frac{x - y}{2}\right)$

(d) $\cos x - \cos y = -2 \sin\left(\frac{x + y}{2}\right) \sin\left(\frac{x - y}{2}\right)$

Vocabulary Check

1. $2 \sin u \cos u$

2. $\frac{1 + \cos 2u}{2}$

3. $\cos 2u$

4. $\tan \frac{u}{2}$

5. $\frac{2 \tan u}{1 - \tan^2 u}$

6. $\frac{1}{2}[\cos(u - v) + \cos(u + v)]$

7. $\sin^2 u$

8. $\cos \frac{u}{2}$

9. $\frac{1}{2}[\sin(u + v) + \sin(u - v)]$

10. $2 \sin\left(\frac{u + v}{2}\right) \cos\left(\frac{u - v}{2}\right)$

1. (a) $\sin \theta = \frac{3}{5}$

(b) $\cos \theta = \frac{4}{5}$

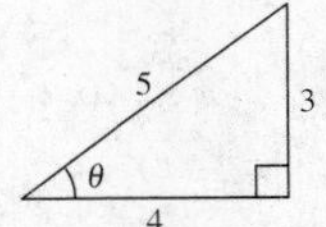

(c) $\cos 2\theta = \cos^2 \theta - \sin^2 \theta$

$= \frac{16}{25} - \frac{9}{25} = \frac{7}{25}$

(d) $\sin 2\theta = 2 \sin \theta \cos \theta$

$= 2\left(\frac{3}{5}\right)\left(\frac{4}{5}\right) = \frac{24}{25}$

(e) $\tan 2\theta = \frac{\sin 2\theta}{\cos 2\theta} = \frac{24}{7}$

(f) $\sec 2\theta = \frac{1}{\cos 2\theta} = \frac{25}{7}$

(g) $\csc 2\theta = \frac{1}{\sin 2\theta} = \frac{25}{24}$

(h) $\cot 2\theta = \frac{1}{\tan 2\theta} = \frac{7}{24}$

2. (a) $\sin \theta = \frac{12}{13}$

(b) $\cos \theta = \frac{5}{13}$

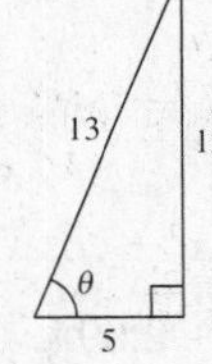

(c) $\sin 2\theta = 2 \sin \theta \cos \theta$

$= 2\left(\frac{12}{13}\right)\left(\frac{5}{13}\right) = \frac{120}{169}$

(d) $\cos 2\theta = \cos^2 \theta - \sin^2 \theta$

$= \frac{25}{169} - \frac{144}{169} = \frac{-119}{169}$

(e) $\tan 2\theta = \frac{\sin 2\theta}{\cos 2\theta} = \frac{-120}{119}$

(f) $\cot 2\theta = \frac{1}{\tan 2\theta} = \frac{-119}{120}$

(g) $\sec 2\theta = \frac{1}{\cos 2\theta} = \frac{-169}{119}$

(h) $\csc 2\theta = \frac{1}{\sin 2\theta} = \frac{169}{120}$

3. $\sin 2x - \sin x = 0$

Solutions: 0, 1.047, 3.142, 5.236

Analytically:

$$\sin 2x - \sin x = 0$$
$$2 \sin x \cos x - \sin x = 0$$
$$\sin x(2 \cos x - 1) = 0$$

$\sin x = 0$ or $2 \cos x - 1 = 0$

$x = 0, \pi$ $\qquad \cos x = \dfrac{1}{2}$

$x = 0, \dfrac{\pi}{3}, \pi, \dfrac{5\pi}{3}$ $\qquad x = \dfrac{\pi}{3}, \dfrac{5\pi}{3}$

4. $\sin 2x + \cos x = 0$

Solutions: 1.5708, 3.6652, 4.7124, 5.7596

Analytically:

$$\sin 2x + \cos x = 0$$
$$2 \sin x \cos x + \cos x = 0$$
$$\cos x(2 \sin x + 1) = 0$$

$\cos x = 0$ $\qquad \sin x = -\dfrac{1}{2}$

$x = \dfrac{\pi}{2}, \dfrac{3\pi}{2}$ $\qquad x = \dfrac{7\pi}{6}, \dfrac{11\pi}{6}$

5. $4 \sin x \cos x = 1$

$x \approx 0.2618, 1.3090, 3.4034, 4.4506$

Analytically:

$$4 \sin x \cos x = 1$$
$$2 \sin(2x) = 1$$
$$\sin(2x) = \frac{1}{2}$$
$$2x = \frac{\pi}{6}, \frac{5\pi}{6}, \frac{13\pi}{6}, \frac{17\pi}{6}$$
$$x = \frac{\pi}{12}, \frac{5\pi}{12}, \frac{13\pi}{12}, \frac{17\pi}{12}$$

6. $\sin 2x \sin x = \cos x$

$x \approx 0.7854, 1.5708, 2.3562, 3.9270, 4.7124, 5.4978$

Analytically:

$$2 \sin x \cos x \sin x - \cos x = 0$$
$$\cos x(2 \sin^2 x - 1) = 0$$

$\cos x = 0$ or $2 \sin^2 x - 1 = 0$

$x = \dfrac{\pi}{2}, \dfrac{3\pi}{2}$ $\qquad \sin^2 x = \dfrac{1}{2}$

$$\sin x = \pm\frac{\sqrt{2}}{2}$$
$$x = \frac{\pi}{4}, \frac{3\pi}{4}, \frac{5\pi}{4}, \frac{7\pi}{4}$$

7. $\cos 2x - \cos x = 0$

$x \approx 0, 2.094, 4.189$, (6.283 not in interval)

Analytically:

$$\cos 2x - \cos x = 0$$
$$2 \cos^2 x - 1 - \cos x = 0$$
$$(2 \cos x + 1)(\cos x - 1) = 0$$

$\cos x = -\dfrac{1}{2}, \qquad \cos x = 1$

$x = \dfrac{2\pi}{3}, \dfrac{4\pi}{3}, 0,$ (2π not in interval)

8. $\tan 2x - \cot x = 0$

$x \approx 0.5236, 1.5708, 2.6180, 3.6652, 4.7124, 5.7596$

Analytically:

$$\frac{2\tan x}{1-\tan^2 x} = \cot x$$

$$2\tan x = \cot x(1-\tan^2 x)$$

$$2\tan x = \cot x - \cot x\tan^2 x$$

$$2\tan x = \cot x - \tan x$$

$$3\tan x = \cot x$$

$$3\tan x - \cot x = 0$$

$$3\tan x - \frac{1}{\tan x} = 0$$

$$\frac{3\tan^2 x - 1}{\tan x} = 0$$

$$\frac{1}{\tan x}(3\tan^2 x - 1) = 0$$

$$\cot x(3\tan^2 x - 1) = 0$$

$\cot x = 0$ or $3\tan^2 x - 1 = 0$

$x = \frac{\pi}{2}, \frac{3\pi}{2}$ $\qquad \tan^2 x = \frac{1}{3}$

$$\tan x = \pm\frac{\sqrt{3}}{3}$$

$$x = \frac{\pi}{6}, \frac{5\pi}{6}, \frac{7\pi}{6}, \frac{11\pi}{6}$$

$$x = \frac{\pi}{6}, \frac{\pi}{2}, \frac{5\pi}{6}, \frac{7\pi}{6}, \frac{3\pi}{2}, \frac{11\pi}{6}$$

9. Solutions: 0, 1.571, 3.142, 4.712

$$\sin 4x = -2\sin 2x$$

$$\sin 4x + 2\sin 2x = 0$$

$$2\sin 2x\cos 2x + 2\sin 2x = 0$$

$$2\sin 2x(\cos 2x + 1) = 0$$

$2\sin 2x = 0$ or $\cos 2x + 1 = 0$

$\sin 2x = 0$ $\qquad \cos 2x = -1$

$2x = n\pi$ $\qquad 2x = \pi + 2n\pi$

$x = \frac{n}{2}\pi$ $\qquad x = \frac{\pi}{2} + n\pi$

$x = 0, \frac{\pi}{2}, \pi, \frac{3\pi}{2}$ $\qquad x = \frac{\pi}{2}, \frac{3\pi}{2}$

10. $(\sin 2x + \cos 2x)^2 = 1$

$x \approx 0.0, 0.7854, 1.5708, 2.3562, 3.1416, 3.9270,$
$4.7124, 5.4978$

Analytically:

$$\sin^2 2x + 2\sin 2x\cos 2x + \cos^2 2x = 1$$

$$2\sin 2x\cos 2x = 0$$

$$\sin 4x = 0$$

$$4x = n\pi$$

$$x = \frac{n\pi}{4}$$

$$x = 0, \frac{\pi}{4}, \frac{\pi}{2}, \frac{3\pi}{4},$$

$$\pi, \frac{5\pi}{4}, \frac{3\pi}{2}, \frac{7\pi}{4}$$

11. $\cos 2x + \sin x = 0$

Using a graphing utility, $x \approx 1.5708, 3.6652, 5.7596$.

Algebraically:

$$\cos 2x + \sin x = 0$$

$$1 - 2\sin^2 x + \sin x = 0$$

$$2\sin^2 x - \sin x - 1 = 0$$

$$(2\sin x + 1)(\sin x - 1) = 0$$

$$\sin x = -\frac{1}{2} \Rightarrow x = \frac{7\pi}{6}, \frac{11\pi}{6}$$

$$\sin x = 1 \Rightarrow x = \frac{\pi}{2}$$

12. $\tan 2x - 2\cos x = 0$

Using a graphing utility,

$x \approx 0.5236, 1.5708, 2.6180, 4.7124.$

Algebraically:

$$\tan 2x = 2\cos x$$

$$\frac{2\tan x}{1 - \tan^2 x} = 2\cos x$$

$$\frac{\sin x}{\cos x} = \cos x\left(1 - \frac{\sin^2 x}{\cos^2 x}\right)$$

$\left(\textbf{Note: } \cos x = 0 \Rightarrow x = \frac{\pi}{2}, \frac{3\pi}{2}\right)$

$$\sin x = \cos^2 x - \sin^2 x$$

$$\sin x = 1 - 2\sin^2 x$$

$$2\sin^2 x + \sin x - 1 = 0$$

$$(2\sin x - 1)(\sin x + 1) = 0$$

$$\sin x = \frac{1}{2} \Rightarrow x = \frac{\pi}{6}, \frac{5\pi}{6}$$

$$\sin x = -1 \Rightarrow x = \frac{3\pi}{2}$$

$$\cos x = 0 \Rightarrow x = \frac{\pi}{2}$$

13. $\sin u = \frac{3}{5}, \ 0 < u < \frac{\pi}{2} \Rightarrow \cos u = \frac{4}{5}$

$$\sin 2u = 2\sin u\cos u = 2 \cdot \frac{3}{5} \cdot \frac{4}{5} = \frac{24}{25}$$

$$\cos 2u = \cos^2 u - \sin^2 u = \frac{16}{25} - \frac{9}{25} = \frac{7}{25}$$

$$\tan 2u = \frac{2\tan u}{1 - \tan^2 u} = \frac{2(3/4)}{1 - (9/16)} = \frac{24}{7}$$

14. $\cos u = -\frac{2}{7}, \frac{\pi}{2} < u < \pi,$ Quadrant II

$$\sin 2u = 2\sin u\cos u = 2\left(\frac{\sqrt{45}}{7}\right)\left(-\frac{2}{7}\right) = -\frac{12\sqrt{5}}{49}$$

$$\cos 2u = \cos^2 u - \sin^2 u = \frac{4}{49} - \frac{45}{49} = -\frac{41}{49}$$

$$\tan 2u = \frac{2\tan u}{1 - \tan^2 u} = \frac{2(-\sqrt{45}/2)}{1 - (45/4)} = \frac{-\sqrt{45}}{(4 - 45)/4} = \frac{12\sqrt{5}}{41}$$

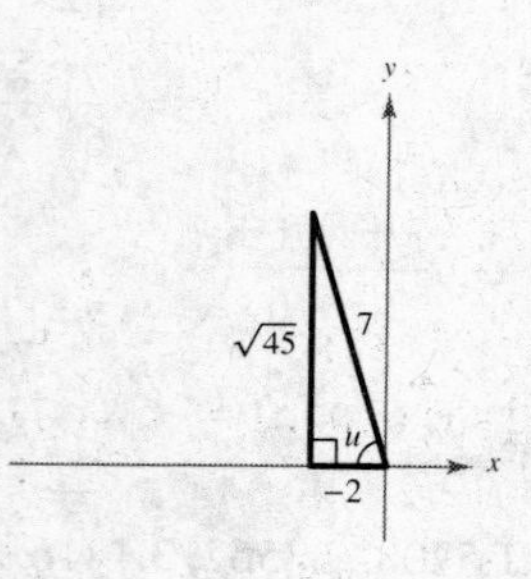

15. $\tan u = \frac{1}{2}, \ \pi < u < \frac{3\pi}{2} \Rightarrow \sin u = -\frac{1}{\sqrt{5}}$ and $\cos u = -\frac{2}{\sqrt{5}}$

$$\sin 2u = 2\sin u\cos u = 2\left(-\frac{1}{\sqrt{5}}\right)\left(-\frac{2}{\sqrt{5}}\right) = \frac{4}{5}$$

$$\cos 2u = \cos^2 u - \sin^2 u = \left(-\frac{2}{\sqrt{5}}\right)^2 - \left(-\frac{1}{\sqrt{5}}\right)^2 = \frac{3}{5}$$

$$\tan 2u = \frac{2\tan u}{1 - \tan^2 u} = \frac{2(1/2)}{1 - (1/4)} = \frac{4}{3}$$

16. $\cot u = -6, \frac{3\pi}{2} < u < 2\pi,$ Quadrant IV

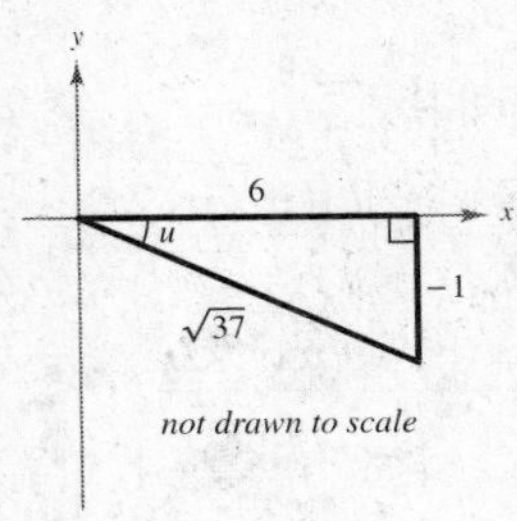

$$\sin 2u = 2\sin u \cos u = 2\left(-\frac{1}{\sqrt{37}}\right)\left(\frac{6}{\sqrt{37}}\right) = -\frac{12}{37}$$

$$\cos 2u = \cos^2 u - \sin^2 u = \frac{36}{37} - \frac{1}{37} = \frac{35}{37}$$

$$\tan 2u = \frac{2\tan u}{1 - \tan^2 u} = \frac{2(-1/6)}{1 - (-1/6)^2} = \frac{-2/6}{35/36} = -\frac{12}{35}$$

17. $\sec u = -\frac{5}{2}, \frac{\pi}{2} < u < \pi$

$$\cos u = -\frac{2}{5} \Rightarrow \sin u = \frac{\sqrt{21}}{5}$$

$$\sin 2u = 2\sin u \cos u = 2\left(\frac{\sqrt{21}}{5}\right)\left(-\frac{2}{5}\right) = \frac{-4\sqrt{21}}{25}$$

$$\cos 2u = \cos^2 u - \sin^2 u = \frac{4}{25} - \frac{21}{25} = -\frac{17}{25}$$

$$\tan 2u = \frac{2\tan u}{1 - \tan^2 u}$$

$$= \frac{2\left(\sqrt{21}/-2\right)}{1 - (21/4)} = \frac{-\sqrt{21}}{-17/4} = \frac{4\sqrt{21}}{17}$$

18. $\csc u = 3, \frac{\pi}{2} < u < \pi$

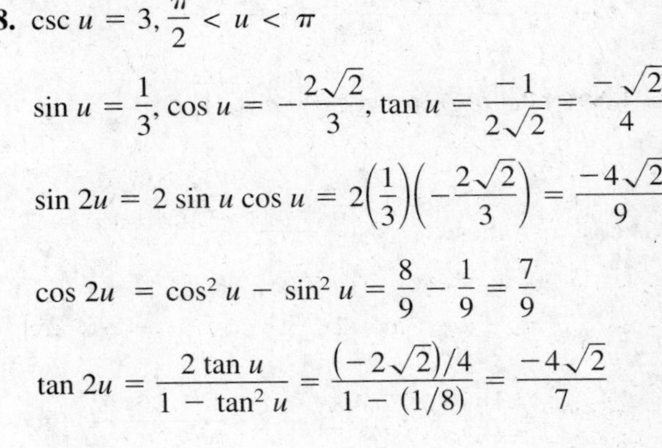

$$\sin u = \frac{1}{3}, \cos u = -\frac{2\sqrt{2}}{3}, \tan u = \frac{-1}{2\sqrt{2}} = \frac{-\sqrt{2}}{4}$$

$$\sin 2u = 2\sin u \cos u = 2\left(\frac{1}{3}\right)\left(-\frac{2\sqrt{2}}{3}\right) = \frac{-4\sqrt{2}}{9}$$

$$\cos 2u = \cos^2 u - \sin^2 u = \frac{8}{9} - \frac{1}{9} = \frac{7}{9}$$

$$\tan 2u = \frac{2\tan u}{1 - \tan^2 u} = \frac{\left(-2\sqrt{2}\right)/4}{1 - (1/8)} = \frac{-4\sqrt{2}}{7}$$

19. $8\sin x \cos x = 4(2\sin x \cos x) = 4\sin 2x$

20. $4\sin x \cos x + 1 = 2\sin 2x + 1$

21. $6 - 12\sin^2 x = 6(1 - 2\sin^2 x) = 6\cos 2x$

22. $(\cos x + \sin x)(\cos x - \sin x) = \cos^2 x - \sin^2 x$

$$= \cos 2x$$

23. $\cos^4 x = (\cos^2 x)(\cos^2 x) = \left(\frac{1 + \cos 2x}{2}\right)\left(\frac{1 + \cos 2x}{2}\right) = \frac{1 + 2\cos 2x + \cos^2 2x}{4}$

$$= \frac{1 + 2\cos 2x + (1 + \cos 4x)/2}{4} = \frac{2 + 4\cos 2x + 1 + \cos 4x}{8}$$

$$= \frac{3 + 4\cos 2x + \cos 4x}{8} = \frac{1}{8}(3 + 4\cos 2x + \cos 4x)$$

24. $\sin^4 x = (\sin^2 x)(\sin^2 x)$

$= \left(\frac{1 - \cos 2x}{2}\right)\left(\frac{1 - \cos 2x}{2}\right)$

$= \frac{1 - 2\cos 2x + \cos^2 2x}{4}$

$= \frac{1 - 2\cos 2x + \left(\frac{1 + \cos 4x}{2}\right)}{4}$

$= \frac{2 - 4\cos 2x + 1 + \cos 4x}{8}$

$= \frac{1}{8}(3 - 4\cos 2x + \cos 4x)$

25. $(\sin^2 x)(\cos^2 x) = \left(\frac{1 - \cos 2x}{2}\right)\left(\frac{1 + \cos 2x}{2}\right)$

$= \frac{1 - \cos^2 2x}{4}$

$= \frac{1}{4}\left(1 - \frac{1 + \cos 4x}{2}\right)$

$= \frac{1}{8}(2 - 1 - \cos 4x)$

$= \frac{1}{8}(1 - \cos 4x)$

26. $\cos^6 x = (\cos^2 x)^3 = \left(\frac{1 + \cos 2x}{2}\right)^3$

$= \frac{1}{8}[1 + 3\cos 2x + 3\cos^2 2x + \cos^3 2x]$

$= \frac{1}{8}\left[1 + 3\cos 2x + 3 \cdot \frac{1 + \cos 4x}{2} + \cos 2x\left(\frac{1 + \cos 4x}{2}\right)\right]$

$= \frac{1}{8}\left[\frac{5}{2} + 3\cos 2x + \frac{3}{2}\cos 4x + \frac{1}{2}\cos 2x + \frac{1}{2}\cos 2x \cdot \cos 4x\right]$

$= \frac{1}{8}\left[\frac{5}{2} + \frac{7}{2}\cos 2x + \frac{3}{2}\cos 4x + \frac{1}{2}\frac{1}{2}(\cos 2x + \cos 6x)\right]$

$= \frac{1}{32}[10 + 15\cos 2x + 6\cos 4x + \cos 6x]$

27. $\sin^2 x\cos^4 x = \sin^2 x\cos^2 x\cos^2 x = \left(\frac{1 - \cos 2x}{2}\right)\left(\frac{1 + \cos 2x}{2}\right)\left(\frac{1 + \cos 2x}{2}\right)$

$= \frac{1}{8}(1 - \cos 2x)(1 + \cos 2x)(1 + \cos 2x)$

$= \frac{1}{8}(1 - \cos^2 2x)(1 + \cos 2x)$

$= \frac{1}{8}(1 + \cos 2x - \cos^2 2x - \cos^3 2x)$

$= \frac{1}{8}\left[1 + \cos 2x - \left(\frac{1 + \cos 4x}{2}\right) - \cos 2x\left(\frac{1 + \cos 4x}{2}\right)\right]$

$= \frac{1}{16}[2 + 2\cos 2x - 1 - \cos 4x - \cos 2x - \cos 2x\cos 4x]$

$= \frac{1}{16}\left[1 + \cos 2x - \cos 4x - \left(\frac{1}{2}\cos 2x + \frac{1}{2}\cos 6x\right)\right]$

$= \frac{1}{32}(2 + 2\cos 2x - 2\cos 4x - \cos 2x - \cos 6x)$

$= \frac{1}{32}(2 + \cos 2x - 2\cos 4x - \cos 6x)$

28. $\sin^4 x \cos^2 x = \sin^2 x \sin^2 x \cos^2 x$

$$= \left(\frac{1 - \cos 2x}{2}\right)\left(\frac{1 - \cos 2x}{2}\right)\left(\frac{1 + \cos 2x}{2}\right)$$

$$= \frac{1}{8}(1 - \cos 2x)(1 - \cos^2 2x)$$

$$= \frac{1}{8}(1 - \cos 2x - \cos^2 2x + \cos^3 2x)$$

$$= \frac{1}{8}\left[1 - \cos 2x - \left(\frac{1 + \cos 4x}{2}\right) + \cos 2x\left(\frac{1 + \cos 4x}{2}\right)\right]$$

$$= \frac{1}{16}[2 - 2\cos 2x - 1 - \cos 4x + \cos 2x + \cos 2x \cos 4x]$$

$$= \frac{1}{16}\left[1 - \cos 2x - \cos 4x + \frac{1}{2}\cos 2x + \frac{1}{2}\cos 6x\right]$$

$$= \frac{1}{32}[2 - 2\cos 2x - 2\cos 4x + \cos 2x + \cos 6x]$$

$$= \frac{1}{32}[2 - \cos 2x - 2\cos 4x + \cos 6x]$$

29. $\sin^2 2x = \dfrac{1 - \cos 4x}{2}$

$$= \frac{1}{2} - \frac{1}{2}\cos 4x$$

$$= \frac{1}{2}(1 - \cos 4x)$$

30. $\cos^2 2x = \dfrac{1 + \cos 4x}{2}$

$$= \frac{1}{2} + \frac{1}{2}\cos 4x$$

$$= \frac{1}{2}(1 + \cos 4x)$$

31. $\cos^2 \dfrac{x}{2} = \dfrac{1 + \cos x}{2}$

$$= \frac{1}{2} + \frac{1}{2}\cos x$$

$$= \frac{1}{2}(1 + \cos x)$$

32. $\sin^2 \dfrac{x}{2} = \dfrac{1 - \cos x}{2}$

$$= \frac{1}{2} - \frac{1}{2}\cos x$$

$$= \frac{1}{2}(1 - \cos x)$$

33. $\sin^2 2x \cos^2 2x = \left(\dfrac{1 - \cos 4x}{2}\right)\left(\dfrac{1 + \cos 4x}{2}\right)$

$$= \frac{1}{4}(1 - \cos 4x)(1 + \cos 4x)$$

$$= \frac{1}{4}(1 - \cos^2 4x)$$

$$= \frac{1}{4}\left(1 - \frac{1 + \cos 8x}{2}\right)$$

$$= \frac{1 - \cos 8x}{8}$$

34. $\sin^2 \dfrac{x}{2} \cos^2 \dfrac{x}{2} = \left(\dfrac{1 - \cos x}{2}\right)\left(\dfrac{1 + \cos x}{2}\right)$

$$= \frac{1}{4}(1 - \cos x)(1 + \cos x)$$

$$= \frac{1}{4}(1 - \cos^2 x)$$

$$= \frac{1}{4}\left(1 - \frac{1 + \cos 2x}{2}\right)$$

$$= \frac{1}{8}(1 - \cos 2x)$$

35. $\sin^4 \frac{x}{2} = \left(\sin^2 \frac{x}{2}\right)\left(\sin^2 \frac{x}{2}\right)$

$= \left(\frac{1 - \cos x}{2}\right)\left(\frac{1 - \cos x}{2}\right)$

$= \frac{1}{4}[1 - 2\cos x + \cos^2 x]$

$= \frac{1}{4}\left[1 - 2\cos x + \frac{1 + \cos 2x}{2}\right]$

$= \frac{1}{8}[2 - 4\cos x + 1 + \cos 2x]$

$= \frac{1}{8}[3 - 4\cos x + \cos 2x]$

36. $\cos^4 \frac{x}{2} = \left(\cos^2 \frac{x}{2}\right)\left(\cos^2 \frac{x}{2}\right)$

$= \left(\frac{1 + \cos x}{2}\right)\left(\frac{1 + \cos x}{2}\right)$

$= \frac{1}{4}[1 + 2\cos x + \cos^2 x]$

$= \frac{1}{4}\left[1 + 2\cos x + \frac{1 + \cos 2x}{2}\right]$

$= \frac{1}{8}[2 + 4\cos x + 1 + \cos 2x]$

$= \frac{1}{8}[3 + 4\cos x + \cos 2x]$

37. (a) $\cos \frac{\theta}{2} = \sqrt{\frac{1 + \cos \theta}{2}} = \sqrt{\frac{1 + (15/17)}{2}} = \sqrt{\frac{16}{17}} = \frac{4}{\sqrt{17}} = \frac{4\sqrt{17}}{17}$

(b) $\sin \frac{\theta}{2} = \sqrt{\frac{1 - \cos \theta}{2}} = \sqrt{\frac{1 - (15/17)}{2}} = \frac{\sqrt{17}}{17}$

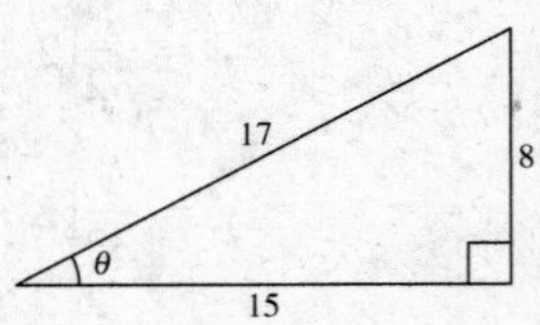

$\sin \theta = \frac{8}{17}$

$\cos \theta = \frac{15}{17}$

(c) $\tan \frac{\theta}{2} = \frac{\sin \theta}{1 + \cos \theta} = \frac{8/17}{1 + (15/17)} = \frac{8}{32} = \frac{1}{4}$

(d) $\sec \frac{\theta}{2} = \frac{1}{\cos(\theta/2)} = \frac{1}{\sqrt{(1 + \cos \theta)/2}} = \frac{\sqrt{2}}{\sqrt{1 + (15/17)}} = \frac{\sqrt{17}}{4}$

(e) $\csc \frac{\theta}{2} = \frac{1}{\sin(\theta/2)} = \frac{1}{\sqrt{(1 - \cos \theta)/2}} = \frac{1}{\sqrt{[1 - (15/17)]/2}} = \frac{1}{1/\sqrt{17}} = \sqrt{17}$

(f) $\cot \frac{\theta}{2} = \frac{1 + \cos \theta}{\sin \theta} = \frac{1 + (15/17)}{8/17} = 4$

(g) $2 \sin \frac{\theta}{2} \cos \frac{\theta}{2} = 2\left(\frac{1}{\sqrt{17}}\right)\left(\frac{4\sqrt{17}}{17}\right) = \frac{8}{17}, \quad (= \sin \theta)$

(h) $2 \cos \frac{\theta}{2} \tan \frac{\theta}{2} = 2 \sin \frac{\theta}{2} = \frac{2\sqrt{17}}{17}$

38. (a) $\sin \frac{\theta}{2} = \sqrt{\frac{1 - \cos \theta}{2}} = \sqrt{\frac{1 - (7/25)}{2}} = \sqrt{\frac{18}{50}} = \frac{3}{5}$

(b) $\cos \frac{\theta}{2} = \sqrt{\frac{1 + \cos \theta}{2}} = \sqrt{\frac{1 + (7/25)}{2}} = \frac{4}{5}$

(c) $\tan \frac{\theta}{2} = \frac{\sin(\theta/2)}{\cos(\theta/2)} = \frac{3}{4}$

(d) $\cot \frac{\theta}{2} = \frac{1}{\tan(\theta/2)} = \frac{4}{3}$

(e) $\sec \frac{\theta}{2} = \frac{1}{\cos(\theta/2)} = \frac{5}{4}$

(f) $\csc \frac{\theta}{2} = \frac{1}{\sin(\theta/2)} = \frac{5}{3}$

(g) $2 \sin \frac{\theta}{2} \cos \frac{\theta}{2} = \sin \theta = \frac{24}{25}$

(h) $\cos 2\theta = 2\cos^2 \theta - 1 = 2\left(\frac{7}{25}\right)^2 - 1 = -\frac{527}{625}$

39. $\sin 15° = \sin\left(\frac{1}{2} \cdot 30°\right) = \sqrt{\frac{1 - \cos 30°}{2}} = \sqrt{\frac{1 - (\sqrt{3}/2)}{2}} = \frac{1}{2}\sqrt{2 - \sqrt{3}}$

$\cos 15° = \cos\left(\frac{1}{2} \cdot 30°\right) = \sqrt{\frac{1 + \cos 30°}{2}} = \sqrt{\frac{1 + (\sqrt{3}/2)}{2}} = \frac{1}{2}\sqrt{2 + \sqrt{3}}$

$\tan 15° = \tan\left(\frac{1}{2} \cdot 30°\right) = \frac{\sin 30°}{1 + \cos 30°} = \frac{1/2}{1 + (\sqrt{3}/2)} = \frac{1}{2 + \sqrt{3}} = 2 - \sqrt{3}$

40. $\sin 165° = \sin\left(\frac{1}{2} \cdot 330°\right) = \sqrt{\frac{1 - \cos 330°}{2}} = \sqrt{\frac{1 - (\sqrt{3}/2)}{2}} = \frac{1}{2}\sqrt{2 - \sqrt{3}}$

$\cos 165° = \cos\left(\frac{1}{2} \cdot 330°\right) = -\sqrt{\frac{1 + \cos 330°}{2}} = -\sqrt{\frac{1 + (\sqrt{3}/2)}{2}} = -\frac{1}{2}\sqrt{2 + \sqrt{3}}$

$\tan 165° = \tan\left(\frac{1}{2} \cdot 330°\right) = \frac{\sin 330°}{1 + \cos 330°} = \frac{-1/2}{1 + (\sqrt{3}/2)} = \frac{-1}{2 + \sqrt{3}} = \sqrt{3} - 2$

41. $\sin 112° 30' = \sin\left(\frac{1}{2} \cdot 225°\right) = \sqrt{\frac{1 - \cos 225°}{2}} = \sqrt{\frac{1 + (\sqrt{2}/2)}{2}} = \frac{1}{2}\sqrt{2 + \sqrt{2}}$

$\cos 112° 30' = \cos\left(\frac{1}{2} \cdot 225°\right) = -\sqrt{\frac{1 + \cos 225°}{2}} = -\sqrt{\frac{1 - (\sqrt{2}/2)}{2}} = -\frac{1}{2}\sqrt{2 - \sqrt{2}}$

$\tan 112° 30' = \tan\left(\frac{1}{2} \cdot 225°\right) = \frac{\sin 225°}{1 + \cos 225°} = \frac{-\sqrt{2}/2}{1 - (\sqrt{2}/2)} = -1 - \sqrt{2}$

42. $157° 30' = 157.5° = \frac{1}{2}(315°)$, Quadrant II

$\sin(157° 30') = \sin\left(\frac{1}{2} \cdot 315°\right) = \sqrt{\frac{1 - \cos 315°}{2}} = \sqrt{\frac{1 - \sqrt{2}/2}{2}} = \frac{\sqrt{2 - \sqrt{2}}}{2}$

$\cos(157° 30') = \cos\left(\frac{1}{2} \cdot 315°\right) = -\sqrt{\frac{1 + \cos 315°}{2}} = -\sqrt{\frac{1 + \sqrt{2}/2}{2}} = -\frac{\sqrt{2 + \sqrt{2}}}{2}$

$\tan(157° 30') = \tan\left(\frac{1}{2} \cdot 315°\right) = \frac{\sin 315°}{1 + \cos 315°} = \frac{-\sqrt{2}/2}{1 + \sqrt{2}/2} = \frac{-\sqrt{2}}{2 + \sqrt{2}} = 1 - \sqrt{2}$

43. $\sin\frac{\pi}{8} = \sin\left[\frac{1}{2}\left(\frac{\pi}{4}\right)\right] = \sqrt{\frac{1 - \cos(\pi/4)}{2}} = \frac{1}{2}\sqrt{2 - \sqrt{2}}$

$\cos\frac{\pi}{8} = \cos\left[\frac{1}{2}\left(\frac{\pi}{4}\right)\right] = \sqrt{\frac{1 + \cos(\pi/4)}{2}} = \frac{1}{2}\sqrt{2 + \sqrt{2}}$

$\tan\frac{\pi}{8} = \tan\left[\frac{1}{2}\left(\frac{\pi}{4}\right)\right] = \frac{\sin(\pi/4)}{1 + \cos(\pi/4)} = \frac{\sqrt{2}/2}{1 + (\sqrt{2}/2)} = \sqrt{2} - 1$

44. $\sin\frac{\pi}{12} = \sin\left[\frac{1}{2}\left(\frac{\pi}{6}\right)\right] = \sqrt{\frac{1 - \cos(\pi/6)}{2}} = \sqrt{\frac{1 - (\sqrt{3}/2)}{2}} = \frac{1}{2}\sqrt{2 - \sqrt{3}}$

$\cos\frac{\pi}{12} = \cos\left[\frac{1}{2}\left(\frac{\pi}{6}\right)\right] = \sqrt{\frac{1 + \cos(\pi/6)}{2}} = \frac{1}{2}\sqrt{2 + \sqrt{3}}$

$\tan\frac{\pi}{12} = \tan\left[\frac{1}{2}\left(\frac{\pi}{6}\right)\right] = \frac{\sin(\pi/6)}{1 + \cos(\pi/6)} = \frac{1/2}{1 + (\sqrt{3}/2)} = 2 - \sqrt{3}$

45. $\sin\frac{3\pi}{8} = \sin\left(\frac{1}{2}\cdot\frac{3\pi}{4}\right) = \sqrt{\frac{1-\cos(3\pi/4)}{2}} = \sqrt{\frac{1+(\sqrt{2}/2)}{2}} = \frac{1}{2}\sqrt{2+\sqrt{2}}$

$\cos\frac{3\pi}{8} = \cos\left(\frac{1}{2}\cdot\frac{3\pi}{4}\right) = \sqrt{\frac{1+\cos(3\pi/4)}{2}} = \sqrt{\frac{1-(\sqrt{2}/2)}{2}} = \frac{1}{2}\sqrt{2-\sqrt{2}}$

$\tan\frac{3\pi}{8} = \tan\left(\frac{1}{2}\cdot\frac{3\pi}{4}\right) = \frac{\sin(3\pi/4)}{1+\cos(3\pi/4)} = \frac{\sqrt{2}/2}{1-(\sqrt{2}/2)} = \frac{\sqrt{2}}{2-\sqrt{2}} = \sqrt{2}+1$

46. $\frac{7\pi}{12} = \frac{1}{2}\left(\frac{7\pi}{6}\right)$, Quadrant II

$\sin\left(\frac{7\pi}{12}\right) = \sin\left(\frac{1}{2}\cdot\frac{7\pi}{6}\right) = \sqrt{\frac{1-\cos(7\pi/6)}{2}} = \sqrt{\frac{1+(\sqrt{3}/2)}{2}} = \frac{\sqrt{2+\sqrt{3}}}{2}$

$\cos\left(\frac{7\pi}{12}\right) = \cos\left(\frac{1}{2}\cdot\frac{7\pi}{6}\right) = -\sqrt{\frac{1+\cos(7\pi/6)}{2}} = -\sqrt{\frac{1-(\sqrt{3}/2)}{2}} = -\frac{\sqrt{2-\sqrt{3}}}{2}$

$\tan\left(\frac{7\pi}{12}\right) = \tan\left(\frac{1}{2}\cdot\frac{7\pi}{6}\right) = \frac{\sin(7\pi/6)}{1+\cos(7\pi/6)} = \frac{-(1/2)}{1-(\sqrt{3}/2)} = \frac{1}{\sqrt{3}-2} = -2-\sqrt{3}$

47. $\sin u = \frac{5}{13}, \frac{\pi}{2} < u < \pi \Rightarrow \cos u = -\frac{12}{13}$

$\sin\left(\frac{u}{2}\right) = \sqrt{\frac{1-\cos u}{2}}$

$= \sqrt{\frac{1+(12/13)}{2}} = \frac{5\sqrt{26}}{26}$

$\cos\left(\frac{u}{2}\right) = \sqrt{\frac{1+\cos u}{2}}$

$= \sqrt{\frac{1-(12/13)}{2}} = \frac{\sqrt{26}}{26}$

$\tan\left(\frac{u}{2}\right) = \frac{\sin u}{1+\cos u} = \frac{5/13}{1-(12/13)} = \frac{5}{1} = 5$

48. $\cos u = \frac{7}{25}, 0 < u < \frac{\pi}{2}$, Quadrant I

$\sin u = \sqrt{1-\cos^2 u} = \sqrt{1-\frac{49}{625}} = \frac{24}{25}$

$\sin\frac{u}{2} = \sqrt{\frac{1-\cos u}{2}}$

$= \sqrt{\frac{1-(7/25)}{2}} = \sqrt{\frac{9}{25}} = 0.6 = \frac{3}{5}$

$\cos\frac{u}{2} = \sqrt{\frac{1+\cos u}{2}}$

$= \sqrt{\frac{1+(7/25)}{2}} = \sqrt{\frac{16}{25}} = 0.8 = \frac{4}{5}$

$\tan\frac{u}{2} = \frac{1-\cos u}{\sin u} = \frac{1-(7/25)}{24/25} = \frac{18}{24} = \frac{3}{4}$

49. $\tan u = -\frac{8}{5}, \frac{3\pi}{2} < u < 2\pi$, Quadrant IV

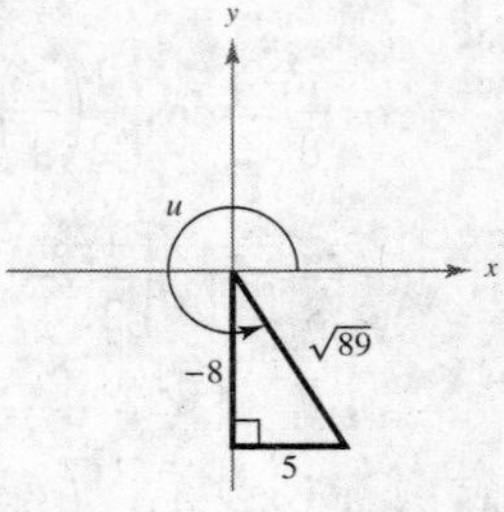

$\sin u = -\frac{8}{\sqrt{89}}, \cos u = \frac{5}{\sqrt{89}}$

$\sin\left(\frac{u}{2}\right) = \sqrt{\frac{1-\cos u}{2}} = \sqrt{\frac{1-(5/\sqrt{89})}{2}} = \sqrt{\frac{\sqrt{89}-5}{2\sqrt{89}}} = \sqrt{\frac{89-5\sqrt{89}}{178}}$

$\cos\left(\frac{u}{2}\right) = -\sqrt{\frac{1+\cos u}{2}} = -\sqrt{\frac{1+(5/\sqrt{89})}{2}} = -\sqrt{\frac{\sqrt{89}+5}{2\sqrt{89}}} = -\sqrt{\frac{89+5\sqrt{89}}{178}}$

$\tan\left(\frac{u}{2}\right) = \frac{1-\cos u}{\sin u} = \frac{1-(5/\sqrt{89})}{-8/\sqrt{89}} = \frac{5-\sqrt{89}}{8}$

50. $\cot u = 7,\ \pi < u < \dfrac{3\pi}{2},$ Quadrant III

$$\sin\frac{u}{2} = \sqrt{\frac{1-\cos u}{2}} = \sqrt{\frac{1+(7/\sqrt{50})}{2}} = \sqrt{\frac{\sqrt{50}+7}{2\sqrt{50}}} = \frac{\sqrt{50+7\sqrt{50}}}{10}$$

$$\cos\frac{u}{2} = -\sqrt{\frac{1+\cos u}{2}} = -\sqrt{\frac{1-7/\sqrt{50}}{2}} = -\sqrt{\frac{\sqrt{50}-7}{2\sqrt{50}}} = -\frac{\sqrt{50-7\sqrt{50}}}{10}$$

$$\tan\frac{u}{2} = \frac{1-\cos u}{\sin u} = \frac{1+7/\sqrt{50}}{-1/\sqrt{50}} = -\left(\sqrt{50}+7\right)$$

not drawn to scale

51. $\csc u = -\dfrac{5}{3},\ \pi < u < \dfrac{3\pi}{2},$ Quadrant III

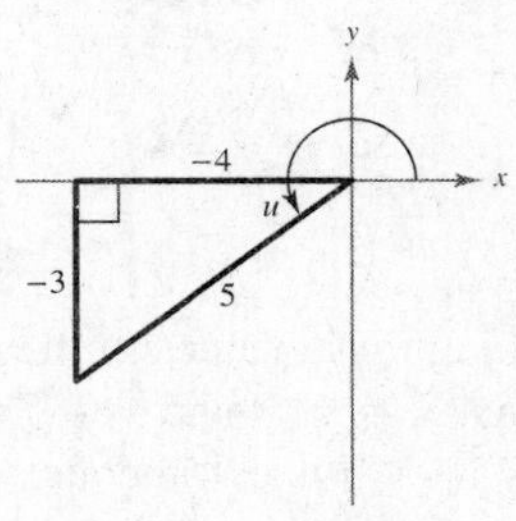

$$\sin u = -\frac{3}{5},\ \cos u = -\frac{4}{5}$$

$$\sin\left(\frac{u}{2}\right) = \sqrt{\frac{1-\cos u}{2}} = \sqrt{\frac{1+(4/5)}{2}} = \frac{3}{\sqrt{10}} = \frac{3\sqrt{10}}{10}$$

$$\cos\left(\frac{u}{2}\right) = -\sqrt{\frac{1+\cos u}{2}} = -\sqrt{\frac{1-(4/5)}{2}} = \frac{-1}{\sqrt{10}} = -\frac{\sqrt{10}}{10}$$

$$\tan\left(\frac{u}{2}\right) = \frac{1-\cos u}{\sin u} = \frac{1+(4/5)}{-3/5} = -3$$

52. $\sec u = \dfrac{-7}{2},\ \dfrac{\pi}{2} < u < \pi$

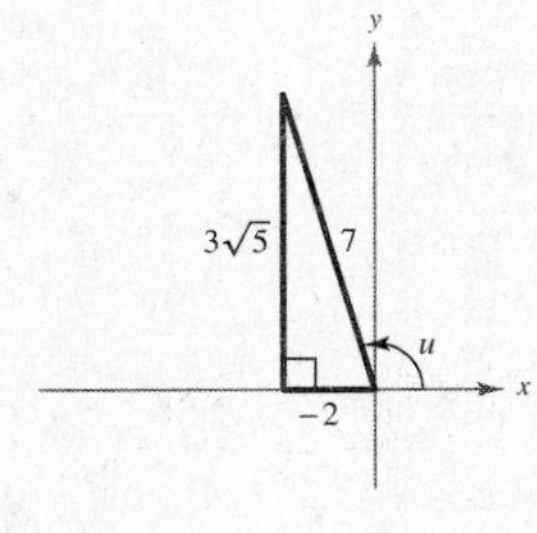

$$\cos u = \frac{-2}{7},\ \sin u = \frac{3\sqrt{5}}{7}$$

$$\sin\frac{u}{2} = \sqrt{\frac{1-\cos u}{2}} = \sqrt{\frac{1+(2/7)}{2}} = \sqrt{\frac{9}{14}} = \frac{3\sqrt{14}}{14}$$

$$\cos\frac{u}{2} = \sqrt{\frac{1+\cos u}{2}} = \sqrt{\frac{1-(2/7)}{2}} = \sqrt{\frac{5}{14}} = \frac{\sqrt{70}}{14}$$

$$\tan\frac{u}{2} = \frac{1-\cos u}{\sin u} = \frac{1+(2/7)}{3\left(\sqrt{5}/7\right)} = \frac{9}{3\sqrt{5}} = \frac{3\sqrt{5}}{5}$$

53. $\sqrt{\dfrac{1-\cos 6x}{2}} = |\sin 3x|$

54. $\sqrt{\dfrac{1+\cos 4x}{2}} = \left|\cos\dfrac{4x}{2}\right| = |\cos 2x|$

55. $-\sqrt{\dfrac{1-\cos 8x}{1+\cos 8x}} = -\dfrac{\sqrt{(1-\cos 8x)/2}}{\sqrt{(1+\cos 8x)/2}}$

$$= -\frac{|\sin 4x|}{|\cos 4x|} = -|\tan 4x|$$

56. $-\sqrt{\dfrac{1-\cos(x-1)}{2}} = -\left|\sin\left(\dfrac{x-1}{2}\right)\right|$

57. $\sin\frac{x}{2} - \cos x = 0$

$$\pm\sqrt{\frac{1-\cos x}{2}} = \cos x$$

$$\frac{1-\cos x}{2} = \cos^2 x$$

$$0 = 2\cos^2 x + \cos x - 1$$

$$= (2\cos x - 1)(\cos x + 1)$$

$\cos x = \frac{1}{2}$ or $\cos x = -1$

$x = \frac{\pi}{3}, \frac{5\pi}{3}$ $\quad x = \pi$

By checking these values in the original equations, we see that $x = \pi/3$ and $x = 5\pi/3$ are the only solutions. $x = \pi$ is extraneous.

58. $h(x) = \sin\frac{x}{2} + \cos x - 1$

$$\sin\frac{x}{2} + \cos x - 1 = 0$$

$$\pm\sqrt{\frac{1-\cos x}{2}} = 1 - \cos x$$

$$\frac{1-\cos x}{2} = 1 - 2\cos x + \cos^2 x$$

$$1 - \cos x = 2 - 4\cos x + 2\cos^2 x$$

$$2\cos^2 x - 3\cos x + 1 = 0$$

$$(2\cos x - 1)(\cos x - 1) = 0$$

$2\cos x - 1 = 0$ or $\cos x - 1 = 0$

$\cos x = \frac{1}{2}$ $\quad \cos x = 1$

$x = \frac{\pi}{3}, \frac{5\pi}{3}$ $\quad x = 0$

59. $\cos\frac{x}{2} - \sin x = 0$

$$\pm\sqrt{\frac{1+\cos x}{2}} = \sin x$$

$$\frac{1+\cos x}{2} = \sin^2 x$$

$$1 + \cos x = 2\sin^2 x$$

$$1 + \cos x = 2 - 2\cos^2 x$$

$$2\cos^2 x + \cos x - 1 = 0$$

$$(2\cos x - 1)(\cos x + 1) = 0$$

$2\cos x - 1 = 0$ or $\cos x + 1 = 0$

$\cos x = \frac{1}{2}$ $\quad \cos x = -1$

$x = \frac{\pi}{3}, \frac{5\pi}{3}$ $\quad x = \pi$

$x = \frac{\pi}{3}, \pi, \frac{5\pi}{3}$

$\pi/3$, π, and $5\pi/3$ are all solutions to the equation.

60. $g(x) = \tan\frac{x}{2} - \sin x$

$$\tan\frac{x}{2} - \sin x = 0$$

$$\frac{1-\cos x}{\sin x} = \sin x$$

$$1 - \cos x = \sin^2 x$$

$$1 - \cos x = 1 - \cos^2 x$$

$$\cos^2 x - \cos x = 0$$

$$\cos x(\cos x - 1) = 0$$

$\cos x = 0$ or $\cos x - 1 = 0$

$x = \frac{\pi}{2}, \frac{3\pi}{2}$ $\quad \cos x = 1$

$x = 0$

0, $\pi/2$, and $3\pi/2$ are all solutions to the equation.

61. $6\sin\frac{\pi}{3}\cos\frac{\pi}{3} = 6 \cdot \frac{1}{2}\left[\sin\left(\frac{\pi}{3}+\frac{\pi}{3}\right) + \sin\left(\frac{\pi}{3}-\frac{\pi}{3}\right)\right] = 3\left[\sin\frac{2\pi}{3} + \sin 0\right] = 3\sin\frac{2\pi}{3}$

62. $4\sin\frac{\pi}{3}\cos\frac{5\pi}{6} = 4 \cdot \frac{1}{2}\left[\sin\left(\frac{\pi}{3}+\frac{5\pi}{6}\right) + \sin\left(\frac{\pi}{3}-\frac{5\pi}{6}\right)\right] = 2\left[\sin\frac{7\pi}{6} + \sin\left(-\frac{\pi}{2}\right)\right] = 2\left(\sin\frac{7\pi}{6} - \sin\frac{\pi}{2}\right)$

63. $\sin 5\theta \cos 3\theta = \frac{1}{2}[\sin(5\theta + 3\theta) + \sin(5\theta - 3\theta)] = \frac{1}{2}(\sin 8\theta + \sin 2\theta)$

64. $5 \sin 3\alpha \sin 4\alpha = 5 \cdot \frac{1}{2}[\cos(3\alpha - 4\alpha) - \cos(3\alpha + 4\alpha)] = \frac{5}{2}[\cos(-\alpha) - \cos(7\alpha)] = \frac{5}{2}[\cos \alpha - \cos 7\alpha]$

65. $10 \cos 75° \cos 15° = 5[\cos(75° - 15°) + \cos(75° + 15°)] = 5[\cos 60° + \cos 90°]$

66. $6 \sin 45° \cos 15° = 3[\sin(45° + 15°) + \sin(45° - 15°) = 3[\sin 60° + \sin 30°]$

67. $5 \cos(-5\beta) \cos 3\beta = 5 \cdot \frac{1}{2}[\cos(-5\beta - 3\beta) + \cos(-5\beta + 3\beta)]$

$$= \frac{5}{2}[\cos(-8\beta) + \cos(-2\beta)] = \frac{5}{2}(\cos 8\beta + \cos 2\beta)$$

68. $\cos 2\theta \cos 4\theta = \frac{1}{2}[\cos(2\theta - 4\theta) + \cos(2\theta + 4\theta)] = \frac{1}{2}[\cos(-2\theta) + \cos 6\theta] = \frac{1}{2}(\cos 2\theta + \cos 6\theta)$

69. $\sin(x + y) \sin(x - y) = \frac{1}{2}[\cos((x + y) - (x - y)) - \cos((x + y) + (x - y))] = \frac{1}{2}[\cos 2y - \cos 2x]$

70. $\sin(x + y) \cos(x - y) = \frac{1}{2}[\sin((x + y) + (x - y)) + \sin((x + y) - (x - y))] = \frac{1}{2}[\sin 2x + \sin 2y]$

71. $\cos(\theta - \pi) \sin(\theta + \pi) = \frac{1}{2}[\sin((\theta - \pi) + (\theta + \pi)) - \sin((\theta - \pi) - (\theta + \pi))]$

$$= \frac{1}{2}[\sin 2\theta - \sin(-2\pi)] = \frac{1}{2}[\sin 2\theta + \sin 2\pi]$$

72. $\sin(\theta + \pi) \sin(\theta - \pi) = \frac{1}{2}[\cos((\theta + \pi) - (\theta - \pi)) - \cos((\theta + \pi) + (\theta - \pi))] = \frac{1}{2}[\cos 2\pi - \cos 2\theta]$

73. $\sin 5\theta - \sin \theta = 2 \cos\left(\frac{5\theta + \theta}{2}\right) \sin\left(\frac{5\theta - \theta}{2}\right)$

$$= 2 \cos 3\theta \cdot \sin 2\theta$$

74. $\sin 3\theta + \sin \theta = 2 \sin\left(\frac{3\theta + \theta}{2}\right) \cos\left(\frac{3\theta - \theta}{2}\right)$

$$= 2 \sin 2\theta \cos \theta$$

75. $\cos 6x + \cos 2x = 2 \cos\left(\frac{6x + 2x}{2}\right) \cos\left(\frac{6x - 2x}{2}\right)$

$$= 2 \cos 4x \cos 2x$$

76. $\sin x + \sin 7x = 2 \sin\left(\frac{x + 7x}{2}\right) \cos\left(\frac{x - 7x}{2}\right)$

$$= 2 \sin 4x \cos(-3x)$$
$$= 2 \sin 4x \cos 3x$$

77. $\sin(\alpha + \beta) - \sin(\alpha - \beta) = 2 \cos\left(\frac{\alpha + \beta + \alpha - \beta}{2}\right) \sin\left(\frac{\alpha + \beta - \alpha + \beta}{2}\right) = 2 \cos \alpha \sin \beta$

78. $\cos(\phi + 2\pi) + \cos \phi = 2 \cos\left(\frac{\phi + 2\pi + \phi}{2}\right) \cos\left(\frac{\phi + 2\pi - \phi}{2}\right) = 2 \cos(\phi + \pi) \cos \pi = -2 \cos(\phi + \pi)$

79. $\cos\left(\theta + \frac{\pi}{2}\right) - \cos\left(\theta - \frac{\pi}{2}\right) = -2 \sin\left(\frac{\theta + (\pi/2) + \theta - (\pi/2)}{2}\right) \sin\left(\frac{\theta + (\pi/2) - \theta + (\pi/2)}{2}\right)$

$$= -2 \sin \theta \sin \frac{\pi}{2} = -2 \sin \theta$$

80. $\sin\left(x + \frac{\pi}{2}\right) + \sin\left(x - \frac{\pi}{2}\right) = 2 \sin\left(\frac{x + (\pi/2) + x - (\pi/2)}{2}\right) \cos\left(\frac{x + (\pi/2) - x + (\pi/2)}{2}\right) = 2 \sin x \cos \frac{\pi}{2} = 0$

81. $\sin 195° + \sin 105° = 2\sin\left(\frac{195° + 105°}{2}\right)\cos\left(\frac{195° - 105°}{2}\right) = 2\sin(150°)\cos(45°) = 2\left(\frac{1}{2}\right)\left(\frac{\sqrt{2}}{2}\right) = \frac{\sqrt{2}}{2}$

82. $\cos 165° - \cos 75° = -2\sin\left(\frac{165° + 75°}{2}\right)\sin\left(\frac{165° - 75°}{2}\right) = -2\sin(120°)\sin(45°)$

$$= -2\left(\frac{\sqrt{3}}{2}\right)\left(\frac{\sqrt{2}}{2}\right) = \frac{-\sqrt{6}}{2}$$

83. $\cos\frac{5\pi}{12} + \cos\frac{\pi}{12} = 2\cos\left(\frac{(5\pi/12) + (\pi/12)}{2}\right)\cos\left(\frac{(5\pi/12) - (\pi/12)}{2}\right)$

$$= 2\cos\left(\frac{\pi}{4}\right)\cos\left(\frac{\pi}{6}\right) = 2\left(\frac{\sqrt{2}}{2}\right)\left(\frac{\sqrt{3}}{2}\right) = \frac{2\sqrt{6}}{4} = \frac{\sqrt{6}}{2}$$

84. $\sin\frac{11\pi}{2} - \sin\frac{7\pi}{12} = 2\cos\left(\frac{(11\pi/12) + (7\pi/12)}{2}\right)\sin\left(\frac{(11\pi/12) - (7\pi/12)}{2}\right)$

$$= 2\cos\left(\frac{3\pi}{4}\right)\sin\left(\frac{\pi}{6}\right) = 2\left(\frac{-\sqrt{2}}{2}\right)\left(\frac{1}{2}\right) = \frac{-\sqrt{2}}{2}$$

85. $\sin 6x + \sin 2x = 0$

$$2\sin\left(\frac{6x + 2x}{2}\right)\cos\left(\frac{6x - 2x}{2}\right) = 0$$

$$\sin 4x \cos 2x = 0$$

$\sin 4x = 0$ or $\cos 2x = 0$

$4x = n\pi$ $\quad$ $2x = \frac{\pi}{2} + n\pi$

$x = \frac{n\pi}{4}$ $\quad$ $x = \frac{\pi}{4} + \frac{n\pi}{2}$

In the interval we have $x = 0, \frac{\pi}{4}, \frac{\pi}{2}, \frac{3\pi}{4}, \pi, \frac{5\pi}{4}, \frac{3\pi}{2}, \frac{7\pi}{4}$.

86. $h(x) = \cos 2x - \cos 6x$

$$\cos 2x - \cos 6x = 0$$

$$-2\sin 4x \sin(-2x) = 0$$

$$2\sin 4x \sin 2x = 0$$

$\sin 4x = 0$ OR $\sin 2x = 0$

$4x = n\pi$ $\quad$ $2x = n\pi$

$x = \frac{n\pi}{4}$ $\quad$ $x = \frac{n\pi}{2}$

$x = 0, \frac{\pi}{4}, \frac{\pi}{2}, \frac{3\pi}{4}, \pi, \frac{5\pi}{4}, \frac{3\pi}{2}, \frac{7\pi}{4}$

87. $$\frac{\cos 2x}{\sin 3x - \sin x} - 1 = 0$$

$$\frac{\cos 2x}{\sin 3x - \sin x} = 1$$

$$\frac{\cos 2x}{2\cos 2x \sin x} = 1$$

$$2\sin x = 1$$

$$\sin x = \frac{1}{2}$$

$$x = \frac{\pi}{6}, \frac{5\pi}{6}$$

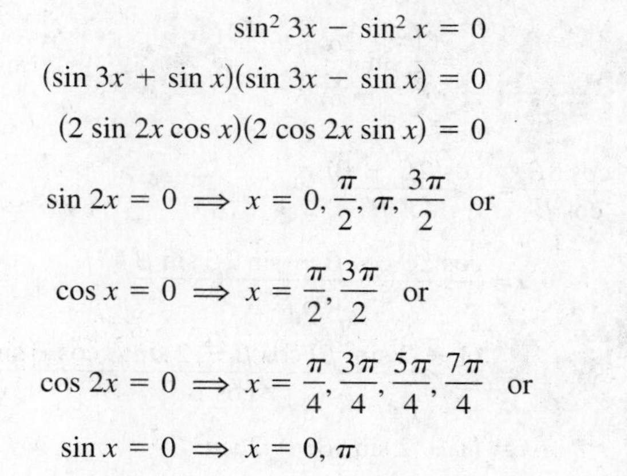

88. $$f(x) = \sin^2 3x - \sin^2 x$$

$$\sin^2 3x - \sin^2 x = 0$$

$$(\sin 3x + \sin x)(\sin 3x - \sin x) = 0$$

$$(2\sin 2x \cos x)(2\cos 2x \sin x) = 0$$

$$\sin 2x = 0 \Rightarrow x = 0, \frac{\pi}{2}, \pi, \frac{3\pi}{2} \text{ or}$$

$$\cos x = 0 \Rightarrow x = \frac{\pi}{2}, \frac{3\pi}{2} \text{ or}$$

$$\cos 2x = 0 \Rightarrow x = \frac{\pi}{4}, \frac{3\pi}{4}, \frac{5\pi}{4}, \frac{7\pi}{4} \text{ or}$$

$$\sin x = 0 \Rightarrow x = 0, \pi$$

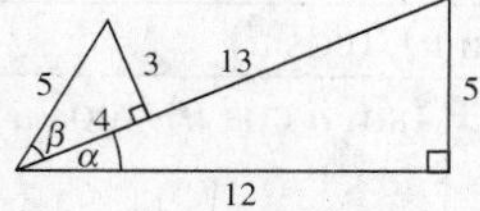

Figure for Exercises 89–92

89. $\sin^2 \alpha = \left(\frac{5}{13}\right)^2 = \frac{25}{169}$

$\sin^2 \alpha = 1 - \cos^2 \alpha = 1 - \left(\frac{12}{13}\right)^2 = 1 - \frac{144}{169} = \frac{25}{169}$

90. $\cos^2 \alpha = (\cos \alpha)^2 = \left(\frac{12}{13}\right)^2 = \frac{144}{169}$

$\cos^2 \alpha = 1 - \sin^2 \alpha = 1 - \left(\frac{5}{13}\right)^2 = 1 - \frac{25}{169} = \frac{144}{169}$

91. $$\sin \alpha \cos \beta = \left(\frac{5}{13}\right)\left(\frac{4}{5}\right) = \frac{4}{13}$$

$$\sin \alpha \cos \beta = \cos\left(\frac{\pi}{2} - \alpha\right)\sin\left(\frac{\pi}{2} - \beta\right)$$

$$= \left(\frac{5}{13}\right)\left(\frac{4}{5}\right) = \frac{4}{13}$$

92. $$\cos \alpha \sin \beta = \left(\frac{12}{13}\right)\left(\frac{3}{5}\right) = \frac{36}{65}$$

$$\cos \alpha \sin \beta = \sin\left(\frac{\pi}{2} - \alpha\right)\cos\left(\frac{\pi}{2} - \beta\right)$$

$$= \left(\frac{12}{13}\right)\left(\frac{3}{5}\right) = \frac{36}{65}$$

93. $$\csc 2\theta = \frac{1}{\sin 2\theta}$$

$$= \frac{1}{2\sin\theta\cos\theta}$$

$$= \frac{1}{\sin\theta} \cdot \frac{1}{2\cos\theta}$$

$$= \frac{\csc\theta}{2\cos\theta}$$

94. $$\sec 2\theta = \frac{1}{\cos 2\theta} = \frac{1}{\cos^2\theta - \sin^2\theta}$$

$$= \frac{1/\cos^2\theta}{1 - (\sin^2\theta/\cos^2\theta)}$$

$$= \frac{\sec^2\theta}{1 - \tan^2\theta}$$

$$= \frac{\sec^2\theta}{1 - (\sec^2\theta - 1)}$$

$$= \frac{\sec^2\theta}{2 - \sec^2\theta}$$

95. $$\cos^2 2\alpha - \sin^2 2\alpha = \cos[2(2\alpha)]$$

$$= \cos 4\alpha$$

96. $$\cos^4 x - \sin^4 x = (\cos^2 x - \sin^2 x)(\cos^2 x + \sin^2 x)$$

$$= (\cos 2x)(1) = \cos 2x$$

97. $$(\sin x + \cos x)^2 = \sin^2 x + 2\sin x\cos x + \cos^2 x$$

$$= (\sin^2 x + \cos^2 x) + 2\sin x\cos x = 1 + \sin 2x$$

98. $\sin\frac{\alpha}{3}\cos\frac{\alpha}{3} = \frac{1}{2}\left[\sin\left(\frac{\alpha}{3}+\frac{\alpha}{3}\right)+\sin\left(\frac{\alpha}{3}-\frac{\alpha}{3}\right)\right]$

$= \frac{1}{2}\sin\frac{2\alpha}{3}$

99. $1 + \cos 10y = 1 + \cos^2 5y - \sin^2 5y$

$= 1 + \cos^2 5y - (1 - \cos^2 5y)$

$= 2\cos^2 5y$

100. $\frac{\cos 3\beta}{\cos\beta} = \frac{\cos(2\beta+\beta)}{\cos\beta}$

$= \frac{\cos 2\beta\cos\beta - \sin 2\beta\sin\beta}{\cos\beta}$

$= \frac{(1-2\sin^2\beta)\cos\beta - 2\sin\beta\cos\beta\sin\beta}{\cos\beta}$

$= (1 - 2\sin^2\beta) - 2\sin^2\beta$

$= 1 - 4\sin^2\beta$

101. $\sec\frac{u}{2} = \frac{1}{\cos(u/2)}$

$= \pm\sqrt{\frac{2}{1+\cos u}}$

$= \pm\sqrt{\frac{2\sin u}{\sin u(1+\cos u)}}$

$= \pm\sqrt{\frac{2\sin u}{\sin u + \sin u\cos u}}$

$= \pm\sqrt{\frac{(2\sin u)/(\cos u)}{(\sin u)/(\cos u) + (\sin u\cos u)/(\cos u)}}$

$= \pm\sqrt{\frac{2\tan u}{\tan u + \sin u}}$

102. $\tan\frac{u}{2} = \frac{1-\cos u}{\sin u} = \frac{1}{\sin u} - \frac{\cos u}{\sin u} = \csc u - \cot u$

103. $\cos 3\beta = \cos(2\beta + \beta)$

$= \cos 2\beta\cos\beta - \sin 2\beta\sin\beta = (\cos^2\beta - \sin^2\beta)\cos\beta - 2\sin\beta\cos\beta\sin\beta$

$= \cos^3\beta - \sin^2\beta\cos\beta - 2\sin^2\beta\cos\beta = \cos^3\beta - 3\sin^2\beta\cos\beta$

104. $\sin 4\beta = 2\sin 2\beta\cos 2\beta$

$= 2[2\sin\beta\cos\beta(\cos^2\beta - \sin^2\beta)]$

$= 2[2\sin\beta\cos\beta(1 - \sin^2\beta - \sin^2\beta)]$

$= 4\sin\beta\cos\beta(1 - 2\sin^2\beta)$

105. $\frac{\cos 4x - \cos 2x}{2\sin 3x} = \frac{-2\sin\left(\frac{4x+2x}{2}\right)\sin\left(\frac{4x-2x}{2}\right)}{2\sin 3x}$

$= \frac{-2\sin 3x\sin x}{2\sin 3x}$

$= -\sin x$

106. $\frac{\cos 3x - \cos x}{\sin 3x - \sin x} = \frac{-2\sin\left(\frac{3x+x}{2}\right)\sin\left(\frac{3x-x}{2}\right)}{2\cos\left(\frac{3x+x}{2}\right)\sin\left(\frac{3x-x}{2}\right)}$

$= \frac{-2\sin 2x\sin x}{2\cos 2x\sin x} = -\tan 2x$

107. $\frac{\cos 4x + \cos 2x}{\sin 4x + \sin 2x} = \frac{2\cos(3x)\cos x}{2\sin(3x)\cos x}$

$= \cot 3x$

108. $\frac{\cos t + \cos 3t}{\sin 3t - \sin t} = \frac{2\cos 2t\cos(-t)}{2\cos 2t\sin t} = \frac{\cos t}{\sin t} = \cot t$

109. $\sin\left(\frac{\pi}{6}+x\right) + \sin\left(\frac{\pi}{6}-x\right) = 2\sin\left(\frac{\frac{\pi}{6}+x+\frac{\pi}{6}-x}{2}\right)\cos\left(\frac{\frac{\pi}{6}+x-\frac{\pi}{6}+x}{2}\right) = 2\sin\frac{\pi}{6}\cos x = \cos x$

110. $\cos\left(\frac{\pi}{3} + x\right) + \cos\left(\frac{\pi}{3} - x\right) = 2\cos\left(\frac{\frac{\pi}{3} + x + \frac{\pi}{3} - x}{2}\right)\cos\left(\frac{\frac{\pi}{3} + x - \frac{\pi}{3} + x}{2}\right) = 2\cos\frac{\pi}{3}\cos x = \cos x$

111. $\sin^2 x = \frac{1 - \cos 2x}{2} = \frac{1}{2} - \frac{\cos 2x}{2}$

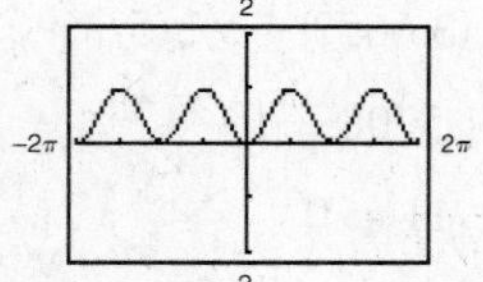

112. $f(x) = \cos^2 x = \frac{1 + \cos 2x}{2} = \frac{1}{2} + \frac{\cos 2x}{2}$

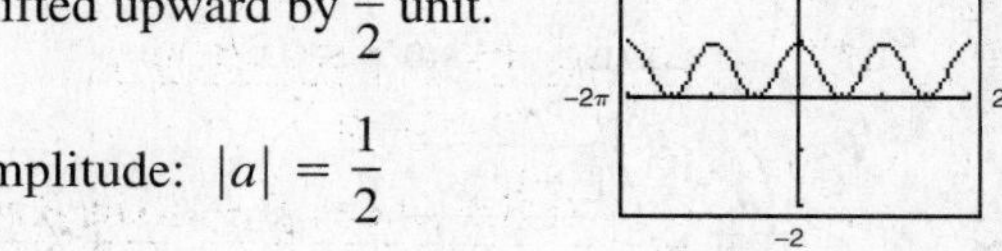

Shifted upward by $\frac{1}{2}$ unit.

Amplitude: $|a| = \frac{1}{2}$

Period: $\frac{2\pi}{2} = \pi$

113. $f(x) = \cos^4 x = \frac{1}{8}(3 + 4\cos 2x + \cos 4x)$

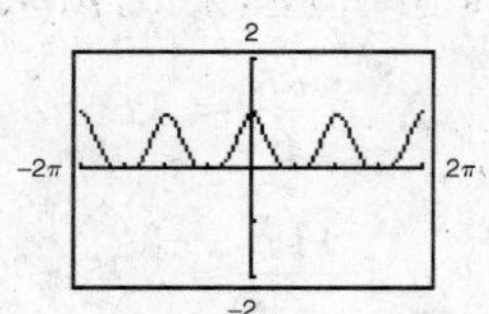

114. $f(x) = \sin^3 x$

$= \sin x\left(\frac{1 - \cos 2x}{2}\right)$

115. $\sin(2 \arcsin x) = 2\sin(\arcsin x)\cos(\arcsin x)$

$= 2x\sqrt{1 - x^2}$

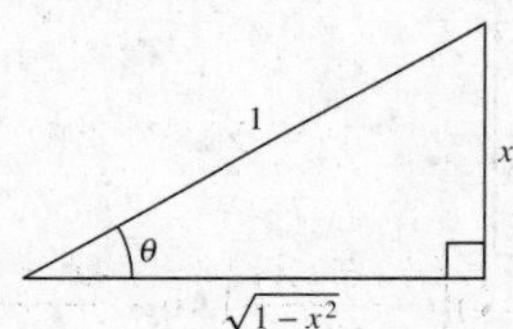

116. Let $\theta = \arccos x$.

$\cos(2 \arccos x) = \cos^2(\arccos x) - \sin^2(\arccos x)$

$= x^2 - (1 - x^2)$

$= 2x^2 - 1$

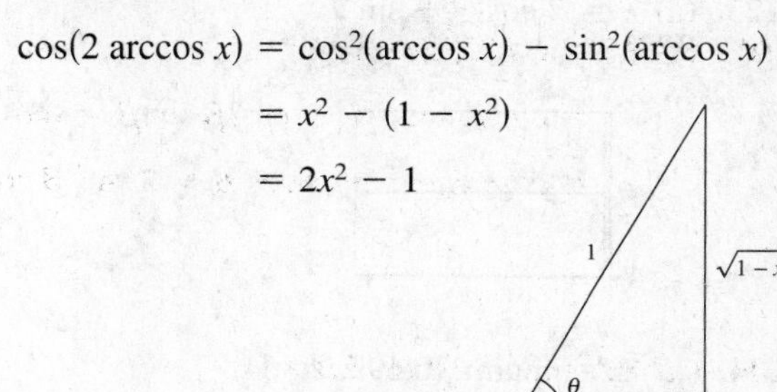

117. $\cos(2 \arcsin x) = 1 - 2\sin^2(\arcsin x)$

$= 1 - 2x^2$

118. Let $u = \arccos x$.

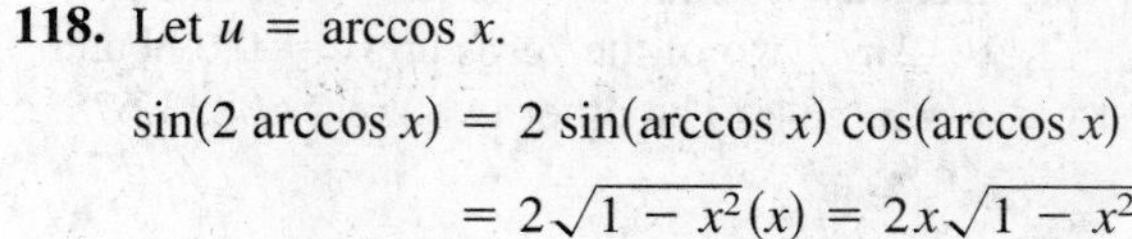

$\sin(2 \arccos x) = 2\sin(\arccos x)\cos(\arccos x)$

$= 2\sqrt{1 - x^2}(x) = 2x\sqrt{1 - x^2}$

119. $\cos(2 \arctan x) = 1 - 2\sin^2(\arctan x)$

$= 1 - 2\left(\frac{x}{\sqrt{1 + x^2}}\right)^2$

$= 1 - \frac{2x^2}{1 + x^2}$

$= \frac{1 - x^2}{1 + x^2}$

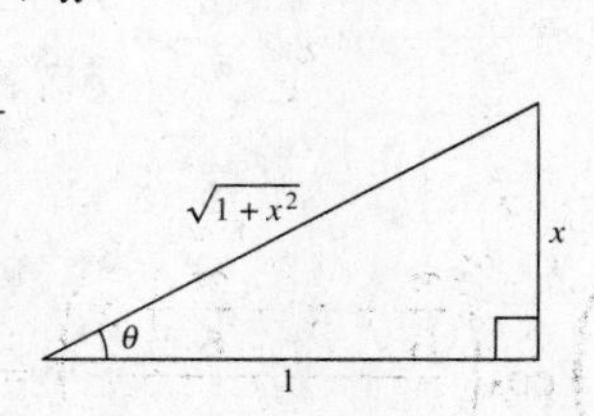

120. Let $u = \arctan x$.

$\sin(2 \arctan x) = 2\sin(\arctan x)\cos(\arctan x)$

$= 2\frac{x}{\sqrt{1 + x^2}} \cdot \frac{1}{\sqrt{1 + x^2}}$

$= \frac{2x}{1 + x^2}$

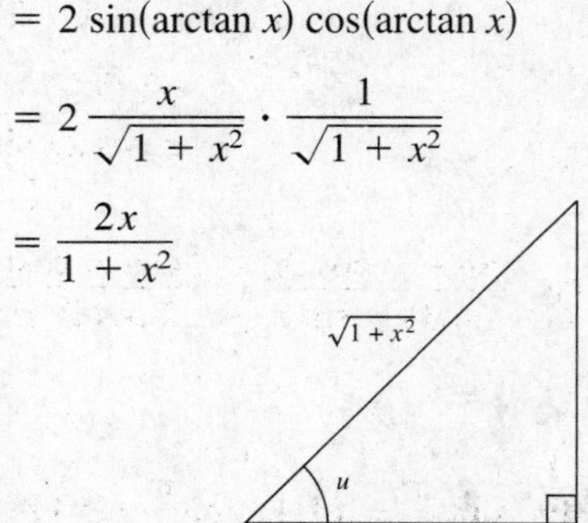

121. (a) $y = 4\sin\frac{x}{2} + \cos x$

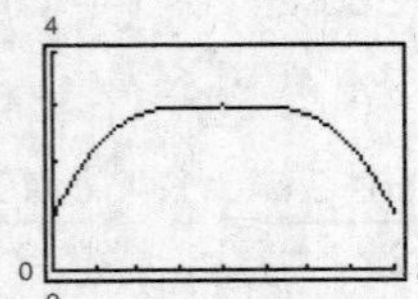

Maximum: $(\pi, 3)$

(b) $2\cos\frac{x}{2} - \sin x = 0$

$$2\left(\pm\sqrt{\frac{1+\cos x}{2}}\right) = \sin x$$

$$4\left(\frac{1+\cos x}{2}\right) = \sin^2 x$$

$$2(1+\cos x) = 1 - \cos^2 x$$

$$\cos^2 x + 2\cos x + 1 = 0$$

$$(\cos x + 1)^2 = 0$$

$$\cos x = -1$$

$$x = \pi$$

122. $f(x) = \cos 2x - 2\sin x$

(a)

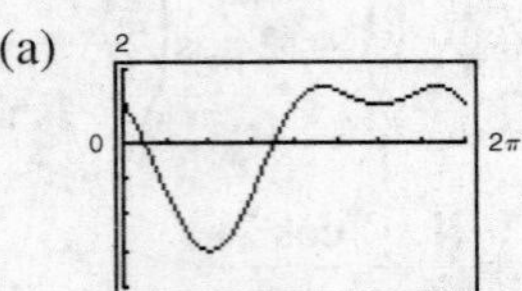

Maximum points: (3.6652, 1.5), (5.7596, 1.5)

Minimum point: (1.5708, −3)

(b) $-2\cos x(2\sin x + 1) = 0$

$-2\cos x = 0$ or $2\sin x + 1 = 0$

$\cos x = 0$ $\qquad \sin x = -\frac{1}{2}$

$x = \frac{\pi}{2}, \frac{3\pi}{2}$ $\qquad x = \frac{7\pi}{6}, \frac{11\pi}{6}$

$\frac{\pi}{2} \approx 1.5708$ $\qquad \frac{7\pi}{6} \approx 3.6652$

$\frac{3\pi}{2} \approx 4.7124$ $\qquad \frac{11\pi}{6} \approx 5.7596$

123. (a) $y = 2\cos\frac{x}{2} + \sin 2x$

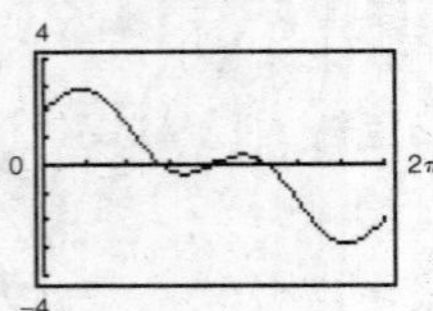

Maximum: (0.699, 2.864)

Minimum: (5.584, −2.864)

(b) $2\cos 2x - \sin(x/2) = 0$ has four zeros on $[0, 2\pi)$. Two of the zeros are $x \approx 0.699$ and $x \approx 5.584$. (The other two are 2.608, 3.675.)

124. $f(x) = 2\sin\frac{x}{2} - 5\cos\left(2x - \frac{\pi}{4}\right)$

(a)

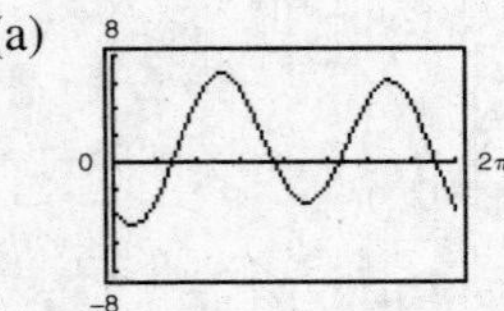

Maximum point: (1.9907, 6.6705)

Minimum point: (0.3434, −4.6340)

(b) $10\sin\left(2x - \frac{\pi}{4}\right) + \cos\frac{x}{2} = 0$

$x \approx 0.343, 1.991, 3.544, 5.064$

The first and second solutions correspond to the maximum and minimum points in part (a).

125. (a) $f(x) = \sin 2x - \sin x = 0$

$2 \sin x \cos x - \sin x = 0$

$\sin x(2 \cos x - 1) = 0$

$\sin x = 0 \Rightarrow x = 0, \pi, 2\pi$

$\cos x = \frac{1}{2} \Rightarrow x = \frac{\pi}{3}, \frac{5\pi}{3}$

(b) $2 \cos 2x - \cos x = 0$

$2(2 \cos^2 x - 1) - \cos x = 0$

$4 \cos^2 x - \cos x - 2 = 0$

$\cos x = \frac{1 \pm \sqrt{1 + 32}}{8} = \frac{1 \pm \sqrt{33}}{8}$

$x = \arccos\left(\frac{1 \pm \sqrt{33}}{8}\right)$

$x = 2\pi - \arccos\left(\frac{1 \pm \sqrt{33}}{8}\right)$

$x \approx 0.5678, 2.2057, 4.0775, 5.7154$

126. (a) $f(x) = \cos 2x + \sin x = 0$

$1 - 2 \sin^2 x + \sin x = 0$

$2 \sin^2 x - \sin x - 1 = 0$

$(2 \sin x + 1)(\sin x - 1) = 0$

$\sin x = -\frac{1}{2} \Rightarrow x = \frac{7\pi}{6}, \frac{11\pi}{6}$

$\sin x = 1 \Rightarrow x = \frac{\pi}{2}$

(b) $-2 \sin 2x + \cos x = 0$

$-4 \sin x \cos x + \cos x = 0$

$\cos x(1 - 4 \sin x) = 0$

$x = \frac{\pi}{2}, \frac{3\pi}{2}, \arcsin\left(\frac{1}{4}\right), \pi - \arcsin\left(\frac{1}{4}\right)$

$x \approx 1.5708, 4.7124, 0.2527, 2.8889$

127. (a) $r = \frac{1}{32}v_0^2 \sin 2\theta$

$= \frac{1}{32}v_0^2(2 \sin \theta \cos \theta)$

$= \frac{1}{16}v_0^2 \sin \theta \cos \theta$

(b) $r = \frac{1}{16}v_0^2 \sin \theta \cos \theta$

$= \frac{1}{16}(80)^2 \sin 42° \cos 42° \approx 198.90$ feet

(c) $r = \frac{1}{16}v_0^2 \sin \theta \cos \theta$

$300 = \frac{1}{16}v_0^2 \sin 40° \cos 40°$

$v_0^2 = \frac{300(16)}{\sin 40° \cos 40°} \approx 9748.0955$

$v_0 \approx 98.73$ feet per second

(d) $\sin 2\theta$ is greatest when $\theta = 45°$.

128. (a) $\sin\left(\frac{\theta}{2}\right) = \frac{b/2}{10} \Rightarrow b = 20 \sin \frac{\theta}{2}$

$\cos\left(\frac{\theta}{2}\right) = \frac{h}{10} \Rightarrow h = 10 \cos \frac{\theta}{2}$

$A = \frac{1}{2}bh = \frac{1}{2}\left(20 \sin \frac{\theta}{2}\right)\left(10 \cos \frac{\theta}{2}\right)$

$= 100 \sin \frac{\theta}{2} \cos \frac{\theta}{2}$

(b) $A = 50\left(2 \sin \frac{\theta}{2} \cos \frac{\theta}{2}\right) = 50 \sin \theta$

The area is maximum when $\theta = \frac{\pi}{2}$, $A = 50$.

129. $\frac{x}{2} = 2r \sin^2 \frac{\theta}{2}, \; x = 4r\left[\sin \frac{\theta}{2}\right]^2 = 4r\frac{1 - \cos \theta}{2} = 2r(1 - \cos \theta)$

130. $\sin \frac{\theta}{2} = \frac{1}{M}$

(a) $\sin \frac{\theta}{2} = \frac{1}{1} = 1 \implies \frac{\theta}{2} = \frac{\pi}{2} \implies \theta = \pi = 180°$

(b) $\sin \frac{\theta}{2} = \frac{1}{4.5} = \frac{2}{9}$

$\frac{\theta}{2} = \arcsin\left(\frac{2}{9}\right) \approx 0.2241$

$\theta \approx 0.4482 \approx 25.7°$

(c) $M = 1 \implies$ Speed $= 760$ mph

$M = 4.5 \implies \frac{\text{Speed}}{760} = 4.5 \implies$ Speed $= 3420$ mph

(d) $\sin \frac{\theta}{2} = \sqrt{\frac{1 - \cos \theta}{2}} = \frac{1}{M}$

$\frac{1 - \cos \theta}{2} = \frac{1}{M^2}$

$1 - \cos \theta = \frac{2}{M^2}$

$\cos \theta = 1 - \frac{2}{M^2}$

131. False. If $x = \pi$, $\sin \frac{x}{2} = \sin \frac{\pi}{2} = 1$, whereas $-\sqrt{\frac{1 - \cos \pi}{2}} = -1$.

132. True. $\sin(\pi) = 0$ and $y = 4 - 8 \sin^2 \pi = 4$, a maximum.

133. $f(x) = 2 \sin x\left[2 \cos^2\left(\frac{x}{2}\right) - 1\right]$

(a)

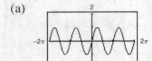

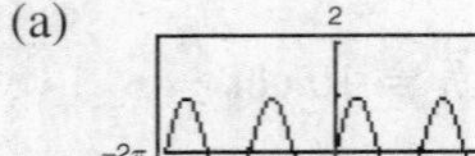

(b) The graph appears to be that of $y = \sin 2x$.

(c) $2 \sin x\left[2 \cos^2\left(\frac{x}{2}\right) - 1\right] = 2 \sin x\left[2 \frac{1 + \cos x}{2} - 1\right]$

$= 2 \sin x[\cos x] = \sin 2x$

134. (a) $f(x) = \sin^4 x + \cos^4 x$. From Example 5 and Exercise 23,

$f(x) = \frac{1}{8}(3 - 4 \cos 2x + \cos 4x) + \frac{1}{8}(3 + 4 \cos 2x + \cos 4x) = \frac{3}{4} + \frac{1}{4} \cos 4x$

(b) Sample answer:

$f(x) = \sin^2 x \cdot \sin^2 x + \cos^2 x \cdot \cos^2 x = \left(\frac{1 - \cos 2x}{2}\right)^2 + \left(\frac{1 + \cos 2x}{2}\right)^2$

$= \frac{1}{4}[2 + 2 \cos^2 2x] = \frac{1}{2}(1 + \cos^2 2x)$

(c) $f(x) = \sin^4 x + 2 \sin^2 x \cos^2 x + \cos^4 x - 2 \sin^2 x \cos^2 x$

$= (\sin^2 x + \cos^2 x)^2 - 2 \sin^2 x \cos^2 x = 1 - 2 \sin^2 x \cos^2 x$

(d) $f(x) = 1 - \frac{1}{2} \sin^2 2x$

(e) Answers will vary.

135. Answers will vary.

136. (a) Sample answer: $\cos(3\theta) = \cos(2\theta + \theta) = \cos 2\theta \cos \theta - \sin 2\theta \sin \theta$

$= (\cos^2 \theta - \sin^2 \theta) \cos \theta - 2 \sin \theta \cos \theta \sin \theta = \cos^3 \theta - 3 \sin^2 \theta \cos \theta$

(b) Sample answer: $\cos 4\theta = 2 \cos^2 2\theta - 1 = 2(2 \cos^2 \theta - 1)^2 - 1 = 8 \cos^4 \theta - 8 \cos^2 \theta + 1$

137. (a)

(b) Distance:

$\sqrt{(5 + 1)^2 + (2 - 4)^2} = \sqrt{40} = 2\sqrt{10}$

(c) Midpoint: $\left(\frac{-1 + 5}{2}, \frac{4 + 2}{2}\right) = (2, 3)$

138. (a)

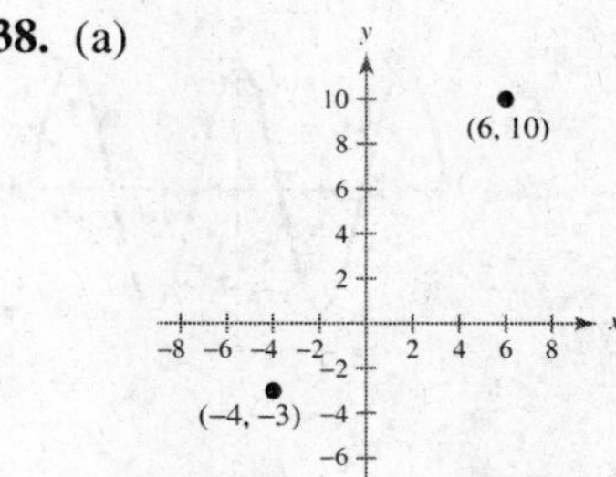

(b) Distance: $\sqrt{(6 + 4)^2 + (10 + 3)^2} = \sqrt{269}$

(c) Midpoint: $\left(\frac{6 - 4}{2}, \frac{10 - 3}{2}\right) = \left(1, \frac{7}{2}\right)$

139. (a)

(b) Distance:

$\sqrt{\left(\frac{4}{3}\right)^2 + \left(\frac{5}{2} - \frac{1}{2}\right)^2} = \sqrt{\frac{16}{9} + 4}$

$= \frac{\sqrt{52}}{3} = \frac{2\sqrt{13}}{3}$

(c) Midpoint: $\left(\frac{0 + (4/3)}{2}, \frac{(1/2) + (5/2)}{2}\right) = \left(\frac{2}{3}, \frac{3}{2}\right)$

140. (a)

(b) Distance: $\sqrt{\left(\frac{1}{3} + 1\right)^2 + \left(\frac{2}{3} + \frac{3}{2}\right)^2} = \frac{\sqrt{233}}{6}$

(c) Midpoint:

$\left(\frac{(1/3) - 1}{2}, \frac{(2/3) - (3/2)}{2}\right) = \left(-\frac{1}{3}, -\frac{5}{12}\right)$

141. (a) Complement: $90° - 55° = 35°$

Supplement: $180° - 55° = 125°$

(b) Complement: None

Supplement: $180° - 162° = 18°$

142. (a) Complement: None

Supplement: $180° - 109° = 71°$

(b) Complement: $90° - 78° = 12°$

Supplement: $180° - 78° = 102°$

143. (a) Complement: $\frac{\pi}{2} - \frac{\pi}{18} = \frac{8\pi}{18} = \frac{4\pi}{9}$

Supplement: $\pi - \frac{\pi}{18} = \frac{17\pi}{18}$

(b) Complement: $\frac{\pi}{2} - \frac{9\pi}{20} = \frac{\pi}{20}$

Supplement: $\pi - \frac{9\pi}{20} = \frac{11\pi}{20}$

144. (a) Complement: $\frac{\pi}{2} - 0.95 \approx 0.6208$

Supplement: $\pi - 0.95 \approx 2.1916$

(b) Complement: None

Supplement: $\pi - 2.76 \approx 0.3816$

145. $s = r\theta \implies \theta = \frac{s}{r} = \frac{7}{15} \approx 0.467$ rad

146. $s = r\,\theta = 21(35^\circ)\left(\frac{\pi}{180^\circ}\right) \approx 12.8282$ cm

147. $f(x) = \frac{3}{2}\cos(2x)$

Period: $\frac{2\pi}{2} = \pi$

Amplitude: $\frac{3}{2}$

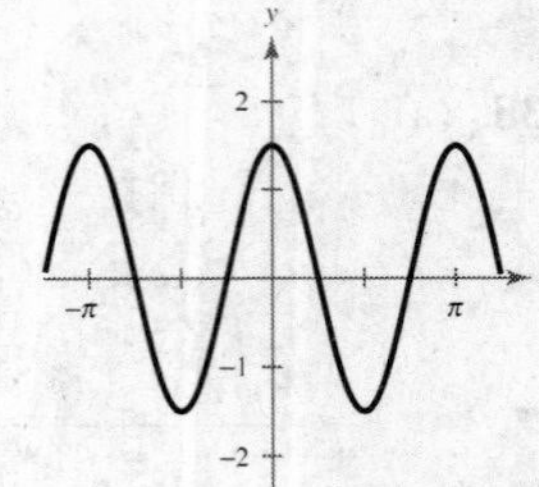

148. $f(x) = \frac{5}{2}\sin\frac{x}{2}$

Period: 4π

Amplitude: $\frac{5}{2}$

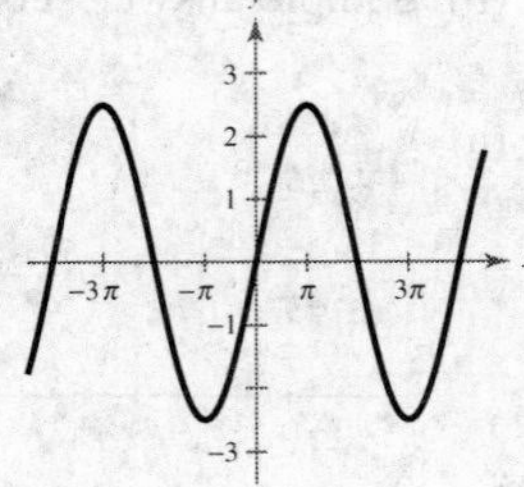

149. $f(x) = \frac{1}{2}\tan(2\pi x)$

Period: $\frac{\pi}{2\pi} = \frac{1}{2}$

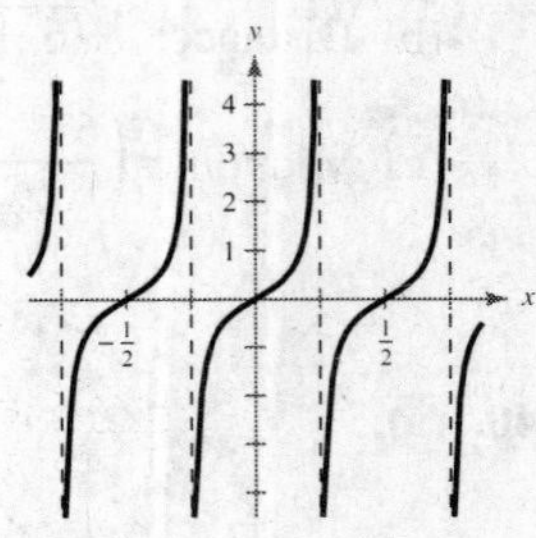

150. $f(x) = \frac{1}{4}\sec\frac{\pi x}{2}$

Period: $\frac{2\pi}{\pi/2} = 4$

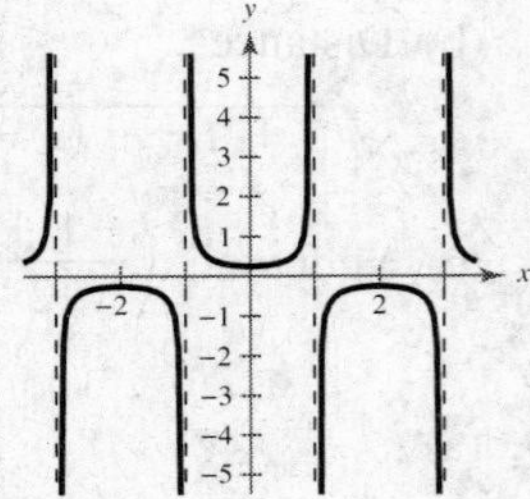

Review Exercises for Chapter 5

1. $\frac{1}{\cos x} = \sec x$

2. $\frac{1}{\sin x} = \csc x$

3. $\frac{1}{\sec x} = \cos x$

4. $\frac{1}{\tan x} = \cot x$

5. $\sqrt{1 - \cos^2 x} = |\sin x|$

6. $\sqrt{1 + \tan^2 x} = |\sec x|$

7. $\csc\left(\frac{\pi}{2} - x\right) = \sec x$

8. $\cot\left(\frac{\pi}{2} - x\right) = \tan x$

9. $\sec(-x) = \sec x$

10. $\tan(-x) = -\tan x$

11. $\sin x = \frac{4}{5}, \cos x = \frac{3}{5}$, Quadrant I

$\tan x = \frac{\sin x}{\cos x} = \frac{4}{3}$

$\cot x = \frac{3}{4}$

$\sec x = \frac{5}{3}$

$\csc x = \frac{5}{4}$

12. $\tan\theta = \frac{2}{3}, \sec\theta = \frac{\sqrt{13}}{3}$, Quadrant I

$\cos\theta = \frac{3\sqrt{13}}{13}$

$\sin\theta = \tan\theta\cos\theta = \frac{2}{3}\left(\frac{3\sqrt{13}}{13}\right) = \frac{2\sqrt{13}}{13}$

$\csc\theta = \frac{\sqrt{13}}{2}$

$\cot\theta = \frac{3}{2}$

13. $\sin\left(\frac{\pi}{2} - x\right) = \cos x = \frac{1}{\sqrt{2}} = \frac{\sqrt{2}}{2},$

$\sin x = -\frac{1}{\sqrt{2}} = -\frac{\sqrt{2}}{2},$ Quadrant IV

$\tan x = -1$

$\cot x = -1$

$\sec x = \sqrt{2}$

$\csc x = -\sqrt{2}$

14. $\csc\left(\frac{\pi}{2} - \theta\right) = \sec\theta = 3, \sin\theta = \frac{2\sqrt{2}}{3},$ Quadrant I

$\cos\theta = \frac{1}{3}$

$\tan\theta = 2\sqrt{2}$

$\cot\theta = \frac{1}{2\sqrt{2}} = \frac{\sqrt{2}}{4}$

$\csc\theta = \frac{3}{2\sqrt{2}} = \frac{3\sqrt{2}}{4}$

15. $\frac{1}{\tan^2 x + 1} = \frac{1}{\sec^2 x} = \cos^2 x$

16. $\frac{\sec^2 x - 1}{\sec x - 1} = \frac{(\sec x - 1)(\sec x + 1)}{\sec x - 1} = \sec x + 1$

17. $\frac{\sin^2\alpha - \cos^2\alpha}{\sin^2\alpha - \sin\alpha\cos\alpha} = \frac{(\sin\alpha + \cos\alpha)(\sin\alpha - \cos\alpha)}{\sin\alpha(\sin\alpha - \cos\alpha)} = \frac{\sin\alpha + \cos\alpha}{\sin\alpha} = 1 + \cot\alpha$

18. $\frac{\sin^3\beta + \cos^3\beta}{\sin\beta + \cos\beta} = \frac{(\sin\beta + \cos\beta)(\sin^2\beta - \sin\beta\cos\beta + \cos^2\beta)}{\sin\beta + \cos\beta} = 1 - \sin\beta\cos\beta$

19. $\tan^2\theta(\csc^2\theta - 1) = \tan^2\theta(\cot^2\theta)$

$= \tan^2\theta\left(\frac{1}{\tan^2\theta}\right) = 1$

20. $\csc^2 x(1 - \cos^2 x) = \csc^2 x(\sin^2 x) = 1$

21. $\tan\left(\frac{\pi}{2} - x\right)\sec x = \cot x \sec x$

$= \frac{\cos x}{\sin x} \cdot \frac{1}{\cos x} = \frac{1}{\sin x} = \csc x$

22. $\frac{\sin(-x)\cot x}{\sin\left(\frac{\pi}{2} - x\right)} = \frac{(-\sin x)\left(\frac{\cos x}{\sin x}\right)}{\cos x} = -1$

23. $\sin^{-1/2} x \cos x = \frac{\cos x}{\sin^{1/2} x}$

$= \frac{\cos x}{\sqrt{\sin x}} \cdot \frac{\sqrt{\sin x}}{\sqrt{\sin x}}$

$= \frac{\cos x}{\sin x}\sqrt{\sin x} = \cot x\sqrt{\sin x}$

24. $\csc^2 x - \csc x \cot x = \frac{1}{\sin^2 x} - \frac{1}{\sin x} \cdot \frac{\cos x}{\sin x}$

$= \frac{1 - \cos x}{\sin^2 x}$

25. $\cos x(\tan^2 x + 1) = \cos x \sec^2 x$

$= \frac{1}{\sec x}\sec^2 x = \sec x$

26. $\sec^2 x \cot x - \cot x = \cot x(\sec^2 x - 1)$

$= \cot x \tan^2 x$

$= \frac{1}{\tan x}\tan^2 x = \tan x$

27. $\sin^3\theta + \sin\theta\cos^2\theta = \sin\theta(\sin^2\theta + \cos^2\theta)$

$= \sin\theta$

28. $\cot^2 x - \cos^2 x = \frac{\cos^2 x}{\sin^2 x} - \cos^2 x$

$= \cos^2 x[\csc^2 x - 1]$

$= \cos^2 x \cdot \cot^2 x$

29. $\sin^5 x \cos^2 x = \sin^4 x \cos^2 x \sin x$

$= (1 - \cos^2 x)^2 \cos^2 x \sin x$

$= (1 - 2\cos^2 x + \cos^4 x) \cos^2 x \sin x$

$= (\cos^2 x - 2\cos^4 x + \cos^6 x) \sin x$

30. $\cos^3 x \sin^2 x = \cos x(\cos^2 x) \sin^2 x$

$= \cos x(1 - \sin^2 x) \sin^2 x$

$= (\sin^2 x - \sin^4 x) \cos x$

31. $\sqrt{\dfrac{1 - \sin\theta}{1 + \sin\theta}} = \sqrt{\dfrac{1 - \sin\theta}{1 + \sin\theta} \cdot \dfrac{1 - \sin\theta}{1 - \sin\theta}} = \sqrt{\dfrac{(1 - \sin\theta)^2}{1 - \sin^2\theta}} = \sqrt{\dfrac{(1 - \sin\theta)^2}{\cos^2\theta}} = \dfrac{|1 - \sin\theta|}{|\cos\theta|} = \dfrac{1 - \sin\theta}{|\cos\theta|}$

Note: We can drop the absolute value on $1 - \sin\theta$ since it is always nonnegative.

32. $\sqrt{1 - \cos x} = \sqrt{(1 - \cos x)\dfrac{1 + \cos x}{1 + \cos x}}$

$= \sqrt{\dfrac{\sin^2 x}{1 + \cos x}} = \dfrac{|\sin x|}{\sqrt{1 + \cos x}}$

33. $\dfrac{\csc(-x)}{\sec(-x)} = -\dfrac{\csc x}{\sec x} = -\dfrac{\cos x}{\sin x} = -\cot x$

34. $\dfrac{1 + \sec(-x)}{\sin(-x) + \tan(-x)} = \dfrac{1 + \sec x}{-\sin x - \tan x}$

$= \dfrac{1 + \sec x}{-\sin x(1 + \sec x)}$

$= -\dfrac{1}{\sin x} = -\csc x$

35. $\csc^2\left(\dfrac{\pi}{2} - x\right) - 1 = \sec^2 x - 1 = \tan^2 x$

36. $\tan\left(\dfrac{\pi}{2} - x\right) \sec x = \cot x \sec x$

$= \dfrac{\cos x}{\sin x} \cdot \dfrac{1}{\cos x}$

$= \dfrac{1}{\sin x} = \csc x$

37. $2\sin x - 1 = 0$

$\sin x = \dfrac{1}{2}$

$x = \dfrac{\pi}{6} + 2n\pi$

$x = \dfrac{5\pi}{6} + 2n\pi$

38. $\tan x + 1 = 0$

$\tan x = -1$

$x = \dfrac{3\pi}{4} + n\pi$

39. $\sin x = \sqrt{3} - \sin x$

$2\sin x = \sqrt{3}$

$\sin x = \dfrac{\sqrt{3}}{2}$

$x = \dfrac{\pi}{3} + 2n\pi$

$x = \dfrac{2\pi}{3} + 2n\pi$

40. $4\cos x = 1 + 2\cos x$

$2\cos x = 1$

$\cos x = \dfrac{1}{2}$

$x = \dfrac{\pi}{3} + 2n\pi$

$x = \dfrac{5\pi}{3} + 2n\pi$

41. $3\sqrt{3}\tan x = 3$

$\tan x = \dfrac{1}{\sqrt{3}}$

$x = \dfrac{\pi}{6} + n\pi$

42. $\frac{1}{2}\sec x - 1 = 0$

$\sec x = 2$

$\cos x = \frac{1}{2}$

$x = \frac{\pi}{3} + 2n\pi$

$x = \frac{5\pi}{3} + 2n\pi$

43. $3\csc^2 x = 4$

$\csc^2 x = \frac{4}{3}$

$\sin^2 x = \frac{3}{4}$

$\sin x = \pm\frac{\sqrt{3}}{2}$

$x = \frac{\pi}{3} + n\pi$

$x = \frac{2\pi}{3} + n\pi$

44. $4\tan^2 x - 1 = \tan^2 x$

$3\tan^2 x = 1$

$\tan^2 x = \frac{1}{3}$

$\tan x = \pm\frac{1}{\sqrt{3}}$

$x = \frac{\pi}{6} + n\pi$

$x = \frac{5\pi}{6} + n\pi$

45. $4\cos^2 x - 3 = 0$

$\cos^2 x = \frac{3}{4}$

$\cos x = \pm\frac{\sqrt{3}}{2}$

$x = \frac{\pi}{6} + n\pi$

$x = \frac{5\pi}{6} + n\pi$

46. $\sin x(\sin x + 1) = 0$

$\sin x = 0$ or $\sin x = -1$

$x = n\pi$ or $x = \frac{3\pi}{2} + 2n\pi$

47. $\sin x - \tan x = 0$

$\sin x - \frac{\sin x}{\cos x} = 0$

$\sin x\cos x - \sin x = 0$

$\sin x(\cos x - 1) = 0$

$\sin x = 0$ or $\cos x - 1 = 0$

$x = n\pi$ $\quad\cos x = 1$

48. $\csc x - 2\cot x = 0$

$\frac{1}{\sin x}(1 - 2\cos x) = 0$

$\cos x = \frac{1}{2}$

$x = \frac{\pi}{3} + 2n\pi$

$x = \frac{5\pi}{3} + 2n\pi$

49. $2\cos^2 x - \cos x - 1 = 0$

$(2\cos x + 1)(\cos x - 1) = 0$

$2\cos x + 1 = 0$ or $\cos x - 1 = 0$

$\cos x = -\frac{1}{2}$ $\quad\cos x = 1$

$x = \frac{2\pi}{3}, \frac{4\pi}{3}$ $\quad x = 0$

50. $2\sin^2 x - 3\sin x + 1 = 0$

$(2\sin x - 1)(\sin x - 1) = 0$

$\sin x = \frac{1}{2}$ or $\sin x = 1$

$x = \frac{\pi}{6}, \frac{5\pi}{6}$ or $x = \frac{\pi}{2}$

51.
$$\cos^2 x + \sin x = 1$$
$$1 - \sin^2 x + \sin x = 1$$
$$\sin x(\sin x - 1) = 0$$
$$\sin x = 0 \quad \text{or} \quad \sin x = 1$$
$$x = 0, \pi \qquad x = \frac{\pi}{2}$$

52.
$$\sin^2 x + 2\cos x = 2$$
$$(1 - \cos^2 x) + 2\cos x - 2 = 0$$
$$\cos^2 x - 2\cos x + 1 = 0$$
$$(\cos x - 1)^2 = 0$$
$$\cos x = 1$$
$$x = 0$$

53. $2\sin 2x = \sqrt{2}$
$$\sin 2x = \frac{\sqrt{2}}{2}$$
$$2x = \frac{\pi}{4}, \frac{3\pi}{4}, \frac{9\pi}{4}, \frac{11\pi}{4}$$
$$x = \frac{\pi}{8}, \frac{3\pi}{8}, \frac{9\pi}{8}, \frac{11\pi}{8}$$

54. $\sqrt{3}\tan 3x = 0$
$$\tan 3x = 0$$
$$3x = k\pi$$
$$x = 0, \frac{\pi}{3}, \frac{2\pi}{3}, \pi, \frac{4\pi}{3}, \frac{5\pi}{3}$$

55. $\cos 4x(\cos x - 1) = 0$

$\cos 4x = 0$ or $\cos x - 1 = 0$
$$4x = \frac{\pi}{2}, \frac{3\pi}{2}, \frac{5\pi}{2}, \frac{7\pi}{2}, \frac{9\pi}{2}, \frac{11\pi}{2}, \frac{13\pi}{2}, \frac{15\pi}{2}$$
or $\cos x = 1$
$$x = \frac{\pi}{8}, \frac{3\pi}{8}, \frac{5\pi}{8}, \frac{7\pi}{8}, \frac{9\pi}{8}, \frac{11\pi}{8}, \frac{13\pi}{8}, \frac{15\pi}{8}, 0$$

56. $3\csc^2 5x = -4$
$$\csc^2 5x = -\frac{4}{3}$$
No solutions

57.
$$\cos 4x - 7\cos 2x = 8$$
$$2\cos^2 2x - 1 - 7\cos 2x = 8$$
$$2\cos^2 2x - 7\cos 2x - 9 = 0$$
$$(2\cos 2x - 9)(\cos 2x + 1) = 0$$
$$2\cos 2x - 9 = 0 \quad \text{or} \quad \cos 2x + 1 = 0$$
$$\cos 2x = \frac{9}{2} \qquad \cos 2x = -1$$
No solution $\qquad 2x = \pi + 2n\pi$
$$x = \frac{\pi}{2} + n\pi$$
$$x = \frac{\pi}{2}, \frac{3\pi}{2}$$

58. $\sin 4x - \sin 2x = 0$
$$2\cos 3x \sin x = 0$$
$$\cos 3x = 0 \quad \text{or} \quad \sin x = 0$$
$$3x = \frac{\pi}{2} + n\pi \qquad x = 0, \pi$$
$$x = \frac{\pi}{6} + \frac{n\pi}{3}$$
$$x = \frac{\pi}{6}, \frac{\pi}{2}, \frac{5\pi}{6}, \frac{7\pi}{6}, \frac{3\pi}{2}, \frac{11\pi}{6}$$

59. $2 \sin 2x - 1 = 0$

$$\sin 2x = \frac{1}{2}$$

$$2x = \frac{\pi}{6} + 2n\pi \quad \text{or} \quad 2x = \frac{5\pi}{6} + 2n\pi$$

$$x = \frac{\pi}{12} + n\pi \quad \text{or} \quad x = \frac{5\pi}{12} + n\pi$$

60. $2 \cos 4x + \sqrt{3} = 0$

$$\cos 4x = \frac{-\sqrt{3}}{2}$$

$$4x = \frac{5\pi}{6} + 2n\pi \quad \text{or} \quad 4x = \frac{7\pi}{6} + 2n\pi$$

$$x = \frac{5\pi}{24} + \frac{n\pi}{2} \quad \text{or} \quad x = \frac{7\pi}{24} + \frac{n\pi}{2}$$

61. $2 \sin^2 3x - 1 = 0$

$$\sin^2 3x = \frac{1}{2}$$

$$\sin 3x = \pm\frac{\sqrt{2}}{2}$$

$$3x = \frac{\pi}{4} + \frac{n\pi}{2}$$

$$x = \frac{\pi}{12} + \frac{n\pi}{6}$$

62. $4 \cos^2 2x - 3 = 0$

$$\cos^2 2x = \frac{3}{4}$$

$$\cos 2x = \pm\frac{\sqrt{3}}{2}$$

$$2x = \frac{\pi}{6} + n\pi \quad \text{or} \quad 2x = \frac{5\pi}{6} + n\pi$$

$$x = \frac{\pi}{12} + \frac{n\pi}{2} \quad \text{or} \quad x = \frac{5\pi}{12} + \frac{n\pi}{2}$$

63. $\sin^2 x - 2 \sin x = 0$

$\sin x(\sin x - 2) = 0$

$\sin x = 0$ or $\sin x = 2$ (impossible)

$x = 0, \pi$

64. $3 \cos^2 x + 5 \cos x = 0$

$\cos x(3 \cos x + 5) = 0$

$\cos x = 0 \Rightarrow x = \frac{\pi}{2}, \frac{3\pi}{2}$

$\cos x = -\frac{5}{3}$ (impossible)

65. $\tan^2 \theta + 3 \tan \theta - 10 = 0$

$(\tan \theta + 5)(\tan \theta - 2) = 0$

$\tan \theta = -5 \Rightarrow$

$\theta = \arctan(-5) + \pi, \arctan(-5) + 2\pi$

$\tan \theta = 2 \Rightarrow \theta = \arctan(2), \arctan(2) + \pi$

$\theta \approx 1.1071, 1.7682, 4.2487, 4.9098$

66. $\sec^2 x + 6 \tan x + 4 = 0$

$(1 + \tan^2 x) + 6 \tan x + 4 = 0$

$\tan^2 x + 6 \tan x + 5 = 0$

$(\tan x + 1)(\tan x + 5) = 0$

$\tan x = -1$ or $\tan x = -5$

$x = \frac{3\pi}{4}, \frac{7\pi}{4}$ or $x \approx 1.7682, 4.9098$

67. $\sin 285° = \sin(315° - 30°)$

$$= \sin 315° \cos 30° - \cos 315° \sin 30°$$

$$= \left(-\frac{\sqrt{2}}{2}\right)\left(\frac{\sqrt{3}}{2}\right) - \left(\frac{\sqrt{2}}{2}\right)\left(\frac{1}{2}\right) = -\frac{\sqrt{6} + \sqrt{2}}{4}$$

$\cos 285° = \cos(315° - 30°) = \cos 315° \cos 30° + \sin 315° \sin 30°$

$$= \left(\frac{\sqrt{2}}{2}\right)\left(\frac{\sqrt{3}}{2}\right) + \left(-\frac{\sqrt{2}}{2}\right)\left(\frac{1}{2}\right) = \frac{\sqrt{6} - \sqrt{2}}{4}$$

$$\tan 285° = -\frac{\sqrt{6} + \sqrt{2}}{\sqrt{6} - \sqrt{2}} = -2 - \sqrt{3}$$

68. $\sin 345° = \sin(300° + 45°) = \sin 300° \cos 45° + \cos 300° \sin 45° = -\frac{\sqrt{3}}{2}\frac{\sqrt{2}}{2} + \frac{1}{2} \cdot \frac{\sqrt{2}}{2} = \frac{\sqrt{2} - \sqrt{6}}{4}$

$\cos 345° = \cos(300° + 45°) = \cos 300° \cos 45° - \sin 300° \sin 45° = \frac{1}{2} \cdot \frac{\sqrt{2}}{2} + \frac{\sqrt{3}}{2}\frac{\sqrt{2}}{2} = \frac{\sqrt{2} + \sqrt{6}}{4}$

$\tan 345° = \frac{\sin 345°}{\cos 345°} = \frac{\sqrt{2} - \sqrt{6}}{\sqrt{2} + \sqrt{6}} = \sqrt{3} - 2$

69. $\sin \frac{31\pi}{12} = \sin\left(\frac{11\pi}{6} + \frac{3\pi}{4}\right) = \sin \frac{11\pi}{6} \cos \frac{3\pi}{4} + \sin \frac{3\pi}{4} \cos \frac{11\pi}{6}$

$= \left(-\frac{1}{2}\right)\left(-\frac{\sqrt{2}}{2}\right) + \left(\frac{\sqrt{2}}{2}\right)\left(\frac{\sqrt{3}}{2}\right) = \frac{\sqrt{2} + \sqrt{6}}{4}$

$\cos \frac{31\pi}{12} = \cos\left(\frac{11\pi}{6} + \frac{3\pi}{4}\right) = \cos \frac{11\pi}{6} \cos \frac{3\pi}{4} - \sin \frac{11\pi}{6} \sin \frac{3\pi}{4}$

$= \left(\frac{\sqrt{3}}{2}\right)\left(-\frac{\sqrt{2}}{2}\right) - \left(-\frac{1}{2}\right)\left(\frac{\sqrt{2}}{2}\right) = \frac{\sqrt{2} - \sqrt{6}}{4}$

$\tan \frac{31\pi}{12} = \frac{\sin(31\pi/12)}{\cos(31\pi/12)} = \frac{\sqrt{2} + \sqrt{6}}{\sqrt{2} - \sqrt{6}} = -2 - \sqrt{3}$

70. $\sin\left(\frac{13\pi}{12}\right) = \sin\left(\frac{11\pi}{6} - \frac{3\pi}{4}\right) = \sin \frac{11\pi}{6} \cos \frac{3\pi}{4} - \sin \frac{3\pi}{4} \cos \frac{11\pi}{6}$

$= \left(-\frac{1}{2}\right)\left(-\frac{\sqrt{2}}{2}\right) - \left(\frac{\sqrt{2}}{2}\right)\left(\frac{\sqrt{3}}{2}\right) = \frac{\sqrt{2} - \sqrt{6}}{4}$

$\cos\left(\frac{13\pi}{12}\right) = \cos\left(\frac{11\pi}{6} - \frac{3\pi}{4}\right) = \cos \frac{11\pi}{6} \cos \frac{3\pi}{4} + \sin \frac{11\pi}{6} \sin \frac{3\pi}{4}$

$= \left(\frac{\sqrt{3}}{2}\right)\left(-\frac{\sqrt{2}}{2}\right) + \left(-\frac{1}{2}\right)\left(\frac{\sqrt{2}}{2}\right) = \frac{-\sqrt{6} - \sqrt{2}}{4}$

$\tan\left(\frac{13\pi}{12}\right) = \frac{\sin(13\pi/12)}{\cos(13\pi/12)} = \frac{\sqrt{2} - \sqrt{6}}{-\sqrt{6} - \sqrt{2}} = 2 - \sqrt{3}$

71. $\sin 130° \cos 50° + \cos 130° \sin 50° = \sin(130° + 50°) = \sin 180° = 0$

72. $\cos 45° \cos 120° - \sin 45° \sin 120° = \cos(45° + 120°) = \cos(165°)$

73. $\frac{\tan 25° + \tan 10°}{1 - \tan 25° \tan 10°} = \tan(25° + 10°) = \tan 35°$

74. $\frac{\tan 63° - \tan 118°}{1 + \tan 63° \tan 118°} = \tan(63° - 118°) = \tan(-55°) = -\tan(55°)$

For Exercises 75–80, $\sin u = \frac{3}{5}$, $\cos v = -\frac{7}{25}$, $\cos u = -\frac{4}{5}$, $\sin v = \frac{24}{25}$.

75. $\sin(u + v) = \sin u \cos v + \sin v \cos u$

$= \frac{3}{5}\left(-\frac{7}{25}\right) + \frac{24}{25}\left(-\frac{4}{5}\right) = \frac{-117}{125}$

76. $\tan(u + v) = \frac{\tan u + \tan v}{1 - \tan u \tan v}$

$= \frac{(-3/4) + (-24/7)}{1 - (-3/4)(-24/7)} = \frac{117}{44}$

77. $\tan(u - v) = \dfrac{\tan u - \tan v}{1 + \tan u \tan v}$

$= \dfrac{(-3/4) - (-24/7)}{1 + (-3/4)(-24/7)} = \dfrac{3}{4}$

78. $\sin(u - v) = \sin u \cos v - \cos u \sin v$

$= \dfrac{3}{5}\left(-\dfrac{7}{25}\right) - \left(-\dfrac{4}{5}\right)\left(\dfrac{24}{25}\right) = \dfrac{3}{5}$

79. $\cos(u + v) = \cos u \cos v - \sin u \sin v$

$= \left(-\frac{4}{5}\right)\left(-\frac{7}{25}\right) - \left(\frac{3}{5}\right)\left(\frac{24}{25}\right) = -\frac{44}{125}$

80. $\cos(u - v) = \cos u \cos v + \sin u \sin v$

$= \left(-\frac{4}{5}\right)\left(-\frac{7}{25}\right) + \left(\frac{3}{5}\right)\left(\frac{24}{25}\right) = \frac{4}{5}$

81. $\sin^{-1} 0 = 0$ and $\cos^{-1}(-1) = \pi$

$\sin(\sin^{-1} 0 + \cos^{-1}(-1)) = \sin(0 + \pi) = 0$

82. $\cos^{-1} 1 = 0$ and $\sin^{-1} 0 = 0$

$\cos(\cos^{-1} 1 + \sin^{-1} 0) = \cos(0 + 0) = 1$

83. $\cos^{-1} 1 = 0$ and $\sin^{-1}(-1) = -\dfrac{\pi}{2}$

$\cos(\cos^{-1} 1 - \sin^{-1}(-1)) = \cos\left(0 + \dfrac{\pi}{2}\right) = 0$

84. $\cos^{-1}(-1) = \pi$ and $\cos^{-1} 1 = 0$

$\tan(\cos^{-1}(-1) + \cos^{-1} 1) = \tan(\pi + 0) = 0$

85. $\cos\left(x + \dfrac{\pi}{2}\right) = \cos x \cos \dfrac{\pi}{2} - \sin x \sin \dfrac{\pi}{2}$

$= (\cos x)(0) - (\sin x)(1) = -\sin x$

86. $\sin\left(x - \dfrac{3\pi}{2}\right) = \sin x \cos \dfrac{3\pi}{2} - \sin \dfrac{3\pi}{2} \cos x$

$= (\sin x)(0) - (-1)(\cos x) = \cos x$

87. $\cot\left(\dfrac{\pi}{2} - x\right) = \dfrac{\cos[(\pi/2) - x]}{\sin[(\pi/2) - x]}$

$= \dfrac{\cos(\pi/2) \cos x + \sin(\pi/2) \sin x}{\sin(\pi/2) \cos x - \sin x \cos(\pi/2)}$

$= \dfrac{\sin x}{\cos x} = \tan x$

88. $\sin(\pi - x) = \sin \pi \cos x - \sin x \cos \pi$

$= (0)(\cos x) - (\sin x)(-1)$

$= \sin x$

89. $\cos 3x = \cos(2x + x)$

$= \cos 2x \cos x - \sin 2x \sin x$

$= (\cos^2 x - \sin^2 x) \cos x - 2 \sin x \cos x \sin x$

$= \cos^3 x - 3 \sin^2 x \cos x$

$= \cos^3 x - 3 \cos x(1 - \cos^2 x)$

$= \cos^3 x - 3 \cos x + 3 \cos^3 x$

$= 4 \cos^3 x - 3 \cos x$

90. $\dfrac{\sin(\alpha + \beta)}{\cos \alpha \cos \beta} = \dfrac{\sin \alpha \cos \beta + \cos \alpha \sin \beta}{\cos \alpha \cos \beta}$

$= \dfrac{\sin \alpha \cos \beta}{\cos \alpha \cos \beta} + \dfrac{\cos \alpha \sin \beta}{\cos \alpha \cos \beta}$

$= \tan \alpha + \tan \beta$

91. $\sin\left(x + \dfrac{\pi}{2}\right) - \sin\left(x - \dfrac{\pi}{2}\right) = \sqrt{2}$

$2 \cos x \sin \dfrac{\pi}{2} = \sqrt{2}$ (Sum-to-Product)

$\cos x = \dfrac{\sqrt{2}}{2}$

$x = \dfrac{\pi}{4}, \dfrac{7\pi}{4}$

92. $\cos\left(x + \dfrac{\pi}{4}\right) - \cos\left(x - \dfrac{\pi}{4}\right) = 1$

$-2 \sin x \sin \dfrac{\pi}{4} = 1$ (Sum-to-Product)

$\sin x = -\dfrac{\sqrt{2}}{2}$

$x = \dfrac{5\pi}{4}, \dfrac{7\pi}{4}$

93. $\sin u = -\frac{5}{7}, \pi < u < \frac{3\pi}{2},$ Quadrant III

$\cos^2 u = 1 - \left(-\frac{5}{7}\right)^2 = \frac{24}{49} \Rightarrow \cos u = -\frac{2\sqrt{6}}{7}$

$\sin 2u = 2 \sin u \cos u = 2\left(-\frac{5}{7}\right)\left(-\frac{2\sqrt{6}}{7}\right) = \frac{20\sqrt{6}}{49}$

$\cos 2u = 1 - 2 \sin^2 u$

$= 1 - 2\left(-\frac{5}{7}\right)^2 = 1 - \frac{50}{49} = -\frac{1}{49}$

$\tan 2u = \frac{\sin 2u}{\cos 2u} = \frac{20\sqrt{6}}{-1} = -20\sqrt{6}$

94. $\cos u = \frac{4}{5}, \frac{3\pi}{2} < u < 2\pi,$ Quadrant IV

$\sin u = \frac{-3}{5}, \tan u = \frac{-3}{4}$

$\sin 2u = 2 \sin u \cos u = 2\left(\frac{-3}{5}\right)\left(\frac{4}{5}\right) = \frac{-24}{25}$

$\cos 2u = \cos^2 u - \sin^2 u = \frac{16}{25} - \frac{9}{25} = \frac{7}{25}$

$\tan 2u = \frac{\sin 2u}{\cos 2u} = \frac{-24}{7}$

95. $\tan u = -\frac{2}{9}, \frac{\pi}{2} < u < \pi,$ Quadrant II

$\sec^2 u = \tan^2 u + 1 = \frac{4}{81} + 1 = \frac{85}{81} \Rightarrow$

$\sec u = -\frac{\sqrt{85}}{9}$

$\cos u = \frac{-9\sqrt{85}}{85}, \sin u = (\tan u)(\cos u) = \frac{2\sqrt{85}}{85}$

$\sin 2u = 2 \sin u \cos u$

$= 2\left(\frac{2\sqrt{85}}{85}\right)\left(\frac{-9\sqrt{85}}{85}\right) = -\frac{36}{85}$

$\cos 2u = 1 - 2 \sin^2 u = 1 - 2\left(\frac{4}{85}\right) = \frac{77}{85}$

$\tan 2u = \frac{\sin 2u}{\cos 2u} = -\frac{36}{77}$

96. $\cos u = -\frac{2}{\sqrt{5}}, \frac{\pi}{2} < u < \pi,$ Quadrant II

$\sin^2 u = 1 - \cos^2 u = 1 - \frac{4}{5} = \frac{1}{5} \Rightarrow \sin u = \frac{1}{\sqrt{5}}$

$\sin 2u = 2 \sin u \cos u = 2\left(\frac{1}{\sqrt{5}}\right)\left(-\frac{2}{\sqrt{5}}\right) = -\frac{4}{5}$

$\cos 2u = \cos^2 u - \sin^2 u = \frac{4}{5} - \frac{1}{5} = \frac{3}{5}$

$\tan 2u = \frac{\sin 2u}{\cos 2u} = -\frac{4}{3}$

97. $6 \sin x \cos x = 3[2 \sin x \cos x] = 3 \sin 2x$

98. $4 \sin x \cos x + 2 = 2(2 \sin x \cos x) + 2$

$= 2 \sin 2x + 2$

99. $1 - 4 \sin^2 x \cos^2 x = 1 - (2 \sin x \cos x)^2$

$= 1 - \sin^2 2x = \cos^2 2x$

100. $\sin 4x = 2 \sin 2x \cos 2x$

$= 2[2 \sin x \cos x(\cos^2 x - \sin^2 x)]$

$= 4 \sin x \cos x(2 \cos^2 x - 1)$

$= 8 \cos^3 x \sin x - 4 \cos x \sin x$

101.

$$r = \frac{1}{32}v_0^2 \sin 2\theta$$
$$100 = \frac{1}{32}(80)^2 \sin 2\theta$$
$$\sin 2\theta = 0.5$$
$$2\theta = 30° \quad \text{or} \quad 2\theta = 180° - 30° = 150°$$
$$\theta = 15° \qquad\qquad \theta = 75°$$

102.

$$r = \frac{1}{32}v_0^2 \sin 2\theta$$
$$77 = \frac{1}{32}(50)^2 \sin 2\theta$$
$$\sin 2\theta = 0.9856$$
$$2\theta = 80.2649° \text{ or } 99.7351°$$
$$\theta = 40.13° \text{ or } 49.87°$$

103. $\sin^6 x = \left(\dfrac{1 - \cos 2x}{2}\right)^3 = \dfrac{1}{8}(1 - 3\cos 2x + 3\cos^2 2x - \cos^3 2x)$

$$= \frac{1}{8}\left[1 - 3\cos 2x + 3\left(\frac{1 + \cos 4x}{2}\right) - \cos 2x\left(\frac{1 + \cos 4x}{2}\right)\right]$$
$$= \frac{1}{8}\left(1 - 3\cos 2x + \frac{3}{2} + \frac{3}{2}\cos 4x - \frac{1}{2}\cos 2x - \frac{1}{2}\cos 2x \cos 4x\right)$$
$$= \frac{1}{16}\left(5 - 7\cos 2x + 3\cos 4x - \frac{1}{2}[\cos 2x + \cos 6x]\right)$$
$$= \frac{1}{32}(10 - 15\cos 2x + 6\cos 4x - \cos 6x)$$

104. $\cos^4 x \sin^4 x = \left(\dfrac{1 + \cos 2x}{2}\right)^2\left(\dfrac{1 - \cos 2x}{2}\right)^2$

$$= \frac{(1 + 2\cos 2x + \cos^2 2x)(1 - 2\cos 2x + \cos^2 2x)}{16}$$
$$= \frac{\left(1 + 2\cos 2x + \dfrac{1 + \cos 4x}{2}\right)\left(1 - 2\cos 2x + \dfrac{1 + \cos 4x}{2}\right)}{16}$$
$$= \frac{(3 + 4\cos 2x + \cos 4x)(3 - 4\cos 2x + \cos 4x)}{64}$$
$$= \frac{1}{64}[(3 + \cos 4x) + 4\cos 2x][(3 + \cos 4x) - 4\cos 2x]$$
$$= \frac{1}{64}[(3 + \cos 4x)^2 - 16\cos^2 2x]$$
$$= \frac{1}{64}[9 + 6\cos 4x + \cos^2 4x - 16\cos^2 2x]$$
$$= \frac{1}{64}\left[9 + 6\cos 4x + \frac{1 + \cos 8x}{2} - 16 \cdot \frac{1 + \cos 4x}{2}\right]$$
$$= \frac{1}{64}\left[\frac{3}{2} + \frac{1}{2}\cos 8x - 2\cos 4x\right]$$
$$= \frac{1}{128}(\cos 8x - 4\cos 4x + 3)$$

105. $\cos^4 2x = \left(\dfrac{1 + \cos 4x}{2}\right)^2$

$= \dfrac{1}{4}(1 + 2\cos 4x + \cos^2 4x)$

$= \dfrac{1}{4}\left(1 + 2\cos 4x + \dfrac{1 + \cos 8x}{2}\right)$

$= \dfrac{1}{8}(2 + 4\cos 4x + 1 + \cos 8x)$

$= \dfrac{1}{8}(3 + 4\cos 4x + \cos 8x)$

106. $\sin^4 2x = \left(\dfrac{1 - \cos 4x}{2}\right)^2$

$= \dfrac{1}{4}[1 - 2\cos 4x + \cos^2 4x]$

$= \dfrac{1}{4}\left[1 - 2\cos 4x + \dfrac{1 + \cos 8x}{2}\right]$

$= \dfrac{1}{4}\left[\dfrac{3}{2} - 2\cos 4x + \dfrac{1}{2}\cos 8x\right]$

$= \dfrac{1}{8}(3 + \cos 8x - 4\cos 4x)$

107. $\sin 105° = \sin\left(\dfrac{1}{2}\cdot 210°\right) = \sqrt{\dfrac{1 - \cos 210°}{2}} = \sqrt{\dfrac{1 + (\sqrt{3}/2)}{2}} = \dfrac{\sqrt{2 + \sqrt{3}}}{2}$

$\cos 105° = \cos\left(\dfrac{1}{2}\cdot 210°\right) = -\sqrt{\dfrac{1 + \cos 210°}{2}} = -\sqrt{\dfrac{1 - (\sqrt{3}/2)}{2}} = \dfrac{-\sqrt{2 - \sqrt{3}}}{2}$

$\tan 105° = \tan\left(\dfrac{1}{2}\cdot 210°\right) = \dfrac{\sin 210°}{1 + \cos 210°} = \dfrac{-1/2}{1 - (\sqrt{3}/2)} = \dfrac{1}{\sqrt{3} - 2} = -2 - \sqrt{3}$

108. $112°\,30' = 112.5°$

$\sin(112.5°) = \sin\left(\dfrac{1}{2}\cdot 225°\right) = \sqrt{\dfrac{1 - \cos 225°}{2}} = \sqrt{\dfrac{1 + (\sqrt{2}/2)}{2}} = \dfrac{\sqrt{2 + \sqrt{2}}}{2}$

$\cos(112.5°) = \cos\left(\dfrac{1}{2}\cdot 225°\right) = -\sqrt{\dfrac{1 + \cos 225°}{2}} = -\sqrt{\dfrac{1 - (\sqrt{2}/2)}{2}} = \dfrac{-\sqrt{2 - \sqrt{2}}}{2}$

$\tan(112.5°) = \tan\left(\dfrac{1}{2}\cdot 225°\right) = \dfrac{\sin 225°}{1 + \cos 225°} = \dfrac{-\sqrt{2}/2}{1 - (\sqrt{2}/2)} = \dfrac{-\sqrt{2}}{2 - \sqrt{2}}\cdot\dfrac{2 + \sqrt{2}}{2 + \sqrt{2}}$

$= \dfrac{-2 - 2\sqrt{2}}{2} = -1 - \sqrt{2}$

109. $\sin\left(\dfrac{7\pi}{8}\right) = \sin\left(\dfrac{1}{2}\cdot\dfrac{7\pi}{4}\right) = \sqrt{\dfrac{1 - \cos(7\pi/4)}{2}} = \sqrt{\dfrac{1 - (\sqrt{2}/2)}{2}} = \dfrac{\sqrt{2 - \sqrt{2}}}{2}$

$\cos\left(\dfrac{7\pi}{8}\right) = \cos\left(\dfrac{1}{2}\cdot\dfrac{7\pi}{4}\right) = -\sqrt{\dfrac{1 + \cos(7\pi/4)}{2}} = -\sqrt{\dfrac{1 + (\sqrt{2}/2)}{2}} = \dfrac{-\sqrt{2 + \sqrt{2}}}{2}$

$\tan\left(\dfrac{7\pi}{8}\right) = \tan\left(\dfrac{1}{2}\cdot\dfrac{7\pi}{4}\right) = \dfrac{\sin(7\pi/4)}{1 + \cos(7\pi/4)} = \dfrac{-\sqrt{2}/2}{1 + (\sqrt{2}/2)} = \dfrac{-\sqrt{2}}{2 + \sqrt{2}} = 1 - \sqrt{2}$

110. $\dfrac{11\pi}{12} = \dfrac{1}{2}\left(\dfrac{11\pi}{6}\right)$, Quadrant II

$\sin\left(\dfrac{11\pi}{12}\right) = \sin\left(\dfrac{1}{2}\cdot\dfrac{11\pi}{6}\right) = \sqrt{\dfrac{1 - \cos(11\pi/6)}{2}} = \sqrt{\dfrac{1 - (\sqrt{3}/2)}{2}} = \dfrac{\sqrt{2 - \sqrt{3}}}{2}$

$\cos\left(\dfrac{11\pi}{12}\right) = \cos\left(\dfrac{1}{2}\cdot\dfrac{11\pi}{6}\right) = -\sqrt{\dfrac{1 + \cos(11\pi/6)}{2}} = -\sqrt{\dfrac{1 + (\sqrt{3}/2)}{2}} = -\dfrac{\sqrt{2 + \sqrt{3}}}{2}$

$\tan\left(\dfrac{11\pi}{12}\right) = \tan\left(\dfrac{1}{2}\cdot\dfrac{11\pi}{6}\right) = \dfrac{\sin(11\pi/6)}{1 + \cos(11\pi/6)} = \dfrac{-1/2}{1 + (\sqrt{3}/2)} = \dfrac{-1}{2 + \sqrt{3}} = -2 + \sqrt{3}$

111. $\sin u = \frac{3}{5}, 0 < u < \frac{\pi}{2} \Rightarrow \cos u = \frac{4}{5}$

$$\sin\left(\frac{u}{2}\right) = \sqrt{\frac{1 - \cos u}{2}}$$

$$= \sqrt{\frac{1 - (4/5)}{2}} = \frac{1}{\sqrt{10}} = \frac{\sqrt{10}}{10}$$

$$\cos\left(\frac{u}{2}\right) = \sqrt{\frac{1 + \cos u}{2}}$$

$$= \sqrt{\frac{1 + (4/5)}{2}} = \frac{3}{\sqrt{10}} = \frac{3\sqrt{10}}{10}$$

$$\tan\left(\frac{u}{2}\right) = \frac{1 - \cos u}{\sin u} = \frac{1 - (4/5)}{3/5} = \frac{1}{3}$$

112. $\tan u = \frac{21}{20}, \pi < u < \frac{3\pi}{2}$, Quadrant III

$$\sec^2 u = \tan^2 u + 1 = \frac{441}{400} + 1 = \frac{841}{400} \Rightarrow$$

$$\sec u = \frac{-29}{20}$$

$$\cos u = \frac{-20}{29}$$

$$\sin u = \cos u \tan u = \frac{-20}{29} \cdot \frac{21}{20} = \frac{-21}{29}$$

$$\sin\frac{u}{2} = \sqrt{\frac{1 - \cos u}{2}} = \sqrt{\frac{1 + (20/29)}{2}} = \frac{7\sqrt{58}}{58}$$

$$\cos\frac{u}{2} = -\sqrt{\frac{1 + \cos u}{2}} = -\sqrt{\frac{1 - (20/29)}{2}}$$

$$= \frac{-3\sqrt{58}}{58}$$

$$\tan\frac{u}{2} = \frac{\sin(u/2)}{\cos(u/2)} = -\frac{7}{3}$$

113. $\cos u = -\frac{2}{7}, \frac{\pi}{2} < u < \pi \Rightarrow \sin u = \sqrt{1 - \frac{4}{49}} = \frac{\sqrt{45}}{7}$

$$\sin\left(\frac{u}{2}\right) = \sqrt{\frac{1 - \cos u}{2}} = \sqrt{\frac{1 + (2/7)}{2}} = \sqrt{\frac{9}{14}} = \frac{3\sqrt{14}}{14}$$

$$\cos\left(\frac{u}{2}\right) = \sqrt{\frac{1 + \cos u}{2}} = \sqrt{\frac{1 - (2/7)}{2}} = \sqrt{\frac{5}{14}} = \frac{\sqrt{70}}{14}$$

$$\tan\left(\frac{u}{2}\right) = \frac{1 - \cos u}{\sin u} = \frac{1 + (2/7)}{\sqrt{45}/7} = \frac{9}{\sqrt{45}} = \frac{9\sqrt{45}}{45} = \frac{\sqrt{45}}{5} = \frac{3\sqrt{5}}{5}$$

114. $\sec u = -6, \frac{\pi}{2} < u < \pi$, Quadrant II

$$\cos u = \frac{-1}{6}, \sin u = \frac{\sqrt{35}}{6}, \tan u = -\sqrt{35}$$

$$\sin\left(\frac{u}{2}\right) = \sqrt{\frac{1 - \cos u}{2}} = \sqrt{\frac{1 + (1/6)}{2}} = \sqrt{\frac{7}{12}} = \frac{\sqrt{21}}{6}$$

$$\cos\left(\frac{u}{2}\right) = \sqrt{\frac{1 + \cos u}{2}} = \sqrt{\frac{1 - (1/6)}{2}} = \sqrt{\frac{5}{12}} = \frac{\sqrt{15}}{6}$$

$$\tan\left(\frac{u}{2}\right) = \frac{1 - \cos u}{\sin u} = \frac{1 + (1/6)}{\sqrt{35}/6} = \frac{7}{\sqrt{35}} = \frac{\sqrt{35}}{5}$$

Note: $u \approx 99.6°$

115. $-\sqrt{\frac{1 + \cos 8x}{2}} = -|\cos 4x|$

116. $\frac{\sin 10x}{1 + \cos 10x} = \tan 5x$

117. Volume V of the trough will be the area A of the isosceles triangle times the length l of the trough.

$V = A \cdot l$

$A = \frac{1}{2}bh$

$\cos\frac{\theta}{2} = \frac{h}{0.5} \Rightarrow h = 0.5\cos\frac{\theta}{2}$

$\sin\frac{\theta}{2} = \frac{b/2}{0.5} \Rightarrow \frac{b}{2} = 0.5\sin\frac{\theta}{2}$

$A = 0.5\sin\frac{\theta}{2}\,0.5\cos\frac{\theta}{2} = (0.5)^2\sin\frac{\theta}{2}\cos\frac{\theta}{2} = 0.25\sin\frac{\theta}{2}\cos\frac{\theta}{2}$ square meters

$V = (0.25)(4)\sin\frac{\theta}{2}\cos\frac{\theta}{2}$ cubic meters $= \sin\frac{\theta}{2}\cos\frac{\theta}{2}$ cubic meters

4 m
b
h
0.5 m
θ
0.5 m
not drawn to scale

118. Volume V of the trough will be the area A of the isosceles triangle times the length l of the trough.

$V = A \cdot l$

$A = \frac{1}{2}bh$

$\cos\frac{\theta}{2} = \frac{h}{0.5} \Rightarrow h = 0.5\cos\frac{\theta}{2}$

$\sin\frac{\theta}{2} = \frac{b/2}{0.5} \Rightarrow \frac{b}{2} = 0.5\sin\frac{\theta}{2}$

$A = 0.5\sin\frac{\theta}{2}\,0.5\cos\frac{\theta}{2} = (0.5)^2\sin\frac{\theta}{2}\cos\frac{\theta}{2} = 0.25\sin\frac{\theta}{2}\cos\frac{\theta}{2}$ square meters

$V = (0.25)(4)\sin\frac{\theta}{2}\cos\frac{\theta}{2}$ cubic meters $= \sin\frac{\theta}{2}\cos\frac{\theta}{2}$ cubic meters

$V = \sin\frac{\theta}{2}\cos\frac{\theta}{2} = \frac{1}{2}\left(2\sin\frac{\theta}{2}\cos\frac{\theta}{2}\right) = \frac{1}{2}\sin\theta$ cubic meters

Volume is maximum when $\theta = \pi/2$.

4 m
b
h
0.5 m
θ
0.5 m
not drawn to scale

119. $6\sin\frac{\pi}{4}\cos\frac{\pi}{4} = 6\left[\frac{1}{2}\sin\left(\frac{\pi}{4}+\frac{\pi}{4}\right) + \sin\left(\frac{\pi}{4}-\frac{\pi}{4}\right)\right] = 3\left(\sin\frac{\pi}{2} + \sin 0\right) = 3$

120. $4\sin 15^\circ \sin 45^\circ = 4 \cdot \frac{1}{2}[\cos(15^\circ - 45^\circ) - \cos(15^\circ + 45^\circ) = 2[\cos(-30^\circ) - \cos(60^\circ)]$

$= 2[\cos(30^\circ) - \cos(60^\circ)]$

121. $\sin 5\alpha \sin 4\alpha = \frac{1}{2}[\cos(5\alpha - 4\alpha) - \cos(5\alpha + 4\alpha)] = \frac{1}{2}[\cos\alpha - \cos 9\alpha]$

122. $\cos 6\theta \sin 8\theta = \frac{1}{2}[\sin(6\theta + 8\theta) - \sin(6\theta - 8\theta)] = \frac{1}{2}[\sin 14\theta - \sin(-2\theta)] = \frac{1}{2}[\sin 14\theta + \sin 2\theta]$

123. $\cos 5\theta + \cos 4\theta = 2\cos\left(\frac{9\theta}{2}\right)\cos\left(\frac{\theta}{2}\right)$

124. $\sin 3\theta + \sin 2\theta = 2\sin\left(\frac{5\theta}{2}\right)\cos\left(\frac{\theta}{2}\right)$

125. $\sin\left(x+\frac{\pi}{4}\right)-\sin\left(x-\frac{\pi}{4}\right)=2\cos x\sin\frac{\pi}{4}=\sqrt{2}\cos x$

126. $\cos\left(x+\frac{\pi}{6}\right)-\cos\left(x-\frac{\pi}{6}\right)=-2\sin\left(\frac{x+\frac{\pi}{6}+x-\frac{\pi}{6}}{2}\right)\sin\left(\frac{x+\frac{\pi}{6}-x+\frac{\pi}{6}}{2}\right)=-2\sin x\sin\frac{\pi}{6}$

127. $y=1.5\sin 8t-0.5\cos 8t$

$a=\frac{3}{2},\ b=-\frac{1}{2},\ B=8,\ C=\arctan\left(-\frac{1/2}{3/2}\right)$

$y=\sqrt{\left(\frac{3}{2}\right)^2+\left(\frac{1}{2}\right)^2}\sin\left(8t+\arctan\left(-\frac{1}{3}\right)\right)$

$y=\frac{1}{2}\sqrt{10}\sin\left(8t-\arctan\frac{1}{3}\right)$

128. $y=\frac{1}{2}\sqrt{10}\sin\left(8t-\arctan\frac{1}{3}\right)$

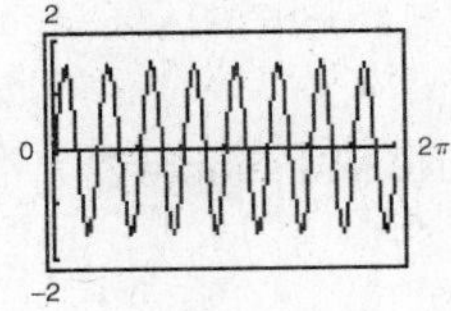

129. The amplitude is $\frac{\sqrt{10}}{2}$.

130. Frequency $=\frac{1}{\text{period}}=\frac{4}{\pi}$

131. If $\frac{\pi}{2}<\theta<\pi$, then $\cos\frac{\theta}{2}<0$. False, if

$\frac{\pi}{2}<\theta<\pi \implies \frac{\pi}{4}<\frac{\theta}{2}<\frac{\pi}{2}$,

which is in Quadrant I $\implies \cos\left(\frac{\theta}{2}\right)>0$.

132. $\sin(x+y)=\sin x+\sin y$. False.

$\sin(x+y)=\sin x\cos y+\cos x\sin y$

133. $4\sin(-x)\cos(-x)=-2\sin 2x$. True.

$4\sin(-x)\cos(-x)=4(-\sin x)(\cos x)=-4\sin x\cos x=-2(2\sin x\cos x)=-2\sin 2x$

134. $4\sin 45^\circ\cos 15^\circ=1+\sqrt{3}$. True.

$4\sin 45^\circ\cos 15^\circ=4\left(\frac{1}{2}[\sin(45^\circ+15^\circ)+\sin(45^\circ-15^\circ)]\right)=2[\sin 60^\circ+\sin 30^\circ]$

$=2\left[\frac{\sqrt{3}}{2}+\frac{1}{2}\right]=2\left(\frac{\sqrt{3}+1}{2}\right)=1+\sqrt{3}$

135. Answers will vary. See page 352.

136. No. $\cos\theta=\pm\sqrt{1-\sin^2\theta}$

137. $y_1=\sec^2\left(\frac{\pi}{2}-x\right)=\csc^2 x$

$y_2=\cot^2 x$

$\csc^2 x=\cot^2 x+1$

Let $y_3=y_2+1=\cot^2 x+1=y_1$.

138. $y_1=\frac{\cos 3x}{\cos x}$

$y_2=(2\sin x)^2$

From the graphs, $y_3=-y_2+1=y_1$.

Chapter 5 Practice Test

1. Find the value of the other five trigonometric functions, given $\tan x = \frac{4}{11}$, $\sec x < 0$.

2. Simplify $\dfrac{\sec^2 x + \csc^2 x}{\csc^2 x(1 + \tan^2 x)}$.

3. Rewrite as a single logarithm and simplify $\ln|\tan \theta| - \ln|\cot \theta|$.

4. True or false: $\cos\left(\dfrac{\pi}{2} - x\right) = \dfrac{1}{\csc x}$

5. Factor and simplify: $\sin^4 x + (\sin^2 x) \cos^2 x$

6. Multiply and simplify: $(\csc x + 1)(\csc x - 1)$

7. Rationalize the denominator and simplify:

$$\frac{\cos^2 x}{1 - \sin x}$$

8. Verify:

$$\frac{1 + \cos \theta}{\sin \theta} + \frac{\sin \theta}{1 + \cos \theta} = 2 \csc \theta$$

9. Verify:

$$\tan^4 x + 2 \tan^2 x + 1 = \sec^4 x$$

10. Use the sum or difference formulas to determine:

(a) $\sin 105°$ (b) $\tan 15°$

11. Simplify: $(\sin 42°) \cos 38° - (\cos 42°) \sin 38°$

12. Verify: $\tan\left(\theta + \dfrac{\pi}{4}\right) = \dfrac{1 + \tan \theta}{1 - \tan \theta}$

13. Write $\sin(\arcsin x - \arccos x)$ as an algebraic expression in x.

14. Use the double-angle formulas to determine:

(a) $\cos 120°$ (b) $\tan 300°$

15. Use the half-angle formulas to determine:

(a) $\sin 22.5°$ (b) $\tan \dfrac{\pi}{12}$

16. Given $\sin \theta = 4/5$, θ lies in Quadrant II, find $\cos \theta/2$.

17. Use the power-reducing identities to write $(\sin^2 x) \cos^2 x$ in terms of the first power of cosine.

18. Rewrite as a sum: $6(\sin 5\theta) \cos 2\theta$

19. Rewrite as a product: $\sin(x + \pi) + \sin(x - \pi)$

20. Verify: $\dfrac{\sin 9x + \sin 5x}{\cos 9x - \cos 5x} = -\cot 2x$

21. Verify: $(\cos u) \sin v = \frac{1}{2}[\sin(u + v) - \sin(u - v)]$

22. Find all solutions in the interval $[0, 2\pi)$:

$$4 \sin^2 x = 1$$

23. Find all solutions in the interval $[0, 2\pi)$:

$$\tan^2 \theta + \left(\sqrt{3} - 1\right) \tan \theta - \sqrt{3} = 0$$

24. Find all solutions in the interval $[0, 2\pi)$:

$$\sin 2x = \cos x$$

25. Use the Quadratic Formula to find all solutions in the interval $[0, 2\pi)$:

$$\tan^2 x - 6 \tan x + 4 = 0$$

CHAPTER 6
Additional Topics in Trigonometry

Section 6.1 Law of Sines **466**

Section 6.2 Law of Cosines **473**

Section 6.3 Vectors in the Plane **482**

Section 6.4 Vectors and Dot Products **495**

Section 6.5 Trigonometric Form of a Complex Number **503**

Review Exercises **528**

Practice Test **547**

CHAPTER 6
Additional Topics in Trigonometry

Section 6.1 Law of Sines

- If ABC is any oblique triangle with sides a, b, and c, then the Law of Sines says

$$\frac{a}{\sin A} = \frac{b}{\sin B} = \frac{c}{\sin C}.$$

- You should be able to use the Law of Sines to solve an oblique triangle for the remaining three parts, given:
  - (a) Two angles and any side (AAS or ASA)
  - (b) Two sides and an angle opposite one of them (SSA)
    1. If A is acute and $h = b \sin A$:
       - (a) $a < h$, no triangle is possible.
       - (b) $a = h$ or $a \geq b$, one triangle is possible.
       - (c) $h < a < b$, two triangles are possible.
    2. If A is obtuse and $h = b \sin A$:
       - (a) $a \leq b$, no triangle is possible.
       - (b) $a > b$, one triangle is possible.
- The area of any triangle equals one-half the product of the lengths of two sides times the sine of their included angle.

$$A = \tfrac{1}{2}ab \sin C = \tfrac{1}{2}ac \sin B = \tfrac{1}{2}bc \sin A$$

Vocabulary Check

1. oblique

2. $\dfrac{b}{\sin B}$

3. (a) Two; any; AAS; ASA

(b) Two; an opposite; SSA

4. $\dfrac{1}{2}bc \sin A$; $\dfrac{1}{2}ab \sin C$; $\dfrac{1}{2}ac \sin B$

1. Given: $A = 25°, B = 60°, a = 12$

$C = 180° - 25° - 60° = 95°$

$$b = \frac{a}{\sin A}(\sin B) = \frac{12}{\sin 25°}(\sin 60°) \approx 24.59 \text{ in.}$$

$$c = \frac{a}{\sin A}(\sin C) = \frac{12}{\sin 25°}(\sin 95°) \approx 28.29 \text{ in.}$$

2. Given: $A = 35°, B = 55°, a = 18$

$C = 180° - 35° - 55° = 90°$

$$b = \frac{a}{\sin A}(\sin B) = \frac{18}{\sin 35°}(\sin 55°) \approx 25.71 \text{ mm}$$

$$c = \frac{a}{\sin A}(\sin C) = \frac{18}{\sin 35°}(\sin 90°) \approx 31.38 \text{ mm}$$

3. Given: $B = 15°, C = 125°, c = 20$

$A = 180° - 15° - 125° = 40°$

$$a = \frac{c}{\sin C}(\sin A) = \frac{20}{\sin 125°}(\sin 40°) \approx 15.69 \text{ cm}$$

$$b = \frac{c}{\sin C}(\sin B) = \frac{20}{\sin 125°}(\sin 15°) \approx 6.32 \text{ cm}$$

4. Given: $B = 40°, C = 110°, c = 30$

$A = 180° - 40° - 110° = 30°$

$$a = \frac{c}{\sin C}(\sin A) = \frac{30}{\sin 110°}(\sin 30°) \approx 15.96 \text{ ft}$$

$$b = \frac{c}{\sin C}(\sin B) = \frac{30}{\sin 110°}(\sin 40°) \approx 20.52 \text{ ft}$$

5. Given: $A = 80° \, 15', B = 25° \, 30', b = 2.8$

$C = 180° - 80° \, 15' - 25° \, 30' = 74° \, 15'$

$$a = \frac{b}{\sin B}(\sin A) = \frac{2.8}{\sin 25° \, 30'}(\sin 80° \, 15') \approx 6.41 \text{ km}$$

$$c = \frac{b}{\sin B}(\sin C) = \frac{2.8}{\sin 25° \, 30'}(\sin 74° \, 15') \approx 6.26 \text{ km}$$

6. Given: $A = 88° \, 35', B = 22° \, 45', b = 50.2$

$C = 180° - 88° \, 35' - 22° \, 45' = 68° \, 40'$

$$a = \frac{b}{\sin B}(\sin A) = \frac{50.2}{\sin 22° \, 45'}(\sin 88° \, 35') \approx 129.77 \text{ yd}$$

$$c = \frac{b}{\sin B}(\sin C) = \frac{50.2}{\sin 22° \, 45'}(\sin 68° \, 40') \approx 120.92 \text{ yd}$$

7. Given: $A = 36°, a = 8, b = 5$

$$\sin B = \frac{b \sin A}{a} = \frac{5 \sin(36°)}{8} \approx 0.3674 \implies B \approx 21.6°$$

$C = 180° - A - B \approx 180° - 36° - 21.6° = 122.4°$

$$c = \frac{a}{\sin A}(\sin C) = \frac{8}{\sin(36°)} \sin(122.4°) \approx 11.49$$

8. Given: $A = 60°, a = 9, c = 10$

$$\sin C = \frac{c \sin A}{a} = \frac{10 \sin 60°}{9} \approx 0.9623 \implies C \approx 74.2° \text{ or } C \approx 105.8°$$

Case 1

$C \approx 74.2°$

$B = 180° - A - C \approx 45.8°$

$$b = \frac{a}{\sin A}(\sin B) \approx \frac{9 \sin 45.8°}{\sin 60°} \approx 7.45$$

Case 2

$C \approx 105.8°$

$B = 180° - A - C \approx 14.2°$

$$b = \frac{a}{\sin A}(\sin B) \approx \frac{9 \sin 14.2°}{\sin 60°} \approx 2.55$$

9. Given: $A = 102.4°, C = 16.7°, a = 21.6$

$B = 180° - A - C = 180° - 102.4° - 16.7° = 60.9°$

$$b = \frac{a}{\sin A}(\sin B) = \frac{21.6}{\sin 102.4°}(\sin 60.9°) \approx 19.32$$

$$c = \frac{a}{\sin A}(\sin C) = \frac{21.6}{\sin 102.4°}(\sin 16.7°) \approx 6.36$$

10. Given: $A = 24.3°, C = 54.6°, c = 2.68$

$B = 180° - A - C = 101.1°$

$$a = \frac{c}{\sin C}(\sin A) = \frac{2.68 \sin 24.3°}{\sin 54.6°} \approx 1.35$$

$$b = \frac{c}{\sin C}(\sin B) = \frac{2.68 \sin 101.1°}{\sin 54.6°} \approx 3.23$$

11. Given: $A = 110° 15', a = 48, b = 16$

$$\sin B = \frac{b \sin A}{a} = \frac{16 \sin 110° 15'}{48} \approx 0.31273 \Rightarrow B \approx 18° 13'$$

$C = 180° - A - B \approx 180° - 110° 15' - 18° 13' = 51° 32'$

$$c = \frac{a}{\sin A}(\sin C) = \frac{48}{\sin 110° 15'}(\sin 51° 32') \approx 40.06$$

12. Given: $B = 2° 45', b = 6.2, c = 5.8$

$$\sin C = \frac{c \sin B}{b} = \frac{5.8 \sin 2° 45'}{6.2} \approx 0.04488 \Rightarrow C \approx 2.57°(2° 34')$$

$A = 180° - B - C \approx 174.68°(174° 41')$

$$a = \frac{b}{\sin B}(\sin A) \approx \frac{6.2 \sin 174° 41'}{\sin 2° 45'} \approx 11.97$$

13. Given: $A = 110°, a = 125, b = 100$

$$\sin B = \frac{b \sin A}{a} = \frac{100 \sin 110°}{125} \approx 0.75175 \Rightarrow B \approx 48.74°$$

$C = 180° - A - B \approx 21.26°$

$$c = \frac{a}{\sin A}(\sin C) = \frac{125 \sin 21.26°}{\sin 110°} \approx 48.23$$

14. Given: $A = 110°, a = 125, b = 200$

A obtuse and $a < b \Rightarrow$ No solution

15. Given: $A = 76°, a = 18, b = 20$

$$\sin B = \frac{b \sin A}{a} = \frac{20 \sin 76°}{18} \approx 1.078$$

No solution

16. Given: $A = 76°, a = 34, b = 21$

$$\sin B = \frac{b \sin A}{a} = \frac{21 \sin 76°}{34} \approx 0.5993 \Rightarrow B \approx 36.8°$$

$C \approx 180° - 76° - 36.8° \approx 67.2°$

$$c = \frac{a}{\sin A} \sin C = \frac{34}{\sin 76°} \sin 67.2° \approx 32.30$$

17. Given: $A = 58°, a = 11.4, b = 12.8$

$$\sin B = \frac{b \sin A}{a} = \frac{12.8 \sin 58°}{11.4} \approx 0.9522 \implies B \approx 72.21° \text{ or } 107.79°$$

Case 1

$B \approx 72.21°$

$C = 180° - 58° - 72.21° = 49.79°$

$$c = \frac{a}{\sin A}(\sin C) = \frac{11.4}{\sin 58°}(\sin 49.79°) \approx 10.27$$

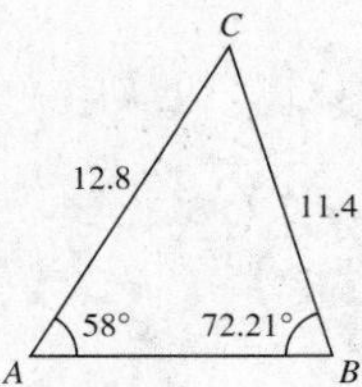

Case 2

$B \approx 107.79°$

$C \approx 180° - 58° - 107.79° = 14.21°$

$$c = \frac{a}{\sin A}(\sin C) = \frac{11.4}{\sin 58°}(\sin 14.21°) \approx 3.30$$

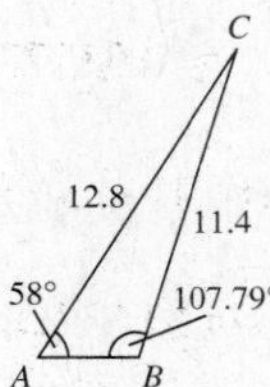

18. Given: $A = 58°, a = 4.5, b = 12.8$

$a < h = b \sin 58°$

$4.5 < 10.86$

No solution

19. $\text{Area} = \frac{1}{2}ab \sin C$

$= \frac{1}{2}(6)(10) \sin(110°)$

≈ 28.2 square units

20. $\text{Area} = \frac{1}{2}ac \sin B$

$= \frac{1}{2}(92)(30) \sin(130°)$

≈ 1057.1 square units

21. $\text{Area} = \frac{1}{2}bc \sin A$

$= \frac{1}{2}(67)(85) \sin(38° \, 45')$

≈ 1782.3 square units

22. $A = 5° \, 15', b = 4.5, c = 22$

$\text{Area} = \frac{1}{2}bc \sin A$

$= \left(\frac{1}{2}\right)(4.5)(22) \sin 5.25°$

≈ 4.529 square units

23. $\text{Area} = \frac{1}{2}ac \sin B$

$= \frac{1}{2}(103)(58) \sin 75° \, 15'$

≈ 2888.6 square units

24. $\text{Area} = \frac{1}{2}ab \sin C$

$= \frac{1}{2}(16)(20) \sin 85° \, 45'$

≈ 159.6 square units

25. Angle $CAB = 70°$

Angle $B = 20° + 14° = 34°$

(a)

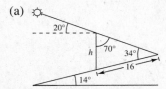

(b) $\dfrac{16}{\sin 70°} = \dfrac{h}{\sin 34°}$

(c) $h = \dfrac{16 \sin 34°}{\sin 70°} \approx 9.52$ meters

26. (a)

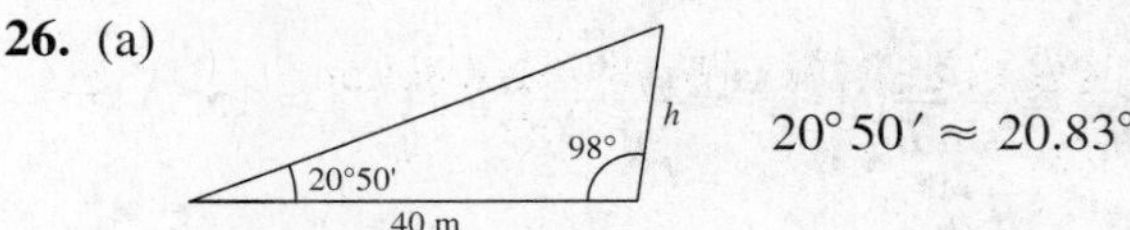

$20° \, 50' \approx 20.83°$

(b) $A = 180° - 98° - 20.83° = 61.17°$ (or $61° \, 10'$)

$$\frac{40}{\sin A} = \frac{h}{\sin (20° \, 50')} \implies h = \frac{40 \sin (20° \, 50')}{\sin 61.17°}$$

(c) $h \approx 16.2$ m

27. $\sin A = \dfrac{a \sin B}{b} = \dfrac{500 \sin(46°)}{720} \approx 0.4995$

$A \approx 29.97°$

$\angle ACD = 90° - 29.97° \approx 60°$

Bearing: S 60° W or (240° in plane navigation)

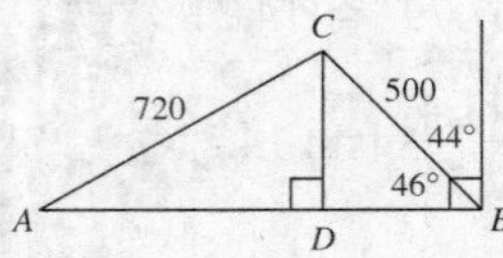

28. Given: $A = 74° - 28° = 46°$,

$B = 180° - 41° - 74° = 65°,\ c = 100$

$C = 180° - 46° - 65° = 69°$

$a = \dfrac{c}{\sin C}(\sin A) = \dfrac{100}{\sin 69°}(\sin 46°) \approx 77$ meters

A, 46°, 100, 65°, B, 69°, C

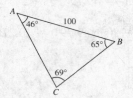

29. (a)

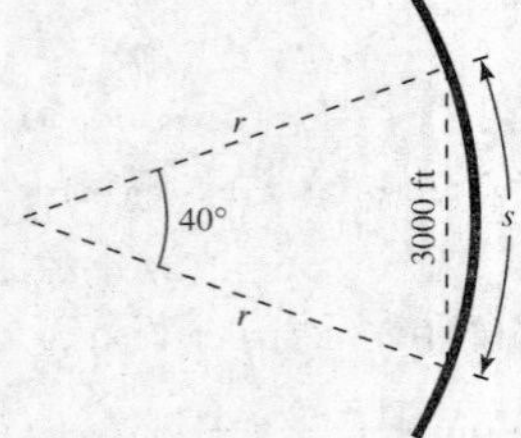

(b) $r = \dfrac{3000 \sin[1/2(180° - 40°)]}{\sin 40°} \approx 4385.71$ feet

(c) $s \approx 40°\left(\dfrac{\pi}{180°}\right)4385.71 \approx 3061.80$ feet

30. (a)

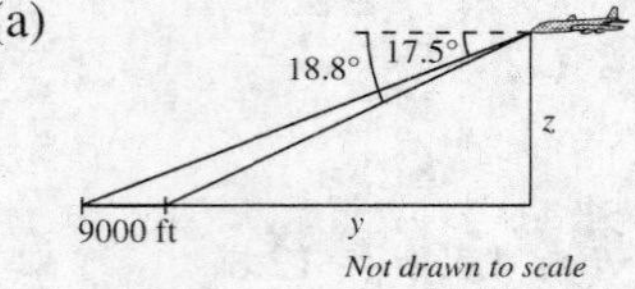

(b) $\dfrac{x}{\sin 17.5°} = \dfrac{9000}{\sin 1.3°}$

$x \approx 119{,}289.1261 \text{ feet } \approx 22.6 \text{ miles}$

(c) $\dfrac{y}{\sin 71.2°} = \dfrac{x}{\sin 90°}$

$y = x \sin 71.2° \approx 119{,}289.1261 \sin 71.2°$

$\approx 112{,}924.963 \text{ feet} \approx 21.4 \text{ miles}$

(d) $z = 119{,}289.1261 \sin 18.8° \approx 38{,}442.8$ feet

31. $\angle ACD = 65°$

$\angle ADC = 180° - 65° - 15° = 100°$

$\angle CDB = 180° - 100° = 80°$

$\angle B = 180° - 80° - 70° = 30°$

$a = \dfrac{b}{\sin B}(\sin A) = \dfrac{30}{\sin 30°}(\sin 15°) \approx 15.53$ km

$c = \dfrac{b}{\sin B}(\sin C) = \dfrac{30}{\sin 30°}(\sin 135°) \approx 42.43$ km

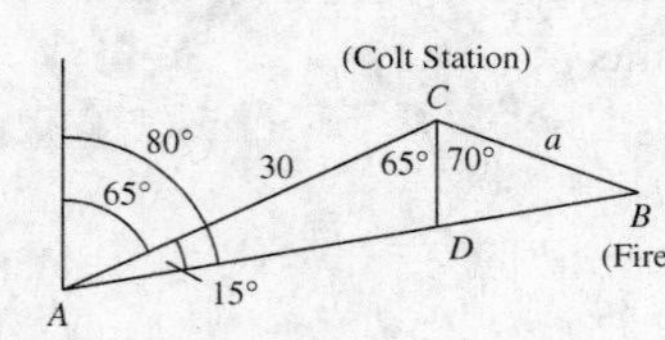

32. $A = 20°, B = 90° + 63° = 153°, c = 10\left(\dfrac{1}{4}\right) = 2.5$

$C = 180° - 20° - 153° = 7°$

$b = \dfrac{c}{\sin C}(\sin B) = \dfrac{2.5 \sin 153°}{\sin 7°} \approx 9.31$

$d \approx b \sin A \approx 9.31 \sin 20° \approx 3.2$ miles

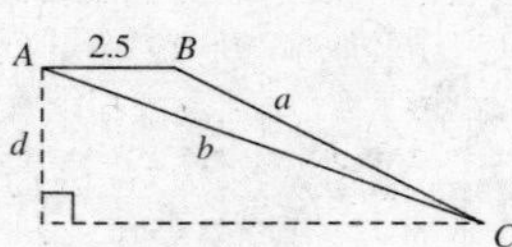

33. $\dfrac{\sin(42° - \theta)}{10} = \dfrac{\sin 48°}{17}$

$$\sin(42° - \theta) = \frac{10}{17}\sin 48° \approx 0.4371$$

$$42° - \theta \approx 25.919$$

$$\theta \approx 16.1°$$

34. (a)

(b) Third angle in triangle $= \alpha$

$$\theta + \alpha + (180° - \phi) = 180° \implies \alpha = \phi - \theta$$

$$\frac{d}{\sin\theta} = \frac{2}{\sin\alpha}$$

$$d = \frac{2\sin\theta}{\sin\alpha} = \frac{2\sin\theta}{\sin(\phi - \theta)}$$

35. (a) $\sin\alpha = \dfrac{5.45}{58.36} \approx 0.0934$

$$\alpha \approx 5.36°$$

(b) $\dfrac{d}{\sin\beta} = \dfrac{58.36}{\sin\theta} \implies \sin\beta = \dfrac{d\sin\theta}{58.36}$

$$\beta = \sin^{-1}\left[\frac{d\sin\theta}{58.36}\right]$$

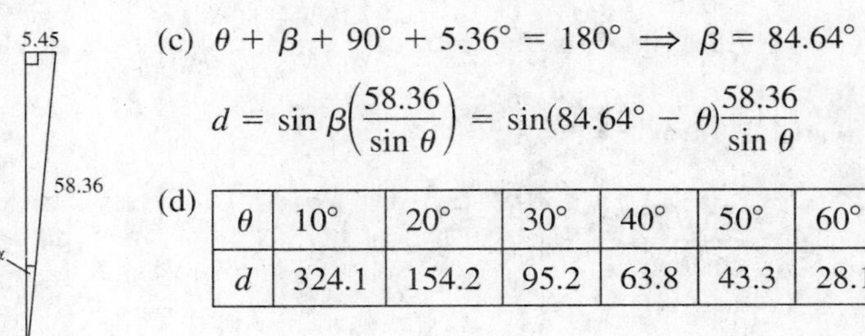

(c) $\theta + \beta + 90° + 5.36° = 180° \implies \beta = 84.64° - \theta$

$$d = \sin\beta\left(\frac{58.36}{\sin\theta}\right) = \sin(84.64° - \theta)\frac{58.36}{\sin\theta}$$

(d)

θ	10°	20°	30°	40°	50°	60°
d	324.1	154.2	95.2	63.8	43.3	28.1

36. (a) $\dfrac{\sin\alpha}{9} = \dfrac{\sin\beta}{18}$

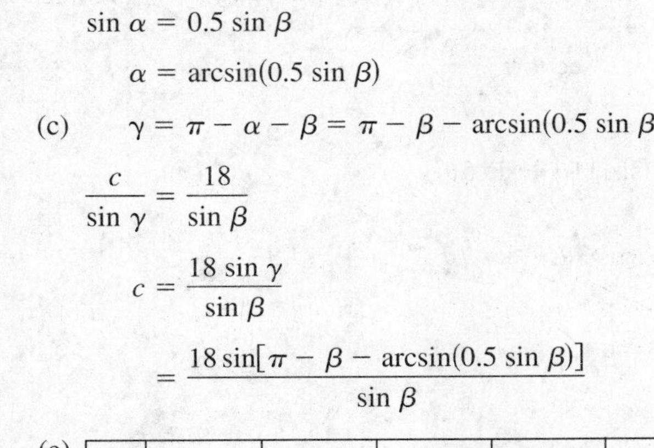

$$\sin\alpha = 0.5\sin\beta$$

$$\alpha = \arcsin(0.5\sin\beta)$$

(b)

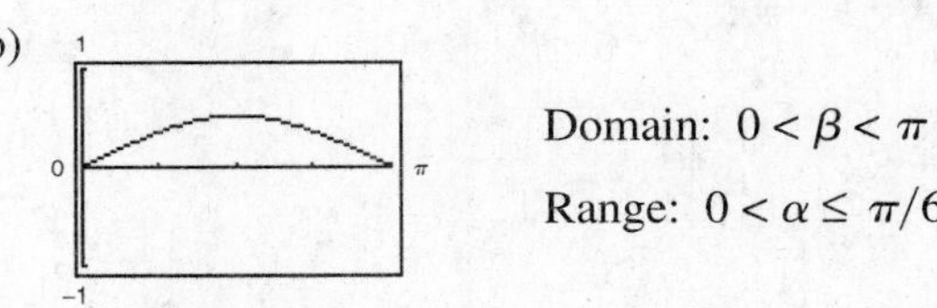

Domain: $0 < \beta < \pi$

Range: $0 < \alpha \le \pi/6$

(c) $\gamma = \pi - \alpha - \beta = \pi - \beta - \arcsin(0.5\sin\beta)$

$$\frac{c}{\sin\gamma} = \frac{18}{\sin\beta}$$

$$c = \frac{18\sin\gamma}{\sin\beta}$$

$$= \frac{18\sin[\pi - \beta - \arcsin(0.5\sin\beta)]}{\sin\beta}$$

(d)

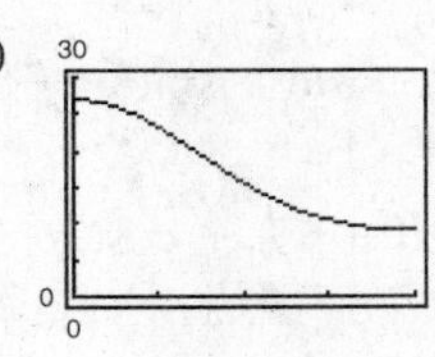

Domain: $0 < \beta < \pi$

Range: $9 < c < 27$

(e)

β	0.4	0.8	1.2	1.6	2.0	2.4	2.8
α	0.1960	0.3669	0.4848	0.5234	0.4720	0.3445	0.1683
c	25.95	23.07	19.19	15.33	12.29	10.31	9.27

As $\beta \to 0$, $c \to 27$.

As $\beta \to \pi$, $c \to 9$.

37. False. If just the three angles are known, the triangle cannot be solved.

38. True. No angle could be 90°.

39. Yes, the Law of Sines can be used to solve a right triangle if you are given at least one side and one angle, or two sides.

40. Answers will vary. $A = 36°, a = 5$

(a) $b = 4$ one solution

(b) $b = 7$ two solutions $[h = b \sin A < a < b]$

(c) $b = 10$ no solution $[a < h = b \sin A]$

41. Given: $A = 45°, B = 52°, a = 16$

$C = 180° - 45° - 52° = 83°$

$b = \frac{a}{\sin A}(\sin B) = \frac{16}{\sin 45°}(\sin 52°) \approx 17.83$

$c = \frac{a}{\sin A}(\sin C) = \frac{16}{\sin 45°}(\sin 83°) \approx 22.46$

$(a + b)\sin\left(\frac{C}{2}\right) = c\cos\left(\frac{A - B}{2}\right)$

$(16 + 17.83)\sin\left(\frac{83°}{2}\right) = 22.46\cos\left(\frac{45° - 52°}{2}\right)$

$22.42 = 22.42$

42. Given: $A = 42°, B = 60°, a = 24$

$C = 180° - 42° - 60° = 78°$

$b = \frac{a}{\sin A}(\sin B) = \frac{24}{\sin 42°}(\sin 60°) \approx 31.06$

$c = \frac{a}{\sin A}(\sin C) = \frac{24}{\sin 42°}(\sin 78°) \approx 35.08$

$(a - b)\cos\left(\frac{C}{2}\right) = c\sin\left(\frac{A - B}{2}\right)$

$(24 - 31.06)\cos\left(\frac{78°}{2}\right) = 35.08\sin\left(\frac{42° - 60°}{2}\right)$

$-5.49 = -5.49$

43. $\tan\theta = \frac{\sin\theta}{\cos\theta} = -\frac{12}{5}$

$\sec\theta = \frac{13}{5}$

$\cot\theta = -\frac{5}{12}$

$\csc\theta = -\frac{13}{12}$

44. $\cot\theta = \frac{9}{2}$

$\sin\theta = -\frac{2}{\sqrt{85}} = -\frac{2\sqrt{85}}{85}$

$\cos\theta = \cot\theta \cdot \sin\theta$

$= \frac{9}{2}\left(-\frac{2}{\sqrt{85}}\right) = -\frac{9}{\sqrt{85}} = -\frac{9\sqrt{85}}{85}$

$\sec\theta = -\frac{\sqrt{85}}{9}$

45. $6\sin 8\theta\cos 3\theta = 6\left(\tfrac{1}{2}\right)[\sin(8\theta + 3\theta) + \sin(8\theta - 3\theta)] = 3(\sin 11\theta + \sin 5\theta)$

46. $2\cos 2\theta\cos 5\theta = 2\left(\tfrac{1}{2}\right)[\cos(2\theta - 5\theta) + \cos(2\theta + 5\theta)] = \cos 3\theta + \cos 7\theta$

47. $3\cos\frac{\pi}{6}\sin\frac{5\pi}{3} = 3\left(\frac{1}{2}\right)\left[\sin\left(\frac{\pi}{6} + \frac{5\pi}{3}\right) - \sin\left(\frac{\pi}{6} - \frac{5\pi}{3}\right)\right]$

$= \frac{3}{2}\left[\sin\left(\frac{11\pi}{6}\right) - \sin\left(-\frac{3\pi}{2}\right)\right]$

$= \frac{3}{2}\left[-\frac{1}{2} - 1\right] = -\frac{9}{4}$

48. $\frac{5}{2}\sin\frac{3\pi}{4}\sin\frac{5\pi}{6} = \frac{5}{2}\cdot\frac{1}{2}\left[\cos\left(\frac{3\pi}{4} - \frac{5\pi}{6}\right) - \cos\left(\frac{3\pi}{4} + \frac{5\pi}{6}\right)\right]$

$= \frac{5}{4}\left[\cos\left(-\frac{\pi}{12}\right) - \cos\left(\frac{19\pi}{12}\right)\right]$

$= \frac{5}{4}\left[\cos\left(\frac{\pi}{12}\right) - \cos\left(\frac{19\pi}{12}\right)\right]$

Section 6.2 Law of Cosines

- If ABC is any oblique triangle with sides a, b, and c, then the Law of Cosines says:

  (a) $a^2 = b^2 + c^2 - 2bc \cos A$ or $\cos A = \dfrac{b^2 + c^2 - a^2}{2bc}$

  (b) $b^2 = a^2 + c^2 - 2ac \cos B$ or $\cos B = \dfrac{a^2 + c^2 - b^2}{2ac}$

  (c) $c^2 = a^2 + b^2 - 2ab \cos C$ or $\cos C = \dfrac{a^2 + b^2 - c^2}{2ab}$

- You should be able to use the Law of Cosines to solve an oblique triangle for the remaining three parts, given:

  (a) Three sides (SSS)

  (b) Two sides and their included angle (SAS)

- Given any triangle with sides of lengths a, b, and c, then the area of the triangle is

  Area $= \sqrt{s(s-a)(s-b)(s-c)}$, where $s = \dfrac{a+b+c}{2}$. (Heron's Formula)

Vocabulary Check

1. $c^2 = a^2 + b^2 - 2ab \cos C$

2. Heron's Area

3. $\frac{1}{2}bh$, $\sqrt{s(s-a)(s-b)(s-c)}$

1. Given: $a = 12$, $b = 16$, $c = 18$

$$\cos A = \frac{b^2 + c^2 - a^2}{2bc} = \frac{16^2 + 18^2 - 12^2}{2(16)(18)} \approx 0.75694 \implies A \approx 40.80°$$

$$\sin B = \frac{b \sin A}{a} \approx 0.8712 \implies B \approx 60.61°$$

$$C \approx 180° - 60.61° - 40.80° = 78.59°$$

2. Given: $a = 8$, $b = 18$, $c = 12$

$$\cos A = \frac{b^2 + c^2 - a^2}{2bc} = \frac{18^2 + 12^2 - 8^2}{2(18)(12)} \approx 0.9352 \implies A \approx 20.74°$$

$$\sin C = \frac{c \sin A}{a} \approx 0.5312 \implies C \approx 32.09°$$

$$B \approx 180° - 32.09° - 20.74° = 127.17°$$

3. Given: $a = 8.5$, $b = 9.2$, $c = 10.8$

$$\cos A = \frac{b^2 + c^2 - a^2}{2bc} = \frac{9.2^2 + 10.8^2 - 8.5^2}{2(9.2)(10.8)} \approx 0.6493 \implies A \approx 49.51°$$

$$\sin B = \frac{b \sin A}{a} \approx \frac{9.2 \sin 49.51°}{8.5} \approx 0.82315 \implies B \approx 55.40°$$

$$C \approx 180° - 55.40° - 49.51° = 75.09°$$

4. Given: $a = 4.2,\ b = 5.4,\ c = 2.1$

$$\cos C = \frac{a^2 + b^2 - c^2}{2ab} = \frac{4.2^2 + 5.4^2 - 2.1^2}{2(4.2)(5.4)} \approx 0.9345 \implies C \approx 20.85°$$

$$\sin A = \frac{a \sin C}{c} \approx \frac{4.2 \sin 20.8°}{2.1} \approx 0.7102 \implies A \approx 45.38°$$

$$B \approx 180° - 20.85° - 45.38° = 113.77°$$

5. Given: $a = 10,\ c = 15,\ B = 20°$

$$b^2 = a^2 + c^2 - 2ac \cos B = 100 + 225 - 2(10)(15) \cos 20° \approx 43.0922 \implies b \approx 6.56 \text{ mm}$$

$$\cos A = \frac{b^2 + c^2 - a^2}{2bc} \approx \frac{43.0922 + 225 - 100}{2(6.56)(15)} \approx 0.8541 \implies A \approx 31.40°$$

$$C \approx 180° - 20° - 31.40° = 128.60°$$

6. Given: $a = 16,\ c = 10,\ B = 40°$

$$b^2 = a^2 + c^2 - 2ac \cos B = 256 + 100 - 2(16)(10) \cos 40° \approx 110.8658 \implies b \approx 10.5293 \approx 10.53 \text{ km}$$

$$\cos C = \frac{a^2 + b^2 - c^2}{2ab} \approx \frac{256 + 110.8658 - 100}{2(16)(10.53)} \approx 0.7920 \implies C \approx 37.62°$$

$$A \approx 180° - 40° - 37.62° = 102.38°$$

7. Given: $a = 10.4,\ c = 12.5,\ B = 50°\ 30' = 50.5°$

$$b^2 = a^2 + c^2 - 2ac \cos B = 10.4^2 + 12.5^2 - 2(10.4)(12.5) \cos 50.5° \approx 99.0297 \implies b \approx 9.95 \text{ ft}$$

$$\cos A = \frac{b^2 + c^2 - a^2}{2bc} \approx \frac{99.0297 + 12.5^2 - 10.4^2}{2(9.95)(12.5)} \approx 0.5914 \implies A \approx 53.75° = 53°\ 45'$$

$$C \approx 180° - 50.5° - 53.75° = 75.75° = 75°\ 45'$$

8. Given: $a = 20.2,\ c = 6.2,\ B = 80°\ 45' = 80.75°$

$$b^2 = a^2 + c^2 - 2ac \cos B = 20.2^2 + 6.2^2 - 2(20.2)(6.2) \cos 80.75° \approx 406.2172 \implies b \approx 20.15 \text{ miles}$$

$$\cos C = \frac{a^2 + b^2 - c^2}{2ab} \approx \frac{20.2^2 + 406.2172 - 6.2^2}{2(20.2)(20.15)} \approx 0.9528 \implies C \approx 17.68° \approx 17°\ 41'$$

$$A \approx 180° - 17.68° - 80.75° = 81.57° = 81°\ 34'$$

9. Given: $a = 6,\ b = 8,\ c = 12$

$$\cos A = \frac{b^2 + c^2 - a^2}{2bc} = \frac{64 + 144 - 36}{2(8)(12)} \approx 0.8958 \implies A \approx 26.4°$$

$$\sin B = \frac{b \sin A}{a} \approx \frac{8 \sin 26.4°}{6} \approx 0.5928 \implies B \approx 36.3°$$

$$C \approx 180° - 26.4° - 36.3° = 117.3°$$

10. Given: $a = 9, b = 3, c = 11$

$$\cos A = \frac{b^2 + c^2 - a^2}{2bc} = \frac{3^2 + 11^2 - 9^2}{2(3)(11)} \approx 0.7424 \Rightarrow A \approx 42.1°$$

$$\cos C = \frac{a^2 + b^2 - c^2}{2ab} = \frac{9^2 + 3^2 - 11^2}{2(9)(3)} \approx -0.574 \Rightarrow C \approx 125.0°$$

$$B = 180° - A - C \approx 12.9°$$

11. Given: $A = 50°, b = 15, c = 30$

$$a^2 = b^2 + c^2 - 2bc \cos A = 225 + 900 - 2(15)(30) \cos 50° \approx 546.49 \Rightarrow a \approx 23.38$$

$$\cos B = \frac{a^2 + c^2 - b^2}{2ac} \approx \frac{546.49 + 900 - 225}{2(23.4)(30)} \approx 0.8708 \Rightarrow B \approx 29.4°$$

$$C = 180° - A - B \approx 180° - 50° - 29.5° = 100.6°$$

12. $C = 108°, a = 10, b = 7$

$$c^2 = a^2 + b^2 - 2ab \cos C = 10^2 + 7^2 - 2(10)(7) \cos 108° \approx 192.2624 \Rightarrow c \approx 13.9$$

$$\sin B = \frac{\sin C}{c} b = \frac{\sin 108°}{13.9}(7) \approx 0.4789 \Rightarrow B \approx 28.7°$$

$$A = 180° - 108° - 28.7° = 43.3°$$

13. Given: $a = 9, \ b = 12, \ c = 15$

$$\cos C = \frac{a^2 + b^2 - c^2}{2ab} = \frac{81 + 144 - 225}{2(9)(12)} = 0 \Rightarrow C = 90°$$

$$\sin A = \frac{9}{15} = \frac{3}{5} \Rightarrow A \approx 36.9°$$

$$B \approx 180° - 90° - 36.9° = 53.1°$$

14. Given: $a = 45, b = 30, c = 72$

$$\cos C = \frac{a^2 + b^2 - c^2}{2ab} = \frac{45^2 + 30^2 - 72^2}{2(45)(30)} \approx -0.8367 \Rightarrow C \approx 146.8°$$

$$\cos B = \frac{a^2 + c^2 - b^2}{2ac} = \frac{45^2 + 72^2 - 30^2}{2(45)(72)} \approx 0.9736 \Rightarrow B \approx 13.2°$$

$$A = 180° - B - C = 20.0°$$

15. Given: $a = 75.4, b = 48, c = 48$

$$\cos A = \frac{b^2 + c^2 - a^2}{2bc} = \frac{48^2 + 48^2 - 75.4^2}{2(48)(48)} \approx -0.2338 \Rightarrow A \approx 103.5°$$

$$\sin B = \frac{b \sin A}{a} \approx \frac{48 \sin (103.5°)}{75.4} \approx 0.6190 \Rightarrow B \approx 38.2°$$

$C = B \approx 38.2°$ (Because of roundoff error, $A + B + C \neq 180°$.)

16. Given: $a = 1.42$, $b = 0.75$, $c = 1.25$

$$\cos A = \frac{b^2 + c^2 - a^2}{2bc} = \frac{(0.75)^2 + (1.25)^2 - (1.42)^2}{2(0.75)(1.25)} = 0.05792 \implies A \approx 86.7°$$

$$\cos B = \frac{a^2 + c^2 - b^2}{2ac} = \frac{(1.42)^2 + (1.25)^2 - (0.75)^2}{2(1.42)(1.25)} \approx 0.8497 \implies B \approx 31.8°$$

$$180° - 86.7° - 31.8° \approx 61.5°$$

17. Given: $B = 8° 15' = 8.25°$, $a = 26$, $c = 18$

$$b^2 = a^2 + c^2 - 2ac \cos B = 26^2 + 18^2 - 2(26)(18)\cos(8.25°) \approx 73.6863 \implies b \approx 8.58$$

$$\sin C = \frac{c \sin B}{b} \approx \frac{18 \sin(8.25°)}{8.58} \approx 0.3 \implies C \approx 17.51° \approx 17° 31'$$

$$A = 180° - B - C \approx 180° - 8.25° - 17.51° = 154.24° \approx 154° 14'$$

18. Given: $B = 10° 35' \approx 10.583°$, $a = 40$, $c = 30$

$$b^2 = a^2 + c^2 - 2ac \cos B \approx 140.8268 \implies b \approx 11.87$$

$$\sin A = \frac{a \sin B}{b} \approx 0.6189 \implies A \approx 141.75° \approx 141° 45'$$

$$C = 180 - A - B = 27.67° \text{ or } 27° 40'$$

19. Given: $B = 75° 20' \approx 75.33°$, $a = 6.2$, $c = 9.5$

$$b^2 = a^2 + c^2 - 2ac \cos B$$

$$= 6.2^2 + 9.5^2 - 2(6.2)(9.5)\cos(75.33°)$$

$$= 98.86$$

$$b \approx 9.94$$

$$\sin C = \frac{c \sin B}{b} = \frac{9.5 \sin(75.33°)}{9.94}$$

$$\approx 0.9246 \implies C \approx 67.6°$$

$$A = 180° - B - C \approx 37.1°$$

20. Given: $C = 15° 15' \approx 15.25°$, $a = 6.25$, $b = 2.15$

$$c^2 = a^2 + b^2 - 2ab \cos C$$

$$= 6.25^2 + 2.15^2 - 2(6.25)(2.15)\cos 15.25°$$

$$\approx 17.7563 \implies c \approx 4.21$$

$$\sin B = \frac{b \sin C}{c}$$

$$\approx 0.1342 \implies B \approx 7.71° \approx 7° 43'$$

$$A = 180° - B - C \approx 157.04° \approx 157° 2'$$

21. $d^2 = 4^2 + 8^2 - 2(4)(8)\cos 30°$

$$\approx 24.57 \implies d \approx 4.96$$

$$2\phi = 360° - 2\theta \implies \phi = 150°$$

$$c^2 = 4^2 + 8^2 - 2(4)(8)\cos 150° \approx 135.43$$

$$c \approx 11.64$$

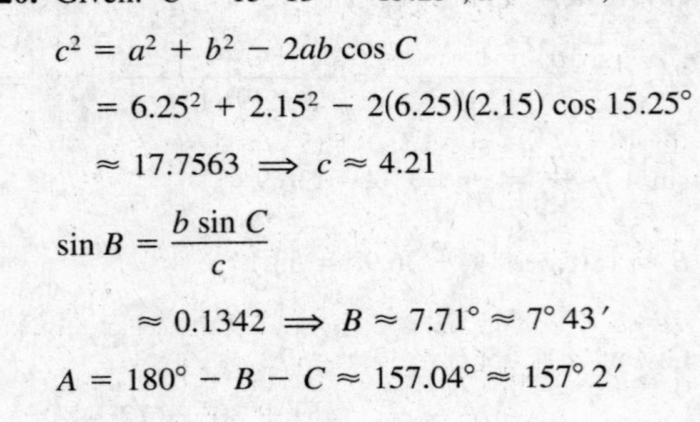

22. $c^2 = 25^2 + 35^2 - 2(25)(35)\cos 120° = 2725 \implies c \approx 52.2$

$$2\theta = 360° - 2(120°) = 120° \implies \theta = 60°$$

$$d^2 = 25^2 + 35^2 - 2(25)(35)\cos 60° = 975 \implies d \approx 31.22$$

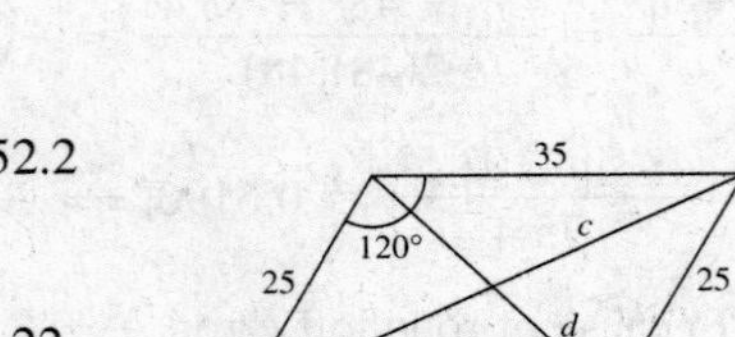

23. $\cos\phi = \dfrac{10^2 + 14^2 - 20^2}{2(10)(14)}$

$\phi \approx 111.8°$

$2\theta \approx 360° - 2(111.80°)$

$\theta = 68.2°$

$d^2 = 10^2 + 14^2 - 2(10)(14)\cos 68.2°$

$d \approx 13.86$

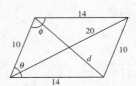

24. $\cos\theta = \dfrac{40^2 + 60^2 - 80^2}{2(40)(60)} \approx -\dfrac{1}{4} \Rightarrow \theta \approx 104.5°$

$2\phi \approx 360° - 2(104.5°) = 151° \Rightarrow \phi = 75.5°$

$c^2 \approx 40^2 + 60^2 - 2(40)(60)\cos 75.5° = 4000$

$c \approx 63.25$

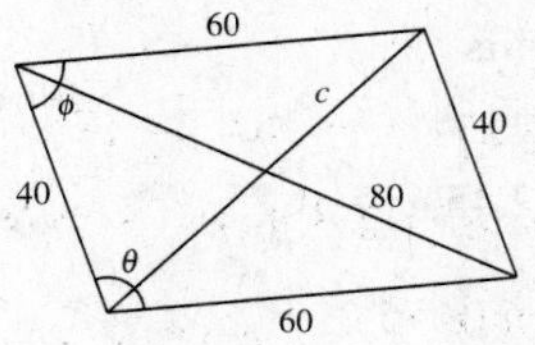

25. $\cos\alpha = \dfrac{15^2 + 12.5^2 - 10^2}{2(15)(12.5)} = 0.75 \Rightarrow \alpha \approx 41.41°$

$\cos\beta = \dfrac{15^2 + 10^2 - 12.5^2}{2(15)(10)} = 0.5625 \Rightarrow \beta \approx 55.77°$

$\delta = 180° - 41.41° - 55.77° \approx 82.82°$

$\mu = 180° - \delta \approx 97.18°$

$b^2 = 12.5^2 + 10^2 - 2(12.5)(10)\cos(97.18°) \approx 287.50$

$b \approx 16.96$

$\sin\omega = \dfrac{10}{16.96}\sin\mu \approx 0.585 \Rightarrow \omega \approx 35.8°$

$\sin\epsilon = \dfrac{12.5}{16.96}\sin\mu \approx 0.731 \Rightarrow \epsilon \approx 47°$

$\theta = \alpha + \omega \approx 77.2°$

$\phi = \beta + \epsilon \approx 102.8°$

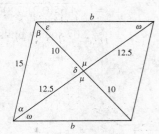

26. $\cos\alpha = \dfrac{25^2 + 17.5^2 - 25^2}{2(25)(17.5)}$

$\alpha \approx 69.513°$

$\beta \approx 180 - \alpha \approx 110.487°$

$a^2 = 17.5^2 + 25^2 - 2(17.5)(25)\cos 110.487°$

$a \approx 35.18$

$z = 180 - 2\alpha \approx 40.974$

$\cos\mu = \dfrac{25^2 + 35.18^2 - 17.5^2}{2(25)(35.18)}$

$\mu \approx 27.772°$

$\theta = \mu + z \approx 68.7°$

$\omega = 180° - \mu - \beta \approx 41.741°$

$\phi = \omega + \alpha \approx 111.3°$

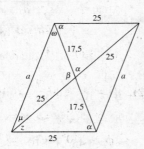

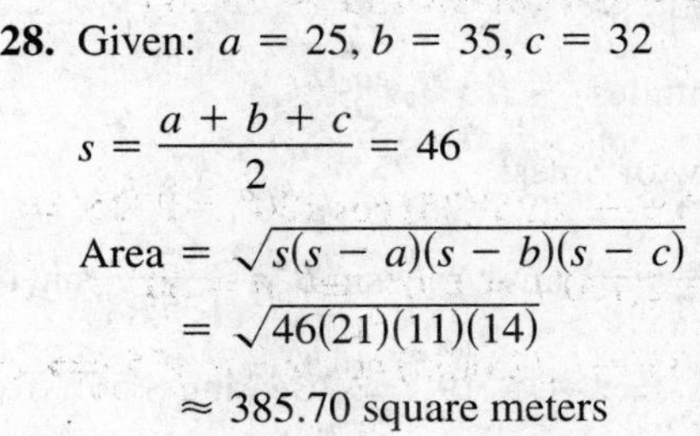

27. Given: $a = 12, b = 24, c = 18$

$s = \dfrac{a + b + c}{2} = 27$

$\text{Area} = \sqrt{s(s-a)(s-b)(s-c)}$

$= \sqrt{27(15)(3)(9)}$

≈ 104.57 square inches

28. Given: $a = 25, b = 35, c = 32$

$s = \dfrac{a + b + c}{2} = 46$

$\text{Area} = \sqrt{s(s-a)(s-b)(s-c)}$

$= \sqrt{46(21)(11)(14)}$

≈ 385.70 square meters

29. Given: $a = 5, b = 8, c = 10$

$s = \frac{a+b+c}{2} = \frac{23}{2} = 11.5$

$\text{Area} = \sqrt{s(s-a)(s-b)(s-c)}$

$= \sqrt{11.5(6.5)(3.5)(1.5)}$

≈ 19.81 square units

30. $s = \frac{a+b+c}{2} = \frac{14+17+7}{2} = 19$

$\text{Area} = \sqrt{s(s-a)(s-b)(s-c)}$

$= \sqrt{19(5)(2)(12)}$

≈ 47.7 square units

31. Given: $a = 1.24, b = 2.45, c = 1.25$

$s = \frac{a+b+c}{2} = 2.47$

$\text{Area} = \sqrt{s(s-a)(s-b)(s-c)}$

$= \sqrt{2.47(1.23)(0.02)(1.22)}$

≈ 0.27 square feet

32. Given: $a = 2.4, b = 2.75, c = 2.25$

$s = \frac{a+b+c}{2} = 3.7$

$\text{Area} = \sqrt{s(s-a)(s-b)(s-c)}$

$= \sqrt{3.7(1.3)(0.95)(1.45)}$

≈ 2.57 square centimeters

33. Given: $a = 3.5, b = 10.2, c = 9$

$s = \frac{a+b+c}{2} = 11.35$

$\text{Area} = \sqrt{s(s-a)(s-b)(s-c)}$

$= \sqrt{11.35(7.85)(1.15)(2.35)}$

≈ 15.52 square units

34. Given: $a = 75.4, b = 52, c = 52$

$s = \frac{75.4+52+52}{2} = 89.7$

$\text{Area} = \sqrt{s(s-a)(s-b)(s-c)}$

$= \sqrt{89.7(14.3)(37.7)(37.7)}$

≈ 1350 square units

35. Given: $a = 10.59, b = 6.65, c = 12.31$

$s = \frac{a+b+c}{2} = 14.775$

$\text{Area} = \sqrt{s(s-a)(s-b)(s-c)}$

$= \sqrt{14.775(4.185)(8.125)(2.465)}$

≈ 35.19 square units

36. $s = \frac{a+b+c}{2} = \frac{4.45+1.85+3.00}{2} = 4.65$

$\text{Area} = \sqrt{s(s-a)(s-b)(s-c)}$

$= \sqrt{4.65(0.2)(2.8)(1.65)}$

≈ 2.07 square units

37. $B = 105° + 32° = 137°$

$b^2 = a^2 + c^2 - 2ac \cdot \cos B$

$= 648^2 + 810^2 - 2(648)(810)\cos(137°)$

$= 1{,}843{,}749.862$

$b = 1357.8$ miles

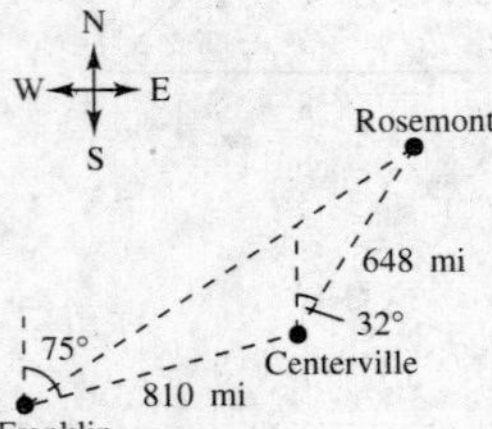

From the Law of Sines:

$\frac{a}{\sin A} = \frac{b}{\sin B} \Rightarrow \sin A = \frac{a}{b}\sin B = \frac{648}{1357.8}\sin(137°) \approx 0.32548$

$\Rightarrow A \approx 19° \Rightarrow$ Bearing S 56° W (or 236° for airplane navigation)

38. Angle at $B = 180° - 80° = 100°$

$b^2 = 240^2 + 380^2 - 2(240)(380)\cos 100°$

$\approx 233{,}673.4 \implies b \approx 483.4$ meters

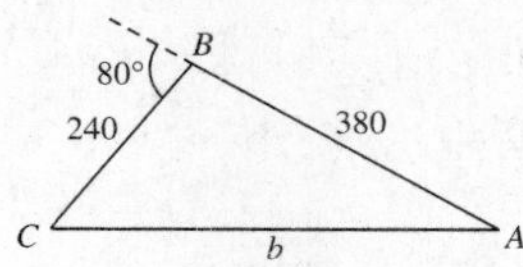

39. $\cos B = \dfrac{1500^2 + 3600^2 - 2800^2}{2(1500)(3600)} \approx 0.6824 \implies B \approx 46.97°$

Bearing at B: $90° - 46.97°$: N 43.03° E

$\cos C = \dfrac{1500^2 + 2800^2 - 3600^2}{2(1500)(2800)} \approx -0.3417 \implies C \approx 109.98°$

Bearing at C: $C - (90° - 46.97°) = 66.95°$

S 66.95° E

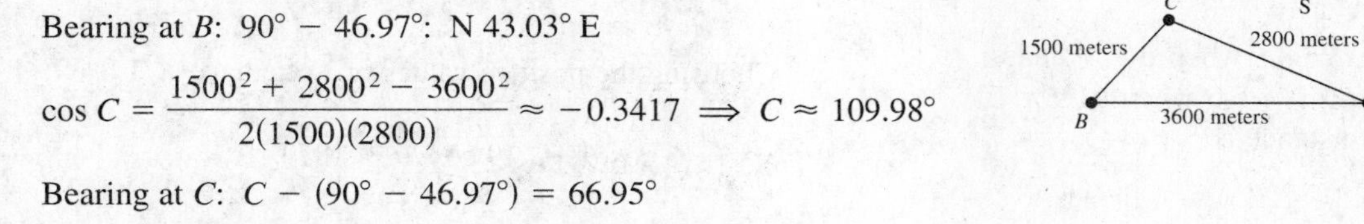

40. $\cos\theta = \dfrac{2^2 + 3^2 - (4.5)^2}{2(2)(3)} \approx -0.60417$

$\theta \approx 127.2°$

41. $C = 180° - 53° - 67° = 60°$

$c^2 = a^2 + b^2 - 2ab\cos C$

$= 36^2 + 48^2 - 2(36)(48)(0.5) = 1872$

$c \approx 43.3$ mi

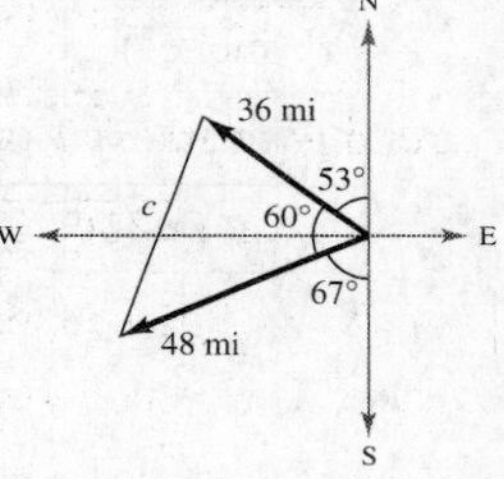

42. The angles at the base of the tower are 96° and 84°. The longer guy wire g_1 is given by:

$g_1{}^2 = 75^2 + 100^2 - 2(75)(100)\cos 96° \approx 17{,}192.9 \implies g_1 \approx 131.1$ feet

The shorter guy wire g_2 is given by: $g_2{}^2 = 75^2 + 100^2 - 2(75)(100)\cos 84° \approx 14{,}057.1 \implies g_2 \approx 118.6$ feet

43. $\overline{RS} = \sqrt{8^2 + 10^2} = \sqrt{164} = 2\sqrt{41} \approx 12.8$ feet

$\overline{PQ} = \dfrac{1}{2}\sqrt{16^2 + 10^2} = \dfrac{1}{2}\sqrt{356} = \sqrt{89} \approx 9.4$ feet

$\tan P = \dfrac{10}{16}$

$P = \arctan\dfrac{5}{8} \approx 32.0°$

$\overline{QS} = \sqrt{8^2 + 9.4^2 - 2(8)(9.4)\cos 32°}$

$\approx \sqrt{24.81} \approx 5.0$ feet

44. $A = 180° - 40° - 20° = 120°$

$x = \dfrac{(\sin 20°)}{\sin 120°}(10)$

≈ 3.95 feet

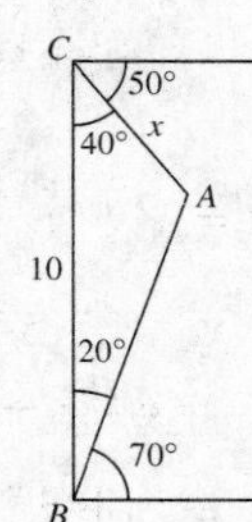

45. $s = \dfrac{a + b + c}{2} = \dfrac{145 + 257 + 290}{2} = 346$

Area $= \sqrt{s(s-a)(s-b)(s-c)}$

$= \sqrt{346(201)(89)(56)} \approx 18{,}617.7$ square feet

46. The height is $h = 70 \sin 70° \approx 65.778$.

Area = base × height

$= (100)(65.778) \approx 6577.8$ square meters

47. (a) $7^2 = 1.5^2 + x^2 - 2(1.5)(x)\cos\theta$

$49 = 2.25 + x^2 - 3x\cos\theta$

(b)
$$x^2 - 3x\cos\theta = 46.75$$
$$x^2 - 3x\cos\theta + \left(\frac{3\cos\theta}{2}\right)^2 = 46.75 + \left(\frac{3\cos\theta}{2}\right)^2$$
$$\left[x - \frac{3\cos\theta}{2}\right]^2 = \frac{187}{4} + \frac{9\cos^2\theta}{4}$$
$$x - \frac{3\cos\theta}{2} = \pm\sqrt{\frac{187 + 9\cos^2\theta}{4}}$$

Choosing the positive values of x, we have

$$x = \frac{1}{2}\left(3\cos\theta + \sqrt{9\cos^2\theta + 187}\right).$$

(c)

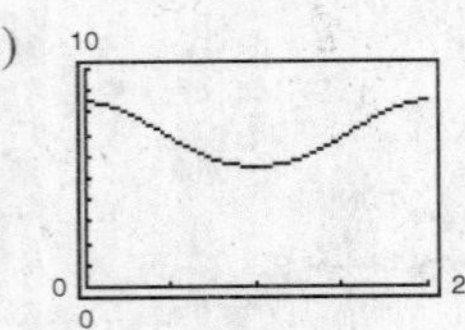

(d) Note that $x = 8.5$ when $\theta = 0$ and $\theta = 2\pi$, and $x = 5.5$ when $\theta = \pi$. Thus, the distance is

$2(8.5 - 5.5) = 2(3) = 6$ inches.

48. (a) $d^2 = 10^2 + 7^2 - 2(10)(7)\cos\theta \Rightarrow d = \sqrt{149 - 140\cos\theta}$

(b) $\theta = \arccos\left[\dfrac{10^2 + 7^2 - d^2}{2(10)(7)}\right] = \arccos\left[\dfrac{149 - d^2}{140}\right]$

(c) $s = \dfrac{360° - \theta}{360°}(2\pi r) = \dfrac{(360° - \theta)\pi}{45°}$

(d)

d (inches)	9	10	12	13	14	15	16
θ (degrees)	60.9°	69.5°	88.0°	98.2°	109.6°	122.9°	139.8°
s (inches)	20.88	20.28	18.99	18.28	17.48	16.55	15.37

49. False. This is not a triangle! $5 + 10 < 16$

50. True. The third side is found by the Law of Cosines. The other angles are determined by the Law of Sines.

51. False. $s = \dfrac{a + b + c}{2}$, not $\dfrac{a + b + c}{3}$.

52.
$$\frac{1}{2}bc(1 + \cos A) = \frac{1}{2}bc\left[1 + \frac{b^2 + c^2 - a^2}{2bc}\right]$$
$$= \frac{1}{2}bc\left[\frac{2bc + b^2 + c^2 - a^2}{2bc}\right]$$
$$= \frac{1}{4}[(b + c)^2 - a^2]$$
$$= \frac{1}{4}[(b + c) + a][(b + c) - a]$$
$$= \frac{b + c + a}{2} \cdot \frac{b + c - a}{2}$$
$$= \frac{a + b + c}{2} \cdot \frac{-a + b + c}{2}$$

53.
$$\frac{1}{2}bc(1 - \cos A) = \frac{1}{2}bc\left[1 - \frac{b^2 + c^2 - a^2}{2bc}\right]$$
$$= \frac{1}{2}bc\left[\frac{2bc - b^2 - c^2 + a^2}{2bc}\right]$$
$$= \frac{1}{4}[a^2 - (b - c)^2]$$
$$= \frac{1}{4}[a - b + c)(a + b - c)]$$
$$= \left(\frac{a - b + c}{2}\right)\left(\frac{a + b - c}{2}\right)$$

54.
$$\frac{\cos A}{a} + \frac{\cos B}{b} + \frac{\cos C}{c} = \frac{b^2 + c^2 - a^2}{a(2bc)} + \frac{a^2 + c^2 - b^2}{b(2ac)} + \frac{a^2 + b^2 - c^2}{c(2ab)}$$
$$= \frac{a^2 + b^2 + c^2}{2abc}$$

55. Since $0 < C < 180°$, $\cos\left(\frac{C}{2}\right) = \sqrt{\frac{1 + \cos C}{2}}$.

Hence, $\cos\left(\frac{C}{2}\right) = \sqrt{\frac{1 + (a^2 + b^2 - c^2)/(2ab)}{2}} = \sqrt{\frac{2ab + a^2 + b^2 - c^2}{4ab}}$.

On the other hand,

$$s(s - c) = \frac{1}{2}(a + b + c)\left(\frac{1}{2}(a + b + c) - c\right)$$

$$= \frac{1}{2}(a + b + c)\frac{1}{2}(a + b - c)$$

$$= \frac{1}{4}((a + b)^2 - c^2)$$

$$= \frac{1}{4}(a^2 + b^2 + 2ab - c^2).$$

Thus, $\sqrt{\frac{s(s - c)}{ab}} = \sqrt{\frac{a^2 + b^2 + 2ab - c^2}{4ab}}$ and we have verified that $\cos\left(\frac{C}{2}\right) = \sqrt{\frac{s(s - c)}{ab}}$.

56. Since $0 < C < 180°$, $\sin\left(\frac{C}{2}\right) = \sqrt{\frac{1 - \cos C}{2}}$.

Hence, $\sin\left(\frac{C}{2}\right) = \sqrt{\frac{1 - (a^2 + b^2 - c^2)/(2ab)}{2}} = \sqrt{\frac{2ab - a^2 - b^2 + c^2}{4ab}}$.

On the other hand,

$$(s - a)(s - b) = \left[\frac{1}{2}(a + b + c) - a\right]\left[\frac{1}{2}(a + b + c) - b\right]$$

$$= \frac{1}{2}(b + c - a)\frac{1}{2}(a + c - b)$$

$$= \frac{1}{4}[c - (a - b)][c + (a - b)]$$

$$= \frac{1}{4}[c^2 - (a - b)^2]$$

$$= \frac{1}{4}(c^2 - a^2 - b^2 + 2ab).$$

Thus, $\sqrt{\frac{(s - a)(s - b)}{ab}} = \sqrt{\frac{c^2 - a^2 - b^2 + 2ab}{4ab}} = \sin\left(\frac{C}{2}\right)$.

57. Given: $a = 12,\ b = 30,\ A = 20°$

$a^2 = b^2 + c^2 - 2bc \cos A$

$12^2 = 30^2 + c^2 - 2(30)(c) \cos 20°$

$c^2 - (60 \cos 20°)c + 756 = 0$

Solving this quadratic equation, $c \approx 21.97, 34.41$.

—CONTINUED—

57. —CONTINUED—

For $c = 21.97$,

$$\cos B = \frac{a^2 + c^2 - b^2}{2ac} \approx \frac{12^2 + 21.97^2 - 30^2}{2(12)(21.97)} \approx -0.5184 \implies B \approx 121.2^\circ$$

$$C \approx 180^\circ - 121.2^\circ - 20^\circ = 38.8^\circ$$

For $c = 34.41$,

$$\cos B = \frac{a^2 + c^2 - b^2}{2ac} \approx \frac{12^2 + 34.41^2 - 30^2}{2(12)(34.41)} \approx 0.5183 \implies B \approx 58.8^\circ$$

$$C \approx 180^\circ - 58.8^\circ - 20^\circ = 101.2^\circ.$$

Using the Law of Sines, $\sin B = \dfrac{b \sin A}{a} = \dfrac{30 \sin 20^\circ}{12} \approx 0.8551 \implies B \approx 58.8^\circ$ or 121.2°.

For $B = 58.8^\circ$, $C = 180^\circ - 58.8^\circ - 20^\circ = 101.2^\circ$ and $c = \dfrac{a \sin C}{\sin A} \approx 34.42$.

For $B = 121.2^\circ$, $C = 180^\circ - 121.2^\circ - 20^\circ = 38.8^\circ$ and $c = \dfrac{a \sin C}{\sin A} \approx 21.98$.

58. Answers will vary. The Law of Cosines can be used to solve the single-solution case of SSA. It cannot be used for the no-solution case.

59. $\arcsin(-1) = -\dfrac{\pi}{2}$ because $\sin\left(-\dfrac{\pi}{2}\right) = -1$.

60. $\cos^{-1} 0 = \dfrac{\pi}{2}$ because $\cos \dfrac{\pi}{2} = 0$.

61. $\tan^{-1}\left(\sqrt{3}\right) = \dfrac{\pi}{3}$ because $\tan\left(\dfrac{\pi}{3}\right) = \sqrt{3}$.

62. $\arcsin\left(\dfrac{-\sqrt{3}}{2}\right) = \dfrac{-\pi}{3}$ because $\sin\left(\dfrac{-\pi}{3}\right) = \dfrac{-\sqrt{3}}{2}$.

Section 6.3 Vectors in the Plane

- A vector $\mathbf{v}$ is the collection of all directed line segments that are equivalent to a given directed line segment $\overrightarrow{PQ}$.
- You should be able to *geometrically* perform the operations of vector addition and scalar multiplication.
- The component form of the vector with initial point $P = (p_1, p_2)$ and terminal point $Q = (q_1, q_2)$ is

  $$\overrightarrow{PQ} = \langle q_1 - p_1, q_2 - p_2 \rangle = \langle v_1, v_2 \rangle = \mathbf{v}.$$
- The magnitude of $\mathbf{v} = \langle v_1, v_2 \rangle$ is given by $\|\mathbf{v}\| = \sqrt{{v_1}^2 + {v_2}^2}$.
- You should be able to perform the operations of scalar multiplication and vector addition in component form.
- You should know the following properties of vector addition and scalar multiplication.

  (a) $\mathbf{u} + \mathbf{v} = \mathbf{v} + \mathbf{u}$
  (b) $(\mathbf{u} + \mathbf{v}) + \mathbf{w} = \mathbf{u} + (\mathbf{v} + \mathbf{w})$
  (c) $\mathbf{u} + \mathbf{0} = \mathbf{u}$
  (d) $\mathbf{u} + (-\mathbf{u}) = \mathbf{0}$
  (e) $c(d\mathbf{u}) = (cd)\mathbf{u}$
  (f) $(c + d)\mathbf{u} = c\mathbf{u} + d\mathbf{u}$
  (g) $c(\mathbf{u} + \mathbf{v}) = c\mathbf{u} + c\mathbf{v}$
  (h) $1(\mathbf{u}) = \mathbf{u}$, $0\mathbf{u} = \mathbf{0}$
  (i) $\|c\mathbf{v}\| = |c|\,\|\mathbf{v}\|$

—CONTINUED—

Section 6.3 —CONTINUED—

- A unit vector in the direction of $\mathbf{v}$ is given by $\mathbf{u} = \dfrac{\mathbf{v}}{\|\mathbf{v}\|}$.
- The standard unit vectors are $\mathbf{i} = \langle 1, 0\rangle$ and $\mathbf{j} = \langle 0, 1\rangle$. $\mathbf{v} = \langle v_1, v_2\rangle$ can be written as $\mathbf{v} = v_1\mathbf{i} + v_2\mathbf{j}$.
- A vector $\mathbf{v}$ with magnitude $\|\mathbf{v}\|$ and direction θ can be written as $\mathbf{v} = a\mathbf{i} + b\mathbf{j} = \|\mathbf{v}\|(\cos\theta)\mathbf{i} + \|\mathbf{v}\|(\sin\theta)\mathbf{j}$ where $\tan\theta = b/a$.

Vocabulary Check

1. directed line segment
2. initial, terminal
3. magnitude
4. vector
5. standard position
6. unit vector
7. multiplication, addition
8. resultant
9. linear combination, horizontal, vertical

1. $\mathbf{u} = \langle 6-2, 5-4\rangle = \langle 4, 1\rangle = \mathbf{v}$

2. $\mathbf{u} = \langle -3-0, -4-4\rangle = \langle -3, -8\rangle$

$\mathbf{v} = \langle 0-3, -5-3\rangle = \langle -3, -8\rangle$

$\mathbf{u} = \mathbf{v}$

3. Initial point: $(0, 0)$

Terminal point: $(4, 3)$

$\mathbf{v} = \langle 4-0, 3-0\rangle = \langle 4, 3\rangle$

$\|\mathbf{v}\| = \sqrt{4^2 + 3^2} = 5$

4. Initial point: $(0, 0)$

Terminal point: $(4, -2)$

$\mathbf{v} = \langle 4-0, -2-0\rangle = \langle 4, -2\rangle$

$\|\mathbf{v}\| = \sqrt{4^2 + (-2)^2} = \sqrt{20} = 2\sqrt{5} \approx 4.47$

5. Initial point: $(2, 2)$

Terminal point: $(-1, 4)$

$\mathbf{v} = \langle -1-2, 4-2\rangle = \langle -3, 2\rangle$

$\|\mathbf{v}\| = \sqrt{(-3)^2 + 2^2} = \sqrt{13} \approx 3.61$

6. Initial point: $(-1, -1)$

Terminal point: $(3, 5)$

$\mathbf{v} = \langle 3-(-1), 5-(-1)\rangle = \langle 4, 6\rangle$

$\|\mathbf{v}\| = \sqrt{4^2 + 6^2} = \sqrt{52} = 2\sqrt{13} \approx 7.21$

7. Initial point: $(3, -2)$

Terminal point: $(3, 3)$

$\mathbf{v} = \langle 3-3, 3-(-2)\rangle = \langle 0, 5\rangle$

$\|\mathbf{v}\| = 5$

8. Initial point: $(-4, -1)$

Terminal point: $(3, -1)$

$\mathbf{v} = \langle 3-(-4), -1-(-1)\rangle = \langle 7, 0\rangle$

$\|\mathbf{v}\| = \sqrt{7^2 + 0^2} = 7$

9. Initial point: $\left(\frac{2}{5}, 1\right)$

Terminal point: $\left(1, \frac{2}{5}\right)$

$\mathbf{v} = \left\langle 1 - \frac{2}{5}, \frac{2}{5} - 1\right\rangle = \left\langle \frac{3}{5}, -\frac{3}{5}\right\rangle$

$\|\mathbf{v}\| = \sqrt{\left(\frac{3}{5}\right)^2 + \left(-\frac{3}{5}\right)^2} = \sqrt{\frac{18}{25}} = \frac{3}{5}\sqrt{2}$

10. Initial point: $\left(\frac{7}{2}, 0\right)$

Terminal point: $\left(0, -\frac{7}{2}\right)$

$\mathbf{v} = \left\langle 0 - \frac{7}{2}, -\frac{7}{2} - 0\right\rangle = \left\langle -\frac{7}{2}, -\frac{7}{2}\right\rangle$

$\|\mathbf{v}\| = \sqrt{\left(-\frac{7}{2}\right)^2 + \left(-\frac{7}{2}\right)^2} = \sqrt{\frac{98}{4}} = \frac{7}{2}\sqrt{2}$

11. Initial point: $\left(\frac{-2}{3}, -1\right)$

Terminal point: $\left(\frac{1}{2}, \frac{4}{5}\right)$

$$\mathbf{v} = \left\langle \frac{1}{2} - \left(-\frac{2}{3}\right), \frac{4}{5} - (-1) \right\rangle = \left\langle \frac{7}{6}, \frac{9}{5} \right\rangle$$

$$\|\mathbf{v}\| = \sqrt{\left(\frac{7}{6}\right)^2 + \left(\frac{9}{5}\right)^2} = \frac{\sqrt{4141}}{30} \approx 2.1450$$

12. Initial point: $\left(\frac{5}{2}, -2\right)$

Terminal point: $\left(1, \frac{2}{5}\right)$

$$\mathbf{v} = \left\langle 1 - \frac{5}{2}, \frac{2}{5} - (-2) \right\rangle = \left\langle -\frac{3}{2}, \frac{12}{5} \right\rangle$$

$$\|\mathbf{v}\| = \sqrt{\left(-\frac{3}{2}\right)^2 + \left(\frac{12}{5}\right)^2} = \frac{3\sqrt{89}}{10} \approx 2.8302$$

13. $-\mathbf{v}$

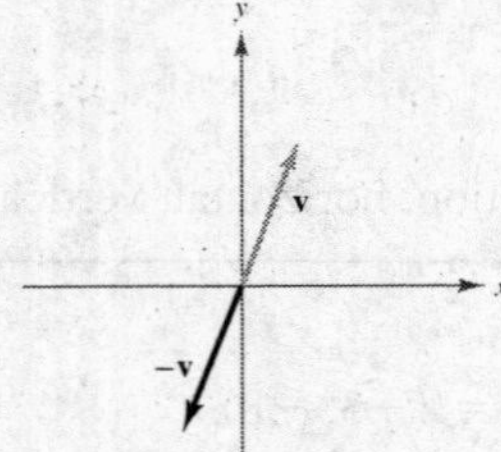

14. $3\mathbf{u}$

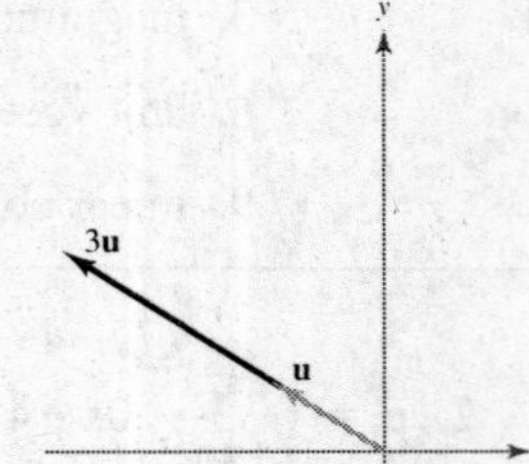

15. $\mathbf{u} + \mathbf{v}$

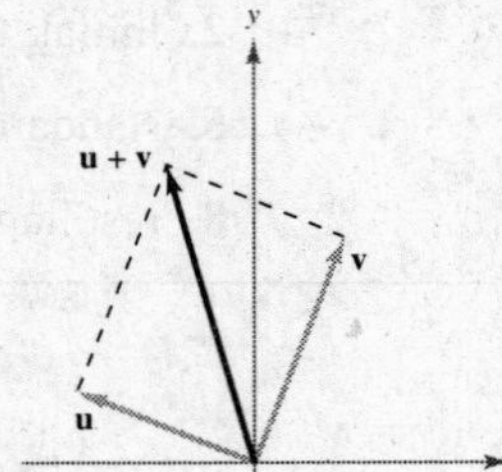

16. $\mathbf{u} - \mathbf{v}$

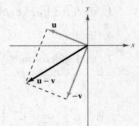

17. $\mathbf{u} + 2\mathbf{v}$

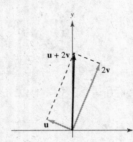

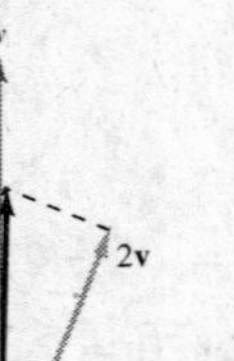

18. $\mathbf{v} - \frac{1}{2}\mathbf{u}$

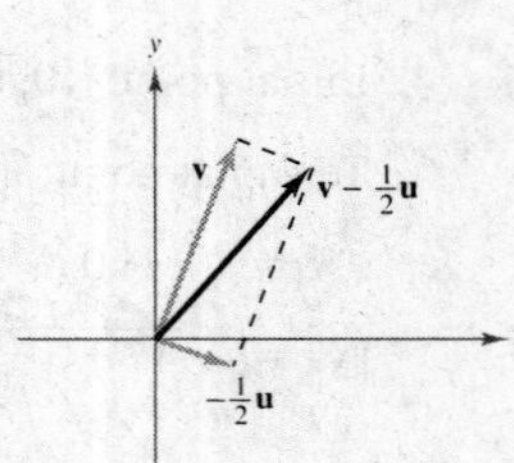

19.

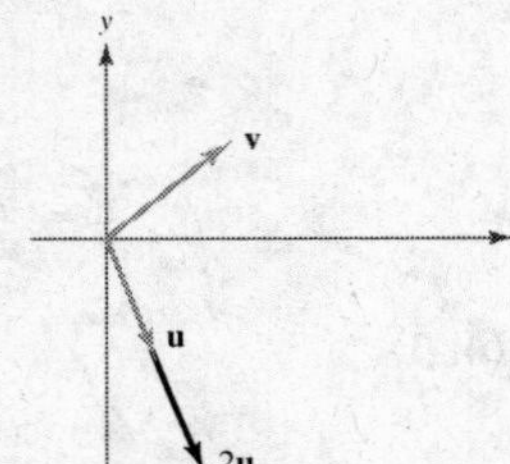

20.

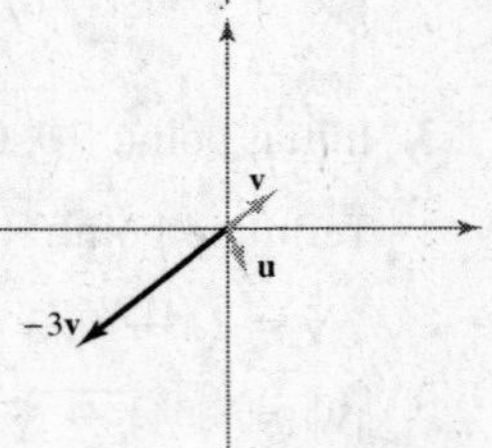

21.

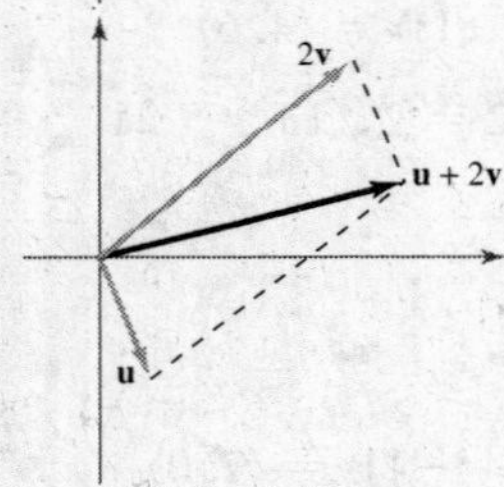

22.

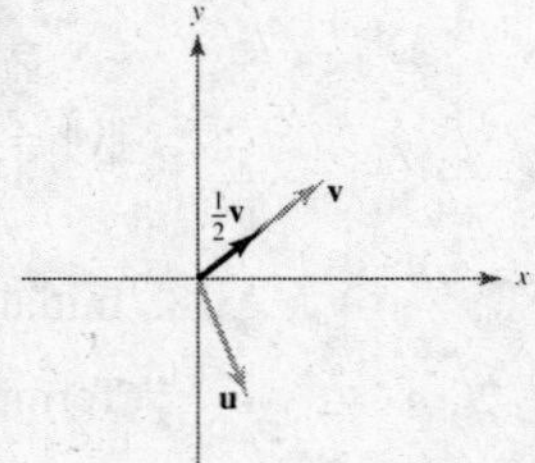

23.

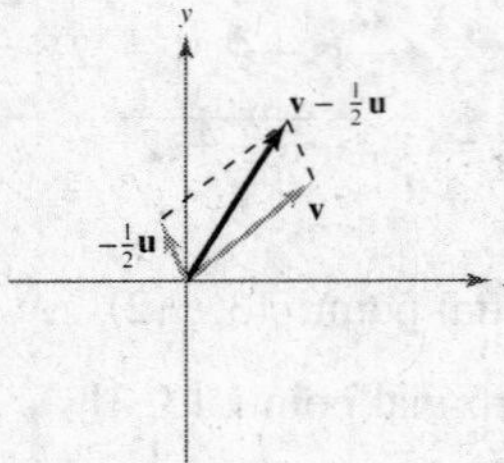

24.

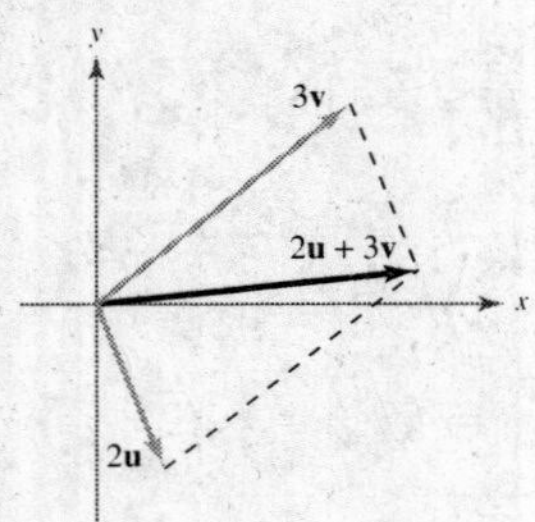

25. $\mathbf{u} = \langle 4, 2 \rangle, \mathbf{v} = \langle 7, 1 \rangle$

(a) $\mathbf{u} + \mathbf{v} = \langle 11, 3 \rangle$

(b) $\mathbf{u} - \mathbf{v} = \langle -3, 1 \rangle$

(c) $2\mathbf{u} - 3\mathbf{v} = \langle 8, 4 \rangle - \langle 21, 3 \rangle = \langle -13, 1 \rangle$

(d) $\mathbf{v} + 4\mathbf{u} = \langle 7, 1 \rangle + \langle 16, 8 \rangle = \langle 23, 9 \rangle$

26. (a) $\mathbf{u} + \mathbf{v} = \langle 5, 3\rangle + \langle -4, 0\rangle = \langle 1, 3\rangle$

(b) $\mathbf{u} - \mathbf{v} = \langle 5, 3\rangle - \langle -4, 0\rangle = \langle 9, 3\rangle$

(c) $2\mathbf{u} - 3\mathbf{v} = 2\langle 5, 3\rangle - 3\langle -4, 0\rangle = \langle 22, 6\rangle$

(d) $\mathbf{v} + 4\mathbf{u} = \langle -4, 0\rangle + 4\langle 5, 3\rangle = \langle 16, 12\rangle$

27. $\mathbf{u} = \langle -6, -8\rangle, \mathbf{v} = \langle 2, 4\rangle$

(a) $\mathbf{u} + \mathbf{v} = \langle -4, -4\rangle$

(b) $\mathbf{u} - \mathbf{v} = \langle -8, -12\rangle$

(c) $2\mathbf{u} - 3\mathbf{v} = \langle -12, -16\rangle - \langle 6, 12\rangle = \langle -18, -28\rangle$

(d) $\mathbf{v} + 4\mathbf{u} = \langle 2, 4\rangle + 4\langle -6, -8\rangle = \langle -22, -28\rangle$

28. (a) $\mathbf{u} + \mathbf{v} = \langle 0, -5\rangle + \langle -3, 9\rangle = \langle -3, 4\rangle$

(b) $\mathbf{u} - \mathbf{v} = \langle 3, -14\rangle$

(c) $2\mathbf{u} - 3\mathbf{v} = \langle 0, -10\rangle - \langle -9, 27\rangle = \langle 9, -37\rangle$

(d) $\mathbf{v} + 4\mathbf{u} = \langle -3, 9\rangle + \langle 0, -20\rangle = \langle -3, -11\rangle$

29. $\mathbf{u} = \mathbf{i} + \mathbf{j}, \mathbf{v} = 2\mathbf{i} - 3\mathbf{j}$

(a) $\mathbf{u} + \mathbf{v} = 3\mathbf{i} - 2\mathbf{j}$

(b) $\mathbf{u} - \mathbf{v} = -\mathbf{i} + 4\mathbf{j}$

(c) $2\mathbf{u} - 3\mathbf{v} = (2\mathbf{i} + 2\mathbf{j}) - (6\mathbf{i} - 9\mathbf{j}) = -4\mathbf{i} + 11\mathbf{j}$

(d) $\mathbf{v} + 4\mathbf{u} = (2\mathbf{i} - 3\mathbf{j}) + (4\mathbf{i} + 4\mathbf{j}) = 6\mathbf{i} + \mathbf{j}$

30. $\mathbf{u} = 2\mathbf{i} - \mathbf{j}, \mathbf{v} = -\mathbf{i} + \mathbf{j}$

(a) $\mathbf{u} + \mathbf{v} = \mathbf{i}$

(b) $\mathbf{u} - \mathbf{v} = 3\mathbf{i} - 2\mathbf{j}$

(c) $2\mathbf{u} - 3\mathbf{v} = (4\mathbf{i} - 2\mathbf{j}) - (-3\mathbf{i} + 3\mathbf{j}) = 7\mathbf{i} - 5\mathbf{j}$

(d) $\mathbf{v} + 4\mathbf{u} = 7\mathbf{i} - 3\mathbf{j}$

31. $\mathbf{w} = \mathbf{u} + \mathbf{v}$

32. $\mathbf{v} = \mathbf{w} - \mathbf{u}$

33. $\mathbf{u} = \mathbf{w} - \mathbf{v}$

34. $2\mathbf{v} = 2(\mathbf{w} - \mathbf{u})$

$= 2\mathbf{w} - 2\mathbf{u}$

35. $\|\langle 6, 0\rangle\| = 6$

Unit vector: $\frac{1}{6}\langle 6, 0\rangle = \langle 1, 0\rangle$

36. $\mathbf{u} = \langle 0, -2\rangle$

$\|\mathbf{u}\| = 2$

Unit vector:

$\frac{1}{2}\langle 0, -2\rangle = \langle 0, -1\rangle$

37. $\mathbf{v} = \langle -1, 1\rangle$

$\|\mathbf{v}\| = \sqrt{2}$

Unit vector $= \frac{1}{\|\mathbf{v}\|}\mathbf{v}$

$= \left\langle -\frac{1}{\sqrt{2}}, \frac{1}{\sqrt{2}}\right\rangle$

$= \left\langle -\frac{\sqrt{2}}{2}, \frac{\sqrt{2}}{2}\right\rangle$

38. $\mathbf{v} = \langle 3, -4\rangle$

$\|\mathbf{v}\| = \sqrt{3^2 + (-4)^2} = 5$

Unit vector: $\frac{1}{5}\langle 3, -4\rangle = \left\langle \frac{3}{5}, -\frac{4}{5}\right\rangle$

39. $\|\mathbf{v}\| = \|\langle -24, -7\rangle\| = \sqrt{(-24)^2 + (-7)^2} = 25$

Unit vector: $\frac{1}{25}\langle -24, -7\rangle = \left\langle -\frac{24}{25}, -\frac{7}{25}\right\rangle$

40. $\mathbf{v} = \langle 8, -20\rangle$

$$\mathbf{u} = \frac{1}{\|\mathbf{v}\|}\mathbf{v} = \frac{1}{\sqrt{64 + 400}}\langle 8, -20\rangle = \frac{1}{\sqrt{29}}\langle 2, -5\rangle = \left\langle \frac{2}{\sqrt{29}}, -\frac{5}{\sqrt{29}}\right\rangle = \left\langle \frac{2\sqrt{29}}{29}, \frac{-5\sqrt{29}}{29}\right\rangle$$

41. $\mathbf{u} = \frac{1}{\|\mathbf{v}\|}\mathbf{v} = \frac{1}{\sqrt{16 + 9}}(4\mathbf{i} - 3\mathbf{j}) = \frac{1}{5}(4\mathbf{i} - 3\mathbf{j}) = \frac{4}{5}\mathbf{i} - \frac{3}{5}\mathbf{j}$

42. $\mathbf{w} = \mathbf{i} - 2\mathbf{j}$

$$\mathbf{u} = \frac{1}{\|\mathbf{w}\|}\mathbf{w} = \frac{1}{\sqrt{1^2 + (-2)^2}}(\mathbf{i} - 2\mathbf{j}) = \frac{1}{\sqrt{5}}(\mathbf{i} - 2\mathbf{j}) = \frac{\sqrt{5}}{5}\mathbf{i} - \frac{2\sqrt{5}}{5}\mathbf{j}$$

43. $\mathbf{u} = \frac{1}{2}(2\mathbf{j}) = \mathbf{j}$

44. $\mathbf{w} = -3\mathbf{i}$

$\|\mathbf{w}\| = 3$

$\mathbf{u} = \frac{1}{3}(-3\mathbf{i}) = -\mathbf{i}$

45. $8\left(\frac{1}{\|\mathbf{u}\|}\mathbf{u}\right) = 8\left(\frac{1}{\sqrt{5^2 + 6^2}}\langle 5, 6\rangle\right)$

$= \frac{8}{\sqrt{61}}\langle 5, 6\rangle$

$= \left\langle \frac{40\sqrt{61}}{61}, \frac{48\sqrt{61}}{61}\right\rangle$

46. $\mathbf{v} = 3\left(\frac{1}{\|\mathbf{u}\|}\mathbf{u}\right)$

$= 3\left(\frac{1}{\sqrt{4^2 + (-4)^2}}\langle 4, -4\rangle\right)$

$= 3\left(\frac{1}{4\sqrt{2}}\langle 4, -4\rangle\right)$

$= \left\langle \frac{3}{\sqrt{2}}, -\frac{3}{\sqrt{2}}\right\rangle$

$= \left\langle \frac{3\sqrt{2}}{2}, \frac{-3\sqrt{2}}{2}\right\rangle$

47. $7\left(\frac{1}{\|\mathbf{u}\|}\mathbf{u}\right) = 7\left(\frac{1}{\sqrt{3^2 + 4^2}}\langle 3, 4\rangle\right)$

$= \frac{7}{5}\langle 3, 4\rangle$

$= \left\langle \frac{21}{5}, \frac{28}{5}\right\rangle$

$= \frac{21}{5}\mathbf{i} + \frac{28}{5}\mathbf{j}$

48. $\mathbf{v} = 10\left(\frac{1}{\|\mathbf{u}\|}\mathbf{u}\right)$

$= 10\left(\frac{1}{\sqrt{4 + 9}}\langle 2, -3\rangle\right)$

$= \left\langle \frac{20}{\sqrt{13}}, -\frac{30}{\sqrt{13}}\right\rangle$

$= \frac{20}{\sqrt{13}}\mathbf{i} - \frac{30}{\sqrt{13}}\mathbf{j}$

$= \frac{20\sqrt{13}}{13}\mathbf{i} - \frac{30\sqrt{13}}{13}\mathbf{j}$

49. $8\left(\frac{1}{\|\mathbf{u}\|}\mathbf{u}\right) = 8\left(\frac{1}{2}\langle -2, 0\rangle\right)$

$= 4\langle -2, 0\rangle$

$= \langle -8, 0\rangle$

$= -8\mathbf{i}$

50. $\mathbf{v} = 4\left(\frac{1}{\|\mathbf{u}\|}\mathbf{u}\right)$

$= 4\left(\frac{1}{5}\langle 0, 5\rangle\right)$

$= \langle 0, 4\rangle = 4\mathbf{j}$

51. $\mathbf{v} = \langle 4 - (-3), 5 - 1\rangle = \langle 7, 4\rangle = 7\mathbf{i} + 4\mathbf{j}$

52. $\langle 3 - 0, 6 - (-2)\rangle = \langle 3, 8\rangle = 3\mathbf{i} + 8\mathbf{j}$

53. $\mathbf{v} = \langle 2 - (-1), 3 - (-5)\rangle = \langle 3, 8\rangle = 3\mathbf{i} + 8\mathbf{j}$

54. $\langle 0 - (-6), 1 - 4\rangle = \langle 6, -3\rangle = 6\mathbf{i} - 3\mathbf{j}$

55. $\mathbf{v} = \frac{3}{2}\mathbf{u}$

$= \frac{3}{2}(2\mathbf{i} - \mathbf{j}) = 3\mathbf{i} - \frac{3}{2}\mathbf{j}$

$= \left\langle 3, -\frac{3}{2}\right\rangle$

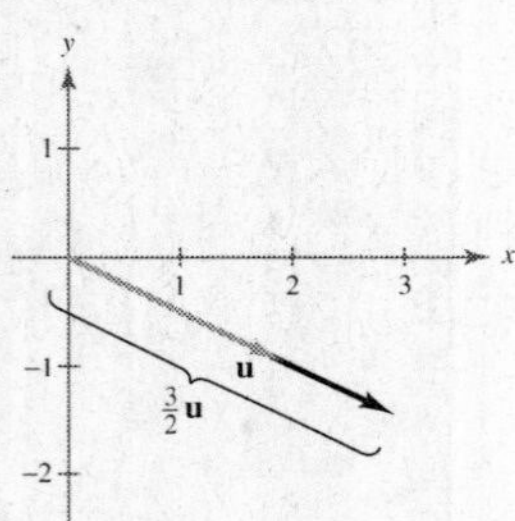

56. $\mathbf{v} = \frac{2}{3}\mathbf{w}$

$= \frac{2}{3}\langle 1, 2\rangle$

$= \left\langle \frac{2}{3}, \frac{4}{3}\right\rangle$

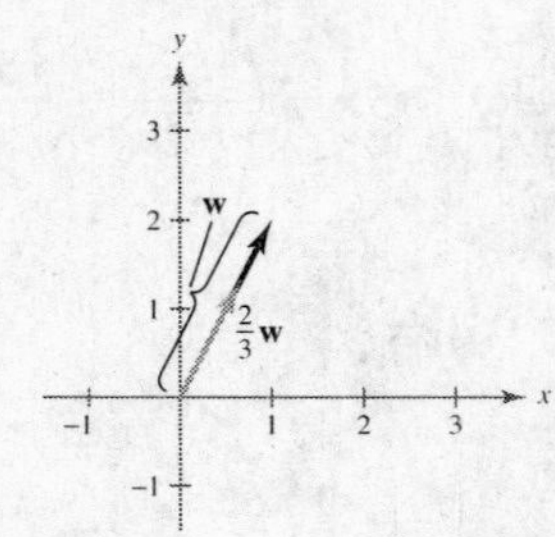

57. $\mathbf{v} = \mathbf{u} + 2\mathbf{w}$

$= (2\mathbf{i} - \mathbf{j}) + 2(\mathbf{i} + 2\mathbf{j})$

$= 4\mathbf{i} + 3\mathbf{j} = \langle 4, 3\rangle$

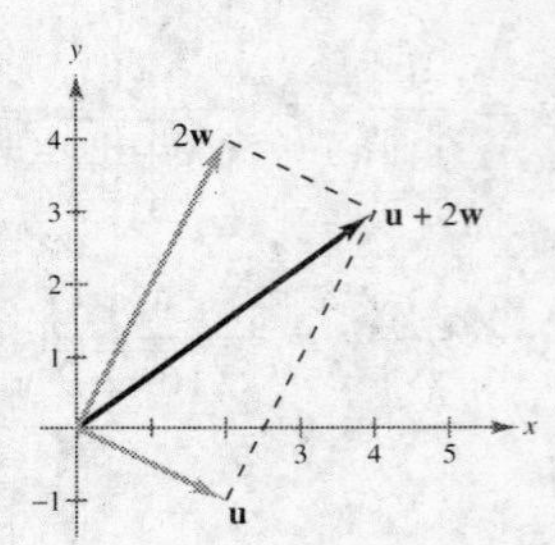

58. $\mathbf{v} = -\mathbf{u} + \mathbf{w}$

$= -(2\mathbf{i} - \mathbf{j}) + (\mathbf{i} + 2\mathbf{j})$

$= -\mathbf{i} + 3\mathbf{j} = \langle -1, 3 \rangle$

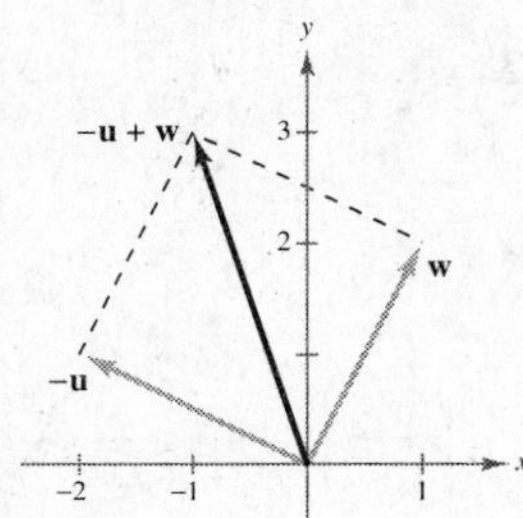

59. $\mathbf{v} = \frac{1}{2}(3\mathbf{u} + \mathbf{w})$

$= \frac{1}{2}(3\langle 2, -1 \rangle + \langle 1, 2 \rangle)$

$= \left\langle \frac{7}{2}, -\frac{1}{2} \right\rangle$

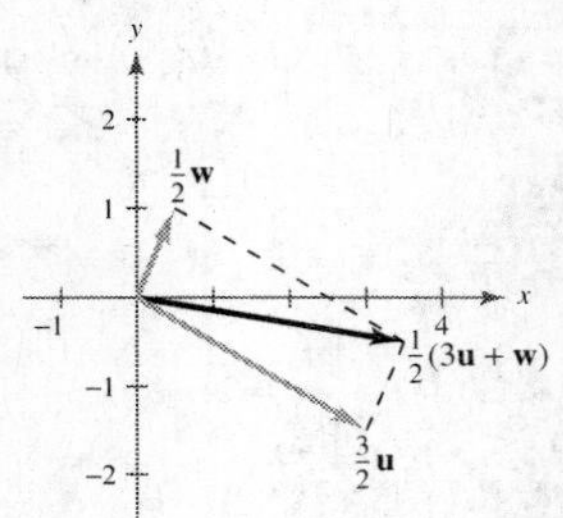

60. $\mathbf{v} = 2\mathbf{u} - 2\mathbf{w}$

$= \langle 4, -2 \rangle - \langle 2, 4 \rangle$

$= \langle 2, -6 \rangle$

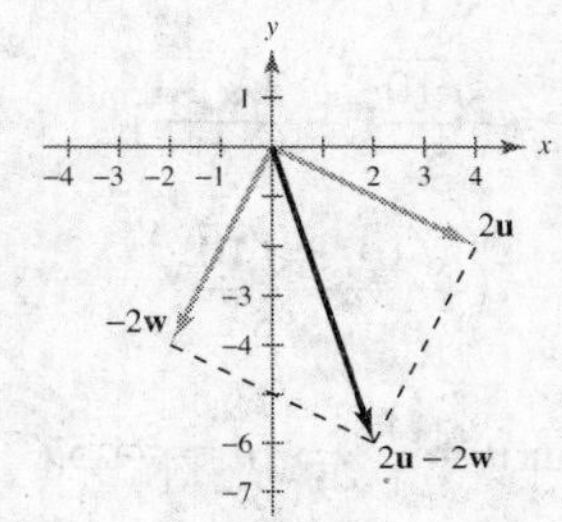

61. $\mathbf{v} = 5(\cos 30°\mathbf{i} + \sin 30°\mathbf{j})$

$\|\mathbf{v}\| = 5, \ \theta = 30°$

62. $\mathbf{v} = 8(\cos 135°\mathbf{i} + \sin 135°\mathbf{j})$

$\|\mathbf{v}\| = 8, \ \theta = 135°$

63. $\mathbf{v} = 6\mathbf{i} - 6\mathbf{j}$

$\|\mathbf{v}\| = \sqrt{6^2 + (-6)^2} = \sqrt{72} = 6\sqrt{2}$

$\tan\theta = -\frac{6}{6} = -1$

Since $\mathbf{v}$ lies in Quadrant IV, $\theta = 315°$.

64. $\mathbf{v} = -4\mathbf{i} - 7\mathbf{j}$, Quadrant III

$\|\mathbf{v}\| = \sqrt{(-4)^2 + (-7)^2} = \sqrt{65}$

$\tan\theta = \frac{-7}{-4} = \frac{7}{4} \implies \theta \approx 240.3°$

65. $\mathbf{v} = -2\mathbf{i} + 5\mathbf{j}$

$\|\mathbf{v}\| = \sqrt{(-2)^2 + 5^2} = \sqrt{29}$

$\tan\theta = -\frac{5}{2}$

Since $\mathbf{v}$ lies in Quadrant II, $\theta \approx 111.8°$.

66. $\mathbf{v} = 12\mathbf{i} + 15\mathbf{j}$, Quadrant I

$\|\mathbf{v}\| = \sqrt{12^2 + 15^2} = \sqrt{369} = 3\sqrt{41}$

$\tan\theta = \frac{15}{12} \implies \theta \approx 51.3°$

67. $\mathbf{v} = \langle 3\cos 0°, 3\sin 0° \rangle$

$= \langle 3, 0 \rangle$

68. $\mathbf{v} = \langle \cos 45°, \sin 45° \rangle$

$= \left\langle \frac{\sqrt{2}}{2}, \frac{\sqrt{2}}{2} \right\rangle$

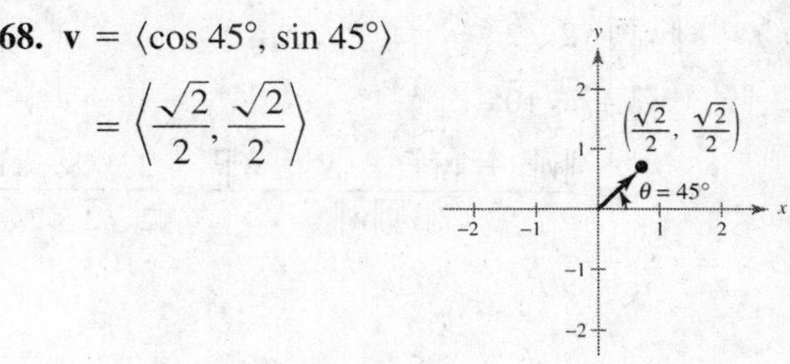

69. $\mathbf{v} = \left\langle 3\sqrt{2}\cos 150°, 3\sqrt{2}\sin 150° \right\rangle$

$= \left\langle -\frac{3\sqrt{6}}{2}, \frac{3\sqrt{2}}{2} \right\rangle$

70. $\mathbf{v} = 4\sqrt{3}\langle \cos 90°, \sin 90° \rangle = \left\langle 0, 4\sqrt{3} \right\rangle$

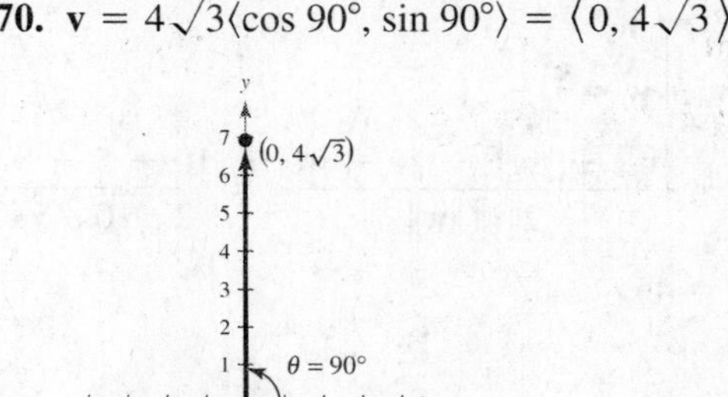

71. $\mathbf{v} = 2\left(\dfrac{1}{\sqrt{3^2 + 1^2}}\right)(\mathbf{i} + 3\mathbf{j})$

$= \dfrac{2}{\sqrt{10}}(\mathbf{i} + 3\mathbf{j})$

$= \dfrac{\sqrt{10}}{5}\mathbf{i} + \dfrac{3\sqrt{10}}{5}\mathbf{j}$

$= \left\langle \dfrac{\sqrt{10}}{5}, \dfrac{3\sqrt{10}}{5} \right\rangle$

$\tan\theta = \dfrac{3}{1} \implies \theta \approx 71.57°$

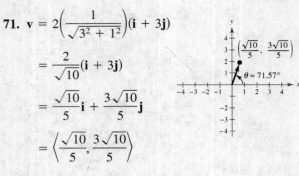

72. $\mathbf{v} = 3\left(\dfrac{1}{\sqrt{3^2 + 4^2}}\right)(3\mathbf{i} + 4\mathbf{j})$

$= \dfrac{3}{5}(3\mathbf{i} + 4\mathbf{j})$

$= \dfrac{9}{5}\mathbf{i} + \dfrac{12}{5}\mathbf{j} = \left\langle \dfrac{9}{5}, \dfrac{12}{5} \right\rangle$

73. $\mathbf{u} = \langle 5\cos 60°, 5\sin 60° \rangle = \left\langle \dfrac{5}{2}, \dfrac{5\sqrt{3}}{2} \right\rangle$

$\mathbf{v} = \langle 5\cos 90°, 5\sin 90° \rangle = \langle 0, 5 \rangle$

$\mathbf{u} + \mathbf{v} = \left\langle \dfrac{5}{2}, \dfrac{5\sqrt{3}}{2} \right\rangle + \langle 0, 5 \rangle = \left\langle \dfrac{5}{2}, 5 + \dfrac{5}{2}\sqrt{3} \right\rangle$

74. $\mathbf{u} = \langle 2\cos 30°, 2\sin 30° \rangle = \langle \sqrt{3}, 1 \rangle$

$\mathbf{v} = \langle 2\cos 90°, 2\sin 90° \rangle = \langle 0, 2 \rangle$

$\mathbf{u} + \mathbf{v} = \langle \sqrt{3}, 3 \rangle$

75. $\mathbf{u} = \langle 20\cos 45°, 20\sin 45° \rangle = \langle 10\sqrt{2}, 10\sqrt{2} \rangle$

$\mathbf{v} = \langle 50\cos 150°, 50\sin 150° \rangle = \langle -25\sqrt{3}, 25 \rangle$

$\mathbf{u} + \mathbf{v} = \langle 10\sqrt{2} - 25\sqrt{3}, 10\sqrt{2} + 25 \rangle$

76. $\mathbf{u} = \langle 35\cos 25°, 35\sin 25° \rangle = \langle 31.72, 14.79 \rangle$

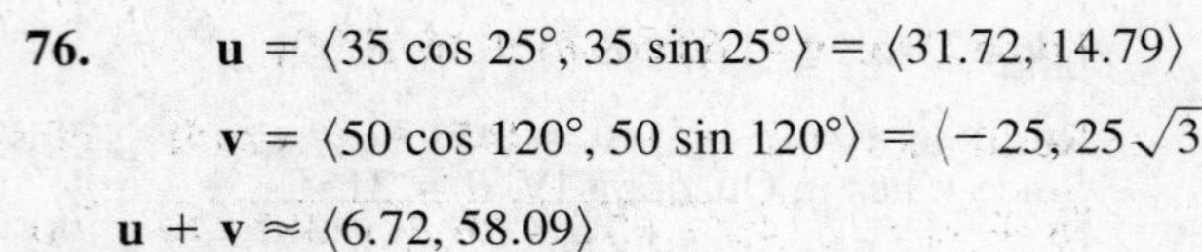

$\mathbf{v} = \langle 50\cos 120°, 50\sin 120° \rangle = \langle -25, 25\sqrt{3} \rangle$

$\mathbf{u} + \mathbf{v} \approx \langle 6.72, 58.09 \rangle$

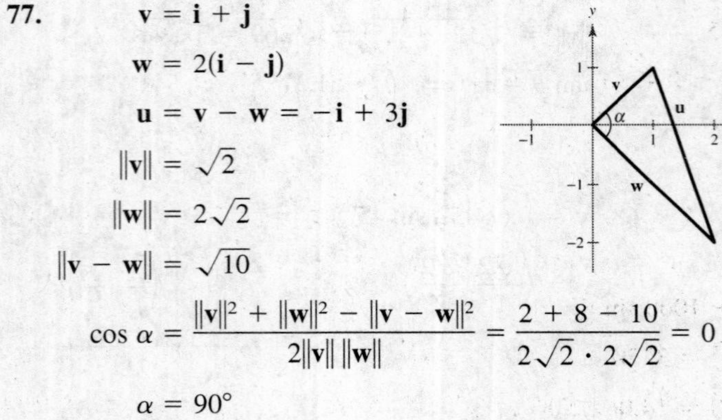

77. $\mathbf{v} = \mathbf{i} + \mathbf{j}$

$\mathbf{w} = 2(\mathbf{i} - \mathbf{j})$

$\mathbf{u} = \mathbf{v} - \mathbf{w} = -\mathbf{i} + 3\mathbf{j}$

$\|\mathbf{v}\| = \sqrt{2}$

$\|\mathbf{w}\| = 2\sqrt{2}$

$\|\mathbf{v} - \mathbf{w}\| = \sqrt{10}$

$\cos\alpha = \dfrac{\|\mathbf{v}\|^2 + \|\mathbf{w}\|^2 - \|\mathbf{v} - \mathbf{w}\|^2}{2\|\mathbf{v}\|\,\|\mathbf{w}\|} = \dfrac{2 + 8 - 10}{2\sqrt{2} \cdot 2\sqrt{2}} = 0$

$\alpha = 90°$

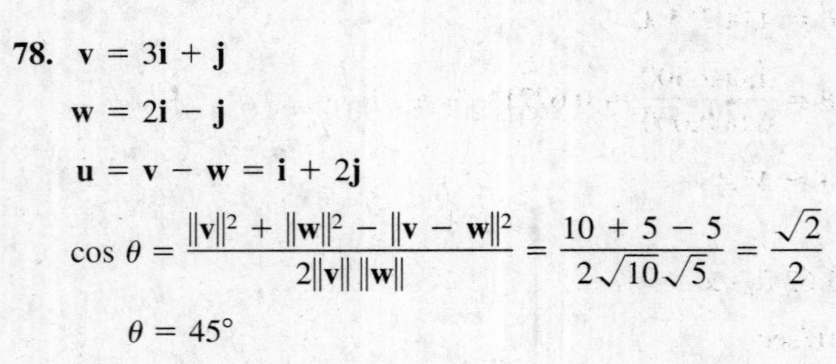

78. $\mathbf{v} = 3\mathbf{i} + \mathbf{j}$

$\mathbf{w} = 2\mathbf{i} - \mathbf{j}$

$\mathbf{u} = \mathbf{v} - \mathbf{w} = \mathbf{i} + 2\mathbf{j}$

$\cos\theta = \dfrac{\|\mathbf{v}\|^2 + \|\mathbf{w}\|^2 - \|\mathbf{v} - \mathbf{w}\|^2}{2\|\mathbf{v}\|\,\|\mathbf{w}\|} = \dfrac{10 + 5 - 5}{2\sqrt{10}\sqrt{5}} = \dfrac{\sqrt{2}}{2}$

$\theta = 45°$

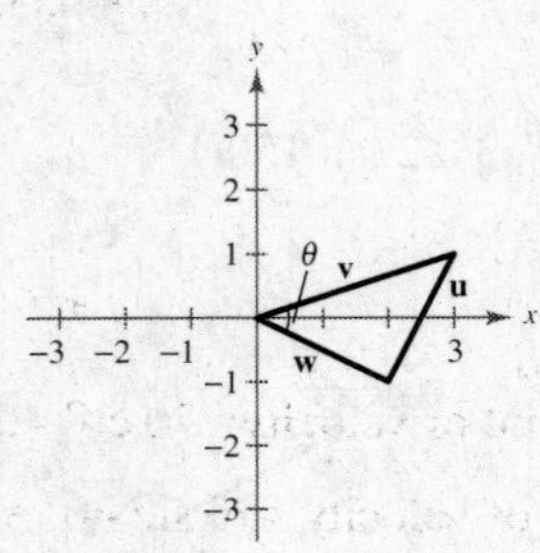

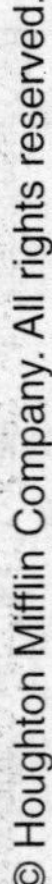

79.
$$\mathbf{u} = 400\cos 25°\mathbf{i} + 400\sin 25°\mathbf{j}$$
$$\mathbf{v} = 300\cos 70°\mathbf{i} + 300\sin 70°\mathbf{j}$$
$$\mathbf{u} + \mathbf{v} \approx 465.13\mathbf{i} + 450.96\mathbf{j}$$
$$\|\mathbf{u} + \mathbf{v}\| \approx \sqrt{(465.13)^2 + (450.96)^2} \approx 647.85$$
$$\alpha = \arctan\left(\frac{450.96}{465.13}\right) \approx 44.11°$$

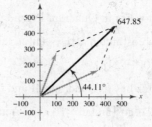

80. Analytically: $\mathbf{v} = 400\langle\cos 25°, \sin 25°\rangle$
$$\mathbf{u} = 300\langle\cos 135°, \sin 135°\rangle$$
$$\mathbf{u} + \mathbf{v} = \langle 150.39, 381.18\rangle$$
$$\|\mathbf{u} + \mathbf{v}\| = 409.77$$
$$\theta = \arctan\left(\frac{381.18}{150.39}\right) = 68.47°$$

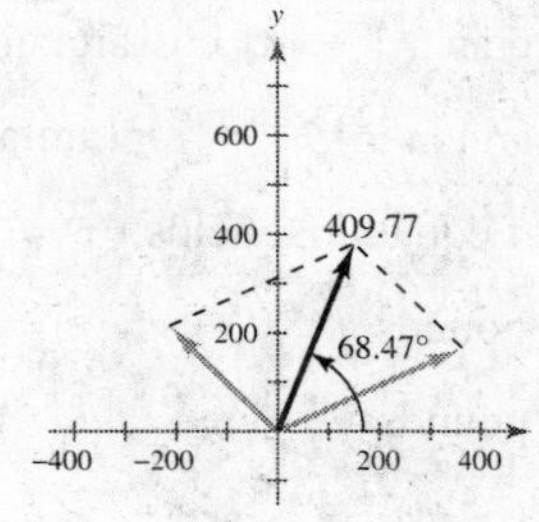

81. Force One: $\mathbf{u} = 45\mathbf{i}$

Force Two: $\mathbf{v} = 60\cos\theta\mathbf{i} + 60\sin\theta\mathbf{j}$

Resultant Force: $\mathbf{u} + \mathbf{v} = (45 + 60\cos\theta)\mathbf{i} + 60\sin\theta\mathbf{j}$

$$\|\mathbf{u} + \mathbf{v}\| = \sqrt{(45 + 60\cos\theta)^2 + (60\sin\theta)^2} = 90$$
$$2025 + 5400\cos\theta + 3600 = 8100$$
$$5400\cos\theta = 2475$$
$$\cos\theta = \tfrac{2475}{5400} \approx 0.4583$$
$$\theta \approx 62.7°$$

82. Force One: $\mathbf{u} = 3000\mathbf{i}$

Force Two: $\mathbf{v} = 1000\cos\theta\mathbf{i} + 1000\sin\theta\mathbf{j}$

Resultant Force: $\mathbf{u} + \mathbf{v} = (3000 + 1000\cos\theta)\mathbf{i} + 1000\sin\theta\mathbf{j}$

$$\|\mathbf{u} + \mathbf{v}\| = \sqrt{(3000 + 1000\cos\theta)^2 + (1000\sin\theta)^2} = 3750$$
$$9{,}000{,}000 + 6{,}000{,}000\cos\theta + 1{,}000{,}000 = 14{,}062,500$$
$$6{,}000{,}000\cos\theta = 4{,}062,500$$
$$\cos\theta = \frac{4{,}062{,}500}{6{,}000{,}000} \approx 0.6771$$
$$\theta \approx 47.4°$$

83. Horizontal component of velocity: $70\cos 40° \approx 53.62$ ft/sec

Vertical component of velocity: $70\sin 40° \approx 45.0$ ft/sec

84. Horizontal component of velocity: $1200\cos 4° \approx 1197.1$ ft/sec

Vertical component of velocity: $1200\sin 4° \approx 83.7$ ft/sec

85. Rope $\overrightarrow{AC}$: $\mathbf{u} = 10\mathbf{i} - 24\mathbf{j}$

The vector lies in Quadrant IV and its reference angle is $\arctan\left(\frac{12}{5}\right)$.

$$\mathbf{u} = \|\mathbf{u}\|\left[\cos\left(\arctan\tfrac{12}{5}\right)\mathbf{i} - \sin\left(\arctan\tfrac{12}{5}\right)\mathbf{j}\right]$$

Rope $\overrightarrow{BC}$: $\mathbf{v} = -20\mathbf{i} - 24\mathbf{j}$

The vector lies in Quadrant III and its reference angle is $\arctan\left(\frac{6}{5}\right)$.

$$\mathbf{v} = \|\mathbf{v}\|\left[-\cos\left(\arctan\tfrac{6}{5}\right)\mathbf{i} - \sin\left(\arctan\tfrac{6}{5}\right)\mathbf{j}\right]$$

Resultant: $\mathbf{u} + \mathbf{v} = -5000\mathbf{j}$

$$\|\mathbf{u}\|\cos\left(\arctan\tfrac{12}{5}\right) - \|\mathbf{v}\|\cos\left(\arctan\tfrac{6}{5}\right) = 0$$

$$-\|\mathbf{u}\|\sin\left(\arctan\tfrac{12}{5}\right) - \|\mathbf{v}\|\sin\left(\arctan\tfrac{6}{5}\right) = -5000$$

Solving this system of equations yields:

$T_{AC} = \|\mathbf{u}\| \approx 3611.1$ pounds

$T_{BC} = \|\mathbf{v}\| \approx 2169.5$ pounds

86. Left cable: $\mathbf{u} = \|\mathbf{u}\|(\cos 155.7°\mathbf{i} + \sin 155.7°\mathbf{j})$

Right cable: $\mathbf{v} = \|\mathbf{v}\|(\cos 44.5°\mathbf{i} + \sin 44.5°\mathbf{j})$

$$\mathbf{u} + \mathbf{v} = 20{,}240\mathbf{j} \implies \|\mathbf{u}\|\cos 155.7° + \|\mathbf{v}\|\cos 44.5° = 0$$

$$\|\mathbf{u}\|\sin 155.7° + \|\mathbf{v}\|\sin 44.5° = 20{,}240$$

$$\implies -0.9114\|\mathbf{u}\| + 0.7133\|\mathbf{v}\| = 0$$

$$0.4115\|\mathbf{u}\| + 0.7009\|\mathbf{v}\| = 20{,}240$$

Solving this system for $\|\mathbf{u}\|$ and $\|\mathbf{v}\|$ yields:

Tension of left cable: $\|\mathbf{u}\| = 15{,}485$ pounds

Tension of right cable: $\|\mathbf{v}\| = 19{,}786$ pounds

87. (a) Tow line 1: $\mathbf{u} = \|\mathbf{u}\|(\cos\theta\mathbf{i} + \sin\theta\mathbf{j})$

Tow line 2: $\mathbf{v} = \|\mathbf{u}\|(\cos(-\theta)\mathbf{i} + \sin(-\theta)\mathbf{j})$

Resultant: $\mathbf{u} + \mathbf{v} = 6000\mathbf{i} = [\|\mathbf{u}\|\cos\theta + \|\mathbf{u}\|\cos(-\theta)]\mathbf{i} \implies$

$$6000 = 2\|\mathbf{u}\|\cos\theta \implies \|\mathbf{u}\| \approx 3000\sec\theta$$

$$T = \|\mathbf{u}\| = 3000\sec\theta$$

Domain: $0° \le \theta < 90°$

(b)

θ	10°	20°	30°	40°	50°	60°
T	3046.3	3192.5	3464.1	3916.2	4667.2	6000.0

(c)

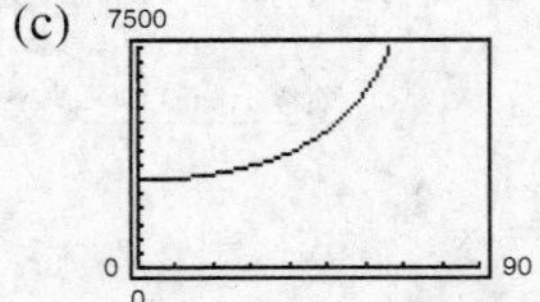

(d) The tension increases because the component in the direction of the motion of the barge decreases.

88. (a) $\mathbf{u} = \|\mathbf{u}\|(\cos(90° - \theta)\mathbf{i} + \sin(90° - \theta)\mathbf{j})$

$\mathbf{v} = \|\mathbf{v}\|(\cos(90° + \theta)\mathbf{i} + \sin(90° + \theta)\mathbf{j})$

$\mathbf{u} + \mathbf{v} = 100\mathbf{j} \Rightarrow \|\mathbf{u}\| \cos(90° - \theta) + \|\mathbf{v}\| \cos(90° + \theta) = 0$

$\Rightarrow \|\mathbf{u}\| = \|\mathbf{v}\|$, and

$100 = \|\mathbf{u}\| \sin(90° - \theta) + \|\mathbf{u}\| \sin(90° + \theta)$

$= 2\|\mathbf{u}\| \cos \theta$

Hence, $\|\mathbf{u}\| = T = \dfrac{50}{\cos \theta} = 50 \sec \theta.$

Domain: $0° \le \theta < 90°$

(b)

θ	10°	20°	30°	40°	50°	60°
T	50.8	53.2	57.7	65.3	77.8	100

(c)

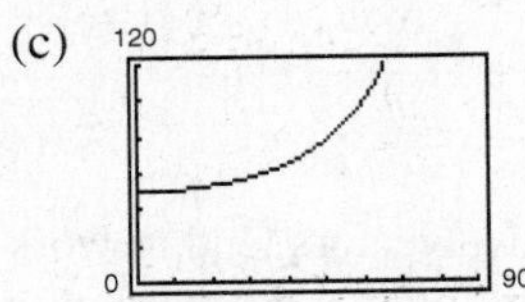

(d) The vertical component of the vectors decreases as θ increases.

89. Airspeed: $\mathbf{v} = 860(\cos 302°\mathbf{i} + \sin 302°\mathbf{j})$

Groundspeed: $\mathbf{u} = 800(\cos 310°\mathbf{i} + \sin 310°\mathbf{j})$

$\mathbf{w} + \mathbf{v} = \mathbf{u}$

$\mathbf{w} = \mathbf{u} - \mathbf{v} = 800(\cos 310°\mathbf{i} + \sin 310°\mathbf{j}) - 860(\cos 302°\mathbf{i} + \sin 302°\mathbf{j}) \approx 58.50\mathbf{i} + 116.49\mathbf{j}$

$\|\mathbf{w}\| = \sqrt{58.50^2 + 116.49^2} \approx 130.35$ km/hr

$\theta = \arctan\left(\dfrac{116.49}{58.50}\right) \approx 63.3°$

Direction: N 26.7° E

90. (a)

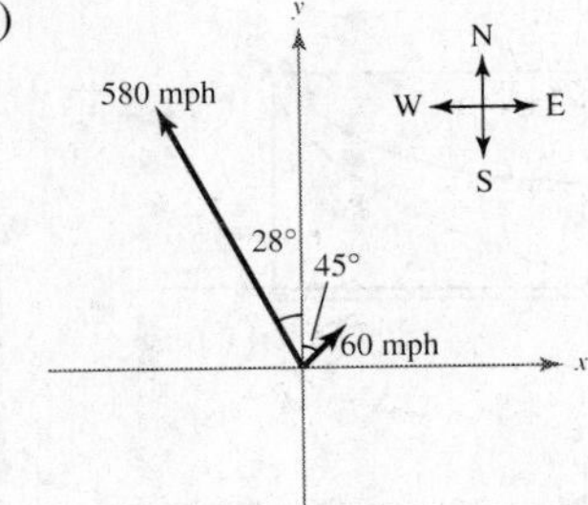

(b) $\mathbf{w} = 60\langle \cos 45°, \sin 45° \rangle = \langle 30\sqrt{2}, 30\sqrt{2} \rangle$

(c) $\mathbf{v} = 580\langle \cos 118°, \sin 118° \rangle = \langle -272.3, 512.1 \rangle$

(d) $\mathbf{w} + \mathbf{v} = \langle -229.9, 554.5 \rangle$

$\|\mathbf{w} + \mathbf{v}\| \approx 600.3$ mph

(e) $\tan \theta = \dfrac{554.5}{-229.9} \Rightarrow \theta \approx 112.5°$

Direction: N 22.5° W (or 337.5° using airplane navigation)

91. (a) $\mathbf{u} = 220\mathbf{i}, \quad \mathbf{v} = 150\cos 30°\mathbf{i} + 150\sin 30°\mathbf{j}$

$$\mathbf{u} + \mathbf{v} = \left(220 + 75\sqrt{3}\right)\mathbf{i} + 75\mathbf{j}$$

$$\|\mathbf{u} + \mathbf{v}\| = \sqrt{\left(220 + 75\sqrt{3}\right)^2 + 75^2} \approx 357.85 \text{ newtons}$$

$$\tan\theta = \frac{75}{220 + 75\sqrt{3}} \implies \theta \approx 12.1°$$

(b) $\mathbf{u} + \mathbf{v} = 220\mathbf{i} + (150\cos\theta\mathbf{i} + 150\sin\theta\mathbf{j})$

$$M = \|\mathbf{u} + \mathbf{v}\| = \sqrt{220^2 + 150^2(\cos^2\theta + \sin^2\theta) + 2(220)(150)\cos\theta}$$

$$= \sqrt{70{,}900 + 66{,}000\cos\theta} = 10\sqrt{709 + 660\cos\theta}$$

$$\alpha = \arctan\left(\frac{15\sin\theta}{22 + 15\cos\theta}\right)$$

(c)

θ	0°	30°	60°	90°	120°	150°	180°
M	370.0	357.9	322.3	266.3	194.7	117.2	70.0
α	0°	12.1°	23.8°	34.3°	41.9°	39.8°	0°

(d)

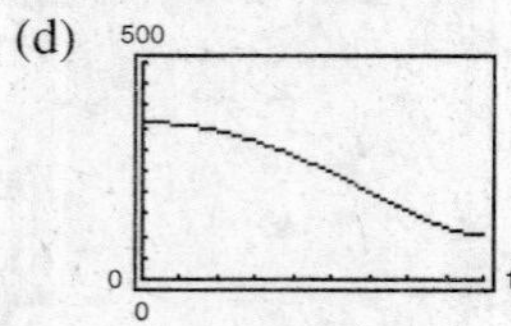

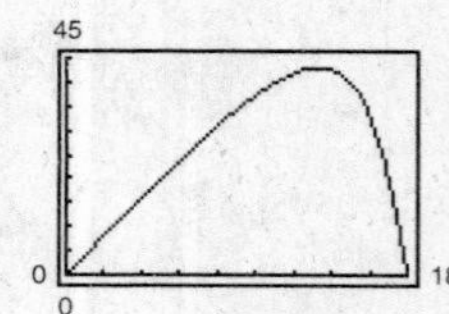

(e) For increasing θ, the two vectors tend to work against each other resulting in a decrease in the magnitude of the resultant.

92. (a)

$$\mathbf{T} = \|\mathbf{T}\|(\cos(90° + \theta)\mathbf{i} + \sin(90° + \theta)\mathbf{j})$$

$$\mathbf{u} + \mathbf{w} + \mathbf{T} = \mathbf{0} \implies \|\mathbf{u}\| + \|\mathbf{T}\|\cos(90° + \theta) = 0$$

$$\|\mathbf{u}\| - \|\mathbf{T}\|\sin\theta = 0$$

$$-1 + \|\mathbf{T}\|\sin(90° + \theta) = 0$$

$$-1 + \|\mathbf{T}\|\cos\theta = 0 \implies$$

$$\|\mathbf{T}\| = \sec\theta,\ 0 \le \theta < \frac{\pi}{2}$$

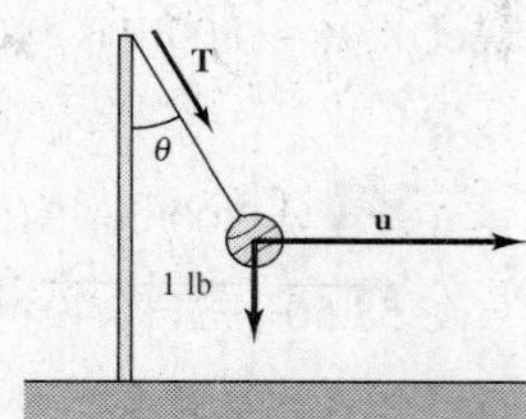

Hence, $\|\mathbf{u}\| = \|\mathbf{T}\|\sin\theta = \sec\theta\sin\theta = \tan\theta, 0 \le \theta < \pi/2$.

(b)

θ	0°	10°	20°	30°	40°	50°	60°
$\|\mathbf{T}\|$	1	1.02	1.06	1.15	1.31	1.56	2
$\|\mathbf{u}\|$	0	0.18	0.36	0.58	0.84	1.19	1.73

(c)

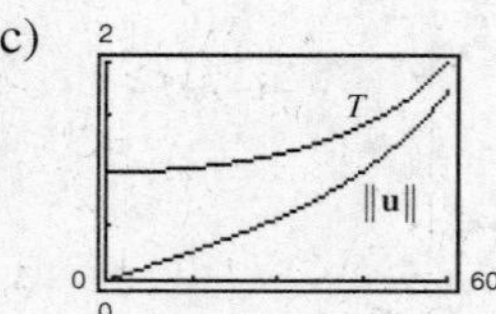

(d) Both $\|\mathbf{T}\|$ and $\|\mathbf{u}\|$ increase as θ increases, and approach each other in magnitude.

93. True. See page 424.

94. True, $\mathbf{u} = \dfrac{\mathbf{v}}{\|\mathbf{v}\|}$.

95. True. In fact, $a = b = 0$.

96. True

97. True. **a** and **d** are parallel, and pointing in opposite directions.

98. True. **c** and **s** are parallel, and pointing in the same direction.

99. True

100. False. In fact, $\mathbf{v} + \mathbf{s} = \mathbf{w}$.

101. True. $\mathbf{a} + \mathbf{w} = 2\mathbf{a} = -2\mathbf{d}$

102. True. $\mathbf{a} + \mathbf{d} = \mathbf{a} + (-\mathbf{a}) = \mathbf{0}$

103. False. $\mathbf{u} - \mathbf{v} = 2\mathbf{u}$ and

$-2(\mathbf{b} + \mathbf{t}) = -2(-2\mathbf{u}) = 4\mathbf{u}$

104. True

$\mathbf{t} - \mathbf{w} = -\mathbf{s}$ and $\mathbf{b} - \mathbf{a} = -\mathbf{c} = -\mathbf{s}$

105. (a) The angle between them is 0°.

(b) The angle between them is 180°.

(c) No. At most it can be equal to the sum when the angle between them is 0°.

106. $\mathbf{F}_1 = \langle 10, 0\rangle$, $\mathbf{F}_2 = 5\langle \cos\theta, \sin\theta\rangle$

(a) $\mathbf{F}_1 + \mathbf{F}_2 = \langle 10 + 5\cos\theta, 5\sin\theta\rangle$

$$\begin{aligned}\|\mathbf{F}_1 + \mathbf{F}_2\| &= \sqrt{(10 + 5\cos\theta)^2 + (5\sin\theta)^2}\\ &= \sqrt{100 + 100\cos\theta + 25\cos^2\theta + 25\sin^2\theta}\\ &= 5\sqrt{4 + 4\cos\theta + \cos^2\theta + \sin^2\theta}\\ &= 5\sqrt{4 + 4\cos\theta + 1}\\ &= 5\sqrt{5 + 4\cos\theta}\end{aligned}$$

(b)

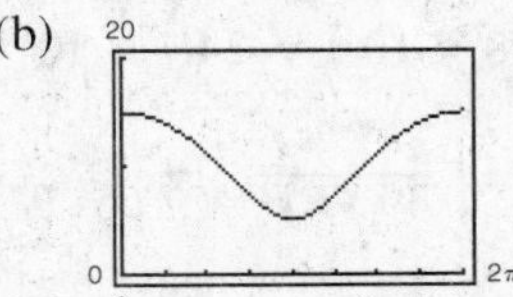

(c) Range: $[5, 15]$

Maximum is 15 when $\theta = 0$.

Minimum is 5 when $\theta = \pi$.

(d) The magnitude of the resultant is never 0 because the magnitudes of $\mathbf{F}_1$ and $\mathbf{F}_2$ are not the same.

107. Let $\mathbf{v} = (\cos\theta)\mathbf{i} + (\sin\theta)\mathbf{j}$.

$\|\mathbf{v}\| = \sqrt{\cos^2\theta + \sin^2\theta} = \sqrt{1} = 1$

Therefore, $\mathbf{v}$ is a unit vector for any value of θ.

108. The following program is written for a TI-82 or TI-83 graphing calculator. The program sketches two vectors $\mathbf{u} = a\mathbf{i} + b\mathbf{j}$ and $\mathbf{v} = c\mathbf{i} + d\mathbf{j}$ in standard position, and then sketches the vector difference $\mathbf{u} - \mathbf{v}$ using the parallelogram law.

```
PROGRAM: SUBVECT
:Input "ENTER A", A
:Input "ENTER B", B
:Input "ENTER C", C
:Input "ENTER D", D
:Line (0, 0, A, B)
:Line (0, 0, C, D)
:Pause
:A-C→E
:B-D→F
:Line (A, B, C, D)
:Line (A, B, E, F)
:Line (0, 0, E, F)
:Pause
:ClrDraw
:Stop
```

109.

$$\begin{aligned}\mathbf{u} &= \langle 5 - 1, 2 - 6\rangle = \langle 4, -4\rangle\\ \mathbf{v} &= \langle 9 - 4, 4 - 5\rangle = \langle 5, -1\rangle\\ \mathbf{u} - \mathbf{v} &= \langle -1, -3\rangle\\ \mathbf{v} - \mathbf{u} &= \langle 1, 3\rangle\end{aligned}$$

110.

$$\begin{aligned}\mathbf{u} &= \langle 80 - 10, 80 - 60\rangle = \langle 70, 20\rangle\\ \mathbf{v} &= \langle -20 - (-100), 70 - 0\rangle = \langle 80, 70\rangle\\ \mathbf{u} - \mathbf{v} &= \langle 70 - 80, 20 - 70\rangle = \langle -10, -50\rangle\\ \mathbf{v} - \mathbf{u} &= \langle 80 - 70, 70 - 20\rangle = \langle 10, 50\rangle\end{aligned}$$

111. $\left(\dfrac{6x^4}{7y^{-2}}\right)(14x^{-1}y^5) = \dfrac{12x^4y^5y^2}{x}$

$= 12x^3y^7,\ x \neq 0, y \neq 0$

112. $(5s^5t^{-5})\left(\dfrac{3s^{-2}}{50t^{-1}}\right) = \dfrac{3s^3}{10t^4},\ s \neq 0$

113. $(18x)^0(4xy)^2(3x^{-1}) = \dfrac{16x^2y^2(3)}{x}$

$= 48xy^2,\ x \neq 0$

114. $(5ab^2)(a^{-3}b^0)(2a^0b)^{-2} = (5ab^2)\dfrac{1}{a^3}\dfrac{1}{(2b)^2}$

$= \dfrac{5}{4a^2},\ b \neq 0$

115. $(2.1 \times 10^9)(3.4 \times 10^{-4}) = 7.14 \times 10^5$

116. $(6.5 \times 10^6)(3.8 \times 10^4) = 24.7 \times 10^{10} = 2.47 \times 10^{11}$

117. $\sin\theta = \dfrac{x}{7} \Rightarrow \sqrt{49 - x^2} = 7\cos\theta$

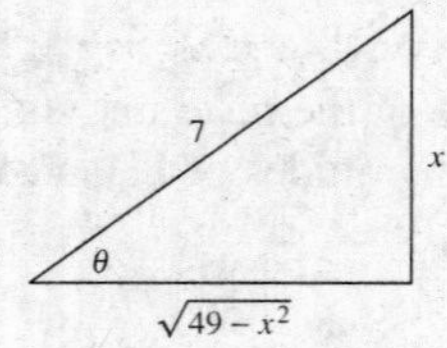

118. $\sqrt{x^2 - 49} = 7\tan\theta$

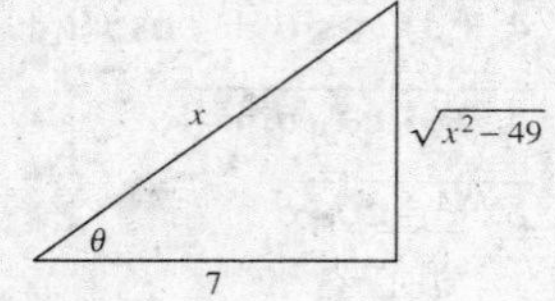

119. $\cot\theta = \dfrac{x}{10} \Rightarrow \sqrt{x^2 + 100} = 10 \cdot \csc\theta$

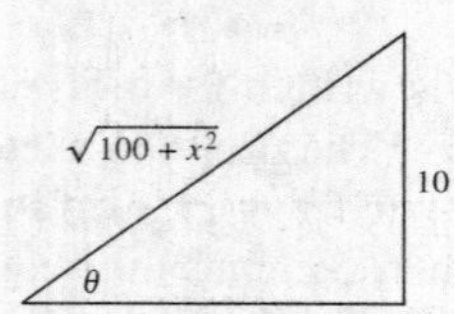

120. $\sqrt{x^2 - 4} = 2\cot\theta$

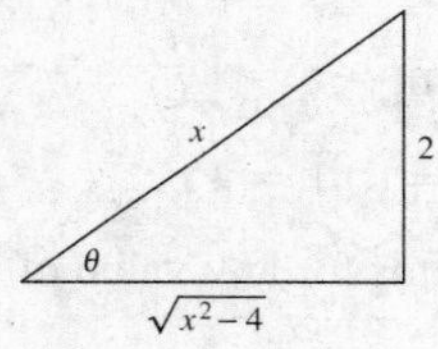

121. $\cos x(\cos x + 1) = 0$

$\cos x = 0 \Rightarrow x = \dfrac{\pi}{2} + n\pi$

$\cos x = -1 \Rightarrow x = \pi + 2n\pi$

122. $\sin x\left(2\sin x + \sqrt{2}\right) = 0$

$\sin x = 0$ or $\sin x = \dfrac{-\sqrt{2}}{2}$

$x = n\pi$ or $x = \dfrac{5\pi}{4} + 2n\pi$

$x = \dfrac{7\pi}{4} + 2n\pi$

123. $3\sec x + 4 = 10$

$\sec x = 2$

$\cos x = \dfrac{1}{2}$

$x = \dfrac{\pi}{3} + 2n\pi, \dfrac{5\pi}{3} + 2n\pi$

124. $\cos x\cot x - \cos x = 0$

$\cos x(\cot x - 1) = 0$

$\cos x = 0$ or $\cot x = 1$

$x = \dfrac{\pi}{2} + n\pi$ or $x = \dfrac{\pi}{4} + n\pi$

Section 6.4 Vectors and Dot Products

- Know the definition of the dot product of $\mathbf{u} = \langle u_1, u_2 \rangle$ and $\mathbf{v} = \langle v_1, v_2 \rangle$.

  $\mathbf{u} \cdot \mathbf{v} = u_1v_1 + u_2v_2$
- Know the following properties of the dot product:
  1. $\mathbf{u} \cdot \mathbf{v} = \mathbf{v} \cdot \mathbf{u}$
  2. $\mathbf{0} \cdot \mathbf{v} = 0$
  3. $\mathbf{u} \cdot (\mathbf{v} + \mathbf{w}) = \mathbf{u} \cdot \mathbf{v} + \mathbf{u} \cdot \mathbf{w}$
  4. $\mathbf{v} \cdot \mathbf{v} = \|\mathbf{v}\|^2$
  5. $c(\mathbf{u} \cdot \mathbf{v}) = c\mathbf{u} \cdot \mathbf{v} = \mathbf{u} \cdot c\mathbf{v}$
- If θ is the angle between two nonzero vectors **u** and **v**, then

  $$\cos\theta = \frac{\mathbf{u} \cdot \mathbf{v}}{\|\mathbf{u}\|\,\|\mathbf{v}\|}.$$
- The vectors **u** and **v** are orthogonal if $\mathbf{u} \cdot \mathbf{v} = 0$.
- Know the definition of vector components. $\mathbf{u} = \mathbf{w}_1 + \mathbf{w}_2$ where $\mathbf{w}_1$ and $\mathbf{w}_2$ are orthogonal, and $\mathbf{w}_1$ is parallel to **v**. $\mathbf{w}_1$ is called the projection of **u** onto **v** and is denoted by

  $$\mathbf{w}_1 = \text{proj}_{\mathbf{v}}\mathbf{u} = \left(\frac{\mathbf{u} \cdot \mathbf{v}}{\|\mathbf{v}\|^2}\right)\mathbf{v}.$$

  Then we have $\mathbf{w}_2 = \mathbf{u} - \mathbf{w}_1$.
- Know the definition of work.
  1. Projection form: $W = \|\text{proj}_{\overrightarrow{PQ}}\mathbf{F}\|\,\|\overrightarrow{PQ}\|$
  2. Dot product form: $W = \mathbf{F} \cdot \overrightarrow{PQ}$

Vocabulary Check

1. dot product
2. $\dfrac{\mathbf{u} \cdot \mathbf{v}}{\|\mathbf{u}\|\,\|\mathbf{v}\|}$
3. orthogonal
4. $\left(\dfrac{\mathbf{u} \cdot \mathbf{v}}{\|\mathbf{v}\|^2}\right)\mathbf{v}$
5. $\|\text{proj}_{\overrightarrow{PQ}}\mathbf{F}\|\,\|\overrightarrow{PQ}\|, \mathbf{F} \cdot \overrightarrow{PQ}$

1. $\mathbf{u} \cdot \mathbf{v} = \langle 6, 3 \rangle \cdot \langle 2, -4 \rangle = 6(2) + 3(-4) = 0$

2. $\mathbf{u} \cdot \mathbf{v} = \langle -4, 1 \rangle \cdot \langle 2, -3 \rangle$
$= (-4)(2) + 1(-3) = -11$

3. $\mathbf{u} \cdot \mathbf{v} = \langle 5, 1 \rangle \cdot \langle 3, -1 \rangle = 5(3) + 1(-1) = 14$

4. $\mathbf{u} \cdot \mathbf{v} = \langle 3, 2 \rangle \cdot \langle -2, 1 \rangle = 3(-2) + 2(1) = -4$

5. $\mathbf{u} = \langle 2, 2 \rangle$
$\mathbf{u} \cdot \mathbf{u} = 2(2) + 2(2) = 8$, scalar

6. $\mathbf{v} \cdot \mathbf{w} = \langle -3, 4 \rangle \cdot \langle 1, -4 \rangle$
$= (-3)(1) + 4(-4) = -19$, scalar

7. $\mathbf{u} = \langle 2, 2 \rangle, \mathbf{v} = \langle -3, 4 \rangle$
$\mathbf{u} \cdot 2\mathbf{v} = 2\mathbf{u} \cdot \mathbf{v} = 4(-3) + 4(4) = 4$, scalar

8. $4\mathbf{u} \cdot \mathbf{v} = 4\langle 2, 2 \rangle \cdot \langle -3, 4 \rangle$
$= 4(-6 + 8)$
$= 8$, scalar

9. $(3\mathbf{w}\cdot\mathbf{v})\mathbf{u} = (3\langle 1, -4\rangle \cdot \langle -3, 4\rangle)\langle 2, 2\rangle$

$= (3(-3) + (-12)(4))\langle 2, 2\rangle$

$= -57\langle 2, 2\rangle$

$= \langle -114, -114\rangle$, vector

10. $(\mathbf{u}\cdot 2\mathbf{v})\mathbf{w} = (\langle 2, 2\rangle \cdot 2\langle -3, 4\rangle)\langle 1, -4\rangle$

$= (2(-6) + 2(8))\langle 1, -4\rangle$

$= 4\langle 1, -4\rangle$

$= \langle 4, -16\rangle$, vector

11. $\mathbf{u} = \langle -5, 12\rangle$

$\|\mathbf{u}\| = \sqrt{\mathbf{u}\cdot\mathbf{u}} = \sqrt{(-5)^2 + 12^2} = 13$

12. $\mathbf{u} = \langle 2, -4\rangle$

$\|\mathbf{u}\| = \sqrt{\mathbf{u}\cdot\mathbf{u}}$

$= \sqrt{2(2) + (-4)(-4)}$

$= \sqrt{20} = 2\sqrt{5}$

13. $\mathbf{u} = 20\mathbf{i} + 25\mathbf{j}$

$\|\mathbf{u}\| = \sqrt{\mathbf{u}\cdot\mathbf{u}} = \sqrt{(20)^2 + (25)^2} = \sqrt{1025} = 5\sqrt{41}$

14. $\mathbf{u} = 6\mathbf{i} - 10\mathbf{j}$

$\|\mathbf{u}\| = \sqrt{\mathbf{u}\cdot\mathbf{u}} = \sqrt{6(6) + (-10)(-10)} = \sqrt{136} = 2\sqrt{34}$

15. $\mathbf{u} = -4\mathbf{j}$

$\|\mathbf{u}\| = \sqrt{\mathbf{u}\cdot\mathbf{u}} = \sqrt{(-4)(-4)} = 4$

16. $\mathbf{u} = 9\mathbf{i}$

$\|\mathbf{u}\| = \sqrt{\mathbf{u}\cdot\mathbf{u}} = \sqrt{9(9) + 0} = \sqrt{81} = 9$

17. $\mathbf{u} = \langle -1, 0\rangle, \mathbf{v} = \langle 0, 2\rangle$

$$\cos\theta = \frac{\mathbf{u}\cdot\mathbf{v}}{\|\mathbf{u}\|\,\|\mathbf{v}\|} = \frac{0}{(1)(2)} = 0 \implies \theta = 90^\circ$$

18. $\mathbf{u} = \langle 4, 4\rangle, \mathbf{v} = \langle -2, 0\rangle$

$$\cos\theta = \frac{\mathbf{u}\cdot\mathbf{v}}{\|\mathbf{u}\|\,\|\mathbf{v}\|}$$

$$= \frac{4(-2) + 4(0)}{(4\sqrt{2})(2)}$$

$$= -\frac{\sqrt{2}}{2}$$

$\theta = 135^\circ$

19. $\mathbf{u} = 3\mathbf{i} + 4\mathbf{j}, \mathbf{v} = -2\mathbf{i} + 3\mathbf{j}$

$$\cos\theta = \frac{\mathbf{u}\cdot\mathbf{v}}{\|\mathbf{u}\|\,\|\mathbf{v}\|} = \frac{-6 + 12}{(5)(\sqrt{13})} = \frac{6}{5\sqrt{13}}$$

$$\theta = \arccos\left(\frac{6}{5\sqrt{13}}\right) \approx 70.56^\circ$$

20. $\mathbf{u} = 2\mathbf{i} - 3\mathbf{j}, \mathbf{v} = \mathbf{i} - 2\mathbf{j}$

$$\cos\theta = \frac{\mathbf{u}\cdot\mathbf{v}}{\|\mathbf{u}\|\,\|\mathbf{v}\|}$$

$$= \frac{2(1) + (-3)(-2)}{\sqrt{2^2 + 3^2}\sqrt{1^2 + 2^2}}$$

$$= \frac{8}{\sqrt{65}} \approx 0.992278$$

$\theta \approx 7.13^\circ$

21. $\mathbf{u} = 2\mathbf{i}, \mathbf{v} = -3\mathbf{j}$

$$\cos\theta = \frac{\mathbf{u}\cdot\mathbf{v}}{\|\mathbf{u}\|\,\|\mathbf{v}\|} = \frac{0}{(2)(3)} = 0 \implies \theta = 90^\circ$$

22. $\mathbf{u}\cdot\mathbf{v} = \langle 0, 4\rangle \cdot \langle -3, 0\rangle = 0 \implies \theta = 90^\circ$

23. $\mathbf{u} = \left(\cos\frac{\pi}{3}\right)\mathbf{i} + \left(\sin\frac{\pi}{3}\right)\mathbf{j} = \frac{1}{2}\mathbf{i} + \frac{\sqrt{3}}{2}\mathbf{j}$

$\mathbf{v} = \left(\cos\frac{3\pi}{4}\right)\mathbf{i} + \left(\sin\frac{3\pi}{4}\right)\mathbf{j} = -\frac{\sqrt{2}}{2}\mathbf{i} + \frac{\sqrt{2}}{2}\mathbf{j}$

$\|\mathbf{u}\| = \|\mathbf{v}\| = 1$

$\cos\theta = \frac{\mathbf{u}\cdot\mathbf{v}}{\|\mathbf{u}\|\,\|\mathbf{v}\|} = \mathbf{u}\cdot\mathbf{v} = \left(\frac{1}{2}\right)\left(-\frac{\sqrt{2}}{2}\right) + \left(\frac{\sqrt{3}}{2}\right)\left(\frac{\sqrt{2}}{2}\right) = \frac{-\sqrt{2}+\sqrt{6}}{4}$

$\theta = \arccos\left(\frac{-\sqrt{2}+\sqrt{6}}{4}\right) = 75° = \frac{5\pi}{12}$

24. $\mathbf{u} = \cos\left(\frac{\pi}{4}\right)\mathbf{i} + \sin\left(\frac{\pi}{4}\right)\mathbf{j} = \frac{\sqrt{2}}{2}\mathbf{i} + \frac{\sqrt{2}}{2}\mathbf{j}$

$\mathbf{v} = \cos\left(\frac{2\pi}{3}\right)\mathbf{i} + \sin\left(\frac{2\pi}{3}\right)\mathbf{j} = -\frac{1}{2}\mathbf{i} + \frac{\sqrt{3}}{2}\mathbf{j}$

$\cos\theta = \frac{\mathbf{u}\cdot\mathbf{v}}{\|\mathbf{u}\|\,\|\mathbf{v}\|} = \frac{-(\sqrt{2}/4) + (\sqrt{6}/4)}{(1)(1)} = \frac{\sqrt{6}-\sqrt{2}}{4} \Rightarrow \theta = 75° = \frac{5\pi}{12}$

25. $\mathbf{u} = 2\mathbf{i} - 4\mathbf{j},\ \mathbf{v} = 3\mathbf{i} - 5\mathbf{j}$

$\cos\theta = \frac{\mathbf{u}\cdot\mathbf{v}}{\|\mathbf{u}\|\,\|\mathbf{v}\|} = \frac{6+20}{\sqrt{20}\sqrt{34}}$

$= \frac{13\sqrt{170}}{170} \Rightarrow \theta \approx 4.40°$

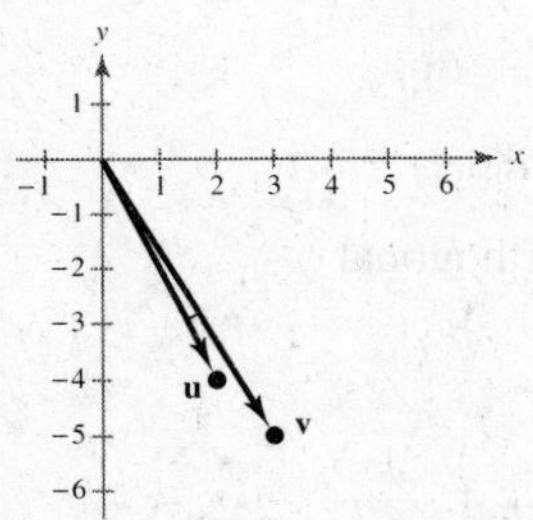

26. $\mathbf{u} = -6\mathbf{i} - 3\mathbf{j},\ \mathbf{v} = -8\mathbf{i} + 4\mathbf{j}$

$\cos\theta = \frac{\mathbf{u}\cdot\mathbf{v}}{\|\mathbf{u}\|\,\|\mathbf{v}\|} = \frac{-6(-8) + (-3)(4)}{\sqrt{45}\sqrt{80}}$

$= \frac{36}{60} = 0.6$

$\theta \approx 53.13°$

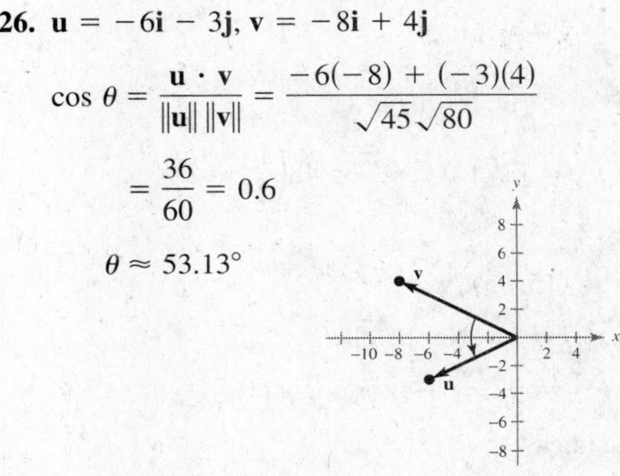

27. $\mathbf{u} = 6\mathbf{i} - 2\mathbf{j},\ \mathbf{v} = 8\mathbf{i} - 5\mathbf{j}$

$\cos\theta = \frac{\mathbf{u}\cdot\mathbf{v}}{\|\mathbf{u}\|\,\|\mathbf{v}\|} = \frac{48+10}{\sqrt{40}\sqrt{89}}$

$= \frac{29\sqrt{890}}{890} \Rightarrow \theta \approx 13.57°$

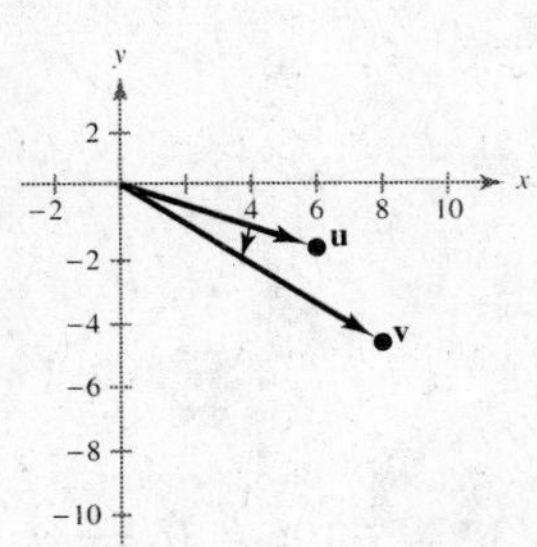

28. $\mathbf{u} = 2\mathbf{i} - 3\mathbf{j},\ \mathbf{v} = 4\mathbf{i} + 3\mathbf{j}$

$\cos\theta = \frac{\mathbf{u}\cdot\mathbf{v}}{\|\mathbf{u}\|\,\|\mathbf{v}\|} = \frac{2(4) + (-3)(3)}{\sqrt{13}\sqrt{25}} \approx -0.0555$

$\theta \approx 93.18°$

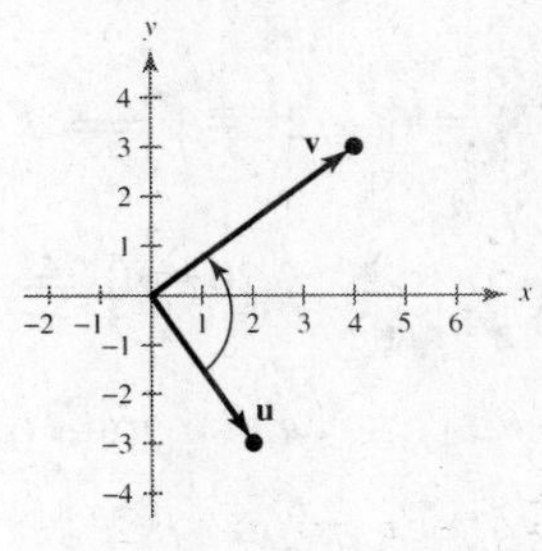

29. $P = (1, 2),\ Q = (3, 4),\ R = (2, 5)$

$\overrightarrow{PQ} = \langle 2, 2 \rangle,\ \overrightarrow{PR} = \langle 1, 3 \rangle,\ \overrightarrow{QR} = \langle -1, 1 \rangle$

$$\cos\alpha = \frac{\overrightarrow{PQ} \cdot \overrightarrow{PR}}{\|\overrightarrow{PQ}\|\,\|\overrightarrow{PR}\|} = \frac{8}{(2\sqrt{2})(\sqrt{10})} \implies \alpha = \arccos\frac{2}{\sqrt{5}} \approx 26.6^\circ$$

$$\cos\beta = \frac{\overrightarrow{PQ} \cdot \overrightarrow{QR}}{\|\overrightarrow{PQ}\|\,\|\overrightarrow{QR}\|} = 0 \implies \beta = 90^\circ$$

Thus, $\gamma \approx 180^\circ - 26.6^\circ - 90^\circ = 63.4^\circ$.

30. $P = (-3, 0), Q = (2, 2), R = (0, 6)$

$\overrightarrow{PQ} = \langle 5, 2 \rangle, \overrightarrow{QR} = \langle -2, 4 \rangle, \overrightarrow{PR} = \langle 3, 6 \rangle,$

$\overrightarrow{QP} = \langle -5, -2 \rangle$

$$\cos\alpha = \frac{\overrightarrow{PQ} \cdot \overrightarrow{PR}}{\|\overrightarrow{PR}\|\,\|\overrightarrow{PR}\|} = \frac{27}{(\sqrt{29})(\sqrt{45})} \implies \alpha \approx 41.6^\circ$$

$$\cos\beta = \frac{\overrightarrow{QR} \cdot \overrightarrow{QP}}{\|\overrightarrow{QR}\|\,\|\overrightarrow{QP}\|} = \frac{2}{(\sqrt{20})(\sqrt{29})} \implies \beta \approx 85.2$$

$\phi = 180^\circ - 41.6^\circ - 85.2^\circ \approx 53.2^\circ$

31. $\mathbf{u} \cdot \mathbf{v} = \|\mathbf{u}\|\,\|\mathbf{v}\| \cos\theta$

$$= (9)(36)\cos\frac{3\pi}{4}$$

$$= 324\left(-\frac{\sqrt{2}}{2}\right)$$

$$= -162\sqrt{2}$$

32. $\mathbf{u} \cdot \mathbf{v} = \|\mathbf{u}\|\,\|\mathbf{v}\| \cos\theta$

$$= (4)(12)\cos\frac{\pi}{3} = 48\left(\frac{1}{2}\right) = 24$$

33. $\mathbf{u} = \langle -12, 30 \rangle,\ \mathbf{v} = \left\langle \frac{1}{2}, -\frac{5}{4} \right\rangle$

$\mathbf{u} = -24\mathbf{v} \implies$ **u** and **v** are parallel.

34. $\mathbf{u} = \langle 15, 45 \rangle, \mathbf{v} = \langle -5, 12 \rangle$

$\mathbf{u} \neq k\mathbf{v} \implies$ Not parallel

$\mathbf{u} \cdot \mathbf{v} \neq 0 \implies$ Not orthogonal

Neither

35. $\mathbf{u} = \frac{1}{4}(3\mathbf{i} - \mathbf{j}),\ \mathbf{v} = 5\mathbf{i} + 6\mathbf{j}$

$\mathbf{u} \neq k\mathbf{v} \implies$ Not parallel

$\mathbf{u} \cdot \mathbf{v} \neq 0 \implies$ Not orthogonal

Neither

36. $\mathbf{u} = \mathbf{j}, \mathbf{v} = \mathbf{i} - 2\mathbf{j}$

$\mathbf{u} \neq k\mathbf{v} \implies$ Not parallel

$\mathbf{u} \cdot \mathbf{v} \neq 0 \implies$ Not orthogonal

Neither

37. $\mathbf{u} = 2\mathbf{i} - 2\mathbf{j},\ \mathbf{v} = -\mathbf{i} - \mathbf{j}$

$\mathbf{u} \cdot \mathbf{v} = 0 \implies$ **u** and **v** are orthogonal.

38. $-4\mathbf{v} = -4(-2\mathbf{i} - \mathbf{j}) = 8\mathbf{i} + 4\mathbf{j} = \mathbf{u} \implies$ parallel

39. $\mathbf{u} \cdot \mathbf{v} = \langle 2, -k \rangle \cdot \langle 3, 2 \rangle = 6 - 2k = 0 \implies k = 3$

40. $\mathbf{u} \cdot \mathbf{v} = \langle 3, 2 \rangle \cdot \langle 2, -k \rangle = 6 - 2k = 0 \implies k = 3$

41. $\mathbf{u} \cdot \mathbf{v} = \langle 1, 4 \rangle \cdot \langle 2k, -5 \rangle = 2k - 20 = 0 \implies k = 10$

42. $\mathbf{u} \cdot \mathbf{v} = \langle -3k, 5 \rangle \cdot \langle 2, -4 \rangle = -6k - 20 = 0 \implies k = -\frac{10}{3}$

43. $\mathbf{u} \cdot \mathbf{v} = \langle -3k, 2 \rangle \cdot \langle -6, 0 \rangle = 18k = 0 \implies k = 0$

44. $\mathbf{u} \cdot \mathbf{v} = \langle 4, -4k \rangle \cdot \langle 0, 3 \rangle = -12k = 0 \implies k = 0$

45. $\mathbf{u} = \langle 3, 4 \rangle, \ \mathbf{v} = \langle 8, 2 \rangle$

$$\mathbf{w}_1 = \text{proj}_{\mathbf{v}}\mathbf{u} = \left(\frac{\mathbf{u} \cdot \mathbf{v}}{\|\mathbf{v}\|^2}\right)\mathbf{v}$$

$$= \left(\frac{32}{68}\right)\mathbf{v} = \frac{8}{17}\langle 8, 2 \rangle = \frac{16}{17}\langle 4, 1 \rangle$$

$$\mathbf{w}_2 = \mathbf{u} - \mathbf{w}_1 = \langle 3, 4 \rangle - \frac{16}{17}\langle 4, 1 \rangle = \frac{13}{17}\langle -1, 4 \rangle$$

$$\mathbf{u} = \mathbf{w}_1 + \mathbf{w}_2 = \frac{16}{17}\langle 4, 1 \rangle + \frac{13}{17}\langle -1, 4 \rangle$$

46. $\mathbf{u} = \langle 4, 2 \rangle, \mathbf{v} = \langle 1, -2 \rangle$

$$\mathbf{w}_1 = \text{proj}_{\mathbf{v}}\mathbf{u} = \left(\frac{\mathbf{u} \cdot \mathbf{v}}{\|\mathbf{v}\|^2}\right)\mathbf{v} = 0\langle 1, -2 \rangle = \langle 0, 0 \rangle$$

$$\mathbf{w}_2 = \mathbf{u} - \mathbf{w}_1 = \langle 4, 2 \rangle - \langle 0, 0 \rangle = \langle 4, 2 \rangle$$

$$\mathbf{u} = \langle 4, 2 \rangle + \langle 0, 0 \rangle$$

47. $\mathbf{u} = \langle 0, 3 \rangle, \ \mathbf{v} = \langle 2, 15 \rangle$

$$\mathbf{w}_1 = \text{proj}_{\mathbf{v}}\mathbf{u} = \left(\frac{\mathbf{u} \cdot \mathbf{v}}{\|\mathbf{v}\|^2}\right)\mathbf{v} = \frac{45}{229}\langle 2, 15 \rangle$$

$$\mathbf{w}_2 = \mathbf{u} - \mathbf{w}_1 = \langle 0, 3 \rangle - \frac{45}{229}\langle 2, 15 \rangle$$

$$= \left\langle -\frac{90}{229}, \frac{12}{229} \right\rangle = \frac{6}{229}\langle -15, 2 \rangle$$

$$\mathbf{u} = \mathbf{w}_1 + \mathbf{w}_2 = \frac{45}{229}\langle 2, 15 \rangle + \frac{6}{229}\langle -15, 2 \rangle$$

48. $\mathbf{u} = \langle -5, -1 \rangle, \mathbf{v} = \langle -1, 1 \rangle$

$$\mathbf{w}_1 = \text{proj}_{\mathbf{v}}\mathbf{u} = \left(\frac{\mathbf{u} \cdot \mathbf{v}}{\|\mathbf{v}\|^2}\right)\mathbf{v} = \frac{4}{2}\langle -1, 1 \rangle = 2\langle -1, 1 \rangle$$

$$\mathbf{w}_2 = \mathbf{u} - \mathbf{w}_1 = \langle -5, -1 \rangle - 2\langle -1, 1 \rangle$$

$$= \langle -3, -3 \rangle = 3\langle -1, -1 \rangle$$

$$\mathbf{u} = \langle -3, -3 \rangle + \langle -2, 2 \rangle$$

49. $\text{proj}_{\mathbf{v}}\mathbf{u} = \mathbf{u}$ since they are parallel.

$$\text{proj}_{\mathbf{v}}\mathbf{u} = \frac{\mathbf{u} \cdot \mathbf{v}}{\|\mathbf{v}\|^2}\mathbf{v}$$

$$= \frac{18 + 8}{36 + 16}\mathbf{v} = \frac{26}{52}\langle 6, 4 \rangle = \langle 3, 2 \rangle = \mathbf{u}$$

50. Because $\mathbf{u}$ and $\mathbf{v}$ are parallel, the projection of $\mathbf{u}$ onto $\mathbf{v}$ is $\mathbf{u}$.

51. $\text{proj}_{\mathbf{v}}\mathbf{u} = \mathbf{0}$ since they are perpendicular.

$$\text{proj}_{\mathbf{v}}\mathbf{u} = \frac{\mathbf{u} \cdot \mathbf{v}}{\|\mathbf{v}\|^2}\mathbf{v} = \mathbf{0}, \text{ since } \mathbf{u} \cdot \mathbf{v} = 0.$$

52. Because $\mathbf{u}$ and $\mathbf{v}$ are orthogonal, the projection of $\mathbf{u}$ onto $\mathbf{v}$ is $\mathbf{0}$.

53. $\mathbf{u} = \langle 2, 6 \rangle$

For $\mathbf{v}$ to be orthogonal to $\mathbf{u}$, $\mathbf{u} \cdot \mathbf{v}$ must equal 0.

Two possibilities: $\langle 6, -2 \rangle$ and $\langle -6, 2 \rangle$

54. For $\mathbf{v}$ to be orthogonal to $\mathbf{u} = \langle -7, 5 \rangle$, their dot product must be zero.

Two possibilities: $\langle 5, 7 \rangle, \langle -5, -7 \rangle$

55. $\mathbf{u} = \frac{1}{2}\mathbf{i} - \frac{3}{4}\mathbf{j}$

For $\mathbf{v}$ to be orthogonal to $\mathbf{u}$, $\mathbf{u} \cdot \mathbf{v}$ must equal 0.

Two possibilities: $\left\langle \frac{3}{4}, \frac{1}{2} \right\rangle$ and $\left\langle -\frac{3}{4}, -\frac{1}{2} \right\rangle$

56. $\mathbf{u} = -\frac{5}{2}\mathbf{i} - 3\mathbf{j}$

For $\mathbf{v}$ to be orthogonal to $\mathbf{u}$, $\mathbf{u} \cdot \mathbf{v}$ must be equal to 0.

Two possibilities: $\mathbf{v} = 3\mathbf{i} - \frac{5}{2}\mathbf{j}$ and $\mathbf{v} = -3\mathbf{i} + \frac{5}{2}\mathbf{j}$

57. $W = \|\text{proj}_{\overrightarrow{PQ}}\mathbf{v}\| \, \|\overrightarrow{PQ}\|$ where $\overrightarrow{PQ} = \langle 4, 7\rangle$ and $\mathbf{v} = \langle 1, 4\rangle$

$$\text{proj}_{\overrightarrow{PQ}}\mathbf{v} = \left(\frac{\mathbf{v}\cdot\overrightarrow{PQ}}{\|\overrightarrow{PQ}\|^2}\right)\overrightarrow{PQ} = \left(\frac{32}{65}\right)\langle 4, 7\rangle$$

$$W = \|\text{proj}_{\overrightarrow{PQ}}\mathbf{v}\|\,\|\overrightarrow{PQ}\| = \left(\frac{32\sqrt{65}}{65}\right)\left(\sqrt{65}\right) = 32$$

58. $P = (1, 3)$, $Q = (-3, 5)$, $\mathbf{v} = -2\mathbf{i} + 3\mathbf{j}$

work $= \|\text{proj}_{\overrightarrow{PQ}}\mathbf{v}\|\,\|\overrightarrow{PQ}\|$ where $\overrightarrow{PQ} = \langle -4, 2\rangle$ and $\mathbf{v} = \langle -2, 3\rangle$.

$$\text{proj}_{\overrightarrow{PQ}}\mathbf{v} = \left(\frac{\mathbf{v}\cdot\overrightarrow{PQ}}{\|\overrightarrow{PQ}\|^2}\right)\overrightarrow{PQ} = \left(\frac{14}{20}\right)\langle -4, 2\rangle$$

$$\text{work} = \|\text{proj}_{\overrightarrow{PQ}}\mathbf{v}\|\,\|\overrightarrow{PQ}\| = \left(\frac{14\sqrt{20}}{20}\right)\left(\sqrt{20}\right) = 14$$

59. (a) $\mathbf{u}\cdot\mathbf{v} = \langle 1245, 2600\rangle \cdot \langle 12.20, 8.50\rangle$

$= 1245(12.20) + 2600(8.50) = 37{,}289$

This is the total dollar value of the picture frames produced.

(b) Multiply $\mathbf{v}$ by 1.02.

60. $\mathbf{u} = \langle 3240, 2450\rangle$, $\mathbf{v} = \langle 1.75, 1.25\rangle$

(a) $\mathbf{u}\cdot\mathbf{v} = 3240(1.75) + 2450(1.25) = 8732.50$

This gives the total revenue earned.

(b) To increase prices by $2\frac{1}{2}$ percent, multiply $\mathbf{v}$ by 1.025:

$1.025\langle 1.75, 1.25\rangle$, scalar multiplication

61. (a) $\mathbf{F} = -30{,}000\vec{\mathbf{j}}$, Gravitational force

$\mathbf{v} = \langle \cos(d°), \sin(d°)\rangle$

$$\mathbf{w}_1 = \text{proj}_{\mathbf{v}}\mathbf{F} = \left(\frac{\mathbf{F}\cdot\mathbf{v}}{\|\mathbf{v}\|^2}\right)\mathbf{v} = (\mathbf{F}\cdot\mathbf{v})\mathbf{v} = -30{,}000\sin(d°)\langle \cos d°, \sin d°\rangle$$

$$= \langle -30{,}000 \sin d° \cos d°, -30{,}000 \sin^2 d°\rangle$$

Force needed: $30{,}000 \sin(d°)$

(b)

d	0°	1°	2°	3°	4°	5°	6°	7°	8°	9°	10°
Force	0	523.6	1047.0	1570.1	2092.7	2614.7	3135.9	3656.1	4175.2	4693.0	5209.4

(c) $\mathbf{w}_2 = \mathbf{F} - \mathbf{w}_1 = -30{,}000\mathbf{j} + 2614.7(\cos(5°)\mathbf{i} + \sin(5°)\mathbf{j}) \approx 2604.75\mathbf{i} - 29{,}772.11\mathbf{j}$

$\|\mathbf{w}_2\| \approx 29{,}885.8$ pounds

62. $\mathbf{F} = -5400\mathbf{j}$, Gravitational force

$\mathbf{v} = \cos 10°\mathbf{i} + \sin 10°\mathbf{j}$

$$\mathbf{w}_1 = \text{proj}_{\mathbf{v}}\mathbf{F} = \frac{\mathbf{F}\cdot\mathbf{v}}{\|\mathbf{v}\|^2}\mathbf{v} = (\mathbf{F}\cdot\mathbf{v})\mathbf{v} \approx -937.7\mathbf{v}$$

Magnitude: 937.7 pounds

$\mathbf{w}_2 = \mathbf{F} - \mathbf{w}_1$

$= -5400\mathbf{j} + 937.7[\cos 10°\mathbf{i} + \sin 10°\mathbf{j}]$

$\approx 923.45\mathbf{i} - 5237.17\mathbf{j}$

$\|\mathbf{w}_2\| \approx 5318$ pounds

63. (a) $\mathbf{F} = 15{,}691\langle \cos 30°, \sin 30°\rangle$

$\overrightarrow{PQ} = d\langle 1, 0\rangle$

$$W = \mathbf{F}\cdot\overrightarrow{PQ} = 15{,}691\frac{\sqrt{3}}{2}d \approx 13{,}588.8d$$

(b)

d	0	200	400	800
Work	0	2,717,761	5,435,522	10,871,044

64. $W = (45)(20)\cos 30° \approx 779.4$ foot-pounds

65. $\|\mathbf{F}\| = 250, \|\overrightarrow{PQ}\| = 100, \theta = 30°$

$$W = \|\mathbf{F}\|\,\|\overrightarrow{PQ}\| \cos\theta$$
$$= (250)(100)\cos 30°$$
$$= 25{,}000\frac{\sqrt{3}}{2}$$
$$= 12{,}500\sqrt{3} \text{ foot-pounds}$$
$$\approx 21{,}650.64 \text{ foot-pounds}$$

66. $\|\mathbf{F}\| = 25, \|\overrightarrow{PQ}\| = 50, \theta = 20°$

$$W = \|\mathbf{F}\|\,\|\overrightarrow{PQ}\| \cos\theta$$
$$= (25)(50)\cos 20°$$
$$\approx 1174.62 \text{ foot-pounds}$$

67. $W = (\cos 25°)(20)(40) \approx 725.05$ foot-pounds

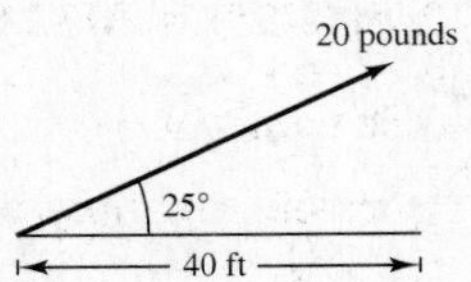

68. Work $= (\cos 20°)(25)(12) \approx 281.9$ foot-pounds

69. True. $\mathbf{u} \cdot \mathbf{v} = 0$

70. False. Work is a scalar, not a vector.

71. $\mathbf{u} \cdot \mathbf{v} = 0 \Rightarrow$ they are orthogonal (unit vectors).

72. (a) $\mathbf{u} \cdot \mathbf{v} = 0 \Rightarrow \mathbf{u}$ and $\mathbf{v}$ are orthogonal and $\theta = \dfrac{\pi}{2}$.

(b) $\mathbf{u} \cdot \mathbf{v} > 0 \Rightarrow \cos\theta > 0 \Rightarrow 0 \le \theta < \dfrac{\pi}{2}$

(c) $\mathbf{u} \cdot \mathbf{v} < 0 \Rightarrow \cos\theta < 0 \Rightarrow \dfrac{\pi}{2} < \theta \le \pi$

73. (a) $\text{proj}_{\mathbf{v}}\mathbf{u} = \mathbf{u} \Rightarrow \mathbf{u}$ and $\mathbf{v}$ are parallel.

(b) $\text{proj}_{\mathbf{v}}\mathbf{u} = \mathbf{0} \Rightarrow \mathbf{u}$ and $\mathbf{v}$ are orthogonal.

74. Let $\mathbf{u}$ and $\mathbf{v}$ be two adjacent sides of the rhombus, $\|\mathbf{u}\| = \|\mathbf{v}\|$. The diagonals are $\mathbf{u} + \mathbf{v}$ and $\mathbf{u} - \mathbf{v}$.

$$(\mathbf{u} + \mathbf{v}) \cdot (\mathbf{u} - \mathbf{v}) = \mathbf{u} \cdot \mathbf{u} + \mathbf{v} \cdot \mathbf{u} - \mathbf{u} \cdot \mathbf{v} - \mathbf{v} \cdot \mathbf{v}$$
$$= \|\mathbf{u}\|^2 - \|\mathbf{v}\|^2 = 0$$

Hence, the diagonals are perpendicular.

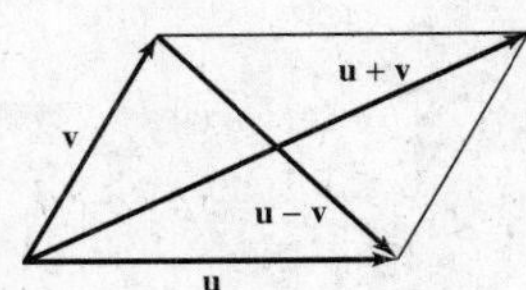

75. Use the Law of Cosines on the triangle:

$$\|\mathbf{u} - \mathbf{v}\|^2 = \|\mathbf{u}\|^2 + \|\mathbf{v}\|^2 - 2\|\mathbf{u}\|\,\|\mathbf{v}\|\cos\theta$$
$$= \|\mathbf{u}\|^2 + \|\mathbf{v}\|^2 - 2\mathbf{u} \cdot \mathbf{v}$$

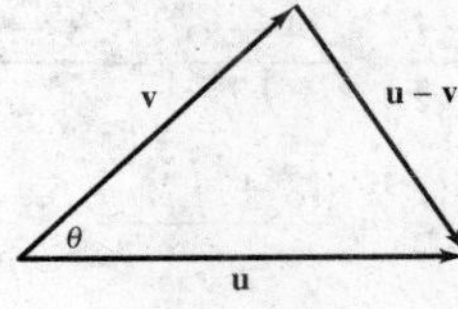

76. $\mathbf{u} \cdot (c\mathbf{v} + d\mathbf{w}) = c(\mathbf{u} \cdot \mathbf{v}) + d(\mathbf{u} \cdot \mathbf{w}) = c0 + d0 = 0$

77. From trigonometry, $x = \cos\theta$ and $y = \sin\theta$. Thus, $\mathbf{u} = \langle x, y\rangle = \cos\theta\,\mathbf{i} + \sin\theta\,\mathbf{j}$.

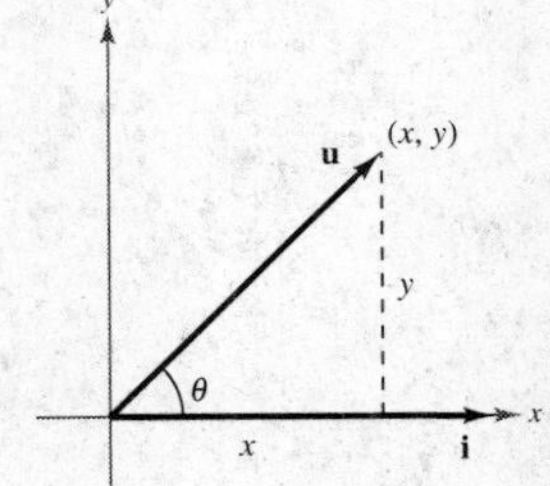

78. From trigonometry,

$x = \cos\left(\frac{\pi}{2} - \theta\right)$ and $y = \sin\left(\frac{\pi}{2} - \theta\right)$.

Thus, $\mathbf{u} = \langle x, y \rangle = \cos\left(\frac{\pi}{2} - \theta\right)\mathbf{i} + \sin\left(\frac{\pi}{2} - \theta\right)\mathbf{j}$.

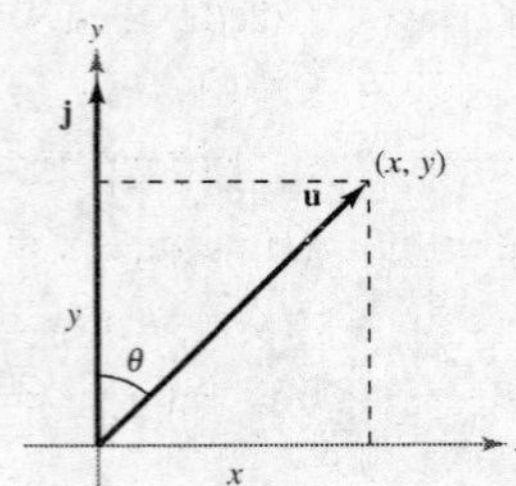

79. $g(x) = f(x - 4)$ is a horizontal shift of f four units to the right.

80. g is a reflection of f with respect to the x-axis.

81. $g(x) = f(x) + 6$ is a vertical shift of f six units upward.

82. g is a horizontal shrink of f.

83. $\sqrt{-4} - 1 = 2i - 1 = -1 + 2i$

84. $\sqrt{-8} + 5 = 2\sqrt{2}i + 5 = 5 + 2\sqrt{2}i$

85. $3i(4 - 5i) = 12i + 15 = 15 + 12i$

86. $-2i(1 + 6i) = -2i + 12 = 12 - 2i$

87. $(1 + 3i)(1 - 3i) = 1 - (3i)^2 = 1 + 9 = 10$

88. $(7 - 4i)(7 + 4i) = 49 + 16 = 65$

89. $$\frac{3}{1+i} + \frac{2}{2-3i} = \frac{3}{1+i} \cdot \frac{1-i}{1-i} + \frac{2}{2-3i} \cdot \frac{2+3i}{2+3i}$$
$$= \frac{3-3i}{2} + \frac{4+6i}{13}$$
$$= \frac{39 - 39i + 8 + 12i}{26}$$
$$= \frac{47}{26} - \frac{27}{26}i$$

90. $$\frac{6}{4-i}\frac{4+i}{4+i} - \frac{3}{1+i} \cdot \frac{1-i}{1-i} = \frac{24+6i}{17} - \frac{3-3i}{2}$$
$$= \frac{48 + 12i - 51 + 51i}{34}$$
$$= \frac{-3}{34} + \frac{63}{34}i$$

91. $-2i$

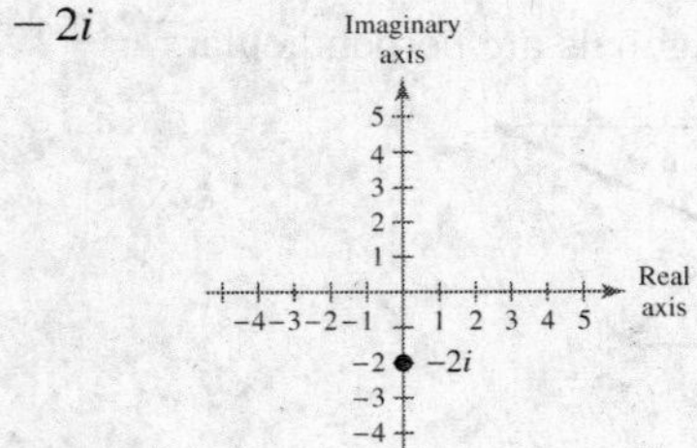

92. $3i$

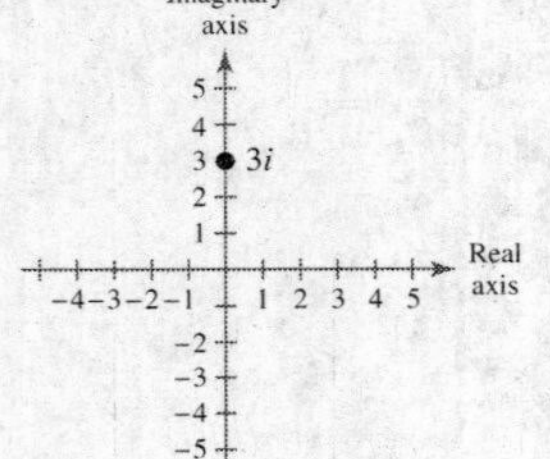

93. $1 + 8i$

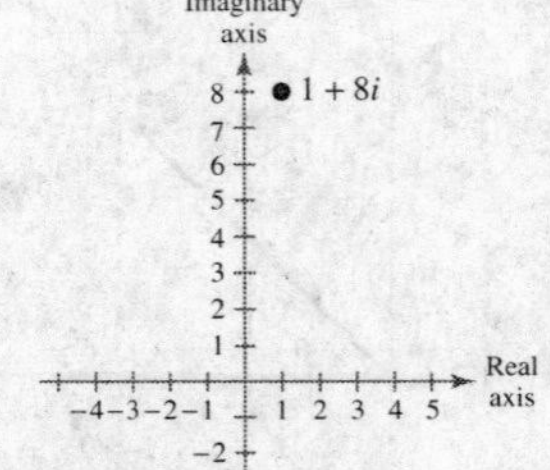

94. $9 - 7i$

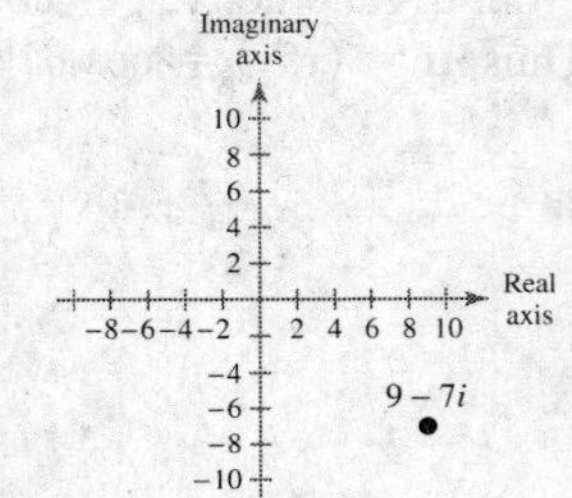

Section 6.5 Trigonometric Form of a Complex Number

- You should be able to graphically represent complex numbers.
- The absolute value of the complex numbers $z = a + bi$ is $|z| = \sqrt{a^2 + b^2}$.
- The trigonometric form of the complex number $z = a + bi$ is $z = r(\cos\theta + i\sin\theta)$ where
  (a) $a = r\cos\theta$ (b) $b = r\sin\theta$
  (c) $r = \sqrt{a^2 + b^2}$; r is called the modulus of z. (d) $\tan\theta = b/a$; θ is called the argument of z.
- Given $z_1 = r_1(\cos\theta_1 + i\sin\theta_1)$ and $z_2 = r_2(\cos\theta_2 + i\sin\theta_2)$:
  (a) $z_1z_2 = r_1r_2[\cos(\theta_1 + \theta_2) + i\sin(\theta_1 + \theta_2)]$
  (b) $\dfrac{z_1}{z_2} = \dfrac{r_1}{r_2}[\cos(\theta_1 - \theta_2) + i\sin(\theta_1 - \theta_2)],\ z_2 \neq 0$
- You should know DeMoivre's Theorem: If $z = r(\cos\theta + i\sin\theta)$, then for any positive integer n,
  $z^n = r^n(\cos n\theta + i\sin n\theta)$.
- You should know that for any positive integer n, $z = r(\cos\theta + i\sin\theta)$ has n distinct nth roots given by
  $$\sqrt[n]{r}\left[\cos\left(\frac{\theta + 2\pi k}{n}\right) + i\sin\left(\frac{\theta + 2\pi k}{n}\right)\right]$$
  where $k = 0, 1, 2, \ldots, n - 1$.

Vocabulary Check

1. absolute value

2. trigonometric form, modulus, argument

3. DeMoivre's

4. nth root

1. $|6i| = 6$

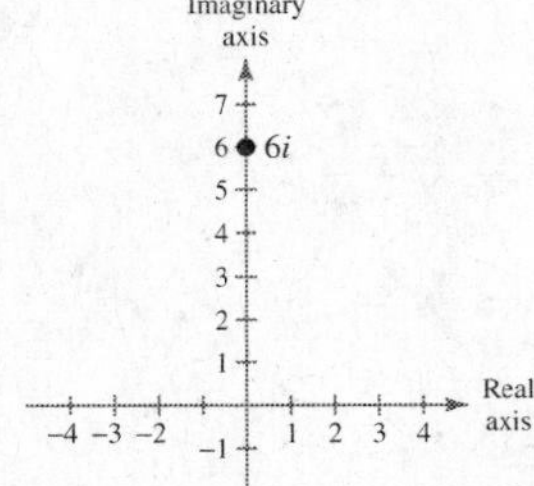

2. $|-2i| = 2$

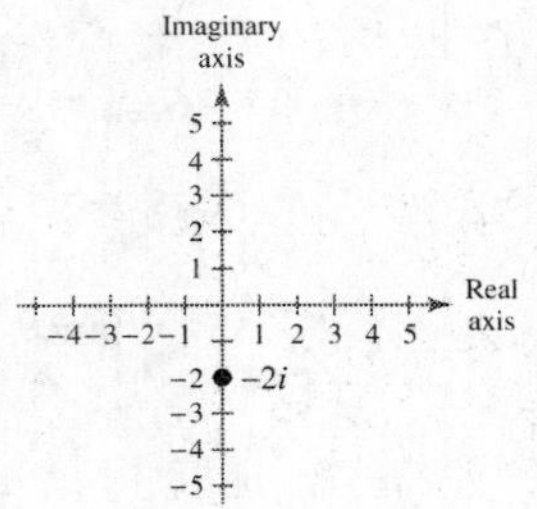

3. $|-4| = \sqrt{(-4)^2 + 0^2} = \sqrt{16} = 4$

4. $|7| = 7$

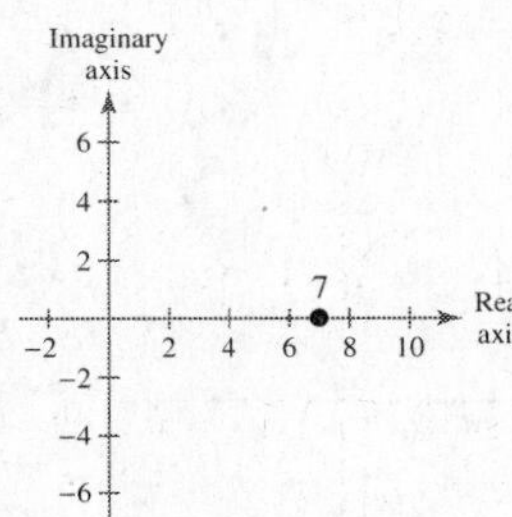

5. $|-4 + 4i| = \sqrt{(-4)^2 + (4)^2} = \sqrt{32} = 4\sqrt{2}$

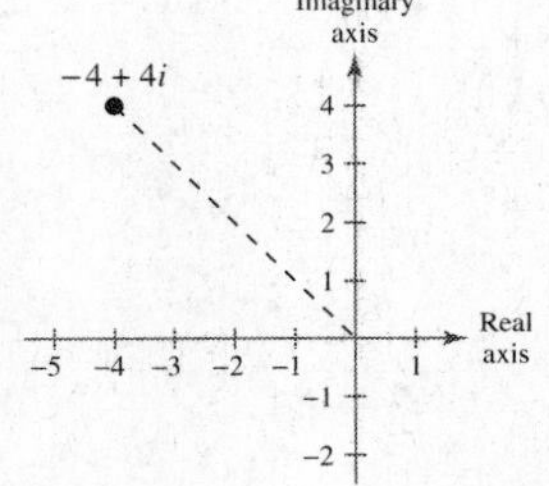

6. $|-5 - 12i| = \sqrt{5^2 + 12^2} = \sqrt{169} = 13$

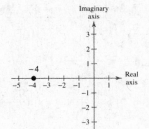

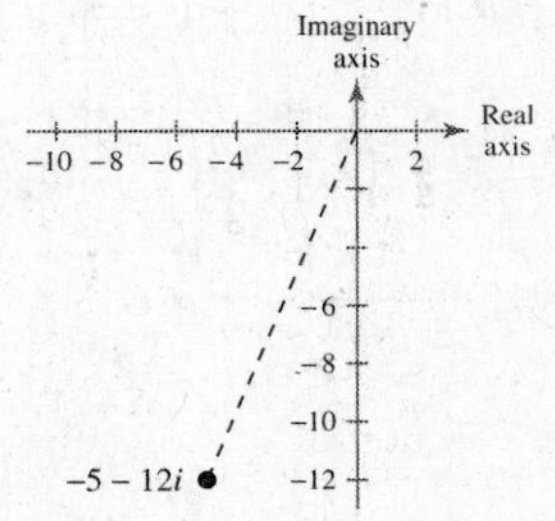

7. $|3 + 6i| = \sqrt{9 + 36}$

$= \sqrt{45} = 3\sqrt{5}$

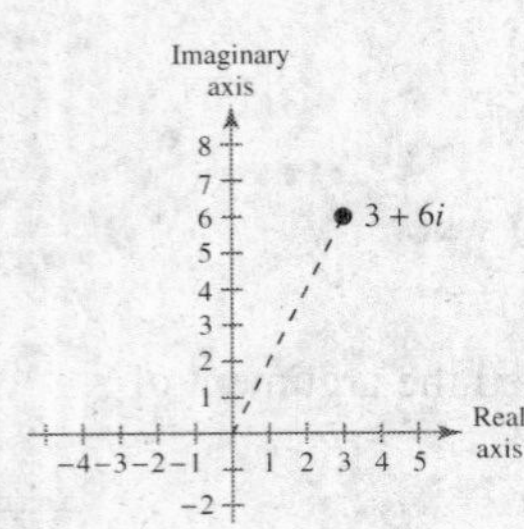

8. $|10 - 3i| = \sqrt{10^2 + (-3)^2}$

$= \sqrt{109}$

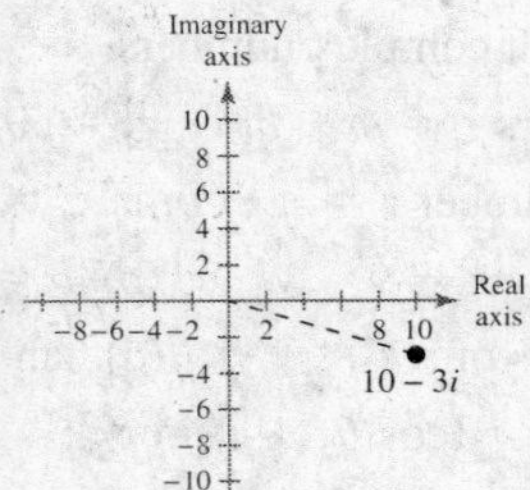

9. $z = 3i$

$r = \sqrt{0^2 + 3^2} = \sqrt{9} = 3$

$\tan\theta = \dfrac{3}{0}$, undefined $\Rightarrow \theta = \dfrac{\pi}{2}$

$z = 3\left(\cos\dfrac{\pi}{2} + i\sin\dfrac{\pi}{2}\right)$

10. $z = 4$

$r = \sqrt{4^2 + 0^2} = \sqrt{16} = 4$

$\tan\theta = \dfrac{0}{4} = 0 \Rightarrow \theta = 0$

$z = 4(\cos 0 + i\sin 0)$

11. $z = -2$

$r = \sqrt{(-2)^2 + 0^2} = 2$

$\tan\theta = \pi \Rightarrow \theta = \pi$

$z = 2(\cos\pi + i\sin\pi)$

12. $z = -i$

$r = \sqrt{0^2 + (-1)^2} = 1$

$\tan\theta$ undefined $\Rightarrow \theta = \dfrac{3\pi}{2}$

$z = \cos\dfrac{3\pi}{2} + i\sin\dfrac{3\pi}{2}$

13. $z = -2 - 2i$

$r = \sqrt{(-2)^2 + (-2)^2} = \sqrt{8} = 2\sqrt{2}$

$\tan\theta = \dfrac{-2}{-2} = 1$, θ is in Quadrant III.

$\theta = \dfrac{5\pi}{4}$

$z = 2\sqrt{2}\left(\cos\dfrac{5\pi}{4} + i\sin\dfrac{5\pi}{4}\right)$

14. $z = 3 + 3i$

$r = \sqrt{3^2 + 3^2} = 3\sqrt{2}$

$\tan\theta = \dfrac{3}{3} = 1 \Rightarrow \theta = \dfrac{\pi}{4}$

$z = 3\sqrt{2}\left(\cos\dfrac{\pi}{4} + i\sin\dfrac{\pi}{4}\right)$

15. $z = \sqrt{3} - i$

$r = \sqrt{(\sqrt{3})^2 + (-1)^2} = 2$

$\tan\theta = \dfrac{-1}{\sqrt{3}} \Rightarrow \theta = \dfrac{11\pi}{6}$

$z = 2\left(\cos\dfrac{11\pi}{6} + i\sin\dfrac{11\pi}{6}\right)$

16. $z = -1 + \sqrt{3}i$

$r = \sqrt{(-1)^2 + (\sqrt{3})^2} = \sqrt{4} = 2$

$\tan\theta = \dfrac{\sqrt{3}}{-1} = -\sqrt{3} \Rightarrow \theta = \dfrac{2\pi}{3}$

$z = 2\left(\cos\dfrac{2\pi}{3} + i\sin\dfrac{2\pi}{3}\right)$

17. $z = 5 - 5i$

$r = \sqrt{5^2 + (-5)^2} = \sqrt{50} = 5\sqrt{2}$

$\tan\theta = -\dfrac{5}{5} = -1 \Rightarrow \theta = \dfrac{7\pi}{4}$

$z = 5\sqrt{2}\left(\cos\dfrac{7\pi}{4} + i\sin\dfrac{7\pi}{4}\right)$

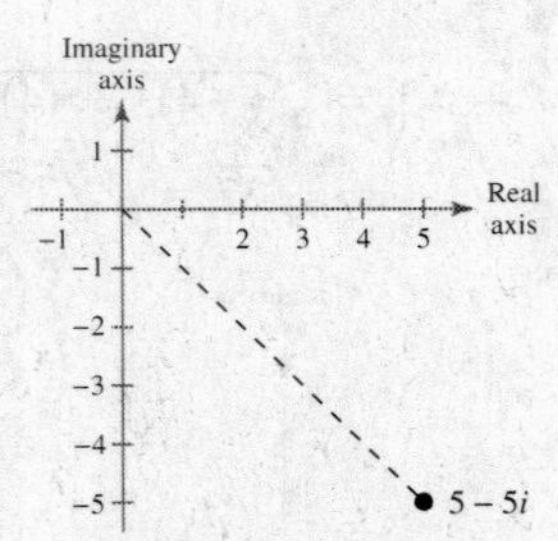

18. $z = 2 + 2i$

$r = \sqrt{4 + 4} = 2\sqrt{2}$

$\tan \theta = \dfrac{2}{2} = 1 \implies \theta = \dfrac{\pi}{4}$

$z = 2\sqrt{2}\left(\cos \dfrac{\pi}{4} + i \sin \dfrac{\pi}{4}\right)$

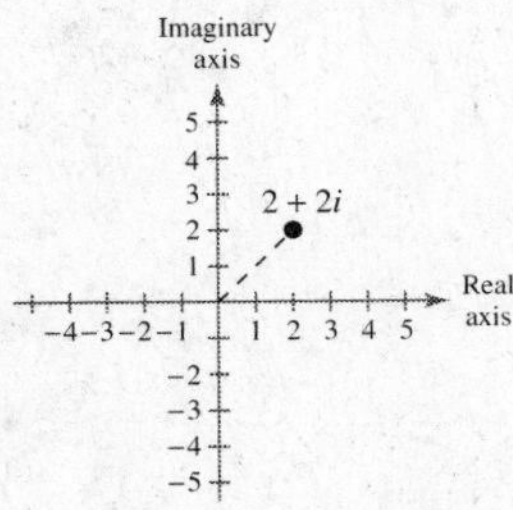

19. $z = \sqrt{3} + i$

$r = \sqrt{\left(\sqrt{3}\right)^2 + 1^2} = \sqrt{4} = 2$

$\tan \theta = \dfrac{1}{\sqrt{3}} = \dfrac{\sqrt{3}}{3} \implies \theta = \dfrac{\pi}{6}$

$z = 2\left(\cos \dfrac{\pi}{6} + i \sin \dfrac{\pi}{6}\right)$

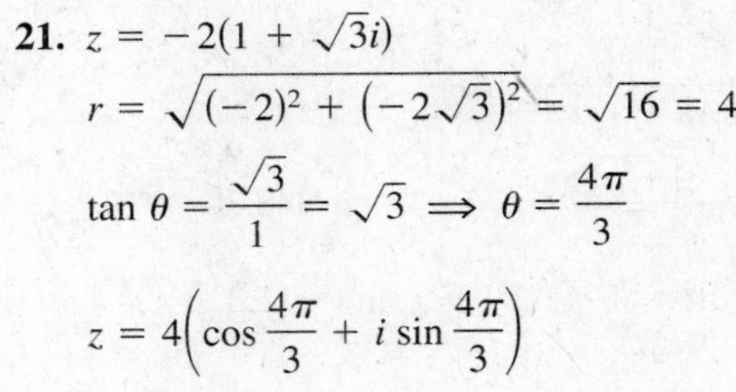

20. $z = -1 - \sqrt{3}i$

$r = \sqrt{1 + 3} = 2$

$\tan \theta = \dfrac{\sqrt{3}}{1} \implies \theta = 240° = \dfrac{4\pi}{3}$

$z = 2\left(\cos \dfrac{4\pi}{3} + i \sin \dfrac{4\pi}{3}\right)$

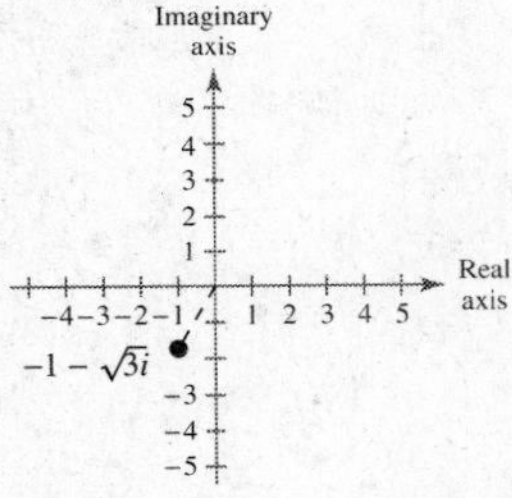

21. $z = -2(1 + \sqrt{3}i)$

$r = \sqrt{(-2)^2 + \left(-2\sqrt{3}\right)^2} = \sqrt{16} = 4$

$\tan \theta = \dfrac{\sqrt{3}}{1} = \sqrt{3} \implies \theta = \dfrac{4\pi}{3}$

$z = 4\left(\cos \dfrac{4\pi}{3} + i \sin \dfrac{4\pi}{3}\right)$

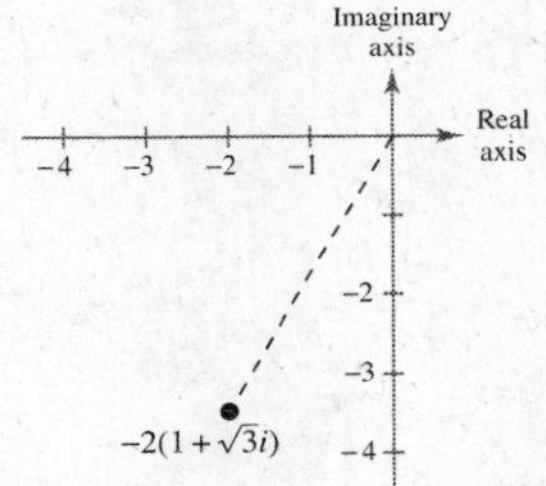

22. $z = \dfrac{5}{2}\left(\sqrt{3} - i\right)$

$r = \sqrt{\left(\dfrac{5}{2}\sqrt{3}\right)^2 + \left(\dfrac{5}{2}(-1)\right)^2} = \sqrt{\dfrac{100}{4}}$

$= \sqrt{25} = 5$

$\tan \theta = \dfrac{-1}{\sqrt{3}} = \dfrac{-\sqrt{3}}{3} \implies \theta = \dfrac{11\pi}{6}$

$z = 5\left(\cos \dfrac{11\pi}{6} + i \sin \dfrac{11\pi}{6}\right)$

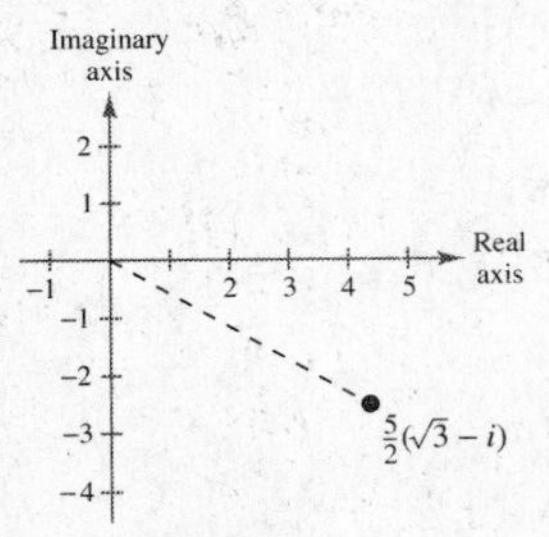

23. $z = -8i$

$r = \sqrt{0 + (-8)^2} = \sqrt{64} = 8$

$\tan \theta = -\dfrac{8}{0}$, undefined $\implies \theta = \dfrac{3\pi}{2}$

$z = 8\left(\cos \dfrac{3\pi}{2} + i \sin \dfrac{3\pi}{2}\right)$

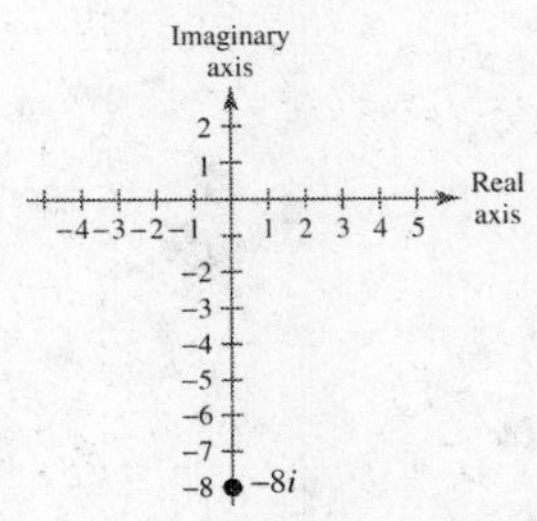

24. $z = 4i$

$r = 4$

$\tan\theta = \dfrac{4}{0}$ undefined $\Rightarrow \theta = \dfrac{\pi}{2}$

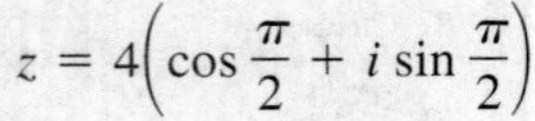

$z = 4\left(\cos\dfrac{\pi}{2} + i\sin\dfrac{\pi}{2}\right)$

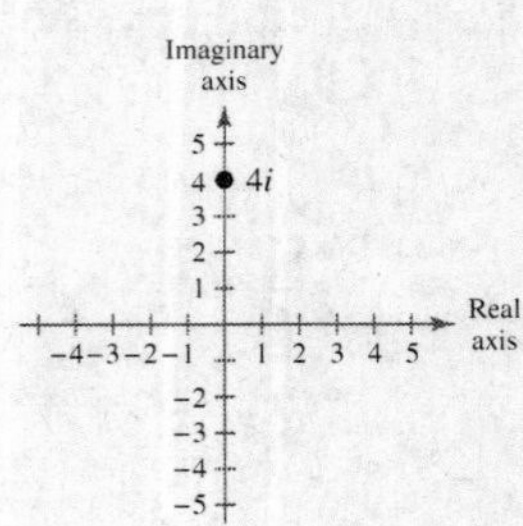

25. $z = -7 + 4i$

$r = \sqrt{49 + 16} = \sqrt{65}$

$\tan\theta = \dfrac{4}{-7} \Rightarrow \theta \approx 2.62$ radians or $150.26°$

$z = \sqrt{65}(\cos 150.26° + i\sin 150.26°)$

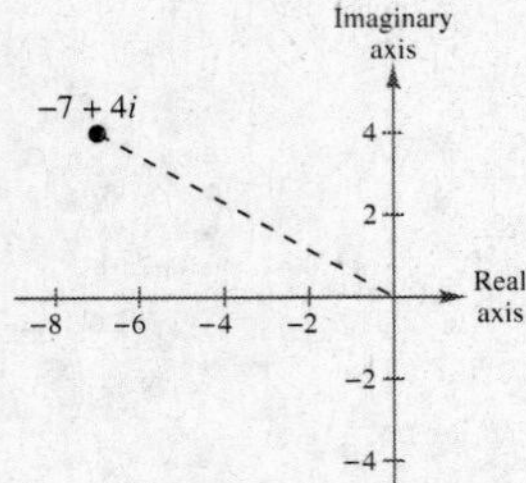

26. $z = 5 - i$

$r = \sqrt{5^2 + (-1)^2} = \sqrt{26}$

$\tan\theta = -\dfrac{1}{5} \Rightarrow \theta \approx -11.3°$ or $348.7°$

$z \approx \sqrt{26}(\cos(-11.3°) + i\sin(-11.3°))$

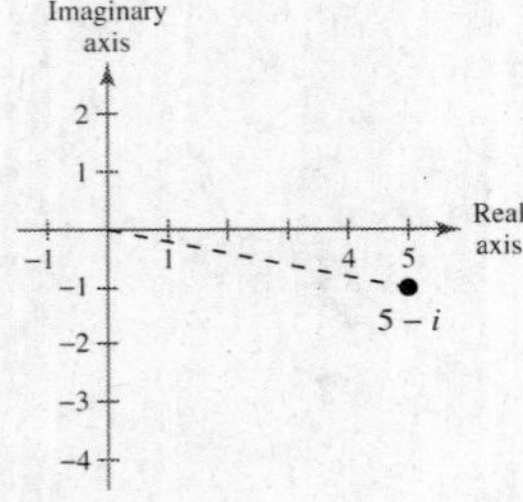

27. $z = 3$

$r = \sqrt{3^2 + 0^2} = 3$

$\tan\theta = \dfrac{0}{3} = 0 \Rightarrow \theta = 0°$

$z = 3(\cos 0° + i\sin 0°)$

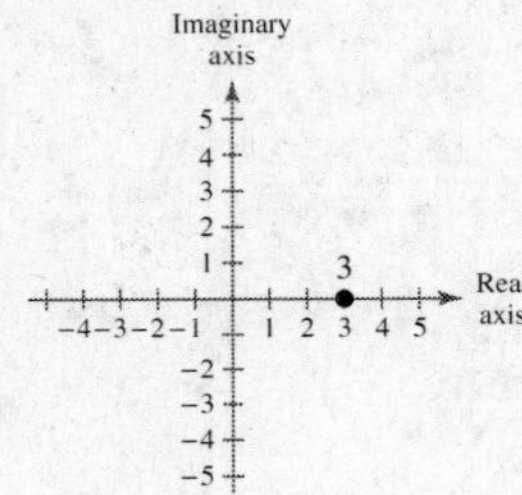

28. $z = 6$

$r = 6$

$\theta = 0$

$z = 6(\cos 0 + i\sin 0)$

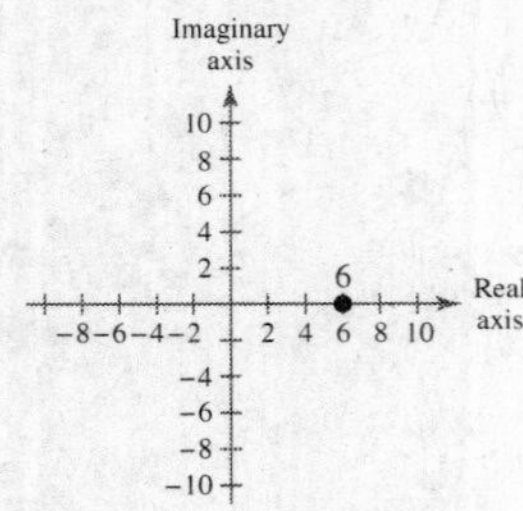

29. $z = 3 + \sqrt{3}i$

$r = \sqrt{9 + 3} = \sqrt{12} = 2\sqrt{3}$

$\tan\theta = \dfrac{\sqrt{3}}{3} \Rightarrow \theta = \dfrac{\pi}{6}$ or $30°$

$z = 2\sqrt{3}\left(\cos\dfrac{\pi}{6} + i\sin\dfrac{\pi}{6}\right)$

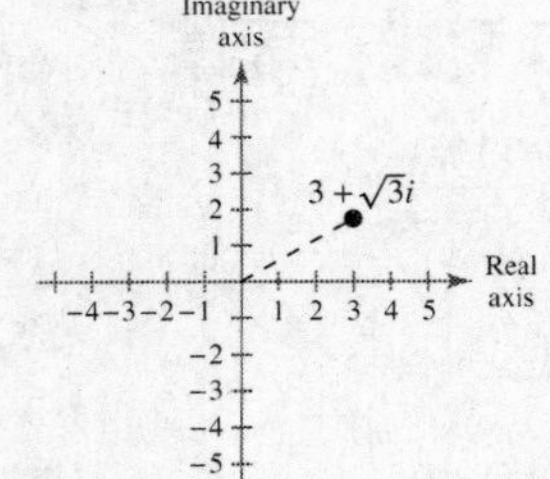

30. $z = 2\sqrt{2} - i$

$r = \sqrt{(2\sqrt{2})^2 + (-1)^2} = \sqrt{9} = 3$

$\tan\theta = \dfrac{-1}{2\sqrt{2}} = -\dfrac{\sqrt{2}}{4} \Rightarrow \theta \approx -19.5° \text{ or } 340.5°$

$z = 3(\cos(-19.5°) + i\sin(-19.5°))$

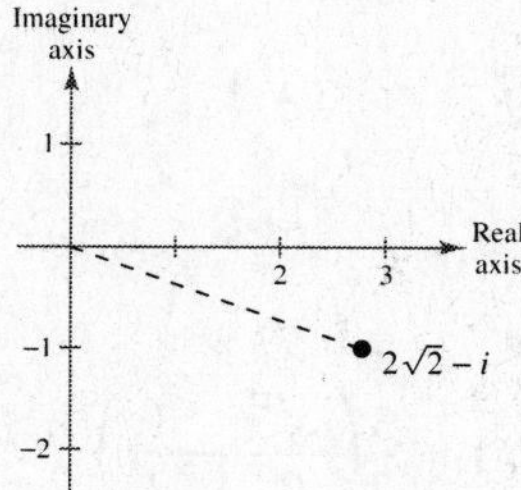

31. $z = -1 - 2i$

$r = \sqrt{1^2 + 2^2} = \sqrt{5}$

$\tan\theta = \dfrac{-2}{-1} = 2 \Rightarrow \theta \approx 243.4°$

$z = \sqrt{5}(\cos 243.4° + i\sin 243.4°)$

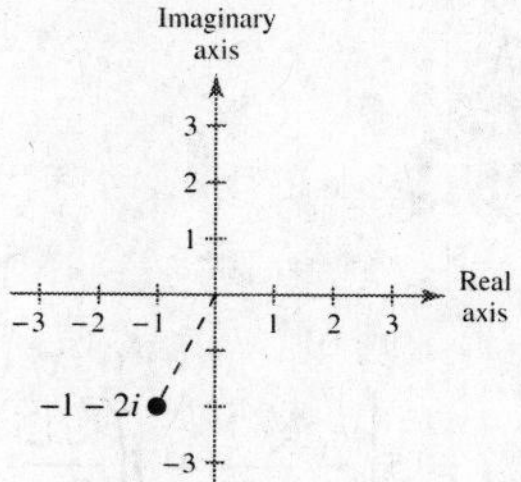

32. $z = 1 + 3i$

$r = \sqrt{1^2 + 3^2} = \sqrt{10}$

$\tan\theta = \frac{3}{1} = 3 \Rightarrow \theta \approx 71.6°$

$z \approx \sqrt{10}(\cos 71.6° + i\sin 71.6°)$

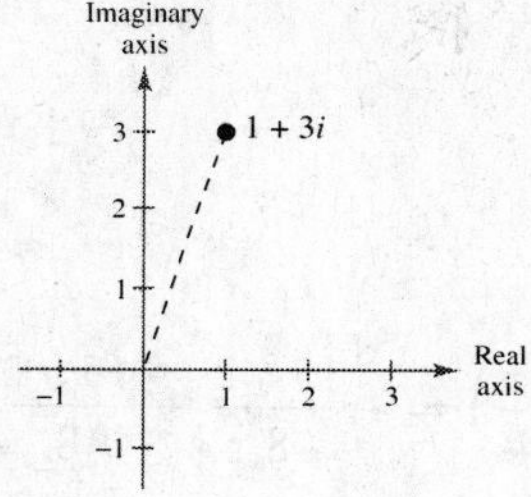

33. $z = 5 + 2i$

$r = \sqrt{25 + 4} = \sqrt{29} \approx 5.385$

$\tan\theta = \frac{2}{5} \Rightarrow \theta \approx 21.80°$

$z = \sqrt{29}(\cos 21.80° + i\sin 21.80°)$

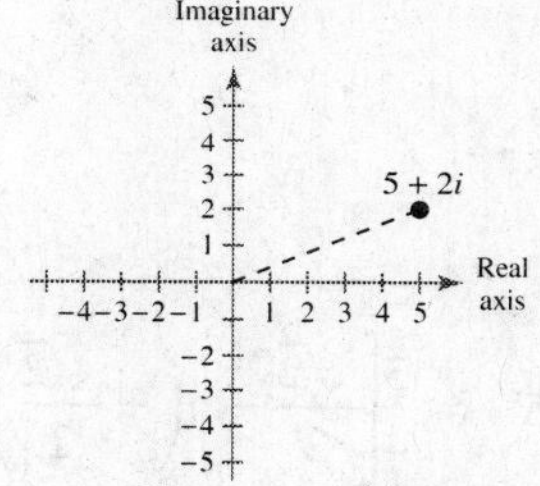

34. $-3 + i \approx 3.16(\cos 161.6° + i\sin 161.6°)$

$= 3.16(\cos 2.82 + i\sin 2.82)$

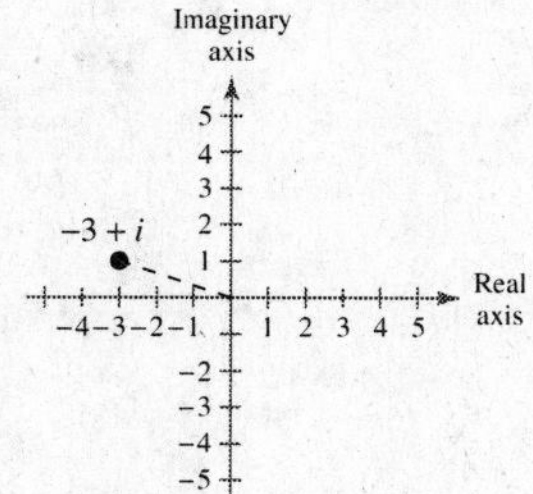

35. $z = 3\sqrt{2} - 7i$

$r = \sqrt{18 + 49} = \sqrt{67} \approx 8.185$

$\tan\theta = \dfrac{-7}{3\sqrt{2}} \approx -1.6499 \Rightarrow \theta \approx 301.22°$

$z = \sqrt{67}(\cos 301.22° + i\sin 301.22°)$

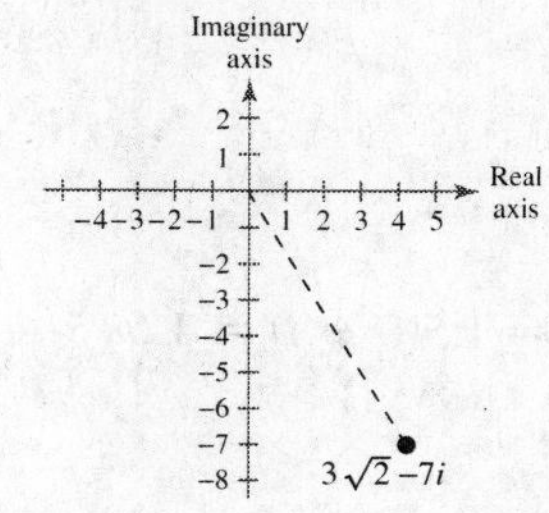

36. $-8 - 5\sqrt{3}i \approx 11.79(\cos 227.3° + i \sin 227.3°)$

$-8 - 5\sqrt{3}i = 11.79(\cos 3.97 + i \sin 3.97)$

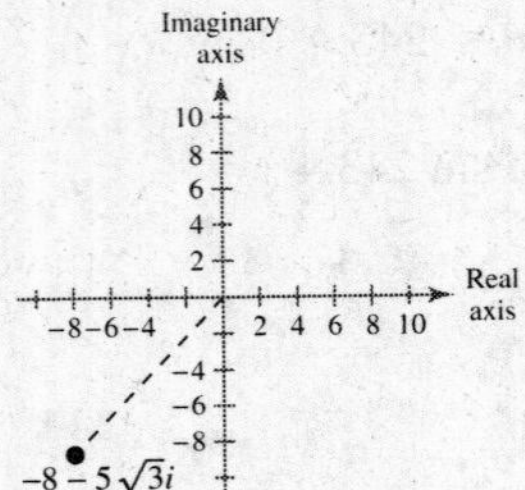

37. $2(\cos 120° + i \sin 120°) = 2\left(-\dfrac{1}{2} + \dfrac{\sqrt{3}}{2}i\right)$

$= -1 + \sqrt{3}i$

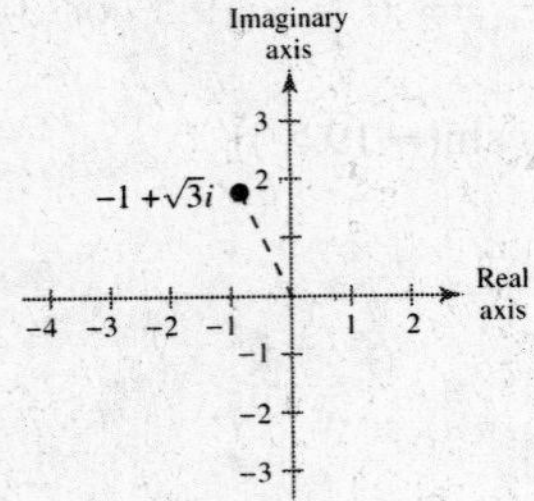

38. $5(\cos 135° + i \sin 135°) = 5\left[-\dfrac{\sqrt{2}}{2} + i\left(\dfrac{\sqrt{2}}{2}\right)\right]$

$= -\dfrac{5\sqrt{2}}{2} + \dfrac{5\sqrt{2}}{2}i$

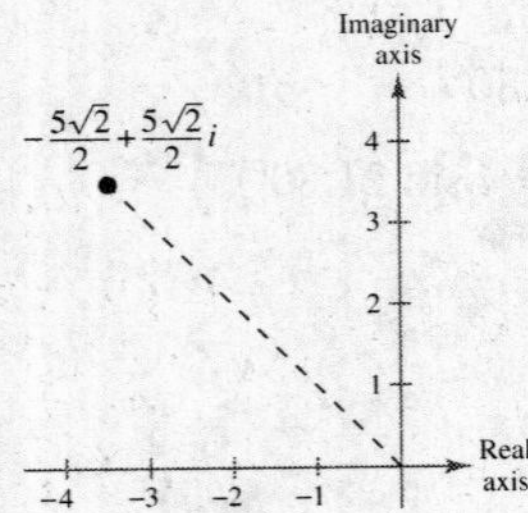

39. $\dfrac{3}{2}(\cos 330° + i \sin 330°) = \dfrac{3}{2}\left(\dfrac{\sqrt{3}}{2} - \dfrac{1}{2}i\right)$

$= \dfrac{3\sqrt{3}}{4} - \dfrac{3}{4}i$

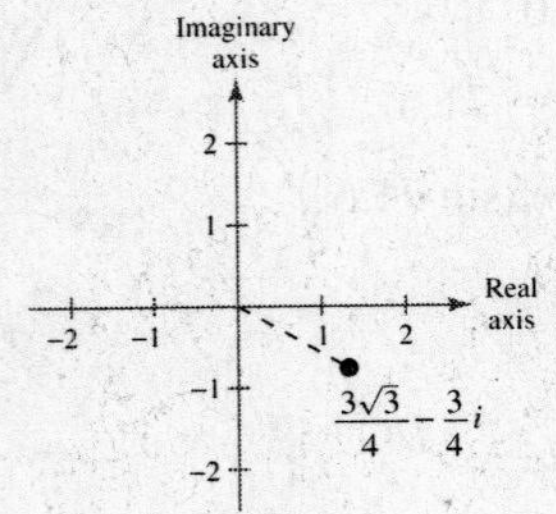

40. $\dfrac{3}{4}(\cos 315° + i \sin 315°) = \dfrac{3}{4}\left[\dfrac{\sqrt{2}}{2} + i\left(-\dfrac{\sqrt{2}}{2}\right)\right]$

$= \dfrac{3\sqrt{2}}{8} - \dfrac{3\sqrt{2}}{8}i$

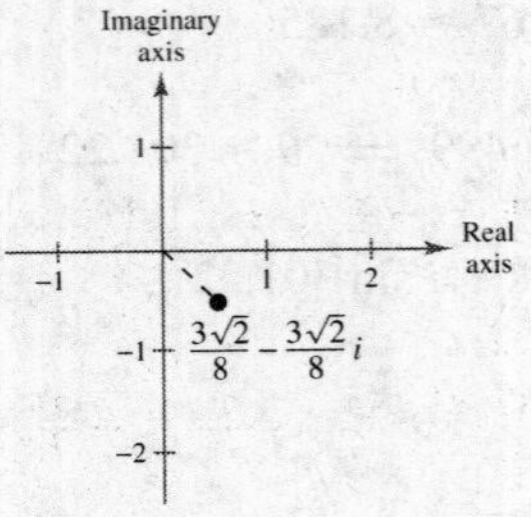

41. $3.75\left(\cos \dfrac{3\pi}{4} + i \sin \dfrac{3\pi}{4}\right) = -\dfrac{15\sqrt{2}}{8} + \dfrac{15\sqrt{2}}{8}i$

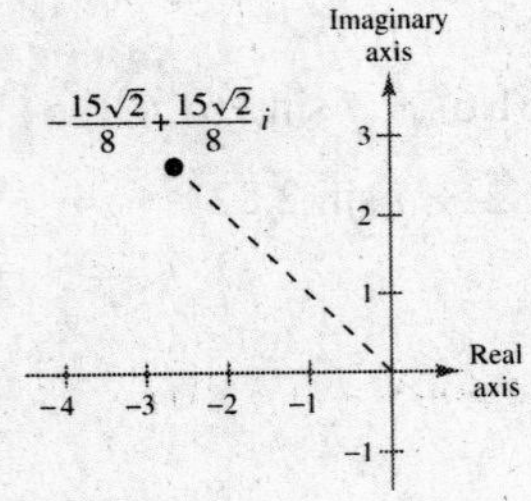

42. $1.5\left(\cos \dfrac{\pi}{2} + i \sin \dfrac{\pi}{2}\right) = 1.5(0 + i) = 1.5i$

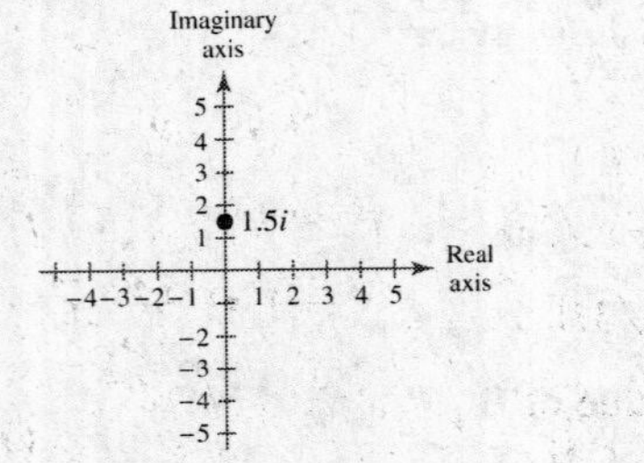

43. $6\left(\cos \dfrac{\pi}{3} + i \sin \dfrac{\pi}{3}\right) = 6\left(\dfrac{1}{2} + \dfrac{\sqrt{3}}{2}i\right) = 3 + 3\sqrt{3}i$

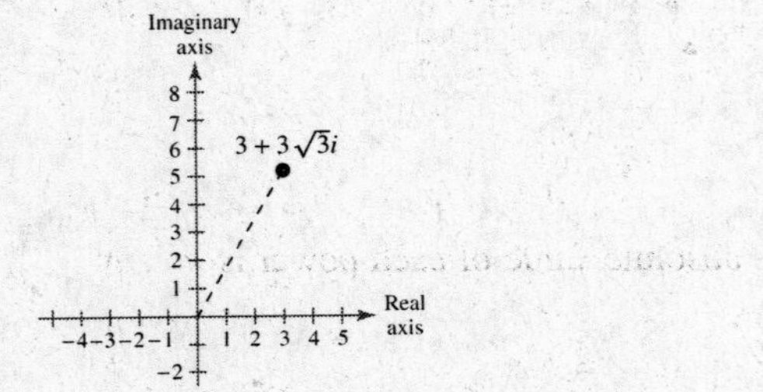

44. $8\left(\cos\dfrac{5\pi}{6} + i\sin\dfrac{5\pi}{6}\right) = 8\left(-\dfrac{\sqrt{3}}{2} + i\dfrac{1}{2}\right)$

$= -4\sqrt{3} + 4i$

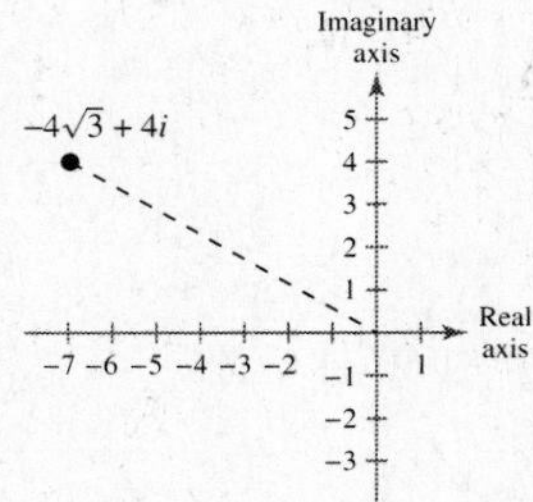

45. $4\left(\cos\dfrac{3\pi}{2} + i\sin\dfrac{3\pi}{2}\right) = 4(0 - i) = -4i$

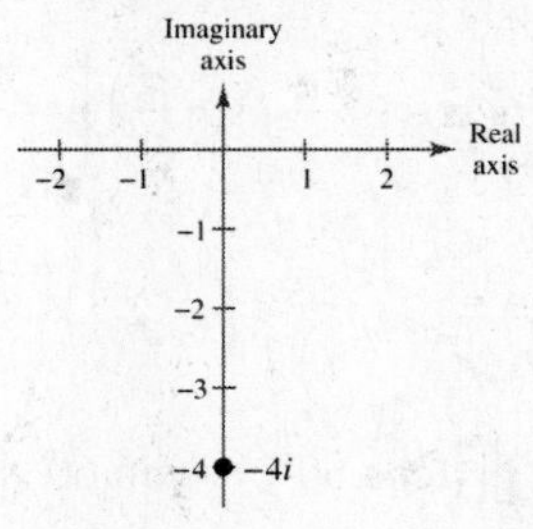

46. $9(\cos 0 + i\sin 0) = 9$

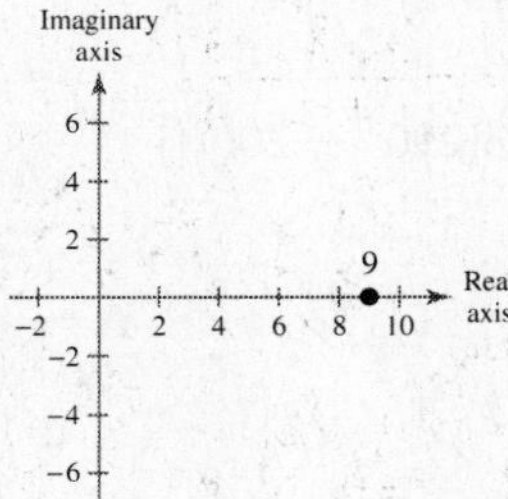

47. $3[\cos(18°\,45') + i\sin(18°\,45')] \approx 2.8408 + 0.9643i$

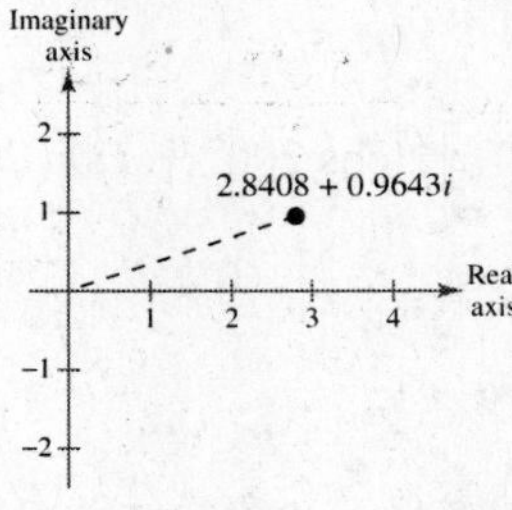

48. $6[\cos(230°\,30') + i\sin(230°\,30')] \approx -3.8165 - 4.6297i$

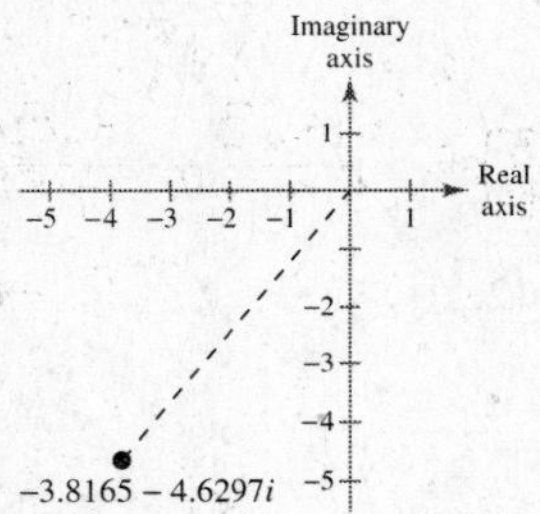

49. $5\left(\cos\dfrac{\pi}{9} + i\sin\dfrac{\pi}{9}\right) \approx 4.6985 + 1.7101i$

50. $12\left(\cos\dfrac{3\pi}{5} + \text{i}\sin\dfrac{3\pi}{5}\right) \approx -3.71 + 11.41i$

51. $9(\cos 58° + i\sin 58°) \approx 4.7693 + 7.6324i$

52. $4(\cos 216.5° + i\sin 216.5°) = -3.22 - 2.38i$

53.

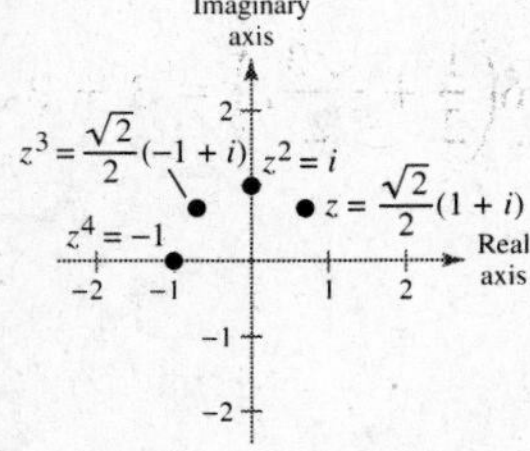

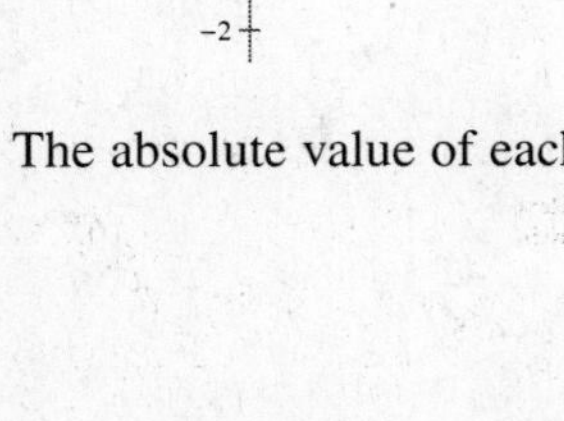

The absolute value of each power is 1.

54. $z = \frac{1}{2}(1 + \sqrt{3}i)$

$z^2 = \frac{1}{2}(1 + \sqrt{3}i)\frac{1}{2}(1 + \sqrt{3}i) = \frac{1}{2}(-1 + \sqrt{3}i)$

$z^3 = z^2z = \frac{1}{2}(-1 + \sqrt{3}i)\frac{1}{2}(1 + \sqrt{3}i)$

$= -1$

$z^4 = z^3z$

$= (-1)\frac{1}{2}(1 + \sqrt{3}i)$

$= \frac{1}{2}(-1 - \sqrt{3}i)$

The absolute value of each is 1.

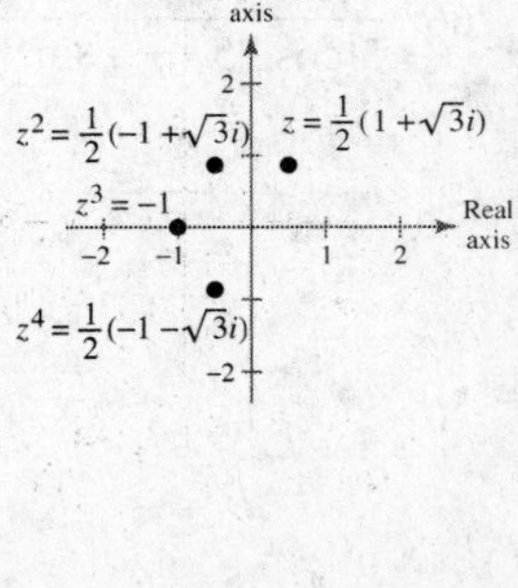

55. $\left[3\left(\cos\frac{\pi}{3} + i\sin\frac{\pi}{3}\right)\right]\left[4\left(\cos\frac{\pi}{6} + i\sin\frac{\pi}{6}\right)\right] = (3)(4)\left[\cos\left(\frac{\pi}{3} + \frac{\pi}{6}\right) + i\sin\left(\frac{\pi}{6} + \frac{\pi}{3}\right)\right] = 12\left(\cos\frac{\pi}{2} + i\sin\frac{\pi}{2}\right)$

56. $\left[\frac{3}{2}\left(\cos\frac{\pi}{6} + i\sin\frac{\pi}{6}\right)\right]\left[6\left(\cos\frac{\pi}{4} + i\sin\frac{\pi}{4}\right)\right] = \frac{3}{2}(6)\left[\cos\left(\frac{\pi}{6} + \frac{\pi}{4}\right) + i\sin\left(\frac{\pi}{6} + \frac{\pi}{4}\right)\right]$

$= 9\left(\cos\frac{5\pi}{12} + i\sin\frac{5\pi}{12}\right)$

57. $\left[\frac{5}{3}(\cos 140° + i\sin 140°)\right]\left[\frac{2}{3}(\cos 60° + i\sin 60°)\right] = \left(\frac{5}{3}\right)\left(\frac{2}{3}\right)[\cos(140° + 60°) + i\sin(140° + 60°)]$

$= \frac{10}{9}(\cos 200° + i\sin 200°)$

58. $\left[\frac{1}{2}(\cos 115° + i\sin 115°)\right]\left[\frac{4}{5}(\cos 300° + i\sin 300°)\right] = \frac{1}{2}\left(\frac{4}{5}\right)[\cos(115° + 300°) + i\sin(115° + 300°)]$

$= \frac{2}{5}(\cos 415° + i\sin 415°) = \frac{2}{5}(\cos 55° + i\sin 55°)$

59. $\left[\frac{11}{20}(\cos 290° + i\sin 290°)\right]\left[\frac{2}{5}(\cos 200° + i\sin 200°)\right] = \left(\frac{11}{20}\right)\left(\frac{2}{5}\right)[\cos(290° + 200°) + i\sin(290° + 200°)]$

$= \frac{11}{50}(\cos 490° + i\sin 490°)$

$= \frac{11}{50}(\cos 130° + i\sin 130°)$

60. $(\cos 5° + i\sin 5°)(\cos 20° + i\sin 20°) = \cos(5° + 20°) + i\sin(5° + 20°)$

$= \cos 25° + i\sin 25°$

61. $\dfrac{\cos 50° + i\sin 50°}{\cos 20° + i\sin 20°} = \cos(50° - 20°) + i\sin(50° - 20°) = \cos 30° + i\sin 30°$

62. $\dfrac{5[\cos(4.3) + i\sin(4.3)]}{4[\cos(2.1) + i\sin(2.1)]} = \frac{5}{4}[\cos(4.3 - 2.1) + i\sin(4.3 - 2.1) = \frac{5}{4}[\cos(2.2) + i\sin(2.2)]$

63. $\dfrac{2(\cos 120° + i\sin 120°)}{4(\cos 40° + i\sin 40°)} = \frac{1}{2}[\cos(120° - 40°) + i\sin(120° - 40°)] = \frac{1}{2}(\cos 80° + i\sin 80°)$

64. $\dfrac{\cos\frac{7\pi}{4} + i\sin\frac{7\pi}{4}}{\cos\pi + i\sin\pi} = \cos\frac{3\pi}{4} + i\sin\frac{3\pi}{4}$

65. $\dfrac{18(\cos 54° + i\sin 54°)}{3(\cos 102° + i\sin 102°)} = 6(\cos(54° - 102°) + i\sin(54° - 102°))$

$= 6(\cos(-48°) + i\sin(-48°)) = 6(\cos 312° + i\sin 312°)$

66. $\dfrac{9(\cos 20° + i\sin 20°)}{5(\cos 75° + i\sin 75°)} = \frac{9}{5}[\cos(20° - 75°) + i\sin(20° - 75°)]$

$= \frac{9}{5}[\cos(-55°) + i\sin(-55°)]$

$= \frac{9}{5}[\cos 305° + i\sin 305°]$

67. (a) $2 - 2i = 2\sqrt{2}\left(\cos\frac{7\pi}{4} + i\sin\frac{7\pi}{4}\right)$

$1 + i = \sqrt{2}\left(\cos\frac{\pi}{4} + i\sin\frac{\pi}{4}\right)$

(b) $(2 - 2i)(1 + i) = 2\sqrt{2}\left(\cos\frac{7\pi}{4} + i\sin\frac{7\pi}{4}\right)\sqrt{2}\left(\cos\frac{\pi}{4} + i\sin\frac{\pi}{4}\right) = 4(\cos 2\pi + i\sin 2\pi) = 4$

(c) $(2 - 2i)(1 + i) = 2 + 2 = 4$

68. (a) $3 - 3i = 3\sqrt{2}\left(\cos\frac{7\pi}{4} + i\sin\frac{7\pi}{4}\right)$

$1 - i = \sqrt{2}\left(\cos\frac{7\pi}{4} + i\sin\frac{7\pi}{4}\right)$

(b) $(3 - 3i)(1 - i) = 3\sqrt{2}\left(\cos\frac{7\pi}{4} + i\sin\frac{7\pi}{4}\right)\sqrt{2}\left(\cos\frac{7\pi}{4} + i\sin\frac{7\pi}{4}\right) = 6\left(\cos\frac{7\pi}{2} + i\sin\frac{7\pi}{2}\right) = -6i$

(c) $(3 - 3i)(1 - i) = 3 - 3 - 6i = -6i$

69. (a) $2 + 2i = 2\sqrt{2}(\cos 45° + i\sin 45°)$

$1 - i = \sqrt{2}[\cos(-45°) + i\sin(-45°)]$

(b) $(2 + 2i)(1 - i) = \left[2\sqrt{2}(\cos 45° + i\sin 45°)\right]\left[\sqrt{2}(\cos(-45°) + i\sin(-45°))\right] = 4(\cos 0° + i\sin 0°) = 4$

(c) $(2 + 2i)(1 - i) = 2 - 2i + 2i - 2i^2 = 2 + 2 = 4$

70. (a) $\sqrt{3} + i = 2(\cos 30° + i\sin 30°)$

$1 + i = \sqrt{2}(\cos 45° + i\sin 45°)$

(b) $\left(\sqrt{3} + i\right)(1 + i) = [2(\cos 30° + i\sin 30°)]\left[\sqrt{2}(\cos 45° + i\sin 45°)\right]$

$= 2\sqrt{2}(\cos 75° + i\sin 75°)$

$= 2\sqrt{2}\left[\left(\frac{\sqrt{6} - \sqrt{2}}{4}\right) + \left(\frac{\sqrt{6} + \sqrt{2}}{4}\right)i\right]$

$= \left(\sqrt{3} - 1\right) + \left(\sqrt{3} + 1\right)i$

(c) $\left(\sqrt{3} + i\right)(1 + i) = \sqrt{3} + \left(\sqrt{3} + 1\right)i + i^2 = \left(\sqrt{3} - 1\right) + \left(\sqrt{3} + 1\right)i$

71. (a) $-2i = 2[\cos(-90°) + i\sin(-90°)]$

$1 + i = \sqrt{2}(\cos 45° + i\sin 45°)$

(b) $-2i(1 + i) = 2[\cos(-90°) + i\sin(-90°)]\left[\sqrt{2}(\cos 45° + i\sin 45°)\right]$

$= 2\sqrt{2}[\cos(-45°) + i\sin(-45°)]$

$= 2\sqrt{2}\left[\frac{1}{\sqrt{2}} - \frac{1}{\sqrt{2}}i\right] = 2 - 2i$

(c) $-2i(1 + i) = -2i - 2i^2 = -2i + 2 = 2 - 2i$

72. (a) $3i = 3\left(\cos\frac{\pi}{2} + i\sin\frac{\pi}{2}\right)$

$1 + i = \sqrt{2}\left(\cos\frac{\pi}{4} + i\sin\frac{\pi}{4}\right)$

(b) $3i(1+i) = 3\left(\cos\frac{\pi}{2} + i\sin\frac{\pi}{2}\right)\sqrt{2}\left(\cos\frac{\pi}{4} + i\sin\frac{\pi}{4}\right)$

$= 3\sqrt{2}\left(\cos\frac{3\pi}{4} + i\sin\frac{3\pi}{4}\right)$

$= 3\sqrt{2}\left(-\frac{\sqrt{2}}{2} + i\frac{\sqrt{2}}{2}\right) = -3 + 3i$

(c) $3i(1+i) = 3i - 3 = -3 + 3i$

73. (a) $-2i = 2\left(\cos\frac{3\pi}{2} + i\sin\frac{3\pi}{2}\right)$

$\sqrt{3} - i = 2\left(\cos\frac{11\pi}{6} + i\sin\frac{11\pi}{6}\right)$

(b) $-2i(\sqrt{3} - i) = 2\left(\cos\frac{3\pi}{2} + i\sin\frac{3\pi}{2}\right)2\left(\cos\frac{11\pi}{6} + i\sin\frac{11\pi}{6}\right)$

$= 4\left(\cos\frac{20\pi}{6} + i\sin\frac{20\pi}{6}\right)$

$= 4\left(-\frac{1}{2} - \frac{\sqrt{3}}{2}i\right)$

$= -2 - 2\sqrt{3}i$

(c) $-2i(\sqrt{3} - i) = -2\sqrt{3}i - 2$

74. (a) $-i = \cos\frac{3\pi}{2} + i\sin\frac{3\pi}{2}$

$1 + \sqrt{3}i = 2\left(\cos\frac{\pi}{3} + i\sin\frac{\pi}{3}\right)$

(b) $-i(1 + \sqrt{3}i) = \left(\cos\frac{3\pi}{2} + i\sin\frac{3\pi}{2}\right)2\left(\cos\frac{\pi}{3} + i\sin\frac{\pi}{3}\right)$

$= 2\left(\cos\frac{11\pi}{6} + i\sin\frac{11\pi}{6}\right)$

$= 2\left(\frac{\sqrt{3}}{2} - i\frac{1}{2}\right) = \sqrt{3} - i$

(c) $(-i)(1 + \sqrt{3}i) = -i + \sqrt{3}$

75. (a) $2 = 2(\cos 0 + i\sin 0)$

$1 - i = \sqrt{2}\left(\cos\frac{7\pi}{4} + i\sin\frac{7\pi}{4}\right)$

(b) $2(1 - i) = 2\sqrt{2}\left(\cos\frac{7\pi}{4} + i\sin\frac{7\pi}{4}\right)$

$= 2\sqrt{2}\left(\frac{\sqrt{2}}{2} - \frac{\sqrt{2}}{2}i\right)$

$= 2(1 - i) = 2 - 2i$

(c) $2(1 - i) = 2 - 2i$

76. (a) $-4 = 4(\cos\pi + i\sin\pi)$

$1 + i = \sqrt{2}\left(\cos\frac{\pi}{4} + i\sin\frac{\pi}{4}\right)$

(b) $-4(1 + i) = 4\sqrt{2}\left(\cos\frac{5\pi}{4} + i\sin\frac{5\pi}{4}\right)$

$= 4\sqrt{2}\left(-\frac{\sqrt{2}}{2} - \frac{\sqrt{2}}{2}i\right)$

$= -4 - 4i$

(c) $-4(1 + i) = -4 - 4i$

77. (a) $3 + 3i = 3\sqrt{2}\left(\cos\dfrac{\pi}{4} + i\sin\dfrac{\pi}{4}\right)$

$1 - \sqrt{3}i = 2\left(\cos\dfrac{5\pi}{3} + i\sin\dfrac{5\pi}{3}\right)$

(b) $\dfrac{3 + 3i}{1 - \sqrt{3}i} = \dfrac{3\sqrt{2}}{2}\left(\cos\left(\dfrac{\pi}{4} - \dfrac{5\pi}{3}\right) + i\sin\left(\dfrac{\pi}{4} - \dfrac{5\pi}{3}\right)\right)$

$= \dfrac{3\sqrt{2}}{2}\left(\cos\left(-\dfrac{17\pi}{12}\right) + i\sin\left(-\dfrac{17\pi}{12}\right)\right)$

$\approx -0.549 + 2.049i$

(c) $\dfrac{3 + 3i}{1 - \sqrt{3}i} \cdot \dfrac{1 + \sqrt{3}i}{1 + \sqrt{3}i} = \dfrac{3 - 3\sqrt{3} + (3 + 3\sqrt{3})i}{4}$

$\approx -0.549 + 2.049i$

78. (a) $2 + 2i = 2\sqrt{2}\left(\cos\dfrac{\pi}{4} + i\sin\dfrac{\pi}{4}\right)$

$1 + \sqrt{3}i = 2\left(\cos\dfrac{\pi}{3} + i\sin\dfrac{\pi}{3}\right)$

(b) $\dfrac{2 + 2i}{1 + \sqrt{3}i} = \dfrac{2\sqrt{2}}{2}\left(\cos\left(\dfrac{\pi}{4} - \dfrac{\pi}{3}\right) + i\sin\left(\dfrac{\pi}{4} - \dfrac{\pi}{3}\right)\right)$

$= \sqrt{2}\left(\cos\left(-\dfrac{\pi}{12}\right) + i\sin\left(-\dfrac{\pi}{12}\right)\right)$

$\approx 1.366 - 0.366i$

(c) $\dfrac{2 + 2i}{1 + \sqrt{3}i} \cdot \dfrac{1 - \sqrt{3}i}{1 - \sqrt{3}i} = \dfrac{2 + 2\sqrt{3} + (2 - 2\sqrt{3})i}{4} = \dfrac{1 + \sqrt{3}}{2} + \dfrac{1 - \sqrt{3}}{2}i$

$\approx 1.366 - 0.366i$

79. (a) $5 = 5(\cos 0 + i\sin 0)$

$2 + 2i = 2\sqrt{2}\left(\cos\dfrac{\pi}{4} + i\sin\dfrac{\pi}{4}\right)$

(b) $\dfrac{5}{2 + 2i} = \dfrac{5(\cos 0 + i\sin 0)}{2\sqrt{2}\left(\cos\dfrac{\pi}{4} + i\sin\dfrac{\pi}{4}\right)}$

$= \dfrac{5}{2\sqrt{2}}\left(\cos\left(-\dfrac{\pi}{4}\right) + i\sin\left(-\dfrac{\pi}{4}\right)\right)$

$= \dfrac{5}{2\sqrt{2}}\left(\dfrac{\sqrt{2}}{2} - \dfrac{\sqrt{2}}{2}i\right) = \dfrac{5}{4} - \dfrac{5}{4}i$

(c) $\dfrac{5}{2 + 2i} \cdot \dfrac{2 - 2i}{2 - 2i} = \dfrac{5(2 - 2i)}{4 + 4} = \dfrac{5}{4} - \dfrac{5}{4}i$

80. (a) $2 = 2(\cos 0 + i\sin 0)$

$\sqrt{3} - i = 2\left(\cos\dfrac{11\pi}{6} + i\sin\dfrac{11\pi}{6}\right)$

(b) $\dfrac{2}{\sqrt{3} - i} = \dfrac{2}{2}\left(\cos\left(-\dfrac{11\pi}{6}\right) + i\sin\left(-\dfrac{11\pi}{6}\right)\right)$

$= \dfrac{\sqrt{3}}{2} + \dfrac{1}{2}i$

(c) $\dfrac{2}{\sqrt{3} - i} \cdot \dfrac{\sqrt{3} + i}{\sqrt{3} + i} = \dfrac{2(\sqrt{3} + i)}{4} = \dfrac{\sqrt{3}}{2} + \dfrac{1}{2}i$

81. (a) $4i = 4\left(\cos\frac{\pi}{2} + i\sin\frac{\pi}{2}\right)$

$-1 + i = \sqrt{2}\left(\cos\frac{3\pi}{4} + i\sin\frac{3\pi}{4}\right)$

(b) $\frac{4i}{-1+i} = \frac{4}{\sqrt{2}}\left(\cos\left(\frac{\pi}{2} - \frac{3\pi}{4}\right) + i\sin\left(\frac{\pi}{2} - \frac{3\pi}{4}\right)\right)$

$= \frac{4}{\sqrt{2}}\left(\cos\left(-\frac{\pi}{4}\right) + i\sin\left(-\frac{\pi}{4}\right)\right)$

$= \frac{4}{\sqrt{2}}\left(\frac{\sqrt{2}}{2} - \frac{\sqrt{2}}{2}i\right) = 2 - 2i$

(c) $\frac{4i}{-1+i} \cdot \frac{-1-i}{-1-i} = \frac{-4i+4}{2} = 2 - 2i$

82. (a) $2i = 2\left(\cos\frac{\pi}{2} + i\sin\frac{\pi}{2}\right)$

$1 - \sqrt{3}i = 2\left(\cos\frac{5\pi}{3} + i\sin\frac{5\pi}{3}\right)$

(b) $\frac{2i}{1-\sqrt{3}i} = \frac{2}{2}\left(\cos\left(\frac{\pi}{2} - \frac{5\pi}{3}\right) + i\sin\left(\frac{\pi}{2} - \frac{5\pi}{3}\right)\right)$

$= \cos\left(-\frac{7\pi}{6}\right) + i\sin\left(-\frac{7\pi}{6}\right) = \frac{-\sqrt{3}}{2} + \frac{1}{2}i$

(c) $\frac{2i}{1-\sqrt{3}i} \cdot \frac{1+\sqrt{3}i}{1+\sqrt{3}i} = \frac{2i - 2\sqrt{3}}{4} = \frac{-\sqrt{3}}{2} + \frac{1}{2}i$

83. Let $z = x + iy$ such that:

$|z| = 2 \Rightarrow 2 = \sqrt{x^2 + y^2} \Rightarrow 4 = x^2 + y^2$

Circle with radius of 2

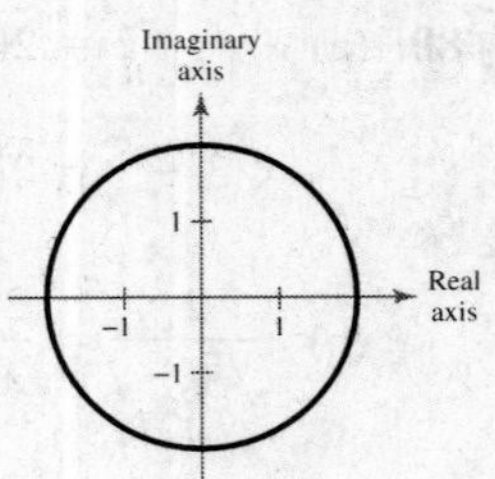

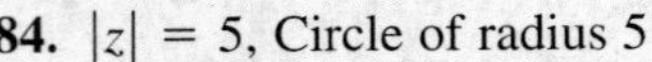

84. $|z| = 5$, Circle of radius 5

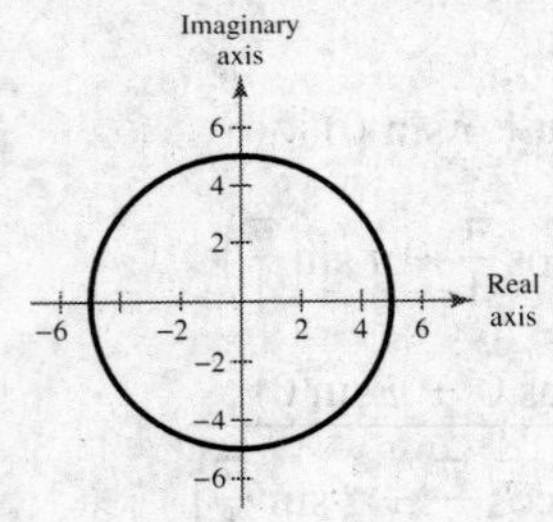

85. Let $z = x + iy$.

$|z| = 4 \Rightarrow 4 = \sqrt{x^2 + y^2} \Rightarrow x^2 + y^2 = 16$

Circle of radius 4

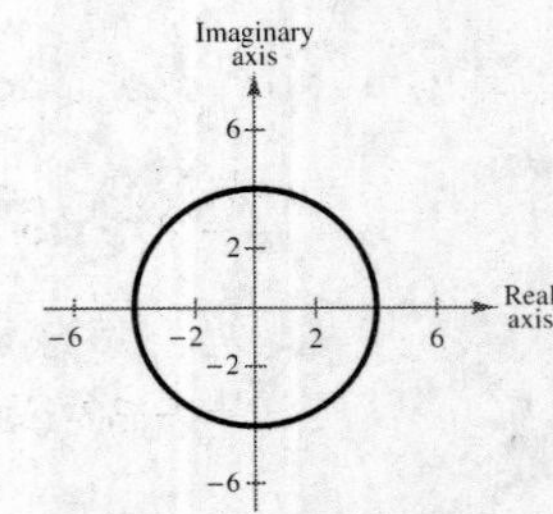

86. Let $z = x + iy$.

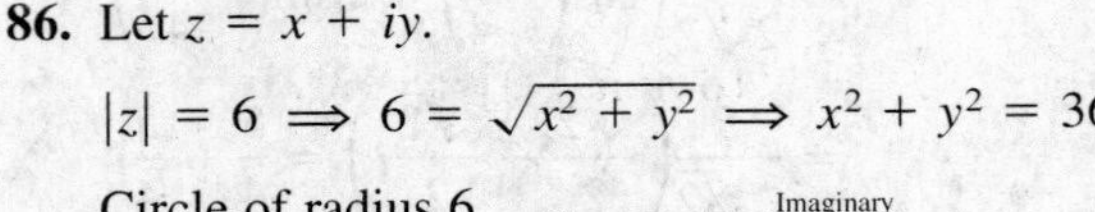

$|z| = 6 \Rightarrow 6 = \sqrt{x^2 + y^2} \Rightarrow x^2 + y^2 = 36$

Circle of radius 6

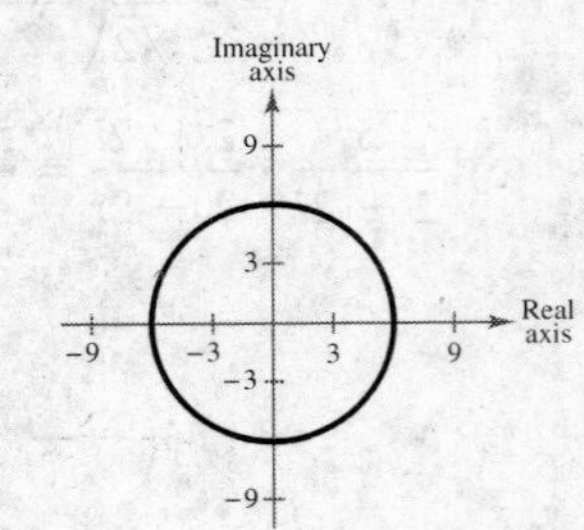

87. $\theta = \dfrac{\pi}{6}$

Let $z = x + iy$ such that:

$\tan \dfrac{\pi}{6} = \dfrac{y}{x} \Rightarrow$

$\dfrac{y}{x} = \dfrac{1}{\sqrt{3}} \Rightarrow y = \dfrac{1}{\sqrt{3}}x$

Line

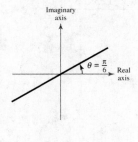

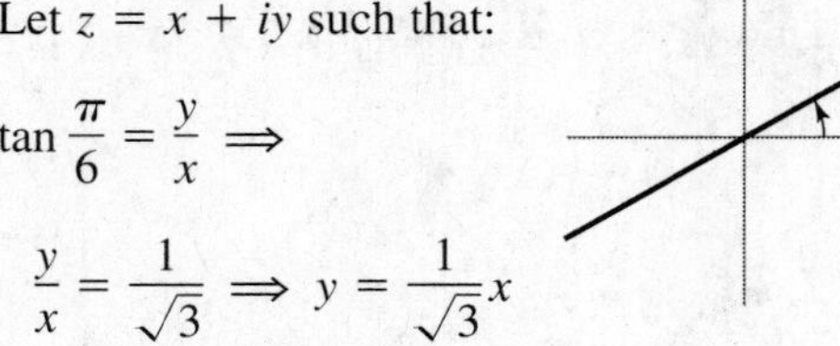

88. $\theta = \dfrac{\pi}{4} = \arctan 1$

Line

$y = x$

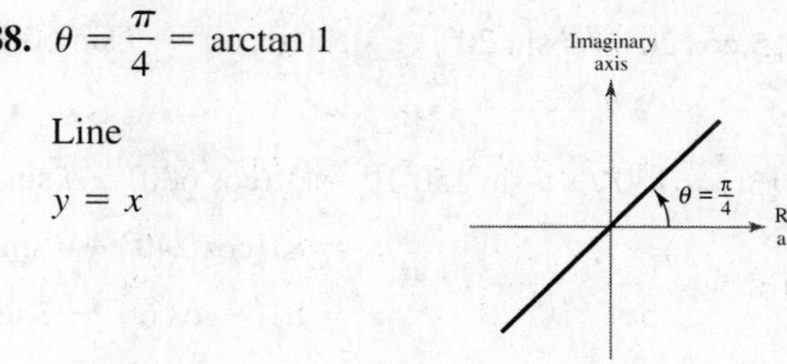

89. $\theta = \dfrac{5\pi}{6}$

Let $z = x + iy$ such that:

$\tan \dfrac{5\pi}{6} = \dfrac{y}{x} \Rightarrow$

$\dfrac{y}{x} = -\dfrac{\sqrt{3}}{3} \Rightarrow y = -\dfrac{\sqrt{3}}{3}x$

Line

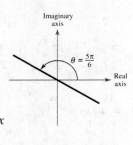

90. $\theta = \dfrac{2\pi}{3}$

Let $z = x + iy$ such that:

$\tan \dfrac{2\pi}{3} = \dfrac{y}{x} \Rightarrow$

$-\sqrt{3} = \dfrac{y}{x} \Rightarrow y = -\sqrt{3}x$

Line

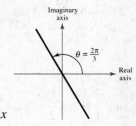

91.
$$\begin{aligned}(1+i)^3 &= \left[\sqrt{2}\left(\cos\frac{\pi}{4} + i\sin\frac{\pi}{4}\right)\right]^3\\ &= \left(\sqrt{2}\right)^3\left(\cos\frac{3\pi}{4} + i\sin\frac{3\pi}{4}\right)\\ &= 2\sqrt{2}\left(-\frac{\sqrt{2}}{2} + \frac{\sqrt{2}}{2}i\right)\\ &= -2 + 2i\end{aligned}$$

92.
$$\begin{aligned}(2+2i)^6 &= \left[2\sqrt{2}\left(\cos\frac{\pi}{4} + i\sin\frac{\pi}{4}\right)\right]^6\\ &= \left(2\sqrt{2}\right)^6\left(\cos\frac{6\pi}{4} + i\sin\frac{6\pi}{4}\right)\\ &= 512\left(\cos\frac{3\pi}{2} + i\sin\frac{3\pi}{2}\right)\\ &= -512i\end{aligned}$$

93.
$$\begin{aligned}(-1+i)^{10} &= \left[\sqrt{2}\left(\cos\frac{3\pi}{4} + i\sin\frac{3\pi}{4}\right)\right]^{10}\\ &= \left(\sqrt{2}\right)^{10}\left(\cos\frac{30\pi}{4} + i\sin\frac{30\pi}{4}\right)\\ &= 32\left[\cos\left(\frac{3\pi}{2} + 6\pi\right) + i\sin\left(\frac{3\pi}{2} + 6\pi\right)\right]\\ &= 32\left(\cos\frac{3\pi}{2} + i\sin\frac{3\pi}{2}\right)\\ &= 32[0 + i(-1)] = -32i\end{aligned}$$

94.
$$\begin{aligned}(1-i)^8 &= \left[\sqrt{2}\left(\cos\frac{7\pi}{4} + i\sin\frac{7\pi}{4}\right)\right]^8\\ &= \left(\sqrt{2}\right)^8(\cos 14\pi + i\sin 14\pi)\\ &= 16\end{aligned}$$

95.
$$\begin{aligned}2\left(\sqrt{3} + i\right)^5 &= 2\left[2\left(\cos\frac{\pi}{6} + i\sin\frac{\pi}{6}\right)\right]^5\\ &= 2\left[2^5\left(\cos\frac{5\pi}{6} + i\sin\frac{5\pi}{6}\right)\right]\\ &= 64\left(-\frac{\sqrt{3}}{2} + \frac{1}{2}i\right)\\ &= -32\sqrt{3} + 32i\end{aligned}$$

96.
$$\begin{aligned}4\left(1 - \sqrt{3}i\right)^3 &= 4\left[2\left(\cos\frac{5\pi}{3} + i\sin\frac{5\pi}{3}\right)\right]^3\\ &= 4[2^3(\cos 5\pi + i\sin 5\pi)]\\ &= 32(-1)\\ &= -32\end{aligned}$$

97. $[5(\cos 20° + i \sin 20°)]^3 = 5^3(\cos 60° + i \sin 60°) = \dfrac{125}{2} + \dfrac{125\sqrt{3}}{2}i$

98.
$$\begin{aligned}[3(\cos 150° + i \sin 150°)]^4 &= 3^4(\cos 600° + i \sin 600°)\\ &= 81(\cos 240° + i \sin 240°)\\ &= 81(-\cos 60° - i \sin 60°)\\ &= -\frac{81}{2} - \frac{81\sqrt{3}}{2}i\end{aligned}$$

99.
$$\begin{aligned}\left(\cos\frac{5\pi}{4} + i \sin\frac{5\pi}{4}\right)^{10} &= \cos\frac{25\pi}{2} + i \sin\frac{25\pi}{2}\\ &= \cos\left(12\pi + \frac{\pi}{2}\right) + i \sin\left(12\pi + \frac{\pi}{2}\right) = \cos\frac{\pi}{2} + i \sin\frac{\pi}{2} = i\end{aligned}$$

100. $\left[2\left(\cos\dfrac{\pi}{2} + i \sin\dfrac{\pi}{2}\right)\right]^{12} = 2^{12}(\cos 6\pi + i \sin 6\pi) = 2^{12} = 4096$

101.
$$\begin{aligned}[2(\cos 1.25 + i \sin 1.25)]^4 &= 2^4(\cos 5 + i \sin 5)\\ &\approx 4.5386 - 15.3428i\end{aligned}$$

102.
$$\begin{aligned}[4(\cos 2.8 + i \sin 2.8)]^5 &= 4^5(\cos 14 + i \sin 14)\\ &\approx 140.02 + 1014.38i\end{aligned}$$

103.
$$\begin{aligned}[2(\cos \pi + i \sin \pi)]^8 &= 2^8(\cos 8\pi + i \sin 8\pi)\\ &= 256(1) = 256\end{aligned}$$

104.
$$\begin{aligned}(\cos 0 + i \sin 0)^{20} &= \cos 0 + i \sin 0\\ &= 1\end{aligned}$$

105. $(3 - 2i)^5 = -597 - 122i$

106.
$$\begin{aligned}(\sqrt{5} - 4i)^4 &= \left[\sqrt{21}(\cos(5.2221) + i \sin(5.2221))\right]^4\\ &= 441[\cos(20.8884) + i \sin(20.8884)]\\ &= -199 + 393.55i\end{aligned}$$

107.
$$\begin{aligned}[4(\cos 10° + i \sin 10°)]^6 &= 4^6(\cos 60° + i \sin 60°)\\ &= 4096\left(\frac{1}{2} + \frac{\sqrt{3}}{2}i\right)\\ &= 2048 + 2048\sqrt{3}i\end{aligned}$$

108.
$$\begin{aligned}[3(\cos 15° + i \sin 15°)]^4 &= 81(\cos 60° + i \sin 60°)\\ &= \frac{81}{2} + \frac{81\sqrt{3}}{2}i\end{aligned}$$

109.
$$\begin{aligned}\left[3\left(\cos\frac{\pi}{8} + i \sin\frac{\pi}{8}\right)\right]^2 &= 3^2\left(\cos\frac{\pi}{4} + i \sin\frac{\pi}{4}\right)\\ &= 9\left(\frac{\sqrt{2}}{2} + i\frac{\sqrt{2}}{2}\right)\\ &= \frac{9}{2}\sqrt{2} + \frac{9}{2}\sqrt{2}i\end{aligned}$$

110.
$$\begin{aligned}\left[2\left(\cos\frac{\pi}{10} + i \sin\frac{\pi}{10}\right)\right]^5 &= 32\left(\cos\frac{\pi}{2} + i \sin\frac{\pi}{2}\right)\\ &= 32i\end{aligned}$$

111.
$$\begin{aligned}\left[-\frac{1}{2}(1 + \sqrt{3}i)\right]^6 &= \left[\cos\frac{4\pi}{3} + i \sin\frac{4\pi}{3}\right]^6\\ &= \cos 8\pi + i \sin 8\pi\\ &= 1\end{aligned}$$

112. $2^{-1/4}(1 - i)$ is a fourth root of -2 if $-2 = [2^{-1/4}(1 - i)]^4$.

$$\begin{aligned}[2^{-1/4}(1 - i)]^4 &= (2^{-1/4})^4(1 - i)^4 \\ &= 2^{-1}(1 - i)^4 \\ &= \tfrac{1}{2}(1 - i)^2(1 - i)^2 \\ &= \tfrac{1}{2}(-2i)(-2i) \\ &= \tfrac{1}{2}(4i^2) \\ &= \tfrac{1}{2}(-4) = -2\end{aligned}$$

113. (a) In trigonometric form we have:

$2(\cos 30° + i \sin 30°)$

$2(\cos 150° + i \sin 150°)$

$2(\cos 270° + i \sin 270°)$

(b) There are three roots evenly spaced around a circle of radius 2. Therefore, they represent the cube roots of some number of modulus 8. Cubing them shows that they are all cube roots of $8i$.

(c) $[2(\cos 30° + i \sin 30°)]^3 = 8i$

$[2(\cos 150° + i \sin 150°)]^3 = 8i$

$[2(\cos 270° + i \sin 270°)]^3 = 8i$

114. (a) In trigonometric form we have:

$3(\cos 45° + i \sin 45°)$

$3(\cos 135° + i \sin 135°)$

$3(\cos 225° + i \sin 225°)$

$3(\cos 315° + i \sin 315°)$

(b) There are four roots evenly spaced around a circle of radius 3. Therefore, they represent the fourth roots of some number of modulus 81. Raising them to the fourth power shows that they are all fourth roots of -81.

(c) $[3(\cos 45° + i \sin 45°)]^4 = -81$

$[3(\cos 135° + i \sin 135°)]^4 = -81$

$[3(\cos 225° + i \sin 225°)]^4 = -81$

$[3(\cos 315° + i \sin 315°)]^4 = -81$

115. (a) In trigonometric form we have:

$\cos 120° + i \sin 120°$

$\cos 240° + i \sin 240°$

$\cos 0° + i \sin 0°$

(b) These are the three cube roots of 1.

(c) $(\cos 120° + i \sin 120°)^3 = 1$

$(\cos 240° + i \sin 240°)^3 = 1$

$(\cos 0° + i \sin 0°)^3 = 1$

116. (a) In trigonometric form we have:

$2(\cos 30° + i \sin 30°)$

$2(\cos 90° + i \sin 90°)$

$2(\cos 150° + i \sin 150°)$

$2(\cos 210° + i \sin 210°)$

$2(\cos 270° + i \sin 270°)$

$2(\cos 330° + i \sin 330°)$

(b) There are six roots evenly spaced around a circle of radius 2. Raising them to the sixth power shows that they are the six sixth roots of -64.

(c) $[2(\cos 30° + i \sin 30°)]^6 = -64$

$[2(\cos 90° + i \sin 90°)]^6 = -64$

$[2(\cos 150° + i \sin 150°)]^6 = -64$

$[2(\cos 210° + i \sin 210°)]^6 = -64$

$[2(\cos 270° + i \sin 270°)]^6 = -64$

$[2(\cos 330° + i \sin 330°)]^6 = -64$

117. $2i = 2\left(\cos\frac{\pi}{2} + i\sin\frac{\pi}{2}\right)$

Square roots:

$\sqrt{2}\left(\cos\frac{\pi}{4} + i\sin\frac{\pi}{4}\right) = 1 + i$

$\sqrt{2}\left(\cos\frac{5\pi}{4} + i\sin\frac{5\pi}{4}\right) = -1 - i$

118. $5i = 5\left(\cos\frac{\pi}{2} + i\sin\frac{\pi}{2}\right)$

Square roots:

$\sqrt{5}\left(\cos\frac{\pi}{4} + i\sin\frac{\pi}{4}\right) = \frac{\sqrt{10}}{2} + \frac{\sqrt{10}}{2}i$

$\sqrt{5}\left(\cos\frac{5\pi}{4} + i\sin\frac{5\pi}{4}\right) = -\frac{\sqrt{10}}{2} - \frac{\sqrt{10}}{2}i$

119. $-3i = 3\left(\cos\frac{3\pi}{2} + i\sin\frac{3\pi}{2}\right)$

Square roots:

$\sqrt{3}\left(\cos\frac{3\pi}{4} + i\sin\frac{3\pi}{4}\right) = -\frac{\sqrt{6}}{2} + \frac{\sqrt{6}}{2}i$

$\sqrt{3}\left(\cos\frac{7\pi}{4} + i\sin\frac{7\pi}{4}\right) = \frac{\sqrt{6}}{2} - \frac{\sqrt{6}}{2}i$

120. $-6i = 6\left(\cos\frac{3\pi}{2} + i\sin\frac{3\pi}{2}\right)$

Square roots:

$\sqrt{6}\left(\cos\frac{3\pi}{4} + i\sin\frac{3\pi}{4}\right) = -\sqrt{3} + \sqrt{3}i$

$\sqrt{6}\left(\cos\frac{7\pi}{4} + i\sin\frac{7\pi}{4}\right) = \sqrt{3} - \sqrt{3}i$

121. $2 - 2i = 2\sqrt{2}\left(\cos\frac{7\pi}{4} + i\sin\frac{7\pi}{4}\right)$

Square roots:

$8^{1/4}\left(\cos\frac{7\pi}{8} + i\sin\frac{7\pi}{8}\right) \approx -1.554 + 0.644i$

$8^{1/4}\left(\cos\frac{15\pi}{8} + i\sin\frac{15\pi}{8}\right) \approx 1.554 - 0.644i$

122. $2 + 2i = 2\sqrt{2}\left(\cos\frac{\pi}{4} + i\sin\frac{\pi}{4}\right)$

Square roots:

$8^{1/4}\left(\cos\frac{\pi}{8} + i\sin\frac{\pi}{8}\right) \approx 1.554 + 0.644i$

$8^{1/4}\left(\cos\frac{9\pi}{8} + i\sin\frac{9\pi}{8}\right) \approx -1.554 - 0.644i$

123. $1 + \sqrt{3}i = 2\left(\cos\frac{\pi}{3} + i\sin\frac{\pi}{3}\right)$

Square roots:

$\sqrt{2}\left(\cos\frac{\pi}{6} + i\sin\frac{\pi}{6}\right) = \frac{\sqrt{6}}{2} + \frac{\sqrt{2}}{2}i$

$\sqrt{2}\left(\cos\frac{7\pi}{6} + i\sin\frac{7\pi}{6}\right) = -\frac{\sqrt{6}}{2} - \frac{\sqrt{2}}{2}i$

124. $1 - \sqrt{3}i = 2\left(\cos\frac{5\pi}{3} + i\sin\frac{5\pi}{3}\right)$

Square roots:

$\sqrt{2}\left(\cos\frac{5\pi}{6} + i\sin\frac{5\pi}{6}\right) = \sqrt{2}\left(-\frac{\sqrt{3}}{2} + \frac{1}{2}i\right)$

$= -\frac{\sqrt{6}}{2} + \frac{\sqrt{2}}{2}i$

$\sqrt{2}\left(\cos\frac{11\pi}{6} + i\sin\frac{11\pi}{6}\right) = \frac{\sqrt{6}}{2} - \frac{\sqrt{2}}{2}i$

125. (a) Square roots of $5(\cos 120° + i\sin 120°)$:

$\sqrt{5}\left[\cos\left(\frac{120° + 360°k}{2}\right) + i\sin\left(\frac{120° + 360°k}{2}\right)\right],\ k = 0, 1$

$\sqrt{5}(\cos 60° + i\sin 60°)$

$\sqrt{5}(\cos 240° + i\sin 240°)$

(c) $\frac{\sqrt{5}}{2} + \frac{\sqrt{15}}{2}i,\ -\frac{\sqrt{5}}{2} - \frac{\sqrt{15}}{2}i$

(b)

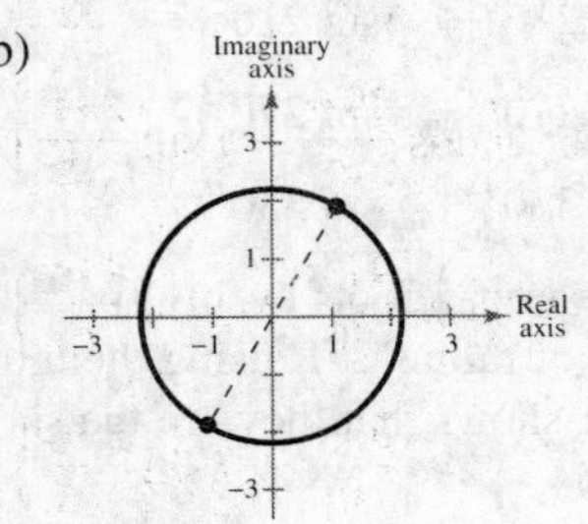

126. (a) Square roots of $16(\cos 60° + i \sin 60°)$:

$$\sqrt{16}\left[\cos\left(\frac{60° + 360° k}{2}\right) + i \sin\left(\frac{60° + 360° k}{2}\right)\right],\ k = 0, 1$$

$4(\cos 30° + i \sin 30°)$

$4(\cos 210° + i \sin 210°)$

(b)

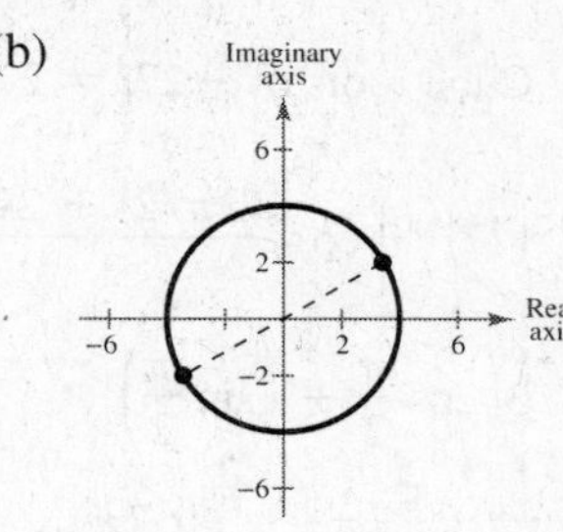

(c) $4\left(\frac{\sqrt{3}}{2} + \frac{1}{2}i\right) = 2\sqrt{3} + 2i$

$4\left(-\frac{\sqrt{3}}{2} - \frac{1}{2}i\right) = -2\sqrt{3} - 2i$

127. (a) Fourth roots of $16\left(\cos \frac{4\pi}{3} + i \sin \frac{4\pi}{3}\right)$:

$$\sqrt[4]{16}\left[\cos\left(\frac{(4\pi/3) + 2k\pi}{4}\right) + i \sin\left(\frac{(4\pi/3) + 2k\pi}{4}\right)\right],\ k = 0, 1, 2, 3$$

$2\left(\cos \frac{\pi}{3} + i \sin \frac{\pi}{3}\right)$

$2\left(\cos \frac{5\pi}{6} + i \sin \frac{5\pi}{6}\right)$

$2\left(\cos \frac{4\pi}{3} + i \sin \frac{4\pi}{3}\right)$

$2\left(\cos \frac{11\pi}{6} + i \sin \frac{11\pi}{6}\right)$

(b)

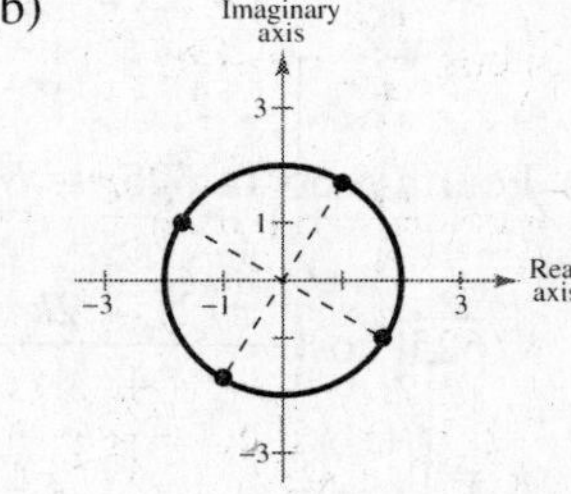

(c) $1 + \sqrt{3}i,\ -\sqrt{3} + i,\ -1 - \sqrt{3}i,\ \sqrt{3} - i$

128. (a) Fifth roots of $32\left(\cos \frac{5\pi}{6} + i \sin \frac{5\pi}{6}\right)$:

$$\sqrt[5]{32}\left[\cos\left(\frac{(5\pi/6) + 2k\pi}{5}\right) + i \sin\left(\frac{(5\pi/6) + 2k\pi}{5}\right)\right]$$

$k = 0, 1, 2, 3, 4$

$k = 0$: $2\left(\cos \frac{\pi}{6} + i \sin \frac{\pi}{6}\right)$

$k = 1$: $2\left(\cos \frac{17\pi}{30} + i \sin \frac{17\pi}{30}\right)$

$k = 2$: $2\left(\cos \frac{29\pi}{30} + i \sin \frac{29\pi}{30}\right)$

$k = 3$: $2\left(\cos \frac{41\pi}{30} + i \sin \frac{41\pi}{30}\right)$

$k = 4$: $2\left(\cos \frac{53\pi}{30} + i \sin \frac{53\pi}{30}\right)$

(b)

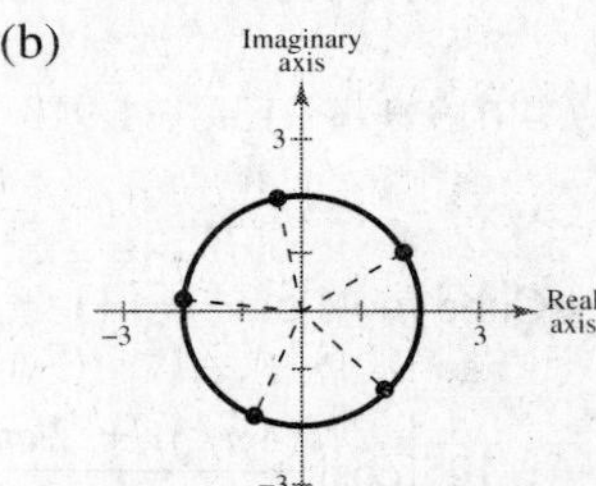

(c) $1.732 + i,\ -0.4158 + 1.956i,\ -1.989 + 0.2091i,$
$-0.8135 - 1.827i,\ 1.486 - 1.338i$

129. (a) Cube roots of $-27i = 27\left(\cos \frac{3\pi}{2} + i \sin \frac{3\pi}{2}\right)$:

$$(27)^{1/3}\left[\cos\left(\frac{(3\pi/2) + 2k\pi}{3}\right) + i \sin\left(\frac{(3\pi/2) + 2k\pi}{3}\right)\right], \quad k = 0, 1, 2$$

$$3\left(\cos \frac{\pi}{2} + i \sin \frac{\pi}{2}\right)$$

$$3\left(\cos \frac{7\pi}{6} + i \sin \frac{7\pi}{6}\right)$$

$$3\left(\cos \frac{11\pi}{6} + i \sin \frac{11\pi}{6}\right)$$

(b)

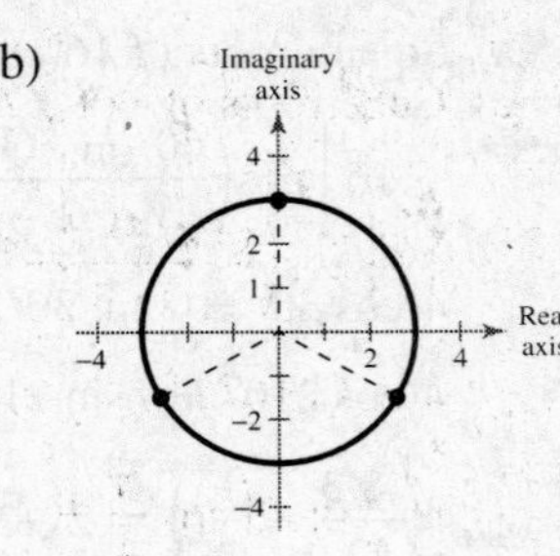

(c) $3i, -\frac{3\sqrt{3}}{2} - \frac{3}{2}i, \frac{3\sqrt{3}}{2} - \frac{3}{2}i$

130. (a) Fourth roots of $625i = 625\left(\cos \frac{\pi}{2} + i \sin \frac{\pi}{2}\right)$:

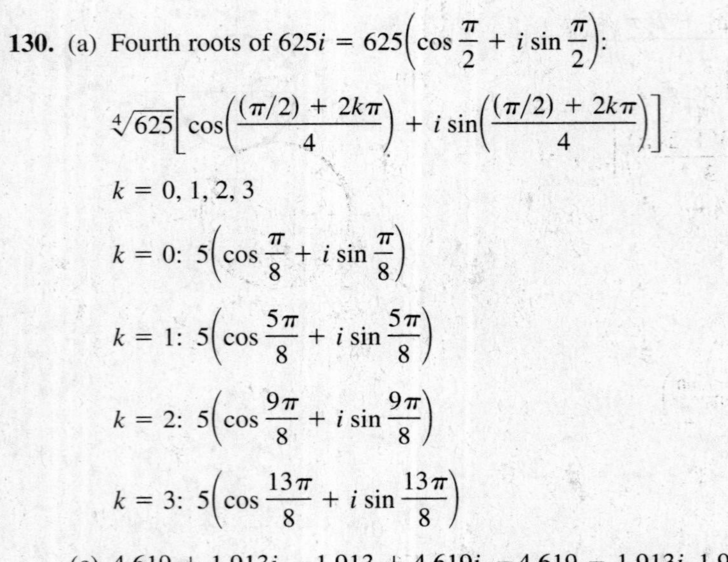

$$\sqrt[4]{625}\left[\cos\left(\frac{(\pi/2) + 2k\pi}{4}\right) + i \sin\left(\frac{(\pi/2) + 2k\pi}{4}\right)\right]$$

$k = 0, 1, 2, 3$

$$k = 0:\ 5\left(\cos \frac{\pi}{8} + i \sin \frac{\pi}{8}\right)$$

$$k = 1:\ 5\left(\cos \frac{5\pi}{8} + i \sin \frac{5\pi}{8}\right)$$

$$k = 2:\ 5\left(\cos \frac{9\pi}{8} + i \sin \frac{9\pi}{8}\right)$$

$$k = 3:\ 5\left(\cos \frac{13\pi}{8} + i \sin \frac{13\pi}{8}\right)$$

(b)

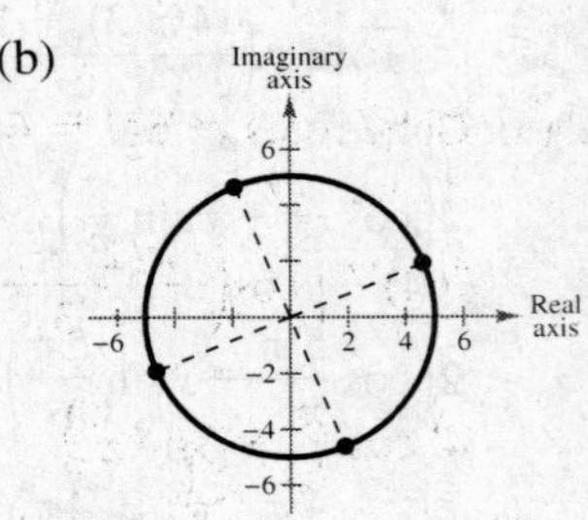

(c) $4.619 + 1.913i, -1.913 + 4.619i, -4.619 - 1.913i, 1.913 - 4.619i$

131. (a) Cube roots of $-\frac{125}{2}(1 + \sqrt{3}i) = 125\left(\cos \frac{4\pi}{3} + i \sin \frac{4\pi}{3}\right)$:

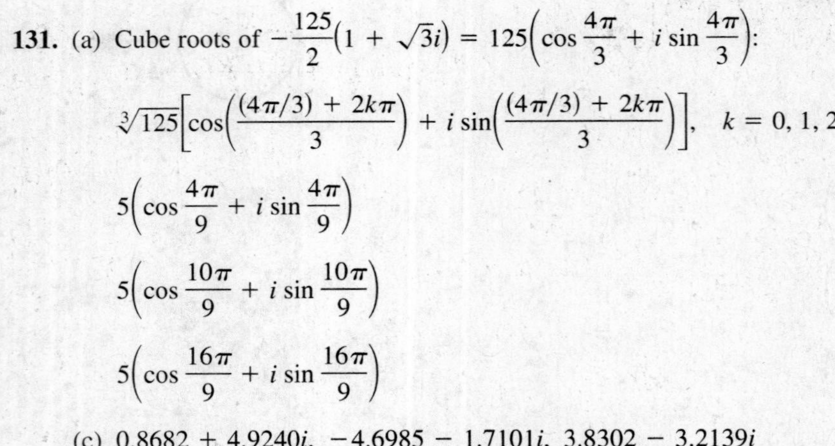

$$\sqrt[3]{125}\left[\cos\left(\frac{(4\pi/3) + 2k\pi}{3}\right) + i \sin\left(\frac{(4\pi/3) + 2k\pi}{3}\right)\right], \quad k = 0, 1, 2$$

$$5\left(\cos \frac{4\pi}{9} + i \sin \frac{4\pi}{9}\right)$$

$$5\left(\cos \frac{10\pi}{9} + i \sin \frac{10\pi}{9}\right)$$

$$5\left(\cos \frac{16\pi}{9} + i \sin \frac{16\pi}{9}\right)$$

(b)

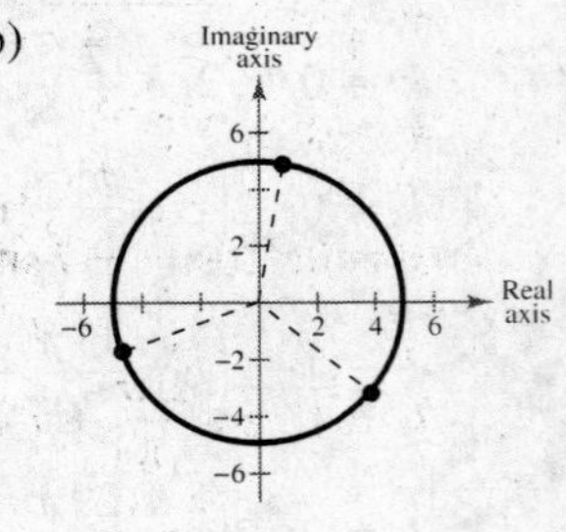

(c) $0.8682 + 4.9240i, \ -4.6985 - 1.7101i, \ 3.8302 - 3.2139i$

132. (a) Cube roots of $-4\sqrt{2}(1 - i) = 8\left(\cos\frac{3\pi}{4} + i\sin\frac{3\pi}{4}\right)$:

$$\sqrt[3]{8}\left[\cos\left(\frac{(3\pi/4) + 2k\pi}{3}\right) + i\sin\left(\frac{(3\pi/4) + 2k\pi}{3}\right)\right]$$

$k = 0, 1, 2$

$k = 0$: $2\left(\cos\frac{\pi}{4} + i\sin\frac{\pi}{4}\right)$

$k = 1$: $2\left(\cos\frac{11\pi}{12} + i\sin\frac{11\pi}{12}\right)$

$k = 2$: $2\left(\cos\frac{19\pi}{12} + i\sin\frac{19\pi}{12}\right)$

(b)

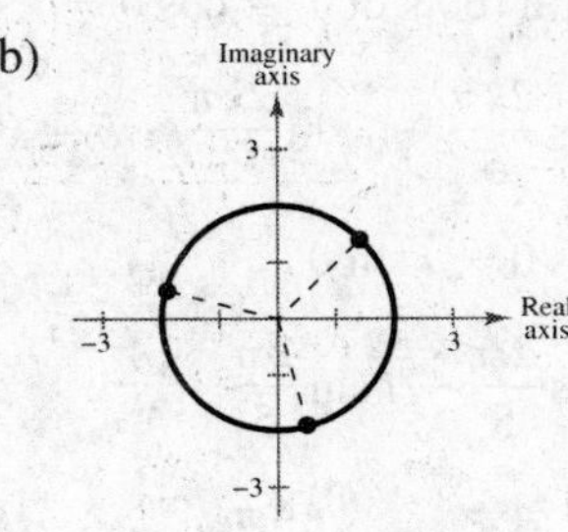

(c) $1.414 + 1.414i, -1.932 + 0.5176i, 0.5176 - 1.9319i$

133. (a) Cube roots of $64i = 64\left(\cos\frac{\pi}{2} + i\sin\frac{\pi}{2}\right)$:

$$(64)^{1/3}\left[\cos\left(\frac{(\pi/2) + 2k\pi}{3}\right) + i\sin\left(\frac{(\pi/2) + 2k\pi}{3}\right)\right], \quad k = 0, 1, 2$$

$4\left(\cos\frac{\pi}{6} + i\sin\frac{\pi}{6}\right)$

$4\left(\cos\frac{5\pi}{6} + i\sin\frac{5\pi}{6}\right)$

$4\left(\cos\frac{9\pi}{6} + i\sin\frac{9\pi}{6}\right) = 4\left(\cos\frac{3\pi}{2} + i\sin\frac{3\pi}{2}\right)$

(b)

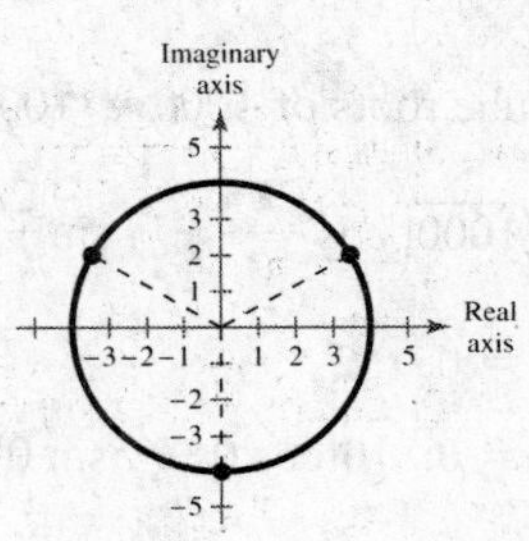

(c) $2\sqrt{3} + 2i, -2\sqrt{3} + 2i, -4i$

134. (a) Fourth roots of $i = \cos\frac{\pi}{2} + i\sin\frac{\pi}{2}$:

$$\sqrt[4]{1}\left[\cos\left(\frac{(\pi/2) + 2k\pi}{4}\right) + i\sin\left(\frac{(\pi/2) + 2k\pi}{4}\right)\right]$$

$k = 0, 1, 2, 3$

$k = 0$: $\cos\frac{\pi}{8} + i\sin\frac{\pi}{8}$

$k = 1$: $\cos\frac{5\pi}{8} + i\sin\frac{5\pi}{8}$

$k = 2$: $\cos\frac{9\pi}{8} + i\sin\frac{9\pi}{8}$

$k = 3$: $\cos\frac{13\pi}{8} + i\sin\frac{13\pi}{8}$

(b)

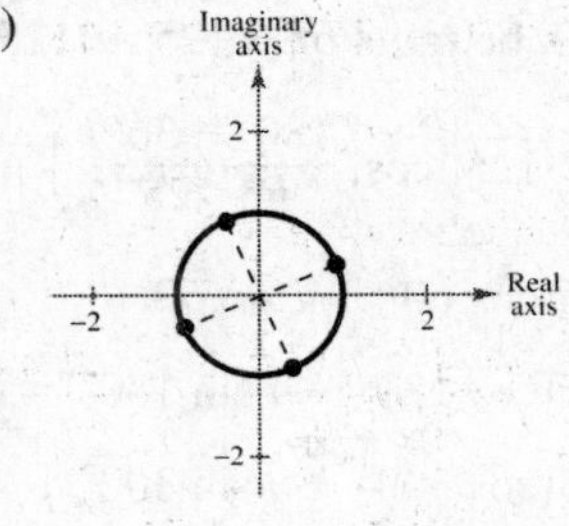

(c) $0.9239 + 0.3827i, -0.3827 + 0.9239i, -0.9239 - 0.3827i, 0.3827 - 0.9239i$

135. (a) Fifth roots of $1 = \cos 0 + i \sin 0$:

$$\cos \frac{2k\pi}{5} + i \sin \frac{2k\pi}{5}, \quad k = 0, 1, 2, 3, 4$$

$$\cos 0 + i \sin 0$$

$$\cos \frac{2\pi}{5} + i \sin \frac{2\pi}{5}$$

$$\cos \frac{4\pi}{5} + i \sin \frac{4\pi}{5}$$

$$\cos \frac{6\pi}{5} + i \sin \frac{6\pi}{5}$$

$$\cos \frac{8\pi}{5} + i \sin \frac{8\pi}{5}$$

(b)

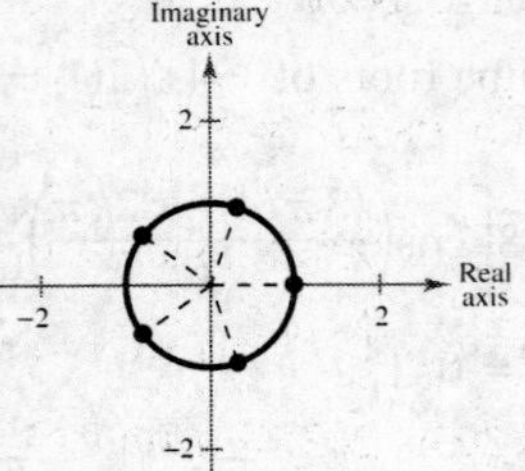

(c) $1, 0.3090 + 0.9511i, -0.8090 + 0.5878i, -0.8090 - 0.5878i, 0.3090 - 0.9511i$

136. (a) Cube roots of $1000 = 1000(\cos 0 + i \sin 0)$:

$$\sqrt[3]{1000}\left(\cos \frac{2k\pi}{3} + i \sin \frac{2k\pi}{3}\right)$$

$k = 0, 1, 2$

$k = 0$: $10(\cos 0 + i \sin 0) = 10$

$k = 1$: $10\left(\cos \frac{2\pi}{3} + i \sin \frac{2\pi}{3}\right)$

$k = 2$: $10\left(\cos \frac{4\pi}{3} + i \sin \frac{4\pi}{3}\right)$

(b)

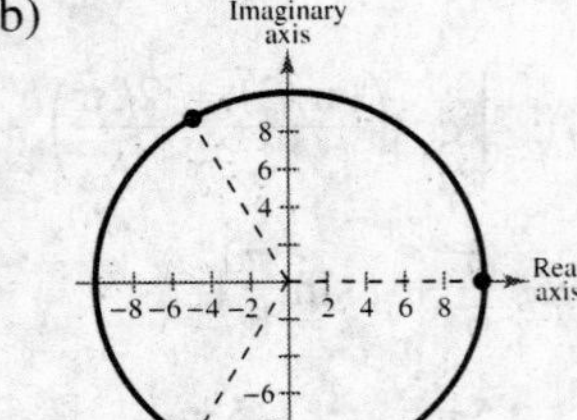

(c) $10, -5 + 5\sqrt{3}i, -5 - 5\sqrt{3}i$

137. (a) Cube roots of $-125 = 125(\cos 180° + i \sin 180°)$ are:

$$\sqrt[3]{125}\left[\cos\left(\frac{180 + 360k}{3}\right) + i \sin\left(\frac{180 + 360k}{3}\right)\right], \quad k = 0, 1, 2$$

$5(\cos 60° + i \sin 60°)$

$5(\cos 180° + i \sin 180°)$

$5(\cos 300° + i \sin 300°)$

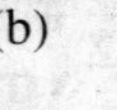
(b)

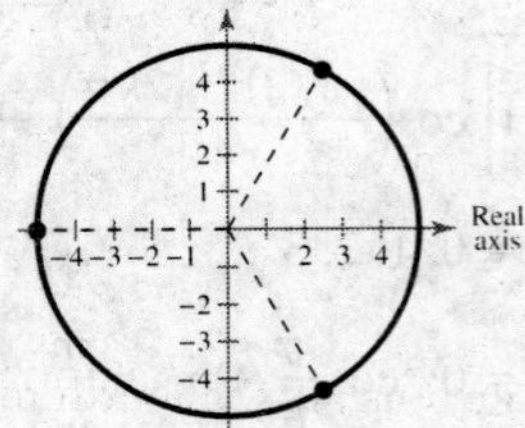

(c) $\frac{5}{2} + \frac{5\sqrt{3}}{2}i, -5, \frac{5}{2} - \frac{5\sqrt{3}}{2}i$

138. (a) Fourth roots of $-4 = 4(\cos 180° + i \sin 180°)$:

$\sqrt{2}(\cos 45° + i \sin 45°)$

$\sqrt{2}(\cos 135° + i \sin 135°)$

$\sqrt{2}(\cos 225° + i \sin 225°)$

$\sqrt{2}(\cos 315° + i \sin 315°)$

(b)

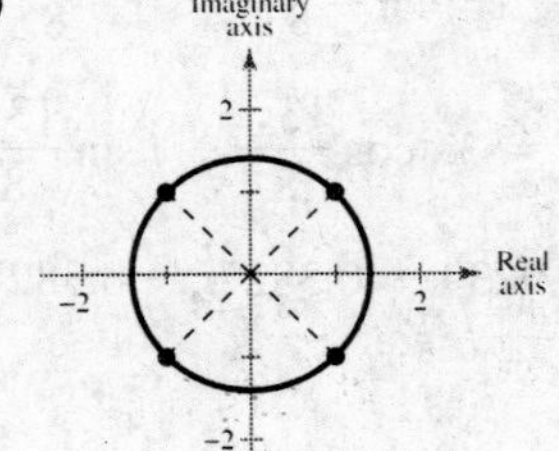

(c) $1 + i, -1 + i, -1 - i, 1 - i$

139. (a) Fifth roots of $128(-1 + i) = 128\sqrt{2}(\cos 135° + i \sin 135°)$ are:

$2\sqrt{2}(\cos 27° + i \sin 27°) = 2\sqrt{2}\left(\cos \frac{3\pi}{20} + i \sin \frac{3\pi}{20}\right)$

$2\sqrt{2}(\cos 99° + i \sin 99°)$

$2\sqrt{2}(\cos 171° + i \sin 171°)$

$2\sqrt{2}(\cos 243° + i \sin 243°)$

$2\sqrt{2}(\cos 315° + i \sin 315°)$

(b)

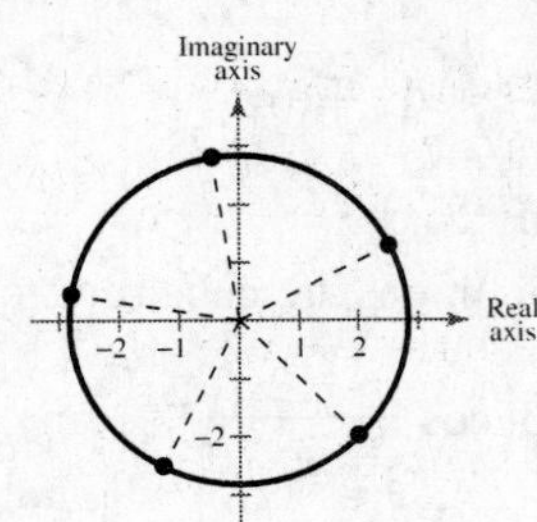

(c) $2.52 + 1.28i, -0.44 + 2.79i, -2.79 + 0.44i, -1.28 - 2.52i, 2 - 2i$

140. (a) Sixth roots of $729i = 729\left(\cos \frac{\pi}{2} + i \sin \frac{\pi}{2}\right)$:

$\sqrt[6]{729}\left[\cos\left(\frac{\pi/2 + 2k\pi}{6}\right) + i \sin\left(\frac{\pi/2 + 2k\pi}{6}\right)\right], k = 0, 1, 2, 3, 4, 5$

$3\left(\cos \frac{\pi}{12} + i \sin \frac{\pi}{12}\right)$

$3\left(\cos \frac{5\pi}{12} + i \sin \frac{5\pi}{12}\right)$

$3\left(\cos \frac{9\pi}{12} + i \sin \frac{9\pi}{12}\right)$

$3\left(\cos \frac{13\pi}{12} + i \sin \frac{13\pi}{12}\right)$

$3\left(\cos \frac{17\pi}{12} + i \sin \frac{17\pi}{12}\right)$

$3\left(\cos \frac{21\pi}{12} + i \sin \frac{21\pi}{12}\right)$

(b)

(c) $2.898 + 0.776i, 0.776 + 2.898i, -2.121 + 2.121i,$
$-2.898 - 0.776i, -0.776 - 2.898i, 2.121 - 2.121i$

141. $x^4 - i = 0$

$x^4 = i$

The solutions are the fourth roots of $i = \cos \frac{\pi}{2} + i \sin \frac{\pi}{2}$:

$\sqrt[4]{1}\left[\cos\left(\frac{(\pi/2) + 2k\pi}{4}\right) + i \sin\left(\frac{(\pi/2) + 2k\pi}{4}\right)\right], \quad k = 0, 1, 2, 3$

$\cos \frac{\pi}{8} + i \sin \frac{\pi}{8}$

$\cos \frac{5\pi}{8} + i \sin \frac{5\pi}{8}$

$\cos \frac{9\pi}{8} + i \sin \frac{9\pi}{8}$

$\cos \frac{13\pi}{8} + i \sin \frac{13\pi}{8}$

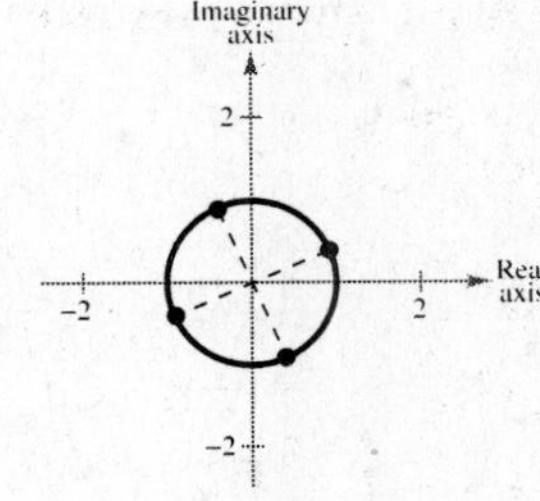

142. $x^3 + 27 = 0$

$x^3 = -27$

Solutions are cube roots of $-27 = 27(\cos \pi + i \sin \pi)$:

$$3\left(\cos \frac{\pi + 2\pi k}{3} + i \sin \frac{\pi + 2\pi k}{3}\right), k = 0, 1, 2$$

$$3\left(\cos \frac{\pi}{3} + i \sin \frac{\pi}{3}\right) = \frac{3}{2} + \frac{3\sqrt{3}}{2}i$$

$$3(\cos \pi + i \sin \pi) = -3$$

$$3\left(\cos \frac{5\pi}{3} + i \sin \frac{5\pi}{3}\right) = \frac{3}{2} - \frac{3\sqrt{3}}{2}i$$

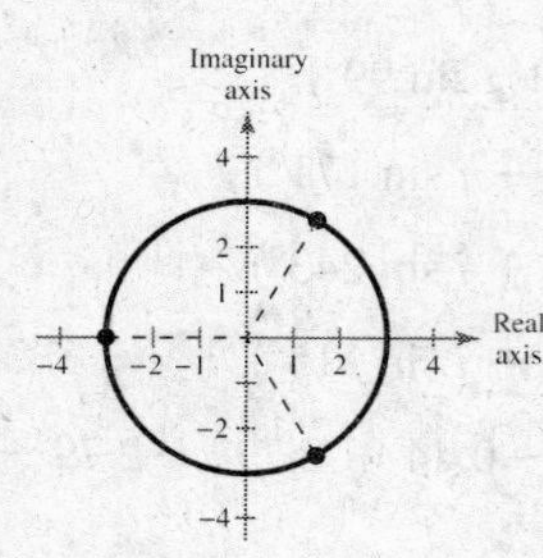

143. $x^5 = -243$

The solutions are the fifth roots of $-243 = 243[\cos \pi + i \sin \pi]$:

$$\sqrt[5]{243}\left[\cos\left(\frac{\pi + 2k\pi}{5}\right) + i \sin\left(\frac{\pi + 2k\pi}{5}\right)\right], \quad k = 0, 1, 2, 3, 4$$

$$3\left(\cos \frac{\pi}{5} + i \sin \frac{\pi}{5}\right)$$

$$3\left(\cos \frac{3\pi}{5} + i \sin \frac{3\pi}{5}\right)$$

$$3\left(\cos \frac{5\pi}{5} + i \sin \frac{5\pi}{5}\right) = -3$$

$$3\left(\cos \frac{7\pi}{5} + i \sin \frac{7\pi}{5}\right)$$

$$3\left(\cos \frac{9\pi}{5} + i \sin \frac{9\pi}{5}\right)$$

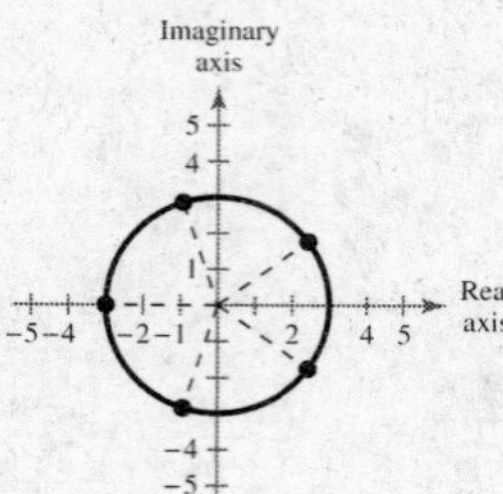

144. $x^4 = 81 = 81(\cos 0 + i \sin 0)$

$$3\left[\cos \frac{2\pi k}{4} + i \sin \frac{2\pi k}{4}\right], k = 0, 1, 2, 3$$

$$3(\cos 0 + i \sin 0) = 3$$

$$3\left(\cos \frac{\pi}{2} + i \sin \frac{\pi}{2}\right) = 3i$$

$$3(\cos \pi + i \sin \pi) = -3$$

$$3\left(\cos \frac{3\pi}{2} + i \sin \frac{3\pi}{2}\right) = -3i$$

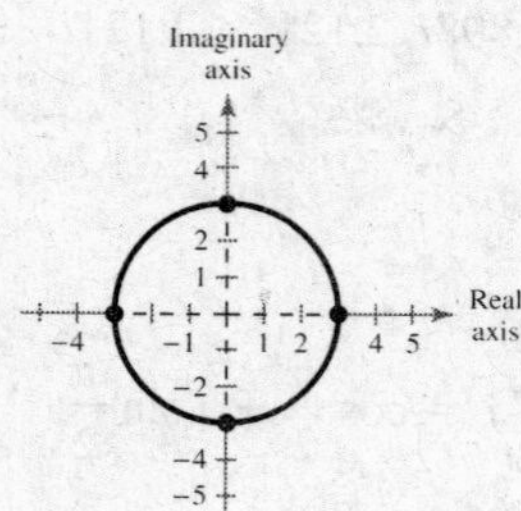

145. $x^4 = -16i$

The solutions are the fourth roots of $-16i = 16\left[\cos\frac{3\pi}{2} + i\sin\frac{3\pi}{2}\right]$:

$$\sqrt[4]{16}\left[\cos\left(\frac{(3\pi/2) + 2k\pi}{4}\right) + i\sin\left(\frac{(3\pi/2) + 2k\pi}{4}\right)\right], \quad k = 0, 1, 2, 3$$

$$2\left[\cos\left(\frac{3\pi}{8}\right) + i\sin\left(\frac{3\pi}{8}\right)\right]$$

$$2\left[\cos\left(\frac{7\pi}{8}\right) + i\sin\left(\frac{7\pi}{8}\right)\right]$$

$$2\left[\cos\left(\frac{11\pi}{8}\right) + i\sin\left(\frac{11\pi}{8}\right)\right]$$

$$2\left[\cos\left(\frac{15\pi}{8}\right) + i\sin\left(\frac{15\pi}{8}\right)\right]$$

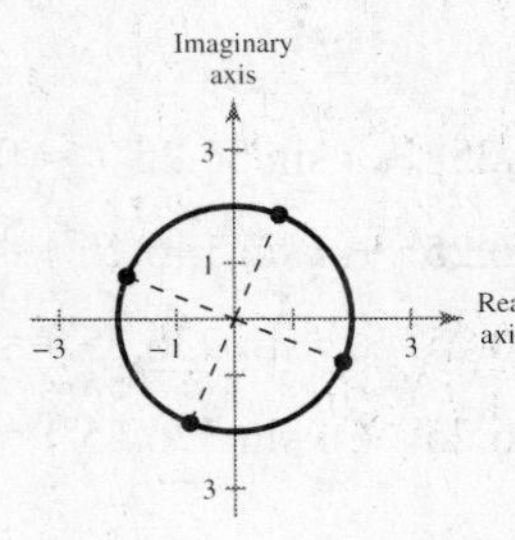

146. $x^6 - 64i = 0$

$x^6 = 64i$

The solutions are the sixth roots of $64i$:

$$\sqrt[6]{64}\left[\cos\left(\frac{(\pi/2) + 2k\pi}{6}\right) + i\sin\left(\frac{(\pi/2) + 2k\pi}{6}\right)\right], \quad k = 0, 1, 2, 3, 4, 5$$

$k = 0$: $2\left(\cos\frac{\pi}{12} + i\sin\frac{\pi}{12}\right) \approx 1.932 + 0.5176i$

$k = 1$: $2\left(\cos\frac{5\pi}{12} + i\sin\frac{5\pi}{12}\right) \approx 0.5176 + 1.932i$

$k = 2$: $2\left(\cos\frac{3\pi}{4} + i\sin\frac{3\pi}{4}\right) \approx -1.414 + 1.414i$

$k = 3$: $2\left(\cos\frac{13\pi}{12} + i\sin\frac{13\pi}{12}\right) \approx -1.932 - 0.5176i$

$k = 4$: $2\left(\cos\frac{17\pi}{12} + i\sin\frac{17\pi}{12}\right) \approx -0.5176 - 1.932i$

$k = 5$: $2\left(\cos\frac{7\pi}{4} + i\sin\frac{7\pi}{4}\right) \approx 1.414 - 1.414i$

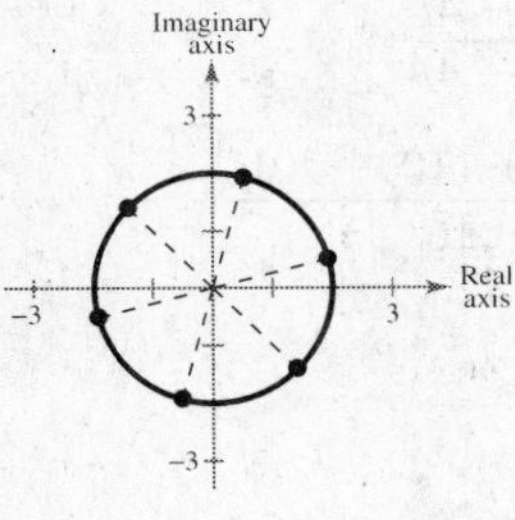

147. $x^3 - (1 - i) = 0$

$x^3 = 1 - i = \sqrt{2}(\cos 315° + i\sin 315°)$

The solutions are the cube roots of $1 - i$:

$$\sqrt[3]{\sqrt{2}}\left[\cos\left(\frac{315° + 360°k}{3}\right) + i\sin\left(\frac{315° + 360°k}{3}\right)\right], \quad k = 0, 1, 2$$

$\sqrt[6]{2}(\cos 105° + i\sin 105°)$

$\sqrt[6]{2}(\cos 225° + i\sin 225°)$

$\sqrt[6]{2}(\cos 345° + i\sin 345°)$

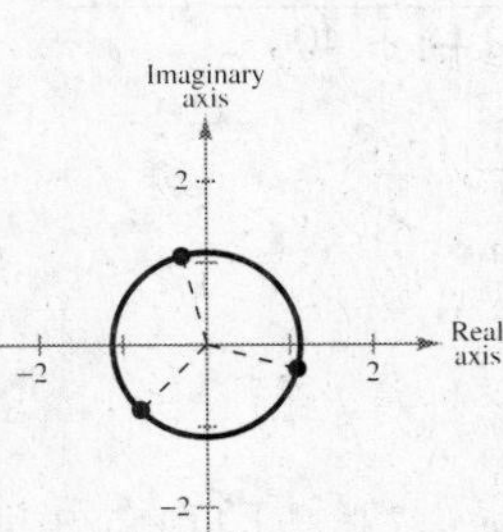

148. $x^4 + (1 + i) = 0$

$$x^4 = -1 - i = \sqrt{2}(\cos 225° + i \sin 225°)$$

The solutions are the fourth roots of $-1 - i$:

$$\sqrt[4]{\sqrt{2}}\left[\cos\left(\frac{225° + 360°k}{4}\right) + i \sin\left(\frac{225° + 360°k}{4}\right)\right]$$

$k = 0, 1, 2, 3$

$k = 0$: $\sqrt[8]{2}(\cos 56.25° + i \sin 56.25°) \approx 0.6059 + 0.9067i$

$k = 1$: $\sqrt[8]{2}(\cos 146.25° + i \sin 146.25°) \approx -0.9067 + 0.6059i$

$k = 2$: $\sqrt[8]{2}(\cos 236.25° + i \sin 236.25°) \approx -0.6059 - 0.9067i$

$k = 3$: $\sqrt[8]{2}(\cos 326.25° + i \sin 326.25°) \approx 0.9067 - 0.6059i$

149. $E = I \cdot Z$

$= (10 + 2i)(4 + 3i)$

$= (40 - 6) + (30 + 8)i$

$= 34 + 38i$

150. $E = I \cdot Z$

$= (12 + 2i)(3 + 5i)$

$= (36 - 10) + (60 + 6)i$

$= 26 + 66i$

151. $Z = \dfrac{E}{I}$

$= \dfrac{5 + 5i}{2 + 4i} \cdot \dfrac{2 - 4i}{2 - 4i}$

$= \dfrac{(10 + 20) + (10 - 20)i}{4 + 16}$

$= \dfrac{30 - 10i}{20}$

$= \dfrac{3}{2} - \dfrac{1}{2}i$

152. $Z = \dfrac{E}{I}$

$= \dfrac{4 + 5i}{10 + 2i} \cdot \dfrac{10 - 2i}{10 - 2i}$

$= \dfrac{(40 + 10) + (50 - 8)i}{100 + 4}$

$= \dfrac{50 + 42i}{104}$

$= \dfrac{25}{52} + \dfrac{21}{52}i$

153. $I = \dfrac{E}{Z}$

$= \dfrac{12 + 24i}{12 + 20i} \cdot \dfrac{12 - 20i}{12 - 20i}$

$= \dfrac{(144 + 480) + (288 - 240)i}{144 + 400}$

$= \dfrac{624 + 48i}{544}$

$= \dfrac{39}{34} + \dfrac{3}{34}i$

154. $I = \dfrac{E}{Z}$

$= \dfrac{15 + 12i}{25 + 24i} \cdot \dfrac{25 - 24i}{25 - 24i}$

$= \dfrac{(375 + 288) + (300 - 360)i}{625 + 576}$

$= \dfrac{663 - 60i}{1201}$

$= \dfrac{663}{1201} - \dfrac{60}{1201}i$

155. True. $\left[\frac{1}{2}(1 - \sqrt{3}i)\right]^9 = \left[\frac{1}{2} - \frac{\sqrt{3}}{2}i\right]^9 = -1$

156. False. $(\sqrt{3} + i)^2 = 2 + 2\sqrt{3}i \neq 8i$

157. True

158. $\dfrac{z_1}{z_2} = \dfrac{r_1(\cos\theta_1 + i\sin\theta_1)}{r_2(\cos\theta_2 + i\sin\theta_2)} \cdot \dfrac{\cos\theta_2 - i\sin\theta_2}{\cos\theta_2 - i\sin\theta_2}$

$= \dfrac{r_1}{r_2(\cos^2\theta_2 + \sin^2\theta_2)}[\cos\theta_1\cos\theta_2 + \sin\theta_1\sin\theta_2 + i(\sin\theta_1\cos\theta_2 - \sin\theta_2\cos\theta_1)]$

$= \dfrac{r_1}{r_2}[\cos(\theta_1 - \theta_2) + i\sin(\theta_1 - \theta_2)]$

159. $z = r(\cos\theta + i\sin\theta)$

$\bar{z} = r(\cos\theta - i\sin\theta)$

$= r(\cos(-\theta) + i\sin(-\theta))$

160. (a) $z\bar{z} = [r(\cos\theta + i\sin\theta)][r(\cos(-\theta) + i\sin(-\theta)]$

$= r^2[\cos(\theta - \theta) + i\sin(\theta - \theta)]$

$= r^2[\cos 0 + i\sin 0]$

$= r^2$

(b) $\dfrac{z}{\bar{z}} = \dfrac{r(\cos\theta + i\sin\theta)}{r[\cos(-\theta) + i\sin(-\theta)]}$

$= \dfrac{r}{r}[\cos(\theta - (-\theta)) + i\sin(\theta - (-\theta))]$

$= \cos 2\theta + i\sin 2\theta$

161. $z = r(\cos\theta + i\sin\theta)$

$-z = -r(\cos\theta + i\sin\theta)$

$= r(-\cos\theta - i\sin\theta)$

$= r(\cos(\theta + \pi) + i\sin(\theta + \pi))$

162. Let $a = 0$ and $b = \pi$ in Euler's Formula:

$e^{a+bi} = e^a(\cos b + i\sin b)$

$e^{0+\pi i} = e^0(\cos\pi + i\sin\pi)$

$e^{\pi i} = -1$

$e^{\pi i} + 1 = 0$

163. $d = 16\cos\left(\dfrac{\pi}{4}t\right)$

Maximum displacement: 16

Lowest possible t-value: $\dfrac{\pi}{4}t = \dfrac{\pi}{2} \Rightarrow t = 2$

164. Maximum displacement: $\dfrac{1}{16}$

Lowest positive value: $t = \dfrac{4}{5}$

165. $d = \dfrac{1}{8}\cos(12\pi t)$

Maximum displacement: $\dfrac{1}{8}$

Lowest possible t-value: $12\pi t = \dfrac{\pi}{2} \Rightarrow t = \dfrac{1}{24}$

166. Maximum displacement: $\dfrac{1}{12}$

Lowest positive value: $t = \dfrac{1}{60}$

167. $2\cos(x+\pi) + 2\cos(x-\pi) = 0$

$$4\cos x \cos \pi = 0$$

$$\cos x = 0$$

$$x = \frac{\pi}{2}, \frac{3\pi}{2}$$

168. $\sin\left(x+\frac{3\pi}{2}\right) - \sin\left(x-\frac{3\pi}{2}\right) = 0$

$$-\cos x - \cos x = 0$$

$$2\cos x = 0$$

$$x = \frac{\pi}{2}, \frac{3\pi}{2}$$

169. $\sin\left(x-\frac{\pi}{3}\right) - \sin\left(x+\frac{\pi}{3}\right) = \frac{3}{2}$

$$\frac{1}{2}\left[\sin\left(x+\frac{\pi}{3}\right) - \sin\left(x-\frac{\pi}{3}\right)\right] = \left(-\frac{3}{2}\right)\frac{1}{2}$$

$$\cos x \sin\frac{\pi}{3} = -\frac{3}{4}$$

$$\cos x\left(\frac{\sqrt{3}}{2}\right) = -\frac{3}{4}$$

$$\cos x = -\frac{\sqrt{3}}{2}$$

$$x = \frac{5\pi}{6}, \frac{7\pi}{6}$$

170. $\tan(x+\pi) - \cos\left(x+\frac{5\pi}{2}\right) = 0$

$$\tan x + \sin x = 0$$

$$\sin x\left(\frac{1}{\cos x} + 1\right) = 0$$

$$x = 0, \pi$$

Review Exercises for Chapter 6

1. Given: $A = 32°, B = 50°, a = 16$

$C = 180° - 32° - 50° = 98°$

$$b = \frac{a\sin B}{\sin A} = \frac{16\sin 50°}{\sin 32°} \approx 23.13$$

$$c = \frac{a\sin C}{\sin A} = \frac{16\sin 98°}{\sin 32°} \approx 29.90$$

2. Given: $A = 38°, B = 58°, a = 12$

$C = 180° - 38° - 58° = 84°$

$$b = \frac{a\sin B}{\sin A} = \frac{12\sin 58°}{\sin 38°} \approx 16.53$$

$$c = \frac{a\sin C}{\sin A} = \frac{12\sin 84°}{\sin 38°} \approx 19.38$$

3. Given: $B = 25°, C = 105°, c = 25$

$A = 180° - 25° - 105° = 50°$

$$b = \frac{c\sin B}{\sin C} = \frac{25\sin 25°}{\sin 105°} \approx 10.94$$

$$a = \frac{c\sin A}{\sin C} = \frac{25\sin 50°}{\sin 105°} \approx 19.83$$

4. Given: $B = 20°, C = 115°, c = 30$

$A = 180° - 20° - 115° = 45°$

$$b = \frac{c\sin B}{\sin C} = \frac{30\sin 20°}{\sin 115°} \approx 11.32$$

$$a = \frac{c\sin A}{\sin C} = \frac{30\sin 45°}{\sin 115°} \approx 23.41$$

5. Given: $A = 60°\,15' = 60.25°,\ B = 45°\,30' = 45.5°,\ b = 4.8$

$C = 180° - 60.25° - 45.5° = 74.25° = 74°\,15'$

$$a = \frac{b\sin A}{\sin B} = \frac{4.8\sin 60.25°}{\sin 45.5°} \approx 5.84$$

$$c = \frac{b\sin C}{\sin B} = \frac{4.8\sin 74.25°}{\sin 45.5°} \approx 6.48$$

6. Given: $A = 82°\,45' = 82.75°,\ B = 28°\,45' = 28.75°,\ b = 40.2$

$C = 180° - 82.75° - 28.75° = 68.5° = 68°\,30'$

$$a = \frac{b \sin A}{\sin B} = \frac{40.2 \sin 82.75°}{\sin 28.75°} \approx 82.91$$

$$c = \frac{b \sin C}{\sin B} = \frac{40.2 \sin 68.5°}{\sin 28.75°} \approx 77.76$$

7. Given: $A = 75°,\ a = 2.5,\ b = 16.5$

$$\sin B = \frac{b \sin A}{a} = \frac{16.5 \sin 75°}{2.5} \approx 6.375 \implies \text{no triangle formed}$$

No solution

8. Given: $A = 15°,\ a = 5,\ b = 10$

$$\sin B = \frac{b \sin A}{a} = \frac{10 \sin 15°}{5} \approx 0.5176 \implies B \approx 31.2° \text{ or } 148.8°$$

Case 1: $B \approx 31.2°$

$C \approx 180° - 15° - 31.2° = 133.8°$

$$c = \frac{a \sin C}{\sin A} \approx \frac{5 \sin 133.8°}{\sin 15°} \approx 13.94$$

Case 2: $B \approx 148.8°$

$C \approx 180° - 15° - 148.8° = 16.2°$

$$c = \frac{a \sin C}{\sin A} \approx \frac{5 \sin 16.2°}{\sin 15°} \approx 5.4$$

9. Given: $B = 115°, a = 9, b = 14.5$

$$\sin A = \frac{a \sin B}{b} = \frac{9 \sin 115°}{14.5} \approx 0.5625 \implies A \approx 34.2°$$

$C \approx 180° - 115° - 34.2° = 30.8°$

$$c = \frac{b}{\sin B}(\sin C) \approx \frac{14.5}{\sin 115°}(\sin 30.8°) \approx 8.18$$

10. Given: $B = 150°, a = 64, b = 10$

$$\sin A = \frac{a \sin B}{b} = \frac{64 \sin 150°}{10} \approx 3.2 \implies \text{no triangle formed}$$

No solution

11. Given: $C = 50°, a = 25, c = 22$

$$\sin A = \frac{a \sin C}{c} = \frac{25 \sin 50°}{22} \approx \frac{25(0.7660)}{22} \approx 0.8705 \implies A \approx 60.5° \text{ or } 119.5°$$

Case 1:

$A \approx 60.5°$

$B \approx 180° - 50° - 60.5° = 69.5°$

$$b = \frac{c \sin B}{\sin C} \approx \frac{22(0.9367)}{0.7660} \approx 26.90$$

Case 2:

$A \approx 119.5°$

$B \approx 180° - 50° - 119.5° = 10.5°$

$$b = \frac{c \sin B}{\sin C} \approx 5.24$$

12. Given: $B = 25°$, $a = 6.2$, $b = 4$

$$\sin A = \frac{a \sin B}{b} \approx \frac{6.2 \sin 25°}{4} \approx 0.6551 \implies A \approx 40.9° \text{ or } 139.1°$$

Case 1: $A \approx 40.9°$

$C \approx 180° - 25° - 40.9° = 114.1°$

$$c = \frac{b \sin C}{\sin B} \approx \frac{4 \sin 114.1°}{\sin 25°} \approx 8.64$$

Case 2: $A \approx 139.1°$

$C \approx 180° - 25° - 139.1° = 15.9°$

$$c = \frac{b \sin C}{\sin B} \approx \frac{4 \sin 15.9°}{\sin 25°} \approx 2.60$$

13. $A = 27°$, $b = 5$, $c = 8$

$$\begin{aligned}\text{Area} &= \tfrac{1}{2}bc \sin A \\ &= \tfrac{1}{2}(5)(8)(\sin 27°) \\ &\approx 9.08 \text{ square units}\end{aligned}$$

14. $B = 80°$, $a = 4$, $c = 8$

$$\begin{aligned}\text{Area} &= \tfrac{1}{2}ac \sin B \\ &= \tfrac{1}{2}(4)(8)(0.9848) \\ &= 15.76 \text{ square units}\end{aligned}$$

15. $C = 122°$, $b = 18$, $a = 29$

$$\begin{aligned}\text{Area} &= \tfrac{1}{2}ab \sin C \\ &= \tfrac{1}{2}(29)(18) \sin 122° \\ &\approx 221.34 \text{ square units}\end{aligned}$$

16.

$$\begin{aligned}\text{Area} &= \tfrac{1}{2}ab \sin C \\ &= \tfrac{1}{2}(120)(74) \sin 100° \\ &\approx 4372.5 \text{ square units}\end{aligned}$$

17. $h = 50 \tan 17° \approx 15.3$ meters

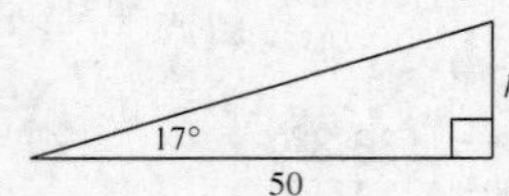

18. In triangle ABC, $A = 90° - 62° = 28°$, $B = 90° + 38° = 128°$, and $C = 180° - A - B = 24°$.

$$b = \frac{c \sin B}{\sin C} = \frac{5 \sin 128°}{\sin 24°} \approx 9.6870$$

$h = b \sin A = b \sin 28° \approx 4.548 \approx 4.5$ miles

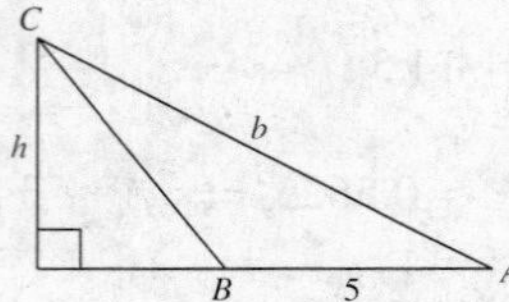

19. $\sin 28° = \dfrac{h}{75}$

$h = 75 \sin 28° \approx 35.21$ feet

$\cos 28° = \dfrac{x}{75}$

$x = 75 \cos 28° \approx 66.22$ feet

$\tan 45° = \dfrac{H}{x}$

$H = x \tan 45° \approx 66.22$ feet

Height of tree: $H - h \approx 31$ feet

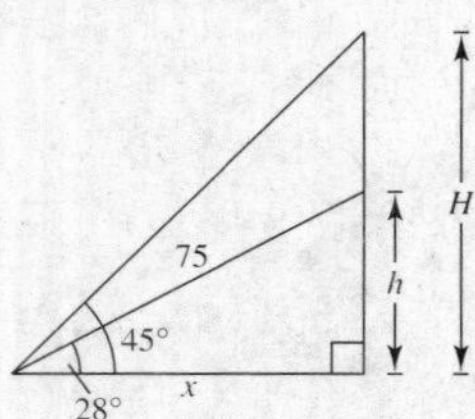

20. $\dfrac{a}{\sin 75°} = \dfrac{400}{\sin 37.5°}$

$$a = \frac{400 \sin 75°}{\sin 37.5°} \approx 634.7 \text{ feet}$$

$\sin 67.5° = \dfrac{w}{a}$

$w = 634.7 \sin 67.5° \approx 586.4$ feet

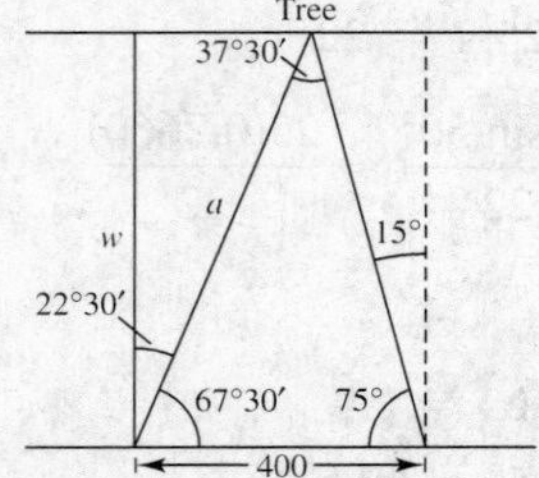

21. Given: $a = 18, b = 12, c = 15$

$$\cos A = \frac{b^2 + c^2 - a^2}{2bc} = \frac{12^2 + 15^2 - 18^2}{2(12)(15)} = 0.125 \Rightarrow A \approx 82.82°$$

$$\cos B = \frac{a^2 + c^2 - b^2}{2ac} = \frac{18^2 + 15^2 - 12^2}{2(18)(15)} = 0.75 \Rightarrow B \approx 41.41°$$

$$C = 180° - A - B \approx 55.77°$$

22. Given: $a = 10, b = 12, c = 16$

$$\cos C = \frac{a^2 + b^2 - c^2}{2ab} = \frac{10^2 + 12^2 - 16^2}{2(10)(12)} = -0.05 \Rightarrow C \approx 92.87°$$

$$\cos B = \frac{a^2 + c^2 - b^2}{2ac} = \frac{10^2 + 16^2 - 12^2}{2(10)(16)} = 0.6625 \Rightarrow B \approx 48.51°$$

$$A = 180° - B - C \approx 38.62°$$

23. Given: $a = 9, b = 12, c = 20$

$$\cos C = \frac{a^2 + b^2 - c^2}{2ab}$$

$$= \frac{81 + 144 - 400}{2(9)(12)}$$

$$\approx -0.8102 \Rightarrow C \approx 144.1°$$

$$\sin A = \frac{a \sin C}{c}$$

$$= \frac{9 \sin(144.1°)}{20}$$

$$\approx 0.264 \Rightarrow A \approx 15.3$$

$$B = 180° - 144.1° - 15.3° = 20.6°$$

24. $a = 7, b = 15, c = 19$

$$\cos C = \frac{a^2 + b^2 - c^2}{2ab} \approx -0.4143 \Rightarrow C \approx 114.5°$$

$$\cos B = \frac{a^2 + c^2 - b^2}{2ac} \approx 0.6955 \Rightarrow B \approx 45.9°$$

$$A = 180° - B - C = 19.6°$$

25. Given: $a = 6.5, b = 10.2, c = 16$

$$\cos A = \frac{b^2 + c^2 - a^2}{2bc} = \frac{10.2^2 + 16^2 - 6.5^2}{2(10.2)(16)} \approx 0.97 \Rightarrow A \approx 13.19°$$

$$\cos B = \frac{a^2 + c^2 - b^2}{2ac} = \frac{6.5^2 + 16^2 - 10.2^2}{2(6.5)(16)} \approx 0.93 \Rightarrow B \approx 20.98°$$

$$C = 180° - A - B \approx 145.83°$$

26. Given: $a = 6.2, b = 6.4, c = 2.1$

$$\cos A = \frac{b^2 + c^2 - a^2}{2bc} = \frac{6.4^2 + 2.1^2 - 6.2^2}{2(6.4)(2.1)} \approx 0.26 \Rightarrow A \approx 75.06°$$

$$\cos B = \frac{a^2 + c^2 - b^2}{2ac} = \frac{6.2^2 + 2.1^2 - 6.4^2}{2(6.2)(2.1)} \approx 0.07 \Rightarrow B \approx 85.84°$$

$$C = 180° - A - B \approx 19.10°$$

27. Given: $C = 65°, a = 25, b = 12$

$c^2 = a^2 + b^2 - 2ab\cos C = 25^2 + 12^2 - 2(25)(12)\cos 65° \approx 515.4290 \implies c \approx 22.70$

$\sin A = \frac{a\sin C}{c} = \frac{25\sin 65°}{22.70} \approx 0.998 \implies A \approx 86.38°$

$B = 180° - A - C \approx 28.62°$

28. Given: $B = 48°, a = 18, c = 12$

$b^2 = a^2 + c^2 - 2ac\cos B = 18^2 + 12^2 - 2(18)(12)\cos 48° \approx 178.9356 \implies b \approx 13.38$

$\sin C = \frac{c\sin B}{b} = \frac{12\sin 48°}{13.38} \approx 0.666663 \implies C \approx 41.81°$

$A = 180° - B - C \approx 90.19°$

(Answers may vary.)

29. Given: $B = 110°, a = 4, c = 4$

$b^2 = a^2 + c^2 - 2ac\cos B = 16 + 16 - 2(4)(4)(\cos 110) \approx 42.94 \implies b \approx 6.55$

$\sin A = \frac{a\sin B}{b} \approx \frac{4\sin 110°}{6.55} \approx 0.5739 \implies A \approx 35°$

$c = a \implies C = A \approx 35°$

30. Given: $B = 150°,\ a = 10,\ c = 20$

$b^2 = a^2 + c^2 - 2ac\cos B \approx 100 + 400 - 400(-0.8660) \approx 846.4 \implies b \approx 29.09$

$\sin C = \frac{c\sin B}{b} \approx \frac{20(0.5)}{29.09} \approx 0.3437 \implies C \approx 20.1°$

$\sin A = \frac{a\sin B}{b} \approx \frac{10(0.5)}{29.09} \approx 0.1719 \implies A \approx 9.9°$

31. Given: $B = 55°\,30' = 55.5°,\ a = 12.4,\ c = 18.5$

$b^2 = a^2 + c^2 - 2ac\cos B = 12.4^2 + 18.5^2 - 2(12.4)(18.5)\cos 55.5° \approx 236.1428 \implies b \approx 15.37$

$\sin A = \frac{a\sin B}{b} \approx \frac{12.4\sin 55.5°}{15.37} \approx 0.665 \implies A \approx 41.68° \approx 41°\,41'$

$C = 180° - A - B = 82.82° \approx 82°\,49'$

32. Given: $B = 85°\,15' = 85.25°,\ a = 24.2,\ c = 28.2$

$b^2 = a^2 + c^2 - 2ac\cos B = 24.2^2 + 28.2^2 - 2(24.2)(28.2)\cos 85.25° \approx 1267.8567 \implies b \approx 35.61$

$\sin A = \frac{a\sin B}{b} \approx \frac{24.2\sin 85.25°}{35.61} \approx 0.677 \implies A \approx 42.63° \approx 42°\,38'$

$C = 180° - A - B = 52.12° \approx 52°\,7'$

33. $a^2 = 5^2 + 8^2 - 2(5)(8)\cos 152° \approx 159.6 \implies a \approx 12.63$ ft

$b^2 = 5^2 + 8^2 - 2(5)(8)\cos 28° \approx 18.36 \implies b \approx 4.285$ ft

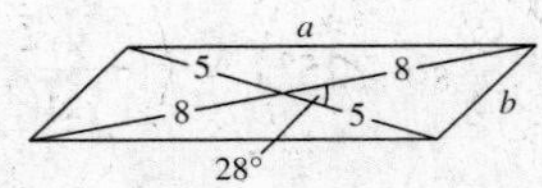

34. $a^2 = 15^2 + 20^2 - 2(15)(20)\cos(146°) \approx 1122.42 \Rightarrow a \approx 33.5$ m

$b^2 = 15^2 + 20^2 - 2(15)(20)\cos(34°) \approx 127.58 \Rightarrow b \approx 11.3$ m

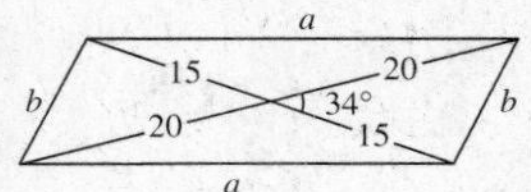

35. Angle between planes is $5° + 67° = 72°$.

In two hours, distances from airport are 850 miles and 1060 miles.

By the Law of Cosines,

$d^2 = 850^2 + 1060^2 - 2(850)(1060)\cos(72°) \approx 1{,}289{,}251.376$

$d \approx 1135.5$ miles.

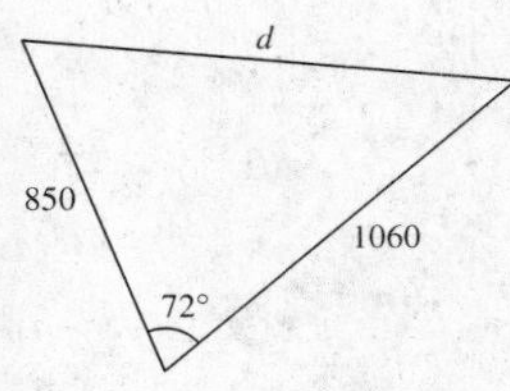

36. $b^2 = a^2 + c^2 - 2ac\cos B$

$= 300^2 + 425^2 - 2(300)(425)\cos(180° - 65°)$

$\approx 378{,}392.66$

$b \approx 615.1$ meters

37. $a = 4,\ b = 5,\ c = 7$

$s = \dfrac{a + b + c}{2} = \dfrac{4 + 5 + 7}{2} = 8$

Area $= \sqrt{s(s - a)(s - b)(s - c)}$

$= \sqrt{8(4)(3)(1)}$

≈ 9.798 square units

38. $a = 15, b = 8, c = 10$

$s = \dfrac{15 + 8 + 10}{2} = 16.5$

Area $= \sqrt{16.5(1.5)(8.5)(6.5)}$

≈ 36.98 square units

39. $a = 64.8, b = 49.2, c = 24.1$

$s = \dfrac{a + b + c}{2} = \dfrac{64.8 + 49.2 + 24.1}{2} = 69.05$

Area $= \sqrt{s(s - a)(s - b)(s - c)}$

$= \sqrt{69.05(4.25)(19.85)(44.95)}$

≈ 511.7 square units

40. $s = \dfrac{8.55 + 5.14 + 12.73}{2} = 13.21$

Area $= \sqrt{s(s - a)(s - b)(s - c)}$

$= \sqrt{13.21(4.66)(8.07)(0.48)}$

≈ 15.4 square units

41. Initial point: $(-5, 4)$

Terminal point: $(2, -1)$

$\mathbf{v} = \langle 2 - (-5), -1 - 4\rangle = \langle 7, -5\rangle$

42. Initial point: $(0, 1)$

Terminal point: $\left(6, \frac{7}{2}\right)$

$\mathbf{v} = \left\langle 6 - 0, \frac{7}{2} - 1\right\rangle = \left\langle 6, \frac{5}{2}\right\rangle$

43. Initial point: $(0, 10)$

Terminal point: $(7, 3)$

$\mathbf{v} = \langle 7 - 0, 3 - 10\rangle = \langle 7, -7\rangle$

44. Initial point: $(1, 5)$

Terminal point: $(15, 9)$

$\mathbf{v} = \langle 15 - 1, 9 - 5\rangle = \langle 14, 4\rangle$

45. $8\cos 120°\mathbf{i} + 8\sin 120°\mathbf{j} = \left\langle -4, 4\sqrt{3}\right\rangle$

46. $\left\langle \dfrac{1}{2}\cos 225°, \dfrac{1}{2}\sin 225°\right\rangle = \left\langle -\dfrac{\sqrt{2}}{4}, -\dfrac{\sqrt{2}}{4}\right\rangle$

47. $2\mathbf{u}$

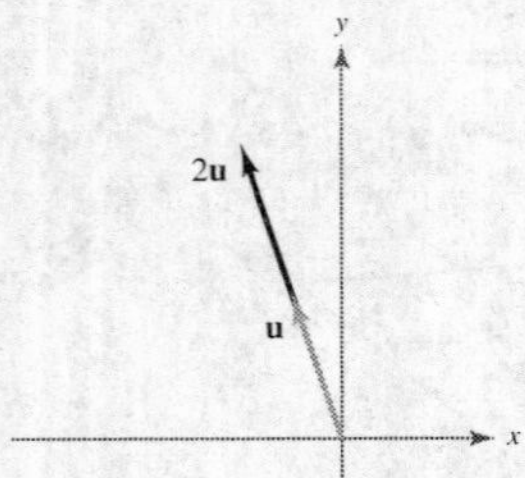

48. $-\frac{1}{2}\mathbf{v}$

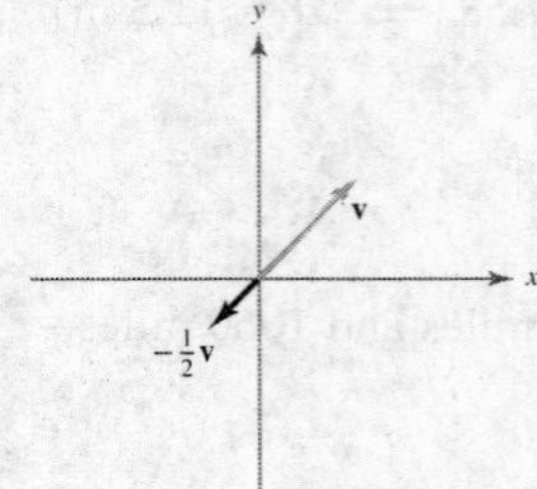

49. $2\mathbf{u} + \mathbf{v}$

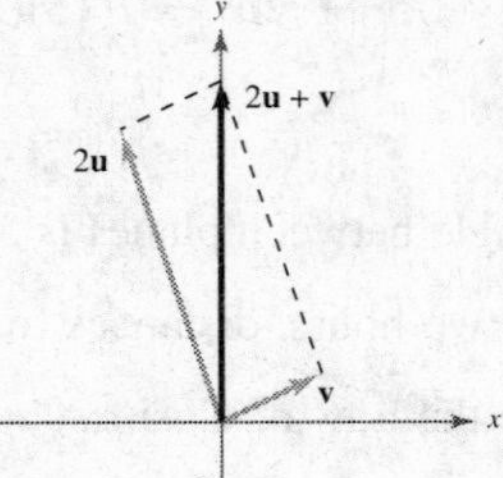

50. $\mathbf{u} + 2\mathbf{v}$

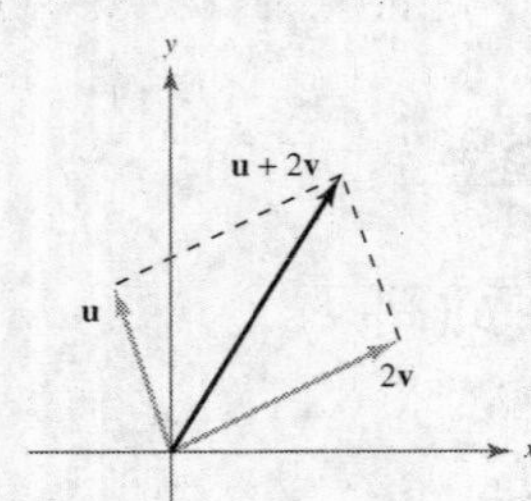

51. $\mathbf{u} - 2\mathbf{v}$

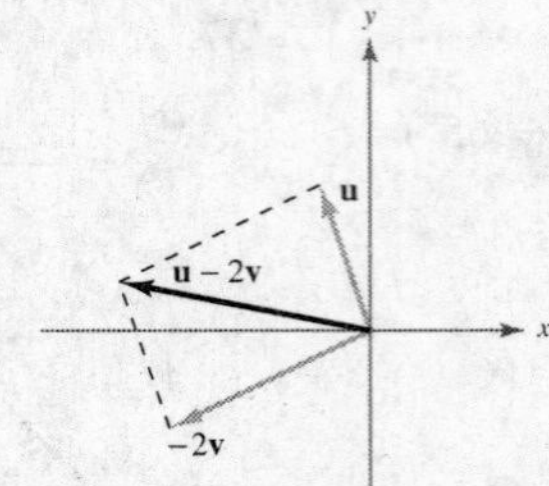

52. $\mathbf{v} - 2\mathbf{u}$

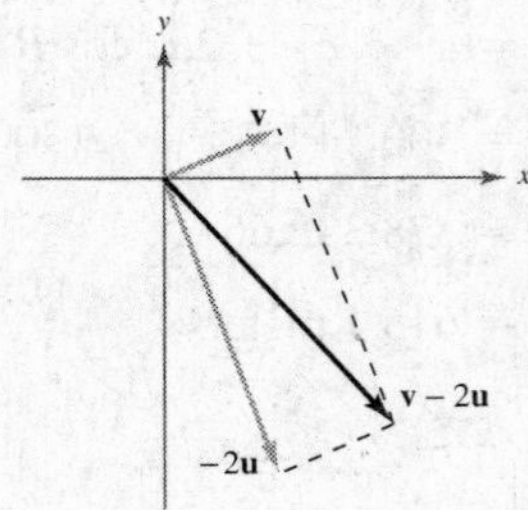

53. (a) $\mathbf{u} + \mathbf{v} = \langle -1, -3\rangle + \langle -3, 6\rangle = \langle -4, 3\rangle$

(b) $\mathbf{u} - \mathbf{v} = \langle 2, -9\rangle$

(c) $3\mathbf{u} = \langle -3, -9\rangle$

(d) $2\mathbf{v} + 5\mathbf{u} = \langle -6, 12\rangle + \langle -5, -15\rangle = \langle -11, -3\rangle$

54. (a) $\mathbf{u} + \mathbf{v} = \langle 4, 5\rangle + \langle 0, -1\rangle = \langle 4, 4\rangle$

(b) $\mathbf{u} - \mathbf{v} = \langle 4, 6\rangle$

(c) $3\mathbf{u} = \langle 12, 15\rangle$

(d) $2\mathbf{v} + 5\mathbf{u} = \langle 0, -2\rangle + \langle 20, 25\rangle = \langle 20, 23\rangle$

55. (a) $\mathbf{u} + \mathbf{v} = \langle -5, 2\rangle + \langle 4, 4\rangle = \langle -1, 6\rangle$

(b) $\mathbf{u} - \mathbf{v} = \langle -9, -2\rangle$

(c) $3\mathbf{u} = \langle -15, 6\rangle$

(d) $2\mathbf{v} + 5\mathbf{u} = \langle 8, 8\rangle + \langle -25, 10\rangle = \langle -17, 18\rangle$

56. (a) $\mathbf{u} + \mathbf{v} = \langle 1, -8\rangle + \langle 3, -2\rangle = \langle 4, -10\rangle$

(b) $\mathbf{u} - \mathbf{v} = \langle -2, -6\rangle$

(c) $3\mathbf{u} = \langle 3, -24\rangle$

(d) $2\mathbf{v} + 5\mathbf{u} = \langle 6, -4\rangle + \langle 5, -40\rangle = \langle 11, -44\rangle$

57. (a) $\mathbf{u} + \mathbf{v} = \langle 2, -1\rangle + \langle 5, 3\rangle = \langle 7, 2\rangle$

(b) $\mathbf{u} - \mathbf{v} = \langle -3, -4\rangle$

(c) $3\mathbf{u} = \langle 6, -3\rangle$

(d) $2\mathbf{v} + 5\mathbf{u} = \langle 10, 6\rangle + \langle 10, -5\rangle = \langle 20, 1\rangle$

58. (a) $\mathbf{u} + \mathbf{v} = \langle 0, -6\rangle + \langle 1, 1\rangle = \langle 1, -5\rangle$

(b) $\mathbf{u} - \mathbf{v} = \langle -1, -7\rangle$

(c) $3\mathbf{u} = \langle 0, -18\rangle$

(d) $2\mathbf{v} + 5\mathbf{u} = \langle 2, 2\rangle + \langle 0, -30\rangle = \langle 2, -28\rangle$

59. (a) $\mathbf{u} + \mathbf{v} = \langle 4, 0\rangle + \langle -1, 6\rangle = \langle 3, 6\rangle$

(b) $\mathbf{u} - \mathbf{v} = \langle 5, -6\rangle$

(c) $3\mathbf{u} = \langle 12, 0\rangle$

(d) $2\mathbf{v} + 5\mathbf{u} = \langle -2, 12\rangle + \langle 20, 0\rangle = \langle 18, 12\rangle$

60. (a) $\mathbf{u} + \mathbf{v} = \langle -7, -3\rangle + \langle 4, -1\rangle = \langle -3, -4\rangle$

(b) $\mathbf{u} - \mathbf{v} = \langle -11, -2\rangle$

(c) $3\mathbf{u} = \langle -21, -9\rangle$

(d) $2\mathbf{v} + 5\mathbf{u} = \langle 8, -2\rangle + \langle -35, -15\rangle = \langle -27, -17\rangle$

61. $3\mathbf{v} = 3(10\mathbf{i} + 3\mathbf{j}) = 30\mathbf{i} + 9\mathbf{j} = \langle 30, 9 \rangle$

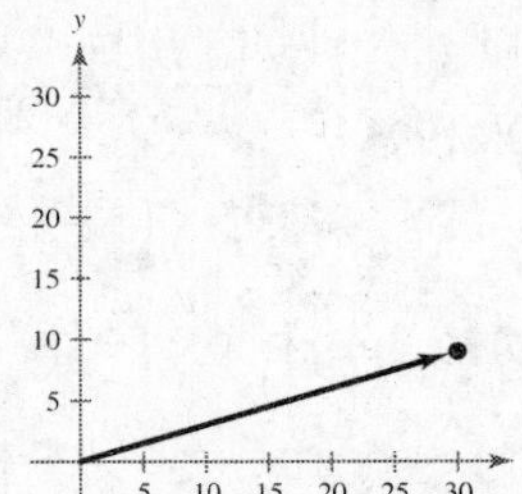

62. $\mathbf{v} = 10\mathbf{i} + 3\mathbf{j}$

$\frac{1}{2}\mathbf{v} = 5\mathbf{i} + \frac{3}{2}\mathbf{j}$

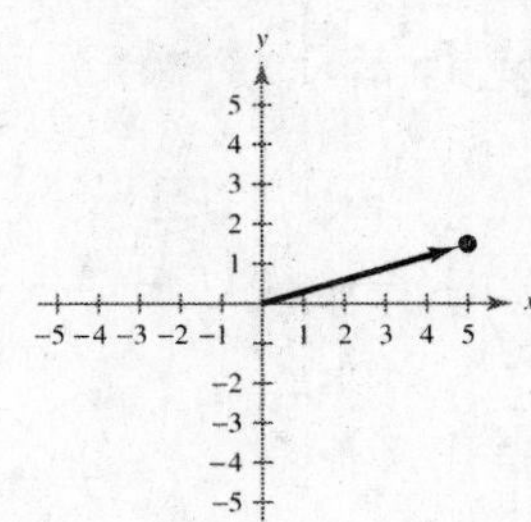

63. $\mathbf{w} = 4\mathbf{u} + 5\mathbf{v} = 4(6\mathbf{i} - 5\mathbf{j}) + 5(10\mathbf{i} + 3\mathbf{j})$

$= 74\mathbf{i} - 5\mathbf{j}$

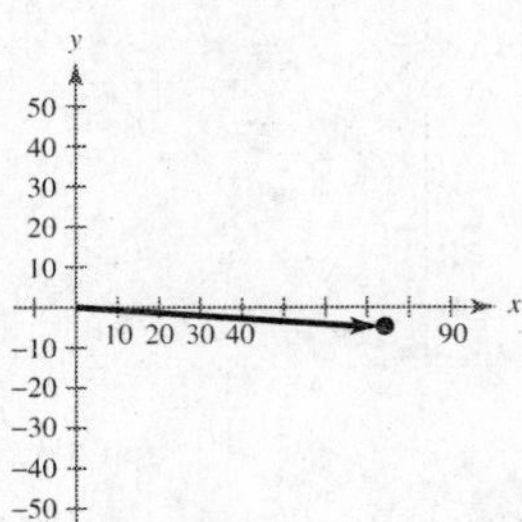

64. $3\mathbf{v} - 2\mathbf{u} = 3(10\mathbf{i} + 3\mathbf{j}) - 2(6\mathbf{i} - 5\mathbf{j}) = 18\mathbf{i} + 19\mathbf{j}$

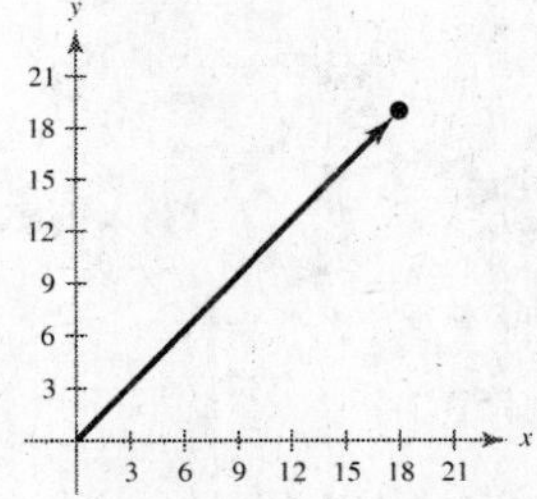

65. $\|\mathbf{u}\| = 6$

Unit vector: $\frac{1}{6}\langle 0, -6 \rangle = \langle 0, -1 \rangle$

66. $\|\mathbf{v}\| = \sqrt{(-12)^2 + (-5)^2} = \sqrt{169} = 13$

Unit vector: $\left\langle -\frac{12}{13}, -\frac{5}{13} \right\rangle$

67. $\|\mathbf{v}\| = \sqrt{5^2 + (-2)^2} = \sqrt{29}$

Unit vector: $\dfrac{1}{\sqrt{29}}\langle 5, -2 \rangle = \left\langle \dfrac{5}{\sqrt{29}}, \dfrac{-2}{\sqrt{29}} \right\rangle$

68. $\|\mathbf{w}\| = 7$

Unit vector: $\dfrac{1}{7}(-7\mathbf{i}) = -\mathbf{i}$

69. $\mathbf{u} = \langle 1 - (-8), -5 - 3 \rangle = \langle 9, -8 \rangle = 9\mathbf{i} - 8\mathbf{j}$

70. $\mathbf{u} = \langle -6.4 - 2, 10.8 - (-3.2) \rangle = -8.4\mathbf{i} + 14\mathbf{j}$

71. $\mathbf{v} = -10\mathbf{i} + 10\mathbf{j}$

$\|\mathbf{v}\| = \sqrt{(-10)^2 + (10)^2} = \sqrt{200} = 10\sqrt{2}$

$\tan\theta = \dfrac{10}{-10} = -1 \Rightarrow \theta = 135°$ since $\mathbf{v}$ is in Quadrant II.

$\mathbf{v} = 10\sqrt{2}(\cos 135°\mathbf{i} + \sin 135°\mathbf{j})$

72. $\mathbf{v} = 4\mathbf{i} - \mathbf{j}$

$\|\mathbf{v}\| = \sqrt{4^2 + (-1)^2} = \sqrt{17}$

$\tan\theta = \dfrac{-1}{4} = -\dfrac{1}{4} \Rightarrow \theta \approx 346°$, since θ is in Quadrant IV.

$\mathbf{v} = \sqrt{17}(\cos 346°\mathrm{i} + \sin 346°\,\mathbf{j})$

73. $\mathbf{u} = 15[(\cos 20°)\mathbf{i} + (\sin 20°)\mathbf{j}]$

$\mathbf{v} = 20[(\cos 63°)\mathbf{i} + (\sin 63°)\mathbf{j}]$

$\mathbf{u} + \mathbf{v} \approx 23.1752\mathbf{i} + 22.9504\mathbf{j}$

$\|\mathbf{u} + \mathbf{v}\| \approx 32.62$

$$\tan\theta = \frac{22.9504}{23.1752} \implies \theta \approx 44.72°$$

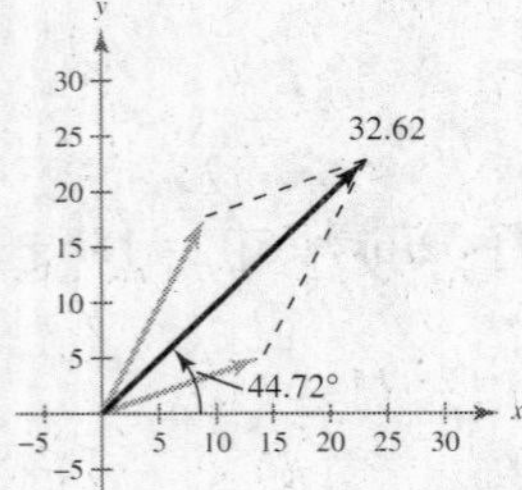

74. $\mathbf{u} = 12[(\cos 82°)\mathbf{i} + (\sin 82°)\mathbf{j}]$

$\mathbf{v} = 8[(\cos(-12°))\mathbf{i} + (\sin(-12°))\mathbf{j}]$

$\mathbf{u} + \mathbf{v} \approx 9.4953\mathbf{i} + 10.2199\mathbf{j}$

$\|\mathbf{u} + \mathbf{v}\| \approx 13.95$

$$\tan\theta = \frac{10.2199}{9.4953} \implies \theta \approx 47.11°$$

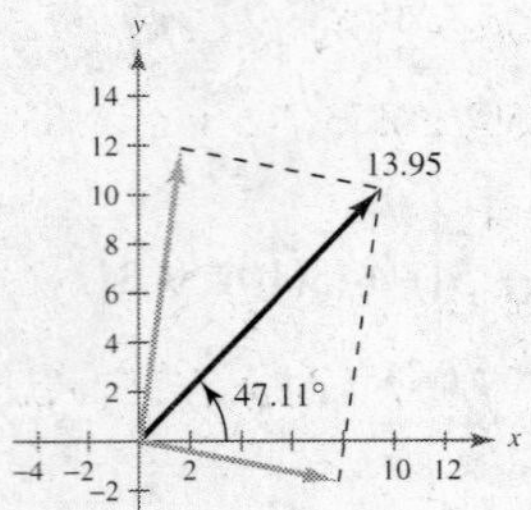

75. $\mathbf{F}_1 = 250\langle\cos 60°, \sin 60°\rangle$

$\mathbf{F}_2 = 100\langle\cos 150°, \sin 150°\rangle$

$\mathbf{F}_3 = 200\langle\cos(-90°), \sin(-90°)\rangle$

$\mathbf{F} = \mathbf{F}_1 + \mathbf{F}_2 + \mathbf{F}_3 \approx \langle 38.39746, 66.50635\rangle$

$$\tan\theta \approx \frac{66.50635}{38.39746} \implies \theta \approx 60°$$

$\|\mathbf{F}\| = \sqrt{38.39746^2 + 66.50635^2} \approx 76.8$ pounds

76. Force One: $\mathbf{u} = 85\mathbf{i}$

Force Two: $\mathbf{v} = 50\cos 15°\mathbf{i} + 50\sin 15°\mathbf{j}$

Resultant Force:

$\mathbf{u} + \mathbf{v} = (85 + 50\cos 15°)\mathbf{i} + (50\sin 15°)\mathbf{j}$

$$\begin{aligned}\|\mathbf{u} + \mathbf{v}\| &= \sqrt{(85 + 50\cos 15°)^2 + (50\sin 15°)^2}\\ &= \sqrt{85^2 + 8500\cos 15° + 50^2}\\ &= 133.92 \text{ lb}\end{aligned}$$

$$\tan\theta = \frac{50\sin 15°}{85 + 50\cos 15°} \implies \theta \approx 5.5° \text{ from the 85-pound force.}$$

77. Rope One: $\mathbf{u} = \|\mathbf{u}\|(\cos 30°\mathbf{i} - \sin 30°\mathbf{j}) = \|\mathbf{u}\|\left(\frac{\sqrt{3}}{2}\mathbf{i} - \frac{1}{2}\mathbf{j}\right)$

Rope Two: $\mathbf{v} = \|\mathbf{u}\|(-\cos 30°\mathbf{i} - \sin 30°\mathbf{j}) = \|\mathbf{u}\|\left(-\frac{\sqrt{3}}{2}\mathbf{i} - \frac{1}{2}\mathbf{j}\right)$

Resultant: $\mathbf{u} + \mathbf{v} = -\|\mathbf{u}\|\mathbf{j} = -180\mathbf{j}$

$\|\mathbf{u}\| = 180$

Therefore, the tension on each rope is $\|\mathbf{u}\| = 180$ pounds.

78. By symmetry, the magnitudes of the tensions are equal.

$\mathbf{T} = \|\mathbf{T}\|(\cos 120°\mathbf{i} + \sin 120°\mathbf{j})$

$\|\mathbf{T}\| \sin 120° = \frac{1}{2}(200) \Rightarrow \|\mathbf{T}\| = \frac{100}{\sqrt{3}/2} = \frac{200}{\sqrt{3}} \approx 115.5 \text{ lbs}$

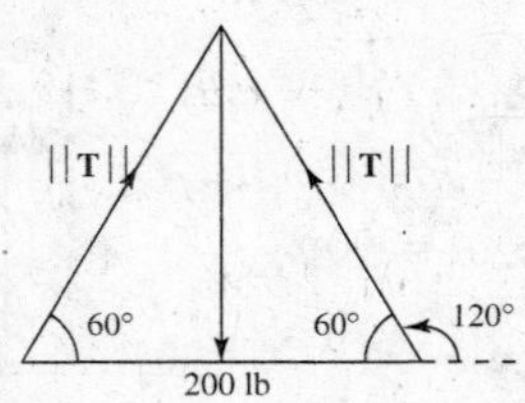

79. Airplane velocity: $\mathbf{u} = 430\langle\cos 315°, \sin 315°\rangle$

Wind velocity: $\mathbf{w} = 35\langle\cos 60°, \sin 60°\rangle$

$\mathbf{u} + \mathbf{w} \approx \langle 321.5559, -273.7450\rangle$

$\|\mathbf{u} + \mathbf{w}\| \approx 422.3 \text{ mph}$

$\tan(\mathbf{u} + \mathbf{w}) = \frac{-273.7450}{321.5559}$

$\approx -0.8513 \Rightarrow \theta \approx -40.4°$

The bearing from the north is $90° + 40.4° = 130.4°$.

80. Airspeed: $\mathbf{u} = 724(\cos 60°\mathbf{i} + \sin 60°\mathbf{j})$

$= 362(\mathbf{i} + \sqrt{3}\mathbf{j})$

Wind: $\mathbf{w} = 32\mathbf{i}$

Groundspeed $= \mathbf{u} + \mathbf{w} = (394\mathbf{i} + 362\sqrt{3}\mathbf{j})$

$\|\mathbf{u} + \mathbf{w}\| = \sqrt{(394)^2 + (362\sqrt{3})^2} \approx 740.5 \text{ km/hr}$

$\tan\theta = \frac{362\sqrt{3}}{394} \Rightarrow \theta \approx 57.9°$

Bearing: N 32.1° E (or 32.1° in airplane navigation)

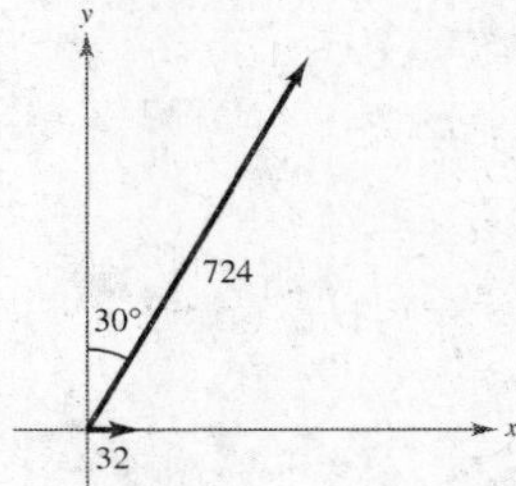

81. $\mathbf{u} \cdot \mathbf{v} = \langle 0, -2\rangle \cdot \langle 1, 10\rangle = 0 - 20 = -20$

82. $\mathbf{u} \cdot \mathbf{v} = \langle -4, 5\rangle \cdot \langle 3, -1\rangle = -12 - 5 = -17$

83. $\mathbf{u} \cdot \mathbf{v} = \langle 6, -1\rangle \cdot \langle 2, 5\rangle = 6(2) + (-1)(5) = 7$

84. $\mathbf{u} \cdot \mathbf{v} = (8\mathbf{i} - 7\mathbf{j}) \cdot (3\mathbf{i} - 4\mathbf{j}) = 24 + 28 = 52$

85. $\mathbf{u} \cdot \mathbf{u} = \langle -3, -4\rangle \cdot \langle -3, -4\rangle$

$= 9 + 16 = 25 = \|\mathbf{u}\|^2$

86. $\|\mathbf{v}\| - 3 = \sqrt{(2)^2 + (1)^2} - 3 = \sqrt{5} - 3$

87. $4\mathbf{u} \cdot \mathbf{v} = 4\langle -3, -4\rangle \cdot \langle 2, 1\rangle = 4(-6 - 4) = -40$

88. $(\mathbf{u} \cdot \mathbf{v})\mathbf{u} = (-10)\langle -3, -4\rangle = \langle 30, 40\rangle$

89. $\mathbf{u} = \langle 2\sqrt{2}, -4\rangle, \mathbf{v} = \langle -\sqrt{2}, 1\rangle$

$\cos\theta = \frac{\mathbf{u} \cdot \mathbf{v}}{\|\mathbf{u}\|\,\|\mathbf{v}\|} = \frac{-8}{(\sqrt{24})(\sqrt{3})} \Rightarrow \theta \approx 160.5°$

90. $\mathbf{u} = \langle 3, 1\rangle, \mathbf{v} = \langle 4, 5\rangle$

$\cos\theta = \frac{\mathbf{u} \cdot \mathbf{v}}{\|\mathbf{u}\|\,\|\mathbf{v}\|} = \frac{17}{(\sqrt{10})(\sqrt{41})} \Rightarrow \theta \approx 32.9°$

91. $\mathbf{u} = \cos\frac{7\pi}{4}\mathbf{i} + \sin\frac{7\pi}{4}\mathbf{j} = \left\langle \frac{1}{\sqrt{2}}, -\frac{1}{\sqrt{2}}\right\rangle$

$\mathbf{v} = \cos\frac{5\pi}{6}\mathbf{i} + \sin\frac{5\pi}{6}\mathbf{j} = \left\langle -\frac{\sqrt{3}}{2}, \frac{1}{2}\right\rangle$

$\cos\theta = \frac{\mathbf{u} \cdot \mathbf{v}}{\|\mathbf{u}\|\,\|\mathbf{v}\|} = \frac{(-\sqrt{3}/(2\sqrt{2})) - (1/(2\sqrt{2}))}{(1)(1)}$

$\approx -0.966 \Rightarrow \theta \approx 165° \text{ or } \frac{11\pi}{12}$

92. Angle $= 45° + 60° = 105°$

93. $\cos\theta = \dfrac{\mathbf{u}\cdot\mathbf{v}}{\|\mathbf{u}\|\,\|\mathbf{v}\|}$

$= 0 \Rightarrow \theta = 90°$

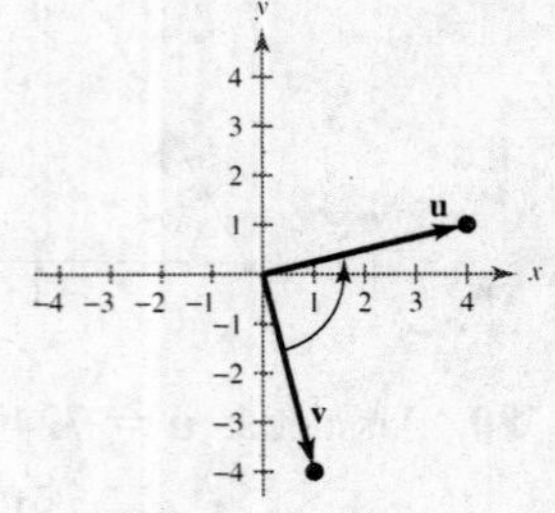

94. 180°

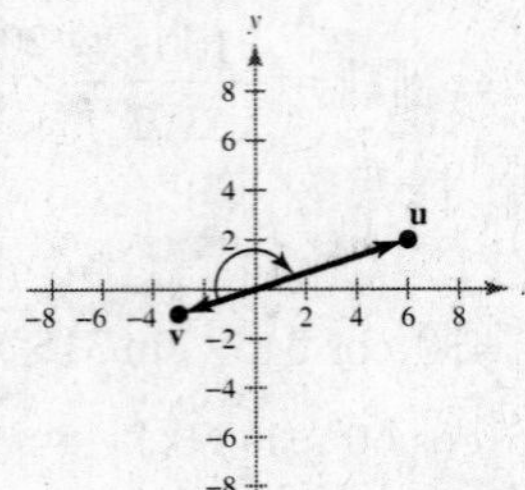

95. $\cos\theta = \dfrac{\mathbf{u}\cdot\mathbf{v}}{\|\mathbf{u}\|\,\|\mathbf{v}\|} = \dfrac{70 - 15}{\sqrt{74}\sqrt{109}}$

≈ 0.612

$\Rightarrow \theta \approx 52.2°$

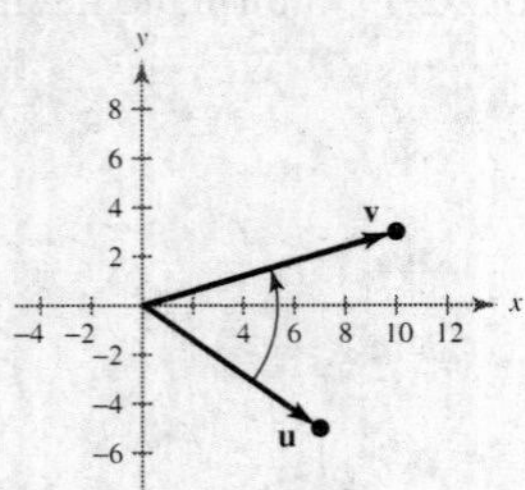

96. 54.1°

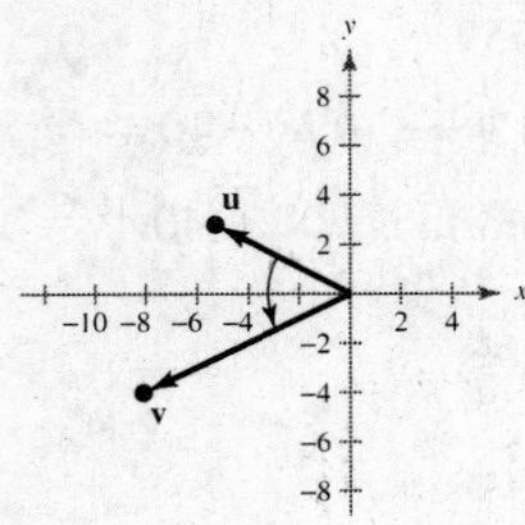

97. $\mathbf{u} = \langle 39, -12\rangle, \mathbf{v} = \langle -26, 8\rangle$

$\mathbf{u}\cdot\mathbf{v} = 39(-26) + (-12)(8)$

$= -1110 \neq 0 \Rightarrow$ **u** and **v** are not orthogonal.

$\mathbf{v} = -\frac{2}{3}\mathbf{u} \Rightarrow$ **u** and **v** are parallel.

98. $\mathbf{u}\cdot\mathbf{v} = \langle 8, -4\rangle \cdot \langle 5, 10\rangle = 40 - 40 = 0 \Rightarrow$ orthogonal

99. $\mathbf{u} = \langle 8, 5\rangle, \mathbf{v} = \langle -2, 4\rangle$

$\mathbf{u}\cdot\mathbf{v} = 8(-2) + (5)(4)$

$= 4 \neq 0 \Rightarrow$ **u** and **v** are not orthogonal.

$\mathbf{u} \neq k\mathbf{v} \Rightarrow$ **u** and **v** are not parallel.

Neither

100. $-\frac{3}{4}\mathbf{v} = -\frac{3}{4}\langle 20, -68\rangle = \langle -15, 51\rangle = \mathbf{u} \Rightarrow$ parallel

101. $\langle 1, -k\rangle \cdot \langle 1, 2\rangle = 1 - 2k = 0 \Rightarrow k = \frac{1}{2}$

102. $\langle 2, 1\rangle \cdot \langle -1, -k\rangle = -2 - k = 0 \Rightarrow k = -2$

103. $\langle k, -1\rangle \cdot \langle 2, -2\rangle = 2k + 2 = 0 \Rightarrow k = -1$

104. $\langle k, -2\rangle \cdot \langle 1, 4\rangle = k - 8 = 0 \Rightarrow k = 8$

105. $\mathbf{u} = \langle -4, 3\rangle,\ \mathbf{v} = \langle -8, -2\rangle$

$$\text{proj}_{\mathbf{v}}\mathbf{u} = \left(\frac{\mathbf{u}\cdot\mathbf{v}}{\|\mathbf{v}\|^2}\right)\mathbf{v} = \left(\frac{26}{68}\right)\langle -8, -2\rangle = -\frac{13}{17}\langle 4, 1\rangle$$

$$\mathbf{u} - \text{proj}_{\mathbf{v}}\mathbf{u} = \langle -4, 3\rangle - \left\langle\frac{-52}{17}, \frac{-13}{17}\right\rangle$$

$$= \left\langle -\frac{16}{17}, \frac{64}{17}\right\rangle$$

$$\mathbf{u} = \left\langle -\frac{52}{17}, -\frac{13}{17}\right\rangle + \left\langle -\frac{16}{17}, \frac{64}{17}\right\rangle$$

106. $\mathbf{u} = \langle 5, 6\rangle,\ \mathbf{v} = \langle 10, 0\rangle$

$$\text{proj}_{\mathbf{v}}\mathbf{u} = \left(\frac{\mathbf{u}\cdot\mathbf{v}}{\|\mathbf{v}\|^2}\right)\mathbf{v} = \frac{50}{100}\langle 10, 0\rangle = \langle 5, 0\rangle$$

$$\mathbf{u} = \langle 5, 0\rangle + \langle 0, 6\rangle$$

107. $\mathbf{u} = \langle 2, 7\rangle,\ \mathbf{v} = \langle 1, -1\rangle$

$$\text{proj}_{\mathbf{v}}\mathbf{u} = \left(\frac{\mathbf{u}\cdot\mathbf{v}}{\|\mathbf{v}\|^2}\right)\mathbf{v} = \frac{-5}{2}\langle 1, -1\rangle = \left\langle -\frac{5}{2}, \frac{5}{2}\right\rangle$$

$$\mathbf{u} - \text{proj}_{\mathbf{v}}\mathbf{u} = \langle 2, 7\rangle - \left\langle -\frac{5}{2}, \frac{5}{2}\right\rangle = \left\langle \frac{9}{2}, \frac{9}{2}\right\rangle$$

$$\mathbf{u} = \left\langle -\frac{5}{2}, \frac{5}{2}\right\rangle + \left\langle \frac{9}{2}, \frac{9}{2}\right\rangle$$

108. $\mathbf{u} = \langle -3, 5\rangle,\ \mathbf{v} = \langle -5, 2\rangle$

$$\text{proj}_{\mathbf{v}}\mathbf{u} = \left(\frac{\mathbf{u}\cdot\mathbf{v}}{\|\mathbf{v}\|^2}\right)\mathbf{v} = \frac{25}{29}\langle -5, 2\rangle$$

$$\mathbf{u} = \left\langle -\frac{125}{29}, \frac{50}{29}\right\rangle + \left\langle \frac{38}{29}, \frac{95}{29}\right\rangle$$

109. 48 inches = 4 feet

Work = 18,000(4) = 72,000 ft · lb

110. Force = 500 sin 12° ≈ 104 lbs

111. $|-i| = 1$

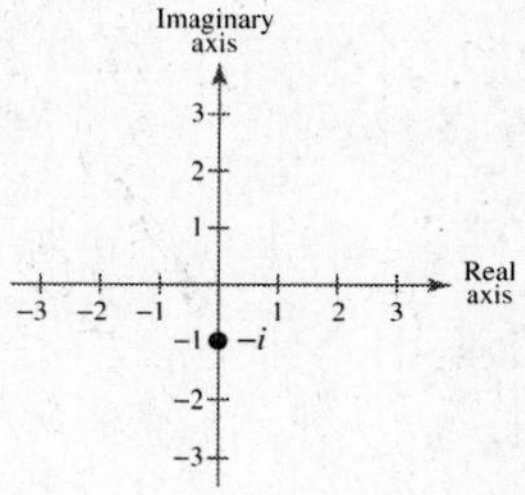

Imaginary axis; Real axis; point $-i$

112. $|5i| = 5$

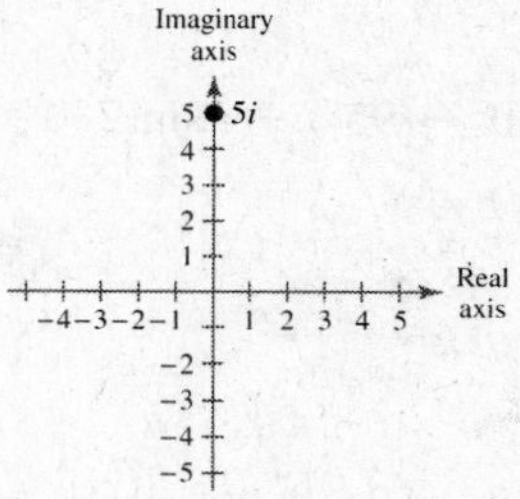

Imaginary axis; Real axis; point $5i$

113. $|7 - 5i| = \sqrt{7^2 + (-5)^2} = \sqrt{74}$

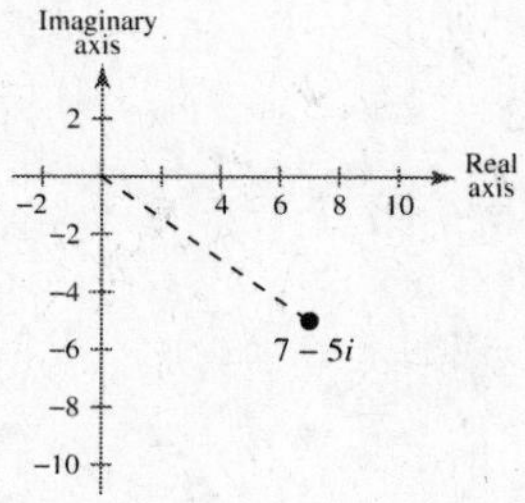

Imaginary axis; Real axis; point $7 - 5i$

114. $|-3 + 9i| = \sqrt{9 + 81} = \sqrt{90} = 3\sqrt{10}$

Imaginary axis; Real axis; point $-3 + 9i$

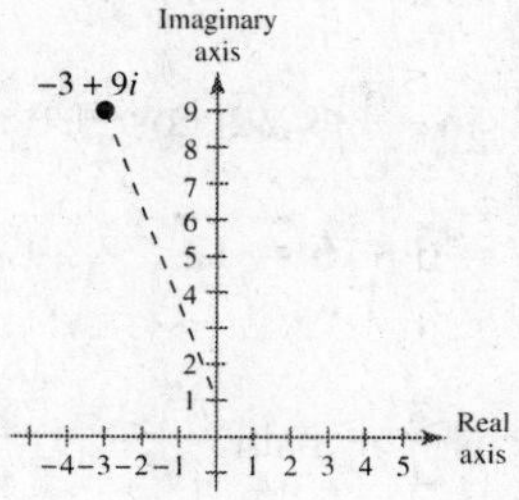

115. $z = 2 - 2i$

$|z| = \sqrt{4 + 4} = 2\sqrt{2}$

$\theta = \dfrac{7\pi}{4}$

$$z = 2\sqrt{2}\left(\cos\frac{7\pi}{4} + i\sin\frac{7\pi}{4}\right)$$

116. $z = -2 + 2i$

$|z| = \sqrt{4 + 4} = 2\sqrt{2}$

$\theta = \dfrac{3\pi}{4}$

$$z = 2\sqrt{2}\left(\cos\frac{3\pi}{4} + i\sin\frac{3\pi}{4}\right)$$

117. $z = -\sqrt{3} - i$

$|z| = \sqrt{3+1} = 2$

$\theta = \frac{7\pi}{6}$

$z = 2\left(\cos \frac{7\pi}{6} + i \sin \frac{7\pi}{6}\right)$

118. $z = -\sqrt{3} + i$

$|z| = \sqrt{3+1} = 2$

$\theta = \frac{5\pi}{6}$

$z = 2\left(\cos \frac{5\pi}{6} + i \sin \frac{5\pi}{6}\right)$

119. $z = -2i$

$|z| = 2$

$\theta = \frac{3\pi}{2}$

$z = 2\left(\cos \frac{3\pi}{2} + i \sin \frac{3\pi}{2}\right)$

120. $z = 4i$

$|z| = 4$

$\theta = \frac{\pi}{2}$

$z = 4\left(\cos \frac{\pi}{2} + i \sin \frac{\pi}{2}\right)$

121. $\left[\frac{5}{2}\left(\cos \frac{\pi}{2} + i \sin \frac{\pi}{2}\right)\right]\left[4\left(\cos \frac{\pi}{4} + i \sin \frac{\pi}{4}\right)\right] = 10\left[\cos \frac{3\pi}{4} + i \sin \frac{3\pi}{4}\right]$

122. $6\left[\cos\left(\frac{2\pi}{3} + \frac{\pi}{6}\right) + i \sin\left(\frac{2\pi}{3} + \frac{\pi}{6}\right)\right] = 6\left(\cos \frac{5\pi}{6} + i \sin \frac{5\pi}{6}\right) = -3\sqrt{3} + 3i$

123. $\frac{20(\cos 320° + i \sin 320°)}{5(\cos 80° + i \sin 80°)} = 4[\cos 240° + i \sin 240°]$

124. $\frac{3}{9}[\cos(230° - 95°) + i \sin(230° - 95°)] = \frac{1}{3}(\cos 135° + i \sin 135°)$

$= -\frac{\sqrt{2}}{6} + \frac{\sqrt{2}}{6}i$

125. (a) $2 - 2i = 2\sqrt{2}\left(\cos \frac{7\pi}{4} + i \sin \frac{7\pi}{4}\right)$

$3 + 3i = 3\sqrt{2}\left(\cos \frac{\pi}{4} + i \sin \frac{\pi}{4}\right)$

(b) $2\sqrt{2}\left(\cos \frac{7\pi}{4} + i \sin \frac{7\pi}{4}\right)3\sqrt{2}\left(\cos \frac{\pi}{4} + i \sin \frac{\pi}{4}\right) = 12(\cos 2\pi + i \sin 2\pi) = 12$

(c) $(2 - 2i)(3 + 3i) = 6 + 6 = 12$

126. (a) $4 + 4i = 4\sqrt{2}\left(\cos \frac{\pi}{4} + i \sin \frac{\pi}{4}\right)$

$-1 - i = \sqrt{2}\left(\cos \frac{5\pi}{4} + i \sin \frac{5\pi}{4}\right)$

(b) $4\sqrt{2}\left(\cos \frac{\pi}{4} + i \sin \frac{\pi}{4}\right)\sqrt{2}\left(\cos \frac{5\pi}{4} + i \sin \frac{5\pi}{4}\right) = 8\left(\cos \frac{3\pi}{2} + i \sin \frac{3\pi}{2}\right) = -8i$

(c) $(4 + 4i)(-1 - i) = -4 - 4i - 4i + 4 = -8i$

127. (a) $-i = \cos\frac{3\pi}{2} + i\sin\frac{3\pi}{2}$

$2 + 2i = 2\sqrt{2}\left(\cos\frac{\pi}{4} + i\sin\frac{\pi}{4}\right)$

(b) $\left(\cos\frac{3\pi}{2} + i\sin\frac{3\pi}{2}\right)2\sqrt{2}\left(\cos\frac{\pi}{4} + i\sin\frac{\pi}{4}\right) = 2\sqrt{2}\left(\cos\frac{7\pi}{4} + i\sin\frac{7\pi}{4}\right)$

$= 2\sqrt{2}\left(\frac{\sqrt{2}}{2} + i\left(-\frac{\sqrt{2}}{2}\right)\right)$

$= 2 - 2i$

(c) $-i(2 + 2i) = -2i + 2 = 2 - 2i$

128. (a) $4i = 4\left(\cos\frac{\pi}{2} + i\sin\frac{\pi}{2}\right)$

$1 - i = \sqrt{2}\left(\cos\left(-\frac{\pi}{4}\right) + i\sin\left(-\frac{\pi}{4}\right)\right)$

(b) $4\left(\cos\frac{\pi}{2} + i\sin\frac{\pi}{2}\right)\sqrt{2}\left(\cos\left(-\frac{\pi}{4}\right) + i\sin\left(-\frac{\pi}{4}\right)\right) = 4\sqrt{2}\left(\cos\frac{\pi}{4} + i\sin\frac{\pi}{4}\right)$

$= 4\sqrt{2}\left(\frac{\sqrt{2}}{2} + i\frac{\sqrt{2}}{2}\right)$

$= 4 + 4i$

(c) $4i(1 - i) = 4i + 4 = 4 + 4i$

129. (a) $3 - 3i = 3\sqrt{2}\left(\cos\frac{7\pi}{4} + i\sin\frac{7\pi}{4}\right)$

$2 + 2i = 2\sqrt{2}\left(\cos\frac{\pi}{4} + i\sin\frac{\pi}{4}\right)$

(b) $\dfrac{3\sqrt{2}\left(\cos\frac{7\pi}{4} + i\sin\frac{7\pi}{4}\right)}{2\sqrt{2}\left(\cos\frac{\pi}{4} + i\sin\frac{\pi}{4}\right)} = \frac{3}{2}\left(\cos\frac{3\pi}{2} + i\sin\frac{3\pi}{2}\right)$

$= \frac{3}{2}(-i) = -\frac{3}{2}i$

(c) $\dfrac{3 - 3i}{2 + 2i} \cdot \dfrac{(2 - 2i)}{(2 - 2i)} = \dfrac{6 - 12i - 6}{8} = -\dfrac{12i}{8} = -\dfrac{3}{2}i$

130. (a) $-1 - i = \sqrt{2}\left(\cos\frac{5\pi}{4} + i\sin\frac{5\pi}{4}\right)$

$-2 - 2i = 2\sqrt{2}\left(\cos\frac{5\pi}{4} + i\sin\frac{5\pi}{4}\right)$

(b) $\dfrac{-1 - i}{-2 - 2i} = \dfrac{\sqrt{2}}{2\sqrt{2}}(\cos 0 + i\sin 0) = \dfrac{1}{2}$

(c) $\dfrac{-1 - i}{-2 - 2i} = \dfrac{-1 - i}{2(-1 - i)} = \dfrac{1}{2}$

131. $\left[5\left(\cos\frac{\pi}{12} + i\sin\frac{\pi}{12}\right)\right]^4 = 5^4\left(\frac{4\pi}{12} + i\sin\frac{4\pi}{12}\right)$

$= 625\left(\cos\frac{\pi}{3} + i\sin\frac{\pi}{3}\right)$

$= 625\left(\frac{1}{2} + \frac{\sqrt{3}}{2}i\right)$

$= \frac{625}{2} + \frac{625\sqrt{3}}{2}i$

132. $\left[2\left(\cos\frac{4\pi}{15} + i\sin\frac{4\pi}{15}\right)\right]^5 = 2^5\left(\cos\frac{4\pi}{3} + i\sin\frac{4\pi}{3}\right)$

$= 32\left(-\frac{1}{2} - \frac{\sqrt{3}}{2}i\right)$

$= -16 - 16\sqrt{3}i$

133. $(2 + 3i)^6 \approx \left[\sqrt{13}(\cos 56.3^\circ + i\sin 56.3^\circ)\right]^6$

$= 13^3(\cos 337.9^\circ + i\sin 337.9^\circ)$

$\approx 13^3(0.9263 - 0.3769i)$

$\approx 2035 - 828i$

134. $(1 - i)^8 = \left[\sqrt{2}(\cos 315^\circ + i\sin 315^\circ)\right]^8$

$= 16(\cos 2520^\circ + i\sin 2520^\circ)$

$= 16(\cos 0^\circ + i\sin 0^\circ)$

$= 16$

135. $-\sqrt{3} + i = 2\left(\cos\frac{5\pi}{6} + i\sin\frac{5\pi}{6}\right)$

Square roots:

$\sqrt{2}\left(\cos\frac{5\pi}{12} + i\sin\frac{5\pi}{12}\right) \approx 0.3660 + 1.3660i$

$\sqrt{2}\left(\cos\frac{17\pi}{12} + i\sin\frac{17\pi}{12}\right) \approx -0.3660 - 1.3660i$

136. $\sqrt{3} - i = 2\left(\cos\frac{11\pi}{6} + i\sin\frac{11\pi}{6}\right)$

Square roots:

$\sqrt{2}\left(\cos\frac{11\pi}{12} + i\sin\frac{11\pi}{12}\right) \approx -1.3660 + 0.3660i$

$\sqrt{2}\left(\cos\frac{23\pi}{12} + i\sin\frac{23\pi}{12}\right) \approx 1.3660 - 0.3660i$

137. $-2i = 2\left(\cos\frac{3\pi}{2} + i\sin\frac{3\pi}{2}\right)$

Square roots:

$\sqrt{2}\left(\cos\frac{3\pi}{4} + i\sin\frac{3\pi}{4}\right) = \sqrt{2}\left(-\frac{\sqrt{2}}{2} + i\frac{\sqrt{2}}{2}\right) = -1 + i$

$\sqrt{2}\left(\cos\frac{7\pi}{4} + i\sin\frac{7\pi}{4}\right) = 1 - i$

138. $-5i = 5\left(\cos\frac{3\pi}{2} + i\sin\frac{3\pi}{2}\right)$

Square roots:

$\sqrt{5}\left(\cos\frac{3\pi}{4} + i\sin\frac{3\pi}{4}\right) = \sqrt{5}\left(-\frac{\sqrt{2}}{2} + \frac{\sqrt{2}}{2}i\right) = -\frac{\sqrt{10}}{2} + \frac{\sqrt{10}}{2}i$

$\sqrt{5}\left(\cos\frac{7\pi}{4} + i\sin\frac{7\pi}{4}\right) = \frac{\sqrt{10}}{2} - \frac{\sqrt{10}}{2}i$

139. $-2 - 2i = 2\sqrt{2}\left(\cos\frac{5\pi}{4} + i\sin\frac{5\pi}{4}\right)$

Square roots:

$2^{3/4}\left(\cos\frac{5\pi}{8} + i\sin\frac{5\pi}{8}\right) \approx -0.6436 + 1.5538i$

$2^{3/4}\left(\cos\frac{13\pi}{8} + i\sin\frac{13\pi}{8}\right) \approx 0.6436 - 1.5538i$

140. $-2 + 2i = 2\sqrt{2}\left(\cos\frac{3\pi}{4} + i\sin\frac{3\pi}{4}\right)$

Square roots:

$2^{3/4}\left(\cos\frac{3\pi}{8} + i\sin\frac{3\pi}{8}\right) \approx 0.6436 + 1.5538i$

$2^{3/4}\left(\cos\frac{11\pi}{8} + i\sin\frac{11\pi}{8}\right) \approx -0.6436 - 1.5538i$

141. (a) Sixth roots of $-729i = 729\left(\cos\frac{3\pi}{2} + i\sin\frac{3\pi}{2}\right)$:

$\sqrt[6]{729}\left(\cos\frac{(3\pi/2) + 2k\pi}{6} + i\sin\frac{(3\pi/2) + 2k\pi}{6}\right),\ k = 0, 1, 2, 3, 4, 5$

$3\left(\cos\frac{\pi}{4} + i\sin\frac{\pi}{4}\right)$

$3\left(\cos\frac{7\pi}{12} + i\sin\frac{7\pi}{12}\right)$

$3\left(\cos\frac{11\pi}{12} + i\sin\frac{11\pi}{12}\right)$

$3\left(\cos\frac{5\pi}{4} + i\sin\frac{5\pi}{4}\right)$

$3\left(\cos\frac{19\pi}{12} + i\sin\frac{19\pi}{12}\right)$

$3\left(\cos\frac{23\pi}{12} + i\sin\frac{23\pi}{12}\right)$

(b) Imaginary axis / Real axis

(c) $\frac{3\sqrt{2}}{2} + \frac{3\sqrt{2}}{2}i,\ -0.7765 + 2.898i,\ -2.898 + 0.7765i,\ -\frac{3\sqrt{2}}{2} - \frac{3\sqrt{2}}{2}i,\ 0.7765 - 2.898i,\ 2.898 - 0.7765i$

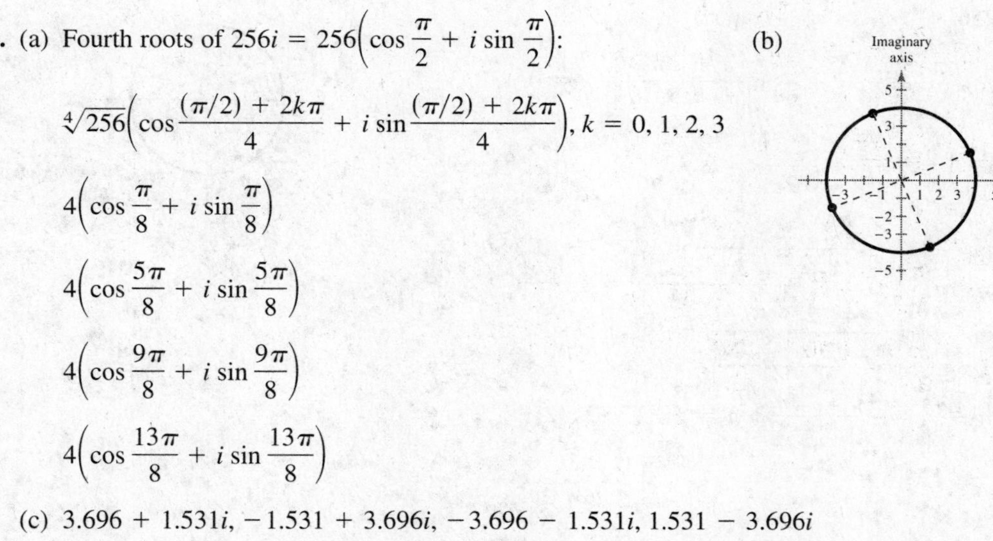

142. (a) Fourth roots of $256i = 256\left(\cos\frac{\pi}{2} + i\sin\frac{\pi}{2}\right)$:

$\sqrt[4]{256}\left(\cos\frac{(\pi/2) + 2k\pi}{4} + i\sin\frac{(\pi/2) + 2k\pi}{4}\right),\ k = 0, 1, 2, 3$

$4\left(\cos\frac{\pi}{8} + i\sin\frac{\pi}{8}\right)$

$4\left(\cos\frac{5\pi}{8} + i\sin\frac{5\pi}{8}\right)$

$4\left(\cos\frac{9\pi}{8} + i\sin\frac{9\pi}{8}\right)$

$4\left(\cos\frac{13\pi}{8} + i\sin\frac{13\pi}{8}\right)$

(b)

(c) $3.696 + 1.531i,\ -1.531 + 3.696i,\ -3.696 - 1.531i,\ 1.531 - 3.696i$

143. (a) Cube roots of $8 = 8(\cos 0 + i \sin 0)$:

(b)

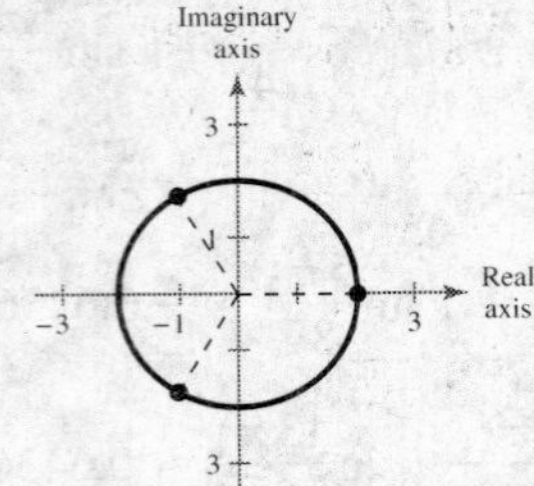

$$\sqrt[3]{8}\left(\cos\left(\frac{2k\pi}{3}\right) + i \sin\left(\frac{2k\pi}{3}\right)\right),\ k = 0, 1, 2$$

$$2(\cos 0 + i \sin 0)$$

$$2\left(\cos \frac{2\pi}{3} + i \sin \frac{2\pi}{3}\right)$$

$$2\left(\cos \frac{4\pi}{3} + i \sin \frac{4\pi}{3}\right)$$

(c) $2, -1 + \sqrt{3}i, -1 - \sqrt{3}i$

144. (a) Fifth roots of $-1024 = 1024(\cos \pi + i \sin \pi)$:

(b)

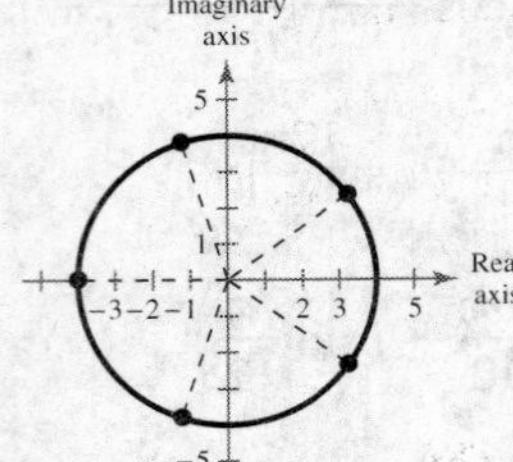
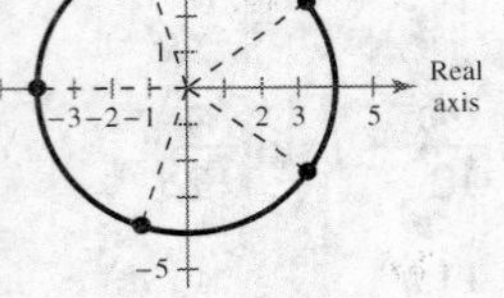

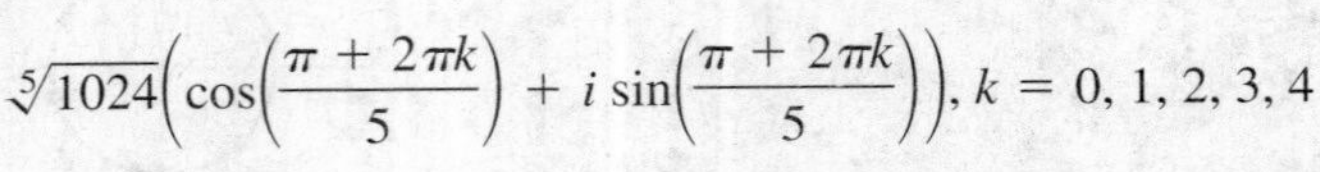

$$\sqrt[5]{1024}\left(\cos\left(\frac{\pi + 2\pi k}{5}\right) + i \sin\left(\frac{\pi + 2\pi k}{5}\right)\right),\ k = 0, 1, 2, 3, 4$$

$$4\left(\cos \frac{\pi}{5} + i \sin \frac{\pi}{5}\right)$$

$$4\left(\cos \frac{3\pi}{5} + i \sin \frac{3\pi}{5}\right)$$

$$4\left(\cos \frac{5\pi}{5} + i \sin \frac{5\pi}{5}\right) = -4$$

$$4\left(\cos \frac{7\pi}{5} + i \sin \frac{7\pi}{5}\right)$$

$$4\left(\cos \frac{9\pi}{5} + i \sin \frac{9\pi}{5}\right)$$

(c) $3.236 \pm 2.351i, -1.236 \pm 3.804i, -4$

145. $x^4 + 256 = 0$

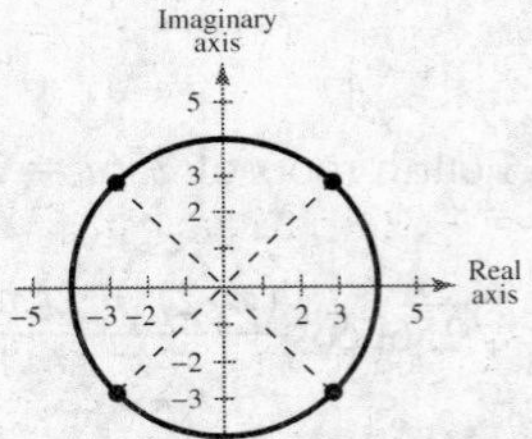

$$x^4 = -256 = 256(\cos \pi + i \sin \pi)$$

$$\sqrt[4]{-256} = 4\left[\cos\left(\frac{\pi + 2\pi k}{4}\right) + i \sin\left(\frac{\pi + 2\pi k}{4}\right)\right],\ k = 0, 1, 2, 3$$

$$4\left(\cos \frac{\pi}{4} + i \sin \frac{\pi}{4}\right) = \frac{4\sqrt{2}}{2} + \frac{4\sqrt{2}}{2}i = 2\sqrt{2} + 2\sqrt{2}i$$

$$4\left(\cos \frac{3\pi}{4} + i \sin \frac{3\pi}{4}\right) = -\frac{4\sqrt{2}}{2} + \frac{4\sqrt{2}}{2}i = -2\sqrt{2} + 2\sqrt{2}i$$

$$4\left(\cos \frac{5\pi}{4} + i \sin \frac{5\pi}{4}\right) = -\frac{4\sqrt{2}}{2} - \frac{4\sqrt{2}}{2}i = -2\sqrt{2} - 2\sqrt{2}i$$

$$4\left(\cos \frac{7\pi}{4} + i \sin \frac{7\pi}{4}\right) = \frac{4\sqrt{2}}{2} - \frac{4\sqrt{2}}{2}i = 2\sqrt{2} - 2\sqrt{2}i$$

146. $x^5 = 32i = 32\left(\cos\dfrac{\pi}{2} + i\sin\dfrac{\pi}{2}\right)$

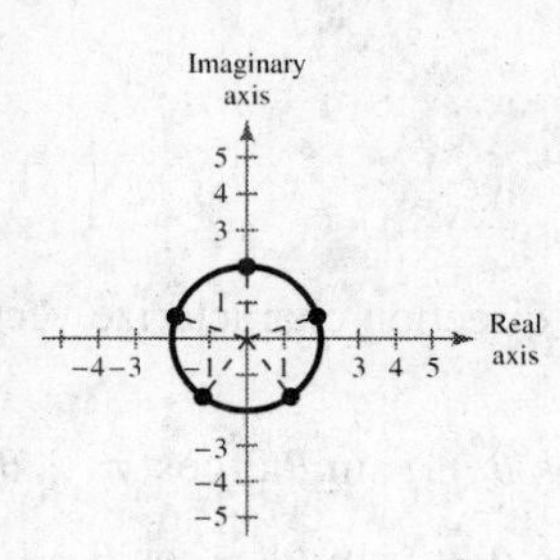

$$\sqrt[5]{32}\left(\cos\left(\frac{\pi/2 + 2k\pi}{5}\right) + i\sin\left(\frac{\pi/2 + 2k\pi}{5}\right)\right), k = 0, 1, 2, 3, 4$$

$$2\left(\cos\frac{\pi}{10} + i\sin\frac{\pi}{10}\right)$$

$$2\left(\cos\frac{\pi}{2} + i\sin\frac{\pi}{2}\right) = 2i$$

$$2\left(\cos\frac{9\pi}{10} + i\sin\frac{9\pi}{10}\right)$$

$$2\left(\cos\frac{13\pi}{10} + i\sin\frac{13\pi}{10}\right)$$

$$2\left(\cos\frac{17\pi}{10} + i\sin\frac{17\pi}{10}\right)$$

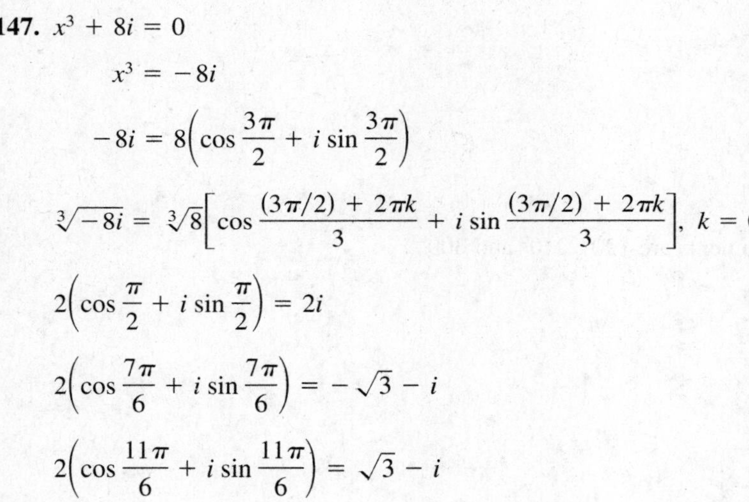

147. $x^3 + 8i = 0$

$$x^3 = -8i$$

$$-8i = 8\left(\cos\frac{3\pi}{2} + i\sin\frac{3\pi}{2}\right)$$

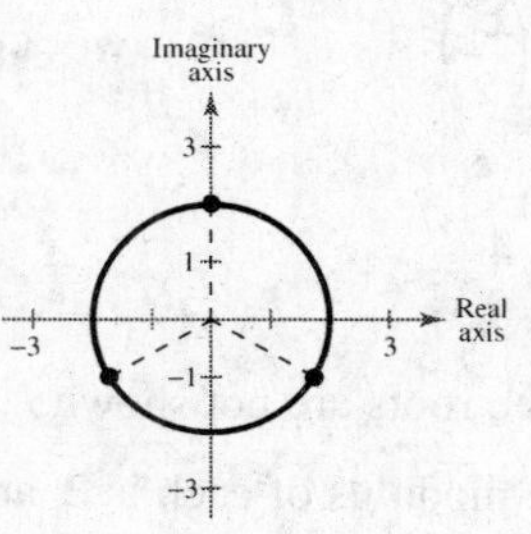

$$\sqrt[3]{-8i} = \sqrt[3]{8}\left[\cos\frac{(3\pi/2) + 2\pi k}{3} + i\sin\frac{(3\pi/2) + 2\pi k}{3}\right], k = 0, 1, 2$$

$$2\left(\cos\frac{\pi}{2} + i\sin\frac{\pi}{2}\right) = 2i$$

$$2\left(\cos\frac{7\pi}{6} + i\sin\frac{7\pi}{6}\right) = -\sqrt{3} - i$$

$$2\left(\cos\frac{11\pi}{6} + i\sin\frac{11\pi}{6}\right) = \sqrt{3} - i$$

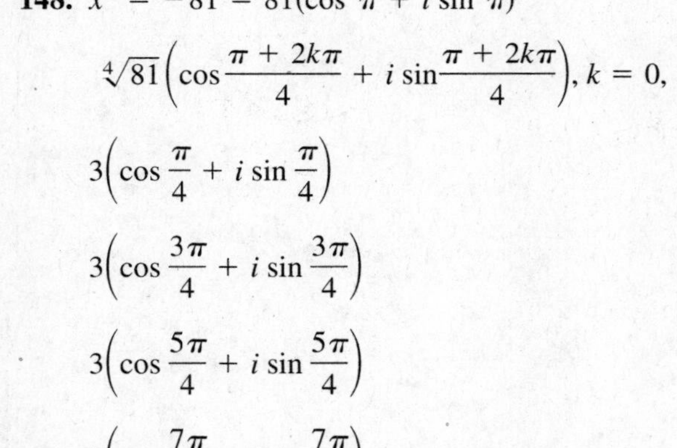

148. $x^4 = -81 = 81(\cos\pi + i\sin\pi)$

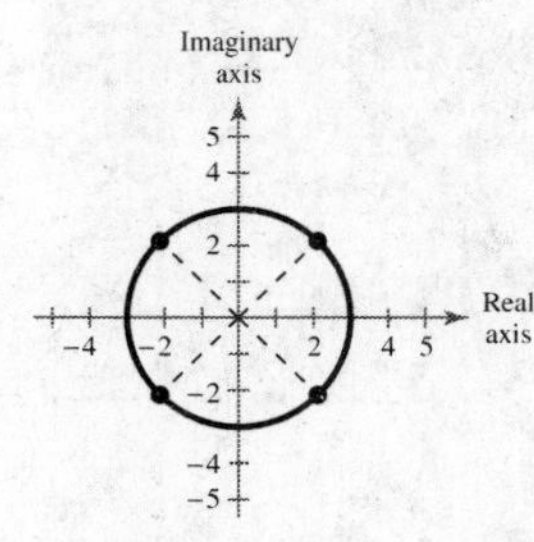

$$\sqrt[4]{81}\left(\cos\frac{\pi + 2k\pi}{4} + i\sin\frac{\pi + 2k\pi}{4}\right), k = 0, 1, 2, 3$$

$$3\left(\cos\frac{\pi}{4} + i\sin\frac{\pi}{4}\right)$$

$$3\left(\cos\frac{3\pi}{4} + i\sin\frac{3\pi}{4}\right)$$

$$3\left(\cos\frac{5\pi}{4} + i\sin\frac{5\pi}{4}\right)$$

$$3\left(\cos\frac{7\pi}{4} + i\sin\frac{7\pi}{4}\right)$$

149. True

150. False. There may be no solution, one solution, or two solutions.

151. Length and direction characterize vectors in plane.

152. **A** and **C** appear equivalent.

153.
$$\begin{aligned}
z_1z_2 &= 2(\cos\theta + i\sin\theta)2(\cos(\pi-\theta) + i\sin(\pi-\theta))\\
&= 4(\cos\theta + i\sin\theta)(-\cos\theta + i\sin\theta)\\
&= 4(-\cos^2\theta - \sin^2\theta) = -4\\
\frac{z_1}{z_2} &= \frac{2(\cos\theta + i\sin\theta)}{2(\cos(\pi-\theta) + i\sin(\pi-\theta))}\\
&= \frac{\cos\theta + i\sin\theta}{-\cos\theta + i\sin\theta}\cdot\frac{-\cos\theta - i\sin\theta}{-\cos\theta - i\sin\theta}\\
&= -\cos^2\theta + \sin^2\theta - 2\sin\theta\cos\theta i\\
&= -(\cos\theta + i\sin\theta)^2\\
&= -\left(\frac{z_1}{2}\right)^2\\
&= -\frac{z_1^{\,2}}{4}
\end{aligned}$$

154. (a) Three roots are not shown.

(b) The modulus of each is 2, and the arguments are 120°, 210° and 300°.

Chapter 6 Practice Test

For Exercises 1 and 2, use the Law of Sines to find the remaining sides and angles of the triangle.

1. $A = 40°,\ B = 12°,\ b = 100$

2. $C = 150°,\ a = 5,\ c = 20$

3. Find the area of the triangle: $a = 3,\ b = 6,\ C = 130°$

4. Determine the number of solutions to the triangle: $a = 10,\ b = 35,\ A = 22.5°$

For Exercises 5 and 6, use the Law of Cosines to find the remaining sides and angles of the triangle.

5. $a = 49,\ b = 53,\ c = 38$

6. $C = 29°,\ a = 100,\ b = 300$

7. Use Heron's Formula to find the area of the triangle: $a = 4.1,\ b = 6.8,\ c = 5.5$.

8. A ship travels 40 miles due east, then adjusts its course 12° southward. After traveling 70 miles in that direction, how far is the ship from its point of departure?

9. $\mathbf{w} = 4\mathbf{u} - 7\mathbf{v}$ where $\mathbf{u} = 3\mathbf{i} + \mathbf{j}$ and $\mathbf{v} = -\mathbf{i} + 2\mathbf{j}$. Find $\mathbf{w}$.

10. Find a unit vector in the direction of $\mathbf{v} = 5\mathbf{i} - 3\mathbf{j}$.

11. Find the dot product and the angle between $\mathbf{u} = 6\mathbf{i} + 5\mathbf{j}$ and $\mathbf{v} = 2\mathbf{i} - 3\mathbf{j}$.

12. $\mathbf{v}$ is a vector of magnitude 4 making an angle of 30° with the positive x-axis. Find $\mathbf{v}$ in component form.

13. Find the projection of $\mathbf{u}$ onto $\mathbf{v}$ given $\mathbf{u} = \langle 3, -1\rangle$ and $\mathbf{v} = \langle -2, 4\rangle$.

14. Give the trigonometric form of $z = 5 - 5i$.

15. Give the standard form of $z = 6(\cos 225° + i \sin 225°)$.

16. Multiply $[7\,(\cos 23° + i \sin 23°)][4(\cos 7° + i \sin 7°)]$.

17. Divide $\dfrac{9\left(\cos \frac{5\pi}{4} + i \sin \frac{5\pi}{4}\right)}{3(\cos \pi + i \sin \pi)}$.

18. Find $(2 + 2i)^8$.

19. Find the cube roots of $8\left(\cos \frac{\pi}{3} + i \sin \frac{\pi}{3}\right)$.

20. Find all the solutions to $x^4 + i = 0$.

CHAPTER 7
Linear Systems and Matrices

Section 7.1 Solving Systems of Equations 549

Section 7.2 Systems of Linear Equations in Two Variables 564

Section 7.3 Multivariable Linear Systems 578

Section 7.4 Matrices and Systems of Equations 603

Section 7.5 Operations with Matrices 620

Section 7.6 The Inverse of a Square Matrix 633

Section 7.7 The Determinant of a Square Matrix 645

Section 7.8 Applications of Matrices and Determinants 654

Review Exercises 662

Practice Test 687

CHAPTER 7
Linear Systems and Matrices

Section 7.1 Solving Systems of Equations

- You should be able to solve systems of equations by the method of substitution.
  1. Solve one of the equations for one of the variables.
  2. Substitute this expression into the other equation and solve.
  3. Back-substitute into the first equation to find the value of the other variable.
  4. Check your answer in each of the original equations.
- You should be able to find solutions graphically. (See Example 5 in textbook.)

Vocabulary Check

1. system, equations **2.** solution **3.** method, substitution

4. point, intersection **5.** break-even point

1. (a) $4(0) - (-3) \stackrel{?}{=} 1$

$6(0) + (-3) \stackrel{?}{=} -6$

$3 \neq 1$

$-3 \neq -6$

No, $(0, -3)$ is not a solution.

(b) $4(-1) - (-5) \stackrel{?}{=} 1$

$6(-1) + (-5) \stackrel{?}{=} -6$

$1 = 1$

$-11 \neq -6$

No, $(-1, -5)$ is not a solution.

(c) $4\left(-\frac{3}{2}\right) - (3) \stackrel{?}{=} 1$

$6\left(-\frac{3}{2}\right) + (3) \stackrel{?}{=} -6$

$-9 \neq 1$

$-6 = -6$

No, $\left(-\frac{3}{2}, 3\right)$ is not a solution.

(d) $4\left(-\frac{1}{2}\right) - (-3) \stackrel{?}{=} 1$

$6\left(-\frac{1}{2}\right) + (-3) \stackrel{?}{=} -6$

$1 = 1$

$-6 = -6$

Yes, $\left(-\frac{1}{2}, -3\right)$ is a solution.

2. (a) $4(2)^2 + (-13) \stackrel{?}{=} 3$

$-2 - (-13) \stackrel{?}{=} 11$

$3 = 3$

$11 = 11$

Yes, $(2, -13)$ is a solution.

(b) $4(-2)^2 + (-9) \stackrel{?}{=} 3$

$-(-2) - (-9) \stackrel{?}{=} 11$

$7 \neq 3$

$11 = 11$

No, $(-2, -9)$ is not a solution.

—CONTINUED—

2. —CONTINUED—

(c) $4\left(-\frac{3}{2}\right)^2 + (6) \stackrel{?}{=} 3$

$-\left(-\frac{3}{2}\right) - (6) \stackrel{?}{=} 11$

$15 \neq 3$

$-\frac{9}{2} \neq 11$

No, $\left(-\frac{3}{2}, 6\right)$ is not a solution.

(d) $4\left(-\frac{7}{4}\right)^2 + \left(-\frac{37}{4}\right) \stackrel{?}{=} 3$

$-\left(-\frac{7}{4}\right) - \left(-\frac{37}{4}\right) \stackrel{?}{=} 11$

$3 = 3$

$11 = 11$

Yes, $\left(-\frac{7}{4}, -\frac{37}{4}\right)$ is a solution.

3. (a) $0 \stackrel{?}{=} -2e^{-2}$

$3(-2) - 0 \stackrel{?}{=} 2$

$0 \neq -2e^{-2}$

$-6 \neq 2$

No, $(-2, 0)$ is not a solution.

(b) $-2 \stackrel{?}{=} -2e^{0}$

$3(0) - (-2) \stackrel{?}{=} 2$

$-2 = -2$

$2 = 2$

Yes, $(0, -2)$ is a solution.

(c) $-3 \stackrel{?}{=} -2e^{0}$

$3(0) - (-3) \stackrel{?}{=} 2$

$-3 \neq -2$

$3 \neq 2$

No, $(0, -3)$ is not a solution.

(d) $-5 \stackrel{?}{=} -2e^{-1}$

$3(-1) - (-5) \stackrel{?}{=} 2$

$-5 \neq -2e^{-1}$

$2 = 2$

No, $(-1, -5)$ is not a solution.

4. (a) $-\log_{10}(100) + 3 \stackrel{?}{=} 1$

$\frac{1}{9}(100) + 1 \stackrel{?}{=} \frac{28}{9}$

$1 = 1$

$\frac{109}{9} \neq \frac{28}{9}$

No, $(100, 1)$ is not a solution.

(b) $-\log_{10} 10 + 3 \stackrel{?}{=} 2$

$\frac{1}{9}(10) + 2 \stackrel{?}{=} \frac{28}{9}$

$2 = 2$

$\frac{28}{9} = \frac{28}{9}$

Yes, $(10, 2)$ is a solution.

(c) $-\log_{10} 1 + 3 \stackrel{?}{=} 3$

$\frac{1}{9}(1) + 3 \stackrel{?}{=} \frac{28}{9}$

$3 = 3$

$\frac{28}{9} = \frac{28}{9}$

Yes, $(1, 3)$ is a solution.

(d) $-\log_{10} 1 + 3 \stackrel{?}{=} 1$

$\frac{1}{9}(1) + 1 \stackrel{?}{=} \frac{28}{9}$

$3 \neq 1$

$\frac{10}{9} \neq \frac{28}{9}$

No, $(1, 1)$ is not a solution.

5. $\begin{cases} 2x + y = 6 & \text{Equation 1} \\ -x + y = 0 & \text{Equation 2} \end{cases}$

Solve for y in Equation 1: $y = 6 - 2x$

Substitute for y in Equation 2: $-x + (6 - 2x) = 0$

Solve for x: $-3x + 6 = 0 \Rightarrow x = 2$

Back-substitute $x = 2$: $y = 6 - 2(2) = 2$

Answer: $(2, 2)$

6. $\begin{cases} x - y = -4 & \text{Equation 1} \\ x + 2y = 5 & \text{Equation 2} \end{cases}$

Solve for x in Equation 1: $x = y - 4$

Substitute for x in Equation 2: $(y - 4) + 2y = 5$

Solve for y: $3y - 4 = 5 \Rightarrow y = 3$

Back-substitute $y = 3$: $x = 3 - 4 = -1$

Answer: $(-1, 3)$

7. $\begin{cases} x - y = -4 & \text{Equation 1} \\ x^2 - y = -2 & \text{Equation 2} \end{cases}$

Solve for y in Equation 1: $y = x + 4$

Substitute for y in Equation 2: $x^2 - (x + 4) = -2$

Solve for x: $x^2 - x - 2 = 0$

$$\Rightarrow (x + 1)(x - 2) = 0$$

$$\Rightarrow x = -1, 2$$

Back-substitute $x = -1$: $y = -1 + 4 = 3$

Back-substitute $x = 2$: $y = 2 + 4 = 6$

Answer: $(-1, 3), (2, 6)$

8. $\begin{cases} -2x + y = -5 & \text{Equation 1} \\ x^2 + y^2 = 25 & \text{Equation 2} \end{cases}$

Solve for y in Equation 1: $y = 2x - 5$

Substitute for y in Equation 2: $x^2 + (2x - 5)^2 = 25$

Solve for x: $x^2 + 4x^2 - 20x + 25 = 25$

$$5x^2 - 20x = 0$$

$$5x(x - 4) = 0$$

$$x = 0, 4$$

Back-substitute $x = 0$: $y = -5$

Back-substitute $x = 4$: $y = 3$

Answer: $(0, -5), (4, 3)$

9. $\begin{cases} 3x + y = 2 & \text{Equation 1} \\ x^3 - 2 + y = 0 & \text{Equation 2} \end{cases}$

Solve for y in Equation 1: $y = 2 - 3x$

Substitute for y in Equation 2: $x^3 - 2 + (2 - 3x) = 0$

Solve for x: $x^3 - 3x = 0 \Longrightarrow x(x^2 - 3) = 0 \Longrightarrow x = 0, \pm\sqrt{3}$

Back-substitute: $x = 0$: $y = 2$

$x = \sqrt{3}$: $y = 2 - 3\sqrt{3}$

$x = -\sqrt{3}$: $y = 2 + 3\sqrt{3}$

Answer: $(0, 2), \left(\sqrt{3}, 2 - 3\sqrt{3}\right), \left(-\sqrt{3}, 2 + 3\sqrt{3}\right)$

10. $\begin{cases} x + y = 0 & \text{Equation 1} \\ x^3 - 5x - y = 0 & \text{Equation 2} \end{cases}$

Solve for y in Equation 1: $y = -x$

Substitute for y in Equation 2: $x^3 - 5x - (-x) = 0$

Solve for x: $x^3 - 4x = 0 \Longrightarrow x(x^2 - 4) = 0 \Longrightarrow x = 0, \pm 2$

Back-substitute $x = 0$: $y = -0 = 0$

Back-substitute $x = 2$: $y = -2$

Back-substitute $x = -2$: $y = -(-2) = 2$

Answer: $(0, 0), (2, -2), (-2, 2)$

11. $\begin{cases} -\frac{7}{2}x - y = -18 & \text{Equation 1} \\ 8x^2 - 2y^3 = 0 & \text{Equation 2} \end{cases}$

Solve for x in Equation 1: $-\frac{7}{2}x = y - 18 \Longrightarrow x = -\frac{2}{7}y + \frac{36}{7}$

Substitute for x in Equation 2: $8\left(-\frac{2}{7}y + \frac{36}{7}\right)^2 - 2y^3 = 0$

Solve for x: $-2y^3 + 8\left(\frac{4}{49}y^2 - \frac{144}{49}y + \frac{36^2}{49}\right) = 0$

$$49y^3 - 16y^2 + 576y - 5184 = 0$$

$$(y - 4)(49y^2 + 180y + 1296) = 0$$

Hence, $y = 4$ and $x = -\frac{2}{7}(4) + \frac{36}{7} = 4$. *Answer:* $(4, 4)$

12. $\begin{cases} y = x^3 - 3x^2 + 4 & \text{Equation 1} \\ y = -2x + 4 & \text{Equation 2} \end{cases}$

Substitute for y in Equation 1:
$-2x + 4 = x^3 - 3x^2 + 4$

Solve for x: $0 = x^3 - 3x^2 + 2x$

$$0 = x(x^2 - 3x + 2)$$

$$0 = x(x - 2)(x - 1) \implies x = 0, 1, 2$$

Back-substitute $x = 0$: $y = -2(0) + 4 = 4$

Back-substitute $x = 1$: $y = -2(1) + 4 = 2$

Back-substitute $x = 2$: $y = -2(2) + 4 = 0$

Answer: $(0, 4), (1, 2), (2, 0)$

13. $\begin{cases} x - y = 0 & \text{Equation 1} \\ 5x - 3y = 10 & \text{Equation 2} \end{cases}$

Solve for y in Equation 1: $y = x$

Substitute for y in Equation 2: $5x - 3x = 10$

Solve for x: $2x = 10 \implies x = 5$

Back-substitute in Equation 1: $y = x = 5$

Answer: $(5, 5)$

14. $\begin{cases} x + 2y = 1 & \text{Equation 1} \\ 5x - 4y = -23 & \text{Equation 2} \end{cases}$

Solve for x in Equation 1: $x = 1 - 2y$

Substitute for x in Equation 2:
$5(1 - 2y) - 4y = -23$

Solve for y: $-14y = -28 \implies y = 2$

Back-substitute $y = 2$: $x = 1 - 2y = 1 - 4 = -3$

Answer: $(-3, 2)$

15. $\begin{cases} 2x - y + 2 = 0 & \text{Equation 1} \\ 4x + y - 5 = 0 & \text{Equation 2} \end{cases}$

Solve for y in Equation 1: $y = 2x + 2$

Substitute for y in Equation 2:
$4x + (2x + 2) - 5 = 0$

Solve for x:
$4x + (2x + 2) - 5 = 0 \implies 6x - 3 = 0 \implies x = \frac{1}{2}$

Back-substitute $x = \frac{1}{2}$: $y = 2x + 2 = 2\left(\frac{1}{2}\right) + 2 = 3$

Answer: $\left(\frac{1}{2}, 3\right)$

16. $\begin{cases} 6x - 3y - 4 = 0 & \text{Equation 1} \\ x + 2y - 4 = 0 & \text{Equation 2} \end{cases}$

Solve for x in Equation 2: $x = 4 - 2y$

Substitute for x in Equation 1: $6(4 - 2y) - 3y - 4 = 0$

Solve for y: $24 - 12y - 3y - 4 = 0 \implies -15y = -20 \implies y = \frac{4}{3}$

Back-substitute $y = \frac{4}{3}$: $x = 4 - 2y = 4 - 2\left(\frac{4}{3}\right) = \frac{4}{3}$

Answer: $\left(\frac{4}{3}, \frac{4}{3}\right)$

17. $\begin{cases} 1.5x + 0.8y = 2.3 \implies 15x + 8y = 23 \\ 0.3x - 0.2y = 0.1 \implies 3x - 2y = 1 \end{cases}$

Solve for y in Equation 2: $-2y = 1 - 3x$

$$y = \frac{3x - 1}{2}$$

Substitute for y in Equation 1: $15x + 8\left(\frac{3x - 1}{2}\right) = 23$

$$15x + 12x - 4 = 23$$

$$27x = 27$$

$$x = 1$$

Then, $y = \frac{3x - 1}{2} = \frac{3(1) - 1}{2} = 1$. *Answer:* $(1, 1)$

18. $\begin{cases} 0.5x + 3.2y = 9.0 & \text{Equation 1} \\ 0.2x - 1.6y = -3.6 & \text{Equation 2} \end{cases}$

Multiply both equations by 10: $5x + 32y = 90$

$2x - 16y = -36$

Solve for x in Equation 2: $x = -18 + 8y$

Substitute for x in Equation 1:

$5(-18 + 8y) + 32y = 90$

Solve for y: $-90 + 40y + 32y = 90$

$72y = 180$

$y = \frac{180}{72} = 2.5$

Back-substitute $y = 2.5$: $x = -18 + 8(2.5) = 2$

Answer: $(2, 2.5)$

19. $\begin{cases} \frac{1}{5}x + \frac{1}{2}y = 8 & \text{Equation 1} \\ x + y = 20 & \text{Equation 2} \end{cases}$

Solve for x in Equation 2: $x = 20 - y$

Substitute for x in Equation 1: $\frac{1}{5}(20 - y) + \frac{1}{2}y = 8$

Solve for y: $4 + \frac{3}{10}y = 8 \Rightarrow y = \frac{40}{3}$

Back-substitute $y = \frac{40}{3}$: $x = 20 - y$

$= 20 - \frac{40}{3} = \frac{20}{3}$

Answer: $\left(\frac{20}{3}, \frac{40}{3}\right)$

20. $\begin{cases} \frac{1}{2}x + \frac{3}{4}y = 10 & \text{Equation 1} \\ \frac{3}{4}x - y = 4 & \text{Equation 2} \end{cases}$

Solve for y in Equation 2: $y = \frac{3}{4}x - 4$

Substitute for y in Equation 1: $\frac{1}{2}x + \frac{3}{4}\left(\frac{3}{4}x - 4\right) = 10$

Solve for x:

$\frac{1}{2}x + \frac{9}{16}x - 3 = 10 \Rightarrow \frac{17}{16}x = 13 \Rightarrow x = \frac{208}{17}$

Back-substitute $x = \frac{208}{17}$: $y = \frac{3}{4}\left(\frac{208}{17}\right) - 4 = \frac{88}{17}$

Answer: $\left(\frac{208}{17}, \frac{88}{17}\right)$

21. $\begin{cases} -\frac{5}{3}x + y = 5 & \text{Equation 1} \\ -5x + 3y = 6 & \text{Equation 2} \end{cases}$

Solve for y in Equation 1: $y = 5 + \frac{5}{3}x$

Substitute for y in Equation 2: $-5x + 3\left(5 + \frac{5}{3}x\right) = 6$

Solve for x: $-5x + 15 + 5x = 6$

$15 \neq 6$ Inconsistent

No solution

22. $\begin{cases} -\frac{2}{3}x + y = 2 & \text{Equation 1} \\ 2x - 3y = 6 & \text{Equation 2} \end{cases}$

From Equation 1, $y = 2 + \frac{2}{3}x$

In Equation 2, $2x - 3\left[2 + \frac{2}{3}x\right] = -6 \neq 6$

No solution

23. $\begin{cases} x^2 - 2x + y = 8 & \text{Equation 1} \\ x - y = -2 & \text{Equation 2} \end{cases}$

Solve for y in Equation 2: $y = x + 2$

Substitute for y in Equation 1:

$x^2 - 2x + (x + 2) = 8$

$x^2 - x - 6 = 0$

$(x - 3)(x + 2) = 0$

$x = 3, -2$

$x = 3 \Rightarrow y = 5$

$x = -2 \Rightarrow y = 0$

Answer: $(3, 5), (-2, 0)$

24. $\begin{cases} 2x^2 - 2x - y = 14 & \text{Equation 1} \\ 2x - y = -2 & \text{Equation 2} \end{cases}$

Solve for y in Equation 2: $y = 2x + 2$

Substitute for y in Equation 1:

$2x^2 - 2x - (2x + 2) = 14$

$2x^2 - 4x - 16 = 0$

$x^2 - 2x - 8 = 0$

$(x - 4)(x + 2) = 0$

$x = 4, -2$

$x = 4 \Rightarrow y = 10$

$x = -2 \Rightarrow y = -2$

Answer: $(4, 10), (-2, -2)$

25. $\begin{cases} 2x^2 - y = 1 & \text{Equation 1} \\ x - y = 2 & \text{Equation 2} \end{cases}$

Solve for y in Equation 2: $y = x - 2$

Substitute for y in Equation 1: $2x^2 - (x - 2) = 1$

$$2x^2 - x + 1 = 0$$

No real solution

26. $\begin{cases} 2x^2 + y = 3 & \text{Equation 1} \\ x + y = 4 & \text{Equation 2} \end{cases}$

Solve for y in Equation 2: $y = -x + 4$

Substitute for y in Equation 1: $2x^2 + (-x + 4) = 3$

$$2x^2 - x + 1 = 0$$

No real solution

27. $\begin{cases} x^3 - y = 0 & \text{Equation 1} \\ x - y = 0 & \text{Equation 2} \end{cases}$

Solve for y in Equation 2: $y = x$

Substitute for y in Equation 1: $x^3 - x = 0$

Solve for x:
$x(x - 1)(x + 1) = 0 \Rightarrow x = 0, 1, -1$

Back-substitute: $x = 0 \Rightarrow y = 0$

$x = 1 \Rightarrow y = 1$

$x = -1 \Rightarrow y = -1$

Answer: $(0, 0), (1, 1), (-1, -1)$

28. $y = -x = x^3 + 3x^2 + 2x$

$x^3 + 3x^2 + 3x = 0$

$x(x^2 + 3x + 3) = 0$

$x = 0 \Rightarrow y = 0$

Answer: $(0, 0)$

29. $\begin{cases} -x + 2y = 2 \\ 3x + y = 15 \end{cases}$

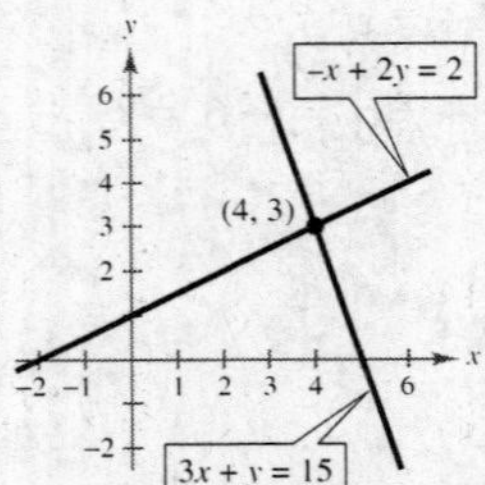

Point of intersection: $(4, 3)$

30. $\begin{cases} x + y = 0 \\ 3x - 2y = 10 \end{cases}$

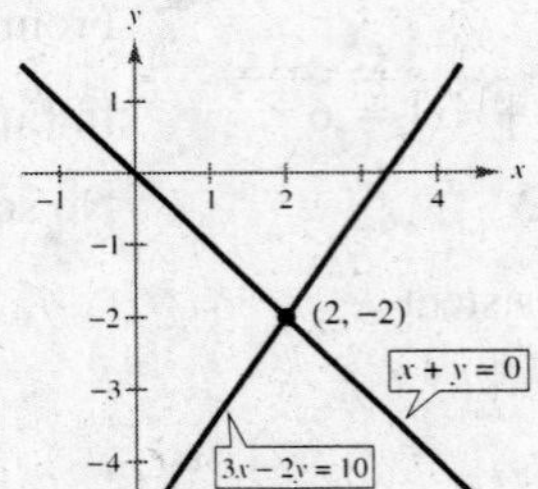

Point of intersection: $(2, -2)$

31. $\begin{cases} x - 3y = -2 \\ 5x + 3y = 17 \end{cases}$

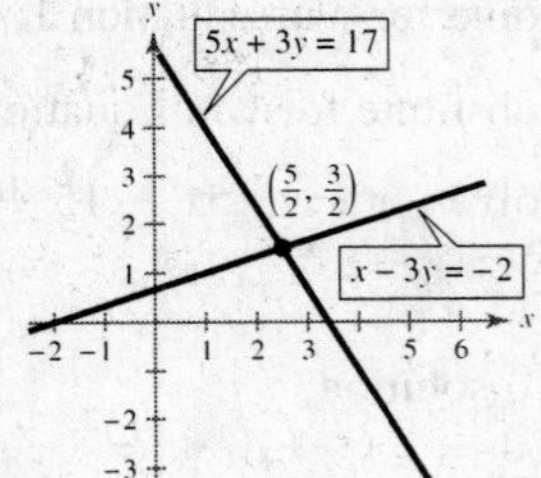

Point of intersection: $\left(\frac{5}{2}, \frac{3}{2}\right)$

32. $\begin{cases} -x + 2y = 1 \\ x - y = 2 \end{cases}$

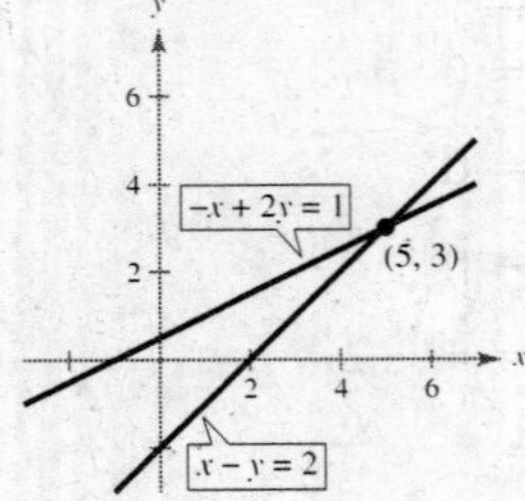

Point of intersection: $(5, 3)$

33. $\begin{cases} x^2 + y = 1 \\ x + y = 2 \end{cases}$

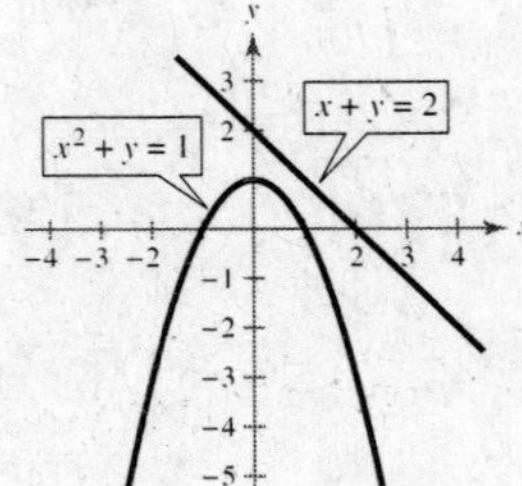

No solution

34. $\begin{cases} x^2 - y = 4 \\ x - y = 2 \end{cases}$

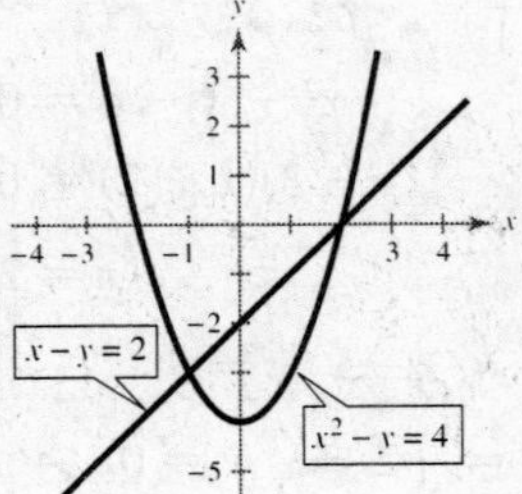

Points of intersection:
$(2, 0), (-1, -3)$

35. $\begin{cases} -x + y = 3 \Rightarrow y_1 = x + 3 \\ x^2 - 6x - 27 + y^2 = 0 \Rightarrow y_2 = \sqrt{6x - x^2 + 27} \end{cases}$

$y_3 = -\sqrt{6x - x^2 + 27}$

Points of intersection: $(-3, 0), (3, 6)$

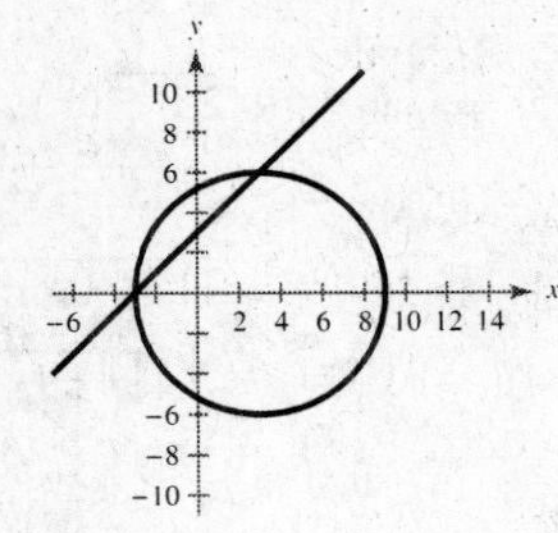

36. $\begin{cases} y^2 - 4x + 11 = 0 \Rightarrow y = \pm\sqrt{4x - 11} \\ -\frac{1}{2}x + y = -\frac{1}{2} \Rightarrow y = \frac{1}{2}x - \frac{1}{2} \end{cases}$

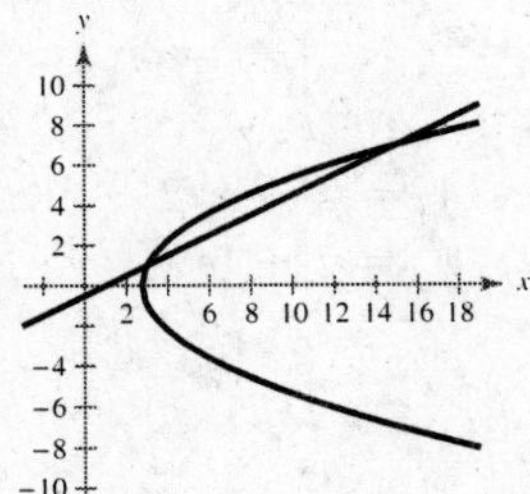

Points of intersection: $(15, 7), (3, 1)$

37. $\begin{cases} 7x + 8y = 24 \Rightarrow y_1 = -\frac{7}{8}x + 3 \\ x - 8y = 8 \Rightarrow y_2 = \frac{1}{8}x - 1 \end{cases}$

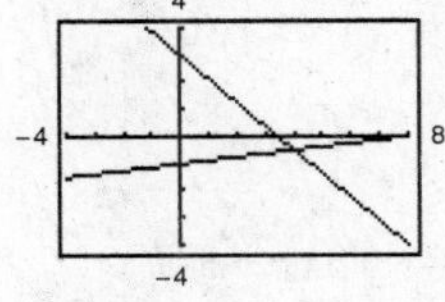

Point of intersection: $\left(4, -\frac{1}{2}\right)$

38. $\begin{cases} x - y = 0 \Rightarrow y_1 = x \\ 5x - 2y = 6 \Rightarrow y_2 = \frac{5}{2}x - 3 \end{cases}$

Point of intersection: $(2, 2)$

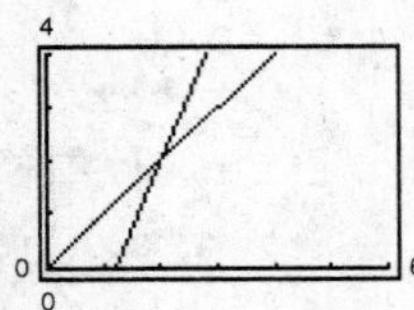

39. $x - y^2 = -1 \Rightarrow y^2 = x + 1 \Rightarrow y_1 = \sqrt{x + 1}$

$y_2 = -\sqrt{x + 1}$

$x - y = 5 \Rightarrow y_3 = x - 5$

Points of intersection: $(8, 3), (3, -2)$

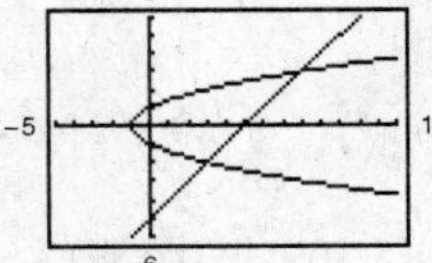

40. $x - y^2 = -2 \Rightarrow y_1 = \sqrt{x + 2}, y_2 = -\sqrt{x + 2}$

$x - 2y = 6 \Rightarrow y_3 = \frac{1}{2}(x - 6)$

Points of intersection: $(2, -2), (14, 4)$

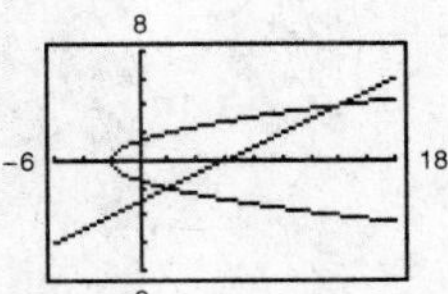

41. $x^2 + y^2 = 8 \Rightarrow y_1 = \sqrt{8 - x^2}, y_2 = -\sqrt{8 - x^2}$

$y = x^2 \Rightarrow y_3 = x^2$

Points of intersection: $(1.540, 2.372), (-1.540, 2.372)$

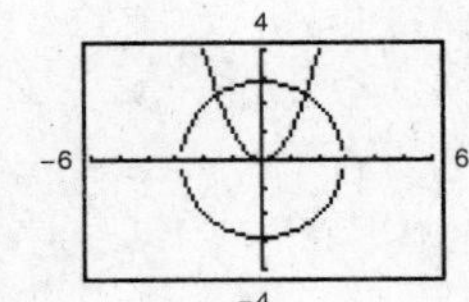

42. $x^2 + y^2 = 25 \Rightarrow y_1 = \sqrt{25 - x^2}$

$y_2 = -\sqrt{25 - x^2}$

$(x - 8)^2 + y^2 = 41 \Rightarrow y_3 = \sqrt{41 - (x - 8)^2}$

$y_4 = -\sqrt{41 - (x - 8)^2}$

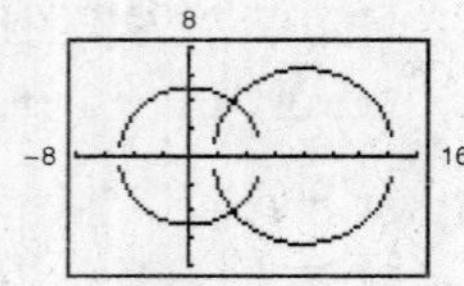

Points of intersection: (3, 4), (3, −4)

43. $\begin{cases} y = e^x \\ x - y + 1 = 0 \Rightarrow y = x + 1 \end{cases}$

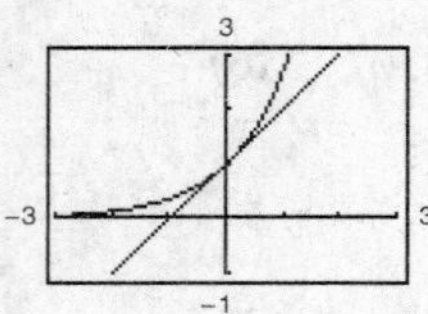

Point of intersection: (0, 1)

44. $\begin{cases} y = -4e^{-x} \\ y + 3x + 8 = 0 \Rightarrow y = -3x - 8 \end{cases}$

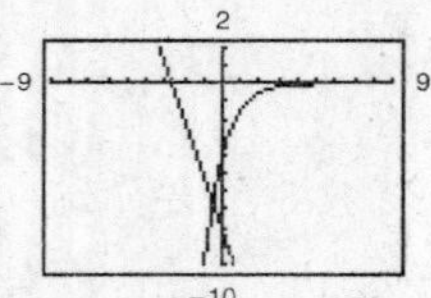

Point of intersection: (−0.490, −6.530)

45. $\begin{cases} x + 2y = 8 \Rightarrow y_1 = 4 - x/2 \\ y = 2 + \ln x \Rightarrow y_2 = 2 + \ln x \end{cases}$

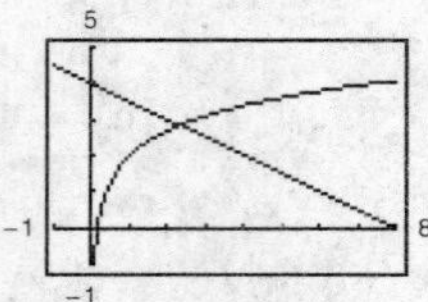

Point of intersection: ≈ (2.318, 2.841)

46. $\begin{cases} y = -2 + \ln(x - 1) \\ 3y + 2x = 9 \Rightarrow y = \frac{1}{3}(9 - 2x) \end{cases}$

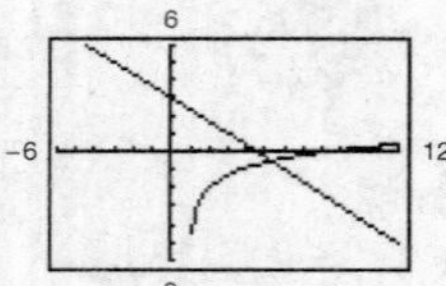

Point of intersection: (5.309, −0.539)

47. $\begin{cases} y = \sqrt{x} + 4 \\ y = 2x + 1 \end{cases}$

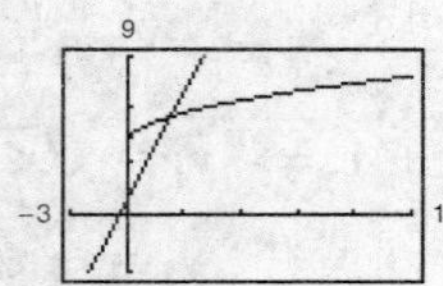

Point of intersection: $\left(\frac{9}{4}, \frac{11}{2}\right)$

48. $\begin{cases} x - y = 3 \Rightarrow y = x - 3 \\ \sqrt{x} - y = 1 \Rightarrow y = \sqrt{x} - 1 \end{cases}$

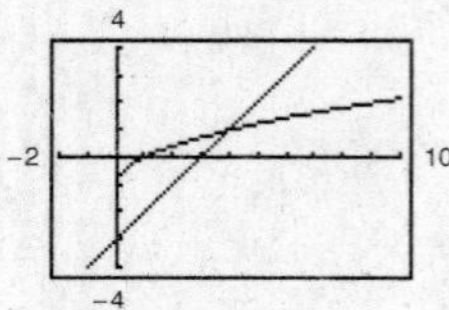

Point of intersection: (4, 1)

49. $\begin{cases} x^2 + y^2 = 169 \Rightarrow y_1 = \sqrt{169 - x^2} \text{ and} \\ \qquad y_2 = -\sqrt{169 - x^2} \\ x^2 - 8y = 104 \Rightarrow y_3 = \frac{1}{8}x^2 - 13 \end{cases}$

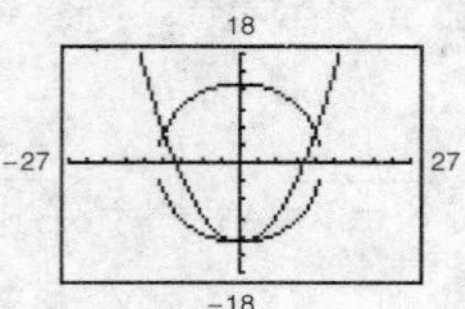

Points of intersection: (0, −13), (±12, 5)

50. $x^2 + y^2 = 4 \Rightarrow y_1 = \sqrt{4 - x^2}$

$y_2 = -\sqrt{4 - x^2}$

$2x^2 - y = 2 \Rightarrow y_3 = 2x^2 - 2$

Points of intersection: $(0, -2), \left(\frac{1}{2}\sqrt{7}, \frac{3}{2}\right), \left(-\frac{1}{2}\sqrt{7}, \frac{3}{2}\right)$
or (0, −2), (±1.323, 1.500)

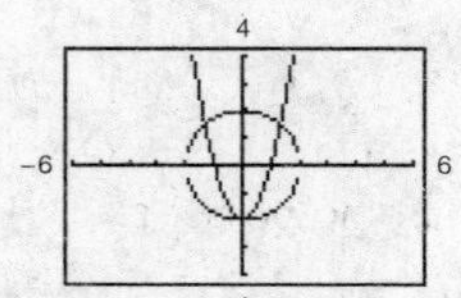

51. $\begin{cases} y = 2x & \text{Equation 1} \\ y = x^2 + 1 & \text{Equation 2} \end{cases}$

Substitute for y in Equation 2: $2x = x^2 + 1$

Solve for x:
$x^2 - 2x + 1 = (x - 1)^2 = 0 \Rightarrow x = 1$

Back-substitute $x = 1$ in Equation 1: $y = 2x = 2$

Answer: $(1, 2)$

52. $\begin{cases} x + y = 4 & \text{Equation 1} \\ x^2 + y = 2 & \text{Equation 2} \end{cases}$

Solve for y in Equation 1: $y = 4 - x$

Substitute for y in Equation 2: $x^2 + (4 - x) = 2$

Solve for x: $x^2 - x + 2 = 0$

No real solutions because the discriminant in the Quadratic Formula is negative.

Inconsistent. No solution

53. $\begin{cases} 3x - 7y + 6 = 0 & \text{Equation 1} \\ x^2 - y^2 = 4 & \text{Equation 2} \end{cases}$

Solve for y in Equation 1: $y = \dfrac{3x + 6}{7}$

Substitute for y in Equation 2: $x^2 - \left(\dfrac{3x + 6}{7}\right)^2 = 4$

Solve for x: $x^2 - \left(\dfrac{9x^2 + 36x + 36}{49}\right) = 4$

$$49x^2 - (9x^2 + 36x + 36) = 196$$

$$40x^2 - 36x - 232 = 0$$

$10x^2 - 9x - 58 = 0 \Rightarrow x = \dfrac{9 \pm \sqrt{81 + 40(58)}}{20} \Rightarrow x = \dfrac{29}{10}, -2$

Back-substitute $x = \dfrac{29}{10}$: $y = \dfrac{3x + 6}{7} = \dfrac{3(29/10) + 6}{7} = \dfrac{21}{10}$

Back-substitute $x = -2$: $y = \dfrac{3x + 6}{7} = 0$

Answers: $\left(\frac{29}{10}, \frac{21}{10}\right), (-2, 0)$

54. $\begin{cases} x^2 + y^2 = 25 & \text{Equation 1} \\ 2x + y = 10 & \text{Equation 2} \end{cases}$

Solve for y in Equation 2: $y = 10 - 2x$

Substitute for y in Equation 1: $x^2 + (10 - 2x)^2 = 25$

Solve for x: $x^2 + 100 - 40x + 4x^2 = 25 \Rightarrow x^2 - 8x + 15 = 0$

$$\Rightarrow (x - 5)(x - 3) = 0 \Rightarrow x = 3, 5$$

Back-substitute $x = 3$: $y = 10 - 2(3) = 4$

Back-substitute $x = 5$: $y = 10 - 2(5) = 0$

Answer: $(3, 4), (5, 0)$

55. $x^2 + y^2 = 1$

$x + y = 4$

Graphing $y_1 = \sqrt{1 - x^2}$, $y_2 = -\sqrt{1 - x^2}$ and $y_3 = 4 - x$, you see that there are no points of intersection.
No solution

56. $x^2 + y^2 = 4$

$x - y = 5$

Graphing $y_1 = \sqrt{4 - x^2}$, $y_2 = -\sqrt{4 - x^2}$ and $y_3 = x - 5$, you see that there are no points of intersection.
No solution

57. 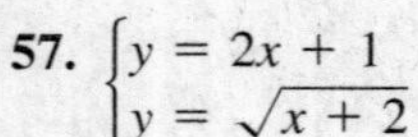

$$\begin{cases} y = 2x + 1 \\ y = \sqrt{x + 2} \end{cases}$$

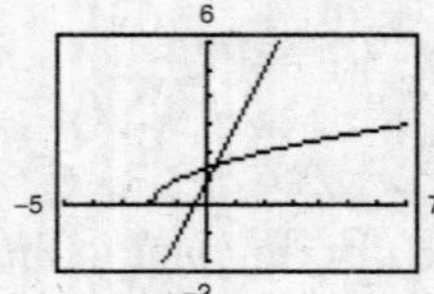

Point of intersection: $\left(\frac{1}{4}, \frac{3}{2}\right)$

58. $\begin{cases} y = 2x - 1 \\ y = \sqrt{x + 1} \end{cases}$

$2x - 1 = \sqrt{x + 1}$

$4x^2 - 4x + 1 = x + 1$

$4x^2 - 5x = 0$

$x(4x - 5) = 0$

$x = 0$ extraneous

$x = \frac{5}{4} \implies y = \frac{3}{2}$

Answer: $\left(\frac{5}{4}, \frac{3}{2}\right)$ or $(1.25, 1.5)$

59. $\begin{cases} y - e^{-x} = 1 \implies y = e^{-x} + 1 \\ y - \ln x = 3 \implies y = \ln x + 3 \end{cases}$

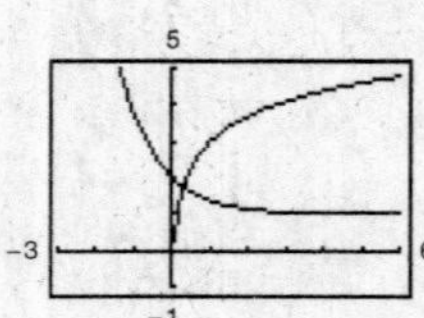

Point of intersection: Approximately $(0.287, 1.751)$

60. Graph $y = 4 - 2 \ln x$ and $y = e^x$

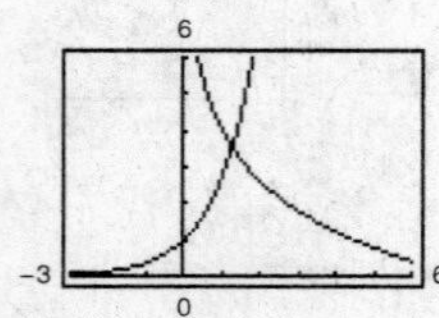

Point of intersection: $(1.262, 3.534)$

61. $\begin{cases} y = x^3 - 2x^2 + 1 & \text{Equation 1} \\ y = 1 - x^2 & \text{Equation 2} \end{cases}$

Substitute for y in Equation 2:

$x^3 - 2x^2 + 1 = 1 - x^2$

Solve for x: $x^3 - x^2 = 0$

$x^2(x - 1) = 0 \implies x = 0, 1$

Back-substitute: $x = 0 \implies y = 1$

$x = 1 \implies y = 0$

Answer: $(0, 1), (1, 0)$

62. $\begin{cases} y = x^3 - 2x^2 + x - 1 & \text{Equation 1} \\ y = -x^2 + 3x - 1 & \text{Equation 2} \end{cases}$

Substitute for y in Equation 1:

$-x^2 + 3x - 1 = x^3 - 2x^2 + x - 1$

Solve for x: $0 = x^3 - x^2 - 2x$

$0 = x(x^2 - x - 2)$

$0 = x(x - 2)(x + 1) \implies x = 0, 2, -1$

Back-substitute $x = 0$ in Equation 2:

$y = -0^2 + 3(0) - 1 = -1$

Back-substitute $x = 2$ in Equation 2:

$y = -2^2 + 3(2) - 1 = 1$

Back-substitute $x = -1$ in Equation 2:

$y = -(-1)^2 + 3(-1) - 1 = -5$

Answer: $(0, -1), (2, 1), (-1, -5)$

63. $\begin{cases} xy - 1 = 0 & \text{Equation 1} \\ 2x - 4y + 7 = 0 & \text{Equation 2} \end{cases}$

Solve for y in Equation 1: $y = \dfrac{1}{x}$

Substitute for y in Equation 2: $2x - 4\left(\dfrac{1}{x}\right) + 7 = 0$

Solve for x: $2x^2 - 4 + 7x = 0$

$\Rightarrow (2x - 1)(x + 4) = 0 \Rightarrow x = \dfrac{1}{2}, -4$

Back-substitute $x = \dfrac{1}{2}$: $y = \dfrac{1}{1/2} = 2$

Back-substitute $x = -4$: $y = \dfrac{1}{-4} = -\dfrac{1}{4}$

Two points of intersection: $\left(\dfrac{1}{2}, 2\right), \left(-4, -\dfrac{1}{4}\right)$

64. $\begin{cases} xy - 2 = 0 & \text{Equation 1} \\ 3x - 2y + 4 = 0 & \text{Equation 2} \end{cases}$

Solve for y in Equation 1: $y = \dfrac{2}{x}$

Substitute for y in Equation 2:

$3x - 2\left(\dfrac{2}{x}\right) + 4 = 0$

$3x^2 + 4x - 4 = 0$ (x cannot be 0.)

$(3x - 2)(x + 2) = 0$

$x = \dfrac{2}{3} \Rightarrow y = 3$

$x = -2 \Rightarrow y = -1$

Two points of intersection: $\left(\dfrac{2}{3}, 3\right), (-2, -1)$

65. $C = 8650x + 250{,}000,\ R = 9950x$

$R = C$

$9950x = 8650x + 250{,}000$

$1300x = 250{,}000$

$x \approx 192$ units

$R \approx \$1{,}910{,}400$ (Answers will vary.)

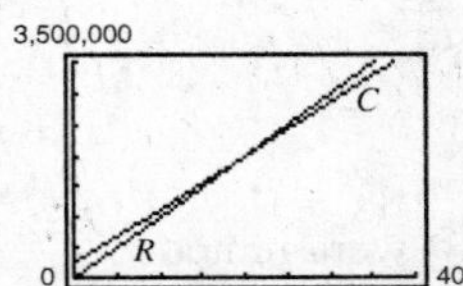

66. $C = 2.65x + 350{,}000,\ R = 4.15x$

$R = C$

$4.15x = 2.65x + 350{,}000$

$1.50x = 350{,}000$

$x \approx 233{,}333$ units, $R \approx \$968{,}333$

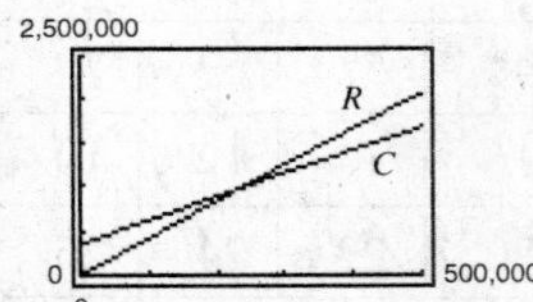

67. $C = 5.5\sqrt{x} + 10{,}000,\ R = 3.29x$

$R = C$

$3.29x = 5.5\sqrt{x} + 10{,}000$

$3.29x - 10{,}000 = 5.5\sqrt{x}$

$10.8241x^2 - 65{,}800x + 100{,}000{,}000 = 30.25x$

$10.8241x^2 - 65{,}830.25x + 100{,}000{,}000 = 0$

$x \approx 3133$ units

In order for the revenue to break even with the cost, 3133 units must be sold, $R \approx \$10{,}308$.

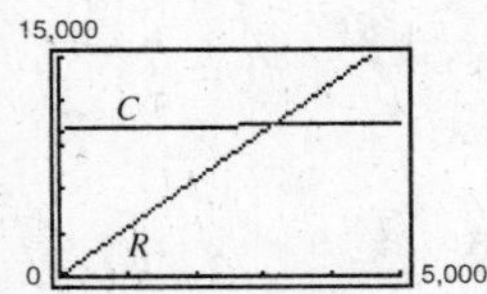

68. $C = 7.8\sqrt{x} + 18{,}500,\ R = 12.84x$

$R = C$

$12.84x = 7.8\sqrt{x} + 18{,}500$

$12.84x - 7.8\sqrt{x} - 18{,}500 = 0$ Quadratic in $\sqrt{x}$

$x \approx 1464$ units, $R \approx \$18{,}798$

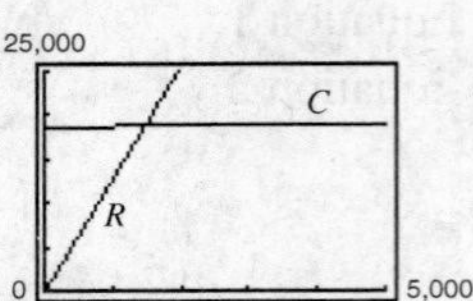

69. $N = 360 - 24x$ Animated film

$N = 24 + 18x$ Horror film

(a)

Week x	1	2	3	4	5	6	7	8	9	10	11	12
Animated	336	312	288	264	240	216	192	168	144	120	96	72
Horror	42	60	78	96	114	132	150	168	186	204	222	240

(b) For $x = 8, N = 168$

(c) $360 - 24x = 24 + 18x$

$336 = 42x$

$x = 8$

$N = 24 + 18(8) = 168$

(d) The answers are the same.

(e) During week 8 the same number (168) were rented.

70. $P_s = 24 - 2x$ Sofia

$P_p = 12 + 2x$ Paige

(a)

x	1	2	3	4	5	6	7	8	9	10	11	12
Sofia	22	20	18	16	14	12	10	8	6	4	2	0
Paige	14	16	18	20	22	24	26	28	30	32	34	36

(b) In the table, $P_s = P_p = 18$ at $x = 3$.

(c) $24 - 2x = 12 + 2x$

$12 = 4x$

$3 = x$

$P_s = P_p = 18$

Answer: (3, 18)

(d) The solutions are the same.

(e) Both girls scored 18 points in game 3.

71. (a) $C = 35.45x + 16{,}000$

$R = 55.95x$

(b) 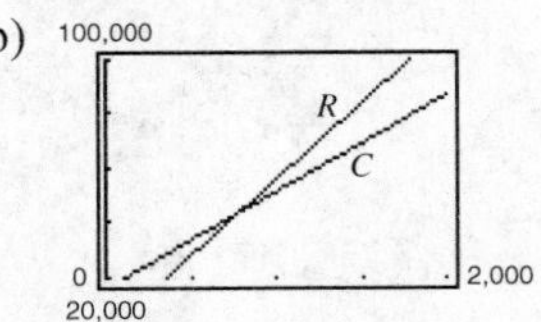

$C = R$ for $x \approx 780$ units

Algebraically,

$$35.45x + 16{,}000 = 55.95x$$
$$16{,}000 = 20.5x$$
$$x = \frac{16{,}000}{20.5} \approx 780 \text{ units}$$

72. (a) $C = 5000 + 2.16x$

$R = 3.49x$

(b) 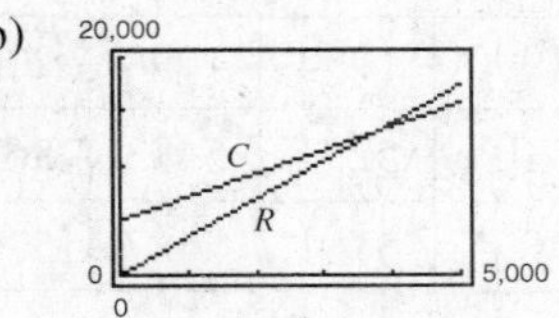

3759 units to break even.

Algebraically,

$$5000 + 2.16x = 3.49x$$
$$5000 = 1.33x$$
$$x \approx 3759.4 = 3759 \text{ units}$$

73. $0.06x = 0.03x + 350$

$0.03x = 350$

$x \approx \$11{,}666.67$

To make the straight commission offer better, you would have to sell more than $11,666.67 per week.

74. $25{,}000 + 0.01x = 20{,}000 + 0.02x$

$5000 = 0.01x$

$500{,}000 = x$

For the second offer to be better, you would have to sell more than $500,000 per year.

75. (a) $\begin{cases} x + y = 20{,}000 \\ 0.065x + 0.085y = 1600 \end{cases}$

(b) 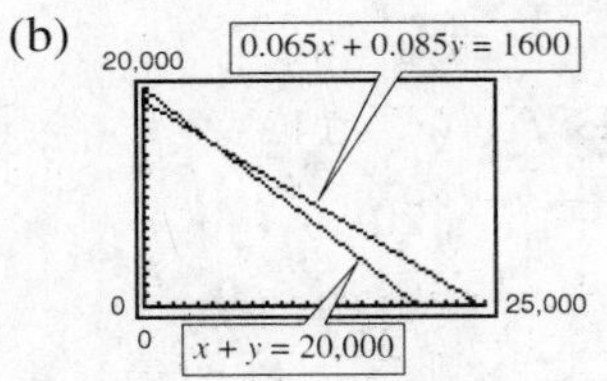

As x increases, y decreases and the amount of interest decreases.

(c) The curves intersect at $x = 5000$. Thus, $5000 should be invested at 6.5%.

76. $V = (D - 4)^2, \; 5 \le D \le 40$

$V = 0.79D^2 - 2D - 4, \; 5 \le D \le 40$

(a) 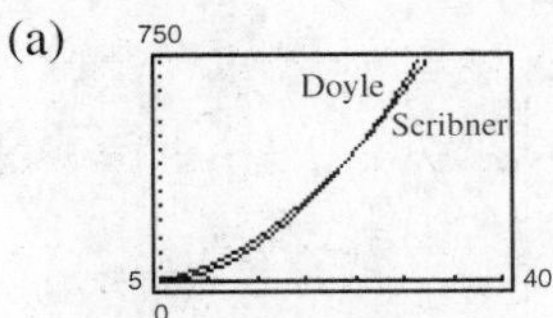

(b) The two graphs intersect at $D = 24.72$. Algebraically:

$$(D - 4)^2 = 0.79D^2 - 2D - 4$$
$$D^2 - 8D + 16 = 0.79D^2 - 2D - 4$$
$$0.21D^2 - 6D + 20 = 0$$
$$D \approx 24.72, \; [illegible].9$$

Since $5 \le D \le 40$, the scales agree when $D \approx 24.72$ inches.

(c) V is larger using the Scribner Log Rule when $5 \le D \le 24.7$. V is larger using the Doyle Log Rule when $24.7 \le D \le 40$. Therefore, for large diameters, you would use the Doyle Log Rule.

77. $M = 47.4t + 5104$

$P = 76.5t + 4875$

(a)

Year	1990	1994	1998	2002	2006	2010
Missouri	5104	5294	5483	5673	5862	6052
Tennessee	4875	5181	5487	5793	6099	6405

(b) From 1998 to 2010

(c)

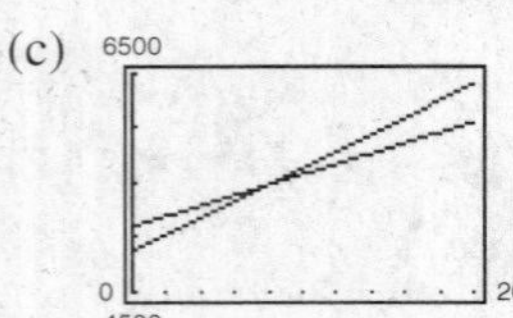

Point of intersection: (7.87, 5477.0)

(d) $47.4t + 5104 = 76.5t + 4875$

$$229 = 29.1t$$

$$t = 229/29.1 \approx 7.87$$

(e) The population of Tennessee surpassed that of Missouri during 1997.

78. (a) $T_{\text{public}} = 55.21x^2 - 25.4x + 2516$

$T_{\text{private}} = 810.5x + 14{,}109$

(b)

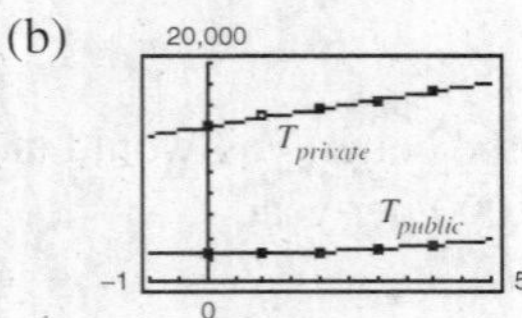

(c) $T_{\text{public}} = T_{\text{private}} \approx 33{,}495$ when $t \approx 23.9$, or late 2023.

(d) $55.21x^2 - 25.4x + 2516 = 810.5x + 14{,}109$

$$55.21x^2 - 835.9 - 11{,}593 = 0$$

$$x = \frac{835.9 \pm \sqrt{835.9^2 - 4(55.21)(-11{,}593)}}{2(55.21)}$$

$$= \frac{835.9 \pm 1805.2}{110.42}$$

Using the positive value, $x \approx 23.9$, or late 2023.

(e) The results are the same.

79. $2l + 2w = 30 \implies l + w = 15$

$l = w + 3 \implies (w + 3) + w = 15$

$$2w = 12$$

$$w = 6$$

$l = w + 3 = 9$

Dimensions: 6 meters × 9 meters

80. $2l + 2w = 280 \implies l + w = 140$

$w = l - 20 \implies l + (l - 20) = 140$

$$2l = 160$$

$$l = 80$$

$w = l - 20 = 80 - 20 = 60$

Dimensions: 60 × 80 centimeters

81. $2l + 2w = 40 \implies l + w = 20 \implies w = 20 - l$

$lw = 96 \implies l(20 - l) = 96$

$$20l - l^2 = 96$$

$$0 = l^2 - 20l + 96$$

$$0 = (l - 8)(l - 12)$$

$$l = 8 \text{ or } l = 12$$

$l = 12, w = 8$

If the length is supposed to be greater than the width, we have $l = 12$ miles and $w = 8$ miles.

82. $A = \frac{1}{2}bh$

$1 = \frac{1}{2}a^2$

$a^2 = 2$

$a = \sqrt{2}$

The dimensions are $b = h = \sqrt{2}$ inches and hypotenuse = 2 inches.

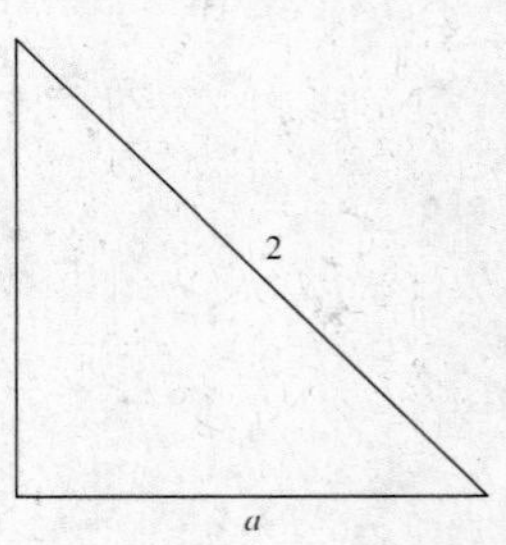

83. False. You could solve for x first.

84. False. There could be four points of intersection. For example, $x^2 + y^2 = 4$ and $y = x^2 - 3$.

85. The system has no solution if you arrive at a false statement, ie. $4 = 8$, or you have a quadratic equation with a negative discriminant, which would yield imaginary roots.

86. The advantage of the method of substitution over the graphical method is that substitution gives an exact answer.

87. (a) The line $y = 2x$ intersects the parabola $y = x^2$ at two points, $(0, 0)$ and $(2, 4)$.

(b) The line $y = 0$ intersects $y = x^2$ at $(0, 0)$ only.

(c) The line $y = x - 2$ does not intersect $y = x^2$.

(Other answers possible.)

88. Answers will vary. For example,

(a) $3x + y = 3$

$3x + y = 5$

(b) $3x + y = 4$

$2x + y = 2$

(c) $6x + 3y = 9$

$2x + y = 3$

89. Answers will vary. For example,

$y = x - 3$

$2y = x - 4$

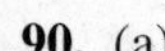

90. (a)

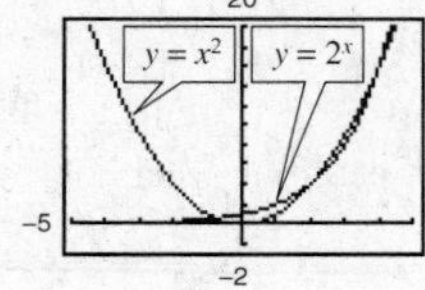

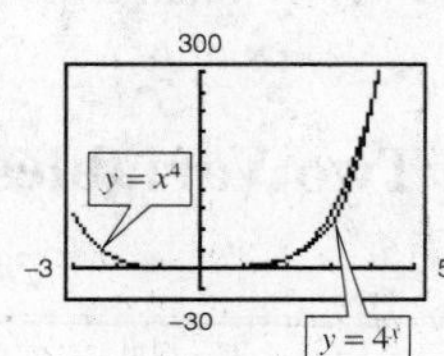

(b) Based on the graphs in part (a) it appears that for $b > 1$, there are three points of intersection for the graphs of $y = b^x$ and $y = x^b$ when b is an even number.

91. $(-2, 7), (5, 5)$

$$m = \frac{5 - 7}{5 - (-2)} = -\frac{2}{7}$$

$$y - 7 = -\frac{2}{7}(x - (-2))$$

$$7y - 49 = -2x - 4$$

$$2x + 7y - 45 = 0$$

92. $(3, 4), (10, 6)$

$$m = \frac{6 - 4}{10 - 3} = \frac{2}{7}$$

$$y - 4 = \frac{2}{7}(x - 3)$$

$$7y - 28 = 2x - 6$$

$$2x - 7y + 22 = 0$$

93. $(6, 3), (10, 3)$

$$m = \frac{3 - 3}{10 - 6} = 0$$

The line is horizontal.

$y = 3 \Rightarrow y - 3 = 0$

94. $(4, -2), (4, 5)$

$x = 4$

95. $\left(\frac{3}{5}, 0\right), (4, 6)$

$$m = \frac{6 - 0}{4 - \frac{3}{5}} = \frac{6}{\frac{17}{5}} = \frac{30}{17}$$

$$y - 6 = \frac{30}{17}(x - 4)$$

$$17y - 102 = 30x - 120$$

$$0 = 30x - 17y - 18$$

96. $\left(-\frac{7}{3}, 8\right), \left(\frac{5}{2}, \frac{1}{2}\right)$

$$m = \frac{8 - \frac{1}{2}}{-\frac{7}{3} - \frac{5}{2}} = \frac{\frac{15}{2}}{-\frac{29}{6}} = -\frac{45}{29}$$

$$y - \frac{1}{2} = \frac{45}{29}\left(x - \frac{5}{2}\right)$$

$$29y - \frac{29}{2} = -45x + \frac{225}{2}$$

$$45x + 29y - 127 = 0$$

97. Domain: all $x \neq 6$

Vertical asymptotes: $x = 6$

Horizontal asymptote: $y = 0$

98. Domain: all $x \neq -\frac{2}{3}$

Vertical asymptote: $x = -\frac{2}{3}$

Horizontal asymptote: $y = \frac{2}{3}$

99. Domain: all $x \neq \pm 4$

Vertical asymptotes: $x = \pm 4$

Horizontal asymptote: $y = 1$

100. $f(x) = 3 - \frac{2}{x^2} = \frac{3x^2 - 2}{x^2}$

Domain: all $x \neq 0$

Vertical asymptote: $x = 0$

Horizontal asymptote: $y = 3$

101. Domain: all real numbers x

Horizontal asymptote: $y = 0$

102. Domain: all real numbers x

Horizontal asymptote: $y = 0$

Section 7.2 Systems of Linear Equations in Two Variables

- You should be able to solve a linear system by the method of elimination.
  1. Obtain coefficients for either x or y that differ only in sign. This is done by multiplying all the terms of one or both equations by appropriate constants.
  2. Add the equations to eliminate one of the variables and then solve for the remaining variable.
  3. Use back-substitution into either original equation and solve for the other variable.
  4. Check your answer.
- You should know that for a system of two linear equations, one of the following is true.
  (a) There are infinitely many solutions; the lines are identical. The system is consistent.
  (b) There is no solution; the lines are parallel. The system is inconsistent.
  (c) There is one solution; the lines intersect at one point. The system is consistent.

Vocabulary Check

1. method, elimination **2.** equivalent **3.** consistent, inconsistent

1. $\begin{cases} 2x + y = 5 & \text{Equation 1} \\ x - y = 1 & \text{Equation 2} \end{cases}$

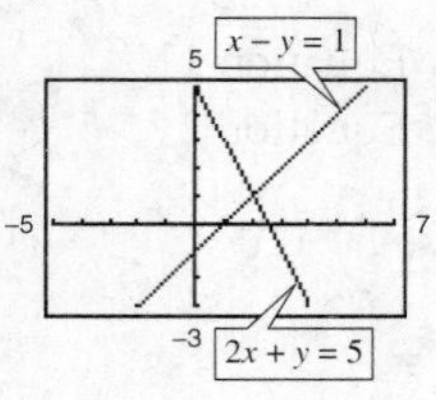

Add to eliminate y: $3x = 6 \implies x = 2$

Substitute $x = 2$ in Equation 2: $2 - y = 1 \implies y = 1$

Answer: $(2, 1)$

2. $\begin{cases} x + 3y = 1 & \text{Equation 1} \\ -x + 2y = 4 & \text{Equation 2} \end{cases}$

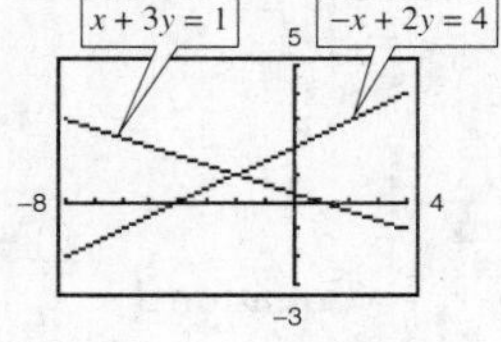

Add to eliminate x: $5y = 5 \implies y = 1$

Substitute $y = 1$ in Equation 1: $x + 3(1) = 1 \implies x = -2$

Answer: $(-2, 1)$

3. $\begin{cases} x + y = 0 & \text{Equation 1} \\ 3x + 2y = 1 & \text{Equation 2} \end{cases}$

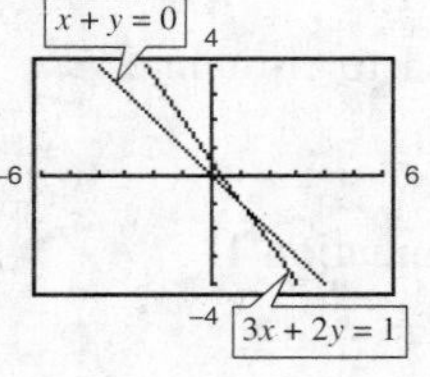

Multiply Equation 1 by -2: $-2x - 2y = 0$

Add this to Equation 2 to eliminate y: $x = 1$

Substitute $x = 1$ in Equation 1: $1 + y = 0 \implies y = -1$

Answer: $(1, -1)$

4. $\begin{cases} 2x - y = 3 & \text{Equation 1} \\ 4x + 3y = 21 & \text{Equation 2} \end{cases}$

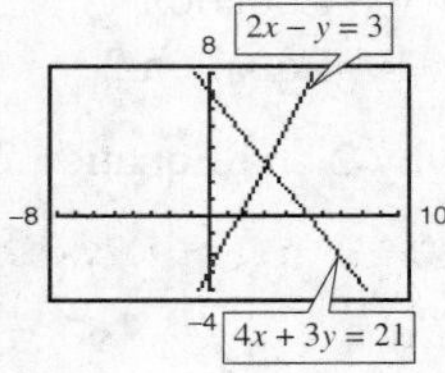

Multiply Equation 1 by 3: $6x - 3y = 9$

Add this to Equation 2 to eliminate y: $10x = 30 \implies x = 3$

Substitute $x = 3$ in Equation 1: $2(3) - y = 3 \implies y = 3$

Answer: $(3, 3)$

5. $\begin{cases} x - y = 2 & \text{Equation 1} \\ -2x + 2y = 5 & \text{Equation 2} \end{cases}$

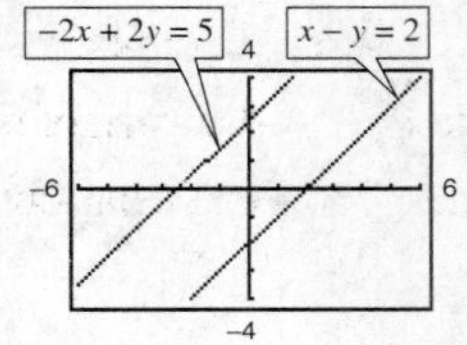

Multiply Equation 1 by 2: $2x - 2y = 4$

Add this to Equation 2: $0 = 9$

There are no solutions.

6. $\begin{cases} 3x - 2y = 5 & \text{Equation 1} \\ -6x + 4y = -10 & \text{Equation 2} \end{cases}$

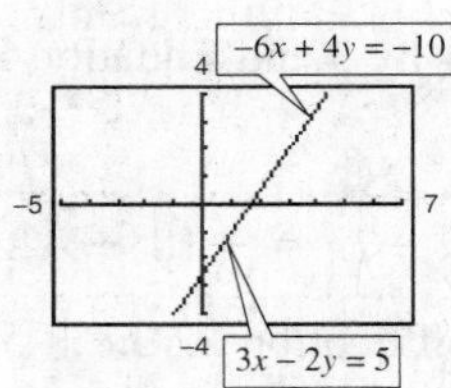

Multiply Equation 1 by 2 and add to Equation 2: $0 + 0 = 0$

There are infinitely many solutions.

All points on line $3x - 2y = 5$.

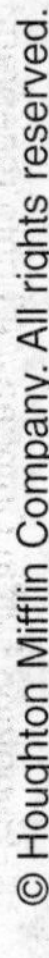

7. $\begin{cases} x + 2y = 4 & \text{Equation 1} \\ x - 2y = 1 & \text{Equation 2} \end{cases}$

Add to eliminate y:

$2x = 5$

$x = \frac{5}{2}$

Substitute $x = \frac{5}{2}$ in Equation 1:

$\frac{5}{2} + 2y = 4 \implies y = \frac{3}{4}$

Answer: $\left(\frac{5}{2}, \frac{3}{4}\right)$

8. $\begin{cases} 3x - 2y = 5 & \text{Equation 1} \\ x + 2y = 7 & \text{Equation 2} \end{cases}$

Adding the equations, $4x = 12 \implies x = 3$.

Then $3 + 2y = 7 \implies y = 2$

Answer: $(3, 2)$

9. $\begin{cases} 2x + 3y = 18 & \text{Equation 1} \\ 5x - y = 11 & \text{Equation 2} \end{cases}$

Multiply Equation 2 by 3: $15x - 3y = 33$

Add this to Equation 1 to eliminate y:

$17x = 51 \implies x = 3$

Substitute $x = 3$ in Equation 1:

$6 + 3y = 18 \implies y = 4$

Answer: $(3, 4)$

10. $\begin{cases} x + 7y = 12 & \text{Equation 1} \\ 3x - 5y = 10 & \text{Equation 2} \end{cases}$

Multiply Equation 1 by -3: $-3x - 21y = -36$

Add this to Equation 2 to eliminate x:

$-26y = -26 \implies y = 1$

Substitute $y = 1$ in Equation 1:

$x + 7 = 12 \implies x = 5$

Answer: $(5, 1)$

11. $\begin{cases} 3r + 2s = 10 & \text{Equation 1} \\ 2r + 5s = 3 & \text{Equation 2} \end{cases}$

Multiply Equation 1 by 2 and Equation 2 by -3:

$6r + 4s = 20$

$-6r - 15s = -9$

Add to eliminate r:

$-11s = 11 \implies s = -1$

Substitute $s = -1$ in Equation 1:

$3r + 2(-1) = 10 \implies r = 4$

Answer: $(4, -1)$

12. $\begin{cases} 2r + 4s = 5 & \text{Equation 1} \\ 16r + 50s = 55 & \text{Equation 2} \end{cases}$

Multiply Equation 1 by -8: $-16r - 32s = -40$

Add this to Equation 2: $18s = 15 \implies s = \frac{5}{6}$

Substitute $s = \frac{5}{6}$ in Equation 1:

$2r + 4\left(\frac{5}{6}\right) = 5 \implies r = \frac{5}{6}$

Answer: $(r, s) = \left(\frac{5}{6}, \frac{5}{6}\right)$

13. $\begin{cases} 5u + 6v = 24 & \text{Equation 1} \\ 3u + 5v = 18 & \text{Equation 2} \end{cases}$

Multiply Equation 1 by 3 and Equation 2 by (-5):

$$15u + 18v = 72$$
$$-15u - 25v = -90$$

Add to eliminate u: $-7v = -18 \implies v = \frac{18}{7}$

Substitute $v = \frac{18}{7}$ in Equation 2: $3u + 5\left(\frac{18}{7}\right) = 18 \implies u = \frac{12}{7}$

Answer: $\left(\frac{12}{7}, \frac{18}{7}\right)$

14. $\begin{cases} 3u + 11v = 4 & \text{Equation 1} \\ -2u - 5v = 9 & \text{Equation 2} \end{cases}$

Multiply Equation 1 by 2 and Equation 2 by 3:

$\begin{cases} 6u + 22v = 8 \\ -6u - 15v = 27 \end{cases}$

Adding, $7v = 35 \implies v = 5$

Then, $3u + 11(5) = 4 \implies u = -17$

Answer: $(-17, 5)$

15. $\begin{cases} 1.8x + 1.2y = 4 & \text{Equation 1} \\ 9x + 6y = 3 & \text{Equation 2} \end{cases}$

Multiply Equation 1 by (-5): $-9x - 6y = -20$

Add this to Equation 2: $0 = -17$

Inconsistent; no solution

16. $\begin{cases} 3.1x - 2.9y = -10.2 & \text{Equation 1} \\ 31x - 12y = 34 & \text{Equation 2} \end{cases}$

Multiply Equation 1 by -10: $-31x + 29y = 102$

Add this to Equation 2: $17y = 136 \implies y = 8.$

Substituting this value into Equation 2:

$$31x - 12(8) = 34 \implies 31x = 130 \implies x = \tfrac{130}{31}$$

Answer: $\left(\frac{130}{31}, 8\right)$

17. $2x - 5y = 0$

$x - y = 3 \implies y = x - 3$

$2x - 5(x - 3) = 0$

$-3x = -15$

$x = 5, y = 2$

Matches (b)

One solution; consistent

18. $-7x + 6y = -4$

$14x - 12y = 8$

Lines coincide.

Matches (a)

Infinite number of solutions; consistent

19. $\left.\begin{array}{l} 2x - 5y = 0 \\ 2x - 3y = -4 \end{array}\right\}$ $\begin{array}{l} -2y = 4 \\ y = -2, x = -5 \end{array}$

One solution; consistent

Matches (c)

20. $7x - 6y = -6$

$-7x + 6y = -4$

Parallel lines

Inconsistent; no solution

21. $\begin{cases} 4x + 3y = 3 & \text{Equation 1} \\ 3x + 11y = 13 & \text{Equation 2} \end{cases}$

Multiply Equation 1 by 3 and Equation 2 by -4:

$\begin{cases} 12x + 9y = 9 \\ -12x - 44y = -52 \end{cases}$

Add to eliminate x: $-35y = -43 \implies y = \frac{43}{35}$

Substitute $y = \frac{43}{35}$ into Equation 1:

$$4x + 3\left(\tfrac{43}{35}\right) = 3 \implies x = -\tfrac{6}{35}$$

Answer: $\left(-\frac{6}{35}, \frac{43}{35}\right)$

22. $\begin{cases} 2x + 5y = 8 & \text{Equation 1} \\ 5x + 8y = 10 & \text{Equation 2} \end{cases}$

Multiply Equation 1 by 5 and Equation 2 by -2:

$$10x + 25y = 40$$

$$-10x - 16y = -20$$

Adding, $9y = 20 \implies y = \frac{20}{9}$

Substituting into Equation 1, $2x + 5\left(\frac{20}{9}\right) = 8 \implies 2x = 8 - \frac{100}{9} \implies x = -\frac{14}{9}$

Answer: $\left(-\frac{14}{9}, \frac{20}{9}\right)$

23. $\begin{cases} \frac{2}{5}x - \frac{3}{2}y = 4 & \text{Equation 1} \\ \frac{1}{5}x - \frac{3}{4}y = -2 & \text{Equation 2} \end{cases}$

Multiply Equation 2 by -2 and add to Equation 1:

$0 = 8$

Inconsistent; no solution

24. $\begin{cases} \frac{2}{3}x + \frac{1}{6}y = \frac{2}{3} & \text{Equation 1} \\ 4x + y = 4 & \text{Equation 2} \end{cases}$

Multiply Equation 1 by -6 and add to Equation 2:

$0 = 0$

There are an infinite number of solutions. All points on the line $4x + y = 4$.

25. $\begin{cases} \frac{3}{4}x + y = \frac{1}{8} & \text{Equation 1} \\ \frac{9}{4}x + 3y = \frac{3}{8} & \text{Equation 2} \end{cases}$

Multiply Equation 1 by -3: $-\frac{9}{4}x - 3y = -\frac{3}{8}$

Add this to Equation 2: $0 = 0$

There are an infinite number of solutions.

The solutions consist of all (x, y) satisfying $\frac{3}{4}x + y = \frac{1}{8}$, or $6x + 8y = 1$.

26. $\begin{cases} \dfrac{1}{4}x + \dfrac{1}{6}y = 1 & \text{Equation 1} \\ -3x - 2y = 0 & \text{Equation 2} \end{cases}$

Multiply Equation 1 by 12 and add to Equation 2:

$0 = 12$

Inconsistent; no solution

27. $\begin{cases} \dfrac{x+3}{4} + \dfrac{y-1}{3} = 1 & \text{Equation 1} \\ 2x - y = 12 & \text{Equation 2} \end{cases}$

Multiply Equation 1 by 12 and Equation 2 by 4:

$\begin{cases} 3x + 4y = 7 \\ 8x - 4y = 48 \end{cases}$

Add to eliminate y: $11x = 55 \Rightarrow x = 5$

Substitute $x = 5$ into Equation 2:

$2(5) - y = 12 \Rightarrow y = -2$

Answer: $(5, -2)$

28. $\begin{cases} \dfrac{x+2}{4} + \dfrac{y-1}{4} = 1 & \text{Equation 1} \\ x - y = 4 & \text{Equation 2} \end{cases}$

Multiply Equation 1 by 4:

$\begin{cases} x + y = 3 \\ x - y = 4 \end{cases}$

Add to eliminate y: $2x = 7 \Rightarrow x = \dfrac{7}{2}$

Substitute $x = \dfrac{7}{2}$ into Equation 2:

$\dfrac{7}{2} - y = 4 \Rightarrow y = -\dfrac{1}{2}$

Answer: $\left(\frac{7}{2}, -\frac{1}{2}\right)$

29. $\begin{cases} \dfrac{x-1}{2} + \dfrac{y+2}{3} = 4 & \text{Equation 1} \\ x - 2y = 5 & \text{Equation 2} \end{cases}$

Multiply Equation 1 by 6:

$3(x - 1) + 2(y + 2) = 24 \Rightarrow 3x + 2y = 23$

Add this to Equation 2 to eliminate y:

$4x = 28 \Rightarrow x = 7$

Substitute $x = 7$ in Equation 2:

$7 - 2y = 5 \Rightarrow y = 1$

Answer: $(7, 1)$

30. $\begin{cases} \dfrac{x-1}{2} + \dfrac{y-2}{2} = 1 & \text{Equation 1} \\ x - y = 2 & \text{Equation 2} \end{cases}$

Multiply Equation 1 by 2:

$$\begin{cases} x + y = 5 \\ x - y = 2 \end{cases}$$

Add to eliminate y: $2x = 7 \Rightarrow x = \dfrac{7}{2}$

Substitute $x = \frac{7}{2}$ into Equation 2:

$$\frac{7}{2} - y = 2 \Rightarrow y = \frac{3}{2}$$

Answer: $\left(\frac{7}{2}, \frac{3}{2}\right)$

31. $\begin{cases} 2.5x - 3y = 1.5 & \text{Equation 1} \\ 10x - 12y = 6 & \text{Equation 2 multiplied by 5} \end{cases}$

Multiply Equation 1 by (-4):

$$-10x + 12y = -6$$

Add this to Equation 2 to eliminate x:

$$0 = 0$$

The solution set consists of all points lying on the line $10x - 12y = 6$.

All points on the line $5x - 6y = 3$.

Let $x = a$, then $y = \frac{5}{6}a - \frac{1}{2}$.

Answer: $\left(a, \frac{5}{6}a - \frac{1}{2}\right)$, where a is any real number.

32. $\begin{cases} 6.3x + 7.2y = 5.4 & \text{Equation 1} \\ 5.6x + 6.4y = 4.8 & \text{Equation 2} \end{cases}$

$$\begin{cases} 7x + 8y = 6 & \text{(Divide by 0.9)} \\ 7x + 8y = 6 & \text{(Divide by 0.8)} \end{cases}$$

There are an infinite number of solutions. All points on the line $7x + 8y = 6$.

33. $\begin{cases} 0.2x - 0.5y = -27.8 & \text{Equation 1} \\ 0.3x + 0.4y = 68.7 & \text{Equation 2} \end{cases}$

Multiply Equation 1 by 40 and Equation 2 by 50:

$$\begin{cases} 8x - 20y = -1112 \\ 15x + 20y = 3435 \end{cases}$$

Adding the equation eliminates y:

$$23x = 2323 \Rightarrow x = 101$$

Substitute $x = 101$ into Equation 1:

$$8(101) - 20y = -1112 \Rightarrow y = 96$$

Answer: $(101, 96)$

34. $\begin{cases} 0.2x + 0.6y = -1 & \text{Equation 1} \\ x - 0.5y = 2 & \text{Equation 2} \end{cases}$

Multiply Equation 1 by 10 and Equation 2 by 2:

$$\begin{cases} 2x + 6y = -10 \\ 2x - y = 4 \end{cases}$$

Subtract to eliminates x:

$$7y = -14 \Rightarrow y = -2.$$

Hence,

$$x = 2 + 0.5(y) = 2 + 0.5(-2) = 1$$

Answer: $(1, -2)$

35. $\begin{cases} 0.05x - 0.03y = 0.21 & \text{Equation 1} \\ 0.07x + 0.02y = 0.16 & \text{Equation 2} \end{cases}$

Multiply Equation 1 by 200 and Equation 2 by 300:

$$\begin{cases} 10x - 6y = 42 \\ 21x + 6y = 48 \end{cases}$$

Add to eliminate y: $31x = 90$

$$x = \tfrac{90}{31}$$

Substitute $x = \frac{90}{31}$ in Equation 2:

$$0.07\left(\tfrac{90}{31}\right) + 0.02y = 0.16$$

$$y = -\tfrac{67}{31}$$

Answer: $\left(\frac{90}{31}, -\frac{67}{31}\right)$

36. $\begin{cases} 0.2x + 0.4y = -0.2 & \text{Equation 1} \\ x + 0.5y = -2.5 & \text{Equation 2} \end{cases}$

Multiply Equation 1 by 10 and Equation 2 by 2:

$\begin{cases} 2x + 4y = -2 \\ 2x + y = -5 \end{cases}$

Subtract to eliminates x:

$3y = 3 \implies y = 1.$

Hence,

$x = -2.5 - 0.5(y) = -2.5 - 0.5(1) = -3$

Answer: $(-3, 1)$

37. Let $X = \dfrac{1}{x}$ and $Y = \dfrac{1}{y}$.

$\begin{cases} X + 3Y = 2 & \text{Equation 1} \\ 4X - Y = -5 & \text{Equation 2} \end{cases}$

Multiply Equation 1 by 4:

$\begin{cases} 4X + 12Y = 8 \\ 4X - Y = -5 \end{cases}$

Subtract to eliminates X:

$13Y = 13 \implies Y = 1.$

Hence,

$X = 2 - 3Y = 2 - 3(1) = -1$

$x = \dfrac{1}{X} = -1, y = \dfrac{1}{Y} = 1$

Answer: $(-1, 1)$

38. Let $X = \dfrac{1}{x}$ and $Y = \dfrac{1}{y}$.

$\begin{cases} 2X - Y = 0 & \text{Equation 1} \\ 4X - 3Y = -1 & \text{Equation 2} \end{cases}$

Multiply Equation 1 by 2:

$\begin{cases} 4X - 2Y = 0 \\ 4X - 3Y = -1 \end{cases}$

Subtract to eliminates X: $Y = 1$

Hence, $X = \dfrac{1}{2}$.

$x = \dfrac{1}{X} = 2, y = \dfrac{1}{Y} = 1$

Answer: $(2, 1)$

39. Let $X = \dfrac{1}{x}$ and $Y = \dfrac{1}{y}$.

$\begin{cases} X + 2Y = 5 & \text{Equation 1} \\ 3X - 4Y = -5 & \text{Equation 2} \end{cases}$

Multiply Equation 1 by 2:

$\begin{cases} 2X + 4Y = 10 \\ 3X - 4Y = -5 \end{cases}$

Adding the equations eliminates Y:

$5X = 5 \implies X = 1.$

Hence,

$2Y = 5 - X = 4 \implies Y = 2.$

$x = \dfrac{1}{X} = 1, y = \dfrac{1}{Y} = \dfrac{1}{2}$

Answer: $\left(1, \frac{1}{2}\right)$

40. Let $X = \dfrac{1}{x}$ and $Y = \dfrac{1}{y}$.

$\begin{cases} 2X - Y = 5 & \text{Equation 1} \\ 6X + Y = 11 & \text{Equation 2} \end{cases}$

Adding the equations, $8X = 16 \implies X = 2$.

Hence,

$Y = 11 - 6X = 11 - 12 = -1.$

$x = \dfrac{1}{X} = \dfrac{1}{2}, y = \dfrac{1}{Y} = -1$

Answer: $\left(\frac{1}{2}, -1\right)$

41. $\begin{cases} 2x - 5y = 0 \implies y = \frac{2}{5}x \\ x - y = 3 \implies y = x - 3 \end{cases}$

The system is consistent.
There is one solution, (5, 2).

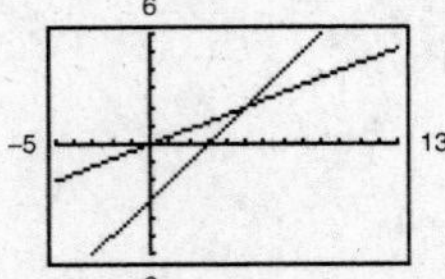

42. $\begin{cases} 2x + y = 5 \\ x - 2y = -1 \end{cases}$

The system is consistent.
There is one solution, $(1.8, 1.4)$

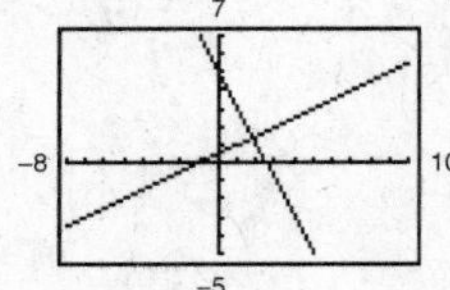

43. $\begin{cases} \frac{3}{5}x - y = 3 \Rightarrow y = \frac{3}{5}x - 3 \\ -3x + 5y = 9 \Rightarrow y = \frac{1}{5}(3x + 9) = \frac{3}{5}x + \frac{9}{5} \end{cases}$

The lines are parallel.
The system is inconsistent.

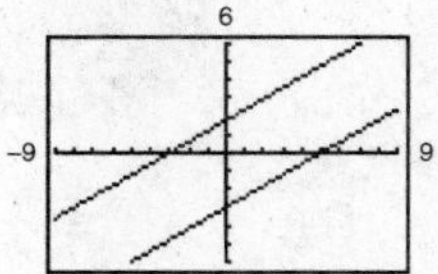

44. $\begin{cases} 4x - 6y = 9 \Rightarrow y = (4x - 9)/6 = \frac{2}{3}x - \frac{3}{2} \\ \frac{16}{3}x - 8y = 12 \Rightarrow y = \left(\frac{16}{3}x - 12\right)/8 = \frac{2}{3}x - \frac{3}{2} \end{cases}$

The system is consistent. The solution set consists of all points on the line $y = \frac{2}{3}x - \frac{3}{2}$, or $4x - 6y - 9 = 0$.

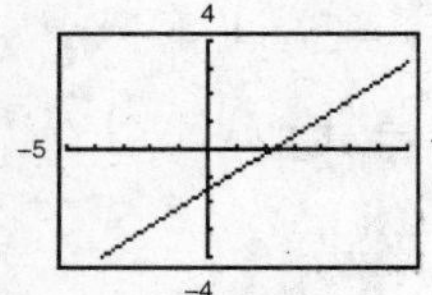

45. $\begin{cases} 8x - 14y = 5 \Rightarrow y = (8x - 5)/14 = \frac{4}{7}x - \frac{5}{14} \\ 2x - 3.5y = 1.25 \Rightarrow y = (2x - 1.25)/3.5 = \frac{4}{7}x - \frac{5}{14} \end{cases}$

The system is consistent. The solution set consists of all points on the line $y = \frac{4}{7}x - \frac{5}{14}$, or $8x - 14y = 5$.

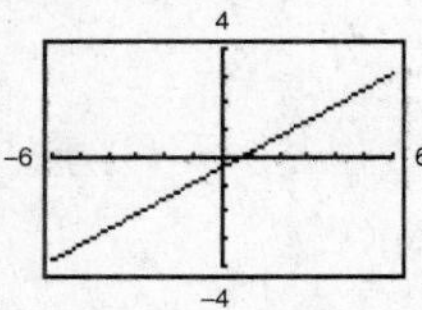

46. $\begin{cases} y = \frac{1}{7}(x + 3) \\ y = 5 + \frac{1}{7}x \end{cases}$

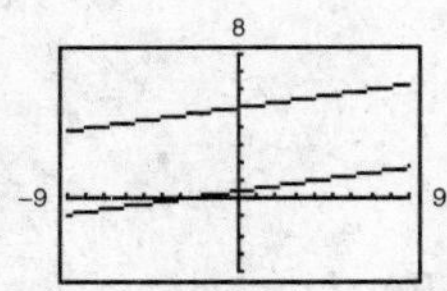

Inconsistent; no solution

47. $\begin{cases} 6y = 42 \Rightarrow y = 7 \\ 6x - y = 16 \Rightarrow y = 6x - 16 \end{cases}$

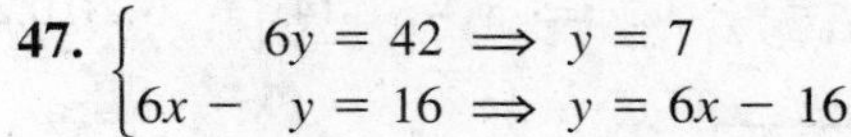

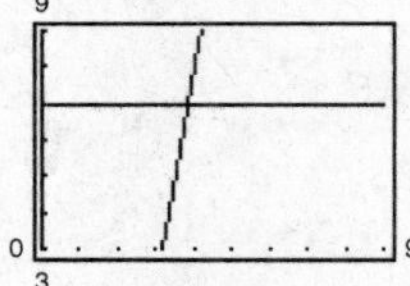

Answer: $\left(\frac{23}{6}, 7\right) \approx (3.833, 7)$

48. $\begin{cases} 4y = -8 \Rightarrow y = -2 \\ 7x - 2y = 25 \Rightarrow y = (7x - 25)/2 \end{cases}$

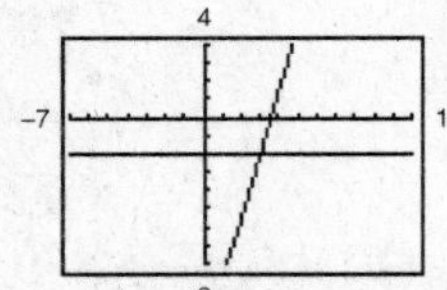

Answer: $(3, -2)$

49. $\begin{cases} \frac{3}{2}x - \frac{1}{5}y = 8 \Rightarrow y = 5\left(\frac{3}{2}x - 8\right) \\ -2x + 3y = 3 \Rightarrow y = \frac{1}{3}(3 + 2x) \end{cases}$

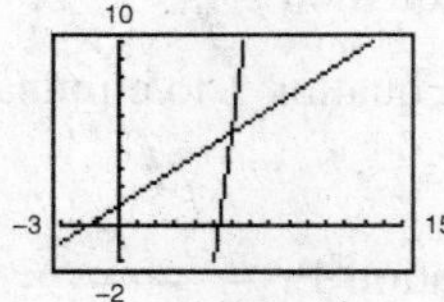

Answer: $(6, 5)$

50. $\begin{cases} \dfrac{3}{4}x - \dfrac{5}{2}y = -9 \Rightarrow y = \dfrac{2}{5}\left(\dfrac{3}{4}x + 9\right) = \dfrac{3}{10}x + \dfrac{18}{5} \\ -x + 6y = 28 \Rightarrow y = (x + 28)/6 = \dfrac{x}{6} + \dfrac{14}{3} \end{cases}$

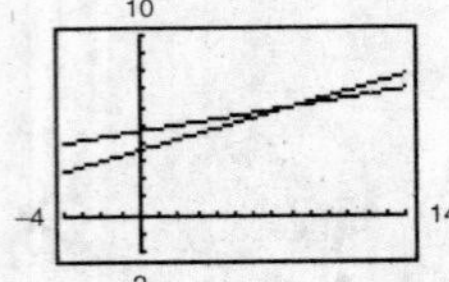

Answer: $(8, 6)$

51. $\dfrac{1}{3}x + y = -\dfrac{1}{3} \Rightarrow y = -\dfrac{1}{3} - \dfrac{1}{3}x$

$5x - 3y = 7 \Rightarrow y = \dfrac{1}{3}(5x - 7)$

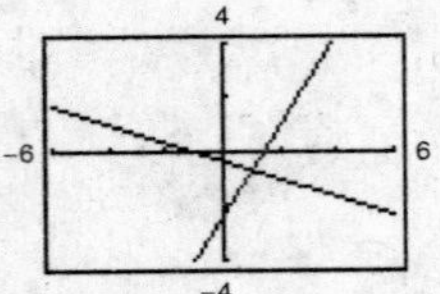

Answer: $(1, -0.667)$

52. $5x - y = -4 \Rightarrow y = 5x + 4$

$2x + \frac{3}{5}y = \frac{2}{5} \Rightarrow y = \frac{5}{3}\left(-2x + \frac{2}{5}\right)$

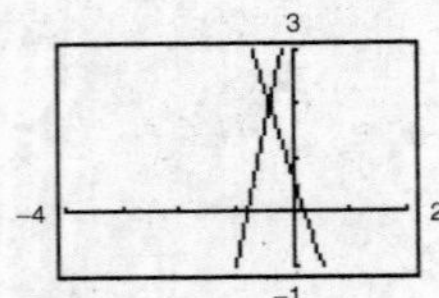

Answer: $(-0.4, 2)$

53. $\begin{cases} 0.5x + 2.2y = 9 \Rightarrow y = 1/2.2(9 - 0.5x) \\ 6x + 0.4y = -22 \Rightarrow y = 1/0.4(-22 - 6x) \end{cases}$

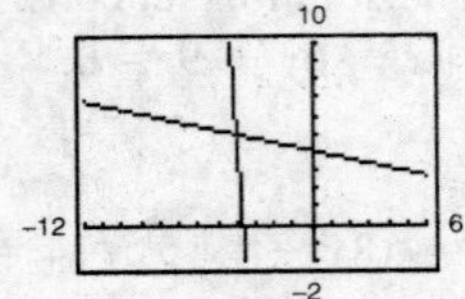

Answer: $(-4, 5)$

54. $\begin{cases} 2.4x + 3.8y = -17.6 \Rightarrow y = (-2.4x - 17.6)/3.8 \\ 4x - 0.2y = -3.2 \Rightarrow y = (4x + 3.2)/0.2 \end{cases}$

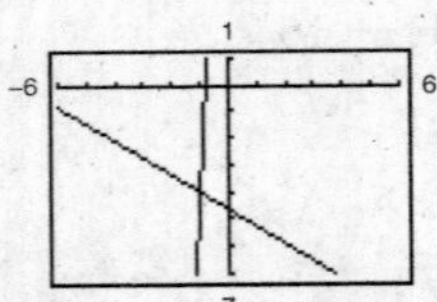

Answer: $(-1, -4)$

55. $\begin{cases} 3x - 5y = 7 & \text{Equation 1} \\ 2x + y = 9 & \text{Equation 2} \end{cases}$

Multiply Equation 2 by 5:

$10x + 5y = 45$

Add this to Equation 1:

$13x = 52 \Rightarrow x = 4$

Back-substitute $x = 4$ into Equation 2:

$2(4) + y = 9 \Rightarrow y = 1$

Answer: $(4, 1)$

56. $\begin{cases} -x + 3y = 17 & \text{Equation 1} \\ 4x + 3y = 7 & \text{Equation 2} \end{cases}$

Subtract Equation 2 from Equation 1 to eliminate y:

$-5x = 10 \Rightarrow x = -2$

Substitute $x = -2$ in Equation 1:

$-(-2) + 3y = 17 \Rightarrow y = 5$

Answer: $(-2, 5)$

57. $\begin{cases} y = 4x + 3 \\ y = -5x - 12 \end{cases}$

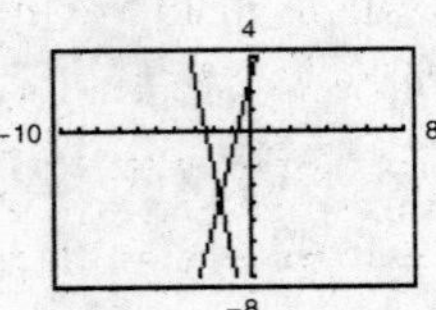

The lines intersect at

$\left(-\frac{5}{3}, -\frac{11}{3}\right) \approx (-1.667, -3.667)$

58. $\begin{cases} 7x + 3y = 16 \\ y = x + 1 \end{cases}$

$7x + 3(x + 1) = 16$

$10x = 13$

$x = \frac{13}{10}$

$y = \frac{13}{10} + 1 = \frac{23}{10}$

Answer: $\left(\frac{13}{10}, \frac{23}{10}\right)$

59. $\begin{cases} x - 5y = 21 \\ 6x + 5y = 21 \end{cases}$

Adding the equations, $7x = 42 \Rightarrow x = 6$.

Back-substituting, $x - 5y = 6 - 5y = 21 \Rightarrow$

$-5y = 15 \Rightarrow y = -3$

Answer: $(6, -3)$

60. $\begin{cases} y = -3x - 8 \\ y = 15 - 2x \end{cases}$

$-3x - 8 = 15 - 2x$

$-x = 23$

$x = -23 \Rightarrow y = -3(-23) - 8 = 61$

Answer: $(-23, 61)$

61. $\begin{cases} -2x + 8y = 19 & \text{Equation 1} \\ y = x - 3 & \text{Equation 2} \end{cases}$

Substitute into Equation 1,

$-2x + 8(x - 3) = 19 \Rightarrow 6x = 43$

$\Rightarrow x = \frac{43}{6}$

Back-substituting, $y = x - 3 = \frac{43}{6} - 3 = \frac{25}{6}$

Answer: $\left(\frac{43}{6}, \frac{25}{6}\right)$

62. $\begin{cases} 4x - 3y = 6 & \text{Equation 1} \\ -5x + 7y = -1 & \text{Equation 2} \end{cases}$

Multiply Equation 1 by 5 and Equation 2 by 4.

$20x - 15y = 30$

$-20x + 28y = -4$

Adding, $13y = 26 \Rightarrow y = 2$

Then, $4x - 3(2) = 6 \Rightarrow x = 3$

Answer: $(3, 2)$

63. There are infinitely many systems that have the solution (0, 8). One possible system is

$\begin{cases} x + y = 8 \\ -x + y = 8 \end{cases}$

64. There are infinitely many systems that have $(3, -4)$ as the solution. For example,

$\begin{cases} x + y = -1 \\ 2x - y = 10 \end{cases}$

65. There are infinitely many systems that have the solution $\left(3, \frac{5}{2}\right)$. One possible system:

$2(3) + 2\left(\frac{5}{2}\right) = 11 \Rightarrow 2x + 2y = 11$

$3 - 4\left(\frac{5}{2}\right) = -7 \Rightarrow x - 4y = -7$

66. There are infinitely many systems that have the solution $\left(-\frac{2}{3}, -10\right)$. One possible system:

$3\left(-\frac{2}{3}\right) + 1(-10) = -12 \Rightarrow 3x + y = -12$

$6\left(-\frac{2}{3}\right) - 1(-10) = 6 \Rightarrow 6x - y = 6$

67. Demand = Supply

$50 - 0.5x = 0.125x$

$50 = 0.625x$

$x = 80$ units

$p = \$10$

Answer: $(80, 10)$

68.

$$\text{Supply} = \text{Demand}$$
$$25 + 0.1x = 100 - 0.05x$$
$$0.15x = 75$$
$$x = 500$$
$$p = 75$$

Answer: (500, 75)

69.

$$\text{Demand} = \text{Supply}$$
$$140 - 0.00002x = 80 + 0.00001x$$
$$60 = 0.00003x$$
$$x = 2{,}000{,}000 \text{ units}$$
$$p = \$100.00$$

Answer: (2,000,000, 100)

70.

$$\text{Supply} = \text{Demand}$$
$$225 + 0.0005x = 400 - 0.0002x$$
$$0.0007x = 175$$
$$x = 250{,}000$$
$$p = 350$$

Answer: (250,000, 350)

71. Let $x =$ the ground speed and $y =$ the wind speed.

$$\begin{cases} 3.6(x - y) = 1800 & \text{Equation 1} \\ 3(x + y) = 1800 & \text{Equation 2} \end{cases}$$

$$\begin{aligned} x - y &= 500 \\ x + y &= 600 \\ \hline 2x \quad &= 1100 \\ x \quad &= 550 \end{aligned}$$

Substituting $x = 550$ in Equation 2:

$$550 + y = 600$$
$$y = 50$$

Answer: $x = 550$ mph, $y = 50$ mph

72. Let $x =$ the speed of the plane that leaves first and $y =$ the speed of the plane that leaves second.

$$\begin{cases} y - x = 80 & \text{Equation 1} \\ 2x + \frac{3}{2}y = 3200 & \text{Equation 2} \end{cases}$$

$$\begin{cases} -2x + 2y = 160 \\ 2x + \frac{3}{2}y = 3200 \end{cases}$$

$$\tfrac{7}{2}y = 3360$$
$$y = 960$$
$$960 - x = 80$$
$$x = 880$$

Answer: First plane: 880 kilometers per hour;
Second plane: 960 kilometers per hour

73. (a) $\begin{cases} A + C = 1175 & \text{Equation 1} \\ 5A + 3.5C = 5087.5 & \text{Equation 2} \end{cases}$

(b) Multiply Equation 1 by 5:

$$5A + 5C = 5875$$
$$5A + 3.5C = 5087.5$$

Subtracting eliminates A:

$$1.5C = 787.5$$
$$C = 525$$

Hence, $A = 1175 - 525 = 650$.

650 adult tickets and 525 child tickets

(c)

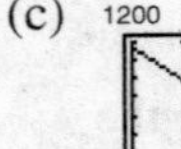

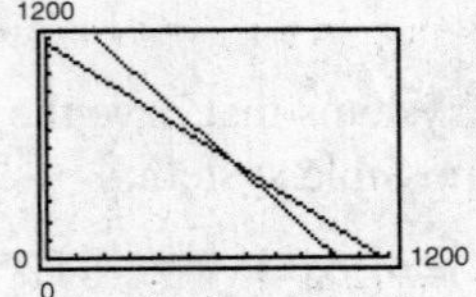

Let $C = y_1 = 1175 - x$

$$C = y_2 = \frac{1}{3.5}(5087.5 - 5x)$$

Point of intersection: $(A, C) = (650, 525)$

74. (a) $\begin{cases} 5C + 3S = 8.50 & \text{Equation 1} \\ 6C + 4S = 10.50 & \text{Equation 2} \end{cases}$

(b) Multiply Equation 1 by 4 and Equation 2 by 3:

$20C + 12S = 34$

$18C + 12S = 31.5$

Subtracting, $2C = 2.5 \Rightarrow C = 1.25$:

Hence, $S = (8.50 - 5C)/3 = 0.75$

$C = \$1.25, S = \$0.75$

(c) Let $C = y_1 = (8.5 - 3S)/5$

$C = y_2 = (10.5 - 4S)/6$

Point of intersection: $(C, S) = (1.25, 0.75)$

75. Let M = number of oranges and let R = number of grapefruit.

$\begin{cases} M + R = 16 & \text{Equation 1} \\ 0.95M + 1.05R = 15.90 & \text{Equation 2} \end{cases}$

Solving for R in Equation 1: $R = 16 - M$.

Substituting into Equation 2:

$0.95M + 1.05(16 - M) = 15.9$

$0.95M + 16.8 - 1.05M = 15.9$

$0.9 = 0.1M$

$M = 9$

Hence, $R = 16 - 9 = 7$.

9 oranges and 7 grapefruit

76. $S - 440.36t = -1023.0$ Family Dollar

$S - 691.48t = -2122.8$ Dollar General

(a) Using a graphing utility, the solution is $(S, T) \approx (905.59, 4.38)$.

(b) In 1994, both stores had sales of \$905.59 million.

77. Let m = number of movies and let v = number of videos.

$\begin{cases} m + v = 310 & \text{Equation 1} \\ 3m + 2.5v = 867.5 & \text{Equation 2} \end{cases}$

Solve for m in Equation 1: $m = 310 - v$.

Substitute for m Equation 2:

$3(310 - v) + 2.5v = 867.5$

$62.5 = 0.5v$

$v = 125$

$m = 310 - 125 = 185$

185 movies and 125 videos

78. Let x = number of pairs of \$75.50 shoes.

Let y = number of pairs of \$89.95 shoes.

$\begin{cases} x + y = 250 \\ 75.50x + 89.95y = 20{,}031 \end{cases}$

Solving for y in the first equation and substituting into the second equation gives:

$75.50x + 89.95[250 - x] = 20{,}031$

$2456.5 = 14.45x$

$x = 170$

$y = 250 - x = 80$

170 of \$75.50 shoes, 80 of \$89.95 shoes

79. $\begin{cases} 5b + 10a = 20.2 \Rightarrow & -10b - 20a = -40.4 \\ 10b + 30a = 50.1 \Rightarrow & 10b + 30a = 50.1 \end{cases}$

$10a = 9.7$

$a = 0.97$

$b = 2.10$

Least squares regression line: $y = 0.97x + 2.10$

80. $\begin{cases} 5b + 10a = 11.7 \Rightarrow & -10b - 20a = -23.4 \\ 10b + 30a = 25.6 \Rightarrow & 10b + 30a = 25.6 \end{cases}$

$$10a = 2.2$$

$$a = 0.22$$

$$5b + 10(0.22) = 11.7$$

$$b = 1.9$$

Least squares regression line: $y = 0.22x + 1.9$

81. $\begin{cases} 5b + 10a = 2.7 & \text{Equation 1} \\ 10b + 30a = -19.6 & \text{Equation 2} \end{cases}$

Multiply Equation 1 by -2:

$$-10b - 20a = -5.4$$

$$10b + 30a = -19.6$$

Adding,

$$10a = -25.0$$

$$a = -2.5$$

$$b = (2.7 + 10(2.5))/5 = 5.54$$

$y = -2.5x + 5.54$

82. $\begin{cases} 5b + 10a = -2.3 & \text{Equation 1} \\ 10b + 30a = -19.4 & \text{Equation 2} \end{cases}$

Multiply Equation 1 by -2: $\quad -10b - 20a = 4.6$

$$10b + 30a = -19.4$$

Adding, $\quad 10a = -14.8$

$$a = -1.48$$

$$b = (-2.3 + 10(1.48))/5 = 2.5$$

$y = -1.48x + 2.5$

83. (a) $\begin{cases} 4b + 7a = 174 \Rightarrow & 28b + 49a = 1218 \\ 7b + 13.5a = 322 \Rightarrow & -28b - 54a = -1288 \end{cases}$

Adding, $-5a = -70 \Rightarrow a = 14,\ b = 19.$

Thus, $y = 14x + 19$

(b) Using a graphing utility, you obtain $y = 14x + 19$.

(c) 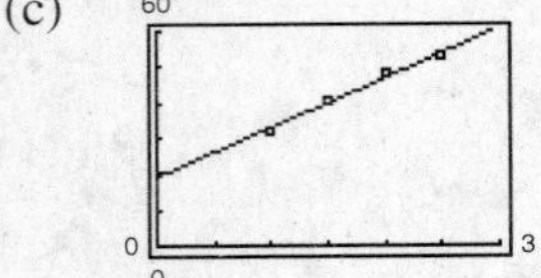

(d) If $x = 1.6$, (160 pounds/acre), $y = 14(1.6) + 19 = 41.4$ bushels per acre.

84. (a) $\begin{cases} 3.00b + 3.70a = 105 \\ 3.70b + 4.69a = 123.9 \end{cases}$

Solving this system, you obtain $a = -44.21$ and $b = 89.53$

$y = -44.21x + 89.53$

(b) $y = -44.21x + 89.53$

(c) 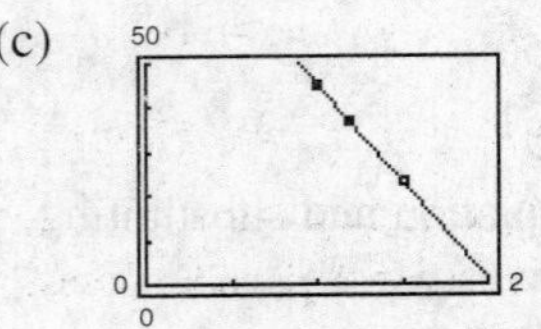

(d) For $x = 1.75$, $y \approx 12$

85. True. A consistent linear system has either one solution or an infinite number of solutions.

86. True

87. $\begin{cases} 100y - x = 200 & \text{Equation 1} \\ 99y - x = -198 & \text{Equation 2} \end{cases}$

Subtract Equation 2 from Equation 1 to eliminate x: $y = 398$

Substitute $y = 398$ into Equation 1: $100(398) - x = 200 \implies x = 39{,}600$

Answer: $(39{,}600, 398)$

The lines are not parallel. The scale on the axes must be changed to see the point of intersection.

88. $\begin{cases} 21x - 20y = 0 & \text{Equation 1} \\ 13x - 12y = 120 & \text{Equation 2} \end{cases}$

Multiply Equation 2 by $\left(-\frac{5}{3}\right)$: $-\frac{65}{3}x + 20y = -200$

Add this to Equation 1 to eliminate y: $-\frac{2}{3}x = -200 \implies x = 300$

Substitute $x = 300$ in Equation 1: $21(300) - 20y = 0 \implies y = 315$

Answer: $(300, 315)$

The lines are not parallel. The scale on the axes must be changed to see the point of intersection.

89. No, it is not possible for a consistent system of linear equations to have exactly two solutions. Either the lines will intersect once or they will coincide and then the system would have infinite solutions.

90. (a) $\begin{cases} x + y = 10 & \text{Equation 1} \\ x + y = 20 & \text{Equation 2} \end{cases}$

Subtract Equation 2 from Equation 1: $0 = -10$

System is inconsistent $\implies$ no solution

(b) $\begin{cases} x + y = 3 & \text{Equation 1} \\ 2x + 2y = 6 & \text{Equation 2} \end{cases}$

Multiply Equation 1 by (-2): $-2x - 2y = -6$

Add this to Equation 2: $0 = 0$ (dependent)

The system has an infinite number of solutions.

91. $\begin{cases} 4x - 8y = -3 & \text{Equation 1} \\ 2x + ky = 16 & \text{Equation 2} \end{cases}$

Multiply Equation 2 by -2: $-4x - 2ky = -32$

Add this to Equation 1: $-8y - 2ky = -35$

The system is inconsistent if $-8y - 2ky = 0$.

This occurs when $k = -4$. Note that for $k = -4$, the two original equations represent parallel lines.

92. $\begin{cases} 15x + 3y = 6 & \text{Equation 1} \\ -10x + ky = 9 & \text{Equation 2} \end{cases}$

Multiply Equation 1 by $\frac{2}{3}$: $10x + 2y = 4$

Add this to Equation 2: $ky + 2y = 13$

$(k + 2)y = 13$

The system is inconsistent if $k = -2$.

93. $u \sin x + v \cos x = 0$

$u \cos x - v \sin x = \sec x$

Multiply the first equation by $\sin x$, the second by $\cos x$, and add the equations:

$$u \sin^2 x + u \cos^2 x = \sec x \cdot \cos x$$
$$u = 1$$

Hence, $v \cos x = -u \sin x = -\sin x$

$$v = -\tan x.$$

94. $u \cos 2x + v \sin 2x = 0$

$u(-2 \sin 2x) + v(2 \cos 2x) = \csc 2x$

Multiply the first equation by $2 \sin 2x$, the second by $\cos 2x$, and add the equations:

$$2v \sin^2 2x + 2v \cos^2 2x = \csc 2x \cdot \cos 2x$$
$$2v = \cot 2x$$
$$v = \frac{1}{2} \cot 2x$$

Hence, $u \cos 2x + \frac{1}{2} \cot 2x \cdot \sin 2x = 0$

$$u = -\frac{1}{2}.$$

95. $-11 - 6x \geq 33$

$-6x \geq 44$

$x \leq -\frac{44}{6} = -\frac{22}{3}$

96. $-6 \leq 3x - 10 < 6$

$4 \leq 3x < 16$

$\frac{4}{3} \leq x < \frac{16}{3}$

97. $|x - 8| < 10$

$-10 < x - 8 < 10$

$-2 < x < 18$

98. $|x + 10| \geq -3$ is true for all x, since $|x + 10| \geq 0$.

99. $2x^2 + 3x - 35 < 0$

$(2x - 7)(x + 5) < 0$

Critical numbers: $\frac{7}{2}, -5$.
Testing the three intervals, $-5 < x < \frac{7}{2}$.

100. $3x^2 + 12x > 0$

$3x(x + 4) > 0$

Critical numbers: $0, -4$.
Checking the three intervals, you obtain $x < -4$ and $x > 0$.

101. $\ln x + \ln 6 = \ln 6x$

102. $\ln x - 5\ln(x + 3) = \ln x - \ln(x + 3)^5$

$= \ln \frac{x}{(x + 3)^5}$

103. $\log_9 12 - \log_9 x = \log_9 \frac{12}{x}$

104. $\frac{1}{4}\log_6 3 + \frac{1}{4}\log_6 x = \frac{1}{4}\log_6(3x)$

$= \log_6(3x)^{1/4}$

105. $2\ln x - \ln(x + 2) = \ln x^2 - \ln(x + 2)$

$= \ln\left[\frac{x^2}{x + 2}\right]$

106. $\frac{1}{2}\ln(x^2 + 4) - \ln x = \ln(x^2 + 4)^{1/2} - \ln x$

$= \ln\left(\frac{\sqrt{x^2 + 4}}{x}\right)$

107. Answers will vary.

Section 7.3 Multivariable Linear Systems

- You should know the operations that lead to equivalent systems of linear equations:
  - (a) Interchange any two equations.
  - (b) Multiply all terms of an equation by a nonzero constant.
  - (c) Replace an equation by the sum of itself and a constant multiple of any other equation in the system.
- You should be able to use the method of elimination.

Vocabulary Check

1. row-echelon
2. ordered triple
3. Gaussian
4. independent, dependent
5. nonsquare
6. three-dimensional
7. partial fraction decomposition

1. (a) $3(3) - 5 + (-3) \stackrel{?}{=} 1$ Yes

$2(3) - 3(-3) \stackrel{?}{=} -14$ No

$5(5) + 2(-3) \stackrel{?}{=} 8$ No

No, $(3, 5, -3)$ is not a solution.

(b) $3(-1) - (0) + 4 \stackrel{?}{=} 1$ Yes

$2(-1) - 3(4) \stackrel{?}{=} -14$ Yes

$5(0) + 2(4) \stackrel{?}{=} 8$ Yes

Yes, $(-1, 0, 4)$ is a solution.

(c) $3(-4) - 1 + 2 \stackrel{?}{=} 1$ No

$2(-4) - 3(2) \stackrel{?}{=} -14$ Yes

$5(1) + 2(2) \stackrel{?}{=} 8$ No

No, $(-4, 1, 2)$ is not a solution.

(d) $3(1) - 0 + 4 \stackrel{?}{=} 1$ No

$2(1) - 3(4) \stackrel{?}{=} -14$ No

$5(0) + 2(4) \stackrel{?}{=} 8$ Yes

No, $(1, 0, 4)$ is not a solution.

2. (a) $3(1) + 4(5) - 6 \stackrel{?}{=} 17$ Yes

$5(1) - 5 + 2(6) \stackrel{?}{=} -2$ No

$2(1) - 3(5) + 7(6) \stackrel{?}{=} -21$ No

No, $(1, 5, 6)$ is not a solution.

(b) $3(-2) + 4(-4) - 2 \stackrel{?}{=} 17$ No

$5(-2) - (-4) + 2(2) \stackrel{?}{=} -2$ Yes

$2(-2) - 3(-4) + 7(2) \stackrel{?}{=} -21$ No

No, $(-2, -4, 2)$ is not a solution.

(c) $3(1) + 4(3) - (-2) \stackrel{?}{=} 17$ Yes

$5(1) - 3 + 2(-2) \stackrel{?}{=} -2$ Yes

$2(1) - 3(3) + 7(-2) \stackrel{?}{=} -21$ Yes

Yes, $(1, 3, -2)$ is a solution.

(d) $3(0) + 4(7) - 0 \stackrel{?}{=} 17$ No

$5(0) - 7 + 2(0) \stackrel{?}{=} -2$ No

$2(0) - 3(7) + 7(0) \stackrel{?}{=} -21$ Yes

No, $(0, 7, 0)$ is not a solution.

3. (a) $4(0) + 1 - 1 \stackrel{?}{=} 0$ Yes

$-8(0) - 6(1) + 1 \stackrel{?}{=} -\frac{7}{4}$ No

$3(0) - 1 \stackrel{?}{=} -\frac{9}{4}$ No

No, $(0, 1, 1)$ is not a solution.

(b) $4\left(-\frac{3}{2}\right) + \frac{5}{4} - \left(-\frac{5}{4}\right) \stackrel{?}{=} 0$ No

$-8\left(-\frac{3}{2}\right) - 6\left(\frac{5}{4}\right) + \left(-\frac{5}{4}\right) \stackrel{?}{=} -\frac{7}{4}$ No

$3\left(-\frac{3}{2}\right) - \left(\frac{5}{4}\right) \stackrel{?}{=} -\frac{9}{4}$ No

No, $\left(-\frac{3}{2}, \frac{5}{4}, -\frac{5}{4}\right)$ is not a solution.

(c) $4\left(-\frac{1}{2}\right) + \frac{3}{4} - \left(-\frac{5}{4}\right) \stackrel{?}{=} 0$ Yes

$-8\left(-\frac{1}{2}\right) - 6\left(\frac{3}{4}\right) - \frac{5}{4} \stackrel{?}{=} -\frac{7}{4}$ Yes

$3\left(-\frac{1}{2}\right) - \frac{3}{4} \stackrel{?}{=} -\frac{9}{4}$ Yes

Yes, $\left(-\frac{1}{2}, \frac{3}{4}, -\frac{5}{4}\right)$ is a solution.

(d) $4\left(-\frac{1}{2}\right) + 2 - 0 \stackrel{?}{=} 0$ Yes

$-8\left(-\frac{1}{2}\right) - 6(2) + 0 \stackrel{?}{=} -\frac{7}{2}$ No

$3\left(-\frac{1}{2}\right) - 2 \stackrel{?}{=} -\frac{9}{4}$ No

No, $\left(-\frac{1}{2}, 2, 0\right)$ is not a solution.

4. (a) $-4(-2) - (-2) - 8(2) \stackrel{?}{=} -6$ Yes

$-2 + 2 \stackrel{?}{=} 0$ Yes

$4(-2) - 7(-2) \stackrel{?}{=} 6$ Yes

$(-2, -2, 2)$ is a solution.

(b) $-4\left(-\frac{33}{2}\right) - (-10) - 8(10) \stackrel{?}{=} -6$ No

$-10 + 10 \stackrel{?}{=} 0$ Yes

$4\left(-\frac{33}{2}\right) - 7(-10) \stackrel{?}{=} 6$ No

$\left(-\frac{33}{2}, -10, 10\right)$ is not a solution.

(c) $-4\left(\frac{1}{8}\right) - \left(-\frac{1}{2}\right) - 8\left(\frac{1}{2}\right) \stackrel{?}{=} -6$ No

$-\frac{1}{2} + \frac{1}{2} \stackrel{?}{=} 0$ Yes

$4\left(\frac{1}{8}\right) - 7\left(-\frac{1}{2}\right) \stackrel{?}{=} 6$ No

$\left(\frac{1}{8}, -\frac{1}{2}, \frac{1}{2}\right)$ is not a solution.

(d) $-4\left(-\frac{11}{2}\right) - (-4) - 8(4) \stackrel{?}{=} -6$ Yes

$-4 + 4 \stackrel{?}{=} 0$ Yes

$4\left(-\frac{11}{2}\right) - 7(-4) \stackrel{?}{=} 6$ Yes

$\left(-\frac{11}{2}, -4, 4\right)$ is a solution.

5. $\begin{cases} 2x - y + 5z = 16 & \text{Equation 1} \\ y + 2z = 2 & \text{Equation 2} \\ z = 2 & \text{Equation 3} \end{cases}$

Back-substitute $z = 2$ into Equation 2:

$y + 2(2) = 2$

$y = -2$

Back-substitute $z = 2$ and $y = -2$ into Equation 1:

$2x - (-2) + 5(2) = 16$

$2x = 4$

$x = 2$

Answer: $(2, -2, 2)$

6. $\begin{cases} 4x - 3y - 2z = -17 & \text{Equation 1} \\ 6y - 5z = -12 & \text{Equation 2} \\ z = -2 & \text{Equation 3} \end{cases}$

Back-substitute $z = -2$ into Equation 2:

$6y - 5(-2) = -12$

$6y = -22$

$y = -11/3$

Back-substitute $z = -2$ and $y = -11/3$ into Equation 1:

$4x - 3(-11/3) - 2(-2) = -17$

$4x = -32$

$x = -8$

Answer: $(-8, -11/3, -2)$

7. $\begin{cases} 2x + y - 3z = 10 & \text{Equation 1} \\ y + z = 12 & \text{Equation 2} \\ z = 2 & \text{Equation 3} \end{cases}$

Back-substitute $z = 2$ into Equation 2:

$y + 2 = 12$

$y = 10$

Back-substitute $y = 10$ and $z = 2$ into Equation 1:

$2x + 10 - 3(2) = 10$

$2x = 6$

$x = 3$

Answer: $(3, 10, 2)$

8. $\begin{cases} x - y + 2z = 22 \\ 3y - 8z = -9 \\ z = -3 \end{cases}$

$z = -3$

$3y = 8(-3) - 9 = -33 \Rightarrow y = -11$

$x = -11 - 2(-3) + 22 = 17$

Answer: $(17, -11, -3)$

9. $\begin{cases} 4x - 2y + z = 8 & \text{Equation 1} \\ -y + z = 4 & \text{Equation 2} \\ z = 2 & \text{Equation 3} \end{cases}$

Back-substitute $z = 2$ into Equation 2:

$$-y + 2 = 4$$
$$y = -2$$

Back-substitute $y = -2$ and $z = 2$ into Equation 1:

$$4x - 2(-2) + 2 = 8$$
$$4x = 2$$
$$x = \tfrac{1}{2}$$

Answer: $\left(\tfrac{1}{2}, -2, 2\right)$

10. $\begin{cases} 5x \quad - 8z = 22 \\ 3y - 5z = 10 \\ z = -4 \end{cases}$

Back-substitute $z = -4$ in Equation 2:

$3y - 5(-4) = 10 \Rightarrow y = -\tfrac{10}{3}$

Back-substitute $z = -4$ in Equation 1:

$5x - 8(-4) = 22 \Rightarrow x = -2$

Answer: $\left(-2, -\tfrac{10}{3}, -4\right)$

11. $\begin{cases} x - 2y + 3z = 5 & \text{Equation 1} \\ -x + 3y - 5z = 4 & \text{Equation 2} \\ 2x \quad - 3z = 0 & \text{Equation 3} \end{cases}$

Add Equation 1 to Equation 2.

$y - 2z = 9$ New Equation 2

This is the first step in putting the system in row-echelon form.

$$\begin{cases} x - 2y + 3z = 5 \\ y - 2z = 9 \\ 2x \quad - 3z = 0 \end{cases}$$

12. $\begin{cases} x - 2y + 3z = 5 \\ -x + 3y - 5z = 4 \\ 2x \quad - 3z = 0 \end{cases}$

Add -2 times Equation 1 to Equation 3.

$4y - 9z = -10$

This is a step in putting the system in row-echelon form.

13. $\begin{cases} x - 2y + z = 1 & \text{Equation 1} \\ 2x - y + 3z = 0 & \text{Equation 2} \\ 3x - y - 4z = 1 & \text{Equation 3} \end{cases}$

Add -2 times Equation 1 to Equation 2.

$3y + z = -2$ New Equation 2

This is the first step in putting the system in row-echelon form.

14. $\begin{cases} x + 2y - 4z = 2 & \text{Equation 1} \\ -x + 4y - z = -2 & \text{Equation 2} \\ 3x - 4y + z = 1 & \text{Equation 3} \end{cases}$

Add -3 times Equation 1 to Equation 3.

$-10y + 13z = -5$ New Equation 3

This eliminates the term $3x$ in Equation 3.

15. $\begin{cases} x + y + z = 6 & \text{Equation 1} \\ 2x - y + z = 3 & \text{Equation 2} \\ 3x \quad - z = 0 & \text{Equation 3} \end{cases}$

$$\begin{cases} x + y + z = 6 & \\ -3y - z = -9 & (-2)\text{ Eq. } 1 + \text{Eq. } 2 \\ -3y - 4z = -18 & (-3)\text{ Eq. } 1 + \text{Eq. } 3 \end{cases}$$

$$\begin{cases} x + y + z = 6 & \\ -3y - z = -9 & \\ -3z = -9 & (-1)\text{ Eq. } 2 + \text{Eq. } 3 \end{cases}$$

$-3z = -9 \Rightarrow z = 3$

$-3y - 3 = -9 \Rightarrow y = 2$

$x + 2 + 3 = 6 \Rightarrow x = 1$

Answer: $(1, 2, 3)$

16. $\begin{cases} x + y + z = 2 \\ -x + 3y + 2z = 8 \\ 4x + y = 4 \end{cases}$ Equation 1, Equation 2, Equation 3

$\begin{cases} x + y + z = 2 \\ 4y + 3z = 10 \\ -3y - 4z = -4 \end{cases}$ Eq. 1 + Eq. 2; -4 Eq. 1 + Eq. 3

$\begin{cases} x + y + z = 2 \\ 12y + 9z = 30 \\ -12y - 16z = -16 \end{cases}$ 3 Eq. 2; 4 Eq. 3

$\begin{cases} x + y + z = 2 \\ 12y + 9z = 30 \\ -7z = 14 \end{cases}$ Eq. 2 + Eq. 3

$-7z = 14 \Rightarrow z = -2$

$12y + 9(-2) = 30 \Rightarrow y = 4$

$x + 4 - 2 = 2 \Rightarrow x = 0$

Answer: $(0, 4, -2)$

17. $\begin{cases} 2x + 2z = 2 \\ 5x + 3y = 4 \\ 3y - 4z = 4 \end{cases}$ Equation 1, Equation 2, Equation 3

$\begin{cases} x + z = 1 \\ 5x + 3y = 4 \\ 3y - 4z = 4 \end{cases}$ $(\frac{1}{2})$ Eq. 1

$\begin{cases} x + z = 1 \\ 3y - 5z = -1 \\ 3y - 4z = 4 \end{cases}$ (-5) Eq. 1 + Eq. 2

$\begin{cases} x + z = 1 \\ 3y - 5z = -1 \\ z = 5 \end{cases}$ (-1) Eq. 2 + Eq. 3

$3y - 5(5) = -1 \Rightarrow y = 8$

$x + 5 = 1 \Rightarrow x = -4$

Answer: $(-4, 8, 5)$

18. $\begin{cases} 6y + 4z = -18 \\ 3x + 3y = 9 \\ 2x - 3z = 12 \end{cases}$ Equation 1, Equation 2, Equation 3

$\begin{cases} 3x + 3y = 9 \\ 6y + 4z = -18 \\ 2x - 3z = 12 \end{cases}$ Interchange equations 1 and 2.

$\begin{cases} x + y = 3 \\ 6y + 4z = -18 \\ 2x - 3z = 12 \end{cases}$ $\frac{1}{3}$ (New Eq. 1)

$\begin{cases} x + y = 3 \\ 6y + 4z = -18 \\ -2y - 3z = 6 \end{cases}$ (-2) Eq. 1 + Eq. 3

$\begin{cases} x + y = 3 \\ -2y - 3z = 6 \\ 6y + 4z = -18 \end{cases}$ Interchange the equations.

$\begin{cases} x + y = 3 \\ -2y - 3z = 6 \\ -5z = 0 \end{cases}$ 3 Eq. 2 + Eq. 3

$-5z = 0 \Rightarrow z = 0$

$-2y - 3(0) = 6 \Rightarrow y = -3$

$x + (-3) = 3 \Rightarrow x = 6$

Answer: $(6, -3, 0)$

19. $\begin{cases} 4x + y - 3z = 11 \\ 2x - 3y + 2z = 9 \\ x + y + z = -3 \end{cases}$ Equation 1, Equation 2, Equation 3

$\begin{cases} x + y + z = -3 \\ 2x - 3y + 2z = 9 \\ 4x + y - 3z = 11 \end{cases}$ Interchange equations 1 and 3

$\begin{cases} x + y + z = -3 \\ -5y = 15 \\ -3y - 7z = 23 \end{cases}$ (-2) Eq. 1 + Eq. 2; (-4) Eq. 1 + Eq. 3

$y = -3 \Rightarrow -3(-3) - 7z = 23$

$\Rightarrow -7z = 14$

$\Rightarrow z = -2$

$x + (-3) + (-2) = -3 \Rightarrow x = 2$

Answer: $(2, -3, -2)$

20. $$\begin{cases} 2x + 4y + z = -4 & \text{Equation 1} \\ 2x - 4y + 6z = 13 & \text{Equation 2} \\ 4x - 2y + z = 6 & \text{Equation 3} \end{cases}$$

$$\begin{cases} 2x + 4y + z = -4 & \\ -8y + 5z = 17 & -\text{Eq. 1} + \text{Eq. 2} \\ -10y - z = 14 & -2\ \text{Eq.} + \text{Eq. 3} \end{cases}$$

$$\begin{cases} 2x + 4y + z = -4 & \\ -40y + 25z = 85 & 5\ \text{Eq. 2} \\ -40y - 4z = 56 & 4\ \text{Eq. 3} \end{cases}$$

$$\begin{cases} 2x + 4y + z = -4 & \\ -40y + 25z = 85 & \\ -29z = -29 & -\text{Eq. 2} + \text{Eq. 3} \end{cases}$$

$-29z = -29 \Rightarrow z = 1$

$-40y + 25(1) = 85 \Rightarrow y = -\frac{3}{2}$

$2x + 4\left(-\frac{3}{2}\right) + 1 = -4 \Rightarrow x = \frac{1}{2}$

Answer: $\left(\frac{1}{2}, -\frac{3}{2}, 1\right)$

21. $$\begin{cases} x + y - 2z = 3 & \text{Interchange} \\ 3x - 2y + 4z = 1 & \text{the equations.} \\ 2x - 3y + 6z = 8 & \end{cases}$$

$$\begin{cases} x + y - 2z = 3 & \\ -5y + 10z = -8 & -3\ \text{Eq. 1} + \text{Eq. 2} \\ -5y + 10z = 2 & -2\ \text{Eq. 1} + \text{Eq. 3} \end{cases}$$

$$\begin{cases} x + y - 2z = 3 & \\ -5y + 10z = -8 & \\ 0 = 10 & -\text{Eq. 2} + \text{Eq. 3} \end{cases}$$

Inconsistent; no solution.

22. $$\begin{cases} 5x - 3y + 2z = 3 & \text{Equation 1} \\ 2x + 4y - z = 7 & \text{Equation 2} \\ x - 11y + 4z = 3 & \text{Equation 3} \end{cases}$$

$$\begin{cases} x - 11y + 4z = 3 & \text{Interchange rows} \\ 5x - 3y + 2z = 3 & \\ 2x + 4y - z = 7 & \end{cases}$$

$$\begin{cases} x - 11y + 4z = 3 & \\ 52y - 18z = -12 & -5\ \text{Eq. 1} + \text{Eq. 2} \\ 26y - 9z = 1 & -2\ \text{Eq. 1} + \text{Eq. 3} \end{cases}$$

$$\begin{cases} x - 11y + 4z = 3 & \\ 52y - 18z = -12 & \\ 0 = 7 & -\frac{1}{2}\ \text{Eq. 2} + \text{Eq. 3} \end{cases}$$

Inconsistent; no solution.

23. $$\begin{cases} 3x + 3y + 5z = 1 \\ 3x + 5y + 9z = 0 \\ 5x + 9y + 17z = 0 \end{cases}$$

$$\begin{cases} 6x + 6y + 10z = 2 & 2\ \text{Eq. 1} \\ 3x + 5y + 9z = 0 & \\ 5x + 9y + 17z = 0 & \end{cases}$$

$$\begin{cases} x - 3y - 7z = 2 & -\text{Eq. 3} + \text{Eq. 1} \\ 3x + 5y + 9z = 0 & \\ 5x + 9y + 17z = 0 & \end{cases}$$

$$\begin{cases} x - 3y - 7z = 2 & \\ 14y + 30z = -6 & -3\ \text{Eq. 1} + \text{Eq. 2} \\ 24y + 52z = -10 & -5\ \text{Eq. 1} + \text{Eq. 3} \end{cases}$$

$$\begin{cases} x - 3y - 7z = 2 & \\ 84y + 180z = -36 & 6\ \text{Eq. 2} \\ 84y + 182z = -35 & 3.5\ \text{Eq. 3} \end{cases}$$

$$\begin{cases} x - 3y - 7z = 2 & \\ 84y + 180z = -36 & \\ 2z = 1 & -\text{Eq. 2} + \text{Eq. 3} \end{cases}$$

$2z = 1 \Rightarrow z = \frac{1}{2}$

$84y + 180\left(\frac{1}{2}\right) = -36 \Rightarrow y = -\frac{3}{2}$

$x - 3\left(-\frac{3}{2}\right) - 7\left(\frac{1}{2}\right) = 2 \Rightarrow x = 1$

Answer: $\left(1, -\frac{3}{2}, \frac{1}{2}\right)$

24. $\begin{cases} 2x + y + 3z = 1 & \text{Equation 1} \\ 2x + 6y + 8z = 3 & \text{Equation 2} \\ 6x + 8y + 18z = 5 & \text{Equation 3} \end{cases}$

$\begin{cases} 2x + y + 3z = 1 & \\ 5y + 5z = 2 & -\text{Eq. 1} + \text{Eq. 2} \\ 5y + 9z = 2 & -3\text{ Eq. 1} + \text{Eq. 3} \end{cases}$

$\begin{cases} 2x + y + 3z = 1 & \\ 5y + 5z = 2 & \\ 4z = 0 & -\text{Eq. 2} + \text{Eq. 3} \end{cases}$

$4z = 0 \Rightarrow z = 0$

$5y + 5(0) = 2 \Rightarrow y = \frac{2}{5}$

$2x + \frac{2}{5} + 3(0) = 1 \Rightarrow x = \frac{3}{10}$

Answer: $\left(\frac{3}{10}, \frac{2}{5}, 0\right)$

25. $\begin{cases} x + 2y - 7z = -4 & \text{Equation 1} \\ 2x + y + z = 13 & \text{Equation 2} \\ 3x + 9y - 36z = -33 & \text{Equation 3} \end{cases}$

$\begin{cases} x + 2y - 7z = -4 & \\ -3y + 15z = 21 & -2\text{ Eq. 1} + \text{Eq. 2} \\ 3y - 15z = -21 & -3\text{ Eq. 1} + \text{Eq. 3} \end{cases}$

$\begin{cases} x + 2y - 7z = -4 & \\ -3y + 15z = 21 & \\ 0 = 0 & \text{Eq. 2} + \text{Eq. 3} \end{cases}$

$\begin{cases} x + 2y - 7z = -4 & \\ y - 5z = -7 & -\frac{1}{3}\text{ Eq. 2} \end{cases}$

$\begin{cases} x + 3z = 10 & -2\text{ Eq. 2} + \text{Eq. 1} \\ y - 5z = -7 & \end{cases}$

Let $z = a$, then:

$y = 5a - 7$

$x = -3a + 10$

Answer: $(-3a + 10, 5a - 7, a)$

26. $\begin{cases} 2x + y - 3z = 4 & \text{Equation 1} \\ 4x + 2z = 10 & \text{Equation 2} \\ -2x + 3y - 13z = -8 & \text{Equation 3} \end{cases}$

$\begin{cases} 2x + y - 3z = 4 & \\ -2y + 8z = 2 & -2\text{ Eq. 1} + \text{Eq. 2} \\ 4y - 16z = -4 & \text{Eq. 1} + \text{Eq. 3} \end{cases}$

$\begin{cases} 2x + y - 3z = 4 & \\ y - 4z = -1 & -\frac{1}{2}\text{ Eq. 2} \\ 0 = 0 & 2\text{ Eq. 2} + \text{Eq. 3} \end{cases}$

$\begin{cases} 2x + z = 5 & -\text{Eq. 2} + \text{Eq. 1} \\ y - 4z = -1 & \end{cases}$

$z = a$

$y = 4a - 1$

$x = -\frac{1}{2}a + \frac{5}{2}$

Answer: $\left(-\frac{1}{2}a + \frac{5}{2}, 4a - 1, a\right)$

27. $\begin{cases} x - y + 2z = 6 & \text{Equation 1} \\ 2x + y + z = 3 & \text{Equation 2} \\ x + y + z = 2 & \text{Equation 3} \end{cases}$

$\begin{cases} x - y + 2z = 6 & \\ 3y - 3z = -9 & (-2)\text{ Eq. 1} + \text{Eq. 2} \\ 2y - z = -4 & (-1)\text{ Eq. 1} + \text{Eq. 3} \end{cases}$

$\begin{cases} x - y + 2z = 6 & \\ y - z = -3 & \left(\frac{1}{3}\right)\text{ Eq. 2} \\ 2y - z = -4 & \end{cases}$

$\begin{cases} x - y + 2z = 6 & \\ y - z = -3 & \\ z = 2 & (-2)\text{ Eq. 2} + \text{Eq. 3} \end{cases}$

$y - z = -3 \Rightarrow y = 2 - 3 = -1$

$x - y + 2z = 6 \Rightarrow x = 6 + (-1) - 2(2) = 1$

Answer: $(1, -1, 2)$

28. $\begin{cases} x + y - z = 3 & \text{Equation 1} \\ 2x - y - z = 1 & \text{Equation 2} \\ x + y - 2z = 5 & \text{Equation 3} \end{cases}$

$\begin{cases} x + y - z = 3 & \\ -3y + z = -5 & (-2)\text{ Eq. 1} + \text{Eq. 2} \\ -z = 2 & (-1)\text{ Eq. 1} + \text{Eq. 3} \end{cases}$

$z = -2$

$-3y + z = -5 \Rightarrow -3y = 2 - 5 = -3 \Rightarrow y = 1$

$x + y - z = 3 \Rightarrow x = 3 - 1 - 2 = 0$

Answer: $(0, 1, -2)$

29. $\begin{cases} 3x - 3y + 6z = 6 & \text{Equation 1} \\ x + 2y - z = 5 & \text{Equation 2} \\ 5x - 8y + 13z = 7 & \text{Equation 3} \end{cases}$

$\begin{cases} x - y + 2z = 2 & \left(\frac{1}{3}\right) \text{Equation 1} \\ x + 2y - z = 5 \\ 5x - 8y + 13z = 7 \end{cases}$

$\begin{cases} x - y + 2z = 2 \\ 3y - 3z = 3 & (-1)\text{ Eq. 1 + Eq. 2} \\ -3y + 3z = -3 & (-5)\text{ Eq. 1 + Eq. 3} \end{cases}$

$\begin{cases} x - y + 2z = 2 \\ y - z = 1 \\ 0 = 0 \end{cases}$

$\begin{cases} x + z = 3 \\ y - z = 1 \end{cases}$

Let $z = a$, then:

$y = a + 1$

$x = -a + 3$

Answer: $(-a + 3, a + 1, a)$

30. $\begin{cases} x + 4z = 13 & \text{Equation 1} \\ 4x - 2y + z = 7 & \text{Equation 2} \\ 2x - 2y - 7z = -19 & \text{Equation 3} \end{cases}$

$\begin{cases} x + 4z = 13 \\ -2y - 15z = -45 & -4\text{ Eq. 1 + Eq. 2} \\ -2y - 15z = -45 & -2\text{ Eq. 1 + Eq. 3} \end{cases}$

$\begin{cases} x + 4z = 13 \\ -2y - 15z = -45 \\ 0 = 0 & -\text{Eq. 2 + Eq. 3} \end{cases}$

$z = a$

$y = -\frac{15}{2}a + \frac{45}{2}$

$x = -4a + 13$

Answer: $\left(-4a + 13, -\frac{15}{2}a + \frac{45}{2}, a\right)$

31. $\begin{cases} x - 2y + 3z = 4 & \text{Equation 1} \\ 3x - y + 2z = 0 & \text{Equation 2} \\ x + 3y - 4z = -2 & \text{Equation 3} \end{cases}$

$\begin{cases} x - 2y + 3z = 4 \\ 5y - 7z = -12 & -3\text{ Eq. 1 + Eq. 2} \\ 5y - 7z = -6 & -1\text{ Eq. 1 + Eq. 3} \end{cases}$

$\begin{cases} x - 2y + 3z = 4 \\ 5y - 7z = -12 \\ 0 = 6 & -\text{Eq. 2 + Eq. 3} \end{cases}$

No solution; inconsistent.

32. $\begin{cases} -x + 3y + z = 4 & \text{Equation 1} \\ 4x - 2y - 5z = -7 & \text{Equation 2} \\ 2x + 4y - 3z = 12 & \text{Equation 3} \end{cases}$

$\begin{cases} -x + 3y + z = 4 \\ 10y - z = 9 & 4\text{ Eq. 1 + Eq. 2} \\ 10y - z = 20 & 2\text{ Eq. 1 + Eq. 3} \end{cases}$

$\begin{cases} -x + 3y + z = 4 \\ 10y - z = 9 \\ 0 = 11 & -\text{Eq. 2 + Eq. 3} \end{cases}$

No solution; inconsistent.

33. $\begin{cases} x + 4z = 1 \\ x + y + 10z = 10 \\ 2x - y + 2z = -5 \end{cases}$

$\begin{cases} x + 4z = 1 \\ y + 6z = 9 & -\text{Eq. 1 + Eq. 2} \\ -y - 6z = -7 & -2\text{ Eq. + Eq. 3} \end{cases}$

$\begin{cases} x + 4z = 1 \\ y + 6z = 9 \\ 0 = 2 & \text{Eq. 2 + Eq. 3} \end{cases}$

No solution; inconsistent.

34. $\begin{cases} 3x - 2y - 6z = -4 & \text{Equation 1} \\ -3x + 2y + 6z = 1 & \text{Equation 2} \\ x - y - 5z = -3 & \text{Equation 3} \end{cases}$

$\begin{cases} x - y - 5z = -3 & \text{Interchange the} \\ 3x - 2y - 6z = -4 & \text{equations} \\ -3x + 2y + 6z = 1 \end{cases}$

$\begin{cases} x - y - 5z = -3 \\ y + 9z = 5 & -3\text{ Eq. 1 + Eq. 2} \\ -y - 9z = -8 & 3\text{ Eq. 1 + Eq. 3} \end{cases}$

$\begin{cases} x - y - 5z = -3 \\ y + 9z = 5 \\ 0 = -3 & \text{Eq. 2 + Eq. 3} \end{cases}$

No solution; inconsistent.

35. $\begin{cases} x + 2y + z = 1 \\ x - 2y + 3z = -3 \\ 2x + y + z = -1 \end{cases}$ Equation 1, Equation 2, Equation 3

$\begin{cases} x + 2y + z = 1 \\ -4y + 2z = -4 \\ -3y - z = -3 \end{cases}$ (-1) Eq. 1 + Eq. 2; (-2) Eq. 1 + Eq. 3

$\begin{cases} x + 2y + z = 1 \\ y - \frac{1}{2}z = 1 \\ 3y + z = 3 \end{cases}$ $\left(-\frac{1}{4}\right)$ Eq. 2; (-1) Eq. 3

$\begin{cases} x + 2y + z = 1 \\ y - \frac{1}{2}z = 1 \\ \frac{5}{2}z = 0 \end{cases}$ (-3) Eq. 2 + Eq. 3

$z = 0$

$y = 1 - 0 = 1$

$x + 2y + z = 1 \Rightarrow x = 1 - 2 = -1$

Answer: $(-1, 1, 0)$

36. $\begin{cases} x - 2y + z = 2 \\ 2x + 2y - 3z = -4 \\ 5x + z = 1 \end{cases}$ Equation 1, Equation 2, Equation 3

$\begin{cases} x - 2y + z = 2 \\ 6y - 5z = -8 \\ 10y - 4z = -9 \end{cases}$ (-2) Eq. 1 + Eq. 2; (-5) Eq. 1 + Eq. 3

$\begin{cases} x - 2y + z = 2 \\ 6y - 5z = -8 \\ \frac{13}{3}z = \frac{13}{3} \end{cases}$ $\left(-\frac{5}{3}\right)$ Eq. 2 + Eq. 3

$z = 1$

$6y - 5z = -8 \Rightarrow 6y = -8 + 5 = -3 \Rightarrow y = -\frac{1}{2}$

$x - 2y + z = 2 \Rightarrow x = 2 + 2\left(-\frac{1}{2}\right) - 1 = 0$

Answer: $\left(0, -\frac{1}{2}, 1\right)$

37. $\begin{cases} x - 2y + 5z = 2 \\ 4x - z = 0 \end{cases}$

$\begin{cases} x - 2y + 5z = 2 \\ 8y - 21z = -8 \end{cases}$ -4 Eq. 1 + Eq. 2

$\begin{cases} x - 2y + 5z = 2 \\ y - \frac{21}{8}z = -1 \end{cases}$ $\frac{1}{8}$ Eq. 2

$\begin{cases} x - \frac{1}{4}z = 0 \\ y - \frac{21}{8}z = -1 \end{cases}$ 2 Eq. 2 + Eq. 1

Let $z = a$. Then $y = \frac{21}{8}a - 1$ and $x = \frac{1}{4}a$

Answer: $\left(\frac{1}{4}a, \frac{21}{8}a - 1, a\right)$

38. $\begin{cases} 23x + 4y - z = 0 \\ 12x + 5y + z = 0 \end{cases}$ Interchange the equations.

$\begin{cases} x + 6y + 3z = 0 \\ -67y - 35z = 0 \end{cases}$ 2 Eq. 2 − Eq. 1; − 12 Eq. 1 + Eq. 2

To avoid fractions, let $z = 67a$, then:

$-67y - 35(67a) = 0$

$y = -35a$

$x + 6(-35a) + 3(67a) = 0$

$x = 9a$

Answer: $(9a, -35a, 67a)$

39. $\begin{cases} 2x - 3y + z = -2 \\ -4x + 9y = 7 \end{cases}$

$\begin{cases} 2x - 3y + z = -2 \\ 3y + 2z = 3 \end{cases}$ 2 Eq. 1 + Eq. 2

$\begin{cases} 2x + 3z = 1 \\ 3y + 2z = 3 \end{cases}$ Eq. 2 + Eq. 1

Let $z = a$, then:

$$y = -\frac{2}{3}a + 1$$

$$x = -\frac{3}{2}a + \frac{1}{2}$$

Answer: $\left(-\frac{3}{2}a + \frac{1}{2}, -\frac{2}{3}a + 1, a\right)$

40. $\begin{cases} 10x - 3y + 2z = 0 \\ 19x - 5y - z = 0 \end{cases}$ Equation 1, Equation 2

$\begin{cases} x - y + 5z = 0 \\ 19x - 5y - z = 0 \end{cases}$ 2 Eq. 1 − Eq. 2

$\begin{cases} x - y + 5z = 0 \\ 14y - 96z = 0 \end{cases}$ − 19 Eq. 1 + Eq. 2

Infinite number of solutions. Let $z = 7a$. Then

$$y = \frac{96z}{14} = \frac{96(7a)}{14} = 48a$$

$$x = y - 5z = 48a - 5(7a) = 13a$$

Answer: $(13a, 48a, 7a)$ or $\left(\frac{13}{7}a, \frac{48}{7}a, a\right)$

41. $\begin{cases} x - 3y + 2z = 18 \\ 5x - 13y + 12z = 80 \end{cases}$ Equation 1, Equation 2

$\begin{cases} x - 3y + 2z = 18 \\ 2y + 2z = -10 \end{cases}$ -5 Eq. 1 + Eq. 2

$\begin{cases} x - 3y + 2z = 18 \\ y + z = -5 \end{cases}$ $\frac{1}{2}$ Eq. 2

$\begin{cases} x + 5z = 3 \\ y + z = -5 \end{cases}$ 3 Eq. 2 + Eq. 1

Let $z = a$, then $y = -a - 5$, and $x = -5a + 3$.

Answer: $(-5a + 3, -a - 5, a)$

42. $\begin{cases} 2x + 3y + 3z = 7 \\ 4x + 18y + 15z = 44 \end{cases}$ Equation 1, Equation 2

$\begin{cases} 2x + 3y + 3z = 7 \\ 12y + 9z = 30 \end{cases}$ -2 Eq. 1 + Eq. 2

$\begin{cases} 2x + \frac{3}{4}z = -\frac{1}{2} \\ 12y + 9z = 30 \end{cases}$ $-\frac{1}{4}$ Eq. 2 + Eq. 1

Let $z = a$, then:

$12y + 9a = 30 \Rightarrow y = -\frac{3}{4}a + \frac{5}{2}$

$2x + \frac{3}{4}a = -\frac{1}{2} \Rightarrow x = -\frac{3}{8}a - \frac{1}{4}$

Answer: $\left(-\frac{3}{8}a - \frac{1}{4}, -\frac{3}{4}a + \frac{5}{2}, a\right)$

43. $\begin{cases} x - y + 2z - w = 0 \\ 2x + y + z - w = 0 \\ x + y - w = -1 \\ x + y - 2z + w = 1 \end{cases}$ Equation 1, Equation 2, Equation 3, Equation 4

$\begin{cases} x - y + 2z - w = 0 \\ 3y - 3z + w = 0 \\ 2y - 2z = -1 \\ 2y - 4z + 2w = 1 \end{cases}$ (-2) Eq. 1 + Eq. 2, (-1) Eq. 1 + Eq. 3, (-1) Eq. 1 + Eq. 4

$\begin{cases} x - y + 2z - w = 0 \\ 2y - 2z = -1 \\ 3y - 3z + w = 0 \\ 2y - 4z + 2w = 1 \end{cases}$ Interchange Eq. 2 and 3

$\begin{cases} x - y + 2z - w = 0 \\ 2y - 2z = -1 \\ w = \frac{3}{2} \\ -2z + 2w = 2 \end{cases}$ $\left(-\frac{3}{2}\right)$ Eq. 2 + Eq. 3, (-1) Eq. 2 + Eq. 4

$w = \frac{3}{2}$

$-2z + 2w = 2 \Rightarrow -2z = 2 - 2\left(\frac{3}{2}\right) = -1 \Rightarrow z = \frac{1}{2}$

$2y - 2z = -1 \Rightarrow 2y = -1 + 2\left(\frac{1}{2}\right) = 0 \Rightarrow y = 0$

$x - y + 2z - w = 0 \Rightarrow x = -2\left(\frac{1}{2}\right) + \frac{3}{2} = \frac{1}{2}$

Answer: $\left(\frac{1}{2}, 0, \frac{1}{2}, \frac{3}{2}\right)$

44. $\begin{cases} x - 2y - z + 2w = 6 & \text{Equation 1} \\ 2x - 3y + z + w = 3 & \text{Equation 2} \\ x - 2y + z + w = 2 & \text{Equation 3} \\ y - z + w = 3 & \text{Equation 4} \end{cases}$

$\begin{cases} x - 2y - z + 2w = 6 & \\ y + 3z - 3w = -9 & (-2)\text{ Eq. 1} + \text{Eq. 2} \\ 2z - w = -4 & (-1)\text{ Eq. 1} + \text{Eq. 3} \\ y - z + w = 3 & \end{cases}$

$\begin{cases} x - 2y - z + 2w = 6 & \\ y + 3z - 3w = -9 & \\ 2z - w = -4 & \\ -4z + 4w = 12 & (-1)\text{ Eq. 2} + \text{Eq. 4} \end{cases}$

$\begin{cases} x - 2y - z + 2w = 6 & \\ y + 3z - 3w = -9 & \\ 2z - w = -4 & \\ 2w = 4 & (2)\text{ Eq. 3} + \text{Eq. 4} \end{cases}$

$w = 2$

$2z - w = -4 \implies 2z = -4 + 2 = -2 \implies z = -1$

$y + 3z - 3w = -9 \implies y = -9 - 3(-1) + 3(2) = 0$

$x - 2y - z + 2w = 6 \implies x = 6 + 2(0) + (-1) - 2(2) = 1$

Answer: $(1, 0, -1, 2)$

45. Let $X = \frac{1}{x}, Y = \frac{1}{y}, Z = \frac{1}{z}$.

$\begin{cases} X + 2Y - 3Z = 3 & \text{Equation 1} \\ X - 2Y + Z = 1 & \text{Equation 2} \\ 2X + 2Y - 3Z = 4 & \text{Equation 3} \end{cases}$

$\begin{cases} X + 2Y - 3Z = 3 & \\ -4Y + 4Z = -2 & (-1)\text{ Eq. 1} + \text{Eq. 2} \\ -2Y + 3Z = -2 & (-2)\text{ Eq. 1} + \text{Eq. 3} \end{cases}$

$\begin{cases} X + 2Y - 3Z = 3 & \\ 2Y - 2Z = 1 & \left(-\frac{1}{2}\right)\text{ Eq. 2} \\ -2Y + 3Z = -2 & \end{cases}$

$\begin{cases} X + 2Y - 3Z = 3 & \\ 2Y - 2Z = 1 & \\ Z = -1 & \text{Eq. 2} + \text{Eq. 3} \end{cases}$

$2Y - 2Z = 1 \implies 2Y = 1 + 2Z = -1 \implies Y = -\frac{1}{2}$

$X + 2Y - 3Z = 3 \implies X = 3 - 2\left(-\frac{1}{2}\right) + 3(-1) = 1$

$x = \frac{1}{X} = 1, y = \frac{1}{Y} = -2, z = \frac{1}{Z} = -1$

Answer: $(1, -2, -1)$

46. Let $X = \frac{1}{x}, Y = \frac{1}{y}, Z = \frac{1}{z}$.

$\begin{cases} 4X - 2Y + Z = -3 & \text{Equation 1} \\ X + 2Y - 2Z = -1 & \text{Equation 2} \\ 2X + Y - 3Z = 0 & \text{Equation 3} \end{cases}$

$\begin{cases} X + 2Y - 2Z = -1 & \text{Interchange} \\ 4X - 2Y + Z = -3 & \text{Eq. 1 and 2} \\ 2X + Y - 3Z = 0 & \end{cases}$

$\begin{cases} X + 2Y - 2Z = -1 & \\ -10Y + 9Z = 1 & (-4)\text{ Eq. 1} + \text{Eq. 2} \\ -3Y + Z = 2 & (-2)\text{ Eq. 1} + \text{Eq. 3} \end{cases}$

$\begin{cases} X + 2Y - 2Z = -1 & \\ -10Y + 9Z = 1 & \\ -\frac{17}{10}Z = \frac{17}{10} & \left(-\frac{3}{10}\right)\text{ Eq. 2} + \text{Eq. 3} \end{cases}$

$Z = -1, Y = -1, X = -1$

$x = \frac{1}{X} = y = z = -1$

Answer: $(-1, -1, -1)$

47. Let $X = \frac{1}{x}, Y = \frac{1}{y}, Z = \frac{1}{z}$.

$$\begin{cases} 2X - Y + 2Z = 4 & \text{Equation 1} \\ X + 2Y - 2Z = -2 & \text{Equation 2} \\ 3X + 3Y + 4Z = 2 & \text{Equation 3} \end{cases}$$

$$\begin{cases} X + 2Y - 2Z = -2 & \text{Interchange} \\ 2X - Y + 2Z = 4 & \text{Eq. 1 and 2} \\ 3X + 3Y + 4Z = 2 & \end{cases}$$

$$\begin{cases} X + 2Y - 2Z = -2 & \\ -5Y + 6Z = 8 & (-2)\text{ Eq. 1 + Eq. 2} \\ -3Y + 10Z = 8 & (-3)\text{ Eq. 1 + Eq. 3} \end{cases}$$

$$\begin{cases} X + 2Y - 2Z = -2 & \\ -5Y + 6Z = 8 & \\ \frac{32}{5}Z = \frac{16}{5} & (-\frac{3}{5})\text{Eq. 2 + Eq. 3} \end{cases}$$

$$Z = \frac{1}{2}$$

$$-5Y + 6Z = 8 \Rightarrow -5Y = 8 - 6\left(\frac{1}{2}\right) = 5 \Rightarrow Y = -1$$

$$X + 2Y - 2Z = -2 \Rightarrow X = -2 - 2(-1) + 2\left(\frac{1}{2}\right) = 1$$

$$x = \frac{1}{X} = 1, y = \frac{1}{Y} = -1, z = \frac{1}{Z} = 2$$

Answer: $(1, -1, 2)$

48. Let $X = \frac{1}{x}, Y = \frac{1}{y}, Z = \frac{1}{z}$.

$$\begin{cases} X + Y + 2Z = 1 & \text{Equation 1} \\ 2X + Y - 2Z = 0 & \text{Equation 2} \\ 3X - Y + 4Z = 6 & \text{Equation 3} \end{cases}$$

$$\begin{cases} X + Y + 2Z = 1 & \\ -Y - 6Z = -2 & (-2)\text{ Eq. 1 + Eq. 2} \\ -4Y - 2Z = 3 & (-3)\text{ Eq. 1 + Eq. 3} \end{cases}$$

$$\begin{cases} X + Y + 2Z = 1 & \\ Y + 6Z = 2 & (-1)\text{ Eq. 2} \\ 22Z = 11 & (4)\text{ Eq. 2 + Eq. 3} \end{cases}$$

$$Z = \frac{1}{2}, Y = -1, X = 1$$

$$x = 1, y = -1, z = 2$$

Answer: $(1, -1, 2)$

49. There are an infinite number of linear systems that have $(4, -1, 2)$ as their solution. One such system is as follows:

$$3(4) + (-1) - (2) = 9 \Rightarrow 3x + y - z = 9$$
$$(4) + 2(-1) - (2) = 0 \Rightarrow x + 2y - z = 0$$
$$-(4) + (-1) + 3(2) = 1 \Rightarrow -x + y + 3z = 1$$

50. There are an infinite number of linear systems that have $(-5, -2, 1)$ as their solution. One such system is:

$$1(-5) + 1(-2) + 1 = -6 \Rightarrow x + y + z = -6$$
$$2(-2) + 1 = -3 \qquad 2y + z = -3$$
$$2(1) = 2 \qquad 2z = 2$$

51. There are an infinite numbers of linear systems that have $\left(3, -\frac{1}{2}, \frac{7}{4}\right)$ as their solution. One such system is:

$$1(3) + 2\left(-\tfrac{1}{2}\right) + 4\left(\tfrac{7}{4}\right) = 9 \Rightarrow x + 2y + 4z = 9$$
$$4\left(-\tfrac{1}{2}\right) + 8\left(\tfrac{7}{4}\right) = 12 \Rightarrow 4y + 8z = 12$$
$$4\left(\tfrac{7}{4}\right) = 7 \Rightarrow 4z = 7$$

52. There are an infinite number of linear systems that have $\left(-\frac{3}{2}, 4, -7\right)$ as their solution. One such system is:

$$\begin{aligned} 2\left(-\tfrac{3}{2}\right) + 4 - (-7) &= 8 \Rightarrow \\ 4\left(-\tfrac{3}{2}\right) + 2(4) + (-7) &= -5 \Rightarrow \\ -2\left(-\tfrac{3}{2}\right) + 5(4) - 3(-7) &= 44 \Rightarrow \end{aligned} \begin{cases} 2x + y - z = 8 \\ 4x + 2y + z = -5 \\ -2x + 5y - 3z = 44 \end{cases}$$

53. $2x + 3y + 4z = 12$

$(6, 0, 0)$, $(0, 4, 0)$, $(0, 0, 3)$, $(4, 0, 1)$

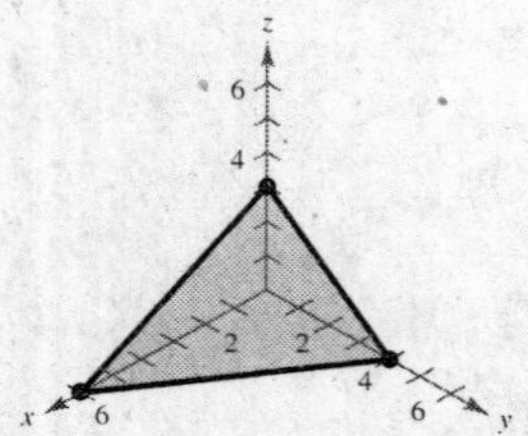

54. $x + y + z = 6$

$(6, 0, 0)$, $(0, 6, 0)$, $(0, 0, 6)$, $(1, 1, 4)$

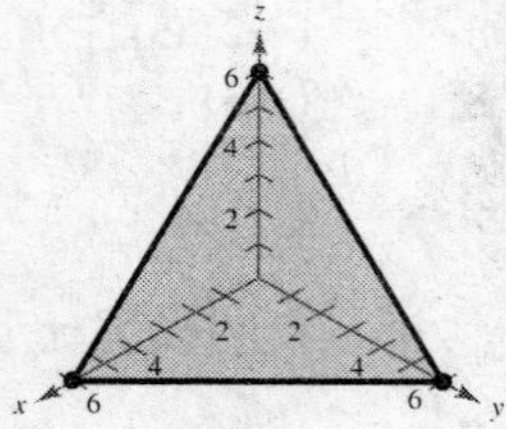

55. $2x + y + z = 4$

$(2, 0, 0)$, $(0, 4, 0)$, $(0, 0, 4)$, $(0, 2, 2)$

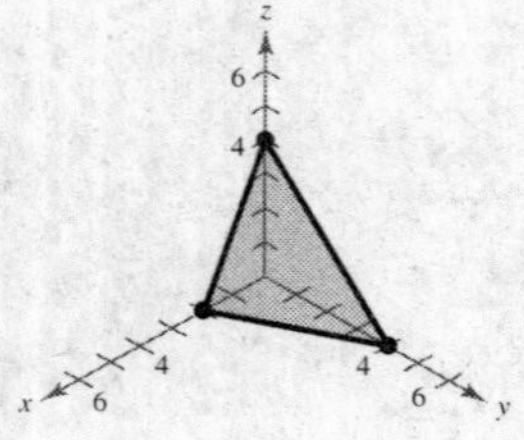

56. $x + 2y + 2z = 6$

$(6, 0, 0)$, $(0, 3, 0)$, $(0, 0, 3)$, $(2, 1, 1)$

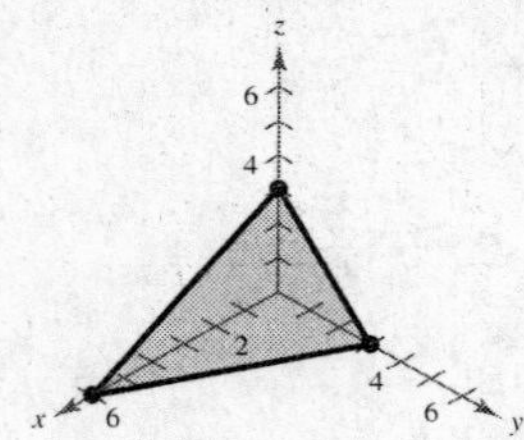

57. $\dfrac{7}{x^2 - 14x} = \dfrac{7}{x(x - 14)} = \dfrac{A}{x} + \dfrac{B}{x - 14}$

58. $\dfrac{x - 2}{x^2 + 4x + 3} = \dfrac{A}{x + 3} + \dfrac{B}{x + 1}$

59. $\dfrac{12}{x^3 - 10x^2} = \dfrac{12}{x^2(x - 10)} = \dfrac{A}{x} + \dfrac{B}{x^2} + \dfrac{C}{x - 10}$

60. $\dfrac{x^2 - 3x + 2}{4x^3 + 11x^2} = \dfrac{x^2 - 3x + 2}{x^2(4x + 11)} = \dfrac{A}{x} + \dfrac{B}{x^2} + \dfrac{C}{4x + 11}$

61. $\dfrac{4x^2 + 3}{(x - 5)^3} = \dfrac{A}{(x - 5)} + \dfrac{B}{(x - 5)^2} + \dfrac{C}{(x - 5)^3}$

62. $\dfrac{6x + 5}{(x + 2)^4} = \dfrac{A}{x + 2} + \dfrac{B}{(x + 2)^2} + \dfrac{C}{(x + 2)^3} + \dfrac{D}{(x + 2)^4}$

63. $\dfrac{1}{x^2 - 1} = \dfrac{A}{x + 1} + \dfrac{B}{x - 1}$

$1 = A(x - 1) + B(x + 1) = (A + B)x + (B - A)$

$\begin{cases} A + B = 0 \\ -A + B = 1 \end{cases}$

$2B = 1 \Rightarrow B = \frac{1}{2} \Rightarrow A = -\frac{1}{2}$

$\dfrac{1}{x^2 - 1} = \dfrac{-1/2}{x + 1} + \dfrac{1/2}{x - 1} = \dfrac{1}{2}\left[\dfrac{1}{x - 1} - \dfrac{1}{x + 1}\right]$

64. $\dfrac{1}{4x^2 - 9} = \dfrac{A}{2x + 3} + \dfrac{B}{2x - 3}$

$1 = A(2x - 3) + B(2x + 3)$

Let $x = -\dfrac{3}{2}$: $1 = -6A \Rightarrow A = -\dfrac{1}{6}$

Let $x = \dfrac{3}{2}$: $1 = 6B \Rightarrow B = \dfrac{1}{6}$

$\dfrac{1}{4x^2 - 9} = \dfrac{1}{6}\left[\dfrac{1}{2x - 3} - \dfrac{1}{2x + 3}\right]$

65. $\dfrac{1}{x^2 + x} = \dfrac{1}{x(x + 1)} = \dfrac{A}{x} + \dfrac{B}{x + 1}$

$1 = A(x + 1) + Bx = (A + B)x + A$

$\begin{cases} A + B = 0 \\ \quad A = 1 \Rightarrow B = -1 \end{cases}$

$\dfrac{1}{x^2 + x} = \dfrac{1}{x} + \dfrac{-1}{x + 1} = \dfrac{1}{x} - \dfrac{1}{x + 1}$

66. $\dfrac{3}{x^2 - 3x} = \dfrac{A}{x - 3} + \dfrac{B}{x}$

$3 = Ax + B(x - 3)$

Let $x = 3$: $3 = 3A \Rightarrow A = 1$

Let $x = 0$: $3 = -3B \Rightarrow B = -1$

$\dfrac{3}{x^2 - 3x} = \dfrac{1}{x - 3} - \dfrac{1}{x}$

67. $\dfrac{1}{2x^2 + x} = \dfrac{1}{x(2x + 1)} = \dfrac{A}{2x + 1} + \dfrac{B}{x}$

$1 = Ax + B(2x + 1) = (A + 2B)x + B$

$\begin{cases} A + 2B = 0 \\ \quad B = 1 \Rightarrow A = -2 \end{cases}$

$\dfrac{1}{2x^2 + x} = \dfrac{-2}{2x + 1} + \dfrac{1}{x} = \dfrac{1}{x} - \dfrac{2}{2x + 1}$

68. $\dfrac{5}{x^2 + x - 6} = \dfrac{A}{x + 3} + \dfrac{B}{x - 2}$

$5 = A(x - 2) + B(x + 3)$

Let $x = -3$: $5 = -5A \Rightarrow A = -1$

Let $x = 2$: $5 = 5B \Rightarrow B = 1$

$\dfrac{5}{x^2 + x - 6} = \dfrac{1}{x - 2} - \dfrac{1}{x + 3}$

69. $\dfrac{5 - x}{2x^2 + x - 1} = \dfrac{5 - x}{(2x - 1)(x + 1)}$

$= \dfrac{A}{2x - 1} + \dfrac{B}{x + 1}$

$5 - x = A(x + 1) + B(2x - 1)$

$= (A + 2B)x + (A - B)$

$\begin{cases} A + 2B = -1 \Rightarrow A = -1 - 2B \\ A - B = 5 \end{cases}$

$(-1 - 2B) - B = 5 \Rightarrow B = -2$ and $A = 3$

$\dfrac{5 - x}{2x^2 + x - 1} = \dfrac{3}{2x - 1} + \dfrac{-2}{x + 1}$

70. $\dfrac{x - 2}{x^2 + 4x + 3} = \dfrac{A}{x + 3} + \dfrac{B}{x + 1}$

$A(x + 1) + B(x + 3) = x - 2$

$(A + B)x + (A + 3B) = x - 2$

$\begin{cases} A + B = 1 \\ A + 3B = -2 \end{cases}$

Solving for A and B, $A = \frac{5}{2}, B = -\frac{3}{2}$

$\dfrac{x - 2}{x^2 + 4x + 3} = \dfrac{5/2}{x + 3} - \dfrac{3/2}{x + 1}$

71. $\dfrac{x^2+12x+12}{x^3-4x} = \dfrac{x^2+12x+12}{x(x-2)(x+2)} = \dfrac{A}{x} + \dfrac{B}{x+2} + \dfrac{C}{x-2}$

$$\begin{aligned} x^2+12x+12 &= A(x+2)(x-2) + Bx(x-2) + Cx(x+2) \\ &= (A+B+C)x^2 + (-2B+2C)x + (-4A) \end{aligned}$$

$$\begin{cases} A + B + C = 1 \\ -2B + 2C = 12 \\ -4A = 12 \implies A = -3 \end{cases}$$

$$\begin{cases} B + C = 4 \\ -B + C = 6 \end{cases}$$

$2C = 10 \implies C = 5 \implies B = -1$

$$\frac{x^2+12x+12}{x^3-4x} = \frac{-3}{x} + \frac{-1}{x+2} + \frac{5}{x-2}$$

72. $\dfrac{x^2+12x-9}{x^3-9x} = \dfrac{x^2+12x-9}{x(x-3)(x+3)} = \dfrac{A}{x} + \dfrac{B}{x-3} + \dfrac{C}{x+3}$

$A(x^2-9) + Bx(x+3) + Cx(x-3) = x^2+12x-9$

$$\begin{cases} A + B + C = 1 \\ 3B - 3C = 12 \\ -9A = -9 \end{cases}$$

Solving, $A = 1$, $B = 2$ and $C = -2$

$$\frac{x^2+12x-9}{x^3-9x} = \frac{1}{x} + \frac{2}{x-3} - \frac{2}{x+3}$$

73. $\dfrac{4x^2+2x-1}{x^2(x+1)} = \dfrac{A}{x} + \dfrac{B}{x^2} + \dfrac{C}{x+1}$

$$\begin{aligned} 4x^2+2x-1 &= Ax(x+1) + B(x+1) + Cx^2 \\ &= (A+C)x^2 + (A+B)x + B \end{aligned}$$

$$\begin{cases} A + C = 4 \\ A + B = 2 \\ B = -1 \end{cases}$$

$B = -1 \implies A = 3 \implies C = 1$

$$\frac{4x^2+2x-1}{x^2(x+1)} = \frac{3}{x} + \frac{-1}{x^2} + \frac{1}{x+1}$$

74. $\dfrac{2x-3}{(x-1)^2} = \dfrac{A}{x-1} + \dfrac{B}{(x-1)^2}$

$2x - 3 = A(x-1) + B$

Let $x = 1$: $-1 = B$

Let $x = 0$: $-3 = -A + B$

$-3 = -A - 1$

$2 = A$

$$\frac{2x-3}{(x-1)^2} = \frac{2}{x-1} - \frac{1}{(x-1)^2}$$

75. $\dfrac{27-7x}{x(x-3)^2} = \dfrac{A}{x} + \dfrac{B}{x-3} + \dfrac{C}{(x-3)^2}$

$27 - 7x = A(x-3)^2 + Bx(x-3) + Cx = (A+B)x^2 + (-6A-3B+C)x + 9A$

$$\begin{cases} A + B = 0 \\ -6A - 3B + C = -7 \\ 9A = 27 \end{cases}$$

$A = 3 \implies B = -3 \implies C = -7 + 18 - 9 = 2$

$$\frac{27-7x}{x(x-3)^2} = \frac{3}{x} + \frac{-3}{x-3} + \frac{2}{(x-3)^2}$$

76. $\dfrac{x^2 - x + 2}{x(x-1)^2} = \dfrac{A}{x} + \dfrac{B}{x-1} + \dfrac{C}{(x-1)^2}$

$A(x-1)^2 + Bx(x-1) + Cx = x^2 - x + 2$

$$\begin{cases} A + B = 1 \\ -2A - B + C = -1 \\ A = 2 \end{cases}$$

Solving, $A = 2, B = -1$ and $C = 2$

$$\frac{x^2 - x + 2}{x(x-1)^2} = \frac{2}{x} - \frac{1}{x-1} + \frac{2}{(x-1)^2}$$

77. $\dfrac{2x^3 - x^2 + x + 5}{x^2 + 3x + 2} = 2x - 7 + \dfrac{18x + 19}{(x+1)(x+2)}$

$\dfrac{18x + 19}{(x+1)(x+2)} = \dfrac{A}{x+1} + \dfrac{B}{x+2}$

$18x + 19 = A(x+2) + B(x+1)$

$= (A + B)x + (2A + B)$

$$\begin{cases} A + B = 18 \\ 2A + B = 19 \end{cases}$$

$A = 1 \implies B = 17$

$$\frac{2x^3 - x^2 + x + 5}{x^2 + 3x + 2} = 2x - 7 + \frac{1}{x+1} + \frac{17}{x+2}$$

78. $\dfrac{x^3 + 2x^2 - x + 1}{x^2 + 3x - 4} = x - 1 + \dfrac{6x - 3}{(x+4)(x-1)}$

$\dfrac{6x - 3}{(x+4)(x-1)} = \dfrac{A}{x+4} + \dfrac{B}{x-1}$

$6x - 3 = A(x-1) + B(x+4)$

Let $x = 1$: $3 = 5B \implies B = \dfrac{3}{5}$

Let $x = -4$: $-27 = -5A \implies A = \dfrac{27}{5}$

$$\frac{x^3 + 2x^2 - x + 1}{x^2 + 3x - 4} = x - 1 + \frac{27}{5(x+4)} + \frac{3}{5(x-1)}$$

79. $\dfrac{x^4}{(x-1)^3} = x + 3 + \dfrac{6x^2 - 8x + 3}{(x-1)^3}$

$\dfrac{6x^2 - 8x + 3}{(x-1)^3} = \dfrac{A}{x-1} + \dfrac{B}{(x-1)^2} + \dfrac{C}{(x-1)^3}$

$6x^2 - 8x + 3 = A(x-1)^2 + B(x-1) + C = Ax^2 + (-2A + B)x + (A - B + C)$

$$\begin{cases} A = 6 \\ -2A + B = -8 \\ A - B + C = 3 \end{cases}$$

$A = 6 \implies B = -8 + 2(6) = 4 \implies C = 3 - 6 + 4 = 1$

$$\frac{x^4}{(x-1)^3} = \frac{6}{x-1} + \frac{4}{(x-1)^2} + \frac{1}{(x-1)^3} + x + 3$$

80. $\dfrac{4x^4}{(2x-1)^3} = \dfrac{x}{2} + \dfrac{3}{4} + \dfrac{24x^2 - 16x + 3}{4(2x-1)^3}$

$$\frac{24x^2 - 16x + 3}{4(2x-1)^3} = \frac{1}{4}\left[\frac{A}{2x-1} + \frac{B}{(2x-1)^2} + \frac{C}{(2x-1)^3}\right]$$

$$24x^2 - 16x + 3 = A(2x-1)^2 + B(2x-1) + C = A4x^2 + (-4A + 2B)x + (A - B + C)$$

$4A = 24 \Rightarrow A = 6$

$-4A + 2B = -16 \Rightarrow 2B = 8 \Rightarrow B = 4$

$A - B + C = 3 \Rightarrow C = 1$

Answer: $\dfrac{x}{2} + \dfrac{3}{4} + \dfrac{3}{2(2x-1)} + \dfrac{1}{(2x-1)^2} + \dfrac{1}{4(2x-1)^3}$

81. $\dfrac{x-12}{x(x-4)} = \dfrac{A}{x} + \dfrac{B}{x-4}$

$x - 12 = A(x-4) + Bx$

$$\begin{cases} A + B = 1 \\ -4A = -12 \end{cases} \Rightarrow A = 3,\ B = -2$$

$\dfrac{x-12}{x(x-4)} = \dfrac{3}{x} - \dfrac{2}{x-4}$

$y = \dfrac{x-12}{x(x-4)}$ $\qquad$ $y = \dfrac{3}{x},\ y = -\dfrac{2}{x-4}$

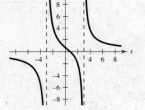

Vertical asymptotes: $x = 0$ and $x = 4$ $\qquad$ Vertical asymptotes: $x = 0$ and $x = 4$

The combination of the vertical asymptotes of the terms of the decompositions are the same as the vertical asymptotes of the rational function.

82. $\dfrac{2(4x-3)}{x^2-9} = \dfrac{A}{x-3} + \dfrac{B}{x+3}$

$2(4x-3) = A(x+3) + B(x-3)$

Let $x = 3$: $18 = 6A \Rightarrow A = 3$

Let $x = -3$: $-30 = -6B \Rightarrow B = 5$

$\dfrac{2(4x-3)}{x^2-9} = \dfrac{3}{x-3} + \dfrac{5}{x+3}$

$y = \dfrac{2(4x-3)}{x^2-9}$ $\qquad$ $y = \dfrac{3}{x-3},\ y = \dfrac{5}{x+3}$

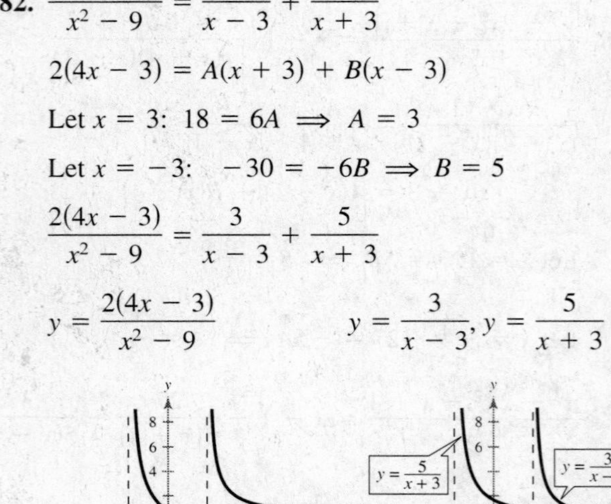

Vertical asymptotes: $x = \pm 3$ $\qquad$ Vertical asymptotes: $x = 3,\ x = -3$

The combination of the vertical asymptotes of the terms of the decompositions are the same as the vertical asymptotes of the rational function.

83. $s = \frac{1}{2}at^2 + v_0t + s_0$

$(1, 128), (2, 80), (3, 0)$

$$\begin{cases} 128 = \frac{1}{2}a + v_0 + s_0 \Rightarrow a + 2v_0 + 2s_0 = 256 \\ 80 = 2a + 2v_0 + s_0 \Rightarrow 2a + 2v_0 + s_0 = 80 \\ 0 = \frac{9}{2}a + 3v_0 + s_0 \Rightarrow 9a + 6v_0 + 2s_0 = 0 \end{cases}$$

Solving the system, $a = -32$, $v_0 = 0$, $s_0 = 144$.

Thus, $s = \frac{1}{2}(-32)t^2 + (0)t + 144$

$= -16t^2 + 144.$

84. $s = \frac{1}{2}at^2 + v_0t + s_0$

$(1, 48), (2, 64), (3, 48)$

$$\begin{cases} 48 = \frac{1}{2}a + v_0 + s_0 \Rightarrow a + 2v_0 + 2s_0 = 96 \\ 64 = 2a + 2v_0 + s_0 \Rightarrow 2a + 2v_0 + s_0 = 64 \\ 48 = \frac{9}{2}a + 3v_0 + s_0 \Rightarrow 9a + 6v_0 + 2s_0 = 96 \end{cases}$$

Solving the system, $a = -32$, $v_0 = 64$, $s_0 = 0$.

Thus, $s = \frac{1}{2}(-32)t^2 + 64t + 0$

$= -16t^2 + 64t.$

85. $s = \frac{1}{2}at^2 + v_0t + a_0$

$(1, 452), (2, 372), (3, 260)$

$$\begin{cases} 452 = \frac{1}{2}a + v_0 + s_0 \Rightarrow a + 2v_0 + 2s_0 = 904 \\ 372 = 2a + 2v_0 + s_0 \Rightarrow 2a + 2v_0 + s_0 = 372 \\ 260 = \frac{9}{2}a + 3v_0 + s_0 \Rightarrow 9a + 6v_0 + 2s_0 = 520 \end{cases}$$

Solving the system, $a = -32$, $v_0 = -32$, $s_0 = 500$

$$\begin{aligned} \text{Thus, } s &= \tfrac{1}{2}(-32)t^2 - 32t + 500 \\ &= -16t^2 - 32t + 500 \end{aligned}$$

86. $s = \frac{1}{2}at^2 + v_0t + s_0$

$(1, 132), (2, 100), (3, 36)$

$$\begin{cases} 132 = \frac{1}{2}a + v_0 + s_0 \Rightarrow a + 2v_0 + 2s_0 = 264 \\ 100 = 2a + 2v_0 + s_0 \Rightarrow 2a + 2v_0 + s_0 = 100 \\ 36 = \frac{9}{2}a + 3v_0 + s_0 \Rightarrow 9a + 6v_0 + 2s_0 = 72 \end{cases}$$

Solving the system $a = -32$, $s_0 = 16$, $s_0 = 132$.

$$\begin{aligned} \text{Thus, } s &= \tfrac{1}{2}(-32)t^2 + 16t + 132 \\ &= -16t^2 + 16t + 132. \end{aligned}$$

87. $y = ax^2 + bx + c$ passing through $(0, 0), (2, -2), (4, 0)$

$$\begin{cases} (0, 0): \quad 0 = 4a + 2b + c \Rightarrow c = -4a - 2b \\ (2, -2): -2 = 4a + 2b + c \Rightarrow -1 = 2a + b \\ (4, 0): \quad 0 = 16a + 4b + c \Rightarrow 0 = 4a + b \end{cases}$$

Answer: $a = \frac{1}{2}$, $b = -2$, $c = 0$

The equation of the parabola is $y = \frac{1}{2}x^2 - 2x$.

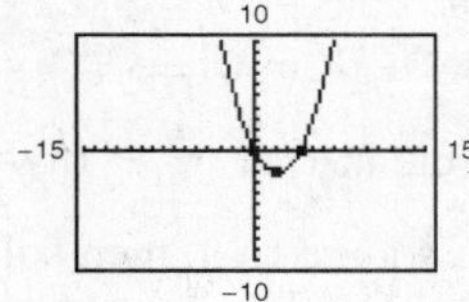

88. $y = ax^2 + bx + c$ passing through $(0, 3), (1, 4), (2, 3)$

$$\begin{cases} (0, 3): 3 = c \\ (1, 4): 4 = a + b + c \Rightarrow 1 = a + b \\ (2, 3): 3 = 4a + 2b + c \Rightarrow 0 = 2a + b \end{cases}$$

Answer: $a = -1$, $b = 2$, $c = 3$

The equation of the parabola is $y = -x^2 + 2x + 3$.

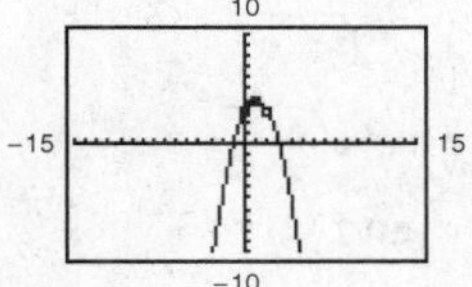

89. $y = ax^2 + bx + c$ passing through $(2, 0), (3, -1), (4, 0)$

$$\begin{cases} (2, 0): \quad 0 = 4a + 2b + c \Rightarrow c = -4a - 2b \\ (3, -1): -1 = 9a + 3b + c \Rightarrow -1 = 5a + b \\ (4, 0): \quad 0 = 16a + 4b + c \Rightarrow 0 = 12a + 2b \end{cases}$$

Answer: $a = 1$, $b = -6$, $c = 8$

The equation of the parabola is $y = x^2 - 6x + 8$.

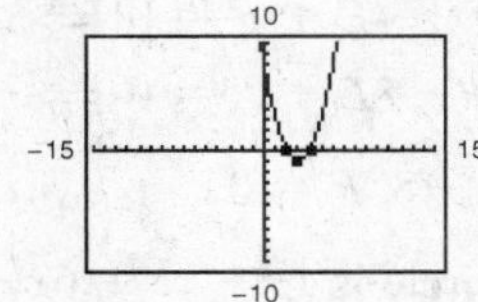

90. $y = ax^2 + bx + c$ passing through $(1, 3), (2, 2), (3, -3)$

$$\begin{cases} (1, 3): \quad 3 = a + b + c \\ (2, 2): \quad 2 = 4a + 2b + c \Rightarrow -1 = 3a + b \\ (3, -3): -3 = 9a + 3b + c \Rightarrow -6 = 8a + 2b \end{cases}$$

Answer: $a = -2$, $b = 5$, $c = 0$

The equation of the parabola is $y = -2x^2 + 5x$.

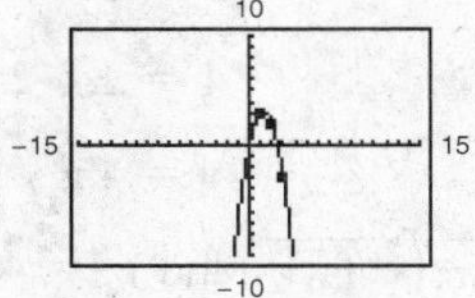

91. $x^2 + y^2 + Dx + Ey + F = 0$ passing through $(0, 0)$, $(2, 2)$, $(4, 0)$

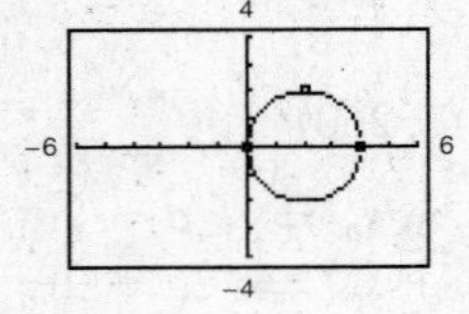

$$\begin{aligned}
(0, 0)&: \quad F = 0 \\
(2, 2)&: \quad 8 + 2D + 2E + F = 0 \Rightarrow D + E = -4 \\
(4, 0)&: \quad 16 + 4D + F = 0 \Rightarrow D = -4 \text{ and } E = 0
\end{aligned}$$

The equation of the circle is $x^2 + y^2 - 4x = 0$.

To graph, let $y_1 = \sqrt{4x - x^2}$ and $y_2 = -\sqrt{4x - x^2}$.

92. $x^2 + y^2 + Dx + Ey + F = 0$ passes through $(0, 0)$, $(0, 6)$, $(3, 3)$.

$$\begin{cases}
(0, 0): & F = 0 \\
(0, 6): & 36 + 6E + F = 0 \Rightarrow E = -6 \\
(3, 3): & 18 + 3D + 3E + F = 0 \Rightarrow D = 0
\end{cases}$$

The equation of the circle is $x^2 + y^2 - 6y = 0$.

To graph, complete the square first, then solve for y.

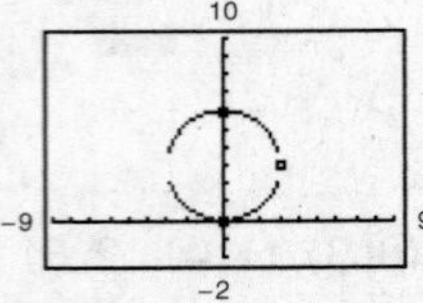

$$\begin{aligned}
x^2 + y^2 - 6y + 9 &= 9 \\
x^2 + (y - 3)^2 &= 9 \\
(y - 3)^2 &= 9 - x^2 \\
y - 3 &= \pm\sqrt{9 - x^2} \\
y &= 3 \pm \sqrt{9 - x^2}
\end{aligned}$$

Let $y_1 = 3 + \sqrt{9 - x^2}$ and $y_2 = 3 - \sqrt{9 - x^2}$.

93. $x^2 + y^2 + Dx + Ey + F = 0$ passes through $(-3, -1)$, $(2, 4)$, $(-6, 8)$.

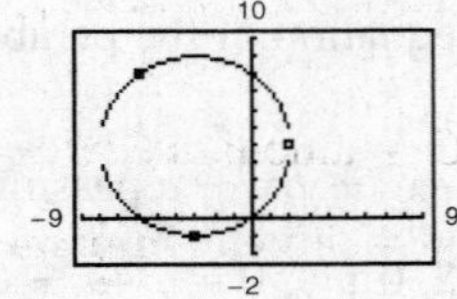

$$\begin{aligned}
(-3, -1)&: \quad 10 - 3D - E + F = 0 \Rightarrow 10 = 3D + E - F \\
(2, 4)&: \quad 20 + 2D + 4E + F = 0 \Rightarrow 20 = -2D - 4E - F \\
(-6, 8)&: \quad 100 - 6D + 8E + F = 0 \Rightarrow 100 = 6D - 8E - F
\end{aligned}$$

Answer: $D = 6$, $E = -8$, $F = 0$

The equation of the circle is $x^2 + y^2 + 6x - 8y = 0$. To graph, complete the squares first, then solve for y.

$$\begin{aligned}
(x^2 + 6x + 9) + (y^2 - 8y + 16) &= 0 + 9 + 16 \\
(x + 3)^2 + (y - 4)^2 &= 25 \\
(y - 4)^2 &= 25 - (x + 3)^2 \\
y - 4 &= \pm\sqrt{25 - (x + 3)^2} \\
y &= 4 \pm \sqrt{25 - (x + 3)^2}
\end{aligned}$$

Let $y_1 = 4 + \sqrt{25 - (x + 3)^2}$ and $y_2 = 4 - \sqrt{25 - (x + 3)^2}$.

94. $x^2 + y^2 + Dx + Ey + F = 0$ passes through $(-6, -1), (-4, 3), (2, -5)$.

$$\begin{cases} (-6,-1): & 36 + 1 - 6D - E + F = 0 \Rightarrow 6D + E - F = 37 \\ (-4,3): & 16 + 9 - 4D + 3E + F = 0 \Rightarrow 4D - 3E - F = 25 \\ (2,-5): & 4 + 25 + 2D - 5E + F = 0 \Rightarrow 2D - 5E + F = -29 \end{cases}$$

Solving the system $D = 2, E = 2, F = -23$, and the circle is

$$x^2 + y^2 + 2x + 2y - 23 = 0$$
$$(x^2 + 2x + 1) + (y^2 + 2y + 1) = 23 + 1 + 1$$
$$(x + 1)^2 + (y + 1)^2 = 25$$
$$y_1 = -1 + \sqrt{25 - (x + 1)^2}$$
$$y_2 = -1 - \sqrt{25 - (x + 1)^2}$$

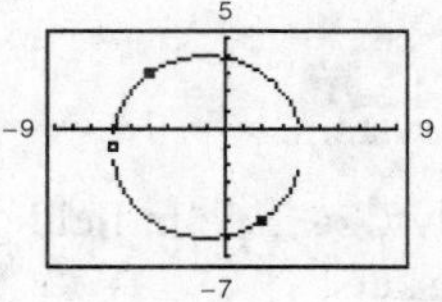

95. Let x = amount at 8%.

Let y = amount at 9%.

Let z = amount at 10%.

$$\begin{cases} x + y + z = 775{,}000 \\ 0.08x + 0.09y + 0.10z = 67{,}000 \\ x = 4z \end{cases}$$

$$\begin{cases} x + y + z = 775{,}000 \\ 8x + 9y + 10z = 6{,}700{,}000 \\ x - 4z = 0 \end{cases}$$

Solving the system, $x = \$366{,}666.67$ at 8%, $y = \$316{,}666.67$ at 9%, $z = \$91{,}666.67$ at 10%.

96. Let x = amount at 8%.

Let y = amount at 10%.

Let z = amount at 12%.

$$\begin{cases} 0.08x + 0.10y + 0.12z = 97{,}200 \\ x + y + z = 1{,}000{,}000 \\ x - 2y = 0 \end{cases}$$

Solving the system, $x = \$456{,}000$ at 8%, $y = \$228{,}000$ at 10%, $z = \$316{,}000$ at 12%.

97. Let C = amount in certificates of deposit.

Let M = amount in municipal bonds.

Let B = amount in blue chip stocks.

Let G = amount in growth or speculative stocks.

$$\begin{cases} C + M + B + G = 500{,}000 \\ 0.08C + 0.09M + 0.12B + 0.15G = 0.10(500{,}000) \\ M = \frac{1}{4}(500{,}000) \end{cases}$$

Solving the system

$C = 156{,}250 + 0.75s$

$M = 125{,}000$

$B = 218{,}750 - 1.75s$

$G = s$

98. Let C = amount in certificates of deposit.

Let M = amount in municipal bonds.

Let B = amount in blue-chip stocks.

Let G = amount in growth or speculative stocks.

$$\begin{cases} C + M + B + G = 500{,}000 \\ 0.09C + 0.05M + 0.12B + 0.14G = 0.10(500{,}000) \\ B + G = \frac{1}{4}(500{,}000) \end{cases}$$

The system has infinitely many solutions.

Let $G = s$, then $B = 125{,}000 - s$

$M = \frac{1}{2}s - 31{,}250$

$C = 406{,}250 - \frac{1}{2}s.$

Answer:

$\left(406{,}250 - \frac{1}{2}s, -31{,}250 + \frac{1}{2}s, 125{,}000 - s, s\right)$

One possible solution is to let $s = \$100{,}000$.

Certificates of deposit: \$356,250

Municipal bonds: \$18,750

Blue-chip stocks: \$25,000

Growth or speculative stocks: \$100,000

99. Let x = number of 1-point free throws.

Let y = number of 2-point field goals.

Let z = number of 3-point basket.

$$\begin{cases} x + 2y + 3z = 84 \\ -x + y = 6 \\ y - 4z = 0 \end{cases}$$

Solving the system, $x = 18, y = 24, z = 6$.

18 free throws, 24 2-point field goals, 6 3-point baskets.

100. Let x = number of 1-point free throws.

Let y = number of 2-point field goals.

Let z = number of 3-point baskets.

$$\begin{cases} x + 2y + 3z = 75 \\ x - z = 3 \\ x - y = -6 \end{cases}$$

Solving the system, $x = 12, y = 18, z = 9$.

12 free throws, 18 2-point field goals, 9 3-point baskets.

101. Let x = number of touchdowns.

Let y = number of extra-point kicks.

Let z = number of field goals.

$$\begin{cases} x + y + z = 9 \\ 6x + y + 3z = 31 \\ x - 4z = 0 \\ x - y = 0 \end{cases}$$

Solving the system, $x = 4, y = 4, z = 1$.

4 touchdowns, 4 extra-points and 1 field goal

102. Let x = number of touchdowns.

Let y = number of extra points.

Let z = number of field goals.

$$\begin{cases} x + y + z = 11 \\ 6x + y + 3z = 39 \\ x - z = 0 \end{cases}$$

Solving the system, $x = 4$ touchdowns, $y = 3$ extra points, $z = 4$ field goals

103. $$\begin{cases} I_1 - I_2 + I_3 = 0 & \text{Equation 1} \\ 3I_1 + 2I_2 = 7 & \text{Equation 2} \\ 2I_2 + 4I_3 = 8 & \text{Equation 3} \end{cases}$$

$$\begin{cases} I_1 - I_2 + I_3 = 0 \\ 5I_2 - 3I_3 = 7 & -3\text{ Eq. 1} + \text{Eq. 2} \\ 2I_2 + 4I_3 = 8 \end{cases}$$

$$\begin{cases} I_1 - I_2 + I_3 = 0 \\ 10I_2 - 6I_3 = 14 & 2\text{ Eq. 2} \\ 10I_2 + 20I_3 = 40 & 5\text{ Eq. 3} \end{cases}$$

$$\begin{cases} I_1 - I_2 + I_3 = 0 \\ 10I_2 - 6I_3 = 14 \\ 26I_3 = 26 & -\text{Eq. 2} + \text{Eq. 3} \end{cases}$$

$$26I_3 = 26 \Rightarrow I_3 = 1$$

$$10I_2 - 6(1) = 14 \Rightarrow I_2 = 2$$

$$I_1 - 2 + 1 = 0 \Rightarrow I_1 = 1$$

Answer: $I_1 = 1$ ampere, $I_2 = 2$ amperes, $I_3 = 1$ ampere

104. $$\begin{cases} t_1 - 2t_2 = 0 \Rightarrow \\ t_1 - 2a = 128 \Rightarrow \\ t_2 + a = 32 \Rightarrow \end{cases}$$

$$\begin{aligned} 2t_2 - 2a &= 128 \\ -2t_2 - 2a &= -64 \\ \hline -4a &= 64 \\ a &= -16 \\ t_2 &= 48 \\ t_1 &= 96 \end{aligned}$$

Answer: $t_1 = 96$ lb, $t_2 = 48$ lb, $a = -16\text{ ft/sec}^2$

105. Let x = number of par-3 holes.

Let y = number of par-4 holes.

Let z = number of par-5 holes.

$$\begin{cases} 3x + 4y + 5z = 72 \\ y - 2z = 2 \\ x - z = 0 \end{cases}$$

Solving the system, $x = 4, y = 10, z = 4$.

4 par-3 holes, 10 par-4 holes, and 4 par-5 holes

106. Let x = number of par-3 holes.

Let y = number of par-4 holes.

Let z = number of par-5 holes.

$$\begin{cases} 3x + 4y + 5z = 72 \\ y - 7z = 0 \\ x + z = 4 \end{cases}$$

Solving the system, $x = 2, y = 14, z = 2$.

2 par-3 holes, 14 par-4 holes, and 2 par-5 holes

107. Least squares regression parabola through $(-4, 5), (-2, 6), (2, 6), (4, 2)$

$$\begin{cases} 4c + 40a = 19 \\ 40b = -12 \\ 40c + 544a = 160 \end{cases}$$

Solving the system, $a = -\frac{5}{24}$, $b = -\frac{3}{10}$, and $c = \frac{41}{6}$.

Thus, $y = -\frac{5}{24}x^2 - \frac{3}{10}x + \frac{41}{6}$.

108. Least squares regression parabola through $(-2, 0), (-1, 0), (0, 1), (1, 2), (2, 5)$

$$\begin{cases} 5c + 10a = 8 \\ 10b = 12 \\ 10c + 34a = 22 \end{cases}$$

Solving the system, $a = \frac{3}{7}$, $b = \frac{6}{5}$, $c = \frac{26}{35}$.

Thus, $y = \frac{3}{7}x^2 + \frac{6}{5}x + \frac{26}{35}$.

109. Least squares regression parabola through $(0, 0), (2, 2), (3, 6), (4, 12)$

$$\begin{cases} 4c + 9b + 29a = 20 \\ 9c + 29b + 99a = 70 \\ 29c + 99b + 353a = 254 \end{cases}$$

Solving the system, $a = 1, b = -1$, and $c = 0$.
Thus, $y = x^2 - x$.

110. Least squares regression parabola through $(0, 10), (1, 9), (2, 6), (3, 0)$

$$\begin{cases} 4c + 6b + 14a = 25 \\ 6c + 14b + 36a = 21 \\ 14c + 36b + 98a = 33 \end{cases}$$

Solving the system, $a = -\frac{5}{4}$, $b = \frac{9}{20}$, $c = \frac{199}{20}$.
Thus, $y = -\frac{5}{4}x^2 + \frac{9}{20}x + \frac{199}{20}$.

111. (a) $\begin{cases} a(30)^2 + b(30) + c = 55 \\ a(40)^2 + b(40) + c = 105 \\ a(50)^2 + b(50) + c = 188 \end{cases}$

Solving the system, $a = 0.165, b = -6.55$ and $c = 103$.

$y = 0.165x^2 - 6.55x + 103$

(b) 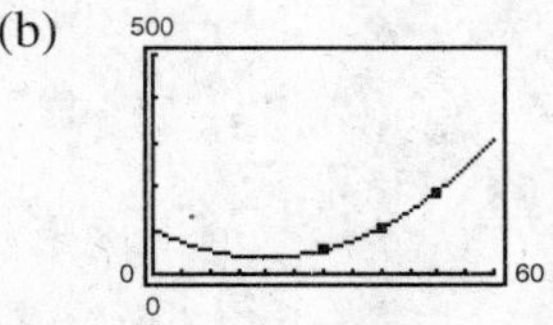

(c) For $x = 70$, $y = 453$ feet.

112. (a) $\begin{cases} a(120)^2 + b(120) + c = 68 \\ a(140)^2 + b(140) + c = 55 \\ a(160)^2 + b(160) + c = 30 \end{cases}$

Solving the system, $a = -0.015, b = 3.25$ and $c = -106$.

Parabola: $y = -0.015x^2 + 3.25x - 106$

(b) 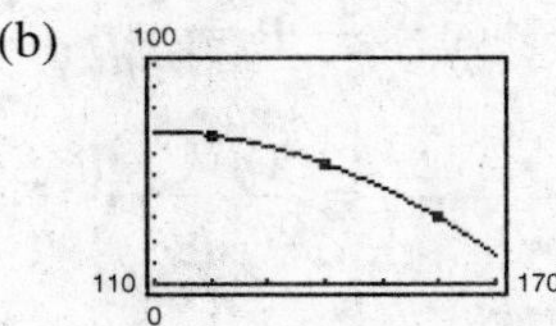

(c) For $x = 170$, $y = 13\%$

113. (a) $\dfrac{2000(4-3x)}{(11-7x)(7-4x)} = \dfrac{A}{11-7x} + \dfrac{B}{7-4x},\ 0 \le x \le 1$

$$2000(4-3x) = A(7-4x) + B(11-7x)$$

$$\begin{cases} -6000 = -4A - 7B \\ 8000 = 7A + 11B \end{cases} \Rightarrow \begin{matrix} A = -2000 \\ B = 2000 \end{matrix}$$

$$\frac{2000(4-3x)}{(11-7x)(7-4x)} = \frac{-2000}{11-7x} + \frac{2000}{7-4x} = \frac{2000}{7-4x} - \frac{2000}{11-7x}$$

(b) $y_1 = \dfrac{2000}{7-4x}$

$y_2 = \dfrac{2000}{11-7x}$

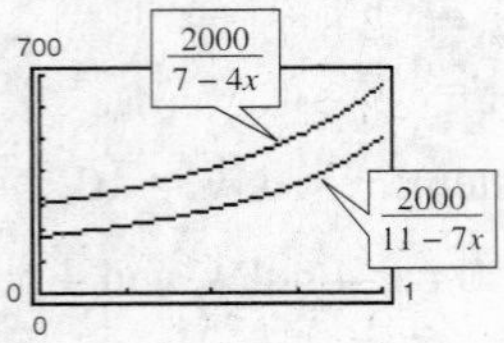

114. $C = \dfrac{120p}{10{,}000 - p^2} = \dfrac{120p}{(100-p)(100+p)},\ 0 \le p < 100$

$$\frac{120p}{(100-p)(100+p)} = \frac{A}{100-p} + \frac{B}{100+p}$$

$$A(100+p) + B(100-p) = 120p$$

$$\begin{cases} A - B = 120 \\ 100A + 100B = 0 \end{cases}$$

Hence, $A = 60$, $B = -60$ and $\dfrac{60}{100-p} - \dfrac{60}{100+p} = \dfrac{120p}{10{,}000 - p^2}$.

115. False. The coefficient of y in the second equation is not 1.

116. True. A common point would be a solution.

117. False. The correct form is

$$\frac{A}{x+10} + \frac{B}{x-10} + \frac{C}{(x-10)^2}.$$

118. $A = -1 \Rightarrow B = 1$. No, the problem was not worked correctly. You must first divide the improper fraction.

119. $\dfrac{1}{a^2 - x^2} = \dfrac{1}{(a+x)(a-x)} = \dfrac{A}{a+x} + \dfrac{B}{a-x}$

$$1 = A(a-x) + B(a+x) = (-A+B)x + (Aa+Ba)$$

$$\begin{cases} -A + B = 0 \\ Aa + Ba = 1 \end{cases} \Rightarrow A = \frac{1}{2a}, B = \frac{1}{2a}$$

$$\frac{1}{a^2-x^2} = \frac{1/2a}{a+x} + \frac{1/2a}{a-x} = \frac{1}{2a}\left[\frac{1}{a+x} + \frac{1}{a-x}\right]$$

120. $\dfrac{1}{(x+1)(a-x)} = \dfrac{A}{x+1} + \dfrac{B}{a-x}$

$$1 = A(a-x) + B(x+1)$$

Let $x = -1$: $1 = A(a+1) \Rightarrow A = \dfrac{1}{a+1}$

Let $x = a$: $B(a+1) \Rightarrow B = \dfrac{1}{a+1}$

$$\frac{1}{(x+1)(a-x)} = \frac{1}{a+1}\left[\frac{1}{x+1} + \frac{1}{a-x}\right]$$

121. $\dfrac{1}{y(a-y)} = \dfrac{A}{y} + \dfrac{B}{a-y}$

$$1 = A(a-y) + By = (-A+B)y + aA$$

$$A = \frac{1}{a}, B = \frac{1}{a}$$

$$\frac{1}{y(a-y)} = \frac{1}{a}\left(\frac{1}{y} + \frac{1}{a-y}\right)$$

122. $\dfrac{1}{x(x+a)} = \dfrac{A}{x} + \dfrac{B}{x+a}$, a is a constant.

$$1 = A(x+a) + Bx$$

Let $x = 0$: $1 = aA \Rightarrow A = \dfrac{1}{a}$

Let $x = -a$: $1 = -aB \Rightarrow B = -\dfrac{1}{a}$

$$\frac{1}{x(x+a)} = \frac{1}{a}\left[\frac{1}{x} - \frac{1}{x+a}\right]$$

123. No, they are not equivalent. In the second system, the constant in the second equation should be -11 and the coefficient of z in the third equation should be 2.

124. When using Gaussian elimination to solve a system of linear equations, a system has no solution when there is a row representing a contradictory equation such as $0 = N$, where N is a nonzero real number.

For instance: $\begin{cases} x + y = 3 & \text{Equation 1} \\ -x - y = 3 & \text{Equation 2} \end{cases}$

$\begin{cases} x + y = 3 & \\ 0 = 6 & \text{Eq. 1 + Eq. 2} \end{cases}$

No solution

125. $\begin{cases} y + \quad \lambda = \\ x + \quad \lambda = \\ x + y - 10 = \end{cases}$ $\Rightarrow x = y = -\lambda$, $\Rightarrow 2x - 10 = 0$

$x = 5$

$y = 5$

$\lambda = -5$

126. $\begin{cases} 2x + \lambda = 0 \\ 2y + \lambda = 0 \\ x + y - 4 = 0 \end{cases}$ $\Rightarrow x = y = -\lambda/2$, $\Rightarrow 2x - 4 = 0$

$2x = 4$

$x = 2$

$y = 2$

$\lambda = -4$

127. $\begin{cases} 2x - 2x\lambda = 0 \Rightarrow x = x\lambda \\ -2y + \lambda = 0 \Rightarrow 2y = \lambda \\ y - x^2 = 0 \Rightarrow y = x^2 \end{cases}$

From the first equation, $x = 0$ or $\lambda = 1$.

If $x = 0$, then $y = 0^2 = 0$ and $\lambda = 0$.

If $x \neq 0$, then $\lambda = 1 \Rightarrow y = \frac{1}{2}$ and $x = \pm\sqrt{\frac{1}{2}}$.

Thus, the solutions are:

(1) $x = y = \lambda = 0$

(2) $x = \dfrac{\sqrt{2}}{2}$, $y = \dfrac{1}{2}$, $\lambda = 1$

(3) $x = -\dfrac{\sqrt{2}}{2}$, $y = \dfrac{1}{2}$, $\lambda = 1$

128. $\begin{cases} 2 + 2x + 2\lambda = 0 \\ 2x + 1 + \lambda = 0 \Rightarrow \lambda = -2x - 1 \\ 2x + y - 100 = 0 \end{cases}$

$2 + 2x + 2(-2x - 1) = 0$

$-2x = 0$

$x = 0$

Then, $\lambda = -1$ and $y = 100 - 2x = 100$

Answer: $x = 0$, $y = 100$, $\lambda = -1$.

129. $y = -3x + 7$

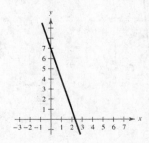

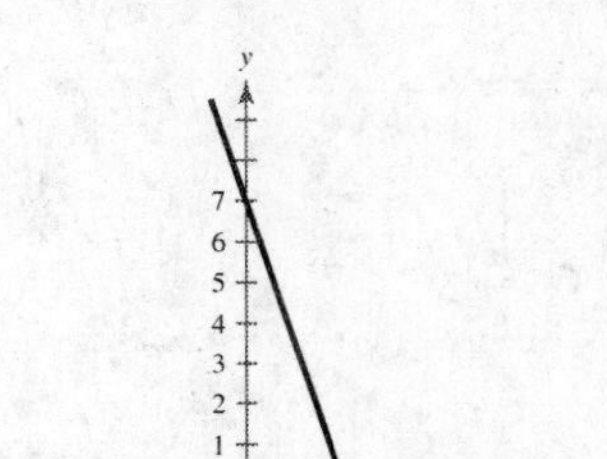

130.

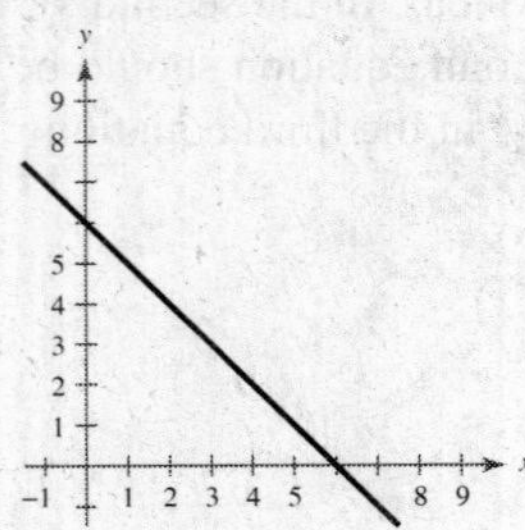

131. $y = -2x^2$

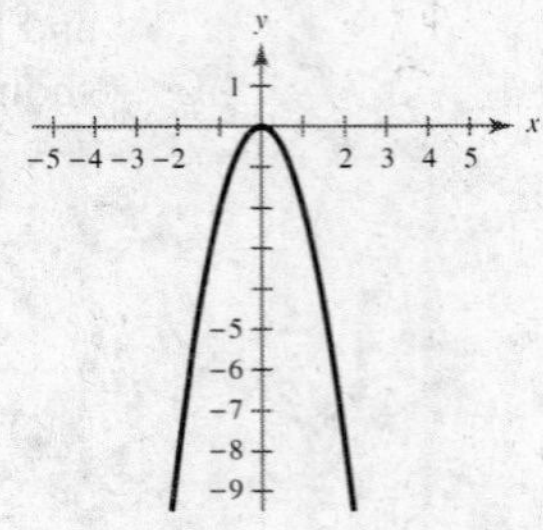

132. $y = \frac{1}{4}x^2 + 1$

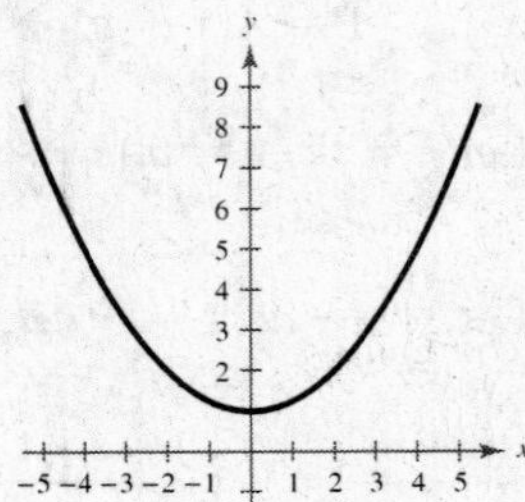

133. $y = -x^2(x - 3)$

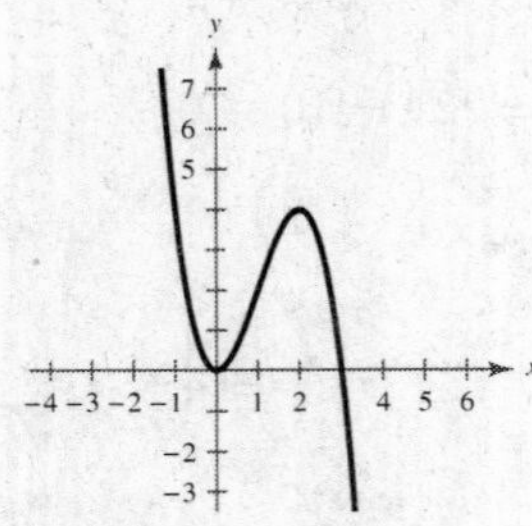

134. $y = \frac{1}{2}x^3 - 1$

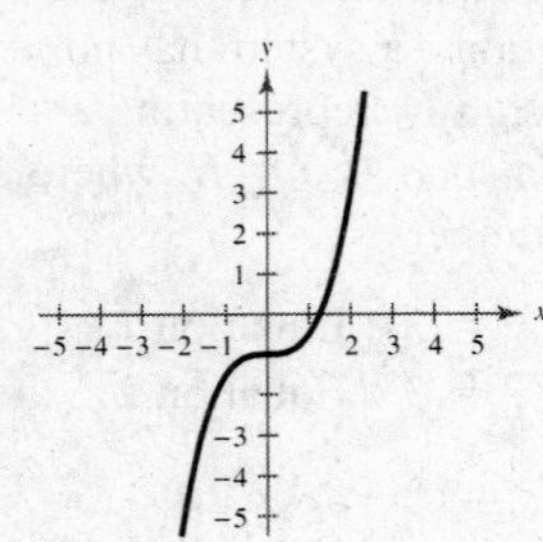

135. (a) $f(x) = x^3 + x^2 - 12x$

$= x(x^2 + x - 12) = x(x + 4)(x - 3)$

$\Longrightarrow x = 0, -4, 3$

(b)

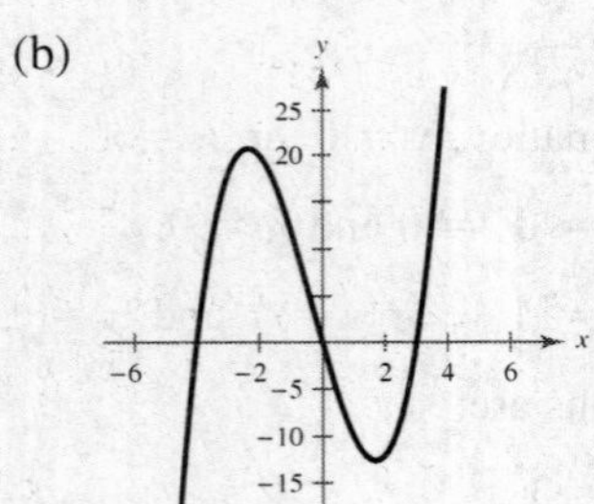

136. (a) $f(x) = -8x^4 + 32x^2$

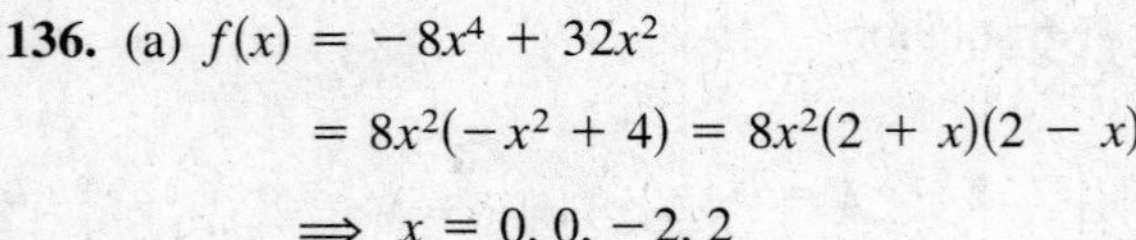

$= 8x^2(-x^2 + 4) = 8x^2(2 + x)(2 - x)$

$\Longrightarrow x = 0, 0, -2, 2$

(b)

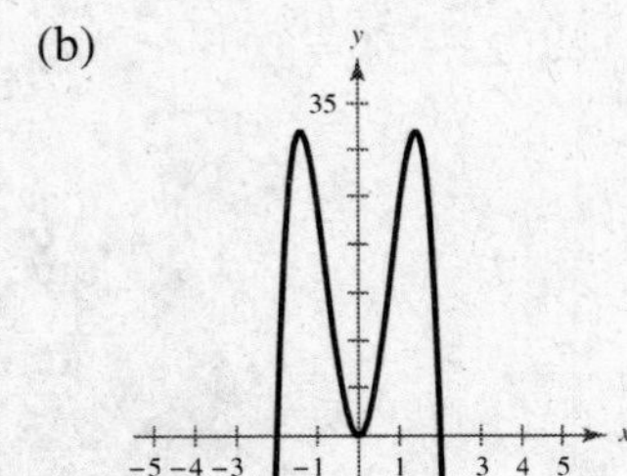

137. (a) $f(x) = 2x^3 + 5x^2 - 21x - 36$

$= (2x + 3)(x + 4)(x - 3)$

$\Longrightarrow x = -\frac{3}{2}, -4, 3$

(b)

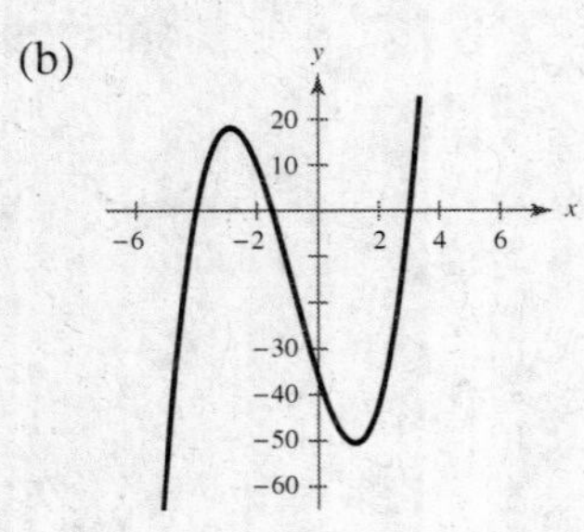

138. (a) $f(x) = 6x^3 - 29x^2 - 6x + 5$

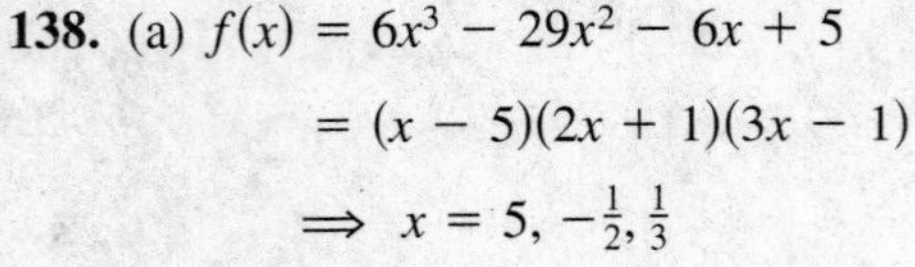

$= (x - 5)(2x + 1)(3x - 1)$

$\Longrightarrow x = 5, -\frac{1}{2}, \frac{1}{3}$

(b)

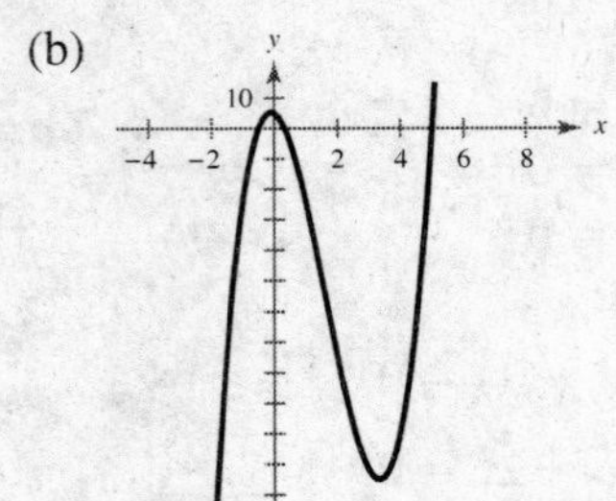

139.

x	-2	-1	0	1	2
y	16	8	4	2	1

$y = \left(\frac{1}{2}\right)^{x-2}$

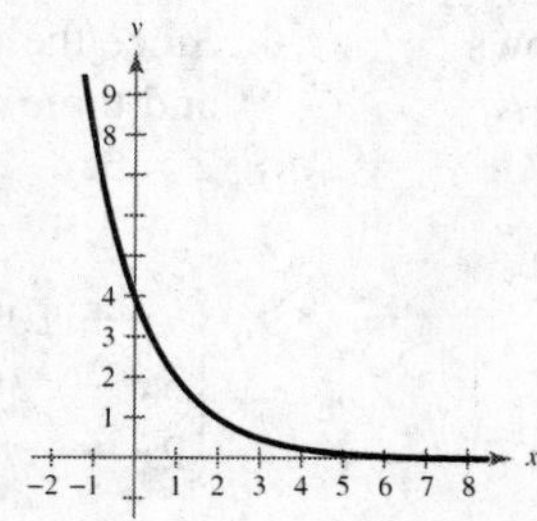

140.

x	-2	-1	0	1
y	10	4	2	1.33

$y = \left(\frac{1}{3}\right)^{x} + 1$

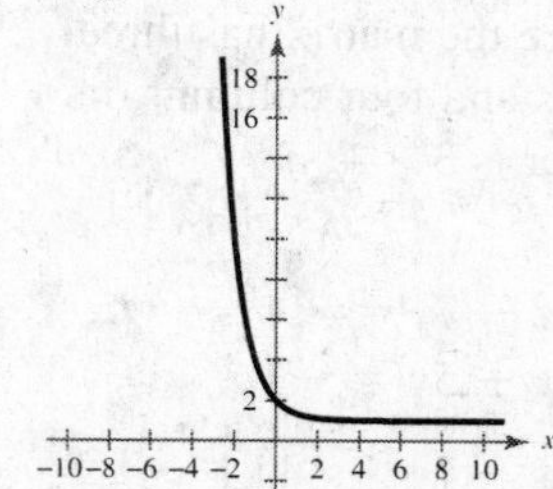

141.

x	-2	-1	0	1	2
y	$-\frac{1}{2}$	0	1	3	7

$y = 2^{x+1} - 1$

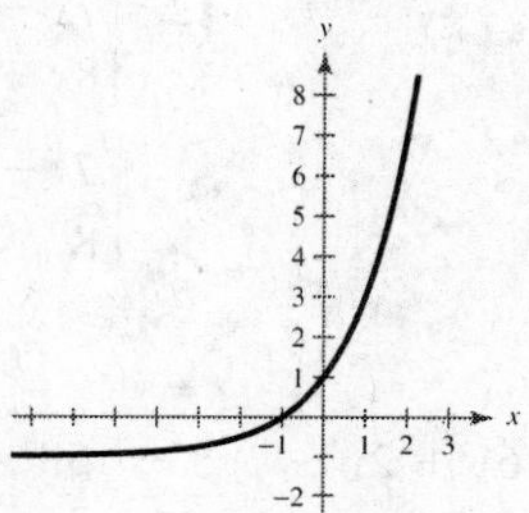

142.

x	-2	0	1	2
y	2.037	2.33	3	5

$y = 3^{x-1} + 2$

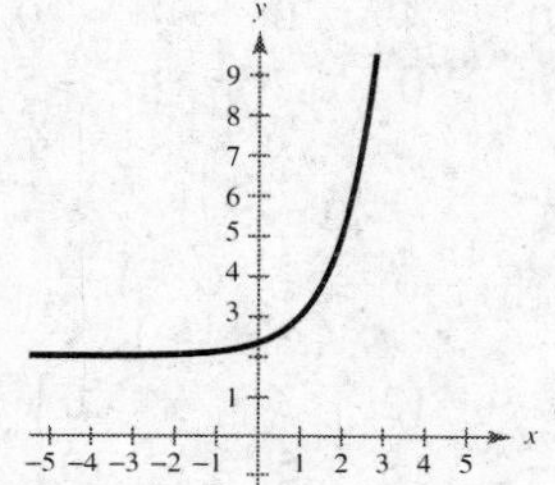

143. Answers will vary.

Section 7.4 Matrices and Systems of Equations

- You should be able to use elementary row operations to produce a row-echelon form (or reduced row-echelon form) of a matrix.
  1. Interchange two rows
  2. Multiply a row by a nonzero constant
  3. Add a multiple of one row to another row
- You should be able to use either Gaussian elimination with back-substitution or Gauss-Jordan elimination to solve a system of linear equations.

Vocabulary Check

1. matrix **2.** square **3.** row matrix, column matrix

4. augmented matrix **5.** coefficient matrix **6.** row-equivalent

7. reduced row-echelon form **8.** Gauss-Jordan elimination

1. Since the matrix has one row and two columns, its order is 1×2.

2. Since the matrix has one row and four columns, its order is 1×4.

3. Since the matrix has three rows and one column, its order is 3×1.

4. Since the matrix has three rows and four columns, its order is 3×4.

5. Since the matrix has two rows and two columns, its order is 2×2.

6. Since the matrix has two rows and three columns, its order is 2×3.

7. $\begin{aligned} 6x - 7y &= 11 \\ -2x + 5y &= -1 \end{aligned}$

$$\left[\begin{array}{cc:c} 6 & -7 & 11 \\ -2 & 5 & -1 \end{array}\right]$$

8. $\begin{cases} 7x + 4y = 22 \\ 5x - 9y = 15 \end{cases}$

$$\left[\begin{array}{cc:c} 7 & 4 & 22 \\ 5 & -9 & 15 \end{array}\right]$$

9. $\begin{cases} x + 10y - 2z = 2 \\ 5x - 3y + 4z = 0 \\ 2x + y \qquad = 6 \end{cases}$

$$\left[\begin{array}{ccc:c} 1 & 10 & -2 & 2 \\ 5 & -3 & 4 & 0 \\ 2 & 1 & 0 & 6 \end{array}\right]$$

10. $\left[\begin{array}{ccc:c} 1 & -3 & 1 & 1 \\ 0 & 4 & 0 & 0 \\ 0 & 0 & 7 & -5 \end{array}\right]$

11. $\begin{aligned} 3x + 4y &= 9 \\ x - y &= -3 \end{aligned}$

$$\left[\begin{array}{cc:c} 3 & 4 & 9 \\ 1 & -1 & -3 \end{array}\right]$$

12. $\begin{cases} 7x - 5y = 0 \\ 8x + 3y = -2 \end{cases}$

$$\left[\begin{array}{cc:c} 7 & -5 & 0 \\ 8 & 3 & -2 \end{array}\right]$$

13. $\left[\begin{array}{ccc:c} 9 & 12 & 3 & 0 \\ -2 & 18 & 5 & 10 \\ 1 & 7 & -8 & -4 \end{array}\right]$

$$\begin{cases} 9x + 12y + 3z = 0 \\ -2x + 18y + 5z = 10 \\ x + 7y - 8z = -4 \end{cases}$$

14. $\begin{cases} 6x + 2y - z - 5w = -25 \\ -x + 7z + 3w = 7 \\ 4x - y - 10z + 6w = 23 \\ 8y + z - 11w = -21 \end{cases}$

15. $\begin{bmatrix} 1 & 4 & 3 \\ 2 & 10 & 5 \end{bmatrix}$

$$\begin{matrix} \\ -2R_1 + R_2 \rightarrow \end{matrix} \begin{bmatrix} 1 & 4 & 3 \\ 0 & \boxed{2} & \boxed{-1} \end{bmatrix}$$

16. $\begin{bmatrix} 3 & 6 & 8 \\ 4 & -3 & 6 \end{bmatrix}$

$$\begin{matrix} \frac{1}{3}R_1 \rightarrow \\ \\ \end{matrix} \begin{bmatrix} 1 & \boxed{2} & \boxed{\frac{8}{3}} \\ 4 & -3 & 6 \end{bmatrix}$$

17. $\begin{bmatrix} 1 & 1 & 4 & -1 \\ 3 & 8 & 10 & 3 \\ -2 & 1 & 12 & 6 \end{bmatrix}$

$$\begin{matrix} \\ -3R_1 + R_2 \rightarrow \\ 2R_1 + R_3 \rightarrow \end{matrix} \begin{bmatrix} 1 & 1 & 4 & -1 \\ 0 & 5 & \boxed{-2} & \boxed{6} \\ 0 & 3 & \boxed{20} & \boxed{4} \end{bmatrix}$$

$$\begin{matrix} \\ \frac{1}{5}R_2 \rightarrow \\ \\ \end{matrix} \begin{bmatrix} 1 & 1 & 4 & -1 \\ 0 & 1 & -\frac{2}{5} & \frac{6}{5} \\ 0 & 3 & \boxed{20} & \boxed{4} \end{bmatrix}$$

18. $\begin{bmatrix} 2 & 4 & 8 & 3 \\ 1 & -1 & -3 & 2 \\ 2 & 6 & 4 & 9 \end{bmatrix}$

$$\begin{matrix} \frac{1}{2}R_1 \rightarrow \\ \\ \\ \end{matrix} \begin{bmatrix} 1 & \boxed{2} & \boxed{4} & \boxed{\frac{3}{2}} \\ 1 & -1 & -3 & 2 \\ 2 & 6 & 4 & 9 \end{bmatrix}$$

$$\begin{matrix} \\ -R_1 + R_2 \rightarrow \\ -2R_1 + R_3 \rightarrow \end{matrix} \begin{bmatrix} 1 & 2 & 4 & \frac{3}{2} \\ 0 & \boxed{-3} & -7 & \frac{1}{2} \\ 0 & 2 & \boxed{-4} & \boxed{6} \end{bmatrix}$$

19. Add -3 times Row 2 to Row 1.

20. 3 times Row 1 added to Row 2.

21. Interchange Rows 1 and 2.

22. 5 times Row 1 added to Row 3.

23. $\begin{bmatrix} 1 & 0 & 0 & 0 \\ 0 & 1 & 1 & 5 \\ 0 & 0 & 0 & 0 \end{bmatrix}$

This matrix is in reduced row-echelon form.

24. $\begin{bmatrix} 1 & 3 & 0 & 0 \\ 0 & 0 & 1 & 8 \\ 0 & 0 & 0 & 0 \end{bmatrix}$

This matrix is in reduced row-echelon form.

25. $\begin{bmatrix} 3 & 0 & 3 & 7 \\ 0 & -2 & 0 & 4 \\ 0 & 0 & 1 & 5 \end{bmatrix}$

The first nonzero entries in rows one and two are not one. The matrix is not in row-echelon form.

26. $\begin{bmatrix} 1 & 0 & 2 & 1 \\ 0 & 1 & -3 & 10 \\ 0 & 0 & 1 & 0 \end{bmatrix}$

This matrix is in row-echelon form, but not reduced row-echelon form.

27. $\begin{bmatrix} 1 & 0 & 0 & 1 \\ 0 & 1 & 0 & -1 \\ 0 & 0 & 0 & 2 \end{bmatrix}$

The first nonzero entry in row three is two, not one. The matrix is not in row-echelon form.

28. $\begin{bmatrix} 1 & 0 & 1 & 0 \\ 0 & 1 & 0 & 2 \\ 0 & 0 & 1 & 0 \end{bmatrix}$

The matrix is in row-echelon form, but not reduced row-echelon form. There is a one above the leading one of row three.

29. $\begin{bmatrix} 1 & 2 & 3 \\ 2 & -1 & -4 \\ 3 & 1 & -1 \end{bmatrix}$

(a) $\begin{bmatrix} 1 & 2 & 3 \\ 0 & -5 & -10 \\ 3 & 1 & -1 \end{bmatrix}$ (b) $\begin{bmatrix} 1 & 2 & 3 \\ 0 & -5 & -10 \\ 0 & -5 & -10 \end{bmatrix}$ (c) $\begin{bmatrix} 1 & 2 & 3 \\ 0 & -5 & -10 \\ 0 & 0 & 0 \end{bmatrix}$

(d) $\begin{bmatrix} 1 & 2 & 3 \\ 0 & 1 & 2 \\ 0 & 0 & 0 \end{bmatrix}$ (e) $\begin{bmatrix} 1 & 0 & -1 \\ 0 & 1 & 2 \\ 0 & 0 & 0 \end{bmatrix}$ This matrix is in reduced row-echelon form.

30. $\begin{bmatrix} 7 & 1 \\ 0 & 2 \\ -3 & 4 \\ 4 & 1 \end{bmatrix}$

(a) $\begin{bmatrix} 7 & 1 \\ 0 & 2 \\ -3 & 4 \\ 1 & 5 \end{bmatrix}$ (b) $\begin{bmatrix} 1 & 5 \\ 0 & 2 \\ -3 & 4 \\ 7 & 1 \end{bmatrix}$ (c) $\begin{bmatrix} 1 & 5 \\ 0 & 2 \\ 0 & 19 \\ 7 & 1 \end{bmatrix}$ (d) $\begin{bmatrix} 1 & 5 \\ 0 & 2 \\ 0 & 19 \\ 0 & -34 \end{bmatrix}$

(e) $\begin{bmatrix} 1 & 5 \\ 0 & 1 \\ 0 & 19 \\ 0 & -34 \end{bmatrix}$ (f) $\begin{bmatrix} 1 & 0 \\ 0 & 1 \\ 0 & 0 \\ 0 & 0 \end{bmatrix}$ This matrix is in reduced row-echelon form.

31. (See Exercise 29.) (Answer is a series of screens.)

(a)
```
*row+(-2,[A],1,2
)→[B]
      [[1 2  3  ]
       [0 -5 -10]
       [3 1  -1 ]]
```

(b)
```
*row+(-3,[B],1,3
)→[C]
      [[1 2  3  ]
       [0 -5 -10]
       [0 -5 -10]]
```

(c)
```
*row+(-1,[C],2,3
)→[D]
      [[1 2  3  ]
       [0 -5 -10]
       [0 0  0  ]]
```

(d)
```
*row(-1/5,[D],2)
→[E]
         [[1 2 3]
          [0 1 2]
          [0 0 0]]
```

(e)
```
*row+(-2,[E],2,1
)
        [[1 0 -1]
         [0 1 2 ]
         [0 0 0 ]]
```

32. (a)
```
row+([A],3,4)→[B
]
         [[7  1]
          [0  2]
          [-3 4]
          [1  5]]
```

(b)
```
rowSwap([B],1,4)
→[C]
         [[1  5]
          [0  2]
          [-3 4]
          [7  1]]
```

(c)
```
*row+(3,[C],1,3)
→[D]
         [[1 5 ]
          [0 2 ]
          [0 19]
          [7 1 ]]
```

(d)
```
*row+(-7,[D],1,4
)→[E]
         [[1 5  ]
          [0 2  ]
          [0 19 ]
          [0 -34]]
```

(e)
```
*row(1/2,[E],2)→
[F]
         [[1 5  ]
          [0 1  ]
          [0 19 ]
          [0 -34]]
```

(f)
```
*row+(-19,[F],2,
3)→[G]
         [[1 5  ]
          [0 1  ]
          [0 0  ]
          [0 -34]]
```

33.
$$\begin{bmatrix} 1 & 2 & 3 & 0 \\ -1 & 4 & 0 & -5 \\ 2 & 6 & 3 & 10 \end{bmatrix}$$

$$\begin{matrix} \\ R_1 + R_2 \rightarrow \\ -2R_1 + R_3 \rightarrow \end{matrix} \begin{bmatrix} 1 & 2 & 3 & 0 \\ 0 & 6 & 3 & -5 \\ 0 & 2 & -3 & 10 \end{bmatrix}$$

$$\begin{matrix} \\ \frac{1}{6}R_2 \rightarrow \\ \\ \end{matrix} \begin{bmatrix} 1 & 2 & 3 & 0 \\ 0 & 1 & \frac{1}{2} & -\frac{5}{6} \\ 0 & 2 & -3 & 10 \end{bmatrix}$$

$$\begin{matrix} \\ \\ -2R_2 + R_3 \rightarrow \end{matrix} \begin{bmatrix} 1 & 2 & 3 & 0 \\ 0 & 1 & \frac{1}{2} & -\frac{5}{6} \\ 0 & 0 & -4 & \frac{35}{3} \end{bmatrix}$$

$$\begin{matrix} \\ \\ -\frac{1}{4}R_3 \rightarrow \end{matrix} \begin{bmatrix} 1 & 2 & 3 & 0 \\ 0 & 1 & \frac{1}{2} & -\frac{5}{6} \\ 0 & 0 & 1 & -\frac{35}{12} \end{bmatrix}$$

(Answers may vary.)

34.
$$\begin{bmatrix} 1 & 2 & -1 & 3 \\ 3 & 7 & -5 & 14 \\ -2 & -1 & -3 & 8 \end{bmatrix}$$

$$\begin{matrix} \\ -3R_1 + R_2 \rightarrow \\ 2R_1 + R_3 \rightarrow \end{matrix} \begin{bmatrix} 1 & 2 & -1 & 3 \\ 0 & 1 & -2 & 5 \\ 0 & 3 & -5 & 14 \end{bmatrix}$$

$$\begin{matrix} \\ \\ -3R_2 + R_3 \rightarrow \end{matrix} \begin{bmatrix} 1 & 2 & -1 & 3 \\ 0 & 1 & -2 & 5 \\ 0 & 0 & 1 & -1 \end{bmatrix}$$

35.
$$\begin{bmatrix} 1 & -1 & -1 & 1 \\ 5 & -4 & 1 & 8 \\ -6 & 8 & 18 & 0 \end{bmatrix}$$

$$\begin{matrix} \\ -5R_1 + R_2 \rightarrow \\ 6R_1 + R_3 \rightarrow \end{matrix} \begin{bmatrix} 1 & -1 & -1 & 1 \\ 0 & 1 & 6 & 3 \\ 0 & 2 & 12 & 6 \end{bmatrix}$$

$$\begin{matrix} \\ \\ -2R_2 + R_3 \rightarrow \end{matrix} \begin{bmatrix} 1 & -1 & -1 & 1 \\ 0 & 1 & 6 & 3 \\ 0 & 0 & 0 & 0 \end{bmatrix}$$

36.
$$\begin{bmatrix} 1 & -3 & 0 & -7 \\ -3 & 10 & 1 & 23 \\ 4 & -10 & 2 & -24 \end{bmatrix}$$

$$\begin{matrix} \\ 3R_1 + R_2 \rightarrow \\ -4R_1 + R_3 \rightarrow \end{matrix} \begin{bmatrix} 1 & -3 & 0 & -7 \\ 0 & 1 & 1 & 2 \\ 0 & 2 & 2 & 4 \end{bmatrix}$$

$$\begin{matrix} \\ \\ -2R_2 + R_3 \rightarrow \end{matrix} \begin{bmatrix} 1 & -3 & 0 & -7 \\ 0 & 1 & 1 & 2 \\ 0 & 0 & 0 & 0 \end{bmatrix}$$

37.
$$\begin{bmatrix} 3 & 3 & 3 \\ -1 & 0 & -4 \\ 2 & 4 & -2 \end{bmatrix}$$

$$\tfrac{1}{3}R_1 \rightarrow \begin{bmatrix} 1 & 1 & 1 \\ -1 & 0 & -4 \\ 2 & 4 & -2 \end{bmatrix}$$

$$\begin{matrix} \\ R_1 + R_2 \rightarrow \\ -2R_1 + R_3 \rightarrow \end{matrix} \begin{bmatrix} 1 & 1 & 1 \\ 0 & 1 & -3 \\ 0 & 2 & -4 \end{bmatrix}$$

$$\begin{matrix} -R_2 + R_1 \rightarrow \\ \\ -2R_2 + R_3 \rightarrow \end{matrix} \begin{bmatrix} 1 & 0 & 4 \\ 0 & 1 & -3 \\ 0 & 0 & 2 \end{bmatrix}$$

$$\begin{matrix} \\ \\ \tfrac{1}{2}R_3 \rightarrow \end{matrix} \begin{bmatrix} 1 & 0 & 4 \\ 0 & 1 & -3 \\ 0 & 0 & 1 \end{bmatrix}$$

$$\begin{matrix} -4R_3 + R_1 \rightarrow \\ 3R_3 + R_2 \rightarrow \\ \\ \end{matrix} \begin{bmatrix} 1 & 0 & 0 \\ 0 & 1 & 0 \\ 0 & 0 & 1 \end{bmatrix}$$

38.
$$\begin{bmatrix} 1 & 3 & 2 \\ 5 & 15 & 9 \\ 2 & 6 & 10 \end{bmatrix}$$

$$\begin{matrix} \\ -5R_1 + R_2 \rightarrow \\ -2R_1 + R_3 \rightarrow \end{matrix} \begin{bmatrix} 1 & 3 & 2 \\ 0 & 0 & -1 \\ 0 & 0 & 6 \end{bmatrix}$$

$$\begin{matrix} 2R_2 + R_1 \rightarrow \\ \\ 6R_2 + R_3 \rightarrow \end{matrix} \begin{bmatrix} 1 & 3 & 0 \\ 0 & 0 & -1 \\ 0 & 0 & 0 \end{bmatrix}$$

$$\begin{matrix} \\ -1R_2 \rightarrow \\ \\ \end{matrix} \begin{bmatrix} 1 & 3 & 0 \\ 0 & 0 & 1 \\ 0 & 0 & 0 \end{bmatrix}$$

39.
$$\begin{bmatrix} -4 & 1 & 0 & 6 \\ 1 & -2 & 3 & -4 \end{bmatrix}$$

$$\begin{matrix} R_1 \rightarrow \\ R_2 \rightarrow \end{matrix} \begin{bmatrix} 1 & -2 & 3 & -4 \\ -4 & 1 & 0 & 6 \end{bmatrix}$$

$$\begin{matrix} \\ 4R_1 + R_2 \rightarrow \end{matrix} \begin{bmatrix} 1 & -2 & 3 & -4 \\ 0 & -7 & 12 & -10 \end{bmatrix}$$

$$\begin{matrix} \\ -\tfrac{1}{7}R_2 \rightarrow \end{matrix} \begin{bmatrix} 1 & -2 & 3 & -4 \\ 0 & 1 & -\tfrac{12}{7} & \tfrac{10}{7} \end{bmatrix}$$

$$\begin{matrix} 2R_2 + R_1 \rightarrow \\ \\ \end{matrix} \begin{bmatrix} 1 & 0 & -\tfrac{3}{7} & -\tfrac{8}{7} \\ 0 & 1 & -\tfrac{12}{7} & \tfrac{10}{7} \end{bmatrix}$$

40.
$$\begin{bmatrix} 5 & 1 & 2 & 4 \\ -1 & 5 & 10 & -32 \end{bmatrix} \begin{matrix} R_1 \\ R_2 \end{matrix} \begin{bmatrix} -1 & 5 & 10 & -32 \\ 5 & 1 & 2 & 4 \end{bmatrix}$$

$$\begin{matrix} \\ 5R_1 + R_2 \rightarrow \end{matrix} \begin{bmatrix} -1 & 5 & 10 & -32 \\ 0 & 26 & 52 & -156 \end{bmatrix}$$

$$\begin{matrix} (-1)R_1 \rightarrow \\ \tfrac{1}{26}R_2 \rightarrow \end{matrix} \begin{bmatrix} 1 & -5 & -10 & 32 \\ 0 & 1 & 2 & -6 \end{bmatrix}$$

$$\begin{matrix} 5R_2 + R_1 \rightarrow \\ \\ \end{matrix} \begin{bmatrix} 1 & 0 & 0 & 2 \\ 0 & 1 & 2 & -6 \end{bmatrix}$$

41. $x - 2y = 4$

$y = -3$

$x = 2y + 4 = 2(-3) + 4 = -2$

Answer: $(x, y) = (-2, -3)$

42. $x + 8y = 12$

$y = 3$

$x + 8(3) = 12$

$x = -12$

Answer: $(-12, 3)$

43. $\begin{cases} x - y + 2z = 4 \\ y - z = 2 \\ z = -2 \end{cases}$

$y - (-2) = 2$

$y = 0$

$x - 0 + 2(-2) = 4$

$x = 8$

Answer: $(8, 0, -2)$

44. $x + 2y - 2z = -1$

$y + z = 9$

$z = -3$

$y = -z + 9 = 3 + 9 = 12$

$x = -2y + 2z - 1 = -24 - 6 - 1 = -31$

Answer: $(x, y, z) = (-31, 12, -3)$

45. $\begin{bmatrix} 1 & 0 & \vdots & 7 \\ 0 & 1 & \vdots & -5 \end{bmatrix}$

$x = 7$

$y = -5$

Answer: $(7, -5)$

46. $\begin{bmatrix} 1 & 0 & \vdots & -2 \\ 0 & 1 & \vdots & 4 \end{bmatrix}$

$x = -2$

$y = 4$

Answer: $(-2, 4)$

47. $\begin{bmatrix} 1 & 0 & 0 & \vdots & -4 \\ 0 & 1 & 0 & \vdots & -8 \\ 0 & 0 & 1 & \vdots & 2 \end{bmatrix}$

$x = -4$

$y = -8$

$z = 2$

Answer: $(-4, -8, 2)$

48. $\begin{bmatrix} 1 & 0 & 0 & \vdots & 3 \\ 0 & 1 & 0 & \vdots & -1 \\ 0 & 0 & 1 & \vdots & 0 \end{bmatrix}$

$x = 3$

$y = -1$

$z = 0$

Answer: $(3, -1, 0)$

49. $\begin{cases} x + 2y = 7 \\ 2x + y = 8 \end{cases}$

$$\begin{bmatrix} 1 & 2 & \vdots & 7 \\ 2 & 1 & \vdots & 8 \end{bmatrix}$$

$$-2R_1 + R_2 \rightarrow \begin{bmatrix} 1 & 2 & \vdots & 7 \\ 0 & -3 & \vdots & -6 \end{bmatrix}$$

$$-\tfrac{1}{3}R_2 \rightarrow \begin{bmatrix} 1 & 2 & \vdots & 7 \\ 0 & 1 & \vdots & 2 \end{bmatrix}$$

$y = 2$

$x + 2(2) = 7 \Rightarrow x = 3$

Answer: $(3, 2)$

50. $\begin{bmatrix} 2 & 6 & \vdots & 16 \\ 2 & 3 & \vdots & 7 \end{bmatrix}$

$$\begin{bmatrix} 2 & 6 & \vdots & 16 \\ 0 & -3 & \vdots & -9 \end{bmatrix}$$

$$\begin{bmatrix} 2 & 0 & \vdots & -2 \\ 0 & 1 & \vdots & 3 \end{bmatrix}$$

$y = 3, x = -1$

Answer: $(-1, 3)$

51. $\begin{cases} -x + y = -22 \\ 3x + 4y = 4 \\ 4x - 8y = 32 \end{cases}$

$$\begin{bmatrix} -1 & 1 & \vdots & -22 \\ 3 & 4 & \vdots & 4 \\ 4 & -8 & \vdots & 32 \end{bmatrix}$$

$$\begin{matrix} \\ 3R_1 + R_2 \rightarrow \\ 4R_1 + R_3 \rightarrow \end{matrix} \begin{bmatrix} -1 & 1 & \vdots & -22 \\ 0 & 7 & \vdots & -62 \\ 0 & -4 & \vdots & -56 \end{bmatrix}$$

$$\begin{matrix} \\ R_2 \rightarrow \\ R_3 \rightarrow \end{matrix} \begin{bmatrix} -1 & 1 & \vdots & -22 \\ 0 & -4 & \vdots & -56 \\ 0 & 7 & \vdots & -62 \end{bmatrix}$$

$$\begin{matrix} \\ -\frac{1}{4}R_2 \rightarrow \\ -7R_2 + R_3 \rightarrow \end{matrix} \begin{bmatrix} -1 & 1 & \vdots & -22 \\ 0 & 1 & \vdots & 14 \\ 0 & 0 & \vdots & -160 \end{bmatrix}$$

No solution, inconsistent

52. $\begin{cases} x + 2y = 0 \\ x + y = 6 \\ 3x - 2y = 8 \end{cases}$

$$\begin{bmatrix} 1 & 2 & \vdots & 0 \\ 1 & 1 & \vdots & 6 \\ 3 & -2 & \vdots & 8 \end{bmatrix}$$

$$\begin{matrix} \\ -R_1 + R_2 \rightarrow \\ -3R_1 + R_3 \rightarrow \end{matrix} \begin{bmatrix} 1 & 2 & \vdots & 0 \\ 0 & -1 & \vdots & 6 \\ 0 & -8 & \vdots & 8 \end{bmatrix}$$

$$\begin{matrix} \\ -R_2 \rightarrow \\ -8R_2 + R_3 \rightarrow \end{matrix} \begin{bmatrix} 1 & 2 & \vdots & 0 \\ 0 & 1 & \vdots & 6 \\ 0 & 0 & \vdots & -40 \end{bmatrix}$$

No solution, inconsistent

53. $$\begin{bmatrix} 3 & 2 & -1 & 1 & \vdots & 0 \\ 1 & -1 & 4 & 2 & \vdots & 25 \\ -2 & 1 & 2 & -1 & \vdots & 2 \\ 1 & 1 & 1 & 1 & \vdots & 6 \end{bmatrix}$$

$$\begin{bmatrix} 1 & -1 & 4 & 2 & \vdots & 25 \\ 0 & 5 & -13 & -5 & \vdots & -75 \\ 0 & -1 & 10 & 3 & \vdots & 52 \\ 0 & 2 & -3 & -1 & \vdots & -19 \end{bmatrix}$$

$$\begin{bmatrix} 1 & -1 & 4 & 2 & \vdots & 25 \\ 0 & 1 & -10 & -3 & \vdots & -52 \\ 0 & 0 & 37 & 10 & \vdots & 185 \\ 0 & 0 & 17 & 5 & \vdots & 85 \end{bmatrix}$$

$$\begin{bmatrix} 1 & -1 & 4 & 2 & \vdots & 25 \\ 0 & 1 & -10 & -3 & \vdots & -52 \\ 0 & 0 & 37 & 10 & \vdots & 185 \\ 0 & 0 & 0 & \frac{15}{37} & \vdots & 0 \end{bmatrix}$$

$w = 0, z = \frac{185}{37} = 5, y = -52 + 10(5) = -2$

$x = 25 + (-2) - 4(5) = 3$

Answer: $(3, -2, 5, 0)$

54. $$\begin{bmatrix} 1 & -4 & 3 & -2 & \vdots & 9 \\ 3 & -2 & 1 & -4 & \vdots & -13 \\ -4 & 3 & -2 & 1 & \vdots & -4 \\ -2 & 1 & -4 & 3 & \vdots & -10 \end{bmatrix}$$

$$\begin{bmatrix} 1 & -4 & 3 & -2 & \vdots & 9 \\ 0 & 10 & -8 & 2 & \vdots & -40 \\ 0 & -13 & 10 & -7 & \vdots & 32 \\ 0 & -7 & 2 & -1 & \vdots & 8 \end{bmatrix}$$

$$\begin{bmatrix} 1 & -4 & 3 & -2 & \vdots & 9 \\ 0 & 1 & -\frac{4}{5} & \frac{1}{5} & \vdots & -4 \\ 0 & 0 & -\frac{2}{5} & -\frac{22}{5} & \vdots & -20 \\ 0 & 0 & -\frac{18}{5} & \frac{2}{5} & \vdots & -20 \end{bmatrix}$$

$$\begin{bmatrix} 1 & -4 & 3 & -2 & \vdots & 9 \\ 0 & 1 & -\frac{4}{5} & \frac{1}{5} & \vdots & -4 \\ 0 & 0 & 1 & 11 & \vdots & 50 \\ 0 & 0 & 0 & 40 & \vdots & 160 \end{bmatrix}$$

$w = \frac{160}{40} = 4, z = 50 - 4(11) = 6$

$y = -4 + \frac{4}{5}(6) - \frac{1}{5}(4) = 0$

$x = 9 + 4(0) - 3(6) + 2(4) = -1$

Answer: $(-1, 0, 6, 4)$

55. $\begin{cases} x - 3z = -2 \\ 3x + y - 2z = 5 \\ 2x + 2y + z = 4 \end{cases}$

$$\begin{bmatrix} 1 & 0 & -3 & \vdots & -2 \\ 3 & 1 & -2 & \vdots & 5 \\ 2 & 2 & 1 & \vdots & 4 \end{bmatrix}$$

$$\begin{matrix} \\ -3R_1 + R_2 \rightarrow \\ -2R_1 + R_3 \rightarrow \end{matrix} \begin{bmatrix} 1 & 0 & -3 & \vdots & -2 \\ 0 & 1 & 7 & \vdots & 11 \\ 0 & 2 & 7 & \vdots & 8 \end{bmatrix}$$

$$\begin{matrix} \\ \\ -2R_2 + R_3 \rightarrow \end{matrix} \begin{bmatrix} 1 & 0 & -3 & \vdots & -2 \\ 0 & 1 & 7 & \vdots & 11 \\ 0 & 0 & -7 & \vdots & -14 \end{bmatrix}$$

$$\begin{matrix} \\ \\ -\frac{1}{7}R_3 \rightarrow \end{matrix} \begin{bmatrix} 1 & 0 & -3 & \vdots & -2 \\ 0 & 1 & 7 & \vdots & 11 \\ 0 & 0 & 1 & \vdots & 2 \end{bmatrix}$$

$$\begin{matrix} 3R_3 + R_1 \rightarrow \\ -7R_3 + R_2 \rightarrow \\ \\ \end{matrix} \begin{bmatrix} 1 & 0 & 0 & \vdots & 4 \\ 0 & 1 & 0 & \vdots & -3 \\ 0 & 0 & 1 & \vdots & 2 \end{bmatrix}$$

Answer: $(4, -3, 2)$

56. $\begin{bmatrix} 2 & -1 & 3 & \vdots & 24 \\ 0 & 2 & -1 & \vdots & 14 \\ 7 & -5 & 0 & \vdots & 6 \end{bmatrix}$

$$\begin{bmatrix} 14 & -7 & 21 & \vdots & 168 \\ 0 & 2 & -1 & \vdots & 14 \\ 14 & -10 & 0 & \vdots & 12 \end{bmatrix}$$

$$\begin{bmatrix} 14 & -7 & 21 & \vdots & 168 \\ 0 & 2 & -1 & \vdots & 14 \\ 0 & -3 & -21 & \vdots & -156 \end{bmatrix}$$

$$\begin{bmatrix} 14 & -7 & 21 & \vdots & 168 \\ 0 & 1 & 7 & \vdots & 52 \\ 0 & 0 & -15 & \vdots & -90 \end{bmatrix}$$

$$\begin{matrix} \frac{1}{7}R_1 \rightarrow \\ \\ -\frac{1}{15}R_3 \rightarrow \end{matrix} \begin{bmatrix} 2 & -1 & 3 & \vdots & 24 \\ 0 & 1 & 7 & \vdots & 52 \\ 0 & 0 & 1 & \vdots & 6 \end{bmatrix}$$

$$\begin{matrix} R_2 + R_1 \rightarrow \\ -7R_3 + R_2 \rightarrow \\ \\ \end{matrix} \begin{bmatrix} 2 & 0 & 10 & \vdots & 76 \\ 0 & 1 & 0 & \vdots & 10 \\ 0 & 0 & 1 & \vdots & 6 \end{bmatrix}$$

$$\begin{matrix} \frac{1}{2}R_1 \rightarrow \\ \\ \\ \end{matrix} \begin{bmatrix} 1 & 0 & 5 & \vdots & 38 \\ 0 & 1 & 0 & \vdots & 10 \\ 0 & 0 & 1 & \vdots & 6 \end{bmatrix}$$

$$\begin{matrix} -5R_3 + R_1 \rightarrow \\ \\ \\ \end{matrix} \begin{bmatrix} 1 & 0 & 0 & \vdots & 8 \\ 0 & 1 & 0 & \vdots & 10 \\ 0 & 0 & 1 & \vdots & 6 \end{bmatrix}$$

Answer: $(8, 10, 6)$

57. $\begin{cases} x + y - 5z = 3 \\ x - 2z = 1 \\ 2x - y - z = 0 \end{cases}$

$$\begin{bmatrix} 1 & 1 & -5 & \vdots & 3 \\ 1 & 0 & -2 & \vdots & 1 \\ 2 & -1 & -1 & \vdots & 0 \end{bmatrix}$$

$$\begin{matrix} \\ -R_1 + R_2 \rightarrow \\ -2R_1 + R_3 \rightarrow \end{matrix} \begin{bmatrix} 1 & 1 & -5 & \vdots & 3 \\ 0 & -1 & 3 & \vdots & -2 \\ 0 & -3 & 9 & \vdots & -6 \end{bmatrix}$$

$$\begin{matrix} \\ \\ -3R_2 + R_3 \rightarrow \end{matrix} \begin{bmatrix} 1 & 1 & -5 & \vdots & 3 \\ 0 & -1 & 3 & \vdots & -2 \\ 0 & 0 & 0 & \vdots & 0 \end{bmatrix}$$

$$\begin{matrix} R_2 + R_1 \rightarrow \\ -R_2 \rightarrow \\ \\ \end{matrix} \begin{bmatrix} 1 & 0 & -2 & \vdots & 1 \\ 0 & 1 & -3 & \vdots & 2 \\ 0 & 0 & 0 & \vdots & 0 \end{bmatrix}$$

Let $z = a$, any real number

$y - 3a = 2 \Rightarrow y = 3a + 2$

$x - 2a = 1 \Rightarrow x = 2a + 1$

Answer: $(2a + 1, 3a + 2, a)$

58. $\begin{cases} 2x + 3z = 3 \\ 4x - 3y + 7z = 5 \\ 8x - 9y + 15z = 9 \end{cases}$

$$\begin{bmatrix} 2 & 0 & 3 & \vdots & 3 \\ 4 & -3 & 7 & \vdots & 5 \\ 8 & -9 & 15 & \vdots & 9 \end{bmatrix}$$

$$\begin{matrix} \\ -2R_1 + R_2 \rightarrow \\ -4R_1 + R_3 \rightarrow \end{matrix} \begin{bmatrix} 2 & 0 & 3 & \vdots & 3 \\ 0 & -3 & 1 & \vdots & -1 \\ 0 & -9 & 3 & \vdots & -3 \end{bmatrix}$$

$$\begin{matrix} \\ \\ -3R_2 + R_3 \rightarrow \end{matrix} \begin{bmatrix} 2 & 0 & 3 & \vdots & 3 \\ 0 & -3 & 1 & \vdots & -1 \\ 0 & 0 & 0 & \vdots & 0 \end{bmatrix}$$

$$\begin{matrix} \frac{1}{2}R_1 \rightarrow \\ -\frac{1}{3}R_2 \rightarrow \\ \\ \end{matrix} \begin{bmatrix} 1 & 0 & \frac{3}{2} & \vdots & \frac{3}{2} \\ 0 & 1 & -\frac{1}{3} & \vdots & \frac{1}{3} \\ 0 & 0 & 0 & \vdots & 0 \end{bmatrix}$$

$z = a$

$y = \frac{1}{3}a + \frac{1}{3}$

$x = -\frac{3}{2}a + \frac{3}{2}$

Answer: $\left(-\frac{3}{2}a + \frac{3}{2}, \frac{1}{3}a + \frac{1}{3}, a\right)$

59. $\begin{cases} -x + y - z = -14 \\ 2x - y + z = 21 \\ 3x + 2y + z = 19 \end{cases}$

$$\begin{bmatrix} -1 & 1 & -1 & \vdots & -14 \\ 2 & -1 & 1 & \vdots & 21 \\ 3 & 2 & 1 & \vdots & 19 \end{bmatrix}$$

$$\begin{array}{r} \\ 2R_1 + R_2 \rightarrow \\ 3R_1 + R_3 \rightarrow \end{array} \begin{bmatrix} -1 & 1 & -1 & \vdots & -14 \\ 0 & 1 & -1 & \vdots & -7 \\ 0 & 5 & -2 & \vdots & -23 \end{bmatrix}$$

$$\begin{array}{r} -R_1 \rightarrow \\ \\ -5R_2 + R_3 \rightarrow \end{array} \begin{bmatrix} 1 & -1 & 1 & \vdots & 14 \\ 0 & 1 & -1 & \vdots & -7 \\ 0 & 0 & 3 & \vdots & 12 \end{bmatrix}$$

$$\begin{array}{r} \\ \\ \frac{1}{3}R_3 \rightarrow \end{array} \begin{bmatrix} 1 & -1 & 1 & \vdots & 14 \\ 0 & 1 & -1 & \vdots & -7 \\ 0 & 0 & 1 & \vdots & 4 \end{bmatrix}$$

$$\begin{array}{r} -R_3 + R_1 \rightarrow \\ R_3 + R_2 \rightarrow \\ \\ \end{array} \begin{bmatrix} 1 & -1 & 0 & \vdots & 10 \\ 0 & 1 & 0 & \vdots & -3 \\ 0 & 0 & 1 & \vdots & 4 \end{bmatrix}$$

$$\begin{array}{r} R_2 + R_1 \rightarrow \\ \\ \\ \end{array} \begin{bmatrix} 1 & 0 & 0 & \vdots & 7 \\ 0 & 1 & 0 & \vdots & -3 \\ 0 & 0 & 1 & \vdots & 4 \end{bmatrix}$$

Answer: $(7, -3, 4)$

60. $\begin{bmatrix} 2 & 2 & -1 & \vdots & 2 \\ 1 & -3 & 1 & \vdots & 28 \\ -1 & 1 & 0 & \vdots & 14 \end{bmatrix}$

$$\begin{bmatrix} 1 & -3 & 1 & \vdots & 28 \\ 0 & 8 & -3 & \vdots & -54 \\ 0 & -2 & 1 & \vdots & 42 \end{bmatrix}$$

$$\begin{bmatrix} 1 & -3 & 1 & \vdots & 28 \\ 0 & -2 & 1 & \vdots & 42 \\ 0 & 0 & 1 & \vdots & 114 \end{bmatrix}$$

$$\begin{array}{r} -R_3 + R_1 \rightarrow \\ -R_3 + R_2 \rightarrow \\ \\ \end{array} \begin{bmatrix} 1 & -3 & 0 & \vdots & -86 \\ 0 & -2 & 0 & \vdots & -72 \\ 0 & 0 & 1 & \vdots & 114 \end{bmatrix}$$

$$\begin{array}{r} 3R_2 + R_1 \rightarrow \\ -\frac{1}{2}R_2 \rightarrow \\ \\ \end{array} \begin{bmatrix} 1 & 0 & 0 & \vdots & 22 \\ 0 & 1 & 0 & \vdots & 36 \\ 0 & 0 & 1 & \vdots & 114 \end{bmatrix}$$

Answer: $(22, 36, 114)$

61. $\begin{cases} 3x + 3y + 12z = 6 \\ x + y + 4z = 2 \\ 2x + 5y + 20z = 10 \\ -x + 2y + 8z = 4 \end{cases}$

$$\begin{bmatrix} 3 & 3 & 12 & \vdots & 6 \\ 1 & 1 & 4 & \vdots & 2 \\ 2 & 5 & 20 & \vdots & 10 \\ -1 & 2 & 8 & \vdots & 4 \end{bmatrix} \Rightarrow \begin{bmatrix} 1 & 0 & 0 & \vdots & 0 \\ 0 & 1 & 4 & \vdots & 2 \\ 0 & 0 & 0 & \vdots & 0 \\ 0 & 0 & 0 & \vdots & 0 \end{bmatrix}$$

Let $z = a$, any real number

$y = -4a + 2$

$x = 0$

Answer: $(0, -4a + 2, a)$

62. $\begin{cases} x + y + z = 0 \\ 2x + 3y + z = 0 \\ 3x + 5y + z = 0 \end{cases}$

$$\begin{bmatrix} 1 & 1 & 1 & \vdots & 0 \\ 2 & 3 & 1 & \vdots & 0 \\ 3 & 5 & 1 & \vdots & 0 \end{bmatrix} \Rightarrow \begin{bmatrix} 1 & 0 & 2 & \vdots & 0 \\ 0 & 1 & -1 & \vdots & 0 \\ 0 & 0 & 0 & \vdots & 0 \end{bmatrix}$$

Let $z = a$, any real number

$y = a$

$x = -2a$

Answer: $(-2a, a, a)$

63. $\begin{cases} 2x + 10y + 2z = 6 \\ x + 5y + 2z = 6 \\ x + 5y + z = 3 \\ -3x - 15y - 3z = -9 \end{cases}$ $\begin{bmatrix} 2 & 10 & 2 & \vdots & 6 \\ 1 & 5 & 2 & \vdots & 6 \\ 1 & 5 & 1 & \vdots & 3 \\ -3 & -15 & -3 & \vdots & -9 \end{bmatrix} \Rightarrow \begin{bmatrix} 1 & 5 & 0 & \vdots & 0 \\ 0 & 0 & 1 & \vdots & 3 \\ 0 & 0 & 0 & \vdots & 0 \\ 0 & 0 & 0 & \vdots & 0 \end{bmatrix}$

$z = 3, y = a, x = -5a$

Answer: $(-5a, a, 3)$

64. $\begin{bmatrix} 2 & 1 & -1 & 2 & \vdots & -6 \\ 3 & 4 & 0 & 1 & \vdots & 1 \\ 1 & 5 & 2 & 6 & \vdots & -3 \\ 5 & 2 & -1 & -1 & \vdots & 3 \end{bmatrix}$ row reduces to $\begin{bmatrix} 1 & 0 & 0 & 0 & \vdots & 1 \\ 0 & 1 & 0 & 0 & \vdots & 0 \\ 0 & 0 & 1 & 0 & \vdots & 4 \\ 0 & 0 & 0 & 1 & \vdots & -2 \end{bmatrix}$

Answer: $(1, 0, 4, -2)$

65. Yes, the systems yield the same solutions.

(a) $z = -3; y = 5(-3) + 16 = 1; x = 2(1) - (-3) - 6 = -1$

Answer: $(-1, 1, -3)$

(b) $z = -3, y = -3(-3) - 8 = 1, x = -1 + 2(-3) + 6 = -1$

Answer: $(-1, 1, -3)$

66. The solutions are not the same.

(a) $z = 2, y = 2 - 4 = -2, x = 3(-2) - 4(2) - 11 = -25.$

Answer: $(-25, -2, 2)$

(b) $z = 2, y = -3(2) + 4 = -2, x = -4(-2) - 11 = -3.$

Answer: $(-3, -2, 2)$

67. No, solutions are different.

(a) $z = 8, y = 7(8) - 54 = 2, x = 4(2) - 5(8) + 27 = -5$

Answer: $(-5, 2, 8)$

(b) $z = 8, y = -5(8) + 42 = 2, x = 6(2) - 8 + 15 = 19$

Answer: $(19, 2, 8)$

68. The solutions are not the same.

(a) $z = -4, y = -6(-4) - 18 = 6, x = -3(6) + (-4) + 19 = -3.$

Answer: $(-3, 6, -4)$

(b) $z = -4, y = 2(-4) + 14 = 6, x = 6 - 3(-4) - 15 = 3.$

Answer: $(3, 6, -4)$

69. $f(x) = ax^2 + bx + c$

$$\begin{cases} f(1) = a + b + c = 8 \\ f(2) = 4a + 2b + c = 13 \\ f(3) = 9a + 3b + c = 20 \end{cases}$$

$$\begin{bmatrix} 1 & 1 & 1 & \vdots & 8 \\ 4 & 2 & 1 & \vdots & 13 \\ 9 & 3 & 1 & \vdots & 20 \end{bmatrix}$$

$$\begin{matrix} \\ -4R_1 + R_2 \rightarrow \\ -9R_1 + R_3 \rightarrow \end{matrix} \begin{bmatrix} 1 & 1 & 1 & \vdots & 8 \\ 0 & -2 & -3 & \vdots & -19 \\ 0 & -6 & -8 & \vdots & -52 \end{bmatrix}$$

$$\begin{matrix} \\ -\frac{1}{2}R_2 \rightarrow \\ -3R_2 + R_3 \rightarrow \end{matrix} \begin{bmatrix} 1 & 1 & 1 & \vdots & 8 \\ 0 & 1 & \frac{3}{2} & \vdots & \frac{19}{2} \\ 0 & 0 & 1 & \vdots & 5 \end{bmatrix}$$

$c = 5$

$b + \frac{3}{2}(5) = \frac{19}{2} \Rightarrow b = 2$

$a + 2 + 5 = 8 \Rightarrow a = 1$

Answer: $y = x^2 + 2x + 5$

70. $f(x) = ax^2 + bx + c$

$$\begin{cases} f(1) = a + b + c = 9 \\ f(2) = 4a + 2b + c = 8 \\ f(3) = 9a + 3b + c = 5 \end{cases}$$

$$\begin{bmatrix} 1 & 1 & 1 & \vdots & 9 \\ 4 & 2 & 1 & \vdots & 8 \\ 9 & 3 & 1 & \vdots & 5 \end{bmatrix}$$

$$\begin{matrix} \\ -4R_1 + R_2 \rightarrow \\ -9R_1 + R_3 \rightarrow \end{matrix} \begin{bmatrix} 1 & 1 & 1 & \vdots & 9 \\ 0 & -2 & -3 & \vdots & -28 \\ 0 & -6 & -8 & \vdots & -76 \end{bmatrix}$$

$$\begin{matrix} \\ -\frac{1}{2}R_2 \rightarrow \\ -3R_2 + R_3 \rightarrow \end{matrix} \begin{bmatrix} 1 & 1 & 1 & \vdots & 9 \\ 0 & 1 & \frac{3}{2} & \vdots & 14 \\ 0 & 0 & 1 & \vdots & 8 \end{bmatrix}$$

$c = 8$

$b + \frac{3}{2}(8) = 14 \Rightarrow b = 2$

$a + 8 + 2 = 9 \Rightarrow a = -1$

Answer: $y = -x^2 + 2x + 8$

71. $f(x) = ax^2 + bx + c$

$$\begin{cases} f(1) = a + b + c = 2 \\ f(-2) = 4a - 2b + c = 11 \\ f(3) = 9a + 3b + c = 16 \end{cases}$$

$$\begin{bmatrix} 1 & 1 & 1 & \vdots & 2 \\ 4 & -2 & 1 & \vdots & 11 \\ 9 & 3 & 1 & \vdots & 16 \end{bmatrix}$$

$$\begin{matrix} \\ -4R_1 + R_2 \rightarrow \\ -9R_1 + R_3 \rightarrow \end{matrix} \begin{bmatrix} 1 & 1 & 1 & \vdots & 2 \\ 0 & -6 & -3 & \vdots & 3 \\ 0 & -6 & -8 & \vdots & -2 \end{bmatrix}$$

$$\begin{matrix} \\ \\ (-1)R_2 + R_3 \rightarrow \end{matrix} \begin{bmatrix} 1 & 1 & 1 & \vdots & 2 \\ 0 & -6 & -3 & \vdots & 3 \\ 0 & 0 & -5 & \vdots & -5 \end{bmatrix}$$

$-5c = -5 \Rightarrow c = 1$

$-6b - 3c = 3 \Rightarrow -6b = 3 + 3 = 6 \Rightarrow b = -1$

$a + b + c = 2 \Rightarrow a = 2 + 1 - 1 = 2$

Answer: $y = 2x^2 - x + 1$

72. $f(x) = ax^2 + bx + c$

$$\begin{cases} f(1) = a + b + c = -1 \\ f(-2) = 4a - 2b + c = 2 \\ f(2) = 4a + 2b + c = -6 \end{cases}$$

$$\begin{bmatrix} 1 & 1 & 1 & \vdots & -1 \\ 4 & -2 & 1 & \vdots & 2 \\ 4 & 2 & 1 & \vdots & -6 \end{bmatrix}$$

$$\begin{matrix} \\ -4R_1 + R_2 \rightarrow \\ -4R_1 + R_3 \rightarrow \end{matrix} \begin{bmatrix} 1 & 1 & 1 & \vdots & -1 \\ 0 & -6 & -3 & \vdots & 6 \\ 0 & -2 & -3 & \vdots & -2 \end{bmatrix}$$

$$\begin{matrix} \\ -\frac{1}{3}R_2 \rightarrow \\ \end{matrix} \begin{bmatrix} 1 & 1 & 1 & \vdots & -1 \\ 0 & 2 & 1 & \vdots & -2 \\ 0 & -2 & -3 & \vdots & -2 \end{bmatrix}$$

$$\begin{matrix} \\ \\ R_2 + R_3 \rightarrow \end{matrix} \begin{bmatrix} 1 & 1 & 1 & \vdots & -1 \\ 0 & 2 & 1 & \vdots & -2 \\ 0 & 0 & -2 & \vdots & -4 \end{bmatrix}$$

$-2c = -4 \Rightarrow c = 2$

$2b + c = -2 \Rightarrow 2b = -2 - 2 = -4 \Rightarrow b = -2$

$a + b + c = -1 \Rightarrow a = -1 + 2 - 2 = -1$

Answer: $y = -x^2 - 2x + 2$

73. $f(x) = ax^2 + bx + c$

$$\begin{aligned} f(-2) &= 4a - 2b + c = -15 \\ f(-1) &= a - b + c = 7 \\ f(1) &= a + b + c = -3 \end{aligned}$$

Solving the system, $a = -9, b = -5, c = 11$.

$f(x) = -9x^2 - 5x + 11$

74. $f(x) = ax^2 + bx + c$

$$\begin{aligned} f(-2) &= 4a - 2b + c = -3 \\ f(1) &= a + b + c = -3 \\ f(2) &= 4a + 2b + c = -11 \end{aligned}$$

Solving the system, $a = -2, b = -2, c = 1$.

$f(x) = -2x^2 - 2x + 1$

75. $f(x) = ax^3 + bx^2 + cx + d$

$$\begin{aligned} f(-2) &= -8a + 4b - 2c + d = -7 \\ f(-1) &= -a + b - c + d = 2 \\ f(1) &= a + b + c + d = -4 \\ f(2) &= 8a + 4b + 2c + d = -7 \end{aligned}$$

Solving the system,
$a = 1, b = -2, c = -4, d = 1$.

$f(x) = x^3 - 2x^2 - 4x + 1$

76. $f(x) = ax^3 + bx^2 + cx + d$

$$\begin{aligned} f(-2) &= -8a + 4b - 2c + d = -17 \\ f(-1) &= -a + b - c + d = -5 \\ f(1) &= a + b + c + d = 1 \\ f(2) &= 8a + 4b + 2c + d = 7 \end{aligned}$$

Solving the system,
$a = 1, b = -1, c = 2, d = -1$.

$f(x) = x^3 - x^2 + 2x - 1$

77. x = amount at 7%, y = amount at 8%, z = amount at 10%

$$\begin{cases} x + y + z = 1{,}500{,}000 \\ 0.07x + 0.08y + 0.1z = 130{,}500 \\ 4x - z = 0 \end{cases}$$

$$\left[\begin{array}{ccc:c} 1 & 1 & 1 & 1{,}500{,}000 \\ 0.07 & 0.08 & 0.1 & 130{,}500 \\ 4 & 0 & -1 & 0 \end{array}\right]$$

$$\begin{array}{r} \\ -0.07R_1 + R_2 \rightarrow \\ -4R_1 + R_3 \rightarrow \end{array} \left[\begin{array}{ccc:c} 1 & 1 & 1 & 1{,}500{,}000 \\ 0 & 0.01 & 0.03 & 25{,}500 \\ 0 & -4 & -5 & -6{,}000{,}000 \end{array}\right]$$

$$\begin{array}{r} \\ 100R_2 \rightarrow \\ 4R_2 + R_3 \rightarrow \end{array} \left[\begin{array}{ccc:c} 1 & 1 & 1 & 1{,}500{,}000 \\ 0 & 1 & 3 & 2{,}550{,}000 \\ 0 & 0 & 7 & 4{,}200{,}000 \end{array}\right]$$

$7z = 4{,}200{,}000 \implies z = 600{,}00$

$y + 3(600{,}000) = 2{,}550{,}000 \implies y = 750{,}000$

$x + 750{,}000 + 600{,}000 = 1{,}500{,}000 \implies x = 150{,}000$

Answers: \$150,000 at 7%, \$750,000 at 8%, \$600,000 at 10%

78. $x =$ amount at 9%, $y =$ amount at 10%, $z =$ amount at 12%

$$\begin{cases} x + y + z = 500{,}000 \\ 0.09x + 0.10y + 0.12z = 52{,}000 \\ 2.5x - y = 0 \end{cases}$$

$$\begin{bmatrix} 1 & 1 & 1 & \vdots & 500{,}000 \\ 0.09 & 0.10 & 0.12 & \vdots & 52{,}000 \\ 2.5 & -1 & 0 & \vdots & 0 \end{bmatrix}$$

$$\begin{array}{r} \\ -0.09R_1 + R_2 \rightarrow \\ -2.5R_1 + R_3 \rightarrow \end{array} \begin{bmatrix} 1 & 1 & 1 & \vdots & 500{,}000 \\ 0 & 0.01 & 0.03 & \vdots & 7{,}000 \\ 0 & -3.5 & -2.5 & \vdots & -1{,}250{,}000 \end{bmatrix}$$

$$\begin{array}{r} \\ 100R_2 \rightarrow \\ 2R_3 \rightarrow \end{array} \begin{bmatrix} 1 & 1 & 1 & \vdots & 500{,}000 \\ 0 & 1 & 3 & \vdots & 700{,}000 \\ 0 & -7 & -5 & \vdots & -2{,}500{,}000 \end{bmatrix}$$

$$\begin{array}{r} -R_2 + R_1 \rightarrow \\ \\ 7R_2 + R_3 \rightarrow \end{array} \begin{bmatrix} 1 & 0 & -2 & \vdots & -200{,}000 \\ 0 & 1 & 3 & \vdots & 700{,}000 \\ 0 & 0 & 16 & \vdots & 2{,}400{,}000 \end{bmatrix}$$

$$\begin{array}{r} \\ \\ \frac{1}{16}R_3 \rightarrow \end{array} \begin{bmatrix} 1 & 0 & -2 & \vdots & -200{,}000 \\ 0 & 1 & 3 & \vdots & 700{,}000 \\ 0 & 0 & 1 & \vdots & 150{,}000 \end{bmatrix}$$

$z = 150{,}000$, $y = 250{,}000$, $x = 100{,}000$

Answers: \$100,000 at 9%, \$250,000 at 10%, \$150,000 at 12%

79. $$\begin{cases} I_1 - I_2 + I_3 = 0 \\ 2I_1 + 2I_2 = 7 \\ 2I_2 + 4I_3 = 8 \end{cases}$$

$$\begin{bmatrix} 1 & -1 & 1 & \vdots & 0 \\ 2 & 2 & 0 & \vdots & 7 \\ 0 & 2 & 4 & \vdots & 8 \end{bmatrix}$$

$$\begin{array}{r} \\ -2R_1 + R_2 \rightarrow \\ \\ \end{array} \begin{bmatrix} 1 & -1 & 1 & \vdots & 0 \\ 0 & 4 & -2 & \vdots & 7 \\ 0 & 2 & 4 & \vdots & 8 \end{bmatrix}$$

$$\begin{array}{r} \\ R_3 \rightarrow \\ R_2 \rightarrow \end{array} \begin{bmatrix} 1 & -1 & 1 & \vdots & 0 \\ 0 & 2 & 4 & \vdots & 8 \\ 0 & 4 & -2 & \vdots & 7 \end{bmatrix}$$

$$\begin{array}{r} \\ \frac{1}{2}R_2 \rightarrow \\ \\ \end{array} \begin{bmatrix} 1 & -1 & 1 & \vdots & 0 \\ 0 & 1 & 2 & \vdots & 4 \\ 0 & 4 & -2 & \vdots & 7 \end{bmatrix}$$

$$\begin{array}{r} \\ \\ -4R_2 + R_3 \rightarrow \end{array} \begin{bmatrix} 1 & -1 & 1 & \vdots & 0 \\ 0 & 1 & 2 & \vdots & 4 \\ 0 & 0 & -10 & \vdots & -9 \end{bmatrix}$$

$$\begin{array}{r} \\ \\ -\frac{1}{10}R_3 \rightarrow \end{array} \begin{bmatrix} 1 & -1 & 1 & \vdots & 0 \\ 0 & 1 & 2 & \vdots & 4 \\ 0 & 0 & 1 & \vdots & \frac{9}{10} \end{bmatrix}$$

$I_3 = \frac{9}{10}$ amperes; $I_2 + 2\left(\frac{9}{10}\right) = 4 \Rightarrow I_2 = \frac{11}{5}$ amperes; $I_1 - \frac{11}{5} + \frac{9}{10} = 0 \Rightarrow I_1 = \frac{13}{10}$ amperes

80. (a) $f(x) = ax^2 + bx + c$

$$\begin{cases} f(0) = \quad c = 5.0 \\ f(15) = 225a + 15b + c = 9.6 \\ f(30) = 900a + 30b + c = 12.4 \end{cases}$$

$$\begin{bmatrix} 0 & 0 & 1 & \vdots & 5.0 \\ 225 & 15 & 1 & \vdots & 9.6 \\ 900 & 30 & 1 & \vdots & 12.4 \end{bmatrix} \Rightarrow \begin{bmatrix} 1 & 0 & 0 & \vdots & -0.004 \\ 0 & 1 & 0 & \vdots & 0.367 \\ 0 & 0 & 1 & \vdots & 5 \end{bmatrix}$$

$y = -0.004x^2 + 0.367x + 5$

(b)

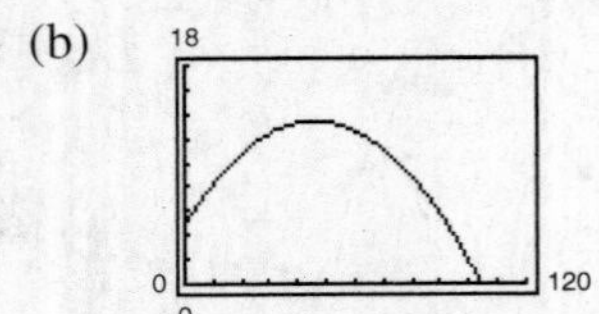

(c) Maximum height $\approx$ 13 feet

Strikes ground ($y = 0$) when $x \approx 104$ feet.

(d) Complete the square:

$-0.004(x^2 - 91.75x + 2104.5) + 5 + 8.418$

Maximum height $=$ 13.418 feet

Range: $y = 0 \Longrightarrow x = \dfrac{-0.367 \pm \sqrt{0.367^2 + 4(0.004)5}}{-0.008} \approx 103.793$ feet

81. (a) (2, 55.37) (3, 59.52) (4, 63.59)

$$\begin{cases} 4a + 2b + c = 55.37 \\ 9a + 3b + c = 59.52 \\ 16a + 4b + c = 63.59 \end{cases}$$

Solving the system using matrices,

$$\begin{bmatrix} 4 & 2 & 1 & \vdots & 55.37 \\ 9 & 3 & 1 & \vdots & 59.52 \\ 16 & 4 & 1 & \vdots & 63.59 \end{bmatrix} \Rightarrow \begin{bmatrix} 1 & 0 & 0 & \vdots & -0.04 \\ 0 & 1 & 0 & \vdots & 4.35 \\ 0 & 0 & 1 & \vdots & 46.83 \end{bmatrix}$$

you obtain $a = -0.04$, $b = 4.35$, $c = 46.83$.

$y = -0.04t^2 + 4.35t + 46.83$

(b)

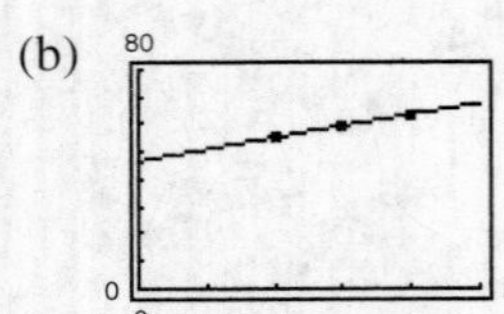

(c) For 2005, $t = 5$ and $y \approx 67.58$ dollars

For 2010, $t = 10$ and $y \approx 86.33$ dollars

For 2015, $t = 15$ and $y \approx 103.08$ dollars

82. (a) (2, 43.8) (3, 45.0) (4, 45.6)

$$\begin{cases} 4a + 2b + c = 43.8 \\ 9a + 3b + c = 45.0 \\ 16a + 4b + c = 45.6 \end{cases}$$

Solving the system using matrices,

$$\begin{bmatrix} 4 & 2 & 1 & \vdots & 43.8 \\ 9 & 3 & 1 & \vdots & 45.0 \\ 16 & 4 & 1 & \vdots & 45.6 \end{bmatrix} \Rightarrow \begin{bmatrix} 1 & 0 & 0 & \vdots & -0.3 \\ 0 & 1 & 0 & \vdots & 2.7 \\ 0 & 0 & 1 & \vdots & 39.6 \end{bmatrix}$$

you obtain $a = -0.3$, $b = 2.7$, $c = 39.6$.

$y = -0.3t^2 + 2.7t + 39.6$

(b)

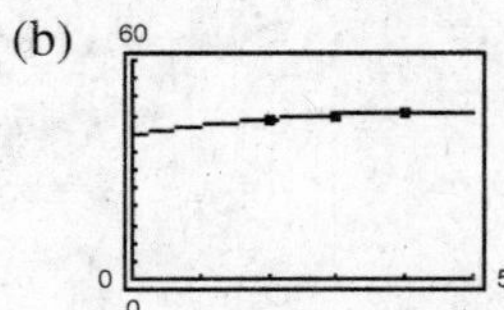

(c) For 2005, $t = 5$ and $y \approx 45.6$ thousand

For 2010, $t = 10$ and $y \approx 36.6$ thousand

For 2015, $t = 15$ and $y \approx 12.6$ thousand

(d) Answers will vary.

83. Let x = number of pounds of glossy.

Let y = number of pounds of semi-glossy

Let z = number of pounds of matte

$$\begin{cases} x + y + z = 100 \\ 5.5x + 4.25y + 3.75z = 480 \\ y + z = 50 \end{cases}$$

Solving the system, $x = 50$, $y = 35$ and $z = 15$.

50 pounds of glossy, 35 pounds of semi-glossy and 15 pounds of matte

84. Let x = number of adults

Let y = number of students

Let z = number of children

$$\begin{cases} 5x + 3.5y + 2.5z = 1030 \\ x - 2z = 0 \\ -\frac{1}{2}x + y = 20 \end{cases}$$

Solving the system, $x = 120$, $y = 80$ and $z = 60$.

120 adults, 80 students and 60 children

85. (a)
$$\begin{cases} x_1 + x_3 = 600 \\ x_1 = x_2 + x_4 \Rightarrow x_1 - x_2 - x_4 = 0 \\ x_2 + x_5 = 500 \\ x_3 + x_6 = 600 \\ x_4 + x_7 = x_6 \Rightarrow x_4 - x_6 + x_7 = 0 \\ x_5 + x_7 = 500 \end{cases}$$

$$\begin{bmatrix} 1 & 0 & 1 & 0 & 0 & 0 & 0 & \vdots & 600 \\ 1 & -1 & 0 & -1 & 0 & 0 & 0 & \vdots & 0 \\ 0 & 1 & 0 & 0 & 1 & 0 & 0 & \vdots & 500 \\ 0 & 0 & 1 & 0 & 0 & 1 & 0 & \vdots & 600 \\ 0 & 0 & 0 & 1 & 0 & -1 & 1 & \vdots & 0 \\ 0 & 0 & 0 & 0 & 1 & 0 & 1 & \vdots & 500 \end{bmatrix}$$

$$\begin{matrix} \\ -R_1 + R_2 \rightarrow \\ R_2 + R_3 \rightarrow \\ R_3 + R_4 \rightarrow \\ R_4 + R_5 \rightarrow \\ -R_5 + R_6 \rightarrow \end{matrix} \begin{bmatrix} 1 & 0 & 1 & 0 & 0 & 0 & 0 & \vdots & 600 \\ 0 & -1 & -1 & -1 & 0 & 0 & 0 & \vdots & -600 \\ 0 & 0 & -1 & -1 & 1 & 0 & 0 & \vdots & -100 \\ 0 & 0 & 0 & -1 & 1 & 1 & 0 & \vdots & 500 \\ 0 & 0 & 0 & 0 & 1 & 0 & 1 & \vdots & 500 \\ 0 & 0 & 0 & 0 & 0 & 0 & 0 & \vdots & 0 \end{bmatrix}$$

$$\begin{matrix} \\ -R_3 + R_2 \rightarrow \\ -R_4 + R_3 \rightarrow \\ -R_4 \rightarrow \\ \\ \\ \end{matrix} \begin{bmatrix} 1 & 0 & 1 & 0 & 0 & 0 & 0 & \vdots & 600 \\ 0 & -1 & 0 & 0 & -1 & 0 & 0 & \vdots & -500 \\ 0 & 0 & -1 & 0 & 0 & -1 & 0 & \vdots & -600 \\ 0 & 0 & 0 & 1 & -1 & -1 & 0 & \vdots & -500 \\ 0 & 0 & 0 & 0 & 1 & 0 & 1 & \vdots & 500 \\ 0 & 0 & 0 & 0 & 0 & 0 & 0 & \vdots & 0 \end{bmatrix}$$

Let $x_7 = t$ and $x_6 = s$, then:

$x_5 = 500 - t$

$x_4 = -500 + s + (500 - t) = s - t$

$x_3 = 600 - s$

$x_2 = 500 - (500 - t) = t$

$x_1 = 600 - (600 - s) = s$

(b) If $x_6 = x_7 = 0$, then $s = t = 0$, and

$x_1 = 0$

$x_2 = 0$

$x_3 = 600$

$x_4 = 0$

$x_5 = 500$

$x_6 = x_7 = 0$

(c) If $x_5 = 1000$ and $x_6 = 0$, then $s = 0$ and $t = -500$. Thus:

$x_1 = 0$

$x_2 = -500$

$x_3 = 600$

$x_4 = 500$

$x_5 = 1000$

$x_6 = 0$

$x_7 = -500$

86. (a) $\begin{cases} x_1 + \quad x_2 = 300 \\ x_1 + \quad x_3 = 150 + x_4 \Rightarrow x_1 + x_3 - x_4 = 150 \\ x_2 + 200 = \quad x_3 + x_5 \Rightarrow x_2 - x_3 - x_5 = -200 \\ x_4 + \quad x_5 = 350 \end{cases}$

$$\left[\begin{array}{rrrrr:r} 1 & 1 & 0 & 0 & 0 & 300 \\ 1 & 0 & 1 & -1 & 0 & 150 \\ 0 & 1 & -1 & 0 & -1 & -200 \\ 0 & 0 & 0 & 1 & 1 & 350 \end{array}\right]$$

$$\begin{array}{r} \\ -R_1 + R_2 \rightarrow \\ \\ \\ \end{array}\left[\begin{array}{rrrrr:r} 1 & 1 & 0 & 0 & 0 & 300 \\ 0 & -1 & 1 & -1 & 0 & -150 \\ 0 & 1 & -1 & 0 & -1 & -200 \\ 0 & 0 & 0 & 1 & 1 & 350 \end{array}\right]$$

$$\begin{array}{r} \\ \\ R_2 + R_3 \rightarrow \\ \\ \end{array}\left[\begin{array}{rrrrr:r} 1 & 1 & 0 & 0 & 0 & 300 \\ 0 & -1 & 1 & -1 & 0 & -150 \\ 0 & 0 & 0 & -1 & -1 & -350 \\ 0 & 0 & 0 & 1 & 1 & 350 \end{array}\right]$$

$$\begin{array}{r} \\ -R_2 \rightarrow \\ -R_3 \rightarrow \\ R_3 + R_4 \rightarrow \end{array}\left[\begin{array}{rrrrr:r} 1 & 1 & 0 & 0 & 0 & 300 \\ 0 & 1 & -1 & 1 & 0 & 150 \\ 0 & 0 & 0 & 1 & 1 & 350 \\ 0 & 0 & 0 & 0 & 0 & 0 \end{array}\right]$$

Let $x_5 = t$.

$x_4 + t = 350 \Rightarrow x_4 = 350 - t$

Let $x_3 = s$.

$x_2 - s + 350 - t = 150 \Rightarrow x_2 = -200 + s + t$

$x_1 - 200 + s + t = 300 \Rightarrow x_1 = 500 - s - t$

(b) When $x_2 = 200$ and $x_3 = 50$:

$x_2 = -200 + s + t$

$200 = -200 + 50 + t \Rightarrow t = 350.$

$x_5 = 350, x_4 = 0, x_3 = 50, x_2 = 200,$

$x_1 = 100$

(c) When $x_2 = 150$ and $x_3 = 0$:

$x_2 = -200 + s + t$

$150 = -200 + 0 + t \Rightarrow t = 350.$

$x_5 = 350, x_4 = 0, x_3 = 0, x_2 = 150,$

$x_1 = 150$

87. False. It is a 2×4 matrix.

88. False. Gauss-Jordan elimination reduces a matrix to reduced row-echelon form.

89. $\begin{cases} x + 3z = -2 & \text{Equation 1} \\ y + 4z = \quad 1 & \text{Equation 2} \end{cases}$

(Equation 1) + (Equation 2) $\rightarrow$ new Equation 1

(Equation 1) + 2(Equation 2) $\rightarrow$ new Equation 2

2(Equation 1) + (Equation 2) $\rightarrow$ new Equation 3

$\begin{cases} x + \quad y + \quad 7z = -1 \\ x + 2y + 11z = \quad 0 \\ 2x + \quad y + 10z = -3 \end{cases}$

90. (a) In the row-echelon form of an augmented matrix that corresponds to an inconsistent system of linear equations, there exists a row consisting of all zeros except for the entry in the last column.

(b) In the row-echelon form of an augmented matrix that corresponds to a system with an infinite number of solutions, there are fewer rows with nonzero entries than there are variables. Nor does the last row consist of all zeros except for the entry in the last column.

91. The row operation $-2R_1 + R_2$ was not performed on the last column. Nor was $-R_2 + R_1$.

92. Answers will vary.

93. $f(x) = \dfrac{7}{-x-1}$

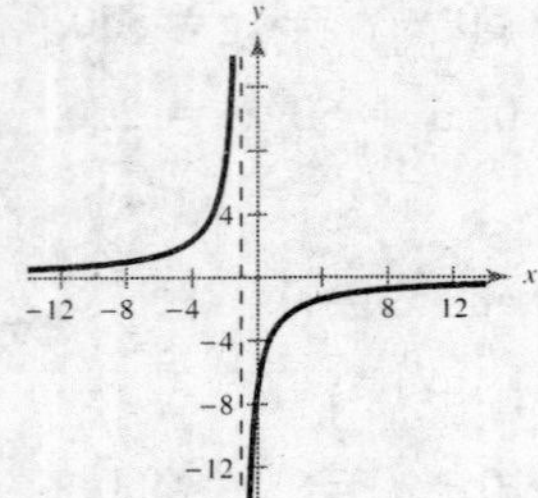

Asymptotes: $x = -1, y = 0$

94. $f(x) = \dfrac{4x}{5x^2 + 2}$

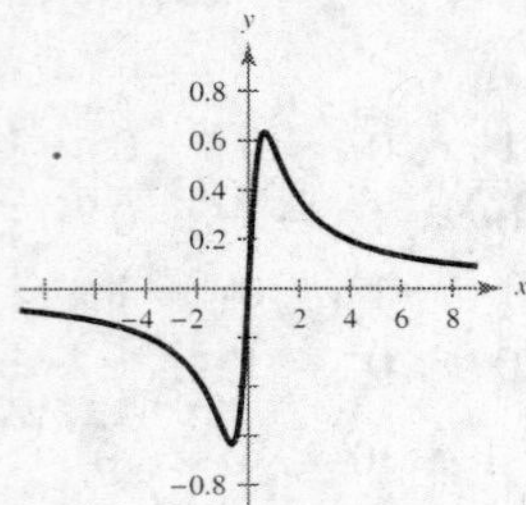

Horizontal asymptote: $y = 0$

95. $f(x) = \dfrac{x^2 - 2x - 3}{x - 4} = x + 2 + \dfrac{5}{x - 4}$

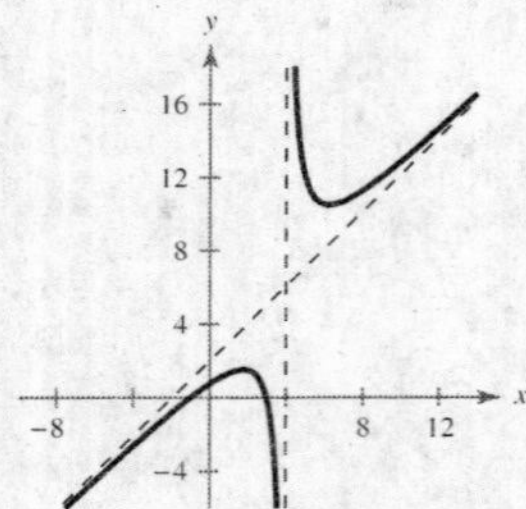

Asymptotes: $x = 4, y = x + 2$

96. $f(x) = \dfrac{x^2 - 36}{x + 1}$

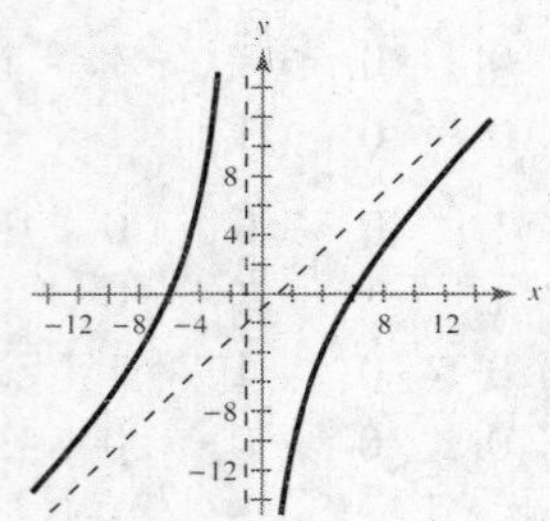

Vertical asymptote: $x = -1$,

Slant asymptote: $y = x - 1$

Section 7.5 Operations with Matrices

- $A = B$ if and only if they have the same order and $a_{ij} = b_{ij}$.
- You should be able to perform the operations of matrix addition, scalar multiplication, and matrix multiplication.
- Some properties of matrix addition and scalar multiplication are:
  (a) $A + B = B + A$ (b) $A + (B + C) = (A + B) + C$
  (c) $(cd)A = c(dA)$ (d) $1A = A$
  (e) $c(A + B) = cA + cB$ (f) $(c + d)A = cA + dA$
- Some properties of matrix multiplication are:
  (a) $A(BC) = (AB)C$ (b) $A(B + C) = AB + AC$
  (c) $(A + B)C = AC + BC$ (d) $c(AB) = (cA)B = A(cB)$
- You should remember that $AB \neq BA$ in general.

Vocabulary Check

1. equal **2.** scalars **3.** zero, 0 **4.** identity

5. (a) iii (b) i (c) iv (d) v (e) ii **6.** (a) ii (b) iv (c) i (d) iii

1. $x = -4,\ y = 22$

2. $x = 13,\ y = 12$

3. $2x + 7 = 5 \Rightarrow x = -1$

$3y = 12 \Rightarrow y = 4$

$3z - 14 = 4 \Rightarrow z = 6$

4. $x + 4 = 2x + 9 \Rightarrow x = -5$

$2y = -8 \Rightarrow y = -4$

$z + 2 = 11 \Rightarrow z = 9$

5. (a) $A + B = \begin{bmatrix} 1 & -1 \\ 2 & -1 \end{bmatrix} + \begin{bmatrix} 2 & -1 \\ -1 & 8 \end{bmatrix} = \begin{bmatrix} 1+2 & -1-1 \\ 2-1 & -1+8 \end{bmatrix} = \begin{bmatrix} 3 & -2 \\ 1 & 7 \end{bmatrix}$

(b) $A - B = \begin{bmatrix} 1 & -1 \\ 2 & -1 \end{bmatrix} - \begin{bmatrix} 2 & -1 \\ -1 & 8 \end{bmatrix} = \begin{bmatrix} 1-2 & -1+1 \\ 2+1 & -1-8 \end{bmatrix} = \begin{bmatrix} -1 & 0 \\ 3 & -9 \end{bmatrix}$

(c) $3A = 3\begin{bmatrix} 1 & -1 \\ 2 & -1 \end{bmatrix} = \begin{bmatrix} 3(1) & 3(-1) \\ 3(2) & 3(-1) \end{bmatrix} = \begin{bmatrix} 3 & -3 \\ 6 & -3 \end{bmatrix}$

(d) $3A - 2B = \begin{bmatrix} 3 & -3 \\ 6 & -3 \end{bmatrix} - 2\begin{bmatrix} 2 & -1 \\ -1 & 8 \end{bmatrix} = \begin{bmatrix} 3 & -3 \\ 6 & -3 \end{bmatrix} + \begin{bmatrix} -4 & 2 \\ 2 & -16 \end{bmatrix} = \begin{bmatrix} -1 & -1 \\ 8 & -19 \end{bmatrix}$

6. (a) $A + B = \begin{bmatrix} 1 & 2 \\ 2 & 1 \end{bmatrix} + \begin{bmatrix} -3 & -2 \\ 4 & 2 \end{bmatrix} = \begin{bmatrix} 1-3 & 2-2 \\ 2+4 & 1+2 \end{bmatrix} = \begin{bmatrix} -2 & 0 \\ 6 & 3 \end{bmatrix}$

(b) $A - B = \begin{bmatrix} 1 & 2 \\ 2 & 1 \end{bmatrix} - \begin{bmatrix} -3 & -2 \\ 4 & 2 \end{bmatrix} = \begin{bmatrix} 1+3 & 2+2 \\ 2-4 & 1-2 \end{bmatrix} = \begin{bmatrix} 4 & 4 \\ -2 & -1 \end{bmatrix}$

(c) $3A = 3\begin{bmatrix} 1 & 2 \\ 2 & 1 \end{bmatrix} = \begin{bmatrix} 3(1) & 3(2) \\ 3(2) & 3(1) \end{bmatrix} = \begin{bmatrix} 3 & 6 \\ 6 & 3 \end{bmatrix}$

(d) $3A - 2B = \begin{bmatrix} 3 & 6 \\ 6 & 3 \end{bmatrix} - 2\begin{bmatrix} -3 & -2 \\ 4 & 2 \end{bmatrix} = \begin{bmatrix} 3+6 & 6+4 \\ 6-8 & 3-4 \end{bmatrix} = \begin{bmatrix} 9 & 10 \\ -2 & -1 \end{bmatrix}$

7. $A = \begin{bmatrix} 8 & -1 \\ 2 & 3 \\ -4 & 5 \end{bmatrix},\ B = \begin{bmatrix} 1 & 6 \\ -1 & -5 \\ 1 & 10 \end{bmatrix}$

(a) $A + B = \begin{bmatrix} 9 & 5 \\ 1 & -2 \\ -3 & 15 \end{bmatrix}$

(b) $A - B = \begin{bmatrix} 7 & -7 \\ 3 & 8 \\ -5 & -5 \end{bmatrix}$

(c) $3A = \begin{bmatrix} 24 & -3 \\ 6 & 9 \\ -12 & 15 \end{bmatrix}$

(d) $3A - 2B = \begin{bmatrix} 24 & -3 \\ 6 & 9 \\ -12 & 15 \end{bmatrix} - \begin{bmatrix} 2 & 12 \\ -2 & -10 \\ 2 & 20 \end{bmatrix} = \begin{bmatrix} 22 & -15 \\ 8 & 19 \\ -14 & -5 \end{bmatrix}$

8. (a) $A + B = \begin{bmatrix} 1 & -1 & 3 \\ 0 & 6 & 9 \end{bmatrix} + \begin{bmatrix} -2 & 0 & -5 \\ -3 & 4 & -7 \end{bmatrix} = \begin{bmatrix} -1 & -1 & -2 \\ -3 & 10 & 2 \end{bmatrix}$

(b) $A - B = \begin{bmatrix} 3 & -1 & 8 \\ 3 & 2 & 16 \end{bmatrix}$

(c) $3A = \begin{bmatrix} 3 & -3 & 9 \\ 0 & 18 & 27 \end{bmatrix}$

(d) $3A - 2B = \begin{bmatrix} 3 & -3 & 9 \\ 0 & 18 & 27 \end{bmatrix} - \begin{bmatrix} -4 & 0 & -10 \\ -6 & 8 & -14 \end{bmatrix} = \begin{bmatrix} 7 & -3 & 19 \\ 6 & 10 & 41 \end{bmatrix}$

9. $A = \begin{bmatrix} 4 & 5 & -1 & 3 & 4 \\ 1 & 2 & -2 & -1 & 0 \end{bmatrix}$, $B = \begin{bmatrix} 1 & 0 & -1 & 1 & 0 \\ -6 & 8 & 2 & -3 & -7 \end{bmatrix}$

(a) $A + B = \begin{bmatrix} 5 & 5 & -2 & 4 & 4 \\ -5 & 10 & 0 & -4 & -7 \end{bmatrix}$

(b) $A - B = \begin{bmatrix} 3 & 5 & 0 & 2 & 4 \\ 7 & -6 & -4 & 2 & 7 \end{bmatrix}$

(c) $3A = \begin{bmatrix} 12 & 15 & -3 & 9 & 12 \\ 3 & 6 & -6 & -3 & 0 \end{bmatrix}$

(d) $3A - 2B = \begin{bmatrix} 12 & 15 & -3 & 9 & 12 \\ 3 & 6 & -6 & -3 & 0 \end{bmatrix} - \begin{bmatrix} 2 & 0 & -2 & 2 & 0 \\ -12 & 16 & 4 & -6 & -14 \end{bmatrix}$

$= \begin{bmatrix} 10 & 15 & -1 & 7 & 12 \\ 15 & -10 & -10 & 3 & 14 \end{bmatrix}$

10. (a) $A + B = \begin{bmatrix} -4 & 9 & 1 \\ 5 & -6 & -5 \\ 15 & -5 & -2 \\ 3 & 10 & -10 \\ -4 & 0 & -2 \end{bmatrix}$

(b) $A - B = \begin{bmatrix} 2 & -1 & -1 \\ 1 & 2 & 9 \\ -5 & 13 & 0 \\ -3 & 6 & -2 \\ -4 & -2 & 2 \end{bmatrix}$

(c) $3A = \begin{bmatrix} -3 & 12 & 0 \\ 9 & -6 & 6 \\ 15 & 12 & -3 \\ 0 & 24 & -18 \\ -12 & -3 & 0 \end{bmatrix}$

(d) $3A - 2B = \begin{bmatrix} 3 & 2 & -2 \\ 5 & 2 & 20 \\ -5 & 30 & -1 \\ -6 & 20 & -10 \\ -12 & -5 & 4 \end{bmatrix}$

11. $A = \begin{bmatrix} 6 & 0 & 3 \\ -1 & -4 & 0 \end{bmatrix}$, $B = \begin{bmatrix} 8 & -1 \\ 4 & -3 \end{bmatrix}$

(a) $A + B$ is not possible.

(b) $A - B$ is not possible.

(c) $3A = \begin{bmatrix} 18 & 0 & 9 \\ -3 & -12 & 0 \end{bmatrix}$

(d) $3A - 2B$ is not possible.

12. (a) $A + B$ is not defined.

(b) $A - B$ is not defined.

(c) $3A = 3\begin{bmatrix} 3 \\ 2 \\ -1 \end{bmatrix} = \begin{bmatrix} 9 \\ 6 \\ -3 \end{bmatrix}$

(d) $3A - 2B$ is not defined.

13. $\begin{bmatrix} -5 & 0 \\ 3 & -6 \end{bmatrix} + \begin{bmatrix} 7 & 1 \\ -2 & -1 \end{bmatrix} + \begin{bmatrix} -10 & -8 \\ 14 & 6 \end{bmatrix} = \begin{bmatrix} -5 & 0 \\ 3 & -6 \end{bmatrix} + \begin{bmatrix} -3 & -7 \\ 12 & 5 \end{bmatrix} = \begin{bmatrix} -8 & -7 \\ 15 & -1 \end{bmatrix}$

14. $\left(\begin{bmatrix} 6 & 9 \\ -1 & 0 \\ 7 & 1 \end{bmatrix} + \begin{bmatrix} 0 & 5 \\ -2 & -1 \\ 3 & -6 \end{bmatrix}\right) + \begin{bmatrix} -13 & -7 \\ 4 & -1 \\ -6 & 0 \end{bmatrix} = \begin{bmatrix} 6 & 14 \\ -3 & -1 \\ 10 & -5 \end{bmatrix} + \begin{bmatrix} -13 & -7 \\ 4 & -1 \\ -6 & 0 \end{bmatrix} = \begin{bmatrix} -7 & 7 \\ 1 & -2 \\ 4 & -5 \end{bmatrix}$

15. $4\left(\begin{bmatrix} -4 & 0 & 1 \\ 0 & 2 & 3 \end{bmatrix} - \begin{bmatrix} 2 & 1 & -2 \\ 3 & -6 & 0 \end{bmatrix}\right) = 4\begin{bmatrix} -6 & -1 & 3 \\ -3 & 8 & 3 \end{bmatrix} = \begin{bmatrix} -24 & -4 & 12 \\ -12 & 32 & 12 \end{bmatrix}$

16. $\frac{1}{2}(\begin{bmatrix} 5 & -2 & 4 & 0 \end{bmatrix} + \begin{bmatrix} 14 & 6 & -18 & 9 \end{bmatrix}) = \frac{1}{2}\begin{bmatrix} 19 & 4 & -14 & 9 \end{bmatrix} = \begin{bmatrix} \frac{19}{2} & 2 & -7 & \frac{9}{2} \end{bmatrix}$

17. $\begin{bmatrix} 2 & 5 \\ -1 & -4 \end{bmatrix} + \begin{bmatrix} -3 & 0 \\ 2 & 2 \end{bmatrix} = \begin{bmatrix} -1 & 5 \\ 1 & -2 \end{bmatrix}$

18. $\begin{bmatrix} -8 & 9 \\ -9 & 25 \end{bmatrix}$

19. $-\frac{1}{2}\begin{bmatrix} 3.211 & 6.829 \\ -1.004 & 4.914 \\ 0.055 & -3.889 \end{bmatrix} - 8\begin{bmatrix} 1.630 & -3.090 \\ 5.256 & 8.335 \\ -9.768 & 4.251 \end{bmatrix} = \begin{bmatrix} -14.645 & 21.305 \\ -41.546 & -69.137 \\ 78.117 & -32.064 \end{bmatrix}$

20. $(-1)\begin{bmatrix} 4 & 11 \\ -2 & -1 \\ 9 & 3 \end{bmatrix} + \frac{1}{6}\left(\begin{bmatrix} -5 & -1 \\ 3 & 4 \\ 0 & 13 \end{bmatrix} + \begin{bmatrix} 7 & 5 \\ -9 & -1 \\ 6 & -1 \end{bmatrix}\right) = \begin{bmatrix} -4 & -11 \\ 2 & 1 \\ -9 & -3 \end{bmatrix} + \frac{1}{6}\begin{bmatrix} 2 & 4 \\ -6 & 3 \\ 6 & 12 \end{bmatrix}$

$$= \begin{bmatrix} -4 & -11 \\ 2 & 1 \\ -9 & -3 \end{bmatrix} + \begin{bmatrix} \frac{1}{3} & \frac{2}{3} \\ -1 & \frac{1}{2} \\ 1 & 2 \end{bmatrix} = \begin{bmatrix} -\frac{11}{3} & -\frac{31}{3} \\ 1 & \frac{3}{2} \\ -8 & -1 \end{bmatrix}$$

21. $X = 3\begin{bmatrix} -2 & -1 \\ 1 & 0 \\ 3 & -4 \end{bmatrix} - 2\begin{bmatrix} 0 & 3 \\ 2 & 0 \\ -4 & -1 \end{bmatrix} = \begin{bmatrix} -6 & -3 \\ 3 & 0 \\ 9 & -12 \end{bmatrix} - \begin{bmatrix} 0 & 6 \\ 4 & 0 \\ -8 & -2 \end{bmatrix} = \begin{bmatrix} -6 & -9 \\ -1 & 0 \\ 17 & -10 \end{bmatrix}$

22. $2X = 2A - B$

$$X = A - \tfrac{1}{2}B = \begin{bmatrix} -2 & -1 \\ 1 & 0 \\ 3 & -4 \end{bmatrix} - \frac{1}{2}\begin{bmatrix} 0 & 3 \\ 2 & 0 \\ -4 & -1 \end{bmatrix} = \begin{bmatrix} -2 & -1 \\ 1 & 0 \\ 3 & -4 \end{bmatrix} - \begin{bmatrix} 0 & \frac{3}{2} \\ 1 & 0 \\ -2 & -\frac{1}{2} \end{bmatrix} = \begin{bmatrix} -2 & -\frac{5}{2} \\ 0 & 0 \\ 5 & -\frac{7}{2} \end{bmatrix}$$

23. $X = -\frac{3}{2}A + \frac{1}{2}B = -\frac{3}{2}\begin{bmatrix} -2 & -1 \\ 1 & 0 \\ 3 & -4 \end{bmatrix} + \frac{1}{2}\begin{bmatrix} 0 & 3 \\ 2 & 0 \\ -4 & -1 \end{bmatrix} = \begin{bmatrix} 3 & 3 \\ -\frac{1}{2} & 0 \\ -\frac{13}{2} & \frac{11}{2} \end{bmatrix}$

24. $2A + 4B = -2X$

$$X = -A - 2B = -1\begin{bmatrix} -2 & -1 \\ 1 & 0 \\ 3 & -4 \end{bmatrix} - 2\begin{bmatrix} 0 & 3 \\ 2 & 0 \\ -4 & -1 \end{bmatrix} = \begin{bmatrix} 2 & 1 \\ -1 & 0 \\ -3 & 4 \end{bmatrix} + \begin{bmatrix} 0 & -6 \\ -4 & 0 \\ 8 & 2 \end{bmatrix} = \begin{bmatrix} 2 & -5 \\ -5 & 0 \\ 5 & 6 \end{bmatrix}$$

25. A is 3×2 and B is $3 \times 3 \implies AB$ is not defined.

26. $AB = \begin{bmatrix} 0 & -1 & 2 \\ 6 & 0 & 3 \\ 7 & -1 & 8 \end{bmatrix}\begin{bmatrix} 2 & -1 \\ 4 & -5 \\ 1 & 6 \end{bmatrix} = \begin{bmatrix} -2 & 17 \\ 15 & 12 \\ 18 & 46 \end{bmatrix}$

27. $AB = \begin{bmatrix} -1 & 6 \\ -4 & 5 \\ 0 & 3 \end{bmatrix}\begin{bmatrix} 2 & 3 \\ 0 & 9 \end{bmatrix} = \begin{bmatrix} -2 & 51 \\ -8 & 33 \\ 0 & 27 \end{bmatrix}$

28. A is 3×3, B is $3 \times 3 \implies AB$ is 3×3.

$$\begin{bmatrix} 1 & 0 & 0 \\ 0 & 4 & 0 \\ 0 & 0 & -2 \end{bmatrix}\begin{bmatrix} 3 & 0 & 0 \\ 0 & -1 & 0 \\ 0 & 0 & 5 \end{bmatrix} = \begin{bmatrix} 3 & 0 & 0 \\ 0 & -4 & 0 \\ 0 & 0 & -10 \end{bmatrix}$$

29. A is 3×3, B is $3 \times 3 \implies AB$ is 3×3.

$$AB = \begin{bmatrix} 5 & 0 & 0 \\ 0 & -8 & 0 \\ 0 & 0 & 7 \end{bmatrix}\begin{bmatrix} \frac{1}{5} & 0 & 0 \\ 0 & -\frac{1}{8} & 0 \\ 0 & 0 & \frac{1}{2} \end{bmatrix} = \begin{bmatrix} 1 & 0 & 0 \\ 0 & 1 & 0 \\ 0 & 0 & \frac{7}{2} \end{bmatrix}$$

30. $\begin{bmatrix} 0 & 0 & 5 \\ 0 & 0 & -3 \\ 0 & 0 & 4 \end{bmatrix}\begin{bmatrix} 6 & -11 & 4 \\ 8 & 16 & 4 \\ 0 & 0 & 0 \end{bmatrix} = \begin{bmatrix} 0 & 0 & 0 \\ 0 & 0 & 0 \\ 0 & 0 & 0 \end{bmatrix}$

31. $AB = \begin{bmatrix} 5 \\ 6 \end{bmatrix}\begin{bmatrix} -3 & -1 & -5 & -9 \end{bmatrix} = \begin{bmatrix} -15 & -5 & -25 & -45 \\ -18 & -6 & -30 & -54 \end{bmatrix}$

32. A is 2×4, B is $2 \times 2 \implies AB$ is not defined.

33. (a) $AB = \begin{bmatrix} 1 & 2 \\ 5 & 2 \end{bmatrix}\begin{bmatrix} 2 & -1 \\ -1 & 8 \end{bmatrix} = \begin{bmatrix} 2-2 & -1+16 \\ 10-2 & -5+16 \end{bmatrix} = \begin{bmatrix} 0 & 15 \\ 8 & 11 \end{bmatrix}$

(b) $BA = \begin{bmatrix} 2 & -1 \\ -1 & 8 \end{bmatrix}\begin{bmatrix} 1 & 2 \\ 5 & 2 \end{bmatrix} = \begin{bmatrix} 2-5 & 4-2 \\ -1+40 & -2+16 \end{bmatrix} = \begin{bmatrix} -3 & 2 \\ 39 & 14 \end{bmatrix}$

(c) $A^2 = \begin{bmatrix} 1 & 2 \\ 5 & 2 \end{bmatrix}\begin{bmatrix} 1 & 2 \\ 5 & 2 \end{bmatrix} = \begin{bmatrix} 1+10 & 2+4 \\ 5+10 & 10+4 \end{bmatrix} = \begin{bmatrix} 11 & 6 \\ 15 & 14 \end{bmatrix}$

34. (a) $AB = \begin{bmatrix} 6 & 3 \\ -2 & -4 \end{bmatrix}\begin{bmatrix} -2 & 0 \\ 2 & 4 \end{bmatrix} = \begin{bmatrix} -6 & 12 \\ -4 & -16 \end{bmatrix}$ (b) $BA = \begin{bmatrix} -12 & -6 \\ 4 & -10 \end{bmatrix}$

(c) $A^2 = AA = \begin{bmatrix} 30 & 6 \\ -4 & 10 \end{bmatrix}$

35. (a) $AB = \begin{bmatrix} 3 & -1 \\ 1 & 3 \end{bmatrix}\begin{bmatrix} 1 & -3 \\ 3 & 1 \end{bmatrix} = \begin{bmatrix} 3-3 & -9-1 \\ 1+9 & -3+3 \end{bmatrix} = \begin{bmatrix} 0 & -10 \\ 10 & 0 \end{bmatrix}$

(b) $BA = \begin{bmatrix} 1 & -3 \\ 3 & 1 \end{bmatrix}\begin{bmatrix} 3 & -1 \\ 1 & 3 \end{bmatrix} = \begin{bmatrix} 3-3 & -1-9 \\ 9+1 & -3+3 \end{bmatrix} = \begin{bmatrix} 0 & -10 \\ 10 & 0 \end{bmatrix}$

(c) $A^2 = \begin{bmatrix} 3 & -1 \\ 1 & 3 \end{bmatrix}\begin{bmatrix} 3 & -1 \\ 1 & 3 \end{bmatrix} = \begin{bmatrix} 9-1 & -3-3 \\ 3+3 & -1+9 \end{bmatrix} = \begin{bmatrix} 8 & -6 \\ 6 & 8 \end{bmatrix}$

36. (a) $AB = \begin{bmatrix} 1 & -1 \\ 1 & 1 \end{bmatrix}\begin{bmatrix} 1 & 3 \\ -3 & 1 \end{bmatrix} = \begin{bmatrix} 1(1)+(-1)(-3) & 1(3)+(-1)(1) \\ 1(1)+1(-3) & 1(3)+1(1) \end{bmatrix} = \begin{bmatrix} 4 & 2 \\ -2 & 4 \end{bmatrix}$

(b) $BA = \begin{bmatrix} 1 & 3 \\ -3 & 1 \end{bmatrix}\begin{bmatrix} 1 & -1 \\ 1 & 1 \end{bmatrix} = \begin{bmatrix} 1(1)+(3)1 & 1(-1)+3(1) \\ -3(1)+(1)(1) & -3(-1)+1(1) \end{bmatrix} = \begin{bmatrix} 4 & 2 \\ -2 & 4 \end{bmatrix}$

(c) $A^2 = \begin{bmatrix} 1 & -1 \\ 1 & 1 \end{bmatrix}\begin{bmatrix} 1 & -1 \\ 1 & 1 \end{bmatrix} = \begin{bmatrix} 1(1)+(-1)(1) & 1(-1)+(-1)(1) \\ 1(1)+(1)(1) & 1(-1)+1(1) \end{bmatrix} = \begin{bmatrix} 0 & -2 \\ 2 & 0 \end{bmatrix}$

37. (a) $AB = \begin{bmatrix} 7 \\ 8 \\ -1 \end{bmatrix}\begin{bmatrix} 1 & 1 & 2 \end{bmatrix} = \begin{bmatrix} 7 & 7 & 14 \\ 8 & 8 & 16 \\ -1 & -1 & -2 \end{bmatrix}$

(b) $BA = \begin{bmatrix} 1 & 1 & 2 \end{bmatrix}\begin{bmatrix} 7 \\ 8 \\ -1 \end{bmatrix} = [7+8-2] = [13]$

(c) A^2 is not defined.

38. (a) $AB = \begin{bmatrix} 3 & 2 & 1 \end{bmatrix}\begin{bmatrix} 2 \\ 3 \\ 0 \end{bmatrix} = [3(2) + 2(3) + 1(0)] = [12]$

(b) $BA = \begin{bmatrix} 2 \\ 3 \\ 0 \end{bmatrix}\begin{bmatrix} 3 & 2 & 1 \end{bmatrix} = \begin{bmatrix} 2(3) & 2(2) & 2(1) \\ 3(3) & 3(2) & 3(1) \\ 0(3) & 0(2) & 0(1) \end{bmatrix} = \begin{bmatrix} 6 & 4 & 2 \\ 9 & 6 & 3 \\ 0 & 0 & 0 \end{bmatrix}$

(c) The number of columns of A does not equal the number of rows of A; the multiplication is not possible.

39. $AB = \begin{bmatrix} 70 & -17 & 73 \\ 32 & 11 & 6 \\ 16 & -38 & 70 \end{bmatrix}$

40. $AB = \begin{bmatrix} 124 & -70 \\ 228 & 452 \\ 192 & -72 \end{bmatrix}$

41. $\begin{bmatrix} -3 & 8 & -6 & 8 \\ -12 & 15 & 9 & 6 \\ 5 & -1 & 1 & 5 \end{bmatrix}\begin{bmatrix} 3 & 1 & 6 \\ 24 & 15 & 14 \\ 16 & 10 & 21 \\ 8 & -4 & 10 \end{bmatrix} = \begin{bmatrix} 151 & 25 & 48 \\ 516 & 279 & 387 \\ 47 & -20 & 87 \end{bmatrix}$

42. A is 3×3, B is $4 \times 2 \Rightarrow AB$ is not defined.

43. A is 2×4 and B is $2 \times 4 \Rightarrow AB$ is not defined.

44. $AB = \begin{bmatrix} -238 & 50 & -484 \\ 119 & 115 & 342 \\ 210 & 135 & 555 \end{bmatrix}$

45. $\left(\begin{bmatrix} 3 & 1 \\ 0 & -2 \end{bmatrix} - \begin{bmatrix} 1 & 0 \\ -2 & 2 \end{bmatrix}\right)\begin{bmatrix} 1 & 0 \\ 2 & 4 \end{bmatrix} = \begin{bmatrix} 1 & 2 \\ 4 & -4 \end{bmatrix}\begin{bmatrix} 1 & 0 \\ 2 & 4 \end{bmatrix} = \begin{bmatrix} 5 & 8 \\ -4 & -16 \end{bmatrix}$

46. $\begin{bmatrix} 27 & -6 \\ -6 & -27 \end{bmatrix}$

47. $\begin{bmatrix} 0 & 2 & -2 \\ 4 & 1 & 2 \end{bmatrix}\left(\begin{bmatrix} 4 & 0 \\ 0 & -1 \\ -1 & 2 \end{bmatrix} + \begin{bmatrix} -2 & 3 \\ -3 & 5 \\ 0 & -3 \end{bmatrix}\right) = \begin{bmatrix} 0 & 2 & -2 \\ 4 & 1 & 2 \end{bmatrix}\begin{bmatrix} 2 & 3 \\ -3 & 4 \\ -1 & -1 \end{bmatrix} = \begin{bmatrix} -4 & 10 \\ 3 & 14 \end{bmatrix}$

48. $\begin{bmatrix} 3 \\ -1 \\ 5 \\ 7 \end{bmatrix}\begin{bmatrix} 4 & 2 \end{bmatrix} = \begin{bmatrix} 12 & 6 \\ -4 & -2 \\ 20 & 10 \\ 28 & 14 \end{bmatrix}$

49. $\left[\begin{array}{cc|c} 1 & 2 & 4 \\ 3 & 2 & 0 \end{array}\right]$

(a) $\begin{bmatrix} 1 & 2 \\ 3 & 2 \end{bmatrix}\begin{bmatrix} 2 \\ 1 \end{bmatrix} = \begin{bmatrix} 4 \\ 8 \end{bmatrix} \Rightarrow \begin{bmatrix} 2 \\ 1 \end{bmatrix}$ is not a solution.

(b) $\begin{bmatrix} 1 & 2 \\ 3 & 2 \end{bmatrix}\begin{bmatrix} -2 \\ 3 \end{bmatrix} = \begin{bmatrix} 4 \\ 0 \end{bmatrix} \Rightarrow \begin{bmatrix} -2 \\ 3 \end{bmatrix}$ is a solution.

(c) $\begin{bmatrix} 1 & 2 \\ 3 & 2 \end{bmatrix}\begin{bmatrix} -4 \\ 4 \end{bmatrix} = \begin{bmatrix} 4 \\ -4 \end{bmatrix} \Rightarrow \begin{bmatrix} -4 \\ 4 \end{bmatrix}$ is not a solution.

(d) $\begin{bmatrix} 1 & 2 \\ 3 & 2 \end{bmatrix}\begin{bmatrix} 2 \\ -3 \end{bmatrix} = \begin{bmatrix} -4 \\ 0 \end{bmatrix} \Rightarrow \begin{bmatrix} 2 \\ -3 \end{bmatrix}$ is not a solution.

50. $\left[\begin{array}{rr|r} 6 & 2 & 0 \\ -1 & 5 & 16 \end{array}\right]$. Let $A = \begin{bmatrix} 6 & 2 \\ -1 & 5 \end{bmatrix}$

(a) $A\begin{bmatrix} -1 \\ 3 \end{bmatrix} = \begin{bmatrix} 0 \\ 16 \end{bmatrix} \Rightarrow \begin{bmatrix} -1 \\ 3 \end{bmatrix}$ is a solution.

(b) $A\begin{bmatrix} 2 \\ -6 \end{bmatrix} = \begin{bmatrix} 0 \\ -32 \end{bmatrix} \Rightarrow \begin{bmatrix} 2 \\ -6 \end{bmatrix}$ is not a solution.

(c) $A\begin{bmatrix} 3 \\ -9 \end{bmatrix} = \begin{bmatrix} 0 \\ -48 \end{bmatrix} \Rightarrow \begin{bmatrix} 3 \\ -9 \end{bmatrix}$ is not a solution.

(d) $A\begin{bmatrix} -3 \\ 9 \end{bmatrix} = \begin{bmatrix} 0 \\ 48 \end{bmatrix} \Rightarrow \begin{bmatrix} -3 \\ 9 \end{bmatrix}$ is not a solution.

51. $\left[\begin{array}{rr|r} -2 & -3 & -6 \\ 4 & 2 & 20 \end{array}\right]$

(a) $\begin{bmatrix} -2 & -3 \\ 4 & 2 \end{bmatrix}\begin{bmatrix} 3 \\ 0 \end{bmatrix} = \begin{bmatrix} -6 \\ 12 \end{bmatrix} \Rightarrow \begin{bmatrix} 3 \\ 0 \end{bmatrix}$ is not a solution.

(b) $\begin{bmatrix} -2 & -3 \\ 4 & 2 \end{bmatrix}\begin{bmatrix} 6 \\ -2 \end{bmatrix} = \begin{bmatrix} -6 \\ 20 \end{bmatrix} \Rightarrow \begin{bmatrix} 6 \\ -2 \end{bmatrix}$ is a solution.

(c) $\begin{bmatrix} -2 & -3 \\ 4 & 2 \end{bmatrix}\begin{bmatrix} -6 \\ 6 \end{bmatrix} = \begin{bmatrix} -6 \\ -12 \end{bmatrix} \Rightarrow \begin{bmatrix} -6 \\ 6 \end{bmatrix}$ is not a solution.

(d) $\begin{bmatrix} -2 & -3 \\ 4 & 2 \end{bmatrix}\begin{bmatrix} 4 \\ 2 \end{bmatrix} = \begin{bmatrix} -14 \\ 20 \end{bmatrix} \Rightarrow \begin{bmatrix} 4 \\ 2 \end{bmatrix}$ is not a solution.

52. $\left[\begin{array}{rr|r} 5 & -7 & -15 \\ 3 & 1 & 17 \end{array}\right]$. Let $A = \begin{bmatrix} 5 & -7 \\ 3 & 1 \end{bmatrix}$

(a) $A\begin{bmatrix} 4 \\ 5 \end{bmatrix} = \begin{bmatrix} -15 \\ 17 \end{bmatrix} \Rightarrow \begin{bmatrix} 4 \\ 5 \end{bmatrix}$ is a solution.

(b) $A\begin{bmatrix} 5 \\ 2 \end{bmatrix} = \begin{bmatrix} 11 \\ 17 \end{bmatrix} \Rightarrow \begin{bmatrix} 5 \\ 2 \end{bmatrix}$ is not a solution.

(c) $A\begin{bmatrix} -4 \\ -5 \end{bmatrix} = \begin{bmatrix} 15 \\ -17 \end{bmatrix} \Rightarrow \begin{bmatrix} -4 \\ -5 \end{bmatrix}$ is not a solution.

(d) $A\begin{bmatrix} 2 \\ 11 \end{bmatrix} = \begin{bmatrix} -67 \\ 17 \end{bmatrix} \Rightarrow \begin{bmatrix} 2 \\ 11 \end{bmatrix}$ is not a solution.

53. (a) $A = \begin{bmatrix} -1 & 1 \\ -2 & 1 \end{bmatrix}$, $X = \begin{bmatrix} x_1 \\ x_2 \end{bmatrix}$, $B = \begin{bmatrix} 4 \\ 0 \end{bmatrix}$

(b) By Gauss-Jordan elimination on

$$\left[\begin{array}{rr|r} -1 & 1 & 4 \\ -2 & 1 & 0 \end{array}\right]$$

$$\begin{array}{r} -R_1 \rightarrow \\ 2R_1 + R_2 \rightarrow \end{array} \left[\begin{array}{rr|r} 1 & -1 & -4 \\ 0 & -1 & -8 \end{array}\right]$$

$$\begin{array}{r} -R_2 + R_1 \rightarrow \\ -R_2 \rightarrow \end{array} \left[\begin{array}{rr|r} 1 & 0 & 4 \\ 0 & 1 & 8 \end{array}\right], \text{ we have}$$

$x_1 = 4$ and $x_2 = 8$. Thus, $X = \begin{bmatrix} 4 \\ 8 \end{bmatrix}$.

54. (a) $A = \begin{bmatrix} 2 & 3 \\ 1 & 4 \end{bmatrix}$, $X = \begin{bmatrix} x_1 \\ x_2 \end{bmatrix}$, $B = \begin{bmatrix} 5 \\ 10 \end{bmatrix}$

(b) By Gauss-Jordan elimination on

$$\left[\begin{array}{rr|r} 1 & 4 & 10 \\ 2 & 3 & 5 \end{array}\right]$$

$$-2R_1 + R_2 \rightarrow \left[\begin{array}{rr|r} 1 & 4 & 10 \\ 0 & -5 & -15 \end{array}\right]$$

$$\begin{array}{r} -4R_2 + R_1 \rightarrow \\ -\frac{1}{5}R_2 \rightarrow \end{array} \left[\begin{array}{rr|r} 1 & 0 & -2 \\ 0 & 1 & 3 \end{array}\right],$$

we have $x_1 = -2$ and $x_2 = 3$.

Answer: $\begin{bmatrix} -2 \\ 3 \end{bmatrix}$

55. (a) $A = \begin{bmatrix} -2 & -3 \\ 6 & 1 \end{bmatrix}$, $X = \begin{bmatrix} x_1 \\ x_2 \end{bmatrix}$, $B = \begin{bmatrix} -4 \\ -36 \end{bmatrix}$

(b) $\left[\begin{array}{rr|r} -2 & -3 & -4 \\ 6 & 1 & -36 \end{array}\right]$

$$3R_1 + R_2 \left[\begin{array}{rr|r} -2 & -3 & -4 \\ 0 & -8 & -48 \end{array}\right]$$

$$\left(-\tfrac{1}{8}\right)R_2 \left[\begin{array}{rr|r} -2 & -3 & -4 \\ 0 & 1 & 6 \end{array}\right]$$

$$3R_2 + R_1 \left[\begin{array}{rr|r} -2 & 0 & 14 \\ 0 & 1 & 6 \end{array}\right]$$

$$-\tfrac{1}{2}R_1 \left[\begin{array}{rr|r} 1 & 0 & -7 \\ 0 & 1 & 6 \end{array}\right]$$

$x_1 = -7$, $x_2 = 6$.

Answer: $X = \begin{bmatrix} -7 \\ 6 \end{bmatrix}$

56. (a) $A = \begin{bmatrix} -4 & 9 \\ 1 & -3 \end{bmatrix}, x = \begin{bmatrix} x_1 \\ x_2 \end{bmatrix}, B = \begin{bmatrix} -13 \\ 12 \end{bmatrix}$

(b) $\begin{bmatrix} -4 & 9 & -13 \\ 1 & -3 & 12 \end{bmatrix} \begin{matrix} R_1 \\ R_2 \end{matrix} \begin{bmatrix} 1 & -3 & 12 \\ -4 & 9 & -13 \end{bmatrix}$

$$4R_1 + R_2 \rightarrow \begin{bmatrix} 1 & -3 & \vdots & 12 \\ 0 & -3 & \vdots & 35 \end{bmatrix}$$

$$(-1)R_2 + R_1 \rightarrow \begin{bmatrix} 1 & 0 & \vdots & -23 \\ 0 & -3 & \vdots & 35 \end{bmatrix}$$

$$-\tfrac{1}{3}R_2 \rightarrow \begin{bmatrix} 1 & 0 & \vdots & -23 \\ 0 & 1 & \vdots & -\frac{35}{3} \end{bmatrix}$$

$x_1 = -23, x_2 = -\frac{35}{3}$

Answer: $\begin{bmatrix} -23 \\ -\frac{35}{3} \end{bmatrix}$

57. (a) $A = \begin{bmatrix} 1 & -2 & 3 \\ -1 & 3 & -1 \\ 2 & -5 & 5 \end{bmatrix}, X = \begin{bmatrix} x_1 \\ x_2 \\ x_3 \end{bmatrix}, B = \begin{bmatrix} 9 \\ -6 \\ 17 \end{bmatrix}$

(b) $\begin{bmatrix} 1 & -2 & 3 & \vdots & 9 \\ -1 & 3 & -1 & \vdots & -6 \\ 2 & -5 & 5 & \vdots & 17 \end{bmatrix}$

$$\begin{matrix} \\ R_1 + R_2 \rightarrow \\ -2R_1 + R_3 \rightarrow \end{matrix} \begin{bmatrix} 1 & -2 & 3 & \vdots & 9 \\ 0 & 1 & 2 & \vdots & 3 \\ 0 & -1 & -1 & \vdots & -1 \end{bmatrix}$$

$$\begin{matrix} 2R_2 + R_1 \rightarrow \\ \\ R_2 + R_3 \rightarrow \end{matrix} \begin{bmatrix} 1 & 0 & 7 & \vdots & 15 \\ 0 & 1 & 2 & \vdots & 3 \\ 0 & 0 & 1 & \vdots & 2 \end{bmatrix}$$

$$\begin{matrix} -7R_3 + R_1 \rightarrow \\ -2R_3 + R_2 \rightarrow \\ \\ \end{matrix} \begin{bmatrix} 1 & 0 & 0 & \vdots & 1 \\ 0 & 1 & 0 & \vdots & -1 \\ 0 & 0 & 1 & \vdots & 2 \end{bmatrix}$$

$x_1 = 1, x_2 = -1, x_3 = 2.$

Answer: $X = \begin{bmatrix} 1 \\ -1 \\ 2 \end{bmatrix}.$

58. (a) $A = \begin{bmatrix} 1 & 1 & -3 \\ -1 & 2 & 0 \\ 1 & -1 & 1 \end{bmatrix}, X = \begin{bmatrix} x_1 \\ x_2 \\ x_3 \end{bmatrix}, B = \begin{bmatrix} -1 \\ 1 \\ 2 \end{bmatrix}$

(b) $\begin{bmatrix} 1 & 1 & -3 & \vdots & -1 \\ -1 & 2 & 0 & \vdots & 1 \\ 1 & -1 & 1 & \vdots & 2 \end{bmatrix}$ row reduces to $\begin{bmatrix} 1 & 0 & 0 & 2 \\ 0 & 1 & 0 & 1.5 \\ 0 & 0 & 1 & 1.5 \end{bmatrix}$

Answer: $\begin{bmatrix} 2 \\ \frac{3}{2} \\ \frac{3}{2} \end{bmatrix}$

59. (a) $A = \begin{bmatrix} 1 & -5 & 2 \\ -3 & 1 & -1 \\ 0 & -2 & 5 \end{bmatrix}, X = \begin{bmatrix} x_1 \\ x_2 \\ x_3 \end{bmatrix}, B = \begin{bmatrix} -20 \\ 8 \\ -16 \end{bmatrix}$

(b) $\begin{bmatrix} 1 & -5 & 2 & \vdots & -20 \\ -3 & 1 & -1 & \vdots & 8 \\ 0 & -2 & 5 & \vdots & -16 \end{bmatrix}$

$$\begin{matrix} \\ 3R_1 + R_2 \\ \\ \end{matrix} \begin{bmatrix} 1 & -5 & 2 & \vdots & -20 \\ 0 & -14 & 5 & \vdots & -52 \\ 0 & -2 & 5 & \vdots & -16 \end{bmatrix}$$

$$\begin{matrix} R_2 \\ R_3 \end{matrix} \begin{bmatrix} 1 & -5 & 2 & \vdots & -20 \\ 0 & -2 & 5 & \vdots & -16 \\ 0 & -14 & 5 & \vdots & -52 \end{bmatrix}$$

$$\begin{matrix} \\ \\ -7R_2 + R_3 \end{matrix} \begin{bmatrix} 1 & -5 & 2 & \vdots & -20 \\ 0 & -2 & 5 & \vdots & -16 \\ 0 & 0 & -30 & \vdots & 60 \end{bmatrix}$$

$$\begin{matrix} \\ \\ -\frac{1}{30}R_3 \end{matrix} \begin{bmatrix} 1 & -5 & 2 & \vdots & -20 \\ 0 & -2 & 5 & \vdots & -16 \\ 0 & 0 & 1 & \vdots & -2 \end{bmatrix}$$

$$\begin{matrix} -2R_3 + R_1 \\ -5R_3 + R_2 \\ \\ \end{matrix} \begin{bmatrix} 1 & -5 & 0 & \vdots & -16 \\ 0 & -2 & 0 & \vdots & -6 \\ 0 & 0 & 1 & \vdots & -2 \end{bmatrix}$$

$$\begin{matrix} \\ \left(-\frac{1}{2}\right)R_2 \\ \\ \end{matrix} \begin{bmatrix} 1 & -5 & 0 & \vdots & -16 \\ 0 & 1 & 0 & \vdots & 3 \\ 0 & 0 & 1 & \vdots & -2 \end{bmatrix}$$

$$\begin{matrix} 5R_2 + R_1 \\ \\ \\ \end{matrix} \begin{bmatrix} 1 & 0 & 0 & \vdots & -1 \\ 0 & 1 & 0 & \vdots & 3 \\ 0 & 0 & 1 & \vdots & -2 \end{bmatrix}$$

$x_1 = -1, x_2 = 3, x_3 = -2$ *Answer:* $X = \begin{bmatrix} -1 \\ 3 \\ -2 \end{bmatrix}$

60. (a) $A = \begin{bmatrix} 1 & -1 & 4 \\ 1 & 3 & 0 \\ 0 & -6 & 5 \end{bmatrix}, x = \begin{bmatrix} x_1 \\ x_2 \\ x_3 \end{bmatrix}, B = \begin{bmatrix} 17 \\ -11 \\ 40 \end{bmatrix}$

(b) $\begin{bmatrix} 1 & -1 & 4 & \vdots & 17 \\ 1 & 3 & 0 & \vdots & -11 \\ 0 & -6 & 5 & \vdots & 40 \end{bmatrix} \begin{matrix} \\ (-1)R_1 + R_2 \rightarrow \\ \\ \end{matrix} \begin{bmatrix} 1 & -1 & 4 & \vdots & 17 \\ 0 & 4 & -4 & \vdots & -28 \\ 0 & -6 & 5 & \vdots & 40 \end{bmatrix}$

$$\begin{matrix} \\ \frac{1}{4}R_2 \rightarrow \\ \\ \end{matrix} \begin{bmatrix} 1 & -1 & 4 & \vdots & 17 \\ 0 & 1 & -1 & \vdots & -7 \\ 0 & -6 & 5 & \vdots & 40 \end{bmatrix}$$

$$\begin{matrix} \\ \\ 6R_2 + R_3 \rightarrow \end{matrix} \begin{bmatrix} 1 & -1 & 4 & \vdots & 17 \\ 0 & 1 & -1 & \vdots & -7 \\ 0 & 0 & -1 & \vdots & -2 \end{bmatrix}$$

$$\begin{matrix} 4R_3 + R_1 \rightarrow \\ -R_3 + R_2 \rightarrow \\ -R_3 \rightarrow \end{matrix} \begin{bmatrix} 1 & -1 & 0 & \vdots & 9 \\ 0 & 1 & 0 & \vdots & -5 \\ 0 & 0 & 1 & \vdots & 2 \end{bmatrix}$$

$$\begin{matrix} R_2 + R_1 \rightarrow \\ \\ \\ \end{matrix} \begin{bmatrix} 1 & 0 & 0 & \vdots & 4 \\ 0 & 1 & 0 & \vdots & -5 \\ 0 & 0 & 1 & \vdots & 2 \end{bmatrix}$$

$x_3 = 2, x_2 = -5, x_1 = 4$ *Answer:* $\begin{bmatrix} 4 \\ -5 \\ 2 \end{bmatrix}$

61. (a) $A(B + C) = \begin{bmatrix} 7 & -2 & 5 \\ -6 & 13 & -8 \\ 16 & 11 & -3 \end{bmatrix}$

(b) $AB + AC = \begin{bmatrix} 7 & -2 & 5 \\ -6 & 13 & -8 \\ 16 & 11 & -3 \end{bmatrix}$

The answers are the same.

62. (a) $(B + C)A = \begin{bmatrix} 9 & 5 & 0 \\ 4 & -5 & 5 \\ -10 & -8 & 13 \end{bmatrix}$

(b) $BA + CA = \begin{bmatrix} 9 & 5 & 0 \\ 4 & -5 & 5 \\ -10 & -8 & 13 \end{bmatrix}$

The answers are the same.

63. (a) $(A + B)^2 = \begin{bmatrix} 26 & 11 & 0 \\ 11 & 20 & -3 \\ 11 & 14 & 0 \end{bmatrix}$

(b) $A^2 + AB + BA + B^2 = \begin{bmatrix} 26 & 11 & 0 \\ 11 & 20 & -3 \\ 11 & 14 & 0 \end{bmatrix}$

The answers are the same.

64. (a) $(A - B)^2 = \begin{bmatrix} 0 & 9 & -6 \\ 41 & -12 & -1 \\ 25 & 0 & -26 \end{bmatrix}$

(b) $A^2 - AB - BA + B^2 = \begin{bmatrix} 0 & 9 & -6 \\ 41 & -12 & -1 \\ 25 & 0 & -26 \end{bmatrix}$

The answers are the same.

65. (a) $A(BC) = \begin{bmatrix} 25 & -34 & 28 \\ -53 & 34 & -7 \\ -76 & 30 & 21 \end{bmatrix}$

(b) $(AB)C = \begin{bmatrix} 25 & -34 & 28 \\ -53 & 34 & -7 \\ -76 & 30 & 21 \end{bmatrix}$

The answers are the same.

66. (a) $c(AB) = \begin{bmatrix} 33 & 9 & -12 \\ -33 & 12 & 12 \\ -18 & 39 & 18 \end{bmatrix}$

(b) $(cA)B = \begin{bmatrix} 33 & 9 & -12 \\ -33 & 12 & 12 \\ -18 & 39 & 18 \end{bmatrix}$

The answers are the same.

67. (a) $A + cB = \begin{bmatrix} -1 & 10 & -4 \\ -5 & -1 & 0 \end{bmatrix}$

(b) $A + cB = \begin{bmatrix} 1 & 2 & -2 \\ -1 & 1 & 0 \end{bmatrix} + 2\begin{bmatrix} -1 & 4 & -1 \\ -2 & -1 & 0 \end{bmatrix} = \begin{bmatrix} -1 & 10 & -4 \\ -5 & -1 & 0 \end{bmatrix}$

68. (*a*), (*b*) $A(B + C)$ Not possible

B and C have different orders.

69. (*a*), (*b*) $c(AB)$ Not possible

Number of columns of A (3) does not equal the number of rows of B (2).

70. (a) $B + dA = \begin{bmatrix} -4 & -2 & 5 \\ 1 & -4 & 0 \end{bmatrix}$

(b) $B + dA = \begin{bmatrix} -1 & 4 & -1 \\ -2 & -1 & 0 \end{bmatrix} + (-3)\begin{bmatrix} 1 & 2 & -2 \\ -1 & 1 & 0 \end{bmatrix} = \begin{bmatrix} -4 & -2 & 5 \\ 1 & -4 & 0 \end{bmatrix}$

71. (*a*), (*b*) $CA - BC$ Not possible

CA is 3×3, BC is 2×2.

72. (*a*), (*b*) dAB^2 Not possible

AB not defined, nor B^2

73. (a) $cd\,A = \begin{bmatrix} -6 & -12 & 12 \\ 6 & -6 & 0 \end{bmatrix}$

(b) $cd\,A = 2(-3)\begin{bmatrix} 1 & 2 & -2 \\ -1 & 1 & 0 \end{bmatrix} = \begin{bmatrix} -6 & -12 & 12 \\ 6 & -6 & 0 \end{bmatrix}$

74. (a) $cA + dB = \begin{bmatrix} 5 & -8 & -1 \\ 4 & 5 & 0 \end{bmatrix}$

(b) $cA + dB = 2\begin{bmatrix} 1 & 2 & -2 \\ -1 & 1 & 0 \end{bmatrix} + (-3)\begin{bmatrix} -1 & 4 & -1 \\ -2 & -1 & 0 \end{bmatrix}$

$= \begin{bmatrix} 2 & 4 & -4 \\ -2 & 2 & 0 \end{bmatrix} + \begin{bmatrix} 3 & -12 & 3 \\ 6 & 3 & 0 \end{bmatrix}$

$= \begin{bmatrix} 5 & -8 & -1 \\ 4 & 5 & 0 \end{bmatrix}$

75. $A = \begin{bmatrix} 2 & 0 \\ 4 & 5 \end{bmatrix}$

$f(A) = A^2 - 5A + 2I = \begin{bmatrix} 2 & 0 \\ 4 & 5 \end{bmatrix}\begin{bmatrix} 2 & 0 \\ 4 & 5 \end{bmatrix} - 5\begin{bmatrix} 2 & 0 \\ 4 & 5 \end{bmatrix} + 2\begin{bmatrix} 1 & 0 \\ 0 & 1 \end{bmatrix} = \begin{bmatrix} -4 & 0 \\ 8 & 2 \end{bmatrix}$

76. $A = \begin{bmatrix} 5 & 4 \\ 1 & 2 \end{bmatrix}$

$f(A) = A^2 - 7A + 6 = \begin{bmatrix} 5 & 4 \\ 1 & 2 \end{bmatrix}\begin{bmatrix} 5 & 4 \\ 1 & 2 \end{bmatrix} - 7\begin{bmatrix} 5 & 4 \\ 1 & 2 \end{bmatrix} + 6\begin{bmatrix} 1 & 0 \\ 0 & 1 \end{bmatrix} = \begin{bmatrix} 0 & 0 \\ 0 & 0 \end{bmatrix}$

77. $1.20\begin{bmatrix} 70 & 50 & 25 \\ 35 & 100 & 70 \end{bmatrix} = \begin{bmatrix} 84 & 60 & 30 \\ 42 & 120 & 84 \end{bmatrix}$

78. $1.10\begin{bmatrix} 100 & 90 & 70 & 30 \\ 40 & 20 & 60 & 60 \end{bmatrix} = \begin{bmatrix} 110 & 99 & 77 & 33 \\ 44 & 22 & 66 & 66 \end{bmatrix}$

79. $BA = \begin{bmatrix} 3.50 & 6.00 \end{bmatrix}\begin{bmatrix} 125 & 100 & 75 \\ 100 & 175 & 125 \end{bmatrix} = \begin{bmatrix} 1037.50 & 1400 & 1012.50 \end{bmatrix}$

The entries in the last matrix BA represent the profit for both crops at each of the three outlets.

80. $\begin{bmatrix} 39.50 & 44.50 & 56.50 \end{bmatrix}\begin{bmatrix} 5000 & 4000 \\ 6000 & 10{,}000 \\ 8000 & 5000 \end{bmatrix} = \begin{bmatrix} 916{,}500 & 885{,}500 \end{bmatrix}$

The entries represent the costs of the three models of the product at each of the two warehouses.

81. $ST = \begin{bmatrix} 3 & 2 & 2 & 3 & 0 \\ 0 & 2 & 3 & 4 & 3 \\ 4 & 2 & 1 & 3 & 2 \end{bmatrix}\begin{bmatrix} 840 & 1100 \\ 1200 & 1350 \\ 1450 & 1650 \\ 2650 & 3000 \\ 3050 & 3200 \end{bmatrix} = \begin{bmatrix} \$15{,}770 & \$18{,}300 \\ \$26{,}500 & \$29{,}250 \\ \$21{,}260 & \$24{,}150 \end{bmatrix}$

The entries represent the wholesale and retail prices of the inventory at each outlet.

82. $ST = \begin{bmatrix} 1.0 & 0.5 & 0.2 \\ 1.6 & 1.0 & 0.2 \\ 2.5 & 2.0 & 0.4 \end{bmatrix}\begin{bmatrix} 12 & 10 \\ 9 & 8 \\ 6 & 5 \end{bmatrix} = \begin{bmatrix} \$17.70 & \$15.00 \\ \$29.40 & \$25.00 \\ \$50.40 & \$43.00 \end{bmatrix}$

This represents the labor cost for each boat size at each plant.

83. $P^2 = \begin{bmatrix} 0.6 & 0.1 & 0.1 \\ 0.2 & 0.7 & 0.1 \\ 0.2 & 0.2 & 0.8 \end{bmatrix}\begin{bmatrix} 0.6 & 0.1 & 0.1 \\ 0.2 & 0.7 & 0.1 \\ 0.2 & 0.2 & 0.8 \end{bmatrix} = \begin{bmatrix} 0.40 & 0.15 & 0.15 \\ 0.28 & 0.53 & 0.17 \\ 0.32 & 0.32 & 0.68 \end{bmatrix}$

This product represents the changes in party affiliation after *two* elections.

84. $P^3 = P^2P = \begin{bmatrix} 0.4 & 0.15 & 0.15 \\ 0.28 & 0.53 & 0.17 \\ 0.32 & 0.32 & 0.68 \end{bmatrix}\begin{bmatrix} 0.6 & 0.1 & 0.1 \\ 0.2 & 0.7 & 0.1 \\ 0.2 & 0.2 & 0.8 \end{bmatrix} = \begin{bmatrix} 0.300 & 0.175 & 0.175 \\ 0.308 & 0.433 & 0.217 \\ 0.392 & 0.392 & 0.608 \end{bmatrix}$

$P^4 = P^3P = \begin{bmatrix} 0.300 & 0.175 & 0.175 \\ 0.308 & 0.433 & 0.217 \\ 0.392 & 0.392 & 0.608 \end{bmatrix}\begin{bmatrix} 0.6 & 0.1 & 0.1 \\ 0.2 & 0.7 & 0.1 \\ 0.2 & 0.2 & 0.8 \end{bmatrix} = \begin{bmatrix} 0.250 & 0.188 & 0.188 \\ 0.315 & 0.377 & 0.248 \\ 0.435 & 0.435 & 0.565 \end{bmatrix}$

$P^5 = P^4P = \begin{bmatrix} 0.250 & 0.188 & 0.188 \\ 0.315 & 0.377 & 0.248 \\ 0.435 & 0.435 & 0.565 \end{bmatrix}\begin{bmatrix} 0.6 & 0.1 & 0.1 \\ 0.2 & 0.7 & 0.1 \\ 0.2 & 0.2 & 0.8 \end{bmatrix} = \begin{bmatrix} 0.225 & 0.194 & 0.194 \\ 0.314 & 0.345 & 0.267 \\ 0.461 & 0.461 & 0.539 \end{bmatrix}$

$P^6 = \begin{bmatrix} 0.213 & 0.197 & 0.197 \\ 0.311 & 0.326 & 0.280 \\ 0.477 & 0.477 & 0.523 \end{bmatrix}$

$P^7 = \begin{bmatrix} 0.206 & 0.198 & 0.198 \\ 0.308 & 0.316 & 0.288 \\ 0.486 & 0.486 & 0.514 \end{bmatrix}$

$P^8 = \begin{bmatrix} 0.203 & 0.199 & 0.199 \\ 0.305 & 0.309 & 0.292 \\ 0.492 & 0.492 & 0.508 \end{bmatrix}$

As P is raised to higher and higher powers, the resulting matrices appear to be approaching the matrix

$\begin{bmatrix} 0.2 & 0.2 & 0.2 \\ 0.3 & 0.3 & 0.3 \\ 0.5 & 0.5 & 0.5 \end{bmatrix}.$

85. True

86. False. $\begin{bmatrix} -6 & -2 \\ 2 & -6 \end{bmatrix}\begin{bmatrix} 4 & 0 \\ 0 & -1 \end{bmatrix} = \begin{bmatrix} -24 & 2 \\ 8 & 6 \end{bmatrix}$

$\begin{bmatrix} 4 & 0 \\ 0 & -1 \end{bmatrix}\begin{bmatrix} -6 & -2 \\ 2 & -6 \end{bmatrix} = \begin{bmatrix} -24 & -8 \\ -2 & 6 \end{bmatrix}$

For 87–93, A is of order 2×3, B is of order 2×3, C is of order 3×2 and D is of order 2×2.

87. $A + 2C$ is not possible. A and C are not of the same order.

88. Not possible

89. AB is not possible. The number of columns of A does not equal the number of rows of B.

90. Possible.
Order 2×2

91. $BC - D$ is possible. The resulting order is 2×2.

92. Not possible

93. $D(A - 3B)$ is possible. The resulting order is 2×3.

94. Possible.
Order 2×3

95. $(A + B)^2 = \begin{bmatrix} 1 & 0 \\ 2 & 1 \end{bmatrix}$

$A^2 + 2AB + B^2 = \begin{bmatrix} 0 & 0 \\ 3 & 2 \end{bmatrix}$

96. $(A - B)^2 = \begin{bmatrix} 7 & -16 \\ 8 & 23 \end{bmatrix}$

$A^2 - 2AB + B^2 = \begin{bmatrix} 8 & -16 \\ 7 & 22 \end{bmatrix}$

97. $(A+B)(A-B) = \begin{bmatrix} 3 & -2 \\ 4 & 3 \end{bmatrix}$

$A^2 - B^2 = \begin{bmatrix} 2 & -2 \\ 5 & 4 \end{bmatrix}$

98. $(A+B)^2 = \begin{bmatrix} 1 & 0 \\ 2 & 1 \end{bmatrix} = A^2 + AB + BA + B^2$

99. $AC = \begin{bmatrix} 0 & 1 \\ 0 & 1 \end{bmatrix}\begin{bmatrix} 2 & 3 \\ 2 & 3 \end{bmatrix} = \begin{bmatrix} 2 & 3 \\ 2 & 3 \end{bmatrix}$

$BC = \begin{bmatrix} 1 & 0 \\ 1 & 0 \end{bmatrix}\begin{bmatrix} 2 & 3 \\ 2 & 3 \end{bmatrix} = \begin{bmatrix} 2 & 3 \\ 2 & 3 \end{bmatrix}$

$AC = BC$, but $A \neq B$.

100. $A = \begin{bmatrix} 3 & 3 \\ 4 & 4 \end{bmatrix}, B = \begin{bmatrix} 1 & -1 \\ -1 & 1 \end{bmatrix}$

$AB = \begin{bmatrix} 3 & 3 \\ 4 & 4 \end{bmatrix}\begin{bmatrix} 1 & -1 \\ -1 & 1 \end{bmatrix} = \begin{bmatrix} 0 & 0 \\ 0 & 0 \end{bmatrix}$

$AB = 0$ but $A \neq 0$ and $B \neq 0$.

101. (a) $A^2 = \begin{bmatrix} i & 0 \\ 0 & i \end{bmatrix}\begin{bmatrix} i & 0 \\ 0 & i \end{bmatrix} = \begin{bmatrix} -1 & 0 \\ 0 & -1 \end{bmatrix}$ and $i^2 = -1$

$A^3 = A^2A = \begin{bmatrix} -1 & 0 \\ 0 & -1 \end{bmatrix}\begin{bmatrix} i & 0 \\ 0 & i \end{bmatrix} = \begin{bmatrix} -i & 0 \\ 0 & -i \end{bmatrix}$ and $i^3 = -i$

$A^4 = A^3A = \begin{bmatrix} -i & 0 \\ 0 & -i \end{bmatrix}\begin{bmatrix} i & 0 \\ 0 & i \end{bmatrix} = \begin{bmatrix} 1 & 0 \\ 0 & 1 \end{bmatrix}$ and $i^4 = 1$

(b) $B^2 = \begin{bmatrix} 0 & -i \\ i & 0 \end{bmatrix}\begin{bmatrix} 0 & -i \\ i & 0 \end{bmatrix} = \begin{bmatrix} 1 & 0 \\ 0 & 1 \end{bmatrix}$,

The identity matrix

102. The product of two diagonal matrices of the same order is a diagonal matrix whose entries are the products of the corresponding diagonal entries of A and B.

103. (a) $A = \begin{bmatrix} 0 & 2 \\ 0 & 0 \end{bmatrix}, B = \begin{bmatrix} 0 & 2 & 3 \\ 0 & 0 & 4 \\ 0 & 0 & 0 \end{bmatrix}$

(b) A^2 and B^3 are both zero matrices.

(c) If A is 4×4, then A^4 will be the zero matrix.

(d) If A is $n \times n$, then A^n is the zero matrix.

104. Matrix multiplication can be used to find the number of subscribers each company will have one year later. Multiply a 3×1 matrix containing the current number of subscribers per company on the left by the given matrix.

105. $3 \ln 4 - \frac{1}{3}\ln(x^2+3) = \ln 4^3 - \ln(x^2+3)^{1/3} = \ln\left[\frac{64}{(x^2+3)^{1/3}}\right]$

106. $\ln x - 3[\ln(x+6) + \ln(x-6)] = \ln x - 3[\ln(x+6)(x-6)]$

$= \ln x - \ln(x^2-36)^3$

$= \ln\left[\frac{x}{(x^2-36)^3}\right]$

107. $\frac{1}{2}[2\ln(x+5) + \ln x - \ln(x-8)] = \ln(x+5) + \ln x^{1/2} - \ln(x-8)^{1/2}$

$= \ln\left[\frac{(x+5)\sqrt{x}}{\sqrt{x-8}}\right]$

108. $\frac{3}{2}\ln 7t^4 - \frac{3}{5}\ln t^5 = \ln(7t^4)^{3/2} - \ln(t^5)^{3/5}$

$= \ln(7^{3/2}t^6) - \ln t^3$

$= \ln\left[\frac{7^{3/2}t^6}{t^3}\right] = \ln(7^{3/2}t^3)$

Section 7.6 The Inverse of a Square Matrix

- You should be able to find the inverse, if it exists, of a square matrix.
  (a) Write the $n \times 2n$ matrix that consists of the given matrix A on the left and the $n \times n$ identity matrix I on the right to obtain $[A \;\vdots\; I]$. Note that we separate the matrices A and I by a dotted line. We call this process **adjoining** the matrices A and I.
  (b) If possible, row reduce A to I using elementary row operations on the *entire* matrix $[A \;\vdots\; I]$. The result will be the matrix $[I \;\vdots\; A^{-1}]$. If this is not possible, then A is not invertible.
  (c) Check your work by multiplying to see that $AA^{-1} = I = A^{-1}A$.
- You should be able to use inverse matrices to solve systems of equation.
- You should be able to find inverses using a graphing utility.

Vocabulary Check

1. square **2.** inverse **3.** nonsingular, singular

1. $AB = \begin{bmatrix} 2 & 1 \\ 5 & 3 \end{bmatrix}\begin{bmatrix} 3 & -1 \\ -5 & 2 \end{bmatrix} = \begin{bmatrix} 2(3) + 1(-5) & 2(-1) + 1(2) \\ 5(3) + 3(-5) & 5(-1) + 3(2) \end{bmatrix} = \begin{bmatrix} 1 & 0 \\ 0 & 1 \end{bmatrix}$

$BA = \begin{bmatrix} 3 & -1 \\ -5 & 2 \end{bmatrix}\begin{bmatrix} 2 & 1 \\ 5 & 3 \end{bmatrix} = \begin{bmatrix} 3(2) + (-1)(5) & 3(1) + (-1)(3) \\ -5(2) + 2(5) & -5(1) + 2(3) \end{bmatrix} = \begin{bmatrix} 1 & 0 \\ 0 & 1 \end{bmatrix}$

2. $AB = \begin{bmatrix} 1 & -1 \\ -1 & 2 \end{bmatrix}\begin{bmatrix} 2 & 1 \\ 1 & 1 \end{bmatrix} = \begin{bmatrix} 2 - 1 & 1 - 1 \\ -2 + 2 & -1 + 2 \end{bmatrix} = \begin{bmatrix} 1 & 0 \\ 0 & 1 \end{bmatrix}$

$BA = \begin{bmatrix} 2 & 1 \\ 1 & 1 \end{bmatrix}\begin{bmatrix} 1 & -1 \\ -1 & 2 \end{bmatrix} = \begin{bmatrix} 2 - 1 & -2 + 2 \\ 1 - 1 & -1 + 2 \end{bmatrix} = \begin{bmatrix} 1 & 0 \\ 0 & 1 \end{bmatrix}$

3. $AB = \begin{bmatrix} 1 & 2 \\ 3 & 4 \end{bmatrix}\begin{bmatrix} -2 & 1 \\ \frac{3}{2} & -\frac{1}{2} \end{bmatrix} = \begin{bmatrix} -2 + 3 & 1 - 1 \\ -6 + 6 & 3 - 2 \end{bmatrix} = \begin{bmatrix} 1 & 0 \\ 0 & 1 \end{bmatrix}$

$BA = \begin{bmatrix} -2 & 1 \\ \frac{3}{2} & -\frac{1}{2} \end{bmatrix}\begin{bmatrix} 1 & 2 \\ 3 & 4 \end{bmatrix} = \begin{bmatrix} -2 + 3 & -4 + 4 \\ \frac{3}{2} - \frac{3}{2} & 3 - 2 \end{bmatrix} = \begin{bmatrix} 1 & 0 \\ 0 & 1 \end{bmatrix}$

4. $AB = \begin{bmatrix} 1 & -1 \\ 2 & 3 \end{bmatrix}\begin{bmatrix} \frac{3}{5} & \frac{1}{5} \\ -\frac{2}{5} & \frac{1}{5} \end{bmatrix} = \begin{bmatrix} \frac{3}{5} + \frac{2}{5} & \frac{1}{5} - \frac{1}{5} \\ \frac{6}{5} - \frac{6}{5} & \frac{2}{5} + \frac{3}{5} \end{bmatrix} = \begin{bmatrix} 1 & 0 \\ 0 & 1 \end{bmatrix}$

$BA = \begin{bmatrix} \frac{3}{5} & \frac{1}{5} \\ -\frac{2}{5} & \frac{1}{5} \end{bmatrix}\begin{bmatrix} 1 & -1 \\ 2 & 3 \end{bmatrix} = \begin{bmatrix} \frac{3}{5} + \frac{2}{5} & -\frac{3}{5} + \frac{3}{5} \\ -\frac{2}{5} + \frac{2}{5} & \frac{2}{5} + \frac{3}{5} \end{bmatrix} = \begin{bmatrix} 1 & 0 \\ 0 & 1 \end{bmatrix}$

5. $AB = \begin{bmatrix} 2 & -17 & 11 \\ -1 & 11 & -7 \\ 0 & 3 & -2 \end{bmatrix}\begin{bmatrix} 1 & 1 & 2 \\ 2 & 4 & -3 \\ 3 & 6 & -5 \end{bmatrix}$

$= \begin{bmatrix} 2 - 34 + 33 & 2 - 68 + 66 & 4 + 51 - 55 \\ -1 + 22 - 21 & -1 + 44 - 42 & -2 - 33 + 35 \\ 6 - 6 & 12 - 12 & -9 + 10 \end{bmatrix} = \begin{bmatrix} 1 & 0 & 0 \\ 0 & 1 & 0 \\ 0 & 0 & 1 \end{bmatrix}$

$BA = \begin{bmatrix} 1 & 1 & 2 \\ 2 & 4 & -3 \\ 3 & 6 & -5 \end{bmatrix}\begin{bmatrix} 2 & -17 & 11 \\ -1 & 11 & -7 \\ 0 & 3 & -2 \end{bmatrix} = \begin{bmatrix} 2 - 1 & -17 + 11 + 6 & 11 - 7 - 4 \\ 4 - 4 & -34 + 44 - 9 & 22 - 28 + 6 \\ 6 - 6 & -51 + 66 - 15 & 33 - 42 + 10 \end{bmatrix} = \begin{bmatrix} 1 & 0 & 0 \\ 0 & 1 & 0 \\ 0 & 0 & 1 \end{bmatrix}$

6. $AB = \begin{bmatrix} 1 & 0 & -1 \\ -1 & 1 & 0 \\ 1 & 2 & 0 \end{bmatrix}\frac{1}{3}\begin{bmatrix} 0 & -2 & 1 \\ 0 & 1 & 1 \\ -3 & -2 & 1 \end{bmatrix} = \begin{bmatrix} 1 & 0 & 0 \\ 0 & 1 & 0 \\ 0 & 0 & 1 \end{bmatrix}$

$BA = \begin{bmatrix} 1 & 0 & 0 \\ 0 & 1 & 0 \\ 0 & 0 & 1 \end{bmatrix}$

7. $AB = \begin{bmatrix} -1 & -4 \\ 1 & 2 \end{bmatrix}\begin{bmatrix} 1 & 2 \\ -\frac{1}{2} & -\frac{1}{2} \end{bmatrix} = \begin{bmatrix} 1 & 0 \\ 0 & 1 \end{bmatrix}; BA = \begin{bmatrix} 1 & 0 \\ 0 & 1 \end{bmatrix}$

8. $AB = \begin{bmatrix} 11 & -12 \\ 2 & -2 \end{bmatrix}\begin{bmatrix} -1 & 6 \\ -1 & \frac{11}{2} \end{bmatrix} = \begin{bmatrix} 1 & 0 \\ 0 & 1 \end{bmatrix}; BA = \begin{bmatrix} 1 & 0 \\ 0 & 1 \end{bmatrix}$

9. $AB = \begin{bmatrix} 1.6 & 2 \\ -3.5 & -4.5 \end{bmatrix}\begin{bmatrix} 22.5 & 10 \\ -17.5 & -8 \end{bmatrix} = \begin{bmatrix} 1 & 0 \\ 0 & 1 \end{bmatrix}; BA = \begin{bmatrix} 1 & 0 \\ 0 & 1 \end{bmatrix}$

10. $AB = \begin{bmatrix} 4 & 0 & -2 \\ 1 & 2 & -4 \\ 0 & 3 & 1 \end{bmatrix}\begin{bmatrix} 0.28 & -0.12 & 0.08 \\ -0.02 & 0.08 & 0.28 \\ 0.06 & -0.24 & 0.16 \end{bmatrix} = \begin{bmatrix} 1 & 0 & 0 \\ 0 & 1 & 0 \\ 0 & 0 & 1 \end{bmatrix}$

$BA = \begin{bmatrix} 1 & 0 & 0 \\ 0 & 1 & 0 \\ 0 & 0 & 1 \end{bmatrix}$

11. $[A \ \vdots \ I] = \left[\begin{array}{cc|cc} 2 & 0 & 1 & 0 \\ 0 & 3 & 0 & 1 \end{array}\right]$

$\begin{array}{l} \frac{1}{2}R_1 \rightarrow \\ \frac{1}{3}R_2 \rightarrow \end{array}\left[\begin{array}{cc|cc} 1 & 0 & \frac{1}{2} & 0 \\ 0 & 1 & 0 & \frac{1}{3} \end{array}\right] = [I \ \vdots \ A^{-1}]$

$A^{-1} = \begin{bmatrix} \frac{1}{2} & 0 \\ 0 & \frac{1}{3} \end{bmatrix} = \frac{1}{6}\begin{bmatrix} 3 & 0 \\ 0 & 2 \end{bmatrix}$

12. $[A \ \vdots \ I] = \begin{bmatrix} 1 & 2 & \vdots & 1 & 0 \\ 3 & 7 & \vdots & 0 & 1 \end{bmatrix}$

$$\begin{matrix} \\ -3R_1 + R_2 \rightarrow \end{matrix}\begin{bmatrix} 1 & 2 & \vdots & 1 & 0 \\ 0 & 1 & \vdots & -3 & 1 \end{bmatrix}$$

$$\begin{matrix} -2R_2 + R_1 \rightarrow \\ \\ \end{matrix}\begin{bmatrix} 1 & 0 & \vdots & 7 & -2 \\ 0 & 1 & \vdots & -3 & 1 \end{bmatrix} = [I \ \vdots \ A^{-1}]$$

$$A^{-1} = \begin{bmatrix} 7 & -2 \\ -3 & 1 \end{bmatrix}$$

13. $[A \ \vdots \ I] = \begin{bmatrix} 1 & -2 & \vdots & 1 & 0 \\ 2 & -3 & \vdots & 0 & 1 \end{bmatrix}$

$$\begin{matrix} \\ -2R_1 + R_2 \rightarrow \end{matrix}\begin{bmatrix} 1 & -2 & \vdots & 1 & 0 \\ 0 & 1 & \vdots & -2 & 1 \end{bmatrix}$$

$$\begin{matrix} 2R_2 + R_1 \rightarrow \\ \\ \end{matrix}\begin{bmatrix} 1 & 0 & \vdots & -3 & 2 \\ 0 & 1 & \vdots & -2 & 1 \end{bmatrix}$$

$$A^{-1} = \begin{bmatrix} -3 & 2 \\ -2 & 1 \end{bmatrix}$$

14. $[A \ \vdots \ I] = \begin{bmatrix} -7 & 33 & \vdots & 1 & 0 \\ 4 & -19 & \vdots & 0 & 1 \end{bmatrix}$

$$\begin{matrix} -\frac{1}{7}R_1 \rightarrow \\ \\ \end{matrix}\begin{bmatrix} 1 & -\frac{33}{7} & \vdots & -\frac{1}{7} & 0 \\ 4 & -19 & \vdots & 0 & 1 \end{bmatrix}$$

$$\begin{matrix} \\ -4R_1 + R_2 \rightarrow \end{matrix}\begin{bmatrix} 1 & -\frac{33}{7} & \vdots & -\frac{1}{7} & 0 \\ 0 & -\frac{1}{7} & \vdots & \frac{4}{7} & 1 \end{bmatrix}$$

$$\begin{matrix} -33R_2 + R_1 \rightarrow \\ \\ \end{matrix}\begin{bmatrix} 1 & 0 & \vdots & -19 & -33 \\ 0 & -\frac{1}{7} & \vdots & \frac{4}{7} & 1 \end{bmatrix}$$

$$\begin{matrix} \\ -7R_2 \rightarrow \end{matrix}\begin{bmatrix} 1 & 0 & \vdots & -19 & -33 \\ 0 & 1 & \vdots & -4 & -7 \end{bmatrix}$$

$$A^{-1} = \begin{bmatrix} -19 & -33 \\ -4 & -7 \end{bmatrix}$$

15. $A = \begin{bmatrix} 2 & 7 & 1 \\ -3 & -9 & 2 \end{bmatrix}$

A has no inverse because it is not square.

16. $A = \begin{bmatrix} -2 & 5 \\ 6 & -15 \\ 0 & 1 \end{bmatrix}$

A has no inverse because it is not square.

17. $[A \ \vdots \ I] = \begin{bmatrix} 1 & 1 & 1 & \vdots & 1 & 0 & 0 \\ 3 & 5 & 4 & \vdots & 0 & 1 & 0 \\ 3 & 6 & 5 & \vdots & 0 & 0 & 1 \end{bmatrix}$

$$\begin{matrix} \\ -3R_1 + R_2 \rightarrow \\ -3R_1 + R_3 \rightarrow \end{matrix}\begin{bmatrix} 1 & 1 & 1 & \vdots & 1 & 0 & 0 \\ 0 & 2 & 1 & \vdots & -3 & 1 & 0 \\ 0 & 3 & 2 & \vdots & -3 & 0 & 1 \end{bmatrix}$$

$$\begin{matrix} -R_2 + R_1 \rightarrow \\ \frac{1}{2}R_2 \rightarrow \\ -3R_2 + R_3 \rightarrow \end{matrix}\begin{bmatrix} 1 & 0 & \frac{1}{2} & \vdots & \frac{5}{2} & -\frac{1}{2} & 0 \\ 0 & 1 & \frac{1}{2} & \vdots & -\frac{3}{2} & \frac{1}{2} & 0 \\ 0 & 0 & \frac{1}{2} & \vdots & \frac{3}{2} & -\frac{3}{2} & 1 \end{bmatrix}$$

$$\begin{matrix} -R_3 + R_1 \rightarrow \\ -R_3 + R_2 \rightarrow \\ 2R_3 \rightarrow \end{matrix}\begin{bmatrix} 1 & 0 & 0 & \vdots & 1 & 1 & -1 \\ 0 & 1 & 0 & \vdots & -3 & 2 & -1 \\ 0 & 0 & 1 & \vdots & 3 & -3 & 2 \end{bmatrix}$$

$$= [I \ \vdots \ A^{-1}]$$

$$A^{-1} = \begin{bmatrix} 1 & 1 & -1 \\ -3 & 2 & -1 \\ 3 & -3 & 2 \end{bmatrix}$$

18. $[A \ \vdots \ I] = \left[\begin{array}{rrr|rrr} 1 & 2 & 2 & 1 & 0 & 0 \\ 3 & 7 & 9 & 0 & 1 & 0 \\ -1 & -4 & -7 & 0 & 0 & 1 \end{array}\right]$

$\begin{array}{r} \\ -3R_1 + R_2 \rightarrow \\ R_1 + R_3 \rightarrow \end{array} \left[\begin{array}{rrr|rrr} 1 & 2 & 2 & 1 & 0 & 0 \\ 0 & 1 & 3 & -3 & 1 & 0 \\ 0 & -2 & -5 & 1 & 0 & 1 \end{array}\right]$

$\begin{array}{r} -2R_2 + R_1 \rightarrow \\ \\ 2R_2 + R_3 \rightarrow \end{array} \left[\begin{array}{rrr|rrr} 1 & 0 & -4 & 7 & -2 & 0 \\ 0 & 1 & 3 & -3 & 1 & 0 \\ 0 & 0 & 1 & -5 & 2 & 1 \end{array}\right]$

$\begin{array}{r} 4R_3 + R_1 \rightarrow \\ -3R_3 + R_2 \rightarrow \\ \\ \end{array} \left[\begin{array}{rrr|rrr} 1 & 0 & 0 & -13 & 6 & 4 \\ 0 & 1 & 0 & 12 & -5 & -3 \\ 0 & 0 & 1 & -5 & 2 & 1 \end{array}\right]$

$= [I \ \vdots \ A^{-1}]$

$A^{-1} = \begin{bmatrix} -13 & 6 & 4 \\ 12 & -5 & -3 \\ -5 & 2 & 1 \end{bmatrix}$

19. $[A \ \vdots \ I] = \left[\begin{array}{rrr|rrr} -5 & 0 & 0 & 1 & 0 & 0 \\ 2 & 0 & 0 & 0 & 1 & 0 \\ -1 & 5 & 7 & 0 & 0 & 1 \end{array}\right]$

$\begin{array}{r} \left(-\frac{1}{5}\right)R_1 \rightarrow \\ (-2)R_1 + R_2 \rightarrow \\ \\ \end{array} \left[\begin{array}{rrr|rrr} 1 & 0 & 0 & -\frac{1}{5} & 0 & 0 \\ 0 & 0 & 0 & \frac{2}{5} & 1 & 0 \\ -1 & 5 & 7 & 0 & 0 & 1 \end{array}\right]$

Not invertible (row of zeros)

A^{-1} does not exist.

20. $[A \ \vdots \ I] = \left[\begin{array}{rrr|rrr} 1 & 0 & 0 & 1 & 0 & 0 \\ 3 & 5 & 0 & 0 & 1 & 0 \\ 2 & 5 & 0 & 0 & 0 & 1 \end{array}\right]$

$\rightarrow \left[\begin{array}{rrr|rrr} 1 & 0 & 0 & 1 & 0 & 0 \\ 0 & 5 & 0 & -3 & 1 & 0 \\ 0 & 5 & 0 & -2 & 0 & 1 \end{array}\right]$

$\rightarrow \left[\begin{array}{rrr|rrr} 1 & 0 & 0 & 1 & 0 & 0 \\ 0 & 5 & 0 & -3 & 1 & 0 \\ 0 & 0 & 0 & 1 & -1 & 1 \end{array}\right]$

Since the first 3 entries of row 3 are all zeros, the inverse does not exist.

21. Not invertible.

A^{-1} does not exist.

22. $A^{-1} = \begin{bmatrix} -175 & 37 & -13 \\ 95 & -20 & 7 \\ 14 & -3 & 1 \end{bmatrix}$

23. $A = \begin{bmatrix} -\frac{1}{2} & \frac{3}{4} & \frac{1}{4} \\ 1 & 0 & -\frac{3}{2} \\ 0 & -1 & \frac{1}{2} \end{bmatrix}$

$A^{-1} = \begin{bmatrix} -12 & -5 & -9 \\ -4 & -2 & -4 \\ -8 & -4 & -6 \end{bmatrix}$

24. $A = \begin{bmatrix} -\frac{5}{6} & \frac{1}{3} & \frac{11}{6} \\ 0 & \frac{2}{3} & 2 \\ 1 & -\frac{1}{2} & -\frac{5}{2} \end{bmatrix}$

A^{-1} does not exist.

25. $A = \begin{bmatrix} 0.1 & 0.2 & 0.3 \\ -0.3 & 0.2 & 0.2 \\ 0.5 & 0.4 & 0.4 \end{bmatrix}$

$A^{-1} = \frac{5}{11}\begin{bmatrix} 0 & -4 & 2 \\ -22 & 11 & 11 \\ 22 & -6 & -8 \end{bmatrix}$

26. $A = \begin{bmatrix} 0.6 & 0 & -0.3 \\ 0.7 & -1 & 0.2 \\ 1 & 0 & -0.9 \end{bmatrix}$

$A^{-1} = \begin{bmatrix} 3.75 & 0 & -1.25 \\ 3.4583 & -1 & -1.375 \\ 4.1667 & 0 & -2.5 \end{bmatrix}$

27. $A = \begin{bmatrix} -1 & 0 & 1 & 0 \\ 0 & 2 & 0 & -1 \\ 2 & 0 & -1 & 0 \\ 0 & -1 & 0 & 1 \end{bmatrix}$

$A^{-1} = \begin{bmatrix} 1 & 0 & 1 & 0 \\ 0 & 1 & 0 & 1 \\ 2 & 0 & 1 & 0 \\ 0 & 1 & 0 & 2 \end{bmatrix}$

28. $A = \begin{bmatrix} 1 & -2 & -1 & -2 \\ 3 & -5 & -2 & -3 \\ 2 & -5 & -2 & -5 \\ -1 & 4 & 4 & 11 \end{bmatrix}$

$A^{-1} = \begin{bmatrix} -24 & 7 & 1 & -2 \\ -10 & 3 & 0 & -1 \\ -29 & 7 & 3 & -2 \\ 12 & -3 & -1 & 1 \end{bmatrix}$

29. $\begin{bmatrix} 5 & 1 \\ -2 & -2 \end{bmatrix}^{-1} = \dfrac{1}{5(-2)-(-2)(1)}\begin{bmatrix} -2 & -1 \\ 2 & 5 \end{bmatrix} = \dfrac{1}{-8}\begin{bmatrix} -2 & -1 \\ 2 & 5 \end{bmatrix} = \begin{bmatrix} \frac{1}{4} & \frac{1}{8} \\ -\frac{1}{4} & -\frac{5}{8} \end{bmatrix}$

30. $\begin{bmatrix} -8 & 0 \\ 11 & -10 \end{bmatrix}^{-1} = \dfrac{1}{(-8)(-10)-11(0)}\begin{bmatrix} -10 & 0 \\ -11 & -8 \end{bmatrix} = \dfrac{1}{80}\begin{bmatrix} -10 & 0 \\ -11 & -8 \end{bmatrix}$

31. $\begin{bmatrix} \frac{7}{2} & -\frac{3}{4} \\ \frac{1}{5} & \frac{4}{5} \end{bmatrix}^{-1} = \dfrac{1}{\left(\frac{7}{2}\right)\left(\frac{4}{5}\right)-\left(-\frac{3}{4}\right)\left(\frac{1}{5}\right)}\begin{bmatrix} \frac{4}{5} & \frac{3}{4} \\ -\frac{1}{5} & \frac{7}{2} \end{bmatrix} = \dfrac{20}{59}\begin{bmatrix} \frac{4}{5} & \frac{3}{4} \\ -\frac{1}{5} & \frac{7}{2} \end{bmatrix} = \dfrac{1}{59}\begin{bmatrix} 16 & 15 \\ -4 & 70 \end{bmatrix}$

32. $\begin{bmatrix} -\frac{1}{4} & -\frac{2}{3} \\ \frac{1}{3} & \frac{8}{9} \end{bmatrix}^{-1} = \dfrac{1}{\left(-\frac{1}{4}\right)\left(\frac{8}{9}\right)-\left(\frac{1}{3}\right)\left(-\frac{2}{3}\right)}\begin{bmatrix} \frac{8}{9} & \frac{2}{3} \\ -\frac{1}{3} & -\frac{1}{4} \end{bmatrix} = \dfrac{1}{0}\begin{bmatrix} \frac{8}{9} & \frac{2}{3} \\ -\frac{1}{3} & -\frac{1}{4} \end{bmatrix} \Rightarrow$ Inverse does not exist.

33. $\begin{bmatrix} 2 & 3 \\ -1 & 5 \end{bmatrix}^{-1} = \dfrac{1}{2(5)-(3)(-1)}\begin{bmatrix} 5 & -3 \\ 1 & 2 \end{bmatrix} = \dfrac{1}{13}\begin{bmatrix} 5 & -3 \\ 1 & 2 \end{bmatrix} = \begin{bmatrix} \frac{5}{13} & -\frac{3}{13} \\ \frac{1}{13} & \frac{2}{13} \end{bmatrix}$

34. $\begin{bmatrix} 1 & -2 \\ -3 & 2 \end{bmatrix}^{-1} = \dfrac{1}{1(2)-(-2)(-3)}\begin{bmatrix} 2 & 2 \\ 3 & 1 \end{bmatrix} = \dfrac{-1}{4}\begin{bmatrix} 2 & 2 \\ 3 & 1 \end{bmatrix} = \begin{bmatrix} -\frac{1}{2} & -\frac{1}{2} \\ -\frac{3}{4} & -\frac{1}{4} \end{bmatrix}$

35. $\begin{bmatrix} -1 & 0 \\ 3 & -2 \end{bmatrix}^{-1} = \dfrac{1}{(-1)(-2)-0(3)}\begin{bmatrix} -2 & 0 \\ -3 & -1 \end{bmatrix} = \dfrac{1}{2}\begin{bmatrix} -2 & 0 \\ -3 & -1 \end{bmatrix} = \begin{bmatrix} -1 & 0 \\ -\frac{3}{2} & -\frac{1}{2} \end{bmatrix}$

36. $\begin{bmatrix} 2 & -5 \\ 3 & 1 \end{bmatrix}^{-1} = \dfrac{1}{2(1)-(-5)(3)}\begin{bmatrix} 1 & 5 \\ -3 & 2 \end{bmatrix} = \dfrac{1}{17}\begin{bmatrix} 1 & 5 \\ -3 & 2 \end{bmatrix} = \begin{bmatrix} \frac{1}{17} & \frac{5}{17} \\ -\frac{3}{17} & \frac{2}{17} \end{bmatrix}$

37. $\begin{bmatrix} 1 & 2 \\ -2 & 0 \end{bmatrix}^{-1} = \begin{bmatrix} 0 & -\frac{1}{2} \\ \frac{1}{2} & \frac{1}{4} \end{bmatrix} \Rightarrow k = 0$

38. $\begin{bmatrix} -1 & 1 \\ 2 & 1 \end{bmatrix}^{-1} = \begin{bmatrix} -\frac{1}{3} & \frac{1}{3} \\ \frac{2}{3} & \frac{1}{3} \end{bmatrix} \Rightarrow k = \frac{2}{3}$

39. $\begin{bmatrix} -1 & 2 \\ -3 & 1 \end{bmatrix}^{-1} = \begin{bmatrix} \frac{1}{5} & -\frac{2}{5} \\ \frac{3}{5} & -\frac{1}{5} \end{bmatrix} \Rightarrow k = \frac{3}{5}$

40. $\begin{bmatrix} -1 & -2 \\ 0 & 2 \end{bmatrix}^{-1} = \begin{bmatrix} -1 & -1 \\ 0 & \frac{1}{2} \end{bmatrix} \Rightarrow k = \frac{1}{2}$

41. $\begin{bmatrix} x \\ y \end{bmatrix} = \begin{bmatrix} -3 & 2 \\ -2 & 1 \end{bmatrix} \begin{bmatrix} 5 \\ 10 \end{bmatrix} = \begin{bmatrix} 5 \\ 0 \end{bmatrix}$

Answer: (5, 0)

42. $\begin{bmatrix} x \\ y \end{bmatrix} = \begin{bmatrix} -3 & 2 \\ -2 & 1 \end{bmatrix} \begin{bmatrix} 0 \\ 3 \end{bmatrix} = \begin{bmatrix} 6 \\ 3 \end{bmatrix}$

Answer: (6, 3)

43. $\begin{bmatrix} x \\ y \end{bmatrix} = \begin{bmatrix} -3 & 2 \\ -2 & 1 \end{bmatrix} \begin{bmatrix} 4 \\ 2 \end{bmatrix} \begin{bmatrix} -8 \\ -6 \end{bmatrix}$

Answer: (−8, −6)

44. $\begin{bmatrix} x \\ y \end{bmatrix} = \begin{bmatrix} -3 & 2 \\ -2 & 1 \end{bmatrix} \begin{bmatrix} 1 \\ -2 \end{bmatrix} = \begin{bmatrix} -7 \\ -4 \end{bmatrix}$

Answer: (−7, −4)

45. $\begin{bmatrix} x \\ y \\ z \end{bmatrix} = \begin{bmatrix} 1 & 1 & -1 \\ -3 & 2 & -1 \\ 3 & -3 & 2 \end{bmatrix} \begin{bmatrix} 0 \\ 5 \\ 2 \end{bmatrix} = \begin{bmatrix} 3 \\ 8 \\ -11 \end{bmatrix}$

Answer: (3, 8, −11)

46. $\begin{bmatrix} x \\ y \\ z \end{bmatrix} = \begin{bmatrix} 1 & 1 & -1 \\ -3 & 2 & -1 \\ 3 & -3 & 2 \end{bmatrix} \begin{bmatrix} -1 \\ 2 \\ 0 \end{bmatrix} = \begin{bmatrix} 1 \\ 7 \\ -9 \end{bmatrix}$

Answer: (1, 7, −9)

47. $\begin{bmatrix} x_1 \\ x_2 \\ x_3 \\ x_4 \end{bmatrix} = \begin{bmatrix} -24 & 7 & 1 & -2 \\ -10 & 3 & 0 & -1 \\ -29 & 7 & 3 & -2 \\ 12 & -3 & -1 & 1 \end{bmatrix} \begin{bmatrix} 0 \\ 1 \\ -1 \\ 2 \end{bmatrix} = \begin{bmatrix} 2 \\ 1 \\ 0 \\ 0 \end{bmatrix}$

Answer: (2, 1, 0, 0)

48. $\begin{bmatrix} x \\ y \\ z \\ w \end{bmatrix} = \begin{bmatrix} -24 & 7 & 1 & -2 \\ -10 & 3 & 0 & -1 \\ -29 & 7 & 3 & -2 \\ 12 & -3 & -1 & 1 \end{bmatrix} \begin{bmatrix} 1 \\ -2 \\ 0 \\ -3 \end{bmatrix} = \begin{bmatrix} -32 \\ -13 \\ -37 \\ 15 \end{bmatrix}$

Answer: (−32, −13, −37, 15)

49. $A = \begin{bmatrix} 3 & 4 \\ 5 & 3 \end{bmatrix}$

$$A^{-1} = \frac{1}{9 - 20} \begin{bmatrix} 3 & -4 \\ -5 & 3 \end{bmatrix}$$

$$\begin{bmatrix} x \\ y \end{bmatrix} = -\frac{1}{11} \begin{bmatrix} 3 & -4 \\ -5 & 3 \end{bmatrix} \begin{bmatrix} -2 \\ 4 \end{bmatrix} = -\frac{1}{11} \begin{bmatrix} -22 \\ 22 \end{bmatrix} = \begin{bmatrix} 2 \\ -2 \end{bmatrix}$$

Answer: (2, −2)

50. $A = \begin{bmatrix} 18 & 12 \\ 30 & 24 \end{bmatrix}$

$$A^{-1} = \frac{1}{18(24) - 12(30)} \begin{bmatrix} 24 & -12 \\ -30 & 18 \end{bmatrix} = \frac{1}{12} \begin{bmatrix} 4 & -2 \\ -5 & 3 \end{bmatrix}$$

$$\begin{bmatrix} x \\ y \end{bmatrix} = A^{-1}b = \frac{1}{12} \begin{bmatrix} 4 & -2 \\ -5 & 3 \end{bmatrix} \begin{bmatrix} 13 \\ 23 \end{bmatrix} = \begin{bmatrix} \frac{1}{2} \\ \frac{1}{3} \end{bmatrix}$$

Answer: $\left(\frac{1}{2}, \frac{1}{3}\right)$

51. $A = \begin{bmatrix} -0.4 & 0.8 \\ 2 & -4 \end{bmatrix}$

$$A^{-1} = \frac{1}{1.6 - 1.6} \begin{bmatrix} -4 & -0.8 \\ -2 & -0.4 \end{bmatrix}$$

A^{-1} does not exist.

[The system actually has no solution.]

52. $A = \begin{bmatrix} 0.2 & -0.6 \\ -1 & 1.4 \end{bmatrix}$

$$A^{-1} = \frac{-1}{8} \begin{bmatrix} 35 & 15 \\ 25 & 5 \end{bmatrix}$$

$$\begin{bmatrix} x \\ y \end{bmatrix} = \frac{-1}{8} \begin{bmatrix} 35 & 15 \\ 25 & 5 \end{bmatrix} \begin{bmatrix} 2.4 \\ -8.8 \end{bmatrix} = \begin{bmatrix} 6 \\ -2 \end{bmatrix}$$

Answer: (6, −2)

53. $A = \begin{bmatrix} -\frac{1}{4} & \frac{3}{8} \\ \frac{3}{2} & \frac{3}{4} \end{bmatrix}$

$A^{-1} = \begin{bmatrix} -1 & \frac{1}{2} \\ 2 & \frac{1}{3} \end{bmatrix}$

$\begin{bmatrix} x \\ y \end{bmatrix} = A^{-1}b = \begin{bmatrix} -1 & \frac{1}{2} \\ 2 & \frac{1}{3} \end{bmatrix}\begin{bmatrix} -2 \\ -12 \end{bmatrix} = \begin{bmatrix} -4 \\ -8 \end{bmatrix}$

Answer: $(-4, -8)$

54. $A = \begin{bmatrix} \frac{5}{6} & -1 \\ \frac{4}{3} & -\frac{7}{2} \end{bmatrix}$

$A^{-1} = \dfrac{1}{\left(\frac{5}{6}\right)\left(-\frac{7}{2}\right) - \left(\frac{4}{3}\right)(-1)}\begin{bmatrix} -\frac{7}{2} & 1 \\ -\frac{4}{3} & \frac{5}{6} \end{bmatrix} = \dfrac{-12}{19}\begin{bmatrix} -\frac{7}{2} & 1 \\ -\frac{4}{3} & \frac{5}{6} \end{bmatrix} = \dfrac{1}{19}\begin{bmatrix} 42 & -12 \\ 16 & -10 \end{bmatrix}$

$\begin{bmatrix} x \\ y \end{bmatrix} = \dfrac{1}{19}\begin{bmatrix} 42 & -12 \\ 16 & -10 \end{bmatrix}\begin{bmatrix} -20 \\ -51 \end{bmatrix} = \begin{bmatrix} -12 \\ 10 \end{bmatrix}$

Answer: $(-12, 10)$

55. $A = \begin{bmatrix} 4 & -1 & 1 \\ 2 & 2 & 3 \\ 5 & -2 & 6 \end{bmatrix}$

$A^{-1} = \frac{1}{55}\begin{bmatrix} 18 & 4 & -5 \\ 3 & 19 & -10 \\ -14 & 3 & 10 \end{bmatrix}$

$\begin{bmatrix} x \\ y \\ z \end{bmatrix} = \frac{1}{55}\begin{bmatrix} 18 & 4 & -5 \\ 3 & 19 & -10 \\ -14 & 3 & 10 \end{bmatrix}\begin{bmatrix} -5 \\ 10 \\ 1 \end{bmatrix}$

$= \frac{1}{55}\begin{bmatrix} -55 \\ 165 \\ 110 \end{bmatrix} = \begin{bmatrix} -1 \\ 3 \\ 2 \end{bmatrix}$

Answer: $(-1, 3, 2)$

56. $A = \begin{bmatrix} 4 & -2 & 3 \\ 2 & 2 & 5 \\ 8 & -5 & -2 \end{bmatrix}$

$A^{-1} = \dfrac{1}{82}\begin{bmatrix} -21 & 19 & 16 \\ -44 & 32 & 14 \\ 26 & -4 & -12 \end{bmatrix}$

$\begin{bmatrix} x \\ y \\ z \end{bmatrix} = \dfrac{1}{82}\begin{bmatrix} -21 & 19 & 16 \\ -44 & 32 & 14 \\ 26 & -4 & -12 \end{bmatrix}\begin{bmatrix} -2 \\ 16 \\ 4 \end{bmatrix} = \begin{bmatrix} 5 \\ 8 \\ -2 \end{bmatrix}$

Answer: $(5, 8, -2)$

57. $A = \begin{bmatrix} 5 & -3 & 2 \\ 2 & 2 & -3 \\ -1 & 7 & -8 \end{bmatrix}$

A^{-1} does not exist.

The system actually has an infinite number of solutions of the form

$x = 0.3125t + 0.8125$

$y = 1.1875t + 0.6875$

$z = t$

where t is any real number.

58. $A = \begin{bmatrix} 2 & 3 & 5 \\ 3 & 5 & -9 \\ 5 & 9 & 17 \end{bmatrix}$ $B = \begin{bmatrix} 4 \\ 7 \\ 13 \end{bmatrix}$

$\begin{bmatrix} x \\ y \\ z \end{bmatrix} = A^{-1}B = \begin{bmatrix} -1 \\ 2 \\ 0 \end{bmatrix}$

Answer: $(-1, 2, 0)$

59. $\begin{bmatrix} 7 & -3 & 0 & 2 & \vdots & 41 \\ -2 & 1 & 0 & -1 & \vdots & -13 \\ 4 & 0 & 1 & -2 & \vdots & 12 \\ -1 & 1 & 0 & -1 & \vdots & -8 \end{bmatrix}$ row reduces to $\begin{bmatrix} 1 & 0 & 0 & 0 & \vdots & 5 \\ 0 & 1 & 0 & 0 & \vdots & 0 \\ 0 & 0 & 1 & 0 & \vdots & -2 \\ 0 & 0 & 0 & 1 & \vdots & 3 \end{bmatrix}$

Answer: $(5, 0, -2, 3)$

60. $A = \begin{bmatrix} 2 & 5 & 0 & 1 \\ 1 & 4 & 2 & -2 \\ 2 & -2 & 5 & 1 \\ 1 & 0 & 0 & -3 \end{bmatrix}$

$$A^{-1} \approx \begin{bmatrix} 0.338 & -0.352 & 0.141 & 0.394 \\ 0.042 & 0.164 & -0.066 & -0.117 \\ -0.141 & 0.230 & 0.108 & -0.164 \\ 0.113 & -0.117 & 0.047 & -0.202 \end{bmatrix}$$

$$\begin{bmatrix} x \\ y \\ z \\ w \end{bmatrix} = \begin{bmatrix} 0.338 & -0.352 & 0.141 & 0.394 \\ 0.042 & 0.164 & -0.066 & -0.117 \\ -0.141 & 0.230 & 0.108 & -0.164 \\ 0.113 & -0.117 & 0.047 & -0.202 \end{bmatrix}\begin{bmatrix} 11 \\ -7 \\ 3 \\ -1 \end{bmatrix} = \begin{bmatrix} 6.21 \\ -0.77 \\ -2.67 \\ 2.40 \end{bmatrix}$$

Answer: $(6.21, -0.77, -2.67, 2.40)$

61. (a) $(x, y) = (-3, 2)$ (b) $(x + h, y + k) = (-3 + 2, 2 + (-1)) = (-1, 1)$

(c) $B = AX = \begin{bmatrix} -1 \\ 1 \\ 1 \end{bmatrix}$ (d) $A^{-1} = \begin{bmatrix} 1 & 0 & -2 \\ 0 & 1 & 1 \\ 0 & 0 & 1 \end{bmatrix}$ (e) $A^{-1}B = \begin{bmatrix} -3 \\ 2 \\ 1 \end{bmatrix}$

The point $(-1, 1)$ has been translated back to $(-3, 2)$.

62. (a) $(x, y) = (1, -2)$ (b) $(x + h, y + k) = (1 - 2, -2 + 3) = (-1, 1)$

(c) $B = AX = \begin{bmatrix} -1 \\ 1 \\ 1 \end{bmatrix}$ (d) $A^{-1} = \begin{bmatrix} 1 & 0 & 2 \\ 0 & 1 & -3 \\ 0 & 0 & 1 \end{bmatrix}$ (e) $A^{-1}B = \begin{bmatrix} 1 \\ -2 \\ 1 \end{bmatrix}$

The point $(-1, 1)$ has been translated back to $(1, -2)$.

63. (a) $(x, y) = (2, -4)$ (b) $(x + h, y + k) = (2 - 3, -4 + 4) = (-1, 0)$

(c) $B = AX = \begin{bmatrix} -1 \\ 0 \\ 1 \end{bmatrix}$ (d) $A^{-1} = \begin{bmatrix} 1 & 0 & 3 \\ 0 & 1 & -4 \\ 0 & 0 & 1 \end{bmatrix}$ (e) $A^{-1}B = \begin{bmatrix} 2 \\ -4 \\ 1 \end{bmatrix}$

The point $(-1, 0)$ has been translated back to $(2, -4)$.

64. (a) $(x, y) = (0, -3)$ (b) $(x + h, y + k) = (0 + 3, -3 - 2) = (3, -5)$

(c) $B = AX = \begin{bmatrix} 3 \\ -5 \\ 1 \end{bmatrix}$ (d) $A^{-1} = \begin{bmatrix} 1 & 0 & -3 \\ 0 & 1 & 2 \\ 0 & 0 & 1 \end{bmatrix}$ (e) $A^{-1}B = \begin{bmatrix} 0 \\ -3 \\ 1 \end{bmatrix}$

The point $(3, -5)$ has been translated back to $(0, -3)$.

For 65–68 use $A = \begin{bmatrix} 1 & 1 & 1 \\ 0.065 & 0.07 & 0.09 \\ 0 & 2 & -1 \end{bmatrix}$. **Using the methods of this section, we have** $A^{-1} = \frac{1}{11}\begin{bmatrix} 50 & -600 & -4 \\ -13 & 200 & 5 \\ -26 & 400 & -1 \end{bmatrix}$.

65. $X = A^{-1}B = \frac{1}{11}\begin{bmatrix} 50 & -600 & -4 \\ -13 & 200 & 5 \\ -26 & 400 & -1 \end{bmatrix}\begin{bmatrix} 25{,}000 \\ 1900 \\ 0 \end{bmatrix} = \begin{bmatrix} 10{,}000 \\ 5000 \\ 10{,}000 \end{bmatrix}$

Answer: \$10,000 in AAA bonds, \$5000 in A-bonds and \$10,000 in B-bonds.

66. $X = A^{-1}B = \frac{1}{11}\begin{bmatrix} 50 & -600 & -4 \\ -13 & 200 & 5 \\ -26 & 400 & -1 \end{bmatrix}\begin{bmatrix} 10{,}000 \\ 760 \\ 0 \end{bmatrix} = \begin{bmatrix} 4000 \\ 2000 \\ 4000 \end{bmatrix}$

Answer: 4000 in AAA bonds, 2000 in A bonds, 4000 in B bonds.

67. $X = A^{-1}B = \frac{1}{11}\begin{bmatrix} 50 & -600 & -4 \\ -13 & 200 & 5 \\ -26 & 400 & -1 \end{bmatrix}\begin{bmatrix} 65{,}000 \\ 5050 \\ 0 \end{bmatrix} = \begin{bmatrix} 20{,}000 \\ 15{,}000 \\ 30{,}000 \end{bmatrix}$

Answer: \$20,000 in AAA bonds, \$15,000 in A-bonds and \$30,000 in B-bonds.

68. $X = A^{-1}B = \frac{1}{11}\begin{bmatrix} 50 & -600 & -4 \\ -13 & 200 & 5 \\ -26 & 400 & -1 \end{bmatrix}\begin{bmatrix} 500{,}000 \\ 38{,}000 \\ 0 \end{bmatrix} = \begin{bmatrix} 200{,}000 \\ 100{,}000 \\ 200{,}000 \end{bmatrix}$

Answer: \$200,000 in AAA bonds, \$100,000 in A bonds, and \$200,000 in B bonds.

69. $A = \begin{bmatrix} 2 & 0 & 4 \\ 0 & 1 & 4 \\ 1 & 1 & -1 \end{bmatrix}$

$A^{-1} = \frac{1}{14}\begin{bmatrix} 5 & -4 & 4 \\ -4 & 6 & 8 \\ 1 & 2 & -2 \end{bmatrix}$

$\begin{bmatrix} I_1 \\ I_2 \\ I_3 \end{bmatrix} = \frac{1}{14}\begin{bmatrix} 5 & -4 & 4 \\ -4 & 6 & 8 \\ 1 & 2 & -2 \end{bmatrix}\begin{bmatrix} 14 \\ 28 \\ 0 \end{bmatrix} = \begin{bmatrix} -3 \\ 8 \\ 5 \end{bmatrix}$

Answer: $I_1 = -3$ amps, $I_2 = 8$ amps, $I_3 = 5$ amps

70. $A = \begin{bmatrix} 2 & 0 & 4 \\ 0 & 1 & 4 \\ 1 & 1 & -1 \end{bmatrix}$

$A^{-1} = \frac{1}{14}\begin{bmatrix} 5 & -4 & 4 \\ -4 & 6 & 8 \\ 1 & 2 & -2 \end{bmatrix}$

$\begin{bmatrix} I_1 \\ I_2 \\ I_3 \end{bmatrix} = \frac{1}{14}\begin{bmatrix} 5 & -4 & 4 \\ -4 & 6 & 8 \\ 1 & 2 & -2 \end{bmatrix}\begin{bmatrix} 10 \\ 10 \\ 0 \end{bmatrix} = \begin{bmatrix} 5/7 \\ 10/7 \\ 15/7 \end{bmatrix}$

Answer: $I_1 = 5/7$ amps, $I_2 = 10/7$ amps, $I_3 = 15/7$ amps

For Exercises 71–74, let x = number of muffins, y = number of bones, z = number of cookies.

$$\begin{bmatrix} 2 & 1 & 2 \\ 3 & 1 & 1 \\ 2 & 1 & 1.5 \end{bmatrix}\begin{bmatrix} x \\ y \\ z \end{bmatrix} = \begin{bmatrix} \text{Beef} \\ \text{Chicken} \\ \text{Liver} \end{bmatrix}$$

$A \quad X$

$$A^{-1} = \begin{bmatrix} 1 & 1 & -2 \\ -5 & -2 & 8 \\ 2 & 0 & -2 \end{bmatrix}$$

71. $A^{-1}\begin{bmatrix} 700 \\ 500 \\ 600 \end{bmatrix} = \begin{bmatrix} 0 \\ 300 \\ 200 \end{bmatrix}$

300 units of bones

200 units of cookies

72. $A^{-1}\begin{bmatrix} 525 \\ 480 \\ 500 \end{bmatrix} = \begin{bmatrix} 5 \\ 415 \\ 50 \end{bmatrix}$

5 units of muffins

415 units of bones

50 units of cookies

73. $A^{-1}\begin{bmatrix} 800 \\ 750 \\ 725 \end{bmatrix} = \begin{bmatrix} 100 \\ 300 \\ 150 \end{bmatrix}$

100 units of muffins

300 units of bones

150 units of cookies

74. $A^{-1}\begin{bmatrix} 1000 \\ 950 \\ 900 \end{bmatrix} = \begin{bmatrix} 150 \\ 300 \\ 200 \end{bmatrix}$

150 units of muffins

300 units of bones

200 units of cookies

75. (a) $f + h + s = 10$
$2f + 2.5h + 3s = 26$
$h - s = 0$

(b) $\begin{bmatrix} 1 & 1 & 1 \\ 2 & 2.5 & 3 \\ 0 & 1 & -1 \end{bmatrix}\begin{bmatrix} f \\ h \\ s \end{bmatrix} = \begin{bmatrix} 10 \\ 26 \\ 0 \end{bmatrix}$

$A \quad X = B$

(c) $X = A^{-1}B = \begin{bmatrix} \frac{11}{3} & -\frac{4}{3} & -\frac{1}{3} \\ -\frac{4}{3} & \frac{2}{3} & \frac{2}{3} \\ -\frac{4}{3} & \frac{2}{3} & -\frac{1}{3} \end{bmatrix}\begin{bmatrix} 10 \\ 26 \\ 0 \end{bmatrix} = \begin{bmatrix} 2 \\ 4 \\ 4 \end{bmatrix}$

2 pounds French vanilla

4 pounds hazelnut

4 pounds Swiss chocolate

76. (a) Let x = number of roses.

Let y = number of lilies.

Let z = number of irises.

$x + y + z = 120$
$2.5x + 4y + 2z = 300$
$x - 2y - 2z = 0$

(b) $\begin{bmatrix} 1 & 1 & 1 \\ 2.5 & 4 & 2 \\ 1 & -2 & -2 \end{bmatrix}\begin{bmatrix} x \\ y \\ z \end{bmatrix} = \begin{bmatrix} 120 \\ 300 \\ 0 \end{bmatrix}$

$A \quad X = B$

(c) $X = A^{-1}B = \begin{bmatrix} \frac{2}{3} & 0 & \frac{1}{3} \\ -\frac{7}{6} & \frac{1}{2} & -\frac{1}{12} \\ \frac{3}{2} & -\frac{1}{2} & -\frac{1}{4} \end{bmatrix}\begin{bmatrix} 120 \\ 300 \\ 0 \end{bmatrix} = \begin{bmatrix} 80 \\ 10 \\ 30 \end{bmatrix}$

80 roses, 10 lilies, 30 irises

77. (a) $(2, 5343) \quad \vdots \quad 4a + 2b + c = 5343$
$(3, 5589) \quad \vdots \quad 9a + 3b + c = 5589$
$(4, 6309) \quad \vdots \quad 16a + 4b + c = 6309$

(b) $A = \begin{bmatrix} 4 & 2 & 1 \\ 9 & 3 & 1 \\ 16 & 4 & 1 \end{bmatrix}, A^{-1} = \begin{bmatrix} \frac{1}{2} & -1 & \frac{1}{2} \\ -\frac{7}{2} & 6 & -\frac{5}{2} \\ 6 & -8 & 3 \end{bmatrix}$

$$A^{-1}\begin{bmatrix} 5343 \\ 5589 \\ 6309 \end{bmatrix} = \begin{bmatrix} a \\ b \\ c \end{bmatrix} = \begin{bmatrix} 237 \\ -939 \\ 6273 \end{bmatrix}$$

$y = 237t^2 - 939t + 6273$

(c)

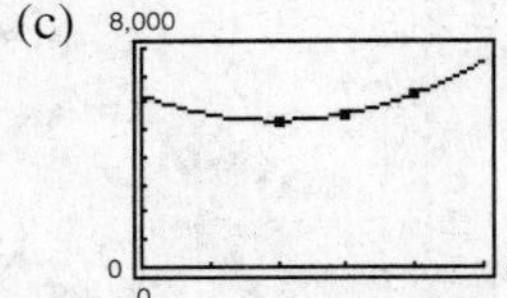

(d) For 2005, $t = 5$ and $y = 7503$ thousand.

For 2010, $t = 10$ and $y = 20{,}583$ thousand.

For 2015, $t = 15$ and $y = 45{,}513$ thousand.

(e) Answers will vary.

78. (a) $(2, 8603) \quad \vdots \quad 4a + 2b + c = 8603$
$(3, 8639) \quad \vdots \quad 9a + 3b + c = 8639$
$(4, 9686) \quad \vdots \quad 16a + 4b + c = 9686$

(b) $A = \begin{bmatrix} 4 & 2 & 1 \\ 9 & 3 & 1 \\ 16 & 4 & 1 \end{bmatrix}, A^{-1} = \begin{bmatrix} \frac{1}{2} & -1 & \frac{1}{2} \\ -\frac{7}{2} & 6 & -\frac{5}{2} \\ 6 & -8 & 3 \end{bmatrix}$

$$A^{-1}\begin{bmatrix} 8603 \\ 8639 \\ 9686 \end{bmatrix} = \begin{bmatrix} a \\ b \\ c \end{bmatrix} = \begin{bmatrix} 505.5 \\ -2491.5 \\ 11{,}564 \end{bmatrix}$$

$y = 505.5t^2 - 2491.5t + 11{,}564$

(c)

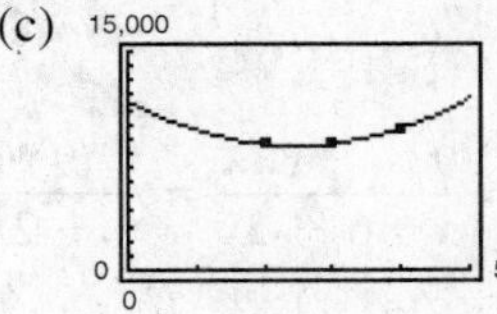

(d) For 2005, $t = 5$ and $y = 11{,}744$ millions.

For 2010, $t = 10$ and $y = 37{,}199$ millions.

For 2015, $t = 15$ and $y = 87{,}929$ millions.

(e) Answers will vary.

79. True. $AA^{-1} = A^{-1}A = I$

80. True

81. $$AA^{-1} = \begin{bmatrix} a & b \\ c & d \end{bmatrix}\left(\frac{1}{ad - bc}\right)\begin{bmatrix} d & -b \\ -c & a \end{bmatrix} = \frac{1}{ad - bc}\begin{bmatrix} a & b \\ c & d \end{bmatrix}\begin{bmatrix} d & -b \\ -c & a \end{bmatrix}$$

$$= \frac{1}{ad - bc}\begin{bmatrix} ad - bc & 0 \\ 0 & ad - bc \end{bmatrix} = \begin{bmatrix} 1 & 0 \\ 0 & 1 \end{bmatrix}$$

$$A^{-1}A = \frac{1}{ad - bc}\begin{bmatrix} d & -b \\ -c & a \end{bmatrix}\begin{bmatrix} a & b \\ c & d \end{bmatrix} = \frac{1}{ad - bc}\begin{bmatrix} ad - bc & 0 \\ 0 & ad - bc \end{bmatrix} = \begin{bmatrix} 1 & 0 \\ 0 & 1 \end{bmatrix}$$

82. (a) Given $A = \begin{bmatrix} a_{11} & 0 \\ 0 & a_{22} \end{bmatrix}$, $A^{-1} = \begin{bmatrix} \frac{1}{a_{11}} & 0 \\ 0 & \frac{1}{a_{22}} \end{bmatrix}$, $a_{11} \neq 0, a_{22} \neq 0$

Given $A = \begin{bmatrix} a_{11} & 0 & 0 \\ 0 & a_{22} & 0 \\ 0 & 0 & a_{33} \end{bmatrix}$, $A^{-1} = \begin{bmatrix} \frac{1}{a_{11}} & 0 & 0 \\ 0 & \frac{1}{a_{22}} & 0 \\ 0 & 0 & \frac{1}{a_{33}} \end{bmatrix}$, $a_{11}, a_{22}, a_{33}, \neq 0$

—CONTINUED—

82. —CONTINUED—

(b) In general, the inverse of the diagonal matrix A is

$$\begin{bmatrix} \frac{1}{a_{11}} & 0 & 0 & \cdots & 0 \\ 0 & \frac{1}{a_{22}} & 0 & \cdots & 0 \\ 0 & 0 & \frac{1}{a_{33}} & \cdots & 0 \\ \vdots & \vdots & \vdots & \vdots & \vdots \\ 0 & 0 & 0 & \cdots & \frac{1}{a_{nn}} \end{bmatrix} \quad \text{(assuming } a_{ii} \neq 0)$$

83. $$\frac{\left(\frac{9}{x}\right)}{\left(\frac{6}{x}+2\right)} = \frac{\left(\frac{9}{x}\right)}{\left(\frac{6+2x}{x}\right)} = \frac{9}{x} \cdot \frac{x}{6+2x} = \frac{9}{6+2x}, \quad x \neq 0$$

84. $$\frac{1+\frac{2}{x}}{1-\frac{4}{x}} = \frac{x+2}{x-4}, x \neq 0$$

85. $$\frac{\frac{4}{x^2-9}+\frac{2}{x-2}}{\frac{1}{x+3}+\frac{1}{x-3}} \cdot \frac{(x^2-9)(x-2)}{(x^2-9)(x-2)}$$

$$= \frac{4(x-2)+2(x^2-9)}{(x-3)(x-2)+(x+3)(x-2)}$$

$$= \frac{2x^2+4x-26}{2x^2-4x}$$

$$= \frac{x^2+2x-13}{x(x-2)}, \quad x \neq \pm 3$$

86. $$\frac{\frac{1}{x+1}+\frac{1}{2}}{\frac{3}{2x^2+4x+2}} = \frac{2+x+1}{2(x+1)} \cdot \frac{2(x+1)^2}{3} = \frac{(x+3)(x+1)}{3} = \frac{x^2+4x+3}{3}, x \neq -1$$

87. $e^{2x} + 2e^x - 15 = (e^x + 5)(e^x - 3) = 0 \Rightarrow e^x = 3 \Rightarrow x = \ln 3 \approx 1.099$

88. $e^{2x} - 10e^x + 24 = (e^x - 6)(e^x - 4) = 0$

$e^x = 6 \Rightarrow x = \ln 6 \approx 1.792$

$e^x = 4 \Rightarrow x = \ln 4 \approx 1.386$

89. $7 \ln 3x = 12$

$\ln 3x = \frac{12}{7}$

$3x = e^{12/7}$

$x = \frac{1}{3}e^{12/7} \approx 1.851$

90. $\ln(x + 9) = 2$

$x + 9 = e^2$

$x = e^2 - 9 \approx -1.611$

91. Answers will vary.

Section 7.7 The Determinant of a Square Matrix

- You should be able to determine the determinant of a matrix of order 2 × 2 by using the products of the diagonals.
- You should be able to use expansion by cofactors to find the determinant of a matrix of order 3 or greater.
- The determinant of a triangular matrix equals the product of the entries on the main diagonal.
- You should be able to calculate determinants using a graphing utility.

Vocabulary Check

1. determinant
2. minor
3. cofactor
4. expanding by cofactors
5. triangular
6. diagonal

1. $|4| = 4$

2. $\det([-10]) = -10$

3. $\begin{vmatrix} 8 & 4 \\ 2 & 3 \end{vmatrix} = 8(3) - 4(2) = 24 - 8 = 16$

4. $\begin{vmatrix} -9 & 0 \\ 6 & 2 \end{vmatrix} = (-9)(2) - 0 = -18$

5. $\begin{vmatrix} 6 & 2 \\ -5 & 3 \end{vmatrix} = 6(3) - (2)(-5) = 18 + 10 = 28$

6. $\begin{vmatrix} 3 & -3 \\ 4 & -8 \end{vmatrix} = 3(-8) - (-3)(4) = -24 + 12 = -12$

7. $\begin{vmatrix} -7 & 6 \\ \frac{1}{2} & 3 \end{vmatrix} = -7(3) - 6\left(\frac{1}{2}\right) = -21 - 3 = -24$

8. $\begin{vmatrix} 4 & -3 \\ 0 & 0 \end{vmatrix} = (4)(0) - (0)(-3) = 0$

9. $\begin{vmatrix} 2 & -1 & 0 \\ 4 & 2 & 1 \\ 4 & 2 & 1 \end{vmatrix} = 2\begin{vmatrix} 2 & 1 \\ 2 & 1 \end{vmatrix} - 4\begin{vmatrix} -1 & 0 \\ 2 & 1 \end{vmatrix} + 4\begin{vmatrix} -1 & 0 \\ 2 & 1 \end{vmatrix} = 2(0) - 4(-1) + 4(-1) = 0$

10. $\begin{vmatrix} -2 & 2 & 3 \\ 1 & -1 & 0 \\ 0 & 1 & 4 \end{vmatrix} = 0\begin{vmatrix} 2 & 3 \\ -1 & 0 \end{vmatrix} - 1\begin{vmatrix} -2 & 3 \\ 1 & 0 \end{vmatrix} + 4\begin{vmatrix} -2 & 2 \\ 1 & -1 \end{vmatrix} = 0(3) - 1(-3) + 4(0) = 3$

11. $\begin{vmatrix} -1 & 2 & -5 \\ 0 & 3 & 4 \\ 0 & 0 & 3 \end{vmatrix} = (-1)(3)(3) = -9$ (Upper Triangular)

12. $\begin{vmatrix} 1 & 0 & 0 \\ -4 & -1 & 0 \\ 5 & 1 & 5 \end{vmatrix} = (1)(-1)(5) = -5$ (Lower Triangular)

13. $\begin{vmatrix} 0.3 & 0.2 & 0.2 \\ 0.2 & 0.2 & 0.2 \\ -0.4 & 0.4 & 0.3 \end{vmatrix} = -0.002$

14. $\begin{vmatrix} 0.1 & 0.2 & 0.3 \\ -0.3 & 0.2 & 0.2 \\ 0.5 & 0.4 & 0.4 \end{vmatrix} = -0.022$

15. $\begin{bmatrix} 3 & 4 \\ 2 & -5 \end{bmatrix}$

(a) $M_{11} = -5$, $M_{12} = 2$, $M_{21} = 4$, $M_{22} = 3$

(b) $C_{11} = M_{11} = -5$, $C_{12} = -M_{12} = -2$, $C_{21} = -M_{21} = -4$, $C_{22} = M_{22} = 3$

16. $\begin{bmatrix} 11 & 0 \\ -3 & 2 \end{bmatrix}$

(a) $M_{11} = 2$, $M_{12} = -3$, $M_{21} = 0$, $M_{22} = 11$

(b) $C_{11} = M_{11} = 2$, $C_{12} = -M_{12} = 3$, $C_{21} = -M_{21} = 0$, $C_{22} = M_{22} = 11$

17. $\begin{bmatrix} -4 & 6 & 3 \\ 7 & -2 & 8 \\ 1 & 0 & -5 \end{bmatrix}$

(a) $M_{11} = \begin{vmatrix} -2 & 8 \\ 0 & -5 \end{vmatrix} = 10$

$M_{12} = \begin{vmatrix} 7 & 8 \\ 1 & -5 \end{vmatrix} = -43$

$M_{13} = \begin{vmatrix} 7 & -2 \\ 1 & 0 \end{vmatrix} = 2$

$M_{21} = \begin{vmatrix} 6 & 3 \\ 0 & -5 \end{vmatrix} = -30$

$M_{22} = \begin{vmatrix} -4 & 3 \\ 1 & -5 \end{vmatrix} = 17$

$M_{23} = \begin{vmatrix} -4 & 6 \\ 1 & 0 \end{vmatrix} = -6$

$M_{31} = \begin{vmatrix} 6 & 3 \\ -2 & 8 \end{vmatrix} = 54$

$M_{32} = \begin{vmatrix} -4 & 3 \\ 7 & 8 \end{vmatrix} = -53$

$M_{33} = \begin{vmatrix} -4 & 6 \\ 7 & -2 \end{vmatrix} = -34$

(b) $C_{11} = 10$, $C_{12} = 43$, $C_{13} = 2$, $C_{21} = 30$, $C_{22} = 17$, $C_{23} = 6$, $C_{31} = 54$, $C_{32} = 53$, $C_{33} = -34$

18. $\begin{bmatrix} -2 & 9 & 4 \\ 7 & -6 & 0 \\ 6 & 7 & -6 \end{bmatrix}$

(a) $M_{11} = \begin{vmatrix} -6 & 0 \\ 7 & -6 \end{vmatrix} = 36$

$M_{12} = \begin{vmatrix} 7 & 0 \\ 6 & -6 \end{vmatrix} = -42$

$M_{13} = \begin{vmatrix} 7 & -6 \\ 6 & 7 \end{vmatrix} = 85$

$M_{21} = \begin{vmatrix} 9 & 4 \\ 7 & -6 \end{vmatrix} = -82$

$M_{22} = \begin{vmatrix} -2 & 4 \\ 6 & -6 \end{vmatrix} = -12$

$M_{23} = \begin{vmatrix} -2 & 9 \\ 6 & 7 \end{vmatrix} = -68$

$M_{31} = \begin{vmatrix} 9 & 4 \\ -6 & 0 \end{vmatrix} = 24$

$M_{32} = \begin{vmatrix} -2 & 4 \\ 7 & 0 \end{vmatrix} = -28$

$M_{33} = \begin{vmatrix} -2 & 9 \\ 7 & -6 \end{vmatrix} = -51$

(b) $C_{11} = (-1)^2 M_{11} = 36$

$C_{12} = (-1)^3 M_{12} = 42$

$C_{13} = (-1)^4 M_{13} = 85$

$C_{21} = (-1)^3 M_{21} = 82$

$C_{22} = (-1)^4 M_{22} = -12$

$C_{23} = (-1)^5 M_{23} = 68$

$C_{31} = (-1)^4 M_{31} = 24$

$C_{32} = (-1)^5 M_{32} = 28$

$C_{33} = (-1)^6 M_{33} = -51$

19. (a) $\begin{vmatrix} -3 & 2 & 1 \\ 4 & 5 & 6 \\ 2 & -3 & 1 \end{vmatrix} = -3\begin{vmatrix} 5 & 6 \\ -3 & 1 \end{vmatrix} - 2\begin{vmatrix} 4 & 6 \\ 2 & 1 \end{vmatrix} + \begin{vmatrix} 4 & 5 \\ 2 & -3 \end{vmatrix} = -3(23) - 2(-8) - 22 = -75$

(b) $\begin{vmatrix} -3 & 2 & 1 \\ 4 & 5 & 6 \\ 2 & -3 & 1 \end{vmatrix} = -2\begin{vmatrix} 4 & 6 \\ 2 & 1 \end{vmatrix} + 5\begin{vmatrix} -3 & 1 \\ 2 & 1 \end{vmatrix} + 3\begin{vmatrix} -3 & 1 \\ 4 & 6 \end{vmatrix} = -2(-8) + 5(-5) + 3(-22) = -75$

20. (a) $\begin{vmatrix} -3 & 4 & 2 \\ 6 & 3 & 1 \\ 4 & -7 & -8 \end{vmatrix} = -6\begin{vmatrix} 4 & 2 \\ -7 & -8 \end{vmatrix} + 3\begin{vmatrix} -3 & 2 \\ 4 & -8 \end{vmatrix} - 1\begin{vmatrix} -3 & 4 \\ 4 & -7 \end{vmatrix} = -6(-18) + 3(16) - (5) = 151$

(b) $\begin{vmatrix} -3 & 4 & 2 \\ 6 & 3 & 1 \\ 4 & -7 & -8 \end{vmatrix} = 2\begin{vmatrix} 6 & 3 \\ 4 & -7 \end{vmatrix} - \begin{vmatrix} -3 & 4 \\ 4 & -7 \end{vmatrix} - 8\begin{vmatrix} -3 & 4 \\ 6 & 3 \end{vmatrix} = 2(-54) - (5) - 8(-33) = 151$

21. (a) $\begin{vmatrix} 6 & 0 & -3 & 5 \\ 4 & 13 & 6 & -8 \\ -1 & 0 & 7 & 4 \\ 8 & 6 & 0 & 2 \end{vmatrix} = -4\begin{vmatrix} 0 & -3 & 5 \\ 0 & 7 & 4 \\ 6 & 0 & 2 \end{vmatrix} + 13\begin{vmatrix} 6 & -3 & 5 \\ -1 & 7 & 4 \\ 8 & 0 & 2 \end{vmatrix} - 6\begin{vmatrix} 6 & 0 & 5 \\ -1 & 0 & 4 \\ 8 & 6 & 2 \end{vmatrix} - 8\begin{vmatrix} 6 & 0 & -3 \\ -1 & 0 & 7 \\ 8 & 6 & 0 \end{vmatrix}$

$= -4(-282) + 13(-298) - 6(-174) - 8(-234) = 170$

(b) $\begin{vmatrix} 6 & 0 & -3 & 5 \\ 4 & 13 & 6 & -8 \\ -1 & 0 & 7 & 4 \\ 8 & 6 & 0 & 2 \end{vmatrix} = 0\begin{vmatrix} 4 & 6 & -8 \\ -1 & 7 & 4 \\ 8 & 0 & 2 \end{vmatrix} + 13\begin{vmatrix} 6 & -3 & 5 \\ -1 & 7 & 4 \\ 8 & 0 & 2 \end{vmatrix} + 0\begin{vmatrix} 6 & -3 & 5 \\ 4 & 6 & -8 \\ 8 & 0 & 2 \end{vmatrix} + 6\begin{vmatrix} 6 & -3 & 5 \\ 4 & 6 & -8 \\ -1 & 7 & 4 \end{vmatrix}$

$= 0 + 13(-298) + 0 + 6(674) = 170$

22. (a) $\begin{vmatrix} 10 & 8 & 3 & -7 \\ 4 & 0 & 5 & -6 \\ 0 & 3 & 2 & 7 \\ 1 & 0 & -3 & 2 \end{vmatrix} = 0\begin{vmatrix} 8 & 3 & -7 \\ 0 & 5 & -6 \\ 0 & -3 & 2 \end{vmatrix} - 3\begin{vmatrix} 10 & 3 & -7 \\ 4 & 5 & -6 \\ 1 & -3 & 2 \end{vmatrix} + 2\begin{vmatrix} 10 & 8 & -7 \\ 4 & 0 & -6 \\ 1 & 0 & 2 \end{vmatrix} - 7\begin{vmatrix} 10 & 8 & 3 \\ 4 & 0 & 5 \\ 1 & 0 & -3 \end{vmatrix}$

$= 0(-64) - 3(-3) + 2(-112) - 7(136) = -1167$

(b) $\begin{vmatrix} 10 & 8 & 3 & -7 \\ 4 & 0 & 5 & -6 \\ 0 & 3 & 2 & 7 \\ 1 & 0 & -3 & 2 \end{vmatrix} = 10\begin{vmatrix} 0 & 5 & -6 \\ 3 & 2 & 7 \\ 0 & -3 & 2 \end{vmatrix} - 4\begin{vmatrix} 8 & 3 & -7 \\ 3 & 2 & 7 \\ 0 & -3 & 2 \end{vmatrix} + 0\begin{vmatrix} 8 & 3 & -7 \\ 0 & 5 & -6 \\ 0 & -3 & 2 \end{vmatrix} - 1\begin{vmatrix} 8 & 3 & -7 \\ 0 & 5 & -6 \\ 3 & 2 & 7 \end{vmatrix}$

$= 10(24) - 4(245) + 0(-64) - 1(427) = -1167$

23. Expand by Column 3.

$\begin{vmatrix} 1 & 4 & -2 \\ 3 & 2 & 0 \\ -1 & 4 & 3 \end{vmatrix} = -2\begin{vmatrix} 3 & 2 \\ -1 & 4 \end{vmatrix} + 3\begin{vmatrix} 1 & 4 \\ 3 & 2 \end{vmatrix} = -2(14) + 3(-10) = -58$

24. $\begin{vmatrix} -3 & 0 & 0 \\ 7 & 11 & 0 \\ 1 & 2 & 2 \end{vmatrix} = -3\begin{vmatrix} 11 & 0 \\ 2 & 2 \end{vmatrix} = -3(22) = -66$ (Lower Triangular)

25. Expand by Column 3.

$\begin{vmatrix} 2 & 6 & 6 & 2 \\ 2 & 7 & 3 & 6 \\ 1 & 5 & 0 & 1 \\ 3 & 7 & 0 & 7 \end{vmatrix} = 6\begin{vmatrix} 2 & 7 & 6 \\ 1 & 5 & 1 \\ 3 & 7 & 7 \end{vmatrix} - 3\begin{vmatrix} 2 & 6 & 2 \\ 1 & 5 & 1 \\ 3 & 7 & 7 \end{vmatrix} = 6(-20) - 3(16) = -168$

26. Expand by Row 2.

$$\begin{vmatrix} 3 & 6 & -5 & 4 \\ -2 & 0 & 6 & 0 \\ 1 & 1 & 2 & 2 \\ 0 & 3 & -1 & -1 \end{vmatrix} = -(-2)\begin{vmatrix} 6 & -5 & 4 \\ 1 & 2 & 2 \\ 3 & -1 & -1 \end{vmatrix} - 6\begin{vmatrix} 3 & 6 & 4 \\ 1 & 1 & 2 \\ 0 & 3 & -1 \end{vmatrix} = 2(-63) - 6(-3) = -108$$

27. Expand by Column 2.

$$\begin{vmatrix} 3 & 2 & 4 & -1 & 5 \\ -2 & 0 & 1 & 3 & 2 \\ 1 & 0 & 0 & 4 & 0 \\ 6 & 0 & 2 & -1 & 0 \\ 3 & 0 & 5 & 1 & 0 \end{vmatrix} = -2\begin{vmatrix} -2 & 1 & 3 & 2 \\ 1 & 0 & 4 & 0 \\ 6 & 2 & -1 & 0 \\ 3 & 5 & 1 & 0 \end{vmatrix} = (-2)(-2)\begin{vmatrix} 1 & 0 & 4 \\ 6 & 2 & -1 \\ 3 & 5 & 1 \end{vmatrix} = 4(103) = 412$$

28. Expand by Column 1.

$$\begin{vmatrix} 5 & 2 & 0 & 0 & -2 \\ 0 & 1 & 4 & 3 & 2 \\ 0 & 0 & 2 & 6 & 3 \\ 0 & 0 & 3 & 4 & 1 \\ 0 & 0 & 0 & 0 & 2 \end{vmatrix} = 5\begin{vmatrix} 1 & 4 & 3 & 2 \\ 0 & 2 & 6 & 3 \\ 0 & 3 & 4 & 1 \\ 0 & 0 & 0 & 2 \end{vmatrix} = 5 \cdot 1\begin{vmatrix} 2 & 6 & 3 \\ 3 & 4 & 1 \\ 0 & 0 & 2 \end{vmatrix} = 5(-20) = -100$$

29. $\begin{vmatrix} 4 & 0 & 0 & 0 \\ 6 & -5 & 0 & 0 \\ 1 & 3 & 1 & 0 \\ 1 & -2 & 7 & 3 \end{vmatrix} = (4)(-5)(1)(3) = -60$ (Lower Triangular)

30. $|A| = (5)(6)(-2)(-1) = 60$

(Upper Triangular)

31. $\det(A) = (-6)(-1)(-7)(-2)(-2) = -168$

(Upper Triangular)

32. $|A| = (-2)(4)(1)(10)(-3) = 240$

(Lower Triangular)

33. $\begin{vmatrix} 1 & -1 & 8 & 4 \\ 2 & 6 & 0 & -4 \\ 2 & 0 & 2 & 6 \\ 0 & 2 & 8 & 0 \end{vmatrix} = -336$

34. $\begin{vmatrix} 0 & -3 & 8 & 2 \\ 8 & 1 & -1 & 6 \\ -4 & 6 & 0 & 9 \\ -7 & 0 & 0 & 14 \end{vmatrix} = 7441$

35. $\begin{vmatrix} 3 & -2 & 4 & 3 & 1 \\ -1 & 0 & 2 & 1 & 0 \\ 5 & -1 & 0 & 3 & 2 \\ 4 & 7 & -8 & 0 & 0 \\ 1 & 2 & 3 & 0 & 2 \end{vmatrix} = 410$

36. $\begin{vmatrix} -2 & 0 & 0 & 0 & 0 \\ 0 & 3 & 0 & 0 & 0 \\ 0 & 0 & -1 & 0 & 0 \\ 0 & 0 & 0 & 2 & 0 \\ 0 & 0 & 0 & 0 & -4 \end{vmatrix} = -48$

37. (a) $\begin{vmatrix} -1 & 0 \\ 0 & 3 \end{vmatrix} = -3$

(b) $\begin{vmatrix} 2 & 0 \\ 0 & -1 \end{vmatrix} = -2$

(c) $\begin{bmatrix} -1 & 0 \\ 0 & 3 \end{bmatrix}\begin{bmatrix} 2 & 0 \\ 0 & -1 \end{bmatrix} = \begin{bmatrix} -2 & 0 \\ 0 & -3 \end{bmatrix}$

(d) $\begin{vmatrix} -2 & 0 \\ 0 & -3 \end{vmatrix} = 6$ **[Note:** $|AB| = |A|\,|B|$]

38. (a) $|A| = -8$

(b) $|B| = 0$

(c) $AB = \begin{bmatrix} -4 & 4 \\ 1 & -1 \end{bmatrix}$

(d) $|AB| = 0$

39. (a) $\begin{vmatrix} -1 & 2 & 1 \\ 1 & 0 & 1 \\ 0 & 1 & 0 \end{vmatrix} = 2$

(b) $\begin{vmatrix} -1 & 0 & 0 \\ 0 & 2 & 0 \\ 0 & 0 & 3 \end{vmatrix} = -6$

(c) $\begin{bmatrix} -1 & 2 & 1 \\ 1 & 0 & 1 \\ 0 & 1 & 0 \end{bmatrix}\begin{bmatrix} -1 & 0 & 0 \\ 0 & 2 & 0 \\ 0 & 0 & 3 \end{bmatrix} = \begin{bmatrix} 1 & 4 & 3 \\ -1 & 0 & 3 \\ 0 & 2 & 0 \end{bmatrix}$

(d) $\begin{vmatrix} 1 & 4 & 3 \\ -1 & 0 & 3 \\ 0 & 2 & 0 \end{vmatrix} = -12$ **[Note:** $|AB| = |A|\,|B|$]

40. (a) $|A| = \begin{vmatrix} 2 & 0 & 1 \\ 1 & -1 & 2 \\ 3 & 1 & 0 \end{vmatrix} = 0$

(b) $|B| = \begin{vmatrix} 2 & -1 & 4 \\ 0 & 1 & 3 \\ 3 & -2 & 1 \end{vmatrix} = -7$

(c) $AB = \begin{bmatrix} 2 & 0 & 1 \\ 1 & -1 & 2 \\ 3 & 1 & 0 \end{bmatrix}\begin{bmatrix} 2 & -1 & 4 \\ 0 & 1 & 3 \\ 3 & -2 & 1 \end{bmatrix} = \begin{bmatrix} 7 & -4 & 9 \\ 8 & -6 & 3 \\ 6 & -2 & 15 \end{bmatrix}$

(d) $|AB| = \begin{vmatrix} 7 & -4 & 9 \\ 8 & -6 & 3 \\ 6 & -2 & 15 \end{vmatrix} = 0$

41. (a) $|A| = -25$

(b) $|B| = -220$

(c) $AB = \begin{bmatrix} -7 & -16 & -1 & -28 \\ -4 & -14 & -11 & 8 \\ 13 & 4 & 4 & -4 \\ -2 & 3 & 2 & 2 \end{bmatrix}$

(d) $|AB| = 5500$ [Note: $|AB| = |A|\,|B|$]

42. (a) $|A| = -46$

(b) $|B| = 89$

(c) $AB = \begin{bmatrix} 53 & -10 & 10 & 22 \\ -1 & 2 & 5 & 1 \\ -29 & 18 & -6 & -13 \\ 35 & 16 & -1 & 12 \end{bmatrix}$

(d) $|AB| = -4094$

43. $\begin{vmatrix} w & x \\ y & z \end{vmatrix} = wz - xy$

$-\begin{vmatrix} y & z \\ w & x \end{vmatrix} = -(xy - wz) = wz - xy$

Thus, $\begin{vmatrix} w & x \\ y & z \end{vmatrix} = -\begin{vmatrix} y & z \\ w & x \end{vmatrix}$.

44. $\begin{vmatrix} w & cx \\ y & cz \end{vmatrix} = cwz - cxy = c(wz - xy)$

$c\begin{vmatrix} w & x \\ y & z \end{vmatrix} = c(wz - xy)$

Thus, $\begin{vmatrix} w & cx \\ y & cz \end{vmatrix} = c\begin{vmatrix} w & x \\ y & z \end{vmatrix}$.

45. $\begin{vmatrix} w & x \\ y & z \end{vmatrix} = wz - xy$

$\begin{vmatrix} w & x + cw \\ y & z + cy \end{vmatrix} = w(z + cy) - y(x + cw) = wz - xy$

Thus, $\begin{vmatrix} w & x \\ y & z \end{vmatrix} = \begin{vmatrix} w & x + cw \\ y & z + cy \end{vmatrix}$.

46. $\begin{vmatrix} w & x \\ cw & cx \end{vmatrix} = cxw - cxw = 0$

Thus, $\begin{vmatrix} w & x \\ cw & cx \end{vmatrix} = 0$.

47. $\begin{vmatrix} 1 & x & x^2 \\ 1 & y & y^2 \\ 1 & z & z^2 \end{vmatrix} = \begin{vmatrix} y & y^2 \\ z & z^2 \end{vmatrix} - \begin{vmatrix} x & x^2 \\ z & z^2 \end{vmatrix} + \begin{vmatrix} x & x^2 \\ y & y^2 \end{vmatrix}$

$$= (yz^2 - y^2z) - (xz^2 - x^2z) + (xy^2 - x^2y)$$
$$= yz^2 - xz^2 - y^2z + x^2z + xy(y - x)$$
$$= z^2(y - x) - z(y^2 - x^2) + xy(y - x)$$
$$= z^2(y - x) - z(y - x)(y + x) + xy(y - x)$$
$$= (y - x)[z^2 - z(y + x) + xy]$$
$$= (y - x)[z^2 - zy - zx + xy]$$
$$= (y - x)[z^2 - zx - zy + xy]$$
$$= (y - x)[z(z - x) - y(z - x)]$$
$$= (y - x)(z - x)(z - y)$$

48. $\begin{vmatrix} a+b & a & a \\ a & a+b & a \\ a & a & a+b \end{vmatrix} = (a+b)\begin{vmatrix} a+b & a \\ a & a+b \end{vmatrix} - a\begin{vmatrix} a & a \\ a & a+b \end{vmatrix} + a\begin{vmatrix} a & a \\ a+b & a \end{vmatrix}$

$$= (a + b)[(a + b)^2 - a^2] - a[a(a + b) - a^2] + a[a^2 - a(a + b)]$$
$$= (a + b)^3 - a^2(a + b) - a^2(a + b) + a^3 + a^3 - a^2(a + b)$$
$$= (a + b)^3 - 3a^2(a + b) + 2a^3$$
$$= a^3 + 3a^2b + 3ab^2 + b^3 - 3a^3 - 3a^2b + 2a^3$$
$$= 3ab^2 + b^3 = b^2(3a + b)$$

49. $\begin{vmatrix} x & 2 \\ 1 & x \end{vmatrix} = 2$

$x^2 - 2 = 2$

$x^2 = 4$

$x = \pm 2$

50. $\begin{vmatrix} x & 4 \\ -1 & x \end{vmatrix} = 20$

$x^2 + 4 = 20$

$x^2 = 16$

$x = \pm 4$

51. $\begin{vmatrix} 2x & -3 \\ -2 & 2x \end{vmatrix} = 3$

$4x^2 - 6 = 3$

$4x^2 = 9$

$x^2 = \frac{9}{4}$

$x = \pm \frac{3}{2}$

52. $\begin{vmatrix} x & 2 \\ 4 & 9x \end{vmatrix} = 8$

$9x^2 - 8 = 8$

$9x^2 = 16$

$x^2 = \dfrac{16}{9}$

$x = \pm \dfrac{4}{3}$

53. $\begin{vmatrix} x & 1 \\ 2 & x-2 \end{vmatrix} = -1$

$x^2 - 2x - 2 = -1$

$x^2 - 2x - 1 = 0$

$x = \dfrac{2 \pm \sqrt{4 + 4}}{2}$

$x = 1 \pm \sqrt{2}$

54. $\begin{vmatrix} x+1 & 2 \\ -1 & x \end{vmatrix} = 4$

$x^2 + x + 2 = 4$

$x^2 + x - 2 = 0$

$(x + 2)(x - 1) = 0$

$x = -2, 1$

55. $\begin{vmatrix} x+3 & 2 \\ 1 & x+2 \end{vmatrix} = 0$

$(x+3)(x+2) - 2 = 0$

$x^2 + 5x + 4 = 0$

$(x+4)(x+1) = 0$

$x = -4, -1$

56. $\begin{vmatrix} x-2 & -1 \\ -3 & x \end{vmatrix} = 0$

$x(x-2) - (-3)(-1) = 0$

$x^2 - 2x - 3 = 0$

$(x+1)(x-3) = 0$

$x = -1$ or $x = 3$

57. $\begin{vmatrix} 2x & 1 \\ -1 & x-1 \end{vmatrix} = x$

$2x^2 - 2x + 1 = x$

$2x^2 - 3x + 1 = 0$

$(x-1)(2x-1) = 0$

$x = 1, \frac{1}{2}$

58. $\begin{vmatrix} x-1 & x \\ x+1 & 2 \end{vmatrix} = -8$

$2x - 2 - x^2 - x = -8$

$-x^2 + x + 6 = 0$

$x^2 - x - 6 = 0$

$(x-3)(x+2) = 0$

$x = 3, -2$

59. $\begin{vmatrix} 1 & 2 & x \\ -1 & 3 & 2 \\ 3 & -2 & 1 \end{vmatrix} = 0$

$1\begin{vmatrix} 3 & 2 \\ -2 & 1 \end{vmatrix} - 2\begin{vmatrix} -1 & 2 \\ 3 & 1 \end{vmatrix} + x\begin{vmatrix} -1 & 3 \\ 3 & -2 \end{vmatrix} = 0$

$7 - 2(-7) + x(-7) = 0$

$21 = 7x$

$x = 3$

60. $\begin{vmatrix} 1 & x & -2 \\ 1 & 3 & 3 \\ 0 & 2 & -2 \end{vmatrix} = 0$

$1\begin{vmatrix} 3 & 3 \\ 2 & -2 \end{vmatrix} - 1\begin{vmatrix} x & -2 \\ 2 & -2 \end{vmatrix} = 0$ (Expand first column)

$-12 - (-2x + 4) = 0$

$2x = 16$

$x = 8$

61. $\begin{vmatrix} 4u & -1 \\ -1 & 2v \end{vmatrix} = 8uv - 1$

62. $\begin{vmatrix} 3x^2 & -3y^2 \\ 1 & 1 \end{vmatrix} = 3x^2 - (-3y^2) = 3x^2 + 3y^2$

63. $\begin{vmatrix} e^{2x} & e^{3x} \\ 2e^{2x} & 3e^{3x} \end{vmatrix} = 3e^{5x} - 2e^{5x} = e^{5x}$

64. $\begin{vmatrix} e^{-x} & xe^{-x} \\ -e^{-x} & (1-x)e^{-x} \end{vmatrix} = (1-x)e^{-2x} - (-xe^{-2x})$

$= e^{-2x} - xe^{-2x} + xe^{-2x}$

$= e^{-2x}$

65. $\begin{vmatrix} x & \ln x \\ 1 & \frac{1}{x} \end{vmatrix} = 1 - \ln x$

66. $\begin{vmatrix} x & x \ln x \\ 1 & 1 + \ln x \end{vmatrix} = x(1 + \ln x) - x \ln x$

$= x + x \ln x - x \ln x = x$

67. True. Expand along the row of zeros.

68. True

69. Let $A = \begin{bmatrix} 1 & 3 \\ -2 & 4 \end{bmatrix}$ and $B = \begin{bmatrix} -4 & 0 \\ 3 & 5 \end{bmatrix}$.

$$|A| = \begin{vmatrix} 1 & 3 \\ -2 & 4 \end{vmatrix} = 10, \quad |B| = \begin{vmatrix} -4 & 0 \\ 3 & 5 \end{vmatrix} = -20$$

$$A + B = \begin{bmatrix} -3 & 3 \\ 1 & 9 \end{bmatrix}, \quad |A + B| = \begin{vmatrix} -3 & 3 \\ 1 & 9 \end{vmatrix} = -30$$

Thus, $|A + B| \neq |A| + |B|$. Your answer may differ, depending on how you choose A and B.

70. $\begin{vmatrix} 4 & 5 & 6 \\ 7 & 8 & 9 \\ 10 & 11 & 12 \end{vmatrix} = 0$ $\quad\begin{vmatrix} 10 & 11 & 12 \\ 13 & 14 & 15 \\ 16 & 17 & 18 \end{vmatrix} = 0$

$\begin{vmatrix} 33 & 34 & 35 \\ 36 & 37 & 38 \\ 39 & 40 & 41 \end{vmatrix} = 0$ $\quad\begin{vmatrix} -5 & -4 & -3 \\ -2 & -1 & 0 \\ 1 & 2 & 3 \end{vmatrix} = 0$

$\begin{vmatrix} 19 & 20 & 21 & 22 \\ 23 & 24 & 25 & 26 \\ 27 & 28 & 29 & 30 \\ 31 & 32 & 33 & 34 \end{vmatrix} = 0$ $\quad\begin{vmatrix} 57 & 58 & 59 & 60 \\ 61 & 62 & 63 & 64 \\ 65 & 66 & 67 & 68 \\ 69 & 70 & 71 & 72 \end{vmatrix} = 0$

For an $n \times n$ matrix $(n > 2)$ with consecutive integer entries, the determinant appears to be 0.

$$\begin{vmatrix} x & x+1 & x+2 \\ x+3 & x+4 & x+5 \\ x+6 & x+7 & x+8 \end{vmatrix} = x\begin{vmatrix} x+4 & x+5 \\ x+7 & x+8 \end{vmatrix} - (x+1)\begin{vmatrix} x+3 & x+5 \\ x+6 & x+8 \end{vmatrix} + (x+2)\begin{vmatrix} x+3 & x+4 \\ x+6 & x+7 \end{vmatrix}$$

$$= x[(x+4)(x+8) - (x+7)(x+5)] - (x+1)[(x+3)(x+8) - (x+6)(x+5)] + (x+2)[(x+3)(x+7) - (x+6)(x+4)]$$

$$= x[(x^2 + 12x + 32) - (x^2 + 12x + 35)] - (x+1)[(x^2 + 11x + 24) - (x^2 + 11x + 30)] + (x+2)[(x^2 + 10x + 21) - (x^2 + 10x + 24)]$$

$$= -3x - (x+1)(-6) + (x+2)(-3)$$

$$= -3x + 6x + 6 - 3x - 6 = 0$$

71. (a) $|A| = 6$

(b) $A^{-1} = \begin{bmatrix} \frac{1}{3} & -\frac{1}{3} \\ \frac{1}{3} & \frac{1}{6} \end{bmatrix}$

(c) $\det(A^{-1}) = \dfrac{1}{6}$

(d) In general, $\det(A^{-1}) = \dfrac{1}{\det A}$.

72. (a) $|A| = -3$

(b) $A^{-1} = \begin{bmatrix} \frac{1}{3} & -\frac{1}{3} \\ \frac{2}{3} & -\frac{5}{3} \end{bmatrix}$

(c) $\det(A^{-1}) = -\dfrac{1}{3}$

(d) In general, $\det(A^{-1}) = \dfrac{1}{\det A}$.

73. (a) $|A| = 2$

(b) $A^{-1} = \begin{bmatrix} -4 & -5 & 1.5 \\ -1 & -1 & 0.5 \\ -1 & -1 & 0 \end{bmatrix}$

(c) $\det(A^{-1}) = \frac{1}{2}$

(d) In general, $\det(A^{-1}) = \frac{1}{\det A}$.

74. (a) $|A| = 4$

(b) $A^{-1} = \begin{bmatrix} -1.25 & 2 & -2.25 \\ 0.25 & 0 & 0.25 \\ -0.5 & 1 & -1.5 \end{bmatrix}$

(c) $\det(A^{-1}) = \frac{1}{4}$

(d) In general, $\det(A^{-1}) = \frac{1}{\det A}$.

75. (a) Columns 2 and 3 are interchanged.

(b) Rows 1 and 3 are interchanged.

76. (a) (-5) times Row 1 is added to Row 2.

(b) (-2) times Row 2 is added to Row 1.

77. (a) 5 is factored out of the first row of A.

(b) 4 and 3 are factored out of columns 2 and 3.

78. Answers will vary.

79. $x^2 - 3x + 2 = (x - 2)(x - 1)$

80. $x^2 + 5x + 6 = (x + 2)(x + 3)$

81. $4y^2 - 12y + 9 = (2y - 3)^2$

82. $4y^2 - 28y + 49 = (2y - 7)^2$

83. $3x - 10y = 46$

$x + y = -2$

$y = -x - 2$

$3x - 10(-x - 2) = 46$

$13x = 26$

$x = 2$

$y = -2 - 2 = -4$

Answer: $(2, -4)$

84. $\begin{cases} 5x + 7y = 23 \\ -4x - 2y = -4 \end{cases} \Rightarrow 2x + y = 2 \Rightarrow y = 2 - 2x$

$5x + 7(2 - 2x) = 23$

$-9x = 9$

$x = -1, y = 2 - 2(-1) = 4$

Answer: $(-1, 4)$

Section 7.8 Applications of Matrices and Determinants

- You should be able to find the area of a triangle with vertices (x_1, y_1), (x_2, y_2), and (x_3, y_3).

$$\text{Area} = \pm\frac{1}{2}\begin{vmatrix} x_1 & y_1 & 1 \\ x_2 & y_2 & 1 \\ x_3 & y_3 & 1 \end{vmatrix}$$

  The $\pm$ symbol indicates that the appropriate sign should be chosen so that the area is positive.
- You should be able to test to see if three points, (x_1, y_1), (x_2, y_2), and (x_3, y_3), are collinear.

$$\begin{vmatrix} x_1 & y_1 & 1 \\ x_2 & y_2 & 1 \\ x_3 & y_3 & 1 \end{vmatrix} = 0, \text{ if and only if they are collinear.}$$

- You should be able to use Cramer's Rule to solve a system of linear equations.
- Now you should be able to solve a system of linear equations by substitution, elimination, elementary row operations on an augmented matrix, using the inverse matrix, or Cramer's Rule.
- You should be able to encode and decode messages by using an invertible $n \times n$ matrix.

Vocabulary Check

1. collinear **2.** Cramer's Rule **3.** cryptogram **4.** uncoded, coded

1. Vertices: $(-2, 4), (2, 3), (-1, 5)$

$$\frac{1}{2}\begin{vmatrix} -2 & 4 & 1 \\ 2 & 3 & 1 \\ -1 & 5 & 1 \end{vmatrix} = \frac{1}{2}\left[-2\begin{vmatrix} 3 & 1 \\ 5 & 1 \end{vmatrix} - 4\begin{vmatrix} 2 & 1 \\ -1 & 1 \end{vmatrix} + \begin{vmatrix} 2 & 3 \\ -1 & 5 \end{vmatrix}\right]$$

$$= \frac{1}{2}[-2(-2) - 4(3) + 13] = \frac{1}{2}(5) = \frac{5}{2}$$

Area $= \frac{5}{2}$ square units

2. Vertices: $(-3, 5), (2, 6), (3, -5)$

$$\frac{1}{2}\begin{vmatrix} -3 & 5 & 1 \\ 2 & 6 & 1 \\ 3 & -5 & 1 \end{vmatrix} = \frac{1}{2}[(-3)11 - 5(-1) + 1(-28)] = \frac{1}{2}(-56)$$

Area = 28 square units

3. Vertices: $\left(0, \frac{1}{2}\right), \left(\frac{5}{2}, 0\right), (4, 3)$

$$\frac{1}{2}\begin{vmatrix} 0 & \frac{1}{2} & 1 \\ \frac{5}{2} & 0 & 1 \\ 4 & 3 & 1 \end{vmatrix} = \frac{1}{2}\left[-\frac{1}{2}\left(-\frac{3}{2}\right) + \frac{15}{2}\right] = \frac{1}{2}\left[\frac{33}{4}\right] = \frac{33}{8}.$$

Area $= \frac{33}{8}$ square units

4. Vertices: $\left(\frac{9}{2}, 0\right), (2, 6), \left(0, -\frac{3}{2}\right)$

$$\frac{1}{2}\begin{vmatrix} \frac{9}{2} & 0 & 1 \\ 2 & 6 & 1 \\ 0 & -\frac{3}{2} & 1 \end{vmatrix} = \frac{1}{2}\left[\frac{9}{2}\left(6 + \frac{3}{2}\right) + 1(-3)\right]$$

$$= \frac{1}{2}(30.75) = 15.375 = \frac{123}{8}.$$

Area $= \frac{123}{8}$ square units

5. $\begin{vmatrix} -3 & 2 & 1 \\ 1 & 2 & 1 \\ -1 & -4 & 1 \end{vmatrix} = -3(6) - 2(2) + 1(-2) = -24$

Area rhombus $= |-24| = 24$ square units

6. $\begin{vmatrix} -4 & 4 & 1 \\ 6 & 8 & 1 \\ 2 & 1 & 1 \end{vmatrix} = -4(7) - 4(4) + 1(-10) = -54$

Area rhombus $= |-54| = 54$ square units

7. $4 = \pm\frac{1}{2}\begin{vmatrix} -1 & 5 & 1 \\ -2 & 0 & 1 \\ x & 2 & 1 \end{vmatrix}$

$8 = \pm[(-1)(-2) - 5(-2 - x) + 1(-4)]$

$8 = \pm[5x + 8]$

$5x + 8 = 8$ or $5x + 8 = -8$

$x = 0$ or $x = -\frac{16}{5}$

$x = 0, -\frac{16}{5}$

8. $4 = \pm\frac{1}{2}\begin{vmatrix} -4 & 2 & 1 \\ -3 & 5 & 1 \\ -1 & x & 1 \end{vmatrix}$

$8 = \pm[-4(5 - x) - 2(-2) + 1(-3x + 5)]$

$8 = \pm[x - 11]$

$x - 11 = 8$ or $x - 11 = -8$

$x = 19$ or $x = 3$

$x = 3, 19$

9. Points: $(3, -1), (0, -3), (12, 5)$

$\begin{vmatrix} 3 & -1 & 1 \\ 0 & -3 & 1 \\ 12 & 5 & 1 \end{vmatrix} = 3(-8) + 12(2) = 0$

The points are collinear.

10. Points: $(3, -5), (6, 1), (4, 2)$

$$\begin{vmatrix} 3 & -5 & 1 \\ 6 & 1 & 1 \\ 4 & 2 & 1 \end{vmatrix} = \begin{vmatrix} 6 & 1 \\ 4 & 2 \end{vmatrix} - \begin{vmatrix} 3 & -5 \\ 4 & 2 \end{vmatrix} + \begin{vmatrix} 3 & -5 \\ 6 & 1 \end{vmatrix}$$

$$= 8 - 26 + 33 = 15 \neq 0$$

The points are not collinear.

11. Points: $\left(2, -\frac{1}{2}\right), (-4, 4), (6, -3)$

$$\begin{vmatrix} 2 & -\frac{1}{2} & 1 \\ -4 & 4 & 1 \\ 6 & -3 & 1 \end{vmatrix} = 2(7) + \frac{1}{2}(-10) + 1(-12)$$

$$= -3 \neq 0$$

The points are not collinear.

12. Points: $\left(0, \frac{1}{2}\right), (2, -1), \left(-4, \frac{7}{2}\right)$

$$\begin{vmatrix} 0 & \frac{1}{2} & 1 \\ 2 & -1 & 1 \\ -4 & \frac{7}{2} & 1 \end{vmatrix} = -\frac{1}{2}(2 + 4) + 1(7 - 4)$$

$$= -3 + 3 = 0$$

The points are collinear.

13. $\begin{vmatrix} 1 & -2 & 1 \\ x & 2 & 1 \\ 5 & 6 & 1 \end{vmatrix} = 0$

$$1(-4) + 2(x - 5) + 1(6x - 10) = 0$$
$$8x - 24 = 0$$
$$x = 3$$

14. $\begin{vmatrix} -6 & 2 & 1 \\ -5 & x & 1 \\ -3 & 5 & 1 \end{vmatrix} = 0$

$$\begin{vmatrix} -5 & x \\ -3 & 5 \end{vmatrix} - \begin{vmatrix} -6 & 2 \\ -3 & 5 \end{vmatrix} + \begin{vmatrix} -6 & 2 \\ -5 & x \end{vmatrix} = 0$$
$$-25 + 3x + 24 - 6x + 10 = 0$$
$$-3x = -9$$
$$x = 3$$

15. $\begin{cases} -7x + 11y = -1 \\ 3x - 9y = 9 \end{cases}$

$$x = \frac{\begin{vmatrix} -1 & 11 \\ 9 & -9 \end{vmatrix}}{\begin{vmatrix} -7 & 11 \\ 3 & -9 \end{vmatrix}} = \frac{-90}{30} = -3$$

$$y = \frac{\begin{vmatrix} -7 & -1 \\ 3 & 9 \end{vmatrix}}{\begin{vmatrix} -7 & 11 \\ 3 & -9 \end{vmatrix}} = \frac{-60}{30} = -2$$

Answer: $(-3, -2)$

16. $\begin{cases} 4x - 3y = -10 \\ 6x + 9y = 12 \end{cases}$

$$x = \frac{\begin{vmatrix} -10 & -3 \\ 12 & 9 \end{vmatrix}}{\begin{vmatrix} 4 & -3 \\ 6 & 9 \end{vmatrix}} = \frac{-54}{54} = -1$$

$$y = \frac{\begin{vmatrix} 4 & -10 \\ 6 & 12 \end{vmatrix}}{\begin{vmatrix} 4 & -3 \\ 6 & 9 \end{vmatrix}} = \frac{108}{54} = 2$$

Answer: $(-1, 2)$

17. $\begin{cases} 3x + 2y = -2 \\ 6x + 4y = 4 \end{cases}$

$$\begin{vmatrix} 3 & 2 \\ 6 & 4 \end{vmatrix} = 12 - 17 = 0$$

Cramer's rule cannot be used.

(In fact, the system is inconsistent.)

18. $\begin{cases} 6x - 5y = 17 \\ -13x + 3y = -76 \end{cases}$

$$x = \frac{\begin{vmatrix} 17 & -5 \\ -76 & 3 \end{vmatrix}}{\begin{vmatrix} 6 & -5 \\ -13 & 3 \end{vmatrix}} = \frac{-329}{-47} = 7$$

$$y = \frac{\begin{vmatrix} 6 & 17 \\ -13 & -76 \end{vmatrix}}{\begin{vmatrix} 6 & -5 \\ -13 & 3 \end{vmatrix}} = \frac{-235}{-47} = 5$$

Answer: $(7, 5)$

19. $\begin{cases} -0.4x + 0.8y = 1.6 \\ 0.2x + 0.3y = 2.2 \end{cases}$

$$D = \begin{vmatrix} -0.4 & 0.8 \\ 0.2 & 0.3 \end{vmatrix} = -0.28$$

$$x = \frac{\begin{vmatrix} 1.6 & 0.8 \\ 2.2 & 0.3 \end{vmatrix}}{-0.28} = \frac{-1.28}{-0.28} = \frac{32}{7}$$

$$y = \frac{\begin{vmatrix} -0.4 & 1.6 \\ 0.2 & 2.2 \end{vmatrix}}{-0.28} = \frac{-1.20}{-0.28} = \frac{30}{7}$$

Answer: $\left(\frac{32}{7}, \frac{30}{7}\right)$

20. $\begin{cases} 2.4x - 0.8y = 10.8 \\ 4.6x + 1.2y = 24.8 \end{cases}$

$$D = \begin{vmatrix} 2.4 & -0.8 \\ 4.6 & 1.2 \end{vmatrix} = 6.56$$

$$x = \frac{\begin{vmatrix} 10.8 & -0.8 \\ 24.8 & 1.2 \end{vmatrix}}{6.56} = \frac{32.8}{6.56} = 5$$

$$y = \frac{\begin{vmatrix} 2.4 & 10.8 \\ 4.6 & 24.8 \end{vmatrix}}{6.56} = \frac{9.84}{6.56} = 1.5$$

Answer: $(5, 1.5)$

21. $\begin{cases} 4x - y + z = -5 \\ 2x + 2y + 3z = 10 \\ 5x - 2y + 6z = 1 \end{cases}$ $D = \begin{vmatrix} 4 & -1 & 1 \\ 2 & 2 & 3 \\ 5 & -2 & 6 \end{vmatrix} = 55$

$$x = \frac{\begin{vmatrix} -5 & -1 & 1 \\ 10 & 2 & 3 \\ 1 & -2 & 6 \end{vmatrix}}{55} = \frac{-55}{55} = -1, \quad y = \frac{\begin{vmatrix} 4 & -5 & 1 \\ 2 & 10 & 3 \\ 5 & 1 & 6 \end{vmatrix}}{55} = \frac{165}{55} = 3, \quad z = \frac{\begin{vmatrix} 4 & -1 & -5 \\ 2 & 2 & 10 \\ 5 & -2 & 1 \end{vmatrix}}{55} = \frac{110}{55} = 2$$

Answer: $(-1, 3, 2)$

22. $\begin{cases} 4x - 2y + 3z = -2 \\ 2x + 2y + 5z = 16 \\ 8x - 5y - 2z = 4 \end{cases}$ $D = \begin{vmatrix} 4 & -2 & 3 \\ 2 & 2 & 5 \\ 8 & -5 & -2 \end{vmatrix} = -82$

$$x = \frac{\begin{vmatrix} -2 & -2 & 3 \\ 16 & 2 & 5 \\ 4 & -5 & -2 \end{vmatrix}}{-82} = \frac{-410}{-82} = 5 \quad y = \frac{\begin{vmatrix} 4 & -2 & 3 \\ 2 & 16 & 5 \\ 8 & 4 & -2 \end{vmatrix}}{-82} = \frac{-656}{-82} = 8 \quad z = \frac{\begin{vmatrix} 4 & -2 & -2 \\ 2 & 2 & 16 \\ 8 & -5 & 4 \end{vmatrix}}{-82} = \frac{164}{-82} = -2$$

Answer: $(5, 8, -2)$

23. (a) $\begin{cases} 3x + 3y + 5z = 1 \\ 3x + 5y + 9z = 2 \\ 5x + 9y + 17z = 4 \end{cases}$

$\begin{cases} 3x + 3y + 5z = 1 \\ 2y + 4z = 1 \\ 4y + \frac{26}{3}z = \frac{7}{3} \end{cases}$

$\begin{cases} 3x + 3y + 5z = 1 \\ 2y + 4z = 1 \\ \frac{2}{3}z = \frac{1}{3} \end{cases}$

$z = \frac{1}{2}$

$2y + 4\left(\frac{1}{2}\right) = 1 \Rightarrow y = -\frac{1}{2}$

$3x + 3\left(-\frac{1}{2}\right) + 5\left(\frac{1}{2}\right) = 1 \Rightarrow x = 0$

Answer: $\left(0, -\frac{1}{2}, \frac{1}{2}\right)$

(b) $D = \begin{vmatrix} 3 & 3 & 5 \\ 3 & 5 & 9 \\ 5 & 9 & 17 \end{vmatrix} = 4$

$$x = \frac{\begin{vmatrix} 1 & 3 & 5 \\ 2 & 5 & 9 \\ 4 & 9 & 17 \end{vmatrix}}{4} = 0$$

$$y = \frac{\begin{vmatrix} 3 & 1 & 5 \\ 3 & 2 & 9 \\ 5 & 4 & 17 \end{vmatrix}}{4} = -\frac{1}{2}$$

$$z = \frac{\begin{vmatrix} 3 & 3 & 1 \\ 3 & 5 & 2 \\ 5 & 9 & 4 \end{vmatrix}}{4} = \frac{1}{2}$$

Answer: $\left(0, -\frac{1}{2}, \frac{1}{2}\right)$

24. (a) $\begin{cases} 2x + 3y - 5z = 1 \\ 3x + 5y + 9z = -16 \\ 5x + 9y + 17z = -30 \end{cases}$

$\begin{cases} 2x + 3y - 5z = 1 \\ \frac{1}{2}y + \frac{33}{2}z = -\frac{35}{2} \\ \frac{3}{2}y + \frac{59}{2}z = -\frac{65}{2} \end{cases}$

$\begin{cases} 2x + 3y - 5z = 1 \\ y + 33z = -35 \\ -20z = 20 \end{cases}$

$z = -1$

$y = -35 + 33 = -2$

$x = (1 - 5 + 6)/2 = 1$

Answer: $(1, -2, -1)$

(b) $D = \begin{vmatrix} 2 & 3 & -5 \\ 3 & 5 & 9 \\ 5 & 9 & 17 \end{vmatrix} = -20$

$$x = \frac{\begin{vmatrix} 1 & 3 & -5 \\ -16 & 5 & 9 \\ -30 & 9 & 17 \end{vmatrix}}{-20} = \frac{-20}{-20} = 1$$

$$y = \frac{\begin{vmatrix} 2 & 1 & -5 \\ 3 & -16 & 9 \\ 5 & -30 & 17 \end{vmatrix}}{-20} = \frac{40}{-20} = -2$$

$$z = \frac{\begin{vmatrix} 2 & 3 & 1 \\ 3 & 5 & -16 \\ 5 & 9 & -30 \end{vmatrix}}{-20} = \frac{20}{-20} = -1$$

Answer: $(1, -2, -1)$

25. (a) $\begin{cases} 2x - y + z = 5 \\ x - 2y - z = 1 \\ 3x + y + z = 4 \end{cases}$

$\begin{cases} x - 2y - z = 1 \\ 3y + 3z = 3 \\ 7y + 4z = 1 \end{cases}$

$\begin{cases} x - 2y - z = 1 \\ y + z = 1 \\ -3z = -6 \end{cases}$

$z = 2$

$y + 2 = 1 \Rightarrow y = -1$

$x - 2(-1) - 2 = 1 \Rightarrow x = 1$

Answer: $(1, -1, 2)$

(b) $D = \begin{vmatrix} 2 & -1 & 1 \\ 1 & -2 & -1 \\ 3 & 1 & 1 \end{vmatrix} = 9$

$$x = \frac{\begin{vmatrix} 5 & -1 & 1 \\ 1 & -2 & -1 \\ 4 & 1 & 1 \end{vmatrix}}{9} = 1$$

$$y = \frac{\begin{vmatrix} 2 & 5 & 1 \\ 1 & 1 & -1 \\ 3 & 4 & 1 \end{vmatrix}}{9} = -1$$

$$z = \frac{\begin{vmatrix} 2 & -1 & 5 \\ 1 & -2 & 1 \\ 3 & 1 & 4 \end{vmatrix}}{9} = 2$$

Answer: $(1, -1, 2)$

26. (a) $\begin{cases} 3x - y - 3z = 1 \\ 2x + y + 2z = -4 \\ x + y - z = 5 \end{cases}$

$$\begin{aligned} x + \quad y - z &= 5 \\ -y + 4z &= -14 \\ -4y \quad &= -14 \end{aligned}$$

$$y = \frac{7}{2}$$

$$-\frac{7}{2} + 4z = -14 \Rightarrow z = -\frac{21}{8}$$

$$x + \frac{7}{2} + \frac{21}{8} = 5 \Rightarrow x = -\frac{9}{8}$$

Answer: $\left(-\frac{9}{8}, \frac{7}{2}, -\frac{21}{8}\right)$

(b) $D = \begin{vmatrix} 3 & -1 & -3 \\ 2 & 1 & 2 \\ 1 & 1 & -1 \end{vmatrix} = -16$

$$x = \frac{\begin{vmatrix} 1 & -1 & -3 \\ -4 & 1 & 2 \\ 5 & 1 & -1 \end{vmatrix}}{-16} = -\frac{9}{8}$$

$$y = \frac{\begin{vmatrix} 3 & 1 & -3 \\ 2 & -4 & 2 \\ 1 & 5 & -1 \end{vmatrix}}{-16} = \frac{7}{2}$$

$$z = \frac{\begin{vmatrix} 3 & -1 & 1 \\ 2 & 1 & -4 \\ 1 & 1 & 5 \end{vmatrix}}{-16} = -\frac{21}{8}$$

27. (a) $D = \begin{vmatrix} 5 & 10 & 30 \\ 10 & 30 & 100 \\ 30 & 100 & 354 \end{vmatrix} = 700$

$$c = \frac{\begin{vmatrix} 5543 & 10 & 30 \\ 12{,}447 & 30 & 100 \\ 38{,}333 & 100 & 354 \end{vmatrix}}{700} = \frac{548{,}580}{700} \approx 784$$

$$b = \frac{\begin{vmatrix} 5 & 5543 & 30 \\ 10 & 12{,}447 & 100 \\ 30 & 38{,}333 & 354 \end{vmatrix}}{700} = \frac{169{,}070}{700} \approx 241.5$$

$$a = \frac{\begin{vmatrix} 5 & 10 & 5543 \\ 10 & 30 & 12{,}447 \\ 30 & 100 & 38{,}333 \end{vmatrix}}{700} = \frac{-18{,}450}{700} \approx -26.36$$

$$y = -26.36t^2 + 241.5t + 784$$

(b)

(c) No, because of the negative t^2 coefficient.

28. (a) $D = \begin{vmatrix} 5 & 10 & 30 \\ 10 & 30 & 100 \\ 30 & 100 & 354 \end{vmatrix} = 700$

$$c = \frac{\begin{vmatrix} 53{,}729 & 10 & 30 \\ 103{,}385 & 30 & 100 \\ 296{,}433 & 100 & 354 \end{vmatrix}}{700} = \frac{7{,}127{,}380}{700} \approx 10{,}182$$

$$b = \frac{\begin{vmatrix} 5 & 53{,}729 & 30 \\ 10 & 103{,}385 & 100 \\ 30 & 296{,}433 & 354 \end{vmatrix}}{700} = \frac{1{,}644{,}690}{700} \approx 2349.6$$

$$a = \frac{\begin{vmatrix} 5 & 10 & 53{,}729 \\ 10 & 30 & 103{,}385 \\ 30 & 100 & 296{,}433 \end{vmatrix}}{700} = \frac{-482{,}450}{700} \approx -689.21$$

$$y = -689.21t^2 + 2349.6t + 10{,}182$$

(b)

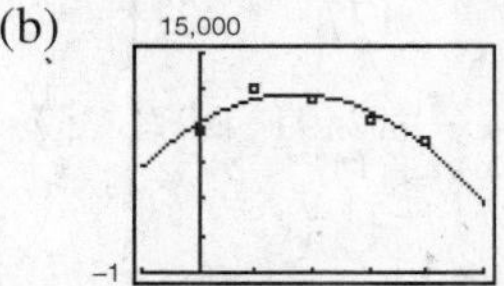

(c) $y = 1500$ for $t \approx 4.3$, or 2004.

29. The uncoded row matrices are the rows of the 6×3 matrix on the left.

$$\begin{array}{ccc} C & A & L \\ L & & M \\ E & & T \\ O & M & O \\ R & R & O \\ W & & \end{array} \begin{bmatrix} 3 & 1 & 12 \\ 12 & 0 & 13 \\ 5 & 0 & 20 \\ 15 & 13 & 15 \\ 18 & 18 & 15 \\ 23 & 0 & 0 \end{bmatrix} \begin{bmatrix} 1 & -1 & 0 \\ 1 & 0 & -1 \\ -6 & 2 & 3 \end{bmatrix} = \begin{bmatrix} -68 & 21 & 35 \\ -66 & 14 & 39 \\ -115 & 35 & 60 \\ -62 & 15 & 32 \\ -54 & 12 & 27 \\ 23 & -23 & 0 \end{bmatrix}$$

Answer: $[-68, 21, 35], [-66, 14, 39], [-115, 35, 60]$

$[-62, 15, 32], [-54, 12, 27], [23, -23, 0]$

30. The uncoded row matrices are the rows of the 6×3 matrix on the left.

$$\begin{array}{ccc} P & L & E \\ A & S & E \\ & S & E \\ N & D & \\ M & O & N \\ E & Y & \end{array} \begin{bmatrix} 16 & 12 & 5 \\ 1 & 19 & 5 \\ 0 & 19 & 5 \\ 14 & 4 & 0 \\ 13 & 15 & 14 \\ 5 & 25 & 0 \end{bmatrix} \begin{bmatrix} 4 & 2 & 1 \\ -3 & -3 & -1 \\ 3 & 2 & 1 \end{bmatrix} = \begin{bmatrix} 43 & 6 & 9 \\ -38 & -45 & -13 \\ -42 & -47 & -14 \\ 44 & 16 & 10 \\ 49 & 9 & 12 \\ -55 & -65 & -20 \end{bmatrix}$$

Answer: $[43 \; 6 \; 9], [-38 \; -45 \; -13], [-42 \; -47 \; -14], [44 \; 16 \; 10], [49 \; 9 \; 12], [-55 \; -65 \; -20]$

31. $$\begin{array}{ccc} G & O & N \\ E & & F \\ I & S & H \\ I & N & G \end{array} \begin{bmatrix} 7 & 15 & 14 \\ 5 & 0 & 6 \\ 9 & 19 & 8 \\ 9 & 14 & 7 \end{bmatrix} \begin{bmatrix} 1 & 2 & 2 \\ 3 & 7 & 9 \\ -1 & -4 & -7 \end{bmatrix} = \begin{bmatrix} 38 & 63 & 51 \\ -1 & -14 & -32 \\ 58 & 119 & 133 \\ 44 & 88 & 95 \end{bmatrix}$$

Cryptogram: 38 63 51 −1 −14 −32 58 119 133 44 88 95

32. H A P P Y _ B I R T H D A Y _

$[8 \; 1 \; 16]$ $[16 \; 25 \; 0]$ $[2 \; 9 \; 18]$ $[20 \; 8 \; 4]$ $[1 \; 25 \; 0]$

$[8 \; 1 \; 16]A = [-5 \; -41 \; -87]$

$[16 \; 25 \; 0]A = [91 \; 207 \; 257]$

$[2 \; 9 \; 18]A = [11 \; -5 \; -41]$

$[20 \; 8 \; 4]A = [40 \; 80 \; 84]$

$[1 \; 25 \; 0]A = [76 \; 177 \; 227]$

Cryptogram: −5 −41 −87 91 207 257 11 −5 −41 40 80 84 76 177 227

33. $A^{-1} = \begin{bmatrix} 1 & 2 \\ 3 & 5 \end{bmatrix}^{-1} = \begin{bmatrix} -5 & 2 \\ 3 & -1 \end{bmatrix}$

$$\begin{bmatrix} 11 & 21 \\ 64 & 112 \\ 25 & 50 \\ 29 & 53 \\ 23 & 46 \\ 40 & 75 \\ 55 & 92 \end{bmatrix} \begin{bmatrix} -5 & 2 \\ 3 & -1 \end{bmatrix} = \begin{bmatrix} 8 & 1 \\ 16 & 16 \\ 25 & 0 \\ 14 & 5 \\ 23 & 0 \\ 25 & 5 \\ 1 & 18 \end{bmatrix} \begin{array}{cc} H & A \\ P & P \\ Y & \\ N & E \\ W & \\ Y & E \\ A & R \end{array}$$

Message: HAPPY NEW YEAR

34. $A = \begin{bmatrix} 2 & 3 \\ 3 & 4 \end{bmatrix}, A^{-1} = \begin{bmatrix} -4 & 3 \\ 3 & -2 \end{bmatrix}$

$$\begin{bmatrix} 85 & 120 \\ 6 & 8 \\ 10 & 15 \\ 84 & 117 \\ 42 & 56 \\ 90 & 125 \\ 60 & 80 \\ 30 & 45 \\ 19 & 26 \end{bmatrix} \begin{bmatrix} -4 & 3 \\ 3 & -2 \end{bmatrix} = \begin{bmatrix} 20 & 15 \\ 0 & 2 \\ 5 & 0 \\ 15 & 18 \\ 0 & 14 \\ 15 & 20 \\ 0 & 20 \\ 15 & 0 \\ 2 & 5 \end{bmatrix} \begin{matrix} \text{T} & \text{O} \\ \text{—} & \text{B} \\ \text{E} & \text{—} \\ \text{O} & \text{R} \\ \text{—} & \text{N} \\ \text{O} & \text{T} \\ \text{—} & \text{T} \\ \text{O} & \text{—} \\ \text{B} & \text{E} \end{matrix}$$

TO BE OR NOT TO BE

35. $A^{-1} = \begin{bmatrix} 1 & 2 & 1 \\ -1 & 0 & 2 \\ 1 & -1 & -2 \end{bmatrix}^{-1} = \begin{bmatrix} \frac{2}{3} & 1 & \frac{4}{3} \\ 0 & -1 & -1 \\ \frac{1}{3} & 1 & \frac{2}{3} \end{bmatrix}$

$$\begin{bmatrix} 38 & 36 & -1 \\ 11 & 17 & 11 \\ 42 & 15 & -27 \\ -5 & 18 & 37 \\ 26 & 28 & 17 \\ 8 & 24 & 20 \\ 32 & 20 & -7 \\ 23 & -1 & -19 \end{bmatrix} \begin{bmatrix} \frac{2}{3} & 1 & \frac{4}{3} \\ 0 & -1 & -1 \\ \frac{1}{3} & 1 & \frac{2}{3} \end{bmatrix} = \begin{bmatrix} 25 & 1 & 14 \\ 11 & 5 & 5 \\ 19 & 0 & 23 \\ 9 & 14 & 0 \\ 23 & 15 & 18 \\ 12 & 4 & 0 \\ 19 & 5 & 18 \\ 9 & 5 & 19 \end{bmatrix} \begin{matrix} \text{Y} & \text{A} & \text{N} \\ \text{K} & \text{E} & \text{E} \\ \text{S} & - & \text{W} \\ \text{I} & \text{N} & - \\ \text{W} & \text{O} & \text{R} \\ \text{L} & \text{D} & - \\ \text{S} & \text{E} & \text{R} \\ \text{I} & \text{E} & \text{S} \end{matrix}$$

YANKEES WIN WORLD SERIES

36. Let A be the 2×2 matrix needed to decode the message.

$$\begin{bmatrix} -18 & -18 \\ 1 & 16 \end{bmatrix} A = \begin{bmatrix} 0 & 18 \\ 15 & 14 \end{bmatrix} \begin{matrix} & \text{R} \\ \text{O} & \text{N} \end{matrix}$$

$$A = \begin{bmatrix} -18 & -18 \\ 1 & 16 \end{bmatrix}^{-1} \begin{bmatrix} 0 & 18 \\ 15 & 14 \end{bmatrix} = \begin{bmatrix} -\frac{8}{135} & -\frac{1}{15} \\ \frac{1}{270} & \frac{1}{15} \end{bmatrix} \begin{bmatrix} 0 & 18 \\ 15 & 14 \end{bmatrix} = \begin{bmatrix} -1 & -2 \\ 1 & 1 \end{bmatrix}$$

$$\begin{bmatrix} 8 & 21 \\ -15 & -10 \\ -13 & -13 \\ 5 & 10 \\ 5 & 25 \\ 5 & 19 \\ -1 & 6 \\ 20 & 40 \\ -18 & -18 \\ 1 & 16 \end{bmatrix} \begin{bmatrix} -1 & -2 \\ 1 & 1 \end{bmatrix} = \begin{bmatrix} 13 & 5 \\ 5 & 20 \\ 0 & 13 \\ 5 & 0 \\ 20 & 15 \\ 14 & 9 \\ 7 & 8 \\ 20 & 0 \\ 0 & 18 \\ 15 & 14 \end{bmatrix} \begin{matrix} \text{M} & \text{E} \\ \text{E} & \text{T} \\ & \text{M} \\ \text{E} & \\ \text{T} & \text{O} \\ \text{N} & \text{I} \\ \text{G} & \text{H} \\ \text{T} & \\ & \text{R} \\ \text{O} & \text{N} \end{matrix}$$

Message: MEET ME TONIGHT RON

37. True. Cramer's Rule requires that the determinant of the coefficient matrix be nonzero.

38. False. The system $\begin{cases} x + y = 1 \\ 2x + 2y = 2 \end{cases}$ has solutions,

yet $\det\left(\begin{bmatrix} 1 & 1 \\ 2 & 2 \end{bmatrix}\right) = 0$.

39. Answers will vary.

40. Answers will vary.

41. $$y - 5 = \frac{5 - 3}{-1 - 7}(x + 1) = \frac{-1}{4}(x + 1)$$

$$4y - 20 = -x - 1$$

$$4y + x = 19$$

$$x + 4y - 19 = 0$$

42. $$y + 6 = \frac{10 - (-6)}{-2 - 0}(x - 0) = -8x$$

$$y = -8x - 6$$

$$8x + y + 6 = 0$$

43. $$y + 3 = \frac{-3 + 1}{3 - 10}(x - 3) = \frac{2}{7}(x - 3)$$

$$7y + 21 = 2x - 6$$

$$7y - 2x = -27$$

$$2x - 7y - 27 = 0$$

44. $$y - 12 = \frac{12 - 2}{-4 - 4}(x + 4) = -\frac{5}{4}(x + 4)$$

$$4y - 48 = -5x - 20$$

$$4y + 5x = 28$$

$$5x + 4y - 28 = 0$$

45. $f(x) = \dfrac{2x^2}{x^2 + 4}$

Horizontal asymptote: $y = 2$

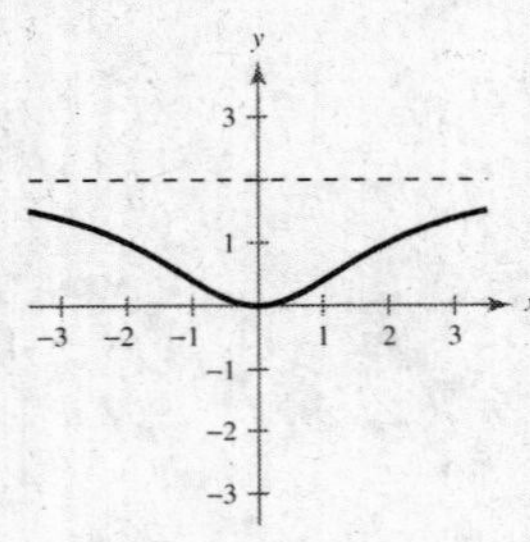

46. $f(x) = \dfrac{2x}{x^2 + 3x - 18} = \dfrac{2x}{(x + 6)(x - 3)}$

Vertical asymptotes: $x = -6, 3$

Horizontal asymptote: $y = 0$

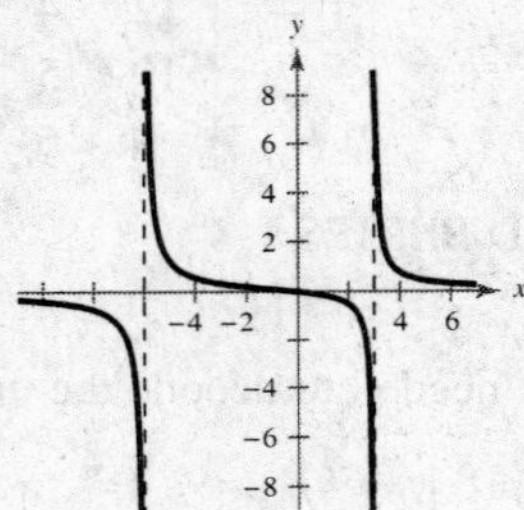

Review Exercises for Chapter 7

1. $$\begin{cases} x + y = 2 \Rightarrow & y = 2 - x \\ x - y = 0 \Rightarrow & x - (2 - x) = 0 \end{cases}$$

$$2x - 2 = 0$$

$$x = 1$$

$$y = 2 - 1 = 1$$

Answer: $(1, 1)$

2. $$\begin{cases} 2x - 3y = 3 \\ x - y = 0 \Rightarrow y = x \end{cases}$$

$$2x - 3(x) = 3$$

$$-x = 3$$

$$x = -3 \Rightarrow y = -3$$

Answer: $(-3, -3)$

3. $\begin{cases} x^2 - y^2 = 9 \\ x - y = 1 \Rightarrow \quad x = y + 1 \end{cases}$

$$(y + 1)^2 - y^2 = 9$$
$$2y + 1 = 9$$
$$y = 4$$
$$x = 5$$

Answer: $(5, 4)$

4. $\begin{cases} x^2 + y^2 = 169 \\ 3x + 2y = 39 \Rightarrow x = \frac{1}{3}(39 - 2y) \end{cases}$

$$\left[\tfrac{1}{3}(39 - 2y)\right]^2 + y^2 = 169$$
$$\tfrac{1}{9}(1521 - 156y + 4y^2) + y^2 = 169$$
$$169 - \tfrac{52}{3}y + \tfrac{4}{9}y^2 + y^2 = 169$$
$$\tfrac{13}{9}y^2 - \tfrac{52}{3}y = 0$$
$$\tfrac{13}{3}y\left(\tfrac{1}{3}y - 4\right) = 0 \Rightarrow y = 0, 12$$

$y = 0$: $x = \frac{1}{3}(39 - 2(0)) = 13$

$y = 12$: $x = \frac{1}{3}(39 - 2(12)) = 5$

Answer: $(13, 0), (5, 12)$

5. $\begin{cases} y = 2x^2 \\ y = x^4 - 2x^2 \Rightarrow 2x^2 = x^4 - 2x^2 \end{cases}$

$$0 = x^4 - 4x^2$$
$$0 = x^2(x^2 - 4)$$
$$0 = x^2(x + 2)(x - 2)$$
$$x = 0, x = -2, x = 2$$
$$y = 0, y = 8, y = 8$$

Answer: $(0, 0), (-2, 8), (2, 8)$

6. $\begin{cases} x = y + 3 \\ x = y^2 + 1 \end{cases}$

$$y + 3 = y^2 + 1$$
$$0 = y^2 - y - 2$$
$$0 = (y - 2)(y + 1) \Rightarrow y = 2, -1$$

$y = 2$: $x = 2 + 3 = 5$

$y = -1$: $x = -1 + 3 = 2$

Answer: $(5, 2), (2, -1)$

7. $\begin{cases} 5x + 6y = 7 \Rightarrow y_1 = \dfrac{1}{6}(7 - 5x) \\ -x - 4y = 0 \Rightarrow y_2 = -\dfrac{x}{4} \end{cases}$

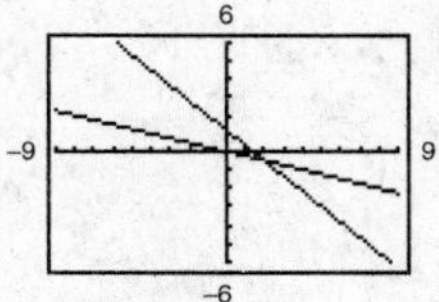

Answer: $\left(2, -\frac{1}{2}\right)$

8. $\begin{cases} 8x - 3y = -3 \Rightarrow y = \frac{1}{3}(8x + 3) = \frac{8}{3}x + 1 \\ 2x + 5y = 28 \Rightarrow y = \frac{1}{5}(28 - 2x) \end{cases}$

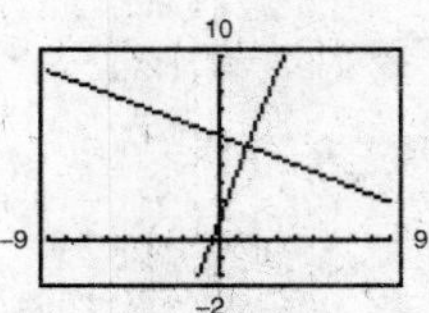

Answer: $(1.5, 5)$

9. $\begin{cases} y^2 - 4x = 0 \Rightarrow y^2 = 4x \Rightarrow y = \pm 2\sqrt{x} \\ x + y = 0 \Rightarrow y = -x \end{cases}$

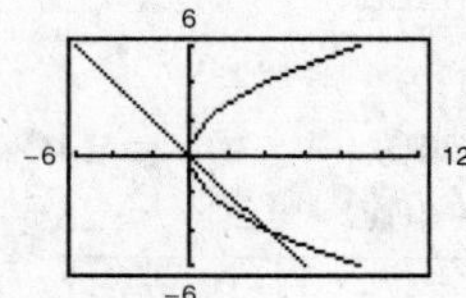

Points of intersection: $(0, 0), (4, -4)$

10. $\begin{cases} y^2 - x = -1 \Rightarrow y^2 = x - 1 \Rightarrow y = \pm\sqrt{x - 1} \\ y + 2x = 5 \Rightarrow y = 5 - 2x \end{cases}$

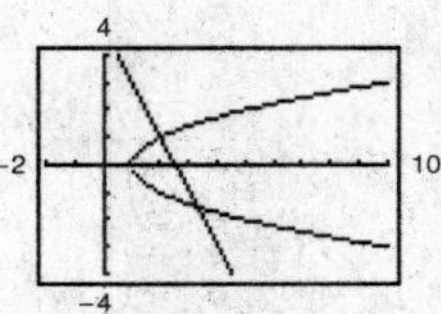

Points of intersection: $(2, 1), (3.25, -1.5)$

11. $\begin{cases} y = 3 - x^2 \\ y = 2x^2 + x + 1 \end{cases}$

Points of intersection:

(0.67, 2.56), (−1, 2)

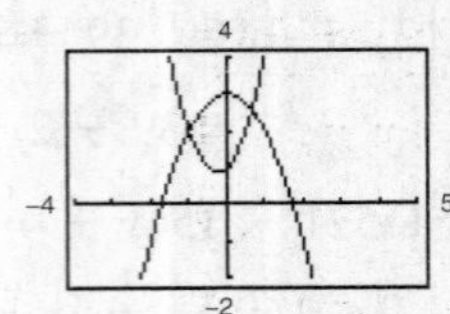

12. $\begin{cases} y = 2x^2 - 4x + 1 \\ y = x^2 - 4x + 3 \end{cases}$

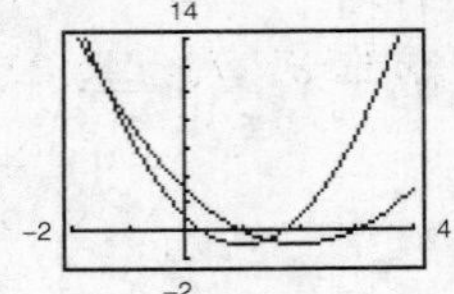

Points of intersection:

$(\sqrt{2}, 5 - 4\sqrt{2}), (-\sqrt{2}, 5 + 4\sqrt{2})$ or

(1.41, −0.66), (−1.41, 10.66)

13. $\begin{cases} y = 2(6 - x) \\ y = 2^{x-2} \end{cases}$

Point of intersection: (4, 4)

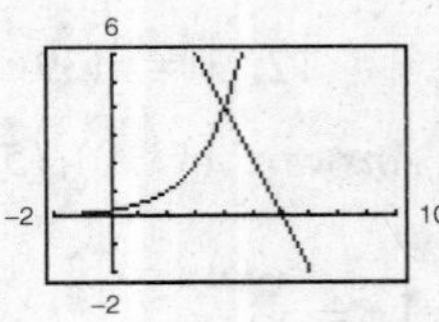

14. $\begin{cases} 3x + y = 16 \\ y = 1 + 3^x \end{cases}$

$y = 16 - 3x$

Point of intersection: (2, 10)

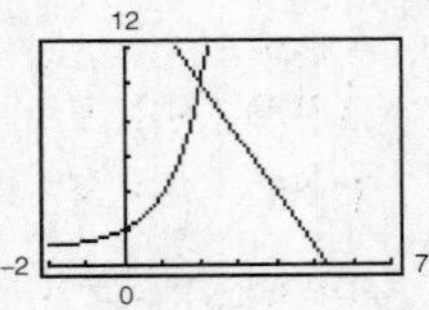

15. $\begin{cases} y = \ln(x + 2) + 1 \\ y = -x \end{cases}$

Point of intersection: (−1, 1)

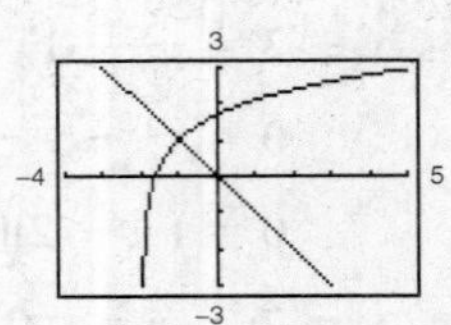

16. $\begin{cases} y = \ln(x - 1) + 3 \\ y = 4 - \frac{1}{2}x \end{cases}$

Point of intersection: (2, 3)

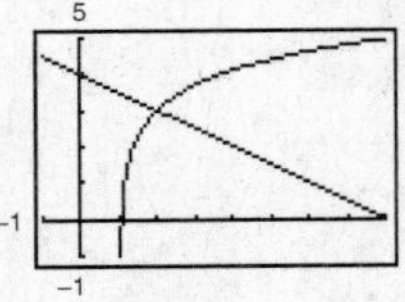

17. Revenue = $4.95x$

Cost = $2.85x + 10{,}000$

Break even when Revenue = Cost

$4.95x = 2.85x + 10{,}000$

$2.10x = 10{,}000$

$x \approx 4762$ units

18. $\begin{cases} y = 22{,}500 + 0.015x \\ y = 20{,}000 + 0.02x \end{cases}$

$22{,}500 + 0.015x = 20{,}000 + 0.02x$

$2500 = 0.005x$

$\$500{,}000 = x$

Answer: More than $500,000

19. $\begin{cases} 2l + 2w = 480 \\ l = 1.50w \end{cases}$

$2(1.50w) + 2w = 480$

$5w = 480$

$w = 96$

$l = 144$

The dimensions are 96×144 meters.

20. $\begin{cases} 2l + 2w = 68 \\ w = \frac{8}{9}l \end{cases}$

$2l + 2\left(\frac{8}{9}l\right) = 68$

$\frac{34l}{9} = 68$

$l = 18$

$w = 16$

The dimensions are 16×18 feet.

21. $\begin{cases} 2x - y = 2 \implies 16x - 8y = 16 \\ 6x + 8y = 39 \implies 6x + 8y = 39 \end{cases}$

$22x = 55$

$x = \frac{55}{22} = \frac{5}{2}$

$y = 3$

Answer: $\left(\frac{5}{2}, 3\right)$

22. $\begin{cases} 40x + 30y = 24 \implies 40x + 30y = 24 \\ 20x - 50y = -14 \implies -40x + 100y = 28 \end{cases}$

$130y = 52$

$y = \frac{2}{5}$

$x = \frac{3}{10}$

Answer: $\left(\frac{3}{10}, \frac{2}{5}\right)$

23. $\begin{cases} 1/5x + 3/10y = 7/50 \Rightarrow 20x + 30y = 14 \Rightarrow \\ 2/5x + 1/2y = 1/5 \Rightarrow 4x + 5y = 2 \Rightarrow \end{cases}$ $\begin{aligned} 20x + 30y &= 14 \\ -20x - 25y &= -10 \\ \hline 5y &= 4 \\ y &= \tfrac{4}{5} \\ x &= -\tfrac{1}{2} \end{aligned}$

Answer: $\left(-\frac{1}{2}, \frac{4}{5}\right)$ or $(-0.5, 0.8)$

24. Interchange the equations: $\begin{cases} -x + \frac{7}{8}y = -\frac{38}{5} & \text{Equation 1} \\ \frac{5}{12}x - \frac{3}{4}y = \frac{25}{4} & \text{Equation 2} \end{cases}$

$\frac{5}{12}$ times Eq. 1 added to Eq. 2 produces: $-\frac{37}{96}y = \frac{37}{12} \Rightarrow y = -8$

Then $-x + \frac{7}{8}(-8) = -\frac{38}{5} \Rightarrow x = \frac{3}{5}$

Answer: $\left(\frac{3}{5}, -8\right)$

25. $\begin{cases} 3x - 2y = 0 \Rightarrow 3x - 2y = 0 \\ 3x + 2(y + 5) = 10 \Rightarrow 3x + 2y = 0 \end{cases}$

$$\begin{aligned} 6x &= 0 \\ x &= 0 \\ y &= 0 \end{aligned}$$

Answer: $(0, 0)$

26. $\begin{cases} 7x + 12y = 63 \Rightarrow -7x - 12y = -63 \\ 2x + 3y = 15 \Rightarrow 8x + 12y = 60 \end{cases}$

$$\begin{aligned} x &= -3 \\ y &= 7 \end{aligned}$$

Answer: $(-3, 7)$

27. $\begin{cases} 1.25x - 2y = 3.5 \Rightarrow 5x - 8y = 14 \\ 5x - 8y = 14 \Rightarrow -5x + 8y = -14 \end{cases}$

$$0 = 0$$

Infinite number of solutions

Let $y = a$, then $5x - 8a = 14 \Rightarrow x = \frac{14}{5} + \frac{8}{5}a$.

Answer: $\left(\frac{14}{5} + \frac{8}{5}a, a\right)$

28. $\begin{cases} 1.5x + 2.5y = 8.5 \Rightarrow 3x + 5y = 17 \\ 6x + 10y = 24 \Rightarrow -3x - 5y = -12 \end{cases}$

$$0 = 5$$

Inconsistent; no solution

29. $\begin{cases} 3x + 2y = 0 \Rightarrow y = -\frac{3}{2}x \\ x - y = 4 \Rightarrow y = x - 4 \end{cases}$

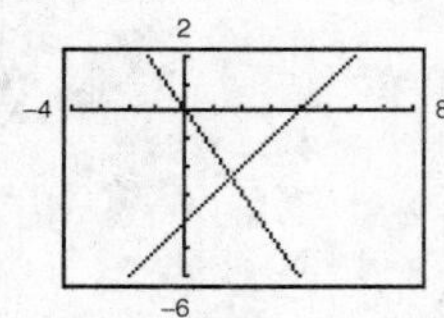

Consistent.

Answer: $(1.6, -2.4)$

30. $\begin{cases} x + y = 6 \Rightarrow y = 6 - x \\ -2y = -12 + 2x \Rightarrow y = 6 - x \end{cases}$

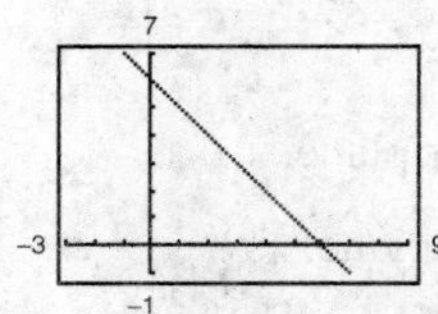

Consistent. Infinite number of solutions of form $(x, 6 - x)$ or $(6 - y, y)$. All points on line $y = 6 - x$.

31. $\begin{cases} \frac{1}{4}x - \frac{1}{5}y = 2 \Rightarrow y = \frac{5}{4}x - 10 \\ -5x + 4y = 8 \Rightarrow y = \frac{1}{4}(8 + 5x) = \frac{5}{4}x + 2 \end{cases}$

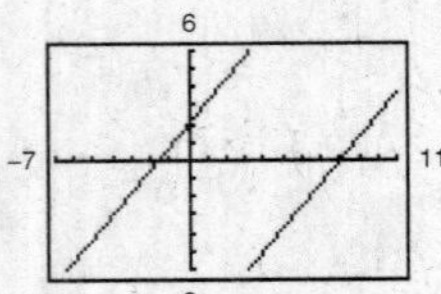

Inconsistent; lines are parallel.

32.

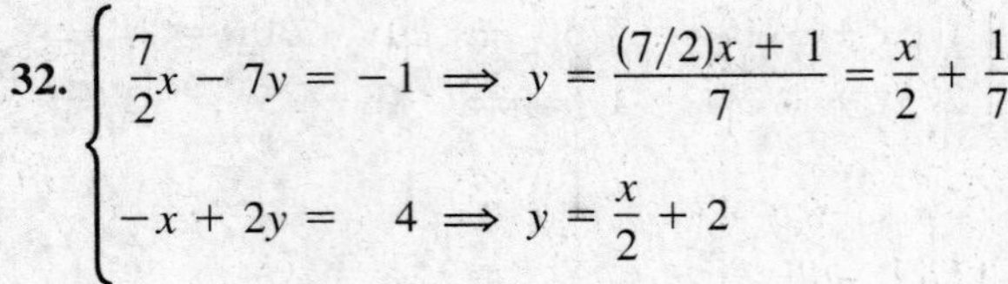

$\begin{cases} \dfrac{7}{2}x - 7y = -1 \Rightarrow y = \dfrac{(7/2)x + 1}{7} = \dfrac{x}{2} + \dfrac{1}{7} \\ -x + 2y = \quad 4 \Rightarrow y = \dfrac{x}{2} + 2 \end{cases}$

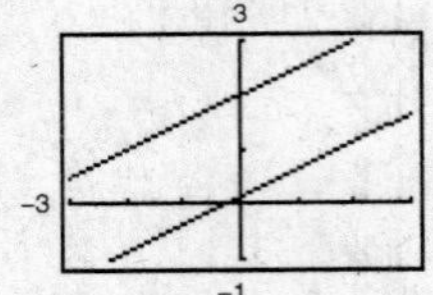

Inconsistent; lines are parallel.

33. $\begin{cases} 2x - \quad 2y = \quad 8 \Rightarrow y = x - 4 \\ 4x - 1.5y = -5.5 \Rightarrow y = \frac{8}{3}x + \frac{11}{3} \end{cases}$

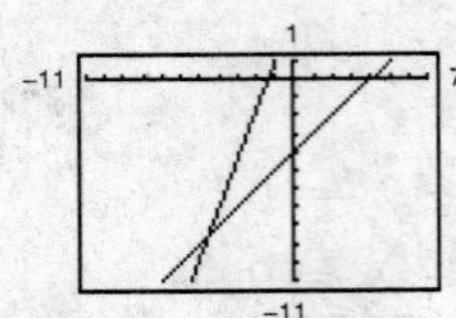

Consistent

Answer: $(-4.6, -8.6)$

34. $\begin{cases} -x + 3.2y = 10.4 \Rightarrow y = \dfrac{1}{3.2}(x + 10.4) \\ -2x - 9.6y = 6.4 \Rightarrow y = \dfrac{-1}{9.6}(2x + 6.4) \end{cases}$

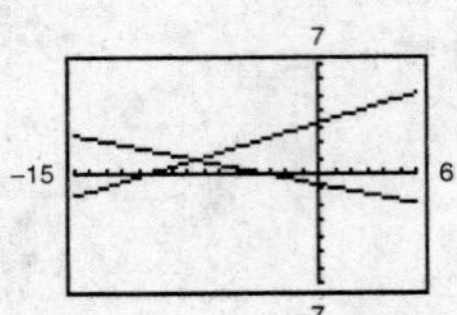

Consistent

Answer: $(-7.52, 0.9)$

35. Demand = Supply

$$37 - 0.0002x = 22 + 0.00001x$$

$$15 = 0.00021x$$

$$x = \frac{500{,}000}{7}, p = \frac{159}{7}$$

Point of equilibrium: $\left(\dfrac{500{,}000}{7}, \dfrac{159}{7}\right)$

36. Supply = Demand

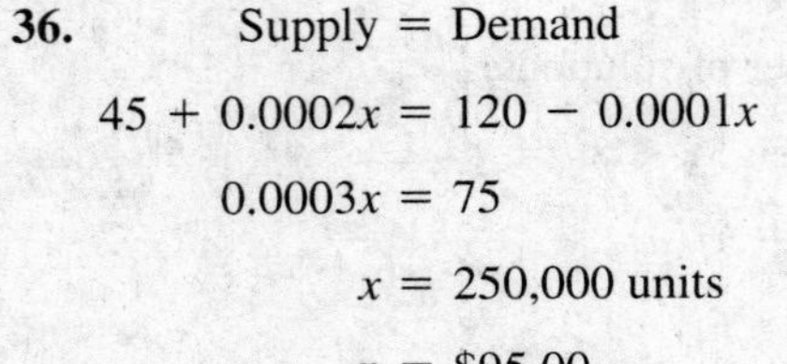

$$45 + 0.0002x = 120 - 0.0001x$$

$$0.0003x = 75$$

$$x = 250{,}000 \text{ units}$$

$$p = \$95.00$$

Points of equilibrium: $(250{,}000, 95)$

37. Let x = speed of the slower plane.

Let y = speed of the faster plane.

Then, distance of first plane + distance of second plane = 275 miles.

(rate of first plane)(time) + (rate of second plane)(time) = 275 miles

$$\begin{cases} x\left(\frac{40}{60}\right) + y\left(\frac{40}{60}\right) = 275 \\ y = x + 25 \end{cases}$$

$$\frac{2}{3}x + \frac{2}{3}(x + 25) = 275$$

$$4x + 50 = 825$$

$$4x = 775$$

$$x = 193.75 \text{ mph}$$

$$y = x + 25 = 218.75 \text{ mph}$$

38. Let x = amount invested in 6.75% bond.

Let y = amount invested in 7.25% bond.

$$\begin{cases} x + y = 46{,}000 \\ 0.0675x + 0.0725y = 3245 \end{cases}$$

Solving the system, $x = 18{,}000$, $y = 28{,}000$.

At most \$18,000 can be invested in the 6.75% bond.

39. $z = -2$

$-y + z = -5 \Rightarrow -y - 2 = -5 \Rightarrow y = 3$

$x - 4y + 3z = -14$

$\Rightarrow x = 4(3) - 3(-2) - 14 = 4$

Answer: $(4, 3, -2)$

40. $z = -3$

$y - 9z = 26 \Rightarrow y = 9(-3) + 26 = -1$

$x - 7y + 8z = -14 \Rightarrow x = -14 + 7(-1) - 8(-3) = 3$

Answer: $(3, -1, -3)$

41. $$\begin{cases} x + 3y - z = 13 \\ 2x - 5z = 23 \\ 4x - y - 2z = 14 \end{cases}$$

$$\begin{cases} x + 3y - z = 13 \\ -6y - 3z = -3 \\ -13y + 2z = -38 \end{cases}$$

$$\begin{cases} x + 3y - z = 13 \\ -6y - 3z = -3 \\ \frac{17}{2}z = -\frac{63}{2} \end{cases}$$

$\frac{17}{2}z = -\frac{63}{2} \Rightarrow z = -\frac{63}{17}$

$-6y - 3\left(-\frac{63}{17}\right) = -3 \Rightarrow y = \frac{40}{17}$

$x + 3\left(\frac{40}{17}\right) - \left(-\frac{63}{17}\right) = 13 \Rightarrow x = \frac{38}{17}$

Answer: $\left(\frac{38}{17}, \frac{40}{17}, -\frac{63}{17}\right)$

42. $$\begin{cases} x + 2y + 6z = 4 \\ 3x - 2y + z = 4 \\ 4x + 2z = 0 \end{cases}$$

$$\begin{cases} x + 2y + 6z = 4 \\ -8y - 17z = -8 \\ -8y - 22z = -16 \end{cases}$$

$$\begin{cases} x + 2y + 6z = 4 \\ -8y - 17z = -8 \\ -5z = -8 \end{cases}$$

$z = \frac{8}{5} = 1.6$

$y = [-8 + 17(1.6)]/(-8) = -2.4$

$x = 4 - 6(1.6) - 2(-2.4) = -0.8$

Answer: $(-0.8, -2.4, 1.6)$

43. $$\begin{cases} x - 2y + z = -6 \\ 2x - 3y = -7 \\ -x + 3y - 3z = 11 \end{cases}$$

$$\begin{cases} x - 2y + z = -6 \\ y - 2z = 5 & -2\text{ Eq.1} + \text{Eq. 2} \\ y - 2z = 5 & \text{Eq. 1} + \text{Eq. 3} \end{cases}$$

$$\begin{cases} x - 2y + z = -6 \\ y - 2z = 5 \\ 0 = 0 & -\text{Eq. 2} + \text{Eq. 3} \end{cases}$$

Let $z = a$, then $y = 2a + 5$.

$x - 2(2a + 5) + a = -6$

$x - 3a - 10 = -6$

$x = 3a + 4$

Answer: $(3a + 4, 2a + 5, a)$ where a is any real number.

44. $$\begin{cases} 2x + 6z = -9 & \text{Equation 1} \\ 3x - 2y + 11z = -16 & \text{Equation 2} \\ 3x - y + 7z = -11 & \text{Equation 3} \end{cases}$$

$$\begin{cases} -x + 2y - 5z = 7 & -\text{Eq. 2} + \text{Eq. 1} \\ 3x - 2y + 11z = -16 \\ 3x - y + 7z = -11 \end{cases}$$

$$\begin{cases} -x + 2y - 5z = 7 \\ 4y - 4z = 5 & 3\text{ Eq. 1} + \text{Eq. 2} \\ 5y - 8z = 10 & 3\text{ Eq. 1} + \text{Eq. 3} \end{cases}$$

$$\begin{cases} -x + 2y - 5z = 7 \\ 4y - 4z = 5 \\ -3y = 0 & -2\text{ Eq. 2} + \text{Eq. 3} \end{cases}$$

$-3y = 0 \Rightarrow y = 0$

$4(0) - 4z = 5 \Rightarrow z = -\frac{5}{4}$

$-x + 2(0) - 5\left(-\frac{5}{4}\right) = 7 \Rightarrow x = -\frac{3}{4}$

Answer: $\left(-\frac{3}{4}, 0, -\frac{5}{4}\right)$

45. $\begin{cases} x - 2y + 3z = -5 \\ 2x + 4y + 5z = 1 \\ x + 2y + z = 0 \end{cases}$

$\begin{cases} x - 2y + 3z = -5 \\ 8y - z = 11 \\ 4y - 2z = 5 \end{cases}$

$\begin{cases} x - 2y + 3z = -5 \\ 4y - 2z = 5 \\ 3z = 1 \end{cases}$

$z = \frac{1}{3}$

$4y = 5 + 2\left(\frac{1}{3}\right) = \frac{17}{3} \Rightarrow y = \frac{17}{12}$

$x = 2\left(\frac{17}{12}\right) - 3\left(\frac{1}{3}\right) - 5 = -\frac{19}{6}$

Answer: $\left(-\frac{19}{6}, \frac{17}{12}, \frac{1}{3}\right)$

46. $\begin{cases} x - 2y + z = 5 \\ 2x + 3y + z = 5 \\ x + y + 2z = 3 \end{cases}$

$\begin{cases} x - 2y + z = 5 \\ 7y - z = -5 \\ 3y + z = -2 \end{cases}$

Adding the second and third equations,

$10y = -7 \Rightarrow y = -\frac{7}{10}$

$z = 7y + 5 = 7\left(-\frac{7}{10}\right) + 5 = \frac{1}{10}$

$x = 2y - z + 5 = 2\left(-\frac{7}{10}\right) - \frac{1}{10} + 5 = \frac{7}{2}$

Answer: $\left(\frac{7}{2}, -\frac{7}{10}, \frac{1}{10}\right)$

47. $\begin{cases} 5x - 12y + 7z = 16 & \text{Equation 1} \\ 3x - 7y + 4z = 9 & \text{Equation 2} \end{cases}$

3 times Eq. 1 and (-5) times Eq. 2:

$\begin{cases} 15x - 36y + 21z = 48 \\ -15x + 35y - 20z = -45 \end{cases}$

Adding, $-y + z = 3 \Rightarrow y = z - 3$.

$5x - 12(z - 3) + 7z = 16$

$5x - 5z + 36 = 16$

$5x = 5z - 20$

$x = z - 4$

Let $z = a$, then $x = a - 4$ and $y = a - 3$.

Answer: $(a - 4, a - 3, a)$ where a is any real number.

48. $\begin{cases} 2x + 5y - 19z = 34 \\ 3x + 8y - 31z = 54 \end{cases}$

$\begin{cases} 6x + 15y - 57z = 102 \\ 6x + 16y - 62z = 108 \end{cases}$

$\begin{cases} 6x + 15y - 57z = 102 \\ y - 5z = 6 \end{cases}$

Let $z = a$

$y = 5a + 6$

$x = [102 + 57a - 15(5a + 6)]/6 = -3a + 2$

Answer: $(2 - 3a, 5a + 6, a)$

49.

$(4, 0, 0), (0, -2, 0), (0, 0, 8), (1, 0, 6)$

50.

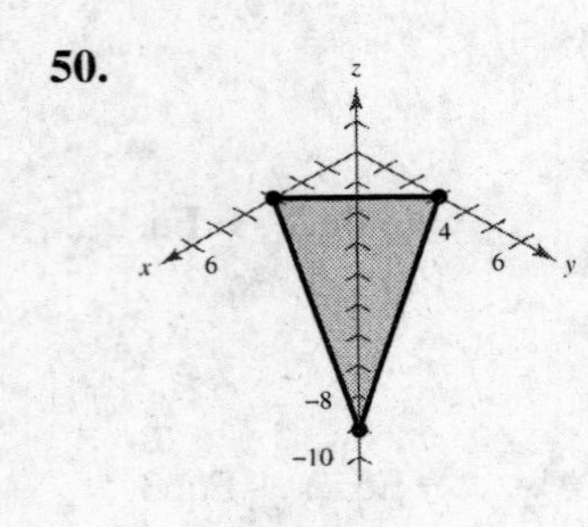

$(0, 0, -9), (0, 3, 0), (3, 0, 0), (1, 1, -3)$

51. $\dfrac{4-x}{x^2+6x+8} = \dfrac{A}{x+2} + \dfrac{B}{x+4}$

$4 - x = A(x+4) + B(x+2)$

$= (A+B)x + (4A+2B)$

$\begin{cases} A + B = -1 \\ 4A + 2B = 4 \end{cases} \Rightarrow A = 3, B = -4$

$\dfrac{4-x}{x^2+6x+8} = \dfrac{3}{x+2} - \dfrac{4}{x+4}$

52. $\dfrac{-x}{x^2+3x+2} = \dfrac{A}{x+1} + \dfrac{B}{x+2}$

$-x = A(x+2) + B(x+1)$

Let $x = -1$: $1 = A$

Let $x = -2$: $2 = -B \Rightarrow B = -2$

$\dfrac{-x}{x^2+3x+2} = \dfrac{1}{x+1} - \dfrac{2}{x+2}$

53. $\dfrac{x^2+2x}{x^3-x^2+x-1} = \dfrac{A}{x-1} + \dfrac{Bx+C}{x^2+1}$

$x^2 + 2x = A(x^2+1) + (Bx+C)(x-1) = (A+B)x^2 + (C-B)x + (A-C)$

$\begin{cases} A + B = 1 \\ -B + C = 2 \\ A - C = 0 \end{cases} \Rightarrow A = \frac{3}{2}, B = -\frac{1}{2}, C = \frac{3}{2}$

$\dfrac{x^2+2x}{x^3-x^2+x-1} = \dfrac{3/2}{x-1} + \dfrac{-(1/2)x+3/2}{x^2+1} = \dfrac{1}{2}\left(\dfrac{3}{x-1} - \dfrac{x-3}{x^2+1}\right)$

54. $\dfrac{3x^3+4x}{x^4+2x^2+1} = \dfrac{3x^3+4x}{(x^2+1)^2} = \dfrac{Ax+B}{x^2+1} + \dfrac{Cx+D}{(x^2+1)^2}$

$3x^3 + 4x = (Ax+B)(x^2+1) + Cx + D$

$\begin{cases} A = 3 \\ B = 0 \\ A + C = 4 \\ B + D = 0 \end{cases}$

$A = 3$

$B = 0$

$C = 1$

$D = 0$

$\dfrac{3x^3+4x}{x^4+2x^2+1} = \dfrac{3x}{x^2+1} + \dfrac{x}{(x^2+1)^2}$

55. $\dfrac{x^2+3x-3}{x^3+2x^2+x+2} = \dfrac{x^2+3x-3}{(x+2)(x^2+1)}$

$= \dfrac{A}{x+2} + \dfrac{Bx+C}{x^2+1}$

$x^2 + 3x - 3 = A(x^2+1) + (Bx+C)(x+2)$

$\begin{cases} A + B = 1 \\ 2B + C = 3 \\ A + 2C = -3 \end{cases}$

$\begin{cases} A + B = 1 \\ 2B + C = 3 \\ -B + 2C = -4 \end{cases}$

$\begin{cases} A + B = 1 \\ B - 2C = 4 \\ 5C = -5 \end{cases}$

$C = -1, B = 2(-1) + 4 = 2, A = 1 - 2 = -1$

$\dfrac{x^2+3x-3}{x^3+2x^2+x+2} = \dfrac{-1}{x+2} + \dfrac{2x-1}{x^2+1}$

56. $\dfrac{2x^2 - x + 7}{x^4 + 8x^2 + 16} = \dfrac{2x^2 - x + 7}{(x^2 + 4)^2} = \dfrac{Ax + B}{x^2 + 4} + \dfrac{Cx + D}{(x^2 + 4)^2}$

$2x^2 - x + 7 = (Ax + B)(x^2 + 4) + Cx + D$

$$\begin{cases} A = 0 \\ B = 2 \\ 4A + C = -1 \\ 4B + D = 7 \end{cases}$$

$A = 0, B = 2, C = -1, D = -1$

$\dfrac{2x^2 - x + 7}{x^4 + 8x^2 + 16} = \dfrac{2}{x^2 + 4} + \dfrac{-x - 1}{(x^2 + 4)^2}$

57. $y = ax^2 + bx + c$

$(-1, -4):\ a - b + c = -4$
$(1, -2):\ a + b + c = -2$
$(2, 5):\ 4a + 2b + c = 5$

Solving the system,
$a = 2, b = 1, c = -5.$

$y = 2x^2 + x - 5$

58. $y = ax^2 + bx + c$

$(-1, 0):\ a - b + c = 0$
$(1, 4):\ a + b + c = 4$
$(2, 3):\ 4a + 2b + c = 3$

Solving the system,
$a = -1, b = 2, c = 3.$

$y = -x^2 + 2x + 3$

59. Let x = gallons of spray X

Let y = gallons of spray Y

Let z = gallons of spray Z

$$\begin{cases} \text{Chemical A: } \frac{1}{5}x + \frac{1}{3}z = 6 \\ \text{Chemical B: } \frac{2}{5}x + \frac{1}{3}z = 8 \\ \text{Cehmical C: } \frac{2}{5}x + y + \frac{1}{3}z = 13 \end{cases}$$

Subtracting Eq. 2 − Eq. 1 gives $\frac{1}{5}x = 2 \Rightarrow x = 10.$

Then $z = 12$ and $y = 5.$

Answer: 10 gallons of spray X
5 gallons of spray Y
12 gallons of spray Z

60. Let x be amount invested at 7%.

Let y be amount invested at 9%.

Let z be amount invested at 11%.

$$\begin{cases} x + y + z = 20{,}000 \\ 0.07x + 0.09y + 0.11z = 1780 \\ x - y = 3000 \\ x - z = 1000 \end{cases}$$

Solving the system,
$x = \$8000, y = \$5000, z = \$7000.$

61. Order 3×1

62. Order 2×4

63. Order 1×1

64. Order 1×5

65. $\left[\begin{array}{cc:c} 3 & -10 & 15 \\ 5 & 4 & 22 \end{array}\right]$

66. $\left[\begin{array}{cc:c} -1 & 1 & 12 \\ 10 & -4 & -90 \end{array}\right]$

67. $\left[\begin{array}{ccc:c} 8 & -7 & 4 & 12 \\ 3 & -5 & 2 & 20 \\ 5 & 3 & -3 & 26 \end{array}\right]$

68. $\left[\begin{array}{ccc:c} 3 & -5 & 1 & 25 \\ -4 & 0 & -2 & -14 \\ 6 & 1 & 0 & 15 \end{array}\right]$

69. $\left[\begin{array}{ccc:c} 5 & 1 & 7 & -9 \\ 4 & 2 & 0 & 10 \\ 9 & 4 & 2 & 3 \end{array}\right]$

$$\begin{cases} 5x + y + 7z = -9 \\ 4x + 2y = 10 \\ 9x + 4y + 2z = 3 \end{cases}$$

70. $\begin{bmatrix} 13 & 16 & 7 & 3 & \vdots & 2 \\ 1 & 21 & 8 & 5 & \vdots & 12 \\ 4 & 10 & -4 & 3 & \vdots & -1 \end{bmatrix}$

$$\begin{cases} 13x + 16y + 7z + 3w = 2 \\ x + 21y + 8z + 5w = 12 \\ 4x + 10y - 4z + 3w = -1 \end{cases}$$

71. $\begin{bmatrix} 0 & 1 & 1 \\ 1 & 2 & 3 \\ 2 & 2 & 2 \end{bmatrix}$

$\begin{matrix} R_1 + R_2 \rightarrow \\ -R_1 + R_2 \rightarrow \\ -2R_1 + R_3 \rightarrow \end{matrix} \begin{bmatrix} 1 & 3 & 4 \\ 0 & -1 & -1 \\ 0 & -4 & -6 \end{bmatrix}$

$\begin{matrix} 3R_2 + R_1 \rightarrow \\ -R_2 \rightarrow \\ -4R_2 + R_3 \rightarrow \end{matrix} \begin{bmatrix} 1 & 0 & 1 \\ 0 & 1 & 1 \\ 0 & 0 & -2 \end{bmatrix}$

72. $\begin{bmatrix} 3 & 5 & 2 \\ 1 & -2 & 4 \\ -2 & 0 & 5 \end{bmatrix} \Rightarrow \begin{bmatrix} 1 & -2 & 4 \\ 0 & 11 & -10 \\ 0 & -4 & 13 \end{bmatrix} \Rightarrow \begin{bmatrix} 1 & -2 & 4 \\ 0 & 1 & -29 \\ 0 & 0 & 1 \end{bmatrix}$

Other answers possible

73. $\begin{bmatrix} 3 & -2 & 1 & 0 \\ 4 & -3 & 0 & 1 \end{bmatrix} \Rightarrow \begin{bmatrix} 1 & 0 & 3 & -2 \\ 0 & 1 & 4 & -3 \end{bmatrix}$

74. $\begin{bmatrix} 1 & 0 & 0 & -6 & -4 & 3 \\ 0 & 1 & 0 & 11 & 6 & -5 \\ 0 & 0 & 1 & -2 & -1 & 1 \end{bmatrix}$

75. $\begin{bmatrix} 1.5 & 3.6 & 4.2 \\ 0.2 & 1.4 & 1.8 \\ 2.0 & 4.4 & 6.4 \end{bmatrix} \Rightarrow \begin{bmatrix} 1 & 0 & 0 \\ 0 & 1 & 0 \\ 0 & 0 & 1 \end{bmatrix}$

76. $\begin{bmatrix} 1 & 0 & 0 \\ 0 & 1 & 0 \\ 0 & 0 & 1 \end{bmatrix}$

77. $\begin{bmatrix} 5 & 4 & \vdots & 2 \\ -1 & 1 & \vdots & -22 \end{bmatrix}$

$\begin{matrix} 4R_2 + R_1 \rightarrow \\ R_1 + R_2 \rightarrow \end{matrix} \begin{bmatrix} 1 & 8 & \vdots & -86 \\ 0 & 9 & \vdots & -108 \end{bmatrix}$

$9y = -108$

$y = -12$

$x = -8(-12) - 86 = 10$

Answer: $(10, -12)$

78. $\begin{bmatrix} 2 & -5 & \vdots & 2 \\ 3 & -7 & \vdots & 1 \end{bmatrix}$

$R_2 - R_1 \rightarrow \begin{bmatrix} 1 & -2 & \vdots & -1 \\ 3 & -7 & \vdots & 1 \end{bmatrix}$

$-3R_1 + R_2 \rightarrow \begin{bmatrix} 1 & -2 & \vdots & -1 \\ 0 & -1 & \vdots & 4 \end{bmatrix}$

$y = -4$

$x = 2(-4) - 1 = -9$

Answer: $(-9, -4)$

79. $\begin{bmatrix} 2 & 1 & \vdots & 0.3 \\ 3 & -1 & \vdots & -1.3 \end{bmatrix}$

$-R_1 + R_2 \rightarrow \begin{bmatrix} 2 & 1 & \vdots & 0.3 \\ 1 & -2 & \vdots & -1.6 \end{bmatrix}$

$\begin{bmatrix} 1 & -2 & \vdots & -1.6 \\ 2 & 1 & \vdots & 0.3 \end{bmatrix}$

$-2R_1 + R_2 \rightarrow \begin{bmatrix} 1 & -2 & \vdots & -1.6 \\ 0 & 5 & \vdots & 3.5 \end{bmatrix}$

$5y = 3.5 \Rightarrow y = 0.7$

$x = 2(0.7) - 1.6 = -0.2$

$x = -0.2,\ y = 0.7$

Answer: $(-0.2, 0.7)$

80. $\begin{bmatrix} 0.2 & -0.1 & \vdots & 0.07 \\ 0.4 & -0.5 & \vdots & -0.01 \end{bmatrix}$

$\begin{matrix} 5R_1 \rightarrow \\ -2R_1 + R_2 \rightarrow \end{matrix} \begin{bmatrix} 1 & -0.5 & \vdots & 0.35 \\ 0 & -0.3 & \vdots & -0.15 \end{bmatrix}$

$y = 0.5$

$x = 0.5(0.5) + 0.35 = 0.6$

Answer: $(0.6, 0.5)$

81. $\begin{bmatrix} 2 & 3 & 3 & \vdots & 3 \\ 6 & 6 & 12 & \vdots & 13 \\ 12 & 9 & -1 & \vdots & 2 \end{bmatrix}$

$\begin{matrix} \\ -3R_1 + R_2 \rightarrow \\ -6R_1 + R_3 \rightarrow \end{matrix}\begin{bmatrix} 2 & 3 & 3 & \vdots & 3 \\ 0 & -3 & 3 & \vdots & 4 \\ 0 & -9 & -19 & \vdots & -16 \end{bmatrix}$

$\begin{matrix} R_2 + R_1 \rightarrow \\ \\ -3R_2 + R_3 \rightarrow \end{matrix}\begin{bmatrix} 2 & 0 & 6 & \vdots & 7 \\ 0 & -3 & 3 & \vdots & 4 \\ 0 & 0 & -28 & \vdots & -28 \end{bmatrix}$

$\begin{matrix} \frac{1}{2}R_1 \rightarrow \\ -\frac{1}{3}R_2 \rightarrow \\ -\frac{1}{28}R_3 \rightarrow \end{matrix}\begin{bmatrix} 1 & 0 & 3 & \vdots & \frac{7}{2} \\ 0 & 1 & -1 & \vdots & -\frac{4}{3} \\ 0 & 0 & 1 & \vdots & 1 \end{bmatrix}$

$z = 1$

$y - 1 = -\frac{4}{3} \implies y = -\frac{1}{3}$

$x + 3(1) = \frac{7}{2} \implies x = \frac{1}{2}$

Answer: $\left(\frac{1}{2}, -\frac{1}{3}, 1\right)$

82. $\begin{bmatrix} 1 & 2 & 6 & \vdots & 1 \\ 2 & 5 & 15 & \vdots & 4 \\ 3 & 1 & 3 & \vdots & -6 \end{bmatrix}$

$\begin{matrix} \\ -2R_1 + R_2 \rightarrow \\ -3R_1 + R_3 \rightarrow \end{matrix}\begin{bmatrix} 1 & 2 & 6 & \vdots & 1 \\ 0 & 1 & 3 & \vdots & 2 \\ 0 & -5 & -15 & \vdots & -9 \end{bmatrix}$

$\begin{matrix} -2R_2 + R_1 \rightarrow \\ \\ 5R_2 + R_3 \rightarrow \end{matrix}\begin{bmatrix} 1 & 0 & 0 & \vdots & -3 \\ 0 & 1 & 3 & \vdots & 2 \\ 0 & 0 & 0 & \vdots & 1 \end{bmatrix}$

$0 = 1$

Inconsistent, no solution

83. $\begin{cases} x + 2y - z = 1 \\ \quad\;\; y + z = 0 \end{cases}$

$\begin{bmatrix} 1 & 2 & -1 & \vdots & 1 \\ 0 & 1 & 1 & \vdots & 0 \end{bmatrix} \implies \begin{bmatrix} 1 & 0 & -3 & \vdots & 1 \\ 0 & 1 & 1 & \vdots & 0 \end{bmatrix}$

$y = -z$

$x = 1 + 3z$

Answer: $(1 + 3a, -a, a)$, a is a real number.

84. $\begin{cases} x - y + 4z - w = 4 \\ x + 3y - 2z + w = -4 \\ \quad\; y - z + w = -3 \\ 2x \quad + z + w = 0 \end{cases}$

$\begin{bmatrix} 1 & -1 & 4 & -1 & \vdots & 4 \\ 1 & 3 & -2 & 1 & \vdots & -4 \\ 0 & 1 & -1 & 1 & \vdots & -3 \\ 2 & 0 & 1 & 1 & \vdots & 0 \end{bmatrix} \implies \begin{bmatrix} 1 & 0 & 0 & 0 & \vdots & 1 \\ 0 & 1 & 0 & 0 & \vdots & -1 \\ 0 & 0 & 1 & 0 & \vdots & 0 \\ 0 & 0 & 0 & 1 & \vdots & -2 \end{bmatrix}$

Answer: $(1, -1, 0, -2)$

85. $\begin{bmatrix} -1 & 1 & 2 & \vdots & 1 \\ 2 & 3 & 1 & \vdots & -2 \\ 5 & 4 & 2 & \vdots & 4 \end{bmatrix}$

$\begin{matrix} -R_1 \rightarrow \\ 2R_1 + R_2 \rightarrow \\ 5R_1 + R_3 \rightarrow \end{matrix} \begin{bmatrix} 1 & -1 & -2 & \vdots & -1 \\ 0 & 5 & 5 & \vdots & 0 \\ 0 & 9 & 12 & \vdots & 9 \end{bmatrix}$

$\begin{matrix} \\ \frac{1}{5}R_2 \rightarrow \\ \\ \end{matrix} \begin{bmatrix} 1 & -1 & -2 & \vdots & -1 \\ 0 & 1 & 1 & \vdots & 0 \\ 0 & 9 & 12 & \vdots & 9 \end{bmatrix}$

$\begin{matrix} R_2 + R_1 \rightarrow \\ \\ -9R_2 + R_3 \rightarrow \end{matrix} \begin{bmatrix} 1 & 0 & -1 & \vdots & -1 \\ 0 & 1 & 1 & \vdots & 0 \\ 0 & 0 & 3 & \vdots & 9 \end{bmatrix}$

$\begin{matrix} \\ \\ \frac{1}{3}R_3 \rightarrow \end{matrix} \begin{bmatrix} 1 & 0 & -1 & \vdots & -1 \\ 0 & 1 & 1 & \vdots & 0 \\ 0 & 0 & 1 & \vdots & 3 \end{bmatrix}$

$\begin{matrix} R_3 + R_1 \rightarrow \\ -R_3 + R_2 \rightarrow \\ \\ \end{matrix} \begin{bmatrix} 1 & 0 & 0 & \vdots & 2 \\ 0 & 1 & 0 & \vdots & -3 \\ 0 & 0 & 1 & \vdots & 3 \end{bmatrix}$

$x = 2, y = -3, z = 3$

Answer: $(2, -3, 3)$

86. $\begin{bmatrix} 4 & 4 & 4 & \vdots & 5 \\ 4 & -2 & -8 & \vdots & 1 \\ 5 & 3 & 8 & \vdots & 6 \end{bmatrix}$

$\begin{matrix} R_3 - R_1 \rightarrow \\ -4R_1 + R_2 \rightarrow \\ -5R_1 + R_3 \rightarrow \end{matrix} \begin{bmatrix} 1 & -1 & 4 & \vdots & 1 \\ 0 & 2 & -24 & \vdots & -3 \\ 0 & 8 & -12 & \vdots & 1 \end{bmatrix}$

$\begin{matrix} R_2 + R_1 \rightarrow \\ \frac{1}{2}R_2 \rightarrow \\ -8R_2 + R_3 \rightarrow \end{matrix} \begin{bmatrix} 1 & 0 & -8 & \vdots & -\frac{1}{2} \\ 0 & 1 & -12 & \vdots & -\frac{3}{2} \\ 0 & 0 & 84 & \vdots & 13 \end{bmatrix}$

$\begin{matrix} 8R_3 + R_1 \rightarrow \\ 12R_3 + R_2 \rightarrow \\ \frac{1}{84}R_3 \rightarrow \end{matrix} \begin{bmatrix} 1 & 0 & 0 & \vdots & \frac{31}{42} \\ 0 & 1 & 0 & \vdots & \frac{5}{14} \\ 0 & 0 & 1 & \vdots & \frac{13}{84} \end{bmatrix}$

$x = \frac{31}{42}, y = \frac{5}{14}, z = \frac{13}{84}$

Answer: $\left(\frac{31}{42}, \frac{5}{14}, \frac{13}{84}\right)$

87. $\begin{cases} x + y + 2z = 4 \\ x - y + 4z = 1 \\ 2x - y + 2z = 1 \end{cases}$ $\begin{bmatrix} 1 & 1 & 2 & \vdots & 4 \\ 1 & -1 & 4 & \vdots & 1 \\ 2 & -1 & 2 & \vdots & 1 \end{bmatrix} \Rightarrow \begin{bmatrix} 1 & 0 & 0 & \vdots & 1 \\ 0 & 1 & 0 & \vdots & 2 \\ 0 & 0 & 1 & \vdots & \frac{1}{2} \end{bmatrix}$

Answer: $\left(1, 2, \frac{1}{2}\right)$

88. $\begin{cases} x + y + 4z = 0 \\ 2x + y + 2z = 0 \\ -x + y - 2z = -1 \end{cases}$

$\begin{bmatrix} 1 & 1 & 4 & \vdots & 0 \\ 2 & 1 & 2 & \vdots & 0 \\ -1 & 1 & -2 & \vdots & -1 \end{bmatrix} \Rightarrow \begin{bmatrix} 1 & 0 & 0 & \vdots & \frac{1}{5} \\ 0 & 1 & 0 & \vdots & -\frac{3}{5} \\ 0 & 0 & 1 & \vdots & \frac{1}{10} \end{bmatrix}$

Answer: $\left(\frac{1}{5}, -\frac{3}{5}, \frac{1}{10}\right)$

89. $\begin{bmatrix} 1 & 2 & -1 & \vdots & 7 \\ 0 & -1 & -1 & \vdots & 4 \\ 4 & 0 & -1 & \vdots & 16 \end{bmatrix}$ reduces to $\begin{bmatrix} 1 & 0 & 0 & \vdots & 3 \\ 0 & 1 & 0 & \vdots & 0 \\ 0 & 0 & 1 & \vdots & -4 \end{bmatrix}$

Answer: $(3, 0, -4)$

90. $\begin{bmatrix} 3 & 0 & 6 & \vdots & 0 \\ -2 & 1 & 0 & \vdots & 5 \\ 0 & 1 & 2 & \vdots & 3 \end{bmatrix} \Rightarrow \begin{bmatrix} 1 & 0 & 0 & \vdots & -2 \\ 0 & 1 & 0 & \vdots & 1 \\ 0 & 0 & 1 & \vdots & 1 \end{bmatrix}$

$(x, y, z) = (-2, 1, 1)$

91. $\begin{bmatrix} 3 & -1 & 5 & -2 & \vdots & -44 \\ 1 & 6 & 4 & -1 & \vdots & 1 \\ 5 & -1 & 1 & 3 & \vdots & -15 \\ 0 & 4 & -1 & -8 & \vdots & 58 \end{bmatrix}$ reduces to $\begin{bmatrix} 1 & 0 & 0 & 0 & \vdots & 2 \\ 0 & 1 & 0 & 0 & \vdots & 6 \\ 0 & 0 & 1 & 0 & \vdots & -10 \\ 0 & 0 & 0 & 1 & \vdots & -3 \end{bmatrix}$

Answer: $(2, 6, -10, -3)$

92. $\begin{bmatrix} 4 & 12 & 2 & \vdots & 20 \\ 1 & 6 & 4 & \vdots & 12 \\ 1 & 6 & 1 & \vdots & 8 \\ -2 & -10 & -2 & \vdots & -10 \end{bmatrix} \Rightarrow \begin{bmatrix} 1 & 0 & 0 & \vdots & 0 \\ 0 & 1 & 0 & \vdots & 0 \\ 0 & 0 & 1 & \vdots & 0 \\ 0 & 0 & 0 & \vdots & 1 \end{bmatrix}$

Inconsistent. No solution $(0 = 1)$

93. $x = 12$

$y = -7$

94. $x = 8$

$y = 0$

95. $x + 3 = 5x - 1 \Rightarrow x = 1$

$-4y = -44 \Rightarrow y = 11$

$y + 5 = 16 \Rightarrow y = 11$

$6x = 6 \Rightarrow x = 1$

Answer: $x = 1, y = 11$

96. $2 = x - 10 \Rightarrow x = 12$

$-4 = 2y \Rightarrow y = -2$

$6 = \frac{1}{2}x \Rightarrow x = 12$

Answer: $x = 12, y = -2$

97. (a) $A + B = \begin{bmatrix} 7 & 3 \\ -1 & 5 \end{bmatrix} + \begin{bmatrix} 10 & -20 \\ 14 & -3 \end{bmatrix} = \begin{bmatrix} 17 & -17 \\ 13 & 2 \end{bmatrix}$

(b) $A - B = \begin{bmatrix} -3 & 23 \\ -15 & 8 \end{bmatrix}$

(c) $4A = \begin{bmatrix} 28 & 12 \\ -4 & 20 \end{bmatrix}$

(d) $A + 3B = \begin{bmatrix} 7 & 3 \\ -1 & 5 \end{bmatrix} + \begin{bmatrix} 30 & -60 \\ 42 & -9 \end{bmatrix} = \begin{bmatrix} 37 & -57 \\ 41 & -4 \end{bmatrix}$

98. (a) $A + B$ not possible

(b) $A - B$ not possible

(c) $4A = \begin{bmatrix} -44 & 64 & 76 \\ -28 & -8 & 4 \end{bmatrix}$

(d) $A + 3B$ not possible

99. (a) $A + B = \begin{bmatrix} 6 & 0 & 7 \\ 5 & -1 & 2 \\ 3 & 2 & 3 \end{bmatrix} + \begin{bmatrix} 0 & 5 & 1 \\ -4 & 8 & 6 \\ 2 & -1 & 1 \end{bmatrix} = \begin{bmatrix} 6 & 5 & 8 \\ 1 & 7 & 8 \\ 5 & 1 & 4 \end{bmatrix}$

(b) $A - B = \begin{bmatrix} 6 & -5 & 6 \\ 9 & -9 & -4 \\ 1 & 3 & 2 \end{bmatrix}$

(c) $4A = \begin{bmatrix} 24 & 0 & 28 \\ 20 & -4 & 8 \\ 12 & 8 & 12 \end{bmatrix}$

(d) $A + 3B = \begin{bmatrix} 6 & 0 & 7 \\ 5 & -1 & 2 \\ 3 & 2 & 3 \end{bmatrix} + \begin{bmatrix} 0 & 15 & 3 \\ -12 & 24 & 18 \\ 6 & -3 & 3 \end{bmatrix} = \begin{bmatrix} 6 & 15 & 10 \\ -7 & 23 & 20 \\ 9 & -1 & 6 \end{bmatrix}$

100. (a) $A + B = \begin{bmatrix} -1 & 2 & 11 \\ 1 & 5 & 2 \end{bmatrix}$ (b) $A - B = \begin{bmatrix} 5 & -8 & 1 \\ -1 & 3 & 0 \end{bmatrix}$

(c) $4A = \begin{bmatrix} 8 & -12 & 24 \\ 0 & 16 & 4 \end{bmatrix}$ (d) $A + 3B = \begin{bmatrix} -7 & 12 & 21 \\ 3 & 7 & 4 \end{bmatrix}$

101. $\begin{bmatrix} 2 & 1 & 0 \\ 0 & 5 & -4 \end{bmatrix} - 3\begin{bmatrix} 5 & 3 & -6 \\ 0 & -2 & 5 \end{bmatrix} = \begin{bmatrix} 2 & 1 & 0 \\ 0 & 5 & -4 \end{bmatrix} - \begin{bmatrix} 15 & 9 & -18 \\ 0 & -6 & 15 \end{bmatrix}$

$= \begin{bmatrix} -13 & -8 & 18 \\ 0 & 11 & -19 \end{bmatrix}$

102. $-2\begin{bmatrix} 1 & 2 \\ 5 & -4 \\ 6 & 0 \end{bmatrix} + 8\begin{bmatrix} 7 & 1 \\ 1 & 2 \\ 1 & 4 \end{bmatrix} = \begin{bmatrix} -2 & -4 \\ -10 & 8 \\ -12 & 0 \end{bmatrix} + \begin{bmatrix} 56 & 8 \\ 8 & 16 \\ 8 & 32 \end{bmatrix} = \begin{bmatrix} 54 & 4 \\ -2 & 24 \\ -4 & 32 \end{bmatrix}$

103. $-\begin{bmatrix} 8 & -1 \\ -2 & 4 \end{bmatrix} - 5\begin{bmatrix} -2 & 0 \\ 3 & -1 \end{bmatrix} + \begin{bmatrix} 7 & -8 \\ 4 & 3 \end{bmatrix} = \begin{bmatrix} -8 & 1 \\ 2 & -4 \end{bmatrix} - \begin{bmatrix} -10 & 0 \\ 15 & -5 \end{bmatrix} + \begin{bmatrix} 7 & -8 \\ 4 & 3 \end{bmatrix}$

$= \begin{bmatrix} 9 & -7 \\ -9 & 4 \end{bmatrix}$

104. $6\left(\begin{bmatrix} -4 & -1 & -3 & 4 \\ 2 & -5 & 7 & -10 \end{bmatrix} + \begin{bmatrix} -1 & 1 & 13 & -7 \\ 14 & -3 & 8 & -1 \end{bmatrix}\right) = 6\begin{bmatrix} -5 & 0 & 10 & -3 \\ 16 & -8 & 15 & -11 \end{bmatrix}$

$= \begin{bmatrix} -30 & 0 & 60 & -18 \\ 96 & -48 & 90 & -66 \end{bmatrix}$

105. $\begin{bmatrix} 32 & -\frac{17}{2} & -\frac{3}{2} \\ 6 & 46 & 33 \end{bmatrix}$

106. $\begin{bmatrix} 4.1 & -10.2 \\ -10.1 & 60.9 \\ -49 & 5.1 \end{bmatrix}$

107. $X = 3A - 2B = 3\begin{bmatrix} -4 & 0 \\ 1 & -5 \\ -3 & 2 \end{bmatrix} - 2\begin{bmatrix} 1 & 2 \\ -2 & 1 \\ 4 & 4 \end{bmatrix} = \begin{bmatrix} -14 & -4 \\ 7 & -17 \\ -17 & -2 \end{bmatrix}$

108. $X = \frac{1}{6}(4A + 3B) = \frac{1}{6}\left(4\begin{bmatrix} -4 & 0 \\ 1 & -5 \\ -3 & 2 \end{bmatrix} + 3\begin{bmatrix} 1 & 2 \\ -2 & 1 \\ 4 & 4 \end{bmatrix}\right) = \frac{1}{6}\begin{bmatrix} -13 & 6 \\ -2 & -17 \\ 0 & 20 \end{bmatrix}$

109. $X = \frac{1}{3}[B - 2A] = \frac{1}{3}\left(\begin{bmatrix} 1 & 2 \\ -2 & 1 \\ 4 & 4 \end{bmatrix} - 2\begin{bmatrix} -4 & 0 \\ 1 & -5 \\ -3 & 2 \end{bmatrix}\right) = \frac{1}{3}\begin{bmatrix} 9 & 2 \\ -4 & 11 \\ 10 & 0 \end{bmatrix}$

110. $X = \frac{1}{3}(2A - 5B) = \frac{1}{3}\left(2\begin{bmatrix} -4 & 0 \\ 1 & -5 \\ -3 & 2 \end{bmatrix} - 5\begin{bmatrix} 1 & 2 \\ -2 & 1 \\ 4 & 4 \end{bmatrix}\right) = \frac{1}{3}\begin{bmatrix} -13 & -10 \\ 12 & -15 \\ -26 & -16 \end{bmatrix}$

111. $\begin{bmatrix} 1 & 2 \\ 5 & -4 \\ 6 & 0 \end{bmatrix}\begin{bmatrix} 6 & -2 & 8 \\ 4 & 0 & 0 \end{bmatrix} = \begin{bmatrix} 1(6)+2(4) & 1(-2)+2(0) & 1(8)+2(0) \\ 5(6)+(-4)(4) & 5(-2)+(-4)(0) & 5(8)+(-4)(0) \\ 6(6)+(0)(4) & 6(-2)+(0)(0) & 6(8)+(0)(0) \end{bmatrix} = \begin{bmatrix} 14 & -2 & 8 \\ 14 & -10 & 40 \\ 36 & -12 & 48 \end{bmatrix}$

112. $\begin{bmatrix} 1 & 5 & 6 \\ 2 & -4 & 0 \end{bmatrix}\begin{bmatrix} 7 & 5 & 2 \\ 0 & 1 & 0 \end{bmatrix}$ is undefined.

113. $AB = \begin{bmatrix} 3 & -2 & 0 \\ 1 & 4 & 9 \end{bmatrix}\begin{bmatrix} 7 & 0 \\ 5 & 3 \\ -1 & 3 \end{bmatrix} = \begin{bmatrix} 11 & -6 \\ 18 & 39 \end{bmatrix}$

114. $AB = \begin{bmatrix} 1 & 3 & 2 \\ 0 & 2 & -4 \\ 1 & -1 & 3 \end{bmatrix}\begin{bmatrix} 4 & -3 & 2 \\ 0 & 3 & -1 \\ 0 & 6 & 2 \end{bmatrix} = \begin{bmatrix} 4 & 18 & 3 \\ 0 & -18 & -10 \\ 4 & 12 & 9 \end{bmatrix}$

115. $\begin{bmatrix} 4 & 1 \\ 11 & -7 \\ 12 & 3 \end{bmatrix}\begin{bmatrix} 3 & -5 & 6 \\ 2 & -2 & -2 \end{bmatrix} = \begin{bmatrix} 14 & -22 & 22 \\ 19 & -41 & 80 \\ 42 & -66 & 66 \end{bmatrix}$

116. $\begin{bmatrix} -2 & 3 & 10 \\ 4 & -2 & 2 \end{bmatrix}\begin{bmatrix} 1 & 1 \\ -5 & 2 \\ 3 & 2 \end{bmatrix} = \begin{bmatrix} 13 & 24 \\ 20 & 4 \end{bmatrix}$

117. $\begin{bmatrix} 2 & 1 \\ 6 & 0 \end{bmatrix}\left(\begin{bmatrix} 4 & 2 \\ -3 & 1 \end{bmatrix} + \begin{bmatrix} -2 & 4 \\ 0 & 4 \end{bmatrix}\right) = \begin{bmatrix} 2 & 1 \\ 6 & 0 \end{bmatrix}\begin{bmatrix} 2 & 6 \\ -3 & 5 \end{bmatrix}$

$$= \begin{bmatrix} 2(2)+1(-3) & 2(6)+1(5) \\ 6(2)+0 & 6(6)+0 \end{bmatrix}$$

$$= \begin{bmatrix} 1 & 17 \\ 12 & 36 \end{bmatrix}$$

118. $\begin{bmatrix} 1 & -1 \\ 4 & 2 \end{bmatrix}\left(\begin{bmatrix} 0 & 3 \\ 1 & 2 \end{bmatrix}\begin{bmatrix} 1 & 0 \\ 5 & -3 \end{bmatrix}\right) = \begin{bmatrix} 1 & -1 \\ 4 & 2 \end{bmatrix}\begin{bmatrix} 15 & -9 \\ 11 & -6 \end{bmatrix} = \begin{bmatrix} 4 & -3 \\ 82 & -48 \end{bmatrix}$

119. (a) $AB = \begin{bmatrix} 40 & 64 & 52 \\ 60 & 82 & 76 \\ 76 & 96 & 84 \end{bmatrix}\begin{bmatrix} 2.65 & 0.25 \\ 2.81 & 0.30 \\ 2.93 & 0.35 \end{bmatrix}$

$$= \begin{bmatrix} 438.2 & 47.4 \\ 612.1 & 66.2 \\ 717.28 & 77.2 \end{bmatrix}$$

This is the sales and profit for milk on Friday, Saturday and Sunday.

(b) Profit $= 47.4 + 66.2 + 77.2 = \$190.80$

120. (a) $A = \begin{bmatrix} 2 & \frac{1}{2} & 3 \end{bmatrix}$

(b) $A = \begin{bmatrix} 2 & \frac{1}{2} & 3 \end{bmatrix}\begin{bmatrix} 109 & 136 \\ 127 & 159 \\ 64 & 79 \end{bmatrix} = \begin{bmatrix} 473.5 & 588.5 \end{bmatrix}$

(c) This gives the total number of calories burned by a 120 pound person and a 150 pound person who perform the given exercises for the given amount of time.

121. $AB = \begin{bmatrix} -4 & -1 \\ 7 & 2 \end{bmatrix}\begin{bmatrix} -2 & -1 \\ 7 & 4 \end{bmatrix} = \begin{bmatrix} 1 & 0 \\ 0 & 1 \end{bmatrix}$; $BA = I_2$

122. $AB = \begin{bmatrix} 1 & 1 & 0 \\ 1 & 0 & 1 \\ 6 & 2 & 3 \end{bmatrix}\begin{bmatrix} -2 & -3 & 1 \\ 3 & 3 & -1 \\ 2 & 4 & -1 \end{bmatrix} = \begin{bmatrix} 1 & 0 & 0 \\ 0 & 1 & 0 \\ 0 & 0 & 1 \end{bmatrix}$; $BA = I_3$

123. $\left[\begin{array}{cc:cc} -6 & 5 & 1 & 0 \\ -5 & 4 & 0 & 1 \end{array}\right]$ row reduces to $\left[\begin{array}{cc:cc} 1 & 0 & 4 & -5 \\ 0 & 1 & 5 & -6 \end{array}\right]$

$\begin{bmatrix} -6 & 5 \\ -5 & 4 \end{bmatrix}^{-1} = \begin{bmatrix} 4 & -5 \\ 5 & -6 \end{bmatrix}$

124. $\begin{bmatrix} -3 & -5 & \vdots & 1 & 0 \\ 2 & 3 & \vdots & 0 & 1 \end{bmatrix}$ reduces to $\begin{bmatrix} 1 & 0 & \vdots & 3 & 5 \\ 0 & 1 & \vdots & -2 & -3 \end{bmatrix}$

$\begin{bmatrix} -3 & -5 \\ 2 & 3 \end{bmatrix}^{-1} = \begin{bmatrix} 3 & 5 \\ -2 & -3 \end{bmatrix}$

125. $\begin{bmatrix} -1 & -2 & -2 & \vdots & 1 & 0 & 0 \\ 3 & 7 & 9 & \vdots & 0 & 1 & 0 \\ 1 & 4 & 7 & \vdots & 0 & 0 & 1 \end{bmatrix}$ row reduces to $\begin{bmatrix} 1 & 0 & 0 & \vdots & 13 & 6 & -4 \\ 0 & 1 & 0 & \vdots & -12 & -5 & 3 \\ 0 & 0 & 1 & \vdots & 5 & 2 & -1 \end{bmatrix}$

$\begin{bmatrix} -1 & -2 & -2 \\ 3 & 7 & 9 \\ 1 & 4 & 7 \end{bmatrix}^{-1} = \begin{bmatrix} 13 & 6 & -4 \\ -12 & -5 & 3 \\ 5 & 2 & -1 \end{bmatrix}$

126. $\begin{bmatrix} 0 & -2 & 1 & \vdots & 1 & 0 & 0 \\ -5 & -2 & -3 & \vdots & 0 & 1 & 0 \\ 7 & 3 & 4 & \vdots & 0 & 0 & 1 \end{bmatrix}$ reduces to $\begin{bmatrix} 1 & 0 & 0 & \vdots & 1 & 11 & 8 \\ 0 & 1 & 0 & \vdots & -1 & -7 & -5 \\ 0 & 0 & 1 & \vdots & -1 & -14 & -10 \end{bmatrix}$

$\begin{bmatrix} 0 & -2 & 1 \\ -5 & -2 & -3 \\ 7 & 3 & 4 \end{bmatrix}^{-1} = \begin{bmatrix} 1 & 11 & 8 \\ -1 & -7 & -5 \\ -1 & -14 & -10 \end{bmatrix}$

127. $\begin{bmatrix} 2 & 6 \\ 3 & -6 \end{bmatrix}^{-1} = \begin{bmatrix} \frac{1}{5} & \frac{1}{5} \\ \frac{1}{10} & -\frac{1}{15} \end{bmatrix}$

128. $\begin{bmatrix} 3 & -10 \\ 4 & 2 \end{bmatrix}^{-1} = \begin{bmatrix} \frac{1}{23} & \frac{5}{23} \\ -\frac{2}{23} & \frac{3}{46} \end{bmatrix}$

129. $\begin{bmatrix} 1 & 2 & 0 \\ -1 & 1 & 1 \\ 0 & -1 & 0 \end{bmatrix}^{-1} = \begin{bmatrix} 1 & 0 & 2 \\ 0 & 0 & -1 \\ 1 & 1 & 3 \end{bmatrix}$

130. $\begin{bmatrix} 1 & -1 & -2 \\ 0 & 1 & -2 \\ 1 & 2 & -4 \end{bmatrix}^{-1} = \begin{bmatrix} 0 & -2 & 1 \\ -\frac{1}{2} & -\frac{1}{2} & \frac{1}{2} \\ -\frac{1}{4} & -\frac{3}{4} & \frac{1}{4} \end{bmatrix}$

131. $\begin{bmatrix} -7 & 2 \\ -8 & 2 \end{bmatrix}^{-1} = \dfrac{1}{(-7)(2) - (2)(-8)}\begin{bmatrix} 2 & -2 \\ 8 & -7 \end{bmatrix} = \begin{bmatrix} 1 & -1 \\ 4 & -\frac{7}{2} \end{bmatrix}$

132. $\begin{bmatrix} 10 & 4 \\ 7 & 3 \end{bmatrix}^{-1} = \dfrac{1}{(10)(3) - 4(7)}\begin{bmatrix} 3 & -4 \\ -7 & 10 \end{bmatrix} = \begin{bmatrix} \frac{3}{2} & -2 \\ -\frac{7}{2} & 5 \end{bmatrix}$

133. $\begin{bmatrix} -1 & 10 \\ 2 & 20 \end{bmatrix}^{-1} = \dfrac{1}{(-1)(20) - 10(2)}\begin{bmatrix} 20 & -10 \\ -2 & -1 \end{bmatrix} = \dfrac{1}{-40}\begin{bmatrix} 20 & -10 \\ -2 & -1 \end{bmatrix} = \begin{bmatrix} -\frac{1}{2} & \frac{1}{4} \\ \frac{1}{20} & \frac{1}{40} \end{bmatrix}$

134. $\begin{bmatrix} -6 & -5 \\ 3 & 3 \end{bmatrix}^{-1} = \dfrac{1}{(-6)(3) - (-5)(3)}\begin{bmatrix} 3 & 5 \\ -3 & -6 \end{bmatrix} = \dfrac{1}{-3}\begin{bmatrix} 3 & 5 \\ -3 & -6 \end{bmatrix} = \begin{bmatrix} -1 & -\frac{5}{3} \\ 1 & 2 \end{bmatrix}$

135. $\begin{cases} x + 5y = -1 \\ 3x - 5y = 5 \end{cases}$

$\begin{bmatrix} 1 & 5 \\ 3 & -5 \end{bmatrix}^{-1} = \begin{bmatrix} \frac{1}{4} & \frac{1}{4} \\ \frac{3}{20} & -\frac{1}{20} \end{bmatrix}$

$\begin{bmatrix} x \\ y \end{bmatrix} = \begin{bmatrix} \frac{1}{4} & \frac{1}{4} \\ \frac{3}{20} & -\frac{1}{20} \end{bmatrix}\begin{bmatrix} -1 \\ 5 \end{bmatrix} = \begin{bmatrix} 1 \\ -\frac{2}{5} \end{bmatrix}$

Answer: $\left(1, -\frac{2}{5}\right)$

136. $\begin{bmatrix} 2 & 3 \\ 4 & -1 \end{bmatrix}^{-1} = \begin{bmatrix} \frac{1}{14} & \frac{3}{14} \\ \frac{2}{7} & -\frac{1}{7} \end{bmatrix}$

$\begin{bmatrix} x \\ y \end{bmatrix} = \begin{bmatrix} \frac{1}{14} & \frac{3}{14} \\ \frac{2}{7} & -\frac{1}{7} \end{bmatrix}\begin{bmatrix} -10 \\ 1 \end{bmatrix} = \begin{bmatrix} -\frac{1}{2} \\ -3 \end{bmatrix}$

Answer: $\left(-\frac{1}{2}, -3\right)$

137. $\begin{bmatrix} 3 & 2 & -1 \\ 1 & -1 & 2 \\ 5 & 1 & 1 \end{bmatrix}^{-1} = \begin{bmatrix} -1 & -1 & 1 \\ 3 & \frac{8}{3} & -\frac{7}{3} \\ 2 & \frac{7}{3} & -\frac{5}{3} \end{bmatrix}$

$$\begin{bmatrix} x \\ y \\ z \end{bmatrix} = \begin{bmatrix} -1 & -1 & 1 \\ 3 & \frac{8}{3} & -\frac{7}{3} \\ 2 & \frac{7}{3} & -\frac{5}{3} \end{bmatrix} \begin{bmatrix} 6 \\ -1 \\ 7 \end{bmatrix} = \begin{bmatrix} 2 \\ -1 \\ -2 \end{bmatrix}$$

Answer: $(2, -1, -2)$

138. $\begin{bmatrix} -1 & 4 & -2 \\ 2 & -9 & 5 \\ -1 & 5 & -4 \end{bmatrix}^{-1} = \begin{bmatrix} -11 & -6 & -2 \\ -3 & -2 & -1 \\ -1 & -1 & -1 \end{bmatrix}$

$$\begin{bmatrix} x \\ y \\ z \end{bmatrix} = \begin{bmatrix} -11 & -6 & -2 \\ -3 & -2 & -1 \\ -1 & -1 & -1 \end{bmatrix} \begin{bmatrix} 12 \\ -25 \\ 10 \end{bmatrix} = \begin{bmatrix} 2 \\ -4 \\ 3 \end{bmatrix}$$

Answer: $(2, -4, 3)$

139. $\begin{bmatrix} 1 & 2 & 1 & -1 \\ 2 & 1 & 1 & 1 \\ 1 & -1 & -3 & 0 \\ 0 & 0 & 1 & 1 \end{bmatrix}^{-1} = \begin{bmatrix} -1 & \frac{4}{3} & -\frac{2}{3} & -\frac{7}{3} \\ 2 & -\frac{5}{3} & \frac{4}{3} & \frac{11}{3} \\ -1 & 1 & -1 & -2 \\ 1 & -1 & 1 & 3 \end{bmatrix}^{-1}$

$$\begin{bmatrix} x \\ y \\ z \\ w \end{bmatrix} = \begin{bmatrix} -1 & \frac{4}{3} & -\frac{2}{3} & -\frac{7}{3} \\ 2 & -\frac{5}{3} & \frac{4}{3} & \frac{11}{3} \\ -1 & 1 & -1 & -2 \\ 1 & -1 & 1 & 3 \end{bmatrix} \begin{bmatrix} -2 \\ 1 \\ 0 \\ 1 \end{bmatrix} = \begin{bmatrix} 1 \\ -2 \\ 1 \\ 0 \end{bmatrix}$$

Answer: $(1, -2, 1, 0)$

140. $\begin{bmatrix} 1 & 1 & 1 & 1 \\ 1 & -1 & 2 & 1 \\ 0 & 1 & 0 & 1 \\ 1 & 0 & 0 & 1 \end{bmatrix}^{-1} = \begin{bmatrix} \frac{2}{3} & -\frac{1}{3} & -1 & \frac{2}{3} \\ \frac{2}{3} & -\frac{1}{3} & 0 & -\frac{1}{3} \\ \frac{1}{3} & \frac{1}{3} & 0 & -\frac{2}{3} \\ -\frac{2}{3} & \frac{1}{3} & 1 & \frac{1}{3} \end{bmatrix}^{-1}$

$$\begin{bmatrix} x \\ y \\ z \\ w \end{bmatrix} = \begin{bmatrix} \frac{2}{3} & -\frac{1}{3} & -1 & \frac{2}{3} \\ \frac{2}{3} & -\frac{1}{3} & 0 & -\frac{1}{3} \\ \frac{1}{3} & \frac{1}{3} & 0 & -\frac{2}{3} \\ -\frac{2}{3} & \frac{1}{3} & 1 & \frac{1}{3} \end{bmatrix} \begin{bmatrix} 1 \\ -3 \\ 2 \\ 2 \end{bmatrix} = \begin{bmatrix} 1 \\ 1 \\ -2 \\ 1 \end{bmatrix}$$

Answer: $(1, 1, -2, 1)$

141. $\begin{cases} x + 2y = -1 \\ 3x + 4y = -5 \end{cases}$

$$\begin{bmatrix} 1 & 2 \\ 3 & 4 \end{bmatrix}^{-1} = \begin{bmatrix} -2 & 1 \\ \frac{3}{2} & -\frac{1}{2} \end{bmatrix} \Rightarrow \begin{bmatrix} x \\ y \end{bmatrix} = \begin{bmatrix} -2 & 1 \\ \frac{3}{2} & -\frac{1}{2} \end{bmatrix} \begin{bmatrix} -1 \\ -5 \end{bmatrix} = \begin{bmatrix} -3 \\ 1 \end{bmatrix}$$

$x = -3, y = 1$

Answer: $(-3, 1)$

142. $\begin{cases} x + 3y = 23 \\ -6x + 2y = -18 \end{cases}$

$$\begin{bmatrix} 1 & 3 \\ -6 & 2 \end{bmatrix}^{-1} = \begin{bmatrix} 0.1 & -0.15 \\ 0.3 & 0.05 \end{bmatrix} \Rightarrow \begin{bmatrix} x \\ y \end{bmatrix} = \begin{bmatrix} 0.1 & -0.15 \\ 0.3 & 0.05 \end{bmatrix} \begin{bmatrix} 23 \\ -18 \end{bmatrix} = \begin{bmatrix} 5 \\ 6 \end{bmatrix}$$

$x = 5, y = 6$

Answer: $(5, 6)$

143. $\begin{cases} -3x - 3y - 4z = 2 \\ y + z = -1 \\ 4x + 3y + 4z = -1 \end{cases}$

$$\begin{bmatrix} -3 & -3 & -4 \\ 0 & 1 & 1 \\ 4 & 3 & 4 \end{bmatrix}^{-1} = \begin{bmatrix} 1 & 0 & 1 \\ 4 & 4 & 3 \\ 4 & -3 & -3 \end{bmatrix} \Rightarrow \begin{bmatrix} x \\ y \\ z \end{bmatrix} = \begin{bmatrix} 1 & 0 & 1 \\ 4 & 4 & 3 \\ -4 & -3 & -3 \end{bmatrix}\begin{bmatrix} 2 \\ -1 \\ -1 \end{bmatrix} = \begin{bmatrix} 1 \\ 1 \\ -2 \end{bmatrix}$$

$x = 1, y = 1, z = -2$

Answer: $(1, 1, -2)$

144. $\begin{cases} 2x + 3y - 4z = 1 \\ x - y + 2z = -4 \\ 3x + 7y - 10z = 0 \end{cases}$

$\begin{bmatrix} 2 & 3 & -4 \\ 1 & -1 & 2 \\ 3 & 7 & -10 \end{bmatrix}^{-1}$ does not exist.

Inconsistent; no solution.

145. $\begin{vmatrix} 8 & 5 \\ 2 & -4 \end{vmatrix} = 8(-4) - 2(5) = -42$

146. $\begin{vmatrix} -9 & 11 \\ 7 & -4 \end{vmatrix} = (-9)(-4) - (11)(7)$

$= 36 - 77 = -41$

147. $\begin{vmatrix} 50 & -30 \\ 10 & 5 \end{vmatrix} = 50(5) - (-30)(10) = 550$

148. $\begin{vmatrix} 14 & -24 \\ 12 & -15 \end{vmatrix} = 14(-15) - (-24)(12) = 78$

149. $A = \begin{bmatrix} 2 & -1 \\ 7 & 4 \end{bmatrix}$

Minors: $M_{11} = 4$ $M_{21} = -1$

$M_{12} = 7$ $M_{22} = 2$

Cofactors: $C_{11} = 4$ $C_{21} = 1$

$C_{12} = -7$ $C_{22} = 2$

150. $A = \begin{bmatrix} 3 & 6 \\ 5 & -4 \end{bmatrix}$

Minors: $M_{11} = -4$ $M_{12} = 5$

$M_{21} = 6$ $M_{22} = 3$

Cofactors: $C_{11} = -4$ $C_{12} = -5$

$C_{21} = -6$ $C_{22} = 3$

151. $A = \begin{bmatrix} 3 & 2 & -1 \\ -2 & 5 & 0 \\ 1 & 8 & 6 \end{bmatrix}$

Minors: $M_{11} = \begin{vmatrix} 5 & 0 \\ 8 & 6 \end{vmatrix} = 30, M_{12} = \begin{vmatrix} -2 & 0 \\ 1 & 6 \end{vmatrix} = -12, M_{13} = \begin{vmatrix} -2 & 5 \\ 1 & 8 \end{vmatrix} = -21$

$M_{21} = \begin{vmatrix} 2 & -1 \\ 8 & 6 \end{vmatrix} = 20, M_{22} = \begin{vmatrix} 3 & -1 \\ 1 & 6 \end{vmatrix} = 19, M_{23} = \begin{vmatrix} 3 & 2 \\ 1 & 8 \end{vmatrix} = 22$

$M_{31} = \begin{vmatrix} 2 & -1 \\ 5 & 0 \end{vmatrix} = 5, M_{32} = \begin{vmatrix} 3 & -1 \\ -2 & 0 \end{vmatrix} = -2, M_{33} = \begin{vmatrix} 3 & 2 \\ -2 & 5 \end{vmatrix} = 19$

Cofactors: $C_{11} = 30, C_{12} = 12, C_{13} = -21$

$C_{21} = -20, C_{22} = 19, C_{23} = -22$

$C_{31} = 5, C_{32} = 2, C_{33} = 19$

152. Minors: $M_{11} = \begin{vmatrix} 5 & -9 \\ 1 & 2 \end{vmatrix} = 19,\ M_{12} = \begin{vmatrix} 6 & -9 \\ -4 & 2 \end{vmatrix} = -24,\ M_{13} = \begin{vmatrix} 6 & 5 \\ -4 & 1 \end{vmatrix} = 26$

$M_{21} = \begin{vmatrix} 3 & 4 \\ 1 & 2 \end{vmatrix} = 2,\ M_{22} = \begin{vmatrix} 8 & 4 \\ -4 & 2 \end{vmatrix} = 32,\ M_{23} = \begin{vmatrix} 8 & 3 \\ -4 & 1 \end{vmatrix} = 20$

$M_{31} = \begin{vmatrix} 3 & 4 \\ 5 & -9 \end{vmatrix} = -47,\ M_{32} = \begin{vmatrix} 8 & 4 \\ 6 & -9 \end{vmatrix} = -96,\ M_{33} = \begin{vmatrix} 8 & 3 \\ 6 & 5 \end{vmatrix} = 22$

Cofactors: $C_{11} = 19, C_{12} = 24, C_{13} = 26$

$C_{21} = -2, C_{22} = 32, C_{23} = -20$

$C_{31} = -47, C_{32} = 96, C_{33} = 22$

153. $\begin{vmatrix} -2 & 4 & 1 \\ -6 & 0 & 2 \\ 5 & 3 & 4 \end{vmatrix} = 6\begin{vmatrix} 4 & 1 \\ 3 & 4 \end{vmatrix} - 2\begin{vmatrix} -2 & 4 \\ 5 & 3 \end{vmatrix} = 6(13) - 2(-26) = 130$

154. $\begin{vmatrix} 4 & 7 & -1 \\ 2 & -3 & 4 \\ -5 & 1 & -1 \end{vmatrix} = 4(3 - 4) - 7(-2 + 20) - 1(2 - 15) = -4 - 126 + 13 = -117$

155. $\begin{vmatrix} 1 & 0 & -2 \\ 0 & 1 & 0 \\ -2 & 0 & 1 \end{vmatrix} = 1\begin{vmatrix} 1 & -2 \\ -2 & 1 \end{vmatrix} = 1(1) - (-2)(-2) = 1 - 4 = -3$

156. $\begin{vmatrix} 0 & 3 & 1 \\ 5 & -2 & 1 \\ 1 & 6 & 1 \end{vmatrix} = -3(5 - 1) + 1(30 + 2) = -12 + 32 = 20$

157. $\begin{vmatrix} 3 & 0 & -4 & 0 \\ 0 & 8 & 1 & 2 \\ 6 & 1 & 8 & 2 \\ 0 & 3 & -4 & 1 \end{vmatrix} = 3\begin{vmatrix} 8 & 1 & 2 \\ 1 & 8 & 2 \\ 3 & -4 & 1 \end{vmatrix} + (-4)\begin{vmatrix} 0 & 8 & 2 \\ 6 & 1 & 2 \\ 0 & 3 & 1 \end{vmatrix}$ (Expansion along Row 1)

$= 3[8(8 - (-8)) - 1(1 - 6) + 2(-4 - 24)] - 4[0 - 6(8 - 6) + 0]$

$= 3[128 + 5 - 56] - 4[-12]$

$= 279$

158. $\begin{vmatrix} -5 & 6 & 0 & 0 \\ 0 & 1 & -1 & 2 \\ -3 & 4 & -5 & 1 \\ 1 & 6 & 0 & 3 \end{vmatrix} = -5\begin{vmatrix} 1 & -1 & 2 \\ 4 & -5 & 1 \\ 6 & 0 & 3 \end{vmatrix} - 6\begin{vmatrix} 0 & -1 & 2 \\ -3 & -5 & 1 \\ 1 & 0 & 3 \end{vmatrix}$ (Expansion along Row 1.)

$= -5[6(-1 + 10) + 3(-5 + 4)] - 6[(-1 + 10) + 3(0 - 3)]$

$= -5[54 \quad -3] - 6[9 \quad -9]$

$= -255$

159. $\det(A) = 8(-1)(4)(3) = -96$ (Upper Triangular)

160. $\det = (-5)(-2)(2)(14) = 280$ (Lower Triangular)

161. $(1, 0),\ (5, 0),\ (5, 8)$

$$\frac{1}{2}\begin{vmatrix} 1 & 0 & 1 \\ 5 & 0 & 1 \\ 5 & 8 & 1 \end{vmatrix} = \frac{1}{2}(32) = 16$$

Area = 16 square units

162. $(-4, 0), (4, 0), (0, 6)$

$$\text{Area} = \frac{1}{2}\begin{vmatrix} -4 & 0 & 1 \\ 4 & 0 & 1 \\ 0 & 6 & 1 \end{vmatrix} = \frac{1}{2}(48) = 24$$

Area = 24 square units

163. $\frac{1}{2}\begin{vmatrix} \frac{1}{2} & 1 & 1 \\ 2 & -\frac{5}{2} & 1 \\ \frac{3}{2} & 1 & 1 \end{vmatrix} = \frac{1}{2}\left(\frac{7}{2}\right) = \frac{7}{4}$

Area = $\frac{7}{4}$ square units

164. $\left(\frac{3}{2}, 1\right), \left(4, -\frac{1}{2}\right), (4, 2)$

$$\text{Area} = \frac{1}{2}\begin{vmatrix} \frac{3}{2} & 1 & 1 \\ 4 & -\frac{1}{2} & 1 \\ 4 & 2 & 1 \end{vmatrix} = \frac{1}{2}\left(\frac{25}{4}\right) = \frac{25}{8} \text{ square units}$$

165. $\frac{1}{2}\begin{vmatrix} 2 & 4 & 1 \\ 5 & 6 & 1 \\ 4 & 1 & 1 \end{vmatrix} = \frac{1}{2}(-13)$

Area = $\frac{13}{2}$ square units

166. $\frac{1}{2}\begin{vmatrix} -3 & 2 & 1 \\ 2 & -3 & 1 \\ -4 & -4 & 1 \end{vmatrix} = \frac{1}{2}(-35)$

Area = $\frac{35}{2}$ square units

167. The figure is a rhombus.

$$\begin{vmatrix} -2 & -1 & 1 \\ 4 & 9 & 1 \\ -2 & -9 & 1 \end{vmatrix} = -48$$

Area = 48 square units

168. The figure is a rhombus.

$$\begin{vmatrix} -4 & 8 & 1 \\ 4 & 0 & 1 \\ -4 & 0 & 1 \end{vmatrix} = -64$$

Area = 64 square units

169. $\begin{vmatrix} -1 & 7 & 1 \\ 2 & 5 & 1 \\ 4 & 1 & 1 \end{vmatrix} = -8 \neq 0$

Not collinear

170. $\begin{vmatrix} 0 & -5 & 1 \\ 2 & 1 & 1 \\ 4 & 7 & 1 \end{vmatrix} = -2(-12) + 4(-6) = 0$

Collinear

171. $x = \dfrac{\begin{vmatrix} 5 & 2 \\ 1 & 1 \end{vmatrix}}{\begin{vmatrix} 1 & 2 \\ -1 & 1 \end{vmatrix}} = \dfrac{3}{3} = 1$

$y = \dfrac{\begin{vmatrix} 1 & 5 \\ -1 & 1 \end{vmatrix}}{\begin{vmatrix} 1 & 2 \\ -1 & 1 \end{vmatrix}} = \dfrac{6}{3} = 2$

Answer: $(1, 2)$

172. $x = \dfrac{\begin{vmatrix} -10 & -1 \\ -1 & 2 \end{vmatrix}}{\begin{vmatrix} 2 & -1 \\ 3 & 2 \end{vmatrix}} = \dfrac{-21}{7} = -3$

$y = \dfrac{\begin{vmatrix} 2 & -10 \\ 3 & -1 \end{vmatrix}}{\begin{vmatrix} 2 & -1 \\ 3 & 2 \end{vmatrix}} = \dfrac{28}{7} = 4$

Answer: $(x, y) = (-3, 4)$

173. $x = \dfrac{\begin{vmatrix} 6 & -2 \\ -23 & 3 \end{vmatrix}}{\begin{vmatrix} 5 & -2 \\ -11 & 3 \end{vmatrix}} = \dfrac{-28}{-7} = 4$

$y = \dfrac{\begin{vmatrix} 5 & 6 \\ -11 & -23 \end{vmatrix}}{\begin{vmatrix} 5 & -2 \\ -11 & 3 \end{vmatrix}} = \dfrac{-49}{-7} = 7$

Answer: (4, 7)

174. $x = \dfrac{\begin{vmatrix} -7 & 8 \\ 37 & -5 \end{vmatrix}}{\begin{vmatrix} 3 & 8 \\ 9 & -5 \end{vmatrix}} = \dfrac{-261}{-87} = 3$

$y = \dfrac{\begin{vmatrix} 3 & -7 \\ 9 & 37 \end{vmatrix}}{\begin{vmatrix} 3 & 8 \\ 9 & -5 \end{vmatrix}} = \dfrac{174}{-87} = -2$

Answer: (3, −2)

175. $x = \dfrac{\begin{vmatrix} -11 & 3 & -5 \\ -3 & -1 & 1 \\ 15 & -4 & 6 \end{vmatrix}}{\begin{vmatrix} -2 & 3 & -5 \\ 4 & -1 & 1 \\ -1 & -4 & 6 \end{vmatrix}} = \dfrac{-14}{14} = -1$

$y = \dfrac{\begin{vmatrix} -2 & -11 & -5 \\ 4 & -3 & 1 \\ -1 & 15 & 6 \end{vmatrix}}{14} = \dfrac{56}{14} = 4$

$z = \dfrac{\begin{vmatrix} -2 & 3 & -11 \\ 4 & -1 & -3 \\ -1 & -4 & 15 \end{vmatrix}}{14} = \dfrac{70}{14} = 5$

Answer: (−1, 4, 5)

176. $x = \dfrac{\begin{vmatrix} 15 & -2 & 1 \\ -7 & -3 & -1 \\ -3 & -1 & -7 \end{vmatrix}}{\begin{vmatrix} 5 & -2 & 1 \\ 3 & -3 & -1 \\ 2 & -1 & -7 \end{vmatrix}} = \dfrac{390}{65} = 6$

$y = \dfrac{\begin{vmatrix} 5 & 15 & 1 \\ 3 & -7 & -1 \\ 2 & -3 & -7 \end{vmatrix}}{65} = \dfrac{520}{65} = 8$

$z = \dfrac{\begin{vmatrix} 5 & -2 & 15 \\ 3 & -3 & -7 \\ 2 & -1 & -3 \end{vmatrix}}{65} = \dfrac{65}{65} = 1$

Answer: (6, 8, 1)

177. $\begin{vmatrix} 1 & -3 & 2 \\ 2 & 2 & -3 \\ 1 & -7 & 8 \end{vmatrix} = 20$

$|A_1| = 0$

$|A_2| = -48$

$|A_3| = -52$

$x = 0,\ y = -\frac{48}{20} = -2.4,\ z = -\frac{52}{20} = -2.6$

Answer: (0, −2.4, −2.6)

178. $x = \dfrac{\begin{vmatrix} 10 & -21 & -7 \\ 4 & 2 & -2 \\ 5 & -21 & 7 \end{vmatrix}}{\begin{vmatrix} 14 & -21 & -7 \\ -4 & 2 & -2 \\ 56 & -21 & 7 \end{vmatrix}} = \dfrac{1176}{1568} = \dfrac{3}{4}$

$y = \dfrac{\begin{vmatrix} 14 & 10 & -7 \\ -4 & 4 & -2 \\ 56 & 5 & 7 \end{vmatrix}}{\begin{vmatrix} 14 & -21 & -7 \\ -4 & 2 & -2 \\ 56 & -21 & 7 \end{vmatrix}} = \dfrac{1400}{1568} = \dfrac{25}{28}$

$z = \dfrac{\begin{vmatrix} 14 & -21 & 10 \\ -4 & 2 & 4 \\ 56 & -21 & 5 \end{vmatrix}}{\begin{vmatrix} 14 & -21 & -7 \\ -4 & 2 & -2 \\ 56 & -21 & 7 \end{vmatrix}} = \dfrac{-4088}{1568} = -\dfrac{73}{28}$

Answer: $(x, y, z) = \left(\dfrac{3}{4}, \dfrac{25}{28}, -\dfrac{73}{28}\right)$

179. (a) $\begin{cases} x - 3y + 2z = 5 \\ 2x + y - 4z = -1 \\ 2x + 4y + 2z = 3 \end{cases}$

$\begin{cases} x - 3y + 2z = 5 \\ 7y - 8z = -11 \\ 10y - 2z = -7 \end{cases}$

$\begin{cases} x - 3y + 2z = 5 \\ 7y - 8z = -11 \\ \frac{66}{7}z = \frac{61}{7} \end{cases}$

$z = \dfrac{61}{66}$

$7y - 8\left(\dfrac{61}{66}\right) = -11 \Rightarrow y = -\dfrac{17}{33}$

$x - 3\left(-\dfrac{17}{33}\right) + 2\left(\dfrac{61}{66}\right) = 5 \Rightarrow x = \dfrac{53}{33}$

Answer: $\left(\dfrac{53}{33}, -\dfrac{17}{33}, \dfrac{61}{66}\right)$

(b) $D = \begin{vmatrix} 1 & -3 & 2 \\ 2 & 1 & -4 \\ 2 & 4 & 2 \end{vmatrix} = 66$

$x = \dfrac{\begin{vmatrix} 5 & -3 & 2 \\ -1 & 1 & -4 \\ 3 & 4 & 2 \end{vmatrix}}{66} = \dfrac{106}{66} = \dfrac{53}{33}$

$y = \dfrac{\begin{vmatrix} 1 & 5 & 2 \\ 2 & -1 & -4 \\ 2 & 3 & 2 \end{vmatrix}}{66} = \dfrac{-34}{66} = \dfrac{-17}{33}$

$z = \dfrac{\begin{vmatrix} 1 & -3 & 5 \\ 2 & 1 & -1 \\ 2 & 4 & 3 \end{vmatrix}}{66} = \dfrac{61}{66}$

Answer: $\left(\dfrac{53}{33}, -\dfrac{17}{33}, \dfrac{61}{66}\right)$

180. (a) $\begin{cases} x + 2y - z = -3 \\ 2x - y + z = -1 \\ 4x - 2y - z = 5 \end{cases}$

$\begin{cases} x + 2y - z = -3 \\ -5y + 3z = 5 \\ -10y + 3z = 17 \end{cases}$

$\begin{cases} x + 2y - z = -3 \\ -5y + 3z = 5 \\ -3z = 7 \end{cases}$

$z = -\dfrac{7}{3}$

$-5y + 3\left(-\dfrac{7}{3}\right) = 5 \Rightarrow y = -\dfrac{12}{5}$

$x + 2\left(-\dfrac{12}{5}\right) - \left(-\dfrac{7}{3}\right) = -3 \Rightarrow x = -\dfrac{8}{15}$

Answer: $\left(\dfrac{-8}{15}, \dfrac{-12}{5}, \dfrac{-7}{3}\right)$

(b) $D = \begin{vmatrix} 1 & 2 & -1 \\ 2 & -1 & 1 \\ 4 & -2 & -1 \end{vmatrix} = 15$

$x = \dfrac{\begin{vmatrix} -3 & 2 & -1 \\ -1 & -1 & 1 \\ 5 & -2 & -1 \end{vmatrix}}{15} = \dfrac{-8}{15}$

$y = \dfrac{\begin{vmatrix} 1 & -3 & -1 \\ 2 & -1 & 1 \\ 4 & 5 & -1 \end{vmatrix}}{15} = \dfrac{-36}{15} = \dfrac{-12}{5}$

$z = \dfrac{\begin{vmatrix} 1 & 2 & -3 \\ 2 & -1 & -1 \\ 4 & -2 & 5 \end{vmatrix}}{15} = \dfrac{-35}{15} = \dfrac{-7}{3}$

Answer: $\left(\dfrac{-8}{15}, \dfrac{-12}{5}, \dfrac{-7}{3}\right)$

181. I _ H A V E _ A _ D R E A M

[9 0 8] [1 22 5] [0 1 0] [4 18 5] [1 13 0]

$[9\ \ 0\ \ 8]A = [-30\ \ -2\ \ 24]$

$[1\ \ 22\ \ 5]A = [38\ \ 8\ \ -51]$

$[0\ \ 1\ \ 0]A = [3\ \ 0\ \ -3]$

$[4\ \ 18\ \ 5]A = [32\ \ 2\ \ -39]$

$[1\ \ 13\ \ 0]A = [41\ \ -2\ \ -39]$

Cryptogram: −30 −2 24 38 8 −51 3 0 −3
32 2 −39 41 −2 −39

182. J U S T _ D O _ I T

[10 21 19] [20 0 4] [15 0 9] [20 0 0]

$[10\ \ 21\ \ 19]A = [-49\ \ -78\ \ -23]$

$[20\ \ 0\ \ 4]A = [52\ \ 28\ \ 4]$

$[15\ \ 0\ \ 9]A = [57\ \ 33\ \ 9]$

$[20\ \ 0\ \ 0]A = [40\ \ 20\ \ 0]$

Cryptogram: −49 −78 −23 52 28 4
57 33 9 40 20 0

183. $A^{-1} = \begin{bmatrix} \frac{1}{2} & -\frac{1}{4} & \frac{1}{4} \\ -\frac{1}{4} & -\frac{3}{8} & -\frac{1}{8} \\ -\frac{1}{2} & -\frac{1}{4} & \frac{1}{4} \end{bmatrix}$

$$\begin{bmatrix} 32 & -46 & 37 \\ 9 & -48 & 15 \\ 3 & -14 & 10 \\ -1 & -6 & 2 \\ -8 & -22 & -3 \end{bmatrix} \begin{bmatrix} \frac{1}{2} & -\frac{1}{4} & \frac{1}{4} \\ -\frac{1}{4} & -\frac{3}{8} & -\frac{1}{8} \\ -\frac{1}{2} & -\frac{1}{4} & \frac{1}{4} \end{bmatrix} = \begin{bmatrix} 9 & 0 & 23 \\ 9 & 12 & 12 \\ 0 & 2 & 5 \\ 0 & 2 & 1 \\ 3 & 11 & 0 \end{bmatrix} = \begin{matrix} \text{I} & \text{\_} & \text{W} \\ \text{I} & \text{L} & \text{L} \\ \text{\_} & \text{B} & \text{E} \\ \text{\_} & \text{B} & \text{A} \\ \text{C} & \text{K} & \text{\_} \end{matrix}$$

Message: I WILL BE BACK

184. $A^{-1} = \begin{bmatrix} \frac{1}{4} & -\frac{1}{4} & \frac{1}{4} \\ \frac{3}{8} & \frac{1}{8} & -\frac{1}{8} \\ -\frac{1}{16} & \frac{5}{16} & \frac{3}{16} \end{bmatrix}$

$$\begin{bmatrix} 30 & -7 & 30 \\ 5 & 10 & 80 \\ 37 & 34 & 16 \\ 40 & -7 & 38 \\ -3 & 8 & 36 \\ 16 & -1 & 58 \\ 23 & 46 & 0 \end{bmatrix} \begin{bmatrix} \frac{1}{4} & -\frac{1}{4} & \frac{1}{4} \\ \frac{3}{8} & \frac{1}{8} & -\frac{1}{8} \\ -\frac{1}{16} & \frac{5}{16} & \frac{3}{16} \end{bmatrix} = \begin{bmatrix} 3 & 1 & 14 \\ 0 & 25 & 15 \\ 21 & 0 & 8 \\ 5 & 1 & 18 \\ 0 & 13 & 5 \\ 0 & 14 & 15 \\ 23 & 0 & 0 \end{bmatrix} \quad \begin{matrix} \text{C} & \text{A} & \text{N} \\ \text{\_} & \text{Y} & \text{O} \\ \text{U} & \text{\_} & \text{H} \\ \text{E} & \text{A} & \text{R} \\ \text{\_} & \text{M} & \text{E} \\ \text{\_} & \text{N} & \text{O} \\ \text{W} & \text{\_} & \text{\_} \end{matrix}$$

Message: CAN YOU HEAR ME NOW

185. $A^{-1} = \begin{bmatrix} \frac{2}{3} & \frac{1}{3} & \frac{1}{3} \\ -\frac{1}{3} & \frac{1}{3} & \frac{1}{3} \\ \frac{1}{6} & \frac{1}{3} & -\frac{1}{6} \end{bmatrix}$

$$\begin{bmatrix} 21 & -11 & 14 \\ 29 & -11 & -18 \\ 32 & -6 & -26 \\ 31 & -19 & -12 \\ 10 & 6 & 26 \\ 13 & -11 & -2 \\ 37 & 28 & -8 \\ 5 & 13 & 36 \end{bmatrix} \begin{bmatrix} \frac{2}{3} & \frac{1}{3} & \frac{1}{3} \\ -\frac{1}{3} & \frac{1}{3} & \frac{1}{3} \\ \frac{1}{6} & \frac{1}{3} & -\frac{1}{6} \end{bmatrix} = \begin{bmatrix} 20 & 8 & 1 \\ 20 & 0 & 9 \\ 19 & 0 & 13 \\ 25 & 0 & 6 \\ 9 & 14 & 1 \\ 12 & 0 & 1 \\ 14 & 19 & 23 \\ 5 & 18 & 0 \end{bmatrix} \quad \begin{matrix} T & H & A \\ T & - & I \\ S & - & M \\ Y & - & F \\ I & N & A \\ L & - & A \\ N & S & W \\ E & R & - \end{matrix}$$

Message: THAT IS MY FINAL ANSWER

186. $A^{-1} = \begin{bmatrix} \frac{3}{5} & -\frac{1}{5} & \frac{1}{5} \\ \frac{2}{5} & \frac{1}{5} & -\frac{1}{5} \\ \frac{1}{10} & -\frac{1}{5} & -\frac{3}{10} \end{bmatrix}$

$$\begin{bmatrix} 9 & 15 & -54 \\ 13 & 32 & -26 \\ 8 & -6 & -14 \\ -4 & 26 & -70 \\ -1 & 56 & -38 \\ 28 & 27 & -46 \\ -13 & 27 & -30 \\ 26 & 23 & -48 \\ 25 & 4 & -26 \\ -11 & 31 & -58 \\ 13 & 39 & -34 \end{bmatrix} \begin{bmatrix} \frac{3}{5} & -\frac{1}{5} & \frac{1}{5} \\ \frac{2}{5} & \frac{1}{5} & -\frac{1}{5} \\ \frac{1}{10} & -\frac{1}{5} & -\frac{3}{10} \end{bmatrix} = \begin{bmatrix} 6 & 12 & 15 \\ 18 & 9 & 4 \\ 1 & 0 & 7 \\ 1 & 20 & 15 \\ 18 & 19 & 0 \\ 23 & 9 & 14 \\ 0 & 14 & 1 \\ 20 & 9 & 15 \\ 14 & 1 & 12 \\ 0 & 20 & 9 \\ 20 & 12 & 5 \end{bmatrix} \quad \begin{matrix} F & L & O \\ R & I & D \\ A & - & G \\ A & T & O \\ R & S & - \\ W & I & N \\ - & N & A \\ T & I & O \\ N & A & L \\ - & T & I \\ T & L & E \end{matrix}$$

Message: FLORIDA GATORS WIN NATIONAL TITLE

187. (a) $\begin{cases} 4b + 44a = 65 \\ 44b + 504a = 723.2 \end{cases}$

Using Cramer's Rule, you obtain,

$a = 0.41$ and $b = 11.74$

$y = 0.41t + 11.74$

(b)

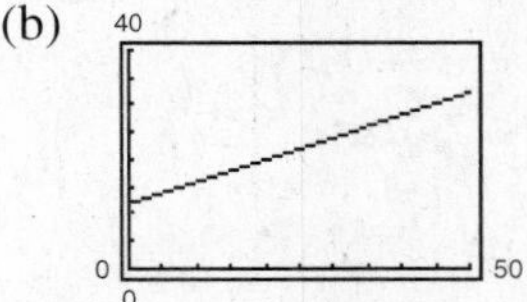

(c) $y = 20$ when $t \approx 20.15$, or 2010

(d) $0.41t + 11.74 > 20$

$0.41t > 8.26$

$t > 20.15$

That is, year 2010.

188. False

189. True. Expansion by Row 3 gives

$$\begin{vmatrix} a_{11} & a_{12} & a_{13} \\ a_{21} & a_{22} & a_{23} \\ a_{31}+c_1 & a_{32}+c_2 & a_{33}+c_3 \end{vmatrix} = (a_{31}+c_1)\begin{vmatrix} a_{12} & a_{13} \\ a_{22} & a_{23} \end{vmatrix} - (a_{32}+c_2)\begin{vmatrix} a_{11} & a_{13} \\ a_{21} & a_{23} \end{vmatrix} + (a_{33}+c_3)\begin{vmatrix} a_{11} & a_{12} \\ a_{21} & a_{22} \end{vmatrix}$$

$$= a_{31}\begin{vmatrix} a_{12} & a_{13} \\ a_{22} & a_{23} \end{vmatrix} - a_{32}\begin{vmatrix} a_{11} & a_{13} \\ a_{21} & a_{23} \end{vmatrix} + a_{33}\begin{vmatrix} a_{11} & a_{12} \\ a_{21} & a_{22} \end{vmatrix}$$

$$+ c_1\begin{vmatrix} a_{12} & a_{13} \\ a_{22} & a_{23} \end{vmatrix} - c_2\begin{vmatrix} a_{11} & a_{13} \\ a_{21} & a_{23} \end{vmatrix} + c_3\begin{vmatrix} a_{11} & a_{12} \\ a_{21} & a_{22} \end{vmatrix}$$

$$= \begin{vmatrix} a_{11} & a_{12} & a_{13} \\ a_{21} & a_{22} & a_{23} \\ a_{31} & a_{32} & a_{33} \end{vmatrix} + \begin{vmatrix} a_{11} & a_{12} & a_{13} \\ a_{21} & a_{22} & a_{23} \\ c_1 & c_2 & c_3 \end{vmatrix}$$

Note: Expand each of these matrices by Row 3 to see the previous step.

190. The row operations on matrices are equivalent to the operations used in the method of elimination.

191. A square $n \times n$ matrix has an inverse if $\det(A) \neq 0$.

Chapter 7 Practice Test

For Exercises 1–3, solve the given system by the method of substitution.

1. $x + y = 1$
$3x - y = 15$

2. $x - 3y = -3$
$x^2 + 6y = 5$

3. $x + y + z = 6$
$2x - y + 3z = 0$
$5x + 2y - z = -3$

4. Find the two numbers whose sum is 110 and product is 2800.

5. Find the dimensions of a rectangle if its perimeter is 170 feet and its area is 2800 square feet.

For Exercises 6–7, solve the linear system by elimination.

6. $2x + 15y = 4$
$x - 3y = 23$

7. $x + y = 2$
$38x - 19y = 7$

8. Use a graphing utility to graph the two equations. Use the graph to approximate the solution of the system. Verify your answer analytically.

$0.4x + 0.5y = 0.112$
$0.3x - 0.7y = -0.131$

9. Herbert invests \$17,000 in two funds that pay 11% and 13% simple interest, respectively. If he receives \$2080 in yearly interest, how much is invested in each fund?

10. Find the least squares regression line for the points $(4, 3)$, $(1, 1)$, $(-1, -2)$, and $(-2, -1)$.

For Exercises 11–13, solve the system of equations.

11. $x + y = -2$
$2x - y + z = 11$
$4y - 3z = -20$

12. $4x - y + 5z = 4$
$2x + y - z = 0$
$2x + 4y + 8z = 0$

13. $3x + 2y - z = 5$
$6x - y + 5z = 2$

14. Find the equation of the parabola $y = ax^2 + bx + c$ passing through the points $(0, -1)$, $(1, 4)$ and $(2, 13)$.

15. Find the position equation $s = \frac{1}{2}at^2 + v_0t + s_0$ given that $s = 12$ feet after 1 second, $s = 5$ feet after 2 seconds, and $s = 4$ feet after 3 seconds.

16. Write the matrix in reduced row-echelon form.

$$\begin{bmatrix} 1 & -2 & 4 \\ 3 & -5 & 9 \end{bmatrix}$$

For Exercises 17–19, use matrices to solve the system of equations.

17. $3x + 5y = 3$
$2x - y = -11$

18. $2x + 3y = -3$
$3x + 2y = 8$
$x + y = 1$

19. $x + 3z = -5$
$2x + y = 0$
$3x + y - z = 3$

20. Multiply $\begin{bmatrix} 1 & 4 & 5 \\ 2 & 0 & -3 \end{bmatrix} \begin{bmatrix} 1 & 6 \\ 0 & -7 \\ -1 & 2 \end{bmatrix}$

21. Given $A = \begin{bmatrix} 9 & 1 \\ -4 & 8 \end{bmatrix}$ and $B = \begin{bmatrix} 6 & -2 \\ 3 & 5 \end{bmatrix}$, find $3A - 5B$.

22. Find $f(A)$:

$f(x) = x^2 - 7x + 8$, $A = \begin{bmatrix} 3 & 0 \\ 7 & 1 \end{bmatrix}$

23. True or false:

$(A + B)(A + 3B) = A^2 + 4AB + 3B^2$ where A and B are matrices.

(Assume that A^2, AB, and B^2 exist.)

For Exercises 24 and 25, find the inverse of the matrix, if it exists.

24. $\begin{bmatrix} 1 & 2 \\ 3 & 5 \end{bmatrix}$

25. $\begin{bmatrix} 1 & 1 & 1 \\ 3 & 6 & 5 \\ 6 & 10 & 8 \end{bmatrix}$

26. Use an inverse matrix to solve the systems.

(a) $x + 2y = 4$
$3x + 5y = 1$

(b) $x + 2y = 3$
$3x + 5y = -2$

For Exercises 27 and 28, find the determinant of the matrix.

27. $\begin{bmatrix} 6 & -1 \\ 3 & 4 \end{bmatrix}$

28. $\begin{bmatrix} 1 & 3 & -1 \\ 5 & 9 & 0 \\ 6 & 2 & -5 \end{bmatrix}$

29. Use a graphing utility to find the determinant of the matrix.

$$\begin{bmatrix} 1 & 4 & 2 & 3 \\ 0 & 1 & -2 & 0 \\ 3 & 5 & -1 & 1 \\ 2 & 0 & 6 & 1 \end{bmatrix}$$

30. Evaluate $\begin{vmatrix} 6 & 4 & 3 & 0 & 6 \\ 0 & 5 & 1 & 4 & 8 \\ 0 & 0 & 2 & 7 & 3 \\ 0 & 0 & 0 & 9 & 2 \\ 0 & 0 & 0 & 0 & 1 \end{vmatrix}$.

31. Use a determinant to find the area of the triangle with vertices (0, 7), (5, 0), and (3, 9).

32. Use a determinant to find the equation of the line through (2, 7) and (−1, 4).

For Exercises 33–35, use Cramer's Rule to find the indicated value.

33. Find x.

$6x - 7y = 4$
$2x + 5y = 11$

34. Find z.

$3x + z = 1$
$y + 4z = 3$
$x - y = 2$

35. Find y.

$721.4x - 29.1y = 33.77$
$45.9x + 105.6y = 19.85$

CHAPTER 8
Sequences, Series, and Probability

Section 8.1	Sequences and Series	**690**
Section 8.2	Arithmetic Sequences and Partial Sums	**705**
Section 8.3	Geometric Sequences and Series	**713**
Section 8.4	Mathematical Induction	**724**
Section 8.5	The Binomial Theorem	**738**
Section 8.6	Counting Principles	**748**
Section 8.7	Probability	**753**
Review Exercises		**759**
Practice Test		**770**

CHAPTER 8
Sequences, Series, and Probability

Section 8.1 Sequences and Series

- Given the general nth term in a sequence, you should be able to find, or list, some of the terms.
- You should be able to find an expression for the nth term of a sequence.
- You should be able to use and evaluate factorials.
- You should be able to use sigma notation for a sum.

Vocabulary Check

1. infinite sequence

2. terms

3. finite

4. recursively

5. factorial

6. summation notation

7. index, upper limit, lower limit

8. series

9. nth partial sum

1. $a_n = 2n + 5$

$a_1 = 2(1) + 5 = 7$

$a_2 = 2(2) + 5 = 9$

$a_3 = 2(3) + 5 = 11$

$a_4 = 2(4) + 5 = 13$

$a_5 = 2(5) + 5 = 15$

2. $a_n = 4n - 7$

$a_1 = 4(1) - 7 = -3$

$a_2 = 4(2) - 7 = 1$

$a_3 = 4(3) - 7 = 5$

$a_4 = 4(4) - 7 = 9$

$a_5 = 4(5) - 7 = 13$

3. $a_n = 2^n$

$a_1 = 2^1 = 2$

$a_2 = 2^2 = 4$

$a_3 = 2^3 = 8$

$a_4 = 2^4 = 16$

$a_5 = 2^5 = 32$

4. $a_n = \left(\frac{1}{2}\right)^n$

$a_1 = \left(\frac{1}{2}\right)^1 = \frac{1}{2}$

$a_2 = \left(\frac{1}{2}\right)^2 = \frac{1}{4}$

$a_3 = \left(\frac{1}{2}\right)^3 = \frac{1}{8}$

$a_4 = \left(\frac{1}{2}\right)^4 = \frac{1}{16}$

$a_5 = \left(\frac{1}{2}\right)^5 = \frac{1}{32}$

5. $a_n = \left(-\frac{1}{2}\right)^n$

$a_1 = \left(-\frac{1}{2}\right)^1 = -\frac{1}{2}$

$a_2 = \left(-\frac{1}{2}\right)^2 = \frac{1}{4}$

$a_3 = \left(-\frac{1}{2}\right)^3 = -\frac{1}{8}$

$a_4 = \left(-\frac{1}{2}\right)^4 = \frac{1}{16}$

$a_5 = \left(-\frac{1}{2}\right)^5 = -\frac{1}{32}$

6. $a_n = (-2)^n$

$a_1 = (-2)^1 = -2$

$a_2 = (-2)^2 = 4$

$a_3 = (-2)^3 = -8$

$a_4 = (-2)^4 = 16$

$a_5 = (-2)^5 = -32$

7. $a_n = \dfrac{n+1}{n}$

$a_1 = \dfrac{1+1}{1} = 2$

$a_2 = \dfrac{3}{2}$

$a_3 = \dfrac{4}{3}$

$a_4 = \dfrac{5}{4}$

$a_5 = \dfrac{6}{5}$

8. $a_n = \dfrac{n}{n+1}$

$a_1 = \dfrac{1}{1+1} = \dfrac{1}{2}$

$a_2 = \dfrac{2}{2+1} = \dfrac{2}{3}$

$a_3 = \dfrac{3}{3+1} = \dfrac{3}{4}$

$a_4 = \dfrac{4}{4+1} = \dfrac{4}{5}$

$a_5 = \dfrac{5}{5+1} = \dfrac{5}{6}$

9. $a_n = \dfrac{n}{n^2+1}$

$a_1 = \dfrac{1}{1^2+1} = \dfrac{1}{2}$

$a_2 = \dfrac{2}{2^2+1} = \dfrac{2}{5}$

$a_3 = \dfrac{3}{3^2+1} = \dfrac{3}{10}$

$a_4 = \dfrac{4}{4^2+1} = \dfrac{4}{17}$

$a_5 = \dfrac{5}{5^2+1} = \dfrac{5}{26}$

10. $a_n = \dfrac{2n}{n+1}$

$a_1 = \dfrac{2(1)}{1+1} = 1$

$a_2 = \dfrac{4}{3}$

$a_3 = \dfrac{6}{4} = \dfrac{3}{2}$

$a_4 = \dfrac{8}{5}$

$a_5 = \dfrac{10}{6} = \dfrac{5}{3}$

11. $a_n = \dfrac{1+(-1)^n}{n}$

$a_1 = 0$

$a_2 = \dfrac{2}{2} = 1$

$a_3 = 0$

$a_4 = \dfrac{2}{4} = \dfrac{1}{2}$

$a_5 = 0$

12. $a_n = \dfrac{1+(-1)^n}{2n}$

$a_1 = \dfrac{1-1}{2} = 0$

$a_2 = \dfrac{1+1}{2(2)} = \dfrac{1}{2}$

$a_3 = \dfrac{1-1}{2(3)} = 0$

$a_4 = \dfrac{1+1}{2(4)} = \dfrac{1}{4}$

$a_5 = \dfrac{1-1}{2(5)} = 0$

13. $a_n = 1 - \dfrac{1}{2^n}$

$a_1 = 1 - \dfrac{1}{2^1} = \dfrac{1}{2}$

$a_2 = 1 - \dfrac{1}{2^2} = 1 - \dfrac{1}{4} = \dfrac{3}{4}$

$a_3 = 1 - \dfrac{1}{2^3} = \dfrac{7}{8}$

$a_4 = 1 - \dfrac{1}{2^4} = \dfrac{15}{16}$

$a_5 = 1 - \dfrac{1}{2^5} = \dfrac{31}{32}$

14. $a_n = \dfrac{3^n}{4^n}$

$a_1 = \dfrac{3^1}{4^1} = \dfrac{3}{4}$

$a_2 = \dfrac{3^2}{4^2} = \dfrac{9}{16}$

$a_3 = \dfrac{3^3}{4^3} = \dfrac{27}{64}$

$a_4 = \dfrac{3^4}{4^4} = \dfrac{81}{256}$

$a_5 = \dfrac{3^5}{4^5} = \dfrac{243}{1024}$

15. $a_n = \dfrac{1}{n^{3/2}}$

$a_1 = \dfrac{1}{1} = 1$

$a_2 = \dfrac{1}{2^{3/2}}$

$a_3 = \dfrac{1}{3^{3/2}}$

$a_4 = \dfrac{1}{4^{3/2}} = \dfrac{1}{8}$

$a_5 = \dfrac{1}{5^{3/2}}$

16. $a_n = \dfrac{1}{\sqrt{n}}$

$a_1 = 1$

$a_2 = \dfrac{1}{\sqrt{2}}$

$a_3 = \dfrac{1}{\sqrt{3}}$

$a_4 = \dfrac{1}{\sqrt{4}} = \dfrac{1}{2}$

$a_5 = \dfrac{1}{\sqrt{5}}$

17. $a_n = \dfrac{(-1)^n}{n^2}$

$a_1 = \dfrac{-1}{1} = -1$

$a_2 = \dfrac{1}{4}$

$a_3 = \dfrac{-1}{9}$

$a_4 = \dfrac{1}{16}$

$a_5 = \dfrac{-1}{25}$

18. $a_n = (-1)^n\left(\dfrac{n}{n+1}\right)$

$a_1 = (-1)^1\dfrac{1}{1+1} = -\dfrac{1}{2}$

$a_2 = (-1)^2\dfrac{2}{1+2} = \dfrac{2}{3}$

$a_3 = (-1)^3\dfrac{3}{3+1} = -\dfrac{3}{4}$

$a_4 = (-1)^4\dfrac{4}{4+1} = \dfrac{4}{5}$

$a_5 = (-1)^5\dfrac{5}{5+1} = -\dfrac{5}{6}$

19. $a_n = (2n-1)(2n+1)$

$a_1 = (1)(3) = 3$

$a_2 = (3)(5) = 15$

$a_3 = (5)(7) = 35$

$a_4 = (7)(9) = 63$

$a_5 = (9)(11) = 99$

20. $a_n = n(n-1)(n-2)$

$a_1 = 1(1-1)(1-2) = 0$

$a_2 = 2(2-1)(2-2) = 0$

$a_3 = 3(3-1)(3-2) = 6$

$a_4 = 4(4-1)(4-2) = 24$

$a_5 = 5(5-1)(5-2) = 60$

21. $a_{25} = (-1)^{25}[3(25) - 2] = -73$

22. $a_{16} = (-1)^{15}[16(15)] = -240$

23. $a_{10} = \dfrac{10^2}{10^2+1} = \dfrac{100}{101}$

24. $a_n = \dfrac{n^2}{2n+1}$

$a_5 = \dfrac{5^2}{2(5)+1} = \dfrac{25}{11}$

25. $a_6 = \dfrac{2^6}{2^6+1} = \dfrac{64}{65}$

26. $a_7 = \dfrac{2^{7+1}}{2^7+1} = \dfrac{2^8}{2^7+1} = \dfrac{256}{129}$

27. $a_n = \dfrac{2}{3}n$

28. $a_n = 2 - \dfrac{4}{n}$

29. $a_n = 16(-0.5)^{n-1}$

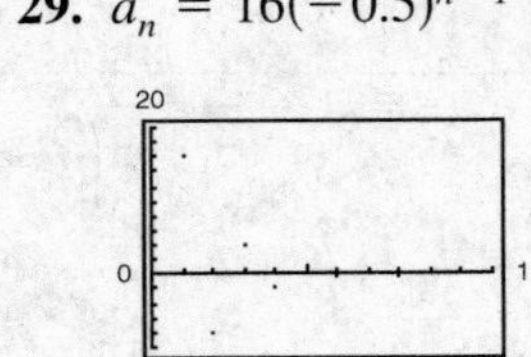

30. $a_n = 8(0.75)^{n-1}$

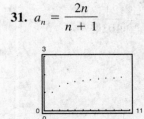

31. $a_n = \dfrac{2n}{n+1}$

32. $a_n = \dfrac{3n^2}{n^2+1}$

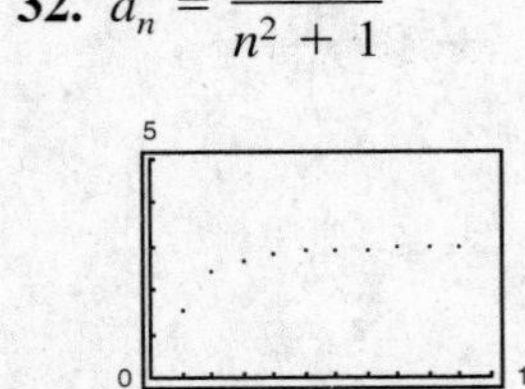

33. $a_n = 2(3n - 1) + 5$

n	1	2	3	4	5	6	7	8	9	10
a_n	9	15	21	27	33	39	45	51	57	63

34. $a_n = 2n(n + 1)(n + 2)$

n	1	2	3	4	5	6	7	8	9	10
a_n	12	48	120	240	420	672	1008	1440	1980	2640

35. $a_n = 1 + \dfrac{n + 1}{n}$

n	1	2	3	4	5	6	7	8	9	10
a_n	3	2.5	2.33	2.25	2.2	2.17	2.14	2.13	2.11	2.1

36. $a_n = \dfrac{4n^2}{(n + 2)}$

n	1	2	3	4	5	6	7	8	9	10
a_n	$\frac{4}{3}$	4	7.2	10.67	14.29	18	21.78	25.6	29.45	33.33

37. $a_n = (-1)^n + 1$

n	1	2	3	4	5	6	7	8	9	10
a_n	0	2	0	2	0	2	0	2	0	2

38. $a_n = (-1)^{n+1} + 1$

n	1	2	3	4	5	6	7	8	9	10
a_n	2	0	2	0	2	0	2	0	2	0

39. $a_n = \dfrac{8}{n + 1}$

$a_n \to 0$ as $n \to \infty$

$a_1 = 4,\ a_{10} = \dfrac{8}{11}$

Matches graph (c).

40. $a_n = \dfrac{8n}{n + 1}$

$a_n \to 8$ as $n \to \infty$

$a_1 = 4,\ a_4 = \dfrac{8(4)}{5} = \dfrac{32}{5}$

Matches graph (b).

41. $a_n = 4(0.5)^{n-1}$

$a_n \to 0$ as $n \to \infty$

$a_1 = 4,\ a_{10} \approx 0.008$

Matches graph (d).

42. $a_n = \dfrac{4^n}{n!}$

$a_n \to 0$ as $n \to \infty$

$a_1 = 4, a_4 = \dfrac{4^4}{4!} = \dfrac{256}{24} = 10\dfrac{2}{3}$

Matches graph (a).

43. 1, 4, 7, 10, 13, . . .

$a_n = 1 + (n - 1)3 = 3n - 2$

44. 3, 7, 11, 15, 19, . . .

$a_n = 4n - 1$

45. 0, 3, 8, 15, 24, . . .

$a_n = n^2 - 1$

46. $1, \dfrac{1}{4}, \dfrac{1}{9}, \dfrac{1}{16}, \dfrac{1}{25}, \ldots$

$a_n = \dfrac{1}{n^2}$

47. $\dfrac{2}{3}, \dfrac{3}{4}, \dfrac{4}{5}, \dfrac{5}{6}, \dfrac{6}{7}, \ldots$

$a_n = \dfrac{n+1}{n+2}$

48. $\dfrac{2}{1}, \dfrac{3}{3}, \dfrac{4}{5}, \dfrac{5}{7}, \dfrac{6}{9}, \ldots$

$a_n = \dfrac{n+1}{2n-1}$

49. $\dfrac{1}{2}, \dfrac{-1}{4}, \dfrac{1}{8}, \dfrac{-1}{16}, \ldots$

$a_n = \dfrac{(-1)^{n+1}}{2^n}$

50. $\dfrac{1}{3}, \dfrac{-2}{9}, \dfrac{4}{27}, \dfrac{-8}{81}, \ldots$

$a_n = \dfrac{(-1)^{n+1}2^{n-1}}{3^n} = \dfrac{(-2)^{n-1}}{3^n}$

51. $1 + \dfrac{1}{1}, 1 + \dfrac{1}{2}, 1 + \dfrac{1}{3}, 1 + \dfrac{1}{4}, 1 + \dfrac{1}{5}, \ldots$

$a_n = 1 + \dfrac{1}{n}$

52. $1 + \dfrac{1}{2}, 1 + \dfrac{3}{4}, 1 + \dfrac{7}{8}, 1 + \dfrac{15}{16}, 1 + \dfrac{31}{32}, \ldots$

$a_n = 1 + \dfrac{2^n - 1}{2^n}$

53. $1, \dfrac{1}{2}, \dfrac{1}{6}, \dfrac{1}{24}, \dfrac{1}{120}, \ldots$

$a_n = \dfrac{1}{n!}$

54. $1, 2, \dfrac{2^2}{2}, \dfrac{2^3}{6}, \dfrac{2^4}{24}, \dfrac{2^5}{120}, \ldots$

$a_n = \dfrac{2^{n-1}}{(n-1)!}$

55. 1, 3, 1, 3, 1, 3, . . .

$a_n = 2 + (-1)^n$

56. 1, −1, 1, −1, 1, −1, . . .

$a_n = (-1)^{n+1}$

57. $a_1 = 28$ and $a_{k+1} = a_k - 4$

$a_1 = 28$

$a_2 = a_1 - 4 = 28 - 4 = 24$

$a_3 = a_2 - 4 = 24 - 4 = 20$

$a_4 = a_3 - 4 = 20 - 4 = 16$

$a_5 = a_4 - 4 = 16 - 4 = 12$

58. $a_1 = 15, \quad a_{k+1} = a_k + 3$

$a_1 = 15$

$a_2 = a_1 + 3 = 15 + 3 = 18$

$a_3 = a_2 + 3 = 18 + 3 = 21$

$a_4 = a_3 + 3 = 21 + 3 = 24$

$a_5 = a_4 + 3 = 24 + 3 = 27$

59. $a_1 = 3$ and $a_{k+1} = 2(a_k - 1)$

$a_1 = 3$

$a_2 = 2(a_1 - 1) = 2(3 - 1) = 4$

$a_3 = 2(a_2 - 1) = 2(4 - 1) = 6$

$a_4 = 2(a_3 - 1) = 2(6 - 1) = 10$

$a_5 = 2(a_4 - 1) = 2(10 - 1) = 18$

60. $a_1 = 32, \quad a_{k+1} = \frac{1}{2}a_k$

$a_1 = 32$

$a_2 = \frac{1}{2}a_1 = \frac{1}{2}(32) = 16$

$a_3 = \frac{1}{2}a_2 = \frac{1}{2}(16) = 8$

$a_4 = \frac{1}{2}a_3 = \frac{1}{2}(8) = 4$

$a_5 = \frac{1}{2}a_4 = \frac{1}{2}(4) = 2$

61. $a_1 = 6$ and $a_{k+1} = a_k + 2$

$a_1 = 6$

$a_2 = a_1 + 2 = 6 + 2 = 8$

$a_3 = a_2 + 2 = 8 + 2 = 10$

$a_4 = a_3 + 2 = 10 + 2 = 12$

$a_5 = a_4 + 2 = 12 + 2 = 14$

In general, $a_n = 2n + 4$.

62. $a_1 = 25,\ a_{k+1} = a_k - 5$

$a_1 = 25$

$a_2 = a_1 - 5 = 25 - 5 = 20$

$a_3 = a_2 - 5 = 20 - 5 = 15$

$a_4 = a_3 - 5 = 15 - 5 = 10$

$a_5 = a_4 - 5 = 10 - 5 = 5$

In general, $a_n = 30 - 5n$.

63. $a_1 = 81$ and $a_{k+1} = \frac{1}{3}a_k$

$a_1 = 81$

$a_2 = \frac{1}{3}a_1 = \frac{1}{3}(81) = 27$

$a_3 = \frac{1}{3}a_2 = \frac{1}{3}(27) = 9$

$a_4 = \frac{1}{3}a_3 = \frac{1}{3}(9) = 3$

$a_5 = \frac{1}{3}a_4 = \frac{1}{3}(3) = 1$

In general, $a_n = 81\left(\frac{1}{3}\right)^{n-1} = 81(3)\left(\frac{1}{3}\right)^n = \frac{243}{3^n}$.

64. $a_1 = 14,\ a_{k+1} = (-2)a_k$

$a_1 = 14$

$a_2 = (-2)a_1 = (-2)(14) = -28$

$a_3 = (-2)a_2 = (-2)(-28) = 56$

$a_4 = (-2)a_3 = (-2)(56) = -112$

$a_5 = (-2)(a_4) = (-2)(-112) = 224$

In general, $a_n = 14(-2)^{n-1}$.

65. $a_n = \frac{1}{n!}$

$a_0 = \frac{1}{0!} = 1$

$a_1 = \frac{1}{1!} = 1$

$a_2 = \frac{1}{2}$

$a_3 = \frac{1}{3!} = \frac{1}{6}$

$a_4 = \frac{1}{4!} = \frac{1}{24}$

66. $a_n = \frac{1}{(n+1)!}$

$a_0 = \frac{1}{1!} = 1$

$a_1 = \frac{1}{2!} = \frac{1}{2}$

$a_2 = \frac{1}{3!} = \frac{1}{6}$

$a_3 = \frac{1}{4!} = \frac{1}{24}$

$a_4 = \frac{1}{5!} = \frac{1}{120}$

67. $a_n = \frac{n!}{2n+1}$

$a_0 = \frac{0!}{1} = 1$

$a_1 = \frac{1!}{2+1} = \frac{1}{3}$

$a_2 = \frac{2!}{4+1} = \frac{2}{5}$

$a_3 = \frac{3!}{6+1} = \frac{6}{7}$

$a_4 = \frac{4!}{8+1} = \frac{24}{9} = \frac{8}{3}$

68. $a_n = \frac{n^2}{(n+1)!}$

$a_0 = 0$

$a_1 = \frac{1}{2}$

$a_2 = \frac{2^2}{3!} = \frac{2}{3}$

$a_3 = \frac{3^2}{4!} = \frac{9}{24} = \frac{3}{8}$

$a_4 = \frac{16}{5!} = \frac{16}{120} = \frac{2}{15}$

69. $a_n = \frac{(-1)^{2n}}{(2n)!}$

$a_0 = \frac{(-1)^0}{0!} = 1$

$a_1 = \frac{(-1)^2}{2!} = \frac{1}{2}$

$a_2 = \frac{(-1)^4}{4!} = \frac{1}{24}$

$a_3 = \frac{(-1)^6}{6!} = \frac{1}{720}$

$a_4 = \frac{(-1)^8}{8!} = \frac{1}{40,320}$

70. $a_n = \frac{(-1)^{2n+1}}{(2n+1)!}$

$a_0 = \frac{-1^1}{1!} = -1$

$a_1 = \frac{(-1)^3}{3!} = \frac{-1}{6}$

$a_2 = \frac{-1}{5!} = \frac{-1}{120}$

$a_3 = \frac{-1}{7!} = \frac{-1}{5040}$

$a_4 = \frac{-1}{9!} = \frac{-1}{362,880}$

71. $\frac{2!}{4!} = \frac{2!}{4 \cdot 3 \cdot 2!} = \frac{1}{12}$

72. $\frac{5!}{7!} = \frac{5!}{7(6)(5!)} = \frac{1}{42}$

73. $\frac{12!}{4!8!} = \frac{12 \cdot 11 \cdot 10 \cdot 9 \cdot 8!}{4!8!}$

$= \frac{12 \cdot 11 \cdot 10 \cdot 9}{4 \cdot 3 \cdot 2} = 495$

74. $\frac{10!\,3!}{4!\,6!} = \frac{10 \cdot 9 \cdot 8 \cdot 7 \cdot 6! \cdot 3!}{4 \cdot 3! \cdot 6!}$

$= \frac{10 \cdot 9 \cdot 8 \cdot 7}{4} = 1260$

75. $\frac{(n+1)!}{n!} = \frac{(n+1)n!}{n!} = n + 1$

76. $\frac{(n+2)!}{n!} = \frac{(n+2)(n+1)n!}{n!} = (n+2)(n+1)$

77. $\frac{(2n-1)!}{(2n+1)!} = \frac{(2n-1)!}{(2n+1)(2n)(2n-1)!}$

$= \frac{1}{2n(2n+1)}$

78. $\frac{(2n+2)!}{(2n)!} = \frac{(2n+2)(2n+1)(2n)!}{(2n)!}$

$= (2n+2)(2n+1)$

79. $\sum_{i=1}^{5} (2i + 1) = (2 + 1) + (4 + 1) + (6 + 1) + (8 + 1) + (10 + 1) = 35$

80. $\sum_{i=1}^{6} (3i - 1) = (3 \cdot 1 - 1) + (3 \cdot 2 - 1) + (3 \cdot 3 - 1) + (3 \cdot 4 - 1) + (3 \cdot 5 - 1) + (3 \cdot 6 - 1) = 57$

81. $\sum_{k=1}^{4} 10 = 10 + 10 + 10 + 10 = 40$

82. $\sum_{k=1}^{5} 6 = 6 + 6 + 6 + 6 + 6 = 30$

83. $\sum_{i=0}^{4} i^2 = 0^2 + 1^2 + 2^2 + 3^2 + 4^2 = 30$

84. $\sum_{k=0}^{5} 3i^2 = 3\sum_{i=0}^{5} i^2$

$= 3(0^2 + 1^2 + 2^2 + 3^2 + 4^2 + 5^2) = 165$

85. $\sum_{k=0}^{3} \frac{1}{k^2 + 1} = \frac{1}{1} + \frac{1}{1+1} + \frac{1}{4+1} + \frac{1}{9+1} = \frac{9}{5}$

86. $\sum_{j=3}^{5} \frac{1}{j} = \frac{1}{3} + \frac{1}{4} + \frac{1}{5} = \frac{47}{60}$

87. $\sum_{i=1}^{4}[(i-1)^2+(i+1)^3] = [(0)^2+(2)^3]+[(1)^2+(3)^3]+[(2)^2+(4)^3]+[(3)^2+(5)^3] = 238$

88. $\sum_{k=2}^{5}(k+1)(k-3) = (2+1)(2-3)+(3+1)(3-3)+(4+1)(4-3)+(5+1)(5-3) = 14$

89. $\sum_{i=1}^{4}2^i = 2^1+2^2+2^3+2^4 = 30$

90. $\sum_{j=0}^{4}(-2)^j = (-2)^0+(-2)^1+(-2)^2+(-2)^3+(-2)^4 = 11$

91. $\sum_{j=1}^{6}(24-3j) = 81$

92. $\sum_{j=1}^{10}\frac{3}{j+1} \approx 6.06$

93. $\sum_{k=0}^{4}\frac{(-1)^k}{k+1} = \frac{47}{60}$

94. $\sum_{k=0}^{4}\frac{(-1)^k}{k!} = \frac{3}{8} = 0.375$

95. $\frac{1}{3(1)}+\frac{1}{3(2)}+\frac{1}{3(3)}+\cdots+\frac{1}{3(9)} = \sum_{i=1}^{9}\frac{1}{3i} \approx 0.94299$

96. $\frac{5}{1+1}+\frac{5}{1+2}+\frac{5}{1+3}+\cdots+\frac{5}{1+15} = \sum_{i=1}^{15}\frac{5}{1+i} \approx 11.904$

97. $\left[2\left(\frac{1}{8}\right)+3\right]+\left[2\left(\frac{2}{8}\right)+3\right]+\left[2\left(\frac{3}{8}\right)+3\right]+\cdots+\left[2\left(\frac{8}{8}\right)+3\right] = \sum_{i=1}^{8}\left[2\left(\frac{i}{8}\right)+3\right] = 33$

98. $\left[1-\left(\frac{1}{6}\right)^2\right]+\left[1-\left(\frac{2}{6}\right)^2\right]+\cdots+\left[1-\left(\frac{6}{6}\right)^2\right] = \sum_{k=1}^{6}\left[1-\left(\frac{k}{6}\right)^2\right] \approx 3.472$

99. $3-9+27-81+243-729 = \sum_{i=1}^{6}(-1)^{i+1}3^i = -546$

100. $1-\frac{1}{2}+\frac{1}{4}-\frac{1}{8}+\cdots-\frac{1}{128} = \frac{1}{2^0}-\frac{1}{2^1}+\frac{1}{2^2}-\frac{1}{2^3}+\cdots-\frac{1}{2^7} = \sum_{n=0}^{7}\left(-\frac{1}{2}\right)^n \approx 0.664$

101. $\frac{1}{1^2}-\frac{1}{2^2}+\frac{1}{3^2}-\frac{1}{4^2}+\cdots-\frac{1}{20^2} = \sum_{i=1}^{20}\frac{(-1)^{i+1}}{i^2} \approx 0.82128$

102. $\frac{1}{1\cdot 3}+\frac{1}{2\cdot 4}+\frac{1}{3\cdot 5}+\cdots+\frac{1}{10\cdot 12} = \sum_{k=1}^{10}\frac{1}{k(k+2)} \approx 0.663$

103. $\frac{1}{4}+\frac{3}{8}+\frac{7}{16}+\frac{15}{32}+\frac{31}{64} = \sum_{i=1}^{5}\frac{2^i-1}{2^{i+1}} = \frac{129}{64} = 2.015625$

104. $\frac{1}{2} + \frac{2}{4} + \frac{6}{8} + \frac{24}{16} + \frac{120}{32} + \frac{720}{64} = \sum_{k=1}^{6} \frac{k!}{2^k} = 18.25$

105. $\sum_{i=1}^{4} 5\left(\frac{1}{2}\right)^i = 4.6875 = \frac{75}{16}$

106. $\sum_{i=1}^{5} 2\left(\frac{1}{3}\right)^i = \frac{242}{243} \approx 0.9959$

107. $\sum_{n=1}^{3} 4\left(-\frac{1}{2}\right)^n = -1.5 = -\frac{3}{2}$

108. $\sum_{n=1}^{4} 8\left(-\frac{1}{4}\right)^n = \frac{-51}{32} \approx -1.59375$

109. (a) $\sum_{i=1}^{4} 6\left(\frac{1}{10}\right)^i = 6\left(\frac{1}{10}\right) + 6\left(\frac{1}{10}\right)^2 + 6\left(\frac{1}{10}\right)^3 + 6\left(\frac{1}{10}\right)^4$

$= 0.6666$

$= \frac{3333}{5000}$

(b) $\sum_{i=1}^{\infty} 6\left(\frac{1}{10}\right)^i = 6[0.1 + 0.01 + 0.001 + \dots]$

$= 6[0.111\dots]$

$= 0.666\dots$

$= \frac{2}{3}$

110. (a) $\sum_{k=1}^{4} 4\left(\frac{1}{10}\right)^k = 4\left(\frac{1}{10}\right) + 4\left(\frac{1}{10}\right)^2 + 4\left(\frac{1}{10}\right)^3 + 4\left(\frac{1}{10}\right)^4$

$= 0.4444$

$= \frac{1111}{2500}$

(b) $\sum_{k=1}^{\infty} 4\left(\frac{1}{10}\right)^k = 4[0.1 + 0.01 + 0.001 + \dots]$

$= 4[0.111\dots]$

$= 0.444\dots$

$= \frac{4}{9}$

111. (a) $\sum_{k=1}^{4} \left(\frac{1}{10}\right)^k = \frac{1}{10} + \frac{1}{100} + \frac{1}{1000} + \frac{1}{10,000}$

$= 0.1111$

$= \frac{1111}{10,000}$

(b) $\sum_{k=1}^{\infty} \left(\frac{1}{10}\right)^k = 0.1 + 0.01 + 0.001 + \dots$

$= 0.111\dots$

$= \frac{1}{9}$

112. (a) $\sum_{i=1}^{4} 2\left(\frac{1}{10}\right)^i = 2(0.1) + 2(0.01) + 2(0.001) + 2(0.0001)$

$= 2(0.1111)$

$= 0.2222$

$= \frac{1111}{5000}$

(b) $\sum_{i=1}^{\infty} 2\left(\frac{1}{10}\right)^i = 2(0.1) + 2(0.01) + 2(0.001) + \dots$

$= 0.2222\dots$

$= \frac{2}{9}$

113. $A_n = 5000\left(1 + \frac{0.03}{4}\right)^n, \quad n = 1, 2, 3, \ldots$

(a) $A_1 = 5000\left(1 + \frac{0.03}{4}\right)^1 = \$5037.50$

$A_2 \approx \$5075.28 \qquad A_3 \approx \$5113.35$

$A_4 \approx \$5151.70 \qquad A_5 \approx \$5190.33$

$A_6 \approx \$5229.26 \qquad A_7 \approx \$5268.48$

$A_8 \approx \$5307.99$

(b) $A_{40} \approx \$6741.74$

114. (a) $A_1 = 100(101)[(1.01)^1 - 1] = \$101.00$

$A_2 = 100(101)[(1.01)^2 - 1] = \$203.01$

$A_3 = 100(101)[(1.01)^3 - 1] \approx \$306.04$

$A_4 = 100(101)[(1.01)^4 - 1] \approx \$410.10$

$A_5 = 100(101)[(1.01)^5 - 1] \approx \$515.20$

$A_6 = 100(101)[(1.01)^6 - 1] \approx \$621.35$

(b) $A_{60} = 100(101)[(1.01)^{60} - 1] \approx \$8248.64$

(c) $A_{240} = 100(101)[(1.01)^{240} - 1] \approx \$99{,}914.79$

115. (a) $p_0 = 5500$ (year 2008)

$p_n = 0.75p_{n-1} + 500$

(b) $p_1 = 0.75p_0 + 500 = 4625$ (2009)

$p_2 = 0.75p_1 + 500 \approx 3969$ (2010)

$p_3 = 0.75p_2 + 500 \approx 3477$ (2011)

(Answers will vary slightly.)

(c) The population approaches 2000 trout because $0.75(2000) + 500 = 2000$.

116. (a) $t_0 = 10{,}000$ (year 2010)

$t_n = 0.9t_{n-1} + 750$

(b) $t_1 = 0.9t_0 + 750 = 9750$

$t_2 = 0.9t_1 + 750 = 9525$

$t_3 \approx 9323$

$t_4 \approx 9140$

(c) The number of trees approaches 7500 because $0.9(7500) + 750 = 7500$.

117. (a) $a_0 = 50$ (end of January)

$a_n = \left(1 + \frac{0.06}{12}\right)a_{n-1} + 50 = 1.005a_{n-1} + 50$

(b) $a_1 = 1.005\, a_0 + 50 = 100.25$ (end of February)

$a_2 = 1.005\, a_1 + 50 = 150.75$

$a_3 = 201.51 \qquad a_4 = 252.51$

$a_5 = 303.78 \qquad a_6 = 355.29$

$a_7 = 407.07 \qquad a_8 = 459.11$

$a_9 = 511.40 \qquad a_{10} = 563.96$

$a_{11} = 616.78$ (end of December)

After one year, the IRA has \$616.78.

(c) After 50 deposits, $a_{49} \approx \$2832.26$.

118. Monthly interest rate is $\frac{0.09}{12} = 0.0075$.

(a) $b_0 = 150{,}000$

$b_1 = b_0(1.0075) - 1206.94 = 149{,}918.06$

$b_n = b_{n-1}(1.0075) - 1206.94$

(b)

n	0	60	120	180	240	300	360
b_n	150,000	143,819.75	134,143.44	118,993.43	95,273.35	58,135.27	−11.12

(c) Total amount: $1206.94 \times 360 - 11.12 = \$434.487.28$

(d) Total interest: $434{,}487.28 - \$150{,}000 = \$284{,}487.28$

119. (a)

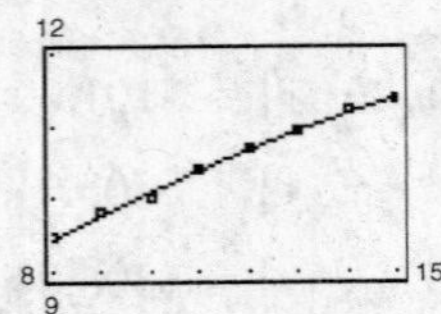

(b) For 2010, $n = 20$ and $r_{20} \approx \$12.25$.

For 2015, $n = 25$ and $r_{25} \approx \$12.64$.

(c) Answers will vary.

(d) $r_{18} = 11.97$ and $r_{19} = 12.12$. So, the average hourly wage reaches \$12 in 2008.

120. (a)

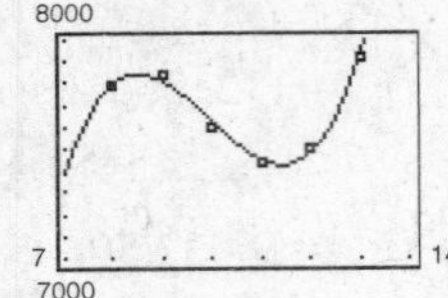

(b) For 2005, $n = 15$ and $S_{15} \approx 10{,}876$ thousand.

For 2010, $n = 20$ and $S_{20} \approx 39{,}671$ thousand.

For 2015, $n = 25$ and $S_{25} \approx 119{,}349$ thousand.

(c) Answers will vary.

121. (a)

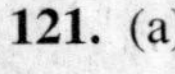

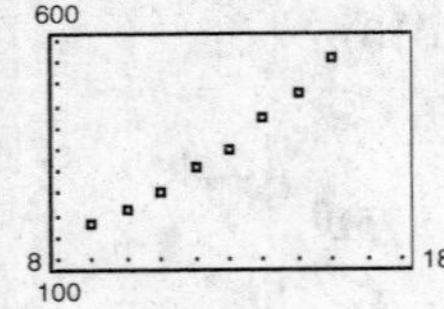

(b) Linear: $R_n = 54.58n - 336.3$

Quadratic: $R_n = 3.088n^2 - 22.62n + 130.0$

Coefficient of determination for linear model: 0.98656

Coefficient of determination for quadratic model: 0.99919

(c)

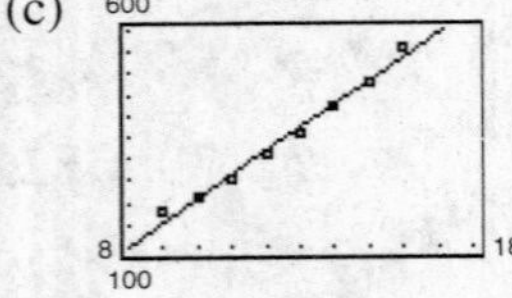

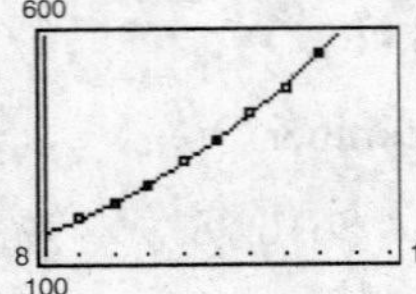

(d) The quadratic model is better.

The quadratic model is better because its coefficient of determination is closer to 1.

(e) For 2010, $n = 20$ and $R_{20} \approx 912.8$ million.

For 2015, $n = 25$ and $R_{25} \approx 1494.5$ million.

(f) $R_n = 1000$ when $n \approx 20.8$, or in 2010.

122. (a)

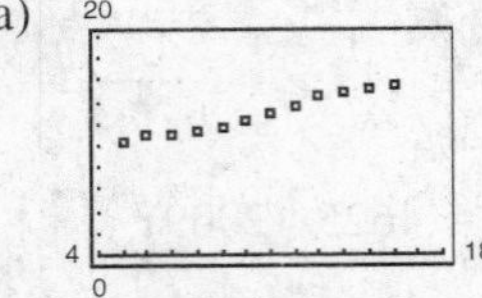

(b) Linear: $S_n = 0.50n + 7.6$

Quadratic: $S_n = 0.012n^2 + 0.24n + 8.8$

Coefficient of determination for linear model: 0.98201

Coefficient of determination for quadratic model: 0.98759

(c)

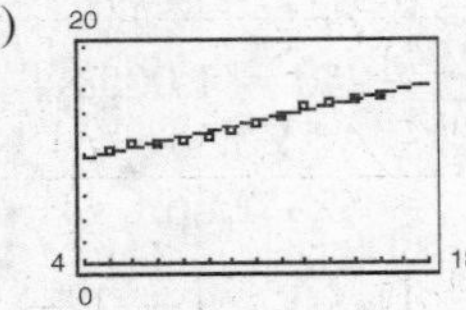

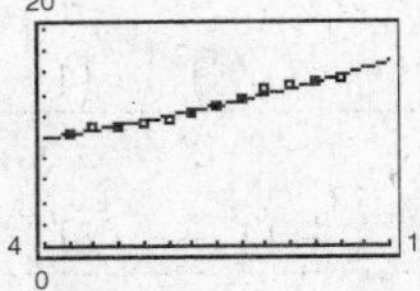

(d) The quadratic model is better.

The quadratic model is better because its coefficient of determination is closer to 1.

(e) For 2010, $n = 20$ and $S_{20} \approx 18.4$ million.

For 2015, $n = 25$ and $S_{25} \approx 22.3$ million.

(f) $S_{22} \approx 19.9$ when $S_{23} \approx 20.7$. So, sales will reach 20 billion in 2012.

123. True

124. True

$$\sum_{j=1}^{4} 2^j = 2^1 + 2^2 + 2^3 + 2^4 = \sum_{j=3}^{6} 2^{j-2}$$

125. $a_0 = 1, a_1 = 1,\ a_{k+2} = a_{k+1} + a_k$

$a_0 = 1$ $\qquad b_0 = \frac{1}{1} = 1$ $\qquad a_6 = 8 + 5 = 13$ $\qquad b_6 = \frac{21}{13}$

$a_1 = 1$ $\qquad b_1 = \frac{2}{1} = 2$ $\qquad a_7 = 13 + 8 = 21$ $\qquad b_7 = \frac{34}{21}$

$a_2 = 1 + 1 = 2$ $\qquad b_2 = \frac{3}{2}$ $\qquad a_8 = 21 + 13 = 34$ $\qquad b_8 = \frac{55}{34}$

$a_3 = 2 + 1 = 3$ $\qquad b_3 = \frac{5}{3}$ $\qquad a_9 = 34 + 21 = 55$ $\qquad b_9 = \frac{89}{55}$

$a_4 = 3 + 2 = 5$ $\qquad b_4 = \frac{8}{5}$ $\qquad a_{10} = 55 + 34 = 89$

$a_5 = 5 + 3 = 8$ $\qquad b_5 = \frac{13}{8}$ $\qquad a_{11} = 89 + 55 = 144$

126. $$b_n = \frac{a_{n+1}}{a_n} = \frac{a_n + a_{n-1}}{a_n}$$
$$= 1 + \frac{a_{n-1}}{a_n} = 1 + \frac{1}{\dfrac{a_n}{a_{n-1}}} = 1 + \frac{1}{b_{n-1}}$$

127. $$a_n = \frac{(1+\sqrt{5})^n - (1-\sqrt{5})^n}{2^n\sqrt{5}}$$
$$a_1 = \frac{(1+\sqrt{5})^1 - (1-\sqrt{5})^1}{2^1\sqrt{5}} = 1$$
$$a_2 = 1, \quad a_3 = 2$$
$$a_4 = 3, \quad a_5 = 5$$

128. These are the first five terms of the Fibonacci sequence.

129. $$a_{n+1} = \frac{(1+\sqrt{5})^{n+1} - (1-\sqrt{5})^{n+1}}{2^{n+1}\sqrt{5}}$$
$$a_{n+2} = \frac{(1+\sqrt{5})^{n+2} - (1-\sqrt{5})^{n+2}}{2^{n+2}\sqrt{5}}$$

130. $$a_{n+1} + a_n = \frac{(1+\sqrt{5})^{n+1} - (1-\sqrt{5})^{n+1}}{2^{n+1}\sqrt{5}} + \frac{(1+\sqrt{5})^n - (1-\sqrt{5})^n}{2^n\sqrt{5}}$$
$$= \frac{2(1+\sqrt{5})^{n+1} - 2(1-\sqrt{5})^{n+1} + 4(1+\sqrt{5})^n - 4(1-\sqrt{5})^n}{2^{n+2}\sqrt{5}}$$
$$= \frac{(1+\sqrt{5})^n[2(1+\sqrt{5}) + 4] - (1-\sqrt{5})^n[2(1-\sqrt{5}) + 4]}{2^{n+2}\sqrt{5}}$$
$$= \frac{(1+\sqrt{5})^n(1+\sqrt{5})^2 - (1-\sqrt{5})^n(1-\sqrt{5})^2}{2^{n+2}\sqrt{5}}$$
$$= \frac{(1+\sqrt{5})^{n+2} - (1-\sqrt{5})^{n+2}}{2^{n+2}\sqrt{5}}$$
$$= a_{n+2}$$

Yes, this is the recursive formula for the Fibonacci sequence.

131. $a_n = \dfrac{x^n}{n!}$

$a_1 = \dfrac{x}{1} = x$

$a_2 = \dfrac{x^2}{2!} = \dfrac{x^2}{2}$

$a_3 = \dfrac{x^3}{3!} = \dfrac{x^3}{6}$

$a_4 = \dfrac{x^4}{4!} = \dfrac{x^4}{24}$

$a_5 = \dfrac{x^5}{5!} = \dfrac{x^5}{120}$

132. $a_n = \dfrac{x^2}{n^2}$

$a_1 = \dfrac{x^2}{1}$

$a_2 = \dfrac{x^2}{4}$

$a_3 = \dfrac{x^2}{9}$

$a_4 = \dfrac{x^2}{16}$

$a_5 = \dfrac{x^2}{25}$

133. $a_n = \dfrac{(-1)^n x^{2n+1}}{2n+1}$

$a_1 = \dfrac{-x^3}{3}$

$a_2 = \dfrac{x^5}{5}$

$a_3 = -\dfrac{x^7}{7}$

$a_4 = \dfrac{x^9}{9}$

$a_5 = \dfrac{-x^{11}}{11}$

134. $a_n = \dfrac{(-1)^n x^{n+1}}{n+1}$

$a_1 = \dfrac{-x^2}{2}$

$a_2 = \dfrac{x^3}{3}$

$a_3 = \dfrac{-x^4}{4}$

$a_4 = \dfrac{x^5}{5}$

$a_5 = \dfrac{-x^6}{6}$

135. $a_n = \dfrac{(-1)^n x^{2n}}{(2n)!}$

$a_1 = \dfrac{-x^2}{2}$

$a_2 = \dfrac{x^4}{4!} = \dfrac{x^4}{24}$

$a_3 = \dfrac{-x^6}{6!} = \dfrac{-x^6}{720}$

$a_4 = \dfrac{x^8}{8!} = \dfrac{x^8}{40{,}320}$

$a_5 = \dfrac{-x^{10}}{10!} = \dfrac{-x^{10}}{3{,}628{,}800}$

136. $a_n = \dfrac{(-1)^n x^{2n+1}}{(2n+1)!}$

$a_1 = \dfrac{-x^3}{3!} = \dfrac{-x^3}{6}$

$a_2 = \dfrac{x^5}{5!} = \dfrac{x^5}{120}$

$a_3 = -\dfrac{x^7}{7!} = \dfrac{-x^7}{5040}$

$a_4 = \dfrac{x^9}{9!} = \dfrac{x^9}{362{,}880}$

$a_5 = \dfrac{-x^{11}}{11!} = \dfrac{-x^{11}}{39{,}916{,}800}$

137. $a_n = \dfrac{(-1)^n x^n}{n!}$

$a_1 = -x$

$a_2 = \dfrac{x^2}{2}$

$a_3 = \dfrac{-x^3}{3!} = \dfrac{-x^3}{6}$

$a_4 = \dfrac{x^4}{4!} = \dfrac{x^4}{24}$

$a_5 = \dfrac{-x^5}{5!} = -\dfrac{x^5}{120}$

138. $a_n = \dfrac{(-1)^n x^{n+1}}{(n+1)!}$

$a_1 = \dfrac{-x^2}{2}$

$a_2 = \dfrac{x^3}{3!} = \dfrac{x^3}{6}$

$a_3 = \dfrac{-x^4}{4!} = -\dfrac{x^4}{24}$

$a_4 = \dfrac{x^5}{5!} = \dfrac{x^5}{120}$

$a_5 = \dfrac{-x^6}{6!} = -\dfrac{x^6}{720}$

139. $a_n = \dfrac{(-1)^{n+1}(x+1)^n}{n!}$

$a_1 = x + 1$

$a_2 = \dfrac{-(x+1)^2}{2}$

$a_3 = \dfrac{(x+1)^3}{6}$

$a_4 = -\dfrac{(x+1)^4}{24}$

$a_5 = \dfrac{(x+1)^5}{120}$

140. $a_n = \dfrac{(-1)^n(x-1)^n}{(n+1)!}$

$a_1 = \dfrac{-(x-1)}{2}$

$a_2 = \dfrac{(x-1)^2}{6}$

$a_3 = \dfrac{-(x-1)^3}{24}$

$a_4 = \dfrac{(x-1)^4}{120}$

$a_5 = \dfrac{-(x-1)^5}{720}$

141. $a_n = \dfrac{1}{2n} - \dfrac{1}{2n+2}$

$a_1 = \dfrac{1}{2} - \dfrac{1}{4} = \dfrac{1}{4}$

$a_2 = \dfrac{1}{4} - \dfrac{1}{6} = \dfrac{1}{12}$

$a_3 = \dfrac{1}{6} - \dfrac{1}{8} = \dfrac{1}{24}$

$a_4 = \dfrac{1}{8} - \dfrac{1}{10} = \dfrac{1}{40}$

$a_5 = \dfrac{1}{10} - \dfrac{1}{12} = \dfrac{1}{60}$

nth partial sum $= \left(\dfrac{1}{2} - \dfrac{1}{4}\right) + \left(\dfrac{1}{4} - \dfrac{1}{6}\right) + \cdots + \left(\dfrac{1}{2n} - \dfrac{1}{2n+2}\right) = \dfrac{1}{2} - \dfrac{1}{2n+2}$

142. $a_n = \dfrac{1}{n} - \dfrac{1}{n+1}$

$a_1 = 1 - \dfrac{1}{2} = \dfrac{1}{2}$

$a_2 = \dfrac{1}{2} - \dfrac{1}{3} = \dfrac{1}{6}$

$a_3 = \dfrac{1}{3} - \dfrac{1}{4} = \dfrac{1}{12}$

$a_4 = \dfrac{1}{4} - \dfrac{1}{5} = \dfrac{1}{20}$

$a_5 = \dfrac{1}{5} - \dfrac{1}{6} = \dfrac{1}{30}$

nth partial sum $= \left(\dfrac{1}{1} - \dfrac{1}{2}\right) + \left(\dfrac{1}{2} - \dfrac{1}{3}\right) + \cdots + \left(\dfrac{1}{n} - \dfrac{1}{n+1}\right) = 1 - \dfrac{1}{n+1}$

143. $a_n = \frac{1}{n+1} - \frac{1}{n+2}$

$a_1 = \frac{1}{2} - \frac{1}{3} = \frac{1}{6}$

$a_2 = \frac{1}{3} - \frac{1}{4} = \frac{1}{12}$

$a_3 = \frac{1}{4} - \frac{1}{5} = \frac{1}{20}$

$a_4 = \frac{1}{5} - \frac{1}{6} = \frac{1}{30}$

$a_5 = \frac{1}{6} - \frac{1}{7} = \frac{1}{42}$

nth partial sum $= \left(\frac{1}{2} - \frac{1}{3}\right) + \left(\frac{1}{3} - \frac{1}{4}\right) + \cdots + \left(\frac{1}{n+1} - \frac{1}{n+2}\right) = \frac{1}{2} - \frac{1}{n+2}$

144. $a_n = \frac{1}{n} - \frac{1}{n+2}$

$a_1 = 1 - \frac{1}{3} = \frac{2}{3}$

$a_2 = \frac{1}{2} - \frac{1}{4} = \frac{1}{4}$

$a_3 = \frac{1}{3} - \frac{1}{5} = \frac{2}{15}$

$a_4 = \frac{1}{4} - \frac{1}{6} = \frac{1}{12}$

$a_5 = \frac{1}{5} - \frac{1}{7} = \frac{2}{35}$

nth partial sum $= \left(1 - \frac{1}{3}\right) + \left(\frac{1}{2} - \frac{1}{4}\right) + \left(\frac{1}{3} - \frac{1}{5}\right) + \cdots + \left(\frac{1}{n-1} - \frac{1}{n+1}\right) + \left(\frac{1}{n} - \frac{1}{n+2}\right)$

$= \left(1 + \frac{1}{2}\right) - \left(\frac{1}{n+1} + \frac{1}{n+2}\right) = \frac{3}{2} - \frac{1}{n+1} - \frac{1}{n+2}$

145. $a_n = \ln n$

$a_1 = \ln 1 = 0$

$a_2 = \ln 2$

$a_3 = \ln 3$

$a_4 = \ln 4$

$a_5 = \ln 5$

nth partial sum $= \ln 2 + \ln 3 + \cdots + \ln n$

$= \ln(2 \cdot 3 \cdots n)$

$= \ln(n!)$

146. $a_n = 1 - \ln(n + 1)$

$a_1 = 1 - \ln 2$

$a_2 = 1 - \ln 3$

$a_3 = 1 - \ln 4$

$a_4 = 1 - \ln 5$

$a_5 = 1 - \ln 6$

$$\begin{aligned} n\text{th partial sum} &= (1 - \ln 2) + (1 - \ln 3) + \cdots + (1 - \ln(n + 1)) \\ &= n - [\ln 2 + \ln 3 + \cdots + \ln(n + 1)] \\ &= n - \ln(2 \cdot 3 \cdots (n + 1)) \\ &= n - \ln((n + 1)!) \end{aligned}$$

147. (a) $A - B = \begin{bmatrix} 8 & 1 \\ -3 & 7 \end{bmatrix}$

(b) $2B - 3A = \begin{bmatrix} -22 & -7 \\ 3 & -18 \end{bmatrix}$

(c) $AB = \begin{bmatrix} 18 & 9 \\ 18 & 0 \end{bmatrix}$

(d) $BA = \begin{bmatrix} 0 & 6 \\ 27 & 18 \end{bmatrix}$

148. (a) $A - B = \begin{bmatrix} 10 & 19 \\ -12 & -5 \end{bmatrix}$

(b) $2B - 3A = \begin{bmatrix} -30 & -45 \\ 28 & 4 \end{bmatrix}$

(c) $AB = \begin{bmatrix} 56 & -43 \\ 48 & 114 \end{bmatrix}$

(d) $BA = \begin{bmatrix} 48 & -72 \\ 36 & 122 \end{bmatrix}$

149. (a) $A - B = \begin{bmatrix} -3 & -7 & 4 \\ 4 & 4 & 1 \\ 1 & 4 & 3 \end{bmatrix}$

(b) $2B - 3A = \begin{bmatrix} 8 & 17 & -14 \\ -12 & -13 & -9 \\ -3 & -15 & -10 \end{bmatrix}$

(c) $AB = \begin{bmatrix} -2 & 7 & -16 \\ 4 & 42 & 45 \\ 1 & 23 & 48 \end{bmatrix}$

(d) $BA = \begin{bmatrix} 16 & 31 & 42 \\ 10 & 47 & 31 \\ 13 & 22 & 25 \end{bmatrix}$

150. (a) $A - B = \begin{bmatrix} -1 & 0 & 0 \\ 2 & 0 & 4 \\ 1 & -1 & 1 \end{bmatrix}$

(b) $2B - 3A = \begin{bmatrix} 3 & -4 & 0 \\ -9 & -1 & -10 \\ -2 & 3 & -5 \end{bmatrix}$

(c) $AB = \begin{bmatrix} 12 & 0 & -8 \\ 1 & 21 & 2 \\ -6 & -1 & 8 \end{bmatrix}$

(d) $BA = \begin{bmatrix} 20 & 4 & 8 \\ 2 & 15 & -4 \\ 1 & -6 & 6 \end{bmatrix}$

Section 8.2 Arithmetic Sequences and Partial Sums

- You should be able to recognize an arithmetic sequence, find its common difference, and find its nth term.
- You should be able to find the nth partial sum of an arithmetic sequence with common difference d using the formula

$$S_n = \frac{n}{2}(a_1 + a_n).$$

Vocabulary Check

1. arithmetic, common
2. $a_n = dn + c$
3. nth partial sum

1. 10, 8, 6, 4, 2, . . .

Arithmetic sequence, $d = -2$

2. 4, 9, 14, 19, 24, . . .

Arithmetic sequence, $d = 5$

3. $3, \frac{5}{2}, 2, \frac{3}{2}, 1, \ldots$

Arithmetic sequence, $d = -\frac{1}{2}$

4. $\frac{1}{3}, \frac{2}{3}, \frac{4}{3}, \frac{8}{3}, \frac{16}{3}, \ldots$

Not an arithmetic sequence

5. $-24, -16, -8, 0, 8$

Arithmetic sequence, $d = 8$

6. ln 1, ln 2, ln 3, ln 4, ln 5, . . .

Not an arithmetic sequence

7. 3.7, 4.3, 4.9, 5.5, 6.1, . . .

Arithmetic sequence, $d = 0.6$

8. $1^2, 2^2, 3^2, 4^2, 5^2, \ldots$

Not an arithmetic sequence

9. $a_n = 8 + 13n$

21, 34, 47, 60, 73

Arithmetic sequence, $d = 13$

10. $a_n = 2^n + n$

3, 6, 11, 20, 37

Not an arithmetic sequence

11. $a_n = \dfrac{1}{n + 1}$

$\frac{1}{2}, \frac{1}{3}, \frac{1}{4}, \frac{1}{5}, \frac{1}{6}$

Not an arithmetic sequence

12. $a_n = 1 + (n - 1)4$

1, 5, 9, 13, 17

Arithmetic sequence, $d = 4$

13. $a_n = 150 - 7n$

143, 136, 129, 122, 115

Arithmetic sequence, $d = -7$

14. $a_n = 2^{n-1}$

1, 2, 4, 8, 16

Not an arithmetic sequence

15. $a_n = 3 + 2(-1)^n$

1, 5, 1, 5, 1

Not an arithmetic sequence

16. $a_n = 3 - 4(n + 6) = -21 - 4n$

$a_1 = -25$

$a_2 = -29$

$a_3 = -33$

$a_4 = -37$

$a_5 = -41$

Arithmetic sequence, $d = -4$

17. $a_1 = 1,\ d = 3$

$a_n = a_1 + (n - 1)d = 1 + (n - 1)(3) = 3n - 2$

18. $a_1 = 15, d = 4$

$a_n = a_1 + (n - 1)d = 15 + (n - 1)4 = 11 + 4n$

19. $a_1 = 100,\ d = -8$

$a_n = a_1 + (n - 1)d$

$= 100 + (n - 1)(-8) = 108 - 8n$

20. $a_1 = 0, d = -\frac{2}{3}$

$a_n = a_1 + (n - 1)d = (n - 1)\left(-\frac{2}{3}\right) = \frac{2}{3} - \frac{2}{3}n$

21. $4, \frac{3}{2}, -1, -\frac{7}{2}, \ldots, d = -\frac{5}{2}$

$a_n = a_1 + (n - 1)d = 4 + (n - 1)\left(-\frac{5}{2}\right) = \frac{13}{2} - \frac{5}{2}n$

22. $10, 5, 0, -5, -10, \ldots, d = -5$

$a_n = a_1 + (n - 1)d = 10 + (n - 1)(-5)$

$= 15 - 5n$

23. $a_1 = 5,\ a_4 = 15$

$a_4 = a_1 + 3d \Rightarrow 15 = 5 + 3d \Rightarrow d = \frac{10}{3}$

$a_n = a_1 + (n - 1)d = 5 + (n - 1)\left(\frac{10}{3}\right) = \frac{10}{3}n + \frac{5}{3}$

24. $a_1 = -4, a_5 = 16$

$a_n = a_1 + (n - 1) d$

$16 = -4 + 4d$

$d = 5$

$a_n = -4 + (n - 1)5 = -9 + 5n$

25. $a_3 = 94,\ a_6 = 85$

$a_6 = a_3 + 3d \Rightarrow 85 = 94 + 3d \Rightarrow d = -3$

$a_1 = a_3 - 2d \Rightarrow a_1 = 94 - 2(-3) = 100$

$a_n = a_1 + (n - 1)d$

$= 100 + (n - 1)(-3) = 103 - 3n$

26. $a_5 = 190, a_{10} = 115$

$a_{10} = a_5 + 5d \Rightarrow 115 = 190 + 5d \Rightarrow d = -15$

$a_1 = a_5 - 4d \Rightarrow a_1 = 190 - 4(-15) = 250$

$a_n = a_1 + (n - 1) d = 250 + (n - 1)(-15)$

$= 265 - 15n$

27. $a_1 = 5,\ d = 6$

$a_1 = 5$

$a_2 = 5 + 6 = 11$

$a_3 = 11 + 6 = 17$

$a_4 = 17 + 6 = 23$

$a_5 = 23 + 6 = 29$

28. $a_1 = 5, d = -\frac{3}{4}$

$a_1 = 5$

$a_2 = 5 - \frac{3}{4} = \frac{17}{4}$

$a_3 = \frac{17}{4} - \frac{3}{4} = \frac{14}{4} = \frac{7}{2}$

$a_4 = \frac{7}{2} - \frac{3}{4} = \frac{11}{4}$

$a_5 = \frac{11}{4} - \frac{3}{4} = \frac{8}{4} = 2$

29. $a_1 = -10, \quad d = -12$

$a_1 = -10$

$a_2 = -10 - 12 = -22$

$a_3 = -22 - 12 = -34$

$a_4 = -34 - 12 = -46$

$a_5 = -46 - 12 = -58$

30. $a_4 = 16, a_{10} = 46$

$16 = a_4 = a_1 + (n - 1)d = a_1 + 3d$

$46 = a_{10} = a_1 + (n - 1)d = a_1 + 9d$

Answer: $a_1 = 1, d = 5$

$a_1 = 1$

$a_2 = 1 + 5 = 6$

$a_3 = 6 + 5 = 11$

$a_4 = 11 + 5 = 16$

$a_5 = 16 + 5 = 21$

31. $a_8 = 26,\ a_{12} = 42$

$26 = a_8 = a_1 + (n - 1)d = a_1 + 7d$

$42 = a_{12} = a_1 + (n - 1)d = a_1 + 11d$

Answer: $d = 4,\ a_1 = -2$

$a_1 = -2$

$a_2 = -2 + 4 = 2$

$a_3 = 2 + 4 = 6$

$a_4 = 6 + 4 = 10$

$a_5 = 10 + 4 = 14$

32. $a_{11} = a_6 + 5d$

$-73 = -38 + 5d \Rightarrow d = -7$

$a_6 = a_1 + 5d \Rightarrow -38 = a_1 + 5(-7) \Rightarrow a_1 = -3$

$a_2 = -3 - 7 = -10$

$a_3 = -10 - 7 = -17$

$a_4 = -17 - 7 = -24$

$a_5 = -24 - 7 = -31$

33. $a_3 = 19, a_{15} = -1.7$

$a_{15} = a_3 + 12d$

$-1.7 = 19 + 12d \Rightarrow d = -1.725$

$a_3 = a_1 + 2d \Rightarrow 19 = a_1 + 2(-1.725)$

$\Rightarrow a_1 = 22.45$

$a_2 = a_1 - 1.725 = 20.725$

$a_3 = 19$

$a_4 = 19 - 1.725 = 17.275$

$a_5 = 17.275 - 1.725 = 15.55$

34. $a_{14} = a_5 + 9d$

$38.5 = 16 + 9d \implies d = 2.5$

$a_5 = a_1 + 4d \implies 16 = a_1 + 4(2.5) \implies a_1 = 6$

$a_2 = 6 + 2.5 = 8.5$

$a_3 = 8.5 + 2.5 = 11$

$a_4 = 11 + 2.5 = 13.5$

$a_5 = 13.5 + 2.5 = 16$

35. $a_1 = 15, \quad a_{k+1} = a_k + 4$

$a_2 = a_1 + 4 = 15 + 4 = 19$

$a_3 = 19 + 4 = 23$

$a_4 = 23 + 4 = 27$

$a_5 = 27 + 4 = 31$

$d = 4, \quad a_n = 11 + 4n$

36. $a_1 = 200$

$a_{k+1} = a_k - 10$

$a_2 = 200 - 10 = 190$

$a_3 = 190 - 10 = 180$

$a_4 = 180 - 10 = 170$

$a_5 = 170 - 10 = 160$

$d = -10$

$a_n = -10n + 210$

37. $a_1 = \frac{3}{5}, a_{k+1} = -\frac{1}{10} + a_k$

$a_2 = -\frac{1}{10} + \frac{3}{5} = \frac{5}{10} = \frac{1}{2}$

$a_3 = -\frac{1}{10} + \frac{1}{2} = \frac{4}{10} = \frac{2}{5}$

$a_4 = -\frac{1}{10} + \frac{2}{5} = \frac{3}{10}$

$a_5 = -\frac{1}{10} + \frac{3}{10} = \frac{1}{5}$

$d = -\frac{1}{10}$

$a_n = \frac{7}{10} - \frac{1}{10}n$

38. $a_1 = 1.5, a_{k+1} = a_k - 2.5$

$a_2 = 1.5 - 2.5 = -1.0$

$a_3 = -1.0 - 2.5 = -3.5$

$a_4 = -3.5 - 2.5 = -6.0$

$a_5 = -6.0 - 2.5 = -8.5$

$d = -2.5$

$a_n = 4.0 - 2.5n$

39. $a_1 = 5, a_2 = 11 \implies d = 6$

$a_{10} = a_1 + 9d = 5 + 9(6) = 59$

40. $a_2 = a_1 + d$

$13 = 3 + d \implies d = 10$

$a_9 = a_1 + 8d$

$= 3 + 8(10) = 83$

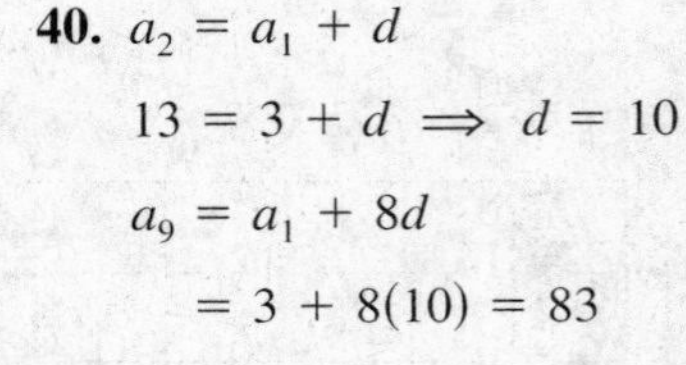

41. $a_1 = 4.2, a_2 = 6.6 \implies d = 2.4$

$a_7 = a_1 + 6d = 4.2 + 6(2.4) = 18.6$

42. $d = a_2 - a_1 = -13.8 - (-0.7) = -13.1$

$a_8 = a_1 + 7d = -0.7 + 7(-13.1) = -92.4$

43. $a_n = 15 - \frac{3}{2}n$

44. $a_n = -5 + 2n$

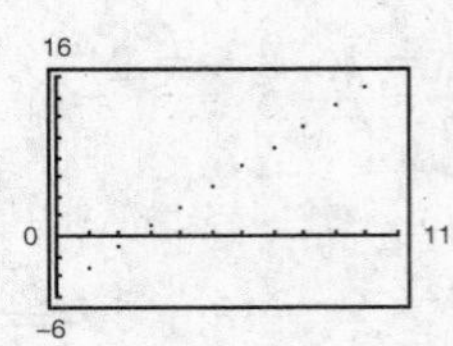

45. $a_n = 0.5n + 4$

46. $a_n = -0.9n + 2$

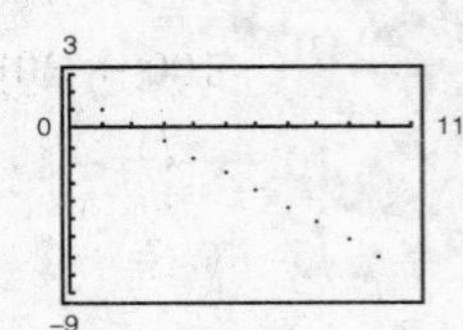

47. $a_n = 4n - 5$

n	1	2	3	4	5	6	7	8	9	10
a_n	−1	3	7	11	15	19	23	27	31	35

48. $a_n = 17 + 3n$

n	1	2	3	4	5	6	7	8	9	10
a_n	20	23	26	29	32	35	38	41	44	47

49. $a_n = 20 - \frac{3}{4}n$

n	1	2	3	4	5	6	7	8	9	10
a_n	19.25	18.5	17.75	17	16.25	15.5	14.75	14	13.25	12.5

50. $a_n = \frac{4}{5}n + 12$

n	1	2	3	4	5	6	7	8	9	10
a_n	12.8	13.6	14.4	15.2	16	16.8	17.6	18.4	19.2	20

51. $a_n = 1.5 + 0.05n$

n	1	2	3	4	5	6	7	8	9	10
a_n	1.55	1.6	1.65	1.7	1.75	1.8	1.85	1.9	1.95	2.0

52. $a_n = 8 - 12.5n$

n	1	2	3	4	5	6	7	8	9	10
a_n	−4.5	−17	−29.5	−42	−54.5	−67	−79.5	−92	−104.5	−117

53. $S_{10} = \frac{10}{2}(2 + 20) = 110$

54. $S_7 = \frac{7}{2}(1 + 19) = 70$

55. $S_5 = \frac{5}{2}(-1 + (-9)) = -25$

56. $S_6 = \frac{6}{2}(-5 + 5) = 0$

57. $S_{50} = \frac{50}{2}(2 + 100) = 2550$

58. $a_1 = 1,\ a_{100} = 199,\ n = 100$

$$\sum_{n=1}^{100}(2n - 1) = \frac{100}{2}(1 + 199)$$

$$= 10{,}000$$

59. $S_{131} = \frac{131}{2}(-100 + 30) = -4585$

60. $a_1 = -10, a_{61} = 50, n = 61$

$$\sum_{i=0}^{60}(i - 10) = \frac{61}{2}(-10 + 50) = 1220$$

61. $8, 20, 32, 44, \ldots n = 10$

$a_1 = 8, a_2 = 20 \implies d = 12$

$a_{10} = a_1 + 9d = 8 + 9(12) = 116$

$S_{10} = \frac{n}{2}[a_1 + a_{10}] = \frac{10}{2}[8 + 116] = 620$

62. $-6, -2, 2, 6, \ldots$

$a_1 = -6, d = 4, n = 50$

$a_{50} = -6 + 49(4) = 190$

$S_{50} = \frac{50}{2}(-6 + 190) = 4600$

63. $a_1 = 0.5, a_2 = 1.3 \implies d = 0.8$

$a_{10} = a_1 + 9d = 0.5 + 9(0.8) = 7.7$

$S_{10} = \frac{10}{2}(a_1 + a_{10}) = 5(0.5 + 7.7) = 41$

64. $4.2, 3.7, 3.2, 2.7, \ldots n = 12$

$a_1 = 4.2$

$d = -0.5$

$n = 12$

$a_{12} = 4.2 + 11(-0.5) = -1.3$

$S_{12} = \frac{12}{2}(4.2 - 1.3) = 17.4$

65. $a_1 = 100, a_{25} = 220$

$S_{25} = \frac{25}{2}(a_1 + a_{25}) = 12.5(100 + 220) = 4000$

66. $a_1 = 15, a_{100} = 307, n = 100$

$S_{100} = \frac{100}{2}(15 + 307) = 16{,}100$

67. $a_1 = 1,\ a_{50} = 50,\ n = 50$

$\sum_{n=1}^{50} n = \frac{50}{2}(1 + 50) = 1275$

68. $a_n = 2n$

$a_1 = 2, a_{100} = 200, n = 100$

$\sum_{n=1}^{100} 2n = \frac{100}{2}(2 + 200) = 10{,}100$

69. $a_1 = 5,\ a_{100} = 500, n = 100$

$\sum_{n=1}^{100} 5n = \frac{100}{2}(5 + 500) = 25{,}250$

70. $a_n = 7n$

$a_{51} = 357, a_{100} = 700$

$\sum_{n=51}^{100} 7n = \frac{50}{2}(357 + 700) = 26{,}425$

71. $\sum_{n=11}^{30} n - \sum_{n=1}^{10} n = \frac{20}{2}(11 + 30) - \frac{10}{2}(1 + 10)$

$= 410 - 55 = 355$

72. $\sum_{n=51}^{100} n - \sum_{n=1}^{50} n = \frac{50}{2}(51 + 100) - \frac{50}{2}(1 + 50)$

$= 3775 - 1275 = 2500$

73. $\sum_{n=1}^{500} (n + 8) = \frac{500}{2}[9 + 508] = 129{,}250$

74. $a_n = 1000 - n$

$a_1 = 999, a_{250} = 750, n = 250$

$\sum_{n=1}^{250} (1000 - n) = \frac{250}{2}(999 + 750) = 218{,}625$

75. $\sum_{n=1}^{20} (2n + 1) = 440$

76. $\sum_{n=0}^{50} (50 - 2n) = 0$

77. $\sum_{n=1}^{100} \frac{n + 1}{2} = 2575$

78. $\sum_{n=0}^{100} \frac{4 - n}{4} = -1161.5$

79. $\sum_{i=1}^{60} \left(250 - \frac{2}{5}i\right) = 14{,}268$

80. $\sum_{j=1}^{200} (10.5 + 0.025j) = 2602.5$

81. $a_1 = 14, a_{18} = 31$

$S_{18} = \frac{18}{2}(14 + 31) = 405$ bricks

82. $a_1 = 15, a_{10} = 24, d = 1, n = 10$

$S_{10} = \frac{10}{2}(15 + 24) = 195$ logs

83. $a_1 = 20{,}000$

$a_2 = 20{,}000 + 5000 = 25{,}000$

$d = 5000$

$a_5 = 20{,}000 + 4(5000) = 40{,}000$

$S_5 = \frac{5}{2}(20{,}000 + 40{,}000) = 150{,}000$

84. $a_1 = 4.9, a_2 = 14.7, a_3 = 24.5,$

$a_4 = 34.3 \implies d = 9.8$

$a_1 = 4.9 = 9.8(1) + c \implies c = -4.9$

$a_n = 9.8n - 4.9$

$a_{10} = 9.8(10) - 4.9 = 93.1$

$S_{10} = \frac{10}{2}(4.9 + 93.1) = 490$ meters

85. (a) $S_n = 0.91n + 5.7$

(b)

Year	1997	1998	1999	2000	2001	2002	2003	2004
Sales (Billions of $)	12.1	13.0	13.9	14.8	15.7	16.6	17.5	18.4

The model is a good fit.

(c) Total $= \frac{8}{2}(12.1 + 18.4) = \$122$ billion

(d) For 2005, $n = 15$ and $S_{15} = 19.35$.

For 2012, $n = 22$ and $S_{22} = 25.72$.

Total $= \frac{8}{2}(19.35 + 25.72) = \$180.3$ billion

Answers will vary.

86. (a) $a_n = 13.5n + 324$, $n = 5$ corresponds to 1995.

(b)

Year	Model
1995	392
1996	405
1997	419
1998	432
1999	446
2000	459
2001	473
2002	486
2003	500

(c) $S = \frac{9}{2}[392 + 500] \approx 4014$ thousand

Adding the table entries,

$398 + \cdots + 512 = 4012$ thousand.

(d) For 2004 to 2014,

$S = \frac{11}{2}(513 + 648) \approx 6386$ thousand.

Answers will vary.

87. True. Given a_1 and a_2, you know $d = a_2 - a_1$. Thus, $a_n = a_1 + (n - 1)d$.

88. False. You need to know how many terms are in the sequence.

89. $a_1 = x$ $\quad a_6 = 11x$

$a_2 = x + 2x = 3x$ $\quad a_7 = 13x$

$a_3 = 3x + 2x = 5x$ $\quad a_8 = 15x$

$a_4 = 7x$ $\quad a_9 = 17x$

$a_5 = 9x$ $\quad a_{10} = 19x$

90. $a_1 = -y$ $\quad a_6 = 24y$

$a_2 = -y + 5y = 4y$ $\quad a_7 = 29y$

$a_3 = 9y$ $\quad a_8 = 34y$

$a_4 = 14y$ $\quad a_9 = 39y$

$a_5 = 19y$ $\quad a_{10} = 44y$

91. $a_{20} = a_1 + 19(3) = a_1 + 57$

$$S = \frac{n}{2}(a_1 + a_{20})$$

$$= \frac{20}{2}(a_1 + (a_1 + 57)) = 650$$

$$10(2a_1 + 57) = 650$$

$$20a_1 = 80$$

$$a_1 = 4$$

92. $S = \frac{n}{2}((a_1 + 5) + (a_n + 5))$

$$= \frac{n}{2}(a_1 + a_2 + 10)$$

$$= \frac{n}{2}(a_1 + a_2) + 5n$$

93. (a) $-7, -4, -1, 2, 5, 8, 11$

$a_{n+1} = a_n + 3,\ a_1 = -7$

(b) 17, 23, 29, 35, 41, 47, 53, 57

$a_{n+1} = a_n + 6,\ a_1 = 17$

(c) Not arithmetic

(d) 4, 7.5, 11, 14.5, 18, 21.5, 25, 28.5

$a_{n+1} = a_n + 3.5,\ a_1 = 4$

(e) Not arithmetic

94. Gauss might have done the following:

$1 + 2 + 3 + \cdots + 99 + 100 = x$

$100 + 99 + \cdots + 2 + 1 = x$

Adding: $101 + 101 + \cdots + 101 + 101 = 2x$

$100(101) = 2x \Rightarrow x = \frac{100(101)}{2} = 5050$

In general, $1 + 2 + \ldots + n = \frac{n(n+1)}{2}$.

95. $S = \frac{n(n+1)}{2} = \frac{200(201)}{2} = 20{,}100$

96. $S = 2 + 4 + 6 + \cdots + 200$

$$= 2(1 + 2 + \cdots + 100)$$

$$= 2\left(\frac{100(101)}{2}\right) = 10{,}100$$

97. $S = 1 + 3 + 5 + \cdots + 101$

$$= (1 + 2 + 3 + \cdots + 101) - (2 + 4 + \cdots + 100)$$

$$= \frac{101(102)}{2} - 2\left(\frac{50(51)}{2}\right)$$

$$= 5151 - 2550 = 2601$$

98. $4 + 8 + \cdots + 400 = 4(1 + 2 + \cdots + 100)$

$$= 4 \cdot \frac{100(101)}{2}$$

$$= 200(101) = 20{,}200$$

99. $\begin{bmatrix} 2 & -1 & 7 & \vdots & -10 \\ 3 & 2 & -4 & \vdots & 17 \\ 6 & -5 & 1 & \vdots & -20 \end{bmatrix}$ row reduces to $\begin{bmatrix} 1 & 0 & 0 & \vdots & 1 \\ 0 & 1 & 0 & \vdots & 5 \\ 0 & 0 & 1 & \vdots & -1 \end{bmatrix}$.

Answer: $(1, 5, -1)$

100. $\begin{bmatrix} -1 & 4 & 10 & \vdots & 4 \\ 5 & -3 & 1 & \vdots & 31 \\ 8 & 2 & -3 & \vdots & -5 \end{bmatrix}$ row reduces to $\begin{bmatrix} 1 & 0 & 0 & \vdots & 2 \\ 0 & 1 & 0 & \vdots & -6 \\ 0 & 0 & 1 & \vdots & 3 \end{bmatrix}$.

Answer: $(2, -6, 3)$

101. $\begin{vmatrix} 0 & 0 & 1 \\ 4 & -3 & 1 \\ 2 & 6 & 1 \end{vmatrix} = 30$

Area $= \frac{1}{2}(30) = 15$ square units

102. $\begin{vmatrix} -1 & 2 & 1 \\ 5 & 1 & 1 \\ 3 & 8 & 1 \end{vmatrix} = 40$

Area $= \frac{1}{2}(40) = 20$ square units

103. Answers will vary.

Section 8.3 Geometric Sequences and Series

- You should be able to identify a geometric sequence, find its common ratio, and find the nth term.
- You should be able to find the nth partial sum of a geometric sequence with common ratio r using the formula.

$$S_n = a_1\left(\frac{1 - r^n}{1 - r}\right)$$

- You should know that if $|r| < 1$, then

$$\sum_{n=1}^{\infty} a_1 r^{n-1} = \frac{a_1}{1 - r}.$$

Vocabulary Check

1. geometric, common

2. $a_n = a_1 r^{n-1}$

3. $S_n = \sum_{i=1}^{n} a_1 r^{i-1} = a_1\left(\frac{1 - r^n}{1 - r}\right)$

4. geometric series

5. $S = \sum_{i=0}^{\infty} a_1 r^i = \dfrac{a_1}{1 - r}$

1. 5, 15, 45, 135, . . .

Geometric sequence

$r = 3$

2. 3, 12, 48, 192, . . .

Geometric sequence

$r = \frac{12}{3} = 4$

3. 6, 18, 30, 42, . . .

Not a geometric sequence

(**Note:** It is an arithmetic sequence with $d = 12$.)

4. $1, -2, 4, -8, \ldots$

Geometric sequence

$r = -2$

5. $1, -\frac{1}{2}, \frac{1}{4}, -\frac{1}{8}, \ldots$

Geometric sequence

$r = -\frac{1}{2}$

6. $5, 1, 0.2, 0.04$

Geometric sequence

$r = \frac{1}{5} = 0.2$

7. $\frac{1}{8}, \frac{1}{4}, \frac{1}{2}, 1, \ldots$

Geometric sequence

$r = 2$

8. $9, -6, 4, -\frac{8}{3}, \ldots$

Geometric sequence

$r = -\frac{2}{3}$

9. $1, \frac{1}{2}, \frac{1}{3}, \frac{1}{4}, \ldots$

Not a geometric sequence

10. $\frac{1}{5}, \frac{2}{7}, \frac{3}{9}, \frac{4}{11}, \ldots$

Not a geometric sequence

11. $a_1 = 6, r = 3$

$a_2 = 6(3) = 18$

$a_3 = 18(3) = 54$

$a_4 = 54(3) = 162$

$a_5 = 162(3) = 486$

12. $a_1 = 4, r = 2$

$a_2 = 4(2) = 8$

$a_3 = 8(2) = 16$

$a_4 = 16(2) = 32$

$a_5 = 32(2) = 64$

13. $a_1 = 1,\ r = \frac{1}{2}$

$a_1 = 1$

$a_2 = 1\left(\frac{1}{2}\right) = \frac{1}{2}$

$a_3 = \frac{1}{2}\left(\frac{1}{2}\right) = \frac{1}{4}$

$a_4 = \frac{1}{4}\left(\frac{1}{2}\right) = \frac{1}{8}$

$a_5 = \frac{1}{8}\left(\frac{1}{2}\right) = \frac{1}{16}$

14. $a_1 = 2, r = \frac{1}{3}$

$a_2 = 2\left(\frac{1}{3}\right) = \frac{2}{3}$

$a_3 = \frac{2}{3}\left(\frac{1}{3}\right) = \frac{2}{9}$

$a_4 = \frac{2}{9}\left(\frac{1}{3}\right) = \frac{2}{27}$

$a_5 = \frac{2}{27}\left(\frac{1}{3}\right) = \frac{2}{81}$

15. $a_1 = 5,\ r = -\frac{1}{10}$

$a_1 = 5$

$a_2 = 5\left(-\frac{1}{10}\right) = -\frac{1}{2}$

$a_3 = \left(-\frac{1}{2}\right)\left(-\frac{1}{10}\right) = \frac{1}{20}$

$a_4 = \frac{1}{20}\left(-\frac{1}{10}\right) = -\frac{1}{200}$

$a_5 = \left(-\frac{1}{200}\right)\left(-\frac{1}{10}\right) = \frac{1}{2000}$

16. $a_1 = 6, r = -\frac{1}{4}$

$a_1 = 6$

$a_2 = 6\left(-\frac{1}{4}\right)^1 = -\frac{3}{2}$

$a_3 = 6\left(-\frac{1}{4}\right)^2 = \frac{3}{8}$

$a_4 = 6\left(-\frac{1}{4}\right)^3 = -\frac{3}{32}$

$a_5 = 6\left(-\frac{1}{4}\right)^4 = \frac{3}{128}$

17. $a_1 = 1,\ r = e$

$a_1 = 1$

$a_2 = 1(e) = e$

$a_3 = (e)(e) = e^2$

$a_4 = (e^2)(e) = e^3$

$a_5 = (e^3)(e) = e^4$

18. $a_1 = 4, r = \sqrt{3}$

$a_2 = 4\sqrt{3}$

$a_3 = 4\sqrt{3}(\sqrt{3}) = 12$

$a_4 = 12(\sqrt{3}) = 12\sqrt{3}$

$a_5 = 12\sqrt{3}(\sqrt{3}) = 36$

19. $a_1 = 64,\ a_{k+1} = \frac{1}{2}a_k$

$a_1 = 64$

$a_2 = \frac{1}{2}(64) = 32$

$a_3 = \frac{1}{2}(32) = 16$

$a_4 = \frac{1}{2}(16) = 8$

$a_5 = \frac{1}{2}(8) = 4$

$r = \frac{1}{2}, a_n = 64\left(\frac{1}{2}\right)^{n-1} = 128\left(\frac{1}{2}\right)^n$

20. $a_1 = 81, a_{k+1} = \frac{1}{3}a_k$

$a_1 = 81$

$a_2 = \frac{1}{3}(81) = 27$

$a_3 = \frac{1}{3}(27) = 9$

$a_4 = \frac{1}{3}(9) = 3$

$a_5 = \frac{1}{3}(3) = 1$

$r = \frac{1}{3}, a_n = 243\left(\frac{1}{3}\right)^n$

21. $a_1 = 9, a_{k+1} = 2a_k$

$a_2 = 2(9) = 18$

$a_3 = 2(18) = 36$

$a_4 = 2(36) = 72$

$a_5 = 2(72) = 144$

$r = 2$

$a_n = \left(\frac{9}{2}\right)2^n = 9(2^{n-1})$

22. $a_1 = 5, a_{k+1} = -3a_k$

$a_2 = -3(5) = -15$

$a_3 = -15(-3) = 45$

$a_4 = 45(-3) = -135$

$a_5 = -135(-3) = 405$

$r = -3, a_n = 5(-3)^{n-1}$

23. $a_1 = 6,\ a_{k+1} = -\frac{3}{2}a_k$

$a_1 = 6$

$a_2 = -\frac{3}{2}(6) = -9$

$a_3 = -\frac{3}{2}(-9) = \frac{27}{2}$

$a_4 = -\frac{3}{2}\left(\frac{27}{2}\right) = -\frac{81}{4}$

$a_5 = -\frac{3}{2}\left(-\frac{81}{4}\right) = \frac{243}{8}$

$r = -\frac{3}{2},\ a_n = 6\left(-\frac{3}{2}\right)^{n-1} = -4\left(-\frac{3}{2}\right)^n$

24. $a_1 = 30,\ a_{k+1} = -\frac{2}{3}a_k$

$a_2 = \frac{-2}{3}a_1 = \frac{-2}{3}(30) = -20$

$a_3 = \frac{-2}{3}(-20) = \frac{40}{3}$

$a_4 = \frac{-2}{3}\left(\frac{40}{3}\right) = \frac{-80}{9}$

$a_5 = \frac{-2}{3}\left(\frac{-80}{9}\right) = \frac{160}{27}$

$r = \frac{-2}{3},\ a_n = 30\left(\frac{-2}{3}\right)^{n-1}$

25. $a_1 = 4,\ a_4 = \frac{1}{2},\ n = 10$

$a_1 r^3 = a_4$

$4r^3 = \frac{1}{2}$

$r^3 = \frac{1}{8}$

$r = \frac{1}{2}$

$a_{10} = a_4 r^6 = \frac{1}{2}\left(\frac{1}{2}\right)^6 = \frac{1}{2^7} = \frac{1}{128}$

26. $a_1 = 5,\ a_3 = \frac{45}{4},\ n = 8$

$a_1 r^2 = a_3$

$5r^2 = \frac{45}{4}$

$r^2 = \frac{9}{4}$

$r = \pm\frac{3}{2}$

$a_8 = a_3 r^5 = \frac{45}{4}\left(\pm\frac{3}{2}\right)^5 = \pm\frac{10{,}935}{128}$

27. $a_1 = 6,\ r = -\frac{1}{3},\ n = 12$

$a_n = a_1 r^{n-1}$

$a_{12} = 6\left(-\frac{1}{3}\right)^{11} = \frac{-2}{3^{10}}$

28. $a_1 = 8,\ r = \frac{-3}{4}$

$a_n = a_1 r^{n-1}$

$a_9 = 8\left(\frac{-3}{4}\right)^8 = \frac{6561}{8192}$

29. $a_1 = 500,\ r = 1.02,\ n = 14$

$a_n = a_1 r^{n-1}$

$a_{14} = 500(1.02)^{13} \approx 646.8$

30. $a_1 = 1000,\ r = 1.005,$
$n = 11$

$a_n = a_1 r^{n-1}$

$a_{11} = 1000(1.005)^{10} \approx 1051.14$

31. $a_2 = a_1 r = -18 \Rightarrow a_1 = \frac{-18}{r}$

$a_5 = a_1 r^4 = (a_1 r)r^3 = -18r^3 = \frac{2}{3} \Rightarrow r = -\frac{1}{3}$

$a_1 = \frac{-18}{r} = \frac{-18}{-1/3} = 54$

$a_6 = a_1 r^5 = 54\left(\frac{-1}{3}\right)^5 = \frac{-54}{243} = -\frac{2}{9}$

32. $a_3 = \frac{16}{3},\ a_5 = \frac{64}{27},\ n = 7$

$a_3 r^2 = a_5$

$\frac{16}{3} r^2 = \frac{64}{27}$

$r^2 = \frac{4}{9}$

$r = \pm\frac{2}{3}$

$a_7 = a_5 r^2 = \frac{64}{27}\left(\pm\frac{2}{3}\right)^2 = \frac{256}{243}$

33. 7, 21, 63

$r = 3$

$a_n = 7(3)^{n-1}$

$a_9 = 7(3)^{9-1} = 45{,}927$

34. 3, 36, 432

$r = \frac{36}{3} = 12$

$a_n = 3(12)^{n-1}$

$a_7 = 3(12)^{7-1} = 8{,}957{,}952$

35. 5, 30, 180

$r = \frac{30}{5} = 6$

$a_n = 5(6)^{n-1}$

$a_{10} = 5(6)^{10-1} = 50{,}388{,}480$

36. 4, 8, 16

$r = \frac{8}{4} = 2$

$a_n = 4(2)^{n-1}$

$a_{22} = 4(2)^{22-1} = 8{,}388{,}608$

37. $a_n = 12(-0.75)^{n-1}$

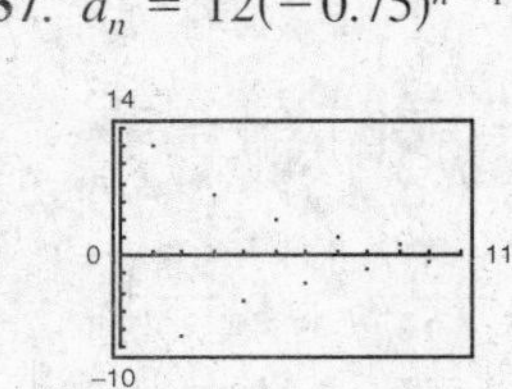

38.

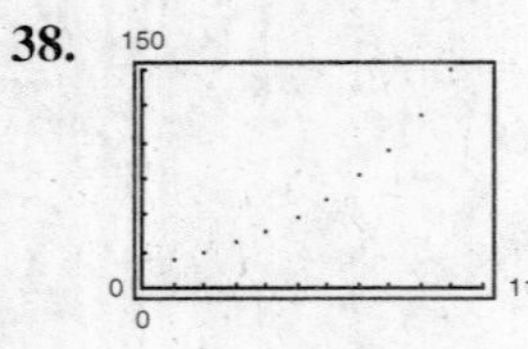

39. $a_n = 2(1.3)^{n-1}$

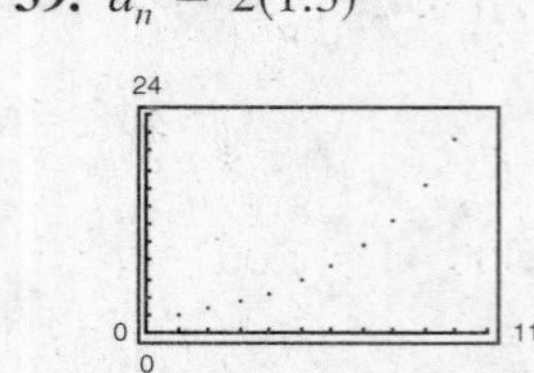

40.

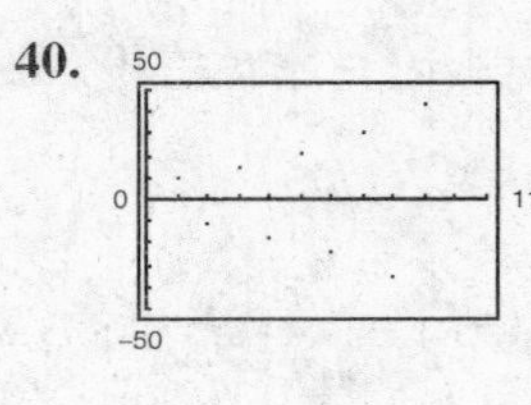

41. $8,\ -4,\ 2,\ -1,\ \frac{1}{2}$

$S_1 = 8$

$S_2 = 8 + (-4) = 4$

$S_3 = 8 + (-4) + 2 = 6$

$S_4 = 8 + (-4) + 2 + (-1) = 5$

42. $8, 12, 18, 27, \frac{81}{2}, \ldots$

$S_1 = 8$

$S_2 = 8 + 12 = 20$

$S_3 = 8 + 12 + 18 = 38$

$S_4 = 8 + 12 + 18 + 27 = 65$

43. $\sum_{n=1}^{\infty} 16\left(-\frac{1}{2}\right)^{n-1}$

n	1	2	3	4	5	6	7	8	9	10
S_n	16	24	28	30	31	31.5	31.75	31.875	31.9375	31.96875

44. $\sum_{n=1}^{\infty} 4(0.2)^{n-1}$

n	1	2	3	4	5	6	7	8	9	10
S_n	4	4.8	4.96	4.992	4.9984	4.99968	4.999936	4.9999872	≈ 5	≈ 5

45. $\sum_{n=1}^{9} 2^{n-1} \Rightarrow a_1 = 1,\ r = 2$

$S_9 = \dfrac{1(1 - 2^9)}{1 - 2} = 511$

46. $\sum_{n=1}^{9} (-2)^{n-1} \Rightarrow a_1 = 1, r = -2$

$S_9 = \dfrac{1(1 - (-2)^9)}{1 - (-2)} = 171$

47. $\sum_{i=1}^{7} 64\left(-\frac{1}{2}\right)^{i-1} \Rightarrow a_1 = 64,\ r = -\frac{1}{2}$

$$S_7 = 64\left[\frac{1-(-1/2)^7}{1-(-1/2)}\right] = \frac{128}{3}\left[1-\left(-\frac{1}{2}\right)^7\right] = 43$$

48. $\sum_{i=1}^{6} 32\left(\frac{1}{4}\right)^{i-1} \Rightarrow a_1 = 32,\ r = \frac{1}{4}$

$$S_6 = 32\frac{(1-(1/4)^6)}{1-(1/4)} = \frac{1365}{32}$$

49. $\sum_{n=0}^{20} 3\left(\frac{3}{2}\right)^n = \sum_{n=1}^{21} 3\left(\frac{3}{2}\right)^{n-1} \Rightarrow a_1 = 3,\ r = \frac{3}{2}$

$$S_{21} = 3\left[\frac{1-(3/2)^{21}}{1-(3/2)}\right]$$

$$= -6\left[1-\left(\frac{3}{2}\right)^{21}\right] \approx 29{,}921.31$$

50. $\sum_{n=0}^{15} 2\left(\frac{4}{3}\right)^n = \sum_{n=1}^{16} 2\left(\frac{4}{3}\right)^{n-1} \Rightarrow a_1 = 2,\ r = \frac{4}{3}$

$$S_{16} = 2\left(\frac{1-(4/3)^{16}}{1-(4/3)}\right) \approx 592.65$$

51. $\sum_{i=1}^{10} 8\left(-\frac{1}{4}\right)^{i-1} \Rightarrow a_1 = 8,\ r = -\frac{1}{4}$

$$S_{10} = 8\left[\frac{1-(-1/4)^{10}}{1-(-1/4)}\right] = \frac{32}{5}\left[1-\left(-\frac{1}{4}\right)^{10}\right] \approx 6.4$$

52. $\sum_{i=1}^{10} 5\left(-\frac{1}{3}\right)^{i-1} \Rightarrow a_1 = 5,\ r = -\frac{1}{3}$

$$S_{10} = 5\left(\frac{1-(-1/3)^{10}}{1-(-1/3)}\right) \approx 3.75$$

53. $\sum_{n=0}^{5} 300(1.06)^n = \sum_{n=1}^{6} 300(1.06)^{n-1} \Rightarrow a_1 = 300,\ r = 1.06$

$$S_6 = 300\left[\frac{1-(1.06)^6}{1-1.06}\right] \approx 2092.60$$

54. $\sum_{n=0}^{6} 500(1.04)^n = \sum_{n=1}^{7} 500(1.04)^{n-1} \Rightarrow a_1 = 500,\ r = 1.04$

$$S_7 = 500\left(\frac{1-(1.04)^7}{1-1.04}\right) \approx 3949.15$$

55. $5 + 15 + 45 + \cdots + 3645$

$r = 3$ and $3645 = 5(3)^{n-1} \Rightarrow n = 7$

Thus, the sum can be written as $\sum_{n=1}^{7} 5(3)^{n-1}$.

56. $7 + 14 + 28 + \cdots + 896$

$r = 2$ and $896 = 7(2)^{n-1} \Rightarrow n = 8$

$\sum_{n=1}^{8} 7(2)^{n-1}$

57. $2 - \frac{1}{2} + \frac{1}{8} - \cdots + \frac{1}{2048}$

$r = -\frac{1}{4}$ and $\frac{1}{2048} = 2\left(-\frac{1}{4}\right)^{n-1} \Rightarrow n = 7$

$\sum_{n=1}^{7} 2\left(-\frac{1}{4}\right)^{n-1}$

58. $15 - 3 + \frac{3}{5} - \cdots - \frac{3}{625}$

$r = -0.2$ and $-\frac{3}{625} = 15(-0.2)^{n-1} \Rightarrow n = 6$

$\sum_{n=1}^{6} 15(-0.2)^{n-1}$

59. $a_1 = 10,\ r = \frac{4}{5}$

$$\sum_{n=0}^{\infty} 10\left(\frac{4}{5}\right)^n = \frac{a_1}{1-r} = \frac{10}{1-\frac{4}{5}} = 50$$

60. $a_1 = 6,\ r = \frac{2}{3}$

$$\sum_{n=0}^{\infty} 6\left(\frac{2}{3}\right)^n = \frac{a_1}{1-r} = \frac{6}{1-\frac{2}{3}} = 18$$

61. $a_1 = 5, r = -\frac{1}{2}$

$$\sum_{n=0}^{\infty} 5\left(-\frac{1}{2}\right)^n = \frac{a_1}{1-r} = \frac{5}{1-\left(-\frac{1}{2}\right)} = \frac{5}{\left(\frac{3}{2}\right)} = \frac{10}{3}$$

62. $a_1 = 9, r = -\frac{2}{3}$

$$\sum_{n=0}^{\infty} 9\left(-\frac{2}{3}\right)^n = \frac{a_1}{1-r} = \frac{9}{1-\left(-\frac{2}{3}\right)} = \frac{9}{\left(\frac{5}{3}\right)} = \frac{27}{5}$$

63. $\sum_{n=1}^{\infty} 2\left(\frac{7}{3}\right)^{n-1}$ does not have a finite sum $\left(\frac{7}{3} > 1\right)$.

64. $\sum_{n=1}^{\infty} 8\left(\frac{5}{3}\right)^{n-1}$ does not have a finite sum $\left(\frac{5}{3} > 1\right)$.

65. $a_1 = 10, r = 0.11$

$$\sum_{n=0}^{\infty} 10(0.11)^n = \frac{a_1}{1-r} = \frac{10}{1-0.11} = \frac{10}{0.89} = \frac{1000}{89} \approx 11.236$$

66. $a_1 = 5, r = 0.45$

$$\sum_{n=0}^{\infty} 5(0.45)^n = \frac{a_1}{1-r} = \frac{5}{1-0.45} = \frac{5}{0.55} = \frac{100}{11} \approx 9.091$$

67. $a_1 = -3, r = -0.9$

$$\sum_{n=0}^{\infty} -3(-0.9)^n = \frac{a_1}{1-r} = \frac{-3}{1-(-0.9)} = \frac{-3}{1.9} = \frac{-30}{19} \approx -1.579$$

68. $a_1 = -10, r = -0.2$

$$\sum_{n=0}^{\infty} -10(-0.2)^n = \frac{a_1}{1-r} = \frac{-10}{1-(-0.2)} = \frac{-10}{1.2} = \frac{-25}{3} \approx -8.333$$

69. $8 + 6 + \frac{9}{2} + \frac{27}{8} + \cdots = \sum_{n=0}^{\infty} 8\left(\frac{3}{4}\right)^n = \frac{8}{1-3/4} = 32$

70. $9 + 6 + 4 + \frac{8}{3} + \cdots = \sum_{n=0}^{\infty} 9\left(\frac{2}{3}\right)^n = \frac{9}{1-2/3} = \frac{9}{1/3} = 27$

71. $3 - 1 + \frac{1}{3} - \frac{1}{9} + \cdots = \sum_{n=0}^{\infty} 3\left(-\frac{1}{3}\right)^n = \frac{a_1}{1-r} = \frac{3}{1-(-1/3)} = 3\left(\frac{3}{4}\right) = \frac{9}{4}$

72. $-6 + 5 - \frac{25}{6} + \frac{125}{36} - \cdots = \sum_{n=0}^{\infty} -6\left(-\frac{5}{6}\right)^n = \frac{-6}{1-(-5/6)} = \frac{-6}{11/6} = \frac{-36}{11} \approx -3.2727$

73. $0.\overline{36} = \sum_{n=0}^{\infty} 0.36(0.01)^n = \frac{0.36}{1-0.01} = \frac{0.36}{0.99} = \frac{36}{99} = \frac{4}{11}$

74. $0.\overline{297} = \sum_{n=0}^{\infty} 0.297(0.001)^n = \frac{0.297}{1-0.001} = \frac{0.297}{0.999} = \frac{297}{999} = \frac{11}{37}$

75. $1.2\overline{5} = 1.2 + \sum_{n=0}^{\infty} 0.05(0.1)^n$

$$= \frac{6}{5} + \frac{0.05}{1-0.1}$$

$$= \frac{6}{5} + \frac{0.05}{0.9}$$

$$= \frac{6}{5} + \frac{5}{90} = \frac{113}{90}$$

76. $1.3\overline{8} = 1.3 + \sum_{n=0}^{\infty} 0.08(0.1)^n$

$$= 1.3 + \frac{0.08}{1-0.1}$$

$$= 1.3 + \frac{0.08}{0.9}$$

$$= 1\frac{3}{10} + \frac{4}{45} = 1\frac{7}{18} = \frac{25}{18}$$

77. $A = P\left(1 + \frac{r}{n}\right)^{nt} = 1000\left(1 + \frac{0.03}{n}\right)^{n(10)}$

(a) $n = 1$: $A = 1000(1 + 0.03)^{10} \approx 1343.92$

(b) $n = 2$: $A = 1000\left(1 + \frac{0.03}{2}\right)^{2(10)} \approx 1346.86$

(c) $n = 4$: $A = 1000\left(1 + \frac{0.03}{4}\right)^{4(10)} \approx 1348.35$

(d) $n = 12$: $A = 1000\left(1 + \frac{0.03}{12}\right)^{12(10)} \approx 1349.35$

(e) $n = 365$: $A = 1000\left(1 + \frac{0.03}{365}\right)^{365(10)} \approx 1349.84$

78. $A = P\left(1 + \frac{r}{n}\right)^{nt} = 2500\left(1 + \frac{0.04}{n}\right)^{20n}$

(a) $n = 1, A = 2500\left(1 + \frac{0.04}{1}\right)^{20(1)} = 5477.81$

(b) $n = 2, A = 5520.10$

(c) $n = 4, A = 5541.79$

(d) $n = 12, A = 5556.46$

(e) $n = 365, A = 5563.61$

79. $A = \sum_{n=1}^{60} 100\left(1 + \frac{0.03}{12}\right)^n$

$= 100\left(1 + \frac{0.03}{12}\right) \cdot \frac{[1 - (1 + 0.03/12)^{60}]}{[1 - (1 + 0.03/12)]}$

$= 100(1.0025) \cdot \left[\frac{1 - 1.0025^{60}}{1 - 1.0025}\right]$

$\approx \$6480.83$

80. $A = \sum_{n=1}^{60} 50\left(1 + \frac{0.02}{12}\right)^n$

$= 50\left(1 + \frac{0.02}{12}\right) \cdot \frac{[1 - (1 + 0.02/12)^{60}]}{[1 - (1 + 0.02/12)]}$

$\approx \$3157.62$

81. Let $N = 12t$ be the total number of deposits.

$$A = P\left(1 + \frac{r}{12}\right) + P\left(1 + \frac{r}{12}\right)^2 + \cdots + P\left(1 + \frac{r}{12}\right)^N$$

$$= \left(1 + \frac{r}{12}\right)\left[P + P\left(1 + \frac{r}{12}\right) + \cdots + P\left(1 + \frac{r}{12}\right)^{N-1}\right]$$

$$= P\left(1 + \frac{r}{12}\right)\sum_{n=1}^{N}\left(1 + \frac{r}{12}\right)^{n-1}$$

$$= P\left(1 + \frac{r}{12}\right)\frac{1 - \left(1 + \frac{r}{12}\right)^N}{1 - \left(1 + \frac{r}{12}\right)}$$

$$= P\left(1 + \frac{r}{12}\right)\left(-\frac{12}{r}\right)\left[1 - \left(1 + \frac{r}{12}\right)^N\right]$$

$$= P\left(\frac{12}{r} + 1\right)\left[-1 + \left(1 + \frac{r}{12}\right)^N\right]$$

$$= P\left[\left(1 + \frac{r}{12}\right)^N - 1\right]\left(1 + \frac{12}{r}\right)$$

$$= P\left[\left(1 + \frac{r}{12}\right)^{12t} - 1\right]\left(1 + \frac{12}{r}\right)$$

82. Let $N = 12t$ be the total number of deposits.

$$A = Pe^{r/12} + Pe^{2r/12} + \cdots + Pe^{Nr/12}$$

$$= \sum_{n=1}^{N} Pe^{r/12 \cdot n}$$

$$= Pe^{r/12}\frac{(1 - (e^{r/12})^N)}{(1 - e^{r/12})}$$

$$= Pe^{r/12}\frac{(1 - (e^{r/12})^{12t})}{1 - e^{r/12}}$$

$$= \frac{Pe^{r/12}(e^{rt} - 1)}{(e^{r/12} - 1)}$$

83. $P = \$50,\ r = 7\%,\ t = 20$ years

(a) Compounded monthly: $A = 50\left[\left(1 + \frac{0.07}{12}\right)^{12(20)} - 1\right]\left(1 + \frac{12}{0.07}\right) \approx \$26{,}198.27$

(b) Compounded continuously: $A = \frac{50e^{0.07/12}(e^{0.07(20)} - 1)}{e^{0.07/12} - 1} \approx \$26{,}263.88$

84. $P = 75,\ r = 0.04,\ t = 25$

(a) $A = 75\left[\left(1 + \frac{0.04}{12}\right)^{12(25)} - 1\right]\left(1 + \frac{12}{0.04}\right) \approx \$38{,}688.25$

(b) $A = \frac{75e^{0.04/12}(e^{0.04(25)} - 1)}{e^{0.04/12} - 1} \approx \$38{,}725.81$

85. $P = 100,\ r = 5\% = 0.05,\ t = 40$

(a) Compounded monthly: $A = 100\left[\left(1 + \frac{0.05}{12}\right)^{12(40)} - 1\right]\left(1 + \frac{12}{0.05}\right) \approx \$153{,}237.86$

(b) Compounded continuously: $A = \frac{100e^{0.05/12}(e^{0.05(40)} - 1)}{e^{0.05/12} - 1} \approx \$153{,}657.02$

86. $P = \$20,\ r = 6\%,\ t = 50$ years

(a) Compounded monthly: $A = 20\left[\left(1 + \frac{0.06}{12}\right)^{12(50)} - 1\right]\left(1 + \frac{12}{0.06}\right) \approx \$76{,}122.54$

(b) Compounded continuously: $A = \frac{20e^{0.06/12}(e^{0.06(50)} - 1)}{e^{0.06/12} - 1} \approx \$76{,}533.16$

87. First shaded area: $\frac{16^2}{4}$ Second shaded area: $\frac{16^2}{4} + \frac{1}{2} \cdot \frac{16^2}{4}$ Third shaded area: $\frac{16^2}{4} + \frac{1}{2}\frac{16^2}{4} + \frac{1}{4}\frac{16^2}{4}$, etc.

Total area of shaded region: $\frac{16^2}{4}\sum_{n=0}^{5}\left(\frac{1}{2}\right)^n = 64\left[\frac{1 - (1/2)^6}{1 - 1/2}\right] = 128\left(1 - \left(\frac{1}{2}\right)^6\right) = 126$ square units

88. $27^2\left(\frac{1}{9}\right) + 27^2\left(\frac{1}{9}\right)\left(\frac{8}{9}\right) + 27^2\left(\frac{1}{9}\right)\left(\frac{8}{9}\right)^2 + 27^2\left(\frac{1}{9}\right)\left(\frac{8}{9}\right)^3 = \sum_{n=0}^{3} 27^2\left(\frac{1}{9}\right)\left(\frac{8}{9}\right)^n = \frac{2465}{9} \approx 273.89$ square inches

89. (a) $a_0 = 70$ degrees

$a_1 = 0.8(70) = 56$ degrees

$\vdots$

$a_n = (0.8)^n(70)$

(b) $a_6 = (0.8)^6(70) \approx 18.35$ degrees

$a_{12} = (0.8)^{12}(70) \approx 4.81$ degrees

(c) 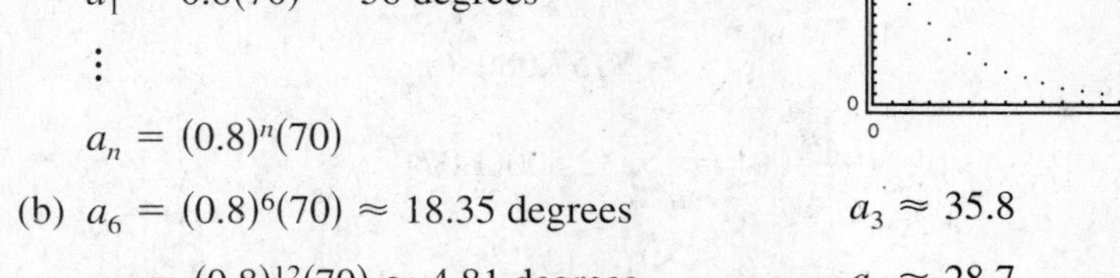

$a_3 \approx 35.8$

$a_4 \approx 28.7$

Thus, the water freezes between 3 and 4 hours, about 3.5 hours.

90. (a) Surface area of a sphere is $4\pi r^2$. The surface area of the sphere flake is

$$S = 4\pi(1)^2 + 9\left(4\pi\left(\frac{1}{3}\right)^2\right) + 9^2\left(4\pi\left(\frac{1}{9}\right)^2\right) + \cdots = 4\pi + 4\pi + 4\pi + \cdots = \sum_{n=1}^{\infty} 4\pi.$$

(b) Volume of a sphere is $\frac{4}{3}\pi r^2$. The volume of the sphere flake is

$$V = \frac{4}{3}\pi(1)^3 + 9\left(\frac{4}{3}\pi\left(\frac{1}{3}\right)^3\right) + 9^2\left(\frac{4}{3}\pi\left(\frac{1}{9}\right)^3\right) + \cdots = \frac{4}{3}\pi + \frac{4}{3}\pi\left(\frac{1}{3}\right) + \frac{4}{3}\pi\left(\frac{1}{3}\right)^2 + \cdots = \sum_{n=0}^{\infty} \frac{4}{3}\pi\left(\frac{1}{3}\right)^n.$$

(c) The surface area is infinite and the volume is finite.

$$V = \frac{4/3\pi}{1 - 1/3} = 2\pi$$

91. $400 + 0.75(400) + (0.75)^2(400) + \cdots = \sum_{n=0}^{\infty} 400(0.75)^n$

$$= \frac{400}{1 - 0.75} = \$1600$$

92. $500 + 0.70(500) + (0.70)^2(500) + \cdots = \sum_{n=0}^{\infty} 500(0.70)^n$

$$= \frac{500}{1 - 0.70} \approx \$1666.67$$

93. $250 + 0.80(250) + (0.80)^2(250) + \cdots = \sum_{n=0}^{\infty} 250(0.80)^2$

$$= \frac{250}{1 - 0.80} = \$1250$$

94. $350 + 0.75(350) + (0.75)^2(350) + \cdots = \sum_{n=0}^{\infty} 350(0.75)^n$

$$= \frac{350}{1 - 0.75} = \$1400$$

95. $600 + 0.725(600) + (0.725)^2(600) + \cdots = \sum_{n=0}^{\infty} 600(0.725)^n$

$$= \frac{600}{1 - 0.725} \approx \$2181.82$$

96. $450 + 0.775(450) + (0.775)^2(450) + \cdots = \sum_{n=0}^{\infty} 450(0.775)^n$

$$= \frac{450}{1 - 0.775} = \$2000$$

97. (a) Option 1: $30{,}000 + 1.025(30{,}000) + \cdots + (1.025)^4(30{,}000) = \sum_{n=0}^{4} 30{,}000(1.025)^n$

$\approx \$157{,}689.86$

Option 2: $32{,}500 + 1.02(32{,}500) + \cdots + (1.02)^4(32{,}500) = \sum_{n=0}^{4} 32{,}500(1.02)^n$

$\approx \$169{,}131.31$

Option 2 has the larger cumulative amount.

(b) Option 1: $(1.025)^4(30{,}000) \approx \$33{,}114.39$

Option 2: $(1.02)^4(32{,}500) \approx \$35{,}179.05$

Option 2 has the larger amount.

98. (a) $8000 + 0.9(8000) + \ldots + (0.9)^{n-1}(8000) = \sum_{i=0}^{n-1} 8000(0.9)^i$

(b) $\sum_{i=0}^{9} 8000(0.9)^i = 52{,}106$ units (10 years)

$\sum_{i=0}^{19} 8000(0.9)^i = 70{,}274$ units (20 years)

$\sum_{i=0}^{49} 8000(0.9)^i = 79{,}588$ units (50 years)

(c) $\sum_{i=0}^{\infty} 8000(0.9)^i = \dfrac{8000}{1 - 0.9} = 80{,}000$

If this trend continues indefinitely, the number of units will be 80,000.

99. (a) Downward: $850 + 0.75(850) + (0.75)^2(850) + \cdots + (0.75)^9(850) = \sum_{n=0}^{9} 850(0.75)^n$

≈ 3208.53 feet

Upward: $0.75(850) + (0.75)^2(850) + \cdots + (0.75)^{10}(850) = \sum_{n=0}^{9} (0.75)(850)(0.75)^n$

$= \sum_{n=0}^{9} 637.5(0.75)^n \approx 2406.4$ feet

Total distance: $3208.53 + 2406.4 = 5614.93$ feet

(b) $\sum_{n=0}^{\infty} 850(0.75)^n + \sum_{n=0}^{\infty} 637.5(0.75)^n = \dfrac{850}{1 - 0.75} + \dfrac{637.5}{1 - 0.75} = 5950$ feet

100. (a) Total distance $= \sum_{n=0}^{\infty} 32(0.81)^n - 16 = \dfrac{32}{1 - 0.81} - 16 \approx 152.42$ feet

(b) Total time $= 1 + 2\sum_{n=1}^{\infty} (0.9)^n = 1 + 2\left[\dfrac{1}{1 - 0.9} - 1\right] = 19$ seconds

101. False. See definition page 535.

102. False. You multiply the first term by the common ratio raised to the $(n - 1)$ power.

103. $a_1 = 3,\ r = \frac{x}{2}$

$a_2 = 3\left(\frac{x}{2}\right) = \frac{3x}{2}$

$a_3 = \frac{3x}{2}\left(\frac{x}{2}\right) = \frac{3x^2}{4}$

$a_4 = \frac{3x^2}{4}\left(\frac{x}{2}\right) = \frac{3x^3}{8}$

$a_5 = \frac{3x^3}{8}\left(\frac{x}{2}\right) = \frac{3x^4}{16}$

104. $a_1 = \frac{1}{2}$

$a_2 = \frac{1}{2}(7x) = \frac{7x}{2}$

$a_3 = \frac{7x}{2}(7x) = \frac{7^2x^2}{2}$

$a_4 = \frac{7^3x^3}{2}$

$a_5 = \frac{7^4x^4}{2}$

105. $a_1 = 100,\ r = e^x,\ n = 9$

$a_n = a_1r^{n-1}$

$a_9 = 100(e^x)^8 = 100e^{8x}$

106. $a_1 = 4, r = \frac{4x}{3}, n = 6$

$a_n = a_1r^{n-1}$

$a_6 = 4\left(\frac{4x}{3}\right)^5 = \frac{4096}{243}x^5$

107. (a) $f(x) = 6\left[\frac{1 - 0.5^x}{1 - 0.5}\right]$

$\sum_{n=0}^{\infty} 6\left(\frac{1}{2}\right)^n = \frac{6}{1 - 1/2} = 12$

The horizontal asymptote of $f(x)$ is $y = 12$. This corresponds to the sum of the series.

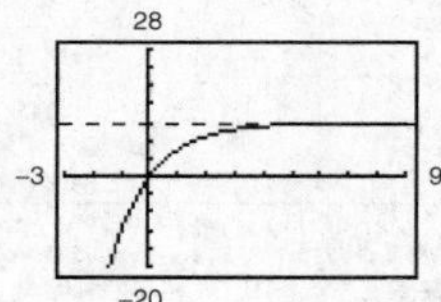

(b) $f(x) = 2\left[\frac{1 - 0.8^x}{1 - 0.8}\right]$

$\sum_{n=0}^{\infty} 2\left(\frac{4}{5}\right)^n = \frac{2}{1 - 4/5} = 10$

The horizontal asymptote of $f(x)$ is $y = 10$. This corresponds to the sum of the series.

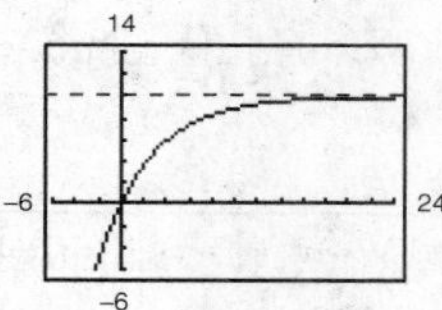

108. Given a real number r between -1 and 1, $|a_n| = |a_{n-1}(r)| < |a_{n-1}|$ which shows that the terms decrease.

109. To use the first two terms of a geometric series to find the nth term, first divide the second term by the first term to obtain the constant ratio. The nth term is the first term multiplied by the common ratio raised to the $(n - 1)$ power.

$r = \frac{a_2}{a_1},\ a_n = a_1r^{n-1}$

110. a_1

$a_2 = a_1r$

$a_3 = a_2r = a_1r^2$

$a_4 = a_1r^3$

$a_n = a_1r^{n-1}$

111. Time $= \frac{\text{Distance}}{\text{Speed}} = \frac{200}{50} + \frac{200}{42} = 200\left[\frac{92}{2100}\right]$ hours

Speed $= \frac{\text{Distance}}{\text{Time}} = \frac{400}{200[92/2100]} = \frac{2(2100)}{92} \approx 45.65$ mph

112. Your friend mows at the rate of $\frac{1}{4}$ lawns/hour, and your rate is $\frac{1}{6}$ lawns/hour. Together, the time would be

$$\frac{1}{(1/4) + (1/6)} = \frac{1}{10/24} = \frac{24}{10} = 2.4 \text{ hours.}$$

113. $\det\begin{bmatrix} -1 & 3 & 4 \\ -2 & 8 & 0 \\ 2 & 5 & -1 \end{bmatrix} = 4(-10 - 16) - 1(-8 + 6)$

$= -104 + 2 = -102$

114. $\det\begin{bmatrix} -1 & 0 & 4 \\ -4 & 3 & 5 \\ 0 & 2 & -3 \end{bmatrix} = -1(-9 - 10) + 4(-8 - 0)$

$= 19 - 32 = -13$

115. Answers will vary.

Section 8.4 Mathematical Induction

- You should be sure that you understand the principle of mathematical induction. If P_n is a statement involving the positive integer n, where P_1 is true and the truth of P_k implies the truth of P_{k+1}, then P_n is true for all positive integers n.
- You should be able to verify (by induction) the formulas for the sums of powers of integers and be able to use these formulas.
- You should be able to work with finite differences.

Vocabulary Check

1. mathematical induction

2. first

3. arithmetic

4. second

1. $P_k = \dfrac{5}{k(k+1)}$

$P_{k+1} = \dfrac{5}{(k+1)[(k+1)+1]} = \dfrac{5}{(k+1)(k+2)}$

2. $P_k = \dfrac{4}{(k+2)(k+3)}$

$P_{k+1} = \dfrac{4}{[(k+1)+2][(k+1)+3]}$

$= \dfrac{4}{(k+3)(k+4)}$

3. $P_k = \dfrac{2^k}{(k+1)!}$

$P_{k+1} = \dfrac{2^{k+1}}{((k+1)+1)!} = \dfrac{2^{k+1}}{(k+2)!}$

4. $P_k = \dfrac{2^{k-1}}{k!}$

$P_{k+1} = \dfrac{2^{(k+1)-1}}{(k+1)!} = \dfrac{2^k}{(k+1)!}$

5. $P_k = 1 + 6 + 11 + \cdots + [5(k-1) - 4] + [5k - 4]$

$P_{k+1} = 1 + 6 + 11 + \cdots + [5k - 4] + [5(k+1) - 4]$

$= 1 + 6 + 11 + \cdots + [5k - 4] + [5k + 1]$

6. $P_k = 7 + 13 + 19 + \cdots + [6(k - 1) + 1] + (6k + 1)$

$$P_{k+1} = 7 + 13 + 19 + \cdots + (6k + 1) + (6(k + 1) + 1)$$

$$= 7 + 13 + 19 + \cdots + (6k + 1) + (6k + 7)$$

7. 1. When $n = 1$, $S_1 = 2 = 1(1 + 1)$.

2. Assume that $S_k = 2 + 4 + 6 + 8 + \cdots + 2k = k(k + 1)$.

Then,

$$S_{k+1} = 2 + 4 + 6 + 8 + \cdots + 2k + 2(k + 1)$$

$$= S_k + 2(k + 1) = k(k + 1) + 2(k + 1) = (k + 1)(k + 2).$$

Therefore, by mathematical induction, the formula is valid for all positive integer values of n.

8. 1. When $n = 1$, $S_1 = 3 = 1(4(1) - 1) = 3$

2. Assume that $S_k = 3 + 11 + \cdots + (8k - 5) = k(4k - 1)$.

Then,

$$S_{k+1} = 3 + 11 + \cdots + (8k - 5) + (8(k + 1) - 5)$$

$$= 3 + 11 + \cdots + (8k - 5) + (8k + 3)$$

$$= S_k + (8k + 3)$$

$$= k(4k - 1) + (8k + 3)$$

$$= 4k^2 + 7k + 3$$

$$= (k + 1)(4k + 3)$$

$$= (k + 1)(4(k + 1) - 1).$$

Therefore, by mathematical induction, the formula is valid for all $n \geq 1$.

9. 1. When $n = 1$, $S_1 = 3 = \frac{1}{2}(5(1) + 1)$

2. Assume that $S_k = 3 + 8 + 13 + \cdots + (5k - 2) = \frac{k}{2}(5k + 1)$.

Then,

$$S_{k+1} = 3 + 8 + 13 + \cdots + (5k - 2) + [5(k + 1) - 2]$$

$$= S_k + [5k + 3] = \frac{k}{2}(5k + 1) + 5k + 3$$

$$= \frac{1}{2}[5k^2 + 11k + 6] = \frac{1}{2}(k + 1)(5k + 6)$$

$$= \frac{1}{2}(k + 1)(5(k + 1) + 1).$$

Therefore, by mathematical induction, the formula is valid for all positive integer values of n.

10. 1. When $n = 1$,

$$S_1 = 1 = \frac{1}{2}(3 \cdot 1 - 1).$$

2. Assume that $S_k = 1 + 4 + 7 + 10 + \cdots + (3k - 2) = \frac{k}{2}(3k - 1)$.

Then,

$$\begin{aligned} S_{k+1} &= 1 + 4 + 7 + 10 + \cdots + (3k - 2) + (3(k + 1) - 2) \\ &= S_k + (3(k + 1) - 2) \\ &= \frac{k}{2}(3k - 1) + (3k + 1) \\ &= \frac{3k^2 - k + 6k + 2}{2} \\ &= \frac{3k^2 + 5k + 2}{2} \\ &= \frac{(k + 1)(3k + 2)}{2} \\ &= \frac{k + 1}{2}[3(k + 1) - 1]. \end{aligned}$$

Therefore, the formula is valid for all positive integer values of n.

11. 1. When $n = 1$, $S_1 = 1 = 2^1 - 1$.

2. Assume that

$S_k = 1 + 2 + 2^2 + 2^3 + \cdots + 2^{k-1} = 2^k - 1$.

Then,

$$\begin{aligned} S_{k+1} &= 1 + 2 + 2^2 + 2^3 + \cdots + 2^{k-1} + 2^k \\ &= S_k + 2^k = 2^k - 1 + 2^k = 2(2^k) - 1 = 2^{k+1} - 1. \end{aligned}$$

Therefore, by mathematical induction, the formula is valid for all positive integer values of n.

12. 1. When $n = 1$, $S_1 = 2 = 3^1 - 1$.

2. Assume that $S_k = 2(1 + 3 + 3^2 + 3^3 + \cdots + 3^{k-1}) = 3^k - 1$.

Then,

$$\begin{aligned} S_{k+1} &= 2(1 + 3 + 3^2 + 3^3 + \cdots + 3^{k-1}) + 2 \cdot 3^{k+1-1} \\ &= S_k + 2 \cdot 3^k \\ &= 3^k - 1 + 2 \cdot 3^k \\ &= 3 \cdot 3^k - 1 \\ &= 3^{k+1} - 1. \end{aligned}$$

Therefore, the formula is valid for all positive integer values of n.

13. 1. When $n = 1$, $S_1 = 1 = \dfrac{1(1+1)}{2}$.

2. Assume that

$$S_k = 1 + 2 + 3 + 4 + \cdots + k = \frac{k(k+1)}{2}.$$

Then,

$$S_{k+1} = 1 + 2 + 3 + 4 + \cdots + k + (k+1)$$
$$= S_k + (k+1) = \frac{k(k+1)}{2} + \frac{2(k+1)}{2} = \frac{(k+1)(k+2)}{2}.$$

Therefore, the formula is valid for all positive integer values of n.

14. 1. When $n = 1$, $S_1 = 1^3 = 1 = \dfrac{1(1+1)^2}{4}$.

2. Assume that $S_k = 1^3 + 2^3 + 3^3 + 4^3 + \cdots + k^3 = \dfrac{k^2(k+1)^2}{4}$.

Then,

$$S_{k+1} = 1^3 + 2^3 + 3^3 + 4^3 + \cdots + k^3 + (k+1)^3$$
$$= S_k + (k+1)^3 = \frac{k^2(k+1)^2}{4} + (k+1)^3 = \frac{k^2(k+1)^2 + 4(k+1)^3}{4}$$
$$= \frac{(k+1)^2[k^2 + 4(k+1)]}{4} = \frac{(k+1)^2(k^2 + 4k + 4)}{4} = \frac{(k+1)^2(k+2)^2}{4}.$$

Therefore, the formula is valid for all positive integer values of n.

15. 1. When $n = 1$,

$$S_1 = 1^4 = \frac{1(1+1)(2\cdot 1 + 1)(3\cdot 1^2 + 3\cdot 1 - 1)}{30}.$$

2. Assume that $S_k = \displaystyle\sum_{i=1}^{k} i^4 = \frac{k(k+1)(2k+1)(3k^2+3k-1)}{30}$.

Then, $S_{k+1} = S_k + (k+1)^4$

$$= \frac{k(k+1)(2k+1)(3k^2+3k-1)}{30} + (k+1)^4 = \frac{k(k+1)(2k+1)(3k^2+3k-1) + 30(k+1)^4}{30}$$
$$= \frac{(k+1)[k(2k+1)(3k^2+3k-1) + 30(k+1)^3]}{30} = \frac{(k+1)(6k^4 + 39k^3 + 91k^2 + 89k + 30)}{30}$$
$$= \frac{(k+1)(k+2)(2k+3)(3k^2+9k+5)}{30} = \frac{(k+1)(k+2)(2(k+1)+1)(3(k+1)^2 + 3(k+1) - 1)}{30}.$$

Therefore, the formula is valid for all positive integer values of n.

16. 1. When $n = 1$, $S_1 = \dfrac{(1)^2(1 + 1)^2(2(1)^2 + 2(1) - 1)}{12} = 1.$

2. Assume that $S_k = \displaystyle\sum_{i=1}^{k} i^5 = \frac{k^2(k + 1)^2(2k^2 + 2k - 1)}{12}.$

Then,

$$\begin{aligned}
S_{k+1} &= \sum_{i=1}^{k+1} i^5 = \sum_{i=1}^{k} i^5 + (k + 1)^5 \\
&= \frac{k^2(k + 1)^2(2k^2 + 2k - 1)}{12} + \frac{12(k + 1)^5}{12} \\
&= \frac{(k + 1)^2[k^2(2k^2 + 2k - 1) + 12(k + 1)^3]}{12} \\
&= \frac{(k + 1)^2[2k^4 + 2k^3 - k^2 + 12(k^3 + 3k^2 + 3k + 1)]}{12} \\
&= \frac{(k + 1)^2[2k^4 + 14k^3 + 35k^2 + 36k + 12]}{12} \\
&= \frac{(k + 1)^2(k^2 + 4k + 4)(2k^2 + 6k + 3)}{12} \\
&= \frac{(k + 1)^2(k + 2)^2[2(k + 1)^2 + 2(k + 1) - 1]}{12}.
\end{aligned}$$

Therefore, the formula is valid for all positive integer values of n.

17. 1. When $n = 1$, $S_1 = 2 = \dfrac{1(2)(3)}{3}.$

2. Assume that $S_k = 1(2) + 2(3) + 3(4) + \cdots + k(k + 1) = \dfrac{k(k + 1)(k + 2)}{3}.$

Then,

$$\begin{aligned}
S_{k+1} &= 1(2) + 2(3) + 3(4) + \cdots + k(k + 1) + (k + 1)(k + 2) \\
&= S_k + (k + 1)(k + 2) \\
&= \frac{k(k + 1)(k + 2)}{3} + \frac{3(k + 1)(k + 2)}{3} \\
&= \frac{(k + 1)(k + 2)(k + 3)}{3}.
\end{aligned}$$

Therefore, the formula is valid for all positive integer values of n.

18. 1. When $n = 1$, $S_1 = \dfrac{1}{(1)(3)} = \dfrac{1}{2 + 1}$.

2. Assume that $S_k = \displaystyle\sum_{i=1}^{k} \frac{1}{(2i - 1)(2i + 1)} = \frac{k}{2k + 1}$.

Then,

$$\begin{aligned}
S_{k+1} &= S_k + \frac{1}{(2(k + 1) - 1)(2(k + 1) + 1)} \\
&= \frac{k}{2k + 1} + \frac{1}{(2k + 1)(2k + 3)} \\
&= \frac{k(2k + 3) + 1}{(2k + 1)(2k + 3)} \\
&= \frac{2k^2 + 3k + 1}{(2k + 1)(2k + 3)} \\
&= \frac{(2k + 1)(k + 1)}{(2k + 1)(2k + 3)} \\
&= \frac{k + 1}{2(k + 1) + 1}.
\end{aligned}$$

Therefore, the formula is valid for all positive integer values of n.

19. 1. When $n = 1$, $S_1 = \dfrac{1}{1(1 + 1)} = \dfrac{1}{2}$

2. Assume $S_k = \displaystyle\sum_{i=1}^{k} \frac{1}{i(i + 1)} = \frac{k}{k + 1}$.

Thus,

$$\begin{aligned}
S_{k+1} &= \sum_{i=1}^{k+1} \frac{1}{i(i + 1)} \\
&= \frac{1}{1(2)} + \frac{1}{2(3)} + \cdots + \frac{1}{k(k + 1)} + \frac{1}{(k + 1)(k + 2)} \\
&= \frac{k}{k + 1} + \frac{1}{(k + 1)(k + 2)} \\
&= \frac{k(k + 2) + 1}{(k + 2)(k + 2)} \\
&= \frac{(k + 1)^2}{(k + 1)(k + 2)} \\
&= \frac{k + 1}{k + 2} \\
&= \frac{k + 1}{(k + 1) + 1}.
\end{aligned}$$

Therefore, the formula is valid for all positive integer values of n.

20. 1. When $n = 1$, $\dfrac{1}{1(2)(3)} = \dfrac{1}{6} = \dfrac{1(4)}{4(2)(3)}$.

2. Assume $\displaystyle\sum_{i=1}^{k} \frac{1}{i(i+1)(i+2)} = \frac{k(k+3)}{4(k+1)(k+2)}$.

Thus,

$$\begin{aligned}
S_{k+1} &= \sum_{i=1}^{k+1} \frac{1}{i(i+1)(i+2)} \\
&= \frac{1}{1 \cdot 2 \cdot 3} + \frac{1}{2 \cdot 3 \cdot 4} + \cdots + \frac{1}{k(k+1)(k+2)} + \frac{1}{(k+1)(k+2)(k+3)} \\
&= \frac{k(k+3)}{4(k+1)(k+2)} + \frac{1}{(k+1)(k+2)(k+3)} \\
&= \frac{k(k+3)(k+3)+4}{4(k+1)(k+2)(k+3)} \\
&= \frac{k^3 + 6k^2 + 9k + 4}{4(k+1)(k+2)(k+3)} \\
&= \frac{(k+1)^2(k+4)}{4(k+1)(k+2)(k+3)} \\
&= \frac{(k+1)(k+4)}{4(k+2)(k+3)}.
\end{aligned}$$

Therefore, the formula is valid for all positive integer values of n.

21. $\displaystyle\sum_{n=1}^{50} n^3 = \frac{50^2(50+1)^2}{4} = 1{,}625{,}625$

22. $$\begin{aligned}\sum_{n=1}^{10} n^4 &= \frac{10(10+1)(2 \cdot 10 + 1)(3 \cdot 10^2 + 3 \cdot 10 - 1)}{30} \\ &= \frac{10(11)(21)(329)}{30} = 25{,}333\end{aligned}$$

23. $$\begin{aligned}\sum_{n=1}^{12} (n^2 - n) &= \sum_{n=1}^{12} n^2 - \sum_{n=1}^{12} n \\ &= \frac{12(12+1)(2 \cdot 12 + 1)}{6} - \frac{12(12+1)}{2} \\ &= 650 - 78 = 572\end{aligned}$$

24. $$\begin{aligned}\sum_{n=1}^{40} (n^3 - n) &= \sum_{n=1}^{40} n^3 - \sum_{n=1}^{40} n \\ &= \frac{40^2(40+1)^2}{4} - \frac{40(40+1)}{2} \\ &= 672{,}400 - 820 = 671{,}580\end{aligned}$$

25. 1. When $n = 4$, $4! = 24$ and $2^4 = 16$, thus $4! > 2^4$.

2. Assume $k! > 2^k$, $k > 4$. Then, $(k+1)! = k!(k+1) > 2^k(2)$ since $k + 1 > 2$. Thus, $(k+1)! > 2^{k+1}$.

Therefore, by mathematical induction, the formula is valid for all integers n such that $n \geq 4$.

26. 1. When $n = 7$, $\left(\frac{4}{3}\right)^7 \approx 7.4915 > 7$.

2. Assume that $\left(\frac{4}{3}\right)^k > k, k > 7$.

Then, $\left(\frac{4}{3}\right)^{k+1} = \left(\frac{4}{3}\right)^k\left(\frac{4}{3}\right) > k\left(\frac{4}{3}\right) = k + \frac{k}{3} > k + 1$ for $k > 7$. Thus, $\left(\frac{4}{3}\right)^{k+1} > k + 1$.

Therefore, $\left(\frac{4}{3}\right)^n > n$.

27. 1. When $n = 2$, $\frac{1}{\sqrt{1}} + \frac{1}{\sqrt{2}} \approx 1.707$ and $\sqrt{2} \approx 1.414$, thus $\frac{1}{\sqrt{1}} + \frac{1}{\sqrt{2}} > \sqrt{2}$.

2. Assume $\frac{1}{\sqrt{1}} + \frac{1}{\sqrt{2}} + \frac{1}{\sqrt{3}} + \cdots + \frac{1}{\sqrt{k}} > \sqrt{k}, k > 2$.

Then, $\frac{1}{\sqrt{1}} + \frac{1}{\sqrt{2}} + \frac{1}{\sqrt{3}} + \cdots + \frac{1}{\sqrt{k}} + \frac{1}{\sqrt{k+1}} > \sqrt{k} + \frac{1}{\sqrt{k+1}}$.

Now we need to show that $\sqrt{k} + \frac{1}{\sqrt{k+1}} > \sqrt{k+1},\ k > 2$.

This is true because $\sqrt{k(k+1)} > k$

$$\sqrt{k(k+1)} + 1 > k + 1$$

$$\frac{\sqrt{k(k+1)} + 1}{\sqrt{k+1}} > \frac{k+1}{\sqrt{k+1}}$$

$$\sqrt{k} + \frac{1}{\sqrt{k+1}} > \sqrt{k+1}.$$

Therefore, $\frac{1}{\sqrt{1}} + \frac{1}{\sqrt{2}} + \frac{1}{\sqrt{3}} + \cdots + \frac{1}{\sqrt{k}} + \frac{1}{\sqrt{k+1}} > \sqrt{k+1}$.

Therefore, by mathematical induction, the formula is valid for all integers n such that $n \geq 2$.

28. 1. When $n = 1$, $\left(\frac{x}{y}\right)^2 < \left(\frac{x}{y}\right)$ and $(0 < x < y)$.

2. Assume that $\left(\frac{x}{y}\right)^{k+1} < \left(\frac{x}{y}\right)^k$

$$\left(\frac{x}{y}\right)^{k+1} < \left(\frac{x}{y}\right)^k \Rightarrow \left(\frac{x}{y}\right)\left(\frac{x}{y}\right)^{k+1} < \left(\frac{x}{y}\right)\left(\frac{x}{y}\right)^k \Rightarrow \left(\frac{x}{y}\right)^{k+2} < \left(\frac{x}{y}\right)^{k+1}.$$

Therefore, $\left(\frac{x}{y}\right)^{n+1} < \left(\frac{x}{y}\right)^n$ for all integers $n \geq 1$.

29. 1. When $n = 1$, $1 + a \geq a$ since $1 > 0$.

2. Assume $(1 + a)^k \geq ka$.

Then, $(1 + a)^{k+1} = (1 + a)^k(1 + a) \geq ka(1 + a)$

$= ka + ka^2 \geq ka + a$ (because $a > 1$)

$= (k + 1)a$.

Therefore, by mathematical induction, the inequality is valid for all integers $n \geq 1$.

30. 1. When $n = 1$, $3^1 > (1)2^1$

2. Assume that $3^k > k2^k$, $k \geq 2$.

First note that $k \geq 2 \Longrightarrow 3k \geq 2k + 2 = 2(k + 1)$

Then, $3^{k+1} = 3(3^k) > 3(k2^k) = (3k)2^k \geq 2(k + 1)2^k = (k + 1)2^{k+1}$.

Therefore $3^n > n2^n$ for all integers $n \geq 1$.

31. 1. When $n = 1$, $(ab)^1 = a^1b^1 = ab$.

2. Assume that $(ab)^k = a^kb^k$.

Then, $(ab)^{k+1} = (ab)^k(ab)$

$= a^kb^kab$

$= a^{k+1}b^{k+1}$.

Thus, $(ab)^n = a^nb^n$.

32. 1. When $n = 1$, $\left(\frac{a}{b}\right)^1 = \frac{a^1}{b^1}$.

2. Assume that $\left(\frac{a}{b}\right)^k = \frac{a^k}{b^k}$.

Then, $\left(\frac{a}{b}\right)^{k+1} = \left(\frac{a}{b}\right)^k\left(\frac{a}{b}\right) = \frac{a^k}{b^k} \cdot \frac{a}{b} = \frac{a^{k+1}}{b^{k+1}}$.

Thus, $\left(\frac{a}{b}\right)^n = \frac{a^n}{b^n}$.

33. 1. When $n = 1$, $(x_1)^{-1} = x_1^{-1}$.

2. Assume that

$(x_1x_2x_3 \cdot \cdot \cdot x_k)^{-1} = x_1^{-1}x_2^{-1}x_3^{-1} \cdot \cdot \cdot x_k^{-1}$.

Then,

$(x_1x_2x_3 \cdot \cdot \cdot x_kx_{k+1})^{-1} = [(x_1x_2x_3 \cdot \cdot \cdot x_k)x_{k+1}]^{-1}$

$= (x_1x_2x_3 \cdot \cdot \cdot x_k)^{-1}x_{k+1}^{-1}$

$= x_1^{-1}x_2^{-1}x_3^{-1} \cdot \cdot \cdot x_k^{-1}x_{k+1}^{-1}$.

Thus, the formula is valid.

34. 1. When $n = 1$, $\ln x_1 = \ln x_1$.

2. Assume that $\ln(x_1x_2x_3 \ldots x_k) = \ln x_1 + \ln x_2 + \ln x_3 + \cdot \cdot \cdot + \ln x_k$.

Then, $\ln(x_1x_2x_3 \ldots x_k x_{k+1}) = \ln[(x_1x_2x_3 \ldots x_k)x_{k+1}]$

$= \ln(x_1x_2x_3 \ldots x_k) + \ln x_{k+1}$

$= \ln x_1 + \ln x_2 + \ln x_3 + \cdot \cdot \cdot + \ln x_k + \ln x_{k+1}$.

Thus, $\ln(x_1x_2x_3 \ldots x_n) = \ln x_1 + \ln x_2 + \ln x_3 + \cdot \cdot \cdot + \ln x_n$.

35. 1. When $n = 1$, $x(y_1) = xy_1$.

2. Assume that $x(y_1 + y_2 + \cdot \cdot \cdot + y_k) = xy_1 + xy_2 + \cdot \cdot \cdot + xy_k$.

Then,

$xy_1 + xy_2 + \cdot \cdot \cdot + xy_k + xy_{k+1} = x(y_1 + y_2 + \cdot \cdot \cdot + y_k) + xy_{k+1}$

$= x[(y_1 + y_2 + \cdot \cdot \cdot + y_k) + y_{k+1}]$

$= x(y_1 + y_2 + \cdot \cdot \cdot + y_k + y_{k+1})$.

Hence, the formula holds.

36. 1. When $n = 1$, $a + bi$ and $a - bi$ are complex conjugates by definition.

2. Assume that $(a + bi)^k$ and $(a - bi)^k$ are complex conjugates.

That is, if $(a + bi)^k = c + di$, then $(a - bi)^k = c - di$.

Then,

$$(a + bi)^{k+1} = (a + bi)^k(a + bi) = (c + di)(a + bi)$$
$$= (ac - bd) + i(bc + ad)$$
$$\text{and } (a - bi)^{k+1} = (a - bi)^k(a - bi) = (c - di)(a - bi)$$
$$= (ac - bd) - i(bc + ad).$$

This implies that $(a + bi)^{k+1}$ and $(a - bi)^{k+1}$ are complex conjugates.
Therefore, $(a + bi)^n$ and $(a - bi)^n$ are complex conjugates for $n \geq 1$.

37. 1. When $n = 1$, $[1^3 + 3(1)^2 + 2(1)] = 6$ and 3 is a factor.

2. Assume that 3 is a factor of $(k^3 + 3k^2 + 2k)$.

Then,

$$[(k + 1)^3 + 3(k + 1)^2 + 2(k + 1)] = k^3 + 3k^2 + 3k + 1 + 3k^2 + 6k + 3 + 2k + 2$$
$$= (k^3 + 3k^2 + 2k) + (3k^2 + 9k + 6)$$
$$= (k^3 + 3k^2 + 2k) + 3(k^2 + 3k + 2).$$

Since 3 is a factor of $(k^3 + 3k^2 + 2k)$ by our assumption, and 3 is a factor of $3(k^2 + 3k + 2)$ then 3 is a factor of the whole sum.

Thus, 3 is a factor of $(n^3 + 3n^2 + 2n)$ for every positive integer n.

38. 1. When $n = 1$, 3 is a factor of $[1^3 + 5(1) + 6] = 12$.

2. Assume that 3 is a factor of $k^3 + 5k + 6$.

Then, $(k + 1)^3 + 5(k + 1) + 6 = k^3 + 3k^2 + 3k + 1 + 5k + 11$

$$= k^3 + 3k^2 + 8k + 12$$
$$= (k^3 + 5k + 6) + (3k^2 + 3k + 6)$$
$$= (k^3 + 5k + 6) + 3(k^2 + k + 2).$$

Because 3 is a factor of both terms, 3 is a factor of $(k + 1)^3 + 5(k + 1) + 6$.

Therefore, 3 is a factor of $n^3 + 5n + 6$ for all $n > 0$.

39. 1. When $n = 1$, $[1^3 - 1 + 3] = 3$, and 3 is a factor.

2. Assume that 3 is a factor of $k^3 - k + 3$. Then,

$$[(k + 1)^3 - (k + 1) + 3] = k^3 + 3k^2 + 3k + 1 - k - 1 + 3$$
$$= k^3 + 3k^2 + 2k + 3$$
$$= (k^3 - k + 3) + 3k^2 + 3k$$
$$= (k^3 - k + 3) + 3(k^2 + k).$$

Since 3 is a factor of $k^3 - k + 3$ by our assumption, and 3 is a factor of $3(k^2 + k)$, then 3 is a factor of the whole sum.

Thus, 3 is a factor of $n^3 - n + 3$ for every positive integer n.

40. 1. When $n = 1$, $[1^4 - 1 + 4] = 4$, and 2 is a factor.

2. Assume that 2 is a factor of $k^4 - k + 4$.

Then,

$$[(k+1)^4 - (k+1) + 4] = (k^4 + 4k^3 + 6k^2 + 4k + 1) - k - 1 + 4$$
$$= k^4 + 4k^3 + 6k^2 + 3k + 4$$
$$= (k^4 - k + 4) + (4k^3 + 6k^2 + 4k).$$

Since 2 is a factor of each term, it is a factor of the sum.

Thus, 2 is a factor of $n^4 - n + 4$ for each positive integer n.

41. 1. When $n = 1$, $2^{2+1} + 1 = 9$, and 3 is a factor.

2. Assume that 3 is a factor of $2^{2k+1} + 1$.

Then,

$$2^{2(k+1)+1} + 1 = 2^{2k+3} + 1$$
$$= 4 \cdot 2^{2k+1} + 1$$
$$= (3+1)2^{2k+1} + 1$$
$$= (2^{2k+1} + 1) + 3 \cdot 2^{2k+1}.$$

Since 3 is a factor of $2^{2k+1} + 1$ by our assumption, and 3 is a factor of $3 \cdot 2^{2k+1}$, then 3 is a factor of the whole sum.

Thus, 3 is a factor of $2^{2n+1} + 1$ for every positive integer n.

42. 1. When $n = 1$, $2^{4(1)-2} + 1 = 5$, and 5 is a factor.

2. Assume that 5 is a factor of $2^{4k-2} + 1$.

Then,

$$2^{4(k+1)-2} + 1 = 2^{4k+2} + 1$$
$$= 16 \cdot 2^{4k-2} + 1$$
$$= (15+1)2^{4k-2} + 1$$
$$= (2^{4k-2} + 1) + 15 \cdot 2^{4k-2}.$$

Since 5 is a factor of $2^{4k-2} + 1$ by our assumption, and 5 is a factor of $15 \cdot 2^{4k-2}$, then 5 is a factor of the whole sum.

Thus, 5 is a factor of $2^{4n-2} + 1$ for every positive integer n.

43. $a_1 = 0,\ a_n = a_{n-1} + 3$

$a_1 = 0$

$a_2 = a_1 + 3 = 0 + 3 = 3$

$a_3 = a_2 + 3 = 3 + 3 = 6$

$a_4 = a_3 + 3 = 6 + 3 = 9$

$a_5 = a_4 + 3 = 9 + 3 = 12$

a_n: 0 3 6 9 12

First differences: 3 3 3 3

Second differences: 0 0 0

Since the first differences are equal, the sequence has a linear model.

44. $a_1 = 2,\ a_n = n - a_{n-1}$

$a_1 = 2$

$a_2 = n - a_1 = 2 - 2 = 0$

$a_3 = n - a_2 = 3 - 0 = 3$

$a_4 = n - a_3 = 4 - 3 = 1$

$a_5 = n - a_5 = 5 - 1 = 4$

a_n: 2 0 3 1 4

First differences: −2 3 −2 3

Second differences: 5 −5 5

Since neither the first differences nor the second differences are equal, the sequence does not have a linear or quadratic model.

45. $a_1 = 3, a_n = a_{n-1} - n$

$a_1 = 3$

$a_2 = a_1 - 2 = 3 - 2 = 1$

$a_3 = a_2 - 3 = 1 - 3 = -2$

$a_4 = a_3 - 4 = -2 - 4 = -6$

$a_5 = a_4 - 5 = -6 - 5 = -11$

a_n: 3 1 −2 −6 −11

First differences: −2 −3 −4 −5

Second differences: −1 −1 −1

Since the second differences are all the same, the sequence has a quadratic model.

46. $a_2 = -3, \; a_n = -2a_{n-1}$

$a_2 = -3$

$a_3 = -2a_2 = -2(-3) = 6$

$a_4 = -2a_3 = -2(6) = -12$

$a_5 = -2a_4 = -2(-12) = 24$

$a_6 = -2a_5 = -2(24) = -48$

a_n: −3 6 −12 24 −48

First differences: 9 −18 36 −72

Second differences: −27 54 −108

Since neither the first nor the second differences are equal, the sequence does not have a linear or quadratic model.

47. $a_0 = 0, a_n = a_{n-1} + n$

$a_0 = 0$

$a_1 = a_0 + 1 = 0 + 1 = 1$

$a_2 = a_1 + 2 = 1 + 2 = 3$

$a_3 = a_2 + 3 = 3 + 3 = 6$

$a_4 = a_3 + 4 = 6 + 4 = 10$

a_n: 0 1 3 6 10

First differences: 1 2 3 4

Second differences: 1 1 1

Since the second differences are equal, the sequence has a quadratic model.

48. $a_0 = 2, \; a_n = (a_{n-1})^2$

$a_0 = 2$

$a_1 = a_0^2 = 2^2 = 4$

$a_2 = a_1^2 = 4^2 = 16$

$a_3 = a_2^2 = 16^2 = 256$

$a_4 = a_3^2 = 256^2 = 65{,}536$

a_n: 2 4 16 256 65,536

First differences: 2 12 240 65,280

Second differences: 10 228 65,040

Since neither the first differences nor the second differences are equal, the sequence does not have a linear or quadratic model.

49. $a_1 = 2, a_n = a_{n-1} + 2$

$a_1 = 2$

$a_2 = a_1 + 2 = 2 + 2 = 4$

$a_3 = a_2 + 2 = 4 + 2 = 6$

$a_4 = a_3 + 2 = 6 + 2 = 8$

$a_5 = a_4 + 2 = 8 + 2 = 10$

a_n: 2 4 6 8 10

First differences: 2 2 2 2

Second differences: 0 0 0

Since the first differences are equal, the sequence has a linear model.

50. $a_1 = 0, \; a_n = a_{n-1} + 2n$

$a_1 = 0$

$a_2 = a_1 + 2(2) = 0 + 4 = 4$

$a_3 = a_2 + 2(3) = 4 + 6 = 10$

$a_4 = a_3 + 2(4) = 10 + 8 = 18$

$a_5 = a_4 + 2(5) = 18 + 10 = 28$

a_n: 0 4 10 18 28

First differences: 4 6 8 10

Second differences: 2 2 2

Since the second differences are equal, the sequence has a quadratic model.

51. $a_1 = 3, a_2 = 3, a_3 = 5$

Let $a_n = an^2 + bn + c$.

$a_1 = a(1)^2 + b(1) + c = 3 \Rightarrow a + b + c = 3$

$a_2 = a(2)^2 + b(2) + c = 3 \Rightarrow 4a + 2b + c = 3$

$a_3 = a(3)^2 + b(3) + c = 5 \Rightarrow 9a + 3b + c = 5$

Solving the system, $a = 1, b = -3, c = 5$,
$a_n = n^2 - 3n + 5, n \geq 1$.

52. $a_1 = 7, a_2 = 6, a_3 = 7$

Let $a_n = an^2 + bn + c$.

$a_1 = a(1)^2 + b(1) + c = 7 \Rightarrow a + b + c = 7$

$a_2 = a(2)^2 + b(2) + c = 6 \Rightarrow 4a + 2b + c = 6$

$a_3 = a(3)^2 + b(3) + c = 7 \Rightarrow 9a + 3b + c = 7$

Solving the system, $a = 1, b = -4, c = 10$,
$a_n = n^2 - 4n + 10, n \geq 1$.

53. $a_0 = -3, a_2 = 1, a_4 = 9$

Let $a_n = an^2 + bn + c$. Then:

$a_0 = a(0)^2 + b(0) + c = -3 \Rightarrow c = -3$

$a_2 = a(2)^2 + b(2) + c = 1 \Rightarrow 4a + 2b + c = 1$

$4a + 2b = 4$

$2a + b = 2$

$a_4 = a(4)^2 + b(4) + c = 9 \Rightarrow 16a + 4b + c = 9$

$16a + 4b = 12$

$4a + b = 3$

By elimination: $-2a - b = -2$

$4a + b = 3$

$2a = 1$

$a = \frac{1}{2} \Rightarrow b = 1$

Thus, $a_n = \frac{1}{2}n^2 + n - 3$.

54. $a_0 = 3, \quad a_2 = 0, \quad a_6 = 36$

Let $a_n = an^2 + bn + c$. Thus:

$a_0 = a(0)^2 + b(0) + c = 3 \Rightarrow c = 3$

$a_2 = a(2)^2 + b(2) + c = 0 \Rightarrow 4a + 2b + c = 0$

$4a + 2b = -3$

$a_6 = a(6)^2 + b(6) + c = 36 \Rightarrow 36a + 6b + c = 36$

$36a + 6b = 33$

$12a + 2b = 11$

By elimination: $-4a - 2b = 3$

$12a + 2b = 11$

$8a = 14$

$a = \frac{7}{4} \Rightarrow b = -5$

Thus, $a_n = \frac{7}{4}n^2 - 5n + 3$.

55. (a) $n = 1$: 3 sides

$n = 2$: $3 \cdot 4 = 12$ sides

$n = 3$: $3 \cdot 4^2 = 48$ sides

nth Koch snowflake: $3(4)^{n-1}$ sides

To prove this, use mathematical induction.

1. For $n - 1$, the number of sides is $3 \cdot 4^{1-1} = 3$.
2. Assume that the number of sides of the kth Koch snowflake is $3 \cdot 4^{k-1}$. When the $(k + 1)^{st}$ Koch snowflake is created, each side is replaced with 4 sides. That is, the number of sides is increased by a factor of 4:

   Number sides $= 4(3 \cdot 4^{k-1}) = 3 \cdot 4^k$.

Hence, the formula is valid for all positive integers n.

(b) $n = 1$: $A_1 = \frac{\sqrt{3}}{4}(1)^2 = \frac{\sqrt{3}}{4}$

$n = 2$: $A_2 = \frac{\sqrt{3}}{4}\left[1 + \frac{1}{3}\right]$

$n = 3$: $A_3 = \frac{\sqrt{3}}{4}\left[1 + \frac{1}{3} + \frac{1}{3}\left(\frac{4}{9}\right)\right]$

$n = 4$: $A_4 = \frac{\sqrt{3}}{4}\left[1 + \frac{1}{3} + \frac{1}{3}\left(\frac{4}{9}\right) + \frac{1}{3}\left(\frac{4}{9}\right)^2\right]$

$$A_n = \frac{\sqrt{3}}{4}\left[1 + \sum_{k=2}^{n} \frac{1}{3}\left(\frac{4}{9}\right)^{k-2}\right], \quad n > 1$$

(c) For the nth Koch snowflake, the length of a single side is $(1/3)^{n-1}$, and the number of sides is $3 \cdot 4^{n-1}$. Hence, the perimeter is

$$\left(\frac{1}{3}\right)^{n-1} 3 \cdot 4^{n-1} = 3\left(\frac{4}{3}\right)^{n-1}.$$

56. (a) One ring → one move

Two rings → three moves

Three rings → seven moves

(b) Four rings: 7 moves to move 3

1 move for fourth ring

7 moves to bring back 3

Total: 15 moves

(c) If n rings, let h_n be the number of moves. Then,

$h_1 = 1$

$h_n = 2h_{n-1} + 1 = 2^n - 1$ moves.

(d) 1. For one ring, $h_1 = 1$.

2. Assume that $h_n = 2h_{n-1} + 1$. For $n + 1$ rings, it takes h_n moves to move n rings, one to move the last ring, and h_n more to move the n rings back.

Total: $h_{n+1} = 2(h_n) + 1$

57. False. P_1 might not even be defined.

58. False. See the Study Tip on page 550.

59. False. It has $n - 2$ second differences.

60. (a) If P_3 is true and P_k implies P_{k+1}, then P_n is true for integers $n \ge 3$.

(b) If $P_1, P_2, P_3, \ldots, P_{50}$ are all true, then P_n is true for integers $1 \le n \le 50$.

(c) If P_1, P_2, and P_3 are all true, but the truth of P_k does not imply that P_{k+1} is true, then you may only conclude that P_1, P_2, and P_3 are true.

(d) If P_2 is true and P_{2k} implies P_{2k+2}, then P_{2n} is true for any positive integer n.

61. $(2x^2 - 1)^2 = 4x^4 - 4x^2 + 1$

62. $(2x - y)^2 = 4x^2 - 4xy + y^2$

63. $(5 - 4x)^3 = -64x^3 + 240x^2 - 300x + 125$

64. $(2x - 4y)^3 = 8x^3 - 48x^2y + 96xy^2 - 64y^3$

65. $3\sqrt{-27} - \sqrt{-12} = 3\sqrt{3 \cdot 3 \cdot (-3)} - \sqrt{2 \cdot 2(-3)} = 9\sqrt{3}i - 2\sqrt{3}i = 7\sqrt{3}i$

66. $\sqrt[3]{125} + 4\sqrt[3]{-8} - 2\sqrt[3]{-54} = 5 + 4(-2) + 6\sqrt[3]{2} = -3 + 6\sqrt[3]{2}$

67. $10\left(\sqrt[3]{64} - 2\sqrt[3]{-16}\right) = 10\left(4 - 2^2\sqrt[3]{-2}\right)$

$= 40 - 40\sqrt[3]{-2}$

$= 40\left(1 + \sqrt[3]{2}\right)$

68. $\left(-5 + \sqrt{-9}\right)^2 = (-5 + 3i)^2$

$= 25 - 9 - 30i = 16 - 30i$

Section 8.5 The Binomial Theorem

- You should be able to use the Binomial Theorem

$$(x + y)^n = x^n + nx^{n-1}y + \frac{n(n-1)}{2!}x^{n-2}y^2 + \cdot \cdot \cdot + {}_nC_r x^{n-r}y^r + \cdot \cdot \cdot + y^n$$

where ${}_nC_r = \dfrac{n!}{(n-r)!r!}$, to expand$(x + y)^n$.

- You should be able to use Pascal's Triangle.

Vocabulary Check

1. binomial coefficients
2. Binomial Theorem, Pascal's Triangle
3. ${}_nC_r$ or $\binom{n}{r}$
4. expanding, binomial

1. ${}_7C_5 = \dfrac{7!}{2!5!} = \dfrac{7 \cdot 6 \cdot 5!}{2 \cdot 5!} = \dfrac{42}{2} = 21$

2. ${}_9C_6 = \dfrac{9!}{6!3!} = \dfrac{9 \cdot 8 \cdot 7 \cdot 6!}{6!\,3 \cdot 2} = \dfrac{9 \cdot 8 \cdot 7}{6} = 84$

3. $\binom{12}{0} = {}_{12}C_0 = \dfrac{12!}{0!12!} = 1$

4. $\binom{20}{20} = {}_{20}C_{20} = \dfrac{20!}{20!0!} = 1$

5. ${}_{20}C_{15} = \dfrac{20!}{15!5!} = \dfrac{20 \cdot 19 \cdot 18 \cdot 17 \cdot 16}{5 \cdot 4 \cdot 3 \cdot 2 \cdot 1} = 15{,}504$

6. ${}_{12}C_3 = \dfrac{12!}{9!3!} = \dfrac{12 \cdot 11 \cdot 10 \cdot 9!}{9!\,3 \cdot 2} = 220$

7. ${}_{14}C_1 = \dfrac{14!}{13!1!} = \dfrac{14 \cdot 13!}{13!} = 14$

8. ${}_{18}C_{17} = \dfrac{18!}{17!1!} = \dfrac{18 \cdot 17!}{17!} = 18$

9. $\binom{100}{98} = {}_{100}C_{98} = \dfrac{100!}{98!2!} = \dfrac{100 \cdot 99}{2 \cdot 1} = 4950$

10. $\binom{10}{7} = \dfrac{10!}{7!3!} = \dfrac{10 \cdot 9 \cdot 8 \cdot 7!}{7!\,3 \cdot 2} = 120$

11. ${}_{41}C_{36} = 749{,}398$

12. ${}_{34}C_4 = 46{,}376$

13. ${}_{100}C_{98} = 4950$

14. ${}_{500}C_{498} = 124{,}750$

15. ${}_{250}C_2 = 31{,}125$

16. ${}_{1000}C_2 = 499{,}500$

17. $(x + 2)^4 = {}_4C_0x^4 + {}_4C_1x^3(2) + {}_4C_2x^2(2)^2 + {}_4C_3x(2)^3 + {}_4C_4(2)^4$
$= x^4 + 8x^3 + 24x^2 + 32x + 16$

18. $(x + 1)^6 = {}_6C_0x^6 + {}_6C_1x^5(1) + {}_6C_2x^4(1)^2 + {}_6C_3x^3(1)^3 + {}_6C_4x^2(1)^4 + {}_6C_5x(1)^5 + {}_6C_6(1)^6$
$= x^6 + 6x^5 + 15x^4 + 20x^3 + 15x^2 + 6x + 1$

19. $(a + 3)^3 = {}_3C_0a^3 + {}_3C_1a^2(3) + {}_3C_2a(3)^2 + {}_3C_3(3)^3$
$= a^3 + 3a^2(3) + 3a(3)^2 + (3)^3 = a^3 + 9a^2 + 27a + 27$

20. $(a + 2)^4 = {}_4C_0a^4 + {}_4C_1a^3(2) + {}_4C_2a^2(2)^2 + {}_4C_3a(2)^3 + {}_4C_4(2)^4 = a^4 + 8a^3 + 24a^2 + 32a + 16$

21. $(y - 2)^4 = {}_4C_0y^4 - {}_4C_1y^3(2) + {}_4C_2y^2(2)^2 - {}_4C_3y(2)^3 + {}_4C_4(2)^4$
$= y^4 - 4y^3(2) + 6y^2(4) - 4y(8) + 16$
$= y^4 - 8y^3 + 24y^2 - 32y + 16$

22. $(y - 2)^5 = {}_5C_0y^5 - {}_5C_1y^4(2) + {}_5C_2y^3(2)^2 - {}_5C_3y^2(2)^3 + {}_5C_4y(2)^4 - {}_5C_5(2)^5$
$= y^5 - 10y^4 + 40y^3 - 80y^2 + 80y - 32$

23. $(x + y)^5 = {}_5C_0x^5 + {}_5C_1x^4y + {}_5C_2x^3y^2 + {}_5C_3x^2y^3 + {}_5C_4xy^4 + {}_5C_5y^5$
$= x^5 + 5x^4y + 10x^3y^2 + 10x^2y^3 + 5xy^4 + y^5$

24. $(x + y)^6 = {}_6C_0x^6 + {}_6C_1x^5y + {}_6C_2x^4y^2 + {}_6C_3x^3y^3 + {}_6C_4x^2y^4 + {}_6C_5xy^5 + {}_6C_6y^6$
$= x^6 + 6x^5y + 15x^4y^2 + 20x^3y^3 + 15x^2y^4 + 6xy^5 + y^6$

25. $(3r + 2s)^6 = {}_6C_0(3r)^6 + {}_6C_1(3r)^5(2s) + {}_6C_2(3r)^4(2s)^2 + {}_6C_3(3r)^3(2s)^3 + {}_6C_4(3r)^2(2s)^4 + {}_6C_5(3r)(2s)^5 + {}_6C_6(2s)^6$
$= 729r^6 + 2916r^5s + 4860r^4s^2 + 4320r^3s^3 + 2160r^2s^4 + 576rs^5 + 64s^6$

26. $(4x + 3y)^4 = 256x^4 + 768x^3y + 864x^2y^2 + 432xy^3 + 81y^4$

27. $(x - y)^5 = {}_5C_0x^5 - {}_5C_1x^4y + {}_5C_2x^3y^2 - {}_5C_3x^2y^3 + {}_5C_4xy^4 - {}_5C_5y^5$
$= x^5 - 5x^4y + 10x^3y^2 - 10x^2y^3 + 5xy^4 - y^5$

28. $(2x - y)^5 = {}_5C_0(2x)^5 - {}_5C_1(2x)^4y + {}_5C_2(2x)^3y^2 - {}_5C_3(2x)^2y^3 + {}_5C_4(2x)y^4 - {}_5C_5y^5$
$= 32x^5 - 5(16x^4)y + 10(8x^3)y^2 - 10(4x^2)y^3 + 5(2x)y^4 - y^5$
$= 32x^5 - 80x^4y + 80x^3y^2 - 40x^2y^3 + 10xy^4 - y^5$

29. $(1 - 4x)^3 = {}_3C_01^3 - {}_3C_11^2(4x) + {}_3C_21(4x)^2 - {}_3C_3(4x)^3$
$= 1 - 3(4x) + 3(4x)^2 - (4x)^3$
$= 1 - 12x + 48x^2 - 64x^3$

30. $(5 - 2y)^3 = 125 - 150y + 60y^2 - 8y^3$

31. $(x^2 + 2)^4 = {}_4C_0(x^2)^4 + {}_4C_1(x^2)^3(2) + {}_4C_2(x^2)^22^2 + {}_4C_3(x^2)2^3 + {}_4C_4(2)^4$
$= x^8 + 8x^6 + 24x^4 + 32x^2 + 16$

32. $(3 - y^2)^3 = {}_3C_0(3)^3 - {}_3C_1(3)^2y^2 + {}_3C_2(3)(y^2)^2 - {}_3C_3(y^2)^3$
$= 27 - 27y^2 + 9y^4 - y^6$
$= -y^6 + 9y^4 - 27y^2 + 27$

33. $(x^2 - 5)^5 = {}_5C_0(x^2)^5 - {}_5C_1(x^2)^4(5) + {}_5C_2(x^2)^3(5^2) - {}_5C_3(x^2)^2(5^3) + {}_5C_4(x^2)(5^4) - {}_5C_5(5^5)$
$= x^{10} - 25x^8 + 250x^6 - 1250x^4 + 3125x^2 - 3125$

34. $(y^2+1)^6 = {}_6C_0(y^2)^6 + {}_6C_1(y^2)^5 + {}_6C_2(y^2)^4 + {}_6C_3(y^2)^3 + {}_6C_4(y^2)^2 + {}_6C_5(y^2) + {}_6C_6$
$= y^{12} + 6y^{10} + 15y^8 + 20y^6 + 15y^4 + 6y^2 + 1$

35. $(x^2+y^2)^4 = {}_4C_0(x^2)^4 + {}_4C_1(x^2)^3(y^2) + {}_4C_2(x^2)^2(y^2)^2 + {}_4C_3(x^2)(y^2)^3 + {}_4C_4(y^2)^4$
$= x^8 + 4x^6y^2 + 6x^4y^4 + 4x^2y^6 + y^8$

36. $(x^2+y^2)^6 = {}_6C_0(x^2)^6 + {}_6C_1(x^2)^5(y^2) + {}_6C_2(x^2)^4(y^2)^2 + {}_6C_3(x^2)^3(y^2)^3 + {}_6C_4(x^2)^2(y^2)^4 + {}_6C_5(x^2)(y^2)^5 + {}_6C_6(y^2)^6$
$= x^{12} + 6x^{10}y^2 + 15x^8y^4 + 20x^6y^6 + 15x^4y^8 + 6x^2y^{10} + y^{12}$

37. $(x^3-y)^6 = {}_6C_0(x^3)^6 - 6C_1(x^3)^5y + {}_6C_2(x^3)^4y^2 - {}_6C_3(x^3)^3y^3 + {}_6C_4(x^3)^2y^4 - {}_6C_5(x^3)y^5 + {}_6C_6y^6$
$= x^{18} - 6x^{15}y + 15x^{12}y^2 - 20x^9y^3 + 15x^6y^4 - 6x^3y^5 + y^6$

38. $(2x^3-y)^5 = {}_5C_0(2x^3)^5 - {}_5C_1(2x^3)^4y + {}_5C_2(2x^3)^3y^2 - {}_5C_3(2x^3)^2y^3 + {}_5C_4(2x^3)y^4 - {}_5C_5y^5$
$= 32x^{15} - 80x^{12}y + 80x^9y^2 - 40x^6y^3 + 10x^3y^4 - y^5$

39. $\left(\frac{1}{x}+y\right)^5 = {}_5C_0\left(\frac{1}{x}\right)^5 + {}_5C_1\left(\frac{1}{x}\right)^4y + {}_5C_2\left(\frac{1}{x}\right)^3y^2 + {}_5C_3\left(\frac{1}{x}\right)^2y^3 + {}_5C_4\left(\frac{1}{x}\right)y^4 + {}_5C_5y^5$
$= \frac{1}{x^5} + \frac{5y}{x^4} + \frac{10y^2}{x^3} + \frac{10y^3}{x^2} + \frac{5y^4}{x} + y^5$

40. $\left(\frac{1}{x}+2y\right)^6 = {}_6C_0\left(\frac{1}{x}\right)^6 + {}_6C_1\left(\frac{1}{x}\right)^5(2y) + {}_6C_2\left(\frac{1}{x}\right)^4(2y)^2 + {}_6C_3\left(\frac{1}{x}\right)^3(2y)^3 + {}_6C_4\left(\frac{1}{x}\right)^2(2y)^4 + {}_6C_5\left(\frac{1}{x}\right)(2y)^5 + {}_6C_6(2y)^6$
$= 1\left(\frac{1}{x}\right)^6 + 6(2)\left(\frac{1}{x}\right)^5y + 15(4)\left(\frac{1}{x}\right)^4y^2 + 20(8)\left(\frac{1}{x}\right)^3y^3 + 15(16)\left(\frac{1}{x}\right)^2y^4 + 6(32)\left(\frac{1}{x}\right)y^5 + 1(64)y^6$
$= \frac{1}{x^6} + \frac{12y}{x^5} + \frac{60y^2}{x^4} + \frac{160y^3}{x^3} + \frac{240y^4}{x^2} + \frac{192y^5}{x} + 64y^6$

41. $\left(\frac{2}{x}-y\right)^4 = {}_4C_0\left(\frac{2}{x}\right)^4 - {}_4C_1\left(\frac{2}{x}\right)^3y + {}_4C_2\left(\frac{2}{x}\right)^2y^2 - {}_4C_3\left(\frac{2}{x}\right)y^3 + {}_4C_4y^4$
$= \frac{16}{x^4} - \frac{32}{x^3}y + \frac{24}{x^2}y^2 - \frac{8}{x}y^3 + y^4$

42. $\left(\frac{2}{x}-3y\right)^5 = {}_5C_0\left(\frac{2}{x}\right)^5 - {}_5C_1\left(\frac{2}{x}\right)^4(3y) + {}_5C_2\left(\frac{2}{x}\right)^3(3y)^2 - {}_5C_3\left(\frac{2}{x}\right)^2(3y)^3 + {}_5C_4\left(\frac{2}{x}\right)(3y)^4 - {}_5C_5(3y)^5$
$= \frac{32}{x^5} - \frac{240}{x^4}y + \frac{720}{x^3}y^2 - \frac{1080}{x^2}y^3 + \frac{810}{x}y^4 - 243y^5$

43. $(4x-1)^3 - 2(4x-1)^4 = (64x^3 - 48x^2 + 12x - 1) - 2(256x^4 - 256x^3 + 96x^2 - 16x + 1)$
$= -512x^4 + 576x^3 - 240x^2 + 44x - 3$

44. $(x+3)^5 - 4(x+3)^4 = (x^5 + 15x^4 + 90x^3 + 270x^2 + 405x + 243) - 4(x^4 + 12x^3 + 54x^2 + 108x + 81)$
$= x^5 + 11x^4 + 42x^3 + 54x^2 - 27x - 81$

45. $2(x-3)^4 + 5(x-3)^2 = 2[x^4 - 4(x^3)(3) + 6(x^2)(3^2) - 4(x)(3^3) + 3^4] + 5[x^2 - 2(x)(3) + 3^2]$

$= 2(x^4 - 12x^3 + 54x^2 - 108x + 81) + 5(x^2 - 6x + 9)$

$= 2x^4 - 24x^3 + 113x^2 - 246x + 207$

46. $3(x+1)^5 + 4(x+1)^3 = (3x^5 + 15x^4 + 30x^3 + 30x^2 + 15x + 3) + (4x^3 + 12x^2 + 12x + 4)$

$= 3x^5 + 15x^4 + 34x^3 + 42x^2 + 27x + 7$

47. $-3(x-2)^3 - 4(x+1)^6 = [-3x^3 + 18x^2 - 36x + 24] - [4x^6 + 24x^5 + 60x^4 + 80x^3 + 60x^2 + 24x + 4]$

$= -4x^6 - 24x^5 - 60x^4 - 83x^3 - 42x^2 - 60x + 20$

48. $5(x+2)^5 - 2(x-1)^2 = [5x^5 + 50x^4 + 200x^3 + 400x^2 + 400x + 160] - [2x^2 - 4x + 2]$

$= 5x^5 + 50x^4 + 200x^3 + 398x^2 + 404x + 158$

49. $(x+8)^{10}, n = 4$

${}_{10}C_3 x^{10-3}(8)^3 = 120x^7(512) = 61{,}440x^7$

50. $(x-5)^6, \quad n = 7$

${}_6C_6\, x^0(-5)^6 = 15{,}625$

51. $(x-6y)^5, n = 3$

${}_5C_2 x^{5-2}(-6y)^2 = 10x^3(36)y^2 = 360x^3y^2$

52. $(x-10z)^7, \quad n = 4$

${}_7C_3\, x^{7-3}(-10z)^3 = -35{,}000\, x^4z^3$

53. $(4x+3y)^9, n = 8$

${}_9C_7(4x)^{9-7}(3y)^7 = 36(16)x^2(3^7)y^7$

$= 1{,}259{,}712x^2y^7$

54. $(5a+6b)^5, \quad n = 5$

${}_5C_4(5a)^{5-4}(6b)^4 = 32{,}400\, a \cdot b^4$

55. $(10x-3y)^{12}, n = 9$

${}_{12}C_8(10x)^{12-8}(-3y)^8 = 495(10^4)(3^8)x^4y^8$

$= 32{,}476{,}950{,}000x^4y^8$

56. $(7x+2y)^{15}, \quad n = 8$

${}_{15}C_7(7x)^{15-7}(2y)^7 \approx 4.7 \times 10^{12}\, x^8y^7$

57. The term involving x^4 in the expansion of $(x+3)^{12}$ is ${}_{12}C_8 x^4(3)^8 = 495x^4(3)^8 = 3{,}247{,}695x^4$. The coefficient is 3,247,695.

58. $(x+4)^{12}, \quad ax^5$

${}_{12}C_7\, x^5(4)^7 = 12{,}976{,}128x^5$

$a = 12{,}976{,}128$

59. The term involving x^8y^2 in the expansion of $(x-2y)^{10}$ is

$${}_{10}C_2 x^8(-2y)^2 = \frac{10!}{2!8!} \cdot 4x^8y^2 = 180x^8y^2.$$

The coefficient is 180.

60. The term involving x^2y^8 in the expansion of $(4x-y)^{10}$ is

$${}_{10}C_8(4x)^2(-y)^8 = \frac{10!}{(10-8)!8!} \cdot 16x^2y^8 = 720x^2y^8.$$

The coefficient is 720.

61. The term involving x^6y^3 in $(3x - 2y)^9$ is

$$_9C_3(3x)^6(-2y)^3 = 84(3)^6(-2)^3x^6y^3$$
$$= -489{,}888x^6y^3.$$

The coefficient is $-489{,}888$.

62. The term involving x^4y^4 in the expansion of $(2x - 3y)^8$ is

$$_8C_4(2x)^4(-3y)^4 = 70(2^4)(-3)^4x^4y^4$$
$$= 90{,}720x^4y^4.$$

$a = 90{,}720$

63. The coefficient of $x^8y^6 = (x^2)^4y^6$ in the expansion of $(x^2 + y)^{10}$ is $_{10}C_6 = 210$.

64. The term involving z^6 in the expansion of $(z^2 - 1)^{12}$ is $_{12}C_9(z^2)^3(-1)^9 = \dfrac{12}{(12 - 9)!9!}z^6(-1) = -220z^6$.

The coefficient is -220.

65. 5th entry of 7th row: $_7C_5 = 21$

66. 3rd entry of 6th row: $_6C_3 = 20$

67. 5th entry of 6th row: $_6C_5 = 6$

68. 2nd entry of 5th row: $_5C_2 = 10$

69. 4th row of Pascal's Triangle: 1 4 6 4 1

$$(3t - 2v)^4 = 1(3t)^4 - 4(3t)^3(2v) + 6(3t)^2(2v)^2 - 4(3t)(2v)^3 + 1(2v)^4$$
$$= 81t^4 - 216t^3v + 216t^2v^2 - 96tv^3 + 16v^4$$

70. 4th row of Pascal's Triangle: 1 4 6 4 1

$$(5v - 2z)^4 = 1(5v)^4 - 4(5v)^3(2z) + 6(5v)^2(2z)^2 - 4(5v)(2z)^3 + 1(2z)^4$$
$$= 625v^4 - 1000v^3z + 600v^2z^2 - 160vz^3 + 16z^4$$

71. 5th row of Pascal's Triangle: 1 5 10 10 5 1

$$(2x - 3y)^5 = 1(2x)^5 - 5(2x)^4(3y) + 10(2x)^3(3y)^2 - 10(2x)^2(3y)^3 + 5(2x)(3y)^4 - (3y)^5$$
$$= 32x^5 - 240x^4y + 720x^3y^2 - 1080x^2y^3 + 810xy^4 - 243y^5$$

72. 5th row of Pascal's Triangle: 1 5 10 10 5 1

$$(5y + 2)^5 = 1(5y)^5 + 5(5y)^42 + 10(5y)^32^2 + 10(5y)^22^3 + 5(5y)2^4 + 2^5$$
$$= 3125y^5 + 6250y^4 + 5000y^3 + 2000y^2 + 400y + 32$$

73. $(\sqrt{x} + 5)^4 = (\sqrt{x})^4 + 4(\sqrt{x})^3(5) + 6(\sqrt{x})^2(5)^2 + 4(\sqrt{x})(5^3) + 5^4$

$$= x^2 + 20x\sqrt{x} + 150x + 500\sqrt{x} + 625$$
$$= x^2 + 20x^{3/2} + 150x + 500x^{1/2} + 625$$

74. $(4\sqrt{t} - 1)^3 = (4\sqrt{t})^3 + 3(4\sqrt{t})^2(-1) + 3(4\sqrt{t})(-1)^2 + (-1)^3$

$$= 64t\sqrt{t} - 48t + 12\sqrt{t} - 1 = 64t^{3/2} - 48t + 12t^{1/2} - 1$$

75. $(x^{2/3} - y^{1/3})^3 = (x^{2/3})^3 - 3(x^{2/3})^2(y^{1/3}) + 3(x^{2/3})(y^{1/3})^2 - (y^{1/3})^3$

$$= x^2 - 3x^{4/3}y^{1/3} + 3x^{2/3}y^{2/3} - y$$

76. $(u^{3/5} + v^{1/5})^5 = u^3 + 5u^{12/5}v^{1/5} + 10u^{9/5}v^{2/5} + 10u^{6/5}v^{3/5} + 5u^{3/5}v^{4/5} + v$

77. $$\frac{f(x+h)-f(x)}{h} = \frac{(x+h)^3 - x^3}{h}$$
$$= \frac{x^3 + 3x^2h + 3xh^2 + h^3 - x^3}{h}$$
$$= \frac{h(3x^2 + 3xh + h^2)}{h}$$
$$= 3x^2 + 3xh + h^2,\ h \neq 0$$

78. $$\frac{f(x+h)-f(x)}{h} = \frac{(x+h)^4 - x^4}{h}$$
$$= \frac{x^4 + 4x^3h + 6x^2h^2 + 4xh^3 + h^4 - x^4}{h}$$
$$= \frac{h(4x^3 + 6x^2h + 4xh^2 + h^3)}{h}$$
$$= 4x^3 + 6x^2h + 4xh^2 + h^3,\ h \neq 0$$

79. $$\frac{f(x+h)-f(x)}{h} = \frac{(x+h)^6 - x^6}{h}$$
$$= \frac{(x^6 + 6x^5h + 15x^4h^2 + 20x^3h^3 + 15x^2h^4 + 6xh^5 + h^6) - x^6}{h}$$
$$= \frac{h(6x^5 + 15x^4h + 20x^3h^2 + 15x^2h^3 + 6xh^4 + h^5)}{h}$$
$$= 6x^5 + 15x^4h + 20x^3h^2 + 15x^2h^3 + 6xh^4 + h^5,\ h \neq 0$$

80. $$\frac{f(x+h)-f(x)}{h} = \frac{(x+h)^8 - x^8}{h}$$
$$= \frac{(x^8 + 8x^7h + 28x^6h^2 + 56x^5h^3 + 70x^4h^4 + 56x^3h^5 + 28x^2h^6 + 8xh^7 + h^8) - x^8}{h}$$
$$= \frac{h(8x^7 + 28x^6h + 56x^5h^2 + 70x^4h^3 + 56x^3h^4 + 28x^2h^5 + 8xh^6 + h^7)}{h}$$
$$= 8x^7 + 28x^6h + 56x^5h^2 + 70x^4h^3 + 56x^3h^4 + 28x^2h^5 + 8xh^6 + h^7,\ h \neq 0$$

81. $$\frac{f(x+h)-f(x)}{h} = \frac{\sqrt{x+h} - \sqrt{x}}{h}$$
$$= \frac{\sqrt{x+h} - \sqrt{x}}{h} \cdot \frac{\sqrt{x+h} + \sqrt{x}}{\sqrt{x+h} + \sqrt{x}}$$
$$= \frac{(x+h) - x}{h\left[\sqrt{x+h} + \sqrt{x}\right]}$$
$$= \frac{1}{\sqrt{x+h} + \sqrt{x}},\ h \neq 0$$

82. $$\frac{f(x+h)-f(x)}{h} = \frac{\dfrac{1}{x+h} - \dfrac{1}{x}}{h}$$
$$= \frac{\dfrac{x-(x+h)}{x(x+h)}}{h}$$
$$= \frac{\dfrac{-h}{x(x+h)}}{h}$$
$$= -\frac{1}{x(x+h)},\ h \neq 0$$

83. $(1 + i)^4 = {}_4C_0 1^4 + {}_4C_1(1)^3 i + {}_4C_2(1)^2 i^2 + {}_4C_3 1 \cdot i^3 + {}_4C_4 i^4$

$= 1 + 4i - 6 - 4i + 1$

$= -4$

84. $(4 - i)^5 = 1024 - 1280i + 640i^2 - 160i^3 + 20i^4 - i^5$

$= 1024 - 1280i - 640 + 160i + 20 - i$

$= 404 - 1121i$

85. $(4 + i)^4 = {}_4C_0(4)^4 + {}_4C_1(4^3)i + {}_4C_2(4^2)(i^2) + {}_4C_3(4)(i^3) + {}_4C_4 i^4$

$= 256 + 256i - 96 - 16i + 1$

$= 161 + 240i$

86. $(2 - i)^5 = 2^5 - 5(2^4)i + 10(2^3)(i^2) - 10(2^2)(i^3) + 5(2)(i^4) - i^5$

$= 32 - 80i - 80 + 40i + 10 - i$

$= -38 - 41i$

87. $(2 - 3i)^6 = {}_6C_0 2^6 - {}_6C_1 2^5(3i) + {}_6C_2 2^4(3i)^2 - {}_6C_3 2^3(3i)^3 + {}_6C_4 2^2(3i)^4 - {}_6C_5 2(3i)^5 + {}_6C_6(3i)^6$

$= 64 - 576i - 2160 + 4320i + 4860 - 2916i - 729$

$= 2035 + 828i$

88. $(3 - 2i)^6 = 3^6 - 6(3^5)(2i) + 15(3^4)(2i)^2 - 20(3^3)(2i)^3 + 15(3^2)(2i)^4 - 6(3)(2i)^5 + (2i)^6$

$= 729 - 2916i - 4860 + 4320i + 2160 - 576i - 64$

$= -2035 + 828i$

89. $\left(5 + \sqrt{-16}\right)^3 = (5 + 4i)^3$

$= 5^3 + 3(5^2)(4i) + 3(5)(4i)^2 + (4i)^3$

$= 125 + 300i - 240 - 64i$

$= -115 + 236i$

90. $\left(5 + \sqrt{-9}\right)^3 = (5 + 3i)^3$

$= 5^3 + 3 \cdot 5^2(3i) + 3 \cdot 5(3i)^2 + (3i)^3$

$= 125 + 225i - 135 - 27i$

$= -10 + 198i$

91. $\left(4 + \sqrt{3}i\right)^4 = 4^4 + 4(4^3)\left(\sqrt{3}i\right) + 6(4^2)\left(\sqrt{3}i\right)^2 + 4(4)\left(\sqrt{3}i\right)^3 + \left(\sqrt{3}\right)^4$

$= 256 + 256\sqrt{3}i - 288 - 48\sqrt{3}i + 9$

$= -23 + 208\sqrt{3}i$

92. $\left(5 - \sqrt{3}i\right)^4 = 5^4 - 4 \cdot 5^3\left(\sqrt{3}i\right) + 6 \cdot 5^2\left(\sqrt{3}i\right)^2 - 4 \cdot 5\left(\sqrt{3}i\right)^3 + \left(\sqrt{3}i\right)^4$

$= 625 - 500\sqrt{3}i - 450 + 60\sqrt{3}i + 9$

$= 184 - 440\sqrt{3}i$

93. $\left(-\frac{1}{2} + \frac{\sqrt{3}}{2}i\right)^3 = \frac{1}{8}(-1 + \sqrt{3}i)^3$

$= \frac{1}{8}\left[(-1)^3 + 3(-1)^2(\sqrt{3}i) + 3(-1)(\sqrt{3}i)^2 + (\sqrt{3}i)^3\right]$

$= \frac{1}{8}\left[-1 + 3\sqrt{3}i + 9 - 3\sqrt{3}i\right]$

$= 1$

94. $\left(\frac{1}{2} - \frac{\sqrt{3}}{2}i\right)^3 = \left(\frac{1}{2}\right)^3 - 3\left(\frac{1}{2}\right)^2\left(\frac{\sqrt{3}}{2}i\right) + 3\left(\frac{1}{2}\right)\left(\frac{\sqrt{3}}{2}i\right)^2 - \left(\frac{\sqrt{3}}{2}i\right)^3$

$= \frac{1}{8} - \frac{3\sqrt{3}}{8}i - \frac{9}{8} + \frac{3\sqrt{3}}{8}i = -1$

95. $\left(\frac{1}{4} - \frac{\sqrt{3}}{4}i\right)^3 = \left(\frac{1}{4}\right)^3 - 3\left(\frac{1}{4}\right)^2\left(\frac{\sqrt{3}}{4}i\right) + 3\left(\frac{1}{4}\right)\left(\frac{-\sqrt{3}}{4}i\right)^2 - \left(\frac{\sqrt{3}}{4}i\right)^3$

$= \left[\frac{1}{64} - \frac{3}{4}\left(\frac{3}{16}\right)\right] + \left[\frac{-3}{16}\frac{\sqrt{3}}{4} + \frac{3\sqrt{3}}{64}\right]i$

$= -\frac{1}{8}$

96. $\left(\frac{1}{3} - \frac{\sqrt{3}}{3}i\right)^3 = \left(\frac{1}{3}\right)^3 - 3\left(\frac{1}{3}\right)^2\left(\frac{\sqrt{3}i}{3}\right) + 3\left(\frac{1}{3}\right)\left(\frac{\sqrt{3}}{3}i\right)^2 - \left(\frac{\sqrt{3}}{3}i\right)^3$

$= \frac{1}{27} - \frac{\sqrt{3}}{9}i - \frac{1}{3} + \frac{\sqrt{3}}{9}i = -\frac{8}{27}$

97. $(1.02)^8 = (1 + 0.02)^8 = 1 + 8(0.02) + 28(0.02)^2 + 56(0.02)^3 + 70(0.02)^4 + 56(0.02)^5$

$+ 28(0.02)^6 + 8(0.02)^7 + (0.02)^8$

$= 1 + 0.16 + 0.0112 + 0.000448 + \cdots \approx 1.172$

98. $(2.005)^{10} = (2 + 0.005)^{10} = 2^{10} + 10(2)^9(0.005) + 45(2)^8(0.005)^2 + 120(2)^7(0.005)^3 + 210(2)^6(0.005)^4$

$+ 252(2)^5(0.005)^5 + 210(2)^4(0.005)^6 + 120(2)^3(0.005)^7 + 45(2)^2(0.005)^8$

$+ 10(2)(0.005)^9 + (0.005)^{10}$

$= 1024 + 25.6 + 0.288 + 0.00192 + 0.0000084 + \cdots$

≈ 1049.890

99. $(2.99)^{12} = (3 - 0.01)^{12}$

$= 3^{12} - 12(3)^{11}(0.01) + 66(3)^{10}(0.01)^2 - 220(3)^9(0.01)^3 + 495(3)^8(0.01)^4$

$- 792(3)^7(0.01)^5 + 924(3)^6(0.01)^6 - 792(3)^5(0.01)^7 + 495(3)^4(0.01)^8$

$- 220(3)^3(0.01)^9 + 66(3)^2(0.01)^{10} - 12(3)(0.01)^{11} + (0.01)^{12}$

$\approx 510{,}568.785$

100. $(1.98)^9 = (2 - 0.02)^9 = 2^9 - 9(2)^8(0.02) + 36(2)^7(0.02)^2 - 84(2)^6(0.02)^3 + 126(2)^5(0.02)^4$

$\quad - 126(2)^4(0.02)^5 + 84(2)^3(0.02)^6 - 36(2)^2(0.02)^7 + 9(2)(0.02)^8 - (0.02)^9$

$= 512 - 46.08 + 1.8432 - 0.043008 + 0.00064512$

≈ 467.721

101. $f(x) = x^3 - 4x$

$g(x) = f(x + 3)$

$= (x + 3)^3 - 4(x + 3)$

$= x^3 + 9x^2 + 27x + 27 - 4x - 12$

$= x^3 + 9x^2 + 23x + 15$

g is shifted three units to the left.

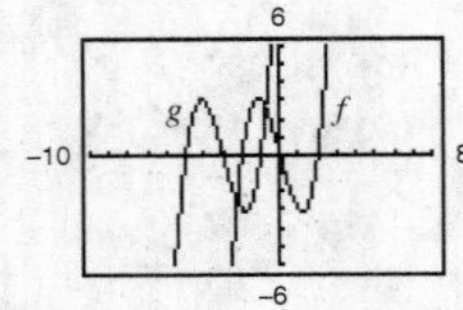

102. $f(x) = -x^4 + 4x^2 - 1$

$g(x) = f(x - 5)$

$= -(x - 5)^4 + 4(x - 5)^2 - 1$

$= -(x^4 - 20x^3 + 150x^2 - 500x + 625)$

$\quad + 4(x^2 - 10x + 25) - 1$

$= -x^4 + 20x^3 - 146x^2 + 460x - 526$

g is shifted five units to the right of f.

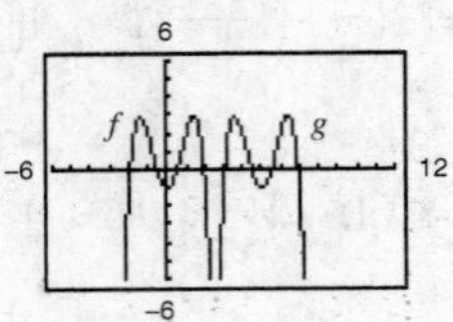

103. $f(x) = (1 - x)^3$

$g(x) = 1 - 3x$

$h(x) = 1 - 3x + 3x^2$

$p(x) = 1 - 3x + 3x^2 - x^3$

Since $p(x)$ is the expansion of $f(x)$, they have the same graph.

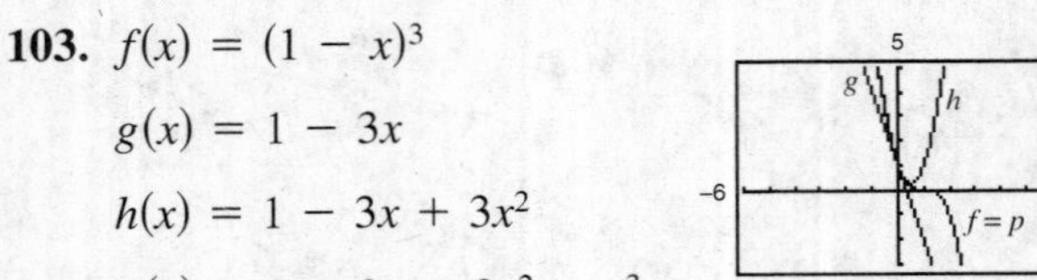

104. $p(x) = 1 - 2x + \frac{3}{2}x^2 - \frac{1}{2}x^3 + \frac{1}{16}x^4 = f(x)$

$p(x)$ is the expansion of $f(x)$.

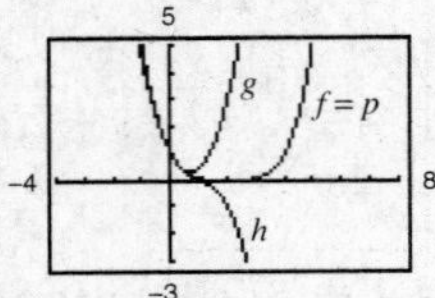

105. ${}_7C_4\left(\frac{1}{2}\right)^4\left(\frac{1}{2}\right)^3 = 35\left(\frac{1}{16}\right)\left(\frac{1}{8}\right) \approx 0.273$

106. ${}_{10}C_3\left(\frac{1}{4}\right)^3\left(\frac{3}{4}\right)^7 = 120\left(\frac{1}{64}\right)\left(\frac{2187}{16,384}\right) \approx 0.2503$

107. ${}_8C_4\left(\frac{1}{3}\right)^4\left(\frac{2}{3}\right)^4 = 70\left(\frac{1}{81}\right)\left(\frac{16}{81}\right) \approx 0.171$

108. ${}_8C_4\left(\frac{1}{2}\right)^4\left(\frac{1}{2}\right)^4 = 70\left(\frac{1}{16}\right)\left(\frac{1}{16}\right) \approx 0.2734$

109. $f(t) = 0.064t^2 - 9.30t + 416.5,\ 5 \le t \le 23$

(a) $g(t) = f(t + 20)$

$= 0.064(t + 20)^2 - 9.30(t + 20) + 416.5$

$= 0.064t^2 - 6.74t + 256.1,\ -15 \le t \le 3$

(b)

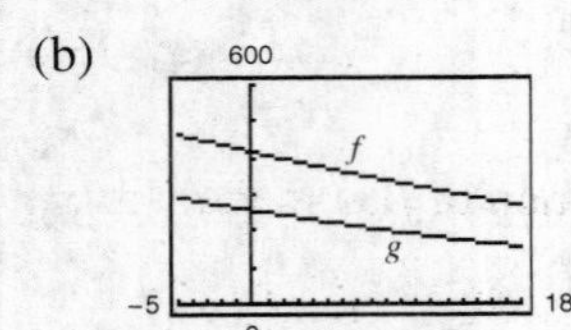

110. $f(t) = 6.22t^2 + 115.2t + 2730,\ 5 \le t \le 25$

(a) $g(t) = f(t + 20)$

$= 6.22(t + 20)^2 + 115.2(t + 20) + 2730$

$= 6.22t^2 + 364t + 7522,\ -15 \le t \le 5$

(b)

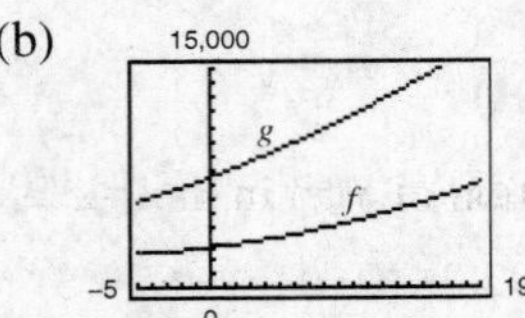

111. False. The x^4y^8 term is

${}_{12}C_4x^4(-2y)^8 = 495x^4(-2)^8y^8 = 126,720x^4y^8$.

[**Note:** 7920 is the coefficient of x^8y^4.]

112. False. The coefficient of x^{10} is 1,732,104 and the coefficient of x^{14} is 192,456.

113. Answers will vary. See page 557.

114. Rows 8–10 of Pascal's Triangle are:

1 8 28 56 70 56 28 8 1

1 9 36 84 126 126 84 36 9 1

1 10 45 120 210 252 210 120 45 10 1

115. The expansions of $(x + y)^n$ and $(x - y)^n$ are almost the same except that the signs of the terms in the expansion of $(x - y)^n$ alternate from positive to negative.

116. (a) Second term of $(2x - 3y)^5$ is

$$5(2x)^4(-3y)^1 = -240x^4y.$$

(b) Fourth term of $\left(\frac{1}{2}x + 7y\right)^6$ is

$${}_6C_3\left(\tfrac{1}{2}x\right)^3(7y)^3 = 857.5x^3y^3.$$

117. $${}_nC_{n-r} = \frac{n!}{[n - (n - r)]!(n - r)!}$$

$$= \frac{n!}{r!(n - r)!} = \frac{n!}{(n - r)!r!} = {}_nC_r$$

118. $$0 = (1 - 1)^n$$

$$= {}_nC_0 - {}_nC_1 + {}_nC_2 - {}_nC_3 + \cdots (\pm {}_nC_n)$$

$$= 0$$

119. $${}_nC_r + {}_nC_{r-1} = \frac{n!}{(n - r)!r!} + \frac{n!}{(n - r + 1)!(r - 1)!}$$

$$= \frac{n!(n - r + 1)}{(n - r)!r!(n - r + 1)} + \frac{n!}{(n - r + 1)!(r - 1)!}\frac{r}{r}$$

$$= \frac{n!(n - r + 1)}{(n - r + 1)!r!} + \frac{n!r}{(n - r + 1)!r!}$$

$$= \frac{n!(n - r + 1 + r)}{(n - r + 1)!r!}$$

$$= \frac{n!(n + 1)}{(n - r + 1)!r!}$$

$$= \frac{(n + 1)!}{(n + 1 - r)!r!} = {}_{n+1}C_r$$

120. $${}_nC_0 + {}_nC_1 + {}_nC_2 + {}_nC_3 + \cdots + {}_nC_n = (1 + 1)^n = 2^n$$

121. $g(x) = f(x) + 8$

$g(x)$ is shifted eight units up from $f(x)$.

122. $g(x) = f(x - 3)$

$g(x)$ is shifted three units to the right of $f(x)$.

123. $g(x) = f(-x)$

$g(x)$ is the reflection of $f(x)$ in the y-axis.

124. $g(x) = -f(x)$

$g(x)$ is the reflection of $f(x)$ in the x-axis.

125. $$\begin{bmatrix} -6 & 5 \\ -5 & 4 \end{bmatrix}^{-1} = \frac{1}{-24 + 25}\begin{bmatrix} 4 & -5 \\ 5 & -6 \end{bmatrix} = \begin{bmatrix} 4 & -5 \\ 5 & -6 \end{bmatrix}$$

126. $$\begin{bmatrix} 1.2 & -2.3 \\ -2 & 4 \end{bmatrix}^{-1} = \frac{1}{4.8 - 4.6}\begin{bmatrix} 4 & 2.3 \\ 2 & 1.2 \end{bmatrix} = \begin{bmatrix} 20 & 11.5 \\ 10 & 6 \end{bmatrix}$$

Section 8.6 Counting Principles

- You should know The Fundamental Counting Principle.
- ${}_nP_r = \dfrac{n!}{(n-r)!}$ is the number of permutations of n elements taken r at a time.
- Given a set of n objects that has n_1 of one kind, n_2 of a second kind, and so on, the number of distinguishable permutations is

$$\frac{n!}{n_1!n_2! \cdot \cdot \cdot n_k!}.$$

- ${}_nC_r = \dfrac{n!}{(n-r)!r!}$ is the number of combinations of n elements taken r at a time.

Vocabulary Check

1. Fundamental Counting Principle
2. permutation
3. ${}_nP_r = \dfrac{n!}{(n-r)!}$
4. distinguishable permutations
5. combinations

1. Odd integers: 1, 3, 5, 7, 9, 11

6 ways

2. Even integers: 2, 4, 6, 8, 10, 12

6 ways

3. Prime integers: 2, 3, 5, 7, 11

5 ways

4. Greater than 6: 7, 8, 9, 10, 11, 12

6 ways

5. Divisible by 4: 4, 8, 12

3 ways

6. Divisible by 3: 3, 6, 9, 12

4 ways

7. Sum is 8:

$1 + 7, 2 + 6, 3 + 5, 4 + 4, 5 + 3, 6 + 2, 7 + 1$

7 ways

8. Distinct integers whose sum is 8:

$1 + 7, 2 + 6, 3 + 5, 5 + 3, 6 + 2, 7 + 1$

6 ways

9. Amplifiers: 4 choices

Compact disc players: 6 choices

Speakers: 5 choices

Total: $4 \cdot 6 \cdot 5 = 120$ ways

10. Math courses: 2

Science courses: 3

Social sciences and humanities courses: 5

Total: $2 \cdot 3 \cdot 5 = 30$ ways

11. $2^{10} = 1024$ ways

12. First lock: $10 \cdot 10 \cdot 10$

Second lock: $10 \cdot 10 \cdot 10$

Hence,
$10^6 = 1{,}000{,}000$ combinations.

13. (a) $9 \cdot 10 \cdot 10 = 900$

(b) $9 \cdot 9 \cdot 8 = 648$

14. (a) $4 \cdot 10 \cdot 10 \cdot 10 = 4000$

(b) $9 \cdot 10 \cdot 10 \cdot 5 = 4500$

15. $2(8 \cdot 10 \cdot 10)(10 \cdot 10 \cdot 10 \cdot 10) = 16{,}000{,}000$ numbers

16. $4(8{,}000{,}000) = 32{,}000{,}000$ telephone numbers

17. (a) $26^3 + 26^3 = 35{,}152$

(b) There are $2 \cdot 25^3$ possibilities that don't have Q. Hence, $2 \cdot 26^3 - 2 \cdot 25^3 = 3902$ have at least one Q.

18. (a) $10^4 = 10{,}000$ ATM codes

(b) $9 \cdot 10^3 = 9000$ ATM codes that don't begin with zero

19. (a) $10^5 = 100{,}000$ zip codes

(b) $2 \cdot 10^4 = 20{,}000$ zip codes beginning with a one or a two

20. (a) 10^9 nine-digit zip codes

(b) $2 \cdot 10^8$ nine-digit zip codes beginning with a one or a two

21. (a) $6 \cdot 5 \cdot 4 \cdot 3 \cdot 2 \cdot 1 = 720$

(b) $6 \cdot 1 \cdot 4 \cdot 1 \cdot 2 \cdot 1 = 48$

22. (a) $8! = 40{,}320$ ways

(b) $(5!)(3!) = 120(6) = 720$ ways

23. $_nP_r = \dfrac{n!}{(n-r)!}$

So, $_4P_4 = \dfrac{4!}{0!} = 4! = 24.$

24. $_nP_r = \dfrac{n!}{(n-r)!}$

$_5P_5 = \dfrac{5!}{(5-5)!} = \dfrac{5!}{0!} = 120$

25. $_8P_3 = \dfrac{8!}{5!} = 8 \cdot 7 \cdot 6 = 336$

26. $_{20}P_2 = \dfrac{20!}{18!} = 20(19) = 380$

27. $_5P_4 = \dfrac{5!}{1!} = 120$

28. $_7P_4 = \dfrac{7!}{3!}$

$= 7 \cdot 6 \cdot 5 \cdot 4 = 840$

29. $_{20}P_6 = 27{,}907{,}200$

30. $_{10}P_8 = 1{,}814{,}400$

31. $_{120}P_4 = 197{,}149{,}680$

32. $_{100}P_5 = 9{,}034{,}502{,}400$

33. $5! = 120$ ways

34. $4! = 24$

35. $9! = 362{,}880$ ways

36. $4! = 24$ ways

37. $_{12}P_4 = \dfrac{12!}{8!}$

$= 12 \cdot 11 \cdot 10 \cdot 9$

$= 11{,}880$ ways

38. $_{15}P_9 = \dfrac{15!}{6!}$

$= 15 \cdot 14 \cdot 13 \cdot 12 \cdot 11 \cdot 10 \cdot 9 \cdot 8 \cdot 7$

$= 1{,}816{,}214{,}400$ ways

39. $37 \cdot 37 \cdot 37 = 50{,}653$

40. $_8P_3 = \dfrac{8!}{5!} = 336$ orders

41.

ABCD	BACD	CABD	DABC
ABDC	BADC	CADB	DACB
ACBD	BCAD	CBAD	DBAC
ACDB	BCDA	CBDA	DBCA
ADBC	BDAC	CDAB	DCAB
ADCB	BDCA	CDBA	DCBA

42. ABCD

ACBD

DBCA

DCBA

43. $\dfrac{7!}{2!1!3!1!} = \dfrac{7!}{2!3!} = 420$

44. $\dfrac{8!}{3!5!} = 56$

45. $\dfrac{7!}{2!1!1!1!1!1!} = \dfrac{7!}{2!}$
$= 7 \cdot 6 \cdot 5 \cdot 4 \cdot 3$
$= 2520$

46. $\dfrac{11!}{1!4!4!2!} = \dfrac{11!}{4!4!2!} = 34{,}650$

47. ${}_5C_2 = \dfrac{5!}{2!3!} = \dfrac{5 \cdot 4}{2} = 10$

48. ${}_6C_3 = \dfrac{6!}{3!3!} = \dfrac{6 \cdot 5 \cdot 4}{6} = 20$

49. ${}_4C_1 = \dfrac{4!}{1!3!} = 4$

50. ${}_5C_1 = \dfrac{5!}{1!4!} = 5$

51. ${}_{25}C_0 = \dfrac{25!}{0!25!} = 1$

52. ${}_{20}C_0 = \dfrac{20!}{0!20!} = 1$

53. ${}_{20}C_4 = 4845$

54. ${}_{10}C_7 = 120$

55. ${}_{42}C_5 = 850{,}668$

56. ${}_{50}C_6 = 15{,}890{,}700$

57. AB, AC, AD, AE, AF,
BC, BD, BE, BF, CD
CE, CF, DE, DF, EF

${}_6C_2 = 15$ ways

58. ABC, ABD, ABE, ABF, ACD, ACE, ACF
ADE, ADF, AEF, BCD, BCE, BCF, BDE
BDF, BEF, CDE, CDF, CEF, DEF

${}_6C_3 = 20$ ways

59. ${}_{100}C_{14} = \dfrac{100!}{14!86!} \approx 4.42 \times 10^{16}$ ways

60. ${}_{14}C_{12} = 91$ ways

61. ${}_{49}C_6 = 13{,}983{,}816$ ways

62. $({}_{55}C_5)({}_{42}C_1) = (3{,}478{,}761)(42)$
$= 146{,}107{,}962$ combinations

63. ${}_9C_2 = 36$ lines

64. There are 22 good sets and 3 defective sets.

(a) ${}_{22}C_4 = 7315$ ways

(b) $({}_{22}C_2)({}_3C_2) = (231)(3) = 693$ ways

(c) ${}_{22}C_4 + ({}_{22}C_3)({}_3C_1) + ({}_{22}C_2)({}_3C_2) = 7315 + (1540)(3) + 693 = 12{,}628$ ways

65. Select type of card for three of a kind: ${}_{13}C_1$

Select three of four cards for three of a kind: ${}_4C_3$

Select type of card for pair: ${}_{12}C_1$

Select two of four cards for pair: ${}_4C_2$

${}_{13}C_1 \cdot {}_4C_3 \cdot {}_{12}C_1 \cdot {}_4C_2 = 13 \cdot 4 \cdot 12 \cdot 6 = 3744$ ways to get a full house

66. Select 2 jacks: ${}_4C_2 = 6$

Select 3 aces: ${}_4C_3 = 4$

Total: $6 \cdot 4 = 24$ ways

67. (a) ${}_{12}C_4 = 495$ ways

(b) $({}_5C_2)({}_7C_2) = (10)(21) = 210$ ways

68. $({}_{13}C_7)({}_{20}C_3) = 1716 \cdot 1140 = 1{,}956{,}240$ ways

69. $({}_7C_1)({}_{12}C_3)({}_{20}C_2) = 7 \cdot 220 \cdot 190$
$= 292{,}600$ ways

70. (a) ${}_3C_2 = \dfrac{3!}{2!1!} = 3$ relationships

(b) ${}_8C_2 = \dfrac{8!}{2!6!} = \dfrac{8 \cdot 7}{2} = 28$ relationships

(c) ${}_{12}C_2 = \dfrac{12!}{2!10!} = \dfrac{12 \cdot 11}{2} = 66$ relationships

(d) ${}_{20}C_2 = \dfrac{20!}{2!18!} = \dfrac{20 \cdot 19}{2} = 190$ relationships

71. ${}_5C_2 - 5 = 10 - 5 = 5$ diagonals

72. ${}_6C_2 - 6 = 15 - 6 = 9$ diagonals

73. ${}_8C_2 - 8 = 28 - 8 = 20$ diagonals

74. ${}_{10}C_2 - 10 = 45 - 10 = 35$ diagonals

75. $14 \cdot {}_nP_3 = {}_{n+2}P_4$

Note: $n \geq 3$ for this to be defined.

$$14\left[\frac{n!}{(n-3)!}\right] = \frac{(n+2)!}{(n-2)!}$$

$$14n(n-1)(n-2) = (n+2)(n+1)n(n-1) \quad \text{(We can divide here by } n(n-1) \text{ since } n \neq 0, n \neq 1.)$$

$$14n - 28 = n^2 + 3n + 2$$

$$0 = n^2 - 11n + 30$$

$$0 = (n-5)(n-6)$$

$$n = 5 \quad \text{or} \quad n = 6$$

76. ${}_nP_5 = 18 \cdot {}_{n-2}P_4$

Note: $n \geq 6$ for this to be defined.

$$\frac{n!}{(n-5)!} = 18\left(\frac{(n-2)!}{(n-6)!}\right) \quad \left(\begin{array}{l}\text{We can divide by } (n-2), (n-3),\\ (n-4) \text{ since } n \neq 2, n \neq 3, \text{ and } n \neq 4.\end{array}\right)$$

$$n(n-1)(n-2)(n-3)(n-4) = 18(n-2)(n-3)(n-4)(n-5)$$

$$n^2 - n = 18n - 90$$

$$n^2 - 19n + 90 = 0$$

$$(n-9)(n-10) = 0$$

$$n = 9 \text{ or } n = 10$$

77. ${}_nP_4 = 10 \cdot {}_{n-1}P_3$

$$\frac{n!}{(n-4)!} = 10\frac{(n-1)!}{(n-4)!}$$

$$n! = 10(n-1)!$$

$$n = 10$$

78. ${}_nP_6 = 12 \cdot {}_{n-1}P_5$

$$\frac{n!}{(n-6)!} = 12\frac{(n-1)!}{(n-6)!}$$

$$n! = 12(n-1)!$$

$$n = 12$$

79. ${}_{n+1}P_3 = 4 \cdot {}_nP_2$

$$\frac{(n+1)!}{(n-2)!} = 4\frac{n!}{(n-2)!}$$

$$(n+1)! = 4n!$$

$$n = 3$$

80. $_{n+2}P_3 = 6 \cdot {_{n+2}P_1}$

$$\frac{(n+2)!}{(n-1)!} = 6\frac{(n+2)!}{(n+1)!}$$

$$(n+1)! = 6(n-1)!$$

$$(n+1)(n) = 6$$

$$n = 2$$

81. $4 \cdot {_{n+1}P_2} = {_{n+2}P_3}$

$$4\frac{(n+1)!}{(n-1)!} = \frac{(n+2)!}{(n-1)!}$$

$$4(n+1)! = (n+2)!$$

$$n = 2$$

82. $5 \cdot {_{n-1}P_1} = {_nP_2}$

$$5\frac{(n-1)!}{(n-2)!} = \frac{n!}{(n-2)!}$$

$$5(n-1)! = n!$$

$$n = 5$$

83. False

84. True

85. $_{100}P_{80} \approx 3.836 \times 10^{139}$.

This number is too large for some calculators to evaluate.

86. The symbol $_nP_r$ means the number of ways to choose and order r elements out of a set of n elements.

87. $_nC_r = {_nC_{n-r}} = \dfrac{n!}{r!(n-r)!}$

88. (b) $_{10}P_6$ is larger than $_{10}C_6$ because the permutations count different orderings as distinct.

89. $_nP_{n-1} = \dfrac{n!}{(n-(n-1))!} = \dfrac{n!}{1!} = \dfrac{n!}{0!} = {_nP_n}$

90. $_nC_n = \dfrac{n!}{(n-n)!n!}$

$$= \frac{n!}{0!n!}$$

$$= \frac{n!}{n!0!} = \frac{n!}{(n-0)!0!} = {_nC_0}$$

91. $_nC_{n-1} = \dfrac{n!}{[n-(n-1)]!(n-1)!}$

$$= \frac{n!}{(1)!(n-1)!}$$

$$= \frac{n!}{(n-1)!1!} = {_nC_1}$$

92. $_nC_r = \dfrac{n!}{(n-r)!r!}$

$$= \frac{1}{r!}\left[\frac{n!}{(n-r)!}\right]$$

$$= \frac{_nP_r}{r!}$$

93. From the graph of $y = \sqrt{x-3} - x + 6$, you see that there is one zero, $x \approx 8.303$. Analytically,

$$\sqrt{x-3} = x - 6$$

$$x - 3 = x^2 - 12x + 36$$

$$0 = x^2 - 13x + 39.$$

By the Quadratic Formula, $x = \dfrac{13 \pm \sqrt{(-13)^2 - 4(39)}}{2} = \dfrac{13 \pm \sqrt{13}}{2}$.

Selecting the larger solution, $x = \dfrac{13 + \sqrt{13}}{2} \approx 8.303$. (The other solution is extraneous.)

94. $\dfrac{4}{t} + \dfrac{3}{2t} = 1$

$$\frac{8+3}{2t} = 1$$

$$11 = 2t$$

$$t = \frac{11}{2} = 5.5$$

95. $\log_2(x-3) = 5$

$$2^5 = x - 3$$

$$2^5 + 3 = x$$

$$x = 35$$

96. $e^{x/3} = 16$

$$\frac{x}{3} = \ln 16$$

$$x = 3\ln 16 \approx 8.318$$

97. $x = \dfrac{\begin{vmatrix} -14 & 3 \\ 2 & -2 \end{vmatrix}}{\begin{vmatrix} -5 & 3 \\ 7 & -2 \end{vmatrix}} = \dfrac{22}{-11} = -2$

$y = \dfrac{\begin{vmatrix} -5 & -14 \\ 7 & 2 \end{vmatrix}}{\begin{vmatrix} -5 & 3 \\ 7 & -2 \end{vmatrix}} = \dfrac{88}{-11} = -8$

Answer: $(-2, -8)$

98. $x = \dfrac{\begin{vmatrix} 35 & 1 \\ 10 & 2 \end{vmatrix}}{\begin{vmatrix} 8 & 1 \\ 6 & 2 \end{vmatrix}} = \dfrac{60}{10} = 6$

$y = \dfrac{\begin{vmatrix} 8 & 35 \\ 6 & 10 \end{vmatrix}}{\begin{vmatrix} 8 & 1 \\ 6 & 2 \end{vmatrix}} = \dfrac{-130}{10} = -13$

Answer: $(6, -13)$

99. $x = \dfrac{\begin{vmatrix} -1 & -4 \\ -4 & 5 \end{vmatrix}}{\begin{vmatrix} -3 & -4 \\ 9 & 5 \end{vmatrix}} = \dfrac{-21}{21} = -1$

$y = \dfrac{\begin{vmatrix} -3 & -1 \\ 9 & -4 \end{vmatrix}}{\begin{vmatrix} -3 & -4 \\ 9 & 5 \end{vmatrix}} = \dfrac{21}{21} = 1$

Answer: $(-1, 1)$

100. $x = \dfrac{\begin{vmatrix} -74 & -11 \\ 8 & -4 \end{vmatrix}}{\begin{vmatrix} 10 & -11 \\ -8 & -4 \end{vmatrix}} = \dfrac{384}{-128} = -3$

$y = \dfrac{\begin{vmatrix} 10 & -74 \\ -8 & 8 \end{vmatrix}}{\begin{vmatrix} 10 & -11 \\ -8 & -4 \end{vmatrix}} = \dfrac{-512}{-128} = 4$

Answer: $(-3, 4)$

Section 8.7 Probability

You should know the following basic principles of probability.

- If an event E has $n(E)$ equally likely outcomes and its sample space has $n(S)$ equally likely outcomes, then the probability of event E is

$$P(E) = \frac{n(E)}{n(S)}, \text{ where } 0 \le P(E) \le 1.$$

- If A and B are mutually exclusive events, then $P(A \cup B) = P(A) + P(B)$.
  If A and B are not mutually exclusive events, then $P(A \cup B) = P(A) + P(B) - P(A \cap B)$.
- If A and B are independent events, then the probability that both A and B will occur is $P(A)P(B)$.
- The probability of the complement of an event A is $P(A') = 1 - P(A)$.

Vocabulary Check

1. experiment, outcomes **2.** sample space **3.** probability

4. impossible, certain **5.** mutually exclusive **6.** independent

7. complement **8.** (a) iii (b) i (c) iv (d) ii

1. $\{(H, 1), (H, 2), (H, 3), (H, 4), (H, 5), (H, 6), (T, 1), (T, 2), (T, 3), (T, 4), (T, 5), (T, 6)\}$

2. $\{2, 3, 4, 5, 6, 7, 8, 9, 10, 11, 12\}$

3. $\{ABC, ACB, BAC, BCA, CAB, CBA\}$

4. $\{(R, R), (R, B), (R, Y), (B, B), (B, Y), (B, R), (Y, B), (Y, R)\}$

5. $\{(A, B), (A, C), (A, D), (A, E), (B, C), (B, D), (B, E), (C, D), (C, E), (D, E)\}$

6. $\{SSS, SSF, SFS, FSS, SFF, FFS, FSF, FFF\}$

7. $E = \{HTT, THT, TTH\}$

$$P(E) = \frac{n(E)}{n(S)} = \frac{3}{8}$$

8. $E = \{HHH, HHT, HTH, HTT\}$

$$P(E) = \frac{n(E)}{n(S)} = \frac{4}{8} = \frac{1}{2}$$

9. $E = \{HHH, HHT, HTH, HTT, THH, THT, TTH\}$

$$P(E) = \frac{n(E)}{n(S)} = \frac{7}{8}$$

10. $E = \{HHH, HHT, HTH, THH\}$

$$P(E) = \frac{n(E)}{n(S)} = \frac{4}{8} = \frac{1}{2}$$

11. $E = \{K, K, K, K, Q, Q, Q, Q, J, J, J, J\}$

$$P(E) = \frac{n(E)}{n(S)} = \frac{12}{52} = \frac{3}{13}$$

12. The probability that the card is not a black face card is the complement of getting a black face card.

$E = \{K, K, Q, Q, J, J\}$

Hence, $P(E) = \frac{6}{52}$ and

$P(E') = 1 - P(E) = 1 - \frac{6}{52} = \frac{23}{26}$.

13. $E = \{A, A, A, A, K, K, K, K, Q, Q, Q, Q, J, J, J, J\}$

$$P(E) = \frac{n(E)}{n(S)} = \frac{16}{52} = \frac{4}{13}$$

14. There are 9 possible cards in each of 4 suits.

$9 \cdot 4 = 36$

$$P(E) = \frac{n(E)}{n(S)} = \frac{36}{52} = \frac{9}{13}$$

15. $E = \{(1, 5), (2, 4), (3, 3), (4, 2), (5, 1)\}$

$$P(E) = \frac{n(E)}{n(S)} = \frac{5}{36}$$

16. $E = \{(2, 6), (3, 5), (3, 6), (4, 4), (4, 5), (4, 6), (5, 3), (5, 4), (5, 5), (5, 6), (6, 2), (6, 3), (6, 4), (6, 5), (6, 6)\}$

$$P(E) = \frac{n(E)}{n(S)} = \frac{15}{36} = \frac{5}{12}$$

17. not $E = \{(5, 6), (6, 5), (6, 6)\}$

$n(E) = n(S) - n(\text{not } E) = 36 - 3 = 33$

$$P(E) = \frac{n(E)}{n(S)} = \frac{33}{36} = \frac{11}{12}$$

18. $E = \{(1, 1), (1, 2), (1, 4), (1, 6), (2, 1), (2, 3), (2, 5), (3, 2), (3, 4), (3, 6), (4, 1), (4, 3), (4, 5), (5, 2), (5, 4), (5, 6), (6, 1), (6, 3), (6, 5)\}$

$$P(E) = \frac{n(E)}{n(S)} = \frac{19}{36}$$

19. $P(E) = \dfrac{{}_3C_2}{{}_6C_2} = \dfrac{3}{15} = \dfrac{1}{5}$

20. $P(E) = \dfrac{{}_2C_2}{{}_6C_2} = \dfrac{1}{15}$

21. $P(E) = \dfrac{{}_4C_2}{{}_6C_2} = \dfrac{6}{15} = \dfrac{2}{5}$

22. $$P(E) = \frac{{}_1C_1 \cdot {}_2C_1 + {}_1C_1 \cdot {}_3C_1 + {}_2C_1 \cdot {}_3C_1}{{}_6C_2} = \frac{2 + 3 + 6}{15} = \frac{11}{15}$$

23. $P(E') = 1 - P(E) = 1 - 0.75 = 0.25$

24. $P(E') = 1 - P(E) = 1 - 0.\overline{2} = 1 - \frac{2}{9} = \frac{7}{9} = 0.\overline{7}$

25. $P(E') = 1 - P(E) = 1 - \frac{2}{3} = \frac{1}{3}$

26. $P(E') = 1 - P(E) = 1 - \frac{7}{8} = \frac{1}{8}$

27. $P(E) = 1 - P(E') = 1 - p = 1 - 0.12 = 0.88$

28. $P(E) = 1 - P(E') = 1 - p = 1 - 0.84 = 0.16$

29. $P(E) = 1 - P(E') = 1 - \frac{13}{20} = \frac{7}{20}$

30. $P(E) = 1 - P(E') = 1 - \frac{61}{100} = \frac{39}{100}$

31. (a) $0.15(8.15) \approx 1.22$ million

(b) $\dfrac{0.41}{1.0} = 0.41$

(c) $\dfrac{0.24}{1.0} = 0.24$

(d) $\dfrac{0.24 + 0.02}{1.0} = 0.26$

32. (a) $0.10(42) \approx 4$ presidents had no children.

(b) $0.19(42) \approx 8$ presidents had four children.

(c) $(0.07 + 0.21) = 0.28$

(d) 0.14

Answers will vary.

33. (a) $(0.128)(293.66) \approx 37.6$ million

(b) $\dfrac{0.01}{1.0} = 0.01$

(c) $\dfrac{0.01 + 0.002}{1.0} = 0.012$

34. (a) $1 - 0.148 = 0.852$ probability of having a high school diploma. Hence,

$0.852(186.88) \approx 159.2$ million.

(b) $0.097(186.88) \approx 18.1$ million

(c) $0.181 + 0.097 = 0.278$

(d) $1 - 0.148 = 0.852$

(e) $0.084 + 0.181 + 0.097 = 0.362$

35. (a) $\dfrac{34}{100} = 0.34$

(b) $\dfrac{45}{100} = 0.45$

(c) $\dfrac{23}{100} = 0.23$

36. (a) $\dfrac{290}{500} = 0.58$

(b) $\dfrac{478}{500} = 0.956$

(c) $\dfrac{2}{500} = 0.004$

37. (a) $\dfrac{672}{1254}$

(b) $\dfrac{582}{1254}$

(c) $\dfrac{672 - 124}{1254} = \dfrac{548}{1254}$

38. (a) $\dfrac{48 + 56}{128} = \dfrac{104}{128} = \dfrac{13}{16}$

(b) $\dfrac{4 + 20}{128} = \dfrac{24}{128} = \dfrac{3}{16}$ $\left[\textbf{Note: } 1 - \dfrac{13}{16} = \dfrac{3}{16}\right]$

(c) $\dfrac{4}{128} = \dfrac{1}{32}$

39. $p + p + 2p = 1$

$p = 0.25$

Taylor: $0.50 = \dfrac{1}{2}$, Moore: $0.25 = \dfrac{1}{4}$

Perez: $0.25 = \dfrac{1}{4}$

40. $\dfrac{54}{31 + 54 + 42 + 20 + 47 + 58} = \dfrac{54}{252} = \dfrac{3}{14}$

41. (a) $\dfrac{{}_{15}C_{10}}{{}_{20}C_{10}} = \dfrac{3003}{184{,}756} = \dfrac{21}{1292} \approx 0.016$

(b) $\dfrac{{}_{15}C_8 \cdot {}_5C_2}{{}_{20}C_{10}} = \dfrac{64{,}350}{184{,}756} = \dfrac{225}{646} \approx 0.348$

(c) $\dfrac{{}_{15}C_9 \cdot {}_5C_1}{{}_{20}C_{10}} + \dfrac{{}_{15}C_{10}}{{}_{20}C_{10}} = \dfrac{25{,}025 + 3003}{184{,}756}$

$= \dfrac{28{,}028}{184{,}756} = \dfrac{49}{323} \approx 0.152$

42. Total ways to insert paychecks: $5! = 120$ ways

5 correct: 1 way

4 correct: not possible

3 correct: 10 ways

2 correct: 20 ways

1 correct: 45 ways

0 correct: 44 ways

(a) $\dfrac{45}{120} = \dfrac{3}{8}$ (b) $\dfrac{45 + 20 + 10 + 1}{120} = \dfrac{19}{30}$

43. (a) $\dfrac{1}{_5P_5} = \dfrac{1}{120}$

(b) $\dfrac{1}{_4P_4} = \dfrac{1}{24}$

44. (a) $\dfrac{(_8C_2)(_{100}C_5)}{_{108}C_7} = 0.0756$

(b) $\dfrac{(_8C_2)(_{25}C_2)(_{25}C_3)}{_{108}C_7} \approx 6.929 \times 10^{-4}$

45. (a) There are three letters to be selected, and two must be Q and Y.

QY__, YQ__, Q__Y, Y__Q, __YQ, __QY

Thus, the probability is

$\dfrac{6(26)}{26^3} = \dfrac{6}{26^2} \approx 0.008876.$

(b) The three letters must be Q, Y, and X.

QYX, QXY, YQX, YXQ, XQY, XYQ

Thus, the probability is $\dfrac{6}{26^3} = \dfrac{3}{8788}.$

46. (a) $\dfrac{1}{10^4} = 0.0001$

(b) $\dfrac{1}{10^2} = 0.01$

47. (a) $\dfrac{100}{(_{55}C_5)(_{42}C_1)} = \dfrac{100}{(3{,}478{,}761)(42)}$

(b) $\dfrac{1000}{(_{55}C_5)(_{42}C_1)} = \dfrac{1000}{(3{,}478{,}761)(42)}$

48. (a) $\dfrac{1}{10^9}$

(b) $\dfrac{1}{10^4}$

(c) $\dfrac{1}{10^2}$

49. (a) $\dfrac{20}{52} = \dfrac{5}{13}$

(b) $\dfrac{13 + 13}{52} = \dfrac{1}{2}$

(c) $\dfrac{4 + 12}{52} = \dfrac{4}{13}$

50. $\dfrac{_{13}C_1 \cdot {_4C_3} \cdot {_{12}C_1} \cdot {_4C_2}}{_{52}C_5} = \dfrac{13 \cdot 4 \cdot 12 \cdot 6}{2{,}598{,}960}$

$= \dfrac{3744}{2{,}598{,}960}$

$= \dfrac{6}{4165}$

51. (a) $\dfrac{_9C_4}{_{12}C_4} = \dfrac{126}{495} = \dfrac{14}{55}$ (4 good units)

(b) $\dfrac{(_9C_2)(_3C_2)}{_{12}C_4} = \dfrac{108}{495} = \dfrac{12}{55}$ (2 good units)

(c) $\dfrac{(_9C_3)(_3C_1)}{_{12}C_4} = \dfrac{252}{495} = \dfrac{28}{55}$ (3 good units)

At least 2 good units: $\dfrac{12}{55} + \dfrac{28}{55} + \dfrac{14}{55} = \dfrac{54}{55}$

52. (a) $P(EE) = \dfrac{20}{40} \cdot \dfrac{20}{40} = \dfrac{1}{4}$

(b) $P(EO \text{ or } OE) = 2\left(\dfrac{20}{40}\right)\left(\dfrac{20}{40}\right) = \dfrac{1}{2}$

(c) $P(N_1 < 30, N_2 < 30) = \dfrac{29}{40} \cdot \dfrac{29}{40} = \dfrac{841}{1600}$

(d) $P(N_1N_1) = \dfrac{40}{40} \cdot \dfrac{1}{40} = \dfrac{1}{40}$

53. $(0.32)^2 = 0.1024$

54. $(0.78)^3 = 0.474552$

55. (a) $P(SS) = (0.985)^2 \approx 0.9702$

(b) $P(S) = 1 - P(FF) = 1 - (0.015)^2 \approx 0.9998$

(c) $P(FF) = (0.015)^2 \approx 0.0002$

56. (a) $P(AA) = (0.90)^2 = 0.81$

(b) $P(NN) = (0.10)^2 = 0.01$

(c) $P(A) = 1 - P(NN) = 1 - 0.01 = 0.99$

57. (a) $\left(\frac{1}{5}\right)^6 = \frac{1}{15{,}625}$

(b) $\left(\frac{4}{5}\right)^6 = \frac{4096}{15{,}625} = 0.262144$

(c) $1 - 0.262144 = 0.737856 = \frac{11{,}529}{15{,}625}$

58. (a) $P(BBBB) = \left(\frac{1}{2}\right)^4 = \frac{1}{16}$

(b) $P(BBBB) + P(GGGG) = \left(\frac{1}{2}\right)^4 + \left(\frac{1}{2}\right)^4 = \frac{1}{8}$

(c) $P(\text{at least one boy}) = 1 - P(\text{no boys})$

$= 1 - P(GGGG)$

$= 1 - \frac{1}{16} = \frac{15}{16}$

59. (a) If the *center* of the coin falls within the circle of radius $d/2$ around a vertex, the coin will cover the vertex.

$$P(\text{coin covers a vertex}) = \frac{\text{Area in which coin may fall so that it covers a vertex}}{\text{Total area}} = \frac{n\left[\pi\left(\frac{d}{2}\right)^2\right]}{nd^2} = \frac{1}{4}\pi$$

(b) Experimental results will vary.

60. $1 - \frac{(45)^2}{(60)^2} = 1 - \left(\frac{45}{60}\right)^2 = 1 - \left(\frac{3}{4}\right)^2 = 1 - \frac{9}{16} = \frac{7}{16}$

61. True

$P(E) + P(E') = 1$

62. False. The first sentence is true, but the second is false. The complement is to roll a number greater than 2, and its probability is $\frac{2}{3}$.

63. (a) As you consider successive people with distinct birthdays, the probabilities must decrease to take into account the birth dates already used. Since the birth dates of people are independent events, multiply the respective probabilities of distinct birthdays.

(b) $\frac{365}{365} \cdot \frac{364}{365} \cdot \frac{363}{365} \cdot \frac{362}{365}$

(c) $P_1 = \frac{365}{365} = 1$

$$P_2 = \frac{365}{365} \cdot \frac{364}{365} = \frac{364}{365} P_1 = \frac{365 - (2 - 1)}{365} P_1$$

$$P_3 = \frac{365}{365} \cdot \frac{364}{365} \cdot \frac{363}{365} = \frac{363}{365} P_2 = \frac{365 - (3 - 1)}{365} P_2$$

$$P_n = \frac{365}{365} \cdot \frac{364}{365} \cdot \frac{363}{365} \cdot \cdots \cdot \frac{365 - (n - 1)}{365} = \frac{365 - (n - 1)}{365} P_{n-1}$$

(d) Q_n is the probability that the birthdays are *not* distinct which is equivalent to at least 2 people having the same birthday.

—CONTINUED—

63. —CONTINUED—

(e)

n	10	15	20	23	30	40	50
P_n	0.88	0.75	0.59	0.49	0.29	0.11	0.03
Q_n	0.12	0.25	0.41	0.51	0.71	0.89	0.97

(f) 23, See the chart above.

64. If a weather forecast indicates that the probability of rain is 40%, this means the meteorological records indicate that over an extended period of time with similar weather conditions it will rain 40% of the time.

65. $\dfrac{2}{x-5} = 4$

$2 = 4(x-5) = 4x - 20$

$4x = 22$

$x = \dfrac{11}{2}$

66. $\dfrac{3}{2x+3} - 4 = \dfrac{-1}{2x+3}$

$\dfrac{4}{2x+3} = 4$

$1 = 2x + 3$

$2x = -2$

$x = -1$

67. $\dfrac{3}{x-2} + \dfrac{x}{x+2} = 1$

$3(x+2) + x(x-2) = (x-2)(x+2)$

$3x + 6 + x^2 - 2x = x^2 - 4$

$x = -10$

68. $\dfrac{2}{x} - \dfrac{5}{x-2} = \dfrac{-13}{x^2-2x} = \dfrac{-13}{x(x-2)}$

$2(x-2) - 5(x) = -13$

$-3x = -9$

$x = 3$

69. $e^x + 7 = 35$

$e^x = 28$

$x = \ln(28) \approx 3.332$

70. $200e^{-x} = 75$

$e^{-x} = \frac{75}{200} = \frac{3}{8}$

$-x = \ln\left(\frac{3}{8}\right)$

$x = -\ln\left(\frac{3}{8}\right) = \ln\left(\frac{8}{3}\right) \approx 0.981$

71. $4 \ln 6x = 16$

$\ln 6x = 4$

$e^4 = 6x$

$x = \frac{1}{6}e^4 \approx 9.10$

72. $5 \ln 2x - 4 = 11$

$\ln 2x = 3$

$2x = e^3$

$x = \frac{1}{2}e^3 \approx 10.043$

73. ${}_5P_3 = \dfrac{5!}{(5-3)!} = \dfrac{120}{2} = 60$

74. ${}_{10}P_4 = \dfrac{10!}{(10-4)!} = \dfrac{10!}{6!} = 10 \cdot 9 \cdot 8 \cdot 7 = 5040$

75. ${}_{11}P_8 = \dfrac{11!}{(11-8)!} = \dfrac{11!}{3!} = 6{,}652{,}800$

76. ${}_9P_2 = \dfrac{9!}{(9-2)!} = \dfrac{9!}{7!} = 9 \cdot 8 = 72$

77. ${}_6C_2 = \dfrac{6!}{4!2!} = \dfrac{6 \cdot 5 \cdot 4!}{4!2} = 15$

78. ${}_9C_5 = 126$

79. ${}_{11}C_8 = \frac{11!}{8!3!} = \frac{11 \cdot 10 \cdot 9 \cdot 8!}{8!6} = 165$

80. ${}_{16}C_{13} = 560$

Review Exercises for Chapter 8

1. $a_n = \frac{2^n}{2^n + 1}$

$a_1 = \frac{2^1}{2^1 + 1} = \frac{2}{3}$

$a_2 = \frac{2^2}{2^2 + 1} = \frac{4}{5}$

$a_3 = \frac{2^3}{2^3 + 1} = \frac{8}{9}$

$a_4 = \frac{2^4}{2^4 + 1} = \frac{16}{17}$

$a_5 = \frac{2^5}{2^5 + 1} = \frac{32}{33}$

2. $a_n = \frac{1}{n} - \frac{1}{n + 1}$

$a_1 = \frac{1}{1} - \frac{1}{2} = \frac{1}{2}$

$a_2 = \frac{1}{2} - \frac{1}{3} = \frac{1}{6}$

$a_3 = \frac{1}{3} - \frac{1}{4} = \frac{1}{12}$

$a_4 = \frac{1}{4} - \frac{1}{5} = \frac{1}{20}$

$a_5 = \frac{1}{5} - \frac{1}{6} = \frac{1}{30}$

3. $a_n = \frac{(-1)^n}{n!}$

$a_1 = \frac{(-1)^1}{1!} = -1$

$a_2 = \frac{(-1)^2}{2!} = \frac{1}{2}$

$a_3 = \frac{(-1)^3}{3!} = -\frac{1}{6}$

$a_4 = \frac{(-1)^4}{4!} = \frac{1}{24}$

$a_5 = \frac{(-1)^5}{5!} = -\frac{1}{120}$

4. $a_n = \frac{(-1)^n}{(2n + 1)!}$

$a_1 = \frac{(-1)^1}{3!} = -\frac{1}{6}$

$a_2 = \frac{(-1)^2}{5!} = \frac{1}{120}$

$a_3 = \frac{(-1)^3}{7!} = \frac{-1}{5040}$

$a_4 = \frac{(-1)^4}{9!} = \frac{1}{362,880}$

$a_5 = \frac{(-1)^5}{11!} = \frac{-1}{39,916,800}$

5. Common difference is 5.

$a_n = 5n, n = 1, 2, \ldots$

6. Common difference is -2.

$a_n = 52 - 2n, n = 1, 2, 3, \ldots$

7. Denominators are successive odd numbers.

$a_n = \frac{2}{2n - 1}, n = 1, 2, 3, \ldots$

8. $a_n = \frac{n + 2}{n + 1}, n = 1, 2, 3, \ldots$

9. $a_1 = 9, a_{k+1} = a_k - 4$

$a_2 = a_1 - 4 = 9 - 4 = 5$

$a_3 = 5 - 4 = 1$

$a_4 = 1 - 4 = -3$

$a_5 = -3 - 4 = -7$

10. $a_1 = 49, a_{k+1} = a_k + 6$

$a_2 = a_1 + 6 = 49 + 6 = 55$

$a_3 = 55 + 6 = 61$

$a_4 = 67$

$a_5 = 73$

11. $\frac{18!}{20!} = \frac{18!}{20 \cdot 19 \cdot 18!}$

$= \frac{1}{20 \cdot 19} = \frac{1}{380}$

12. $\frac{10!}{8!} = \frac{10 \cdot 9 \cdot 8!}{8!} = 90$

13. $\dfrac{(n+1)!}{(n-1)!} = \dfrac{(n+1)n(n-1)!}{(n-1)!} = n(n+1)$

14. $\dfrac{2n!}{(n+1)!} = \dfrac{2n!}{(n+1)n!} = \dfrac{2}{n+1}$

15. $\sum_{i=1}^{6} 5 = 6(5) = 30$

16. $\sum_{k=2}^{5} 4k = 8 + 12 + 16 + 20 = 56$

17. $\sum_{j=1}^{4} \dfrac{6}{j^2} = \dfrac{6}{1^2} + \dfrac{6}{2^2} + \dfrac{6}{3^2} + \dfrac{6}{4^2}$

$= 6 + \dfrac{3}{2} + \dfrac{2}{3} + \dfrac{3}{8} = \dfrac{205}{24}$

18. $\sum_{i=1}^{8} \dfrac{i}{i+1} = \dfrac{1}{2} + \dfrac{2}{3} + \dfrac{3}{4} + \dfrac{4}{5} + \dfrac{5}{6} + \dfrac{6}{7} + \dfrac{7}{8} + \dfrac{8}{9}$

≈ 6.17

19. $\sum_{k=1}^{100} 2k^3 = 2 \cdot \dfrac{100^2(101)^2}{4} = 51{,}005{,}000$

20. $\sum_{j=0}^{40} (j^2 + 1) = \dfrac{40(41)(81)}{6} + 41 = 22{,}181$

21. $\sum_{n=0}^{50} (n^2 + 3) = \dfrac{50(51)(101)}{6} + 3(51) = 43{,}078$

22. $\sum_{n=1}^{100} \left(\dfrac{1}{n} - \dfrac{1}{n+1}\right) = \left(\dfrac{1}{1} - \dfrac{1}{2}\right) + \left(\dfrac{1}{2} - \dfrac{1}{3}\right) + \left(\dfrac{1}{3} - \dfrac{1}{4}\right) + \cdots + \left(\dfrac{1}{99} - \dfrac{1}{100}\right) + \left(\dfrac{1}{100} - \dfrac{1}{101}\right)$

$= \dfrac{1}{1} - \dfrac{1}{101} = \dfrac{100}{101}$

23. $\dfrac{1}{2(1)} + \dfrac{1}{2(2)} + \dfrac{1}{2(3)} + \cdots + \dfrac{1}{2(20)} = \sum_{k=1}^{20} \dfrac{1}{2k}$

≈ 1.799

24. $2(1^2) + 2(2^2) + 2(3^2) + \cdots + 2(9^2) = \sum_{k=1}^{9} 2k^2$

$= 570$

25. $\dfrac{1}{2} + \dfrac{2}{3} + \dfrac{3}{4} + \cdots + \dfrac{9}{10} = \sum_{k=1}^{9} \dfrac{k}{k+1} \approx 7.071$

26. $1 - \dfrac{1}{3} + \dfrac{1}{9} - \dfrac{1}{27} + \cdots = \sum_{k=0}^{\infty} \left(-\dfrac{1}{3}\right)^k = \dfrac{3}{4}$

27. (a) $\sum_{k=1}^{4} \dfrac{5}{10^k} = \dfrac{5}{10} + \dfrac{5}{100} + \dfrac{5}{1000} + \dfrac{5}{10{,}000} = 0.5 + 0.05 + 0.005 + 0.0005 = 0.5555 = \dfrac{1111}{2000}$

(b) $\sum_{k=1}^{\infty} \dfrac{5}{10^k} = \dfrac{5}{10} \sum_{k=0}^{\infty} \dfrac{1}{10^k} = \dfrac{5}{10} \cdot \dfrac{1}{1 - 1/10} = \dfrac{5}{10} \cdot \dfrac{10}{9} = \dfrac{5}{9}$

28. $\sum_{k=1}^{\infty} \dfrac{3}{2^k}$

(a) $\sum_{k=1}^{4} \dfrac{3}{2^k} = \dfrac{3}{2} + \dfrac{3}{4} + \dfrac{3}{8} + \dfrac{3}{16} = \dfrac{45}{16} = 2.8125$

(b) $\sum_{k=1}^{\infty} \dfrac{3}{2^k} = \sum_{k=0}^{\infty} \left(\dfrac{3}{2}\right)\left(\dfrac{1}{2^k}\right) = \dfrac{3/2}{1 - 1/2} = 3$

29. $\sum_{k=1}^{\infty} 2(0.5)^k$

(a) $\sum_{k=1}^{4} 2(0.5)^k = 2(0.5) + 2(0.5)^2 + 2(0.5)^3 + 2(0.5)^4$

$= 1.875 = \dfrac{15}{8}$

(b) $\sum_{k=1}^{\infty} 2(0.5)^k = 2(0.5)\dfrac{1}{1 - 0.5} = 2$

30. $\sum_{k=1}^{\infty} 4(0.25)^k$

(a) $\sum_{k=1}^{\infty} 4(0.25)^k = 4(0.25) + 4(0.25)^2 + 4(0.25)^3 + 4(0.25)^4 = 1.328125 = \frac{85}{64}$

(b) $\sum_{k=1}^{\infty} 4(0.25)^k = \sum_{k=0}^{\infty} 4(0.25)(0.25)^k = \frac{1}{1 - 0.25} = \frac{4}{3}$

31. $a_n = 2500\left(1 + \frac{0.02}{4}\right)^n, n = 1, 2, 3$

(a) $a_1 = 2500\left(1 + \frac{0.02}{4}\right)^1 = 2512.5$

$a_2 = 2525.06 \quad a_3 = 2537.69$

$a_4 = 2550.38 \quad a_5 = 2563.13$

$a_6 = 2575.94 \quad a_7 = 2588.82$

$a_8 = 2601.77$

(b) $a_{40} = 2500\left(1 + \frac{0.02}{4}\right)^{40} = \$3051.99$

32. (a)

n	1	2	3	4	5	6
a_n	535	539	544	549	556	563

n	7	8	9	10	11	12	13
a_n	571	580	590	600	611	623	636

(b)

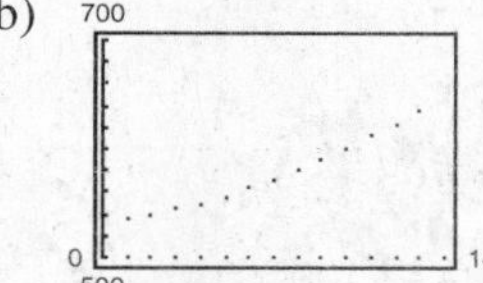

(c)

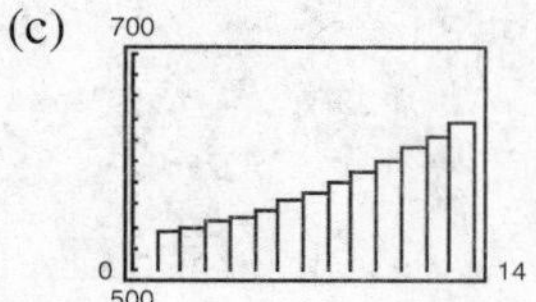

(d) For 2004, $n = 14$ and $a_{14} \approx 650$ thousand.

For 2010, $n = 20$ and $a_{20} \approx 750$ thousand.

The results seem reasonable.

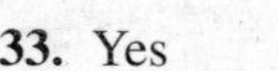

33. Yes

$d = 3 - 5 = -2$

34. Not arithmetic

35. Yes

$d = 1 - \frac{1}{2} = \frac{1}{2}$

36. Arithmetic

$d = \frac{8}{9} - \frac{9}{9} = \frac{-1}{9}$

37. $a_1 = 3, d = 4$

$a_1 = 3$

$a_2 = 3 + 4 = 7$

$a_3 = 7 + 4 = 11$

$a_4 = 11 + 4 = 15$

$a_5 = 15 + 4 = 19$

38. $a_1 = 8, d = -2$

$a_1 = 8$

$a_2 = 8 - 2 = 6$

$a_3 = 6 - 2 = 4$

$a_4 = 4 - 2 = 2$

$a_5 = 2 - 2 = 0$

39. $a_4 = 10, \; a_{10} = 28$

$a_{10} = a_4 + 6d$

$28 = 10 + 6d$

$18 = 6d$

$3 = d$

$a_1 = a_4 - 3d$

$a_1 = 10 - 3(3)$

$a_1 = 1$

$a_2 = 1 + 3 = 4$

$a_3 = 4 + 3 = 7$

$a_4 = 7 + 3 = 10$

$a_5 = 10 + 3 = 13$

40. $a_2 = 14, a_6 = 22$

$a_6 = a_2 + 4d$

$22 = 14 + 4d$

$8 = 4d$

$2 = d$

$a_1 = a_2 - d$

$a_1 = 14 - 2 = 12$

$a_2 = 12 + 2 = 14$

$a_3 = 14 + 2 = 16$

$a_4 = 16 + 2 = 18$

$a_5 = 18 + 2 = 20$

41. $a_1 = 35, a_{k+1} = a_k - 3$

$a_1 = 35$

$a_2 = a_1 - 3 = 35 - 3 = 32$

$a_3 = a_2 - 3 = 32 - 3 = 29$

$a_4 = a_3 - 3 = 29 - 3 = 26$

$a_5 = a_4 - 3 = 26 - 3 = 23$

$a_n = 35 + (n - 1)(-3) = 38 - 3n, d = -3$

42. $a_1 = 15, a_{k+1} = a_k + \frac{5}{2}$

$a_1 = 15$

$a_2 = 15 + \frac{5}{2} = \frac{35}{2}$

$a_3 = \frac{35}{2} + \frac{5}{2} = \frac{40}{2} = 20$

$a_4 = 20 + \frac{5}{2} = \frac{45}{2}$

$a_5 = \frac{45}{2} + \frac{5}{2} = \frac{50}{2} = 25$

$a_n = 15 + \frac{5}{2}(n - 1) = \frac{25}{2} + \frac{5}{2}n, d = \frac{5}{2}$

43. $a_1 = 9, a_{k+1} = a_k + 7$

$a_1 = 9$

$a_2 = a_1 + 7 = 9 + 7 = 16$

$a_3 = a_2 + 7 = 16 + 7 = 23$

$a_4 = a_3 + 7 = 23 + 7 = 30$

$a_5 = a_4 + 7 = 30 + 7 = 37$

$a_n = 9 + (n - 1)(7) = 2 + 7n, d = 7$

44. $a_1 = 100, a_{k+1} = a_k - 5$

$a_1 = 100$

$a_2 = 100 - 5 = 95$

$a_3 = 95 - 5 = 90$

$a_4 = 90 - 5 = 85$

$a_5 = 85 - 5 = 80$

$a_n = 100 - 5(n - 1) = 105 - 5n, d = -5$

45. $a_n = 100 + (n - 1)(-3) = 103 - 3n$

$$\sum_{n=1}^{20}(103 - 3n) = \sum_{n=1}^{20} 103 - 3\sum_{n=1}^{20} n = 20(103) - 3\left[\frac{(20)(21)}{2}\right] = 1430$$

46. $a_3 = a_1 + 2d$

$28 = 10 + 2d$

$18 = 2d$

$9 = d$

$a_n = 10 + (n - 1)9 = 1 + 9n$

$$\sum_{n=1}^{20}(1 + 9n) = \sum_{n=1}^{20} 1 + 9\sum_{n=1}^{20} n = 20(1) + 9\left[\frac{(20)(21)}{2}\right] = 1910$$

47. $$\sum_{j=1}^{10}(2j - 3) = 2\sum_{j=1}^{10} j - \sum_{j=1}^{10} 3 = 2\left[\frac{10(11)}{2}\right] - 10(3) = 80$$

48. $$\sum_{j=1}^{8}(20 - 3j) = \sum_{j=1}^{8} 20 - 3\sum_{j=1}^{8} j = 8(20) - 3\left[\frac{(8)(9)}{2}\right] = 52$$

49. $$\sum_{k=1}^{11}\left(\frac{2}{3}k + 4\right) = \frac{2}{3}\sum_{k=1}^{11} k + \sum_{k=1}^{11} 4 = \frac{2}{3} \cdot \frac{(11)(12)}{2} + 11(4) = 88$$

50. $$\sum_{k=1}^{25}\left(\frac{3k + 1}{4}\right) = \frac{3}{4}\sum_{k=1}^{25} k + \sum_{k=1}^{25} \frac{1}{4} = \frac{3}{4}\left[\frac{(25)(26)}{2}\right] + 25\left(\frac{1}{4}\right) = 250$$

51. $$\sum_{k=1}^{100} 5k = 5\left[\frac{(100)(101)}{2}\right] = 25{,}250$$

52. $$\sum_{n=20}^{80} n = \sum_{n=1}^{80} n - \sum_{n=1}^{19} n = \frac{(80)(81)}{2} - \frac{(19)(20)}{2} = 3050$$

53. (a) $34{,}000 + 4(2250) = \$43{,}000$

(b) $\sum_{k=1}^{5}[34{,}000 + (k-1)(2250)]$

$= \sum_{k=1}^{5}(31{,}750 + 2250k)$

$= \$192{,}500$

54. $a_1 = 123,\ d = 112 - 123 = -11$

$n = 8$

$a_8 = (-11)8 + 134 = 46$

$S_8 = \frac{8}{2}(123 + 46) = 676$ bales

55. 5, 10, 20, 40

Geometric: $r = 2$

56. $\frac{1}{2}, \frac{2}{3}, \frac{3}{4}, \frac{4}{5}$

Not geometric:

$\frac{1}{2}r = \frac{2}{3} \Rightarrow r = \frac{4}{3}$

$\frac{2}{3}r = \frac{3}{4} \Rightarrow r = \frac{9}{8}$

57. Geometric:

$r = -\frac{1}{3}$

58. Geometric:

$r = -2$

59. $a_1 = 4,\ r = -\frac{1}{4}$

$a_1 = 4$

$a_2 = 4\left(-\frac{1}{4}\right) = -1$

$a_3 = -1\left(-\frac{1}{4}\right) = \frac{1}{4}$

$a_4 = \frac{1}{4}\left(-\frac{1}{4}\right) = -\frac{1}{16}$

$a_5 = -\frac{1}{16}\left(-\frac{1}{4}\right) = \frac{1}{64}$

60. $a_1 = 2,\ r = \frac{3}{2}$

$a_1 = 2$

$a_2 = 2\left(\frac{3}{2}\right) = 3$

$a_3 = 3\left(\frac{3}{2}\right) = \frac{9}{2}$

$a_4 = \frac{9}{2}\left(\frac{3}{2}\right) = \frac{27}{4}$

$a_5 = \frac{27}{4}\left(\frac{3}{2}\right) = \frac{81}{8}$

61. $a_1 = 9,\ a_3 = 4$

$a_3 = a_1r^2$

$4 = 9r^2$

$\frac{4}{9} = r^2 \Rightarrow r = \pm\frac{2}{3}$

$a_1 = 9$

$a_2 = 9\left(\frac{2}{3}\right) = 6$

$a_3 = 6\left(\frac{2}{3}\right) = 4$

$a_4 = 4\left(\frac{2}{3}\right) = \frac{8}{3}$

$a_5 = \frac{8}{3}\left(\frac{2}{3}\right) = \frac{16}{9}$

or

$a_1 = 9$

$a_2 = 9\left(-\frac{2}{3}\right) = -6$

$a_3 = -6\left(-\frac{2}{3}\right) = 4$

$a_4 = 4\left(-\frac{2}{3}\right) = -\frac{8}{3}$

$a_5 = -\frac{8}{3}\left(-\frac{2}{3}\right) = \frac{16}{9}$

62. $a_1 = 2,\ a_3 = 12$

$a_3 = a_1r^2$

$12 = 2r^2$

$6 = r^2$

$\pm\sqrt{6} = r$

$a_1 = 2$

$a_2 = 2\left(\sqrt{6}\right) = 2\sqrt{6}$

$a_3 = 2\sqrt{6}\left(\sqrt{6}\right) = 12$

$a_4 = 12\left(\sqrt{6}\right) = 12\sqrt{6}$

$a_5 = 12\sqrt{6}\sqrt{6} = 72$

or

$a_1 = 2$

$a_2 = 2\left(-\sqrt{6}\right) = -2\sqrt{6}$

$a_3 = -2\sqrt{6}\left(-\sqrt{6}\right) = 12$

$a_4 = 12\left(-\sqrt{6}\right) = -12\sqrt{6}$

$a_5 = -12\sqrt{6}\left(-\sqrt{6}\right) = 72$

63. $a_1 = 120,\ a_{k+1} = \frac{1}{3}a_k$

$a_1 = 120$

$a_2 = \frac{1}{3}(120) = 40$

$a_3 = \frac{1}{3}(40) = \frac{40}{3}$

$a_4 = \frac{1}{3}\left(\frac{40}{3}\right) = \frac{40}{9}$

$a_5 = \frac{1}{3}\left(\frac{40}{9}\right) = \frac{40}{27}$

$a_n = 120\left(\frac{1}{3}\right)^{n-1},\ r = \frac{1}{3}$

64. $a_1 = 200,\ a_{k+1} = 0.1a_k$

$a_1 = 200$

$a_2 = 0.1(200) = 20$

$a_3 = 0.1(20) = 2$

$a_4 = 0.1(2) = 0.2$

$a_5 = 0.1(0.2) = 0.02$

$a_n = 200(0.1)^{n-1}$

65. $a_1 = 25,\ a_{k+1} = -\frac{3}{5}a_k$

$a_1 = 25$

$a_2 = -\frac{3}{5}(25) = -15$

$a_3 = -\frac{3}{5}(-15) = 9$

$a_4 = -\frac{3}{5}(9) = -\frac{27}{3}$

$a_5 = -\frac{3}{5}\left(-\frac{27}{5}\right) = \frac{81}{25}$

$a_n = 25\left(-\frac{3}{5}\right)^{n-1},\ r = -\frac{3}{5}$

66. $a_1 = 18, a_{k+1} = \frac{5}{3}a_k$

$a_1 = 18$

$a_2 = \frac{5}{3}(18) = 30$

$a_3 = \frac{5}{3}(30) = 50$

$a_4 = \frac{5}{3}(50) = \frac{250}{3}$

$a_5 = \frac{5}{3}\left(\frac{250}{3}\right) = \frac{1250}{9}$

$a_n = 18\left(\frac{5}{3}\right)^{n-1}$

$r = \frac{5}{3}$

67. $a_2 = a_1 r$

$-8 = 16r$

$-\frac{1}{2} = r$

$a_n = 16\left(-\frac{1}{2}\right)^{n-1}$

$\sum_{n=1}^{20} 16\left(-\frac{1}{2}\right)^{n-1} = 16\left[\frac{1-(-1/2)^{20}}{1-(-1/2)}\right] \approx 10.67$

68. $a_4 = a_3 r$

$1 = 6r \Rightarrow r = \frac{1}{6}$

$a_3 = a_1 r^2 \Rightarrow 6 = a_1\left(\frac{1}{6}\right)^2 \Rightarrow a_1 = 6^3 = 216$

$a_n = a_1 r^{n-1} = 216\left(\frac{1}{6}\right)^{n-1}$

$\sum_{n=1}^{20} 216\left(\frac{1}{6}\right)^{n-1} = 216\,\frac{1-(1/6)^{20}}{1-(1/6)} = 259.2$

69. $a_1 = 100, r = 1.05$

$a_n = 100(1.05)^{n-1}$

$\sum_{n=1}^{20} 100(1.05)^{n-1} = 100\left[\frac{1-(1.05)^{20}}{1-1.05}\right] \approx 3306.60$

70. $a_1 = 5,\ r = 0.2$

$a_n = a_1\, r^{n-1} = 5\left(\frac{1}{5}\right)^{n-1}$

$\sum_{n=1}^{20} 5\left(\frac{1}{5}\right)^{n-1} = 5\left[\frac{1-(1/5)^{20}}{1-1/5}\right] = 6.25$

71. $\sum_{i=1}^{7} 2^{i-1} = \frac{1-2^7}{1-2} = 127$

72. $\sum_{i=1}^{5} 3^{i-1} = \frac{1-3^5}{1-3} = 121$

73. $\sum_{n=1}^{7} (-4)^{n-1} = \frac{1-(-4)^7}{1-(-4)}$

$= 3277$

74. $\sum_{n=1}^{4} 12\left(-\frac{1}{2}\right)^{n-1} = 7.5$

75. $\sum_{n=0}^{4} 250(1.02)^n = 250\left(\frac{1-1.02^5}{1-1.02}\right) = 1301.01004$

76. $\sum_{n=0}^{5} 400(1.08)^n \approx 2934.3716$

77. $\sum_{i=1}^{10} 10\left(\frac{3}{5}\right)^{i-1} \approx 24.849$

78. $\sum_{i=1}^{15} 20(0.2)^{i-1} \approx 25$

79. $\sum_{i=1}^{\infty} 4\left(\frac{7}{8}\right)^{i-1} = \sum_{i=0}^{\infty} 4\left(\frac{7}{8}\right)^{i} = \frac{4}{1 - 7/8} = 32$

80. $\sum_{i=1}^{\infty} 6\left(\frac{1}{3}\right)^{i-1} = \sum_{i=0}^{\infty} 6\left(\frac{1}{3}\right)^{i} = \frac{6}{1 - 1/3} = 9$

81. $\sum_{k=1}^{\infty} 4\left(\frac{2}{3}\right)^{k-1} = \frac{4}{1 - 2/3} = 12$

82. $\sum_{k=1}^{\infty} 1.3\left(\frac{1}{10}\right)^{k-1} = \frac{1.3}{1 - (1/10)} = \frac{13}{9}$

83. (a) $a_t = 120{,}000(0.7)^t$

(b) $a_5 = 120{,}000(0.7)^5 = \$20{,}168.40$

84. $A = \sum_{i=1}^{48} 75\left(1 + \frac{0.04}{12}\right)^i = \$3909.96$

85. 1. When $n = 1$, $2 = \frac{1}{2}(5(1) - 1)$.

2. Assume that $S_k = 2 + 7 + \cdots + (5k - 3) = \frac{k}{2}(5k - 1)$. Then,

$$\begin{aligned} S_{k+1} &= 2 + 7 + \cdots + (5k - 3) + [5(k + 1) - 3] \\ &= S_k + 5k + 2 \\ &= \frac{k}{2}(5k - 1) + 5k + 2 \\ &= \frac{1}{2}[5k^2 + 9k + 4] \\ &= \frac{1}{2}[(5k + 4)(k + 1)] \\ &= \frac{k + 1}{2}(5(k + 1) - 1). \end{aligned}$$

Therefore, by mathematical induction, the formula is true for all positive integers n.

86. 1. When $n = 1$, $1 = \frac{1}{4}(1 + 3) = 1$.

2. Assume that $1 + \frac{3}{2} + 2 + \frac{5}{2} + \cdots + \frac{1}{2}(k + 1) = \frac{k}{4}(k + 3)$. Then,

$$\begin{aligned} 1 + \frac{3}{2} + 2 + \frac{5}{2} + \cdots + \frac{1}{2}(k + 1) + \frac{1}{2}(k + 2) &= \frac{k}{4}(k + 3) + \frac{1}{2}(k + 2) \\ &= \frac{k(k + 3) + 2(k + 2)}{4} \\ &= \frac{k^2 + 5k + 4}{4} \\ &= \frac{(k + 1)(k + 4)}{4} \\ &= \frac{k + 1}{4}[(k + 1) + 3]. \end{aligned}$$

Thus, the formula holds for all positive integers n.

87. 1. When $n = 1$, $a = a\left(\frac{1-r}{1-r}\right)$.

2. Assume that

$$S_k = \sum_{i=0}^{k-1} ar^i = \frac{a(1-r^k)}{1-r}.$$

Then,

$$S_{k+1} = \sum_{i=0}^{k} ar^i = \sum_{i=0}^{k-1} ar^i + ar^k = \frac{a(1-r^k)}{1-r} + ar^k$$

$$= \frac{a(1-r^k+r^k-r^{k+1})}{1-r} = \frac{a(1-r^{k+1})}{1-r}.$$

Therefore, by mathematical induction, the formula is valid for all positive integer values of n.

88. 1. When $n = 1$, $a + 0 \cdot d = a = \frac{1}{2}[2a + (1-1)d] = a$.

2. Assume that $\sum_{k=0}^{i-1}(a + kd) = \frac{i}{2}[2a + (i-1)d]$, using i as the induction variable. Then,

$$\sum_{k=0}^{i+1-1}(a + kd) = \frac{i}{2}[2a + (i-1)d] + [a + id]$$

$$= \frac{2ia + i(i-1)d + 2a + 2id}{2} = \frac{2a(i+1) + id(i+1)}{2} = \left(\frac{i+1}{2}\right)[2a + id].$$

Thus, the formula holds for all positive integers n.

89. $\sum_{n=1}^{30} n = \frac{30(31)}{2} = 465$

90. $\sum_{n=1}^{10} n^2 = \frac{10(10+1)(20+1)}{6} = 385$

91. $\sum_{n=1}^{7}(n^4 - n) = \sum_{n=1}^{7} n^4 - \sum_{n=1}^{7} n$

$$= \frac{7(8)(15)[3(7)^2 + 3(7) - 1]}{30} - \frac{7(8)}{2}$$

$$= \frac{840(167)}{30} - 28 = 4676 - 28 = 4648$$

92. $\sum_{n=1}^{6}(n^5 - n^2) = \frac{6^2(7^2)(2 \cdot 6^2 + 12 - 1)}{12} - \frac{6(7)(2(6)+1)}{6} = 12{,}201 - 91 = 12{,}110$

93. $a_1 = f(1) = 5$

$a_2 = a_1 + 5 = 5 + 5 = 10$

$a_3 = a_2 + 5 = 15$

$a_4 = a_3 + 5 = 20$

$a_5 = a_4 + 5 = 25$

n:	1		2		3		4		5
a_n:	5		10		15		20		25
First differences:		5		5		5		5	
Second difference:			0		0		0		

Linear model: $a_n = 5n$

94. $a_1 = f(1) = -3$

$a_2 = a_1 - 2(2) = -3 - 4 = -7$

$a_3 = -7 - 2(3) = -7 - 6 = -13$

$a_4 = -13 - 2(4) = -13 - 8 = -21$

$a_5 = -21 - 2(5) = -21 - 10 = -31$

n:	1		2		3		4		5
a_n:	-3		-7		-13		-21		-31
First differences:		-4		-6		-8		-10	
Second differences:			-2		-2		-2		

Quadratic model

95. $a_1 = f(1) = 16$

$a_2 = a_1 - 1 = 16 - 1 = 15$

$a_3 = a_2 - 1 = 15 - 1 = 14$

$a_4 = 14 - 1 = 13$

$a_5 = 13 - 1 = 12$

n:	1		2		3		4		5
a_n:	16		15		14		13		12
First differences:		-1		-1		-1		-1	
Second difference:			0		0		0		

Linear model: $a_n = 17 - n$

96. $a_1 = f(1) = 1$

$a_2 = 2 - a_1 = 2 - 1 = 1$

$a_3 = 3 - a_2 = 2$

$a_4 = 4 - 2 = 2$

$a_5 = 5 - 2 = 3$

n:	1		2		3		4		5
a_n:	1		1		2		2		3
First differences:		0		1		0		1	
Second differences:			1		-1		1		

Neither linear nor quadratic

97. ${}_{10}C_8 = 45$

98. ${}_{12}C_5 = 792$

99. $\binom{9}{4} = {}_9C_4 = 126$

100. $\binom{14}{12} = {}_{14}C_{12} = 91$

101. 4th number in 6th row is ${}_6C_3 = 20$.

102. The 8th entry in the 9th row is 36.

103. 5th number in 8th row is $\binom{8}{4} = {}_8C_4 = 70.$

104. The 6th entry in the 10th row is 252.

105. $(x + 5)^4 = x^4 + 4x^3(5) + 6x^2(5^2) + 4x(5^3) + 5^4$
$= x^4 + 20x^3 + 150x^2 + 500x + 625$

106. $(y - 3)^3 = y^3 - 9y^2 + 27y - 27$

107. $(a - 4b)^5 = a^5 - 5a^4(4b) + 10a^3(4b)^2 - 10a^2(4b)^3 + 5a(4b)^4 - (4b)^5$
$= a^5 - 20a^4b + 160a^3b^2 - 640a^2b^3 + 1280ab^4 - 1024b^5$

108. $(3x + y)^7 = 2187x^7 + 5103x^6y + 5103x^5y^2 + 2835x^4y^3 + 945x^3y^4 + 189x^2y^5 + 21xy^6 + y^7$

109. $(7 + 2i)^4 = 7^4 + 4(7)^3(2i) + 6(7)^2(2i)^2 + 4(7)(2i)^3 + (2i)^4$
$= 2401 + 2744i - 1176 - 224i + 16$
$= 1241 + 2520i$

110. $(4 - 5i)^3 = 4^3 - 3(4)^2(5i) + 3(4)(5i)^2 - (5i)^3$
$= 64 - 240i - 300 + 125i$
$= -236 - 115i$

111. $E = \{(1, 11), (2, 10), (3, 9), (4, 8), (5, 7), (7, 5), (8, 4), (9, 3), (10, 2), (11, 1)\}$
$n(E) = 10$

112. $(2!)(6!) = 1440$ ways

113. (a) $(4)(3)(6)(3) = 216$ schedules
(b) $(2)(3)(6)(3) = 108$ schedules
(c) $(2)(3)(2)(3) = 36$ schedules

114. (a) $10^7 = 10{,}000{,}000$ possible calls
(b) $2 \cdot 10^6 = 2{,}000{,}000$ calls
(c) $10{,}000{,}000 - 2{,}000{,}000 = 8{,}000{,}000$ calls

115. ${}_{10}C_8 = \dfrac{10!}{2!8!} = \dfrac{10 \cdot 9}{2} = 45$

116. ${}_8C_6 = \dfrac{8!}{2!6!} = \dfrac{8 \cdot 7}{2} = 28$

117. ${}_{12}P_{10} = \dfrac{12!}{2!} = 239{,}500{,}800$

118. ${}_6P_4 = \dfrac{6!}{2!} = 360$

119. ${}_{100}C_{98} = \dfrac{100!}{2!98!} = \dfrac{100 \cdot 99}{2} = 4950$

120. ${}_{50}C_{48} = \dfrac{50!}{2!48!} = \dfrac{50 \cdot 49}{2} = 1225$

121. ${}_{1000}P_2 = \dfrac{1000!}{998!} = 1000(999) = 999{,}000$

122. ${}_{500}P_2 = \dfrac{500!}{498!} = 500(499) = 249{,}500$

123. $\dfrac{8!}{2!2!2!1!1!} = \dfrac{8!}{8} = 7! = 5040$ permutations

124. $\dfrac{9!}{2!2!} = \dfrac{9!}{4} = 90{,}720$ permutations

125. $10! = 3{,}628{,}800$ ways

126. $({}_7C_2)({}_{11}C_2) = 21 \cdot 55 = 1155$ ways

127. ${}_{20}C_{15} = 15{,}504$ ways

128. ${}_{54}C_6 = 25{,}827{,}165$ ways

129.
$${}_{n+1}P_2 = 4 \cdot {}_nP_1$$
$$\frac{(n+1)!}{(n-1)!} = 4 \cdot \frac{n!}{(n-1)!}$$
$$(n+1)! = 4 \cdot n!$$
$$n = 3$$

130.
$$8 \cdot {}_nP_2 = {}_{n+1}P_3$$
$$8\frac{n!}{(n-2)!} = \frac{(n+1)!}{(n-2)!}$$
$$8n! = (n+1)!$$
$$n = 7$$

131. $\frac{10}{10} \cdot \frac{1}{9} = \frac{1}{9}$

132. $P(E) = \frac{n(E)}{n(S)} = \frac{1}{5!} = \frac{1}{120}$

133. (a) $\frac{208}{500} = 0.416$

(b) $\frac{400}{500} = 0.8$

(c) $\frac{37}{500} = 0.074$

134. $\left(\frac{6}{6}\right)\left(\frac{5}{6}\right)\left(\frac{4}{6}\right)\left(\frac{3}{6}\right)\left(\frac{2}{6}\right)\left(\frac{1}{6}\right) = \frac{6!}{6^6} = \frac{720}{46{,}656} = \frac{5}{324}$

135. $P(2 \text{ pairs}) = \frac{({}_{13}C_2)({}_4C_2)({}_4C_2)({}_{44}C_1)}{({}_{52}C_5)} = 0.0475$

136. $P(\text{club}) = \frac{13}{52} = \frac{1}{4}$

$P(\text{not club}) = 1 - \frac{1}{4} = \frac{3}{4}$

137. True

$$\frac{(n+2)!}{n!} = \frac{(n+2)(n+1)n!}{n!} = (n+2)(n+1)$$

138. True

139. Answers will vary. See pages 526 and 535.

140. They differ by a minus sign.

(a) $-1, \frac{1}{2}, -\frac{1}{3}, \ldots$
(Odd-numbered terms are negative.)

(b) $1, -\frac{1}{2}, \frac{1}{3}, \ldots$
(Even-numbered terms are negative.)

141. (a) Arithmetic-linear model

(b) Geometric model

142. $S_6 = 130 + 70 + 40 = 240$

$S_7 = 240 + 130 + 70 = 440$

$S_8 = 440 + 240 + 130 = 810$

$S_9 = 810 + 440 + 240 = 1490$

$S_{10} = 1490 + 810 + 440 = 2740$

143. Answers will vary. See page 528. To define a sequence recursively, you need to be given one or more of the first few terms. All other terms are defined using previous terms.

144. When $0 < r < 1$, $a_n = a_{n-1}(r) < a_{n-1}$.

145. If n is even, the expansion are the same. If n is odd, the expansion of $(-x + y)^n$ is the negative of that of $(x - y)^n$.

146. In the closed interval $[0, 1]$.

Chapter 8 Practice Test

1. Write out the first five terms of the sequence $a_n = \dfrac{2n}{(n+2)!}$.

2. Write an expression for the nth term of the sequence $\left\{\frac{4}{3}, \frac{5}{9}, \frac{6}{27}, \frac{7}{81}, \frac{8}{243}, \ldots\right\}$.

3. Find the sum $\sum_{i=1}^{6} (2i - 1)$.

4. Write out the first five terms of the arithmetic sequence where $a_1 = 23$ and $d = -2$.

5. Find a_{50} for the arithmetic sequence with $a_1 = 12$, $d = 3$, and $n = 50$.

6. Find the sum of the first 200 positive integers.

7. Write out the first five terms of the geometric sequence with $a_1 = 7$ and $r = 2$.

8. Evaluate $\sum_{n=0}^{9} 6\left(\frac{2}{3}\right)^n$.

9. Evaluate $\sum_{n=0}^{\infty} (0.03)^n$.

10. Use mathematical induction to prove that $1 + 2 + 3 + 4 + \cdots + n = \dfrac{n(n+1)}{2}$.

11. Use mathematical induction to prove that $n! > 2^n$, $n \geq 4$.

12. Evaluate ${}_{13}C_4$. Verify with a graphing utility.

13. Expand $(x + 3)^5$.

14. Find the term involving x^7 in $(x - 2)^{12}$.

15. Evaluate ${}_{30}P_4$.

16. How many ways can six people sit at a table with six chairs?

17. Twelve cars run in a race. How many different ways can they come in first, second, and third place? (Assume that there are no ties.)

18. Two six-sided dice are tossed. Find the probability that the total of the two dice is less than 5.

19. Two cards are selected at random from a deck of 52 playing cards without replacement. Find the probability that the first card is a King and the second card is a black ten.

20. A manufacturer has determined that for every 1000 units it produces, 3 will be faulty. What is the probability that an order of 50 units will have one or more faulty units?

CHAPTER 9
Topics in Analytic Geometry

Section 9.1 Circles and Parabolas **772**

Section 9.2 Ellipses **784**

Section 9.3 Hyperbolas **795**

Section 9.4 Rotation and Systems of Quadratic Equations **807**

Section 9.5 Parametric Equations **825**

Section 9.6 Polar Coordinates **833**

Section 9.7 Graphs of Polar Equations **845**

Section 9.8 Polar Equations of Conics **854**

Review Exercises **863**

Practice Test **886**

CHAPTER 9
Topics in Analytic Geometry

Section 9.1 Circles and Parabolas

- A **parabola** is the set of all points (x, y) that are equidistant from a fixed line **(directrix)** and a fixed point **(focus)** not on the line.
- The standard equation of a parabola with vertex (h, k) and
  (a) Vertical axis $x = h$ and directrix $y = k - p$ is
  $(x - h)^2 = 4p(y - k),\ p \neq 0.$
  (b) Horizontal axis $y = k$ and directrix $x = h - p$ is
  $(y - k)^2 = 4p(x - h),\ p \neq 0.$
- The tangent line to a parabola at a point P makes **equal angles** with
  (a) the line through P and the focus.
  (b) the axis of the parabola.

Vocabulary Check

1. conic section
2. locus
3. circle, center
4. parabola, directrix, focus
5. vertex
6. axis
7. tangent

1. $x^2 + y^2 = \left(\sqrt{18}\right)^2$

$x^2 + y^2 = 18$

2. $x^2 + y^2 = \left(4\sqrt{2}\right)^2$

$x^2 + y^2 = 32$

3. Radius $= \sqrt{(3 - 1)^2 + (7 - 0)^2}$

$= \sqrt{4 + 49} = \sqrt{53}$

$(x - h)^2 + (y - k)^2 = r^2$

$(x - 3)^2 + (y - 7)^2 = 53$

4. Radius $= \sqrt{[6 - (-2)]^2 + [-3 - 4]^2}$

$= \sqrt{64 + 49} = \sqrt{113}$

$(x - h)^2 + (y - k)^2 = r^2$

$(x - 6)^2 + (y + 3)^2 = 113$

5. Diameter $= 2\sqrt{7} \Rightarrow$ radius $= \sqrt{7}$

$(x - h)^2 + (y - k)^2 = r^2$

$(x + 3)^2 + (y + 1)^2 = 7$

6. Diameter $= 4\sqrt{3} \Rightarrow$ radius $= 2\sqrt{3}$

$(x - h)^2 + (y - k)^2 = r^2$

$(x - 5)^2 + (y + 6)^2 = 12$

7. $x^2 + y^2 = 49$

Center: $(0, 0)$

Radius: 7

8. $x^2 + y^2 = 1$

Center: $(0, 0)$

Radius: 1

9. $(x + 2)^2 + (y - 7)^2 = 16$

Center: $(-2, 7)$

Radius: 4

10. $(x + 9)^2 + (y + 1)^2 = 36$

Center: $(-9, -1)$

Radius: 6

11. $(x - 1)^2 + y^2 = 15$

Center: $(1, 0)$

Radius: $\sqrt{15}$

12. $x^2 + (y + 12)^2 = 24$

Center: $(0, -12)$

Radius: $\sqrt{24} = 2\sqrt{6}$

13. $\frac{1}{4}x^2 + \frac{1}{4}y^2 = 1$

$x^2 + y^2 = 4$

Center: $(0, 0)$

Radius: 2

14. $\frac{1}{9}x^2 + \frac{1}{9}y^2 = 1$

$x^2 + y^2 = 9$

Center: $(0, 0)$

Radius: 3

15. $\frac{4}{3}x^2 + \frac{4}{3}y^2 = 1$

$x^2 + y^2 = \frac{3}{4}$

Center: $(0, 0)$

Radius: $\frac{\sqrt{3}}{2}$

16. $\frac{9}{2}x^2 + \frac{9}{2}y^2 = 1$

$x^2 + y^2 = \frac{2}{9}$

Center: $(0, 0)$

Radius: $\frac{\sqrt{2}}{3}$

17. $(x^2 - 2x + 1) + (y^2 + 6y + 9) = -9 + 1 + 9$

$(x - 1)^2 + (y + 3)^2 = 1$

Center: $(1, -3)$

Radius: 1

18. $(x^2 - 10x + 25) + (y^2 - 6y + 9) = -25 + 25 + 9$

$(x - 5)^2 + (y - 3)^2 = 9$

Center: $(5, 3)$

Radius: 3

19. $4\left(x^2 + 3x + \frac{9}{4}\right) + 4(y^2 - 6y + 9) = -41 + 9 + 36$

$4\left(x + \frac{3}{2}\right)^2 + 4(y - 3)^2 = 4$

$\left(x + \frac{3}{2}\right)^2 + (y - 3)^2 = 1$

Center: $\left(-\frac{3}{2}, 3\right)$

Radius: 1

20. $9(x^2 + 6x + 9) + 9(y^2 - 4y + 4) = -17 + 81 + 36$

$9(x + 3)^2 + 9(y - 2)^2 = 100$

$(x + 3)^2 + (y - 2)^2 = \frac{100}{9}$

Center: $(-3, 2)$

Radius: $\frac{10}{3}$

21. $x^2 = 16 - y^2$

$x^2 + y^2 = 16$

Center: $(0, 0)$

Radius: 4

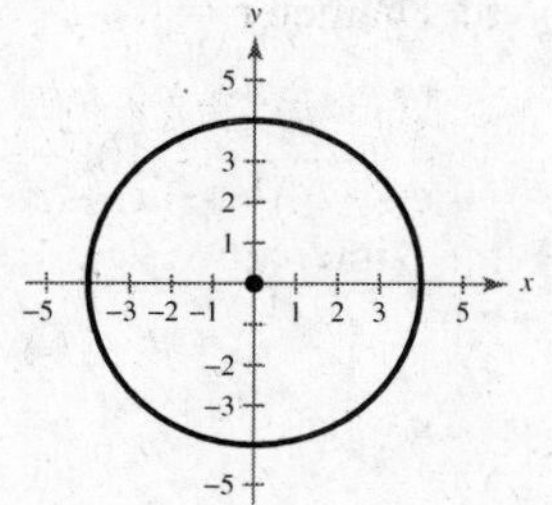

22. $y^2 = 81 - x^2$

$x^2 + y^2 = 81$

Center: $(0, 0)$

Radius: 9

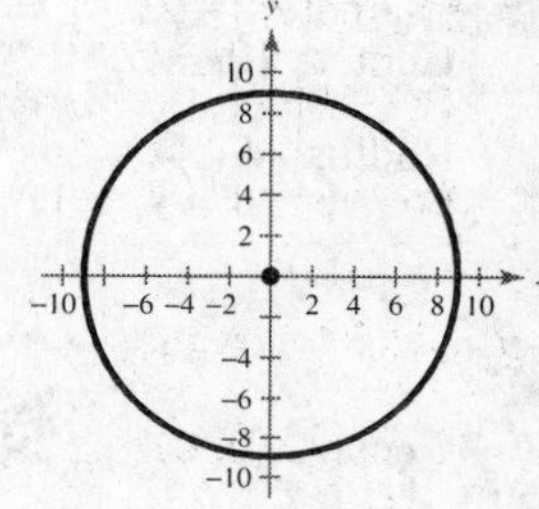

23. $x^2 + 4x + y^2 + 4y - 1 = 0$

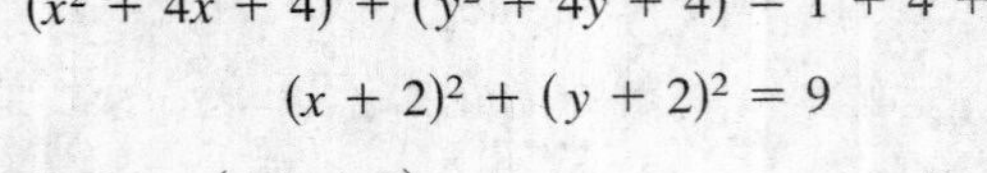

$(x^2 + 4x + 4) + (y^2 + 4y + 4) = 1 + 4 + 4$

$(x + 2)^2 + (y + 2)^2 = 9$

Center: $(-2, -2)$

Radius: 3

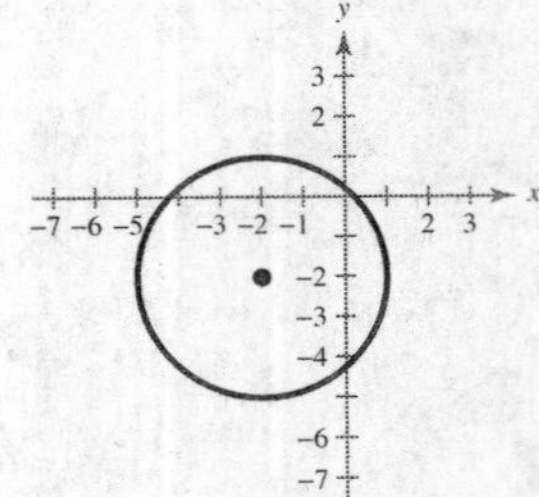

24. $x^2 - 6x + y^2 + 6y + 14 = 0$

$(x^2 - 6x + 9) + (y^2 + 6y + 9) = -14 + 9 + 9$

$(x - 3)^2 + (y + 3)^2 = 4$

Center: $(3, -3)$

Radius: 2

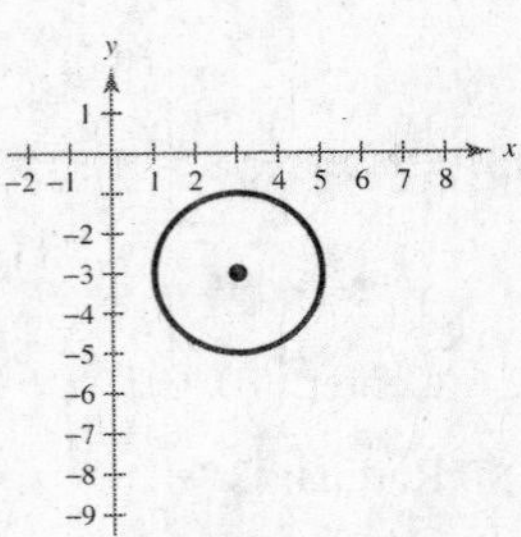

25. $x^2 - 14x + y^2 + 8y + 40 = 0$

$(x^2 - 14x + 4) + (y^2 + 8y + 16) = -40 + 49 + 16$

$(x - 7)^2 + (y + 4)^2 = 25$

Center: $(7, -4)$

Radius: 5

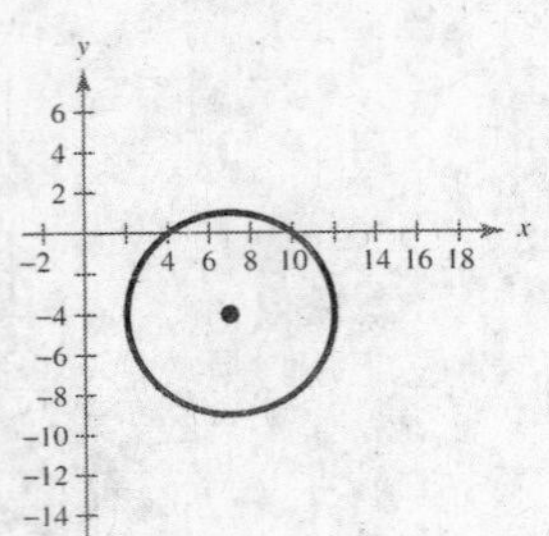

26. $x^2 + 6x + y^2 - 12y + 41 = 0$

$(x^2 + 6x + 9) + (y^2 - 12y + 36) = -41 + 9 + 36$

$(x + 3)^2 + (y - 6)^2 = 4$

Center: $(-3, 6)$

Radius: 2

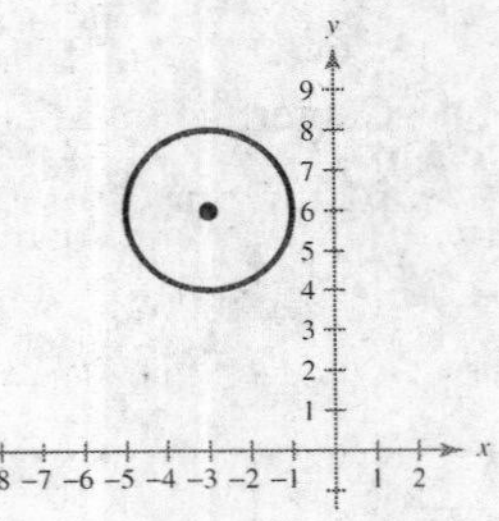

27. $x^2 + 2x + y^2 - 35 = 0$

$(x^2 + 2x + 1) + y^2 = 35 + 1$

$(x + 1)^2 + y^2 = 36$

Center: $(-1, 0)$

Radius: 6

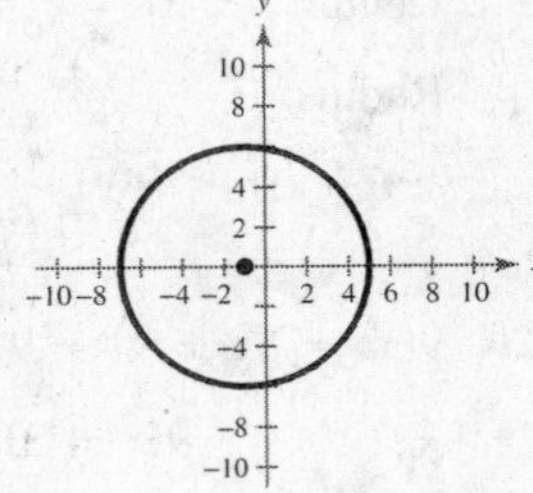

28. $x^2 + y^2 + 10y + 9 = 0$

$x^2 + (y^2 + 10y + 25) = -9 + 25$

$x^2 + (y^2 + 5)^2 = 16$

Center: $(0, -5)$

Radius: 4

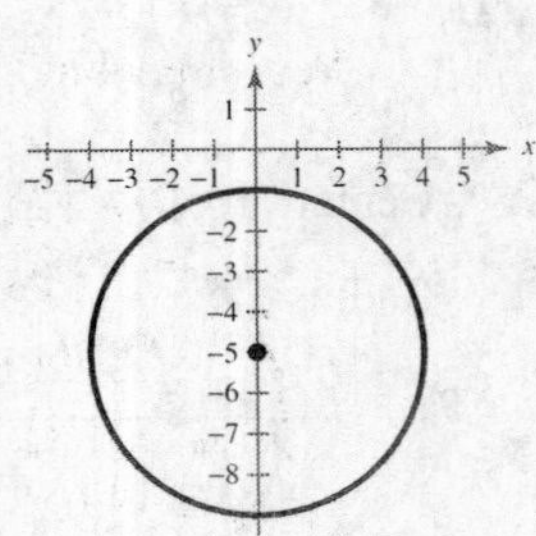

29. y-intercepts: $(0 - 2)^2 + (y + 3)^2 = 9$

$4 + (y + 3)^2 = 9$

$(y + 3)^2 = 5$

$y = -3 \pm \sqrt{5}$

$(0, -3 \pm \sqrt{5})$

x-intercepts: $(x - 2)^2 + (0 + 3)^2 = 9$

$(x - 2)^2 = 0$

$x = 2$

$(2, 0)$

30. y-intercepts: $(0 + 5)^2 + (y - 4)^2 = 25$

$$(y - 4)^2 = 0$$
$$y = 4$$

$(0, 4)$

x-intercepts: $(x + 5)^2 + (0 - 4)^2 = 25$

$$(x + 5)^2 + 16 = 25$$
$$(x + 5)^2 = 9$$
$$x + 5 = \pm 3$$
$$x = -8, -2$$

$(-2, 0), (-8, 0)$

31. y-intercepts: Let $x = 0$.

$$y^2 - 6y - 27 = 0$$
$$y^2 - 6y + 9 = 27 + 9$$
$$(y - 3)^2 = 36$$
$$y - 3 = \pm 6$$
$$y = 9, -3$$

$(0, 9), (0, -3)$

x-intercepts: Let $y = 0$.

$$x^2 - 2x - 27 = 0$$
$$x^2 - 2x + 1 = 27 + 1$$
$$(x - 1)^2 = 28$$
$$x - 1 = \pm\sqrt{28}$$
$$x = 1 \pm 2\sqrt{7}$$

$\left(1 \pm 2\sqrt{7}, 0\right)$

32. y-intercepts: Let $x = 0$.

$$y^2 + 2y + 9 = 0$$

No solution

No y-intercepts

x-intercepts: Let $y = 0$.

$$x^2 + 8x + 9 = 0$$
$$x^2 + 8x + 16 = -9 + 16$$
$$(x + 4)^2 = 7$$
$$x + 4 = \pm\sqrt{7}$$
$$x = -4 \pm \sqrt{7}$$

$\left(-4 \pm \sqrt{7}, 0\right)$

33. y-intercepts: $(0 - 6)^2 + (y + 3)^2 = 16$

$$(y + 3)^2 = 16 - 36$$
$$= -20$$

No solution

No y-intercepts

x-intercepts: $(x - 6)^2 + (0 + 3)^2 = 16$

$$(x - 6)^2 = 7$$
$$x - 6 = \pm\sqrt{7}$$
$$x = 6 \pm \sqrt{7}$$

$\left(6 \pm \sqrt{7}, 0\right)$

34. y-intercepts: $(0 + 7)^2 + (y - 8)^2 = 4$

$$(y - 8)^2 = 4 - 49$$
$$= -45$$

No solution

No y-intercepts

x-intercepts: $(x + 7)^2 + (0 - 8)^2 = 4$

$$(x + 7)^2 = 4 - 64$$
$$= -60$$

No solution

No x-intercepts

35. (a) Radius: 81; Center: $(0, 0)$

$x^2 + y^2 = 81^2 = 6561$

(b) The distance from $(60, 45)$ to $(0, 0)$ is

$\sqrt{60^2 + 45^2} = \sqrt{5625} = 75$ miles.

Yes, you would feel the earthquake.

(c)

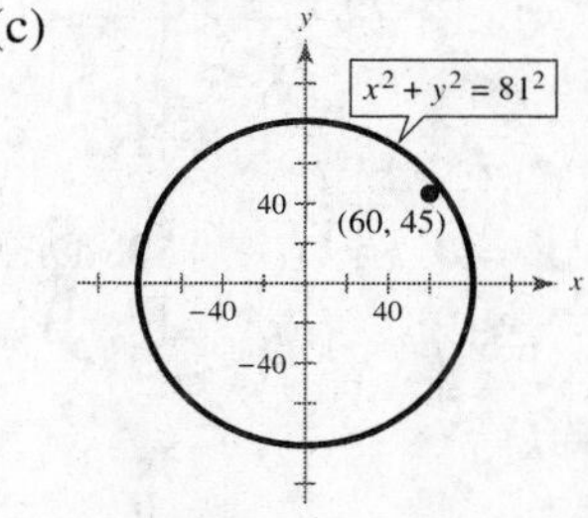

You were $81 - 75 = 6$ miles from the outer boundary.

36. (a) Area $= \pi r^2 = 1800$

$$r^2 = \frac{1800}{\pi}$$

$$r = \sqrt{\frac{1800}{\pi}}$$

$$r \approx 23.937 \text{ feet}$$

(b) $\pi R^2 = 2400$

$$R = \sqrt{\frac{2400}{\pi}} \approx 27.640 \text{ feet}$$

$27.640 - 23.937 \approx 3.703$ longer radius

37. $y^2 = -4x$

Vertex: $(0, 0)$

Opens to the left since p is negative.

Matches graph (e).

38. $x^2 = 2y$

Vertex: $(0, 0)$

$p = \frac{1}{2} > 0$

Opens upward

Matches graph (b).

39. $x^2 = -8y$

Vertex: $(0, 0)$

Opens downward since p is negative.

Matches graph (d).

40. $y^2 = -12x$

Vertex: $(0, 0)$

$p = -3 < 0$

Opens to the left

Matches graph (f).

41. $(y - 1)^2 = 4(x - 3)$

Vertex: $(3, 1)$

Opens to the right since p is positive.

Matches graph (a).

42. $(x + 3)^2 = -2(y - 1)$

Vertex: $(-3, 1)$

$p = -\frac{1}{2} < 0$

Opens downward

Matches graph (c).

43. Vertex: $(0, 0) \Rightarrow h = 0, k = 0$

Graph opens upward.

$x^2 = 4py$

Point on graph: $(3, 6)$

$3^2 = 4p(6)$

$9 = 24p$

$\frac{3}{8} = p$

Thus, $x^2 = 4\left(\frac{3}{8}\right)y \Rightarrow y = \frac{2}{3}x^2$

$\Rightarrow x^2 = \frac{3}{2}y.$

44. Point: $(-2, 6)$

$x = ay^2$

$-2 = a(6)^2$

$-\frac{1}{18} = a$

$x = -\frac{1}{18}y^2$

$y^2 = -18x$

45. Vertex: $(0, 0) \Rightarrow h = 0, k = 0$

Focus: $\left(0, -\frac{3}{2}\right) \Rightarrow p = -\frac{3}{2}$

$(x - h)^2 = 4p(y - k)$

$x^2 = 4\left(-\frac{3}{2}\right)y$

$x^2 = -6y$

46. Focus: $\left(\frac{5}{2}, 0\right) \Rightarrow p = \frac{5}{2}$

$y^2 = 4px = 4\left(\frac{5}{2}\right)x$

$y^2 = 10x$

47. Vertex: $(0, 0) \Rightarrow h = 0, k = 0$

Focus: $(-2, 0) \Rightarrow p = -2$

$(y - k)^2 = 4p(x - h)$

$y^2 = 4(-2)x$

$y^2 = -8x$

48. Focus: $(0, 1) \Rightarrow p = 1$

$x^2 = 4py = 4(1)y$

$x^2 = 4y$

49. Vertex: $(0, 0) \Rightarrow h = 0, k = 0$

Directrix: $y = -1 \Rightarrow p = 1$

$(x - h)^2 = 4p(y - k)$

$(x - 0)^2 = 4(1)(y - 0)$

$x^2 = 4y$ or $y = \frac{1}{4}x^2$

50. Directrix: $y = 3 \Rightarrow p = -3$

$x^2 = 4py$

$x^2 = -12y$

51. Vertex: $(0, 0) \Rightarrow h = 0, k = 0$

Directrix: $x = 2 \Rightarrow p = -2$

$y^2 = 4px$

$y^2 = -8x$

52. Directrix: $x = -3 \Rightarrow p = 3$

$y^2 = 4px$

$y^2 = 12x$

53. Vertex: $(0, 0) \Rightarrow h = 0, k = 0$

Horizontal axis and passes through the point $(4, 6)$

$(y - k)^2 = 4p(x - h)$

$(y - 0)^2 = 4p(x - 0)$

$y^2 = 4px$

$6^2 = 4p(4)$

$36 = 16p \Rightarrow p = \frac{9}{4}$

$y^2 = 4\left(\frac{9}{4}\right)x$

$y^2 = 9x$

54. Vertical axis

Passes through $(-3, -3)$

$x^2 = 4py$

$(-3)^2 = 4p(-3)$

$9 = -12p \Rightarrow p = -\frac{3}{4}$

$x^2 = 4\left(-\frac{3}{4}\right)y$

$x^2 = -3y$

55. $y = \frac{1}{2}x^2$

$x^2 = 2y = 4\left(\frac{1}{2}\right)y;\ p = \frac{1}{2}$

Vertex: $(0, 0)$

Focus: $\left(0, \frac{1}{2}\right)$

Directrix: $y = -\frac{1}{2}$

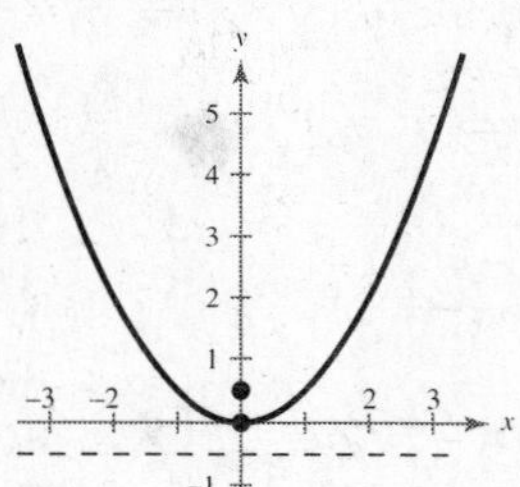

56. $y = -4x^2$

$x^2 = -\frac{1}{4}y = 4\left(-\frac{1}{16}\right)y, p = -\frac{1}{16}$

Vertex: $(0, 0)$

Focus: $\left(0, -\frac{1}{16}\right)$

Directrix: $y = \frac{1}{16}$

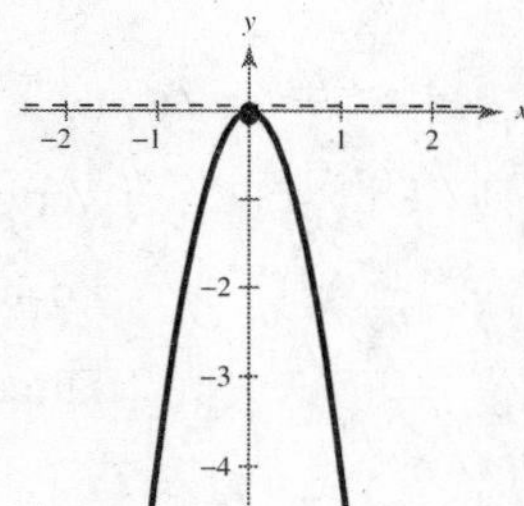

57. $y^2 = -6x$

$y^2 = 4\left(-\frac{3}{2}\right)x;\ p = -\frac{3}{2}$

Vertex: $(0, 0)$

Focus: $\left(-\frac{3}{2}, 0\right)$

Directrix: $x = \frac{3}{2}$

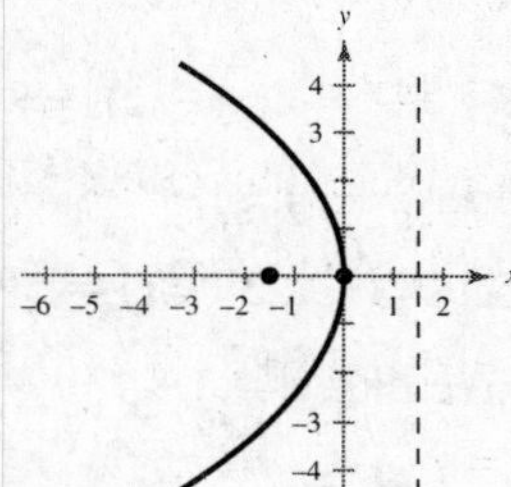

58. $y^2 = 3x$

$y^2 = 4\left(\frac{3}{4}\right)x; p = \frac{3}{4}$

Vertex: $(0, 0)$

Focus: $\left(\frac{3}{4}, 0\right)$

Directrix: $x = -\frac{3}{4}$

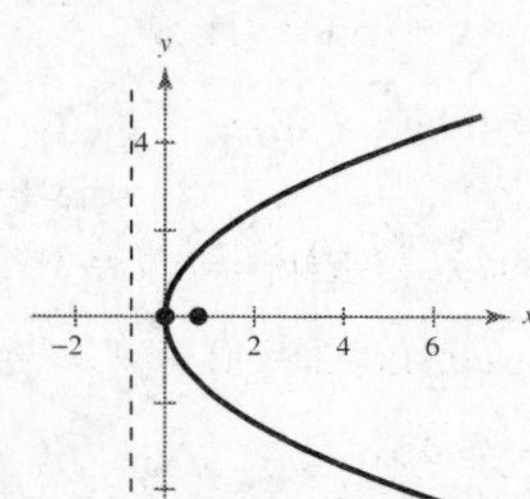

59. $x^2 + 8y = 0$

$x^2 = 4(-2)y;\ p = -2$

Vertex: $(0, 0)$

Focus: $(0, -2)$

Directrix: $y = 2$

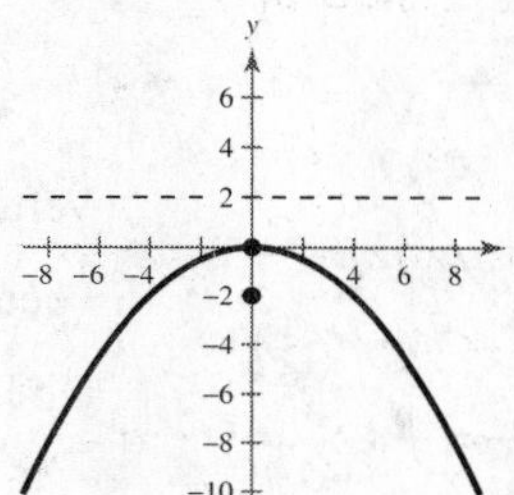

60. $y^2 = -x$

$y^2 = 4\left(-\frac{1}{4}\right)x, p = -\frac{1}{4}$

Vertex: $(0, 0)$

Focus: $\left(-\frac{1}{4}, 0\right)$

Directrix: $x = \frac{1}{4}$

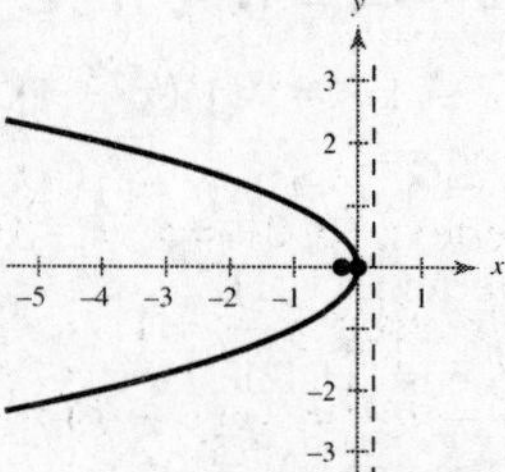

61. $(x + 1)^2 + 8(y + 3) = 0$

$$(x + 1)^2 = 4(-2)(y + 3)$$

$h = -1, k = -3, p = -2$

Vertex: $(-1, -3)$

Focus: $(-1, -5)$

Directrix: $y = -1$

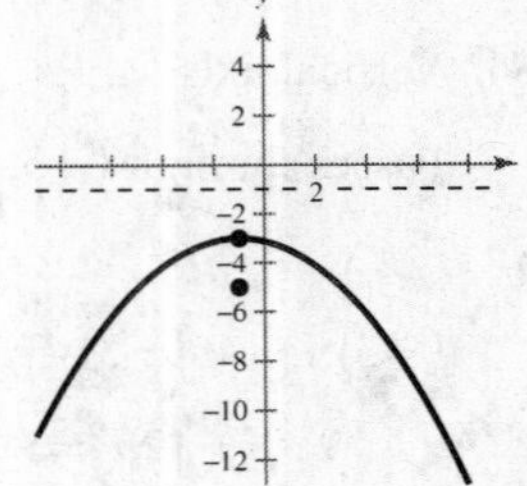

62. $(x - 5) + (y + 4)^2 = 0$

$$(y + 4)^2 = -(x - 5) = 4\left(-\tfrac{1}{4}\right)(x - 5)$$

Vertex: $(5, -4)$

Focus: $\left(5 - \tfrac{1}{4}, -4\right) = \left(\tfrac{19}{4}, -4\right)$

Directrix: $x = \tfrac{21}{4}$

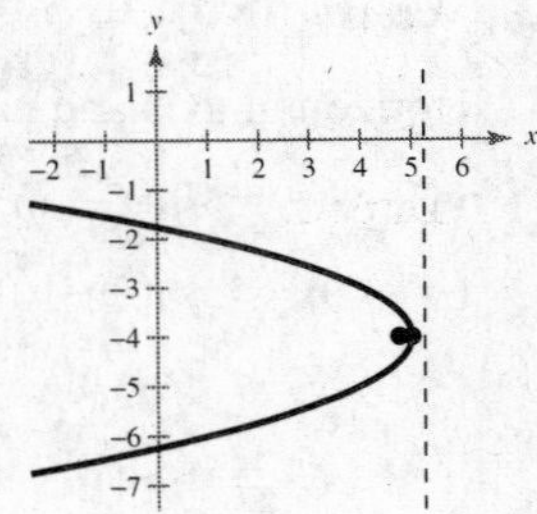

63. $y^2 + 6y + 8x + 25 = 0$

$$(y + 3)^2 = 4(-2)(x + 2);\ p = -2$$

Vertex: $(-2, -3)$

Focus: $(-4, -3)$

Directrix: $x = 0$

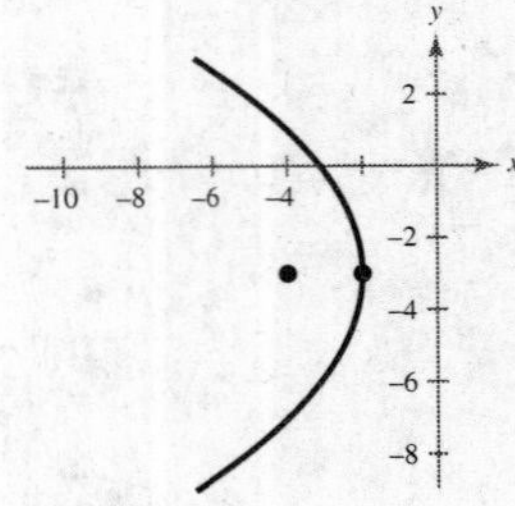

64. $y^2 - 4y - 4x = 0$

$$(y - 2)^2 = 4(x + 1);\ p = 1$$

Vertex: $(-1, 2)$

Focus: $(0, 2)$

Directrix: $x = -2$

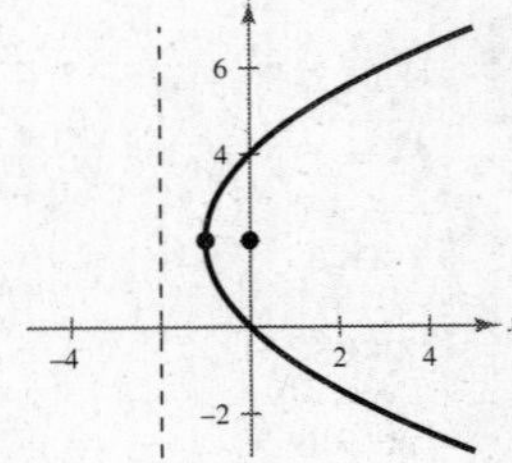

65. $\left(x + \tfrac{3}{2}\right)^2 = 4(y - 2) \implies h = -\tfrac{3}{2}, k = 2, p = 1$

Vertex: $\left(-\tfrac{3}{2}, 2\right)$

Focus: $\left(-\tfrac{3}{2}, 2 + 1\right) = \left(-\tfrac{3}{2}, 3\right)$

Directrix: $y = 1$

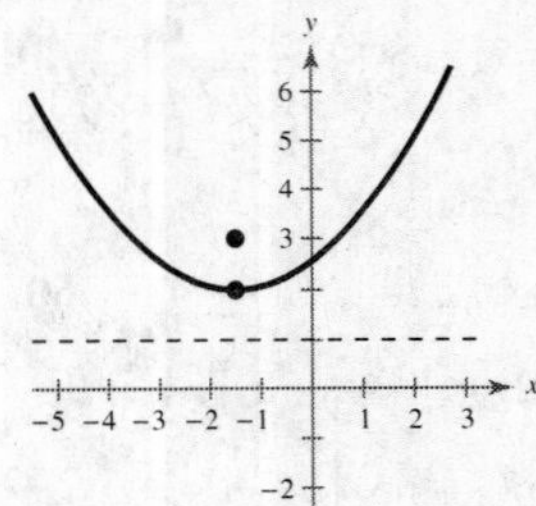

66. $\left(x + \tfrac{1}{2}\right)^2 = 4(y - 1) \implies p = 1$

Vertex: $\left(-\tfrac{1}{2}, 1\right)$

Focus: $\left(-\tfrac{1}{2}, 1 + 1\right) = \left(-\tfrac{1}{2}, 2\right)$

Directrix: $y = 0$

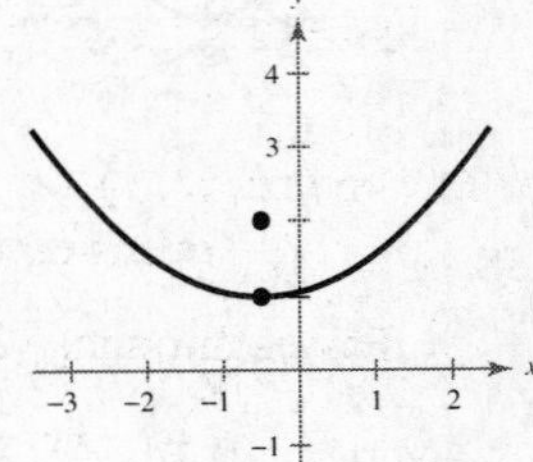

67. $y = \tfrac{1}{4}(x^2 - 2x + 5)$

$4y - 4 = (x - 1)^2$

$(x - 1)^2 = 4(1)(y - 1)$

$h = 1, k = 1, p = 1$

Vertex: $(1, 1)$

Focus: $(1, 2)$

Directrix: $y = 0$

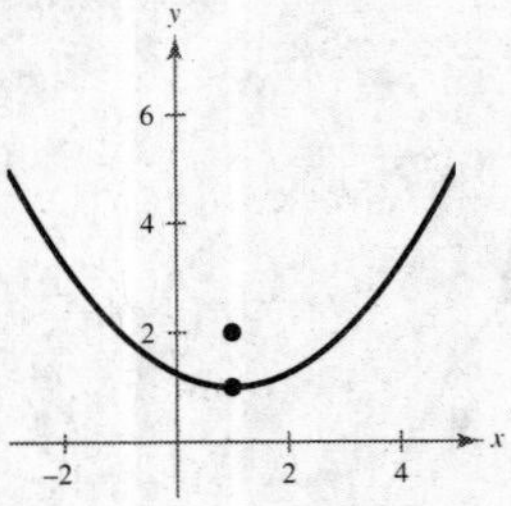

68. $4x - y^2 - 2y - 33 = 0$

$$y^2 + 2y + 1 = 4x - 33 + 1$$

$$(y + 1)^2 = 4(1)(x - 8)$$

Vertex: $(8, -1)$

Focus: $(9, -1)$

Directrix: $x = 7$

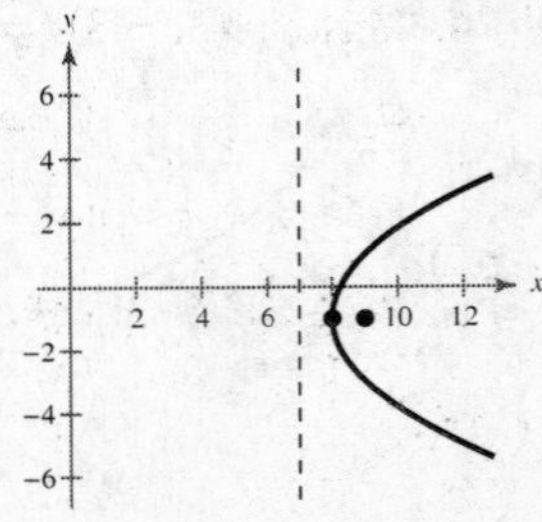

69. $x^2 + 4x + 6y - 2 = 0$

$$x^2 + 4x + 4 = -6y + 2 + 4 = -6y + 6$$
$$(x + 2)^2 = -6(y - 1)$$
$$(x + 2)^2 = 4\left(-\tfrac{3}{2}\right)(y - 1)$$

Vertex: $(-2, 1)$

Focus: $\left(-2, 1 - \frac{3}{2}\right) = \left(-2, -\frac{1}{2}\right)$

Directrix: $y = \frac{5}{2}$

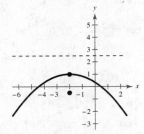

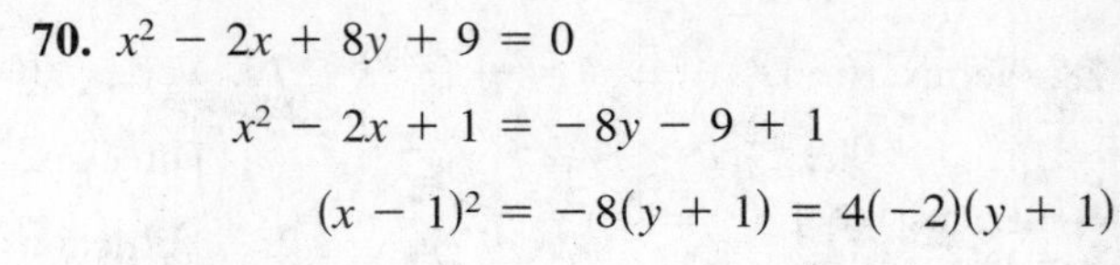

70. $x^2 - 2x + 8y + 9 = 0$

$$x^2 - 2x + 1 = -8y - 9 + 1$$
$$(x - 1)^2 = -8(y + 1) = 4(-2)(y + 1)$$

Vertex: $(1, -1)$

Focus: $(1, -3)$

Directrix: $y = 1$

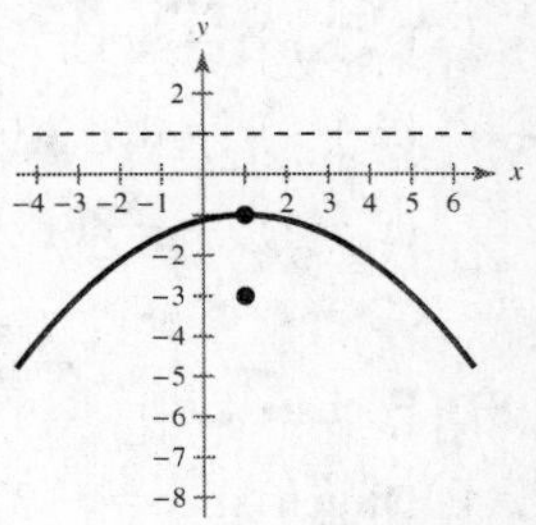

71. $y^2 + x + y = 0$

$$y^2 + y + \tfrac{1}{4} = -x + \tfrac{1}{4}$$
$$\left(y + \tfrac{1}{2}\right)^2 = 4\left(-\tfrac{1}{4}\right)\left(x - \tfrac{1}{4}\right)$$

$h = \frac{1}{4}, k = -\frac{1}{2}, p = -\frac{1}{4}$

Vertex: $\left(\frac{1}{4}, -\frac{1}{2}\right)$

Focus: $\left(0, -\frac{1}{2}\right)$

Directrix: $x = \frac{1}{2}$

To use a graphing calculator, enter:

$y_1 = -\frac{1}{2} + \sqrt{\frac{1}{4} - x}$

$y_2 = -\frac{1}{2} - \sqrt{\frac{1}{4} - x}$

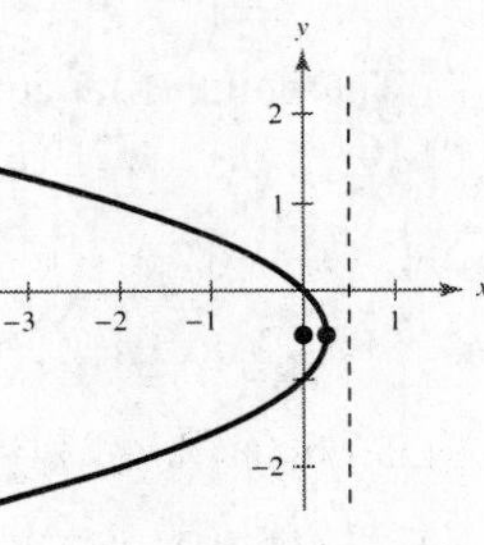

72. $y^2 - 4x - 4 = 0$

$$y^2 = 4x + 4 = 4(1)(x + 1)$$

Vertex: $(-1, 0)$

Focus: $(0, 0)$

Directrix: $x = -2$

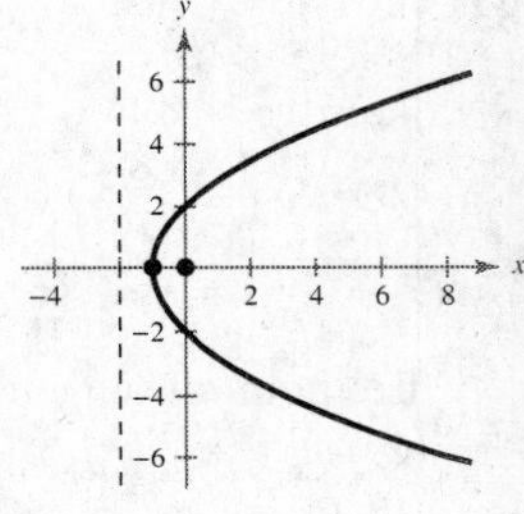

73. Vertex: $(3, 1)$, opens downward

Passes through: $(2, 0)$, $(4, 0)$

$$y = -(x - 2)(x - 4)$$
$$= -x^2 + 6x - 8$$
$$= -(x - 3)^2 + 1$$

$(x - 3)^2 = -(y - 1)$

74. Vertex: $(5, 3) \Rightarrow h = 5, k = 3$

Passes through: $(4.5, 4)$

$$(y - k)^2 = 4p(x - h)$$
$$(y - 3)^2 = 4p(x - 5)$$
$$1 = 4p(4.5 - 5)$$
$$p = -\tfrac{1}{2}$$
$$(y - 3)^2 = -2(x - 5)$$

75. Vertex: $(-2, 0)$, opens to the right

Focus: $\left(-\frac{3}{2}, 0\right)$

$\frac{1}{2} = p$

$y^2 = 4\left(\frac{1}{2}\right)(x + 2)$

$y^2 = 2(x + 2)$

76. Vertex: $(3, -3) \Rightarrow h = 3,\ k = -3$

Focus: $\left(3, -\frac{9}{4}\right) \Rightarrow p = \frac{3}{4}$

$(x - h)^2 = 4p(y - k)$

$(x - 3)^2 = 3(y + 3)$

77. Vertex: $(5, 2)$

Focus: $(3, 2)$

Horizontal axis: $p = 3 - 5 = -2$

$(y - 2)^2 = 4(-2)(x - 5)$

$(y - 2)^2 = -8(x - 5)$

78. Vertex: $(-1, 2) \Rightarrow h = -1, k = 2$

Focus: $(-1, 0) \Rightarrow p = -2$

$(x - h)^2 = 4p(y - k)$

$(x + 1)^2 = 4(-2)(y - 2)$

$(x + 1)^2 = -8(y - 2)$

79. Vertex: $(0, 4)$

Directrix: $y = 2$

Vertical axis

$p = 4 - 2 = 2$

$(x - 0)^2 = 4(2)(y - 4)$

$x^2 = 8(y - 4)$

80. Vertex: $(-2, 1) \Rightarrow h = -2, k = 1$

Directrix: $x = 1 \Rightarrow p = -3$

$(y - k)^2 = 4p(x - h)$

$(y - 1)^2 = 4(-3)(x - (-2))$

$(y - 1)^2 = -12(x + 2)$

81. Focus: $(2, 2)$

Directrix: $x = -2$

Horizontal axis

Vertex: $(0, 2)$

$p = 2 - 0 = 2$

$(y - 2)^2 = 4(2)(x - 0)$

$(y - 2)^2 = 8x$

82. Focus: $(0, 0)$

Directrix: $y = 4 \Rightarrow p = -2$

Vertex: $(0, 2)$

$x^2 = 4(-2)(y - 2)$

$x^2 = -8(y - 2)$

83. $y^2 - 8x = 0$ and $x - y + 2 = 0$

$y^2 = 8x$ $\qquad y_3 = x + 2$

$y_1 = \sqrt{8x}$

$y_2 = -\sqrt{8x}$

The point of tangency is $(2, 4)$.

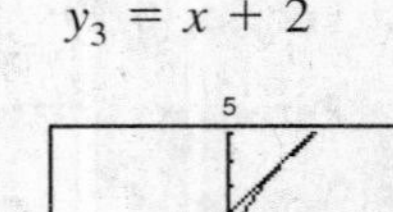

84. $x^2 + 12y = 0$ and $x + y - 3 = 0$

$12y = -x^2$ $\qquad y_2 = 3 - x$

$y_1 = -\frac{1}{12}x^2$

The point of tangency is $(6, -3)$.

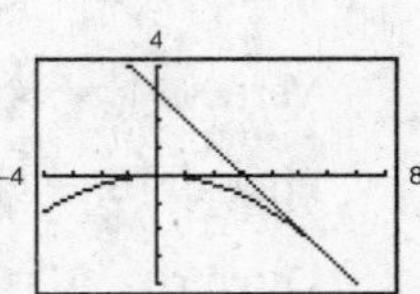

85. $x^2 = 2y$, $(4, 8)$, $p = \frac{1}{2}$, focus: $\left(0, \frac{1}{2}\right)$

Following Example 4, we find the y-intercept $(0, b)$.

$$d_1 = \frac{1}{2} - b$$

$$d_2 = \sqrt{(4 - 0)^2 + \left(8 - \frac{1}{2}\right)^2} = \frac{17}{2}$$

$$d_1 = d_2 \Rightarrow \frac{1}{2} - b = \frac{17}{2} \Rightarrow b = -8$$

$$m = \frac{8 - (-8)}{4 - 0} = 4$$

$y = 4x - 8$, Tangent line

Let $y = 0 \Rightarrow x = 2 \Rightarrow x$-intercept $(2, 0)$.

86. $2y = x^2$

$4\left(\frac{1}{2}\right)y = x^2$

$p = \frac{1}{2}$

Focus: $\left(0, \frac{1}{2}\right)$

$d_1 = \frac{1}{2} - b$

$d_2 = \sqrt{(-3 - 0)^2 + \left(\frac{9}{2} - \frac{1}{2}\right)^2} = 5$

$\frac{1}{2} - b = 5$

$b = -\frac{9}{2}$

$m = \frac{-(9/2) - (9/2)}{0 + 3} = -3$

Tangent line: $y = -3x - \frac{9}{2} \Rightarrow 6x + 2y + 9 = 0$

x-intercept: $\left(-\frac{3}{2}, 0\right)$

87. $y = -2x^2 \Rightarrow x^2 = -\frac{1}{2}y = 4\left(-\frac{1}{8}\right)y$

$\Rightarrow p = -\frac{1}{8}$

Focus: $\left(0, -\frac{1}{8}\right)$

Following Example 4, we find the y-intercept $(0, b)$.

$d_1 = \frac{1}{8} + b$

$d_2 = \sqrt{(-1 - 0)^2 + \left(-2 + \frac{1}{8}\right)^2} = \frac{17}{8}$

$d_1 = d_2 \Rightarrow \frac{1}{8} + b = \frac{17}{8} \Rightarrow b = 2$

$m = \frac{-2 - 2}{-1 - 0} = 4$

$y = 4x + 2$

Let $y = 0 \Rightarrow x = -\frac{1}{2} \Rightarrow x$-intercept $\left(-\frac{1}{2}, 0\right)$.

88. $y = -2x^2, (2, -8)$

$x^2 = -\frac{1}{2}y = 4\left(-\frac{1}{8}\right)y \Rightarrow p = -\frac{1}{8}$

Focus: $\left(0, -\frac{1}{8}\right)$

$d_1 = \frac{1}{8} + b$

$d_2 = \sqrt{(2 - 0)^2 + \left(-8 + \frac{1}{8}\right)^2} = \frac{65}{8}$

$d_1 = d_2 \Rightarrow \frac{1}{8} + b = \frac{65}{8} \Rightarrow b = 8$

$m = \frac{-8 - 8}{2 - 0} = -8$

$y = -8x + 8$

Intercept: $(1, 0)$

89. $R = 375x - \frac{3}{2}x^2$

R is a maximum of \$23,437.50 when $x = 125$ televisions.

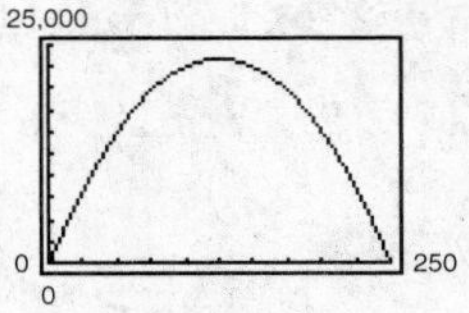

90. (a) $x^2 = 4py$

$32^2 = 4p\left(\frac{1}{12}\right)$

$1024 = \frac{1}{3}p$

$3072 = p$

$x^2 = 4(3072)y$

$y = \frac{x^2}{12{,}288}$

(b) $\frac{1}{24} = \frac{x^2}{12{,}288}$

$\frac{12{,}288}{24} = x^2$

$512 = x^2$

$x \approx 22.6$ feet

91. (a) $x^2 = 4py, p = \frac{3}{2}$

$x^2 = 4\left(\frac{3}{2}\right)y = 6y$

(or $y^2 = 6x$)

(b) When $x = 4$,

$6y = 16$

$y = \frac{16}{6} = \frac{8}{3}$.

Depth: $\frac{8}{3}$ inches

92. $x^2 = 4py$, (6, 4) on parabola

$36 = 4p(4)$

$p = \frac{36}{16} = \frac{9}{4}$

The wire should be inserted $\frac{9}{4}$ inches from the bottom.

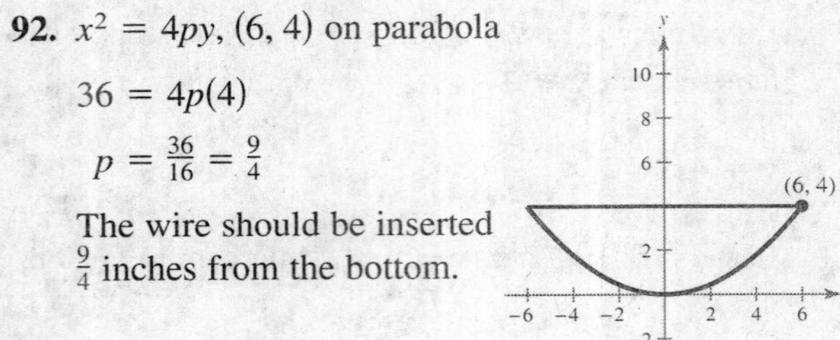

93. (a)

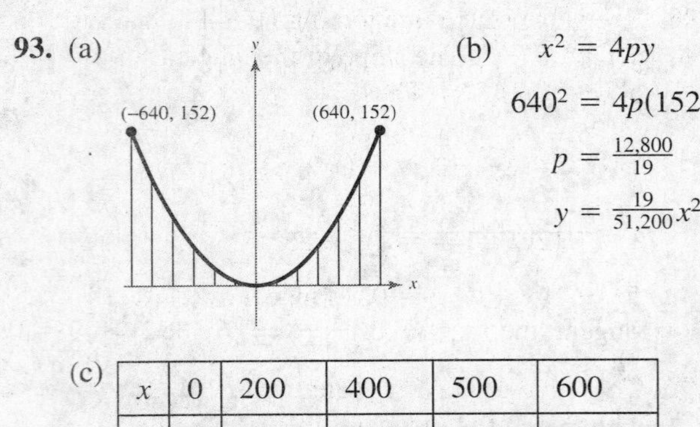

(b) $x^2 = 4py$

$640^2 = 4p(152)$

$p = \frac{12{,}800}{19}$

$y = \frac{19}{51{,}200}x^2$

(c)

x	0	200	400	500	600
y	0	14.84	59.38	92.77	133.59

94. (a) $x^2 = 4py$ passes through point $\left(16, -\frac{2}{5}\right)$.

$256 = 4p\left(-\frac{2}{5}\right) \Rightarrow p = -160$

$x^2 = 4(-160)y$

$x^2 = -640y$ or $y = -\frac{1}{640}x^2$

(b) $-0.1 = -\frac{1}{640}x^2 \Rightarrow x = 8$ feet

95. Vertex: (0, 0)

$y^2 = 4px$

Point: (1000, 800)

$800^2 = 4p(1000) \Rightarrow p = 160$

$y^2 = 4(160)x$

$y^2 = 640x$

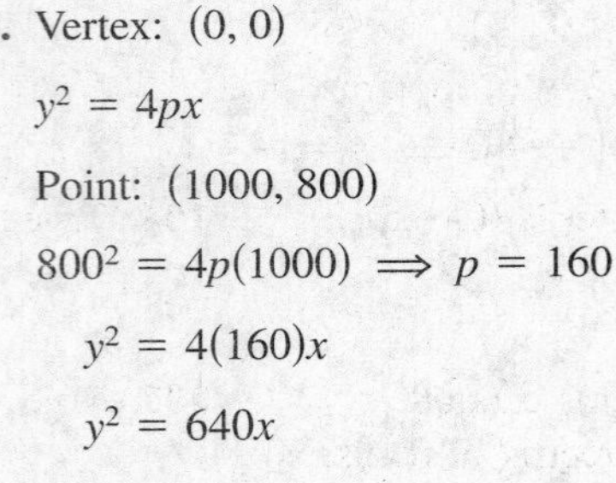

96. (a) $V = 17{,}500\sqrt{2}$ mi/hr $\approx 24{,}750$ mi/hr

(b) $p = -4100, (h, k) = (0, 4100)$

$(x - 0)^2 = 4(-4100)(y - 4100)$

$x^2 = -16{,}400(y - 4100)$

97. $-12.5(y - 7.125) = (x - 6.25)^2$

$-12.5y + 89.0625 = x^2 - 12.5x + 39.0625$

$y = -0.08x^2 + x + 4$

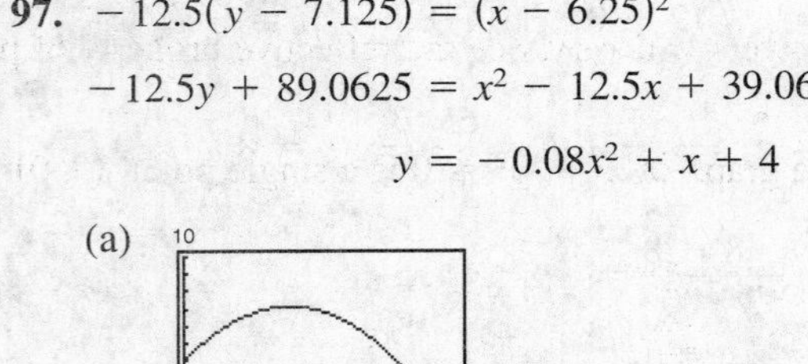

(a)

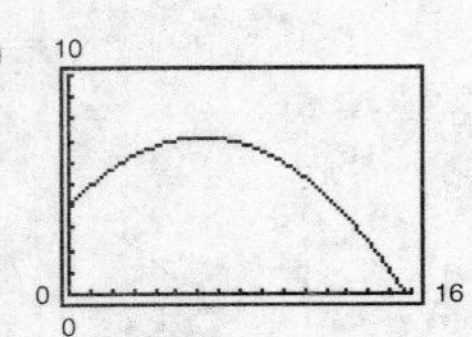

(b) The highest point is at (6.25, 7.125). The distance is the x-intercept of ≈ 15.69 feet.

98. (a) $x^2 = -\frac{1}{16}v^2(y - s)$

$$y = -\frac{16x^2}{v^2} + s$$

$$= -\frac{16x^2}{32^2} + 75$$

$$= -\frac{1}{64}x^2 + 75$$

(b) $y = 0 = -\frac{1}{64}x^2 + 75 \Rightarrow x^2 = 75(64)$

$$\Rightarrow x \approx 69.3 \text{ ft}$$

99. The slope of the line joining $(3, -4)$ and the center is $-\frac{4}{3}$. The slope of the tangent line at $(3, -4)$ is $\frac{3}{4}$. Thus,

$$y + 4 = \frac{3}{4}(x - 3)$$

$$4y + 16 = 3x - 9$$

$$3x - 4y = 25, \quad \text{tangent line.}$$

100. The slope of the line joining $(-5, 12)$ and the center is $-\frac{12}{5}$. The slope of the tangent line at $(-5, 12)$ is $\frac{5}{12}$. Thus,

$$y - 12 = \frac{5}{12}(x + 5)$$

$$12y - 144 = 5x + 25$$

$$5x - 12y + 169 = 0, \quad \text{tangent line.}$$

101. The slope of the line joining $(2, -2\sqrt{2})$ and the center is $(-2\sqrt{2})/2 = -\sqrt{2}$. The slope of the tangent line is $1/\sqrt{2} = \sqrt{2}/2$. Thus,

$$y + 2\sqrt{2} = \frac{\sqrt{2}}{2}(x - 2)$$

$$2y + 4\sqrt{2} = \sqrt{2}x - 2\sqrt{2}$$

$$\sqrt{2}x - 2y = 6\sqrt{2}, \quad \text{tangent line.}$$

102. The slope of the line joining $(-2\sqrt{5}, 2)$ and the center is $2/(-2\sqrt{5}) = -1/\sqrt{5}$. The slope of the tangent line is $\sqrt{5}$. Thus,

$$y - 2 = \sqrt{5}(x + 2\sqrt{5})$$

$$y - 2 = \sqrt{5}x + 10$$

$$\sqrt{5}x - y + 12 = 0, \quad \text{tangent line.}$$

103. False. The center is $(0, -5)$.

104. True

105. False. A circle is a conic section.

106. False. A parabola cannot intersect its directrix or focus.

107. True

108. False. The directrix $y = -\frac{1}{4}$ is below the x-axis.

109. Answers will vary. See the reflective property of parabolas, page 599.

110. The graph of $x^2 + y^2 = 0$ is a single point, $(0, 0)$.

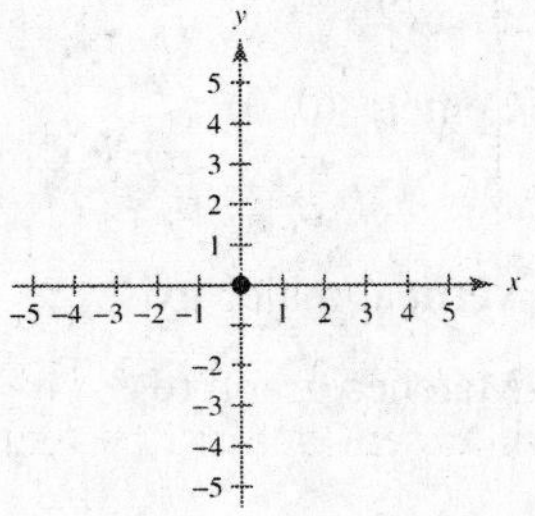

The plane intersects the double-napped cone at the vertices of the cones.

111. $(y - 3)^2 = 6(x + 1)$

For the upper half of the parabola,

$y - 3 = \sqrt{6(x + 1)}$

$y = \sqrt{6(x + 1)} + 3.$

112. $(y + 1)^2 = 2(x - 2)$

For the lower half of the parabola,

$y + 1 = -\sqrt{2(x - 2)}$

$y = -1 - \sqrt{2(x - 2)}.$

113. $f(x) = 3x^3 - 4x + 2$

Relative maximum: $(-0.67, 3.78)$

Relative minimum: $(0.67, 0.22)$

114. $f(x) = 2x^2 + 3x$

Relative minimum: -1.13 at $x = -0.75$

115. $f(x) = x^4 + 2x + 2$

Relative minimum: $(-0.79, 0.81)$

116. $f(x) = x^5 - 3x - 1$

Relative minimum: -3.11 at 0.88

Relative maximum: 1.11 at -0.88

Section 9.2 Ellipses

- An **ellipse** is the set of all points (x, y) the sum of whose distances from two distinct fixed points **(foci)** is constant.
- The standard equation of an ellipse with center (h, k) and major and minor axes of lengths $2a$ and $2b$ is
  (a) $\dfrac{(x - h)^2}{a^2} + \dfrac{(y - k)^2}{b^2} = 1$ if the major axis is horizontal.
  (b) $\dfrac{(x - h)^2}{b^2} + \dfrac{(y - k)^2}{a^2} = 1$ if the major axis is vertical.
- $c^2 = a^2 - b^2$ where c is the distance from the center to a focus.
- The eccentricity of an ellipse is $e = \dfrac{c}{a}$.

Vocabulary Check

1. ellipse

2. major axis, center

3. minor axis

4. eccentricity

1. $\dfrac{x^2}{4} + \dfrac{y^2}{9} = 1$

Center: $(0, 0)$

$a = 3, b = 2$

Vertical major axis

Matches graph (b).

2. $\dfrac{x^2}{9} + \dfrac{y^2}{4} = 1$

Center: $(0, 0)$

$a = 3, b = 2$

Horizontal major axis

Matches graph (c).

3. $\dfrac{x^2}{4} + \dfrac{y^2}{25} = 1$

Center: $(0, 0)$

$a = 5, b = 2$

Vertical major axis

Matches graph (d).

4. $\dfrac{x^2}{4} + y^2 = 1$

Center: $(0, 0)$

$a = 2, b = 1$

Horizontal major axis

Matches graph (f).

5. $\dfrac{(x - 2)^2}{16} + (y + 1)^2 = 1$

Center: $(2, -1)$

$a = 4, b = 1$

Horizontal major axis

Matches graph (a).

6. $\dfrac{(x + 2)^2}{9} + \dfrac{(y + 2)^2}{4} = 1$

Center: $(-2, -2)$

Horizontal major axis

Matches graph (e).

7. $\dfrac{x^2}{64} + \dfrac{y^2}{9} = 1$

Center: $(0, 0)$

$a = 8, b = 3,$

$c = \sqrt{64 - 9} = \sqrt{55}$

Vertices: $(\pm 8, 0)$

Foci: $\left(\pm\sqrt{55}, 0\right)$

$e = \dfrac{c}{a} = \dfrac{\sqrt{55}}{8}$

8. $\dfrac{x^2}{16} + \dfrac{y^2}{81} = 1$

Center: $(0, 0)$

$a = 9, b = 4,$

$c = \sqrt{81 - 16} = \sqrt{65}$

Vertices: $(0, \pm 9)$

Foci: $\left(0, \pm\sqrt{65}\right)$

$e = \dfrac{c}{a} = \dfrac{\sqrt{65}}{9}$

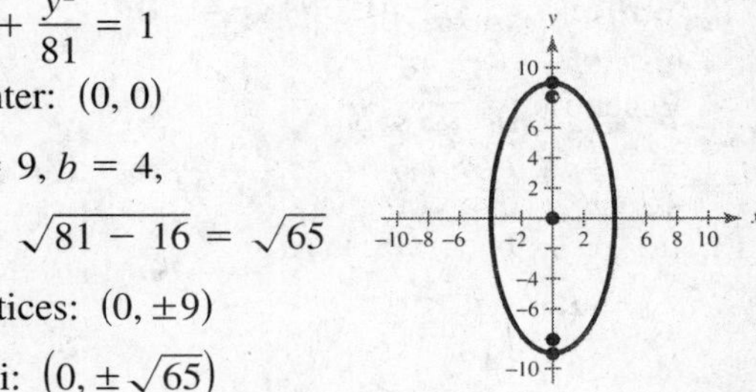

9. $\dfrac{(x - 4)^2}{16} + \dfrac{(y + 1)^2}{25} = 1$

Center: $(4, -1)$

$a = 5, b = 4, c = 3$

Vertices: $(4, -1 \pm 5)$; $(4, -6), (4, 4)$

Foci: $(4, -1 \pm 3)$; $(4, -4), (4, 2)$

$e = \dfrac{c}{a} = \dfrac{3}{5}$

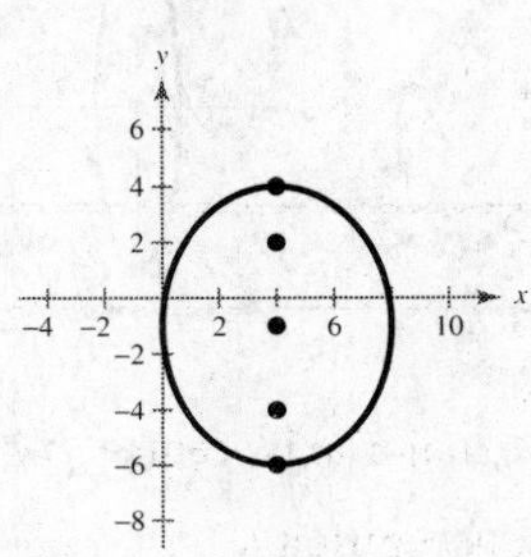

10. $\dfrac{(x + 3)^2}{12} + \dfrac{(y - 2)^2}{16} = 1$

Center: $(-3, 2)$

$a = 4, b = 2\sqrt{3}, c = \sqrt{16 - 12} = 2$

Foci: $(-3, 2 \pm 2)$; $(-3, 0), (-3, 4)$

Vertices: $(-3, 2 \pm 4)$; $(-3, -2), (-3, 6)$

$e = \dfrac{c}{a} = \dfrac{2}{4} = \dfrac{1}{2}$

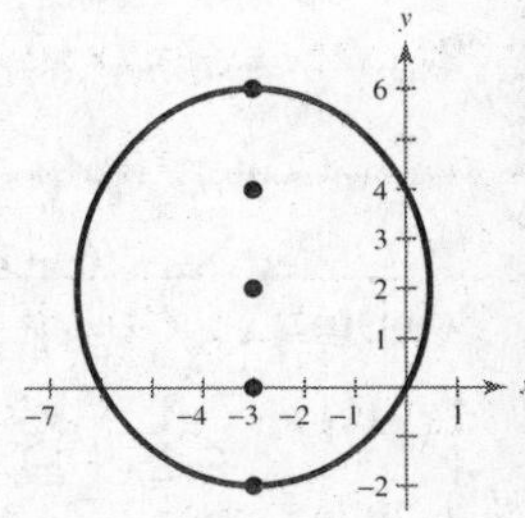

11. $\dfrac{(x + 5)^2}{9/4} + (y - 1)^2 = 1$

Center: $(-5, 1)$

$a = \dfrac{3}{2}, b = 1, c = \sqrt{\dfrac{9}{4} - 1} = \dfrac{\sqrt{5}}{2}$

Foci: $\left(-5 + \dfrac{\sqrt{5}}{2}, 1\right), \left(-5 - \dfrac{\sqrt{5}}{2}, 1\right)$

Vertices: $\left(-5 + \dfrac{3}{2}, 1\right) = \left(-\dfrac{7}{2}, 1\right), \left(-5 - \dfrac{3}{2}, 1\right) = \left(-\dfrac{13}{2}, 1\right)$

$e = \dfrac{\sqrt{5}/2}{3/2} = \dfrac{\sqrt{5}}{3}$

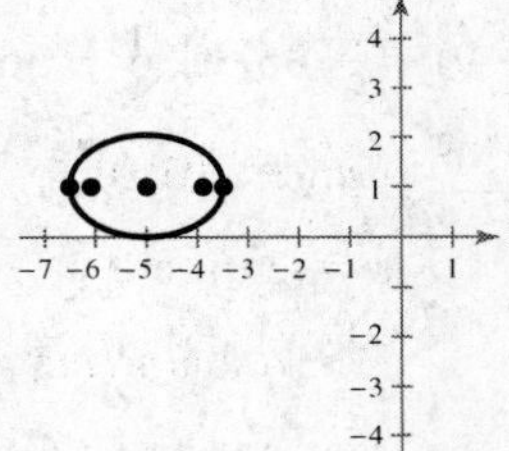

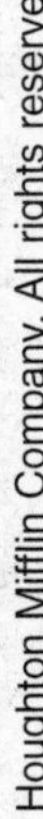

12. $(x+2)^2 + \dfrac{(y+4)^2}{1/4} = 1$

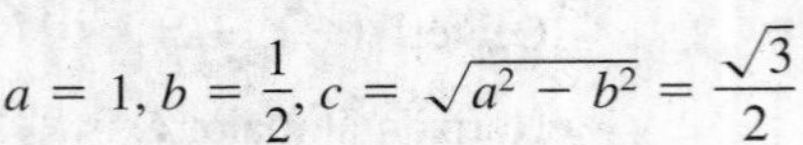

$a = 1, b = \dfrac{1}{2}, c = \sqrt{a^2 - b^2} = \dfrac{\sqrt{3}}{2}$

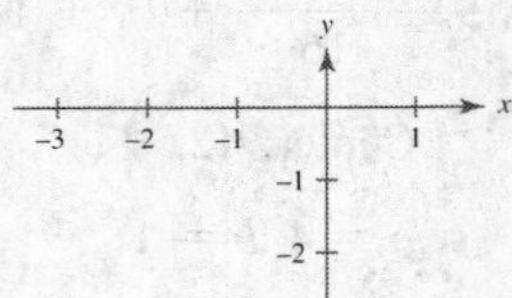

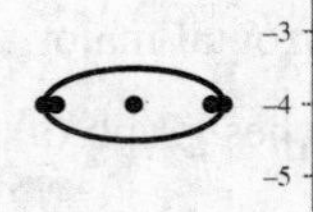

Center: $(-2, -4)$

Foci: $\left(-2 + \dfrac{\sqrt{3}}{2}, -4\right), \left(-2 - \dfrac{\sqrt{3}}{2}, -4\right)$

Vertices: $(-3, -4), (-1, -4)$

Eccentricity: $\dfrac{\sqrt{3}}{2}$

13. (a) $x^2 + 9y^2 = 36$

$\dfrac{x^2}{36} + \dfrac{y^2}{4} = 1$

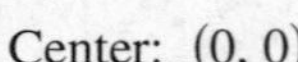

(b) $a = 6, b = 2, c = \sqrt{36 - 4} = \sqrt{32} = 4\sqrt{2}$

Center: $(0, 0)$

Vertices: $(\pm 6, 0)$

Foci: $(\pm 4\sqrt{2}, 0)$

$e = \dfrac{c}{a} = \dfrac{4\sqrt{2}}{6} = \dfrac{2\sqrt{2}}{3}$

(c)

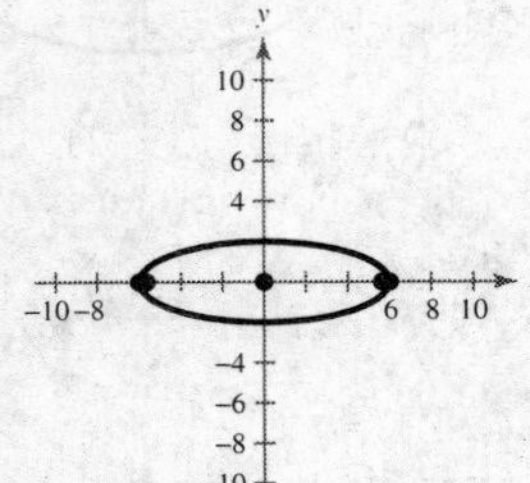

14. (a) $16x^2 + y^2 = 16$

$x^2 + \dfrac{y^2}{16} = 1$

(b) $a = 4, b = 1, c = \sqrt{16 - 1} = \sqrt{15}$

Center: $(0, 0)$

Vertices: $(0, \pm 4)$

Foci: $(0, \pm\sqrt{15})$

$e = \dfrac{c}{a} = \dfrac{\sqrt{15}}{4}$

(c)

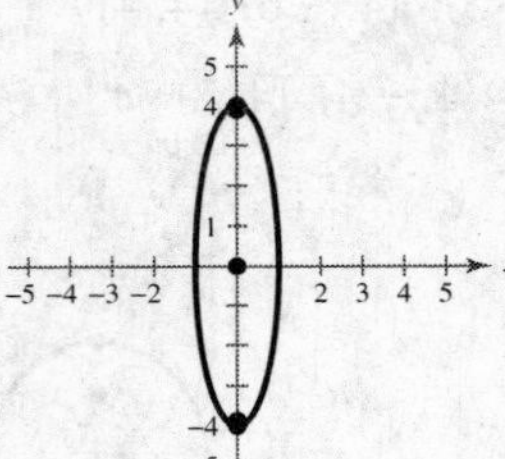

15. (a) $9x^2 + 4y^2 + 36x - 24y + 36 = 0$

$9(x^2 + 4x + 4) + 4(y^2 - 6y + 9) = -36 + 36 + 36$

$\dfrac{(x+2)^2}{4} + \dfrac{(y-3)^2}{9} = 1$

(b) $a = 3, b = 2, c = \sqrt{5}$

Center: $(-2, 3)$

Foci: $(-2, 3 \pm \sqrt{5})$

Vertices: $(-2, 6), (-2, 0)$

$e = \dfrac{\sqrt{5}}{3}$

(c)

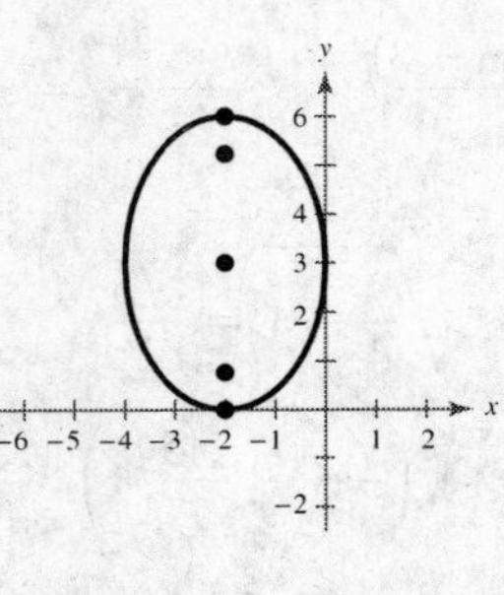

16. (a) $9(x^2 - 6x + 9) + 4(y^2 + 10y + 25) = -37 + 81 + 100$

$$9(x - 3)^2 + 4(y + 5)^2 = 144$$

$$\frac{(x - 3)^2}{16} + \frac{(y + 5)^2}{36} = 1$$

(b) $a = 6, b = 4, c = \sqrt{20} = 2\sqrt{5}$

Center: $(3, -5)$

Foci: $\left(3, -5 \pm 2\sqrt{5}\right)$

Vertices: $(3, -5 \pm 6)$; $(3, 1)$, $(3, -11)$

$e = \dfrac{2\sqrt{5}}{6} = \dfrac{\sqrt{5}}{3}$

(c)

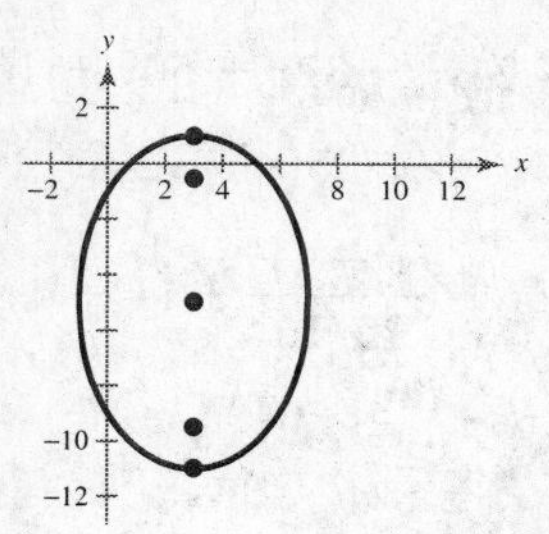

17. (a) $6x^2 + 2y^2 + 18x - 10y + 2 = 0$

$$6\left(x^2 + 3x + \frac{9}{4}\right) + 2\left(y^2 - 5y + \frac{25}{4}\right) = -2 + \frac{27}{2} + \frac{25}{2}$$

$$6\left(x + \frac{3}{2}\right)^2 + 2\left(y - \frac{5}{2}\right)^2 = 24$$

$$\frac{\left(x + \frac{3}{2}\right)^2}{4} + \frac{\left(y - \frac{5}{2}\right)^2}{12} = 1$$

(b) $a = 2\sqrt{3}, b = 2, c = 2\sqrt{2}$

Center: $\left(-\dfrac{3}{2}, \dfrac{5}{2}\right)$

Foci: $\left(-\dfrac{3}{2}, \dfrac{5}{2} \pm 2\sqrt{2}\right)$

Vertices: $\left(-\dfrac{3}{2}, \dfrac{5}{2} \pm 2\sqrt{3}\right)$

$e = \dfrac{\sqrt{2}}{\sqrt{3}} = \dfrac{\sqrt{6}}{3}$

(c)

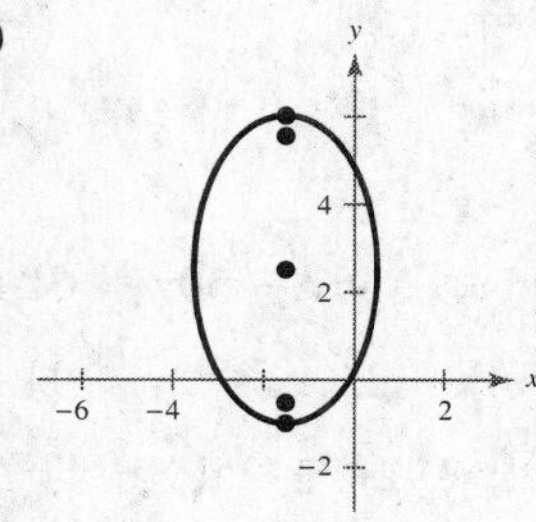

18. (a) $(x^2 - 6x + 9) + 4\left(y^2 + 5y + \dfrac{25}{4}\right) = 2 + 9 + 25$

$$(x - 3)^2 + 4\left(y + \frac{5}{2}\right)^2 = 36$$

$$\frac{(x - 3)^2}{36} + \frac{\left(y + \frac{5}{2}\right)^2}{9} = 1$$

(b) $a = 6, b = 3, c = \sqrt{36 - 9} = \sqrt{27} = 3\sqrt{3}$

Center: $\left(3, -\dfrac{5}{2}\right)$

Foci: $\left(3 \pm 3\sqrt{3}, -\dfrac{5}{2}\right)$

Vertices: $\left(9, -\dfrac{5}{2}\right), \left(-3, -\dfrac{5}{2}\right)$

$e = \dfrac{\sqrt{3}}{2}$

(c)

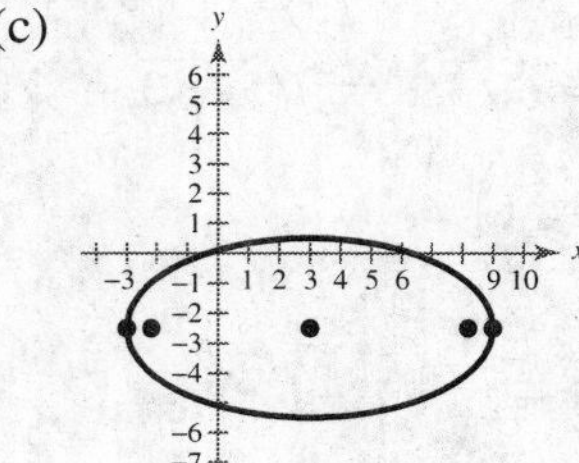

19. (a)
$$16x^2 + 25y^2 - 32x + 50y + 16 = 0$$
$$16(x^2 - 2x + 1) + 25(y^2 + 2y + 1) = -16 + 16 + 25$$
$$\frac{(x-1)^2}{25/16} + (y+1)^2 = 1$$

(b) $a = \frac{5}{4}, b = 1, c = \frac{3}{4}$

Center: $(1, -1)$

Foci: $\left(\frac{7}{4}, -1\right), \left(\frac{1}{4}, -1\right)$

Vertices: $\left(\frac{9}{4}, -1\right), \left(-\frac{1}{4}, -1\right)$

$e = \frac{3}{5}$

(c)

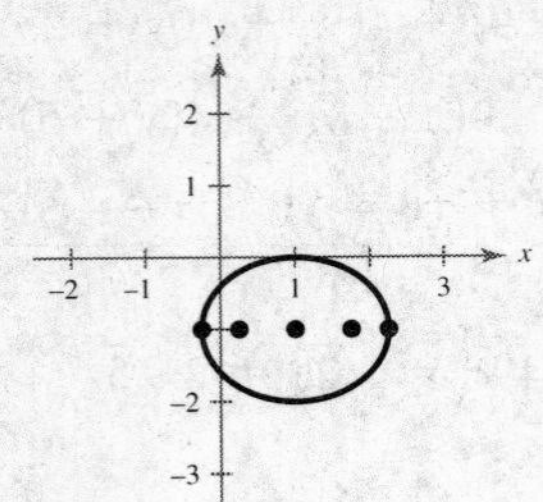

20. (a)
$$9x^2 + 25y^2 - 36x - 50y + 61 = 0$$
$$9(x^2 - 4x + 4) + 25(y^2 - 2y + 1) = -61 + 36 + 25$$
$$9(x-2)^2 + 25(y-1)^2 = 0$$

(b) Degenerate ellipse with center $(2, 1)$ as the only point

(c)

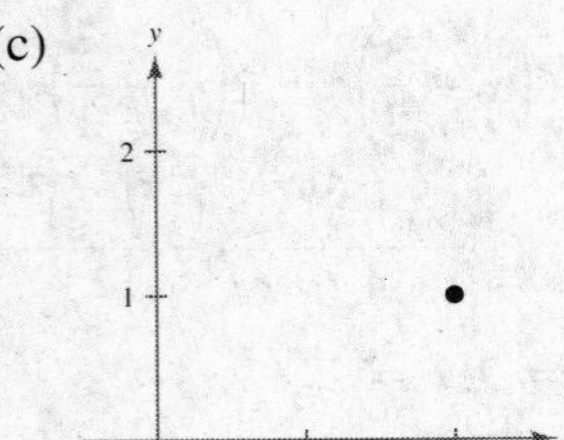

21. (a)

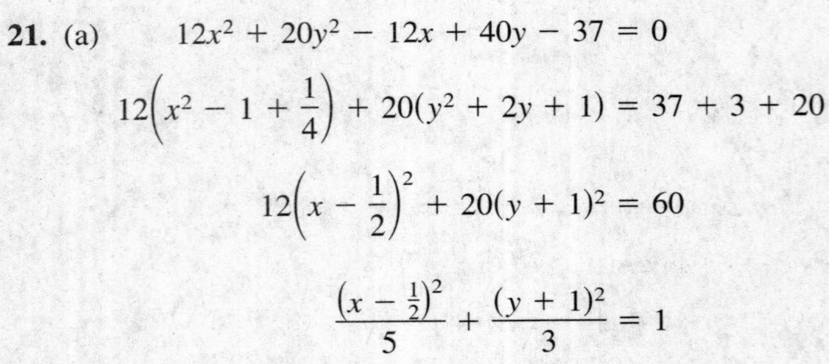

$$12x^2 + 20y^2 - 12x + 40y - 37 = 0$$
$$12\left(x^2 - 1 + \frac{1}{4}\right) + 20(y^2 + 2y + 1) = 37 + 3 + 20$$
$$12\left(x - \frac{1}{2}\right)^2 + 20(y+1)^2 = 60$$
$$\frac{\left(x - \frac{1}{2}\right)^2}{5} + \frac{(y+1)^2}{3} = 1$$

(b) $a = \sqrt{5}, b = \sqrt{3}, c = \sqrt{5 - 3} = \sqrt{2}$

Center: $\left(\frac{1}{2}, -1\right)$

Vertices: $\left(\frac{1}{2} \pm \sqrt{5}, -1\right)$

Foci: $\left(\frac{1}{2} \pm \sqrt{2}, -1\right)$

Eccentricity: $\frac{c}{a} = \frac{\sqrt{2}}{\sqrt{5}} = \frac{\sqrt{10}}{5}$

(c)

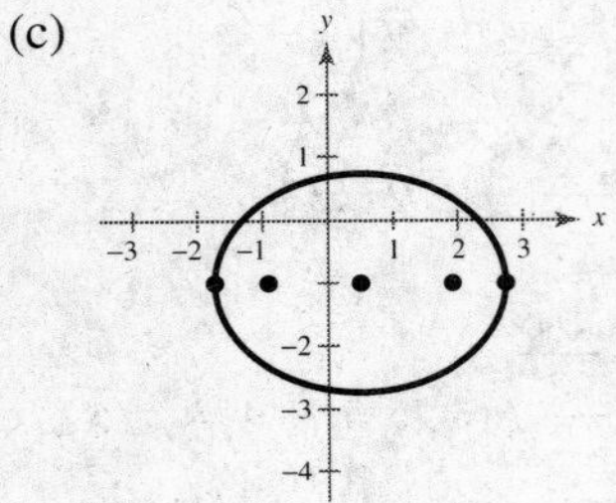

22. (a) $$36x^2 + 9y^2 + 48x - 36y + 43 = 0$$

$$36\left(x^2 + \frac{4}{3}x + \frac{4}{9}\right) + 9(y^2 - 4y + 4) = -43 + 16 + 36$$

$$36\left(x + \frac{2}{3}\right)^2 + 9(y - 2)^2 = 9$$

$$\frac{\left(x + \frac{2}{3}\right)^2}{\frac{1}{4}} + \frac{(y - 2)^2}{1} = 1$$

(b) $a = 1, b = \frac{1}{2}, c = \sqrt{1 - \frac{1}{4}} = \frac{\sqrt{3}}{2}$

Center: $\left(-\frac{2}{3}, 2\right)$

Vertices: $\left(-\frac{2}{3}, 2 \pm 1\right) = \left(-\frac{2}{3}, 1\right), \left(-\frac{2}{3}, 3\right)$

Foci: $\left(-\frac{2}{3}, 2 \pm \frac{\sqrt{3}}{2}\right)$

Eccentricity: $\frac{c}{a} = \frac{\sqrt{3}}{2}$

(c)

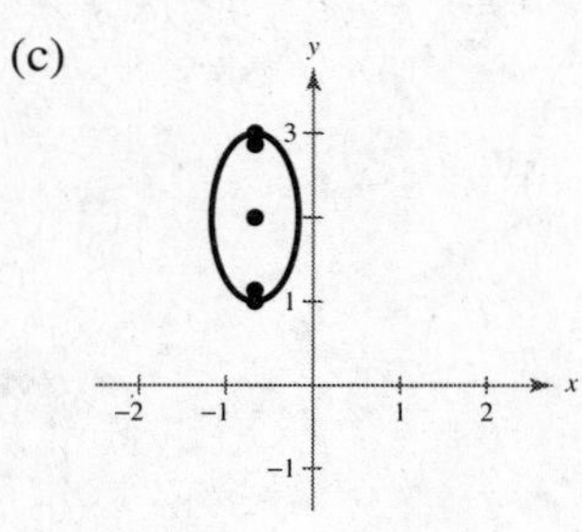

23. Center: $(0, 0)$

$a = 4, b = 2$

Vertical major axis

$$\frac{x^2}{4} + \frac{y^2}{16} = 1$$

24. Vertices: $(\pm 2, 0) \Rightarrow a = 2$

Endpoints of minor axis: $\left(0, \pm\frac{3}{2}\right) \Rightarrow b = \frac{3}{2}$

$$\frac{x^2}{a^2} + \frac{y^2}{b^2} = 1$$

$$\frac{x^2}{2^2} + \frac{y^2}{(3/2)^2} = 1$$

$$\frac{x^2}{4} + \frac{4y^2}{9} = 1$$

25. Center: $(0, 0)$

$a = 3, c = 2 \Rightarrow b = \sqrt{9 - 4} = \sqrt{5}$

Horizontal major axis

$$\frac{x^2}{9} + \frac{y^2}{5} = 1$$

26. Vertices: $(0, \pm 8) \Rightarrow a = 8$

Foci: $(0, \pm 4) \Rightarrow c = 4$

$b^2 = a^2 - c^2 = 64 - 16 = 48$

Center: $(0, 0) = (h, k)$

$$\frac{(y - k)^2}{a^2} + \frac{(x - h)^2}{b^2} = 1$$

$$\frac{y^2}{64} + \frac{x^2}{48} = 1$$

27. Center: $(0, 0)$

$c = 3$

$a = 4 \Rightarrow b = \sqrt{16 - 9} = \sqrt{7}$

Horizontal major axis

$$\frac{x^2}{16} + \frac{y^2}{7} = 1$$

28. Center: $(0, 0)$

$c = 2$

$a = 6 \Rightarrow b = \sqrt{36 - 4} = \sqrt{32} = 4\sqrt{2}$

Horizontal major axis

$$\frac{x^2}{36} + \frac{y^2}{32} = 1$$

29. Vertices: $(0, \pm 5) \implies a = 5$

Center: $(0, 0)$

Vertical major axis

$$\frac{(x-h)^2}{b^2} + \frac{(y-k)^2}{a^2} = 1$$

$$\frac{x^2}{b^2} + \frac{y^2}{25} = 1$$

Point: $(4, 2)$

$$\frac{4^2}{b^2} + \frac{2^2}{25} = 1$$

$$\frac{16}{b^2} = 1 - \frac{4}{25} = \frac{21}{25}$$

$$400 = 21b^2$$

$$\frac{400}{21} = b^2$$

$$\frac{x^2}{400/21} + \frac{y^2}{25} = 1$$

$$\frac{21x^2}{400} + \frac{y^2}{25} = 1$$

30. Vertical major axis

Passes through: $(0, 4)$ and $(2, 0)$

$a = 4, b = 2$

$$\frac{x^2}{b^2} + \frac{y^2}{a^2} = 1$$

$$\frac{x^2}{4} + \frac{y^2}{16} = 1$$

31. Center: $(2, 3)$

$a = 3, b = 1$

Vertical major axis

$$\frac{(x-h)^2}{b^2} + \frac{(y-k)^2}{a^2} = 1$$

$$\frac{(x-2)^2}{1} + \frac{(y-3)^2}{9} = 1$$

32. Vertices: $(0, -1), (4, -1) \implies a = 2$

Center: $(2, -1) \implies h = 2, k = -1$

Endpoints of minor axis: $(2, 0), (2, -2) \implies b = 1$

$$\frac{(x-h)^2}{a^2} + \frac{(y-k)^2}{b^2} = 1$$

$$\frac{(x-2)^2}{4} + \frac{(y+1)^2}{1} = 1$$

33. Center: $(4, 2)$

$a = 4, b = 1 \implies c = \sqrt{16-1} = \sqrt{15}$

Horizontal major axis

$$\frac{(x-4)^2}{16} + \frac{(y-2)^2}{1} = 1$$

34. Center: $(2, 0)$

$c = 2, a = 3 \implies b^2 = a^2 - c^2 = 9 - 4 = 5$

Horizontal major axis

$$\frac{(x-2)^2}{9} + \frac{y^2}{5} = 1$$

35. Center: $(0, 4)$

$c = 4, a = 18 \implies b^2 = a^2 - c^2 = 324 - 16 = 308$

Vertical major axis

$$\frac{x^2}{308} + \frac{(y-4)^2}{324} = 1$$

36. Center: $(2, -1) \Rightarrow h = 2, k = -1$

Vertex: $\left(2, \frac{1}{2}\right) \Rightarrow a = \frac{3}{2}$

Minor axis length: $2 \Rightarrow b = 1$

$$\frac{(x-h)^2}{b^2} + \frac{(y-k)^2}{a^2} = 1$$

$$\frac{(x-2)^2}{1} + \frac{(y+1)^2}{(3/2)^2} = 1$$

$$(x-2)^2 + \frac{4(y+1)^2}{9} = 1$$

37. Vertices: $(3, 1), (3, 9) \Rightarrow a = 4$

Center: $(3, 5)$

Minor axis of length $6 \Rightarrow b = 3$

Vertical major axis

$$\frac{(x-h)^2}{b^2} + \frac{(y-k)^2}{a^2} = 1$$

$$\frac{(x-3)^2}{9} + \frac{(y-5)^2}{16} = 1$$

38. Center: $(3, 2) = (h, k)$

$a = 3c$

Foci: $(1, 2), (5, 2) \Rightarrow c = 2, a = 6$

$b^2 = a^2 - c^2 = 36 - 4 = 32$

$$\frac{(x-h)^2}{a^2} + \frac{(y-k)^2}{b^2} = 1$$

$$\frac{(x-3)^2}{36} + \frac{(y-2)^2}{32} = 1$$

39. Center: $(0, 4)$

Vertices: $(-4, 4), (4, 4) \Rightarrow a = 4$

$a = 2c \Rightarrow 4 = 2c \Rightarrow c = 2$

$2^2 = 4^2 - b^2 \Rightarrow b^2 = 12$

Horizontal major axis

$$\frac{(x-h)^2}{a^2} + \frac{(y-k)^2}{b^2} = 1$$

$$\frac{x^2}{16} + \frac{(y-4)^2}{12} = 1$$

40. Vertices:
$(5, 0), (5, 12) \Rightarrow a = 6$

Endpoints of minor axis:
$(0, 6), (10, 6) \Rightarrow b = 5$

Center: $(5, 6) \Rightarrow h = 5, k = 6$

$$\frac{(x-h)^2}{b^2} + \frac{(y-k)^2}{a^2} = 1$$

$$\frac{(x-5)^2}{25} + \frac{(y-6)^2}{36} = 1$$

41. $\frac{x^2}{4} + \frac{y^2}{9} = 1$

$a = 3, b = 2,$

$c = \sqrt{9-4} = \sqrt{5}$

$e = \frac{c}{a} = \frac{\sqrt{5}}{3}$

42. $\frac{x^2}{25} + \frac{y^2}{36} = 1$

$a = 6, b = 5,$

$c = \sqrt{36-25} = \sqrt{11}$

$e = \frac{c}{a} = \frac{\sqrt{11}}{6}$

43.
$$x^2 + 9y^2 - 10x + 36y + 52 = 0$$

$$(x^2 - 10x + 25) + 9(y^2 + 4y + 4) = -52 + 25 + 36$$

$$(x-5)^2 + 9(y+2)^2 = 9$$

$$\frac{(x-5)^2}{9} + \frac{(y+2)^2}{1} = 1$$

$a = 3, b = 1, c = \sqrt{9-1} = 2\sqrt{2}$

$e = \frac{c}{a} = \frac{2\sqrt{2}}{3}$

44. $$4x^2 + 3y^2 - 8x + 18y + 19 = 0$$

$$4(x^2 - 2x + 1) + 3(y^2 + 6y + 9) = -19 + 4 + 27$$

$$4(x - 1)^2 + 3(y + 3)^2 = 12$$

$$\frac{(x-1)^2}{3} + \frac{(y+3)^2}{4} = 1$$

$a = 2, b = \sqrt{3}, c = \sqrt{4 - 3} = 1$

$e = \dfrac{c}{a} = \dfrac{1}{2}$

45. Vertices: $(\pm 5, 0) \implies a = 5$

Eccentricity: $\dfrac{4}{5} = \dfrac{c}{a} \implies c = \dfrac{4}{5}a = 4$

$b^2 = a^2 - c^2 = 25 - 16 = 9$

Center: $(0, 0)$

Horizontal major axis

$$\frac{x^2}{25} + \frac{y^2}{9} = 1$$

46. Vertices: $(0, \pm 8) \implies a = 8, h = 0, k = 0$

Eccentricity: $e = \dfrac{1}{2} = \dfrac{c}{a}$

$$\frac{1}{2} = \frac{c}{8}$$

$$c = 4$$

$b^2 = a^2 - c^2 = 64 - 16 = 48$

$$\frac{x^2}{b^2} + \frac{y^2}{a^2} = 1$$

$$\frac{x^2}{48} + \frac{y^2}{64} = 1$$

47. (a)

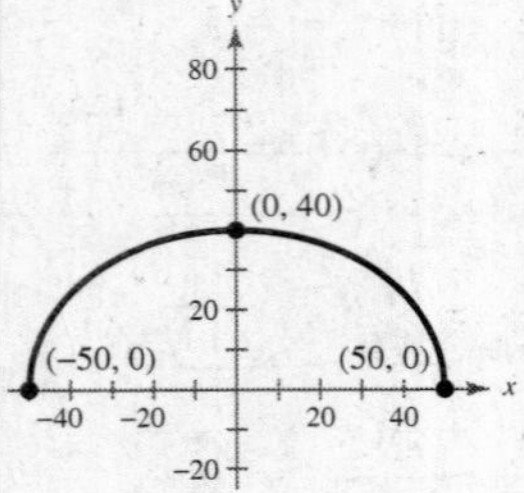

(b) Vertices: $(\pm 50, 0) \implies a = 50$

Height at center: $40 \implies b = 40$

Horizontal major axis

$$\frac{x^2}{a^2} + \frac{y^2}{b^2} = 1$$

$$\frac{x^2}{2500} + \frac{y^2}{1600} = 1, \ y \geq 0$$

(c) For $x = 45$, $\dfrac{45^2}{2500} + \dfrac{y^2}{1600} = 1.$

$$y^2 = 1600\left(1 - \frac{45^2}{2500}\right)$$

$$y^2 = 304$$

$$y \approx 17.44$$

The height five feet from the edge of the tunnel is approximately 17.44 feet.

48. (a)

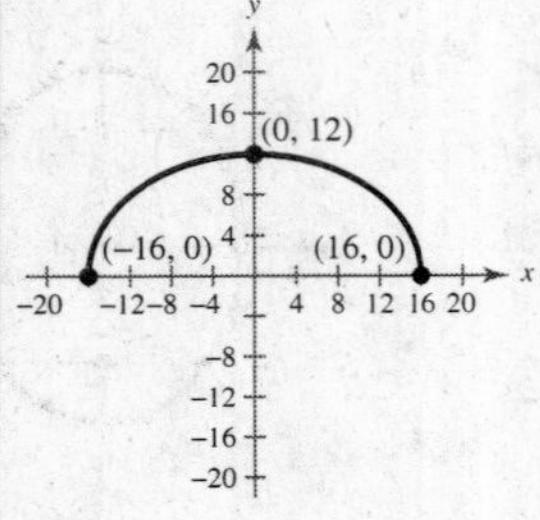

(b) $a = 16, b = 12$

$$\frac{x^2}{256} + \frac{y^2}{144} = 1, \ y \geq 0$$

(c) When $x = 10$,

$$y^2 = 144\sqrt{1 - \frac{10^2}{256}}$$

$$y \approx 9.4 > 9.$$

Hence, the truck will be able to drive through without crossing the center line.

49. Let $\dfrac{x^2}{a^2} + \dfrac{y^2}{b^2} = 1$ be the equation of the ellipse. Then $b = 2$ and $a = 3 \implies c^2 = a^2 - b^2 = 9 - 4 = 5$. Thus, the tacks are placed at $(\pm\sqrt{5}, 0)$. The string has a length of $2a = 6$ feet.

50.

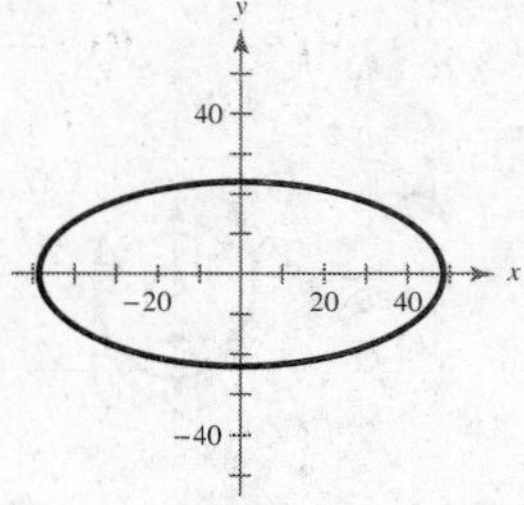

$$\frac{x^2}{(97/2)^2} + \frac{y^2}{23^2} = 1 \quad \left(\text{or } \frac{x^2}{23^2} + \frac{y^2}{(97/2)^2} = 1\right)$$

$$a = \frac{97}{2}, b = 23, c = \sqrt{\left(\frac{97}{2}\right)^2 - (23)^2} \approx 4.7$$

Distance between foci: $2(4.7) \approx 85.4$ feet

51. Area of ellipse = 2(area of circle)

$$\pi ab = 2\pi r^2$$
$$\pi a(10) = 2\pi(10)^2$$
$$\pi a(10) = 200$$
$$a = 20$$

Length of major axis: $2a = 2(20) = 40$ units

52. Center: $(0, 0)$, $e = 0.97$

$2a = 35.88 \implies a = 17.94 \implies a^2 \approx 321.84$

$e = \frac{c}{a} \implies 0.97 = \frac{c}{17.94} \implies c = 17.4018$

$c^2 = a^2 - b^2 \implies b^2 = a^2 - c^2 \approx 19.02$

Ellipse: $\frac{x^2}{321.84} + \frac{y^2}{19.02} = 1$

53. $a + c = 4.08$

$a - c = 0.34$

$2a = 4.42 \implies a = 2.21 \implies c = 1.87$

$b^2 = a^2 - c^2 \implies b^2 = 1.3872$

$$\frac{x^2}{4.8841} + \frac{y^2}{1.3872} = 1$$

54. $a + c = 947 + 6378 = 7325$

$a - c = 228 + 6378 = 6606$

$2a = 13{,}931$

$a = 6965.5$

$c = 7325 - 6965.5$

$= 359.5$

$e = \frac{c}{a} \approx 0.0516$

55. For $\frac{x^2}{a^2} + \frac{y^2}{b^2} = 1$, we have $c^2 = a^2 - b^2$.

When $x = c$,

$$\frac{c^2}{a^2} + \frac{y^2}{b^2} = 1 \implies y^2 = b^2\left(1 - \frac{a^2 - b^2}{a^2}\right)$$
$$\implies y^2 = \frac{b^4}{a^2}$$
$$\implies 2y = \frac{2b^2}{a}.$$

56. $\frac{x^2}{4} + \frac{y^2}{1} = 1$

$a = 2,\ b = 1,\ c = \sqrt{3}$

Points on the ellipse: $(\pm 2, 0), (0, \pm 1)$

Length of latus recta:

$\frac{2b^2}{a} = 1$

Additional points: $\left(\sqrt{3}, \pm\frac{1}{2}\right), \left(-\sqrt{3}, \pm\frac{1}{2}\right)$

57. $\frac{x^2}{9} + \frac{y^2}{16} = 1$

$a = 4, b = 3, c = \sqrt{7}$

Points on the ellipse: $(\pm 3, 0), (0, \pm 4)$

Length of latus recta:

$\frac{2b^2}{a} = \frac{2(3)^2}{4} = \frac{9}{2}$

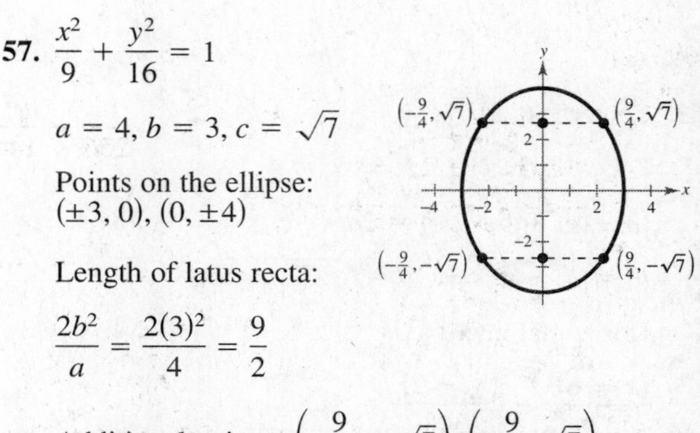

Additional points: $\left(\pm\frac{9}{4}, -\sqrt{7}\right), \left(\pm\frac{9}{4}, \sqrt{7}\right)$

58. $9x^2 + 4y^2 = 36$

$$\frac{x^2}{4} + \frac{y^2}{9} = 1$$

Points on the ellipse: $(\pm 2, 0), (0, \pm 3)$

Length of latus recta:

$$\frac{2b^2}{a} = \frac{2 \cdot 2^2}{3} = \frac{8}{3}$$

Additional points: $\left(\pm\frac{4}{3}, -\sqrt{5}\right), \left(\pm\frac{4}{3}, \sqrt{5}\right)$

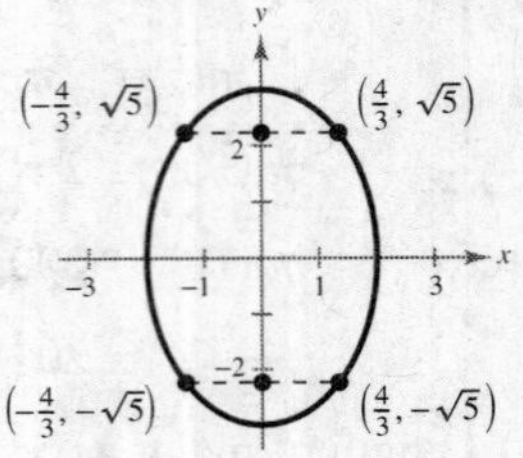

59. $5x^2 + 3y^2 = 15$

$$\frac{x^2}{3} + \frac{y^2}{5} = 1$$

$a = \sqrt{5}, b = \sqrt{3},$

$c = \sqrt{2}$

Points on the ellipse: $(\pm\sqrt{3}, 0), (0, \pm\sqrt{5})$

Length of latus recta: $\frac{2b^2}{a} = \frac{2 \cdot 3}{\sqrt{5}} = \frac{6\sqrt{5}}{5}$

Additional points: $\left(\pm\frac{3\sqrt{5}}{5}, -\sqrt{2}\right), \left(\pm\frac{3\sqrt{5}}{5}, \sqrt{2}\right)$

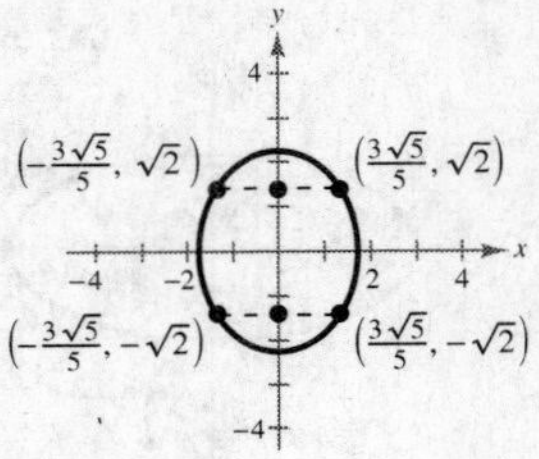

60. Answers will vary.

61. True. If $e \approx 1$ then the ellipse is elongated, not circular.

62. True. The ellipse is inside the circle.

63. (a) The length of the string is $2a$.

(b) The path is an ellipse because the sum of the distances from the two thumbtacks is always the length of the string, that is, it is constant.

64. (a) $a + b = 20 \implies b = 20 - a$

$A = \pi ab = \pi a(20 - a)$

(b) $264 = \pi a(20 - a)$

$\pi a^2 - 20\pi a + 264 = 0$

$a \approx 14$ or $a \approx 6$ by the Quadratic Formula

$b = 6 \qquad b = 14$

Since $a > b$, we choose $a = 14$ and $b = 6$.

$$\frac{x^2}{14^2} + \frac{y^2}{6^2} = 1$$

$$\frac{x^2}{196} + \frac{y^2}{36} = 1$$

(c)

a	8	9	10	11	12	13
A	301.6	311.0	314.2	311.0	301.6	285.9

(d)

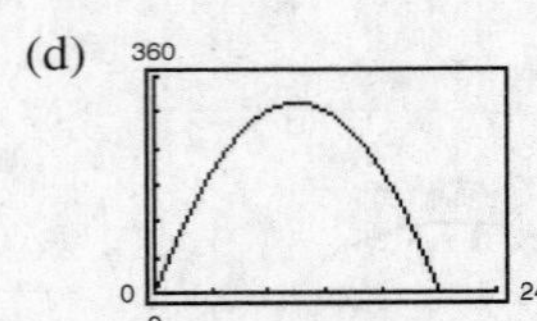

The area is maximum when $a = b = 10$ and it is a circle.

65. Center: $(6, 2)$

Foci: $(2, 2), (10, 2) \implies c = 4$

$(a + c) + (a - c) = 2a = 36 \implies a = 18$

$b^2 = a^2 - b^2 \implies b = \sqrt{18^2 - 16} = \sqrt{308}$

Horizontal major axis

$$\frac{(x - 6)^2}{324} + \frac{(y - 2)^2}{308} = 1$$

66. $\frac{x^2}{a^2} + \frac{y^2}{b^2} = 1$

The sum of the distances from any point on the ellipse to the two foci is constant. Using the vertex $(a, 0)$, you have

$(a + c) + (a - c) = 2a.$

From the figure,

$2\sqrt{b^2 + c^2} = 2a \implies a^2 = b^2 + c^2.$

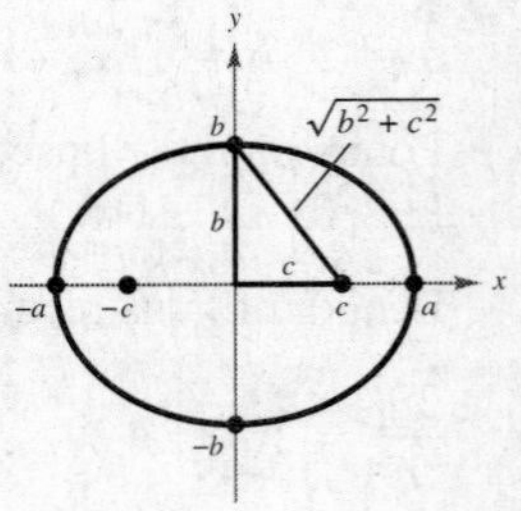

67. Arithmetic: $d = -11$

68. Geometric: $r = \frac{1}{2}$

69. Geometric: $r = 2$

70. Arithmetic: $d = 1$

71. $\sum_{n=0}^{6} 3^n = 1093$

72. $\sum_{n=0}^{6} (-3)^n = 547$

73. $\sum_{n=1}^{10} 4\left(\frac{3}{4}\right)^{n-1} \approx 15.099$

74. $\sum_{n=0}^{10} 5\left(\frac{4}{3}\right)^n \approx 340.155$

Section 9.3 Hyperbolas

- A **hyperbola** is the set of all points (x, y) the difference of whose distances from two distinct fixed points **(foci)** is constant.
- The standard equation of a hyperbola with center (h, k) and transverse and conjugate axes of lengths $2a$ and $2b$ is:

  (a) $\dfrac{(x-h)^2}{a^2} - \dfrac{(y-k)^2}{b^2} = 1$ if the transverse axis is horizontal.

  (b) $\dfrac{(y-k)^2}{a^2} - \dfrac{(x-h)^2}{b^2} = 1$ if the transverse axis is vertical.
- $c^2 = a^2 + b^2$ where c is the distance from the center to a focus.
- The asymptotes of a hyperbola are:

  (a) $y = k \pm \dfrac{b}{a}(x - h)$ if the transverse axis is horizontal.

  (b) $y = k \pm \dfrac{a}{b}(x - h)$ the transverse axis is vertical.
- The eccentricity of a hyperbola is $e = \dfrac{c}{a}$.
- To classify a nondegenerate conic from its general equation $Ax^2 + Cy^2 + Dx + Ey + F = 0$:
  (a) If $A = C$ $(A \neq 0, C \neq 0)$, then it is a circle.
  (b) If $AC = 0$ ($A = 0$ or $C = 0$, but not both), then it is a parabola.
  (c) If $AC > 0$, then it is an ellipse.
  (d) If $AC < 0$, then it is a hyperbola.

Vocabulary Check

1. hyperbola

2. branches

3. transverse axis, center

4. asymptotes

5. $Ax^2 + Cy^2 + Dx + Ey + F = 0$

1. Center: $(0, 0)$

$a = 3, b = 5, c = \sqrt{34}$

Vertical transverse axis

Matches graph (b).

2. Center: $(0, 0)$

$a = 5, b = 3$

Vertical transverse axis

Matches graph (c).

3. Center: $(1, 0)$

$a = 4, b = 2$

Horizontal transverse axis

Matches graph (a).

4. Center: $(-1, 2)$

$a = 4, b = 3$

Horizontal transverse axis

Matches graph (d).

5. $x^2 - y^2 = 1$

$a = 1, b = 1, c = \sqrt{2}$

Center: $(0, 0)$

Vertices: $(\pm 1, 0)$

Foci: $(\pm\sqrt{2}, 0)$

Asymptotes: $y = \pm x$

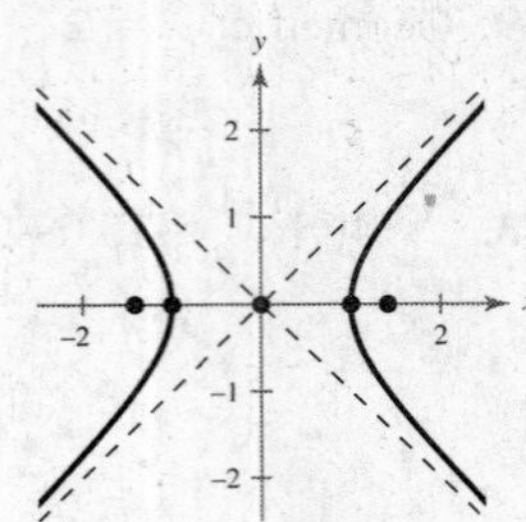

6. $\dfrac{x^2}{9} - \dfrac{y^2}{25} = 1$

Center: $(0, 0)$

$a = 3, b = 5,$

$c = \sqrt{3^2 + 5^2} = \sqrt{34}$

Vertices: $(\pm 3, 0)$

Foci: $(\pm\sqrt{34}, 0)$

Asymptotes: $y = \pm\dfrac{b}{a}x = \pm\dfrac{5}{3}x$

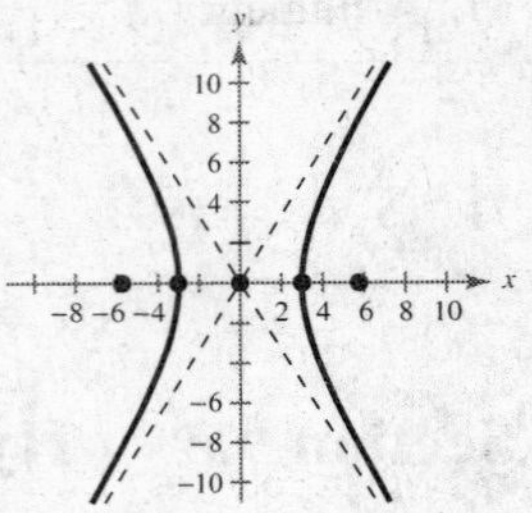

7. $\dfrac{y^2}{1} - \dfrac{x^2}{4} = 1$

$a = 1, b = 2, c = \sqrt{5}$

Center: $(0, 0)$

Vertices: $(0, \pm 1)$

Foci: $(0, \pm\sqrt{5})$

Asymptotes: $y = \pm\dfrac{1}{2}x$

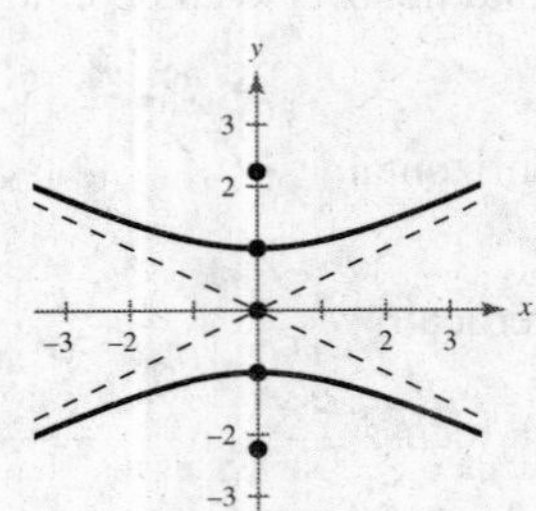

8. $\dfrac{y^2}{9} - \dfrac{x^2}{1} = 1$

$a = 3, b = 1,$

$c = \sqrt{3^2 + 1^2} = \sqrt{10}$

Center: $(0, 0)$

Vertices: $(0, \pm 3)$

Foci: $(0, \pm\sqrt{10})$

Asymptotes: $y = \pm 3x$

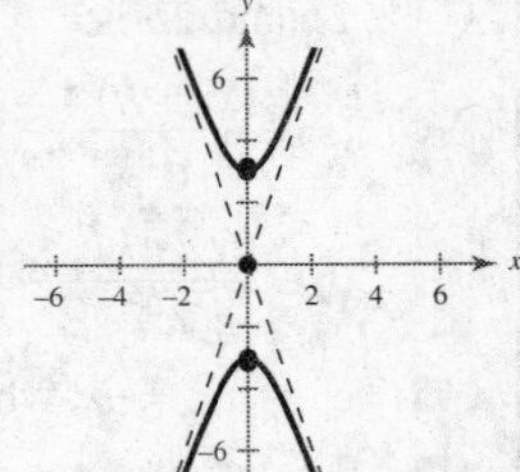

9. $\dfrac{y^2}{25} - \dfrac{x^2}{81} = 1$

$a = 5, b = 9, c = \sqrt{a^2 + b^2} = \sqrt{106}$

Center: $(0, 0)$

Vertices: $(0, \pm 5)$

Foci: $(0, \pm\sqrt{106})$

Asymptotes:

$y = \pm\dfrac{a}{b}x = \pm\dfrac{5}{9}x$

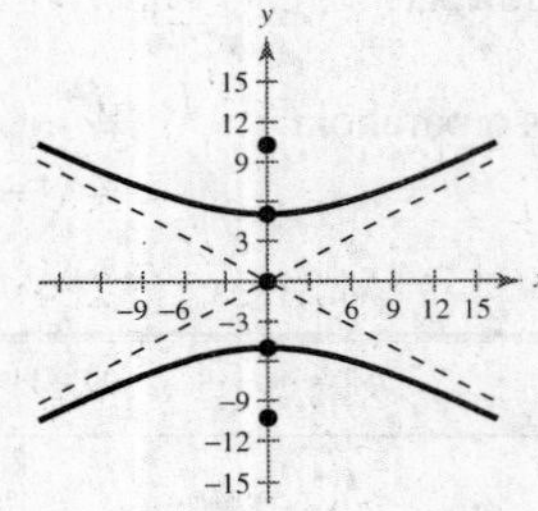

10. $\dfrac{x^2}{36} - \dfrac{y^2}{4} = 1$

$a = 6, b = 2,$

$c = \sqrt{36 + 4} = 2\sqrt{10}$

Center: $(0, 0)$

Vertices: $(\pm 6, 0)$

Foci: $(\pm 2\sqrt{10}, 0)$

Asymptotes: $y = \pm\dfrac{1}{3}x$

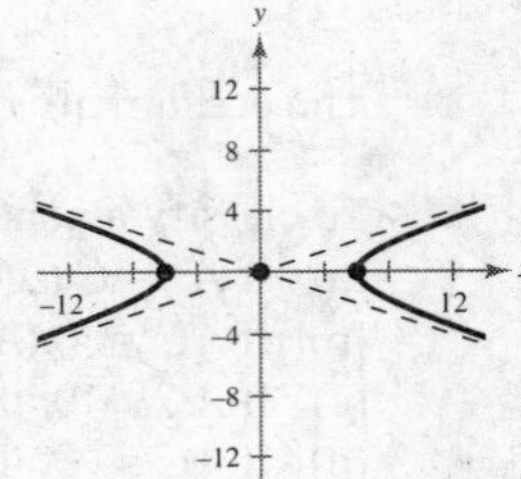

11. $\dfrac{(x - 1)^2}{4} - \dfrac{(y + 2)^2}{1} = 1$

$a = 2, b = 1, c = \sqrt{5}$

Center: $(1, -2)$

Vertices:

$(-1, -2), (3, -2)$

Foci: $(1 \pm \sqrt{5}, -2)$

Asymptotes: $y = -2 \pm \dfrac{1}{2}(x - 1)$

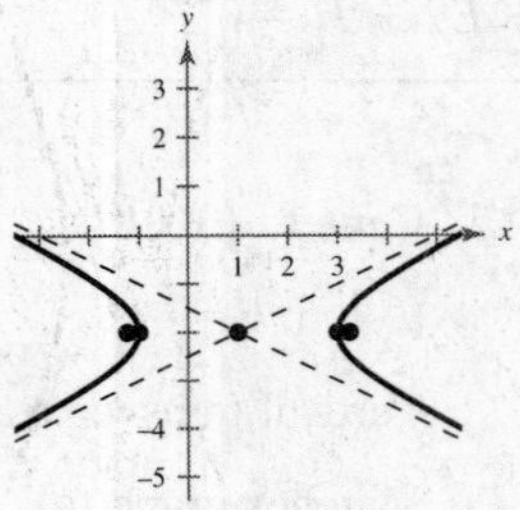

12. $\dfrac{(x + 3)^2}{144} - \dfrac{(y - 2)^2}{25} = 1$

Center: $(-3, 2)$

$a = 12, b = 5, c = 13$

Vertices: $(-15, 2), (9, 2)$

Foci: $(-16, 2), (10, 2)$

Asymptotes:

$y = 2 \pm \dfrac{5}{12}(x + 3)$

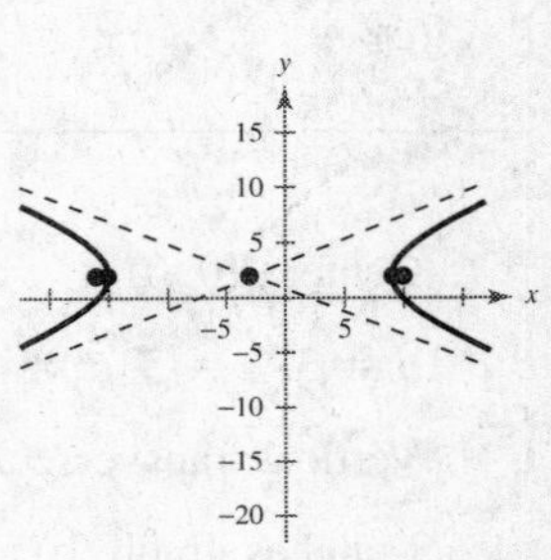

13. $\dfrac{(y+5)^2}{1/9} - \dfrac{(x-1)^2}{1/4} = 1$

$a = \dfrac{1}{3}, b = \dfrac{1}{2}, c = \sqrt{\dfrac{1}{9} + \dfrac{1}{4}} = \dfrac{\sqrt{13}}{6}$

Center: $(1, -5)$

Vertices: $\left(1, -5 \pm \dfrac{1}{3}\right)$: $\left(1, -\dfrac{16}{3}\right), \left(1, -\dfrac{14}{3}\right)$

Foci: $\left(1, -5 \pm \dfrac{\sqrt{13}}{6}\right)$

Asymptotes: $y = k \pm \dfrac{a}{b}(x - h)$

$$y = -5 \pm \frac{2}{3}(x - 1)$$

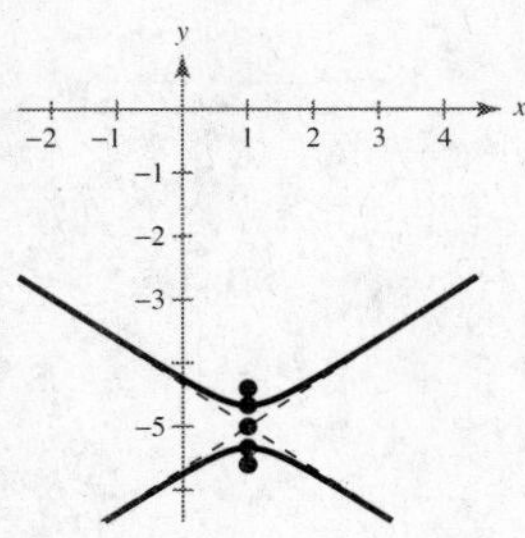

14. $\dfrac{(y-1)^2}{1/4} - \dfrac{(x+3)^2}{1/16} = 1$

Center: $(-3, 1)$

$a = \dfrac{1}{2}, b = \dfrac{1}{4}, c = \sqrt{\dfrac{1}{4} + \dfrac{1}{16}} = \dfrac{\sqrt{5}}{4}$

Vertices: $\left(-3, \dfrac{1}{2}\right), \left(-3, \dfrac{3}{2}\right)$

Foci: $\left(-3, 1 \pm \dfrac{\sqrt{5}}{4}\right)$

Asymptotes: $y = 1 \pm \dfrac{1/2}{1/4}(x + 3) = 1 \pm 2(x + 3)$

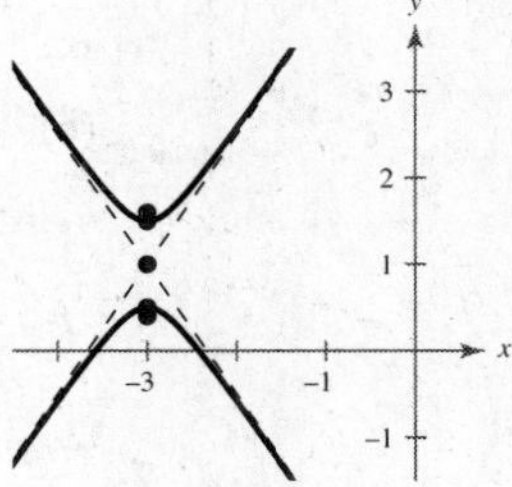

15. (a) $4x^2 - 9y^2 = 36$

$\dfrac{x^2}{9} - \dfrac{y^2}{4} = 1$

(b) Center: $(0, 0)$

$a = 3, b = 2, c = \sqrt{9 + 4} = \sqrt{13}$

Vertices: $(\pm 3, 0)$

Foci: $(\pm\sqrt{13}, 0)$

Asymptotes: $y = \pm\dfrac{b}{a}x = \pm\dfrac{2}{3}x$

(c)

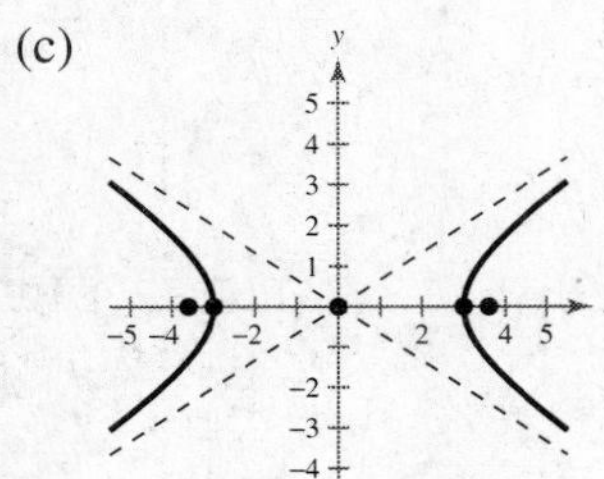

16. (a) $25x^2 - 4y^2 = 100$

$\dfrac{x^2}{4} - \dfrac{y^2}{25} = 1$

(b) Center: $(0, 0)$

$a = 2, b = 5, c = \sqrt{4 + 25} = \sqrt{29}$

Vertices: $(\pm 2, 0)$

Foci: $(\pm\sqrt{29}, 0)$

Asymptotes: $y = \pm\dfrac{b}{a}x = \pm\dfrac{5}{2}x$

(c)

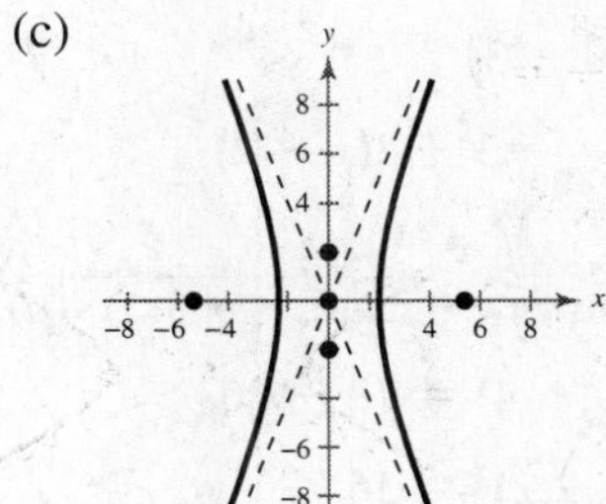

17. (a) $2x^2 - 3y^2 = 6$

$$\frac{x^2}{3} - \frac{y^2}{2} = 1$$

(b) $a = \sqrt{3}, b = \sqrt{2}, c = \sqrt{5}$

Center: $(0, 0)$

Vertices: $(\pm\sqrt{3}, 0)$

Foci: $(\pm\sqrt{5}, 0)$

Asymptotes: $y = \pm\sqrt{\frac{2}{3}}x$

$$= \pm\frac{\sqrt{6}}{3}x$$

(c) To use a graphing calculator, solve first for y.

$$y^2 = \frac{2x^2 - 6}{3}$$

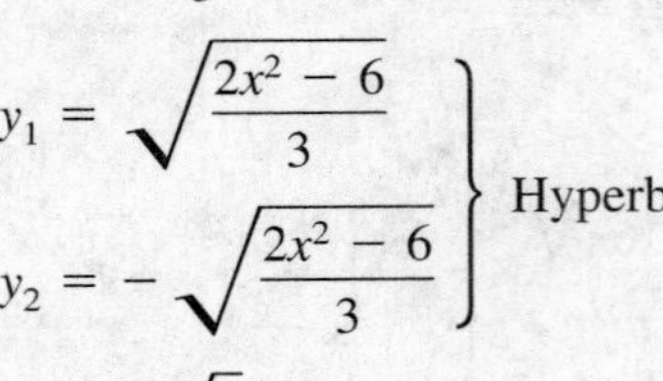

$$y_1 = \sqrt{\frac{2x^2 - 6}{3}}$$
$$y_2 = -\sqrt{\frac{2x^2 - 6}{3}}$$
Hyperbola

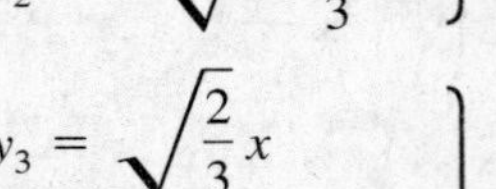

$$y_3 = \sqrt{\frac{2}{3}}x$$
$$y_4 = -\sqrt{\frac{2}{3}}x$$
Asymptotes

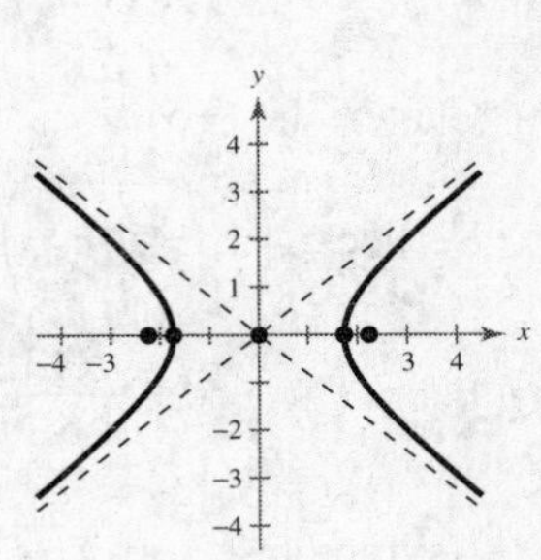

18. (a) $6y^2 - 3x^2 = 18$

$$\frac{y^2}{3} - \frac{x^2}{6} = 1$$

(b) $a = \sqrt{3}, b = \sqrt{6}, c = 3$

Center: $(0, 0)$

Vertices: $(0, \pm\sqrt{3})$

Foci: $(0, \pm 3)$

Asymptotes: $y = \pm\frac{\sqrt{3}}{\sqrt{6}}x = \pm\frac{\sqrt{2}}{2}x$

(c)

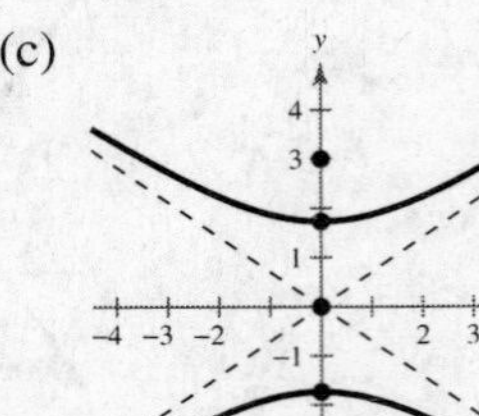

19. (a) $9x^2 - y^2 - 36x - 6y + 18 = 0$

$$9(x^2 - 4x + 4) - (y^2 + 6y + 9) = -18 + 36 - 9$$

$$\frac{(x-2)^2}{1} - \frac{(y+3)^2}{9} = 1$$

(b) $a = 1, b = 3, c = \sqrt{10}$

Center: $(2, -3)$

Vertices: $(1, -3), (3, -3)$

Foci: $(2 \pm \sqrt{10}, -3)$

Asymptotes: $y = -3 \pm 3(x - 2)$

(c)

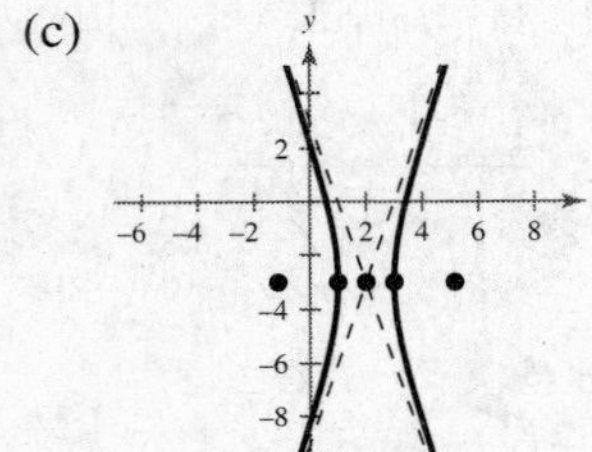

20. (a) $x^2 - 9y^2 + 36y - 72 = 0$

$$x^2 - 9(y^2 - 4y + 4) = 72 - 36$$

$$x^2 - 9(y-2)^2 = 36$$

$$\frac{x^2}{36} - \frac{(y-2)^2}{4} = 1$$

(b) $a = 6, b = 2,$

$c = \sqrt{36 + 4} = 2\sqrt{10}$

Center: $(0, 2)$

Vertices: $(\pm 6, 2)$

Foci: $(\pm 2\sqrt{10}, 2)$

Asymptotes: $y = 2 \pm \frac{1}{3}x$

(c)

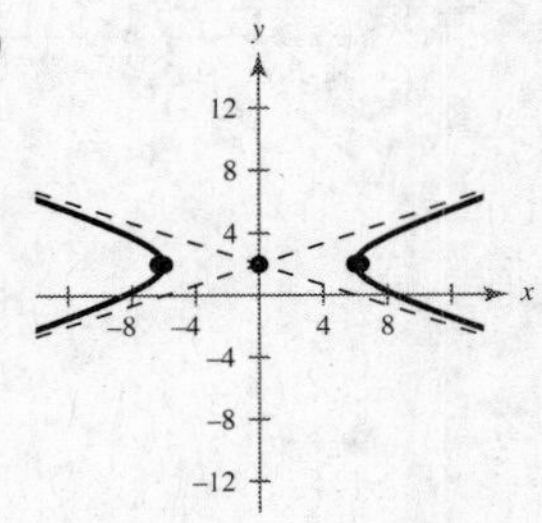

21. (a)
$$x^2 - 9y^2 + 2x - 54y - 80 = 0$$
$$(x^2 + 2x + 1) - 9(y^2 + 6y + 9) = 80 + 1 - 81$$
$$(x + 1)^2 - 9(y + 3)^2 = 0$$
$$y + 3 = \pm\tfrac{1}{3}(x + 1)$$

(b) Degenerate hyperbola is two lines intersecting at $(-1, -3)$.

(c)

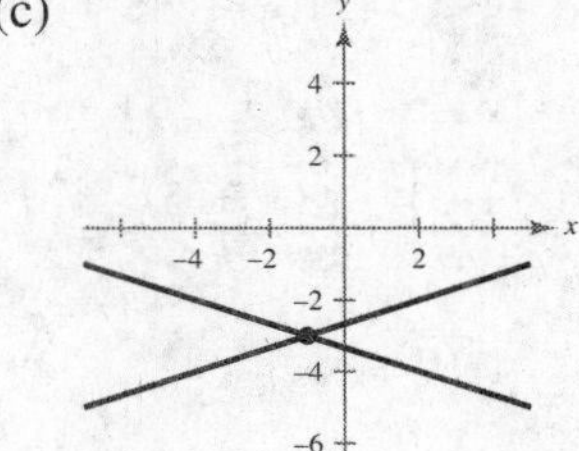

22. (a)

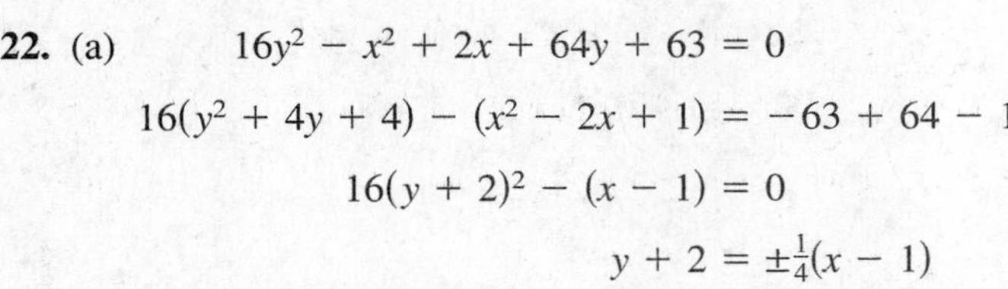

$$16y^2 - x^2 + 2x + 64y + 63 = 0$$
$$16(y^2 + 4y + 4) - (x^2 - 2x + 1) = -63 + 64 - 1$$
$$16(y + 2)^2 - (x - 1) = 0$$
$$y + 2 = \pm\tfrac{1}{4}(x - 1)$$

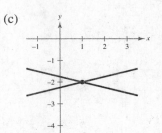

(b) Degenerate hyperbola is two intersecting lines at $(1, -2)$.

(c)

23. (a)
$$9y^2 - x^2 + 2x + 54y + 62 = 0$$
$$9(y^2 + 6y + 9) - (x^2 - 2x + 1) = -62 - 1 + 81$$
$$\frac{(y + 3)^2}{2} - \frac{(x - 1)^2}{18} = 1$$

(b) $a = \sqrt{2}, b = 3\sqrt{2}, c = 2\sqrt{5}$

Center: $(1, -3)$

Vertices: $\left(1, -3 \pm \sqrt{2}\right)$

Foci: $\left(1, -3 \pm 2\sqrt{5}\right)$

Asymptotes: $y = -3 \pm \dfrac{1}{3}(x - 1)$

(c) To use a graphing calculator, solve for y first.

$$9(y + 3)^2 = 18 + (x - 1)^2$$
$$y = -3 \pm \sqrt{\frac{18 + (x - 1)^2}{9}}$$

$$\left.\begin{aligned} y_1 &= -3 + \frac{1}{3}\sqrt{18 + (x - 1)^2} \\ y_2 &= -3 - \frac{1}{3}\sqrt{18 + (x - 1)^2} \end{aligned}\right\} \text{Hyperbola}$$

$$\left.\begin{aligned} y_3 &= -3 + \frac{1}{3}(x - 1) \\ y_4 &= -3 - \frac{1}{3}(x - 1) \end{aligned}\right\} \text{Asymptotes}$$

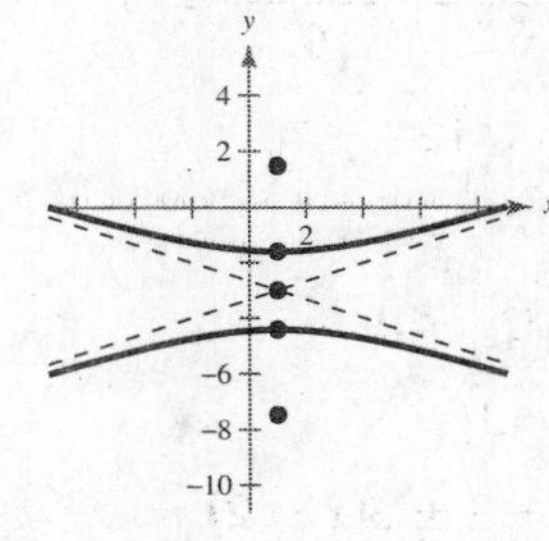

24. (a)
$$9x^2 - y^2 + 54x + 10y + 55 = 0$$
$$9(x^2 + 6x + 9) - (y^2 - 10y + 25) = -55 + 81 - 25$$
$$\frac{(x+3)^2}{1/9} - \frac{(y-5)^2}{1} = 1$$

(b) $a = \frac{1}{3}, b = 1, c = \frac{\sqrt{10}}{3}$

Center: $(-3, 5)$

Vertices: $\left(-3 \pm \frac{1}{3}, 5\right)$

Foci: $\left(-3 \pm \frac{\sqrt{10}}{3}, 5\right)$

Asymptotes: $y = 5 \pm 3(x + 3)$

(c)

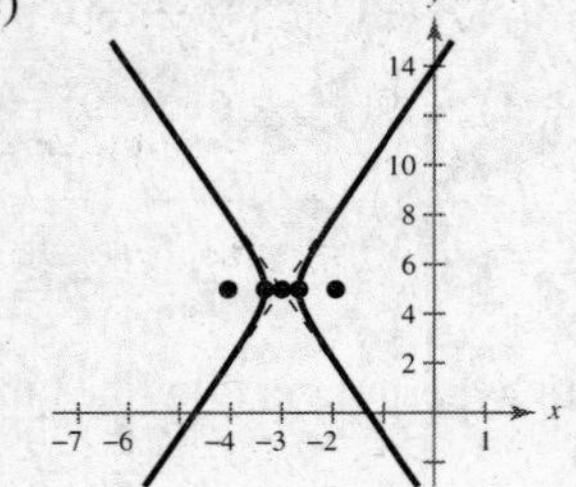

25. Vertices: $(0, \pm 2) \implies a = 2$

Foci: $(0, \pm 4) \implies c = 4$

$b^2 = c^2 - a^2 = 16 - 4 = 12$

Center: $(0, 0) = (h, k)$

$$\frac{(y-k)^2}{a^2} - \frac{(x-h)^2}{b^2} = 1$$
$$\frac{y^2}{4} - \frac{x^2}{12} = 1$$

26. Vertices: $(\pm 3, 0) \implies a = 3$

Foci: $(\pm 6, 0) \implies c = 6$

$b^2 = c^2 - a^2 = 36 - 9 = 27$

$$\frac{x^2}{a^2} - \frac{y^2}{b^2} = 1$$
$$\frac{x^2}{9} - \frac{y^2}{27} = 1$$

27. Vertices: $(\pm 1, 0) \implies a = 1$

Asymptotes:

$$y = \pm 5x \implies \frac{b}{a} = 5$$
$$\implies b = 5$$

Center: $(0, 0)$

$$\frac{x^2}{1} - \frac{y^2}{25} = 1$$

28. Vertices: $(0, \pm 3) \implies a = 3$

Asymptotes: $y = \pm 3x \implies \frac{a}{b} = 3, b = 1$

Center: $(0, 0) = (h, k)$

$$\frac{(y-k)^2}{a^2} - \frac{(x-h)^2}{b^2} = 1$$
$$\frac{y^2}{9} - x^2 = 1$$

29. Foci: $(0, \pm 8) \implies c = 8$

Asymptotes: $y = \pm 4x \implies \frac{a}{b} = 4 \implies a = 4b$

Center: $(0, 0) = (h, k)$

$c^2 = a^2 + b^2 \implies 64 = 16b^2 + b^2$

$\frac{64}{17} = b^2 \implies a^2 = \frac{1024}{17}$

$$\frac{(y-k)^2}{a^2} - \frac{(x-h)^2}{b^2} = 1$$
$$\frac{y^2}{1024/17} - \frac{x^2}{64/17} = 1$$
$$\frac{17y^2}{1024} - \frac{17x^2}{64} = 1$$

30. Foci: $(\pm 10, 0) \implies c = 10$

Asymptotes: $y = \pm\frac{3}{4}x \implies \frac{b}{a} = \frac{3m}{4m}$

$$c^2 = a^2 + b^2 \implies 100 = (3m)^2 + (4m)^2$$
$$100 = 25m^2$$
$$2 = m$$

$a = 4(2) = 8,\ b = 3(2) = 6$

$$\frac{x^2}{a^2} - \frac{y^2}{b^2} = 1$$

$$\frac{x^2}{64} - \frac{y^2}{36} = 1$$

31. Vertices: $(2, 0), (6, 0) \implies a = 2$

Foci: $(0, 0), (8, 0) \implies c = 4$

$b^2 = c^2 - a^2 = 16 - 4 = 12$

Center: $(4, 0) = (h, k)$

$$\frac{(x-h)^2}{a^2} - \frac{(y-k)^2}{b^2} = 1$$

$$\frac{(x-4)^2}{4} - \frac{y^2}{12} = 1$$

32. Vertices: $(2, 3), (2, -3) \implies a = 3$

Center: $(2, 0)$

Foci: $(2, 5), (2, -5) \implies c = 5$

$b^2 = c^2 - a^2 = 25 - 9 = 16$

$$\frac{(y-k)^2}{a^2} - \frac{(x-h)^2}{b^2} = 1$$

$$\frac{y^2}{9} - \frac{(x-2)^2}{16} = 1$$

33. Vertices: $(4, 1), (4, 9) \implies a = 4$

Foci: $(4, 0), (4, 10) \implies c = 5$

$b^2 = c^2 - a^2 = 25 - 16 = 9$

Center: $(4, 5) = (h, k)$

$$\frac{(y-k)^2}{a^2} - \frac{(x-h)^2}{b^2} = 1$$

$$\frac{(y-5)^2}{16} - \frac{(x-4)^2}{9} = 1$$

34. Vertices: $(-2, 1), (2, 1) \implies a = 2$

Center: $(0, 1)$

Foci: $(-3, 1), (3, 1) \implies c = 3$

$b^2 = c^2 - a^2 = 9 - 4 = 5$

$$\frac{(x-h)^2}{a^2} - \frac{(y-k)^2}{b^2} = 1$$

$$\frac{x^2}{4} - \frac{(y-1)^2}{5} = 1$$

35. Vertices: $(2, 3), (2, -3) \implies a = 3$

Solution point: $(0, 5)$

Center: $(2, 0) = (h, k)$

$$\frac{(y-k)^2}{a^2} - \frac{(x-h)^2}{b^2} = 1$$

$$\frac{y^2}{9} - \frac{(x-2)^2}{b^2} = 1 \implies$$

$$b^2 = \frac{9(x-2)^2}{y^2 - 9}$$

$$= \frac{9(-2)^2}{25 - 9} = \frac{36}{16} = \frac{9}{4}$$

$$\frac{y^2}{9} - \frac{(x-2)^2}{9/4} = 1$$

36. Center: $(0, 1), a = 2$

$$\frac{x^2}{4} - \frac{(y-1)^2}{b^2} = 1$$

Solution point: $(5, 4)$

$$\frac{25}{4} - \frac{9}{b^2} = 1$$

$$\frac{9}{b^2} = \frac{21}{4}$$

$$b^2 = \frac{36}{21} = \frac{12}{7}$$

$$\frac{x^2}{4} - \frac{(y-1)^2}{12/7} = 1$$

37. Vertices: $(0, 4), (0, 0)$

Center: $(0, 2), a = 2$

$$\frac{(y-2)^2}{4} - \frac{x^2}{b^2} = 1$$

Passes through $\left(\sqrt{5}, -1\right)$

$$\frac{(-1-2)^2}{4} - \frac{5}{b^2} = 1$$

$$\frac{9}{4} - 1 = \frac{5}{b^2}$$

$$b^2 = 4 \Rightarrow b = 2$$

$$\frac{(y-2)^2}{4} - \frac{x^2}{4} = 1$$

38. Center: $(1, 0), a = 2$

$$\frac{y^2}{4} - \frac{(x-1)^2}{b^2} = 1$$

Solution point: $\left(0, \sqrt{5}\right)$

$$\frac{5}{4} - \frac{1}{b^2} = 1$$

$$\frac{1}{b^2} = \frac{1}{4} \Rightarrow b = 2$$

$$\frac{y^2}{4} - \frac{(x-1)^2}{4} = 1$$

39. Vertices:

$(1, 2), (3, 2) \Rightarrow a = 1$

Center: $(2, 2)$

Asymptotes:

$y = x, y = 4 - x$

$$\frac{b}{a} = 1 \Rightarrow b = 1$$

$$\frac{(x-2)^2}{1} - \frac{(y-2)^2}{1} = 1$$

40. Center: $(3, -3), a = 3$

Asymptotes:

$y = x - 6, y = -x$

$$1 = \frac{a}{b} = \frac{3}{b} \Rightarrow b = 3$$

$$\frac{(y+3)^2}{9} - \frac{(x-3)^2}{9} = 1$$

41. Vertices: $(0, 2), (6, 2) \Rightarrow a = 3$

Asymptotes: $y = \frac{2}{3}x, y = 4 - \frac{2}{3}x$

$$\frac{b}{a} = \frac{2}{3} \Rightarrow b = 2$$

Center: $(3, 2) = (h, k)$

$$\frac{(x-h)^2}{a^2} - \frac{(y-k)^2}{b^2} = 1$$

$$\frac{(x-3)^2}{9} - \frac{(y-2)^2}{4} = 1$$

42. Vertices: $(3, 0), (3, 4) \Rightarrow a = 2$

Asymptotes: $y = \frac{2}{3}x, y = 4 - \frac{2}{3}x$

$$\frac{a}{b} = \frac{2}{3} \Rightarrow b = 3$$

Center: $(3, 2) = (h, k)$

$$\frac{(y-k)^2}{a^2} - \frac{(x-h)^2}{b^2} = 1$$

$$\frac{(y-2)^2}{4} - \frac{(x-3)^2}{9} = 1$$

43. F_1: Friend's location $(-10{,}560, 0)$

F_2: Your location $(10{,}560, 0)$

$P(x, y)$: Location of lightning strike

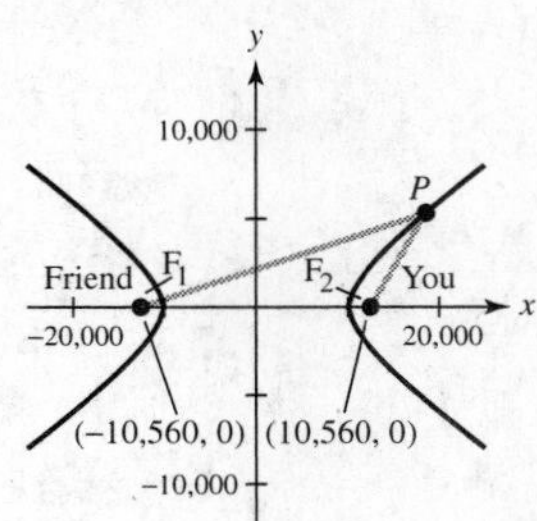

$(1100)(18) = 19{,}800$

$$\frac{x^2}{a^2} - \frac{y^2}{b^2} = 1$$

$$c = 10{,}560,\ a = \frac{19{,}800}{2} = 9900 \Rightarrow a^2 = 98{,}010{,}000$$

$$b^2 = c^2 - a^2 = 13{,}503{,}600$$

$$\frac{x^2}{98{,}010{,}000} - \frac{y^2}{13{,}503{,}600} = 1$$

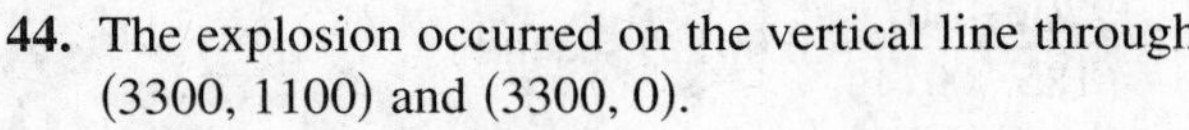

44. The explosion occurred on the vertical line through $(3300, 1100)$ and $(3300, 0)$.

$d_2 - d_1 = 4(1100) = 4400$

Hence,

$2a = 4400$

$a = 2200$

$c = 3300$

$b^2 = c^2 - a^2.$

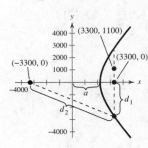

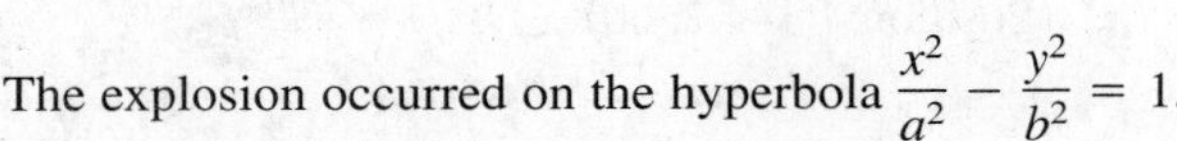

The explosion occurred on the hyperbola $\dfrac{x^2}{a^2} - \dfrac{y^2}{b^2} = 1.$

Letting $x = 3300$,

$$y^2 = b^2\left(\frac{x^2}{a^2} - 1\right) = (3300^2 - 2200^2)\left(\frac{3300^2}{2200^2} - 1\right) \Rightarrow y = -2750.$$

$(3300, -2750)$

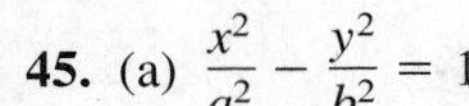

45. (a) $\dfrac{x^2}{a^2} - \dfrac{y^2}{b^2} = 1$

$a = 1$; $(2, 9)$ is on the curve, so

$$\frac{4}{1} - \frac{81}{b^2} = 1 \Rightarrow \frac{81}{b^2} = 3$$

$$\Rightarrow b^2 = \frac{81}{3} \Rightarrow b = 3\sqrt{3}.$$

$$\frac{x^2}{1} - \frac{y^2}{27} = 1, \quad -9 \le y \le 9$$

(b) Because each unit is $\frac{1}{2}$ foot, 4 inches is $\frac{2}{3}$ of a unit. The base is 9 units from the origin, so

$$y = 9 - \frac{2}{3} = 8\frac{1}{3}.$$

When $y = \dfrac{25}{3}$,

$$x^2 = 1 + \frac{(25/3)^2}{27} \Rightarrow x \approx 1.88998.$$

So the width is $2x \approx 3.779956$ units, or 22.68 inches, or 1.88998 feet.

46. Foci: $(\pm 150, 0) \Rightarrow c = 150$

Center: $(0, 0)$

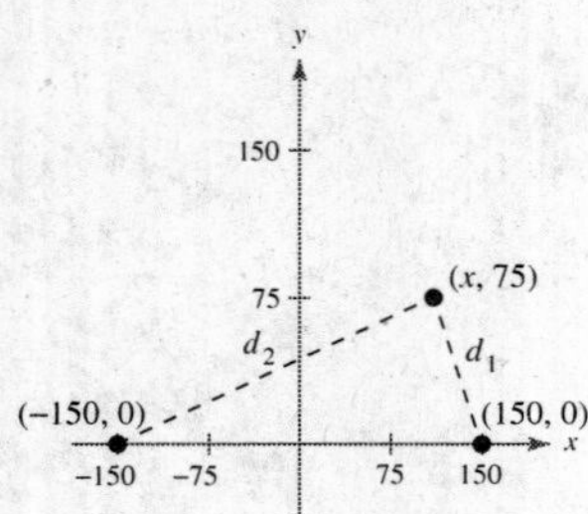

(a) $d_2 - d_1 = (186{,}000)(0.001)$

$= 186 \Rightarrow 2a = 186 \Rightarrow a = 93$

$b^2 = c^2 - a^2 = 150^2 - 93^2 = 13{,}851$

$$\frac{x^2}{93^2} - \frac{y^2}{13{,}851} = 1$$

$$x^2 = 93^2\left(1 + \frac{75^2}{13{,}851}\right) \approx 12{,}161.43$$

$x \approx 110.3$ miles

(b) $150 - 93 = 57$ miles

(c) Bay to Station 1: 30 miles

Bay to Station 2: 270 miles

$$\frac{(270 - 30)}{186{,}000} \approx 0.00129 \text{ second}$$

(d) In this case,

$d_2 - d_1 = 186{,}000(0.00129) \approx 239.94 \Rightarrow a \approx 120$

and $b^2 = c^2 - a^2 = 8100$. The hyperbola is

$$\frac{x^2}{120^2} - \frac{y^2}{90^2} = 1.$$

For $y = 60$, $x^2 = 20{,}800$ and $x \approx 144.2$.

Position: $(144.2, 60)$

47. Center: $(0, 0)$

Focus: $(24, 0)$

$b^2 = c^2 - a^2 = 24^2 - a^2 = 576 - a^2$

$$\frac{x^2}{a^2} - \frac{y^2}{576 - a^2} = 1$$

$$\frac{24^2}{a^2} - \frac{24^2}{576 - a^2} = 1$$

$$\frac{576}{a^2} - \frac{576}{576 - a^2} = 1$$

$576(576 - a^2) - 576a^2 = a^2(576 - a^2)$

$a^4 - 1728a^2 + 331{,}776 = 0$

$$a \approx \pm 38.83 \text{ or } a \approx \pm 14.83$$

Since $a < c$ and $c = 24$, we choose $a = 14.83$. The vertex is approximate at $(14.83, 0)$. [**Note:** By the Quadratic Formula, the exact value of a is $a = 12(\sqrt{5} - 1)$.]

48. $\dfrac{x^2}{25} - \dfrac{y^2}{16} = 1$

$a = 5, b = 4, c = \sqrt{25 + 16} = \sqrt{41}$

The camera is $5 + \sqrt{41}$ units from the mirror.

49. $9x^2 + 4y^2 - 18x + 16y - 119 = 0$

$A = 9, C = 4$

$AC = 36 > 0$, Ellipse

50. $x^2 + y^2 - 4x - 6y - 23 = 0$

$A = C = 1$, Circle

51. $16x^2 - 9y^2 + 32x + 54y - 209 = 0$

$A = 16, C = -9$

$AC = 16(-9) < 0$, Hyperbola

52. $x^2 + 4x - 8y + 20 = 0$

$A = 1, C = 0$

$AC = 0$, Parabola

53. $y^2 + 12x + 4y + 28 = 0$

$C = 1, A = 0$

$AC = 0$, Parabola

54. $4x^2 + 25y^2 + 16x + 250y + 541 = 0$

$A = 4, C = 25$

$AC = 100 > 0$, Ellipse

55. $x^2 + y^2 + 2x - 6y = 0$

$A = C = 1$, Circle

56. $y^2 - x^2 + 2x - 6y - 8 = 0$

$A = -1, C = 1$

$AC < 0$, Hyperbola

57. $x^2 - 6x - 2y + 7 = 0$

$A = 1, C = 0, D = -6,\ E = -2, F = 7$

$AC = 0 \implies$ Parabola

58. $9x^2 + 4y^2 - 90x + 8y + 228 = 0$

$A = 9, C = 4$

$AC = 9(4) = 36 > 0 \implies$ Ellipse

59. True. $e = \dfrac{c}{a} = \dfrac{\sqrt{a^2 + b^2}}{a}$

60. False. $b \neq 0$ because it is in the denominator.

61. False. For example,

$x^2 - y^2 - 2x + 2y = 0$

$(x - 1)^2 - (y - 1)^2 = 0$

is the graph of two intersecting lines.

62. True. The asymptotes are

$$y = \pm\frac{b}{a}x.$$

If they intersect at right angles, then

$$\frac{b}{a} = \frac{-1}{(-b/a)} = \frac{a}{b} \implies a = b.$$

63. Let (x, y) be such that the difference of the distances from $(c, 0)$ and $(-c, 0)$ is $2a$ (again only deriving one of the forms).

$$\begin{aligned}
2a &= \left|\sqrt{(x + c)^2 + y^2} - \sqrt{(x - c) + y^2}\right| \\
2a + \sqrt{(x - c)^2 + y^2} &= \sqrt{(x + c)^2 + y^2} \\
4a^2 + 4a\sqrt{(x - c)^2 + y^2} + (x - c)^2 + y^2 &= (x + c)^2 + y^2 \\
4a\sqrt{(x - c)^2 + y^2} &= 4cx - 4a^2 \\
a\sqrt{(x - c)^2 + y^2} &= cx - a^2 \\
a^2(x^2 - 2cx + c^2 + y^2) &= c^2x^2 - 2a^2cx + a^4 \\
a^2(c^2 - a^2) &= (c^2 - a^2)x^2 - a^2y^2
\end{aligned}$$

Let $b^2 = c^2 - a^2$. Then $a^2b^2 = b^2x^2 - a^2y^2 \implies 1 = \dfrac{x^2}{a^2} - \dfrac{y^2}{b^2}$.

64. Answers will vary. See Example 3.

65. $|d_2 - d_1| =$ constant by definition of hyperbola

At the point $(a, 0)$,

$|d_2 - d_1| = |(a + c) - (c - a)| = 2a.$

66. Center: $(6, 2)$

Horizontal transverse axis

Foci at $(2, 2)$ and $(10, 2) \implies c = 4.$

$(c + a) - (c - a) = 6 \implies a = 3$

$b^2 = c^2 - a^2 = 16 - 9 = 7$

$\dfrac{(x-6)^2}{9} - \dfrac{(y-2)^2}{7} = 1$

67. At the point $(a, 0)$, the difference of the distances to the foci $(\pm c, 0)$ is $(c + a) - (c - a) = 2a.$
Let (x, y) be a point on the hyperbola.

$$2a = \sqrt{(x+c)^2 + y^2} - \sqrt{(x-c)^2 + y^2}$$

$$2a + \sqrt{(x-c)^2 + y^2} = \sqrt{(x+c)^2 + y^2}$$

$$4a^2 + 4a\sqrt{(x-c)^2 + y^2} + (x-c)^2 + y^2 = (x+c)^2 + y^2$$

$$4a\sqrt{(x-c)^2 + y^2} = 4cx - 4a^2$$

$$a\sqrt{(x-c)^2 + y^2} = cx - a^2$$

$$a^2(x^2 - 2cx + c^2 + y^2) = c^2x^2 - 2a^2cx + a^4$$

$$a^2(c^2 - a^2) = (c^2 - a^2)x^2 - a^2y^2$$

$$1 = \frac{x^2}{a^2} - \frac{y^2}{c^2 - a^2}$$

Thus, $c^2 - a^2 = b^2$, as desired.

68. If $A = C \neq 0$, then by completing the square you obtain a circle.

If $A = 0$ and $C \neq 0$, then $Cy^2 + Dx + Ey + F = 0$ is a parabola (complete the square).
Same for $A \neq 0$ and $C = 0$.

If $AC > 0$, then both A and C are positive (or both negative). By completing the square you obtain an ellipse.

If $AC < 0$, then A and C have opposite signs. You obtain a hyperbola.

69. $(x^3 - 3x^2) - (6 - 2x - 4x^2) = x^3 + x^2 + 2x - 6$

70. $\left(3x - \frac{1}{2}\right)(x + 4) = 3x^2 + 12x - \frac{1}{2}x - 2$

$= 3x^2 + \frac{23}{2}x - 2$

71.

$$\begin{array}{r|rrrr} -2 & 1 & 0 & -3 & 4 \\ & & -2 & 4 & -2 \\ \hline & 1 & -2 & 1 & 2 \end{array}$$

$\dfrac{x^3 - 3x + 4}{x + 2} = x^2 - 2x + 1 + \dfrac{2}{x + 2}$

72. $[(x + y) + 3]^2 = (x + y)^2 + 6(x + y) + 9$

$= x^2 + 2xy + y^2 + 6x + 6y + 9$

73. $x^3 - 16x = x(x^2 - 16) = x(x - 4)(x + 4)$

74. $x^2 + 14x + 49 = (x + 7)^2$

75. $2x^3 - 24x^2 + 72x = 2x(x^2 - 12x + 36)$
$= 2x(x - 6)^2$

76. $6x^3 - 11x^2 - 10x = x(6x^2 - 11x - 10)$
$= x(3x + 2)(2x - 5)$

77. $16x^3 + 54 = 2(8x^3 + 27)$
$= 2(2x + 3)(4x^2 - 6x + 9)$

78. $4 - x + 4x^2 - x^3 = (4 - x) + x^2(4 - x)$
$= (4 - x)(x^2 + 1)$
$= (4 - x)(x + i)(x - i)$

Section 9.4 Rotation and Systems of Quadratic Equations

- The general second-degree equation $Ax^2 + Bxy + Cy^2 + Dx + Ey + F = 0$ can be rewritten $A'(x')^2 + C'(y')^2 + D'x' + E'y' + F' = 0$ by rotating the coordinate axes through the angle θ where $\cot 2\theta = (A - C)/B$.
- $x = x' \cos \theta - y' \sin \theta$
  $y = x' \sin \theta + y' \cos \theta$
- The graph of the nondegenerate equation $Ax^2 + Bxy + Cy^2 + Dx + Ey + F = 0$ is:
  (a) An ellipse or circle if $B^2 - 4AC < 0$.
  (b) A parabola if $B^2 - 4AC = 0$.
  (c) A hyperbola if $B^2 - 4AC > 0$.

Vocabulary Check

1. rotation, axes **2.** invariant under rotation **3.** discriminant

1. $\theta = 90°$; Point: $(0, 3)$

$x = x' \cos \theta - y' \sin \theta$ $\quad$ $y = x' \sin \theta + y' \cos \theta$

$0 = x' \cos 90° - y' \sin 90°$ $\quad$ $3 = x' \sin 90° + y' \cos 90°$

$0 = y'$ $\quad$ $3 = x'$

Thus, $(x', y') = (3, 0)$.

2. $\theta = 45°$; Point: $(3, 3)$

$x = x' \cos \theta - y' \sin \theta$ $\quad$ $y = x' \sin \theta + y' \cos \theta$

$3 = x' \cos 45° - y' \sin 45°$ $\quad$ $3 = x' \sin 45° + y' \cos 45°$

$3 = \frac{\sqrt{2}}{2}x' - \frac{\sqrt{2}}{2}y'$ $\quad$ $3 = \frac{\sqrt{2}}{2}x' + \frac{\sqrt{2}}{2}y'$

Adding, $6 = \sqrt{2}x' \Rightarrow x' = \frac{6}{\sqrt{2}} = 3\sqrt{2}$.

Subtracting, $\sqrt{2}y' = 0 \Rightarrow y' = 0$.

Thus, $(x', y') = \left(3\sqrt{2}, 0\right)$.

3. $xy + 1 = 0$

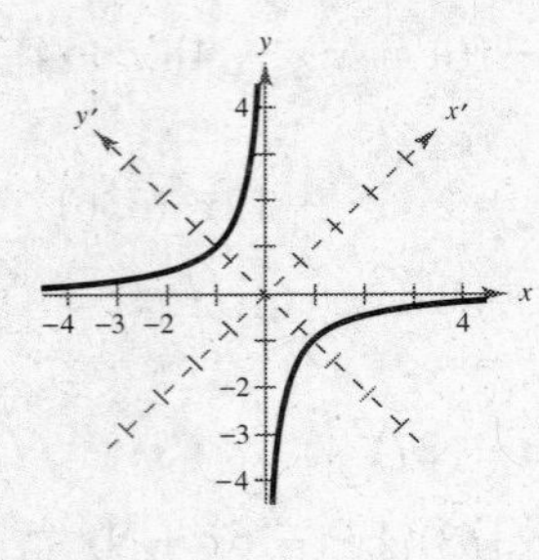

$A = 0, B = 1, C = 0$

$\cot 2\theta = \dfrac{A - C}{B} = 0 \Rightarrow 2\theta = \dfrac{\pi}{2} \Rightarrow \theta = \dfrac{\pi}{4}$

$x = x'\cos\dfrac{\pi}{4} - y'\sin\dfrac{\pi}{4} = x'\left(\dfrac{\sqrt{2}}{2}\right) - y'\left(\dfrac{\sqrt{2}}{2}\right) = \dfrac{x' - y'}{\sqrt{2}}$

$y = x'\sin\dfrac{\pi}{4} + y'\cos\dfrac{\pi}{4} = x'\left(\dfrac{\sqrt{2}}{2}\right) + y'\left(\dfrac{\sqrt{2}}{2}\right) = \dfrac{x' + y'}{\sqrt{2}}$

$$xy + 1 = 0$$

$$\left(\frac{x' - y'}{\sqrt{2}}\right)\left(\frac{x' + y'}{\sqrt{2}}\right) + 1 = 0$$

$$\frac{(y')^2}{2} - \frac{(x')^2}{2} = 1, \text{ Hyperbola}$$

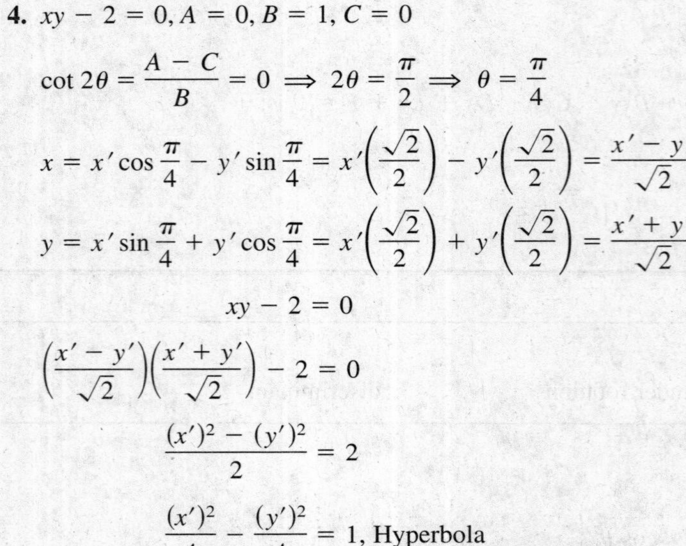

4. $xy - 2 = 0, A = 0, B = 1, C = 0$

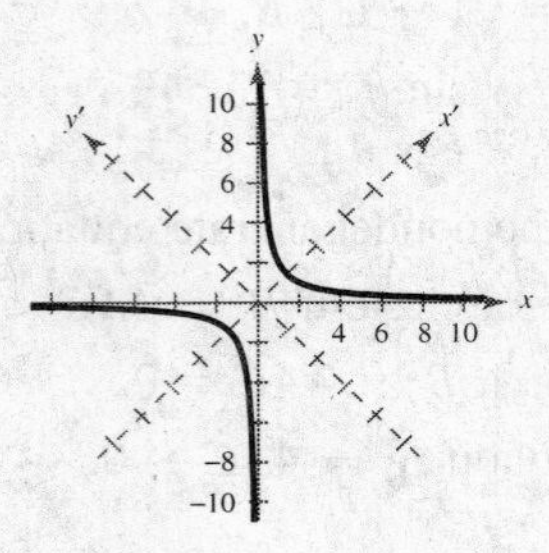

$\cot 2\theta = \dfrac{A - C}{B} = 0 \Rightarrow 2\theta = \dfrac{\pi}{2} \Rightarrow \theta = \dfrac{\pi}{4}$

$x = x'\cos\dfrac{\pi}{4} - y'\sin\dfrac{\pi}{4} = x'\left(\dfrac{\sqrt{2}}{2}\right) - y'\left(\dfrac{\sqrt{2}}{2}\right) = \dfrac{x' - y'}{\sqrt{2}}$

$y = x'\sin\dfrac{\pi}{4} + y'\cos\dfrac{\pi}{4} = x'\left(\dfrac{\sqrt{2}}{2}\right) + y'\left(\dfrac{\sqrt{2}}{2}\right) = \dfrac{x' + y'}{\sqrt{2}}$

$$xy - 2 = 0$$

$$\left(\frac{x' - y'}{\sqrt{2}}\right)\left(\frac{x' + y'}{\sqrt{2}}\right) - 2 = 0$$

$$\frac{(x')^2 - (y')^2}{2} = 2$$

$$\frac{(x')^2}{4} - \frac{(y')^2}{4} = 1, \text{ Hyperbola}$$

5. $x^2 - 4xy + y^2 + 1 = 0$

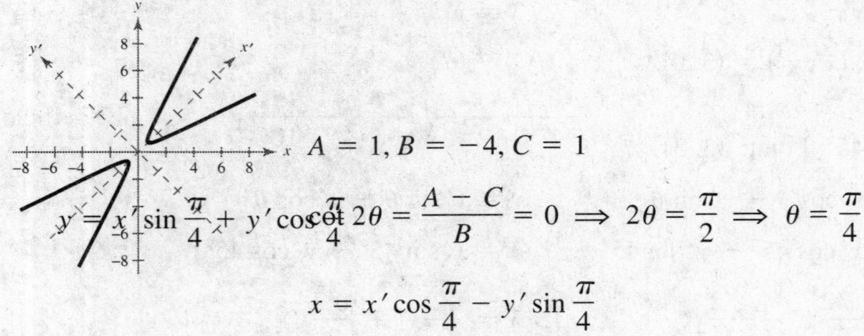

$A = 1, B = -4, C = 1$

$\cot 2\theta = \dfrac{A - C}{B} = 0 \Rightarrow 2\theta = \dfrac{\pi}{2} \Rightarrow \theta = \dfrac{\pi}{4}$

$x = x'\cos\dfrac{\pi}{4} - y'\sin\dfrac{\pi}{4}$

$= x'\left(\dfrac{\sqrt{2}}{2}\right) - y'\left(\dfrac{\sqrt{2}}{2}\right)$

$= \dfrac{\sqrt{2}}{2}(x' - y')$

$y = x'\sin\dfrac{\pi}{4} + y'\cos\dfrac{\pi}{4}$

5. —CONTINUED—

$$x^2 - 4xy + y^2 + 1 = 0$$

$$\left[\frac{\sqrt{2}}{2}(x' - y')\right]^2 - 4\left[\frac{\sqrt{2}}{2}(x' - y')\frac{\sqrt{2}}{2}(x' + y')\right] + \left[\frac{\sqrt{2}}{2}(x' + y')\right]^2 + 1 = 0$$

$$\frac{1}{2}(x')^2 - x'y' + \frac{1}{2}(y')^2 - 2[(x')^2 - (y')^2] + \frac{1}{2}(x')^2 + x'y' + \frac{1}{2}(y')^2 + 1 = 0$$

$$-(x')^2 + 3(y')^2 = -1$$

$$(x')^2 - \frac{(y')^2}{1/3} = 1, \text{ Hyperbola}$$

6. $xy + x - 2y + 3 = 0$

$A = 0, B = 1, C = 0$

$$\cot 2\theta = \frac{A - C}{B} = 0 \Rightarrow 2\theta = \frac{\pi}{2} \Rightarrow \theta = \frac{\pi}{4}$$

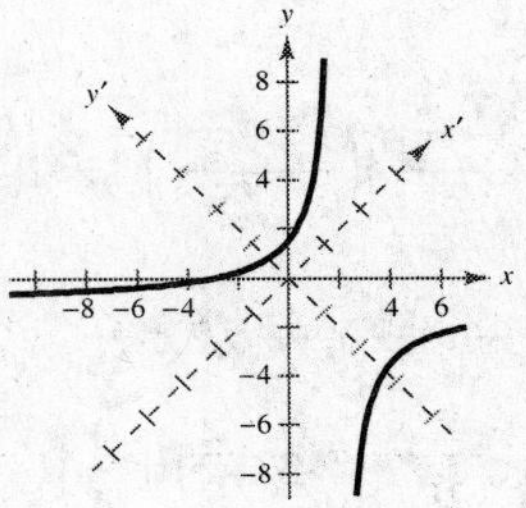

$$x = x'\cos\frac{\pi}{4} - y'\sin\frac{\pi}{4} = x'\left(\frac{\sqrt{2}}{2}\right) - y'\left(\frac{\sqrt{2}}{2}\right) = \frac{x' - y'}{\sqrt{2}}$$

$$y = x'\sin\frac{\pi}{4} + y'\cos\frac{\pi}{4} = x'\left(\frac{\sqrt{2}}{2}\right) + y'\left(\frac{\sqrt{2}}{2}\right) = \frac{x' + y'}{\sqrt{2}}$$

$$xy + x - 2y + 3 = 0$$

$$\left(\frac{x' - y'}{\sqrt{2}}\right)\left(\frac{x' + y'}{\sqrt{2}}\right) + \left(\frac{x' - y'}{\sqrt{2}}\right) - 2\left(\frac{x' + y'}{\sqrt{2}}\right) + 3 = 0$$

$$\frac{(x')^2}{2} - \frac{(y')^2}{2} + \frac{x'}{\sqrt{2}} - \frac{y'}{\sqrt{2}} - \frac{2x'}{\sqrt{2}} - \frac{2y'}{\sqrt{2}} + 3 = 0$$

$$\left[(x')^2 - \sqrt{2}x' + \left(\frac{\sqrt{2}}{2}\right)^2\right] - \left[(y')^2 + 3\sqrt{2}y' + \left(\frac{3\sqrt{2}}{2}\right)^2\right] = -6 + \left(\frac{\sqrt{2}}{2}\right)^2 - \left(\frac{3\sqrt{2}}{2}\right)^2$$

$$\left(x' - \frac{\sqrt{2}}{2}\right)^2 - \left(y' + \frac{3\sqrt{2}}{2}\right)^2 = -10$$

$$\frac{\left(y' + \frac{3\sqrt{2}}{2}\right)^2}{10} - \frac{\left(x' - \frac{\sqrt{2}}{2}\right)^2}{10} = 1, \text{ Hyperbola}$$

7. $xy - 2y - 4x = 0$

$A = 0, B = 1, C = 0$

$$\cot 2\theta = \frac{A - C}{B} = 0 \Rightarrow 2\theta = \frac{\pi}{2} \Rightarrow \theta = \frac{\pi}{4}$$

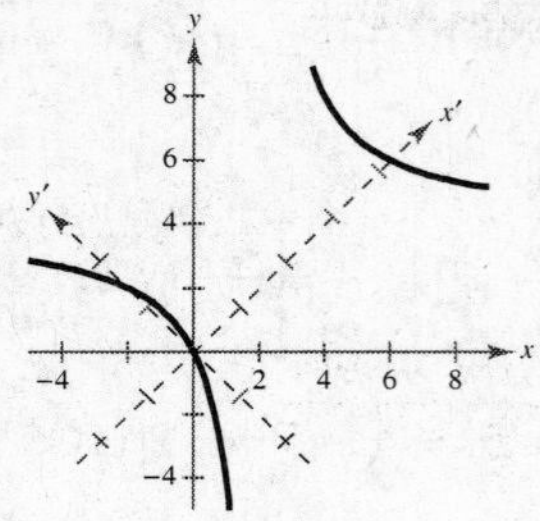

$$x = x'\cos\frac{\pi}{4} - y'\sin\frac{\pi}{4} \qquad y = x'\sin\frac{\pi}{4} + y'\cos\frac{\pi}{4}$$

$$= x'\left(\frac{\sqrt{2}}{2}\right) - y'\left(\frac{\sqrt{2}}{2}\right) \qquad = x'\left(\frac{\sqrt{2}}{2}\right) + y'\left(\frac{\sqrt{2}}{2}\right)$$

$$= \frac{x' - y'}{\sqrt{2}} \qquad = \frac{x' + y'}{\sqrt{2}}$$

$$xy - 2y - 4x = 0$$

$$\left(\frac{x' - y'}{\sqrt{2}}\right)\left(\frac{x' + y'}{\sqrt{2}}\right) - 2\left(\frac{x' + y'}{\sqrt{2}}\right) - 4\left(\frac{x' - y'}{\sqrt{2}}\right) = 0$$

$$\frac{(x')^2}{2} - \frac{(y')^2}{2} - \sqrt{2}x' - \sqrt{2}y' - 2\sqrt{2}x' + 2\sqrt{2}y' = 0$$

$$\left[(x')^2 - 6\sqrt{2}x' + \left(3\sqrt{2}\right)^2\right] - \left[(y')^2 - 2\sqrt{2}y' + \left(\sqrt{2}\right)^2\right] = 0 + \left(3\sqrt{2}\right)^2 - \left(\sqrt{2}\right)^2$$

$$\left(x' - 3\sqrt{2}\right)^2 - \left(y' - \sqrt{2}\right)^2 = 16$$

$$\frac{\left(x' - 3\sqrt{2}\right)^2}{16} - \frac{\left(y' - \sqrt{2}\right)^2}{16} = 1, \quad \text{Hyperbola}$$

8. $2x^2 - 3xy - 2y^2 + 10 = 0$

$A = 2, B = -3, C = -2$

$$\cot 2\theta = \frac{A - C}{B} = -\frac{4}{3} \Rightarrow \theta \approx 71.57^\circ$$

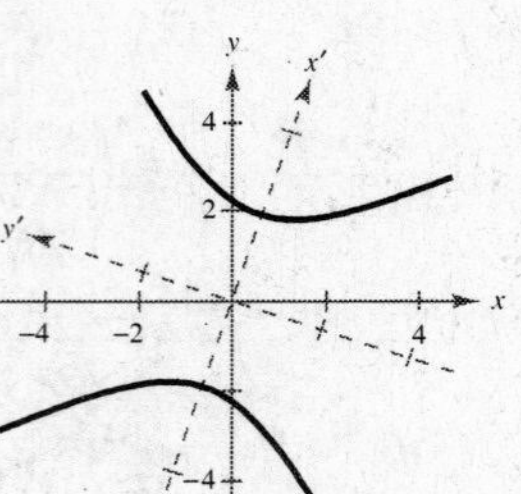

$$\cos 2\theta = -\frac{4}{5}$$

$$\sin\theta = \sqrt{\frac{1 - \cos 2\theta}{2}} = \sqrt{\frac{1 - (-4/5)}{2}} = \frac{3}{\sqrt{10}}$$

$$\cos\theta = \sqrt{\frac{1 + \cos 2\theta}{2}} = \sqrt{\frac{1 + (-4/5)}{2}} = \frac{1}{\sqrt{10}}$$

$$x = x'\cos\theta - y'\sin\theta \qquad y = x'\sin\theta + y'\cos\theta$$

$$= x'\left(\frac{1}{\sqrt{10}}\right) - y'\left(\frac{3}{\sqrt{10}}\right) \qquad = x'\left(\frac{3}{\sqrt{10}}\right) + y'\left(\frac{1}{\sqrt{10}}\right)$$

$$= \frac{x' - 3y'}{\sqrt{10}} \qquad = \frac{3x' + y'}{\sqrt{10}}$$

—CONTINUED—

8. —CONTINUED—

$$2x^2 - 3xy - 2y^2 + 10 = 0$$

$$2\left(\frac{x' - 3y'}{\sqrt{10}}\right)^2 - 3\left(\frac{x' - 3y'}{\sqrt{10}}\right)\left(\frac{3x' + y'}{\sqrt{10}}\right) - 2\left(\frac{3x' + y'}{\sqrt{10}}\right)^2 + 10 = 0$$

$$\frac{(x')^2}{5} - \frac{6x'y'}{5} + \frac{9(y')^2}{5} - \frac{9(x')^2}{10} + \frac{24x'y'}{10} + \frac{9(y')^2}{10} - \frac{9(x')^2}{5} - \frac{6x'y'}{5} - \frac{(y')^2}{5} + 10 = 0$$

$$-\frac{5}{2}(x')^2 + \frac{5}{2}(y')^2 = -10$$

$$\frac{(x')^2}{4} - \frac{(y')^2}{4} = 1, \text{ Hyperbola}$$

9. $5x^2 - 6xy + 5y^2 - 12 = 0$

$A = 5, B = -6, C = 5$

$$\cot 2\theta = \frac{A - C}{B} = 0 \Rightarrow 2\theta = \frac{\pi}{2} \Rightarrow \theta = \frac{\pi}{4}$$

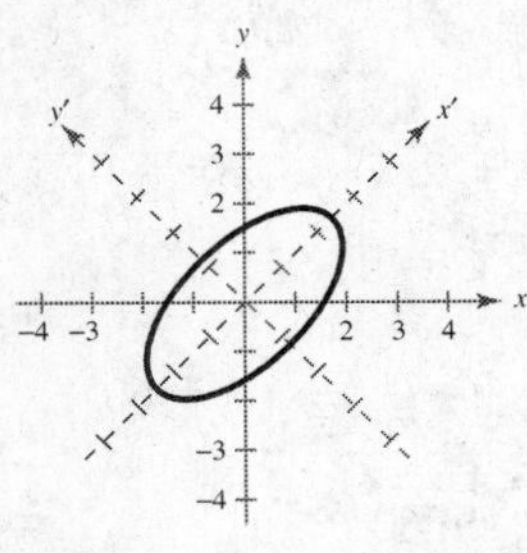

$$x = x' \cos\frac{\pi}{4} - y' \sin\frac{\pi}{4} = \frac{\sqrt{2}}{2}(x' - y')$$

$$y = x' \sin\frac{\pi}{4} + y' \cos\frac{\pi}{4} = \frac{\sqrt{2}}{2}(x' + y')$$

$$5x^2 - 6xy + 5y^2 - 12 = 0$$

$$5\left[\frac{\sqrt{2}}{2}(x' - y')\right]^2 - 6\left[\frac{\sqrt{2}}{2}(x' - y')\frac{\sqrt{2}}{2}(x' + y')\right] + 5\left[\frac{\sqrt{2}}{2}(x' + y')\right]^2 = 12$$

$$\frac{5}{2}(x')^2 - 5x'y' + \frac{5}{2}(y')^2 - 3(x')^2 + 3(y')^2 + \frac{5}{2}(x')^2 + 5x'y' + \frac{5}{2}(y')^2 = 12$$

$$2(x')^2 + 8(y')^2 = 12$$

$$\frac{(x')^2}{6} + \frac{(y')^2}{3/2} = 1, \quad \text{Ellipse}$$

10. $13x^2 + 6\sqrt{3}xy + 7y^2 - 16 = 0$

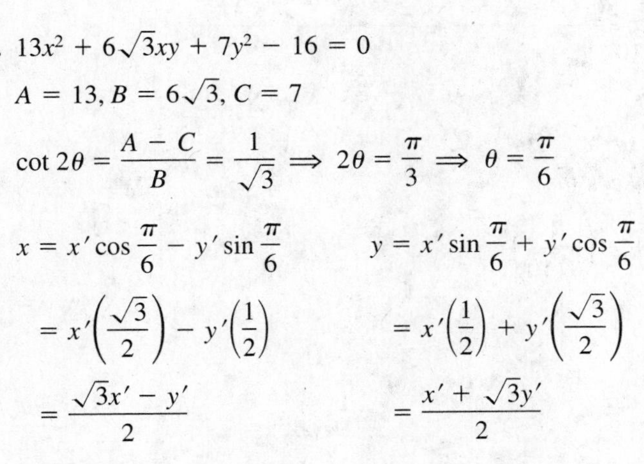

$A = 13, B = 6\sqrt{3}, C = 7$

$$\cot 2\theta = \frac{A - C}{B} = \frac{1}{\sqrt{3}} \Rightarrow 2\theta = \frac{\pi}{3} \Rightarrow \theta = \frac{\pi}{6}$$

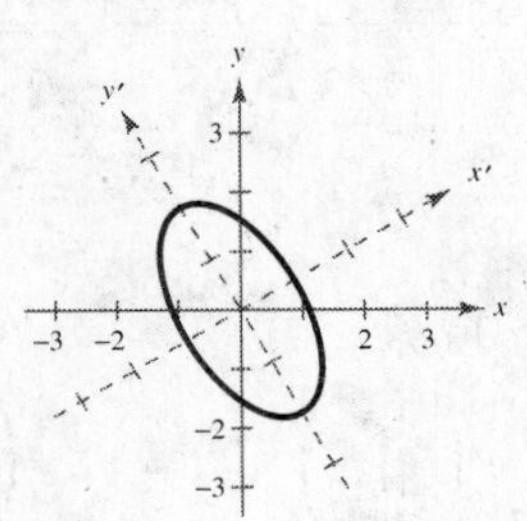

$$x = x' \cos\frac{\pi}{6} - y' \sin\frac{\pi}{6} \qquad y = x' \sin\frac{\pi}{6} + y' \cos\frac{\pi}{6}$$

$$= x'\left(\frac{\sqrt{3}}{2}\right) - y'\left(\frac{1}{2}\right) \qquad = x'\left(\frac{1}{2}\right) + y'\left(\frac{\sqrt{3}}{2}\right)$$

$$= \frac{\sqrt{3}x' - y'}{2} \qquad = \frac{x' + \sqrt{3}y'}{2}$$

—CONTINUED—

10. —CONTINUED—

$$13x^2 + 6\sqrt{3}xy + 7y^2 - 16 = 0$$

$$13\left(\frac{\sqrt{3}x' - y'}{2}\right)^2 + 6\sqrt{3}\left(\frac{\sqrt{3}x' - y'}{2}\right)\left(\frac{x' + \sqrt{3}y'}{2}\right) + 7\left(\frac{x' + \sqrt{3}y'}{2}\right)^2 - 16 = 0$$

$$\frac{39(x')^2}{4} - \frac{13\sqrt{3}x'y'}{2} + \frac{13(y')^2}{4} + \frac{18(x')^2}{4} + \frac{18\sqrt{3}x'y'}{4} - \frac{6\sqrt{3}x'y'}{4}$$

$$-\frac{18(y')^2}{4} + \frac{7(x')^2}{4} + \frac{7\sqrt{3}x'y'}{2} + \frac{21(y')^2}{4} - 16 = 0$$

$$16(x')^2 + 4(y')^2 = 16$$

$$\frac{(x')^2}{1} + \frac{(y')^2}{4} = 1\text{, Ellipse}$$

11. $3x^2 - 2\sqrt{3}xy + y^2 + 2x + 2\sqrt{3}y = 0$

$A = 3, B = -2\sqrt{3}, C = 1$

$$\cot 2\theta = \frac{A - C}{B} = -\frac{1}{\sqrt{3}} \Rightarrow \theta = 60^\circ$$

$$x = x'\cos 60^\circ - y'\sin 60^\circ$$

$$= x'\left(\frac{1}{2}\right) - y'\left(\frac{\sqrt{3}}{2}\right) = \frac{x' - \sqrt{3}y'}{2}$$

$$y = x'\sin\theta + y'\cos\theta = \frac{\sqrt{3}x' + y'}{2}$$

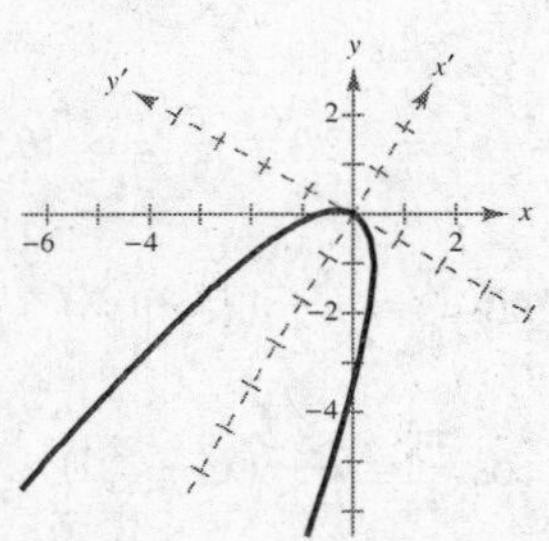

$$3x^2 - 2\sqrt{3}xy + y^2 + 2x + 2\sqrt{3}y = 0$$

$$3\left(\frac{x' - \sqrt{3}y'}{2}\right)^2 - 2\sqrt{3}\left(\frac{x' - \sqrt{3}y'}{2}\right)\left(\frac{\sqrt{3}x' + y'}{2}\right) + \left(\frac{\sqrt{3}x' + y'}{2}\right)^2 + 2\left(\frac{x' - \sqrt{3}y'}{2}\right)$$

$$+ 2\sqrt{3}\left(\frac{\sqrt{3}x' + y'}{2}\right) = 0$$

$$\frac{3(x')^2}{4} - \frac{6\sqrt{3}x'y'}{4} + \frac{9(y')^2}{4} - \frac{6(x')^2}{4} + \frac{4\sqrt{3}x'y'}{4} + \frac{6(y')^2}{4} + \frac{3(x')^2}{4} + \frac{2\sqrt{3}x'y'}{4} + \frac{(y')^2}{4}$$

$$+ x' - \sqrt{3}y' + 3x' + \sqrt{3}y' = 0$$

$$4(y')^2 + 4x' = 0$$

$$x' = -(y')^2, \quad \text{Parabola}$$

12. $16x^2 - 24xy + 9y^2 - 60x - 80y + 100 = 0$

$A = 16, B = -24, C = 9$

$\cot 2\theta = \dfrac{A - C}{B} = -\dfrac{7}{24} \Rightarrow \theta \approx 53.13°$

$\cos 2\theta = -\dfrac{7}{25}$

$\sin \theta = \sqrt{\dfrac{1 - \cos 2\theta}{2}} = \sqrt{\dfrac{1 - (-7/25)}{2}} = \dfrac{4}{5}$

$\cos \theta = \sqrt{\dfrac{1 + \cos 2\theta}{2}} = \sqrt{\dfrac{1 + (-7/25)}{2}} = \dfrac{3}{5}$

$x = x'\cos\theta - y'\sin\theta = x'\left(\dfrac{3}{5}\right) - y'\left(\dfrac{4}{5}\right) = \dfrac{3x' - 4y'}{5}$

$y = x'\sin\theta + y'\cos\theta = x'\left(\dfrac{4}{5}\right) + y'\left(\dfrac{3}{5}\right) = \dfrac{4x' + 3y'}{5}$

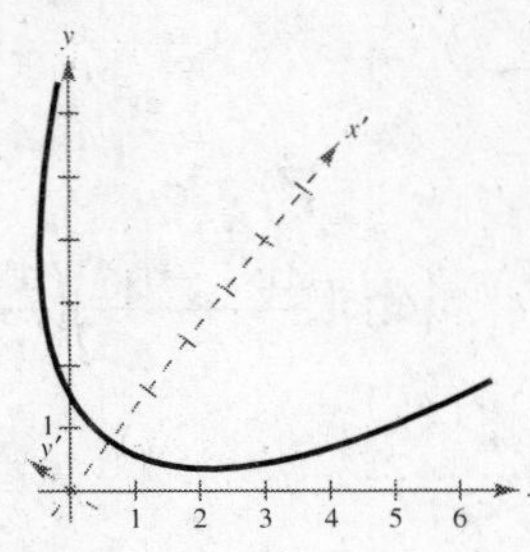

$$16x^2 - 24xy + 9y^2 - 60x - 80y + 100 = 0$$

$$16\left(\frac{3x' - 4y'}{5}\right)^2 - 24\left(\frac{3x' - 4y'}{5}\right)\left(\frac{4x' + 3y'}{5}\right) + 9\left(\frac{4x' + 3y'}{5}\right)^2 - 60\left(\frac{3x' - 4y'}{5}\right) - 80\left(\frac{4x' + 3y'}{5}\right) + 100 = 0$$

$$\frac{144(x')^2}{25} - \frac{384x'y'}{25} + \frac{256(y')^2}{25} - \frac{288(x')^2}{25} + \frac{168x'y'}{25} + \frac{288(y')^2}{25} + \frac{144(x')^2}{25} + \frac{216x'y'}{25}$$

$$+ \frac{81(y')^2}{25} - 36x' + 48y' - 64x' - 48y' + 100 = 0$$

$$25(y')^2 - 100x' + 100 = 0$$

$$(y')^2 = 4(x' - 1)$$

Parabola

13. $9x^2 + 24xy + 16y^2 + 90x - 130y = 0$

$A = 9, B = 24, C = 16$

$\cot 2\theta = \dfrac{A - C}{B} = -\dfrac{7}{24} \Rightarrow \theta \approx 53.13°$

$\cos 2\theta = -\dfrac{7}{25}$

$\sin \theta = \sqrt{\dfrac{1 - \cos 2\theta}{2}} = \sqrt{\dfrac{1 - (-7/25)}{2}} = \dfrac{4}{5}$

$\cos \theta = \sqrt{\dfrac{1 + \cos 2\theta}{2}} = \sqrt{\dfrac{1 + (-7/25)}{2}} = \dfrac{3}{5}$

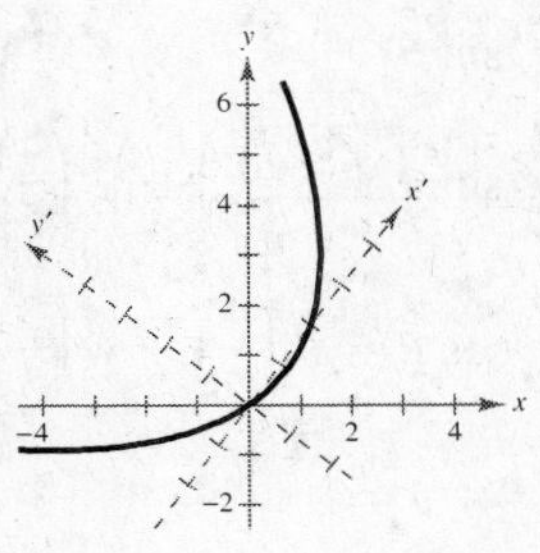

$x = x'\cos\theta - y'\sin\theta$ $\qquad$ $y = x'\sin\theta + y'\cos\theta$

$= x'\left(\dfrac{3}{5}\right) - y'\left(\dfrac{4}{5}\right)$ $\qquad$ $= x'\left(\dfrac{4}{5}\right) + y'\left(\dfrac{3}{5}\right)$

$= \dfrac{3x' - 4y'}{5}$ $\qquad$ $= \dfrac{4x' + 3y'}{5}$

—CONTINUED—

13. —CONTINUED—

$$9x^2 + 24xy + 16y^2 + 90x - 130y = 0$$

$$9\left(\frac{3x' - 4y'}{5}\right)^2 + 24\left(\frac{3x' - 4y'}{5}\right)\left(\frac{4x' + 3y'}{5}\right) + 16\left(\frac{4x' + 3y'}{5}\right)^2 + 90\left(\frac{3x' - 4y'}{5}\right) - 130\left(\frac{4x' + 3y'}{5}\right) = 0$$

$$\frac{81(x')^2}{25} - \frac{216x'y'}{25} + \frac{144(y')^2}{25} + \frac{288(x')^2}{25} - \frac{168x'y'}{25} - \frac{288(y')^2}{25} + \frac{256(x')^2}{25} + \frac{384x'y'}{25} + \frac{144(y')^2}{25} + 54x' - 72y' - 104x' - 78y' = 0$$

$$25(x')^2 - 50x' - 150y' = 0$$

$$(x')^2 - 2x' + 1 = 6y' + 1$$

$$(x' - 1)^2 = 6\left(y' + \frac{1}{6}\right), \text{ Parabola}$$

14. $9x^2 + 24xy + 16y^2 + 80x - 60y = 0$

$A = 9, B = 24, C = 16$

$\cot 2\theta = \frac{A - C}{B} = -\frac{7}{24} \Rightarrow \theta \approx 53.13°$

$\cos 2\theta = -\frac{7}{25}$

$\sin \theta = \sqrt{\frac{1 - \cos 2\theta}{2}} = \sqrt{\frac{1 - (-7/25)}{2}} = \frac{4}{5}$

$\cos \theta = \sqrt{\frac{1 + \cos 2\theta}{2}} = \sqrt{\frac{1 + (-7/25)}{2}} = \frac{3}{5}$

$x = x' \cos \theta - y' \sin \theta \qquad y = x' \sin \theta + y' \cos \theta$

$x = x' \cos \theta - y' \sin \theta = x'\left(\frac{3}{5}\right) - y'\left(\frac{4}{5}\right) = \frac{3x' - 4y'}{5}$

$y = x' \sin \theta + y' \cos \theta = x'\left(\frac{4}{5}\right) + y'\left(\frac{3}{5}\right) = \frac{4x' + 3y'}{5}$

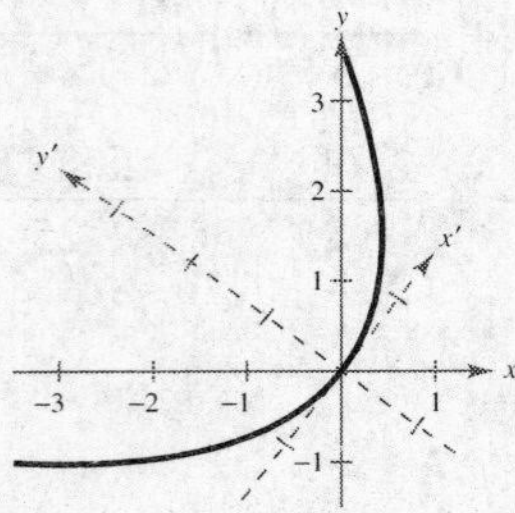

$$9x^2 + 24xy + 16y^2 + 80x - 60y = 0$$

$$9\left(\frac{3x' - 4y'}{5}\right)^2 + 24\left(\frac{3x' - 4y'}{5}\right)\left(\frac{4x' + 3y'}{5}\right) + 16\left(\frac{4x' + 3y'}{5}\right)^2 + 80\left(\frac{3x' - 4y'}{5}\right) - 60\left(\frac{4x' + 3y'}{5}\right) = 0$$

$$\frac{81(x')^2}{25} - \frac{216x'y'}{25} + \frac{144(y')^2}{25} + \frac{288(x')^2}{25} - \frac{168x'y'}{25} - \frac{288(y')^2}{25} + \frac{256(x')^2}{25} + \frac{384x'y'}{25} + \frac{144(y')^2}{25} + 48x' - 64y' - 48x' - 36y' = 0$$

$$25(x')^2 - 100y' = 0$$

$$(x')^2 = 4y',$$

Parabola

15. $x^2 + 3xy + y^2 = 20$

$$\cot 2\theta = \frac{A - C}{B} = \frac{1 - 1}{3} = 0 \Rightarrow \theta = \frac{\pi}{4} = 45°$$

Solve for y in terms of x:

$$y^2 + 3xy = 20 - x^2$$

$$y^2 + 3xy + \frac{9x^2}{4} = 20 - x^2 + \frac{9x^2}{4}$$

$$\left(y + \frac{3}{2}x\right)^2 = 20 + \frac{5x^2}{4} = \frac{80 + 5x^2}{4}$$

$$y = -\frac{3}{2}x \pm \frac{\sqrt{80 + 5x^2}}{2}$$

Graph $y_1 = -\frac{3x}{2} + \frac{\sqrt{80 + 5x^2}}{2}$ and $y_2 = -\frac{3x}{2} - \frac{\sqrt{80 + 5x^2}}{2}$.

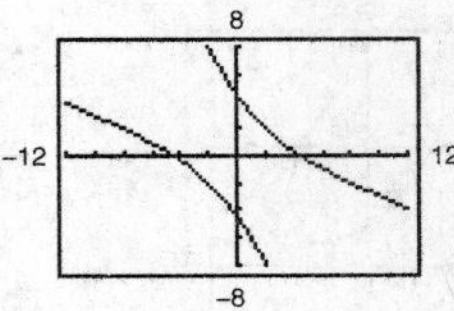

16. $x^2 - 4xy + 2y^2 = 8$

$A = 1, B = -4, C = 2$

$$\cot 2\theta = \frac{A - C}{B} = \frac{1 - 2}{-4} = \frac{1}{4}$$

$$\frac{1}{\tan 2\theta} = \frac{1}{4}$$

$$\tan 2\theta = 4$$

$$2\theta \approx 75.96°$$

$$\theta \approx 37.98°$$

To graph conic with a graphing calculator, we need to solve for y in terms of x.

$$x^2 - 4xy + 2y^2 = 8$$

$$y^2 - 2xy + x^2 = 4 - \frac{x^2}{2} + x^2$$

$$(y - x)^2 = 4 + \frac{x^2}{2}$$

$$y - x = \pm\sqrt{4 + \frac{x^2}{2}}$$

$$y = x \pm \sqrt{4 + \frac{x^2}{2}}$$

Graph $y_1 = x + \sqrt{4 + \frac{x^2}{2}}$ and

$y_2 = x - \sqrt{4 + \frac{x^2}{2}}$.

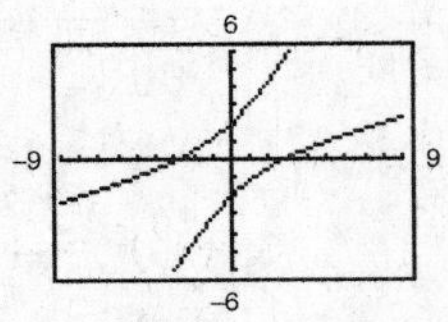

17. $17x^2 + 32xy - 7y^2 = 75$

$$\cot 2\theta = \frac{A - C}{B} = \frac{17 + 7}{32} = \frac{24}{32} = \frac{3}{4} \Rightarrow \theta \approx 26.57°$$

Solve for y in terms of x by completing the square.

$$-7y^2 + 32xy = -17x^2 + 75$$

$$y^2 - \frac{32}{7}xy = \frac{17}{7}x^2 - \frac{75}{7}$$

$$y^2 - \frac{32}{7}xy + \frac{256}{49}x^2 = \frac{119}{49}x^2 - \frac{525}{49} + \frac{256}{49}x^2$$

$$\left(y - \frac{16}{7}x\right)^2 = \frac{375x^2 - 525}{49}$$

$$y = \frac{16}{7}x \pm \sqrt{\frac{375x^2 - 525}{49}}$$

$$y = \frac{16x \pm 5\sqrt{15x^2 - 21}}{7}$$

Graph $y_1 = \frac{16x + 5\sqrt{15x^2 - 21}}{7}$ and

$y_2 = \frac{16x - 5\sqrt{15x^2 - 21}}{7}$.

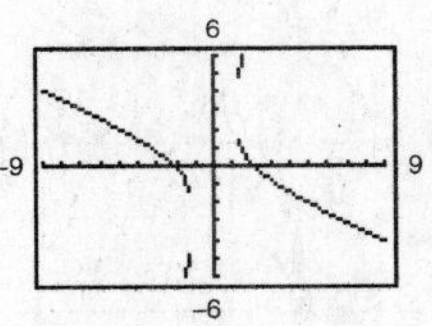

18. $40x^2 + 36xy + 25y^2 = 52$

$A = 40, B = 36, C = 25$

$\cot 2\theta = \frac{A - C}{B} = \frac{40 - 25}{36} = \frac{5}{12}$

$\frac{1}{\tan 2\theta} = \frac{5}{12}$

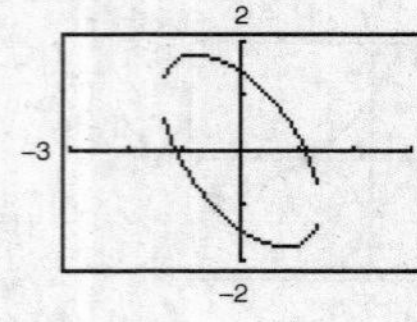

$\tan 2\theta = \frac{12}{5}$

$2\theta \approx 67.38°$

$\theta \approx 33.69°$

Solve for y in terms of x by completing the square:

$$25y^2 + 36xy = 52 - 40x^2$$

$$y^2 + \frac{36}{25}xy = \frac{52}{25} - \frac{40}{25}x^2$$

$$y^2 + \frac{36}{25}xy + \frac{324}{625}x^2 = \frac{52}{25} - \frac{40}{25}x^2 + \frac{324}{625}x^2$$

$$\left(y + \frac{18}{25}x\right)^2 = \frac{1300 - 676x^2}{625}$$

$$y + \frac{18}{25}x = \pm\sqrt{\frac{1300 - 676x^2}{625}}$$

$$y = \frac{-18x \pm \sqrt{1300 - 676x^2}}{25}$$

Graph $y_1 = \frac{-18x + \sqrt{1300 - 676x^2}}{25}$ and

$y_2 = \frac{-18x - \sqrt{1300 - 676x^2}}{25}$.

19. $32x^2 + 48xy + 8y^2 = 50$

$\cot 2\theta = \frac{A - C}{B} = \frac{32 - 8}{48} = \frac{1}{2} \implies \theta \approx 31.72°$

Solve for y in terms of x:

$$8y^2 + 48xy = -32x^2 + 50$$

$$y^2 + 6xy = -4x^2 + \frac{25}{4}$$

$$y^2 + 6xy + 9x^2 = -4x^2 + \frac{25}{4} + 9x^2$$

$$(y + 3x)^2 = 5x^2 + \frac{25}{4} = \frac{20x^2 + 25}{4}$$

$$y = -3x \pm \frac{\sqrt{20x^2 + 25}}{2}$$

Graph $y_1 = -3x + \frac{\sqrt{20x^2 + 25}}{2}$ and

$y_2 = -3x - \frac{\sqrt{20x^2 + 25}}{2}$.

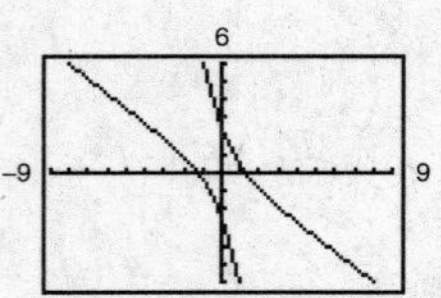

20. $4x^2 - 12xy + 9y^2 + (4\sqrt{13} - 12)x - (6\sqrt{13} + 8)y = 91$

$A = 4, B = -12, C = 9$

$\cot 2\theta = \frac{A - C}{B} = \frac{4 - 9}{-12} = \frac{5}{12}$

$\frac{1}{\tan 2\theta} = \frac{5}{12}$

$\tan 2\theta = \frac{12}{5}$

$2\theta \approx 67.38°$

$\theta \approx 33.69°$

—CONTINUED—

20. —CONTINUED—

Solve for y in terms of x with the Quadratic Formula:

$$4x^2 - 12xy + 9y^2 + (4\sqrt{13} - 12)x - (6\sqrt{13} + 8)y = 91$$

$$9y^2 - (12x + 6\sqrt{13} + 8)y + (4x^2 + 4\sqrt{13}x - 12x - 91) = 0$$

$$a = 9, b = -(12x + 6\sqrt{13} + 8), c = 4x^2 + 4\sqrt{13}x - 12x - 91$$

$$y = \frac{-b \pm \sqrt{b^2 - 4ac}}{2a}$$

$$y = \frac{(12x + 6\sqrt{13} + 8) \pm \sqrt{(12x + 6\sqrt{13} + 8)^2 - 4(9)(4x^2 + 4\sqrt{13}x - 12x - 91)}}{18}$$

$$= \frac{(12x + 6\sqrt{13} + 8) \pm \sqrt{624x + 3808 + 96\sqrt{13}}}{18}$$

Graph $y_1 = \dfrac{12x + 6\sqrt{13} + 8 + \sqrt{624x + 3808 + 96\sqrt{13}}}{18}$ and

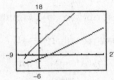

$y_2 = \dfrac{12x + 6\sqrt{13} + 8 - \sqrt{624x + 3808 + 96\sqrt{13}}}{18}$.

21. $xy + 4 = 0$

$B^2 - 4AC = 1 \Rightarrow$ The graph is a hyperbola.

$\cot 2\theta = \dfrac{A - C}{B} = 0 \Rightarrow \theta = 45°$

Matches graph (e).

22. $x^2 + 2xy + y^2 = 0$

$$(x + y)^2 = 0$$

$$x + y = 0$$

$$y = -x$$

The graph is a line. Matches graph (b).

23. $-2x^2 + 3xy + 2y^2 + 3 = 0$

$B^2 - 4AC = (3)^2 - 4(-2)(2)$

$= 25 \Rightarrow$ The graph is a hyperbola.

$\cot 2\theta = \dfrac{A - C}{B} = -\dfrac{4}{3} \Rightarrow \theta \approx -18.43°$

Matches graph (f).

24. $x^2 - xy + 3y^2 - 5 = 0$

$A = 1, B = -1, C = 3$

$B^2 - 4AC = (-1)^2 - 4(1)(3) = -11$

The graph is an ellipse or circle.

$\cot 2\theta = \dfrac{A - C}{B} = \dfrac{1 - 3}{-1} = 2 \Rightarrow \theta \approx 13.28°$

Matches graph (a).

25. $3x^2 + 2xy + y^2 - 10 = 0$

$B^2 - 4AC = (2)^2 - 4(3)(1)$

$= -8 \Rightarrow$ The graph is an ellipse or circle.

$\cot 2\theta = \dfrac{A - C}{B} = 1 \Rightarrow \theta = 22.5°$

Matches graph (d).

26. $x^2 - 4xy + 4y^2 + 10x - 30 = 0$

$A = 1, B = -4, C = 4$

$B^2 - 4AC = (-4)^2 - 4(1)(4) = 0$

The graph is a parabola.

$\cot 2\theta = \dfrac{A - C}{B} = \dfrac{1 - 4}{-4} = \dfrac{3}{4} \Rightarrow \theta \approx 26.57°$

Matches graph (c).

27. $16x^2 - 24xy + 9y^2 - 30x - 40y = 0$

(a) $B^2 - 4AC = (-24)^2 - 4(16)(9) = 0 \implies$ Parabola

(b) $9y^2 - (24x + 40)y + (16x^2 - 30x) = 0$

$$y = \frac{(24x + 40) \pm \sqrt{(24x + 40)^2 - 4(9)(16x^2 - 30x)}}{2(9)}$$

$$= \frac{24x + 40 \pm \sqrt{3000x + 1600}}{18}$$

(c)

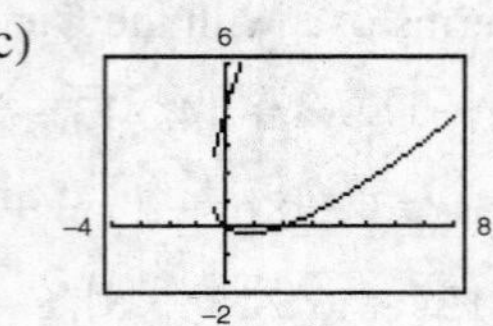

28. (a) $B^2 - 4AC = (-4)^2 - 4(1)(-2)$

$= 16 + 8 = 24$

$> 0 \implies$ Hyperbola

(b) $-2y^2 - 4xy + x^2 - 6 = 0$

$$y = \frac{4x \pm \sqrt{16x^2 - 4(-2)(x^2 - 6)}}{-4}$$

$$= \frac{4x \pm \sqrt{24x^2 - 48}}{-4}$$

(c)

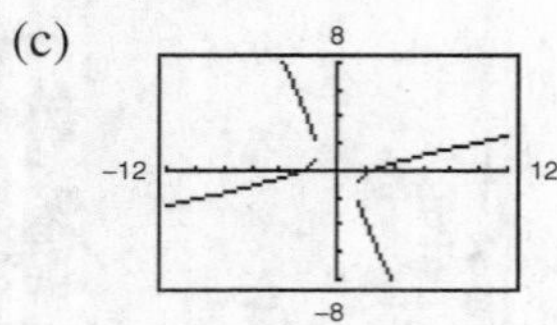

29. $15x^2 - 8xy + 7y^2 - 45 = 0$

(a) $B^2 - 4AC = (-8)^2 - 4(15)(7)$

$= -356 \implies$ Ellipse or circle

(b) $7y^2 - 8xy + (15x^2 - 45) = 0$

$$y = \frac{8x \pm \sqrt{(-8x)^2 - 4(7)(15x^2 - 45)}}{14}$$

$$= \frac{8x \pm \sqrt{1260 - 356x^2}}{14}$$

(c)

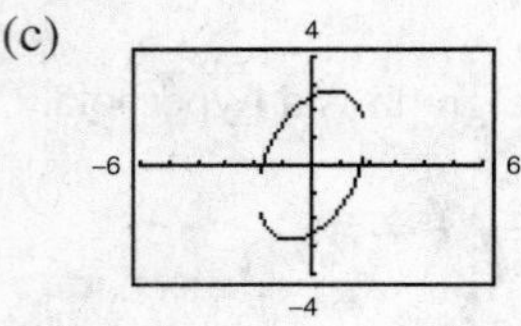

30. (a) $B^2 - 4AC = 4^2 - 4(2)(5)$

$= -24 < 0 \implies$ Ellipse or circle

(b) $5y^2 + (4x - 4)y + (2x^2 + 3x - 20) = 0$

$$y = \frac{(4 - 4x) \pm \sqrt{(4x - 4)^2 - 4(5)(2x^2 + 3x - 20)}}{10}$$

$$= \frac{(4 - 4x) \pm \sqrt{-24x^2 - 92x + 416}}{10}$$

(c)

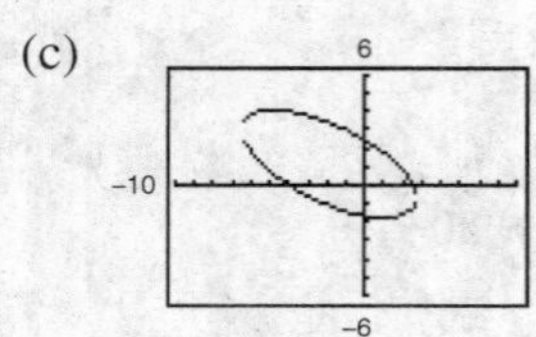

31. $x^2 - 6xy - 5y^2 + 4x - 22 = 0$

(a) $B^2 - 4AC = (-6)^2 - 4(1)(-5)$

$= 56 \implies$ Hyperbola

(b) $-5y^2 - 6xy + (x^2 + 4x - 22) = 0$

$$y = \frac{6x \pm \sqrt{(-6x)^2 - 4(-5)(x^2 + 4x - 22)}}{-10}$$

$$= \frac{6x \pm \sqrt{56x^2 + 80x - 440}}{-10}$$

(c)

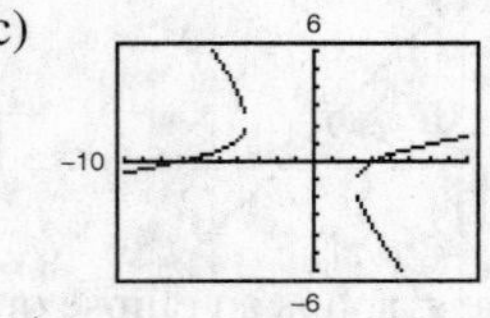

32. (a) $B^2 - 4AC = (-60)^2 - 4(36)(25)$

$= 0 \implies$ Parabola

(b) $25y^2 + (9 - 60x)y + 36x^2 = 0$

$$y = \frac{(60x - 9) \pm \sqrt{(9 - 60x)^2 - 100(36x^2)}}{50}$$

$$= \frac{60x - 9 \pm \sqrt{-1080x + 81}}{50}$$

(c)

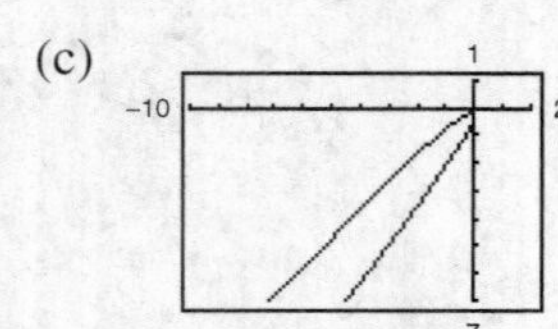

33. $x^2 + 4xy + 4y^2 - 5x - y - 3 = 0$

(a) $B^2 - 4AC = 4^2 - 4(1)(4) = 0 \Rightarrow$ Parabola

(b) $4y^2 + (4x - 1)y + (x^2 - 5x - 3) = 0$

$$y = \frac{(1 - 4x) \pm \sqrt{(4x - 1)^2 - 4(4)(x^2 - 5x - 3)}}{8}$$

$$= \frac{1 - 4x \pm \sqrt{72x + 49}}{8}$$

(c)

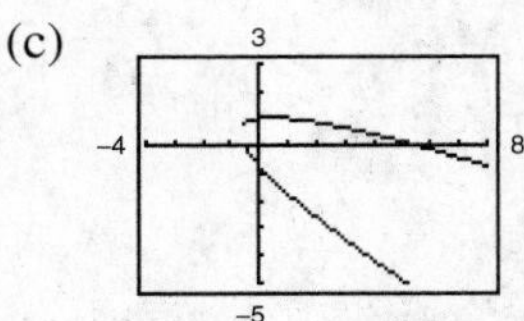

34. (a) $B^2 - 4AC = 1 - 4(1)(4)$

$= -15 < 0 \Rightarrow$ Ellipse or circle

(b) $4y^2 + (x + 1)y + (x^2 + x - 4) = 0$

$$y = \frac{-(x + 1) \pm \sqrt{(x + 1)^2 - 4(4)(x^2 + x - 4)}}{8}$$

$$= \frac{-x - 1 \pm \sqrt{-15x^2 - 14x + 65}}{8}$$

(c)

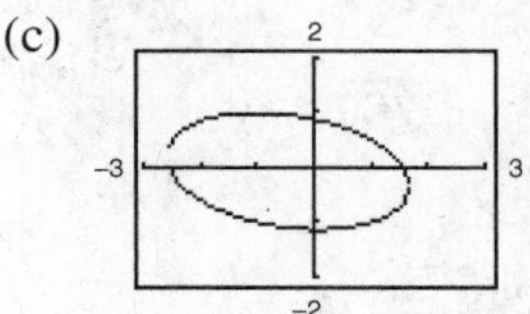

35. $y^2 - 16x^2 = 0$

$y^2 = 16x^2$

$y = \pm 4x$

Two intersecting lines

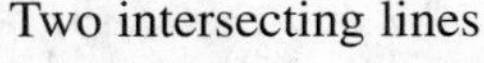

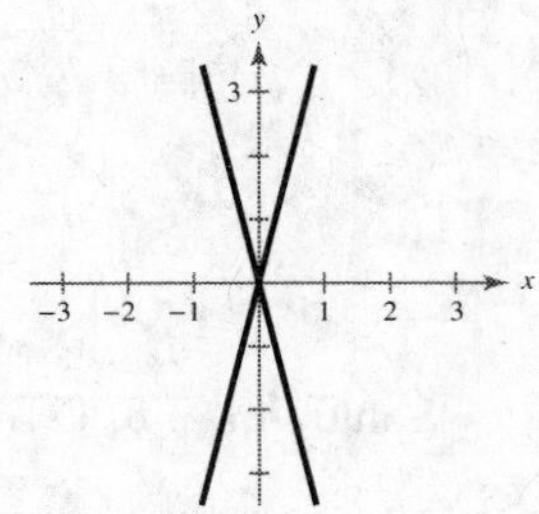

36. $x^2 + y^2 - 2x + 6y + 10 = 0$

$(x^2 - 2x + 1) + (y^2 + 6y + 9) = -10 + 1 + 9$

$(x - 1)^2 + (y + 3)^2 = 0$

Point at $(1, -3)$

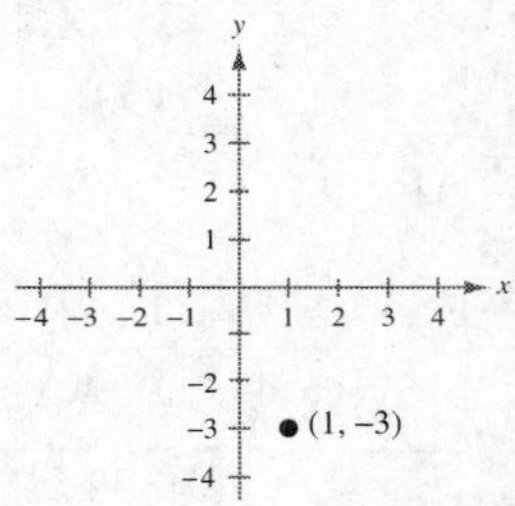

37. $x^2 + 2xy + y^2 - 1 = 0$

$(x + y)^2 - 1 = 0$

$(x + y)^2 = 1$

$x + y = \pm 1$

$y = -x \pm 1$

Two parallel lines

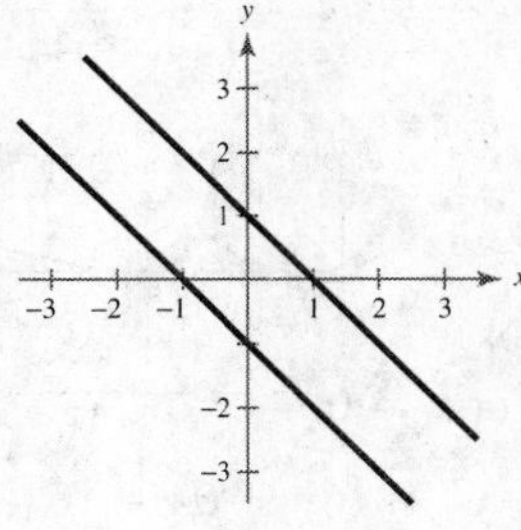

38. $x^2 - 10xy + y^2 = 0$

$y^2 - 10xy + 25x^2 = 25x^2 - x^2$

$(y - 5x)^2 = 24x^2$

$y - 5x = \pm\sqrt{24x^2}$

$y = 5x \pm 2\sqrt{6}x$

$y = (5 \pm 2\sqrt{6})x$

Two lines

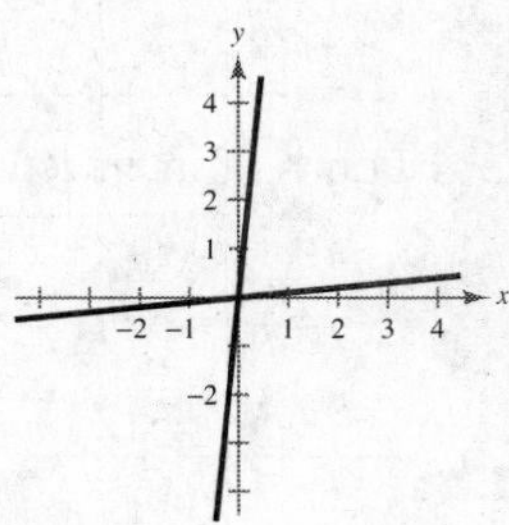

39. $x^2 + y^2 = 4$

$3x - y^2 = 0$

Adding:

$x^2 + 3x - 4 = 0$

$(x + 4)(x - 1) = 0 \Rightarrow x = 1, -4$

For $x = 1, y = \pm\sqrt{3}$.

$x = -4$ is impossible.

Solutions: $(1, \sqrt{3}), (1, -\sqrt{3})$

40. $4x^2 + 9y^2 - 36y = 0$

$x^2 + y^2 - 27 = 0 \Rightarrow x^2 = 27 - y^2$

$4(27 - y^2) + 9y^2 - 36y = 0$

$5y^2 - 36y + 108 = 0$

$$y = \frac{36 \pm \sqrt{36^2 - 4(5)(108)}}{10}$$

$$= \frac{36 \pm \sqrt{-864}}{10}$$

No solution

41. $-4x^2 - y^2 - 16x + 24y - 16 = 0$

$4x^2 + y^2 + 40x - 24y + 208 = 0$

$24x + 192 = 0$

$24x = -192$

$x = -8$

For $x = -8$:

$-4(64) - y^2 - 16(-8) + 24y - 16 = 0$

$-y^2 + 24y - 144 = 0$

$y^2 - 24y + 144 = 0$

$(y - 12)^2 = 0$

$\Rightarrow y = 12$

Solution: $(-8, 12)$

42. $x^2 - 4y^2 - 20x - 64y - 172 = 0 \Rightarrow (x - 10)^2 - 4(y + 8)^2 = 16$

$16x^2 + 4y^2 - 320x + 64y + 1600 = 0 \Rightarrow 16(x - 10)^2 + 4(y + 8)^2 = 256$

$17x^2 - 340x + 1428 = 0$

$(17x - 238)(x - 6) = 0$

$x = 6$ or $x = 14$

When $x = 6$:

$6^2 - 4y^2 - 20(6) - 64y - 172 = 0$

$-4y^2 - 64y - 256 = 0$

$y^2 + 16y + 64 = 0$

$(y + 8)^2 = 0$

$y = -8$

When $x = 14$:

$14^2 - 4y^2 - 20(14) - 64y - 172 = 0$

$4y^2 + 64y + 256 = 0$

$y^2 + 16y + 64 = 0$

$(y + 8)^2 = 0$

$y = -8$

Points of intersection: $(6, -8), (14, -8)$

43. $x^2 - y^2 - 12x + 16y - 64 = 0$

$x^2 + y^2 - 12x - 16y + 64 = 0$

$2x^2 - 24x = 0$

$x^2 - 12x = 0$

$x(x - 12) = 0 \Rightarrow x = 0, 12$

For $x = 0$:

$-y^2 + 16y - 64 = 0$

$y^2 - 16y + 64 = 0$

$(y - 8)^2 = 0 \Rightarrow y = 8$

For $x = 12$:

$144 - y^2 - 12(12) + 16y - 64 = 0$

$-y^2 + 16y - 64 = 0 \Rightarrow y = 8$

Solutions: $(0, 8), (12, 8)$

44.
$$\begin{aligned} x^2 + 4y^2 - 2x - 8y + 1 &= 0 \Rightarrow (x-1)^2 + 4(y-1)^2 = 4 \\ -x^2 \qquad + 2x - 4y - 1 &= 0 \Rightarrow y = -\tfrac{1}{4}(x-1)^2 \\ \hline 4y^2 \qquad - 12y \qquad &= 0 \\ 4y(y-3) &= 0 \\ y = 0 \text{ or } y &= 3 \end{aligned}$$

When $y = 0$:

$$\begin{aligned} x^2 + 4(0)^2 - 2x - 8(0) + 1 &= 0 \\ x^2 - 2x + 1 &= 0 \\ (x-1)^2 &= 0 \\ x &= 1 \end{aligned}$$

When $y = 3$:

$$\begin{aligned} -x^2 + 2x - 4(3) - 1 &= 0 \\ x^2 - 2x + 13 &= 0 \end{aligned}$$

No real solution

Point of intersection: $(1, 0)$

45.
$$\begin{aligned} -16x^2 - \quad y^2 + 24y - \ 80 &= 0 \\ 16x^2 + 25y^2 \qquad - 400 &= 0 \\ \hline 24y^2 + 24y - 480 &= 0 \\ 24(y+5)(y-4) &= 0 \\ y = -5 \text{ or } y &= 4 \end{aligned}$$

When $y = -5$:

$$\begin{aligned} 16x^2 + 25(-5)^2 - 400 &= 0 \\ 16x^2 &= -225 \end{aligned}$$

No real solution

When $y = 4$:

$$\begin{aligned} 16x^2 + 25(4)^2 - 400 &= 0 \\ 16x^2 &= 0 \\ x &= 0 \end{aligned}$$

The point of intersection is $(0, 4)$. In standard form the equations are:

$$\frac{x^2}{4} + \frac{(y-12)^2}{64} = 1$$

$$\frac{x^2}{25} + \frac{y^2}{16} = 1$$

46.
$$\begin{aligned} 16x^2 - y^2 \qquad + 16y - 128 &= 0 \Rightarrow 16x^2 - (y-8)^2 = 64 \\ y^2 - 48x - 16y - \ 32 &= 0 \Rightarrow (y-8)^2 - 48x = 96 \\ \hline 16x^2 \qquad - 48x \qquad - 160 &= 0 \\ 16(x^2 - 3x - 10) &= 0 \\ (x-5)(x+2) &= 0 \\ x = 5 \text{ or } x &= -2 \end{aligned}$$

When $x = 5$:

$$\begin{aligned} y^2 - 48(5) - 16y - 32 &= 0 \\ y^2 - 16y - 272 &= 0 \\ y &= 8 \pm 4\sqrt{21} \end{aligned}$$

When $x = -2$:

$$\begin{aligned} y^2 - 48(-2) - 16y - 32 &= 0 \\ y^2 - 16y + 64 &= 0 \\ (y-8)^2 &= 0 \\ y &= 8 \end{aligned}$$

Points of intersection: $\left(5, 8 + 4\sqrt{21}\right), \left(5, 8 - 4\sqrt{21}\right), (-2, 8)$

47. $2x^2 - y^2 + 6 = 0$

$2x + y = 0 \Rightarrow y = -2x$

$2x^2 - (-2x)^2 + 6 = 0$

$-2x^2 + 6 = 0$

$x^2 = 3 \Rightarrow x = \pm\sqrt{3}$

Two solutions: $(\sqrt{3}, -2\sqrt{3}), (-\sqrt{3}, 2\sqrt{3})$

48. $6x^2 + 3y^2 - 12 = 0$

$x + y - 2 = 0 \Rightarrow y = 2 - x$

$6x^2 + 3(2 - x)^2 - 12 = 0$

$6x^2 + 3(4 - 4x + x^2) - 12 = 0$

$9x^2 - 12x = 0$

$3x(3x - 4) = 0$

$x = 0 \Rightarrow y = 2$

$x = \frac{4}{3} \Rightarrow y = 2 - \frac{4}{3} = \frac{2}{3}$

Solutions: $(0, 2), \left(\frac{4}{3}, \frac{2}{3}\right)$

49. $10x^2 - 25y^2 - 100x + 160 = 0$

$y^2 - 2x + 16 = 0 \Rightarrow y^2 = 2x - 16$

$10x^2 - 25(2x - 16) - 100x + 160 = 0$

$10x^2 - 150x + 560 = 0$

$x^2 - 15x + 56 = 0$

$(x - 8)(x - 7) = 0$

$x = 8 \Rightarrow y^2 = 0 \Rightarrow (8, 0)$

$x = 7 \Rightarrow y^2 = -2$ impossible

One solution: $(8, 0)$

50. $4x^2 - y^2 - 8x + 6y - 9 = 0$

$2x^2 - 3y^2 + 4x + 18y - 43 = 0$

From Equation 1:

$y^2 - 6y = 4x^2 - 8x - 9$

$3y^2 - 18y = 12x^2 - 24x - 27$

In Equation 2:

$2x^2 + 4x - 43 - (3y^2 - 18y) = 0$

$2x^2 + 4x - 43 - (12x^2 - 24x - 27) = 0$

$-10x^2 + 28x - 16 = 0$

$5x^2 - 14x + 8 = 0$

$(x - 2)(5x - 4) = 0$

$x = 2 \Rightarrow y^2 - 6y = -9$

$\Rightarrow (y - 3)^2 = 0 \Rightarrow y = 3$

$x = \frac{4}{5} \Rightarrow y^2 - 6y = -\frac{321}{25}$ No solution

Solution: $(2, 3)$

51. $xy + x - 2y + 3 = 0 \Rightarrow y = \dfrac{-x - 3}{x - 2}$

$x^2 + 4y^2 - 9 = 0$

$x^2 + 4\left(\dfrac{-x - 3}{x - 2}\right)^2 = 9$

$x^2(x - 2)^2 + 4(-x - 3)^2 = 9(x - 2)^2$

$x^2(x^2 - 4x + 4) + 4(x^2 + 6x + 9) = 9(x^2 - 4x + 4)$

$x^4 - 4x^3 + 4x^2 + 4x^2 + 24x + 36 = 9x^2 - 36x + 36$

$x^4 - 4x^3 - x^2 + 60x = 0$

$x(x + 3)(x^2 - 7x + 20) = 0$

$x = 0$ or $x = -3$

Note: $x^2 - 7x + 20 = 0$ has no real solution.

When $x = 0$: $y = \dfrac{-0 - 3}{0 - 2} = \dfrac{3}{2}$

When $x = -3$: $y = \dfrac{-(-3) - 3}{-3 - 2} = 0$

The points of intersection are $\left(0, \frac{3}{2}\right), (-3, 0)$.

52. $5x^2 - 2xy + 5y^2 - 12 = 0$

$$x + y - 1 = 0 \Rightarrow y = 1 - x$$
$$5x^2 - 2x(1 - x) + 5(1 - x)^2 - 12 = 0$$
$$5x^2 - 2x + 2x^2 + 5(1 - 2x + x^2) - 12 = 0$$
$$5x^2 - 2x + 2x^2 + 5 - 10x + 5x^2 - 12 = 0$$
$$12x^2 - 12x - 7 = 0$$
$$x = \frac{3 \pm \sqrt{30}}{6}$$

When $x = \dfrac{3 + \sqrt{30}}{6}$: $y = 1 - \dfrac{3 + \sqrt{30}}{6} = \dfrac{3 - \sqrt{30}}{6}$

When $x = \dfrac{3 - \sqrt{30}}{6}$: $y = 1 - \dfrac{3 - \sqrt{30}}{6} = \dfrac{3 + \sqrt{30}}{6}$

Points of intersection: $\left(\frac{1}{6}(3 + \sqrt{30}), \frac{1}{6}(3 - \sqrt{30})\right), \left(\frac{1}{6}(3 - \sqrt{30}), \frac{1}{6}(3 + \sqrt{30})\right)$

53. True. $B^2 - 4AC = 1 - 4k$

If $k < \frac{1}{4}$, then $B^2 - 4AC > 0$.

54. False. See Example 2. However, $A + C = A' + C'$.

55. $g(x) = \dfrac{2}{2 - x}$

Asymptotes:
$x = 2, y = 0$

Intercepts: $(0, 1)$

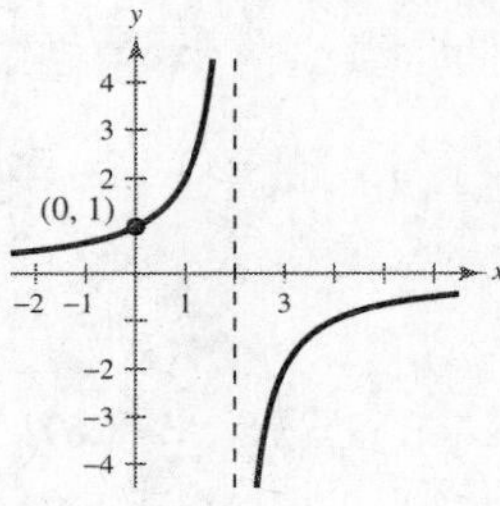

56. $f(x) = \dfrac{2x}{2 - x} = -2 + \dfrac{4}{2 - x}$

Intercept: $(0, 0)$

Asymptotes:
$x = 2, y = -2$

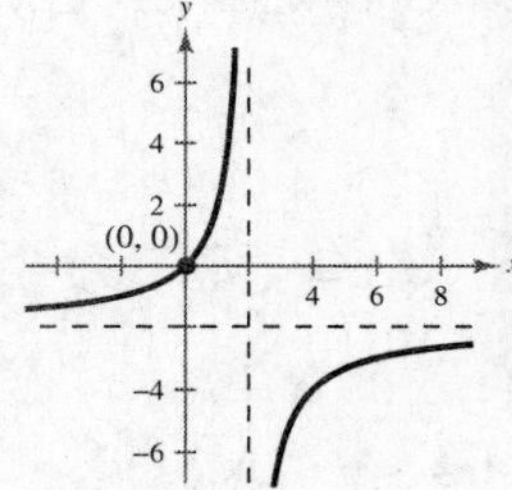

57. $h(t) = \dfrac{t^2}{2 - t} = -t - 2 + \dfrac{4}{2 - t}$

Slant asymptote: $y = -t - 2$

Vertical asymptote: $t = 2$

Intercept: $(0, 0)$

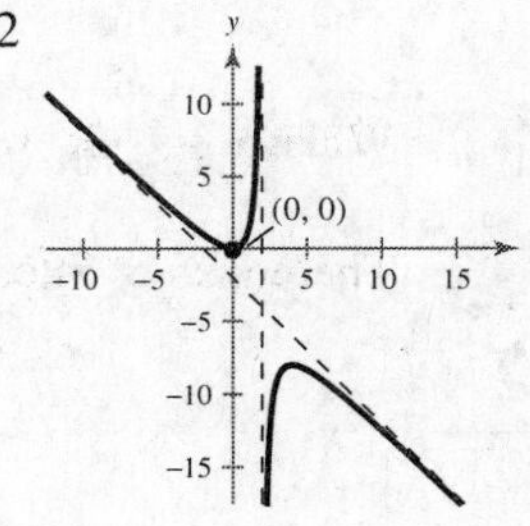

58. $g(s) = \dfrac{2}{4 - s^2}$

Intercept: $\left(0, \dfrac{1}{2}\right)$

Asymptotes:
$s = \pm 2, y = 0$

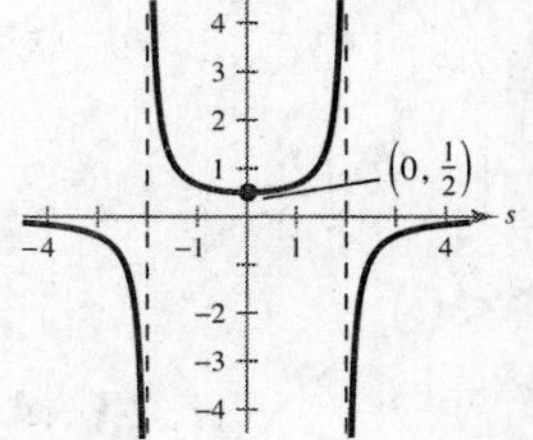

59. (a) $AB = \begin{bmatrix} 1 & -3 \\ 2 & 5 \end{bmatrix}\begin{bmatrix} 0 & 6 \\ 5 & -1 \end{bmatrix} = \begin{bmatrix} -15 & 9 \\ 25 & 7 \end{bmatrix}$

(b) $BA = \begin{bmatrix} 0 & 6 \\ 5 & -1 \end{bmatrix}\begin{bmatrix} 1 & -3 \\ 2 & 5 \end{bmatrix} = \begin{bmatrix} 12 & 30 \\ 3 & -20 \end{bmatrix}$

(c) $A^2 = \begin{bmatrix} 1 & -3 \\ 2 & 5 \end{bmatrix}\begin{bmatrix} 1 & -3 \\ 2 & 5 \end{bmatrix} = \begin{bmatrix} -5 & -18 \\ 12 & 19 \end{bmatrix}$

60. (a) $AB = \begin{bmatrix} 1 & 5 \\ 0 & -2 \end{bmatrix}\begin{bmatrix} 3 & 2 \\ -3 & 8 \end{bmatrix} = \begin{bmatrix} -12 & 42 \\ 6 & -16 \end{bmatrix}$

(b) $BA = \begin{bmatrix} 3 & 2 \\ -3 & 8 \end{bmatrix}\begin{bmatrix} 1 & 5 \\ 0 & -2 \end{bmatrix} = \begin{bmatrix} 3 & 11 \\ -3 & -31 \end{bmatrix}$

(c) $A^2 = \begin{bmatrix} 1 & 5 \\ 0 & -2 \end{bmatrix}\begin{bmatrix} 1 & 5 \\ 0 & -2 \end{bmatrix} = \begin{bmatrix} 1 & -5 \\ 0 & 4 \end{bmatrix}$

61. (a) $AB = \begin{bmatrix} 4 & -2 & 5 \end{bmatrix}\begin{bmatrix} 3 \\ -4 \\ 5 \end{bmatrix} = [12 + 8 + 25] = [45]$

(b) $BA = \begin{bmatrix} 3 \\ -4 \\ 5 \end{bmatrix}\begin{bmatrix} 4 & -2 & 5 \end{bmatrix} = \begin{bmatrix} 12 & -6 & 15 \\ -16 & 8 & -20 \\ 20 & -10 & 25 \end{bmatrix}$

(c) A^2 does not exist.

62. (a) $AB = \begin{bmatrix} 8 & -10 & 2 \\ 27 & 20 & 6 \\ -13 & 20 & -13 \end{bmatrix}$

(b) $BA = \begin{bmatrix} -9 & -14 & 0 \\ 2 & 9 & 25 \\ 9 & -1 & 15 \end{bmatrix}$

(c) $A^2 = \begin{bmatrix} -2 & -2 & -10 \\ 16 & 19 & 5 \\ 4 & -2 & 20 \end{bmatrix}$

63. $f(x) = |x + 3|$

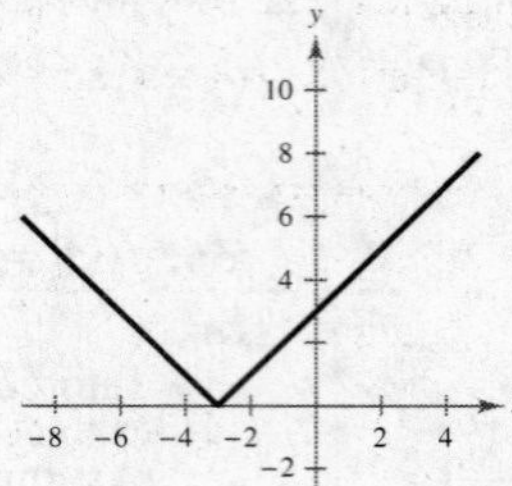

64. $f(x) = |x - 4| + 1$

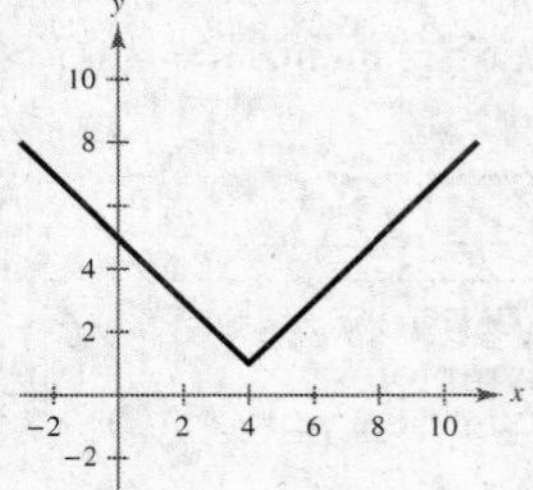

65. $g(x) = \sqrt{4 - x^2}$

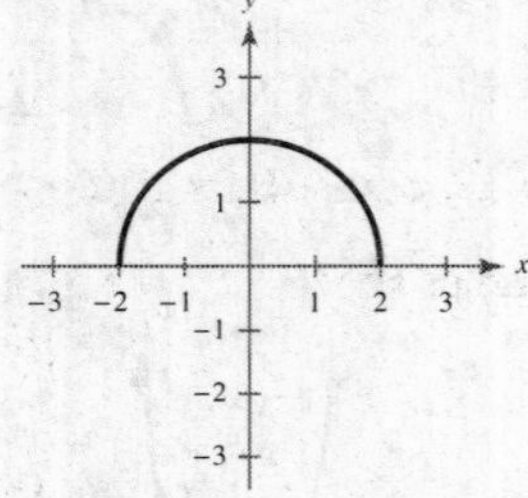

66. $g(x) = \sqrt{3x - 2}$

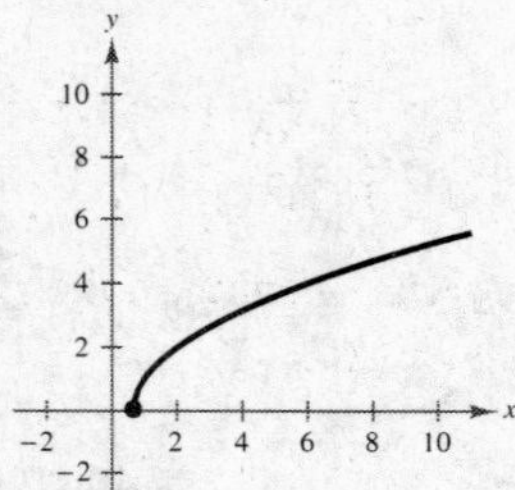

67. $h(t) = -(t - 2)^3 + 3$

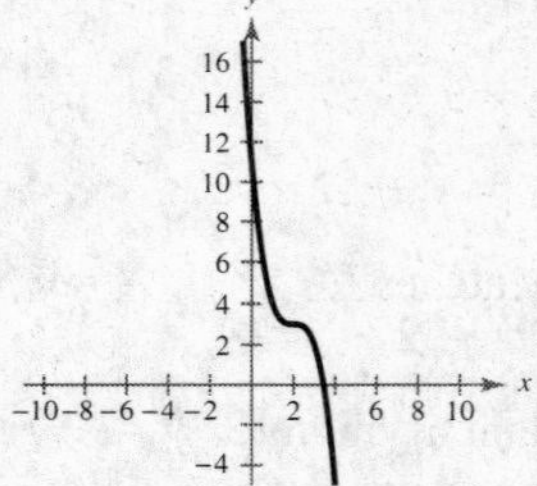

68. $h(t) = \frac{1}{2}(t + 4)^3$

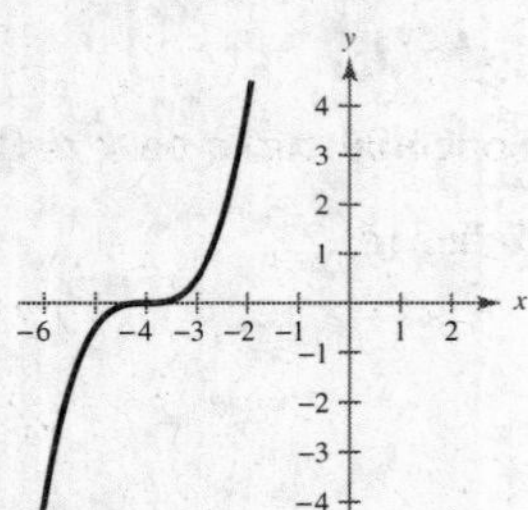

69. $f(t) = [\![t - 5]\!] + 1$

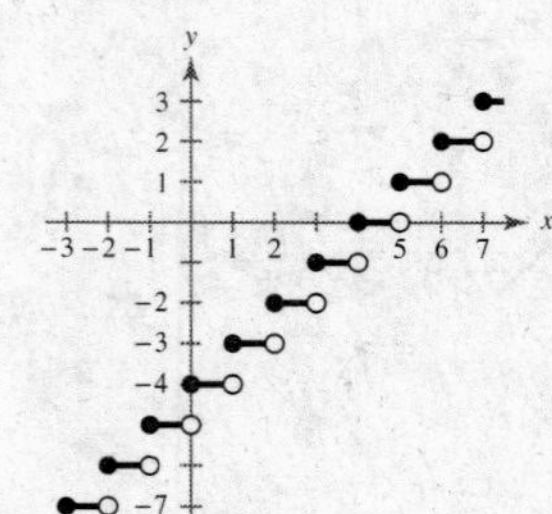

70. $f(t) = -2[\![t]\!] + 3$

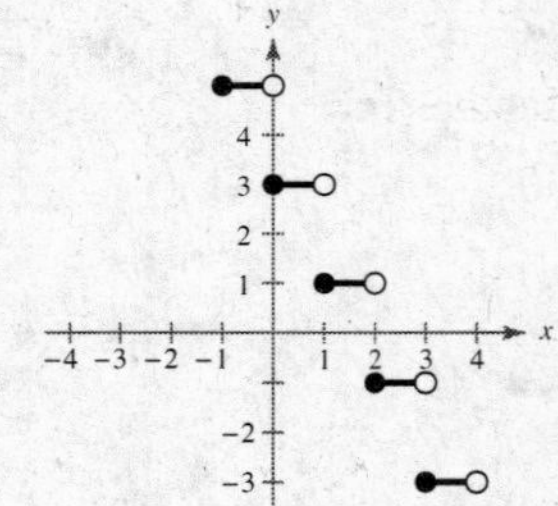

71. Area $= \frac{1}{2}ab \sin C$

$= \frac{1}{2}(8)(12) \sin 110°$

≈ 45.11

72. Area $= \frac{1}{2}ac \sin B$

$= \frac{1}{2}(25)(16) \sin 70°$

≈ 187.94

73. $s = \frac{1}{2}(11 + 18 + 10) = \frac{39}{2}$

Area $= \sqrt{s(s-a)(s-b)(s-c)}$

$= \sqrt{\frac{39}{2}\left(\frac{17}{2}\right)\left(\frac{3}{2}\right)\left(\frac{19}{2}\right)}$

≈ 48.60

74. $s = \frac{1}{2}(23 + 35 + 27) = \frac{85}{2}$

Area $= \sqrt{s(s-a)(s-b)(s-c)}$

$= \sqrt{\frac{85}{2}\left(\frac{39}{2}\right)\left(\frac{15}{2}\right)\left(\frac{31}{2}\right)}$

≈ 310.39

Section 9.5 Parametric Equations

- If f and g are continuous functions of t on an interval I, then the set of ordered pairs $(f(t), g(t))$ is a *plane curve* C. The equations $x = f(t)$ and $y = g(t)$ are *parametric equations* for C and t is the *parameter.*
- You should be able to graph plane curves with your graphing utility.
- To eliminate the parameter:

  Solve for t in one equation and substitute into the second equation.
- You should be able to find the parametric equations for a graph.

Vocabulary Check

1. plane curve, parametric equations, parameter
2. orientation
3. eliminating, parameter

1. $x = t$

$y = t + 2$

$y = x + 2$, line

Matches (c).

2. $x = t^2$

$y = t - 2 \Rightarrow t = y + 2$

$x = (y + 2)^2$

Parabola opening to the right

Matches (d).

3. $x = \sqrt{t}$

$y = t$

$y = x^2$, parabola, $x \geq 0$

Matches (b).

4. $x = \frac{1}{t} \Rightarrow t = \frac{1}{x}$

$y = t + 2 \Rightarrow y = \frac{1}{x} + 2$

Matches (a).

5. $x = \ln t \Leftrightarrow t = e^x$

$y = \frac{1}{2}t - 2$

$y = \frac{1}{2}e^x - 2$

Matches (f).

6. $x = -2\sqrt{t} \Rightarrow t = \left(\frac{x}{-2}\right)^2 = \frac{x^2}{4}$

$y = e^t$

$y = e^{x^2/4}$

Exponential curve on $x \leq 0$

Matches (e).

7. $x = \sqrt{t}, y = 2 - t$

(a)

t	0	1	2	3	4
x	0	1	$\sqrt{2}$	$\sqrt{3}$	2
y	2	1	0	-1	-2

(b) Graph by hand.

Note: $x \geq 0$

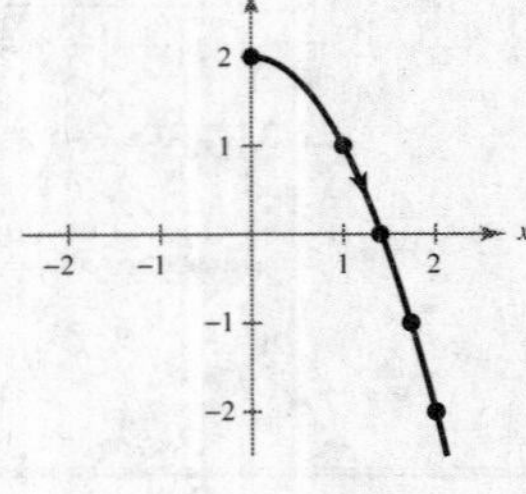

(c)

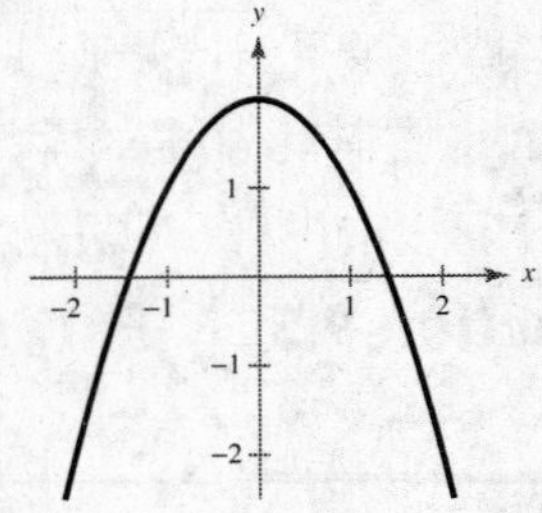

(d) $y = 2 - t = 2 - x^2$,

Parabola

In part (c), $x \geq 0$.

8. $x = 4\cos^2\theta, y = 4\sin\theta$

(a)

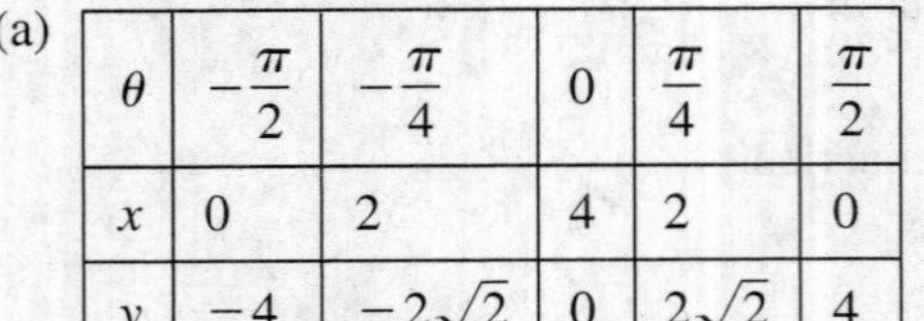

θ	$-\frac{\pi}{2}$	$-\frac{\pi}{4}$	0	$\frac{\pi}{4}$	$\frac{\pi}{2}$
x	0	2	4	2	0
y	-4	$-2\sqrt{2}$	0	$2\sqrt{2}$	4

(b)

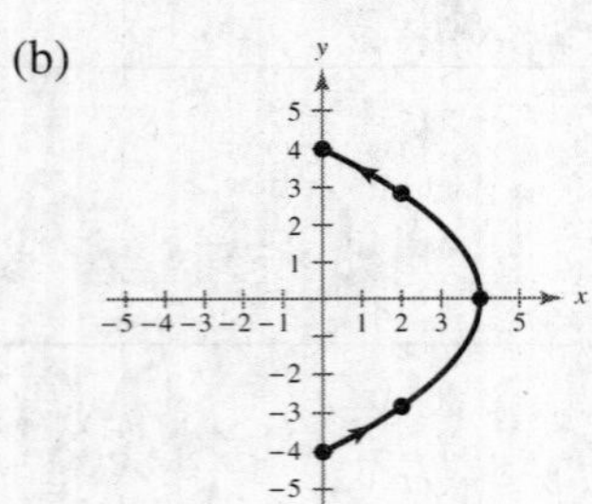

(c)

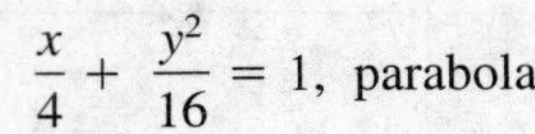

(d) $4x + y^2 = 16\cos^2\theta + 16\sin^2\theta = 16$

$\frac{x}{4} + \frac{y^2}{16} = 1$, parabola

The graph is an entire parabola rather than just the right portion.

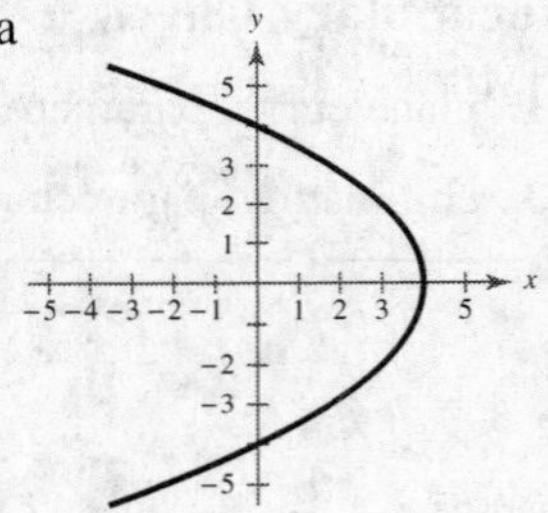

9. The graph opens upward, contains (1, 0), and is oriented left to right. Matches (b).

10. The orientation of the graph is clockwise and the center is (2, 3). Matches (c).

11. $x = t, y = -4t$

$y = -4x$

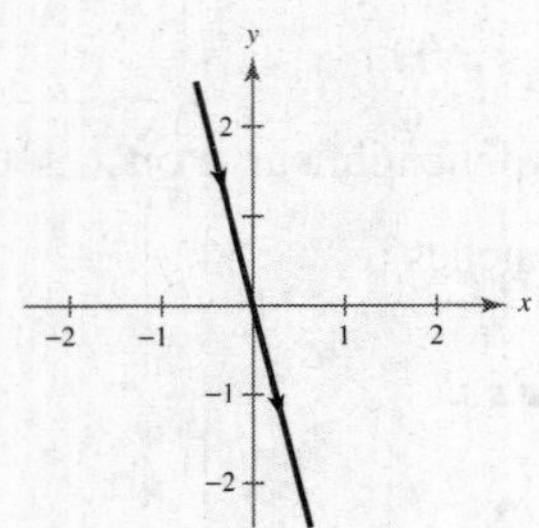

12. $x = t, \ y = \frac{1}{2}t$

$y = \frac{1}{2}x$ or $x - 2y = 0$

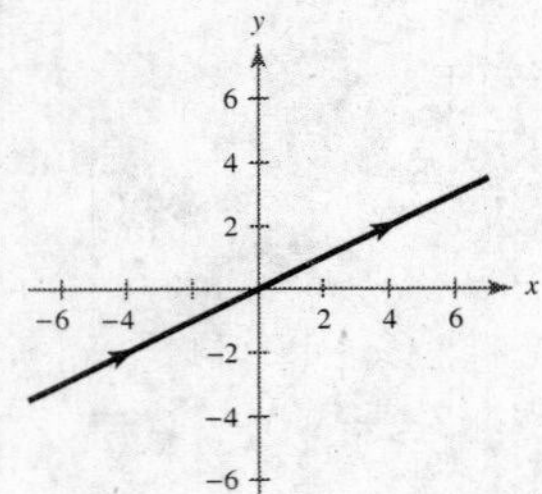

13. $x = 3t - 3, y = 2t + 1$

$$t = \frac{x + 3}{3}$$

$$y = 2\left(\frac{x + 3}{3}\right) + 1$$

$$y = \frac{2}{3}x + 3$$

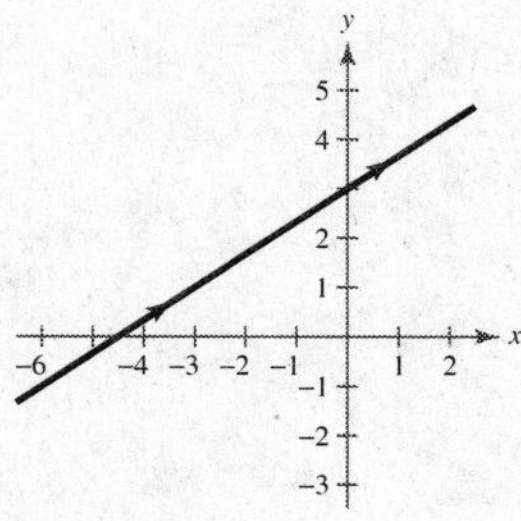

14. $x = 3 - 2t, y = 2 + 3t$

$$y = 2 + 3\left(\frac{3 - x}{2}\right)$$

$$3x + 2y - 13 = 0$$

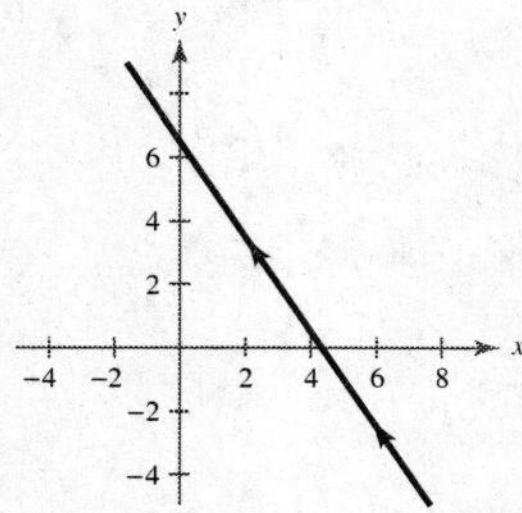

15. $x = \frac{1}{4}t, y = t^2$

$$y = (4x)^2$$

$$y = 16x^2$$

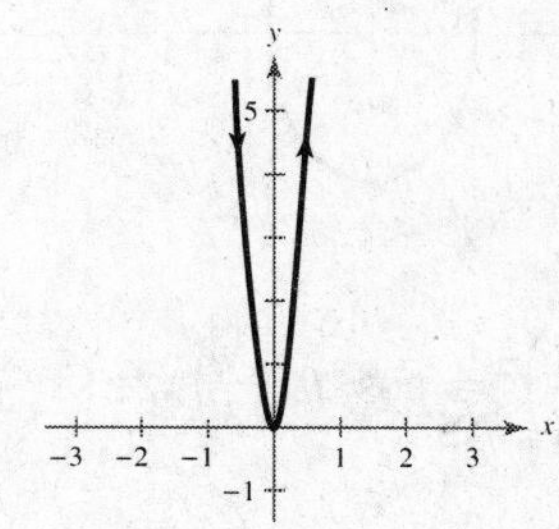

16. $x = t, \ y = t^3$

$$y = x^3$$

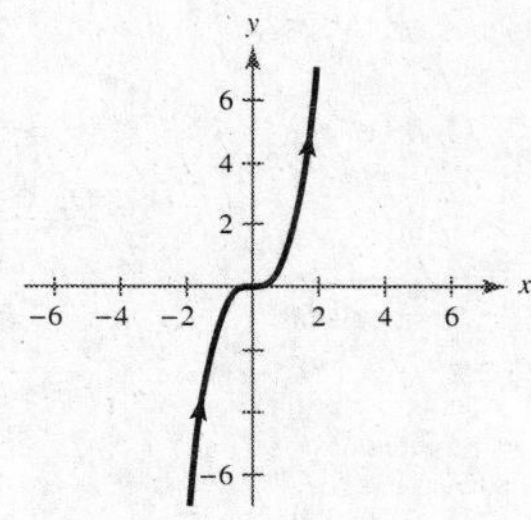

17. $x = t + 2, y = t^2$

$$t = x - 2$$

$$y = (x - 2)^2$$

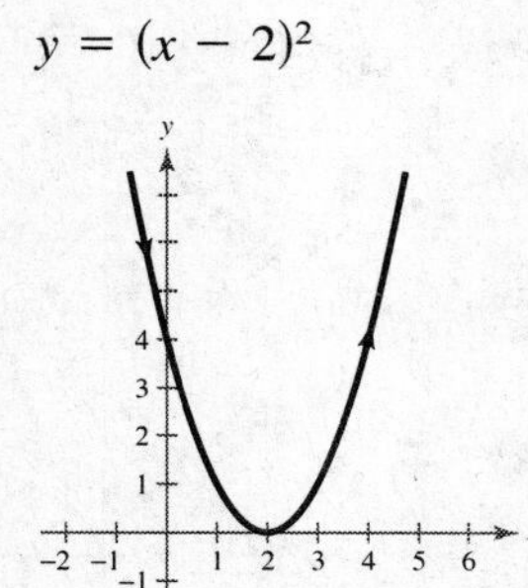

18. $x = \sqrt{t}$

$$y = 1 - t$$

$$y = 1 - x^2, \ x \geq 0$$

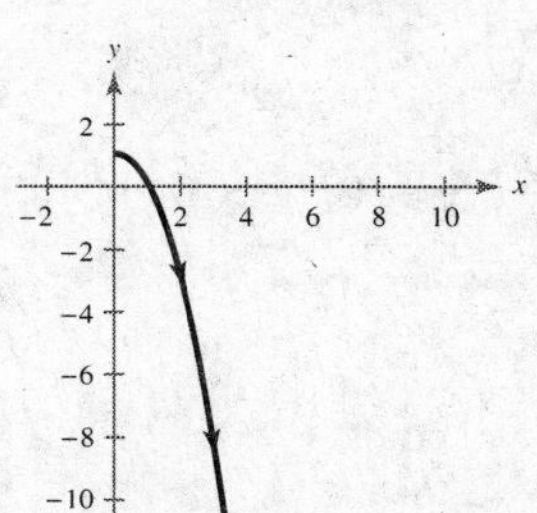

19. $x = 2t, y = |t - 2|$

$$t = \frac{x}{2} \Rightarrow y = |t - 2|$$

$$= \left|\frac{x}{2} - 2\right|$$

$$= \frac{1}{2}|x - 4|$$

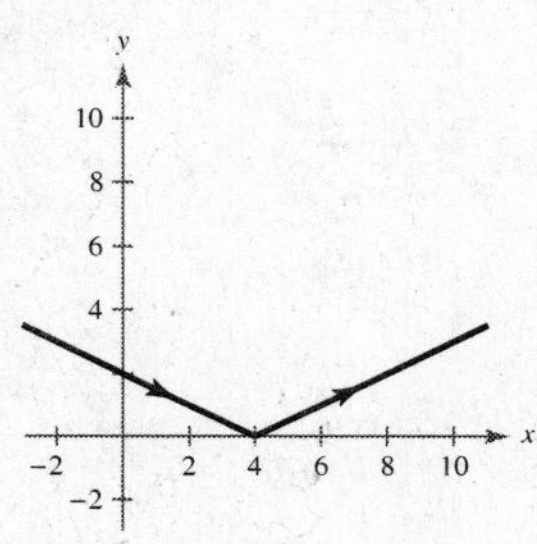

20. $x = |t - 1|$

$y = t + 2$

Eliminating the parameter t, $t = y - 2$ and

$$x = |t - 1|$$

$$= |(y - 2) - 1|$$

$$= |y - 3|.$$

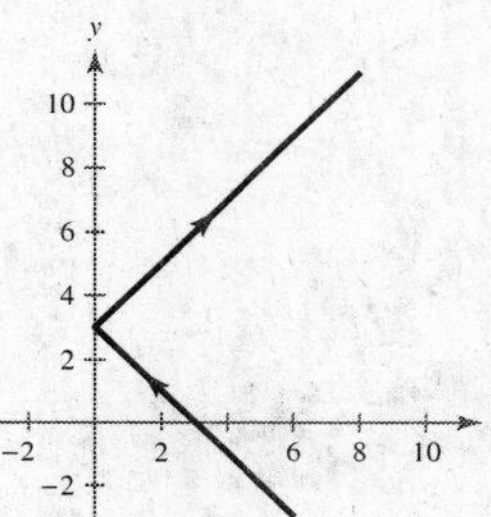

21. $x = 2\cos\theta,\ y = 3\sin\theta$

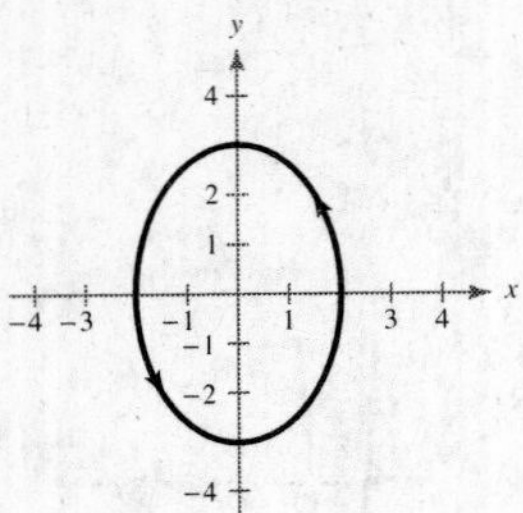

$$\left(\frac{x}{2}\right)^2 = \cos^2\theta,\ \left(\frac{y}{3}\right)^2 = \sin^2\theta$$

$$\frac{x^2}{4} + \frac{y^2}{9} = \cos^2\theta + \sin^2\theta = 1$$

$$\frac{x^2}{4} + \frac{y^2}{9} = 1, \quad \text{ellipse}$$

22. $x = \cos\theta,\ y = 4\sin\theta$

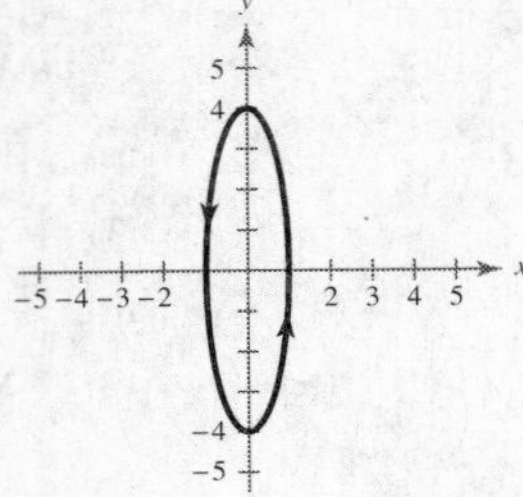

$$x^2 + \left(\frac{y}{4}\right)^2 = \cos^2\theta + \sin^2\theta = 1$$

$$x^2 + \frac{y^2}{16} = 1, \quad \text{ellipse}$$

23. $x = e^{-t} \Rightarrow \dfrac{1}{x} = e^t$

$y = e^{3t} \Rightarrow y = (e^t)^3$

$$y = \left(\frac{1}{x}\right)^3$$

$$y = \frac{1}{x^3},\ x > 0,\ y > 0$$

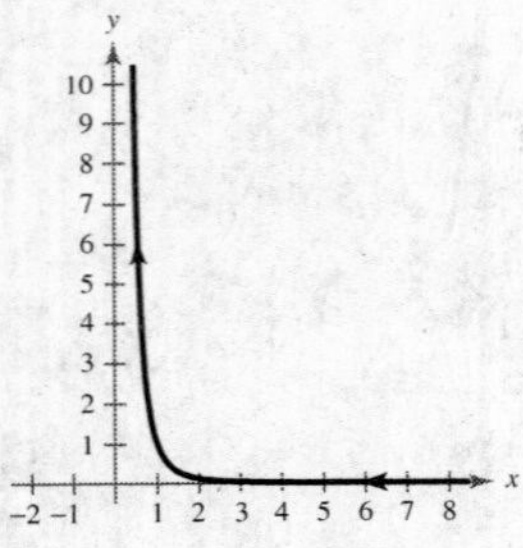

24. $x = e^{2t}$

$y = e^t \Rightarrow y^2 = e^{2t}$

$y^2 = x,\ y > 0;\ y = \sqrt{x},\ x > 0$

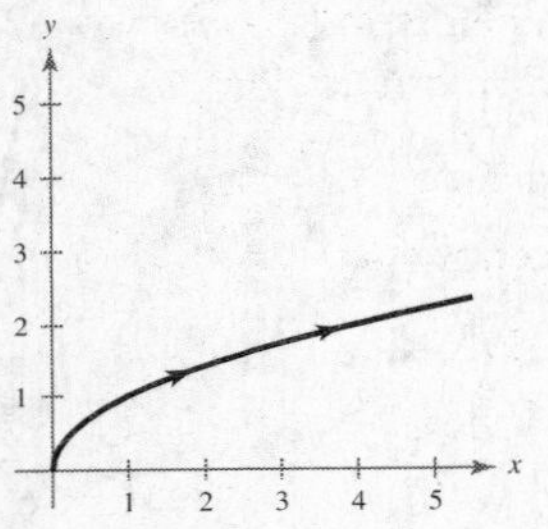

25. $x = t^3 \Rightarrow x^{1/3} = t$

$y = 3\ln t \Rightarrow y = \ln t^3$

$y = \ln(x^{1/3})^3$

$y = \ln x$

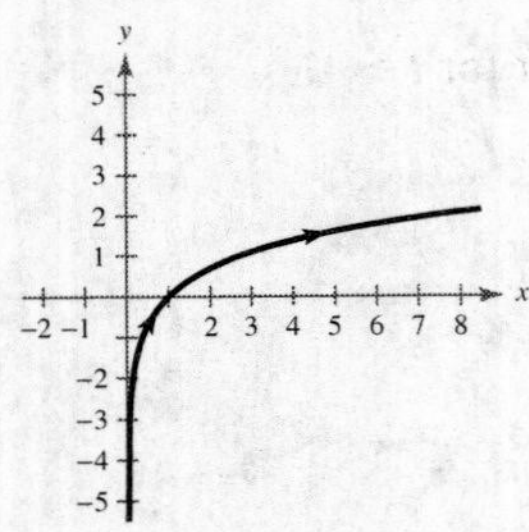

26. $x = \ln 2t \Rightarrow e^x = 2t \Rightarrow t = \frac{1}{2}e^x$

$y = 2t^2 = 2\left(\frac{1}{2}e^x\right)^2 = \frac{1}{2}e^{2x}$

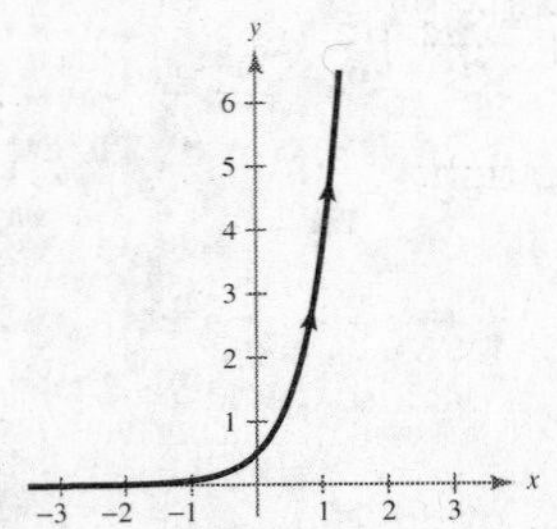

27. $x = 4 + 3\cos\theta,\ y = -2 + \sin\theta$

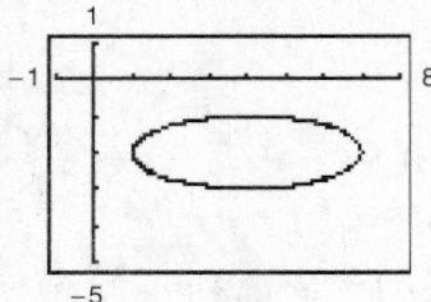

28. $x = 4 + 3\cos\theta,\ y = -2 + 2\sin\theta$

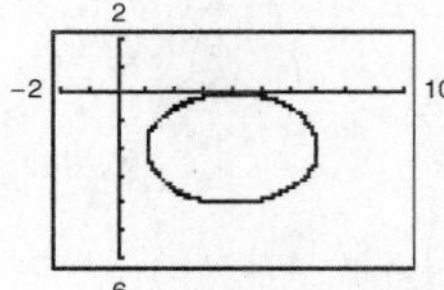

29. $x = 4\sec\theta,\ y = 2\tan\theta$

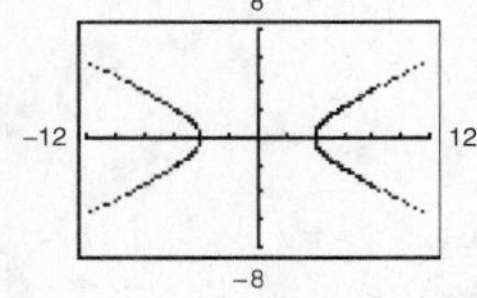

30. $x = \sec\theta$

$y = \tan\theta$

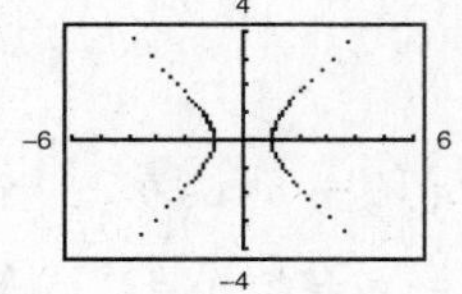

31. $x = \dfrac{t}{2}$

$y = \ln(t^2 + 1)$

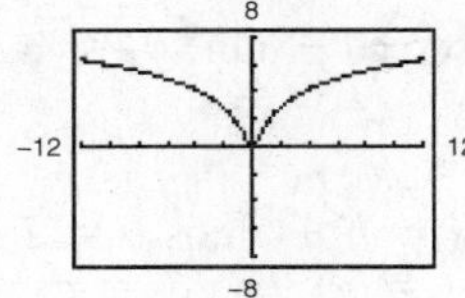

32. $x = 10 - 0.01e^t$

$y = 0.4t^2$

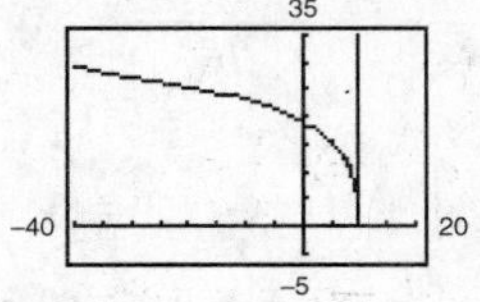

33. By eliminating the parameters in (a)–(d), we get $y = 2x + 1$. They differ from each other in restricted domain and in orientation.

(a) Domain: $-\infty < x < \infty$

Orientation: Left to right

(b) Domain: $-1 \le x \le 1$

Orientation: Depends on θ

(c) Domain: $0 < x < \infty$

Orientation: Right to left

(d) Domain: $0 < x < \infty$

Orientation: Left to right

34. Each curve represents a portion of the line $2y + x - 8 = 0$.

(a) $x = 2\sqrt{t},\ x \ge 0$

$y = 4 - \sqrt{t} = 4 - \dfrac{x}{2},\ y \le 4$

Orientation: Left to right

(b) $x = 2\sqrt[3]{t},\ -\infty < x < \infty$

$y = 4 - \sqrt[3]{t} = 4 - \dfrac{x}{2}$

Orientation: Left to right

(c) $x = 2(t + 1),\ -\infty < x < \infty$

$y = 3 - t = 3 - \left(\dfrac{x - 2}{2}\right) = 4 - \dfrac{x}{2}$

Orientation: Left to right

(d) $x = -2t^2,\ x \le 0$

$y = 4 + t^2 = 4 - \dfrac{x}{2}$

Orientation: Left to right for $t \le 0$

Right to left for $t > 0$

35. $t = \dfrac{(x - x_1)}{(x_2 - x_1)}$

$y = y_1 + \left(\dfrac{x - x_1}{x_2 - x_1}\right)(y_2 - y_1)$

$\Rightarrow y - y_1 = \left(\dfrac{y_2 - y_1}{x_2 - x_1}\right)(x - x_1)$

36. $x = h + r\cos\theta$

$y = k + r\sin\theta$

$\dfrac{(x - h)}{r} = \cos\theta, \quad \dfrac{y - k}{r} = \sin\theta$

$\cos^2\theta + \sin^2\theta = \dfrac{(x - h)^2}{r^2} + \dfrac{(y - k)^2}{r^2} = 1$

$(x - h)^2 + (y - k)^2 = r^2$

37. $x = h + a\cos\theta$

$y = k + b\sin\theta$

$\dfrac{x - h}{a} = \cos\theta, \quad \dfrac{y - k}{b} = \sin\theta$

$\dfrac{(x - h)^2}{a^2} + \dfrac{(y - k)^2}{b^2} = 1$

38. $x = h + a\sec\theta$

$y = k + b\tan\theta$

$\dfrac{x - h}{a} = \sec\theta, \quad \dfrac{y - k}{b} = \tan\theta$

$\sec^2\theta - \tan^2\theta = \dfrac{(x - h)^2}{a^2} - \dfrac{(y - k)^2}{b^2} = 1$

39. $x = x_1 + t(x_2 - x_1) = 1 + t(6 - 1) = 1 + 5t$

$y = y_1 + t(y_2 - y_1) = 4 + t(-3 - 4) = 4 - 7t$

40. $x = h + r\cos\theta = 2 + 4\cos\theta$

$y = k + r\sin\theta = 5 + 4\sin\theta$

41. $a = 5$, $c = 4$, and $b = \sqrt{a^2 - c^2} = 3$.

The center is $(0, 0)$, so $h = 0$ and $k = 0$.

$\cos^2\theta + \sin^2\theta = 1 = \dfrac{x^2}{5^2} + \dfrac{y^2}{3^2}$, so $x = 5\cos\theta$ and $y = 3\sin\theta$. This solution is not unique.

42. $a = 1$, $c = 2$, and $b = \sqrt{c^2 - a^2} = \sqrt{3}$.

The center is $(0, 0)$, so $h = 0$ and $k = 0$.

$\sec^2\theta - \tan^2\theta = 1 = \dfrac{y^2}{1} - \dfrac{x^2}{3}$, so $y = \sec\theta$ and $x = \sqrt{3}\tan\theta$.

43. $y = 5x - 3$

Answers will vary.

$x = t, y = 5t - 3$

$x = \dfrac{1}{5}t, y = t - 3$

44. $y = 4 - 7x$

Answers will vary.

$x = t, y = 4 - 7t$

$x = 2t, y = 4 - 14t$

45. $y = \dfrac{1}{x}$

Sample answers:

$x = t, y = \dfrac{1}{t}$

$x = t^3, y = \dfrac{1}{t^3}$

46. $y = \dfrac{1}{2x}$

Sample answers:

$x = t, y = \dfrac{1}{2t}$

$x = 2t, y = \dfrac{1}{4t}$

47. $y = 6x^2 - 5$

Sample answers:

$x = t, y = 6t^2 - 5$

$x = 2t, y = 24t^2 - 5$

48. $y = x^3 + 2x$

Sample answers:

$x = t, y = t^3 + 2t$

$x = \dfrac{1}{2}t, y = \dfrac{t^3}{8} + t$

49. $x = 2\cot\theta,\ y = 2\sin^2\theta$

50. $x = \dfrac{3t}{1 + t^3}, y = \dfrac{3t^2}{1 + t^3}$

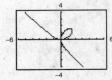

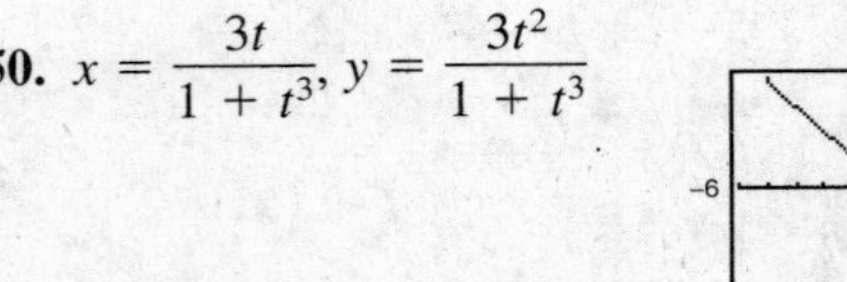

51. Matches (b).

52. Matches (c).

53. Matches (d).

54. Matches (a).

55. $x = (v_0 \cos \theta)t, \; y = h + (v_0 \sin \theta)t - 16t^2$

(a) $100 \text{ miles/hour} = \dfrac{100 \text{ mi/hr} \cdot 5280 \text{ ft/mi}}{3600 \text{ sec/hr}}$

$= 146.67 \text{ ft/sec}$

$x = (146.67 \cos \theta)t$

$y = 3 + (146.67 \sin \theta)t - 16t^2$

(b) $\theta = 15°$

$x = (146.67 \cos 15°)t = 141.7t$

$y = 3 + (146.67 \sin 15°)t - 16t^2$

$= 3 + 38.0t - 16t^2$

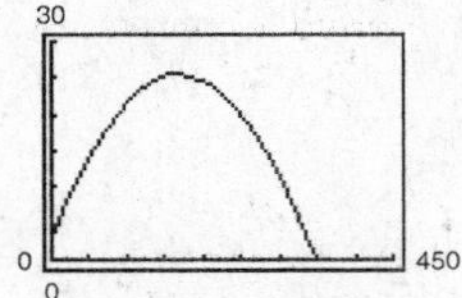

It is not a home run because $y < 10$ when $x = 400$.

(c) $\theta = 23°$

$x = (146.67 \cos 23°)t = 135.0t$

$y = 3 + (146.67 \sin 23°)t - 16t^2$

$= 3 + 57.3t - 16t^2$

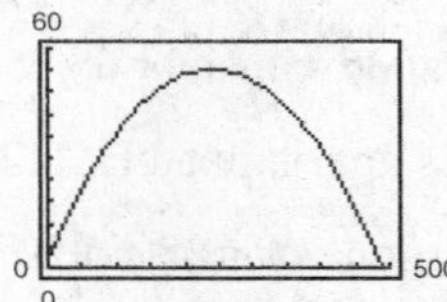

Yes, it is a home run because $y > 10$ when $x = 400$.

(d) $\theta \approx 19.4°$ is the minimum angle.

56. (a) $x = (v_0 \cos \theta)t = (105 \cos 40°)t$

$y = h + (v_0 \sin \theta)t - 16t^2$

$= 2.5 + (105 \sin 40°)t - 16t^2$

(b)

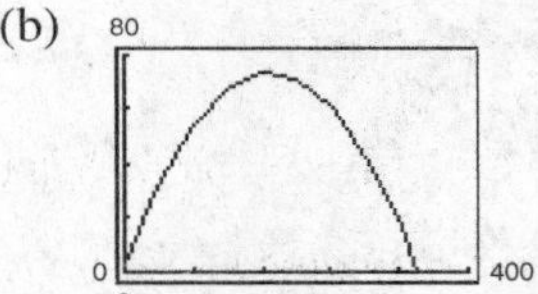

The maximum height is approximately 73.68 feet, when $t \approx 2.109$ seconds.

(c) The horizontal distance is approximately 342.25 feet.

(d) You could use the Quadratic Formula to find the zeros of $y = -16t^2 + (105 \sin 40°)t + 2.5$. The larger zero, 4.255, gives $x \approx 342.25$ feet.

57. (a) $x = (\cos 35°)v_0 t$

$y = 7 + (\sin 35°)v_0 t - 16t^2$

(b) If the ball is caught at time t_1, then:

$90 = (\cos 35°)v_0 t_1$

$4 = 7 + (\sin 35°)v_0 t_1 - 16t_1^2.$

$v_0 t_1 = \dfrac{90}{\cos 35°} \Rightarrow -3 = (\sin 35°)\dfrac{90}{\cos 35°} - 16t_1^2$

$\Rightarrow 16t_1^2 = 90 \tan 35° + 3$

$\Rightarrow t_1 \approx 2.03 \text{ seconds}$

$\Rightarrow v_0 = \dfrac{90}{t_1 \cos 35°} \approx 54.09 \text{ ft/sec}$

(c)

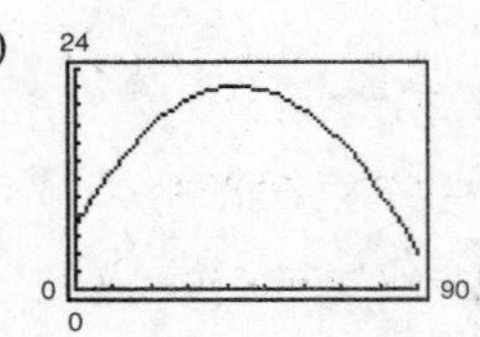

Maximum height ≈ 22 feet

(d) From part (b), $t_1 \approx 2.03$ seconds.

58. (a) $x = (v_0 \cos \theta)t = (85 \cos 50°)t$

$y = h + (v_0 \sin \theta)t - 16t^2 = (85 \sin 50°)t - 16t^2$

(b)

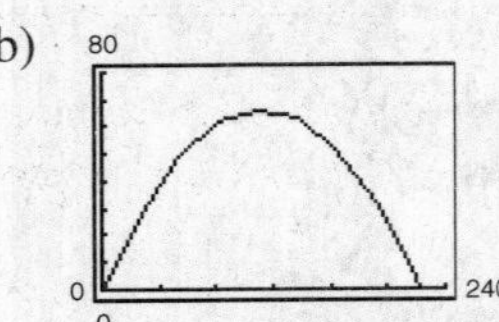

The maximum height is approximately 66.25 feet when $t \approx 2.035$ seconds.

(c) The horizontal distance is approximately 222.35 feet.

(d) You could solve the equation $y = (85 \sin 50°)t - 16t^2 = 0$ for $t \approx 4.0696$. Then, $x \approx 222.35$ feet.

59. True

$x = t$ first set

$y = t^2 + 1 = x^2 + 1$

$x = 3t$ second set

$y = 9t^2 + 1 = (3t)^2 + 1 = x^2 + 1$

60. False. The graph of $x = t^2, y = t^2$ represents the portion of the line $y = x$ in the first quadrant.

61. False. For example, $x = t^2$ and $y = t$ does not represent y as a function of x.

62. False. The equations represent a line.

63. Sample answer: $x = \cos \theta$

$y = -2 \sin \theta$

64. The graph is the same, but the orientation is reversed.

65. $f(-x) = \dfrac{4(-x)^2}{(-x)^2 + 1} = \dfrac{4x^2}{x^2 + 1} = f(x)$

Symmetric about the y-axis

Even function

66. $f(x) = \sqrt{x}, x \geq 0$

No symmetry

Neither even nor odd

67. $y = e^x \neq e^{-x}; e^{-x} \neq -e^x$

No symmetry

Neither even nor odd

68. $(x - 2)^2 = y + 4$

$y = x^2 - 4x$

No symmetry

Neither even nor odd

Section 9.6 Polar Coordinates

- In polar coordinates you do not have unique representation of points. The point (r, θ) can be represented by $(r, \theta \pm 2n\pi)$ or by $(-r, \theta \pm (2n + 1)\pi)$ where n is any integer. The pole is represented by $(0, \theta)$ where θ is any angle.
- To convert from polar coordinates to rectangular coordinates, use the following relationships.

  $x = r\cos\theta$

  $y = r\sin\theta$
- To convert from rectangular coordinates to polar coordinates, use the following relationships.

  $r = \pm\sqrt{x^2 + y^2}$

  $\tan\theta = y/x$

  If θ is in the same quadrant as the point (x, y), then r is positive. If θ is in the opposite quadrant as the point (x, y), then r is negative.
- You should be able to convert rectangular equations to polar form and vice versa.

Vocabulary Check

1. pole **2.** directed distance, directed angle **3.** polar

1. Polar coordinates: $\left(4, \frac{\pi}{2}\right)$

$x = 4\cos\left(\frac{\pi}{2}\right) = 0$

$y = 4\sin\left(\frac{\pi}{2}\right) = 4$

Rectangular coordinates: $(0, 4)$

2. Polar coordinates: $\left(4, \frac{3\pi}{2}\right)$

$x = 4\cos\left(\frac{3\pi}{2}\right) = 0,\ y = 4\sin\left(\frac{3\pi}{2}\right) = -4$

Rectangular coordinates: $(0, -4)$

3. Polar coordinates: $\left(-1, \frac{5\pi}{4}\right)$

$x = -1\cos\left(\frac{5\pi}{4}\right) = \frac{\sqrt{2}}{2}$

$y = -1\sin\left(\frac{5\pi}{4}\right) = \frac{\sqrt{2}}{2}$

Rectangular coordinates: $\left(\frac{\sqrt{2}}{2}, \frac{\sqrt{2}}{2}\right)$

4. Polar coordinates: $\left(2, -\frac{\pi}{4}\right)$

$x = 2\cos\left(-\frac{\pi}{4}\right) = 2\left(\frac{\sqrt{2}}{2}\right) = \sqrt{2}$

$y = 2\sin\left(-\frac{\pi}{4}\right) = 2\left(-\frac{\sqrt{2}}{2}\right) = -\sqrt{2}$

Rectangular coordinates: $\left(\sqrt{2}, -\sqrt{2}\right)$

5.

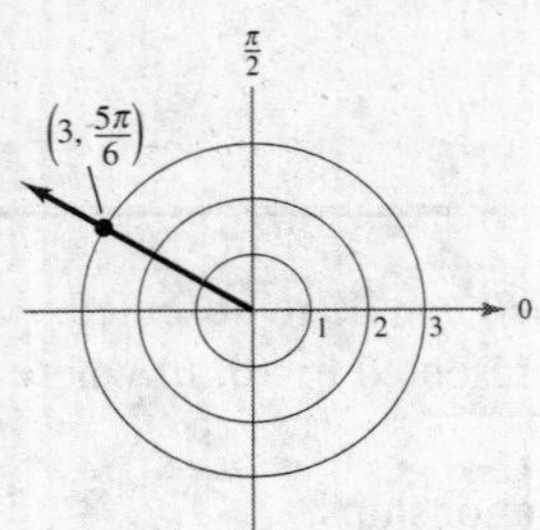

Three additional representations:

$$\left(3, \frac{5\pi}{6} - 2\pi\right) = \left(3, -\frac{7\pi}{6}\right)$$

$$\left(-3, \frac{5\pi}{6} + \pi\right) = \left(-3, \frac{11\pi}{6}\right)$$

$$\left(-3, \frac{5\pi}{6} - \pi\right) = \left(-3, -\frac{\pi}{6}\right)$$

6.

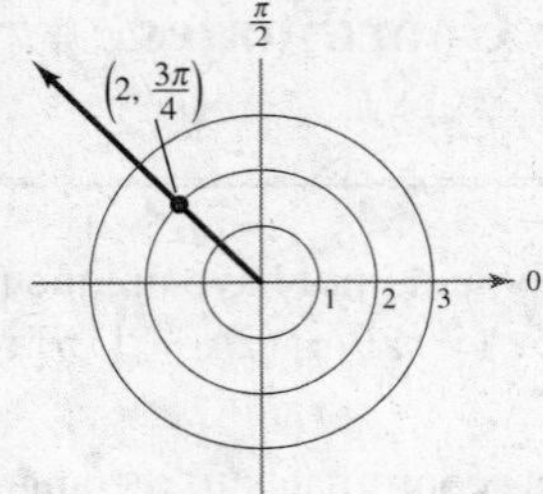

Three additional points:

$$\left(2, \frac{-5\pi}{4}\right), \left(-2, \frac{7\pi}{4}\right), \left(-2, \frac{-\pi}{4}\right)$$

7.

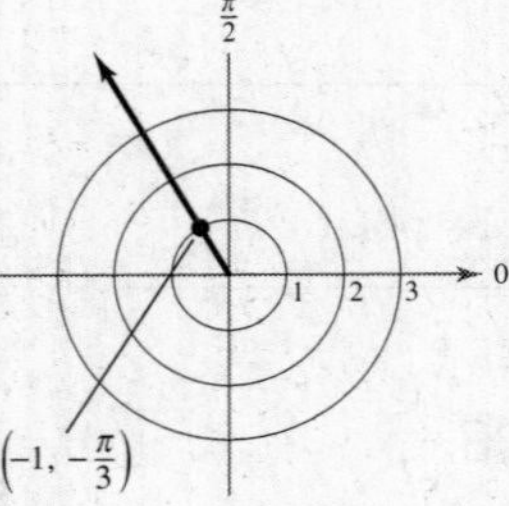

Three additional representations:

$$\left(-1, -\frac{\pi}{3} + 2\pi\right) = \left(-1, \frac{5\pi}{3}\right)$$

$$\left(1, -\frac{\pi}{3} + \pi\right) = \left(1, \frac{2\pi}{3}\right)$$

$$\left(1, -\frac{\pi}{3} - \pi\right) = \left(1, -\frac{4\pi}{3}\right)$$

8.

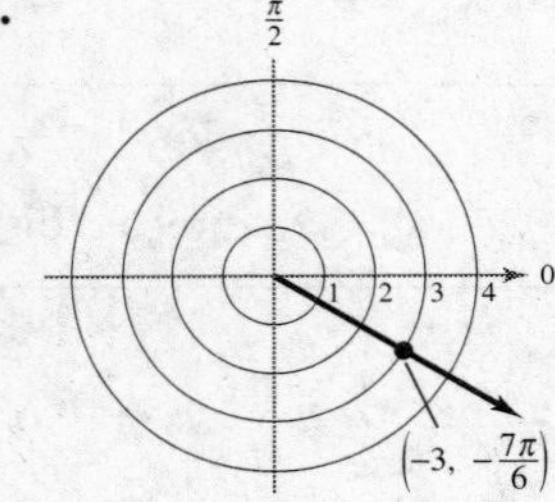

Three additional points:

$$\left(-3, \frac{5\pi}{6}\right), \left(3, \frac{11\pi}{6}\right), \left(3, -\frac{\pi}{6}\right)$$

9.

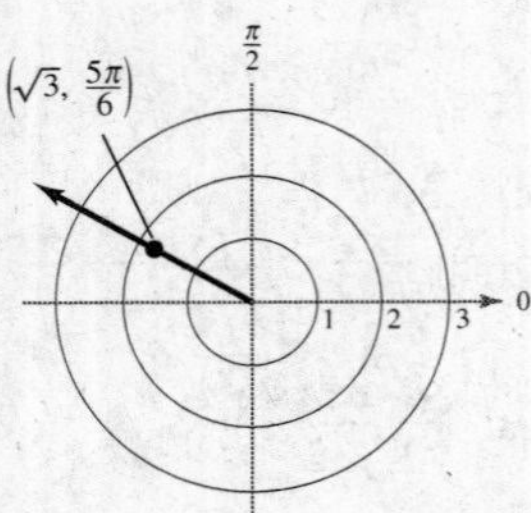

Three additional representations:

$$\left(\sqrt{3}, -\frac{7\pi}{6}\right), \left(-\sqrt{3}, -\frac{\pi}{6}\right), \left(-\sqrt{3}, \frac{11\pi}{6}\right)$$

10.

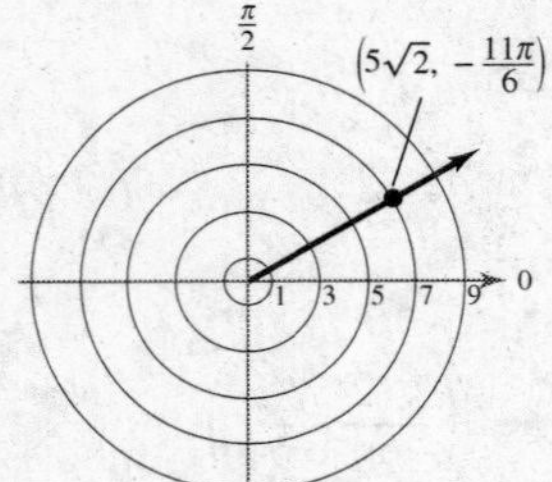

Three additional points:

$$\left(5\sqrt{2}, \frac{\pi}{6}\right), \left(-5\sqrt{2}, -\frac{5\pi}{6}\right), \left(-5\sqrt{2}, \frac{7\pi}{6}\right)$$

11.

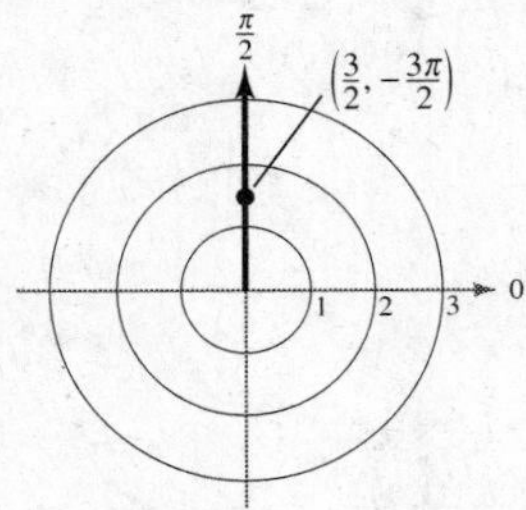

Three additional representations:

$\left(\frac{3}{2}, \frac{\pi}{2}\right), \left(-\frac{3}{2}, \frac{3\pi}{2}\right), \left(-\frac{3}{2}, -\frac{\pi}{2}\right)$

12.

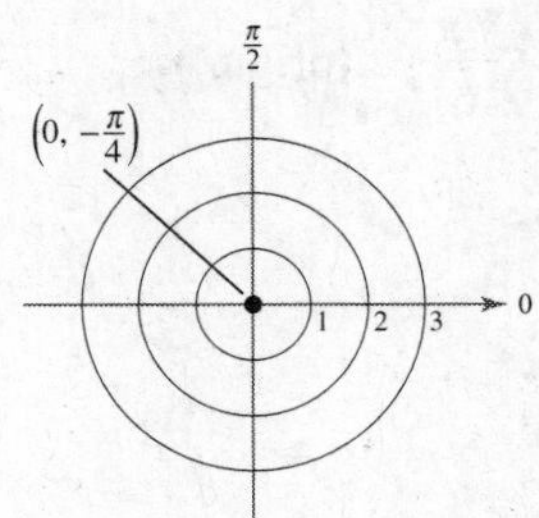

$\left(0, \frac{-\pi}{4}\right)$ is the origin.

Three additional points: $\left(0, \frac{3\pi}{4}\right), \left(0, \frac{-5\pi}{4}\right), \left(0, \frac{7\pi}{4}\right)$

(Any angle will do since $r = 0$.)

13. Polar coordinates: $\left(4, -\frac{\pi}{3}\right)$

$x = 4\cos\left(-\frac{\pi}{3}\right) = 2$

$y = 4\sin\left(-\frac{\pi}{3}\right) = -2\sqrt{3}$

Rectangular coordinates: $\left(2, -2\sqrt{3}\right)$

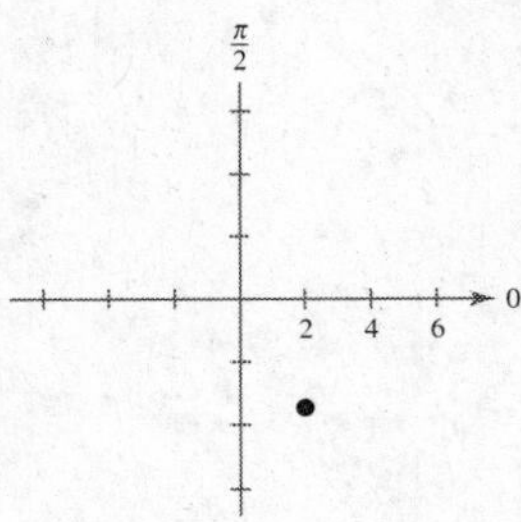

14. Polar coordinates: $\left(2, \frac{7\pi}{6}\right)$

$x = 2\cos\frac{7\pi}{6} = 2\left(-\frac{\sqrt{3}}{2}\right) = -\sqrt{3}$

$y = 2\sin\frac{7\pi}{6} = 2\left(-\frac{1}{2}\right) = -1$

Rectangular coordinates: $\left(-\sqrt{3}, -1\right)$

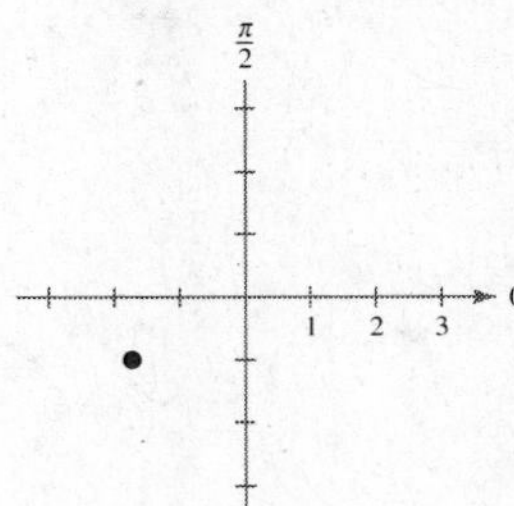

15. Polar coordinates: $\left(-1, \frac{-3\pi}{4}\right)$

$x = -1\cos\left(\frac{-3\pi}{4}\right) = \frac{\sqrt{2}}{2}$

$y = -1\sin\left(\frac{-3\pi}{4}\right) = \frac{\sqrt{2}}{2}$

Rectangular coordinates: $\left(\frac{\sqrt{2}}{2}, \frac{\sqrt{2}}{2}\right)$

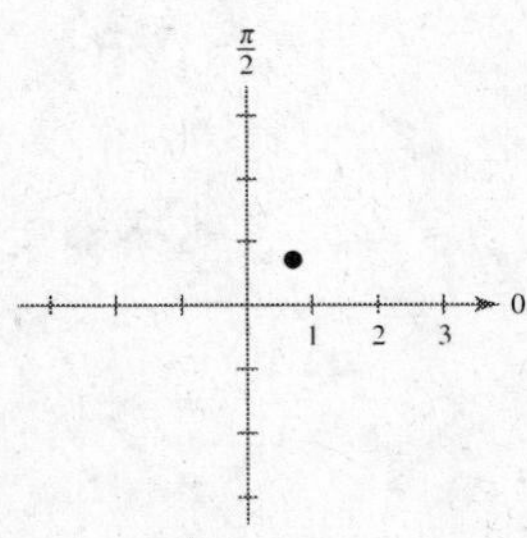

16. Polar coordinates: $\left(-3, -\frac{2\pi}{3}\right) = \left(3, \frac{\pi}{3}\right)$

$x = -3\cos\left(-\frac{2\pi}{3}\right) = -3\left(-\frac{1}{2}\right) = \frac{3}{2}$

$y = -3\sin\left(-\frac{2\pi}{3}\right) = -3\left(-\frac{\sqrt{3}}{2}\right) = \frac{3\sqrt{3}}{2}$

Rectangular coordinates: $\left(\frac{3}{2}, \frac{3\sqrt{3}}{2}\right)$

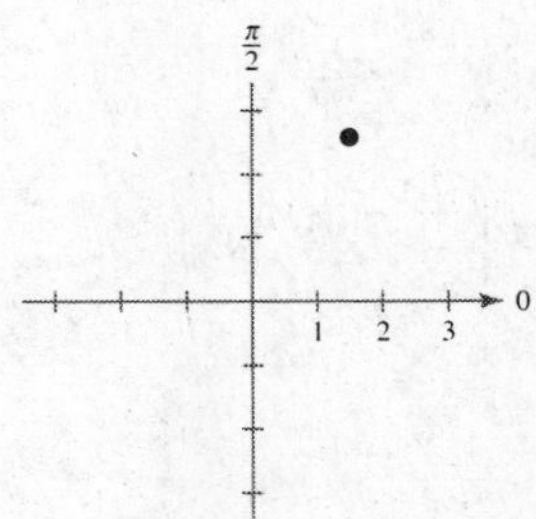

17. Polar coordinates: $\left(0, -\frac{7\pi}{6}\right)$ (origin!)

$x = 0\cos\left(-\frac{7\pi}{6}\right) = 0$

$y = 0\sin\left(-\frac{7\pi}{6}\right) = 0$

Rectangular coordinates: $(0, 0)$

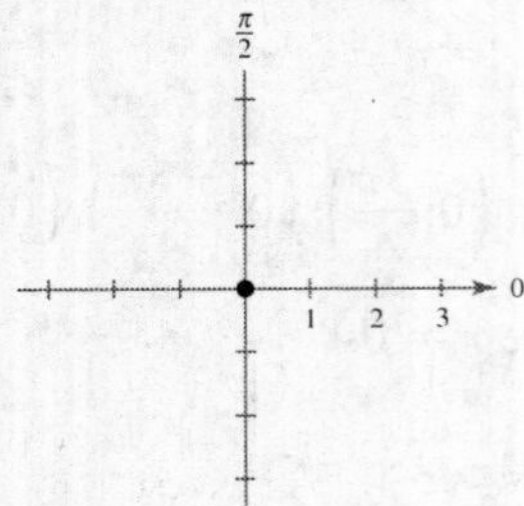

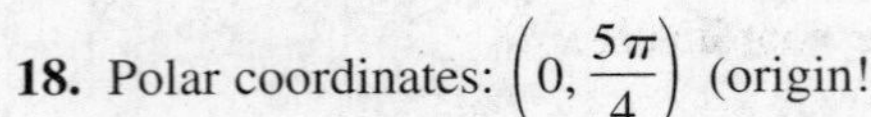

18. Polar coordinates: $\left(0, \frac{5\pi}{4}\right)$ (origin!)

$x = 0\cos\frac{5\pi}{4} = 0$

$y = 0\sin\frac{5\pi}{4} = 0$

Rectangular coordinates: $(0, 0)$

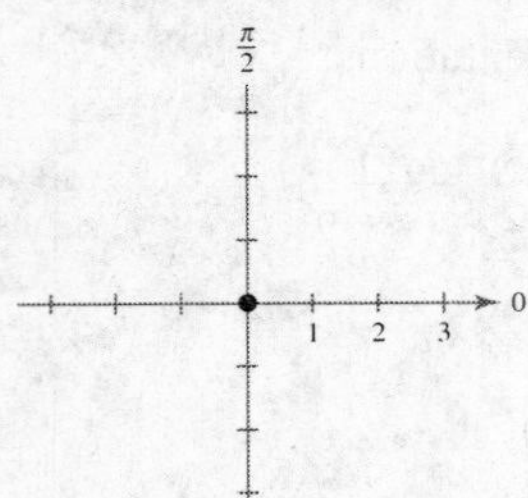

19. Polar coordinates: $(\sqrt{2}, 2.36)$

$x = \sqrt{2}\cos(2.36) \approx -1.004$

$y = \sqrt{2}\sin(2.36) \approx 0.996$

Rectangular coordinates: $(-1.004, 0.996)$

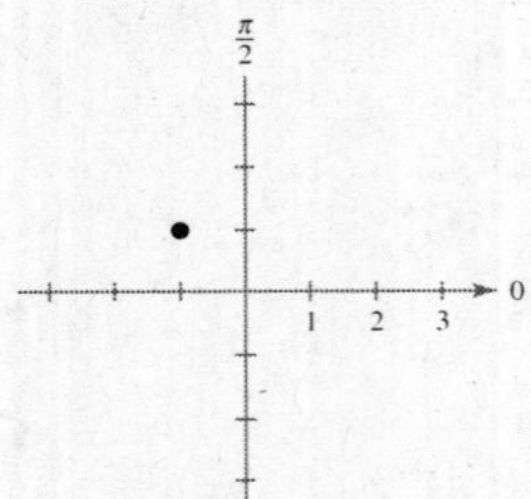

20. Polar coordinates: $(-3, -1.57)$

$x = -3\cos(-1.57) \approx -0.0024$

$y = -3\sin(-1.57) \approx 3.000$

Rectangular coordinates: $(-0.0024, 3)$

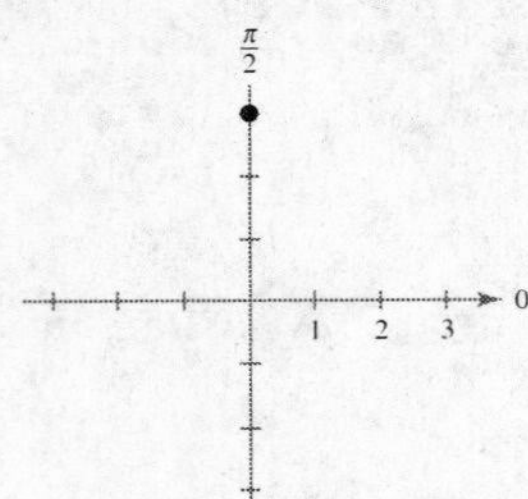

21. $(r, \theta) = \left(2, \frac{2\pi}{9}\right) \Rightarrow (x, y) = (1.53, 1.29)$

22. $(r, \theta) = \left(4, \frac{11\pi}{9}\right) \Rightarrow (x, y) = (-3.06, -2.57)$

23. $(r, \theta) = (-4.5, 1.3) \Rightarrow (x, y) = (-1.204, -4.336)$

24. $(r, \theta) = (8.25, 3.5) \Rightarrow (x, y) = (-7.726, -2.894)$

25. $(r, \theta) = (2.5, 1.58) \Rightarrow (x, y) = (-0.02, 2.50)$

26. $(r, \theta) = (5.4, 2.85) \Rightarrow (x, y) = (-5.17, 1.55)$

27. $(r, \theta) = (-4.1, -0.5) \Rightarrow (x, y) = (-3.60, 1.97)$

28. $(r, \theta) = (8.2, -3.2) \Rightarrow (x, y) = (-8.19, 0.48)$

29. Rectangular coordinates: $(-7, 0)$

$r = 7, \tan\theta = 0, \theta = 0$

Polar coordinates: $(7, \pi), (-7, 0)$

30. Rectangular coordinates: $(0, -5)$

$r = 5$, $\tan\theta$ undefined, $\theta = \dfrac{\pi}{2}$

Polar coordinates: $\left(5, \dfrac{3\pi}{2}\right), \left(-5, \dfrac{\pi}{2}\right)$

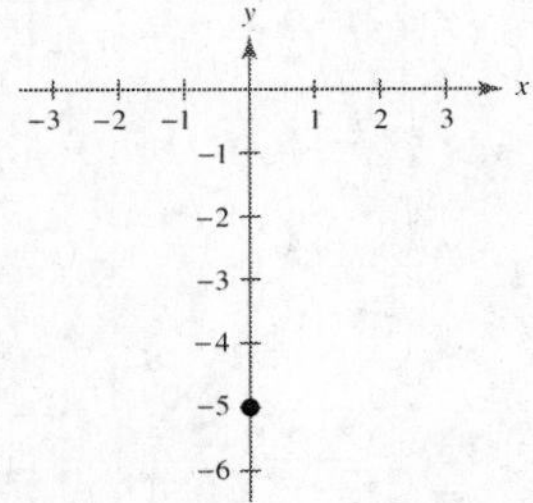

31. Rectangular coordinates: $(1, 1)$

$r = \sqrt{2}$, $\tan\theta = 1$, $\theta = \dfrac{\pi}{4}$

Polar coordinates: $\left(\sqrt{2}, \dfrac{\pi}{4}\right), \left(-\sqrt{2}, \dfrac{5\pi}{4}\right)$

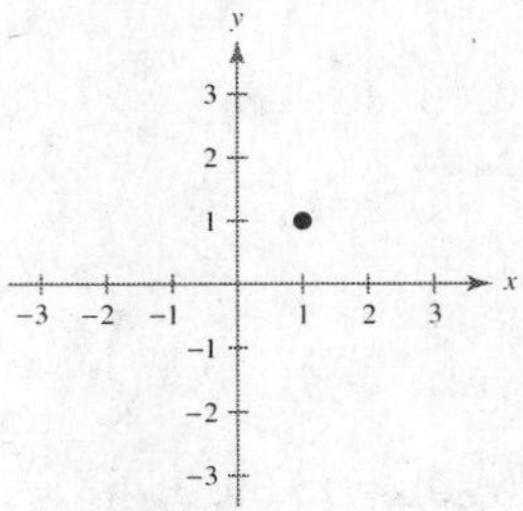

32. Rectangular coordinates: $(-3, -3)$

$r = 3\sqrt{2}$, $\tan\theta = 1$, $\theta = \dfrac{\pi}{4}$

Polar coordinates: $\left(3\sqrt{2}, \dfrac{5\pi}{4}\right), \left(-3\sqrt{2}, \dfrac{\pi}{4}\right)$

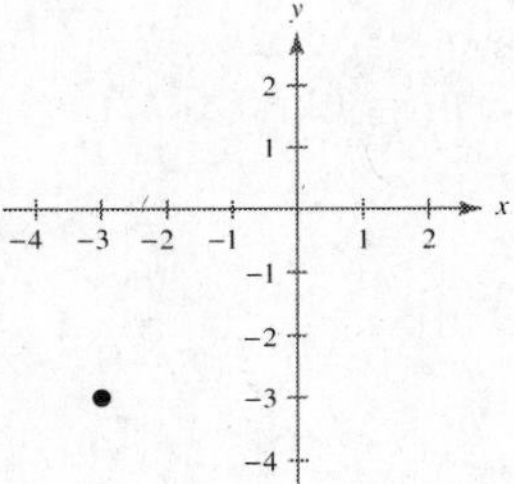

33. Rectangular coordinates: $\left(-\sqrt{3}, -\sqrt{3}\right)$

$r = \sqrt{3+3} = \sqrt{6}$, $\tan\theta = 1$, $\theta = \dfrac{\pi}{4}$

Polar coordinates: $\left(\sqrt{6}, \dfrac{5\pi}{4}\right), \left(-\sqrt{6}, \dfrac{\pi}{4}\right)$

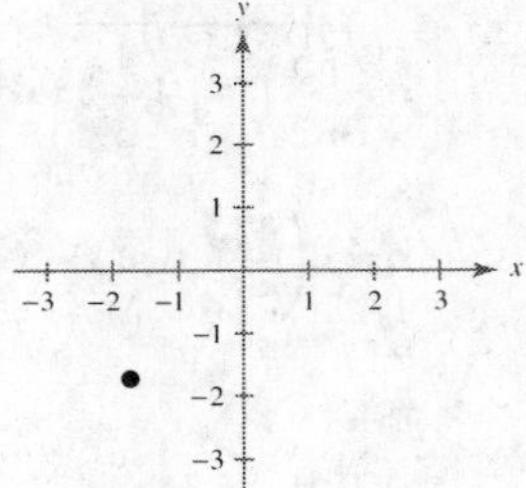

34. Rectangular coordinates: $\left(\sqrt{3}, -1\right)$

$r = \sqrt{3+1} = 2$

$\tan\theta = \dfrac{-1}{\sqrt{3}}$, $\theta = \dfrac{11\pi}{6}$

Polar coordinates: $\left(2, \dfrac{11\pi}{6}\right), \left(-2, \dfrac{5\pi}{6}\right)$

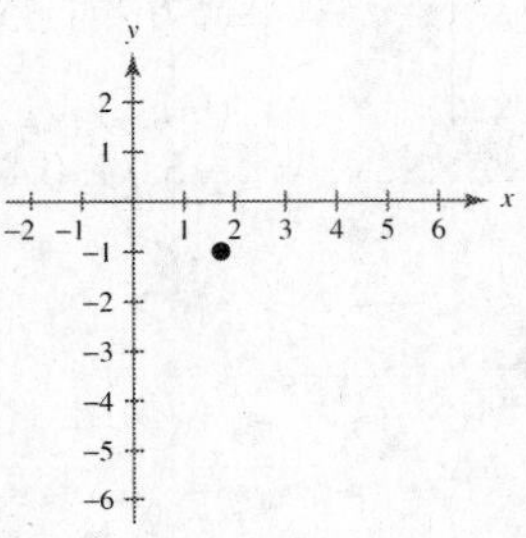

35. $(x, y) = (6, 9)$

$r = \sqrt{6^2 + 9^2} = \sqrt{117} \approx 10.8$

$\tan\theta = \dfrac{9}{6} = \dfrac{3}{2} \Rightarrow \theta \approx 0.983$

Polar coordinates: $(10.8, 0.983), (-10.8, 4.124)$

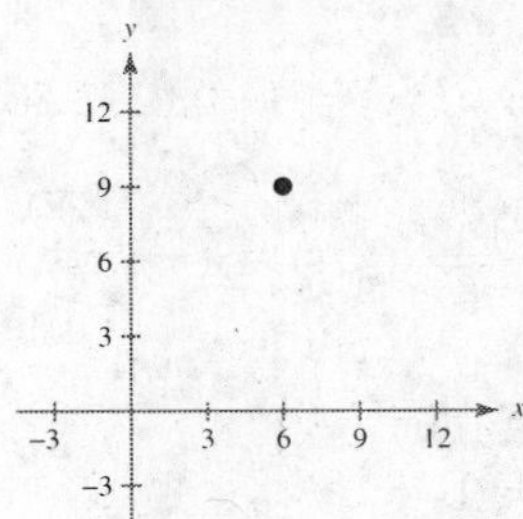

36. Rectangular coordinates: $(5, 12)$

$r = \sqrt{25 + 144} = 13$, $\tan\theta = \frac{12}{5}$, $\theta \approx 1.176$

Polar coordinates: $(13, 1.176)$, $(-13, 4.318)$

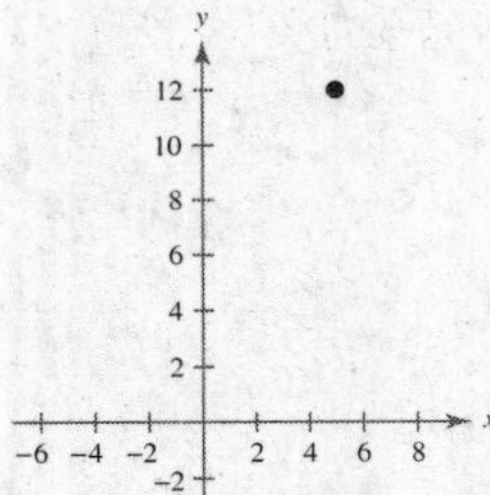

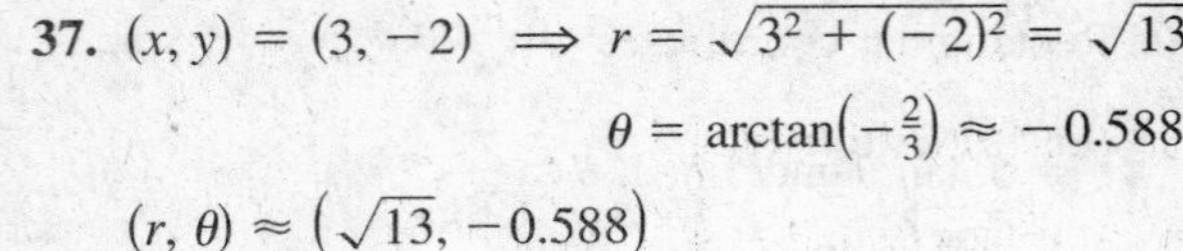

37. $(x, y) = (3, -2) \implies r = \sqrt{3^2 + (-2)^2} = \sqrt{13}$

$\theta = \arctan\left(-\frac{2}{3}\right) \approx -0.588$

$(r, \theta) \approx \left(\sqrt{13}, -0.588\right)$

38. $(x, y) = (-5, 2) \implies (r, \theta) = (5.39, 2.76)$

39. $(x, y) = \left(\sqrt{3}, 2\right) \implies r = \sqrt{3 + 2^2} = \sqrt{7}$

$\theta = \arctan\left(\dfrac{2}{\sqrt{3}}\right) \approx 0.857$

$(r, \theta) \approx \left(\sqrt{7}, 0.857\right)$

40. $(x, y) = \left(3\sqrt{2}, 3\sqrt{2}\right) \implies (r, \theta) = \left(6, \dfrac{\pi}{4}\right) \approx (6.0, 0.785)$

41. $(x, y) = \left(\dfrac{5}{2}, \dfrac{4}{3}\right) \implies r = \sqrt{\left(\dfrac{5}{2}\right)^2 + \left(\dfrac{4}{3}\right)^2} = \dfrac{17}{6}$

$\theta = \arctan\left(\dfrac{4/3}{5/2}\right) \approx 0.490$

$(r, \theta) \approx \left(\dfrac{17}{6}, 0.490\right)$

42. $(x, y) = \left(\dfrac{7}{4}, \dfrac{3}{2}\right) \implies (r, \theta) = (2.30, 0.71)$

43. $x^2 + y^2 = 9$

$r^2 = 9$

$r = 3$

44. $x^2 + y^2 = 16$

$r^2 = 16$

$r = 4$

45. $y = 4$

$r\sin\theta = 4$

$r = 4\csc\theta$

46. $y = x$

$r\sin\theta = r\cos\theta$

$\sin\theta = \cos\theta$

$\tan\theta = 1$

$\theta = \dfrac{\pi}{4}$

47. $x = 8$

$r\cos\theta = 8$

$r = 8\sec\theta$

48. $x = a$

$r\cos\theta = a$

$r = a\sec\theta$

49. $3x - 6y + 2 = 0$

$3r\cos\theta - 6r\sin\theta = -2$

$r(3\cos\theta - 6\sin\theta) = -2$

$r = \dfrac{2}{6\sin\theta - 3\cos\theta}$

50. $4x + 7y - 2 = 0$

$4r\cos\theta + 7r\sin\theta - 2 = 0$

$r(4\cos\theta + 7\sin\theta) = 2$

$r = \dfrac{2}{4\cos\theta + 7\sin\theta}$

51. $xy = 4$

$(r\cos\theta)(r\sin\theta) = 4$

$r^2\cos\theta\sin\theta = 4$

$r^2(2\cos\theta\sin\theta) = 8$

$r^2\sin 2\theta = 8$

$r^2 = 8\csc 2\theta$

52. $2xy = 1$

$2r\cos\theta \cdot r\sin\theta = 1$

$2r^2 = \sec\theta\csc\theta$

$r^2 = \frac{1}{2}\sec\theta\csc\theta = \csc(2\theta)$

53. $(x^2 + y^2)^2 = 9(x^2 - y^2)$

$(r^2)^2 = 9(r^2\cos^2\theta - r^2\sin^2\theta)$

$r^2 = 9(\cos^2\theta - \sin^2\theta)$

$r^2 = 9\cos(2\theta)$

54. $y^2 - 8x - 16 = 0$

$r^2\sin^2\theta - 8r\cos\theta - 16 = 0$

$r^2(1 - \cos^2\theta) - 8r\cos\theta - 16 = 0$

$r^2\cos^2\theta + 8r\cos\theta + 16 = r^2$

$(r\cos\theta + 4)^2 = r^2$

$r = \pm(r\cos\theta + 4)$

$$r = \frac{4}{1 - \cos\theta} \quad \text{or} \quad r = \frac{-4}{1 + \cos\theta}$$

55. $x^2 + y^2 - 6x = 0$

$r^2 - 6r\cos\theta = 0$

$r^2 = 6r\cos\theta$

$r = 6\cos\theta$

56. $x^2 + y^2 - 8y = 0$

$r^2 - 8r\sin\theta = 0$

$r(r - 8\sin\theta) = 0$

$r = 8\sin\theta$

57. $x^2 + y^2 - 2ax = 0$

$r^2 - 2ar\cos\theta = 0$

$r(r - 2a\cos\theta) = 0$

$r = 2a\cos\theta$

58. $x^2 + y^2 - 2ay = 0$

$r^2 - 2a\,r\sin\theta = 0$

$r(r - 2a\sin\theta) = 0$

$r = 2a\sin\theta$

59. $y^2 = x^3$

$(r\sin\theta)^2 = (r\cos\theta)^3$

$\sin^2\theta = r\cos^3\theta$

$$r = \frac{\sin^2\theta}{\cos^3\theta}$$

$= \tan^2\theta\sec\theta$

60. $x^2 = y^3$

$r^2\cos^2\theta = r^3\sin^3\theta$

$$r = \frac{\cos^2\theta}{\sin^3\theta} = \cot^2\theta\csc\theta$$

61. $r = 6\sin\theta$

$r^2 = 6r\sin\theta$

$x^2 + y^2 = 6y$

$x^2 + y^2 - 6y = 0$

62. $r = 2\cos\theta$

$r^2 = 2r\cos\theta$

$x^2 + y^2 = 2x$

63. $\theta = \frac{4\pi}{3}$

$$\tan\theta = \tan\frac{4\pi}{3} = \frac{y}{x}$$

$$\sqrt{3} = \frac{y}{x}$$

$y = \sqrt{3}x$

64. $\theta = \dfrac{5\pi}{3}$

$\tan\theta = \tan\dfrac{5\pi}{3} = -\sqrt{3}$

$\dfrac{y}{x} = -\sqrt{3}$

$y + \sqrt{3}x = 0$

65. $\theta = \dfrac{5\pi}{6}$

$\tan\theta = \tan\dfrac{5\pi}{6} = \dfrac{y}{x}$

$\dfrac{-\sqrt{3}}{3} = \dfrac{y}{x}$

$y = \dfrac{-\sqrt{3}}{3}x$

66. $\theta = \dfrac{11\pi}{6}$

$\tan\theta = \tan\dfrac{11\pi}{6} = \dfrac{y}{x}$

$\dfrac{-\sqrt{3}}{3} = \dfrac{y}{x}$

$y = \dfrac{-\sqrt{3}}{3}x$

67. $\theta = \dfrac{\pi}{2}$, vertical line

$x = 0$

68. $\theta = \pi$, horizontal line

$y = 0$

69. $r = 4$

$r^2 = 16$

$x^2 + y^2 = 16$

70. $r = 10$

$r^2 = 100$

$x^2 + y^2 = 100$

71. $r = -3\csc\theta$

$r\sin\theta = -3$

$y = -3$

72. $r = 2\sec\theta$

$r\cos\theta = 2$

$x = 2$

73. $r^2 = \cos\theta$

$r^3 = r\cos\theta$

$(x^2 + y^2)^{3/2} = x$

$x^2 + y^2 = x^{2/3}$

$(x^2 + y^2)^3 = x^2$

74. $r^2 = \sin 2\theta = 2\sin\theta\cos\theta$

$r^2 = 2\left(\dfrac{y}{r}\right)\left(\dfrac{x}{r}\right) = \dfrac{2xy}{r^2}$

$r^4 = 2xy$

$(x^2 + y^2)^2 = 2xy$

75. $r = 2\sin 3\theta$

$r = 2(3\sin\theta - 4\sin^3\theta)$

$r^4 = 6r^3\sin\theta - 8r^3\sin^3\theta$

$(x^2 + y^2)^2 = 6(x^2 + y^2)y - 8y^3$

$(x^2 + y^2)^2 = 6x^2y - 2y^3$

76. $r = 3\cos 2\theta$

$r = 3(\cos^2\theta - \sin^2\theta)$

$r^3 = 3(r^2\cos^2\theta - r^2\sin^2\theta)$

$(x^2 + y^2)^{3/2} = 3(x^2 - y^2)$ or $(x^2 + y^2)^3 = 9(x^2 - y^2)^2$

77. $r = \dfrac{1}{1 - \cos\theta}$

$r - r\cos\theta = 1$

$\sqrt{x^2 + y^2} - x = 1$

$x^2 + y^2 = 1 + 2x + x^2$

$y^2 = 2x + 1$

78. $r = \dfrac{2}{1 + \sin\theta}$

$r + r\sin\theta = 2$

$\sqrt{x^2 + y^2} + y = 2$

$x^2 + y^2 = (2 - y)^2$

$x^2 + y^2 = 4 - 4y + y^2$

$x^2 + 4y - 4 = 0$

79.
$$r = \frac{6}{2 - 3\sin\theta}$$
$$r(2 - 3\sin\theta) = 6$$
$$2r = 6 + 3r\sin\theta$$
$$2\left(\pm\sqrt{x^2 + y^2}\right) = 6 + 3y$$
$$4(x^2 + y^2) = (6 + 3y)^2$$
$$4x^2 + 4y^2 = 36 + 36y + 9y^2$$
$$4x^2 - 5y^2 - 36y - 36 = 0$$

80.
$$r = \frac{6}{2\cos\theta - 3\sin\theta}$$
$$r = \frac{6}{2(x/r) - 3(y/r)}$$
$$r = \frac{6r}{2x - 3y}$$
$$1 = \frac{6}{2x - 3y}$$
$$2x - 3y = 6$$

81. $r = 7$

$r^2 = 49$

$x^2 + y^2 = 49$

The graph is a circle centered at the origin with radius 7.

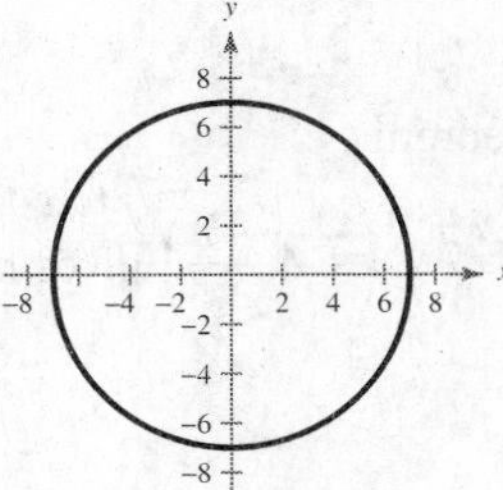

82. $r = 8$

$r^2 = 64$

$x^2 + y^2 = 64$

Circle of radius 8 centered at origin

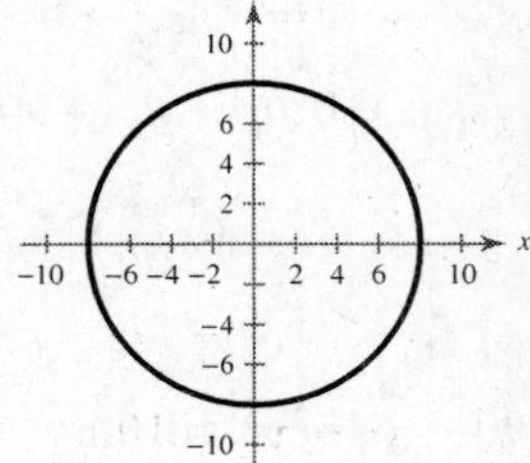

83. $\theta = \dfrac{\pi}{4}$

$\tan\theta = \tan\dfrac{\pi}{4} = 1 = \dfrac{y}{x}$

$y = x$

The graph is the line $y = x$, which makes an angle of $\theta = \pi/4$ with the positive x-axis.

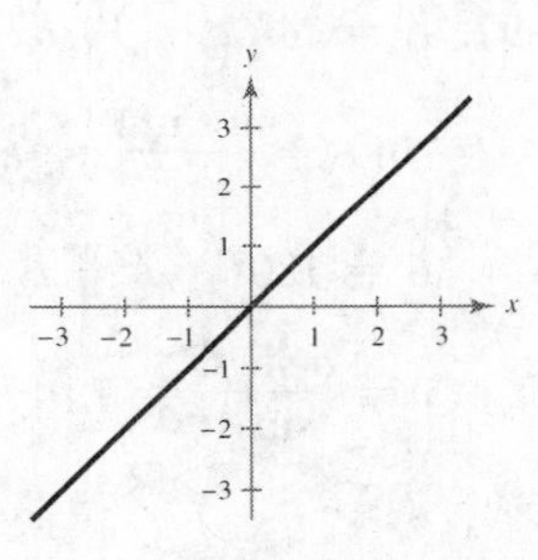

84. $\theta = \dfrac{7\pi}{6}$

$\dfrac{y}{x} = \tan\theta = \tan\dfrac{7\pi}{6} = \dfrac{\sqrt{3}}{3}$

$3y - \sqrt{3}x = 0$

Line through origin making angle of $\pi/6$ with positive x-axis

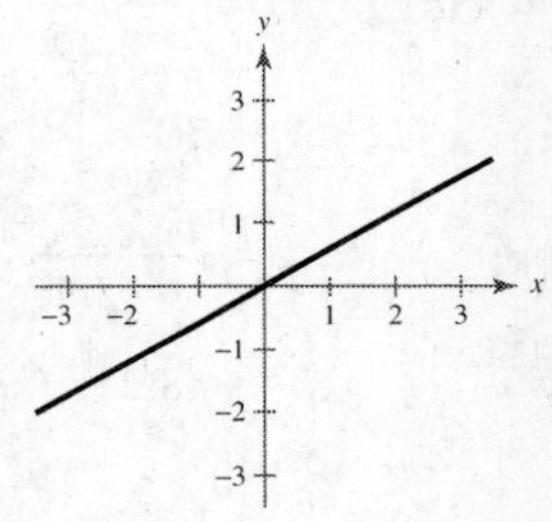

85. $r = 3\sec\theta$

$r\cos\theta = 3$

$x = 3$

$x - 3 = 0$

Vertical line

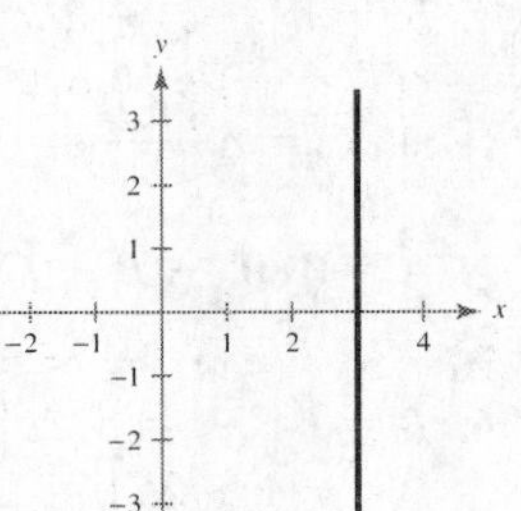

86. $r = 2\csc\theta$

$r\sin\theta = 2$

$y = 2$

$y - 2 = 0$

Horizontal line through $(0, 2)$

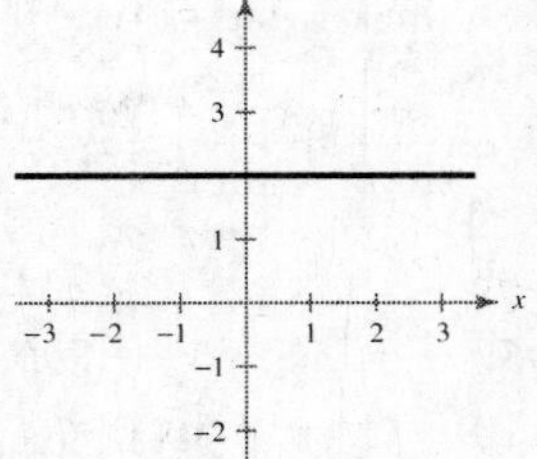

87. True, the distances from the origin are the same.

88. False. For instance when $r = 0$, any value of θ gives the same point.

89. (a) $(r_1, \theta_1) = (x_1, y_1)$ where $x_1 = r_1 \cos \theta_1$ and $y_1 = r_1 \sin \theta_1$.

$(r_2, \theta_2) = (x_2, y_2)$ where $x_2 = r_2 \cos \theta_2$ and $y_2 = r_2 \sin \theta_2$.

Then $x_1^2 + y_1^2 = r_1^2 \cos^2 \theta_1 + r_1^2 \sin^2 \theta_1 = r_1^2$ and $x_2^2 + y_2^2 = r_2^2$. Thus,

$$\begin{aligned} d &= \sqrt{(x_1 - x_2)^2 + (y_1 - y_2)^2} \\ &= \sqrt{x_1^2 - 2x_1x_2 + x_2^2 + y_1^2 - 2y_1y_2 + y_2^2} \\ &= \sqrt{(x_1^2 + y_1^2) + (x_2^2 + y_2^2) - 2(x_1x_2 + y_1y_2)} \\ &= \sqrt{r_1^2 + r_2^2 - 2(r_1r_2 \cos \theta_1 \cos \theta_2 + r_1r_2 \sin \theta_1 \sin \theta_2)} \\ &= \sqrt{r_1^2 + r_2^2 - 2r_1r_2 \cos(\theta_1 - \theta_2)}. \end{aligned}$$

(b) If $\theta_1 = \theta_2$, the points are on the same line through the origin. In this case,

$d = \sqrt{r_1^2 + r_2^2 - 2r_1r_2 \cos(0)} = \sqrt{(r_1 - r_2)^2} = |r_1 - r_2|$.

(c) If $\theta_1 - \theta_2 = 90°$, $d = \sqrt{r_1^2 + r_2^2}$, the Pythagorean Theorem.

(d) For instance, $\left(3, \frac{\pi}{6}\right), \left(4, \frac{\pi}{3}\right)$ gives $d \approx 2.053$ and $\left(-3, \frac{7\pi}{6}\right), \left(-4, \frac{4\pi}{3}\right)$ gives $d \approx 2.053$. (Same!)

90. Answers will vary.

91. $\cos A = \dfrac{b^2 + c^2 - a^2}{2bc} = \dfrac{19^2 + 25^2 - 13^2}{2(19)(25)} = 0.86$

$A \approx 30.7°$

$\cos B = \dfrac{a^2 + c^2 - b^2}{2ac} = \dfrac{13^2 + 25^2 - 19^2}{2(13)(25)} = 0.66615$

$B \approx 48.2°$

$C \approx 180° - 30.7° - 48.2° \approx 101.1°$

92. $A = 24°, a = 10, b = 6$

$\sin B = \dfrac{b \sin A}{a} \approx 0.2440 \implies B \approx 14.1°$

$C = 180° - A - B \approx 141.9°$

$c = \dfrac{a \sin C}{\sin A} \approx 15.17$

93. $B = 180° - 56° - 38° = 86°$

$\dfrac{a}{\sin A} = \dfrac{c}{\sin C} \implies a = \dfrac{c \sin A}{\sin C} = \dfrac{12 \sin(56°)}{\sin(38°)} \approx 16.16$

$\dfrac{b}{\sin B} = \dfrac{c}{\sin C} \implies b = \dfrac{c \sin B}{\sin C} = \dfrac{12 \sin(86°)}{\sin(38°)} \approx 19.44$

94. $B = 71°, a = 21, c = 29$

$b^2 = a^2 + c^2 - 2ac \cos B \approx 885.458 \implies b \approx 29.76$

$\sin C = c\dfrac{\sin B}{b} \approx 0.9214 \implies C \approx 67.1°$

$A = 180° - B - C \approx 41.9°$

95. $c^2 = a^2 + b^2 - 2ab \cos C$

$= 8^2 + 4^2 - 2(8)(4) \cos(35°)$

≈ 27.57

$c \approx 5.25$

$\dfrac{b}{\sin B} = \dfrac{c}{\sin C} \implies \sin B = \dfrac{b \sin C}{c} = \dfrac{4 \sin(35°)}{5.25}$

$\implies B \approx 25.9°$

$A = 180° - B - C = 119.1°$

96. $B = 64°, b = 52, c = 44$

$\sin C = \dfrac{c \sin B}{b} \approx 0.7605 \implies C \approx 49.5°$

$A = 180° - B - C \approx 66.5°$

$a = \dfrac{b \sin A}{\sin B} \approx 53.06$

97. By Cramer's Rule,

$$D = \begin{vmatrix} 5 & -7 \\ -3 & 1 \end{vmatrix} = 5 - 21 = -16$$

$$D_x = \begin{vmatrix} -11 & -7 \\ -3 & 1 \end{vmatrix} = -11 - 21 = -32$$

$$D_y = \begin{vmatrix} 5 & -11 \\ -3 & -3 \end{vmatrix} = -15 - 33 = -48$$

$$x = \frac{D_x}{D} = \frac{-32}{-16} = 2,\ y = \frac{D_y}{D} = \frac{-48}{-16} = 3$$

Solution: $(2, 3)$

98. By Cramer's Rule,

$$D = \begin{vmatrix} 3 & 5 \\ 4 & -2 \end{vmatrix} = -6 - 20 = -26$$

$$D_x = \begin{vmatrix} -10 & 5 \\ -5 & -2 \end{vmatrix} = -20 - (-25) = 5$$

$$D_y = \begin{vmatrix} 3 & 10 \\ 4 & -5 \end{vmatrix} = -15 - 40 = -55$$

$$x = \frac{D_x}{D} = -\frac{5}{26},\ y = \frac{D_y}{D} = \frac{-55}{-26} = \frac{55}{26}$$

Solution: $\left(-\frac{5}{26}, \frac{55}{26}\right)$

99. By Cramer's Rule,

$$D = \begin{vmatrix} 3 & -2 & 1 \\ 2 & 1 & -3 \\ 1 & -3 & 9 \end{vmatrix} = 35$$

$$D_a = \begin{vmatrix} 0 & -2 & 1 \\ 0 & 1 & -3 \\ 0 & -3 & 9 \end{vmatrix} = 0$$

$$D_b = \begin{vmatrix} 3 & 0 & 1 \\ 2 & 0 & -3 \\ 1 & 0 & 9 \end{vmatrix} = 0$$

$$D_c = \begin{vmatrix} 3 & -2 & 0 \\ 2 & 1 & 0 \\ 1 & -3 & 0 \end{vmatrix} = 0$$

$$a = \frac{D_a}{D} = 0,\ b = \frac{D_b}{D} = 0,\ c = \frac{D_c}{D} = 0$$

Solution: $(0, 0, 0)$

100. By Cramer's Rule,

$$D = \begin{vmatrix} 5 & 7 & 9 \\ 1 & -2 & -3 \\ 8 & -2 & 1 \end{vmatrix} = -89$$

$$D_u = \begin{vmatrix} 15 & 7 & 9 \\ 7 & -2 & -3 \\ 0 & -2 & 1 \end{vmatrix} = -295$$

$$D_v = \begin{vmatrix} 5 & 15 & 9 \\ 1 & 7 & -3 \\ 8 & 0 & 1 \end{vmatrix} = -844$$

$$D_w = \begin{vmatrix} 5 & 7 & 15 \\ 1 & -2 & 7 \\ 8 & -2 & 0 \end{vmatrix} = 672$$

$$u = \frac{D_u}{D} = \frac{-295}{-89} = \frac{295}{89},\ v = \frac{D_v}{D} = \frac{-844}{-89} = \frac{844}{89},$$

$$w = \frac{D_w}{D} = \frac{672}{-89} = \frac{-672}{89}$$

Solution: $\left(\frac{295}{89}, \frac{844}{89}, -\frac{672}{89}\right)$

101. By Cramer's Rule,

$$D = \begin{vmatrix} -1 & 1 & 2 \\ 2 & 3 & 1 \\ 5 & 4 & 2 \end{vmatrix} = -15$$

$$D_x = \begin{vmatrix} 1 & 1 & 2 \\ -2 & 3 & 1 \\ 4 & 4 & 2 \end{vmatrix} = -30$$

$$D_y = \begin{vmatrix} -1 & 1 & 2 \\ 2 & -2 & 1 \\ 5 & 4 & 2 \end{vmatrix} = 45$$

$$D_z = \begin{vmatrix} -1 & 1 & 1 \\ 2 & 3 & -2 \\ 5 & 4 & 4 \end{vmatrix} = -45$$

$$x = \frac{D_x}{D} = \frac{-30}{-15} = 2,\ y = \frac{D_y}{D} = \frac{45}{-15} = -3,$$

$$z = \frac{D_z}{D} = \frac{-45}{-15} = 3$$

Solution: $(2, -3, 3)$

102. Cramer's Rule does not apply because

$$D = \begin{vmatrix} 2 & 1 & 2 \\ 2 & 2 & 0 \\ 2 & -1 & 6 \end{vmatrix} = 0.$$

Use elimination to solve the system.

$$\begin{bmatrix} 2 & 1 & 2 & \vdots & 4 \\ 2 & 2 & 0 & \vdots & 5 \\ 2 & -1 & 6 & \vdots & 2 \end{bmatrix} \rightarrow$$

$$\begin{matrix} \\ -R_1 + R_2 \\ -R_1 + R_3 \end{matrix} \begin{bmatrix} 2 & 1 & 2 & \vdots & 4 \\ 0 & 1 & -2 & \vdots & 1 \\ 0 & -2 & 4 & \vdots & -2 \end{bmatrix} \rightarrow$$

$$\begin{matrix} -R_2 + R_1 \\ \\ 2R_2 + R_3 \end{matrix} \begin{bmatrix} 2 & 0 & 4 & \vdots & 3 \\ 0 & 1 & -2 & \vdots & 1 \\ 0 & 0 & 0 & \vdots & 0 \end{bmatrix}$$

Let $x_3 = a$, then $x_2 = 2a + 1$ and $x_1 = -2a + \frac{3}{2}$.

Solution: $\left(-2a + \frac{3}{2}, 2a + 1, a\right)$

103. Points: $(4, -3), (6, -7), (-2, -1)$

$$\begin{vmatrix} 4 & -3 & 1 \\ 6 & -7 & 1 \\ -2 & -1 & 1 \end{vmatrix} = -20 \neq 0$$

The points are not collinear.

104. Points: $(-2, 4), (0, 1), (4, -5)$

$$\begin{vmatrix} -2 & 4 & 1 \\ 0 & 1 & 1 \\ 4 & -5 & 1 \end{vmatrix} = 0 \Rightarrow \text{collinear}$$

105. Points: $(-6, -4), (-1, -3), (1.5, -2.5)$

$$\begin{vmatrix} -6 & -4 & 1 \\ -1 & -3 & 1 \\ 1.5 & -2.5 & 1 \end{vmatrix} = 0$$

The points are collinear.

106. Points: $(-2.3, 5), (-0.5, 0), (1.5, -3)$

$$\begin{vmatrix} -2.3 & 5 & 1 \\ -0.5 & 0 & 1 \\ 1.5 & -3 & 1 \end{vmatrix} = 4.6 \Rightarrow \text{not collinear}$$

Section 9.7 Graphs of Polar Equations

- When graphing polar equations:
  1. Test for symmetry
     (a) $\theta = \pi/2$: Replace (r, θ) by $(r, \pi - \theta)$ or $(-r, -\theta)$.
     (b) Polar axis: Replace (r, θ) by $(r, -\theta)$ or $(-r, \pi - \theta)$.
     (c) Pole: Replace (r, θ) by $(r, \pi + \theta)$ or $(-r, \theta)$.
     (d) $r = f(\sin \theta)$ is symmetric with respect to the line $\theta = \pi/2$.
     (e) $r = f(\cos \theta)$ is symmetric with respect to the polar axis.
  2. Find the θ values for which $|r|$ is maximum.
  3. Find the θ values for which $r = 0$.
  4. Know the different types of polar graphs.

(a) Limaçons	(b) Rose curves, $n \geq 2$	(c) Circles	(d) Lemniscates
$r = a \pm b \cos \theta$	$r = a \cos n\theta$	$r = a \cos \theta$	$r^2 = a^2 \cos 2\theta$
$r = a \pm b \sin \theta$	$r = a \sin n\theta$	$r = a \sin \theta$	$r^2 = a^2 \sin 2\theta$
		$r = a$	

- You should be able to graph polar equations of the form $r = f(\theta)$ with your graphing utility. If your utility does not have a polar mode, use

  $x = f(t) \cos t$
  $y = f(t) \sin t$

  in parametric mode.

Vocabulary Check

1. $\theta = \dfrac{\pi}{2}$
2. polar axis
3. convex limaçon
4. circle
5. lemniscate
6. cardioid

1. $r = 3 \cos 2\theta$ is a rose curve.

2. Cardioid

3. Lemniscate

4. $r = 3 \cos \theta$ is a circle.

5. $r = 6 \sin 2\theta$ is a rose curve.

6. Limaçon

7. The graph is symmetric about the line $\theta = \pi/2$, and passes through $(r, \theta) = (3, 3\pi/2)$. Matches (a).

8. The graph is symmetric about the polar axis and passes through $(r, \theta) = (3, 0)$. Matches (c).

9. The graph has four leaves. Matches (c).

10. The graph has three leaves. Matches (d).

11. $r = 14 + 4\cos\theta$

$\theta = \frac{\pi}{2}$: $-r = 14 + 4\cos(-\theta)$

$-r = 14 + 4\cos\theta$

Not an equivalent equation

$r = 14 + 4\cos(\pi - \theta)$

$r = 14 + 4(\cos\pi\cos\theta + \sin\pi\sin\theta)$

$r = 14 - 4\cos\theta$

Not an equivalent equation

Polar axis: $r = 14 + 4\cos(-\theta)$

$r = 14 + 4\cos\theta$

Equivalent equation

Pole: $-r = 14 + 4\cos\theta$

Not an equivalent equation

$r = 14 + 4\cos(\pi + \theta)$

$r = 14 - 4\cos\theta$

Not an equivalent equation

Answer: Symmetric with respect to polar axis

12. $r = 12\cos 3\theta$

$\theta = \frac{\pi}{2}$: $-r = 12\cos(3(-\theta))$

$-r = 12\cos 3\theta$

Not an equivalent equation

$r = 12\cos(3(\pi - \theta))$

$r = -12\cos 3\theta$

Not an equivalent equation

Polar axis: $r = 12\cos(3(-\theta))$

$r = 12\cos 3\theta$

Equivalent equation

Pole: $-r = 12\cos 3\theta$

Not an equivalent equation

$r = 12\cos(3(\pi + \theta))$

$r = -12\cos 3\theta$

Not an equivalent equation

Answer: Symmetric with respect to polar axis

13. $r = \dfrac{4}{1 + \sin\theta}$

$\theta = \frac{\pi}{2}$: $r = \dfrac{4}{1 + \sin(\pi - \theta)}$

$r = \dfrac{4}{1 + \sin\pi\cos\theta - \cos\pi\sin\theta}$

$r = \dfrac{4}{1 + \sin\theta}$

Equivalent equation

Polar axis: $r = \dfrac{4}{1 + \sin(-\theta)}$

$r = \dfrac{4}{1 - \sin\theta}$

Not an equivalent equation

$-r = \dfrac{4}{1 + \sin(\pi - \theta)}$

$-r = \dfrac{4}{1 + \sin\theta}$

Not an equivalent equation

Pole: $-r = \dfrac{4}{1 + \sin\theta}$

Not an equivalent equation

$r = \dfrac{4}{1 + \sin(\pi + \theta)}$

$r = \dfrac{4}{1 - \sin\theta}$

Not an equivalent equation

Answer: Symmetric with respect to $\theta = \frac{\pi}{2}$

14. $r = \dfrac{2}{1 - \cos\theta}$

$\theta = \dfrac{\pi}{2}$: $-r = \dfrac{2}{1 - \cos(-\theta)}$

$-r = \dfrac{2}{1 - \cos\theta}$

Not an equivalent equation

$r = \dfrac{2}{1 - \cos(\pi - \theta)}$

$r = \dfrac{2}{1 - (\cos\pi\cos\theta + \sin\pi\sin\theta)}$

$r = \dfrac{2}{1 + \cos\theta}$

Not an equivalent equation

Polar axis: $r = \dfrac{2}{1 - \cos(-\theta)}$

$r = \dfrac{2}{1 - \cos\theta}$

Equivalent equation

Pole: $-r = \dfrac{2}{1 - \cos\theta}$

Not an equivalent equation

$r = \dfrac{2}{1 - \cos(\pi + \theta)}$

$r = \dfrac{2}{1 - (\cos\pi\cos\theta - \sin\pi\sin\theta)}$

$r = \dfrac{2}{1 + \cos\theta}$

Not an equivalent equation

Answer: Symmetric with respect to the polar axis

15. $r = 6\sin\theta$

$\theta = \dfrac{\pi}{2}$: $-r = 6\sin(-\theta)$

$r = 6\sin\theta$

Equivalent equation

Polar axis: $r = 6\sin(-\theta)$

$r = -6\sin\theta$

Not an equivalent equation

$-r = 6\sin(\pi - \theta)$

$-r = 6(\sin\pi\cos\theta - \cos\pi\sin\theta)$

$-r = 6\sin\theta$

Not an equivalent equation

Pole: $-r = 6\sin\theta$

Not an equivalent equation

$r = 6\sin(\pi + \theta)$

$r = -6\sin\theta$

Not an equivalent equation

Answer: Symmetric with respect to $\theta = \dfrac{\pi}{2}$

16. $r = 4\csc\theta\cos\theta = 4\cot\theta$

$\theta = \dfrac{\pi}{2}$: $-r = 4\cot(-\theta)$

$r = 4\cot\theta$

Equivalent equation

Polar axis: $-r = 4\cot(\pi - \theta)$

$-r = 4\cot(-\theta)$

$r = 4\cot\theta$

Equivalent equation

Pole: $r = 4\cot(\pi + \theta)$

$r = 4\cot\theta$

Equivalent equation

Answer: Symmetric with respect to $\theta = \dfrac{\pi}{2}$, polar axis and pole

17. $r^2 = 16 \sin 2\theta$

$\theta = \frac{\pi}{2}$: $(-r)^2 = 16 \sin(2(-\theta))$

$r^2 = -16 \sin 2\theta$

Not an equivalent equation

$r^2 = 16 \sin(2(\pi - \theta))$

$r^2 = 16 \sin(2\pi - 2\theta)$

$r^2 = -16 \sin 2\theta$

Not an equivalent equation

Polar axis: $r^2 = 16 \sin(2(-\theta))$

$r^2 = -16 \sin 2\theta$

Not an equivalent equation

$(-r)^2 = 16 \sin(2(\pi - \theta))$

$r^2 = -16 \sin 2\theta$

Not an equivalent equation

Pole: $(-r)^2 = 16 \sin(2\theta)$

$r^2 = 16 \sin 2\theta$

Equivalent equation

Answer: Symmetric with respect to pole

18. $r^2 = 25 \cos 4\theta$

$\theta = \frac{\pi}{2}$: $(-r)^2 = 25 \cos(4(-\theta))$

$r^2 = 25 \cos 4\theta$

Equivalent equation

Polar axis: $r^2 = 25 \cos(4(-\theta))$

$r^2 = 25 \cos 4\theta$

Equivalent equation

Pole: $(-r)^2 = 25 \cos 4\theta$

$r^2 = 25 \cos 4\theta$

Equivalent equation

Answer: Symmetric with respect to $\theta = \frac{\pi}{2}$, polar axis and pole

19. $|r| = |10(1 - \sin \theta)|$

$= 10|1 - \sin \theta| \le 10(2) = 20$

$|1 - \sin \theta| = 2$

$1 - \sin \theta = 2$ or $1 - \sin \theta = -2$

$\sin \theta = -1$ $\quad \sin \theta = 3$

$\theta = \frac{3\pi}{2}$ $\quad$ Not possible

Maximum: $|r| = 20$ when $\theta = \frac{3\pi}{2}$

$r = 0$ when $1 - \sin \theta = 0$

$\sin \theta = 1$

$\theta = \frac{\pi}{2}$

20. $|r| = |6 + 12 \cos \theta| \le |6| + |12 \cos \theta|$

$= 6 + 12|\cos \theta| \le 18$

$\cos \theta = 1$

$\theta = 0$

Maximum: $|r| = 18$ when $\theta = 0$

Zero: $r = 0$ when $\theta = \frac{2\pi}{3}, \frac{4\pi}{3}$

21. $|r| = |4 \cos 3\theta| = 4 |\cos 3\theta| \le 4$

$|\cos 3\theta| = 1$

$\cos 3\theta = \pm 1$

$\theta = 0, \frac{\pi}{3}, \frac{2\pi}{3}, \pi$

Maximum: $|r| = 4$ when $\theta = 0, \frac{\pi}{3}, \frac{2\pi}{3}, \pi$

$r = 0$ when $\cos 3\theta = 0$

$\theta = \frac{\pi}{6}, \frac{\pi}{2}, \frac{5\pi}{6}$

22. $r = \sin 2\theta$

$|r| = |\sin 2\theta|$

Maximum: $|r| = 1$ when $\theta = \frac{\pi}{4}, \frac{3\pi}{4}, \frac{5\pi}{4}, \frac{7\pi}{4}$

Zero: $r = 0$ when $\theta = 0, \frac{\pi}{2}, \pi, \frac{3\pi}{2}, 2\pi$

23. $r = 5$

Circle

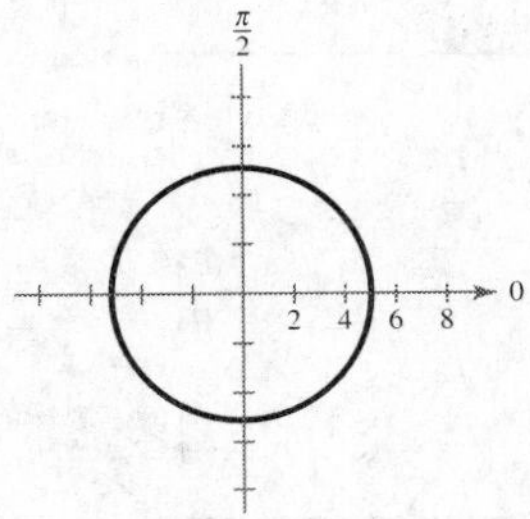

24. $\theta = -\frac{5\pi}{3}$

Line

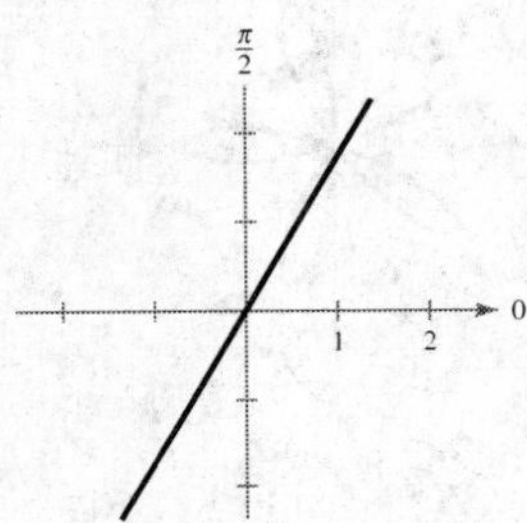

25. $r = 3 \sin \theta$

Symmetric with respect to $\theta = \pi/2$

Circle with radius of $3/2$

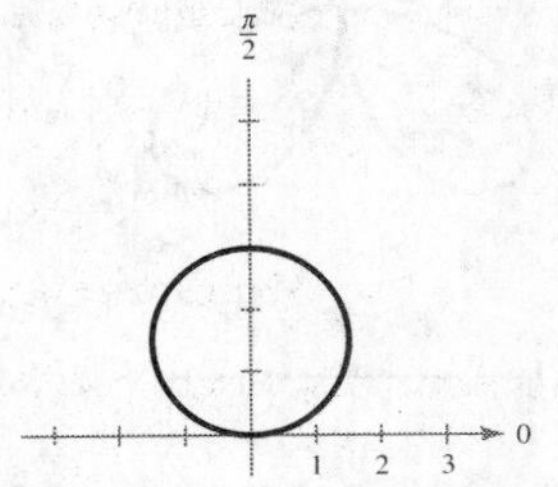

26. $r = 2 \cos \theta$

Circle

Radius: 1, center: (1, 0)

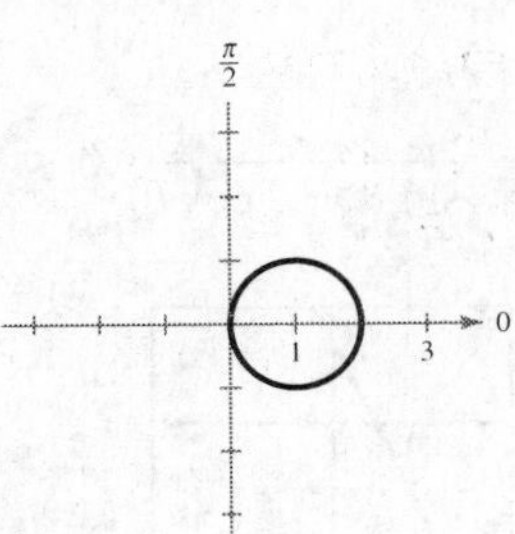

27. $r = 3(1 - \cos \theta)$

Cardioid

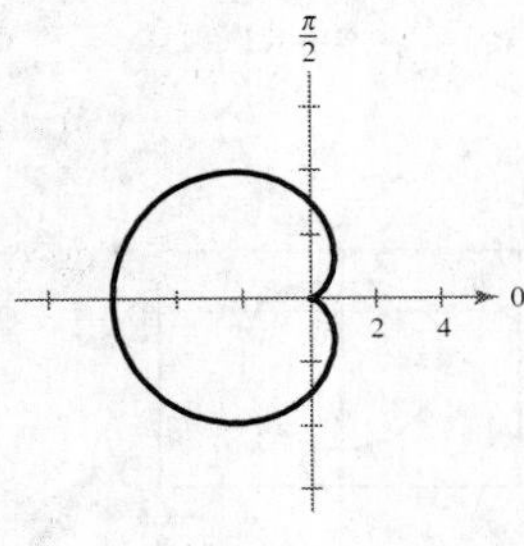

28. $r = 4(1 + \sin \theta)$

Cardioid

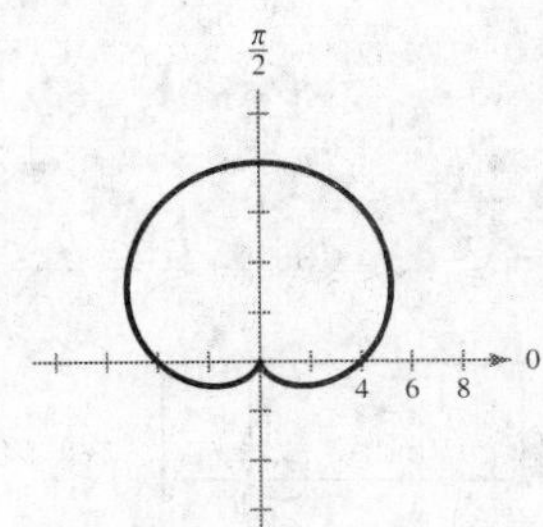

29. $r = 3 - 4 \cos \theta$

Limaçon

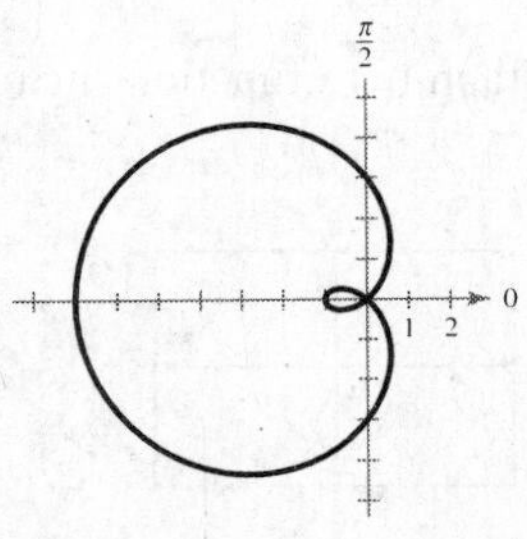

30. $r = 1 - 2 \sin \theta$

Limaçon with inner loop

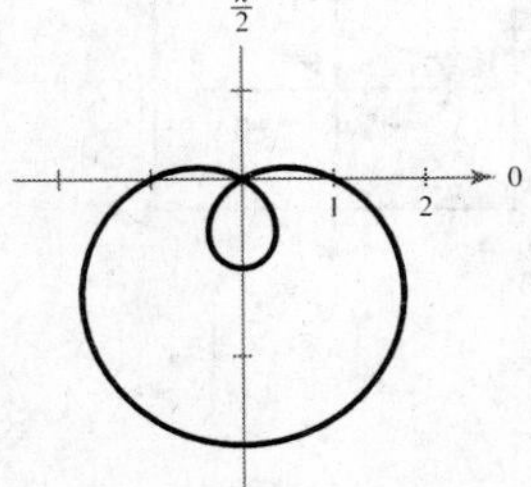

31. $r = 4 + 5 \sin \theta$

Limaçon

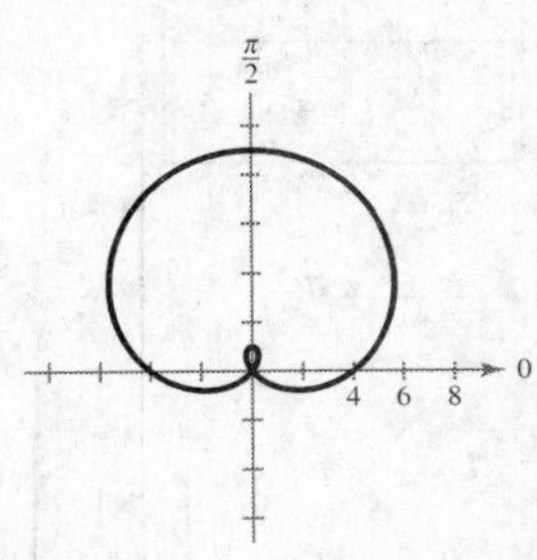

32. $r = 3 + 6\cos\theta$

Limaçon

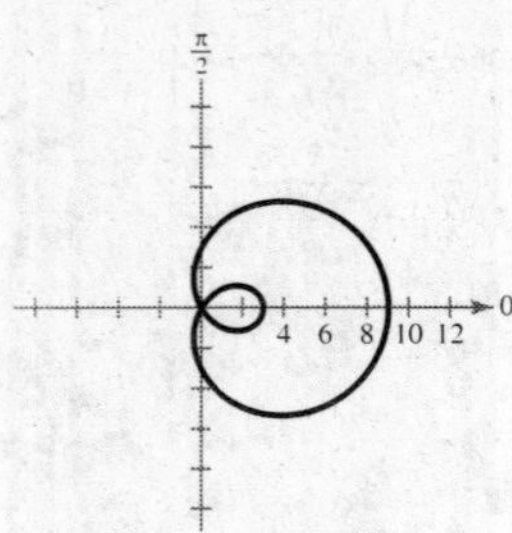

33. $r = 5\cos 3\theta$

Rose curve

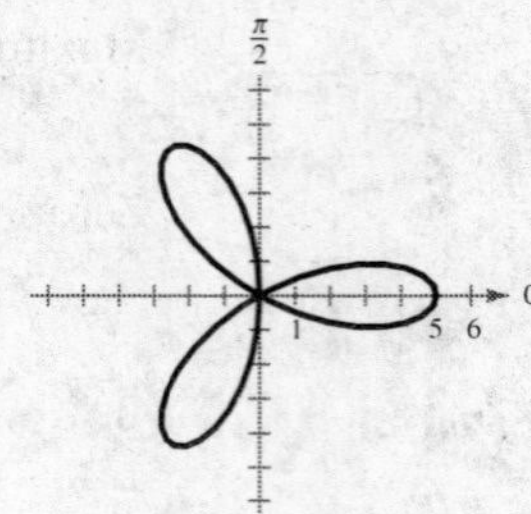

34. $r = -\sin 5\theta$

Rose curve

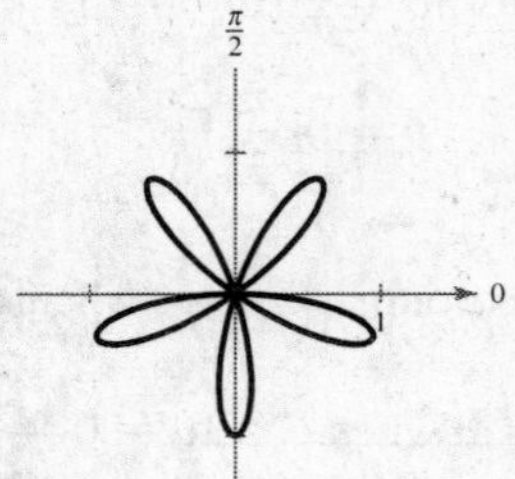

35. $r = 7\sin 2\theta$

Rose curve, four petals

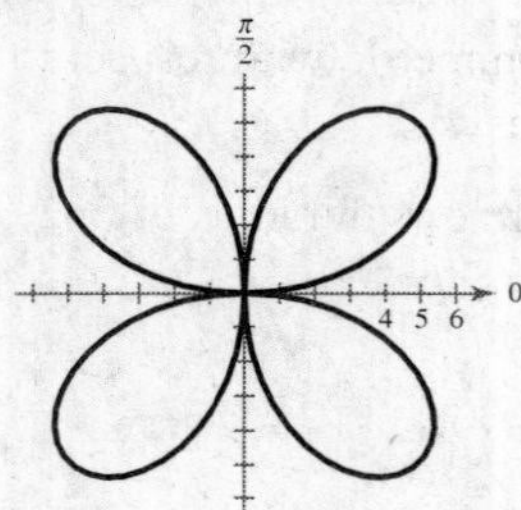

36. $r = 3\cos 5\theta$

Rose curve, five petals

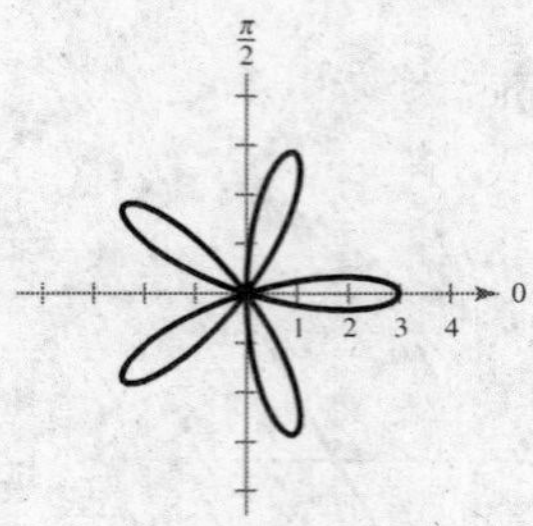

37. $r = 8\cos 2\theta$

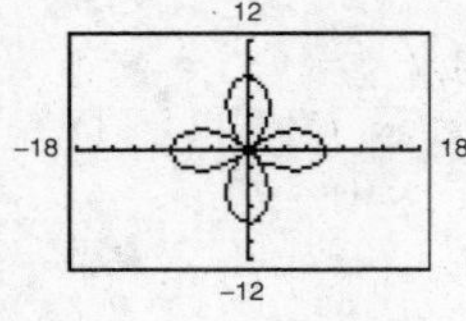

$0 \le \theta < 2\pi$

38.

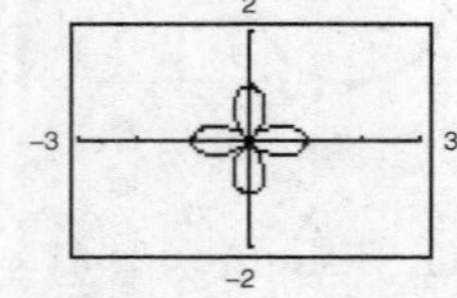

$0 \le \theta \le 2\pi$

39. $r = 2(5 - \sin\theta)$

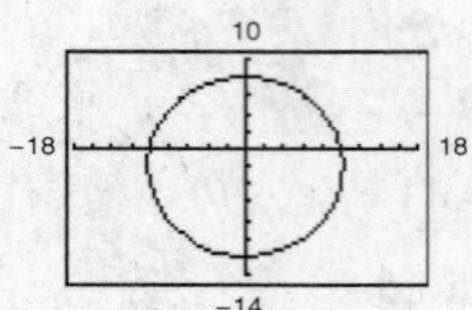

$0 \le \theta < 2\pi$

40.

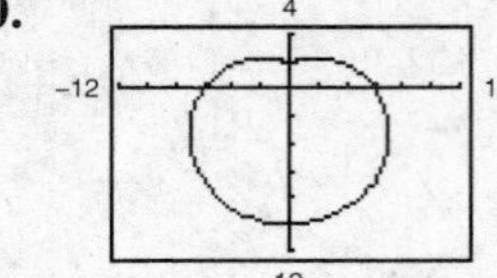

$0 \le \theta \le 2\pi$

41. $r = 3 - 6\cos\theta,\ 0 \le \theta \le 2\pi$

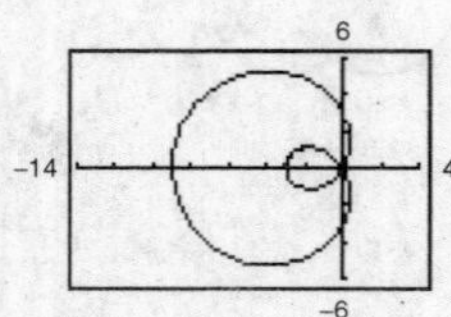

42.

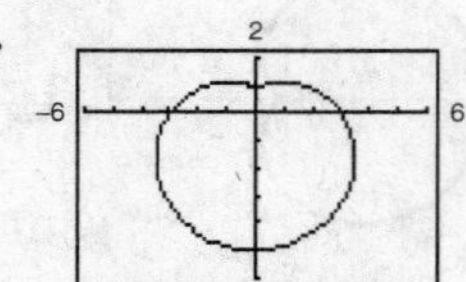

$0 \le \theta \le 2\pi$

43. $r = \dfrac{3}{\sin\theta - 2\cos\theta},\ 0 \le \theta \le \dfrac{\pi}{2}$

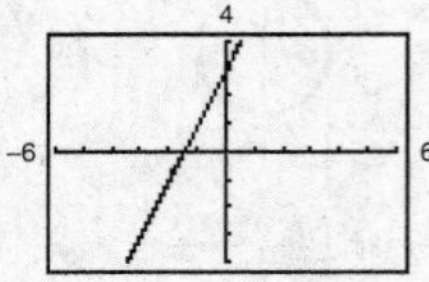

44.

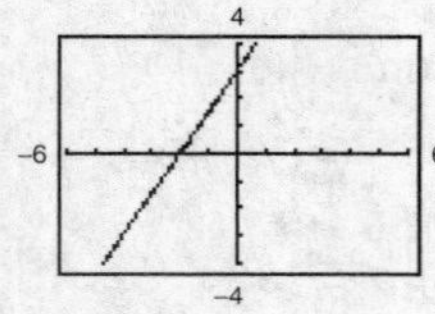

$0 \le \theta \le 2\pi$

45. 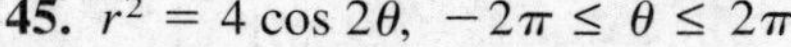 $r^2 = 4\cos 2\theta,\ -2\pi \le \theta \le 2\pi$

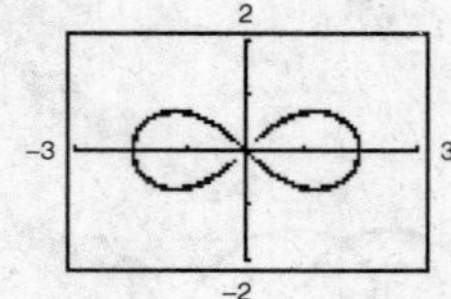

46. $r^2 = 9\sin\theta$

$r = \pm 3\sqrt{\sin\theta}$

Graph both functions using $0 \le \theta \le 2\pi$.

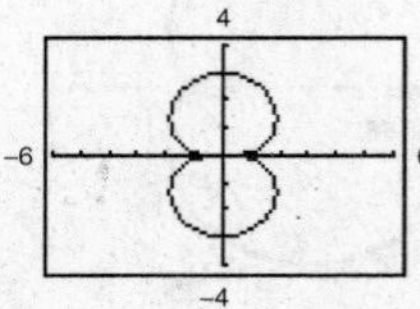

47. $r = 4 \sin \theta \cos^2 \theta,\ 0 \le \theta \le \pi$

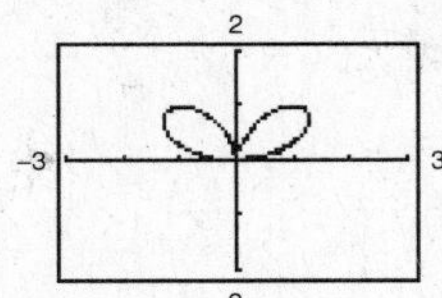

48.

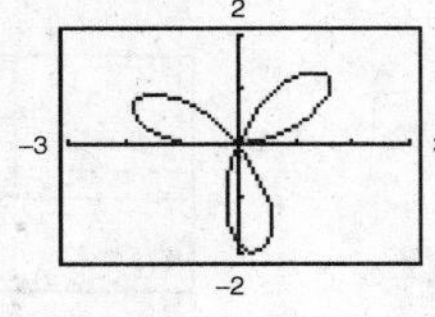

$0 \le \theta \le \pi$

49. $r = 2 \csc \theta + 6$

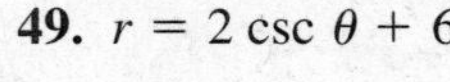

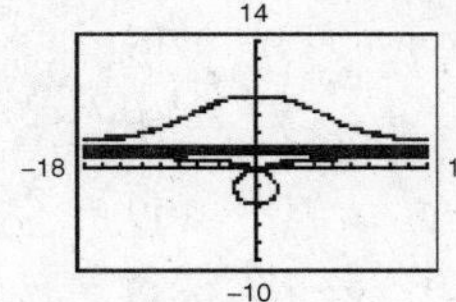

$0 \le \theta < 2\pi$

50.

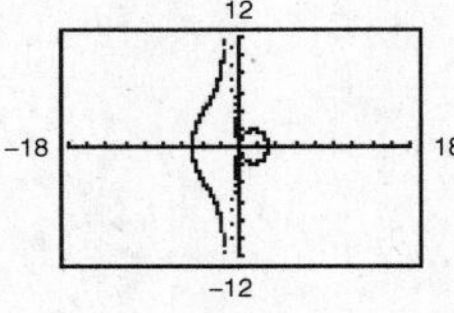

$0 \le \theta \le 2\pi$

51. $r = e^{2\theta}$

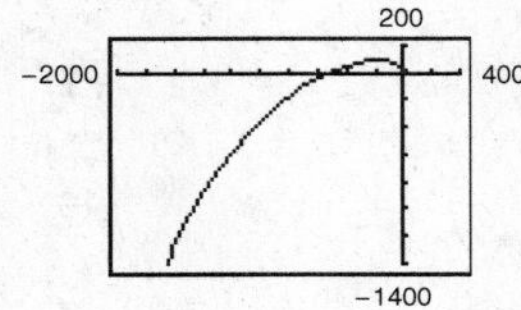

Answers will vary.

52. $r = e^{\theta/2}$

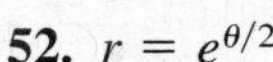

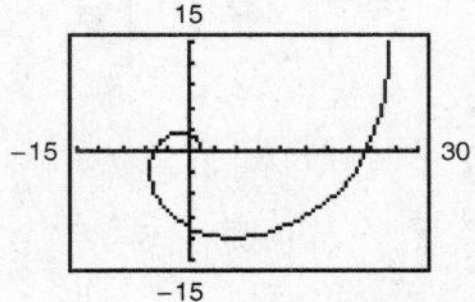

Answers will vary.

53. $r = 3 - 2 \cos \theta,\ 0 \le \theta < 2\pi$

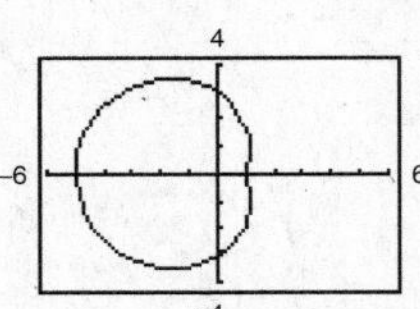

54.

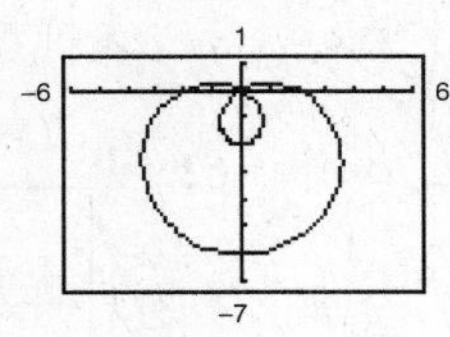

$0 \le \theta < 2\pi$

55. $r = 2 \cos\left(\dfrac{3\theta}{2}\right),\ 0 \le \theta < 4\pi$

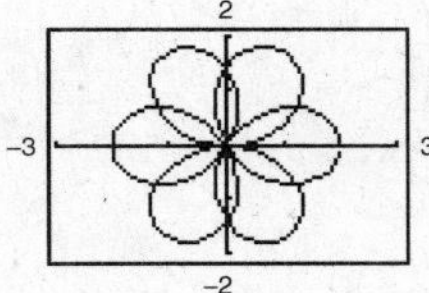

56.

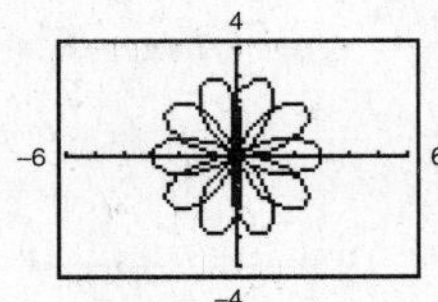

$0 \le \theta < 4\pi$

57. $r^2 = \sin 2\theta,\ 0 \le \theta < \dfrac{\pi}{2}$

(Use $r_1 = \sqrt{\sin 2\theta}$ and $r_2 = -\sqrt{\sin 2\theta}$.)

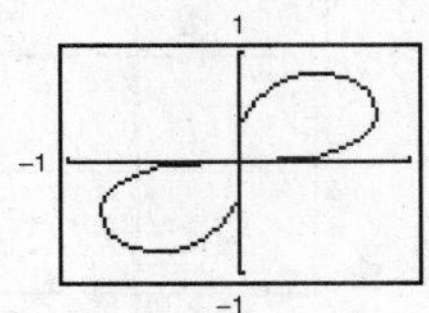

58.

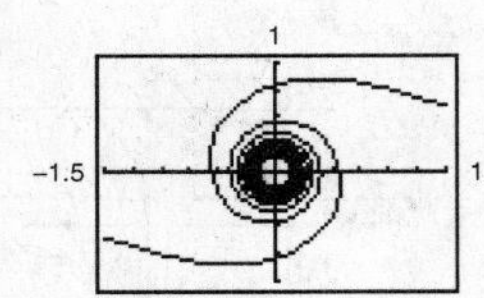

$0 < \theta < \infty$

$r = \dfrac{\pm 1}{\sqrt{\theta}}$

59. $r = 2 - \sec \theta$

$x = -1$ is an asymptote.

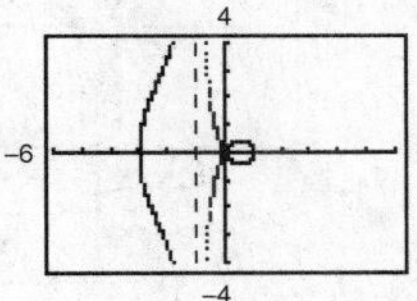

60.

$$r = 2 + \csc\theta = 2 + \frac{1}{\sin\theta}$$

$$r\sin\theta = 2\sin\theta + 1$$

$$r(r\sin\theta) = 2r\sin\theta + r$$

$$\left(\pm\sqrt{x^2+y^2}\right)(y) = 2y + \left(\pm\sqrt{x^2+y^2}\right)$$

$$\left(\pm\sqrt{x^2+y^2}\right)(y-1) = 2y$$

$$\left(\pm\sqrt{x^2+y^2}\right) = \frac{2y}{y-1}$$

$$x^2 + y^2 = \frac{4y^2}{(y-1)^2}$$

$$x^2 = \frac{y^2(3+2y-y^2)}{(y-1)^2}$$

$$x = \pm\sqrt{\frac{y^2(3+2y-y^2)}{(y-1)^2}} = \pm\left|\frac{y}{y-1}\right|\sqrt{3+2y-y^2}$$

The graph has an asymptote at $y = 1$.

61. $r = \dfrac{2}{\theta}$

$y = 2$ is an asymptote.

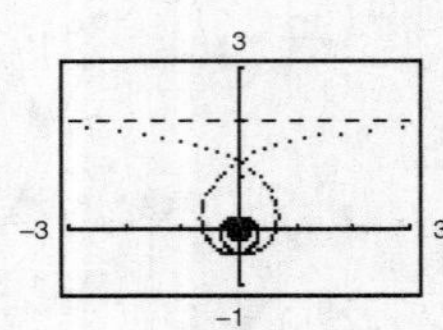

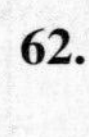

62.

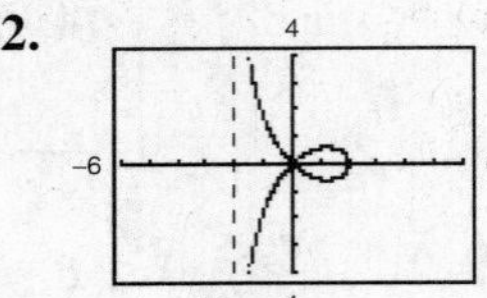

63. True. It has five petals.

64. False. For example, let $r = \cos 3\theta$.

65. $r = \cos(5\theta) + n\cos\theta,\ 0 \le \theta < \pi$; Answers will vary.

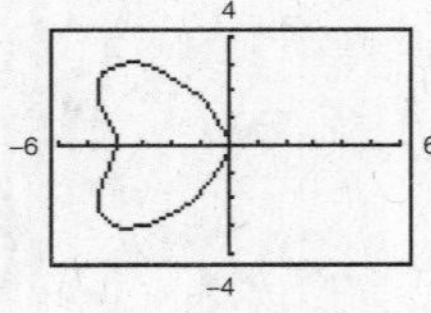

$n = -5$

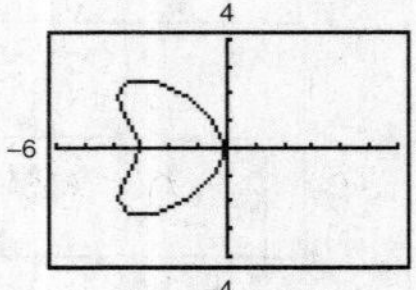

$n = -4$

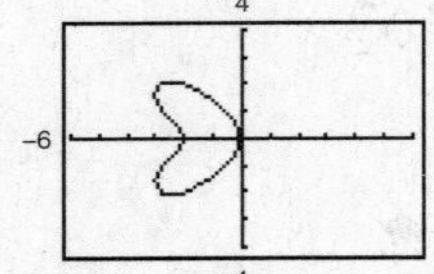

$n = -3$

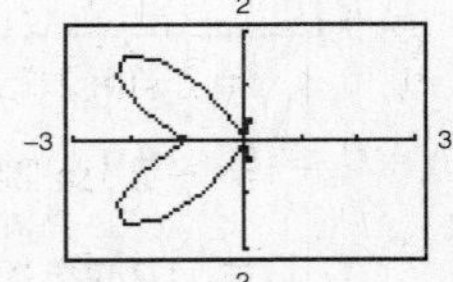

$n = -2$

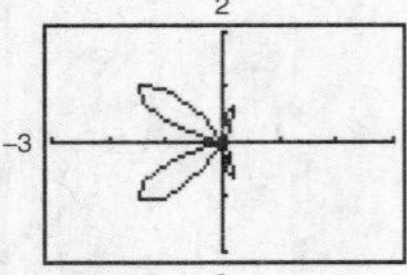

$n = -1$

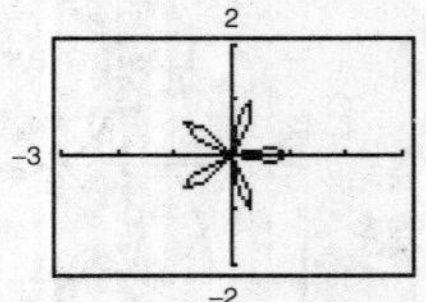

$n = 0$

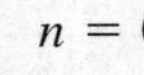

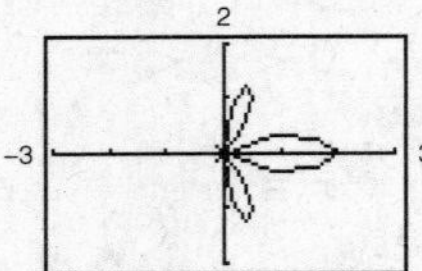

$n = 1$

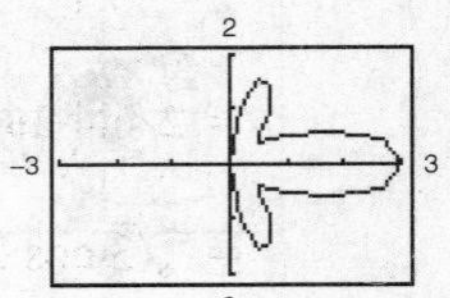

$n = 2$

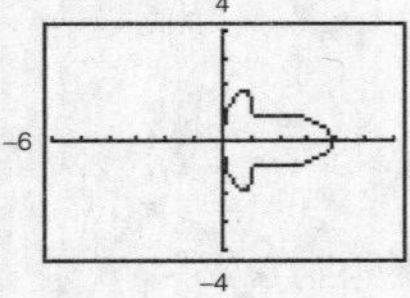

$n = 3$

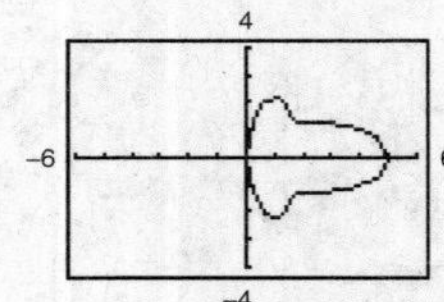

$n = 4$

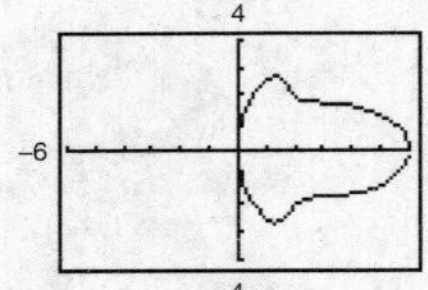

$n = 5$

66. The graph of $r = f(\theta)$ is rotated about the pole through an angle ϕ. Let (r, θ) be any point on the graph of $r = f(\theta)$. Then $(r, \theta + \phi)$ is rotated through the angle ϕ, and since $r = f((\theta + \phi) - \phi) = f(\theta)$, it follows that $(r, \theta + \phi)$ is on the graph of $r = f(\theta - \phi)$.

67. Use the result of Exercise 66.

(a) Rotation: $\phi = \dfrac{\pi}{2}$

Original graph: $r = f(\sin\theta)$

Rotated graph: $r = f\left(\sin\left(\theta - \dfrac{\pi}{2}\right)\right) = f(-\cos\theta)$

(b) Rotation: $\phi = \pi$

Original graph: $r = f(\sin\theta)$

Rotated graph: $r = f(\sin(\theta - \pi)) = f(-\sin\theta)$

(c) Rotation: $\phi = \dfrac{3\pi}{2}$

Original graph: $r = f(\sin\theta)$

Rotated graph: $r = f\left(\sin\left(\theta - \dfrac{3\pi}{2}\right)\right) = f(\cos\theta)$

68. (a) $r = 2 - \sin\left(\theta - \dfrac{\pi}{4}\right)$

$= 2 - \dfrac{\sqrt{2}}{2}(\sin\theta - \cos\theta)$

(b) $r = 2 - \sin\left(\theta - \dfrac{\pi}{2}\right)$

$= 2 + \cos\theta$

(c) $r = 2 - \sin(\theta - \pi)$

$= 2 + \sin\theta$

(d) $r = 2 - \sin\left(\theta - \dfrac{3\pi}{2}\right)$

$= 2 - \cos\theta$

69. (a) $r = 2\sin\left[2\left(\theta - \dfrac{\pi}{6}\right)\right]$

$= 2\sin\left(2\theta - \dfrac{\pi}{3}\right)$

$= \sin 2\theta - \sqrt{3}\cos 2\theta$

(b) $r = 2\sin\left[2\left(\theta - \dfrac{\pi}{2}\right)\right]$

$= 2\sin(2\theta - \pi)$

$= -2\sin 2\theta$

$= -4\sin\theta\cos\theta$

(c) $r = 2\sin\left[2\left(\theta - \dfrac{2\pi}{3}\right)\right]$

$= 2\sin\left(2\theta - \dfrac{4\pi}{3}\right)$

$= \sqrt{3}\cos 2\theta - \sin 2\theta$

(d) $r = 2\sin[2(\theta - \pi)]$

$= 2\sin(2\theta - 2\pi)$

$= 2\sin 2\theta$

$= 4\sin\theta\cos\theta$

70. (a) $r = 1 - \sin\theta$

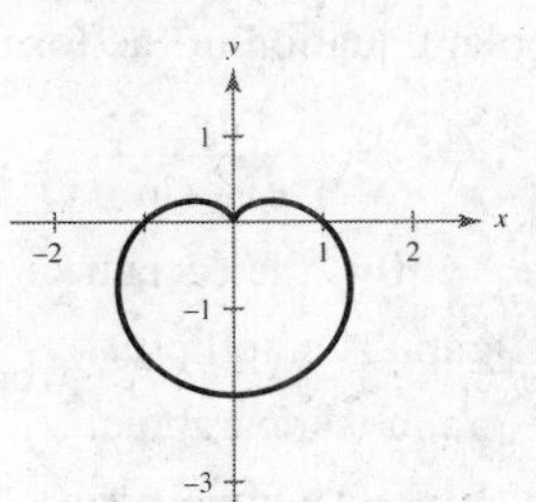

(b) $r = 1 - \sin\left(\theta - \dfrac{\pi}{4}\right)$

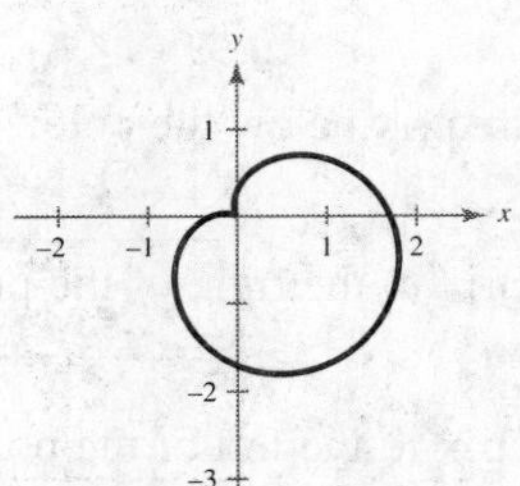

71. $r = 2 + k\cos\theta$

$k = 0$

Circle

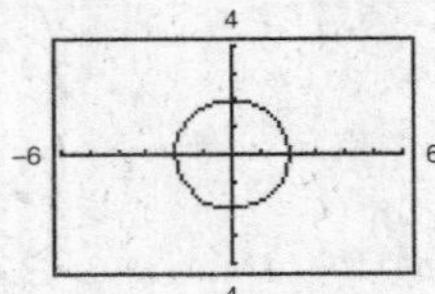

$k = 1$

Convex limaçon

$k = 2$

Cardioid

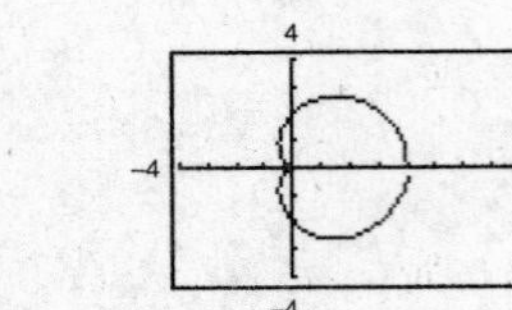

$k = 3$

Limaçon with inner loop

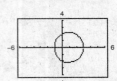

72. $r = 3\sin k\,\theta$

(a)

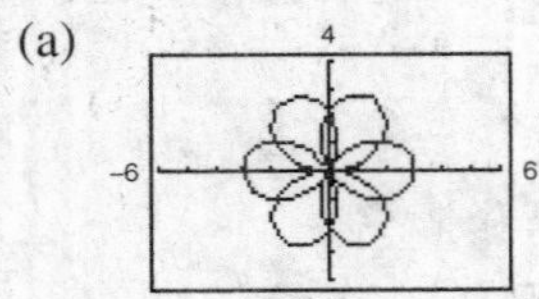

$k = 1.5$: $0 \le \theta < 4\pi$

(b)

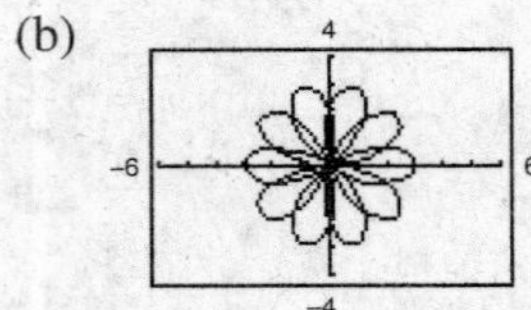

$k = 2.5$: $0 \le \theta < 4\pi$

(c) Yes. Answers will vary.

Section 9.8 Polar Equations of Conics

- The graph of a polar equation of the form

  $$r = \frac{ep}{1 \pm e\cos\theta} \quad \text{or} \quad r = \frac{ep}{1 \pm e\sin\theta}$$

  is a conic, where $e > 0$ is the eccentricity and $|p|$ is the distance between the focus (pole) and the directrix.

  (a) If $e < 1$, the graph is an ellipse.

  (b) If $e = 1$, the graph is a parabola.

  (c) If $e > 1$, the graph is a hyperbola.

- Guidelines for finding polar equations of conics:

  (a) Horizontal directrix above the pole: $r = \dfrac{ep}{1 + e\sin\theta}$

  (b) Horizontal directrix below the pole: $r = \dfrac{ep}{1 - e\sin\theta}$

  (c) Vertical directrix to the right of the pole: $r = \dfrac{ep}{1 + e\cos\theta}$

  (d) Vertical directrix to the left of the pole: $r = \dfrac{ep}{1 - e\cos\theta}$

Vocabulary Check

1. conic

2. eccentricity, e

3. (a) i (b) iii (c) ii

1. $r = \dfrac{2e}{1 + e\cos\theta}$

(a) Parabola

(b) Ellipse

(c) Hyperbola

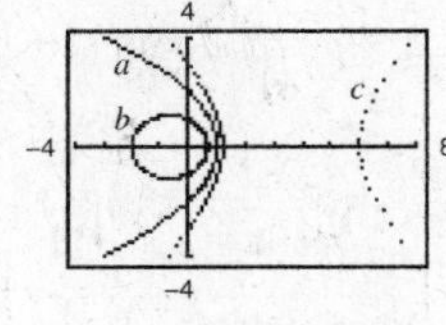

2. (a) Parabola

(b) Ellipse

(c) Hyperbola

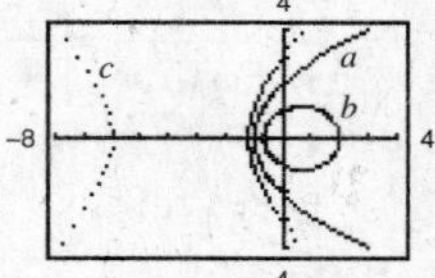

3. $r = \dfrac{2e}{1 - e\sin\theta}$

(a) Parabola

(b) Ellipse

(c) Hyperbola

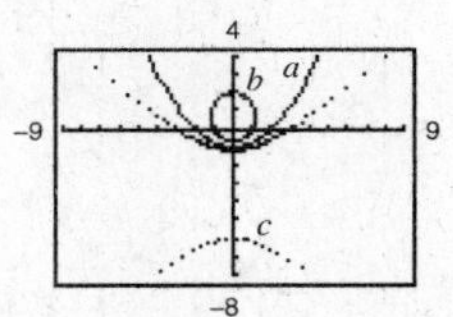

4. (a) Parabola

(b) Ellipse

(c) Hyperbola

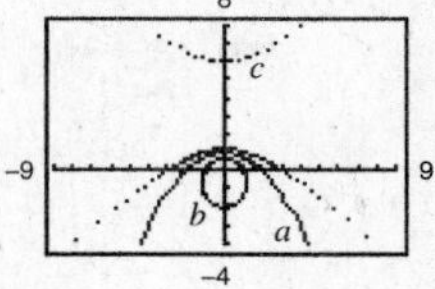

5. $r = \dfrac{4}{1 - \cos\theta}$

$e = 1 \Rightarrow$ parabola

Vertical directrix to left of pole

Matches (b).

6. $r = \dfrac{3}{2 - \cos\theta} = \dfrac{3/2}{1 - (1/2)\cos\theta}$

$e = \dfrac{1}{2} \Rightarrow$ ellipse

Vertical directrix to left of pole

Matches (c).

7. $r = \dfrac{3}{2 + \cos\theta} = \dfrac{3/2}{1 + (1/2)\cos\theta}$

$e = \dfrac{1}{2} \Rightarrow$ ellipse

Vertical directrix to right of pole

Matches (f).

8. $r = \dfrac{4}{1 - 3\sin\theta}$

$e = 3 \Rightarrow$ hyperbola

Horizontal directrix below the pole.

Matches (e).

9. $r = \dfrac{3}{1 + 2\sin\theta}$

$e = 2 \Rightarrow$ hyperbola

Horizontal directrix above the pole.

Matches (d).

10. $r = \dfrac{4}{1 + \sin\theta}$

$e = 1 \Rightarrow$ parabola

Vertex: $\left(2, \dfrac{\pi}{2}\right)$

Matches (a).

11. $r = \dfrac{2}{1 - \cos\theta}$

$e = 1 \Rightarrow$ parabola

Vertex: $(r, \theta) = (1, \pi)$

12. $r = \dfrac{2}{1 + \sin\theta}$

$e = 1 \Rightarrow$ parabola

Vertex: $(1, \pi/2)$

13. $r = \dfrac{4}{4 - \cos\theta} = \dfrac{1}{1 - (1/4)\cos\theta}$

$e = \dfrac{1}{4}, p = 4,$ ellipse

Vertices:

$(r, \theta) = \left(\dfrac{4}{3}, 0\right), \left(\dfrac{4}{5}, \pi\right)$

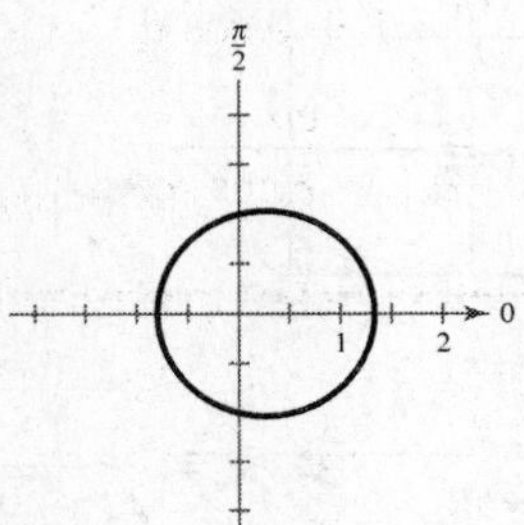

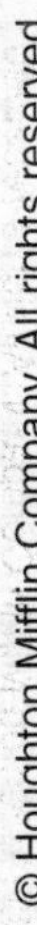

14. $r = \dfrac{7}{7 + \sin\theta} = \dfrac{1}{1 + (1/7)\sin\theta}$

$e = \dfrac{1}{7} \implies$ ellipse

Vertices: $(r, \theta) = \left(\dfrac{7}{8}, \dfrac{\pi}{2}\right), \left(\dfrac{7}{6}, \dfrac{3\pi}{2}\right)$

15. $r = \dfrac{8}{4 + 3\sin\theta} = \dfrac{2}{1 + (3/4)\sin\theta}$

$e = \dfrac{3}{4} \implies$ ellipse

Vertices:

$(r, \theta) = \left(\dfrac{8}{7}, \dfrac{\pi}{2}\right), \left(8, \dfrac{3\pi}{2}\right)$

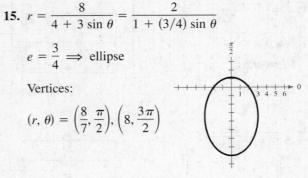

16. $r = \dfrac{6}{3 - 2\cos\theta} = \dfrac{2}{1 - (2/3)\cos\theta}$

$e = \dfrac{2}{3} \implies$ ellipse

Vertices: $(6, 0), \left(\dfrac{6}{5}, \pi\right)$

17. $r = \dfrac{6}{2 + \sin\theta} = \dfrac{(1/2)(6)}{1 + (1/2)\sin\theta}$

$e = \dfrac{1}{2} \implies$ ellipse

Vertices:

$\left(2, \dfrac{\pi}{2}\right), \left(6, \dfrac{3\pi}{2}\right)$

18. $r = \dfrac{5}{-1 + 2\cos\theta} = \dfrac{-5}{1 - 2\cos\theta}$

$e = 2 \implies$ hyperbola

Vertices: $(5, 0), \left(-\dfrac{5}{3}, \pi\right)$

19. $r = \dfrac{3}{4 - 8\cos\theta} = \dfrac{3/4}{1 - 2\cos\theta}$

$e = 2 \implies$ hyperbola

Hyperbola

Vertices:

$(r, \theta) = \left(-\dfrac{3}{4}, 0\right), \left(\dfrac{1}{4}, \pi\right)$

20. $r = \dfrac{10}{3 + 9\sin\theta} = \dfrac{10/3}{1 + 3\sin\theta}$

$e = 3 \implies$ hyperbola

Vertices:

$(r, \theta) = \left(\dfrac{5}{6}, \dfrac{\pi}{2}\right), \left(-\dfrac{5}{3}, \dfrac{3\pi}{2}\right)$

21. $r = \dfrac{-5}{1 - \sin\theta}$

Parabola

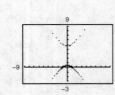

22. $r = \dfrac{-1}{2 + 4\sin\theta}$

Hyperbola

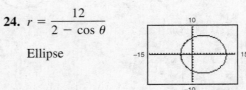

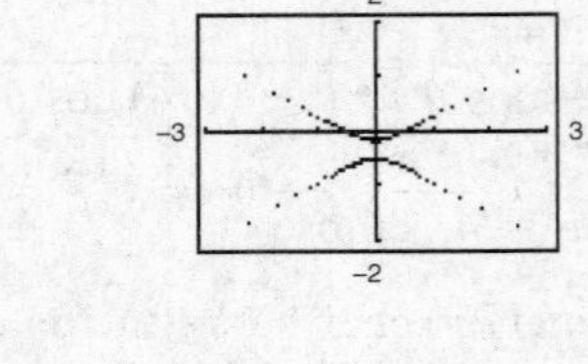

23. $r = \dfrac{14}{14 + 17\sin\theta}$

$= \dfrac{1}{1 + (17/14)\sin\theta}$

Hyperbola

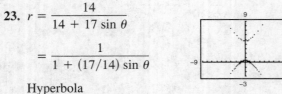

24. $r = \dfrac{12}{2 - \cos\theta}$

Ellipse

25.

Ellipse

26.

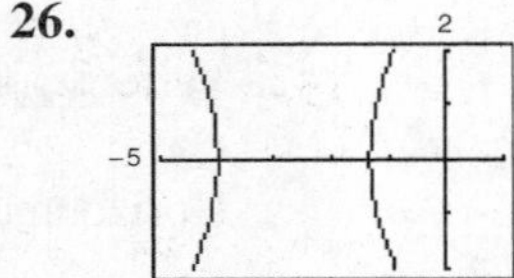

Hyperbola

27.

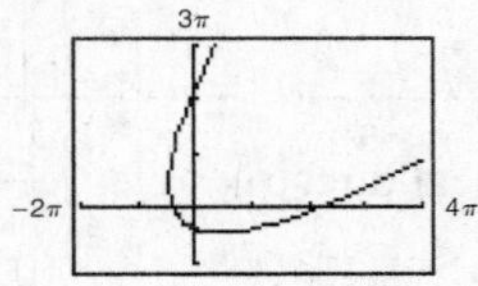

28.

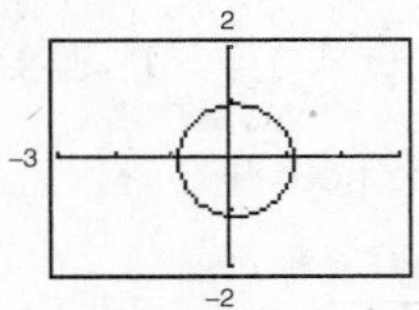

29.

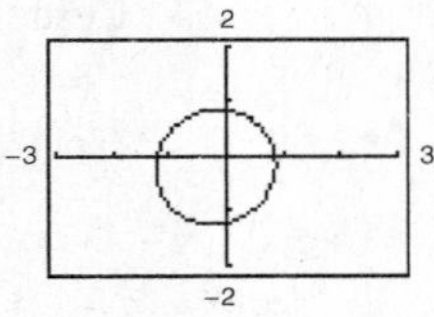

30.

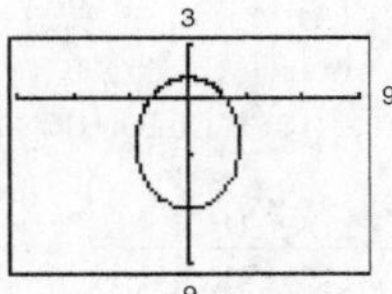

31.

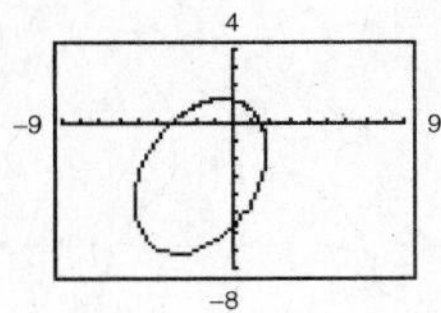

32.

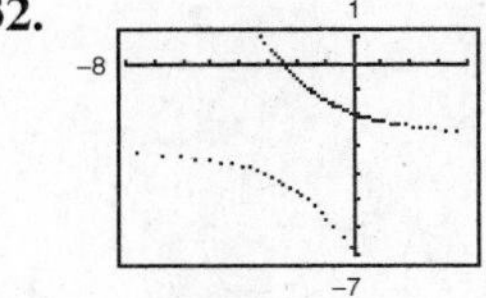

33. $e = 1, x = -1, p = 1$

Vertical directrix to the left of the pole

$$r = \frac{1(1)}{1 - 1\cos\theta} = \frac{1}{1 - \cos\theta}$$

34. $e = 1, y = -4, p = 4$

Horizontal directrix below the pole

$$r = \frac{1(4)}{1 - (1)\sin\theta} = \frac{4}{1 - \sin\theta}$$

35. $e = \frac{1}{2}, y = 1, p = 1$

Horizontal directrix above the pole

$$r = \frac{(1/2)(1)}{1 + (1/2)\sin\theta} = \frac{1}{2 + \sin\theta}$$

36. $e = \frac{3}{4}, y = -4, p = 4$

Horizontal directrix below pole

$$r = \frac{(3/4)4}{1 - (3/4)\sin\theta} = \frac{12}{4 - 3\sin\theta}$$

37. $e = 2, x = 1, p = 1$

Vertical directrix to the right of the pole

$$r = \frac{2(1)}{1 + 2\cos\theta} = \frac{2}{1 + 2\cos\theta}$$

38. $e = \frac{3}{2}, x = -1, p = 1$

Vertical directrix to the left of the pole

$$r = \frac{3/2(1)}{1 - (3/2)\cos\theta} = \frac{3}{2 - 3\cos\theta}$$

39. Vertex: $\left(1, -\frac{\pi}{2}\right) \Rightarrow e = 1, p = 2$

Horizontal directrix below the pole

$$r = \frac{1(2)}{1 - 1\sin\theta} = \frac{2}{1 - \sin\theta}$$

40. Parabola, $e = 1$, vertex: $(8, 0)$

Vertical directrix to right of pole

$$r = \frac{ep}{1 + e\cos\theta} = \frac{16}{1 + \cos\theta}$$

41. Vertex: $(5, \pi) \Rightarrow e = 1, p = 10$

Vertical directrix to left of pole

$$r = \frac{1(10)}{1 - 1\cos\theta} = \frac{10}{1 - \cos\theta}$$

42. Vertex: $\left(10, \frac{\pi}{2}\right) \Rightarrow e = 1, p = 20$

Horizontal directrix above pole

$$r = \frac{1(20)}{1 + 1\sin\theta} = \frac{20}{1 + \sin\theta}$$

43. Center: $(4, \pi), c = 4, a = 6, e = \frac{2}{3}$

Vertical directrix to the right of the pole

$$r = \frac{(2/3)p}{1 + (2/3)\cos\theta} = \frac{2p}{3 + 2\cos\theta}$$

$$2 = \frac{2p}{3 + 2\cos 0} = \frac{2p}{5} \Rightarrow p = 5$$

$$r = \frac{10}{3 + 2\cos\theta}$$

44. Center: $\left(1, \frac{3\pi}{2}\right), c = 1, a = 3, e = \frac{1}{3}$

Horizontal directrix above the pole

$$r = \frac{(1/3)p}{1 + (1/3)\sin\theta} = \frac{p}{3 + \sin\theta}$$

$$2 = \frac{p}{3 + \sin(\pi/2)}$$

$$p = 8$$

$$r = \frac{8}{3 + \sin\theta}$$

45. Center: $(8, 0), c = 8, a = 12, e = \frac{c}{a} = \frac{2}{3}$

Vertical directrix to left of pole

$$r = \frac{(2/3)p}{1 - (2/3)\cos\theta} = \frac{2p}{3 - 2\cos\theta}$$

$$20 = \frac{2p}{3 - 2} = 2p \Rightarrow p = 10$$

$$r = \frac{20}{3 - 2\cos\theta}$$

46. Center: $\left(5, \frac{3\pi}{2}\right), c = 5, a = 4, e = \frac{5}{4}$

Horizontal directrix below the pole

$$r = \frac{(5/4)p}{1 - (5/4)\sin\theta} = \frac{5p}{4 - 5\sin\theta}$$

$$1 = \frac{5p}{4 - 5\sin(3\pi/2)}$$

$$p = \frac{9}{5}$$

$$r = \frac{5(9/5)}{4 - 5\sin\theta} = \frac{9}{4 - 5\sin\theta}$$

47. Center: $\left(\frac{5}{2}, \frac{\pi}{2}\right), c = \frac{5}{2}, a = \frac{3}{2}, e = \frac{5}{3}$

Horizontal directrix above the pole

$$r = \frac{(5/3)p}{1 + (5/3)\sin\theta} = \frac{5p}{3 + 5\sin\theta}$$

Substitute the point $\left(1, \frac{-3\pi}{2}\right)$ rather than $\left(-1, \frac{3\pi}{2}\right)$

in order to get a directrix between the vertices.

$$1 = \frac{5p}{3 + 5\sin(-3\pi/2)}$$

$$p = \frac{8}{5}$$

$$r = \frac{5(8/5)}{3 + 5\sin\theta} = \frac{8}{3 + 5\sin\theta}$$

48. Center: $\left(\frac{5}{2}, \frac{\pi}{2}\right), c = \frac{5}{2}, a = \frac{3}{2}, e = \frac{c}{a} = \frac{5}{3}$

Horizontal directrix above the pole

$$r = \frac{(5/3)p}{1 + (5/3)\sin\theta} = \frac{5p}{3 + 5\sin\theta}$$

$$1 = \frac{5p}{3 + 5\sin(\pi/2)} \Rightarrow p = \frac{8}{5}$$

$$r = \frac{8}{3 + 5\sin\theta}$$

49. When $\theta = 0$, $r = c + a = ea + a = a(1 + e)$.

Therefore,

$$a(1 + e) = \frac{ep}{1 - e\cos 0}$$

$$a(1 + e)(1 - e) = ep$$

$$a(1 - e^2) = ep.$$

Thus, $r = \dfrac{ep}{1 - e\cos\theta} = \dfrac{(1 - e^2)a}{1 - e\cos\theta}$.

50. Minimum distance occurs when $\theta = \pi$.

$$r = \frac{(1 - e^2)a}{1 - e\cos\pi} = \frac{(1 - e)(1 + e)a}{1 + e} = a(1 - e)$$

Maximum distance occurs when $\theta = 0$.

$$r = \frac{(1 - e^2)a}{1 - e\cos 0} = \frac{(1 - e)(1 + e)a}{1 - e} = a(1 + e)$$

51. $r = \dfrac{[1 - (0.0167)^2](92.956 \times 10^6)}{1 - 0.0167\cos\theta}$

$\approx \dfrac{9.2930 \times 10^7}{1 - 0.0167\cos\theta}$

Perihelion distance:

$r = 92.956 \times 10^6(1 - 0.0167) \approx 9.1404 \times 10^7$

Aphelion distance:

$r = 92.956 \times 10^6(1 + 0.0167) \approx 9.4508 \times 10^7$

52. $a = 35.983 \times 10^6$, $e = 0.2056$

$r = \dfrac{(1 - 0.2056^2)(35.983 \times 10^6)}{1 - 0.2056\cos\theta}$

$\approx \dfrac{3.4462 \times 10^7}{1 - 0.2056\cos\theta}$

Perihelion distance: $a(1 - e) \approx 2.8585 \times 10^7$ miles

Aphelion distance: $a(1 + e) \approx 4.3381 \times 10^7$ miles

53. $r = \dfrac{(1 - 0.0484^2)77.841 \times 10^7}{1 - 0.0484\cos\theta}$

$= \dfrac{7.7659 \times 10^8}{1 - 0.0484\cos\theta}$

Perihelion:

$r = 77.841 \times 10^7(1 - 0.0484) \approx 7.4073 \times 10^8$ km

Aphelion:

$r = 77.841 \times 10^7(1 + 0.0484) \approx 8.1609 \times 10^8$ km

54. $a = 142.673 \times 10^7$, $e = 0.0542$

$r = \dfrac{(1 - 0.0542^2)(142.673 \times 10^7)}{1 - 0.0542\cos\theta}$

$\approx \dfrac{1.4225 \times 10^9}{1 - 0.0542\cos\theta}$

Perihelion distance: $a(1 - e) \approx 1.3494 \times 10^9$ km

Aphelion distance: $a(1 + e) \approx 1.5041 \times 10^9$ km

55. $a = 4.498 \times 10^9$, $e = 0.0086$, Neptune

$a = 5.906 \times 10^9$, $e = 0.2488$, Pluto

(a) Neptune: $r = \dfrac{(1 - 0.0086^2)4.498 \times 10^9}{1 - 0.0086\cos\theta} = \dfrac{4.4977 \times 10^9}{1 - 0.0086\cos\theta}$

Pluto: $r = \dfrac{(1 - 0.2488^2)5.906 \times 10^9}{1 - 0.2488\cos\theta} = \dfrac{5.5404 \times 10^9}{1 - 0.2488\cos\theta}$

(b) Neptune: Perihelion: $4.498 \times 10^9(1 - 0.0086) \approx 4.4593 \times 10^9$ km

Aphelion: $4.498 \times 10^9(1 + 0.0086) \approx 4.5367 \times 10^9$ km

Pluto: Perihelion: $5.906 \times 10^9(1 - 0.2488) \approx 4.4366 \times 10^9$ km

Aphelion: $5.906 \times 10^9(1 + 0.2488) \approx 7.3754 \times 10^9$ km

(c)

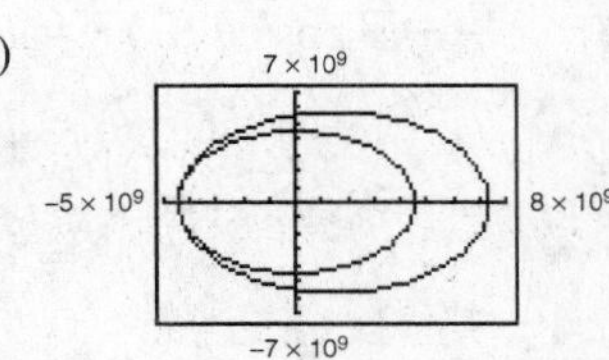

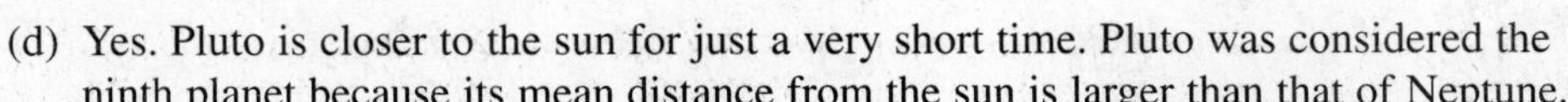

(d) Yes. Pluto is closer to the sun for just a very short time. Pluto was considered the ninth planet because its mean distance from the sun is larger than that of Neptune.

(e) Although the graphs intersect, the orbits do not, and the planets won't collide.

56. (a) Radius of earth $\approx$ 4000 miles. Choose $r = \dfrac{ep}{1 - e\cos\theta}$.

Vertices: $(126{,}800, 0)$ and $(4119, \pi)$

$$a = \frac{126{,}800 + 4119}{2} = 65{,}459.5$$

$$c = 65{,}459.5 - 4119 = 61{,}340.5$$

$$e = \frac{c}{a} = \frac{61{,}340.5}{65{,}459.5} \approx 0.937$$

$$2a = \frac{ep}{1 - e\cos 0} + \frac{ep}{1 - e\cos(\pi)} = \frac{ep}{1-e} + \frac{ep}{1+e} = \frac{2ep}{1-e^2}$$

Thus, $p = \dfrac{a(1-e^2)}{e} \approx 8525.2$. Thus, $r = \dfrac{ep}{1 - e\cos\theta} \approx \dfrac{7988.1}{1 - 0.937\cos\theta}$.

(b) When $\theta = 60°$, $r \approx 15{,}029$ and the distance from the surface of the earth to the satellite is $15{,}029 - 4000 = 11{,}029$ miles.

(c) When $\theta = 30°$, $r \approx 42{,}370$ and distance $= 38{,}370$ miles.

57. $r = \dfrac{4}{-3 - 3\sin\theta} = \dfrac{-4/3}{1 + \sin\theta}$

False. The directrix is below the pole.

58. $r^2 = \dfrac{16}{9 - 4\cos\left(\theta + \dfrac{\pi}{4}\right)}$

False. The graph is not an ellipse.

(It is two ellipses.)

59.

$$\frac{x^2}{a^2} + \frac{y^2}{b^2} = 1$$

$$\frac{r^2\cos^2\theta}{a^2} + \frac{r^2\sin^2\theta}{b^2} = 1$$

$$\frac{r^2\cos^2\theta}{a^2} + \frac{r^2(1 - \cos^2\theta)}{b^2} = 1$$

$$r^2b^2\cos^2\theta + r^2a^2 - r^2a^2\cos^2\theta = a^2b^2$$

$$r^2(b^2 - a^2)\cos^2\theta + r^2a^2 = a^2b^2$$

For an ellipse, $b^2 - a^2 = -c^2$. Hence,

$$-r^2c^2\cos^2\theta + r^2a^2 = a^2b^2$$

$$-r^2\left(\frac{c}{a}\right)^2\cos^2\theta + r^2 = b^2,\ e = \frac{c}{a}$$

$$-r^2e^2\cos^2\theta + r^2 = b^2$$

$$r^2(1 - e^2\cos^2\theta) = b^2$$

$$r^2 = \frac{b^2}{1 - e^2\cos^2\theta}.$$

60.

$$\frac{x^2}{a^2} - \frac{y^2}{b^2} = 1$$

$$\frac{r^2\cos^2\theta}{a^2} - \frac{r^2\sin^2\theta}{b^2} = 1$$

$$\frac{r^2\cos^2\theta}{a^2} - \frac{r^2(1 - \cos^2\theta)}{b^2} = 1$$

$$r^2b^2\cos^2\theta - r^2a^2 + r^2a^2\cos^2\theta = a^2b^2$$

$$r^2(b^2 + a^2)\cos^2\theta - r^2a^2 = a^2b^2$$

$$a^2 + b^2 = c^2$$

$$r^2c^2\cos^2\theta - r^2a^2 = a^2b^2$$

$$r^2\left(\frac{c}{a}\right)^2\cos^2\theta - r^2 = b^2,\ e = \frac{c}{a}$$

$$r^2e^2\cos^2\theta - r^2 = b^2$$

$$r^2(e^2\cos^2\theta - 1) = b^2$$

$$r^2 = \frac{b^2}{e^2\cos^2\theta - 1}$$

$$= \frac{-b^2}{1 - e^2\cos^2\theta}$$

61. $\frac{x^2}{169} + \frac{y^2}{144} = 1$

$a = 13, b = 12, c = 5, e = \frac{5}{13}$

$r^2 = \frac{144}{1 - (25/169)\cos^2\theta} = \frac{24{,}336}{169 - 25\cos^2\theta}$

62. $\frac{x^2}{9} - \frac{y^2}{16} = 1$

$a = 3, b = 4, c = 5, e = \frac{5}{3}$

$r^2 = \frac{-16}{1 - (25/9)\cos^2\theta} = \frac{144}{25\cos^2\theta - 9}$

63. $\frac{x^2}{25} + \frac{y^2}{16} = 1$

$a = 5, b = 4, c = 3, e = \frac{3}{5}$

$r^2 = \frac{b^2}{1 - e^2\cos^2\theta} = \frac{16}{1 - (9/25)\cos^2\theta} = \frac{400}{25 - 9\cos^2\theta}$

64. $\frac{x^2}{36} - \frac{y^2}{4} = 1$

$a = 6, b = 2, c = \sqrt{40} = 2\sqrt{10}, e = \frac{2\sqrt{10}}{6} = \frac{\sqrt{10}}{3}$

$r^2 = \frac{-b^2}{1 - e^2\cos^2\theta} = \frac{-4}{1 - (10/9)\cos^2\theta} = \frac{36}{10\cos^2\theta - 9}$

65. Center: $(x, y) = (0, 0), c = 5, a = 4, e = \frac{5}{4}$

$b^2 = c^2 - a^2 = 25 - 16 = 9 \implies b = 3$

$r^2 = \frac{-b^2}{1 - e^2\cos^2\theta} = \frac{-9}{1 - (25/16)\cos^2\theta} = \frac{144}{25\cos^2\theta - 16}$

66. Center: $(x, y) = (0, 0), c = 4, a = 5, e = \frac{4}{5}$

$b^2 = a^2 - c^2 = 25 - 16 = 9 \implies b = 3$

$r^2 = \frac{b^2}{1 - e^2\cos^2\theta} = \frac{9}{1 - (16/25)\cos^2\theta} = \frac{225}{25 - 16\cos^2\theta}$

67. $r = \frac{4}{1 - 0.4\cos\theta}$

Vertical directrix to left of pole

(a) $e = 0.4 \implies$ ellipse

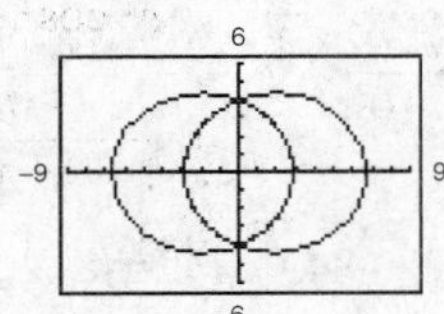

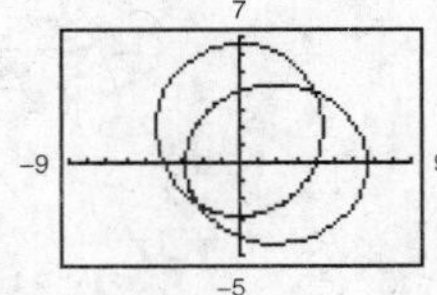

(b) $r = \frac{4}{1 + 0.4\cos\theta}$

Vertical directrix to right of pole

Graph is reflected in line $\theta = \pi/2$.

$r = \frac{4}{1 - 0.4\sin\theta}$

Horizontal directrix below pole

90° rotation counterclockwise

68. The lengths of the major and minor axes increase as p increases.

Example: $r = \dfrac{(0.5)2}{1 + (0.5)\sin\theta}$

$r = \dfrac{(0.5)4}{1 + (0.5)\sin\theta}$

69. Answers will vary.

70. $r = a\sin\theta + b\cos\theta$

$r^2 = a\,r\sin\theta + b\,r\cos\theta$

$x^2 + y^2 = ay + bx$

Circle

71. $4\sqrt{3}\tan\theta - 3 = 1$

$\tan\theta = \dfrac{1}{\sqrt{3}} = \dfrac{\sqrt{3}}{3}$

$\theta = \dfrac{\pi}{6} + n\pi$

72. $6\cos x - 2 = 1$

$\cos x = \dfrac{1}{2}$

$x = \dfrac{\pi}{3} + 2n\pi, \dfrac{5\pi}{3} + 2n\pi$

73. $12\sin^2\theta = 9$

$\sin^2\theta = \dfrac{3}{4}$

$\sin\theta = \pm\dfrac{\sqrt{3}}{2}$

$\theta = \dfrac{\pi}{3} + n\pi, \dfrac{2\pi}{3} + n\pi$

74. $9\csc^2 x - 10 = 2$

$\csc^2 x = \dfrac{4}{3}$

$\sin^2 x = \dfrac{3}{4}$

$\sin x = \dfrac{\pm\sqrt{3}}{2}$

$x = \dfrac{\pi}{3} + n\pi, \dfrac{2\pi}{3} + n\pi$

75. $2\cot x = 5\cos\dfrac{\pi}{2}$

$2\cot x = 0$

$\cot x = 0$

$x = \dfrac{\pi}{2} + n\pi$

76. $\sqrt{2}\sec\theta = 2\csc\dfrac{\pi}{4}$

$\sqrt{2}\sec\theta = 2\sqrt{2}$

$\sec\theta = 2$

$\cos\theta = \dfrac{1}{2}$

$\theta = \dfrac{\pi}{3} + 2n\pi, \dfrac{5\pi}{3} + 2n\pi$

For Exercises 77–80: $\sin u = -\dfrac{3}{5}, \cos u = \dfrac{4}{5}, \cos v = \dfrac{1}{\sqrt{2}}, \sin v = -\dfrac{1}{\sqrt{2}}$

77. $\cos(u + v) = \cos u\cos v - \sin u\sin v$

$= \dfrac{4}{5}\left(\dfrac{1}{\sqrt{2}}\right) - \left(-\dfrac{3}{5}\right)\left(-\dfrac{1}{\sqrt{2}}\right)$

$= \dfrac{1}{5\sqrt{2}} = \dfrac{\sqrt{2}}{10}$

78. $\sin(u + v) = \sin u\cos v + \sin v\cos u$

$= \left(\dfrac{-3}{5}\right)\left(\dfrac{1}{\sqrt{2}}\right) + \left(\dfrac{-1}{\sqrt{2}}\right)\left(\dfrac{4}{5}\right)$

$= \dfrac{-7}{5\sqrt{2}} = \dfrac{-7\sqrt{2}}{10}$

79. $\sin(u - v) = \sin u\cos v - \sin v\cos u$

$= \left(-\dfrac{3}{5}\right)\left(\dfrac{1}{\sqrt{2}}\right) - \left(-\dfrac{1}{\sqrt{2}}\right)\left(\dfrac{4}{5}\right)$

$= \dfrac{1}{5\sqrt{2}} = \dfrac{\sqrt{2}}{10}$

80. $\cos(u - v) = \cos u\cos v + \sin u\sin v$

$= \left(\dfrac{4}{5}\right)\left(\dfrac{1}{\sqrt{2}}\right) + \left(\dfrac{-3}{5}\right)\left(\dfrac{-1}{\sqrt{2}}\right)$

$= \dfrac{7}{5\sqrt{2}} = \dfrac{7\sqrt{2}}{10}$

81. ${}_{12}C_9 = 220$

82. ${}_{18}C_{16} = 153$

83. ${}_{10}P_3 = 720$

84. ${}_{29}P_2 = 812$

Review Exercises for Chapter 9

1. Radius $= \sqrt{(-3-0)^2 + (-4-0)^2}$

$= \sqrt{9+16} = \sqrt{25} = 5$

$x^2 + y^2 = 25$

2. Radius $= \sqrt{(8-0)^2 + (-15-0)^2}$

$= \sqrt{64+225} = \sqrt{289} = 17$

$x^2 + y^2 = 289$

3. Radius $= \frac{1}{2}\sqrt{(5-(-1))^2 + (6-2)^2}$

$= \frac{1}{2}\sqrt{36+16} = \frac{1}{2}\sqrt{52} = \sqrt{13}$

Center $= \left(\frac{5+(-1)}{2}, \frac{6+2}{2}\right) = (2, 4)$

$(x-2)^2 + (y-4)^2 = 13$

4. Radius $= \frac{1}{2}\sqrt{(6-(-2))^2 + (-5-3)^2}$

$= \frac{1}{2}\sqrt{64+64} = 4\sqrt{2}$

Center $= \left(\frac{-2+6}{2}, \frac{3-5}{2}\right) = (2, -1)$

$(x-2)^2 + (y+1)^2 = 32$

5. $\frac{1}{2}x^2 + \frac{1}{2}y^2 = 18$

$x^2 + \quad y^2 = 36$

Center: $(0, 0)$

Radius: 6

6. $\frac{3}{4}x^2 + \frac{3}{4}y^2 = 1$

$x^2 + \quad y^2 = \frac{4}{3}$

Center: $(0, 0)$

Radius: $\frac{2}{\sqrt{3}} = \frac{2\sqrt{3}}{3}$

7.
$$16x^2 + 16y^2 - 16x + 24y - 3 = 0$$
$$16\left(x^2 - x + \tfrac{1}{4}\right) + 16\left(y^2 + \tfrac{3}{2}y + \tfrac{9}{16}\right) = 3 + 4 + 9$$
$$16\left(x - \tfrac{1}{2}\right)^2 + 16\left(y + \tfrac{3}{4}\right)^2 = 16$$
$$\left(x - \tfrac{1}{2}\right)^2 + \left(y + \tfrac{3}{4}\right)^2 = 1$$

Center: $\left(\frac{1}{2}, -\frac{3}{4}\right)$

Radius: 1

8.
$$4x^2 + 4y^2 + 32x - 24y + 51 = 0$$
$$4(x^2 + 8x + 16) + 4(y^2 - 6y + 9) = -51 + 64 + 36$$
$$4(x+4)^2 + 4(y-3)^2 = 49$$
$$(x+4)^2 + (y-3)^2 = \tfrac{49}{4}$$

Center: $(-4, 3)$

Radius: $\frac{7}{2}$

9. $(x^2 + 4x + 4) + (y^2 + 6y + 9) = 3 + 4 + 9$

$$(x + 2)^2 + (y + 3)^2 = 16$$

Center: $(-2, -3)$

Radius: 4

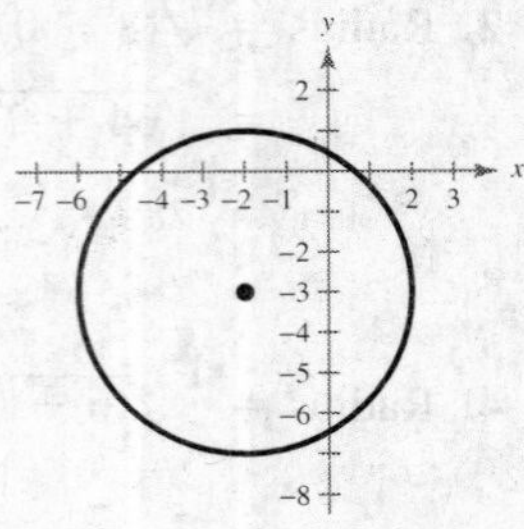

10. $(x^2 + 8x + 16) + (y^2 - 10y + 25) = 8 + 16 + 25$

$$(x + 4)^2 + (y - 5)^2 = 49$$

Center: $(-4, 5)$

Radius: 7

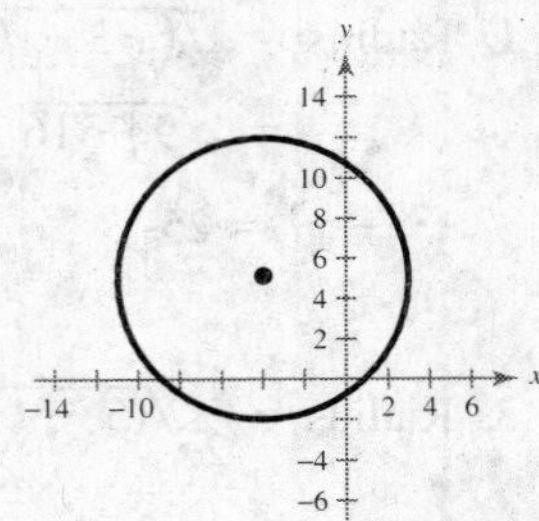

11. x-intercepts: $(x - 3)^2 + (0 + 1)^2 = 7$

$$(x - 3)^2 = 6$$

$$x - 3 = \pm\sqrt{6}$$

$$x = 3 \pm \sqrt{6}$$

$\left(3 \pm \sqrt{6}, 0\right)$

y-intercepts: $(0 - 3)^2 + (y + 1)^2 = 7$

$$(y + 1)^2 = -2, \text{ impossible}$$

No y-intercepts

12. x-intercepts: $(x + 5)^2 + (0 - 6)^2 = 27$

$$(x + 5)^2 = -9, \text{ impossible}$$

No x-intercepts

y-intercepts: $(0 + 5)^2 + (y - 6)^2 = 27$

$$(y - 6)^2 = 2$$

$$y - 6 = \pm\sqrt{2}$$

$$y = 6 \pm \sqrt{2}$$

$\left(0, 6 \pm \sqrt{2}\right)$

13. $4x - y^2 = 0$

$$y^2 = 4(1)x,\ p = 1$$

Vertex: $(0, 0)$

Focus: $(1, 0)$

Directrix: $x = -1$

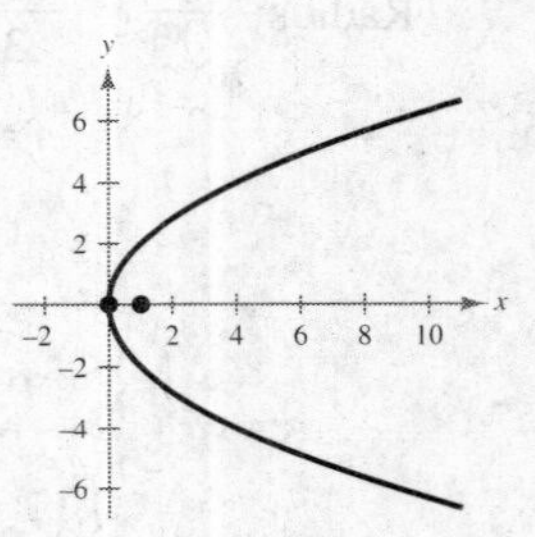

14. $y = -\frac{1}{8}x^2$

$$x^2 = 4(-2)y,\ p = -2$$

Vertex: $(0, 0)$

Focus: $(0, -2)$

Directrix: $y = 2$

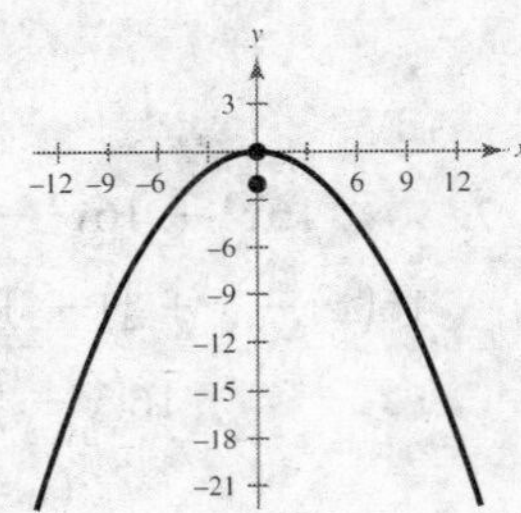

15. $\frac{1}{2}y^2 + 18x = 0$

$$\frac{1}{2}y^2 = -18x$$

$$y^2 = -36x = 4(-9)x,\ p = -9$$

Vertex: $(0, 0)$

Focus: $(-9, 0)$

Directrix: $x = 9$

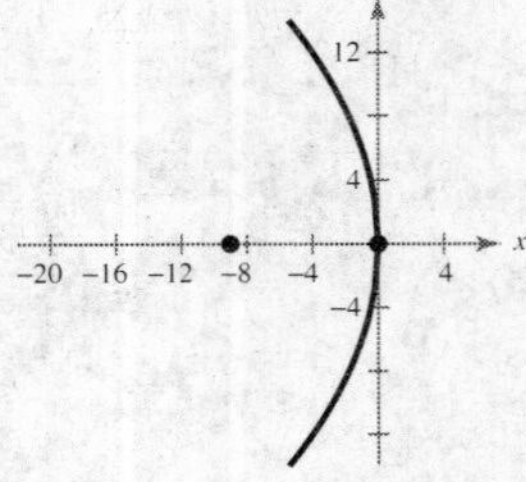

16. $\frac{1}{4}y - 8x^2 = 0$

$$8x^2 = \frac{1}{4}y$$

$$x^2 = \frac{1}{32}y = 4\left(\frac{1}{128}\right)y,\ p = \frac{1}{128}$$

Vertex: $(0, 0)$

Focus: $\left(0, \frac{1}{128}\right)$

Directrix: $y = -\frac{1}{128}$

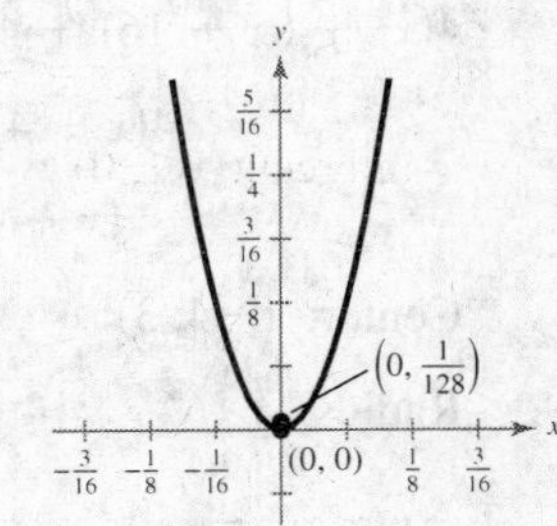

17. Vertex: $(0, 0)$

Focus: $(-6, 0)$

Parabola opens to left.

$y^2 = 4px$

$y^2 = 4(-6)x$

$y^2 = -24x$

18. Vertex: $(4, 2)$

Focus: $(4, 0)$

Vertical axis, $p = -2$

$(x - 4)^2 = 4(-2)(y - 2)$

$(x - 4)^2 = -8(y - 2)$

19. Vertex: $(-6, 4)$

Passes through $(0, 0)$

Vertical axis

$(x + 6)^2 = 4p(y - 4)$

$(0 + 6)^2 = 4p(0 - 4)$

$36 = -16p$

$-\frac{9}{4} = p$

$(x + 6)^2 = 4\left(-\frac{9}{4}\right)(y - 4)$

$(x + 6)^2 = -9(y - 4)$

20. Vertex: $(0, 5)$

$(y - 5)^2 = 4p(x - 0) = 4px$

$(6, 0)$ on graph:

$(0 - 5)^2 = 4p(6) \implies p = \frac{25}{24}$

$(y - 5)^2 = 4\left(\frac{25}{24}\right)x = \frac{25}{6}x$

21. $x^2 = -2y = 4\left(-\frac{1}{2}\right)y, p = -\frac{1}{2}$

Focus: $\left(0, -\frac{1}{2}\right)$

$d_1 = \frac{1}{2} + b$

$d_2 = \sqrt{(2 - 0)^2 + \left(-2 + \frac{1}{2}\right)^2} = \frac{5}{2}$

$d_1 = d_2 \implies \frac{1}{2} + b = \frac{5}{2} \implies b = 2$

Slope of tangent line: $\frac{b + 2}{0 - 2} = \frac{4}{-2} = -2$

Equation: $y + 2 = -2(x - 2)$

$y = -2x + 2$

x-intercept: $(1, 0)$

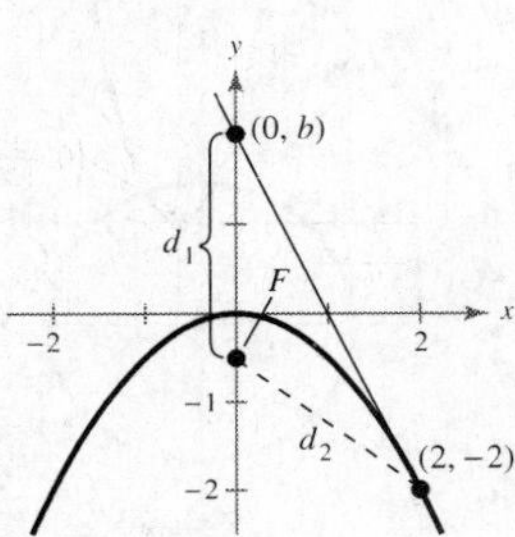

22. $-2x = y^2$

$4\left(-\frac{1}{2}x\right) = y^2$

$p = -\frac{1}{2}$

Focus: $\left(-\frac{1}{2}, 0\right)$

Let $(b, 0)$ be the x-intercept of the tangent line.

$d_1 = \frac{1}{2} + b$

$d_2 = \sqrt{\left(-8 + \frac{1}{2}\right)^2 + (-4 - 0)^2} = \frac{17}{2}$

$\frac{1}{2} + b = \frac{17}{2} \implies b = 8$

$m = \frac{-4 - 0}{-8 - 8} = \frac{1}{4}$

$y - 0 = \frac{1}{4}(x - 8)$

$y = \frac{1}{4}x - 2$

x-intercept: $(8, 0)$

23. $x^2 = 4p(y - 12)$

(4, 10) on curve:

$16 = 4p(10 - 12) = -8p \Rightarrow p = -2$

$x^2 = 4(-2)(y - 12) = -8y + 96$

$y = \dfrac{-x^2 + 96}{8}$

$y = 0$ if $x^2 = 96 \Rightarrow x = 4\sqrt{6} \Rightarrow$ width is $8\sqrt{6}$ meters.

24. (a) Parabola:

Vertex: (0, 4)

Passes through $(\pm4, 0)$

$x^2 = 4p(y - 4)$

$16 = 4p(0 - 4)$

$16 = -16p$

$-1 = p$

$x^2 = -4(y - 4)$

Circle:

Passes through $(\pm4, 0)$

Radius: $r = 8$

Center: $(0, k)$

$x^2 + (y - k)^2 = 8^2$

$(\pm4)^2 + (0 - k)^2 = 8^2$

$16 + k^2 = 64$

$k^2 = 48$

$k = -\sqrt{48} = -4\sqrt{3}$

$x^2 + \left(y + 4\sqrt{3}\right)^2 = 64$

(b) Parabola:

$x^2 = -4(y - 4) \Rightarrow y = -\frac{1}{4}x^2 + 4$

Circle:

$x^2 + \left(y + 4\sqrt{3}\right)^2 = 64 \Rightarrow y = \sqrt{64 - x^2} - 4\sqrt{3}$

$d = \left(-\frac{1}{4}x^2 + 4\right) - \left(\sqrt{64 - x^2} - 4\sqrt{3}\right)$

$= -\frac{1}{4}x^2 - \sqrt{64 - x^2} + 4 + 4\sqrt{3}$

x	0	1	2	3	4
d	2.928	2.741	2.182	1.262	0

25. $\dfrac{x^2}{4} + \dfrac{y^2}{16} = 1$

$a = 4, b = 2, c = \sqrt{16 - 4} = \sqrt{12} = 2\sqrt{3}$

Center: (0, 0)

Vertices: $(0, \pm4)$

Foci: $\left(0, \pm2\sqrt{3}\right)$

Eccentricity $= \dfrac{c}{a}$

$= \dfrac{2\sqrt{3}}{4}$

$= \dfrac{\sqrt{3}}{2}$

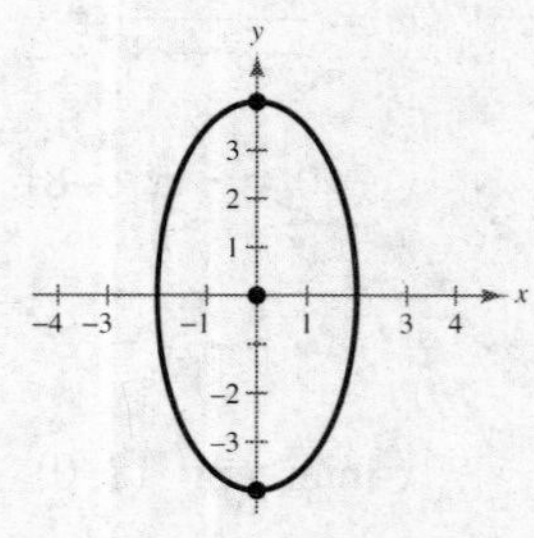

26. $\dfrac{x^2}{9} + \dfrac{y^2}{8} = 1$

$a = 3, b = 2\sqrt{2}, c = \sqrt{9 - 8} = 1$

Center: (0, 0)

Vertices: $(\pm3, 0)$

Foci: $(\pm1, 0)$

Eccentricity $= \dfrac{c}{a} = \dfrac{1}{3}$

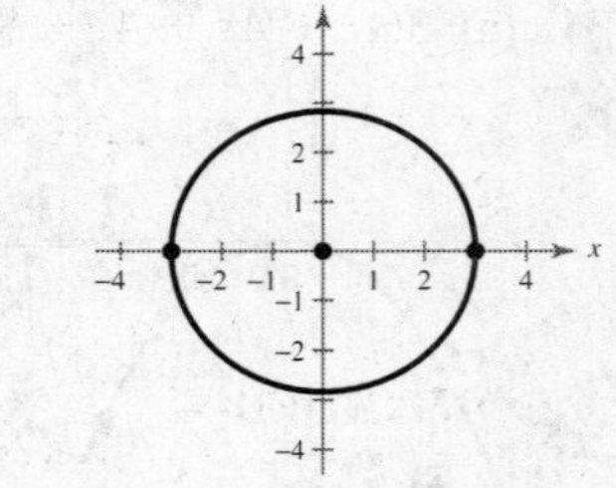

27. $\dfrac{(x-4)^2}{6} + \dfrac{(y+4)^2}{9} = 1$

$a = 3, b = \sqrt{6}, c = \sqrt{9-6} = \sqrt{3}$

Center: $(4, -4)$

Vertices: $(4, -1), (4, -7)$

Foci: $\left(4, -4 \pm \sqrt{3}\right)$

Eccentricity $= \dfrac{c}{a} = \dfrac{\sqrt{3}}{3}$

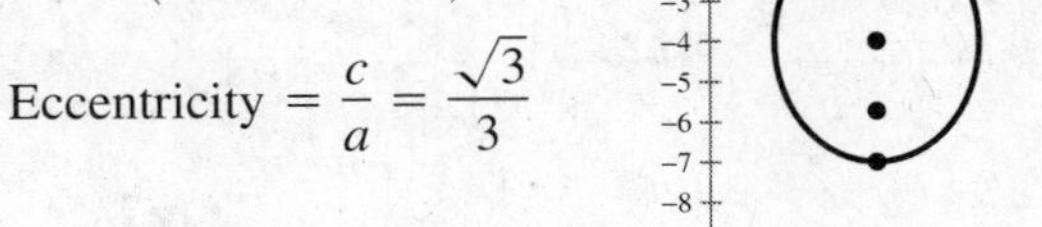

28. $\dfrac{(x+1)^2}{16} + \dfrac{(y-3)^2}{6} = 1$

$a = 4, b = \sqrt{6}, c = \sqrt{16-6} = \sqrt{10}$

Center: $(-1, 3)$

Vertices: $(3, 3), (-5, 3)$

Foci: $\left(-1 \pm \sqrt{10}, 3\right)$

Eccentricity $= \dfrac{c}{a} = \dfrac{\sqrt{10}}{4}$

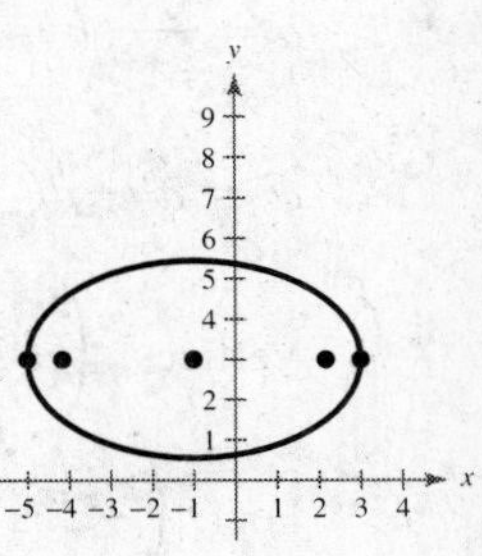

29. (a) $16(x^2 - 2x + 1) + 9(y^2 + 8y + 16) = -16 + 16 + 144$

$$16(x-1)^2 + 9(y+4)^2 = 144$$

$$\frac{(x-1)^2}{9} + \frac{(y+4)^2}{16} = 1$$

(b) Center: $(1, -4)$

$a = 4, b = 3, c = \sqrt{16-9} = \sqrt{7}$

Vertices: $(1, 0), (1, -8)$

Foci: $\left(1, -4 \pm \sqrt{7}\right)$

$e = \dfrac{c}{a} = \dfrac{\sqrt{7}}{4}$

(c)

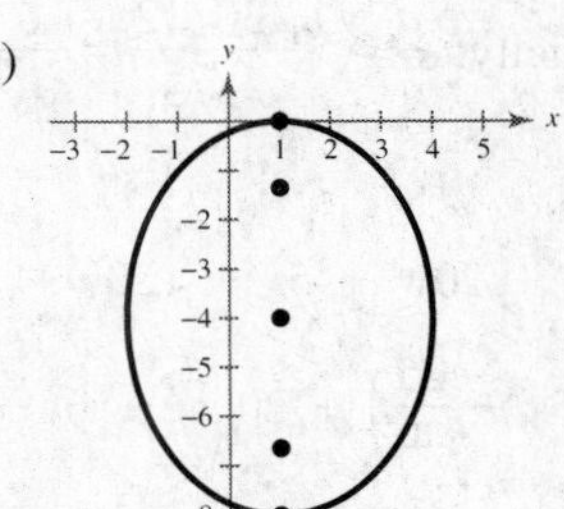

30. (a) $4(x^2 + 4x + 4) + 25(y^2 - 6y + 9) = -141 + 16 + 225$

$$4(x+2)^2 + 25(y-3)^2 = 100$$

$$\frac{(x+2)^2}{25} + \frac{(y-3)^2}{4} = 1$$

(b) $a = 5, b = 2, c = \sqrt{21}$

Center: $(-2, 3)$

Vertices: $(3, 3), (-7, 3)$

Foci: $\left(-2 \pm \sqrt{21}, 3\right)$

$e = \dfrac{\sqrt{21}}{5}$

(c)

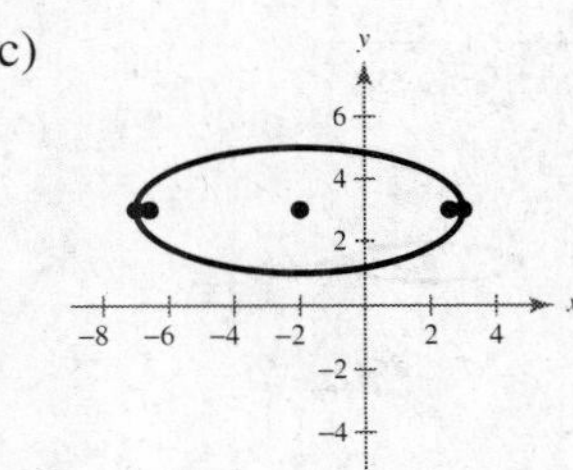

31. (a) $3(x^2 + 4x + 4) + 8(y^2 - 14y + 49) = -403 + 12 + 392$

$$3(x+2)^2 + 8(y-7)^2 = 1$$

$$\frac{(x+2)^2}{1/3} + \frac{(y-7)^2}{1/8} = 1$$

—CONTINUED—

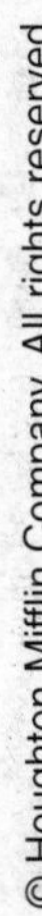

31. —CONTINUED—

(b) Center: $(-2, 7)$

$$a = \frac{\sqrt{3}}{3},\ b = \frac{\sqrt{2}}{4}$$

$$c^2 = a^2 - b^2 = \frac{1}{3} - \frac{1}{8} = \frac{5}{24} \Rightarrow c = \frac{\sqrt{30}}{12}$$

Vertices: $\left(-2 \pm \frac{\sqrt{3}}{3}, 7\right)$

Foci: $\left(-2 \pm \frac{\sqrt{30}}{12}, 7\right)$

Eccentricity: $\frac{c}{a} = \frac{\sqrt{30}/12}{\sqrt{3}/3} = \frac{\sqrt{10}}{4}$

(c)

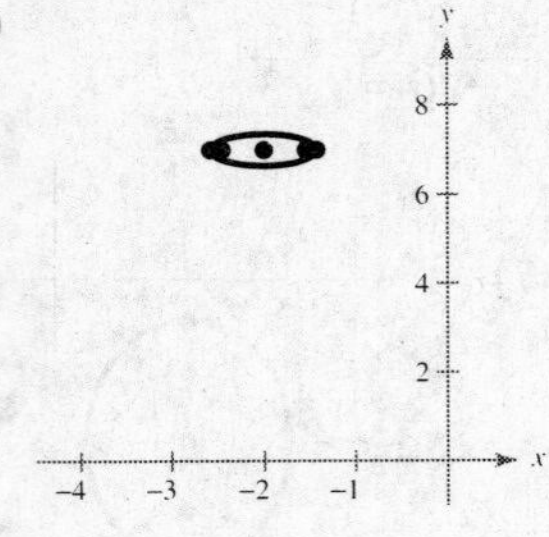

32. (a) $x^2 + 20y^2 - 5x + 120y + 185 = 0$

$$\left(x^2 - 5x + \frac{25}{4}\right) + 20(y^2 + 6y + 9) = -185 + \frac{25}{4} + 180$$

$$\left(x - \frac{5}{2}\right)^2 + 20(y + 3)^2 = \frac{5}{4}$$

$$\frac{[x - (5/2)]^2}{(5/4)} + \frac{(y + 3)^2}{(1/16)} = 1$$

(b)

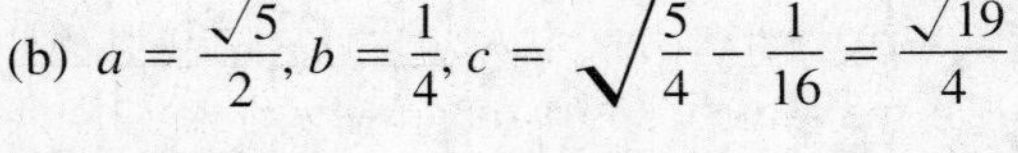

$a = \frac{\sqrt{5}}{2},\ b = \frac{1}{4},\ c = \sqrt{\frac{5}{4} - \frac{1}{16}} = \frac{\sqrt{19}}{4}$

Center: $\left(\frac{5}{2}, -3\right)$

Vertices: $\left(\frac{5}{2} \pm \frac{\sqrt{5}}{2}, -3\right)$

Foci: $\left(\frac{5}{2} \pm \frac{\sqrt{19}}{4}, -3\right)$

$$e = \frac{c}{a} = \frac{\sqrt{19}/4}{\sqrt{5}/2} = \frac{\sqrt{95}}{10}$$

(c)

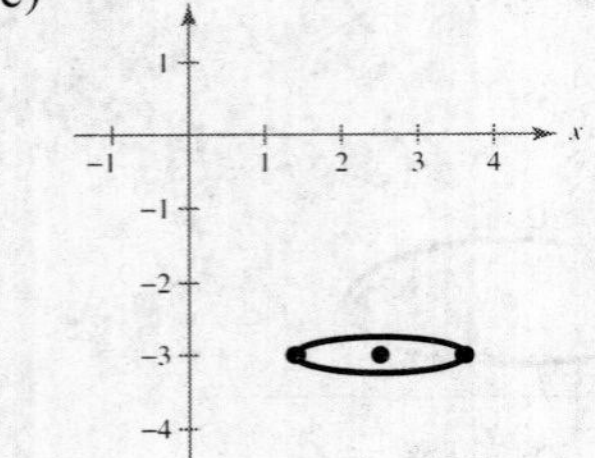

33. Vertices: $(\pm 5, 0)$

Foci: $(\pm 4, 0)$

$a = 5, c = 4 \Rightarrow b = 3$

$$\frac{x^2}{25} + \frac{y^2}{9} = 1$$

34. Vertices: $(0, \pm 6)$

Passes through $(2, 2)$

Vertical major axis

Center: $(0, 0)$, $a = 6$

$$\frac{x^2}{b^2} + \frac{y^2}{36} = 1$$

$$\frac{2^2}{b^2} + \frac{2^2}{36} = 1$$

$$\frac{4}{b^2} = 1 - \frac{1}{9} = \frac{8}{9}$$

$$b^2 = \frac{36}{8} = \frac{9}{2}$$

$$\frac{x^2}{9/2} + \frac{y^2}{36} = 1$$

35. Vertices: $(-3, 0), (7, 0)$

Foci: $(0, 0), (4, 0)$

Horizontal major axis

Center: $(2, 0)$

$a = 5, c = 2,$

$b = \sqrt{25 - 4} = \sqrt{21}$

$$\frac{(x-h)^2}{a^2} + \frac{(y-k)^2}{b^2} = 1$$

$$\frac{(x-2)^2}{25} + \frac{y^2}{21} = 1$$

36. Vertices: $(2, 0), (2, 4)$

Foci: $(2, 1), (2, 3)$

Vertical major axis

Center: $(2, 2)$

$a = 2, c = 1,$

$b = \sqrt{4 - 1} = \sqrt{3}$

$$\frac{(x-h)^2}{b^2} + \frac{(y-k)^2}{a^2} = 1$$

$$\frac{(x-2)^2}{3} + \frac{(y-2)^2}{4} = 1$$

37. $a = 5, b = 4, c = \sqrt{a^2 - b^2} = \sqrt{25 - 16} = 3$

The foci should be placed 3 feet on either side of the center and have the same height as the pillars.

38. $\dfrac{x^2}{324} + \dfrac{y^2}{196} = 1, a = \sqrt{324} = 18, b = \sqrt{196} = 14$

Longest distance: $2a = 2(18) = 36$ feet

Shortest distance: $2b = 2(14) = 28$ feet

$c^2 = a^2 - b^2 = 128$

Foci: $(\pm 8\sqrt{2}, 0)$

Distance between foci: $16\sqrt{2} \approx 22.63$ feet

39. $a - c = 1.3495 \times 10^9$

$a + c = 1.5045 \times 10^9$

Adding, $2a = 2.854 \times 10^9 \implies a = 1.427 \times 10^9$. Then

$c = 1.5045 \times 10^9 - 1.427 \times 10^9 = 0.0775 \times 10^9$

$e = \dfrac{c}{a} \approx 0.0543.$

40. $a = \dfrac{72}{2} = 36$

$e = \dfrac{c}{a} = 0.2056 \implies c = ae = 7.4016$

$b^2 = a^2 - c^2 = 36^2 - 7.4016^2 \approx 1241.2$

$$\frac{x^2}{1296} + \frac{y^2}{1241.2} = 1$$

41. (a) $5y^2 - 4x^2 = 20$

$$\frac{y^2}{4} - \frac{x^2}{5} = 1$$

(b) $a = 2, b = \sqrt{5},$

$c = \sqrt{4 + 5} = 3$

Center: $(0, 0)$

Vertices: $(0, \pm 2)$

Foci: $(0, \pm 3)$

Eccentricity $= \dfrac{c}{a} = \dfrac{3}{2}$

(c)

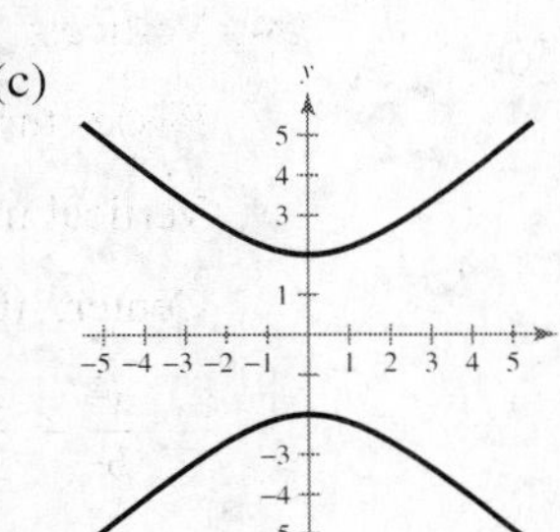

42. (a) $x^2 - y^2 = \dfrac{9}{4}$

$$\frac{x^2}{(9/4)} - \frac{y^2}{(9/4)} = 1$$

(b) $a = \dfrac{3}{2}, b = \dfrac{3}{2},$

$$c = \sqrt{\frac{9}{4} + \frac{9}{4}}$$

$$= \sqrt{\frac{9}{2}} = \frac{3}{\sqrt{2}} = \frac{3\sqrt{2}}{2}$$

Center: $(0, 0)$

Vertices: $\left(\pm\dfrac{3}{2}, 0\right)$

Foci: $\left(\pm\dfrac{3\sqrt{2}}{2}, 0\right)$

Eccentricity $= \dfrac{c}{a} = \dfrac{3\sqrt{2}/2}{3/2} = \sqrt{2}$

(c)

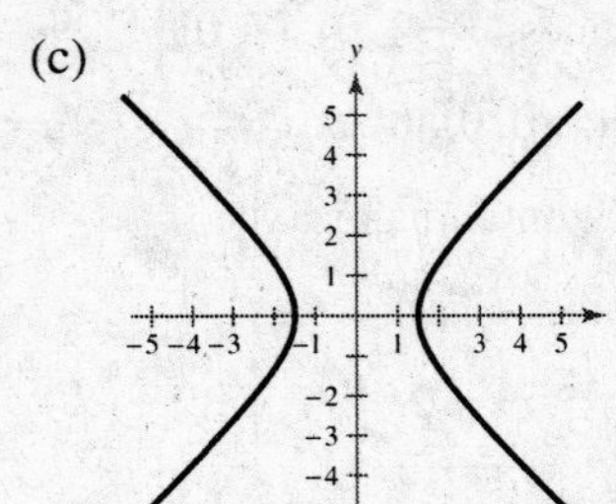

43. (a) $9(x^2 - 2x + 1) - 16(y^2 + 2y + 1) = 151 + 9 - 16$

$$9(x - 1)^2 - 16(y + 1)^2 = 144$$

$$\frac{(x - 1)^2}{16} - \frac{(y + 1)^2}{9} = 1$$

(b) Center: $(1, -1)$, $a = 4$, $b = 3$, $c = 5$

Vertices: $(5, -1), (-3, -1)$

Foci: $(6, -1), (-4, -1)$

Eccentricity: $\dfrac{5}{4}$

(c)

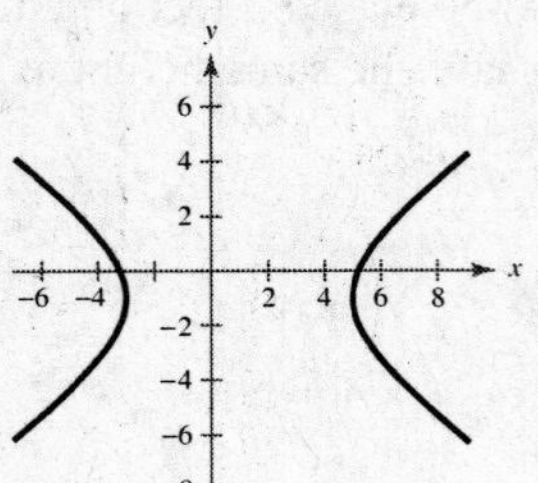

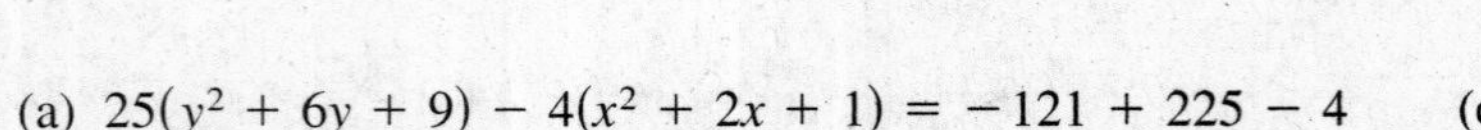

44. (a) $25(y^2 + 6y + 9) - 4(x^2 + 2x + 1) = -121 + 225 - 4$

$$25(y + 3)^2 - 4(x + 1)^2 = 100$$

$$\frac{(y + 3)^2}{4} - \frac{(x + 1)^2}{25} = 1$$

(b) Center: $(-1, -3)$, $a = 2$, $b = 5$, $c = \sqrt{29}$

Vertices: $(-1, -1), (-1, -5)$

Foci: $\left(-1, -3 \pm \sqrt{29}\right)$

Eccentricity: $\dfrac{\sqrt{29}}{2}$

(c)

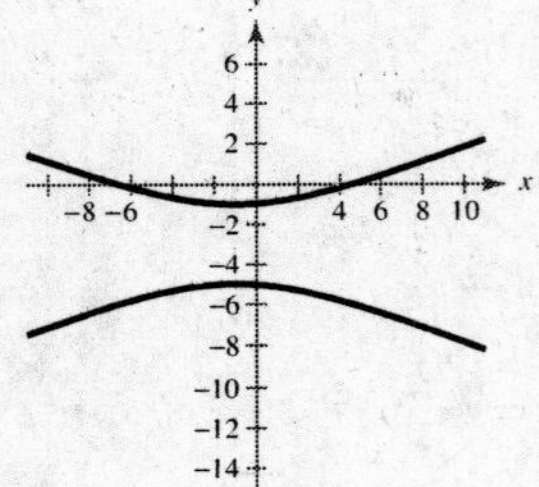

45. (a) $(y^2 - 2y + 1) - 4(x^2 + 12x + 36) = -59 + 1 - 144$

$$(y - 1)^2 - 4(x + 6)^2 = -202$$

$$\frac{(x + 6)^2}{(101/2)} - \frac{(y - 1)^2}{202} = 1$$

(b) Center: $(-6, 1)$

$$a^2 = \frac{101}{2}, b^2 = 202, c^2 = \frac{101}{2} + 202 = \frac{505}{2}$$

Vertices: $\left(-6 \pm \sqrt{\frac{101}{2}}, 1\right)$

Foci: $\left(-6 \pm \sqrt{\frac{505}{2}}, 1\right)$

Eccentricity: $e = \dfrac{c}{a} = \dfrac{\sqrt{505}}{\sqrt{101}} = \sqrt{5}$

(c)

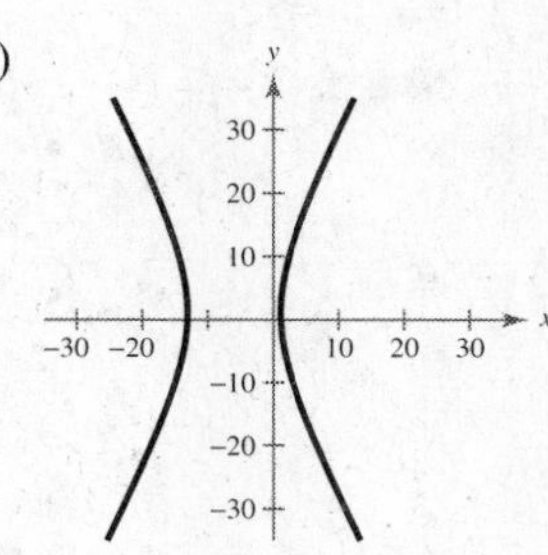

46. (a) $9(x^2 - 8x + 16) - (y^2 - 8y + 16) = -119 + 144 - 16 = 9$

$$9(x - 4)^2 - (y - 4)^2 = 9$$

$$(x - 4)^2 - \frac{(y - 4)^2}{9} = 1$$

(b) Center: $(4, 4)$

$a = 1, b = 3, \ c = \sqrt{10}$

Vertices: $(4 \pm 1, 4)$: $(3, 4), (5, 4)$

Foci: $(4 \pm \sqrt{10}, 4)$

Eccentricity: $e = \sqrt{10}$

(c)

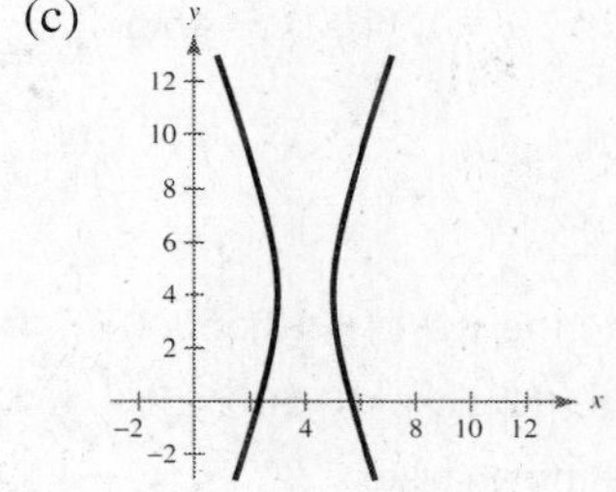

47. $\dfrac{x^2}{a^2} - \dfrac{y^2}{b^2} = 1$

$a = 4$

$c^2 = a^2 + b^2 \implies 36 = 16 + b^2$

$\implies b = \sqrt{20} = 2\sqrt{5}$

$$\frac{x^2}{16} - \frac{y^2}{20} = 1$$

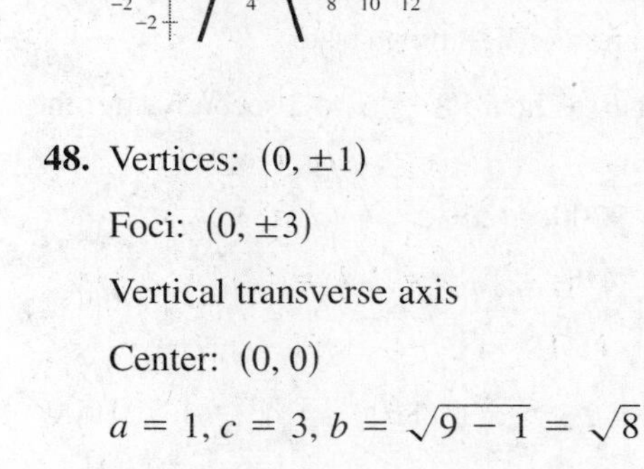

48. Vertices: $(0, \pm 1)$

Foci: $(0, \pm 3)$

Vertical transverse axis

Center: $(0, 0)$

$a = 1, c = 3, b = \sqrt{9 - 1} = \sqrt{8}$

$$\frac{y^2}{1} - \frac{x^2}{8} = 1$$

49. Foci: $(0, 0), (8, 0) \implies c = 4$

Center: $(4, 0)$

Asymptotes:

$$y = \pm 2(x - 4) \implies \frac{b}{a} = 2 \implies b = 2a$$

$$c^2 = a^2 + b^2$$

$$16 = a^2 + (2a)^2 = 5a^2 \implies a = \frac{4}{\sqrt{5}}, b = \frac{8}{\sqrt{5}}$$

$$\frac{(x - 4)^2}{16/5} - \frac{y^2}{64/5} = 1$$

50. Vertical transverse axis

Center: $(3, 0) \implies c = 2$

$$\frac{a}{b} = 2 \implies a = 2b$$

$$c^2 = a^2 + b^2$$

$$4 = (2b)^2 + b^2 = 5b^2 \implies b^2 = \frac{4}{5}, a^2 = \frac{16}{5}$$

$$\frac{5y^2}{16} - \frac{5(x - 3)^2}{4} = 1$$

51. $d_2 - d_1 = 186{,}000(0.0005)$

$2a = 93$

$a = 46.5$

$c = 100$

$b = \sqrt{c^2 - a^2}$

$$\frac{x^2}{a^2} - \frac{y^2}{b^2} = 1$$

$$x = 60 \implies y^2 = b^2\left(\frac{x^2}{a^2} - 1\right) = (100^2 - 46.5^2)\left(\frac{60^2}{46.5^2} - 1\right) \approx 5211.57 \implies y \approx 72.2$$

72.2 miles north

52. Q: Your location $(0, 0)$

F_1: Location of friend to the west $(-10{,}560, 0)$

F_2: Location of friend to the east $(10{,}560, 0)$

$P(x, y)$: Location of lightning strike

The sound at F_1 is heard $8 - 6 = 2$ seconds after the sound at F_2.

$$(1100)(2) = 2200 = 2a$$

$$\frac{x^2}{a^2} - \frac{y^2}{b^2} = 1$$

$$c = 10{,}560, a = \frac{2200}{2} = 1100 \implies a^2 = 1{,}210{,}000$$

$$b^2 = c^2 - a^2 = 110{,}303{,}600$$

The equation of the first hyperbola is

$$\frac{x^2}{1{,}210{,}000} - \frac{y^2}{110{,}303{,}600} = 1.$$

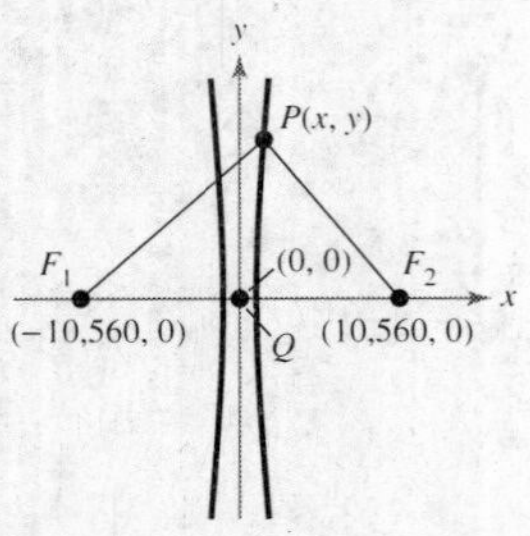

For the second hyperbola, place the center at $(5280, 0)$.

Q: Your location $(0, 0)$

F_2: Location of friend to the east $(10{,}560, 0)$

$P(x, y)$: Location of lightning strike

The sound at F_2 is heard 6 seconds after the sound at Q.

$$(1100)(6) = 6600 = 2a$$

$$\frac{(x - 5280)^2}{a^2} - \frac{y^2}{b^2} = 1$$

$$C = 5280, a = \frac{6600}{2} = 3300 \implies a^2 = 10{,}890{,}000$$

$$b^2 = c^2 - a^2 = 16{,}988{,}400$$

The equation of the second hyperbola is

$$\frac{(x - 5280)^2}{10{,}890{,}000} - \frac{y^2}{16{,}988{,}400} = 1.$$

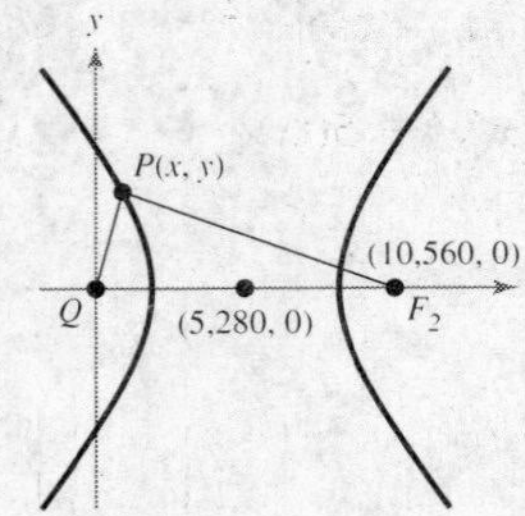

53. $3x^2 + 2y^2 - 12x + 12y + 29 = 0$

$$3(x^2 - 4x + 4) + 2(y^2 + 6y + 9) = -29 + 12 + 18$$

$$3(x - 2)^2 + 2(y + 3)^2 = 1$$

Ellipse

54. $4x^2 + 4y^2 - 4x + 8y - 11 = 0$

$A = C = 4 \implies$ Circle

55. $5x^2 - 2y^2 + 10x - 4y + 17 = 0$

$$5(x^2 + 2x + 1) - 2(y^2 + 2y + 1) = -17 + 5 - 2$$

$$5(x + 1)^2 - 2(y + 1)^2 = -14$$

$$\frac{(y + 1)^2}{7} - \frac{(x + 1)^2}{(14/5)} = 1$$

Hyperbola

56. $-4y^2 + 5x + 3y + 7 = 0$

$A = 0, C = -4, AC = 0$

Parabola

57. $xy - 4 = 0$

$A = 0, B = 1, C = 0$

$$\cot 2\theta = \frac{A - C}{B} = 0 \implies \theta = \frac{\pi}{4}$$

$$x = \frac{\sqrt{2}}{2}(x' - y'), y = \frac{\sqrt{2}}{2}(x' + y')$$

$$xy = 4$$

$$\frac{\sqrt{2}}{2}(x' - y')\frac{\sqrt{2}}{2}(x' + y') = 4$$

$$\frac{1}{2}(x')^2 - \frac{1}{2}(y')^2 = 4$$

$$\frac{(x')^2}{8} - \frac{(y')^2}{8} = 1$$

Hyperbola

58. $x^2 - 10xy + y^2 + 1 = 0$

$$A = C = 1 \implies \cot 2\theta = 0 \implies \theta = \frac{\pi}{4}$$

$$x = \frac{\sqrt{2}}{2}(x' - y'), y = \frac{\sqrt{2}}{2}(x' + y')$$

$$\left[\frac{\sqrt{2}}{2}(x' - y')\right]^2 - 10\left[\frac{\sqrt{2}}{2}(x' - y')\right]\left[\frac{\sqrt{2}}{2}(x' + y')\right] + \left[\frac{\sqrt{2}}{2}(x' + y')\right]^2 + 1 = 0$$

$$\frac{1}{2}(x')^2 + \frac{1}{2}(y')^2 - x'y' - 5((x')^2 - (y')^2) + \frac{1}{2}(x')^2 + x'y' + \frac{1}{2}(y')^2 = -1$$

$$-4(x')^2 + 6(y')^2 = -1$$

$$\frac{(x')^2}{1/4} - \frac{(y')^2}{1/6} = 1$$

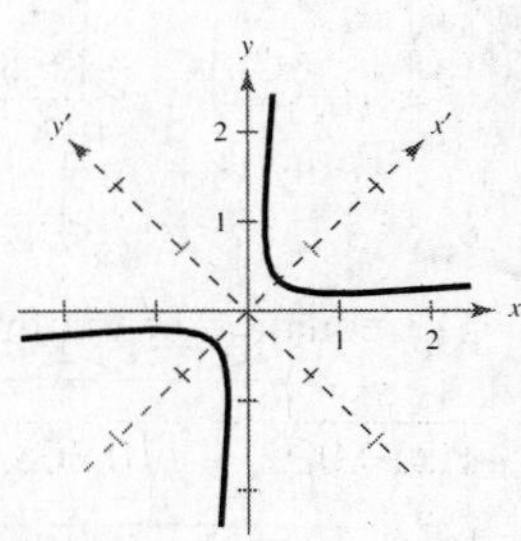

Hyperbola

59. $5x^2 - 2xy + 5y^2 - 12 = 0$

$A = 5, B = -2, C = 5$

$\cot 2\theta = 0 \Rightarrow \theta = \frac{\pi}{4}$

$x = \frac{\sqrt{2}}{2}(x' - y'), y = \frac{\sqrt{2}}{2}(x' + y')$

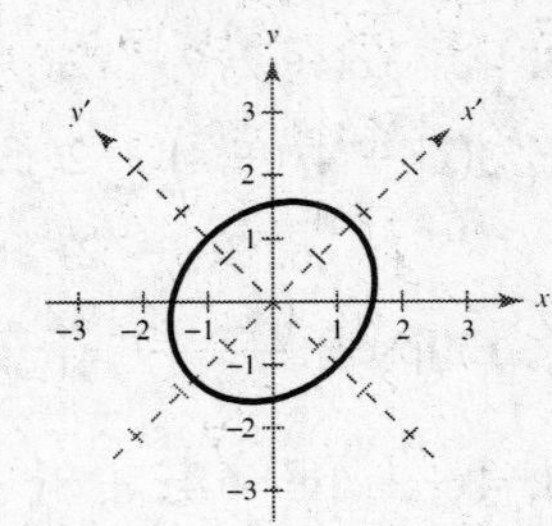

$$5x^2 - 2xy + 5y^2 = 12$$

$$5\left[\frac{\sqrt{2}}{2}(x' - y')\right]^2 - 2\left[\frac{\sqrt{2}}{2}(x' - y')\right]\left[\frac{\sqrt{2}}{2}(x' + y')\right] + 5\left[\frac{\sqrt{2}}{2}(x' + y')\right]^2 = 12$$

$$5\left[\frac{1}{2}(x')^2 - x'y' + \frac{1}{2}(y')^2\right] - (x')^2 + (y')^2 + 5\left[\frac{1}{2}(x')^2 + x'y' + \frac{1}{2}(y')^2\right] = 12$$

$$4(x')^2 + 6(y')^2 = 12$$

$$\frac{(x')^2}{3} + \frac{(y')^2}{2} = 1$$

Ellipse

60. $\cot 2\theta = \frac{4 - 4}{8} = 0 \Rightarrow \theta = \frac{\pi}{4}$

$x = \frac{\sqrt{2}}{2}(x' - y'), y = \frac{\sqrt{2}}{2}(x' + y')$

$$4\left[\frac{\sqrt{2}}{2}(x' - y')\right]^2 + 8\left[\frac{\sqrt{2}}{2}(x' - y')\frac{\sqrt{2}}{2}(x' + y')\right] + 4\left[\frac{\sqrt{2}}{2}(x' + y')\right]^2$$

$$+ 7\sqrt{2}\left[\frac{\sqrt{2}}{2}(x' - y')\right] + 9\sqrt{2}\left[\frac{\sqrt{2}}{2}(x' + y')\right] = 0$$

$$2[(x')^2 + (y')^2 - 2x'y'] + 4[(x')^2 - (y')^2] + 2[(x')^2 + (y')^2 + 2x'y'] + 7(x' - y') + 9(x' + y') = 0$$

$$8(x')^2 + 16x' + 2y' = 0$$

$$y' = -4(x')^2 - 8x'$$

Parabola

61. (a) $B^2 - 4AC = (-8)^2 - 4(16)(1) = 0$

Parabola

(b) $y^2 + (5 - 8x)y + (16x^2 - 10x) = 0$

$$y = \frac{(8x - 5) \pm \sqrt{(5 - 8x)^2 - 4(16x^2 - 10x)}}{2}$$

(c)

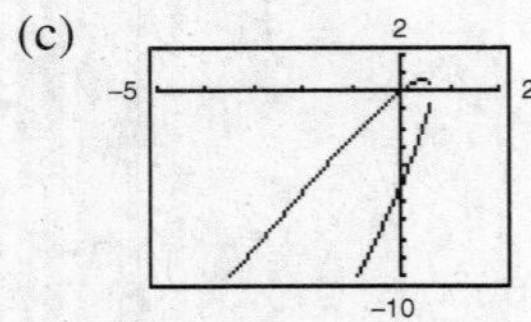

62. (a) $B^2 - 4AC = -300 \Rightarrow$ Ellipse

(b) $7y^2 - 8xy + (13x^2 - 45) = 0$

$$y = \frac{8x \pm \sqrt{(64x^2) - 4(7)(13x^2 - 45)}}{14}$$

(c)

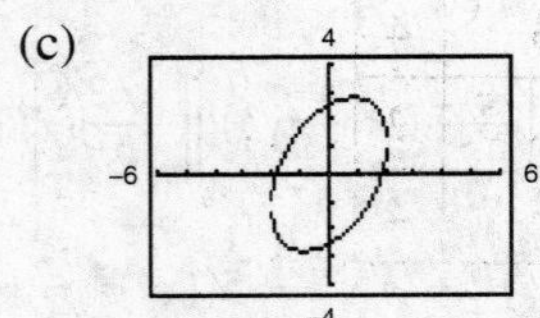

63. (a) $B^2 - 4AC = (2)^2 - 4(1)(1) = 0$

Parabola

(b) $y^2 + (2x - 2\sqrt{2})y + (x^2 + 2\sqrt{2}x + 2) = 0$

$$y = \frac{(2\sqrt{2} - 2x) \pm \sqrt{(2x - 2\sqrt{2})^2 - 4(x^2 + 2\sqrt{2x} + 2)}}{2}$$

(c) 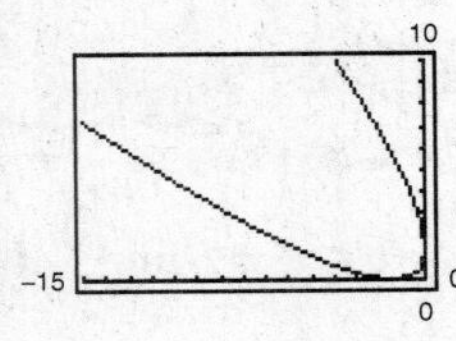

64. (a) $B^2 - 4AC = 100 - 4$

$= 96 > 0 \implies$ Hyperbola

(b) $y^2 - 10xy + (x^2 + 1) = 0$

$$y = \frac{10x \pm \sqrt{100x^2 - 4(x^2 + 1)}}{2}$$

$$y = \frac{10x \pm \sqrt{96x^2 - 4}}{2}$$

$$y = 5x \pm \sqrt{24x^2 - 1}$$

(c) 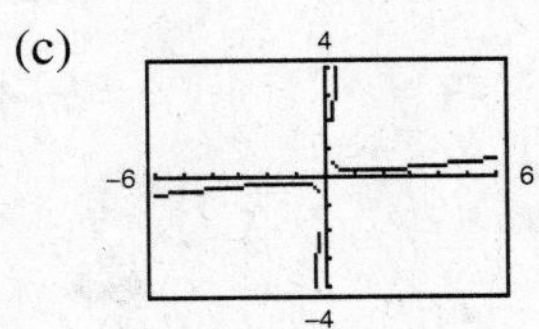

65. Adding the equations,

$24x + 240 = 0 \implies x = -10$. Then:

$4(100) + y^2 - 560 - 24y + 304 = 0$

$y^2 - 24y + 144 = 0$

$(y - 12)^2 = 0 \implies y = 12$

Solution: $(-10, 12)$

66. $4x^2 + 4y^2 = 100$

$9x - 4y^2 = 0$

Adding:

$4x^2 + 9x = 100$

$4x^2 + 9x - 100 = 0$

$(x - 4)(4x + 25) = 0 \implies x = 4, -\frac{25}{4}$

If $x = 4$:

$4y^2 = 9(4) = 36$

$y^2 = 9 \implies y = \pm 3$

If $x = -\frac{25}{4}$, $9\left(-\frac{25}{4}\right) = 4y^2$, impossible.

Answer: $(4, 3), (4, -3)$

67.

t	-2	-1	0	1	2	3
x	-8	-5	-2	1	4	7
y	15	11	7	3	-1	-5

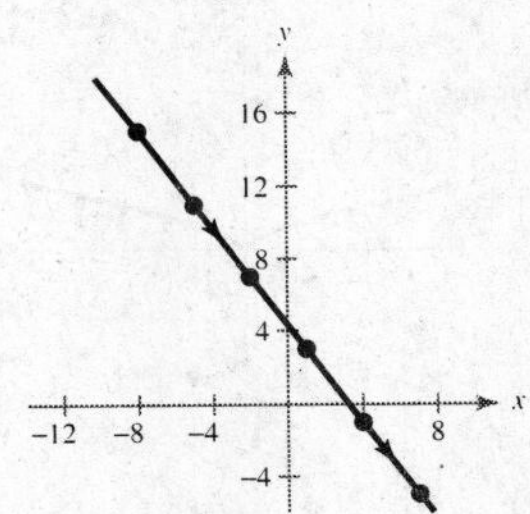

68. $x = \sqrt{t}, y = 8 - t$

t	0	1	2	3	4
x	0	1	$\sqrt{2}$	$\sqrt{3}$	2
y	8	7	6	5	4

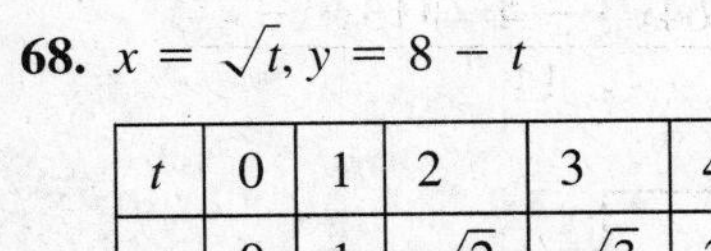

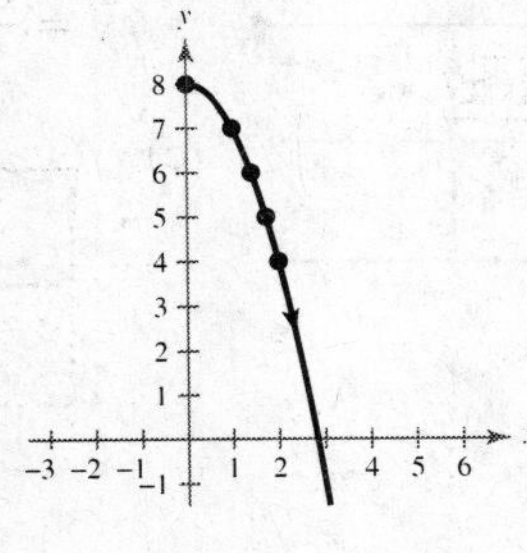

69. $x = 5t - 1, y = 2t + 5$

$t = \frac{1}{5}(x + 1) \Rightarrow$

$y = \frac{2}{5}(x + 1) + 5 = \frac{2}{5}x + \frac{27}{5}$, line

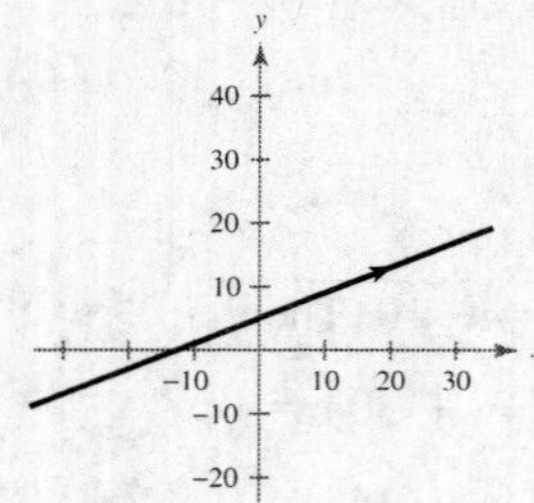

70. $x = 4t + 1,\ y = 8 - 3t$

$t = \frac{1}{4}(x - 1) \Rightarrow$

$y = 8 - 3\left(\frac{1}{4}(x - 1)\right) = -\frac{3}{4}x + \frac{35}{4}$

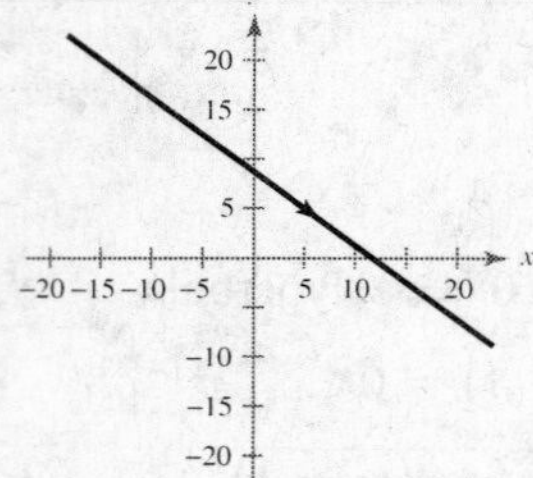

71. $x = t^2 + 2, y = 4t^2 - 3$

$t^2 = x - 2 \Rightarrow$

$y = 4(x - 2) - 3 = 4x - 11, \quad x \geq 2$

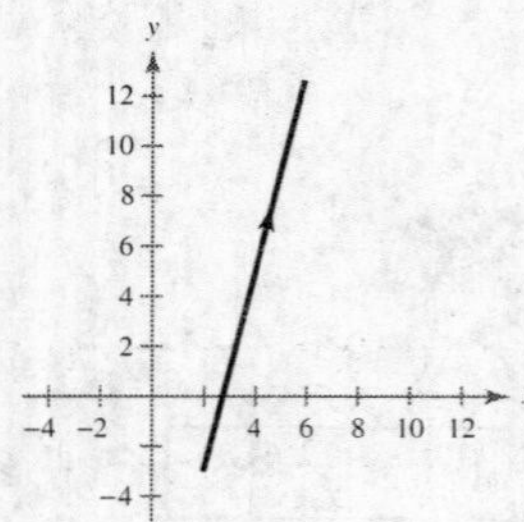

72. $x = \ln 4t,\ y = t^2$

$e^x = 4t, t = \frac{1}{4}e^x \Rightarrow y = \left(\frac{1}{4}e^x\right)^2 = \frac{1}{16}e^{2x}$

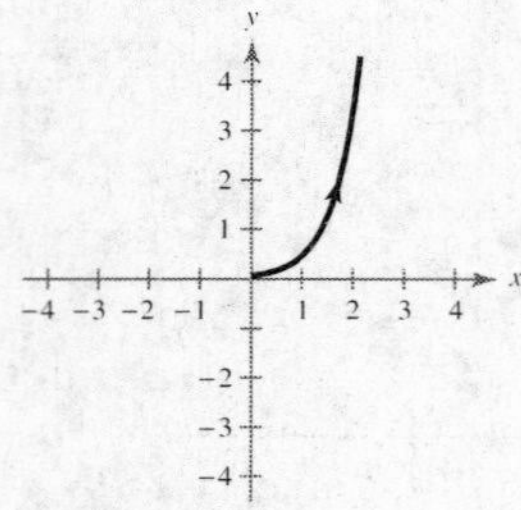

73. $x = t^3, y = \dfrac{1}{2}t^2$

$t = x^{1/3} \Rightarrow y = \dfrac{1}{2}x^{2/3}$

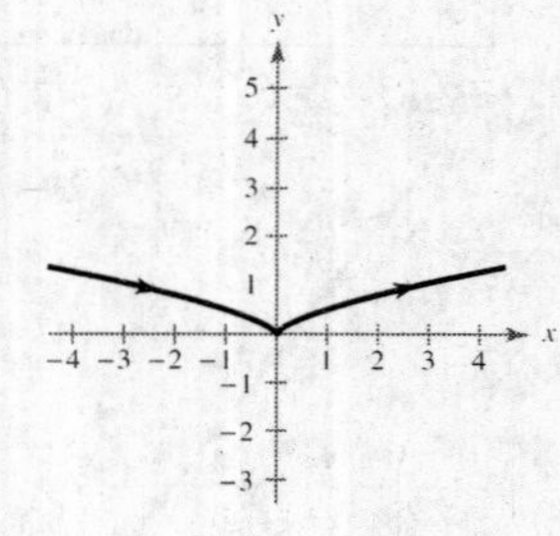

74. $x = \dfrac{4}{t},\ y = t^2 - 1$

$t = \dfrac{4}{x} \Rightarrow y = \dfrac{16}{x^2} - 1$

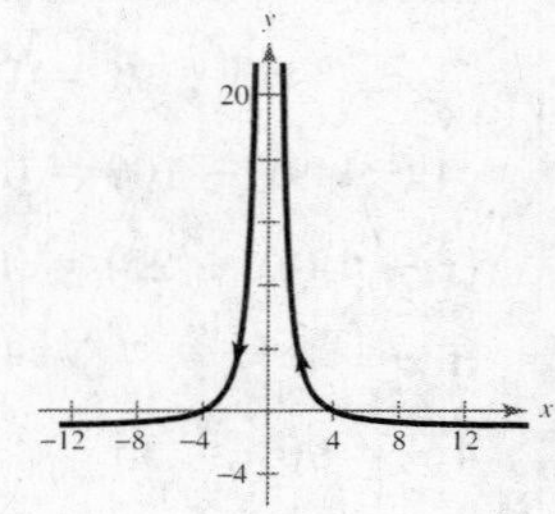

75. $x = \sqrt[3]{t}$

$y = t$

$t = x^3 \Rightarrow y = t = x^3$

$y = x^3$

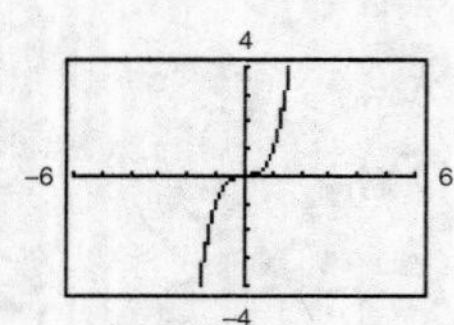

76. $x = t$

$y = \sqrt[3]{t} = \sqrt[3]{x} = x^{1/3}$

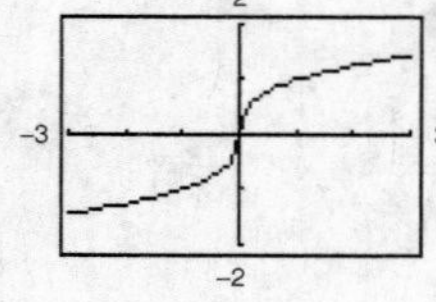

77. $x = \dfrac{1}{t}$

$y = t$

$y = t = \dfrac{1}{x}$

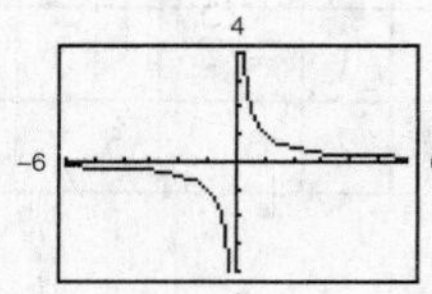

78. $x = t$

$y = \frac{1}{t} = \frac{1}{x}$

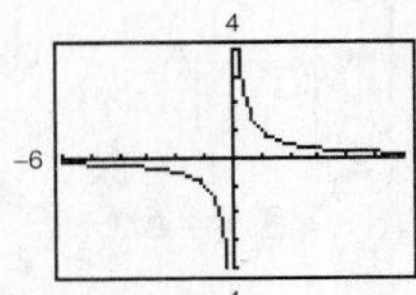

79. $x = 2t$

$y = 4t$

$y = 2(2t) = 2x$

Line

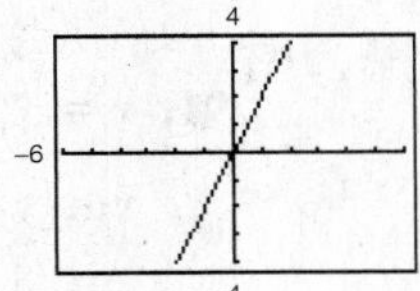

80. $x = t^2, \; y = \sqrt{t}$

$t = y^2$

$x = (y^2)^2 = y^4, \; y \geq 0$

$y = \sqrt[4]{x}, x \geq 0$

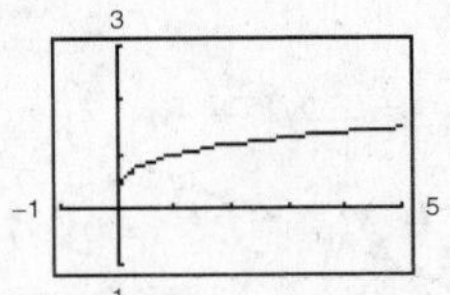

81. $x = 1 + 4t$

$y = 2 - 3t$

$t = \frac{x-1}{4} \Rightarrow y = 2 - 3\left(\frac{x-1}{4}\right) = 2 - \frac{3}{4}x + \frac{3}{4}$

$y = \frac{11}{4} - \frac{3}{4}x$

$3x + 4y - 11 = 0$

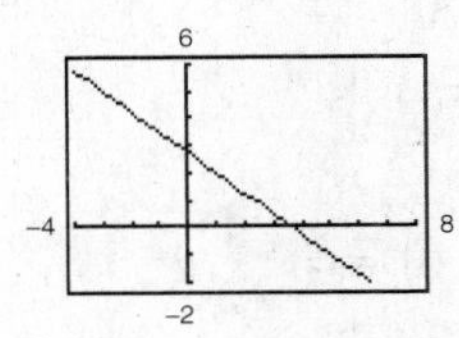

82. $x = t + 4, \; y = t^2$

$t = x - 4$

$y = (x - 4)^2$

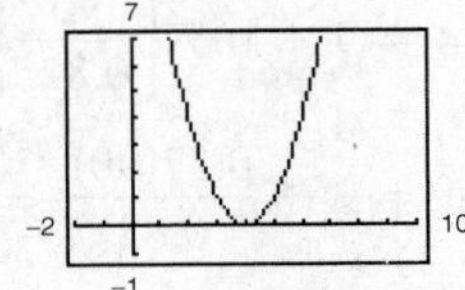

83. $x = 3$

$y = t$

Vertical line: $x = 3$

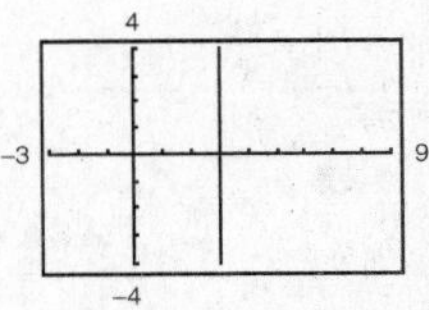

84. $x = t$

$y = 2$

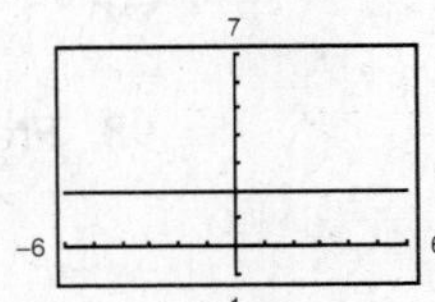

85. $x = 6 \cos \theta, y = 6 \sin \theta$

$\cos \theta = \frac{x}{6}, \sin \theta = \frac{y}{6}$

$\frac{x^2}{36} + \frac{y^2}{36} = 1$

$x^2 + y^2 = 36$

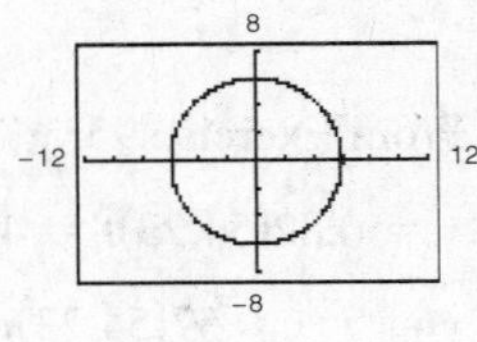

86. $x = 3 + 3 \cos \theta, y = 2 + 5 \sin \theta$

$\cos \theta = \frac{x-3}{3}, \sin \theta = \frac{y-2}{5}$

$\frac{(x-3)^2}{9} + \frac{(y-2)^2}{25} = 1$

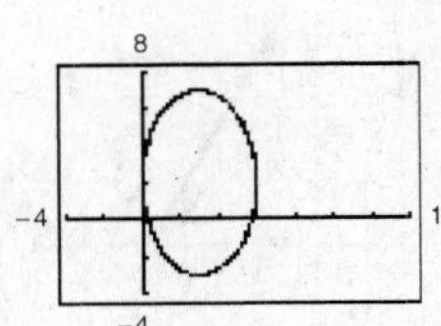

87. $y = 6x + 2$

$x = t, y = 6t + 2$

$x = -t, y = -6t + 2$

Other answers possible

88. $x = t,\ y = 10 - t$

$x = -t,\ y = 10 + t$

Many answers possible

89. $y = x^2 + 2$

$x = t, y = t^2 + 2$

$x = t + 1, y = (t + 1)^2 + 2 = t^2 + 2t + 3$

Other answers possible

90. $x = t,\ y = 2t^3 + 5t$

$x = -t,\ y = -2t^3 - 5t$

Many answers possible

91. $x = x_1 + t(x_2 - x_1) = 3 + t(8 - 3) = 5t + 3$

$y = y_1 + t(y_2 - y_1) = 5 + t(0 - 0) = 5$

or $x = t,\ y = 5$

92. $x = x_1 + t(x_2 - x_1) = 2 + t(2 - 2) = 2$

$y = y_1 + t(y_2 - y_1)$

$= -1 + t(4 - (-1)) = -1 + 5t$

or $x = 2,\ y = t$

93. $x = x_1 + t(x_2 - x_1)$

$= -1 + t[10 - (-1)] = 11t - 1$

$y = y_1 + t(y_2 - y_1) = 6 + t(0 - 6) = -6t + 6$

94. $x = x_1 + t(x_2 - x_1) = 0 + t\left(\frac{5}{2} - 0\right) = \frac{5}{2}t$

$y = y_1 + t(y_2 - y_1) = 0 + t(6 - 0) = 6t$

or $x = 5t,\ y = 12t$

95. (90, 4) is on the curve:

$$90 = 0.82v_0 t \implies v_0 = \frac{90}{0.82t}$$

$$4 = 7 + 0.57\left[\frac{90}{0.82t}\right]t - 16t^2 \implies$$

$$16t^2 = 3 + \frac{0.57(90)}{0.82} \implies t \approx 2.024$$

Hence, $v_0 \approx \dfrac{90}{0.82(2.024)} \approx 54.23$ ft/sec.

96. From Exercise 95, $v_0 = 54.23$.

$x = 0.82(54.23)t = 44.47t$

$y = 7 + 0.57(54.23)t - 16t^2$

$= 7 + 30.91t - 16t^2$

97. From Exercise 96:

The maximum height is approximately 21.9 feet for $t \approx 0.97$.

98. From Exercise 95, $t \approx 2.024$ seconds.

99. $\left(1, \frac{\pi}{4}\right)$

$\left(1, -\frac{7\pi}{4}\right), \left(-1, \frac{5\pi}{4}\right), \left(-1, -\frac{3\pi}{4}\right)$

100.

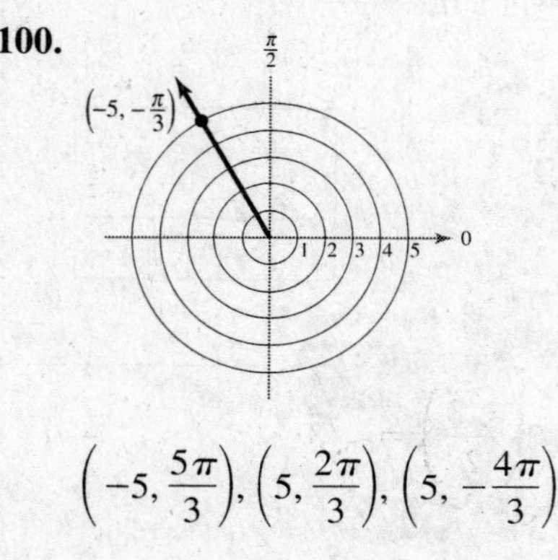

$\left(-5, \frac{5\pi}{3}\right), \left(5, \frac{2\pi}{3}\right), \left(5, -\frac{4\pi}{3}\right)$

101. $(r, \theta) = \left(-2, -\dfrac{11\pi}{6}\right)$

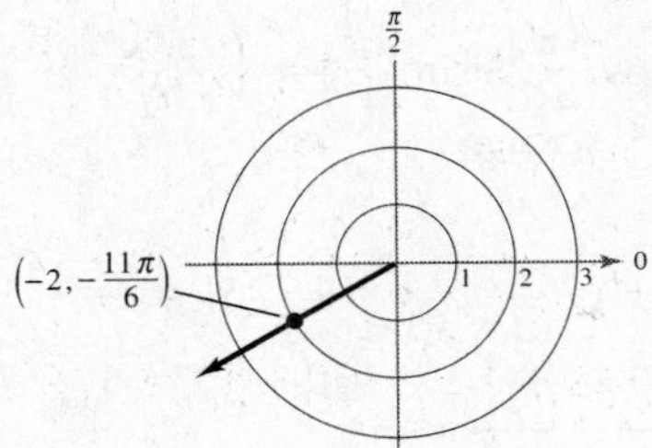

$\left(-2, \dfrac{\pi}{6}\right), \left(2, \dfrac{7\pi}{6}\right), \left(2, -\dfrac{5\pi}{6}\right)$

102. 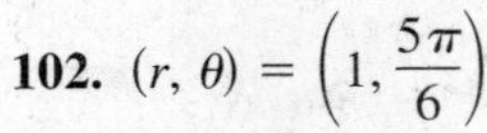 $(r, \theta) = \left(1, \dfrac{5\pi}{6}\right)$

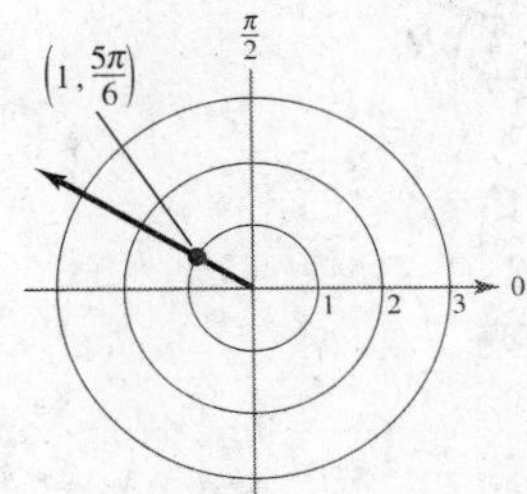

$\left(-1, -\dfrac{\pi}{6}\right), \left(-1, \dfrac{11\pi}{6}\right), \left(1, -\dfrac{7\pi}{6}\right)$

103. $\left(\sqrt{5}, -\dfrac{4\pi}{3}\right)$

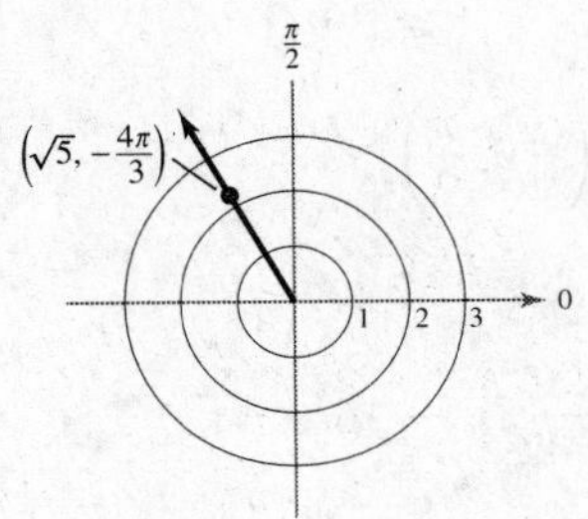

$\left(\sqrt{5}, \dfrac{2\pi}{3}\right), \left(-\sqrt{5}, -\dfrac{\pi}{3}\right), \left(-\sqrt{5}, \dfrac{5\pi}{3}\right)$

104.

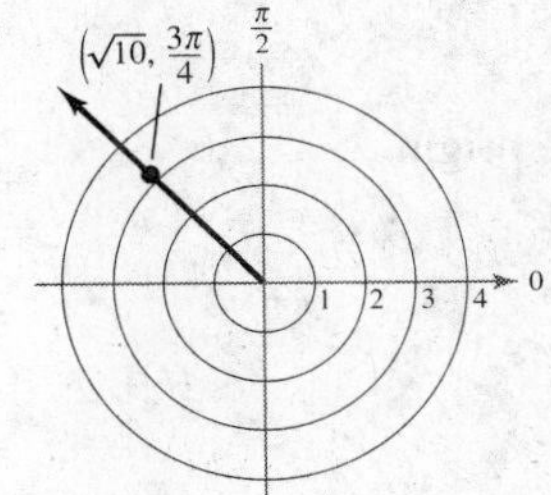

$(r, \theta) = \left(\sqrt{10}, -\dfrac{5\pi}{4}\right), \left(-\sqrt{10}, -\dfrac{\pi}{4}\right), \left(-\sqrt{10}, \dfrac{7\pi}{4}\right)$

105. $(r, \theta) = \left(5, -\dfrac{7\pi}{6}\right)$

$(x, y) = \left(-\dfrac{5\sqrt{3}}{2}, \dfrac{5}{2}\right)$

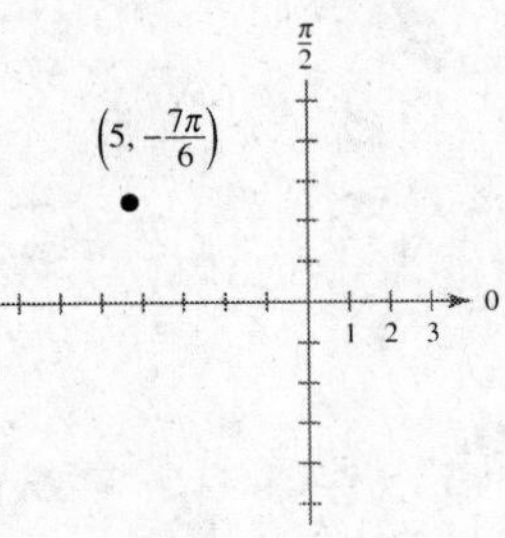

106.

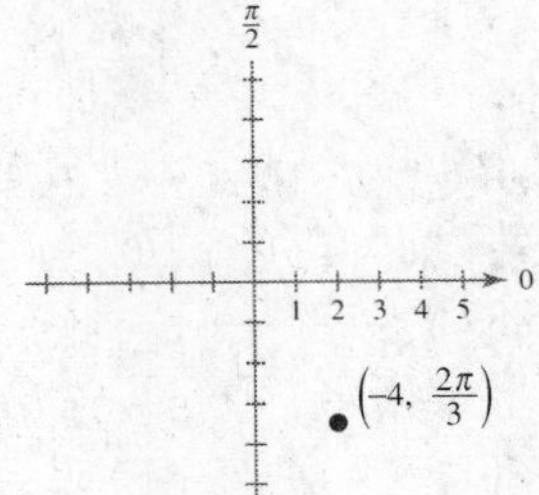

$(r, \theta) = \left(-4, \dfrac{2\pi}{3}\right)$

$(x, y) = \left(-4 \cos \dfrac{2\pi}{3}, -4 \sin \dfrac{2\pi}{3}\right) = \left(2, -2\sqrt{3}\right)$

107. $\left(2, -\dfrac{5\pi}{3}\right)$

$x = r \cos \theta = 2\left(\dfrac{1}{2}\right) = 1$

$y = r \sin \theta = 2\left(\dfrac{\sqrt{3}}{2}\right) = \sqrt{3}$

$(x, y) = \left(1, \sqrt{3}\right)$

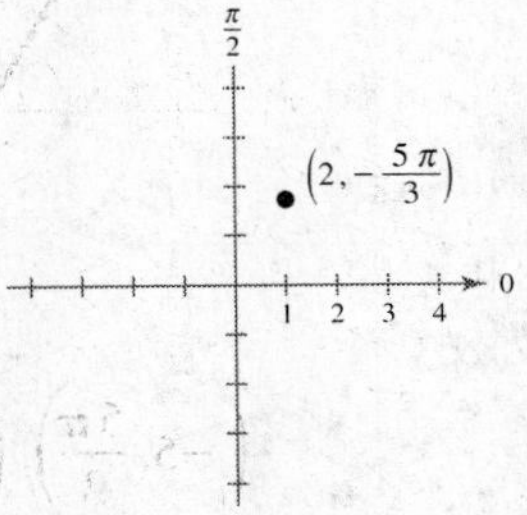

108. $\left(-1, \frac{11\pi}{6}\right)$

$x = r\cos\theta = -1\left(\frac{\sqrt{3}}{2}\right)$

$y = r\sin\theta = -1\left(-\frac{1}{2}\right)$

$(x, y) = \left(-\frac{\sqrt{3}}{2}, \frac{1}{2}\right)$

109. $(r, \theta) = \left(3, \frac{3\pi}{4}\right)$

$(x, y) = \left(3\cos\frac{3\pi}{4}, 3\sin\frac{3\pi}{4}\right) = \left(\frac{-3\sqrt{2}}{2}, \frac{3\sqrt{2}}{2}\right)$

110. $(r, \theta) = \left(0, \frac{\pi}{2}\right)$, the origin

$(x, y) = (0, 0)$

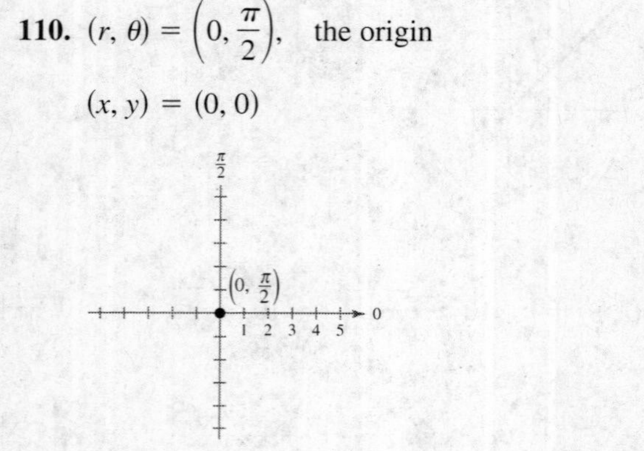

111. $(x, y) = (0, -9)$

$(r, \theta) = \left(9, \frac{3\pi}{2}\right), \left(-9, \frac{\pi}{2}\right)$

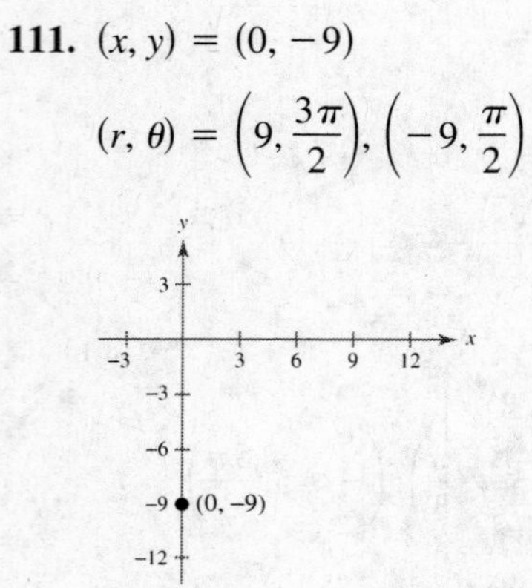

112. $(x, y) = (-3, 4)$

$r = 5, \tan\theta = \frac{-4}{3}$

$(5, 126.87°), (-5, 306.87°)$

or

$(5, 2.214), (-5, 5.356)$

(radians)

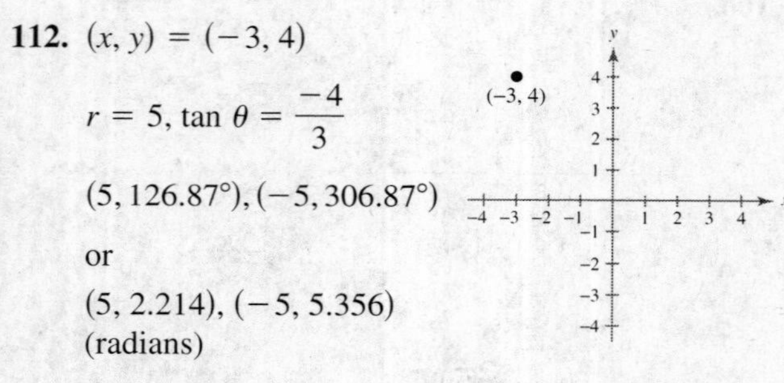

113. $(x, y) = (5, -5)$

$(r, \theta) = \left(5\sqrt{2}, \frac{7\pi}{4}\right), \left(-5\sqrt{2}, \frac{3\pi}{4}\right)$

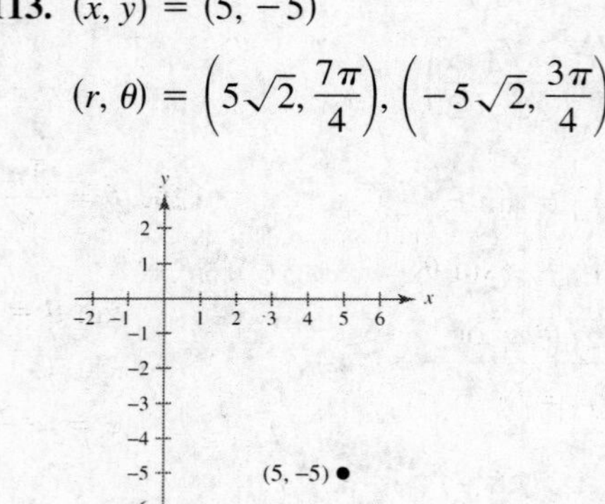

114. $(x, y) = \left(-3, -\sqrt{3}\right)$

Third quadrant, $\theta = \frac{7\pi}{6}$

$r^2 = (-3)^2 + 3 = 12 \implies r = 2\sqrt{3}$

$(r, \theta) = \left(2\sqrt{3}, \frac{7\pi}{6}\right), \left(-2\sqrt{3}, \frac{\pi}{6}\right)$

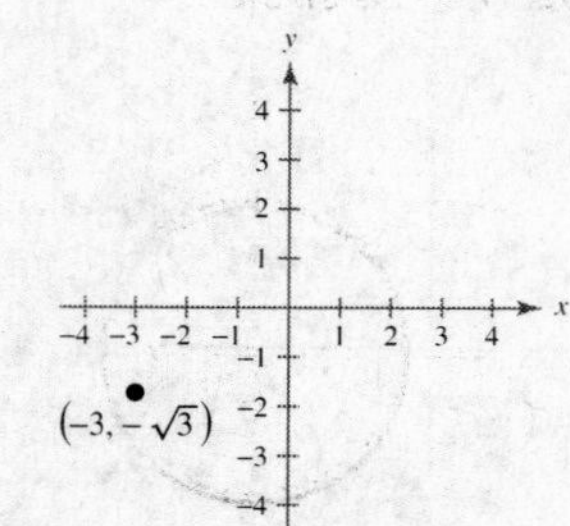

115. $x^2 + y^2 = 9$
$$r^2 = 9$$
$$r = 3$$

116. $x^2 + y^2 = 20$
$$r^2 = 20$$
$$r = 2\sqrt{5}$$

117. $x^2 + y^2 - 4x = 0$
$$r^2 - 4r\cos\theta = 0$$
$$r = 4\cos\theta$$

118. $x^2 + y^2 = 6y$
$$r^2 = 6r\sin\theta$$
$$r = 6\sin\theta$$

119.
$$xy = 5$$
$$(r\cos\theta)(r\sin\theta) = 5$$
$$r^2 = 5\csc\theta\cdot\sec\theta$$

120.
$$xy = -2$$
$$(r\cos\theta)(r\sin\theta) = -2$$
$$r^2 = -2\sec\theta\csc\theta$$

121.
$$4x^2 + y = 1$$
$$4(r\cos\theta)^2 + (r\sin\theta)^2 = 1$$
$$4r^2\cos^2\theta + r^2(1 - \cos^2\theta) = 1$$
$$r^2[3\cos^2\theta + 1] = 1$$
$$r^2 = \frac{1}{3\cos^2\theta + 1}$$

122.
$$2x^2 + 3y^2 = 1$$
$$2(r\cos\theta)^2 + 3(r\sin\theta)^2 = 1$$
$$r^2(2\cos^2\theta + 3\sin^2\theta) = 1$$
$$r^2(2(1 - \sin^2\theta) + 3\sin^2\theta) = 1$$
$$r^2(2 + \sin^2\theta) = 1$$
$$r^2 = \frac{1}{2 + \sin^2\theta}$$

123.
$$r = 5$$
$$x^2 + y^2 = 5^2 = 25$$
Circle

124.
$$r = 12$$
$$x^2 + y^2 = 144$$
Circle

125.
$$r = 3\cos\theta$$
$$r^2 = 3r\cos\theta$$
$$x^2 + y^2 = 3x$$

126.
$$r = 8\sin\theta$$
$$r^2 = 8r\sin\theta$$
$$x^2 + y^2 = 8y$$

127.
$$r^2 = \cos 2\theta$$
$$r^2 = 1 - 2\sin^2\theta$$
$$r^4 = r^2 - 2r^2\sin^2\theta$$
$$(x^2 + y^2)^2 = x^2 + y^2 - 2y^2$$
$$(x^2 + y^2)^2 - x^2 + y^2 = 0$$

128.
$$r^2 = \sin\theta$$
$$r^3 = r\sin\theta$$
$$(x^2 + y^2)^{3/2} = y \text{ or}$$
$$(x^2 + y^2)^3 = y^2$$

129. $\theta = \dfrac{5\pi}{6}$
$$\tan\theta = \frac{y}{x} = -\frac{1}{\sqrt{3}}$$
$$y = -\frac{\sqrt{3}}{3}x, \quad \text{line}$$

130. $\theta = \dfrac{4\pi}{3}$
$$\tan\theta = \frac{y}{x} = \sqrt{3}$$
$$y = \sqrt{3}x$$

131. $r = 5$, circle

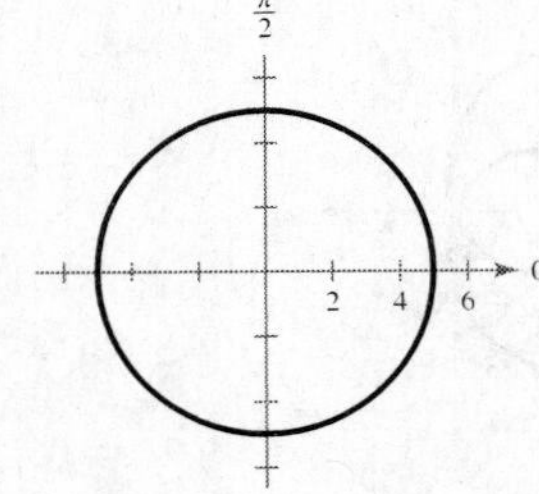

132. $r = 3$, circle

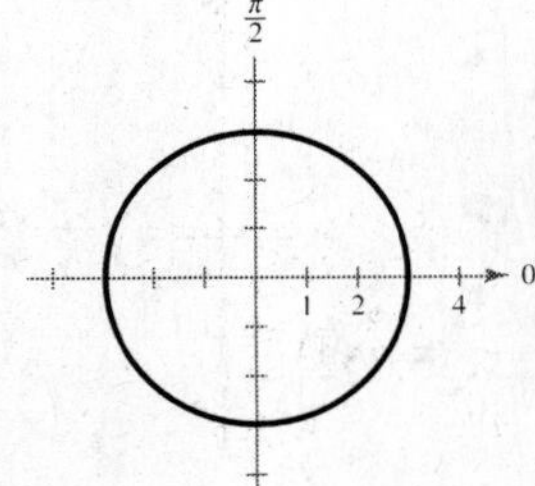

133. $\theta = \dfrac{\pi}{2}$, y-axis

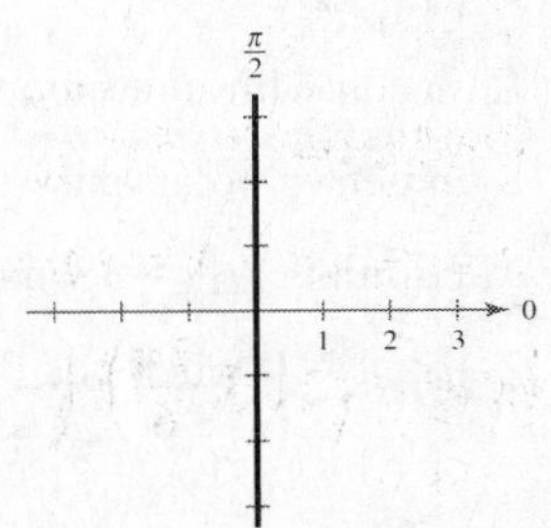

134. $\theta = -\dfrac{5\pi}{6}$, line

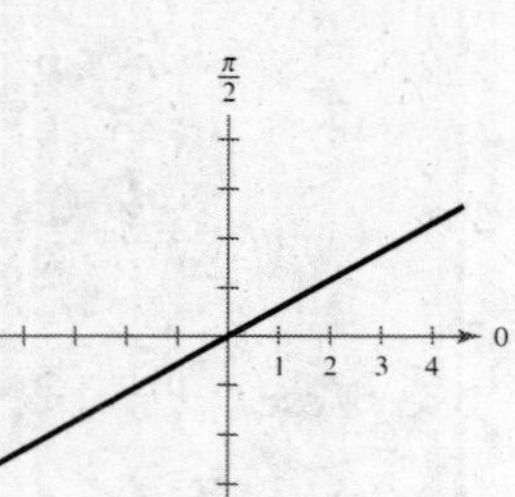

135. $r = 5\cos\theta$, circle

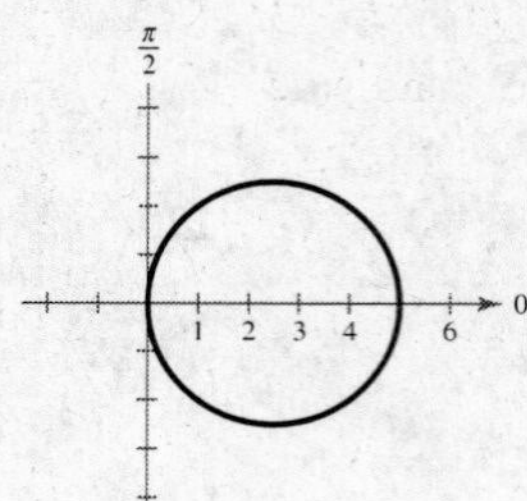

136. $r = 2\sin\theta$, circle

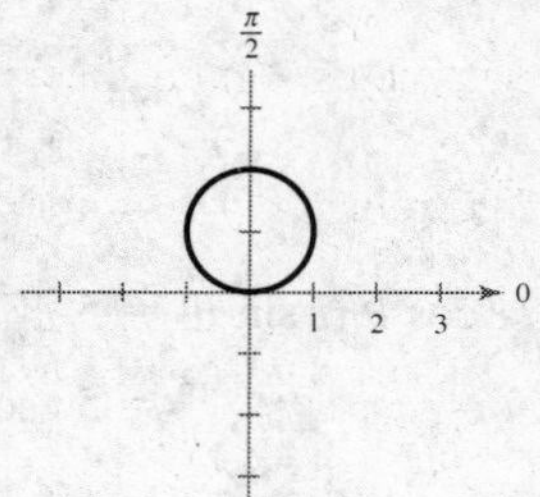

137. $r = 5 + 4\cos\theta$

Dimpled limaçon

Symmetric with respect to polar axis

r is maximum at $\theta = 0$: $(r, \theta) = (9, 0)$

$r \neq 0$ (No zeros)

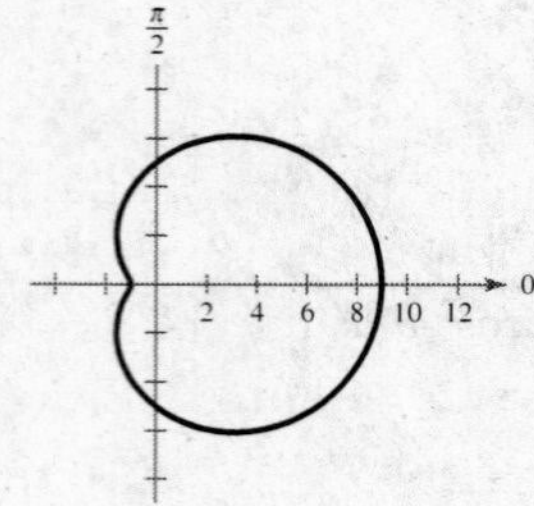

138. $r = 1 + 4\sin\theta$

Limaçon with inner loop

Symmetric with respect to $\theta = \dfrac{\pi}{2}$

$|r|$ is a maximum at $\theta = \dfrac{\pi}{2}$: $\left(5, \dfrac{\pi}{2}\right)$

$r = 0$ when $4\sin\theta = -1 \implies \sin\theta = -\dfrac{1}{4} \implies \theta \approx 3.394, 6.031$

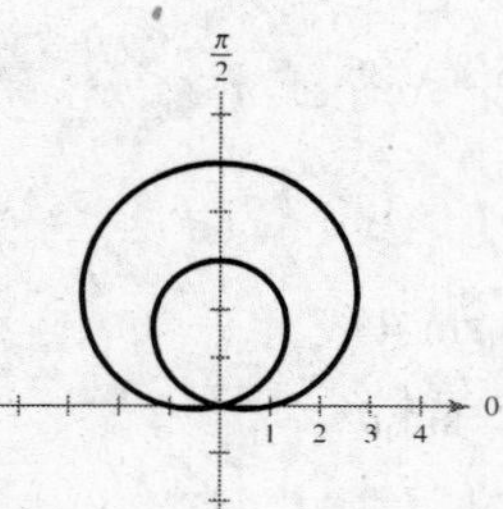

139. $r = 3 - 5\sin\theta$

Limaçon with loop

Symmetry: line $\theta = \dfrac{\pi}{2}$

Maximum $|r|$-value: $|r| = 8$ when $\theta = \dfrac{3\pi}{2}$

Zeros: $r = 0$ when $\theta \approx 0.6435, 2.4981$ $\left(\sin\theta = \dfrac{3}{5}\right)$

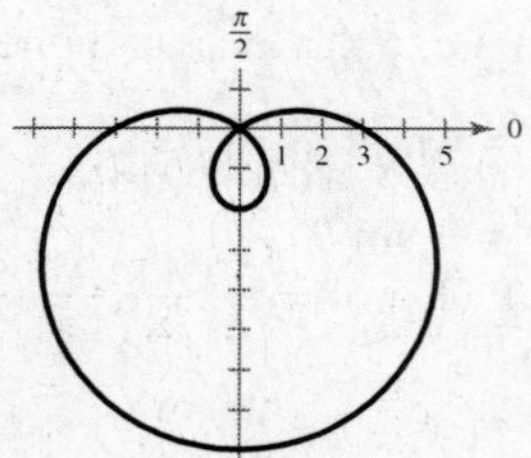

140. $r = 2 - 6\cos\theta$

Limaçon with inner loop

Symmetry: polar axis

Maximum: $|r| = 8$ when $\theta = \pi$

Zero: $r = 0$ when $\cos\theta = \frac{1}{3} \implies \theta \approx 1.231, 5.052$

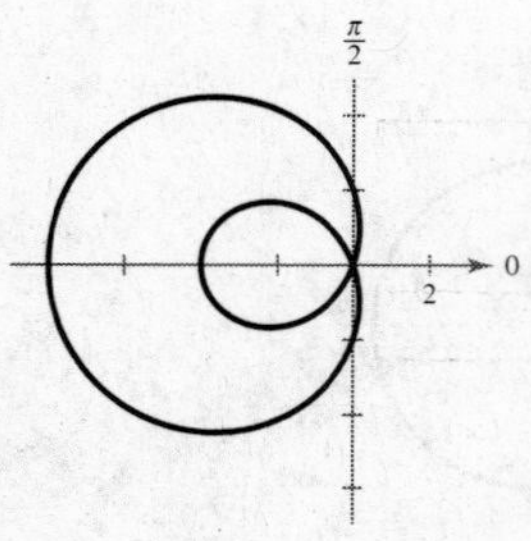

141. $r = -3\cos 2\theta,\ 0 \le \theta \le 2\pi$

Four-leaved rose

Symmetric with respect to $\theta = \dfrac{\pi}{2}$, polar axis, and pole

The value of $|r|$ is a maximum (3) at $\theta = 0, \dfrac{\pi}{2}, \pi, \dfrac{3\pi}{2}$.

$r = 0$ for $\theta = \dfrac{\pi}{4}, \dfrac{3\pi}{4}, \dfrac{5\pi}{4}, \dfrac{7\pi}{4}$

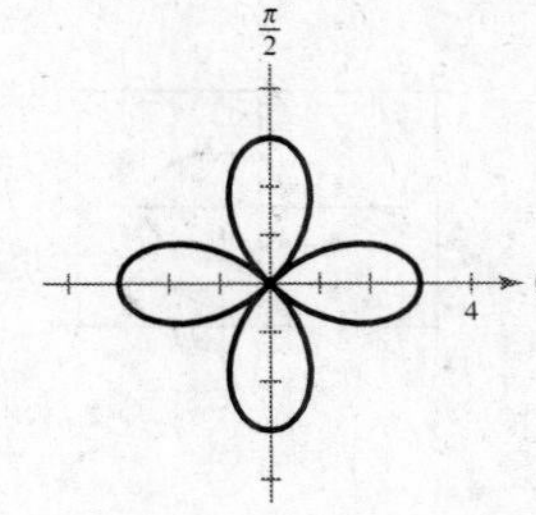

142. $r = \cos 5\theta$

Five-leaved rose

Symmetric with respect to polar axis

$|r|$ is maximum value of 1 at $\theta = \dfrac{n\pi}{5}, n = 0, 1, 2, \ldots$

$r = 0$ for $\theta = \dfrac{\pi}{10} + \dfrac{2n\pi}{10}, n = 0, 1, 2, \ldots$

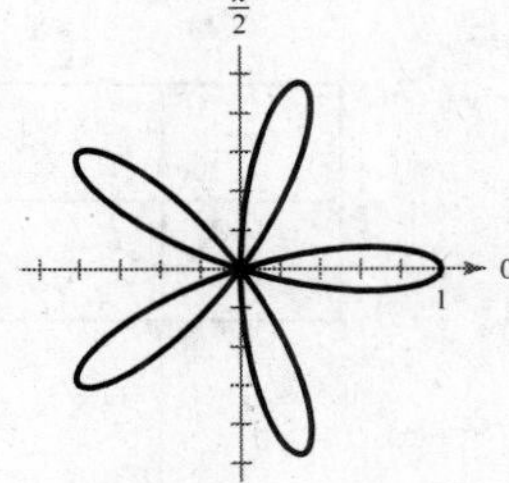

143. $r^2 = 5\sin 2\theta$

Lemniscate

Symmetry with respect to pole

Maximum $|r|$-value: $\sqrt{5}$ when $\theta = \dfrac{\pi}{4}, \dfrac{5\pi}{4}$

Zeros: $r = 0$ when $\theta = 0, \dfrac{\pi}{2}, \pi, \dfrac{3\pi}{2}$

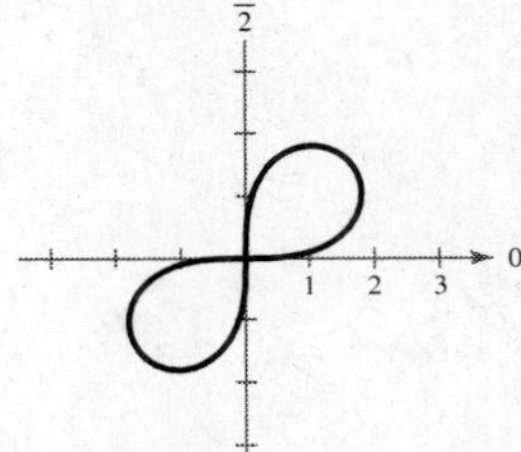

144. $r^2 = \cos 2\theta$

Lemniscate

Symmetry: Pole, polar axis, and line $\theta = \dfrac{\pi}{2}$

Maximum: $|r| = 1$ when $\theta = 0, \pi, 2\pi$

Zeros: $r = 0$ when $\theta = \dfrac{\pi}{4}, \dfrac{3\pi}{4}, \dfrac{5\pi}{4}, \dfrac{7\pi}{4}$

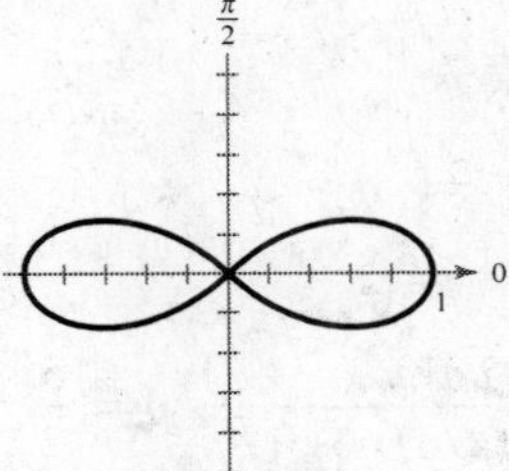

145. $r = \dfrac{2}{1 - \sin\theta}$

$e = 1$

Parabola

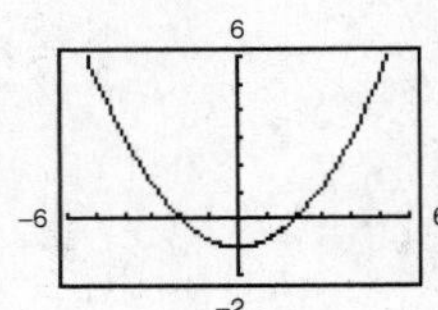

146. $r = \dfrac{1}{1 + 2\sin\theta}, e = 2$

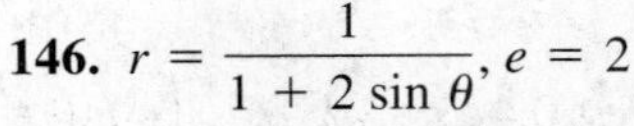

Hyperbola symmetric with $\theta = \pi/2$ and having vertices at $(1/3, \pi/2)$ and $(-1, 3\pi/2)$

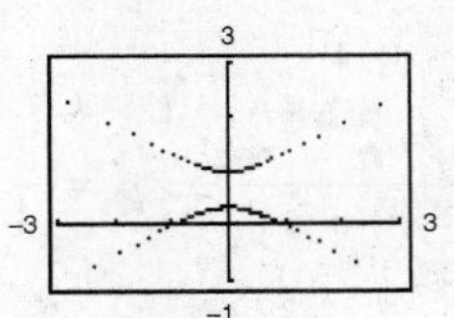

147. $r = \dfrac{4}{5 - 3\cos\theta}$

$= \dfrac{4/5}{1 - (3/5)\cos\theta}$

$e = \dfrac{3}{5}$

Ellipse

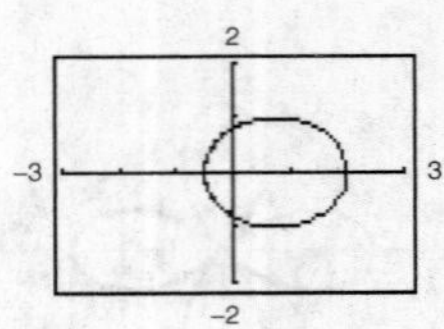

148. $r = \dfrac{6}{-1 + 4\cos\theta} = \dfrac{-6}{1 - 4\cos\theta}$

Hyperbola ($e = 4$)

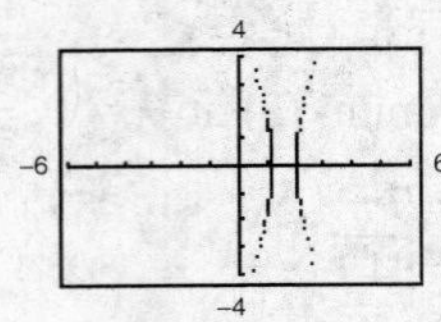

149. $r = \dfrac{5}{6 + 2\sin\theta}$

$= \dfrac{5/6}{1 + (1/3)\sin\theta}$

$e = \dfrac{1}{3}$

Ellipse

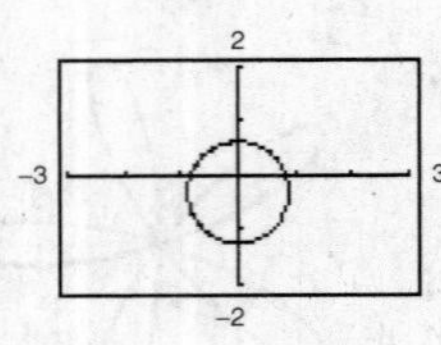

150. $r = \dfrac{3}{4 - 4\cos\theta} = \dfrac{3/4}{1 - \cos\theta}$

Parabola ($e = 1$)

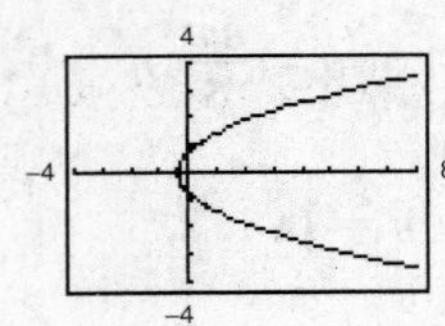

151. $e = 1$

$r = \dfrac{4}{1 - \cos\theta}$

Vertical directrix: $x = -4$

152. Parabola: $r = \dfrac{ep}{1 + e\sin\theta}$, $e = 1$

Vertex: $\left(2, \dfrac{\pi}{2}\right)$

Focus: $(0, 0) \implies p = 4$

$r = \dfrac{4}{1 + \sin\theta}$

153. Ellipse: $r = \dfrac{ep}{1 - e\cos\theta}$

Vertices: $(5, 0), (1, \pi) \implies a = 3$

One focus: $(0, 0) \implies c = 2$

$e = \dfrac{c}{a} = \dfrac{2}{3}, 5 = \dfrac{2/3\,p}{1 - (2/3)\cos 0} \implies p = \dfrac{5}{2}$

$r = \dfrac{(2/3)(5/2)}{1 - (2/3)\cos\theta} = \dfrac{5/3}{1 - (2/3)\cos\theta} = \dfrac{5}{3 - 2\cos\theta}$

154. Hyperbola: $r = \dfrac{ep}{1 + e\cos\theta}$

Vertices: $(1, 0), (7, 0) \implies a = 3$

One focus: $(0, 0) \implies c = 4$

$e = \dfrac{c}{a} = \dfrac{4}{3}, 1 = \dfrac{4/3\,p}{1 + (4/3)\cos 0} \implies p = \dfrac{7}{4}$

$r = \dfrac{(4/3)(7/4)}{1 + (4/3)\cos\theta} = \dfrac{7/3}{1 + (4/3)\cos\theta} = \dfrac{7}{3 + 4\cos\theta}$

155. $e = 0.093$

Use $r = \dfrac{ep}{1 - e\cos\theta}$.

$$2a = \frac{0.093p}{1 - 0.093\cos 0} + \frac{0.093p}{1 - 0.093\cos\pi} = 0.1876p = 3.05 \Rightarrow p \approx 16.258,\ ep \approx 1.512$$

$$r = \frac{1.512}{1 - 0.093\cos\theta}$$

Perihelion: $\dfrac{1.512}{1 + 0.093} \approx 1.383$ astronomical units

Aphelion: $\dfrac{1.512}{1 - 0.093} \approx 1.667$ astronomical units

156. Use $r = \dfrac{ep}{1 - e\sin\theta}$ (horizontal directrix below pole).

$e = 1$ (parabola)

When $\theta = \dfrac{-\pi}{2}$, $r = 6{,}000{,}000$.

$$r = \frac{p}{1 - \sin\left(\frac{-\pi}{2}\right)} = \frac{p}{2} = 6{,}000{,}000 \Rightarrow p = 12{,}000{,}000$$

$$r = \frac{12{,}000{,}000}{1 - \sin\theta}$$

When $\theta = -\dfrac{\pi}{3}$, distance is approximately 6,430,781 miles.

157. False. The y^4-term is not second degree.

158. False. There are many sets possible. For example,

$x = t,\ y = 3 - 2t$

$x = 3t,\ y = 3 - 6t.$

159. (a) Vertical translation

(b) Horizontal translation

(c) Reflection in the y-axis

(d) Parabola opens more slowly.

160. (a) Major axis horizontal

(b) Circle

(c) Ellipse is flatter.

(d) Horizontal translation

161. The number b must be less than 5. The ellipse becomes more circular and approaches a circle of radius 5.

162. The orientation of the graph would be reversed.

163. (a) The speed would double.

(b) The elliptical orbit would be flatter. The length of the major axis is greater.

Chapter 9 Practice Test

1. Find the vertex, focus and directrix of the parabola $x^2 - 6x - 4y + 1 = 0$.

2. Find an equation of the parabola with its vertex at $(2, -5)$ and focus at $(2, -6)$.

3. Find the center, foci, vertices, and eccentricity of the ellipse $x^2 + 4y^2 - 2x + 32y + 61 = 0$.

4. Find an equation of the ellipse with vertices $(0, \pm 6)$ and eccentricity $e = \frac{1}{2}$.

5. Find the center, vertices, foci, and asymptotes of the hyperbola $16y^2 - x^2 - 6x - 128y + 231 = 0$.

6. Find an equation of the hyperbola with vertices at $(\pm 3, 2)$ and foci at $(\pm 5, 2)$.

7. Rotate the axes to eliminate the xy-term. Sketch the graph of the resulting equation, showing both sets of axes.

$5x^2 + 2xy + 5y^2 - 10 = 0$

8. Use the discriminant to determine whether the graph of the equation is a parabola, ellipse, or hyperbola.

(a) $6x^2 - 2xy + y^2 = 0$

(b) $x^2 + 4xy + 4y^2 - x - y + 17 = 0$

For Exercises 9 and 10, eliminate the parameter and write the corresponding rectangular equation.

9. $x = 3 - 2 \sin \theta,\ y = 1 + 5 \cos \theta$

10. $x = e^{2t},\ y = e^{4t}$

11. Convert the polar point $\left(\sqrt{2}, (3\pi)/4\right)$ to rectangular coordinates.

12. Convert the rectangular point $\left(\sqrt{3}, -1\right)$ to polar coordinates.

13. Convert the rectangular equation $4x - 3y = 12$ to polar form.

14. Convert the polar equation $r = 5 \cos \theta$ to rectangular form.

15. Sketch the graph of $r = 1 - \cos \theta$.

16. Sketch the graph of $r = 5 \sin 2\theta$.

17. Sketch the graph of $r = \dfrac{3}{6 - \cos \theta}$.

18. Find a polar equation of the parabola with its vertex at $(6, \pi/2)$ and focus at $(0, 0)$.

CHAPTER 10
Analytic Geometry in Three Dimensions

Section 10.1 The Three-Dimensional Coordinate System **888**

Section 10.2 Vectors in Space **897**

Section 10.3 The Cross Product of Two Vectors **905**

Section 10.4 Lines and Planes in Space **912**

Review Exercises **919**

Practice Test **927**

C H A P T E R 10
Analytic Geometry in Three Dimensions

Section 10.1 The Three-Dimensional Coordinate System

- You should be able to plot points in the three-dimensional coordinate system.
- The distance between the points (x_1, y_1, z_1) and (x_2, y_2, z_2) is
  $d = \sqrt{(x_2 - x_1)^2 + (y_2 - y_1)^2 + (z_2 - z_1)^2}.$
- The midpoint of the line segment joining the points (x_1, y_1, z_1) and (x_2, y_2, z_2) is
  $\left(\frac{x_1 + x_2}{2}, \frac{y_1 + y_2}{2}, \frac{z_1 + z_2}{2}\right).$
- The equation of the sphere with center (h, k, j) and radius r is
  $(x - h)^2 + (y - k)^2 + (z - j)^2 = r^2.$
- You should be able to find the trace of a surface in space.

Vocabulary Check

1. three-dimensional
2. xy-plane, xz-plane, yz-plane
3. octants
4. Distance Formula
5. $\left(\frac{x_1 + x_2}{2}, \frac{y_1 + y_2}{2}, \frac{z_1 + z_2}{2}\right)$
6. sphere
7. surface, space
8. trace

---

1. $A(-1, 4, 3), B(1, 3, -2), C(-3, 0, -2)$
2. $A(6, 2, -3), B(2, -1, 2)\ C(-2, 3, 0)$
3. $A(-2, -1, 4), B(3, -2, 0), C(-2, 2, -3)$
4. $A(0, 5, -3), B(5, -4, -2), C(-4, 1, 5)$

5.

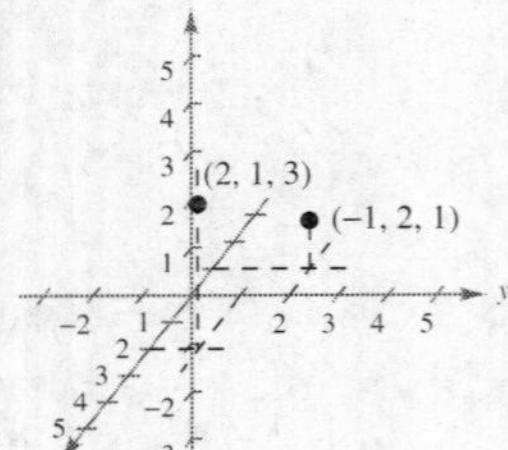

6.

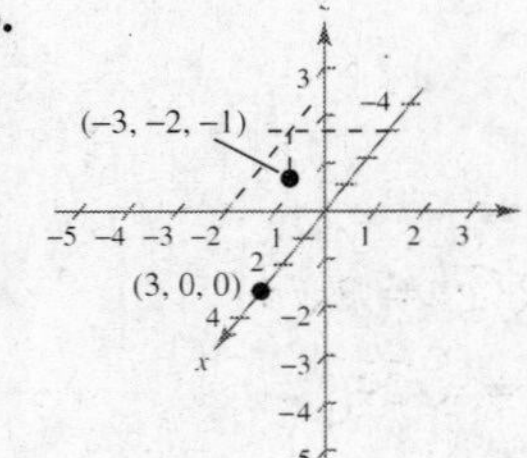

7.

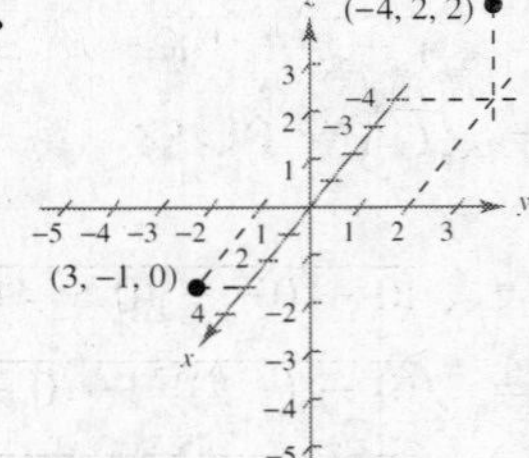

8.

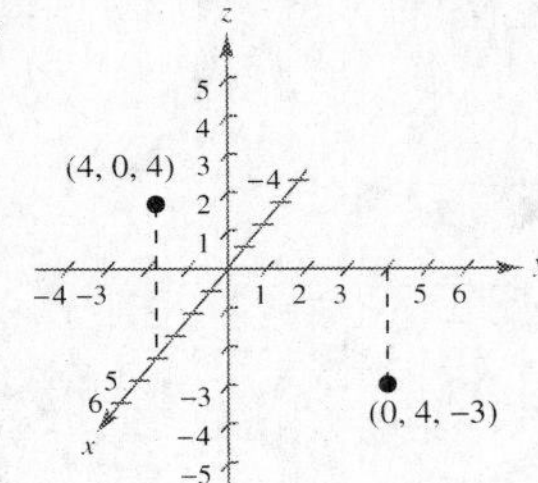

9.

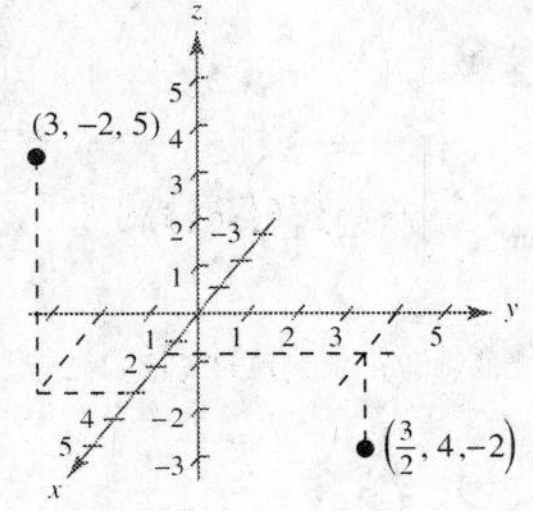

10.

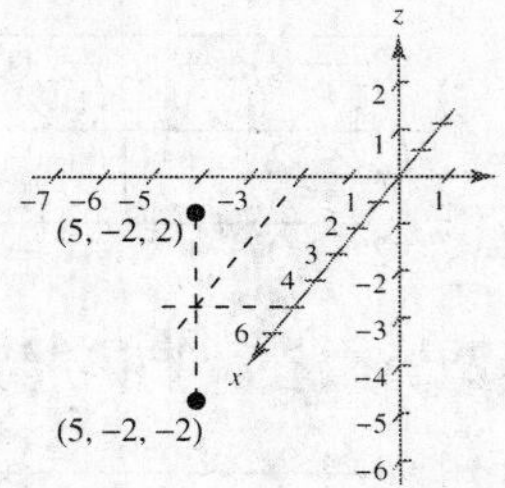

11. $x = -3, y = 3, z = 4$: $(-3, 3, 4)$

12. $x = 6, y = -1, z = -1 \Rightarrow (6, -1, -1)$

13. $y = z = 0, x = 10$: $(10, 0, 0)$

14. $x = 0, y = 2, z = 8 \Rightarrow (0, 2, 8)$

15. Octant IV

16. Octant VI

17. Octants I, II, III, IV (above the *xy*-plane)

18. Octants III, IV, VII, or VIII

19. Octants II, IV, VI, VIII

20. Octants I, II, VII, or VIII

21. $$\begin{aligned} d &= \sqrt{(7-3)^2 + (4-2)^2 + (8-(-5))^2} \\ &= \sqrt{4^2 + 2^2 + 13^2} \\ &= \sqrt{16 + 4 + 169} \\ &= \sqrt{189} \\ &= 3\sqrt{21} \approx 13.748 \end{aligned}$$

22. $$\begin{aligned} d &= \sqrt{(4-2)^2 + (1-1)^2 + (9-6)^2} \\ &= \sqrt{4 + 9} \\ &= \sqrt{13} \end{aligned}$$

23. $$\begin{aligned} d &= \sqrt{[6-(-1)]^2 + [0-4]^2 + [-9-(-2)]^2} \\ &= \sqrt{7^2 + 4^2 + 7^2} \\ &= \sqrt{49 + 16 + 49} \\ &= \sqrt{114} \\ &\approx 10.677 \end{aligned}$$

24. $$\begin{aligned} d &= \sqrt{(1-(-2))^2 + (1-(-3))^2 + (-7-(-7))^2} \\ &= \sqrt{9 + 16} \\ &= \sqrt{25} \\ &= 5 \end{aligned}$$

25. $$\begin{aligned} d &= \sqrt{(1-0)^2 + [0-(-3)]^2 + (-10-0)^2} \\ &= \sqrt{1 + 9 + 100} \\ &= \sqrt{110} \approx 10.488 \end{aligned}$$

26. $$\begin{aligned} d &= \sqrt{(2-0)^2 + (-4-6)^2 + (0-(-3))^2} \\ &= \sqrt{4 + 100 + 9} \\ &= \sqrt{113} \end{aligned}$$

27. $$\begin{aligned} d_1 &= \sqrt{(0-0)^2 + (0-4)^2 + (2-0)^2} = \sqrt{20} = 2\sqrt{5} \\ d_2 &= \sqrt{(0-(-2))^2 + (0-5)^2 + (2-2)^2} = \sqrt{29} \\ d_3 &= \sqrt{(-2-0)^2 + (5-4)^2 + (2-0)^2} = 3 \\ d_1^2 + d_3^2 &= 20 + 9 = 29 = d_2^2 \end{aligned}$$

28. $$\begin{aligned} d_1 &= \sqrt{(2-(-2))^2 + (-1-5)^2 + (2-0)^2} = \sqrt{56} = 2\sqrt{14} \\ d_2 &= (2-(-4))^2 + (-1-4)^2 + (2-1)^2 = \sqrt{62} \\ d_3 &= \sqrt{(-4-(-2))^2 + (4-5)^2 + (1-0)^2} = \sqrt{6} \\ d_1^2 + d_3^2 &= 56 + 6 = 62 = d_2^2 \end{aligned}$$

29. $d_1 = \sqrt{(2-0)^2 + (2-0)^2 + (1-0)^2} = \sqrt{9} = 3$

$d_2 = \sqrt{(2-2)^2 + (-4-2)^2 + (4-1)^2} = \sqrt{45} = 3\sqrt{5}$

$d_3 = \sqrt{(2-0)^2 + (-4-0)^2 + (4-0)^2} = \sqrt{36} = 6$

$d_1^2 + d_3^2 = 9 + 36 = 45 = d_2^2$

30. $d_1 = \sqrt{(1-1)^2 + (3-0)^2 + (1-1)^2} = \sqrt{9} = 3$

$d_2 = \sqrt{(1-1)^2 + (3-0)^2 + (1-3)^2} = \sqrt{13}$

$d_3 = \sqrt{(1-1)^2 + (0-0)^2 + (3-1)^2} = 2$

$d_1^2 + d_3^2 = 9 + 4 = 13 = d_2^2$

31. $d_1 = \sqrt{(5-1)^2 + (-1+3)^2 + (2+2)^2} = \sqrt{16+4+16} = \sqrt{36} = 6$

$d_2 = \sqrt{(5+1)^2 + (-1-1)^2 + (2-2)^2} = \sqrt{36+4} = \sqrt{40} = 2\sqrt{10}$

$d_3 = \sqrt{(-1-1)^2 + (1+3)^2 + (2+2)^2} = \sqrt{4+16+16} = \sqrt{36} = 6$

$d_1 = d_3$, Isosceles triangle

32. $d_1 = \sqrt{(7-5)^2 + (1-3)^2 + (3-4)^2} = \sqrt{4+4+1} = \sqrt{9} = 3$

$d_2 = \sqrt{(3-7)^2 + (5-1)^2 + (3-3)^2} = \sqrt{16+16} = \sqrt{32} = 4\sqrt{2}$

$d_3 = \sqrt{(3-5)^2 + (5-3)^2 + (3-4)^2} = \sqrt{4+4+1} = \sqrt{9} = 3$

$d_1 = d_3 = 3$, Isosceles triangle

33. $d_1 = \sqrt{(8-4)^2 + (1+1)^2 + (2+2)^2} = \sqrt{36} = 6$

$d_2 = \sqrt{(8-2)^2 + (1-3)^2 + (2-2)^2} = \sqrt{40} = 2\sqrt{10}$

$d_3 = \sqrt{(4-2)^2 + (-1-3)^2 + (-2-2)^2} = \sqrt{36} = 6$

Since $d_1 = d_3$, the triangle is isosceles.

34. $d_1 = \sqrt{(3-1)^2 + (0+2)^2 + (0+1)^2} = \sqrt{9} = 3$

$d_2 = \sqrt{(3-3)^2 + (0+6)^2 + (0-3)^2} = \sqrt{45} = 3\sqrt{5}$

$d_3 = \sqrt{(3-1)^2 + (-6+2)^2 + (3+1)^2} = \sqrt{36} = 6$

$d_1^2 + d_3^2 = 9 + 36 = 45 = d_2^2$

Right triangle

35. Midpoint: $\left(\frac{3-3}{2}, \frac{-6+4}{2}, \frac{10+4}{2}\right) = (0, -1, 7)$

36. Midpoint: $\left(\frac{-1+3}{2}, \frac{5+7}{2}, \frac{-3-1}{2}\right) = (1, 6, -2)$

37. Midpoint: $\left(\frac{6-4}{2}, \frac{-2+2}{2}, \frac{5+6}{2}\right) = \left(1, 0, \frac{11}{2}\right)$

38. Midpoint: $\left(\frac{-3-6}{2}, \frac{5+4}{2}, \frac{5+8}{2}\right) = \left(-\frac{9}{2}, \frac{9}{2}, \frac{13}{2}\right)$

39. Midpoint: $\left(\frac{-2+7}{2}, \frac{8-4}{2}, \frac{10+2}{2}\right) = \left(\frac{5}{2}, 2, 6\right)$

40. Midpoint: $\left(\frac{9+9}{2}, \frac{-5-2}{2}, \frac{1-4}{2}\right) = \left(9, -\frac{7}{2}, -\frac{3}{2}\right)$

41. $(x-3)^2 + (y-2)^2 + (z-4)^2 = 16$

42. $(x+3)^2 + (y-4)^2 + (z-3)^2 = 4$

43. $(x + 1)^2 + (y - 2)^2 + z^2 = 3$

44. $x^2 + (y + 1)^2 + (z - 3)^2 = 5$

45. $(x - 0)^2 + (y - 4)^2 + (z - 3)^2 = 3^2$

$x^2 + (y - 4)^2 + (z - 3)^2 = 9$

46. $(x - 2)^2 + (y + 1)^2 + (z - 8)^2 = 36$

47. Radius $= \dfrac{\text{Diameter}}{2} = 5$

$(x + 3)^2 + (y - 7)^2 + (z - 5)^2 = 5^2 = 25$

48. Radius $= \dfrac{\text{Diameter}}{2} = 4$

$(x - 0)^2 + (y - 5)^2 + (z + 9)^2 = 4^2 = 16$

49. Center: $\left(\dfrac{3+0}{2}, \dfrac{0+0}{2}, \dfrac{0+6}{2}\right) = \left(\dfrac{3}{2}, 0, 3\right)$

Radius: $\sqrt{\left(3 - \dfrac{3}{2}\right)^2 + (0 - 0)^2 + (0 - 3)^2} = \sqrt{\dfrac{9}{4} + 9} = \sqrt{\dfrac{45}{4}}$

Sphere: $\left(x - \dfrac{3}{2}\right)^2 + (y - 0)^2 + (z - 3)^2 = \dfrac{45}{4}$

50. Center: $\left(\dfrac{2-1}{2}, \dfrac{-2+4}{2}, \dfrac{2+6}{2}\right) = \left(\dfrac{1}{2}, 1, 4\right)$

Radius: $\sqrt{\left(2 - \dfrac{1}{2}\right)^2 + (-2 - 1)^2 + (2 - 4)^2} = \sqrt{\dfrac{9}{4} + 9 + 4} = \sqrt{\dfrac{61}{4}}$

Sphere: $\left(x - \dfrac{1}{2}\right)^2 + (y - 1)^2 + (z - 4)^2 = \dfrac{61}{4}$

51. $\left(x^2 - 5x + \frac{25}{4}\right) + y^2 + z^2 = \frac{25}{4}$

$\left(x - \frac{5}{2}\right)^2 + y^2 + z^2 = \frac{25}{4}$

Center: $\left(\frac{5}{2}, 0, 0\right)$

Radius: $\frac{5}{2}$

52. $x^2 + y^2 - 8y + 16 + z^2 = 16$

$x^2 + (y - 4)^2 + z^2 = 16$

Center: $(0, 4, 0)$

Radius: 4

53. $(x^2 - 4x + 4) + (y^2 + 2y + 1) + z^2 = 4 + 1$

$(x - 2)^2 + (y + 1)^2 + z^2 = 5$

Center: $(2, -1, 0)$

Radius: $\sqrt{5}$

54. $\left(x^2 - x + \dfrac{1}{4}\right) + \left(y^2 - y + \dfrac{1}{4}\right) + \left(z^2 - z + \dfrac{1}{4}\right) = \dfrac{1}{4} + \dfrac{1}{4} + \dfrac{1}{4}$

$\left(x - \dfrac{1}{2}\right)^2 + \left(y - \dfrac{1}{2}\right)^2 + \left(z - \dfrac{1}{2}\right)^2 = \dfrac{3}{4}$

Center: $\left(\dfrac{1}{2}, \dfrac{1}{2}, \dfrac{1}{2}\right)$

Radius: $\dfrac{\sqrt{3}}{2}$

55. $(x^2 - 4x + 4) + (y^2 + 2y + 1) + (z^2 - 6z + 9) = -10 + 4 + 1 + 9$

$$(x - 2)^2 + (y + 1)^2 + (z - 3)^2 = 4$$

Center: $(2, -1, 3)$

Radius: 2

56. $(x^2 - 6x + 9) + (y^2 + 4y + 4) + z^2 = -9 + 9 + 4$

$$(x - 3)^2 + (y + 2)^2 + z^2 = 4$$

Center: $(3, -2, 0)$

Radius: 2

57. $(x^2 + 4x + 4) + y^2 + (z^2 - 8z + 16) = -19 + 4 + 16$

$$(x + 2)^2 + y^2 + (z - 4)^2 = 1$$

Center: $(-2, 0, 4)$

Radius: 1

58. $x^2 + (y^2 - 8y + 16) + (z^2 - 6z + 9) = -13 + 16 + 9$

$$x^2 + (y - 4)^2 + (z - 3)^2 = 12$$

Center: $(0, 4, 3)$

Radius: $\sqrt{12} = 2\sqrt{3}$

59.
$$x^2 + y^2 + z^2 - 2x - \tfrac{2}{3}y - 8z = -\tfrac{73}{9}$$
$$(x^2 - 2x + 1) + \left(y^2 - \tfrac{2}{3}y + \tfrac{1}{9}\right) + (z^2 - 8z + 16) = -\tfrac{73}{9} + 1 + \tfrac{1}{9} + 16$$
$$(x - 1)^2 + \left(y - \tfrac{1}{3}\right)^2 + (z - 4)^2 = 9$$

Center: $\left(1, \tfrac{1}{3}, 4\right)$

Radius: 3

60.
$$x^2 + y^2 + z^2 - x - 3y - 2z = -\tfrac{5}{2}$$
$$\left(x^2 - x + \tfrac{1}{4}\right) + \left(y^2 - 3y + \tfrac{9}{4}\right) + (z^2 - 2z + 1) = -\tfrac{5}{2} + \tfrac{1}{4} + \tfrac{9}{4} + 1$$
$$\left(x - \tfrac{1}{2}\right)^2 + \left(y - \tfrac{3}{2}\right)^2 + (z - 1)^2 = 1$$

Center: $\left(\tfrac{1}{2}, \tfrac{3}{2}, 1\right)$

Radius: 1

61. $4(x^2 - 2x + 1) + 4(y^2 + 4y + 4) + 4z^2 = 4 + 16 + 1$

$$(x - 1)^2 + (y + 2)^2 + z^2 = \frac{21}{4}$$

Center: $(1, -2, 0)$

Radius: $\dfrac{\sqrt{21}}{2}$

62. $9(x^2 - 2x + 1) + 9(y^2 + 4y + 4) + 9(z^2 + 6z + 9) = 9 + 36 + 81 + 126$

$$9(x-1)^2 + 9(y+2)^2 + 9(z+3)^2 = 252$$

$$(x-1)^2 + (y+2)^2 + (z+3)^2 = 28 = \left(2\sqrt{7}\right)^2$$

Center: $(1, -2, -3)$

Radius: $2\sqrt{7}$

63. $9x^2 - 6x + 9y^2 + 18y + 9z^2 = -1$

$$x^2 - \tfrac{2}{3}x + \tfrac{1}{9} + y^2 + 2y + 1 + z^2 = -\tfrac{1}{9} + \tfrac{1}{9} + 1$$

$$\left(x - \tfrac{1}{3}\right)^2 + (y+1)^2 + z^2 = 1$$

Center: $\left(\tfrac{1}{3}, -1, 0\right)$

Radius: 1

64. $x^2 - x + \dfrac{1}{4} + y^2 - 8y + 16 + z^2 + 2z + 1 = \dfrac{-33}{4} + \dfrac{1}{4} + 16 + 1$

$$\left(x - \frac{1}{2}\right)^2 + (y-4)^2 + (z+1)^2 = 9$$

Center: $\left(\dfrac{1}{2}, 4, -1\right)$

Radius: 3

65. xz-trace $(y = 0)$: $(x-1)^2 + z^2 = 36$, Circle

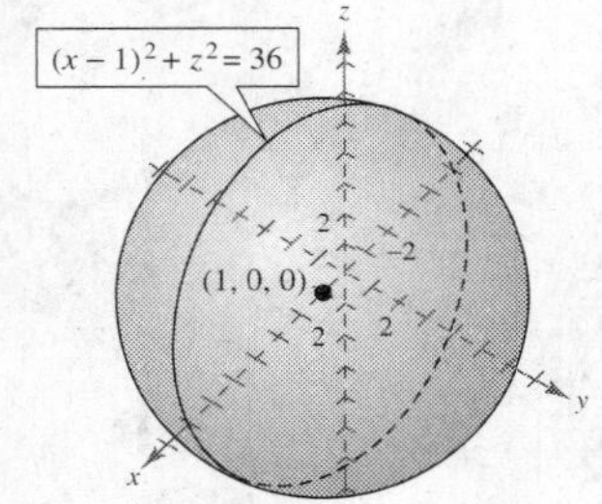

66. yz-trace $(x = 0)$: $(y+3)^2 + z^2 = 25$, Circle

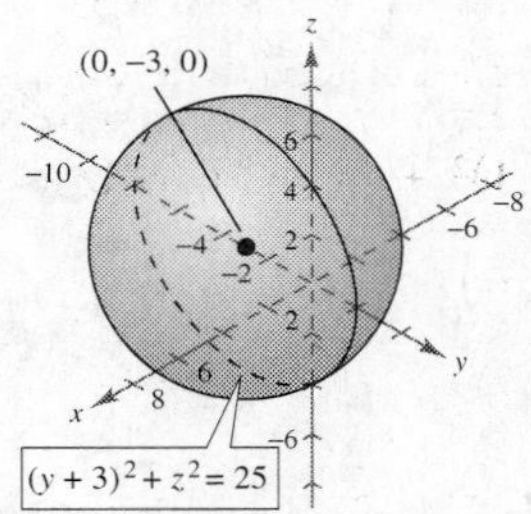

67. yz-trace $(x = 0)$: $(y-3)^2 + z^2 = 9 - 4 = 5$, Circle

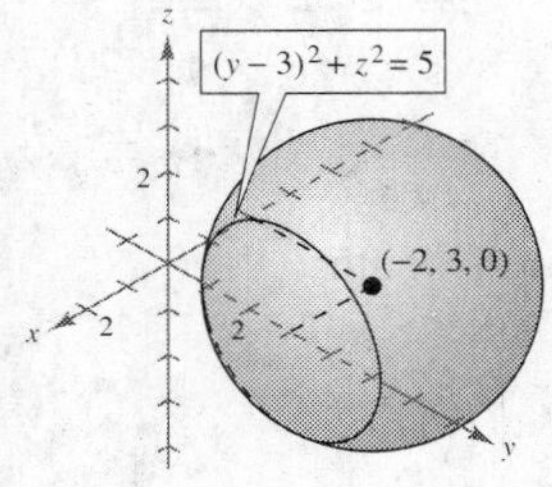

68. xy-trace $(z = 0)$: $x^2 + (y-1)^2 = 3$, Circle

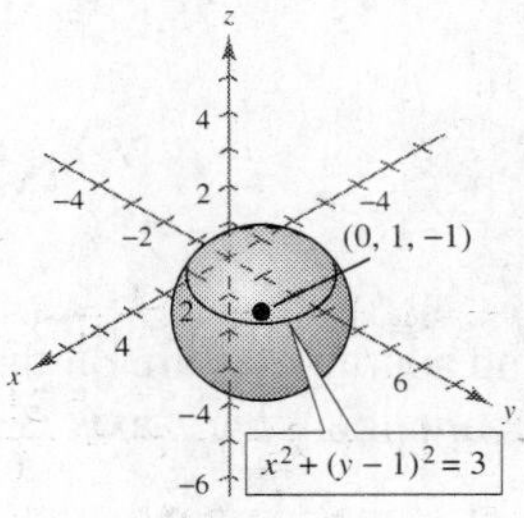

69. $(x^2 - 2x + 1) + y^2 + (z^2 - 4z + 4) = -1 + 1 + 4$

$$(x - 1)^2 + y^2 + (z - 2)^2 = 4$$

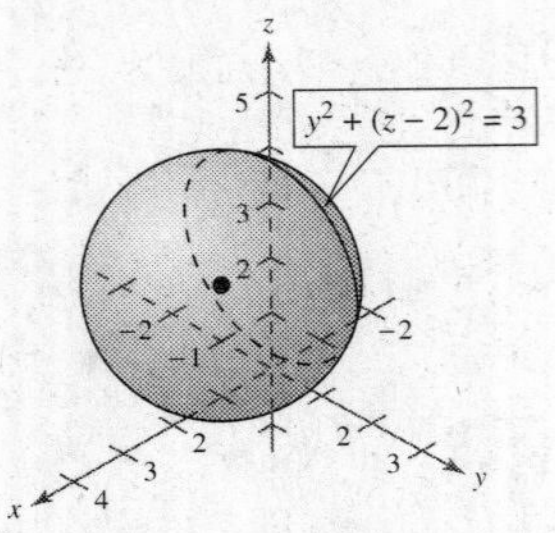

yz − trace: $x = 0$: $y^2 + (z - 2)^2 = 3$

70.

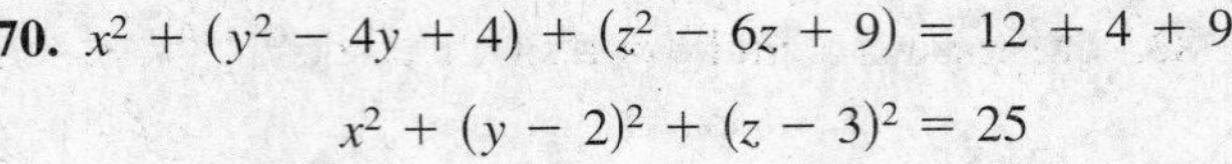

$x^2 + (y^2 - 4y + 4) + (z^2 - 6z + 9) = 12 + 4 + 9$

$$x^2 + (y - 2)^2 + (z - 3)^2 = 25$$

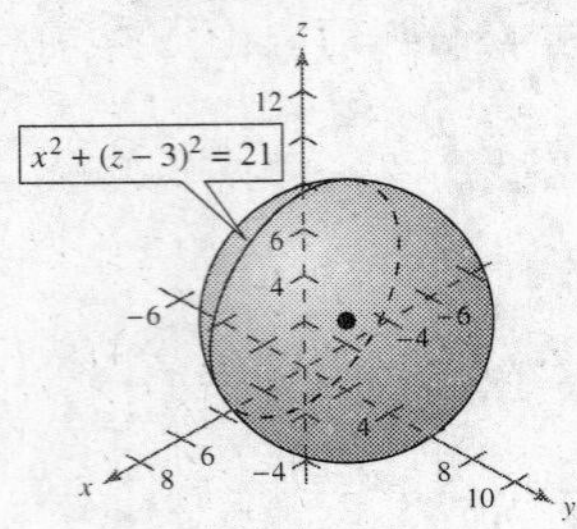

xz − trace: $y = 0$: $x^2 + (z - 3)^2 = 21$

71.

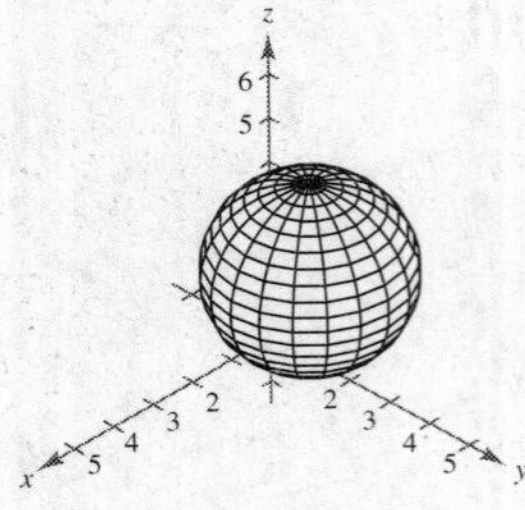

72. $x^2 + y^2 + 6y + (z^2 - 8z + 16) = -21 + 16$

$$x^2 + y^2 + 6y + (z - 4)^2 = -5$$

$$z_1 = 4 + \sqrt{-5 - x^2 - y^2 - 6y}$$

$$z_2 = 4 - \sqrt{-5 - x^2 - y^2 - 6y}$$

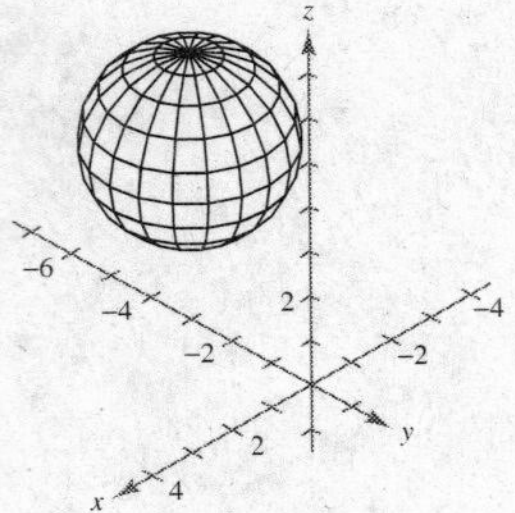

73.

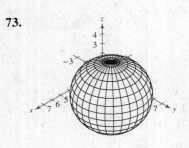

74.

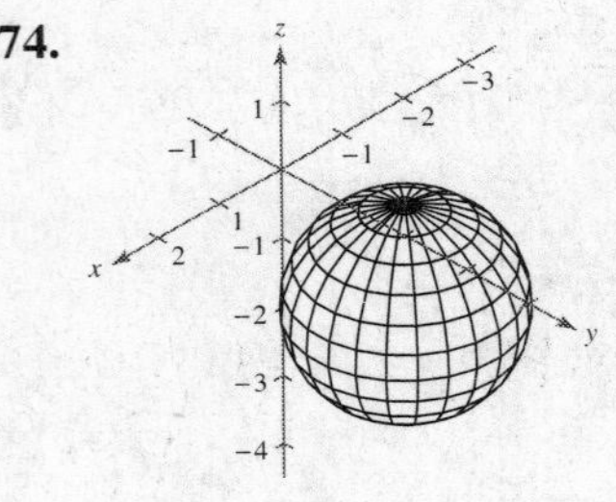

75. The length of each side is 3.
Thus, $(x, y, z) = (3, 3, 3)$.

76. $x = 4, y = 4, z = 8, \quad (4, 4, 8)$

77. $d = 165 \Rightarrow r = \frac{165}{2} = 82.5$

$$x^2 + y^2 + z^2 = \left(\tfrac{165}{2}\right)^2$$

78.

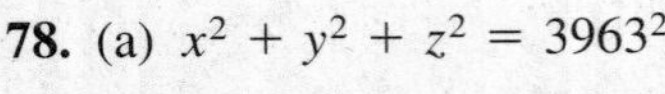

(a) $x^2 + y^2 + z^2 = 3963^2$

(b) Assume the north and south poles are on the z-axis. Lines of longitude that run north–south are traces of planes containing the z-axis. These shapes are circles of radius 3963 miles.

(c) Latitudes are traces of planes perpendicular to the z-axis. These shapes are circles.

79. False. x is the directed distance from the yz-plane to P.

80. False. The trace could be a single point, or empty.

81. In the xy-plane, the z-coordinate is 0.
In the xz-plane, the y-coordinate is 0.
In the yz-plane, the x-coordinate is 0.

82. It is a plane.

83. The trace is a circle, or a single point.

84. The trace will be a line in the xy-plane (unless the plane is the xy-plane).

85. $x_m = \dfrac{x_2 + x_1}{2} \Rightarrow x_2 = 2x_m - x_1$

Similarly for y_2 and z_2,

$(x_2, y_2, z_2) = (2x_m - x_1, 2y_m - y_1, 2z_m - z_1)$.

86. $x_2 = 2x_m - x_1 = 2(5) - 3 = 7$

$y_2 = 2y_m - y_1 = 2(8) - 0 = 16$

$z_2 = 2z_m - z_1 = 2(7) - 2 = 12$

$(7, 16, 12)$

87. $v^2 + 3v + \dfrac{9}{4} = 2 + \dfrac{9}{4}$

$$\left(v + \frac{3}{2}\right)^2 = \frac{17}{4}$$

$$v + \frac{3}{2} = \pm\frac{\sqrt{17}}{2}$$

$$v = -\frac{3}{2} \pm \frac{\sqrt{17}}{2}$$

88. $z^2 - 7z + \dfrac{49}{4} = 19 + \dfrac{49}{4}$

$$\left(z - \frac{7}{2}\right)^2 = \frac{125}{4}$$

$$z - \frac{7}{2} = \pm\frac{5\sqrt{5}}{2}$$

$$z = \frac{7}{2} \pm \frac{5}{2}\sqrt{5}$$

89. $x^2 - 5x + \dfrac{25}{4} = -5 + \dfrac{25}{4}$

$$\left(x - \frac{5}{2}\right)^2 = \frac{5}{4}$$

$$x - \frac{5}{2} = \pm\frac{\sqrt{5}}{2}$$

$$x = \frac{5}{2} \pm \frac{\sqrt{5}}{2}$$

90. $x^2 + 3x + \dfrac{9}{4} = 1 + \dfrac{9}{4}$

$$\left(x + \frac{3}{2}\right)^2 = \frac{13}{4}$$

$$x + \frac{3}{2} = \pm\frac{\sqrt{13}}{2}$$

$$x = \frac{-3}{2} \pm \frac{\sqrt{13}}{2}$$

91. $4y^2 + 4y = 9$

$$y^2 + y + \frac{1}{4} = \frac{9}{4} + \frac{1}{4}$$

$$\left(y + \frac{1}{2}\right)^2 = \frac{10}{4}$$

$$y + \frac{1}{2} = \pm\frac{\sqrt{10}}{2}$$

$$y = -\frac{1}{2} \pm \frac{\sqrt{10}}{2}$$

92. $x^2 + \dfrac{5}{2}x + \dfrac{25}{16} = 4 + \dfrac{25}{16}$

$$\left(x + \frac{5}{4}\right)^2 = \frac{89}{16}$$

$$x + \frac{5}{4} = \pm\frac{\sqrt{89}}{4}$$

$$x = \frac{-5}{4} \pm \frac{\sqrt{89}}{4}$$

93. $\mathbf{v} = 3\mathbf{i} - 3\mathbf{j}$, Quadrant IV

$$\|\mathbf{v}\| = \sqrt{3^2 + (-3)^2} = \sqrt{18} = 3\sqrt{2}$$

$$\tan\theta = -\frac{3}{3} = -1 \Rightarrow$$

$$\theta = -45° \text{ or } 315°$$

94. $\mathbf{v} = \langle -1, 2\rangle$, Quadrant II

$$\|\mathbf{v}\| = \sqrt{1^2 + 2^2} = \sqrt{5}$$

$$\tan\theta = \frac{2}{-1} \Rightarrow \theta \approx 116.6°$$

95. $\mathbf{v} = 4\mathbf{i} + 5\mathbf{j}$, Quadrant I

$$\|\mathbf{v}\| = \sqrt{16 + 25} = \sqrt{41}$$

$$\tan\theta = \frac{5}{4} \Rightarrow \theta \approx 51.34°$$

96. $\mathbf{v} = \langle 10, -7\rangle$, Quadrant IV

$$\|\mathbf{v}\| = \sqrt{100 + 49} = \sqrt{149}$$

$$\tan\theta = \frac{-7}{10} \Rightarrow \theta \approx 325.0°$$

97. $\mathbf{u} \cdot \mathbf{v} = \langle -4, 1\rangle \cdot \langle 3, 5\rangle$

$$= -4(3) + 1(5) = -7$$

98. $\mathbf{u} \cdot \mathbf{v} = \langle -1, 0\rangle \cdot \langle -2, -6\rangle$

$$= 2 + 0 = 2$$

99. $a_0 = 1, a_n = a_{n-1} + n^2$

$a_1 = 1 + 1^2 = 2$

$a_2 = 2 + 2^2 = 6$

$a_3 = 6 + 3^2 = 15$

$a_4 = 15 + 4^2 = 31$

	1		2		6		15		31
First differences:		1		4		9		16	
Second differences:			3		5		7		

Neither model

100. $a_0 = 0, a_n = a_{n-1} - 1$

$a_1 = 0 - 1 = -1$

$a_2 = -1 - 1 = -2$

$a_3 = -3$

$a_4 = -4$

	0		−1		−2		−3		−4
First differences:		−1		−1		−1		−1	
Second differences:			0		0		0		

Linear model

101. $a_1 = -1, a_n = a_{n-1} + 3$

$a_2 = -1 + 3 = 2$

$a_3 = 2 + 3 = 5$

$a_4 = 5 + 3 = 8$

$a_5 = 8 + 3 = 11$

	−1		2		5		8		11
First differences:		3		3		3		3	
Second differences:			0		0		0		

Linear model

102. $a_1 = 4, a_n = a_{n-1} - 2n$

$a_2 = 4 - 2(2) = 0$

$a_3 = 0 - 2(3) = -6$

$a_4 = -6 - 2(4) = -14$

$a_5 = -14 - 2(5) = -24$

	4		0		−6		−14		−24
First differences:		−4		−6		−8		−10	
Second differences:			−2		−2		−2		

Quadratic model

103. $(x + 5)^2 + (y - 1)^2 = 49$

104. $(x - 3)^2 + (y + 6)^2 = 81$

105. $(y - 1)^2 = 4p(x - 4),\ p = -3$

$(y - 1)^2 = 4(-3)(x - 4)$

$(y - 1)^2 = -12(x - 4)$

106. $(x - h)^2 = 4p(y - k),\ p = -5,\ (h, k) = (-2, 5)$

$(x + 2)^2 = 4(-5)(y - 5)$

$(x + 2)^2 = -20(y - 5)$

107. $a = 3, b = 2$, center: $(3, 3)$, horizontal major axis

$$\frac{(x - 3)^2}{9} + \frac{(y - 3)^2}{4} = 1$$

108. Center: $(0, 3)$

Vertical major axis length 9 $\implies a = \frac{9}{2}$

$c = 3 \implies b^2 = a^2 - c^2 = \frac{81}{4} - 9 = \frac{45}{4}$

$$\frac{(x - 0)^2}{(45/4)} + \frac{(y - 3)^2}{(81/4)} = 1$$

109. Center: $(6, 0)$, horizontal transverse axis

$a = 2, c = 6, b^2 = c^2 - a^2 = 36 - 4 = 32$

$$\frac{(x - 6)^2}{4} - \frac{y^2}{32} = 1$$

110. Center: $(3, 5)$, vertical transverse axis

$a = 4, c = 5, b^2 = c^2 - a^2 = 25 - 16 = 9$

$$\frac{(y - 5)^2}{16} - \frac{(x - 3)^2}{9} = 1$$

Section 10.2 Vectors in Space

- Vectors in space $\mathbf{v} = \langle v_1, v_2, v_3 \rangle$ have many of the same properties as vectors in the plane.
- The dot product of two vectors $\mathbf{u} = \langle u_1, u_2, u_3 \rangle$ and $\mathbf{v} = \langle v_1, v_2, v_3 \rangle$ in space is $\mathbf{u} \cdot \mathbf{v} = u_1v_1 + u_2v_2 + u_3v_3$.
- Two nonzero vectors $\mathbf{u}$ and $\mathbf{v}$ are said to be parallel if there is some scalar c such that $\mathbf{u} = c\mathbf{v}$.
- You should be able to use vectors to solve real life problems.

Vocabulary Check

1. zero

2. $\mathbf{v} = v_1\mathbf{i} + v_2\mathbf{j} + v_3\mathbf{k}$

3. component form

4. orthogonal

5. parallel

1. $\mathbf{v} = \langle 0 - 2, 3 - 0, 2 - 1 \rangle = \langle -2, 3, 1 \rangle$

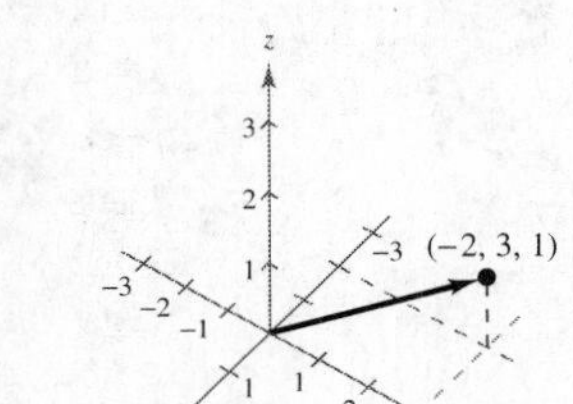

2. (a) $\mathbf{v} = \langle 0 - 1, 4 - (-2), -4 - 4 \rangle$

$= \langle -1, 6, -8 \rangle$

(b)

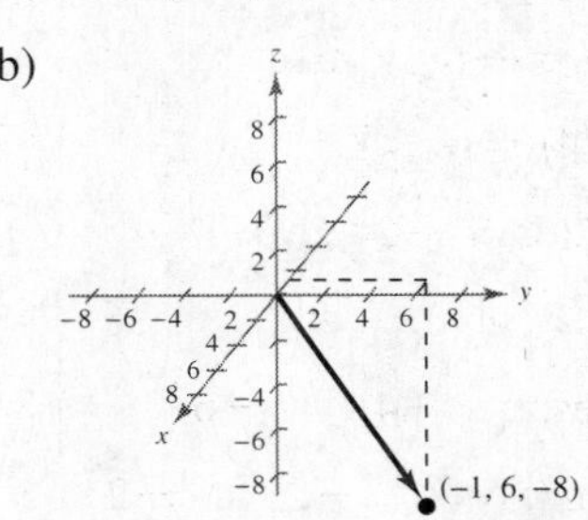

3. (a) $\mathbf{v} = \langle 1 - 1, 4 - 4, 0 - 4 \rangle = \langle 0, 0, -4 \rangle$

(b)

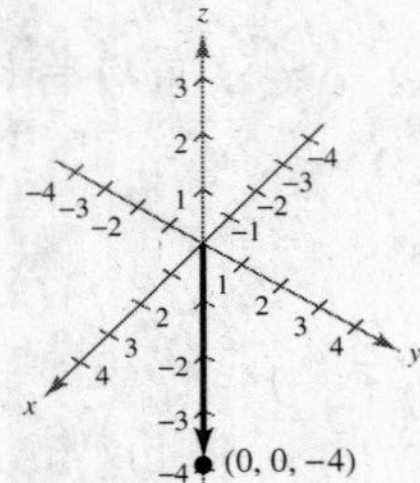

4. (a) $\mathbf{v} = \langle 0 - 4, -2 - (-2), 1 - 1 \rangle = \langle -4, 0, 0 \rangle$

(b)

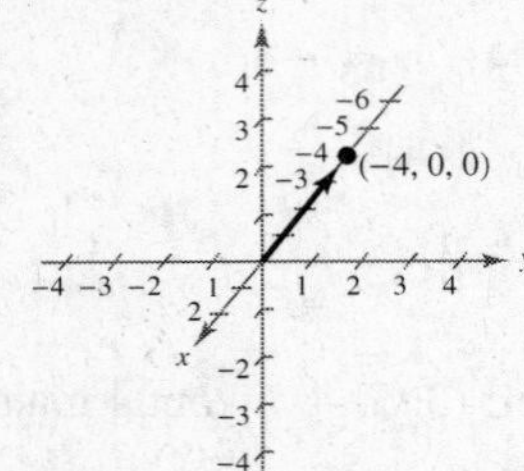

5. (a) $\mathbf{v} = \langle 1 - (-6), -1 - 4, 3 - (-2) \rangle$

$= \langle 7, -5, 5 \rangle$

(b) $\|\mathbf{v}\| = \sqrt{7^2 + (-5)^2 + 5^2}$

$= \sqrt{49 + 25 + 25}$

$= \sqrt{99}$

$= 3\sqrt{11}$

(c) $\dfrac{\mathbf{v}}{\|\mathbf{v}\|} = \dfrac{1}{3\sqrt{11}}\langle 7, -5, 5 \rangle = \dfrac{\sqrt{11}}{33}\langle 7, -5, 5 \rangle$

6. (a) $\mathbf{v} = \langle 0 + 7, 0 - 3, 2 - 5 \rangle = \langle 7, -3, -3 \rangle$

(b) $\|\mathbf{v}\| = \sqrt{49 + 9 + 9} = \sqrt{67}$

(c) Unit vector:

$\dfrac{1}{\sqrt{67}}\langle 7, -3, -3 \rangle = \dfrac{\sqrt{67}}{67}\langle 7, -3, -3 \rangle$

7. (a) $\mathbf{v} = \langle 1 - (-1), 4 - 2, -4 - (-4) \rangle = \langle 2, 2, 0 \rangle$

(b) $\|\mathbf{v}\| = \sqrt{2^2 + 2^2 + 0^2} = \sqrt{8} = 2\sqrt{2}$

(c) Unit vector: $\dfrac{1}{2\sqrt{2}}\langle 2, 2, 0 \rangle = \left\langle \dfrac{\sqrt{2}}{2}, \dfrac{\sqrt{2}}{2}, 0 \right\rangle$

8. (a) $\mathbf{v} = \langle 0 - 0, 2 - (-1), 1 - 1 \rangle = \langle 0, 3, 0 \rangle$

(b) $\|\mathbf{v}\| = \sqrt{0^2 + 3^2 + 0^2} = \sqrt{9} = 3$

(c) Unit vector: $\dfrac{1}{3}\langle 0, 3, 0 \rangle = \langle 0, 1, 0 \rangle$

9. (a)

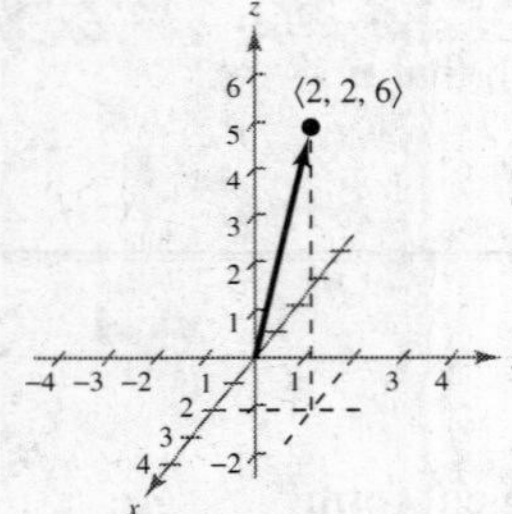

(b)

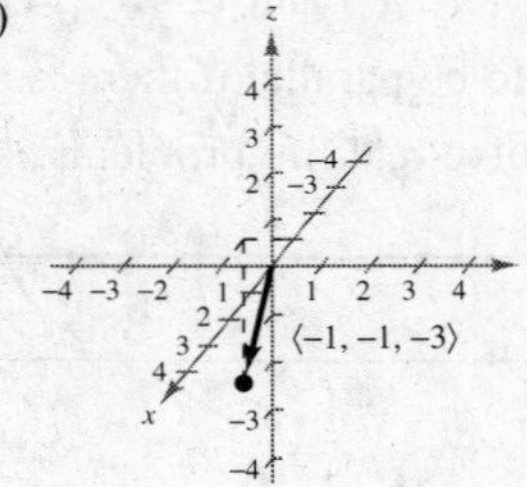

(c)

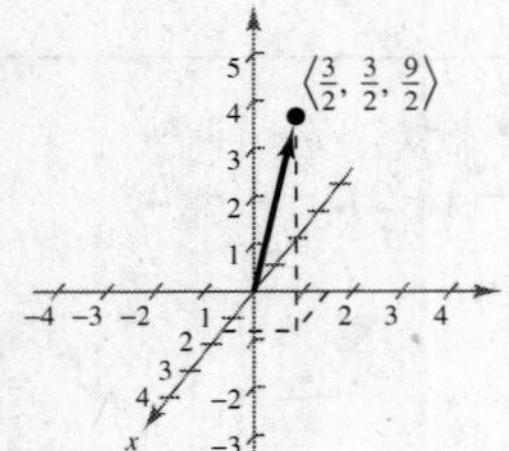

(d)

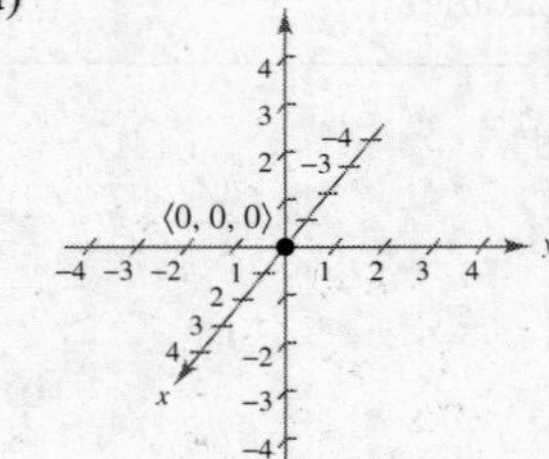

10. $\mathbf{v} = \langle -1, 2, 2\rangle$

(a) $-\mathbf{v} = \langle 1, -2, -2\rangle$

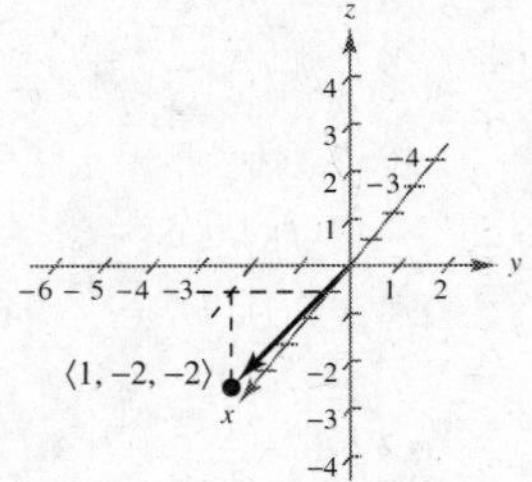

(b) $2\mathbf{v} = \langle -2, 4, 4\rangle$

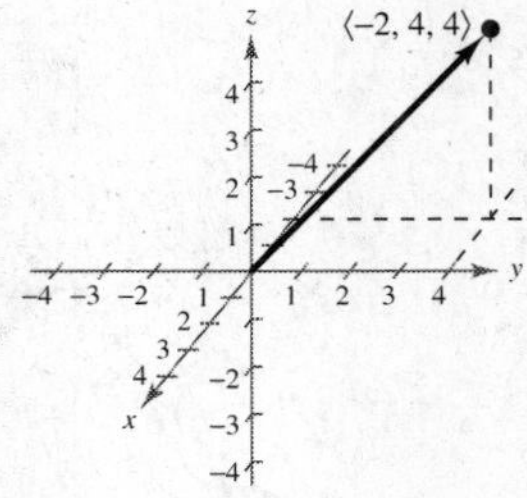

(c) $\dfrac{1}{2}\mathbf{v} = \left\langle -\dfrac{1}{2}, 1, 1\right\rangle$

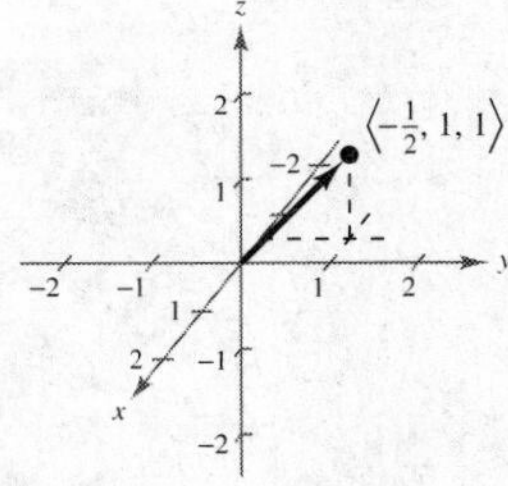

(d) $\dfrac{5}{2}\mathbf{v} = \left\langle \dfrac{-5}{2}, 5, 5\right\rangle$

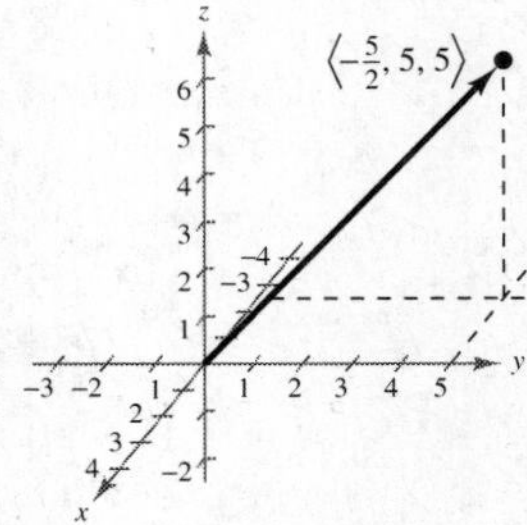

11. $\mathbf{v} = 2\mathbf{i} + 2\mathbf{j} - \mathbf{k}$

(a) $2\mathbf{v} = 4\mathbf{i} + 4\mathbf{j} - 2\mathbf{k}$

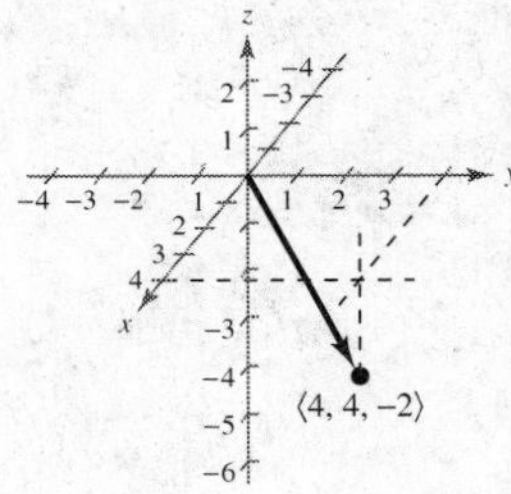

(b) $-\mathbf{v} = -2\mathbf{i} - 2\mathbf{j} + \mathbf{k}$

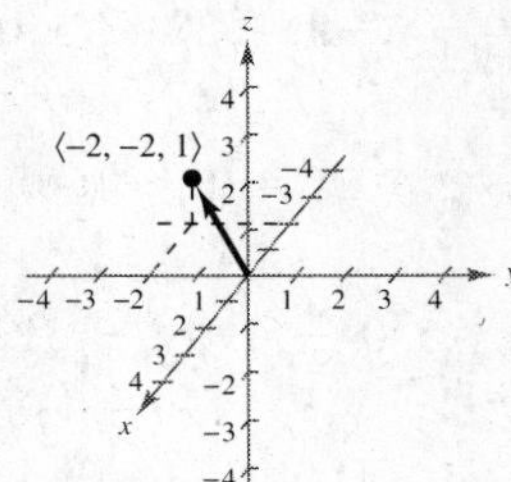

(c) $\dfrac{5}{2}\mathbf{v} = 5\mathbf{i} + 5\mathbf{j} - \dfrac{5}{2}\mathbf{k}$

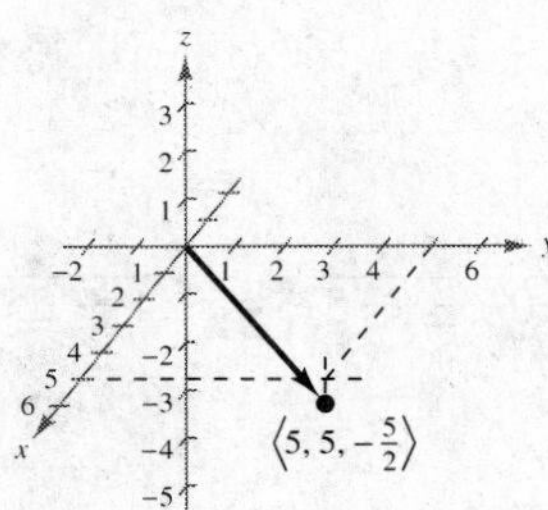

(d) $0\mathbf{v} = \mathbf{0}$

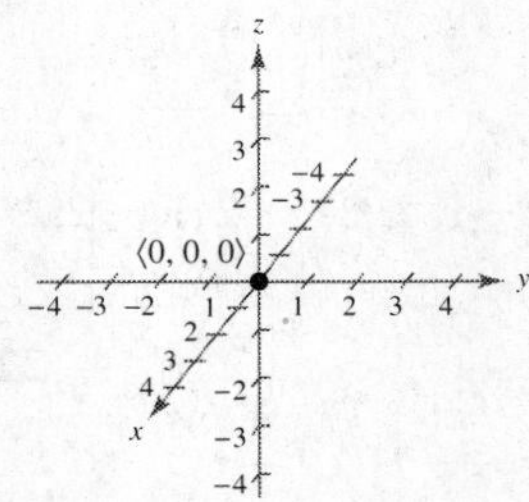

12. $\mathbf{v} = \mathbf{i} - 2\mathbf{j} + \mathbf{k}$

(a) $4\mathbf{v} = 4\mathbf{i} - 8\mathbf{j} + 4\mathbf{k}$

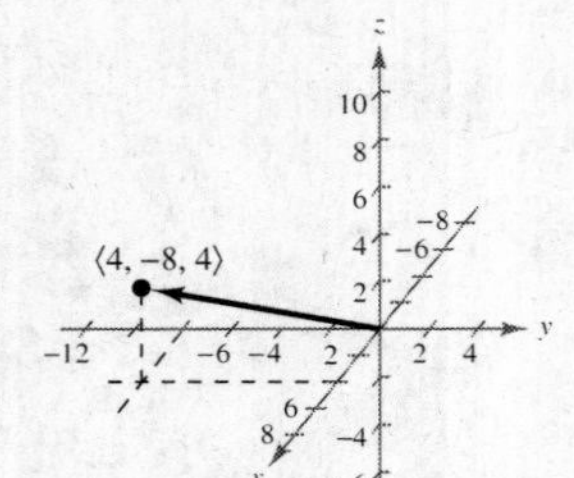

(b) $-2\mathbf{v} = -2\mathbf{i} + 4\mathbf{j} - 2\mathbf{k}$

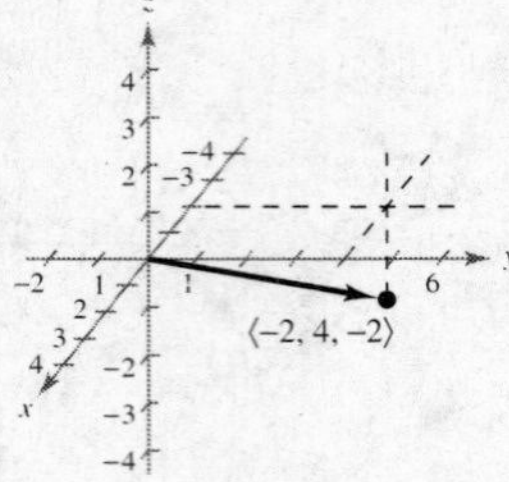

(c) $\frac{1}{2}\mathbf{v} = \frac{1}{2}\mathbf{i} - \mathbf{j} + \frac{1}{2}\mathbf{k}$

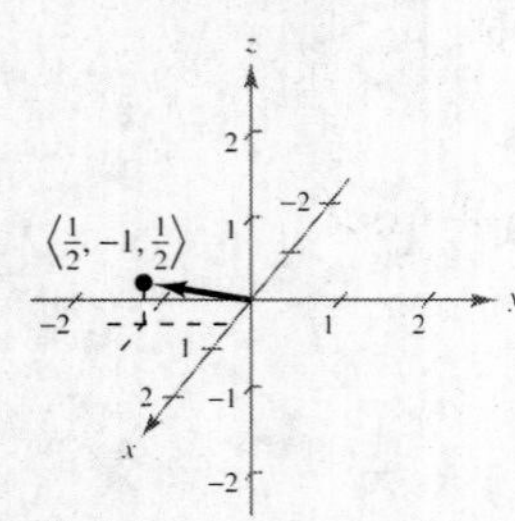

(d) $0\mathbf{v} = \mathbf{0}$

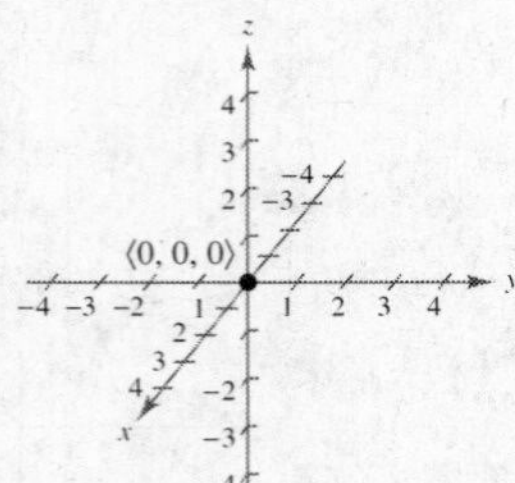

13. $\mathbf{z} = \mathbf{u} - 2\mathbf{v} = \langle -1, 3, 2\rangle - 2\langle 1, -2, -2\rangle = \langle -3, 7, 6\rangle$

14. $\mathbf{z} = 7\langle -1, 3, 2\rangle + \langle 1, -2, -2\rangle - \frac{1}{5}\langle 5, 0, -5\rangle = \langle -7, 19, 13\rangle$

15. $2\mathbf{z} - 4\mathbf{u} = \mathbf{w} \Rightarrow \mathbf{z} = \frac{1}{2}(4\mathbf{u} + \mathbf{w}) = \frac{1}{2}(4\langle -1, 3, 2\rangle + \langle 5, 0, -5\rangle) = \left\langle \frac{1}{2}, 6, \frac{3}{2}\right\rangle$

16. $\mathbf{z} = -\mathbf{u} - \mathbf{v} = -\langle -1, 3, 2\rangle - \langle 1, -2, -2\rangle = \langle 0, -1, 0\rangle$

17. $\mathbf{z} = 2\langle -1, 3, 2\rangle - 3\langle 1, -2, -2\rangle + \frac{1}{2}\langle 5, 0, -5\rangle = \left\langle -\frac{5}{2}, 12, \frac{15}{2}\right\rangle$

18. $\mathbf{z} = 3\langle 5, 0, -5\rangle - 2\langle 1, -2, -2\rangle + \langle -1, 3, 2\rangle = \langle 12, 7, -9\rangle$

19. $4\mathbf{z} = 4\langle 5, 0, -5\rangle - \langle -1, 3, 2\rangle + \langle 1, -2, -2\rangle = \langle 22, -5, -24\rangle$

$\mathbf{z} = \left\langle \frac{11}{2}, -\frac{5}{4}, -6\right\rangle$

20. $\mathbf{z} = \mathbf{w} - \mathbf{u} - 2\mathbf{v} = \langle 5, 0, -5\rangle - \langle -1, 3, 2\rangle - 2\langle 1, -2, -2\rangle = \langle 4, 1, -3\rangle$

21. $\|\mathbf{v}\| = \|\langle 7, 8, 7\rangle\|$

$= \sqrt{49 + 64 + 49} = \sqrt{162} = 9\sqrt{2}$

22. $\|\mathbf{v}\| = \sqrt{(-2)^2 + 0^2 + (-5)^2} = \sqrt{4 + 25} = \sqrt{29}$

23. $\|\mathbf{v}\| = \sqrt{1^2 + (-2)^2 + 4^2} = \sqrt{21}$

24. $\|\mathbf{v}\| = \sqrt{(-1)^2 + 0^2 + 3^2} = \sqrt{10}$

25. $\|\mathbf{v}\| = \sqrt{2^2 + (-4)^2 + 1^2} = \sqrt{21}$

26. $\|\mathbf{v}\| = \sqrt{1^2 + 3^2 + (-1)^2} = \sqrt{11}$

27. $\|\mathbf{v}\| = \sqrt{4^2 + (-3)^2 + (-7)^2}$
$= \sqrt{16 + 9 + 49} = \sqrt{74}$

28. $\|\mathbf{v}\| = \sqrt{2^2 + (-1)^2 + 6^2} = \sqrt{41}$

29. $\mathbf{v} = \langle 1 - 1, 0 - (-3), -1 - 4 \rangle = \langle 0, 3, -5 \rangle$
$\|\mathbf{v}\| = \sqrt{0 + 3^2 + (-5)^2} = \sqrt{34}$

30. $\mathbf{v} = \langle 1 - 0, 2 - (-1), -2 - 0 \rangle = \langle 1, 3, -2 \rangle$
$\|\mathbf{v}\| = \sqrt{1 + 9 + 4} = \sqrt{14}$

31. $\|\mathbf{u}\| = \sqrt{5^2 + (-12)^2} = \sqrt{169} = 13$
(a) $\frac{1}{13}(5\mathbf{i} - 12\mathbf{k})$
(b) $-\frac{1}{13}(5\mathbf{i} - 12\mathbf{k})$

32. $\|\mathbf{u}\| = \sqrt{3^2 + (-4)^2} = \sqrt{25} = 5$
(a) $\frac{1}{5}(3\mathbf{i} - 4\mathbf{k}) = \frac{3}{5}\mathbf{i} - \frac{4}{5}\mathbf{k}$
(b) $-\frac{1}{5}(3\mathbf{i} - 4\mathbf{k}) = -\frac{3}{5}\mathbf{i} + \frac{4}{5}\mathbf{k}$

33. (a) $\dfrac{\mathbf{u}}{\|\mathbf{u}\|} = \dfrac{\langle 8, 3, -1 \rangle}{\sqrt{74}}$
$= \dfrac{1}{\sqrt{74}}(8\mathbf{i} + 3\mathbf{j} - \mathbf{k}) = \dfrac{\sqrt{74}}{74}\langle 8, 3, -1 \rangle$
(b) $-\dfrac{1}{\sqrt{74}}(8\mathbf{i} + 3\mathbf{j} - \mathbf{k}) = -\dfrac{\sqrt{74}}{74}\langle 8, 3, -1 \rangle$

34. (a) $\dfrac{\mathbf{u}}{\|\mathbf{u}\|} = \dfrac{\langle -3, 5, 10 \rangle}{\sqrt{134}} = \dfrac{1}{\sqrt{134}}(-3\mathbf{i} + 5\mathbf{j} + 10\mathbf{k})$
(b) $\dfrac{-1}{\sqrt{134}}(-3\mathbf{i} + 5\mathbf{j} + 10\mathbf{k})$

35. $6\mathbf{u} - 4\mathbf{v} = 6\langle -1, 3, 4 \rangle - 4\langle 5, 4.5, -6 \rangle = \langle -6, 18, 24 \rangle + \langle -20, -18, 24 \rangle = \langle -26, 0, 48 \rangle$

36. $2\mathbf{u} + \frac{5}{2}\mathbf{v} = 2\langle -1, 3, 4 \rangle + \frac{5}{2}\langle 5, 4.5, -6 \rangle = \left\langle \frac{21}{2}, \frac{69}{4}, -7 \right\rangle$

37. $\mathbf{u} + \mathbf{v} = \langle -1, 3, 4 \rangle + \langle 5, 4.5, -6 \rangle = \langle 4, 7.5, -2 \rangle$
$\|\mathbf{u} + \mathbf{v}\| = \sqrt{4^2 + 7.5^2 + (-2)^2} = \frac{1}{2}\sqrt{305} \approx 8.73$

38. $\dfrac{\mathbf{v}}{\|\mathbf{v}\|} = \dfrac{\langle 5, 4.5, -6 \rangle}{\sqrt{25 + 20.25 + 36}} = \dfrac{\langle 5, 4.5, -6 \rangle}{5\sqrt{13/2}} = \left\langle \dfrac{2}{\sqrt{13}}, \dfrac{9}{5\sqrt{13}}, \dfrac{-12}{5\sqrt{13}} \right\rangle \approx \langle 0.5547, 0.4992, -0.6656 \rangle$

39. $\mathbf{u} \cdot \mathbf{v} = \langle 4, 4, -1 \rangle \cdot \langle 2, -5, -8 \rangle$
$= 8 - 20 + 8 = -4$

40. $\mathbf{u} \cdot \mathbf{v} = 3(4) + (-1)(-10) + 6(1) = 28$

41. $\mathbf{u} \cdot \mathbf{v} = \langle 2, -5, 3 \rangle \cdot \langle 9, 3, -1 \rangle$
$= 18 - 15 - 3 = 0$

42. $\mathbf{u} \cdot \mathbf{v} = 0(6) + 3(-4) + (-6)(-2) = 0$

43. $\cos\theta = \dfrac{\mathbf{u} \cdot \mathbf{v}}{\|\mathbf{u}\|\,\|\mathbf{v}\|} = \dfrac{-8}{\sqrt{8}\sqrt{25}} \Rightarrow \theta \approx 124.45°$

44. $\cos\theta = \dfrac{\mathbf{u} \cdot \mathbf{v}}{\|\mathbf{u}\|\,\|\mathbf{v}\|} = \dfrac{5}{\sqrt{10}\sqrt{6}} \Rightarrow \theta \approx 49.80°$

45. $\cos\theta = \dfrac{\mathbf{u} \cdot \mathbf{v}}{\|\mathbf{u}\|\,\|\mathbf{v}\|} = \dfrac{-120}{\sqrt{1700}\sqrt{73}} \Rightarrow \theta \approx 109.92°$

46. $\cos\theta = \dfrac{\mathbf{u} \cdot \mathbf{v}}{\|\mathbf{u}\|\,\|\mathbf{v}\|} = \dfrac{100}{\sqrt{464}\sqrt{125}} \Rightarrow \theta \approx 65.47°$

47. $-\frac{3}{2}\langle 8, -4, -10 \rangle = \langle -12, 6, 15 \rangle \Rightarrow$ parallel

48. $\mathbf{u} \cdot \mathbf{v} = -2 - 3 - 5 = -10 \neq 0$ and
$\mathbf{u} \neq c\mathbf{v} \Rightarrow$ neither

49. $\mathbf{u} \cdot \mathbf{v} = 3 - 5 + 2 = 0 \Rightarrow$ orthogonal

50. $-8\mathbf{u} = -8\langle -1, \frac{1}{2}, -1\rangle = \langle 8, -4, 8\rangle = \mathbf{v} \Rightarrow$ parallel

51. $\mathbf{u} \neq c\mathbf{v}$

$\mathbf{u} \cdot \mathbf{v} = -2 - 6 \neq 0$

Neither parallel nor orthogonal

52. $\mathbf{u} \neq c\mathbf{v}$

$\mathbf{u} \cdot \mathbf{v} = 4 \neq 0$

Neither parallel nor orthogonal

53. $\mathbf{u} \cdot \mathbf{v} = -4 + 3 + 1 = 0$

Orthogonal

54. $\mathbf{u} \cdot \mathbf{v} = -2 + 3 - 1 = 0$

Orthogonal

55. $\mathbf{v} = \langle 7 - 5, 3 - 4, -1 - 1\rangle = \langle 2, -1, -2\rangle$

$\mathbf{u} = \langle 4 - 7, 5 - 3, 3 - (-1)\rangle = \langle -3, 2, 4\rangle$

Since **u** and **v** are not parallel, the points are not collinear.

56. $\mathbf{v} = \langle -4 - (-2), 8 - 7, 1 - 4\rangle = \langle -2, 1, -3\rangle$

$\mathbf{u} = \langle 0 - (-4), 6 - 8, 7 - 1\rangle = \langle 4, -2, 6\rangle$

Since $\mathbf{u} = -2\mathbf{v}$, the points are collinear.

57. $\mathbf{v} = \langle -1 - 1, 2 - 3, 5 - 2\rangle = \langle -2, -1, 3\rangle$

$\mathbf{u} = \langle 3 - (-1), 4 - 2, -1 - 5\rangle = \langle 4, 2, -6\rangle$

Since $\mathbf{u} = -2\mathbf{v}$, the points are collinear.

58. $\mathbf{v} = \langle -1 - 0, 5 - 4, 6 - 4\rangle = \langle -1, 1, 2\rangle$

$\mathbf{u} = \langle -2 - (-1), 6 - 5, 7 - 6\rangle = \langle -1, 1, 1\rangle$

Since **u** and **v** are not parallel, the points are not collinear.

59. The vector $\langle 1, 2, 0\rangle$ joining $(1, 2, 0)$ and $(0, 0, 0)$ is perpendicular to the vector $\langle -2, 1, 0\rangle$ joining $(-2, 1, 0)$ and $(0, 0, 0)$:

$\langle 1, 2, 0\rangle \cdot \langle -2, 1, 0\rangle = -2 + 2 = 0$

The triangle is a right triangle.

60. Consider the vector $\langle -3, 0, 0\rangle$ joining $(0, 0, 0)$ and $(-3, 0, 0)$ and the vector $\langle 1, 2, 3\rangle$ joining $(1, 2, 3)$ and $(0, 0, 0)$:

$\langle -3, 0, 0\rangle \cdot \langle 1, 2, 3\rangle = -3 < 0$

The triangle has an obtuse angle.

Obtuse triangle

61. The three sides of the triangle are given by the vectors:

$\mathbf{u} = \langle -2, 4, -2\rangle$

$\mathbf{v} = \langle -3, 5, -4\rangle$

$\mathbf{w} = \langle -1, 1, -2\rangle$

$\mathbf{u} \cdot \mathbf{v} = 34 > 0$

$\mathbf{u} \cdot \mathbf{w} = 10 > 0$

$\mathbf{v} \cdot \mathbf{w} = 16 > 0$

The triangle has three acute angles.

Acute triangle

62. Consider the vector $\langle -3, 12, 5\rangle$ joining $(-1, 5, 8)$ and $(2, -7, 3)$, and the vector $\langle 5, 1, -9\rangle$ joining $(4, 6, -1)$ and $(-1, 5, 8)$:

$\langle 5, 1, -9\rangle \cdot \langle -3, 12, 5\rangle = -48 < 0$

The triangle has an obtuse angle.

Obtuse triangle

63. $\mathbf{v} = \langle 2, -4, 7\rangle = \langle q_1 - 1, q_2 - 5, q_3 - 0\rangle \Rightarrow$

$$\left.\begin{aligned} 2 &= q_1 - 1 \\ -4 &= q_2 - 5 \\ 7 &= q_3 \end{aligned}\right\} \Rightarrow \left.\begin{aligned} q_1 &= 3 \\ q_2 &= 1 \\ q_3 &= 7 \end{aligned}\right\} \Rightarrow \text{Terminal point is } (3, 1, 7).$$

64. $\langle 4, -1, -1\rangle = \langle x - 6, y + 4, z - 3\rangle \Rightarrow (x, y, z) = (10, -5, 2)$

65. $\mathbf{v} = \left\langle 4, \frac{3}{2}, -\frac{1}{4}\right\rangle = \left\langle q_1 - 2, q_2 - 1, q_3 + \frac{3}{2}\right\rangle$

$4 = q_1 - 2 \Rightarrow q_1 = 6$

$\frac{3}{2} = q_2 - 1 \Rightarrow q_2 = \frac{5}{2}$

$-\frac{1}{4} = q_3 + \frac{3}{2} \Rightarrow q_3 = -\frac{7}{4}$

Terminal point: $\left(6, \frac{5}{2}, -\frac{7}{4}\right)$

66. $\left\langle \frac{5}{2}, -\frac{1}{2}, 4\right\rangle = \left\langle x - 3, y - 2, z + \frac{1}{2}\right\rangle \Rightarrow (x, y, z) = \left(\frac{11}{2}, \frac{3}{2}, \frac{7}{2}\right)$

67. $c\mathbf{u} = c\mathbf{i} + 2c\mathbf{j} + 3c\mathbf{k}$

$\|c\mathbf{u}\| = \sqrt{c^2 + 4c^2 + 9c^2} = |c|\sqrt{14} = 3 \Rightarrow$

$c = \pm\frac{3}{\sqrt{14}} = \pm\frac{3\sqrt{14}}{14}$

68. $\|c\,\mathbf{u}\| = |c|\,\|\mathbf{u}\| = |c|\sqrt{4 + 4 + 16} = |c|\sqrt{24} = 12$

$\Rightarrow |c| = \frac{12}{\sqrt{24}} = \frac{6}{\sqrt{6}} = \sqrt{6} \Rightarrow c = \pm\sqrt{6}$

69. $\mathbf{v} = \langle q_1, q_2, q_3\rangle$

Since $\mathbf{v}$ lies in the yz-plane, $q_1 = 0$. Since $\mathbf{v}$ makes an angle of 45°, $|q_2| = |q_3|$. Finally, $\|\mathbf{v}\| = 4$ implies that $q_2^2 + q_3^2 = 16$. Thus, $q_2 = q_3 = 2\sqrt{2}$ and $\mathbf{v} = \left\langle 0, 2\sqrt{2}, 2\sqrt{2}\right\rangle$, or $q_2 = 2\sqrt{2}$ and $q_3 = -2\sqrt{2}$ and $\mathbf{v} = \left\langle 0, 2\sqrt{2}, -2\sqrt{2}\right\rangle$.

70. $\mathbf{v}$ lies in xz-plane $\Rightarrow y = 0$.

$\mathbf{v} = 10\langle \sin 60°, 0, \cos 60°\rangle = \left\langle 5\sqrt{3}, 0, 5\right\rangle$, or

$\mathbf{v} = 10\langle -\sin 60°, 0, \cos 60°\rangle = \left\langle -5\sqrt{3}, 0, 5\right\rangle$

71. $\overrightarrow{PQ_1} = \left\langle 0, -24, -12\sqrt{21}\right\rangle$

$\overrightarrow{PQ_2} = \left\langle 12\sqrt{3}, 12, -12\sqrt{21}\right\rangle$

$\overrightarrow{PQ_3} = \left\langle -12\sqrt{3}, 12, -12\sqrt{21}\right\rangle$

Let $\mathbf{F}_1$, $\mathbf{F}_2$, and $\mathbf{F}_3$ be the tension on each wire. Since $\|\mathbf{F}_1\| = \|\mathbf{F}_2\| = \|\mathbf{F}_3\|$, there exists a constant c such that

$\mathbf{F}_1 = c\left\langle 0, -24, -12\sqrt{21}\right\rangle$

$\mathbf{F}_2 = c\left\langle 12\sqrt{3}, 12, -12\sqrt{21}\right\rangle$

$\mathbf{F}_3 = c\left\langle -12\sqrt{3}, 12, -12\sqrt{21}\right\rangle$.

The total force is $-30\mathbf{k} = \mathbf{F}_1 + \mathbf{F}_2 + \mathbf{F}_3 \Rightarrow$ the vertical ($\mathbf{k}$) component satisfies

$-10 = -12\sqrt{21}\,c \Rightarrow c = \frac{5}{6\sqrt{21}}$.

Hence,

$\mathbf{F}_1 = \left\langle 0, \frac{-20}{\sqrt{21}}, -10\right\rangle$

$\mathbf{F}_2 = \left\langle \frac{10}{\sqrt{7}}, \frac{10}{\sqrt{21}}, -10\right\rangle$

$\mathbf{F} = \left\langle \frac{-10}{\sqrt{7}}, \frac{10}{\sqrt{21}}, -10\right\rangle$

$\|\mathbf{F}_1\| = \|\mathbf{F}_2\| = \|\mathbf{F}_3\| \approx 10.91$ pounds.

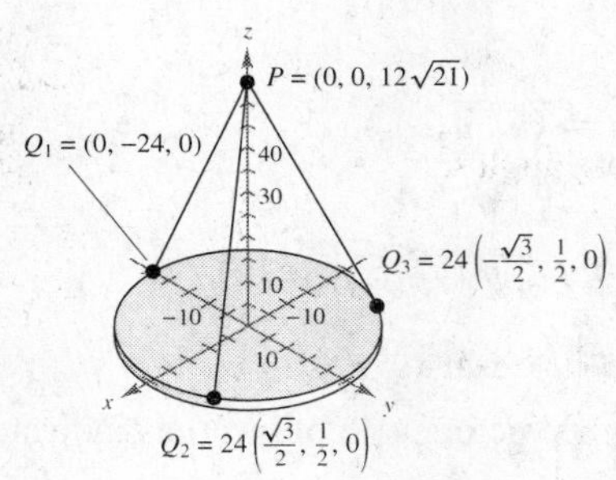

$Q_1 = (0, -24, 0)$

$Q_2 = (20.8, 12, 0)$

$Q_3 = (-20.8, 12, 0)$

$P = (0, 0, 55)$

72. $\overrightarrow{AB} = \langle 0, 70, 115 \rangle$, $\mathbf{F}_1 = C_1\langle 0, 70, 115 \rangle$

$\overrightarrow{AC} = \langle -60, 0, 115 \rangle$, $\mathbf{F}_2 = C_2\langle -60, 0, 115 \rangle$

$\overrightarrow{AD} = \langle 45, -65, 115 \rangle$, $\mathbf{F}_3 = C_3\langle 45, -65, 115 \rangle$

$\mathbf{F}_1 + \mathbf{F}_2 + \mathbf{F}_3 = \langle 0, 0, -500 \rangle$. Thus

$$\begin{aligned} -60C_2 + 45C_3 &= 0 \\ 70C_1 - 65C_3 &= 0 \\ 115C_1 + 115C_2 + 115C_3 &= -500. \end{aligned}$$

Solving this system yields $C_1 = \dfrac{-104}{69}$, $C_2 = \dfrac{-28}{23}$, $C_3 = \dfrac{-112}{69}$.

Thus,

$\|\mathbf{F}_1\| \approx 202.919$ N

$\|\mathbf{F}_2\| \approx 157.909$ N

$\|\mathbf{F}_3\| \approx 226.521$ N.

73. True. $\cos\theta = 0 \implies \theta = 90°$

74. True

75. (a)

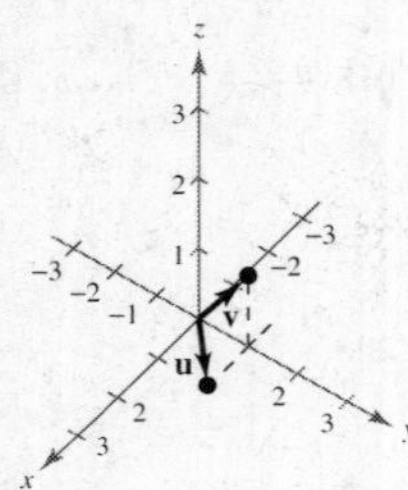

(b) $\mathbf{w} = a\mathbf{u} + b\mathbf{v} = a\langle 1, 1, 0 \rangle + b\langle 0, 1, 1 \rangle$

$\mathbf{0} = \langle a, a + b, b \rangle \Rightarrow a = b = 0$

(c) $\mathbf{w} = \langle 1, 2, 1 \rangle = a\langle 1, 1, 0 \rangle + b\langle 0, 1, 1 \rangle$

$1 = a$

$2 = a + b$

$1 = b$

Hence, $a = b = 1$.

(d) $\mathbf{w} = \langle 1, 2, 3 \rangle = a\langle 1, 1, 0 \rangle + b\langle 0, 1, 1 \rangle$

$1 = a$

$2 = a + b$

$3 = b$

Impossible

76. This set is a sphere.

$(x - x_1)^2 + (y - y_1)^2 + (z - z_1)^2 = 16$

77. If $\mathbf{u} \cdot \mathbf{v} < 0$, then $\cos\theta < 0$ and the angle between $\mathbf{u}$ and $\mathbf{v}$ is obtuse, $180° > \theta > 90°$.

78. Let $\mathbf{v} = \langle v_1, v_2, v_3 \rangle$ and $\mathbf{u} = \langle u_1, u_2, u_3 \rangle$.

Then $t\mathbf{v} = \langle tv_1, tv_2, tv_3 \rangle$,

$\mathbf{u} + t\mathbf{v} = \langle u_1 + tv_1, u_2 + tv_2, u_3 + tv_3 \rangle$, and

$s\mathbf{u} + t\mathbf{v} = \langle su_1 + tv_1, su_2 + tv_2, su_3 + tv_3 \rangle$.

The endpoints of these three vectors are collinear, as indicated in the figure. So, the figure is a line.

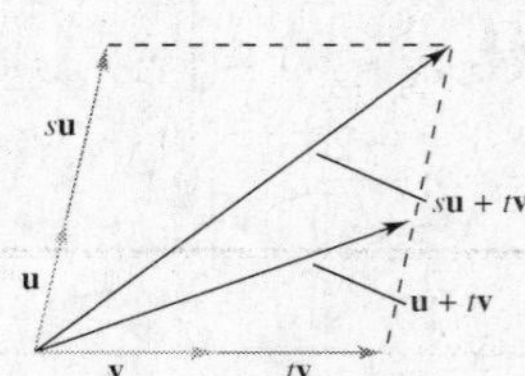

79. (a) $x = t$

$y = 3t + 2$

(b) $x = t - 1$

$y = 3(t - 1) + 2 = 3t - 1$

80. (a) $x = t, y = \dfrac{2}{t}$

(b) $x = t - 1, y = \dfrac{2}{t - 1}$

81. (a) $x = t$

$y = t^2 - 8$

(b) $x = t - 1$

$y = (t - 1)^2 - 8 = t^2 - 2t - 7$

82. (a) $x = t, y = 4t^3$

(b) $x = t - 1, y = 4(t - 1)^3$

Section 10.3 The Cross Product of Two Vectors

- The cross product of two vectors $\mathbf{u} = u_1\mathbf{i} + u_2\mathbf{j} + u_3\mathbf{k}$ and $\mathbf{v} = v_1\mathbf{i} + v_2\mathbf{j} + v_3\mathbf{k}$ is given by

$$\mathbf{u} \times \mathbf{v} = (u_2v_3 - u_3v_2)\mathbf{i} - (u_1v_3 - u_3v_1)\mathbf{j} + (u_1v_2 - u_2v_1)\mathbf{k} = \begin{vmatrix} \mathbf{i} & \mathbf{j} & \mathbf{k} \\ u_1 & u_2 & u_3 \\ v_1 & v_2 & v_3 \end{vmatrix}.$$

- The cross product satisfies the following algebraic properties.
  (a) $\mathbf{u} \times \mathbf{v} = -(\mathbf{v} \times \mathbf{u})$
  (b) $\mathbf{u} \times (\mathbf{v} + \mathbf{w}) = (\mathbf{u} \times \mathbf{v}) + (\mathbf{u} \times \mathbf{w})$
  (c) $c(\mathbf{u} \times \mathbf{v}) = (c\mathbf{u}) \times \mathbf{v} = \mathbf{u} \times (c\mathbf{v})$
  (d) $\mathbf{u} \times \mathbf{0} = \mathbf{0} \times \mathbf{u} = \mathbf{0}$
  (e) $\mathbf{u} \times \mathbf{u} = \mathbf{0}$
  (f) $\mathbf{u} \cdot (\mathbf{v} \times \mathbf{w}) = (\mathbf{u} \times \mathbf{v}) \cdot \mathbf{w}$
- The following geometric properties of the cross product are valid, where θ is the angle between the vectors $\mathbf{u}$ and $\mathbf{v}$:
  (a) $\mathbf{u} \times \mathbf{v}$ is orthogonal to both $\mathbf{u}$ and $\mathbf{v}$.
  (b) $\|\mathbf{u} \times \mathbf{v}\| = \|\mathbf{u}\|\,\|\mathbf{v}\| \sin \theta$
  (c) $\mathbf{u} \times \mathbf{v} = \mathbf{0}$ if and only if $\mathbf{u}$ and $\mathbf{v}$ are scalar multiples.
  (d) $\|\mathbf{u} \times \mathbf{v}\|$ is the area of the parallelogram having $\mathbf{u}$ and $\mathbf{v}$ as sides.
- The absolute value of the triple scalar product is the volume of the parallelepiped having $\mathbf{u}$, $\mathbf{v}$, and $\mathbf{w}$ as sides.

$$\mathbf{u} \cdot (\mathbf{v} \times \mathbf{w}) = \begin{vmatrix} u_1 & u_2 & u_3 \\ v_1 & v_2 & v_3 \\ w_1 & w_2 & w_3 \end{vmatrix}$$

Vocabulary Check

1. cross product

2. 0

3. $\|\mathbf{u}\|\,\|\mathbf{v}\| \sin \theta$

4. triple scalar product

1. $\mathbf{j} \times \mathbf{i} = \begin{vmatrix} \mathbf{i} & \mathbf{j} & \mathbf{k} \\ 0 & 1 & 0 \\ 1 & 0 & 0 \end{vmatrix} = -\mathbf{k}$

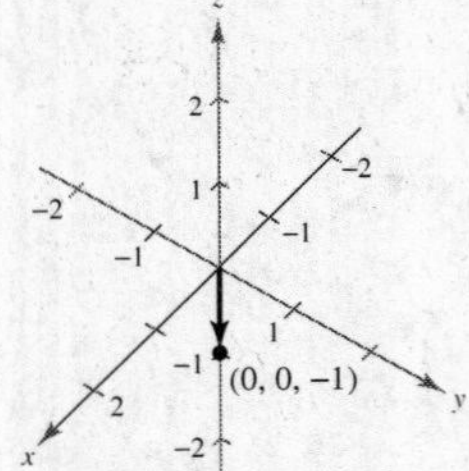

2. $\mathbf{k} \times \mathbf{j} = \begin{vmatrix} \mathbf{i} & \mathbf{j} & \mathbf{k} \\ 0 & 0 & 1 \\ 0 & 1 & 0 \end{vmatrix} = -\mathbf{i}$

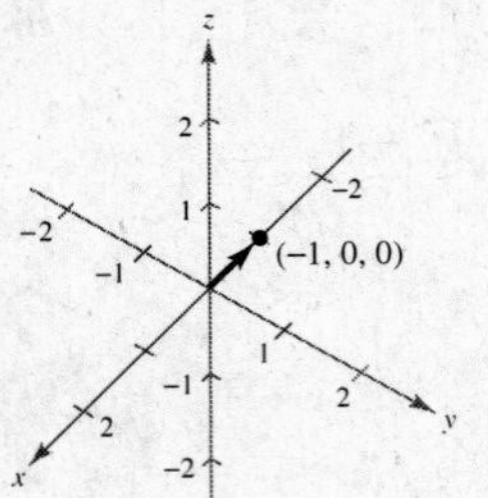

3. $\mathbf{i} \times \mathbf{k} = \begin{vmatrix} \mathbf{i} & \mathbf{j} & \mathbf{k} \\ 1 & 0 & 0 \\ 0 & 0 & 1 \end{vmatrix} = -\mathbf{j}$

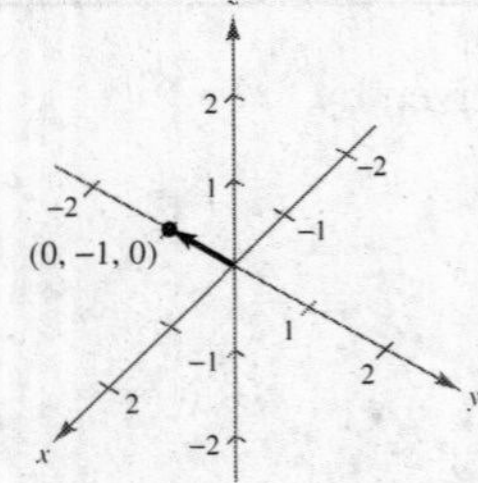

4. $\mathbf{k} \times \mathbf{i} = \begin{vmatrix} \mathbf{i} & \mathbf{j} & \mathbf{k} \\ 0 & 0 & 1 \\ 1 & 0 & 0 \end{vmatrix} = \mathbf{j}$

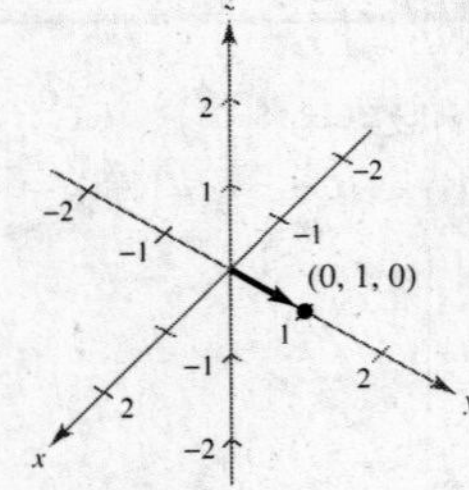

5. $\mathbf{u} \times \mathbf{v} = \begin{vmatrix} \mathbf{i} & \mathbf{j} & \mathbf{k} \\ 1 & -1 & 0 \\ 0 & 1 & -1 \end{vmatrix} = \mathbf{i} + \mathbf{j} + \mathbf{k} = \langle 1, 1, 1 \rangle$

6. $\mathbf{u} \times \mathbf{v} = \begin{vmatrix} \mathbf{i} & \mathbf{j} & \mathbf{k} \\ -1 & 1 & 0 \\ 1 & 0 & -1 \end{vmatrix} = -\mathbf{i} - \mathbf{j} - \mathbf{k} = \langle -1, -1, -1 \rangle$

7. $\mathbf{u} \times \mathbf{v} = \begin{vmatrix} \mathbf{i} & \mathbf{j} & \mathbf{k} \\ 3 & -2 & 5 \\ 0 & -1 & 1 \end{vmatrix} = \langle 3, -3, -3 \rangle$

$(\mathbf{u} \times \mathbf{v}) \cdot \mathbf{u} = \langle 3, -3, -3 \rangle \cdot \langle 3, -2, 5 \rangle = 0$

$(\mathbf{u} \times \mathbf{v}) \cdot \mathbf{v} = \langle 3, -3, -3 \rangle \cdot \langle 0, -1, 1 \rangle = 0$

8. $\mathbf{u} \times \mathbf{v} = \begin{vmatrix} \mathbf{i} & \mathbf{j} & \mathbf{k} \\ 2 & -3 & 1 \\ 1 & -2 & 1 \end{vmatrix} = -\mathbf{i} - \mathbf{j} - \mathbf{k} = \langle -1, -1, -1 \rangle$

9. $\mathbf{u} \times \mathbf{v} = \begin{vmatrix} \mathbf{i} & \mathbf{j} & \mathbf{k} \\ -10 & 0 & 6 \\ 7 & 0 & 0 \end{vmatrix} = \langle 0, 42, 0 \rangle$

$(\mathbf{u} \times \mathbf{v}) \cdot \mathbf{u} = \langle 0, 42, 0 \rangle \cdot \langle -10, 0, 6 \rangle = 0$

$(\mathbf{u} \times \mathbf{v}) \cdot \mathbf{v} = \langle 0, 42, 0 \rangle \cdot \langle 7, 0, 0 \rangle = 0$

10. $\mathbf{u} \times \mathbf{v} = \begin{vmatrix} \mathbf{i} & \mathbf{j} & \mathbf{k} \\ -5 & 5 & 11 \\ 2 & 2 & 3 \end{vmatrix} = \langle -7, 37, -20 \rangle$

11. $\mathbf{u} \times \mathbf{v} = \begin{vmatrix} \mathbf{i} & \mathbf{j} & \mathbf{k} \\ 6 & 2 & 1 \\ 1 & 3 & -2 \end{vmatrix} = \langle -7, 13, 16 \rangle$

$= -7\mathbf{i} + 13\mathbf{j} + 16\mathbf{k}$

12. $\mathbf{u} \times \mathbf{v} = \begin{vmatrix} \mathbf{i} & \mathbf{j} & \mathbf{k} \\ 1 & \frac{3}{2} & -\frac{5}{2} \\ \frac{1}{2} & -\frac{3}{4} & \frac{1}{4} \end{vmatrix} = \left\langle -\frac{3}{2}, -\frac{3}{2}, -\frac{3}{2} \right\rangle = -\frac{3}{2}\mathbf{i} - \frac{3}{2}\mathbf{j} - \frac{3}{2}\mathbf{k}$

13. $\mathbf{u} \times \mathbf{v} = \begin{vmatrix} \mathbf{i} & \mathbf{j} & \mathbf{k} \\ 2 & 4 & 3 \\ -1 & 3 & -2 \end{vmatrix} = -17\mathbf{i} + \mathbf{j} + 10\mathbf{k}$

14. $\mathbf{u} \times \mathbf{v} = \begin{vmatrix} \mathbf{i} & \mathbf{j} & \mathbf{k} \\ 3 & -2 & 1 \\ -2 & 1 & 2 \end{vmatrix} = -5\mathbf{i} - 8\mathbf{j} - \mathbf{k}$

15. $\mathbf{u} \times \mathbf{v} = \begin{vmatrix} \mathbf{i} & \mathbf{j} & \mathbf{k} \\ \frac{1}{2} & -\frac{2}{3} & 1 \\ -\frac{3}{4} & 1 & \frac{1}{4} \end{vmatrix} = -\frac{7}{6}\mathbf{i} - \frac{7}{8}\mathbf{j}$

16. $\mathbf{u} \times \mathbf{v} = \begin{vmatrix} \mathbf{i} & \mathbf{j} & \mathbf{k} \\ \frac{2}{5} & -\frac{1}{4} & \frac{1}{2} \\ -\frac{3}{5} & 1 & \frac{1}{5} \end{vmatrix} = -\frac{11}{20}\mathbf{i} - \frac{19}{50}\mathbf{j} + \frac{1}{4}\mathbf{k}$

17. $\mathbf{u} \times \mathbf{v} = \begin{vmatrix} \mathbf{i} & \mathbf{j} & \mathbf{k} \\ 0 & 0 & 6 \\ -1 & 3 & 1 \end{vmatrix} = \langle -18, -6, 0 \rangle$

$= -18\mathbf{i} - 6\mathbf{j}$

18. $\mathbf{u} \times \mathbf{v} = \begin{vmatrix} \mathbf{i} & \mathbf{j} & \mathbf{k} \\ \frac{2}{3} & 0 & 0 \\ 0 & \frac{1}{3} & -3 \end{vmatrix} = 2\mathbf{j} + \frac{2}{9}\mathbf{k}$

19. $\mathbf{u} \times \mathbf{v} = \begin{vmatrix} \mathbf{i} & \mathbf{j} & \mathbf{k} \\ -1 & 0 & 1 \\ 0 & 1 & -2 \end{vmatrix} = \langle -1, -2, -1 \rangle$

$= -\mathbf{i} - 2\mathbf{j} - \mathbf{k}$

20. $\mathbf{u} \times \mathbf{v} = \begin{vmatrix} \mathbf{i} & \mathbf{j} & \mathbf{k} \\ 1 & 0 & -2 \\ 0 & -1 & 1 \end{vmatrix} = (0 - 2)\mathbf{i} - (1 - 0)\mathbf{j} + (-1 - 0)\mathbf{k} = -2\mathbf{i} - \mathbf{j} - \mathbf{k}$

21. $\mathbf{u} \times \mathbf{v} = \begin{vmatrix} \mathbf{i} & \mathbf{j} & \mathbf{k} \\ 2 & 4 & 3 \\ 0 & -2 & 1 \end{vmatrix} = \langle 10, -2, -4 \rangle$

22. $\mathbf{u} \times \mathbf{v} = \begin{vmatrix} \mathbf{i} & \mathbf{j} & \mathbf{k} \\ 4 & -2 & 6 \\ -1 & 5 & 7 \end{vmatrix} = \langle -44, -34, 18 \rangle$

23. $\mathbf{u} \times \mathbf{v} = \begin{vmatrix} \mathbf{i} & \mathbf{j} & \mathbf{k} \\ 1 & -2 & 4 \\ -4 & 2 & -1 \end{vmatrix} = -6\mathbf{i} - 15\mathbf{j} - 6\mathbf{k}$

24. $\mathbf{u} \times \mathbf{v} = \begin{vmatrix} \mathbf{i} & \mathbf{j} & \mathbf{k} \\ 2 & -1 & 3 \\ -1 & 1 & -4 \end{vmatrix} = \mathbf{i} + 5\mathbf{j} + \mathbf{k}$

25. $\mathbf{u} \times \mathbf{v} = \begin{vmatrix} \mathbf{i} & \mathbf{j} & \mathbf{k} \\ 6 & -5 & 1 \\ \frac{1}{2} & -\frac{3}{4} & \frac{2}{10} \end{vmatrix} = \langle -0.25, -0.7, -2 \rangle$

26. $\mathbf{u} \times \mathbf{v} = \begin{vmatrix} \mathbf{i} & \mathbf{j} & \mathbf{k} \\ 8 & -4 & 2 \\ \frac{1}{2} & \frac{3}{4} & -\frac{1}{4} \end{vmatrix} = -\frac{1}{2}\mathbf{i} + 3\mathbf{j} + 8\mathbf{k}$

27. $\mathbf{u} \times \mathbf{v} = \begin{vmatrix} \mathbf{i} & \mathbf{j} & \mathbf{k} \\ 1 & 2 & 3 \\ 2 & -3 & 0 \end{vmatrix} = \langle 9, 6, -7 \rangle$

$\|\mathbf{u} \times \mathbf{v}\| = \sqrt{166}$

Unit vector: $\frac{\sqrt{166}}{166}\langle 9, 6, -7 \rangle$

28. $\mathbf{u} \times \mathbf{v} = \begin{vmatrix} \mathbf{i} & \mathbf{j} & \mathbf{k} \\ 2 & -1 & 3 \\ 1 & 0 & -2 \end{vmatrix} = \langle 2, 7, 1 \rangle$

$\|\mathbf{u} \times \mathbf{v}\| = \sqrt{54} = 3\sqrt{6}$

Unit vector: $\frac{1}{3\sqrt{6}}\langle 2, 7, 1 \rangle = \frac{\sqrt{6}}{18}\langle 2, 7, 1 \rangle$

29. $\mathbf{u} \times \mathbf{v} = \begin{vmatrix} \mathbf{i} & \mathbf{j} & \mathbf{k} \\ 3 & 1 & 0 \\ 0 & 1 & 1 \end{vmatrix} = \mathbf{i} - 3\mathbf{j} + 3\mathbf{k}$

$\|\mathbf{u} \times \mathbf{v}\| = \sqrt{19}$

$$\text{Unit vector} = \frac{\mathbf{u} \times \mathbf{v}}{\|\mathbf{u} \times \mathbf{v}\|} = \frac{1}{\sqrt{19}}(\mathbf{i} - 3\mathbf{j} + 3\mathbf{k})$$
$$= \frac{\sqrt{19}}{19}\langle 1, -3, 3 \rangle$$

30. $\mathbf{u} \times \mathbf{v} = \begin{vmatrix} \mathbf{i} & \mathbf{j} & \mathbf{k} \\ 1 & 2 & 0 \\ 1 & 0 & -3 \end{vmatrix} = -6\mathbf{i} + 3\mathbf{j} - 2\mathbf{k}$

$\|\mathbf{u} \times \mathbf{v}\| = \sqrt{36 + 9 + 4} = 7$

$$\text{Unit vector} = \frac{\mathbf{u} \times \mathbf{v}}{\|\mathbf{u} \times \mathbf{v}\|} = -\frac{6}{7}\mathbf{i} + \frac{3}{7}\mathbf{j} - \frac{2}{7}\mathbf{k}$$

31. $\mathbf{u} \times \mathbf{v} = \begin{vmatrix} \mathbf{i} & \mathbf{j} & \mathbf{k} \\ -3 & 2 & -5 \\ \frac{1}{2} & -\frac{3}{4} & \frac{1}{10} \end{vmatrix} = \left\langle -\frac{71}{20}, -\frac{11}{5}, \frac{5}{4} \right\rangle$

Consider the parallel vector $\langle -71, -44, 25 \rangle = \mathbf{w}$.

$\|\mathbf{w}\| = \sqrt{71^2 + 44^2 + 25^2} = \sqrt{7602}$

$$\text{Unit vector} = \frac{1}{\sqrt{7602}}\langle -71, -44, 25 \rangle$$
$$= \frac{\sqrt{7602}}{7602}\langle -71, -44, 25 \rangle$$

32. $\mathbf{u} \times \mathbf{v} = \begin{vmatrix} \mathbf{i} & \mathbf{j} & \mathbf{k} \\ 7 & -14 & 5 \\ 14 & 28 & -15 \end{vmatrix} = 70\mathbf{i} + 175\mathbf{j} + 392\mathbf{k}$

$$\|\mathbf{u} \times \mathbf{v}\| = \sqrt{70^2 + 175^2 + 392^2}$$
$$= \sqrt{189{,}189} = 21\sqrt{429}$$

$$\text{Unit vector} = \frac{\mathbf{u} \times \mathbf{v}}{\|\mathbf{u} \times \mathbf{v}\|} = \frac{1}{21\sqrt{249}}\langle 70, 175, 392 \rangle$$
$$= \frac{1}{3\sqrt{429}}\langle 10, 25, 56 \rangle$$
$$= \frac{\sqrt{429}}{1287}\langle 10, 25, 56 \rangle$$

33. $\mathbf{u} \times \mathbf{v} = \begin{vmatrix} \mathbf{i} & \mathbf{j} & \mathbf{k} \\ 1 & 1 & -1 \\ 1 & 1 & 1 \end{vmatrix} = 2\mathbf{i} - 2\mathbf{j}$

$\|\mathbf{u} \times \mathbf{v}\| = 2\sqrt{2}$

$$\text{Unit vector} = \frac{\mathbf{u} \times \mathbf{v}}{\|\mathbf{u} \times \mathbf{v}\|} = \frac{1}{2\sqrt{2}}(2\mathbf{i} - 2\mathbf{j})$$
$$= \frac{1}{\sqrt{2}}\mathbf{i} - \frac{1}{\sqrt{2}}\mathbf{j}$$
$$= \frac{\sqrt{2}}{2}\mathbf{i} - \frac{\sqrt{2}}{2}\mathbf{j}$$

34. $\mathbf{u} \times \mathbf{v} = \begin{vmatrix} \mathbf{i} & \mathbf{j} & \mathbf{k} \\ 1 & -2 & 2 \\ 2 & -1 & -2 \end{vmatrix} = 6\mathbf{i} + 6\mathbf{j} + 3\mathbf{k}$

$\|\mathbf{u} \times \mathbf{v}\| = \sqrt{36 + 36 + 9} = 9$

$$\text{Unit vector} = \frac{\mathbf{u} \times \mathbf{v}}{\|\mathbf{u} \times \mathbf{v}\|} = \frac{1}{9}(6\mathbf{i} + 6\mathbf{j} + 3\mathbf{k})$$
$$= \frac{2}{3}\mathbf{i} + \frac{2}{3}\mathbf{j} + \frac{1}{3}\mathbf{k}$$

35. $\mathbf{u} \times \mathbf{v} = \begin{vmatrix} \mathbf{i} & \mathbf{j} & \mathbf{k} \\ 0 & 0 & 1 \\ 1 & 0 & 1 \end{vmatrix} = \mathbf{j}$

Area $= \|\mathbf{u} \times \mathbf{v}\| = \|\mathbf{j}\| = 1$ square unit

36. $\mathbf{u} \times \mathbf{v} = \begin{vmatrix} \mathbf{i} & \mathbf{j} & \mathbf{k} \\ 1 & 2 & 2 \\ 1 & 0 & 1 \end{vmatrix} = 2\mathbf{i} + \mathbf{j} - 2\mathbf{k}$

Area $= \|\mathbf{u} \times \mathbf{v}\| = \|2\mathbf{i} + \mathbf{j} - 2\mathbf{k}\|$

$= \sqrt{4 + 1 + 4} = 3$ square units

37. $\mathbf{u} \times \mathbf{v} = \begin{vmatrix} \mathbf{i} & \mathbf{j} & \mathbf{k} \\ 3 & 4 & 6 \\ 2 & -1 & 5 \end{vmatrix} = 26\mathbf{i} - 3\mathbf{j} - 11\mathbf{k}$

$\text{Area} = \|\mathbf{u} \times \mathbf{v}\| = \sqrt{26^2 + (-3)^2 + (-11)^2}$

$= \sqrt{806}$ square units

38. $\mathbf{u} \times \mathbf{v} = \begin{vmatrix} \mathbf{i} & \mathbf{j} & \mathbf{k} \\ -2 & 3 & 2 \\ 1 & 2 & 4 \end{vmatrix} = \langle 8, 10, -7 \rangle$

$\text{Area} = \|\mathbf{u} \times \mathbf{v}\| = \sqrt{8^2 + 10^2 + (-7)^2}$

$= \sqrt{213}$ square units

39. $\mathbf{u} \times \mathbf{v} = \begin{vmatrix} \mathbf{i} & \mathbf{j} & \mathbf{k} \\ 2 & 2 & -3 \\ 0 & 2 & 3 \end{vmatrix} = \langle 12, -6, 4 \rangle$

$\text{Area} = \|\mathbf{u} \times \mathbf{v}\| = \sqrt{12^2 + (-6)^2 + 4^2}$

$= 14$ square units

40. $\mathbf{u} \times \mathbf{v} = \begin{vmatrix} \mathbf{i} & \mathbf{j} & \mathbf{k} \\ 4 & -3 & 2 \\ 5 & 0 & 1 \end{vmatrix} = \langle -3, 6, 15 \rangle$

$\text{Area} = \|\mathbf{u} \times \mathbf{v}\| = \sqrt{(-3)^2 + 6^2 + 15^2}$

$= \sqrt{270} = 3\sqrt{30}$ square units

41. (a) $\overrightarrow{AB} = \langle 3 - 2, 1 - (-1), 2 - 4 \rangle = \langle 1, 2, -2 \rangle$ is parallel to

$\overrightarrow{DC} = \langle 0 - (-1), 5 - 3, 6 - 8 \rangle = \langle 1, 2, -2 \rangle.$

$\overrightarrow{AD} = \langle -3, 4, 4 \rangle$ is parallel to $\overrightarrow{BC} = \langle -3, 4, 4 \rangle.$

(b) $\overrightarrow{AB} \times \overrightarrow{AD} = \begin{vmatrix} \mathbf{i} & \mathbf{j} & \mathbf{k} \\ 1 & 2 & -2 \\ -3 & 4 & 4 \end{vmatrix} = \langle 16, 2, 10 \rangle$

$\text{Area} = \|\overrightarrow{AB} \times \overrightarrow{AD}\|$

$= \sqrt{16^2 + 2^2 + 10^2}$

$= \sqrt{360} = 6\sqrt{10}$ square units

(c) $\overrightarrow{AB} \cdot \overrightarrow{AD} = \langle 1, 2, -2 \rangle \cdot \langle -3, 4, 4 \rangle$

$\neq 0 \implies$ not a rectangle

42. (a) $\overrightarrow{AB} = \langle 1, 2, 3 \rangle$

$\overrightarrow{CD} = \langle 1, 2, 3 \rangle$

Opposites are parallel and same length. Thus, *ABCD* form a parallelogram.

(b) $\overrightarrow{AB} \times \overrightarrow{AC} = \begin{vmatrix} \mathbf{i} & \mathbf{j} & \mathbf{k} \\ 1 & 2 & 3 \\ 5 & 4 & 1 \end{vmatrix} = \langle -10, 14, -6 \rangle$

$\text{Area} = \|\overrightarrow{AB} \times \overrightarrow{AC}\| = \sqrt{(-10)^2 + 14^2 + (-6)^2} = 2\sqrt{83}$ square units

(c) $\overrightarrow{AB} \cdot \overrightarrow{AC} = 5 + 8 + 3 = 16 \neq 0 \implies$ not a rectangle

43. $\mathbf{u} = \langle 1, 2, 3 \rangle, \mathbf{v} = \langle -3, 0, 0 \rangle$

$\mathbf{u} \times \mathbf{v} = \begin{vmatrix} \mathbf{i} & \mathbf{j} & \mathbf{k} \\ 1 & 2 & 3 \\ -3 & 0 & 0 \end{vmatrix} = \langle 0, -9, 6 \rangle$

$\text{Area} = \frac{1}{2}\|\mathbf{u} \times \mathbf{v}\| = \frac{1}{2}\sqrt{81 + 36} = \frac{3}{2}\sqrt{13}$

44. $\mathbf{u} = \langle 2 - 1, 0 - (-4), 2 - 3 \rangle = \langle 1, 4, -1 \rangle$

$\mathbf{v} = \langle -2 - 1, 2 - (-4), 0 - 3 \rangle = \langle -3, 6, -3 \rangle$

$\mathbf{u} \times \mathbf{v} = \begin{vmatrix} \mathbf{i} & \mathbf{j} & \mathbf{k} \\ 1 & 4 & -1 \\ -3 & 6 & -3 \end{vmatrix} = \langle -6, 6, 18 \rangle$

$\text{Area} = \frac{1}{2}\|\mathbf{u} \times \mathbf{v}\| = \frac{1}{2}\sqrt{(-6)^2 + 6^2 + 18^2}$

$= \frac{1}{2}\sqrt{396} = 3\sqrt{11}$ square units

45. $\mathbf{u} = \langle -2 - 2, -2 - 3, 0 - (-5) \rangle = \langle -4, -5, 5 \rangle$

$\mathbf{v} = \langle 3 - 2, 0 - 3, 6 - (-5) \rangle = \langle 1, -3, 11 \rangle$

$$\mathbf{u} \times \mathbf{v} = \begin{vmatrix} \mathbf{i} & \mathbf{j} & \mathbf{k} \\ -4 & -5 & 5 \\ 1 & -3 & 11 \end{vmatrix} = \langle -40, 49, 17 \rangle$$

$$\text{Area} = \tfrac{1}{2}\|\mathbf{u} \times \mathbf{v}\| = \tfrac{1}{2}\sqrt{(-40)^2 + 49^2 + 17^2}$$
$$= \tfrac{1}{2}\sqrt{4290} \text{ square units}$$

46. $\mathbf{u} = \langle -2 - 2, -4 - 4, 0 - 0 \rangle = \langle -4, -8, 0 \rangle$

$\mathbf{v} = \langle 0 - 2, 0 - 4, 4 - 0 \rangle = \langle -2, -4, 4 \rangle$

$$\mathbf{u} \times \mathbf{v} = \begin{vmatrix} \mathbf{i} & \mathbf{j} & \mathbf{k} \\ -4 & -8 & 0 \\ -2 & -4 & 4 \end{vmatrix} = \langle -32, 16, 0 \rangle$$

$$\text{Area} = \tfrac{1}{2}\|\mathbf{u} \times \mathbf{v}\| = \tfrac{1}{2}\sqrt{(-32)^2 + 16^2}$$
$$= \tfrac{1}{2}\sqrt{1280} = 8\sqrt{5} \text{ sq. units}$$

47. $$\mathbf{u} \cdot (\mathbf{v} \times \mathbf{w}) = \begin{vmatrix} 2 & 3 & 3 \\ 4 & 4 & 0 \\ 0 & 0 & 4 \end{vmatrix}$$
$$= 2(16) - 3(16) + 3(0) = -16$$

48. $$\mathbf{u} \cdot (\mathbf{v} \times \mathbf{w}) = \begin{vmatrix} 2 & 0 & 1 \\ 0 & 3 & 0 \\ 0 & 0 & 1 \end{vmatrix} = 6$$

49. $$\mathbf{u} \cdot (\mathbf{v} \times \mathbf{w}) = \begin{vmatrix} 2 & 3 & 1 \\ 1 & -1 & 0 \\ 4 & 3 & 1 \end{vmatrix} = 2(-1) - 3(1) + 1(7) = 2$$

50. $$\mathbf{u} \cdot (\mathbf{v} \times \mathbf{w}) = \begin{vmatrix} 1 & 4 & -7 \\ 2 & 0 & 4 \\ 0 & -3 & 6 \end{vmatrix} = 1(0 + 12) - 4(12 - 0) - 7(-6) = 6$$

51. $$\mathbf{u} \cdot (\mathbf{v} \times \mathbf{w}) = \begin{vmatrix} 1 & 1 & 0 \\ 0 & 1 & 1 \\ 1 & 0 & 1 \end{vmatrix} = 1 + 1 = 2$$

Volume $= |\mathbf{u} \cdot (\mathbf{v} \times \mathbf{w})| = 2$ cubic units

52. $$\mathbf{u} \cdot (\mathbf{v} \times \mathbf{w}) = \begin{vmatrix} 1 & 1 & 3 \\ 0 & 3 & 3 \\ 3 & 0 & 3 \end{vmatrix} = 1(9) - 1(-9) + 3(-9) = -9$$

Volume $= |\mathbf{u} \cdot (\mathbf{v} \times \mathbf{w})| = |-9| = 9$ cubic units

53. $$\mathbf{u} \cdot (\mathbf{v} \times \mathbf{w}) = \begin{vmatrix} 0 & 2 & 2 \\ 0 & 0 & -2 \\ 3 & 0 & 2 \end{vmatrix} = 0 - 2(6) + 2(0) = -12$$

Volume $= |\mathbf{u} \cdot (\mathbf{v} \times \mathbf{w})| = 12$ cubic units

54. $$\mathbf{u} \cdot (\mathbf{v} \times \mathbf{w}) = \begin{vmatrix} 1 & 2 & -1 \\ -1 & 2 & 2 \\ 2 & 0 & 1 \end{vmatrix} = 1(2) - 2(-1 - 4) - 1(0 - 4) = 16$$

Volume $= |\mathbf{u} \cdot (\mathbf{v} \times \mathbf{w})| = 16$ cubic units

55. $\mathbf{u} = \langle 4, 0, 0\rangle$, $\mathbf{v} = \langle 0, -2, 3\rangle$, $\mathbf{w} = \langle 0, 5, 3\rangle$

$$\mathbf{u}\cdot(\mathbf{v}\times\mathbf{w}) = \begin{vmatrix} 4 & 0 & 0 \\ 0 & -2 & 3 \\ 0 & 5 & 3 \end{vmatrix} = 4(-21) = -84$$

Volume $= |-84| = 84$ cubic units

56. $\overrightarrow{AB} = \langle 1, 1, 0\rangle$, $\overrightarrow{AC} = \langle 1, 0, 2\rangle$, $\overrightarrow{AD} = \langle 0, 1, 1\rangle$

$$\mathbf{u}\cdot(\mathbf{v}\times\mathbf{w}) = \begin{vmatrix} 1 & 1 & 0 \\ 1 & 0 & 2 \\ 0 & 1 & 1 \end{vmatrix} = 1(-2) - 1(1) = -3$$

Volume $= 3$ cubic units

57. $$\mathbf{V}\times\mathbf{F} = \begin{vmatrix} \mathbf{i} & \mathbf{j} & \mathbf{k} \\ 0 & -\frac{1}{2}\cos 40^\circ & -\frac{1}{2}\sin 40^\circ \\ 0 & 0 & -p \end{vmatrix} = \left(\frac{p}{2}\cos 40^\circ\right)\mathbf{i}$$

(a) $T(p) = \|\mathbf{V}\times\mathbf{F}\| = \dfrac{p}{2}\cos 40^\circ$

(b)

p	15	20	25	30	35	40	45
T	5.75	7.66	9.58	11.49	13.41	15.32	17.24

58. $\overrightarrow{PQ} = 0.16\mathbf{k}$

$$\overrightarrow{PQ}\times\mathbf{F} = \begin{vmatrix} \mathbf{i} & \mathbf{j} & \mathbf{k} \\ 0 & 0 & 0.16 \\ 0 & -1000\sqrt{3} & -1000 \end{vmatrix} = 160\sqrt{3}\,\mathbf{i}$$

$\|\overrightarrow{PQ}\times\mathbf{F}\| = 160\sqrt{3}$ ft-lb

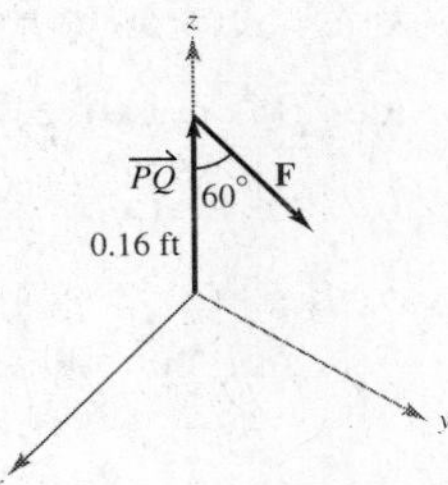

59. True. The cross product is defined for vectors in three-dimensional space.

60. False. $\mathbf{u}\times\mathbf{v} = -(\mathbf{v}\times\mathbf{u})$

61. If $\mathbf{u}$ and $\mathbf{v}$ are orthogonal, then $\sin\theta = 1$ and hence, $\|\mathbf{u}\times\mathbf{v}\| = \|\mathbf{u}\|\,\|\mathbf{v}\|\sin\theta = \|\mathbf{u}\|\,\|\mathbf{v}\|$.

62. $$\mathbf{u}\times(\mathbf{v}\times\mathbf{w}) = \mathbf{u}\times\begin{vmatrix} \mathbf{i} & \mathbf{j} & \mathbf{k} \\ v_1 & v_2 & v_3 \\ w_1 & w_2 & w_3 \end{vmatrix} = \mathbf{u}\times[(v_2w_3 - w_2v_3)\mathbf{i} - (v_1w_3 - w_1v_3)\mathbf{j} + (v_1w_2 - w_1v_2)\mathbf{k}]$$

$$= \begin{vmatrix} \mathbf{i} & \mathbf{j} & \mathbf{k} \\ u_1 & u_2 & u_3 \\ v_2w_3 - w_2v_3 & w_1v_3 - v_1w_3 & v_1w_2 - w_1v_2 \end{vmatrix}$$

$$= [u_2(v_1w_2 - w_1v_2) - u_3(w_1v_3 - v_1w_3)]\mathbf{i}$$
$$\quad - [u_1(v_1w_2 - w_1v_2) - u_3(v_2w_3 - w_2v_3)]\mathbf{j} + [u_1(w_1v_3 - v_1w_3) - u_2(v_2w_3 - w_2v_3)]\mathbf{k}$$

$$= [u_2w_2v_1 + u_3w_3v_1 - u_2v_2w_1 - u_3v_3w_1]\mathbf{i}$$
$$\quad - [-u_1w_1v_2 - u_3w_3v_2 + u_1v_1w_2 + u_3v_3w_2]\mathbf{j} + [u_1w_1v_3 + u_2w_2v_3 - u_1v_1w_3 - u_2v_2w_3]\mathbf{k}$$

$$= (u_1w_1 + u_2w_2 + u_3w_3)(v_1\mathbf{i} + v_2\mathbf{j} + v_3\mathbf{k}) - (u_1v_1 + u_2v_2 + u_3v_3)(w_1\mathbf{i} + w_2\mathbf{j} + w_3\mathbf{k})$$

$$= (u_1w_1 + u_2w_2 + u_3w_3)\mathbf{v} - (u_1v_1 + u_2v_2 + u_3v_3)\mathbf{w}$$

$$= (\mathbf{u}\cdot\mathbf{w})\mathbf{v} - (\mathbf{u}\cdot\mathbf{v})\mathbf{w}$$

63. $\mathbf{v} \times \mathbf{w} = \begin{vmatrix} \mathbf{i} & \mathbf{j} & \mathbf{k} \\ v_1 & v_2 & v_3 \\ w_1 & w_2 & w_3 \end{vmatrix} = (v_2w_3 - w_2v_3)\mathbf{i} - (v_1w_3 - w_1v_3)\mathbf{j} + (v_1w_2 - v_2w_1)\mathbf{k}$

Hence,

$$\mathbf{u} \cdot (\mathbf{v} \times \mathbf{w}) = u_1(v_2w_3 - w_2v_3) - u_2(v_1w_3 - w_1v_3) + u_3(v_1w_2 - v_2w_1) = \begin{vmatrix} u_1 & u_2 & u_3 \\ v_1 & v_2 & v_3 \\ w_1 & w_2 & w_3 \end{vmatrix}.$$

64. $\mathbf{u} \times \mathbf{v} = \begin{vmatrix} \mathbf{i} & \mathbf{j} & \mathbf{k} \\ \cos\alpha & \sin\alpha & 0 \\ \cos\beta & \sin\beta & 0 \end{vmatrix} = (\cos\alpha\ \sin\beta - \sin\alpha\ \cos\beta)\mathbf{k}$

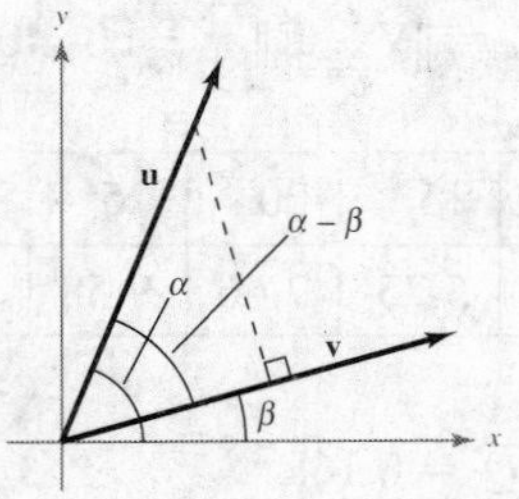

Area of triangle formed by the unit vectors **u** and **v** is

$\frac{1}{2}(\text{base})(\text{height}) = \frac{1}{2}(1)\sin(\alpha - \beta)$.

The area is also given by $\frac{1}{2}\|\mathbf{u} \times \mathbf{v}\| = \frac{1}{2}|\cos\alpha\sin\beta - \sin\alpha\cos\beta|$

Notice that $\cos\alpha\sin\beta - \sin\alpha\ \cos\beta$ is negative.

Thus, $\sin(\alpha - \beta) = \sin\alpha\ \cos\beta - \cos\alpha\sin\beta$.

65. $\cos 480° = \cos 120° = -\frac{1}{2}$

66. $\tan 300° = -\sqrt{3}$

67. $\sin 690° = \sin 330° = -\frac{1}{2}$

68. $\cos 930° = \cos 210° = -\frac{\sqrt{3}}{2}$

69. $\sin\frac{19\pi}{6} = \sin\left(\frac{7\pi}{6}\right) = -\frac{1}{2}$

70. $\cos\frac{17\pi}{6} = \cos\frac{5\pi}{6} = -\frac{\sqrt{3}}{2}$

71. $\tan\frac{15\pi}{4} = \tan\frac{7\pi}{4} = -1$

72. $\tan\frac{10\pi}{3} = \tan\frac{4\pi}{3} = \sqrt{3}$

Section 10.4 Lines and Planes in Space

- The parametric equations of the line in space parallel to the vector $\langle a, b, c\rangle$ and passing through the point (x_1, y_2, z_3) are

  $x = x_1 + at, \quad y = y_1 + bt, \quad z = z_1 + ct.$
- The standard equation of the plane in space containing the point (x_1, y_1, z_1) and having normal vector (a, b, c) is

  $a(x - x_1) + b(y - y_1) + c(z - z_1) = 0.$
- You should be able to find the angle between two planes by calculating the angle between their normal vectors.
- You should be able to sketch a plane in space.
- The distance between a point Q and a plane having normal $\mathbf{n}$ is

  $$D = \|\text{proj}_{\mathbf{n}}\overrightarrow{PQ}\| = \frac{|\overrightarrow{PQ} \cdot \mathbf{n}|}{\|\mathbf{n}\|}$$

  where P is a point in the plane.

Vocabulary Check

1. direction, $\frac{\overrightarrow{PQ}}{t}$
2. parametric equations
3. symmetric equations
4. normal
5. $a(x - x_1) + b(y - y_1) + c(z - z_1) = 0$

1. $x = x_1 + at = 0 + t$

$y = y_1 + bt = 0 + 2t$

$z = z_1 + ct = 0 + 3t$

(a) Parametric equations: $x = t, y = 2t, z = 3t$

(b) Symmetric equations: $\frac{x}{1} = \frac{y}{2} = \frac{z}{3}$

2. $x = x_1 + at = 3 + 3t$

$y = y_1 + bt = -5 - 7t$

$z = z_1 + ct = 1 - 10t$

(a) Parametric equations:
$x = 3 + 3t, y = -5 - 7t, z = 1 - 10t$

(b) Symmetric equations: $\frac{x - 3}{3} = \frac{y + 5}{-7} = \frac{z - 1}{-10}$

3. $x = x_1 + at = -4 + \frac{1}{2}t,\ y = y_1 + bt = 1 + \frac{4}{3}t,\ z = z_1 + ct = 0 - t$

(a) Parametric equations: $x = -4 + \frac{1}{2}t, y = 1 + \frac{4}{3}t, z = -t$

Equivalently: $x = -4 + 3t, y = 1 + 8t, z = -6t$

(b) Symmetric equations: $\frac{x + 4}{3} = \frac{y - 1}{8} = \frac{z}{-6}$

4. $x = x_1 + at = 5 + 4t$

$y = y_1 + bt = 0 + 0t$

$z = z_1 + ct = 10 + 3t$

(a) Parametric equations:
$x = 5 + 4t, y = 0, z = 10 + 3t$

(b) $\frac{x - 5}{4} = \frac{z - 10}{3}, y = 0$

Not possible

5. $x = x_1 + at = 2 + 2t,$

$y = y_1 + bt = -3 - 3t,$

$z = z_1 + ct = 5 + t$

(a) Parametric equations:
$x = 2 + 2t, y = -3 - 3t, z = 5 + t$

(b) Symmetric equations: $\frac{x - 2}{2} = \frac{y + 3}{-3} = z - 5$

6. $\mathbf{v} = \langle 3, -2, 1 \rangle$

(a) $x = 1 + 3t, y = -2t, z = 1 + t$

(b) Symmetric equations: $\frac{x - 1}{3} = \frac{y}{-2} = \frac{z - 1}{1}$

7. $\mathbf{v} = \langle 1 - 2, 4 - 0, -3 - 2 \rangle = \langle -1, 4, -5 \rangle$

Point: $(2, 0, 2)$

(a) $x = 2 - t, y = 4t, z = 2 - 5t$

(b) $\frac{x - 2}{-1} = \frac{y}{4} = \frac{z - 2}{-5}$

8. $\mathbf{v} = \langle 8, 5, 12 \rangle$

Point: $(2, 3, 0)$

(a) Parametric equations:
$x = 2 + 8t, y = 3 + 5t, z = 12t$

(b) Symmetric equations: $\frac{x - 2}{8} = \frac{y - 3}{5} = \frac{z}{12}$

9. $\mathbf{v} = \langle 1 - (-3), -2 - 8, 16 - 15 \rangle = \langle 4, -10, 1 \rangle$

Point: $(-3, 8, 15)$

(a) $x = -3 + 4t, y = 8 - 10t, z = 15 + t$

(b) $\frac{x + 3}{4} = \frac{y - 8}{-10} = \frac{z - 15}{1}$

10. $\mathbf{v} = \langle 1-2, -5-3, 3+1\rangle = \langle -1, -8, 4\rangle$

Point: $(2, 3, -1)$

(a) $x = 2 - t, y = 3 - 8t, z = -1 + 4t$

(b) $\dfrac{x-2}{-1} = \dfrac{y-3}{-8} = \dfrac{z+1}{4}$

11. $\mathbf{v} = \langle -1-3, 1-1, 5-2\rangle = \langle -4, 0, 3\rangle$

Point: $(3, 1, 2)$

(a) $x = 3 - 4t, y = 1, z = 2 + 3t$

(b) $\dfrac{x-3}{-4} = \dfrac{z-2}{3},\ y = 1$

Not possible

12. $\mathbf{v} = \langle 2-2, 1+1, -3-5\rangle = \langle 0, 2, -8\rangle$

Point: $(2, -1, 5)$

(a) $x = 2, y = -1 + 2t, z = 5 - 8t$

(b) $\dfrac{y+1}{2} = \dfrac{z-5}{-8},\ x = 2$

Not possible

13. $\mathbf{v} = \left\langle 1 + \frac{1}{2}, -\frac{1}{2} - 2, 0 - \frac{1}{2}\right\rangle = \left\langle \frac{3}{2}, -\frac{5}{2}, -\frac{1}{2}\right\rangle$

or $\langle 3, -5, -1\rangle$

Point: $\left(-\frac{1}{2}, 2, \frac{1}{2}\right)$

(a) $x = -\frac{1}{2} + 3t, y = 2 - 5t, z = \frac{1}{2} - t$

(b) $\dfrac{x+\frac{1}{2}}{3} = \dfrac{y-2}{-5} = \dfrac{z-\frac{1}{2}}{-1}$

14. $\mathbf{v} = \left\langle 3 - \left(-\frac{3}{2}\right), -5 - \frac{3}{2}, -4 - 2\right\rangle = \left\langle \frac{9}{2}, -\frac{13}{2}, -6\right\rangle$, or $\langle 9, -13, -12\rangle$

Point: $(3, -5, -4)$

(a) Parametric equations: $x = 3 + 9t, y = -5 - 13t, z = -4 - 12t$

(b) Symmetric equations: $\dfrac{x-3}{9} = \dfrac{y+5}{-13} = \dfrac{z+4}{-12}$

15.

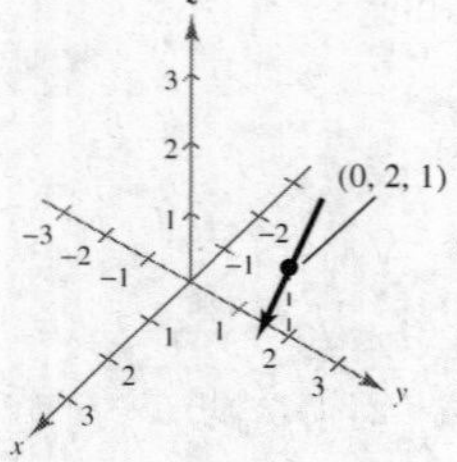

16.

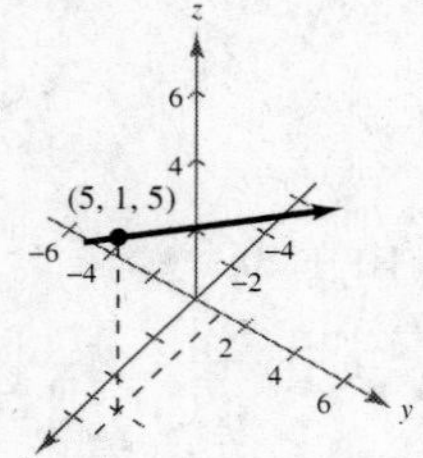

17. $a(x - x_1) + b(y - y_1) + c(z - z_1) = 0$

$1(x-2) + 0(y-1) + 0(z-2) = 0$

$x - 2 = 0$

18. $a(x - x_0) + b(y - y_0) + c(z - z_0) = 0$

$0(x-1) + 0(y-0) + 1(z+3) = 0$

$z + 3 = 0$

19. $-2(x-5) + 1(y-6) - 2(z-3) = 0$

$-2x + y - 2z + 10 = 0$

20. $0(x-0) - 3(y-0) + 5(z-0) = 0$

$-3y + 5z = 0$

21. $\mathbf{n} = \langle -1, -2, 1\rangle \Rightarrow$

$-1(x-2) - 2(y-0) + 1(z-0) = 0$

$-x - 2y + z + 2 = 0$

22. $\mathbf{n} = \langle -1, 1, -2\rangle$

$-1(x-0) + 1(y-0) - 2(z-6) = 0$

$-x + y - 2z + 12 = 0$

23. $\mathbf{u} = \langle 1-0, 2-0, 3-0\rangle = \langle 1, 2, 3\rangle$

$\mathbf{v} = \langle -2-0, 3-0, 3-0\rangle = \langle -2, 3, 3\rangle$

$$\mathbf{n} = \mathbf{u}\times\mathbf{v} = \begin{vmatrix} \mathbf{i} & \mathbf{j} & \mathbf{k} \\ 1 & 2 & 3 \\ -2 & 3 & 3 \end{vmatrix} = \langle -3, -9, 7\rangle$$

$$-3(x-0) - 9(y-0) + 7(z-0) = 0$$
$$-3x - 9y + 7z = 0$$
$$3x + 9y - 7z = 0$$

24. $\mathbf{u} = \langle 2, -6, 2\rangle$, $\mathbf{v} = \langle -3, -3, 0\rangle$

$$\mathbf{u}\times\mathbf{v} = \begin{vmatrix} \mathbf{i} & \mathbf{j} & \mathbf{k} \\ 2 & -6 & 2 \\ -3 & -3 & 0 \end{vmatrix} = \langle 6, -6, -24\rangle$$

$\mathbf{n} = \langle -1, 1, 4\rangle$

Plane: $-1(x-4) + 1(y+1) + 4(z-3) = 0$
$$-x + y + 4z - 7 = 0$$

25. $\mathbf{u} = \langle 3-2, 4-3, 2+2\rangle = \langle 1, 1, 4\rangle$

$\mathbf{v} = \langle 1-2, -1-3, 0+2\rangle = \langle -1, -4, 2\rangle$

$$\mathbf{n} = \mathbf{u}\times\mathbf{v} = \begin{vmatrix} \mathbf{i} & \mathbf{j} & \mathbf{k} \\ 1 & 1 & 4 \\ -1 & -4 & 2 \end{vmatrix} = \langle 18, -6, -3\rangle$$

$$18(x-2) - 6(y-3) - 3(z+2) = 0$$
$$18x - 6y - 3z - 24 = 0$$
$$6x - 2y - z - 8 = 0$$

26. $\mathbf{u} = \langle 4, 0, 2\rangle$, $\mathbf{v} = \langle 1, 2, -5\rangle$

$$\mathbf{u}\times\mathbf{v} = \begin{vmatrix} \mathbf{i} & \mathbf{j} & \mathbf{k} \\ 4 & 0 & 2 \\ 1 & 2 & -5 \end{vmatrix} = \langle -4, 22, 8\rangle$$

$\mathbf{n} = \langle -2, 11, 4\rangle$

Plane: $-2(x-1) + 11(y+1) + 4(z-2) = 0$
$$-2x + 11y + 4z + 5 = 0$$

27. $\mathbf{n} = \mathbf{j}$: $0(x-2) + 1(y-5) + 0(z-3) = 0$
$$y - 5 = 0$$

28. $\mathbf{n} = \langle 1, 0, 0\rangle$, normal to yz-plane

$$1(x-1) + 0(y-2) + 0(z-3) = 0$$
$$x - 1 = 0$$

29. $\langle 0-(-1), 2-(-2), 4-0\rangle = \langle 1, 4, 4\rangle$ and $\langle 1, 0, 0\rangle$ are parallel to the plane.

$$\mathbf{n} = \begin{vmatrix} \mathbf{i} & \mathbf{j} & \mathbf{k} \\ 1 & 4 & 4 \\ 1 & 0 & 0 \end{vmatrix} = \langle 0, 4, -4\rangle$$

$$0(x-0) + 4(y-2) - 4(z-4) = 0$$
$$4y - 4z + 8 = 0$$
$$y - z + 2 = 0$$

30. $\langle 4-1, 0-(-2), -1-4\rangle = \langle 3, 2, -5\rangle$ and $\langle 0, 1, 0\rangle$ are parallel to the plane.

$$\mathbf{n} = \begin{vmatrix} \mathbf{i} & \mathbf{j} & \mathbf{k} \\ 3 & 2 & -5 \\ 0 & 1 & 0 \end{vmatrix} = \langle 5, 0, 3\rangle$$

$$5(x-1) + 0(y+2) + 3(z-4) = 0$$
$$5x + 3z - 17 = 0$$

31. $\langle -1-2, 1-2, -1-1\rangle = \langle -3, -1, -2\rangle$ and $\langle 2, -3, 1\rangle$ are parallel to plane.

$$\mathbf{n} = \begin{vmatrix} \mathbf{i} & \mathbf{j} & \mathbf{k} \\ -3 & -1 & -2 \\ 2 & -3 & 1 \end{vmatrix} = \langle -7, -1, 11\rangle$$

$$-7(x-2) - 1(y-2) + 11(z-1) = 0$$
$$-7x - y + 11z + 5 = 0$$

32. $\langle 1-(-1), 2-(-1), 0-2\rangle = \langle 2, 3, -2\rangle$ and $\langle 2, -3, 1\rangle$ are parallel to the plane.

$$\mathbf{n} = \begin{vmatrix} \mathbf{i} & \mathbf{j} & \mathbf{k} \\ 2 & 3 & -2 \\ 2 & -3 & 1 \end{vmatrix} = \langle -3, -6, -12\rangle$$

$$-3(x-1) - 6(y-2) - 12(z-0) = 0$$
$$-3x - 6y - 12z + 15 = 0$$
$$x + 2y + 4z - 5 = 0$$

33. $\mathbf{v} = \langle 0, 0, 1\rangle$ and $P = (2, 3, 4)$

$x = 2$

$y = 3$

$z = 4 + t$

34. $\mathbf{v} = \langle 0, 1, 0\rangle$ and $P = (-4, 5, 2)$

$x = -4$

$y = 5 + t$

$z = 2$

35. $\mathbf{v} = \langle 3, 2, -1\rangle$ and $P = (2, 3, 4)$

$x = 2 + 3t$

$y = 3 + 2t$

$z = 4 - t$

36. $\mathbf{v} = \langle -1, 2, 1\rangle$ and $P = (-4, 5, 2)$

$x = -4 - t$

$y = 5 + 2t$

$z = 2 + t$

37. $\mathbf{v} = \langle 2, -1, 3\rangle$ and $P = (5, -3, -4)$

$x = 5 + 2t$

$y = -3 - t$

$z = -4 + 3t$

38. $\mathbf{v} = \langle 5, -1, 0\rangle$ and $P = (-1, 4, -3)$

$x = -1 + 5t$

$y = 4 - t$

$z = -3$

39. $\mathbf{v} = \langle -1, 1, 1\rangle$ and $P = (2, 1, 2)$

$x = 2 - t$

$y = 1 + t$

$z = 2 + t$

40. $\mathbf{v} = \langle -2, 2, 0\rangle$ and $P = (-6, 0, 8)$

$x = -6 - 2t$

$y = 2t$

$z = 8$

41. $\mathbf{n}_1 = \langle 5, -3, 1\rangle, \mathbf{n}_2 = \langle 1, 4, 7\rangle$

$\mathbf{n}_1 \cdot \mathbf{n}_2 = 5 - 12 + 7 = 0$; orthogonal

42. $\mathbf{n}_1 = \langle 3, 1, -4\rangle, \mathbf{n}_2 = \langle -9, -3, 12\rangle$

$3\mathbf{n}_1 = \langle 9, 3, -12\rangle = -\mathbf{n}_2 \implies$ parallel planes

43. $\mathbf{n}_1 = \langle 2, 0, -1\rangle, \mathbf{n}_2 = \langle 4, 1, 8\rangle$

$\mathbf{n}_1 \cdot \mathbf{n}_2 = 8 - 8 = 0$; orthogonal

44. $\mathbf{n}_1 = \langle 1, -5, -1\rangle$

$\mathbf{n}_2 = \langle 5, -25, -5\rangle = 5\mathbf{n}_1 \implies$ parallel

45. (a) $\mathbf{n}_1 = \langle 3, -4, 5\rangle, \mathbf{n}_2 = \langle 1, 1, -1\rangle$; normal vectors to planes

$$\cos\theta = \frac{|\mathbf{n}_1 \cdot \mathbf{n}_2|}{\|\mathbf{n}_1\|\,\|\mathbf{n}_2\|} = \frac{|-6|}{\sqrt{50}\sqrt{3}} = \frac{6}{\sqrt{150}} \implies \theta \approx 60.67°$$

(b) $3x - 4y + 5z = 6$ Equation 1

$x + y - z = 2$ Equation 2

(-3) times Equation 2 added to Equation 1 gives

$-7y + 8z = 0$

$y = \frac{8}{7}z.$

Substituting back into Equation 2, $x = 2 - y + z = 2 - \frac{8}{7}z + z = 2 - \frac{1}{7}z.$

Letting $t = z/7$, we obtain $x = 2 - t, y = 8t, z = 7t$.

46. (a) $\mathbf{n}_1 = \langle 1, -3, 1\rangle, \mathbf{n}_2 = \langle 2, 0, 5\rangle$

$$\cos\theta = \frac{|\mathbf{n}_1 \cdot \mathbf{n}_2|}{\|\mathbf{n}_1\|\,\|\mathbf{n}_2\|} = \frac{|7|}{\sqrt{11}\sqrt{29}} = \frac{7}{\sqrt{319}} \implies \theta \approx 66.93°$$

—CONTINUED—

46. —CONTINUED—

(b) $2x + 5z + 3 = 0 \implies x = \frac{1}{2}(-5z - 3)$

Then $3y = x + z + 2 = \frac{1}{2}(-5z - 3) + z + 2 = -\frac{3}{2}z + \frac{1}{2} \implies y = -\frac{1}{2}z + \frac{1}{6}$.

Let $z = t$. Parametric equations: $x = -\frac{5}{2}t - \frac{3}{2}, y = -\frac{1}{2}t + \frac{1}{6}, z = t$

Or equivalently, let $z = 2t$ and you obtain $x = -5t - \frac{3}{2}, y = -t + \frac{1}{6}, z = 2t$.

47. (a) $\mathbf{n}_1 = \langle 1, 1, -1\rangle, \mathbf{n}_2 = \langle 2, -5, -1\rangle$; normal vectors to planes

$\cos\theta = \frac{|\mathbf{n}_1 \cdot \mathbf{n}_2|}{\|\mathbf{n}_1\|\,\|\mathbf{n}_2\|} = \frac{|-2|}{\sqrt{3}\sqrt{30}} = \frac{2}{\sqrt{90}} \implies \theta \approx 77.83°$

(b) $x + y - z = 0$ Equation 1

$2x - 5y - z = 1$ Equation 2

(-2) times Equation 1 added to Equation 2 gives

$-7y + z = 1$

$y = \frac{z - 1}{7}$.

Substituting back into Equation 1, $x = z - y = z - \frac{z-1}{7} = \frac{6z}{7} + \frac{1}{7} = \frac{1}{7}(6z + 1)$.

Letting $z = t, x = \frac{6t + 1}{7}, y = \frac{t - 1}{7}$. Equivalently, let $y = t, z = 7t + 1$ and $x = 6t + 1$.

48. The planes are parallel because $\mathbf{n}_1 = \langle 2, 4, -2\rangle$ is a multiple of $\mathbf{n}_2 = \langle -3, -6, 3\rangle$. The planes do not intersect.

49. $x + 2y + 3z = 6$

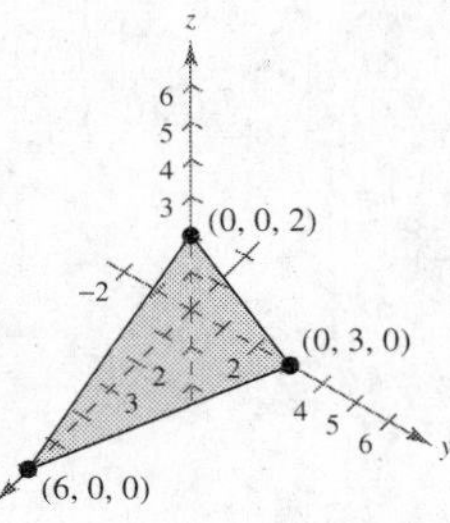

50. $2x - y + 4z = 4$

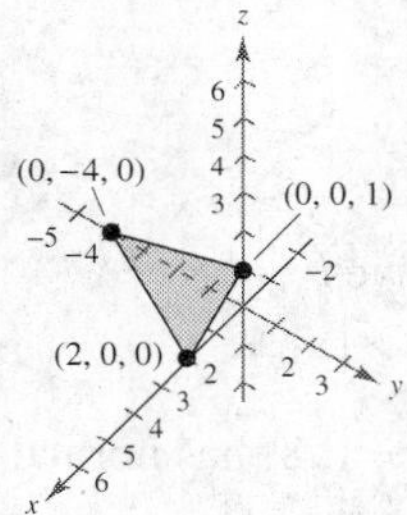

51. $x + 2y = 4$

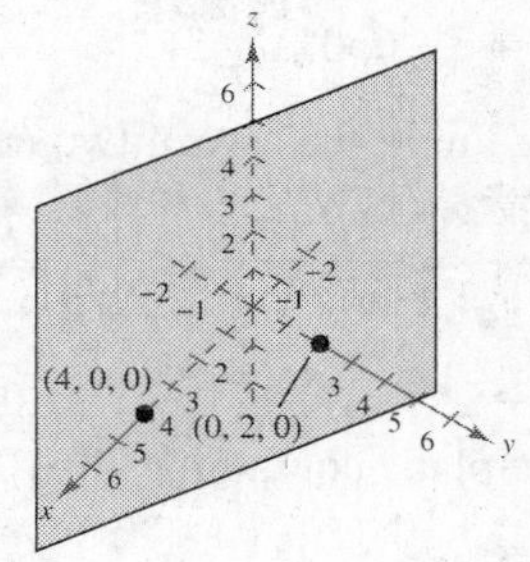

52. $y + z = 5$

53. $3x + 2y - z = 6$

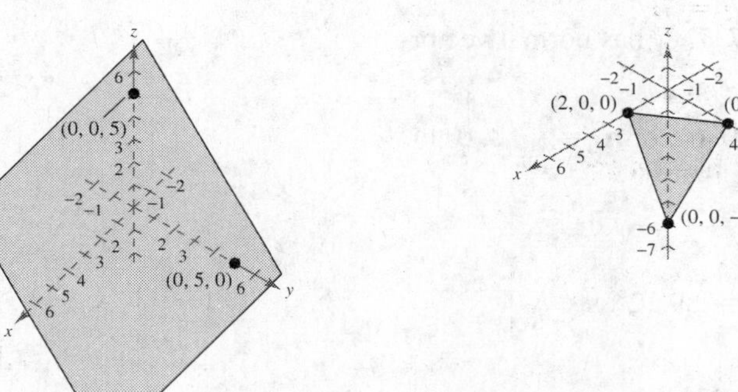

54. $x - 3z = 6$

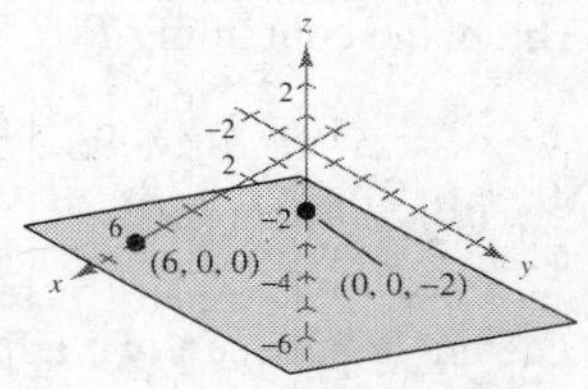

55. $D = \dfrac{|\overrightarrow{PQ} \cdot \mathbf{n}|}{\|\mathbf{n}\|}$

$P = (1, 0, 0)$ on plane, $Q = (0, 0, 0)$,

$\mathbf{n} = \langle 8, -4, 1\rangle, \overrightarrow{PQ} = \langle -1, 0, 0\rangle$

$$D = \frac{|\langle -1, 0, 0\rangle \cdot \langle 8, -4, 1\rangle|}{\sqrt{64 + 16 + 1}} = \frac{|-8|}{\sqrt{81}} = \frac{8}{9}$$

56. $P = (4, 0, 0)$ on plane, $Q = (3, 2, 1), \mathbf{n} = \langle 1, -1, 2\rangle$

$\overrightarrow{PQ} = \langle -1, 2, 1\rangle$

$$D = \frac{|\overrightarrow{PQ} \cdot \mathbf{n}|}{\|\mathbf{n}\|} = \frac{|-1|}{\sqrt{6}} = \frac{1}{\sqrt{6}} = \frac{\sqrt{6}}{6}$$

57. $D = \dfrac{|\overrightarrow{PQ} \cdot \mathbf{n}|}{\|\mathbf{n}\|}$

$P = (2, 0, 0)$ on plane, $Q = (4, -2, -2)$,

$\mathbf{n} = \langle 2, -1, 1\rangle, \overrightarrow{PQ} = \langle 2, -2, -2\rangle$

$$D = \frac{|\langle 2, -2, -2\rangle \cdot \langle 2, -1, 1\rangle|}{\sqrt{6}} = \frac{4}{\sqrt{6}} = \frac{2\sqrt{6}}{3}$$

58. $P = (6, 0, 0)$ on plane, $Q = (-1, 2, 5)$,

$\overrightarrow{PQ} = \langle -7, 2, 5\rangle, \mathbf{n} = \langle 2, 3, 1\rangle$

$$D = \frac{|\overrightarrow{PQ} \cdot \mathbf{n}|}{\|\mathbf{n}\|} = \frac{|-3|}{\sqrt{14}} = \frac{3}{\sqrt{14}} = \frac{3\sqrt{14}}{14}$$

59. The normal vector to plane containing $(0, 0, 0)$, $(2, 2, 12)$ and $(10, 0, 0)$ is obtained as follows.

$\mathbf{v}_1 = \langle 2, 2, 12\rangle, \mathbf{v}_2 = \langle 10, 0, 0\rangle$

$$\mathbf{v}_1 \times \mathbf{v}_2 = \begin{vmatrix} \mathbf{i} & \mathbf{j} & \mathbf{k} \\ 2 & 2 & 12 \\ 10 & 0 & 0 \end{vmatrix} = \langle 0, 120, -20\rangle$$

$\mathbf{n}_1 = \langle 0, 6, -1\rangle$

The normal vector to the plane containing $(0, 0, 0)$, $(2, 2, 12)$ and $(0, 10, 0)$ is obtained as follows.

$\mathbf{u}_1 = \langle 2, 2, 12\rangle, \mathbf{u}_2 = \langle 0, 10, 0\rangle$

$$\mathbf{u}_1 \times \mathbf{u}_2 = \begin{vmatrix} \mathbf{i} & \mathbf{j} & \mathbf{k} \\ 2 & 2 & 12 \\ 0 & 10 & 0 \end{vmatrix} = \langle -120, 0, 20\rangle$$

$\mathbf{n}_2 = \langle -6, 0, 1\rangle$

The angle θ between two adjacent sides is given by

$$\cos\theta = \frac{|\mathbf{n}_1 \cdot \mathbf{n}_2|}{\|\mathbf{n}_1\|\,\|\mathbf{n}_2\|} = \frac{|-1|}{\sqrt{37}\sqrt{37}} = \frac{1}{37} \implies \theta \approx 88.45°.$$

60. The plane containing $P(6, 0, 0)$, $S(0, 0, 0)$, $T(-1, -1, 8)$ has normal vector

$$\langle 6, 0, 0\rangle \times \langle -1, -1, 8\rangle = \begin{vmatrix} \mathbf{i} & \mathbf{j} & \mathbf{k} \\ 6 & 0 & 0 \\ -1 & -1 & 8 \end{vmatrix} = \langle 0, -48, -6\rangle \text{ or } \mathbf{n}_1 = \langle 0, 8, 1\rangle.$$

The plane containing $P(6, 0, 0)$, $Q(6, 6, 0)$, and $R(7, 7, 8)$ has normal vector

$$\langle 0, -6, 0\rangle \times \langle 1, 1, 8\rangle = \begin{vmatrix} \mathbf{i} & \mathbf{j} & \mathbf{k} \\ 0 & -6 & 0 \\ 1 & 1 & 8 \end{vmatrix} = \langle -48, 0, 6\rangle, \text{ or } \mathbf{n}_2 = \langle -8, 0, 1\rangle.$$

The angle between two adjacent sides is given by

$$\cos\theta = \frac{|\mathbf{n}_1 \cdot \mathbf{n}_2|}{\|\mathbf{n}_1\|\,\|\mathbf{n}_2\|} = \frac{1}{\sqrt{65}\sqrt{65}} = \frac{1}{65} \implies \theta \approx 89.12°.$$

61. False. They might be skew lines, such as:

L_1: $x = t, y = 0, z = 0$ (x-axis)

and L_2: $x = 0, y = t, z = 1$

62. True

63. The lines are parallel: $-\frac{3}{2}\langle 10, -18, 20\rangle = \langle -15, 27, -30\rangle$

64. (a) Sphere: $(x-4)^2 + (y+1)^2 + (z-1)^2 = 4$

(b) Two planes parallel to given plane. Let $Q = (x, y, z)$ be a point on one of these planes, and pick $P = (0, 0, 10)$ on the given plane. By the distance formula,

$$2 = \frac{|\overrightarrow{PQ} \cdot \mathbf{n}|}{\|\mathbf{n}\|} = \frac{|\langle x, y, z-10\rangle \cdot \langle 4, -3, 1\rangle|}{\sqrt{26}}$$

$$\pm 2\sqrt{26} = 4x - 3y + z - 10$$

$$4x - 3y + z = 10 \pm 2\sqrt{26} \quad \text{(Two planes parallel to given plane)}$$

65. $x^2 + y^2 = 10^2 = 100$

66. $\theta = \frac{3\pi}{4} \Rightarrow \tan\theta = -1 = \frac{y}{x} \Rightarrow y = -x$ (line)

67. $r = 3\cos\theta, r^2 = 3r\cos\theta, x^2 + y^2 = 3x$

68. $r = \dfrac{1}{2-\cos\theta} \Rightarrow 2r - r\cos\theta = 1 \Rightarrow 2\sqrt{x^2+y^2} - x = 1$

$$\Rightarrow 2\sqrt{x^2+y^2} = x + 1 \Rightarrow 4(x^2+y^2) = x^2 + 2x + 1 \Rightarrow 3x^2 + 4y^2 = 2x + 1$$

69. $r^2 = 49$

$r = 7$

70. $x^2 + y^2 - 4x = 0$

$r^2 - 4r\cos\theta = 0$

$r - 4\cos\theta = 0 \Rightarrow r = 4\cos\theta$

71. $y = 5$

$r\sin\theta = 5$

$r = 5\csc\theta$

72. $2x - y + 1 = 0$

$2r\cos\theta - r\sin\theta = -1$

$r(2\cos\theta - \sin\theta) = -1$

$$r = \frac{1}{\sin\theta - 2\cos\theta}$$

Review Exercises for Chapter 10

1. (a) and (b)

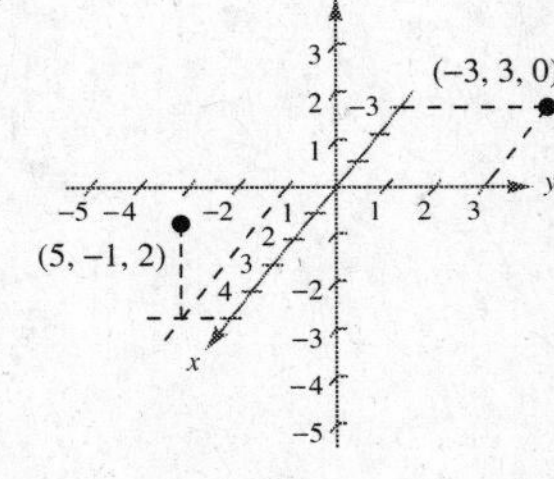

2.

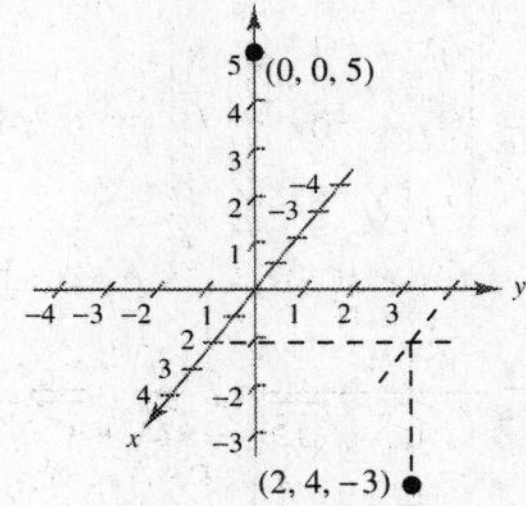

3. $(-5, 4, 0)$

4. y-axis $\Rightarrow x = z = 0$

$(0, -7, 0)$

5. $d = \sqrt{(5-4)^2 + (2-0)^2 + (1-7)^2}$

$= \sqrt{1 + 4 + 36}$

$= \sqrt{41}$

6. $d = \sqrt{(2-(-1))^2 + (3-(-3))^2 + (-4-0)^2}$

$= \sqrt{9 + 36 + 16}$

$= \sqrt{61}$

7. $d_1 = \sqrt{(3-0)^2 + (-2-3)^2 + (0-2)^2} = \sqrt{9 + 25 + 4} = \sqrt{38}$

$d_2 = \sqrt{(0-0)^2 + (5-3)^2 + (-3-2)^2} = \sqrt{4 + 25} = \sqrt{29}$

$d_3 = \sqrt{(0-3)^2 + (5-(-2))^2 + (-3-0)^2} = \sqrt{9 + 49 + 9} = \sqrt{67}$

$d_1^2 + d_2^2 = 38 + 29 = 67 = d_3^2$

8. $d_1 = \sqrt{(4-0)^2 + (3-0)^2 + (2-4)^2} = \sqrt{16 + 9 + 4} = \sqrt{29}$

$d_2 = \sqrt{(4-4)^2 + (5-3)^2 + (5-2)^2} = \sqrt{4 + 9} = \sqrt{13}$

$d_3 = \sqrt{(4-0)^2 + (5-0)^2 + (5-4)^2} = \sqrt{16 + 25 + 1} = \sqrt{42}$

$d_1^2 + d_2^2 = d_3^2 = 42$

9. Midpoint: $\left(\frac{-2+2}{2}, \frac{3-5}{2}, \frac{2+(-2)}{2}\right) = (0, -1, 0)$

10. Midpoint: $\left(\frac{7+1}{2}, \frac{1-1}{2}, \frac{-4+2}{2}\right) = (4, 0, -1)$

11. Midpoint: $\left(\frac{10-8}{2}, \frac{6-2}{2}, \frac{-12-6}{2}\right) = (1, 2, -9)$

12. Midpoint: $\left(\frac{-5-7}{2}, \frac{-3-9}{2}, \frac{1-5}{2}\right) = (-6, -6, -2)$

13. $(x-2)^2 + (y-3)^2 + (z-5)^2 = 1$

14. $(x-3)^2 + (y+2)^2 + (z-4)^2 = 16$

15. Radius: 6

$(x-1)^2 + (y-5)^2 + (z-2)^2 = 36$

16. Radius $= \frac{15}{2}$

$x^2 + (y-4)^2 + (z+1)^2 = \frac{225}{4}$

17. $(x^2 - 4x + 4) + (y^2 - 6y + 9) + z^2 = -4 + 4 + 9$

$(x-2)^2 + (y-3)^2 + z^2 = 9$

Center: $(2, 3, 0)$

Radius: 3

18. $(x^2 - 10x + 25) + (y^2 + 6y + 9) + (z^2 - 4z + 4) = -34 + 25 + 9 + 4$

$(x-5)^2 + (y+3)^2 + (z-2)^2 = 4$

Center: $(5, -3, 2)$

Radius: 2

19. (a) xz-trace $(y = 0)$: $x^2 + z^2 = 7$, circle

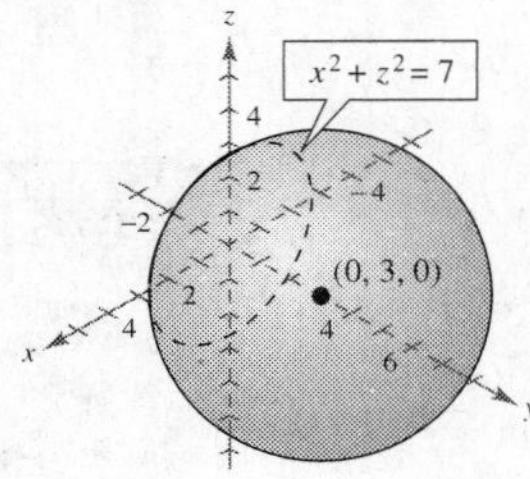

(b) yz-trace $(x = 0)$: $(y - 3)^2 + z^2 = 16$, circle

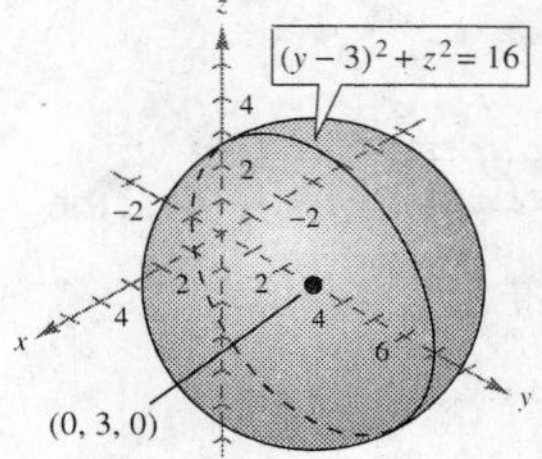

20. (a) xy-trace $(z = 0)$: $(x + 2)^2 + (y - 1)^2 = 9$, circle

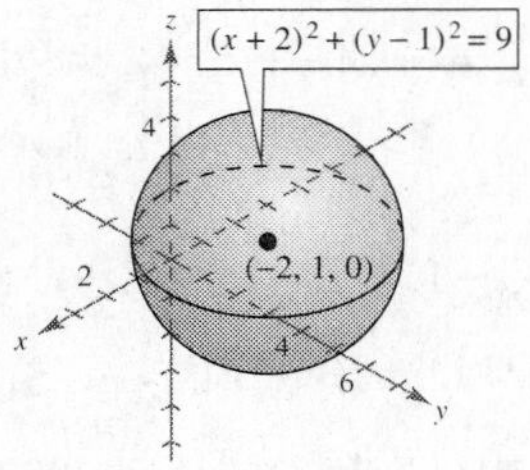

(b) yz-trace $(x = 0)$: $4 + (y - 1)^2 + z^2 = 9$

$(y - 1)^2 + z^2 = 5$, circle

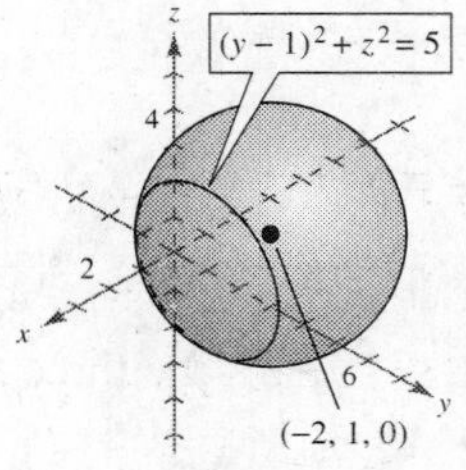

21. (a) $\mathbf{v} = \langle 3 - 2, 3 - (-1), 0 - 4 \rangle = \langle 1, 4, -4 \rangle$

(b) $\|\mathbf{v}\| = \sqrt{1^2 + 4^2 + (-4)^2} = \sqrt{33}$

(c) Unit vector: $\dfrac{\sqrt{33}}{33}\langle 1, 4, -4 \rangle$

22. (a) $\mathbf{v} = \langle -3 - 2, 2 - (-1), 3 - 2 \rangle = \langle -5, 3, 1 \rangle$

(b) $\|\mathbf{v}\| = \sqrt{(-5)^2 + 3^2 + 1^2} = \sqrt{35}$

(c) Unit vector: $\dfrac{\sqrt{35}}{35}\langle -5, 3, 1 \rangle$

23. (a) $\mathbf{v} = \langle -3 - 7, 2 - (-4), 10 - 3 \rangle = \langle -10, 6, 7 \rangle$

(b) $\|\mathbf{v}\| = \sqrt{(-10)^2 + 6^2 + 7^2} = \sqrt{185}$

(c) Unit vector: $\dfrac{\sqrt{185}}{185}\langle -10, 6, 7 \rangle$

24. (a) $\mathbf{v} = \langle 5 - 0, -8 - 3, 6 - (-1) \rangle = \langle 5, -11, 7 \rangle$

(b) $\|\mathbf{v}\| = \sqrt{5^2 + (-11)^2 + 7^2} = \sqrt{195}$

(c) Unit vector: $\dfrac{\sqrt{195}}{195}\langle 5, -11, 7 \rangle$

25. $\mathbf{u} \cdot \mathbf{v} = -1(0) + 4(-6) + 3(5) = -9$

26. $\mathbf{u} \cdot \mathbf{v} = 8(2) - 4(5) + 2(2) = 0$

27. $\mathbf{u} \cdot \mathbf{v} = 2(1) - 1(0) + 1(-1) = 1$

28. $\mathbf{u} \cdot \mathbf{v} = 2(1) + 1(-3) - 2(2) = -5$

29. $\cos\theta = \dfrac{\mathbf{u} \cdot \mathbf{v}}{\|\mathbf{u}\|\,\|\mathbf{v}\|} = \dfrac{12 - 2 - 10}{\sqrt{42}\sqrt{17}} = 0$

$\theta \approx 90°$

The vectors are orthogonal.

30. $\cos\theta = \dfrac{\mathbf{u} \cdot \mathbf{v}}{\|\mathbf{u}\|\,\|\mathbf{v}\|} = \dfrac{-20 - 5 - 45}{\sqrt{350}\sqrt{14}} = \dfrac{-70}{70} = -1$

$\theta \approx 180°$

The vectors are parallel.

31. Since $\mathbf{u} \cdot \mathbf{v} = 0$, the angle is 90°.

32. $\cos\theta = \dfrac{\mathbf{u} \cdot \mathbf{v}}{\|\mathbf{u}\|\,\|\mathbf{v}\|} = \dfrac{12 + 5 - 2}{\sqrt{11}\sqrt{45}}$

$= \dfrac{15}{\sqrt{11}\sqrt{45}} \Rightarrow \theta \approx 47.61°$

33. $\mathbf{u} \cdot \mathbf{v} = 7(-1) + (-2)(4) + 3(5) = 0$

Orthogonal

34. $-4\mathbf{u} = -4\langle -4, 3, -6\rangle = \langle 16, -12, 24\rangle = \mathbf{v}$

Parallel

35. Since $-\frac{2}{3}\langle 39, -12, 21\rangle = \langle -26, 8, -14\rangle$, the vectors are parallel.

36. $\mathbf{u} \cdot \mathbf{v} = \langle 8, 5, -8\rangle \cdot \left\langle -2, 4, \frac{1}{2}\right\rangle$

$= -16 + 20 - 4 = 0$

Orthogonal

37. First two points: $\mathbf{u} = \langle -3, 4, 1\rangle$

Last two points: $\mathbf{v} = \langle 0, -2, 6\rangle$

Since $\mathbf{u} \neq c\mathbf{v}$, the points are not collinear.

38. First two points: $\langle -1, 5, 4\rangle$

Last two points: $\langle 2, -10, -8\rangle$

Since, $\langle 2, -10, -8\rangle = -2\langle -1, 5, 4\rangle$, the three points are collinear.

39. First two points: $\langle 4, -2, -10\rangle$

First and third points: $\langle 2, -1, -5\rangle$

Since $\langle 4, -2, -10\rangle = 2\langle 2, -1, -5\rangle$, the three points are collinear.

40. First two points: $\langle 3, -1, -2\rangle$

Last two points: $\langle 3, 11, -2\rangle$

Since $\langle 3, -1, -2\rangle \neq c\langle 3, 11, -2\rangle$, the three points are not collinear.

41. Let **a**, **b**, and **c** be the three force vectors determined by $A(0, 10, 10)$, $B(-4, -6, 10)$, and $C(4, -6, 10)$.

$$\mathbf{a} = \|\mathbf{a}\|\frac{\langle 0, 10, 10\rangle}{10\sqrt{2}} = \|\mathbf{a}\|\left\langle 0, \frac{1}{\sqrt{2}}, \frac{1}{\sqrt{2}}\right\rangle$$

$$\mathbf{b} = \|\mathbf{b}\|\frac{\langle -4, -6, 10\rangle}{\sqrt{152}} = \|\mathbf{b}\|\left\langle \frac{-2}{\sqrt{38}}, \frac{-3}{\sqrt{38}}, \frac{5}{\sqrt{38}}\right\rangle$$

$$\mathbf{c} = \|\mathbf{c}\|\frac{\langle 4, -6, 10\rangle}{\sqrt{152}} = \|\mathbf{c}\|\left\langle \frac{2}{\sqrt{38}}, \frac{-3}{\sqrt{38}}, \frac{5}{\sqrt{38}}\right\rangle$$

Must have $\mathbf{a} + \mathbf{b} + \mathbf{c} = 300\mathbf{k}$. Thus,

$$\frac{-2}{\sqrt{38}}\|\mathbf{b}\| + \frac{2}{\sqrt{38}}\|\mathbf{c}\| = 0$$

$$\frac{1}{\sqrt{2}}\|\mathbf{a}\| - \frac{3}{\sqrt{38}}\|\mathbf{b}\| - \frac{3}{\sqrt{38}}\|\mathbf{c}\| = 0$$

$$\frac{1}{\sqrt{2}}\|\mathbf{a}\| + \frac{5}{\sqrt{38}}\|\mathbf{b}\| + \frac{5}{\sqrt{38}}\|\mathbf{c}\| = 300.$$

From the first equation, $\|\mathbf{b}\| = \|\mathbf{c}\|$. From the second equation, $\frac{1}{\sqrt{2}}\|\mathbf{a}\| = \frac{6}{\sqrt{38}}\|\mathbf{b}\|$.

From the third equation, $\frac{1}{\sqrt{2}}\|\mathbf{a}\| = 300 - \frac{10}{\sqrt{38}}\|\mathbf{b}\|$. Thus,

$$\frac{6}{\sqrt{38}}\|\mathbf{b}\| = 300 - \frac{10}{\sqrt{38}}\|\mathbf{b}\| \implies \frac{16}{\sqrt{38}}\|\mathbf{b}\| = 300 \text{ and } \|\mathbf{b}\| = \|\mathbf{c}\| = \frac{75\sqrt{38}}{4} \approx 115.58.$$

Finally, $\|\mathbf{a}\| = \sqrt{2}\left(\frac{6}{\sqrt{38}}\right)\left(\frac{75\sqrt{38}}{4}\right) = \frac{225\sqrt{2}}{2} \approx 159.10.$

42. Let **a**, **b**, **c** be the three force vectors determined by $A(0, 10, 10)$, $B(-4, -6, 10)$, and $C(4, -6, 10)$.

$$\mathbf{a} = \|\mathbf{a}\|\frac{\langle 0, 10, 10\rangle}{10\sqrt{2}} = \|\mathbf{a}\|\left\langle 0, \frac{1}{\sqrt{2}}, \frac{1}{\sqrt{2}}\right\rangle$$

$$\mathbf{b} = \|\mathbf{b}\|\frac{\langle -4, -6, 10\rangle}{\sqrt{152}} = \|\mathbf{b}\|\left\langle \frac{-2}{\sqrt{38}}, \frac{-3}{\sqrt{38}}, \frac{5}{\sqrt{38}}\right\rangle$$

$$\mathbf{c} = \|\mathbf{c}\|\frac{\langle 4, -6, 10\rangle}{\sqrt{152}} = \|\mathbf{c}\|\left\langle \frac{2}{\sqrt{38}}, \frac{-3}{\sqrt{38}}, \frac{5}{\sqrt{38}}\right\rangle$$

We must have $\mathbf{a} + \mathbf{b} + \mathbf{c} = 200\mathbf{k}$. Thus,

$$\frac{-2}{\sqrt{38}}\|\mathbf{b}\| + \frac{2}{\sqrt{38}}\|\mathbf{c}\| = 0$$

$$\frac{1}{\sqrt{2}}\|\mathbf{a}\| - \frac{3}{\sqrt{38}}\|\mathbf{b}\| - \frac{3}{\sqrt{38}}\|\mathbf{c}\| = 0$$

$$\frac{1}{\sqrt{2}}\|\mathbf{a}\| + \frac{5}{\sqrt{38}}\|\mathbf{b}\| + \frac{5}{\sqrt{38}}\|\mathbf{c}\| = 200$$

Solving this system, $\|\mathbf{a}\| \approx 106.1$, $\|\mathbf{b}\| = \|\mathbf{c}\| = 77.1$. Thus, the tensions are 106.1, 77.1 and 77.1 pounds.

43. $\mathbf{u} \times \mathbf{v} = \begin{vmatrix} \mathbf{i} & \mathbf{j} & \mathbf{k} \\ -2 & 8 & 2 \\ 1 & 1 & -1 \end{vmatrix} = \langle -10, 0, -10\rangle$

44. $\mathbf{u} \times \mathbf{v} = \begin{vmatrix} \mathbf{i} & \mathbf{j} & \mathbf{k} \\ 10 & 15 & 5 \\ 5 & -3 & 0 \end{vmatrix} = \langle 15, 25, -105\rangle$

45. $\mathbf{u} \times \mathbf{v} = \begin{vmatrix} \mathbf{i} & \mathbf{j} & \mathbf{k} \\ -3 & 2 & -5 \\ 10 & -15 & 2 \end{vmatrix} = \langle -71, -44, 25\rangle$

$\|\mathbf{u} \times \mathbf{v}\| = \sqrt{7602}$

Unit vector: $\frac{1}{\sqrt{7602}}\langle -71, -44, 25\rangle$

46. $\mathbf{u} \times \mathbf{v} = \begin{vmatrix} \mathbf{i} & \mathbf{j} & \mathbf{k} \\ 0 & 0 & 4 \\ 1 & 0 & 12 \end{vmatrix} = 4\mathbf{j} \Rightarrow$ unit vector: $\mathbf{j} = \langle 0, 1, 0\rangle$

47. First two points: $\langle 3, 2, 3\rangle$

Last two points: $\langle 3, 2, 3\rangle$

First and third points: $\langle -2, 2, 0\rangle$

$\begin{vmatrix} \mathbf{i} & \mathbf{j} & \mathbf{k} \\ 3 & 2 & 3 \\ -2 & 2 & 0 \end{vmatrix} = \langle -6, -6, 10\rangle$

$$\begin{aligned} \text{Area} &= \|\langle -6, -6, 10\rangle\| \\ &= \sqrt{36 + 36 + 100} \\ &= \sqrt{172} \\ &= 2\sqrt{43} \text{ square units} \end{aligned}$$

48. $\mathbf{u} = \langle 1, 0, 1\rangle$, $\mathbf{v} = \langle 1, 0, 1\rangle$,

Opposite sides parallel and equal length

Adjacent sides: $\mathbf{u} = \langle 1, 0, 1\rangle$, $\mathbf{w} = \langle 0, 2, 0\rangle$

$\mathbf{u} \times \mathbf{w} = \begin{vmatrix} \mathbf{i} & \mathbf{j} & \mathbf{k} \\ 1 & 0 & 1 \\ 0 & 2 & 0 \end{vmatrix} = \langle -2, 0, 2\rangle$

Area $= \|\mathbf{u} \times \mathbf{w}\| = \sqrt{4 + 4} = 2\sqrt{2}$ square units

49. The parallelogram is determined by the three vectors with initial point $(0, 0, 0)$.

$\mathbf{u} = \langle 3, 0, 0\rangle, \mathbf{v} = \langle 2, 0, 5\rangle, \mathbf{w} = \langle 0, 5, 1\rangle$

$$\mathbf{u} \cdot (\mathbf{v} \times \mathbf{w}) = \begin{vmatrix} 3 & 0 & 0 \\ 2 & 0 & 5 \\ 0 & 5 & 1 \end{vmatrix} = -75$$

$\text{Volume} = |-75| = 75$ cubic units

50. $\mathbf{u} = \langle 2, 0. 0\rangle, \mathbf{v} = \langle 0, 4, 0\rangle, \mathbf{w} = \langle 0, 0, 6\rangle$

$$\mathbf{u} \cdot (\mathbf{v} \times \mathbf{w}) = \begin{vmatrix} 2 & 0 & 0 \\ 0 & 4 & 0 \\ 0 & 0 & 6 \end{vmatrix} = 48$$

$\text{Volume} = |\mathbf{u} \cdot (\mathbf{v} \times \mathbf{w})| = 48$ cubic units

51. $\mathbf{v} = \langle 9 - 3, 11 - 0, 6 - 2\rangle = \langle 6, 11, 4\rangle$

Point: $(3, 0, 2)$

(a) $x = 3 + 6t,\ y = 11t,\ z = 2 + 4t$

(b) $\dfrac{x - 3}{6} = \dfrac{y}{11} = \dfrac{z - 2}{4}$

52. $\mathbf{v} = \langle 9, 6, 2\rangle$

Point: $(-1, 4, 3)$

(a) $x = -1 + 9t,\ y = 4 + 6t,\ z = 3 + 2t$

(b) $\dfrac{x + 1}{9} = \dfrac{y - 4}{6} = \dfrac{z - 3}{2}$

53. $\mathbf{v} = \langle 3 + 1, 6 - 3, -1 - 5\rangle = \langle 4, 3, -6\rangle$, point: $(-1, 3, 5)$

(a) Parametric equations: $x = -1 + 4t, y = 3 + 3t, z = 5 - 6t$

(b) Symmetric equations: $\dfrac{x + 1}{4} = \dfrac{y - 3}{3} = \dfrac{z - 5}{-6}$

54. (a) $\mathbf{v} = \langle 5, 20, -3\rangle$

$x = 5t,\ y = -10 + 20t,\ z = 3 - 3t$

(b) $\dfrac{x}{5} = \dfrac{y + 10}{20} = \dfrac{z - 3}{-3}$

55. Use $2\mathbf{v} = \langle -4, 5, 2\rangle$, point: $(0, 0, 0)$.

(a) Parametric equations: $x = -4t, y = 5t, z = 2t$

(b) Symmetric equations: $\dfrac{x}{-4} = \dfrac{y}{5} = \dfrac{z}{2}$

56. (a) $\mathbf{v} = \langle 1, 1, 1\rangle$

$x = 3 + t, y = 2 + t, z = 1 + t$

(b) $\dfrac{x - 3}{1} = \dfrac{y - 2}{1} = \dfrac{z - 1}{1}$ or

$x - 3 = y - 2 = z - 1$

57. $\mathbf{u} = \langle 5, 0, 2\rangle, \mathbf{v} = \langle 2, 3, 8\rangle$

$$\mathbf{u} \times \mathbf{v} = \begin{vmatrix} \mathbf{i} & \mathbf{j} & \mathbf{k} \\ 5 & 0 & 2 \\ 2 & 3 & 8 \end{vmatrix} = \langle -6, -36, 15\rangle$$

$\mathbf{n} = \langle 2, 12, -5\rangle$

$$a(x - x_0) + b(y - y_0) + c(z - z_0) = 0$$
$$2(x - 0) + 12(y - 0) - 5(z - 0) = 0$$
$$2x + 12y - 5z = 0$$

58. $\mathbf{u} = \langle 5, -5, -2\rangle,\ \mathbf{v} = \langle 3, 5, 2\rangle$

$$\mathbf{n} = \mathbf{u} \times \mathbf{v} = \begin{vmatrix} \mathbf{i} & \mathbf{j} & \mathbf{k} \\ 5 & -5 & -2 \\ 3 & 5 & 2 \end{vmatrix} = \langle 0, -16, 40\rangle$$

Plane: $0(x + 1) - 16(y - 3) + 40(z - 4) = 0$

$$-2(y - 3) + 5(z - 4) = 0$$
$$-2y + 5z - 14 = 0$$

59. $\mathbf{n} = \mathbf{k}$, normal vector

Plane: $0(x - 5) + 0(y - 3) + 1(z - 2) = 0$

$$z - 2 = 0$$

60. $\mathbf{n} = \langle -1, 1, -2 \rangle$, point: $(0, 0, 6)$

$$-1(x - 0) + 1(y - 0) - 2(z - 6) = 0$$
$$-x + y - 2z + 12 = 0$$
$$x - y + 2z - 12 = 0$$

61. $3x - 2y + 3z = 6$

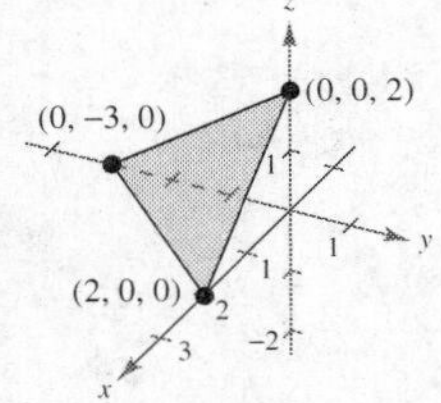

62. $5x - y - 5z = 5$

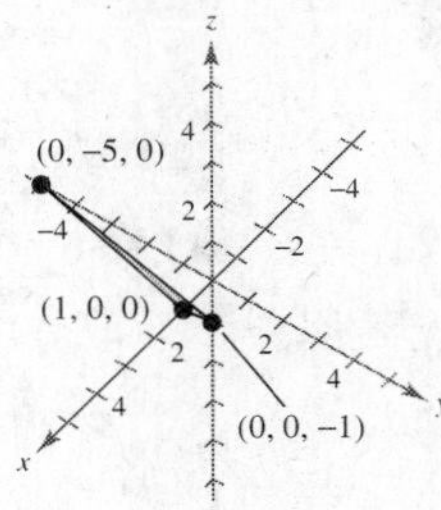

63. $2x - 3z = 6$

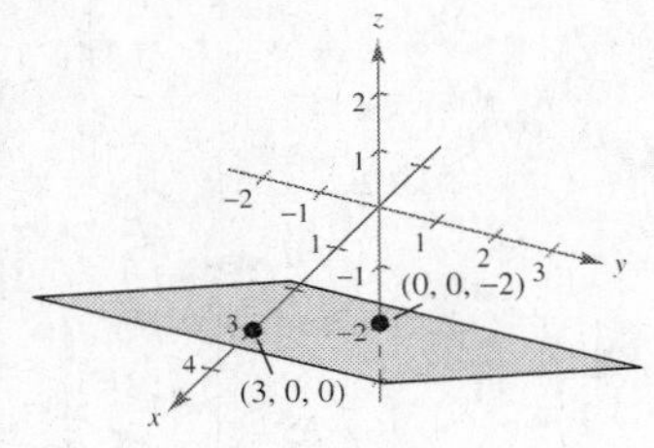

64. $4y - 3z = 12$

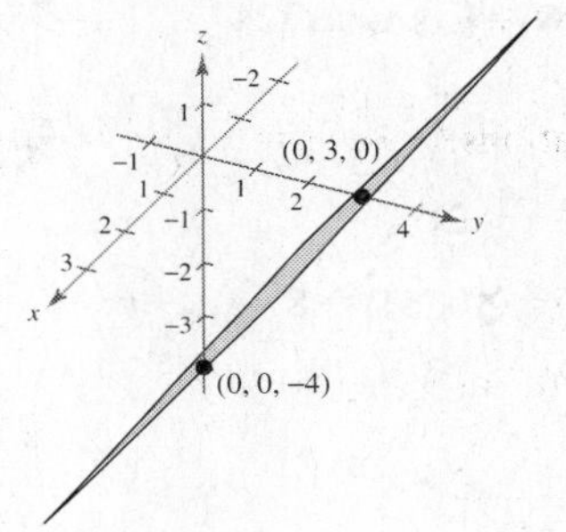

65. $\mathbf{n} = \langle 2, -20, 6 \rangle$, $P = (0, 0, 1)$ in plane, $Q = (2, 3, 10)$, $\overrightarrow{PQ} = \langle 2, 3, 9 \rangle$

$$D = \frac{|\overrightarrow{PQ} \cdot \mathbf{n}|}{\|\mathbf{n}\|} = \frac{|-2|}{\sqrt{440}} = \frac{1}{\sqrt{110}} = \frac{\sqrt{110}}{110} \approx 0.0953$$

66. $D = \dfrac{|\overrightarrow{PQ} \cdot \mathbf{n}|}{\|\mathbf{n}\|}$

$Q = (1, 2, 3)$, $P = (2, 0, 0)$ in plane, $\overrightarrow{PQ} = \langle -1, 2, 3 \rangle$, $\mathbf{n} = \langle 2, -1, 1 \rangle$

$$D = \frac{|\langle -1, 2, 3 \rangle \cdot \langle 2, -1, 1 \rangle|}{\sqrt{6}} = \frac{1}{\sqrt{6}} = \frac{\sqrt{6}}{6}$$

67. $\mathbf{n} = \langle 1, -10, 3 \rangle$, $P = (2, 0, 0)$ in plane, $Q = (0, 0, 0)$, $\overrightarrow{PQ} = \langle -2, 0, 0 \rangle$

$$D = \frac{|\overrightarrow{PQ} \cdot \mathbf{n}|}{\|\mathbf{n}\|} = \frac{|-2|}{\sqrt{1 + 100 + 9}} = \frac{2}{\sqrt{110}} = \frac{2\sqrt{110}}{110} = \frac{\sqrt{110}}{55} \approx 0.191$$

68. $D = \dfrac{|\overrightarrow{PQ} \cdot \mathbf{n}|}{\|\mathbf{n}\|}$

$Q = (0, 0, 0)$, $P = (0, 0, 12)$ in plane, $\overrightarrow{PQ} = \langle 0, 0, -12 \rangle$, $\mathbf{n} = \langle 2, 3, 1 \rangle$

$$D = \frac{|\langle 0, 0, -12 \rangle \cdot \langle 2, 3, 1 \rangle|}{\sqrt{14}} = \frac{12}{\sqrt{14}} = \frac{6\sqrt{14}}{7}$$

69. False. $\mathbf{a} \times \mathbf{b} = -(\mathbf{b} \times \mathbf{a})$

70. True. See page 761.

71. $\mathbf{u} \cdot \mathbf{u} = \langle 3, -2, 1\rangle \cdot \langle 3, -2, 1\rangle$
$= 9 + 4 + 1$
$= 14$
$= \|\mathbf{u}\|^2$

72. $\mathbf{u} \times \mathbf{v} = \begin{vmatrix} \mathbf{i} & \mathbf{j} & \mathbf{k} \\ 3 & -2 & 1 \\ 2 & -4 & -3 \end{vmatrix} = \langle 10, 11, -8\rangle$

$\mathbf{v} \times \mathbf{u} = \begin{vmatrix} \mathbf{i} & \mathbf{j} & \mathbf{k} \\ 2 & -4 & -3 \\ 3 & -2 & 1 \end{vmatrix} = \langle -10, -11, 8\rangle$

Thus, $\mathbf{u} \times \mathbf{v} = -(\mathbf{v} \times \mathbf{u})$.

73. $\mathbf{u} \cdot (\mathbf{v} + \mathbf{w}) = \langle 3, -2, 1\rangle \cdot \langle 1, -2, -1\rangle = 6$

$\mathbf{u} \cdot \mathbf{v} + \mathbf{u} \cdot \mathbf{w} = 11 + (-5) = 6$

74. $\mathbf{u} \times (\mathbf{v} + \mathbf{w}) = \mathbf{u} \times \langle 1, -2, -1\rangle = \begin{vmatrix} \mathbf{i} & \mathbf{j} & \mathbf{k} \\ 3 & -2 & 1 \\ 1 & -2 & -1 \end{vmatrix} = \langle 4, 4, -4\rangle$

$\mathbf{u} \times \mathbf{v} = \langle 10, 11, -8\rangle$ (Exercise 72)

$\mathbf{u} \times \mathbf{w} = \begin{vmatrix} \mathbf{i} & \mathbf{j} & \mathbf{k} \\ 3 & -2 & 1 \\ -1 & 2 & 2 \end{vmatrix} = \langle -6, -7, 4\rangle$

$(\mathbf{u} \times \mathbf{v}) + (\mathbf{u} \times \mathbf{w}) = \langle 10, 11, -8\rangle + \langle -6, -7, 4\rangle = \langle 4, 4, -4\rangle$
$= \mathbf{u} \times (\mathbf{v} + \mathbf{w})$

75. $\mathbf{u} \times \mathbf{v} = \begin{vmatrix} \mathbf{i} & \mathbf{j} & \mathbf{k} \\ u_1 & u_2 & u_3 \\ v_1 & v_2 & v_3 \end{vmatrix} = (u_2v_3 - u_3v_2)\mathbf{i} - (u_1v_3 - u_3v_1)\mathbf{j} + (u_1v_2 - u_2v_1)\mathbf{k}$

76. See table on page 759.

77. The magnitude will increase by a factor of 4.

78. Form vectors for two sides and complete their cross product.

Chapter 10 Practice Test

1. Find the lengths of the sides of the triangle with vertices $(0, 0, 0)$, $(1, 2, -4)$, and $(0, -2, -1)$. Show that the triangle is a right triangle.

2. Find the standard form of the equation of a sphere having center $(0, 4, 1)$ and radius 5.

3. Find the center and radius of the sphere $x^2 + y^2 + z^2 + 2x - 4z - 11 = 0$.

4. Find the vector $\mathbf{u} - 3\mathbf{v}$ given $\mathbf{u} = \langle 1, 0, -1 \rangle$ and $\mathbf{v} = \langle 4, 3, -6 \rangle$.

5. Find the length of $\frac{1}{2}\mathbf{v}$ if $\mathbf{v} = \langle 2, 4, -6 \rangle$.

6. Find the dot product of $\mathbf{u} = \langle 2, 1, -3 \rangle$ and $\mathbf{v} = \langle 1, 1, -2 \rangle$.

7. Determine whether $\mathbf{u} = \langle 1, 1, -1 \rangle$ and $\mathbf{v} = \langle -3, -3, 3 \rangle$ are orthogonal, parallel, or neither.

8. Find the cross product of $\mathbf{u} = \langle -1, 0, 2 \rangle$ and $\mathbf{v} = \langle 1, -1, 3 \rangle$. What is $\mathbf{v} \times \mathbf{u}$?

9. Use the triple scalar product to find the volume of the parallelepiped having adjacent edges $\mathbf{u} = \langle 1, 1, 1 \rangle$, $\mathbf{v} = \langle 0, -1, 1 \rangle$, and $\mathbf{w} = \langle 1, 0, 4 \rangle$.

10. Find a set of parametric equations for the line through the points $(0, -3, 3)$ and $(2, -3, 4)$.

11. Find an equation of the plane passing through $(1, 2, 3)$ and perpendicular to the vector $\mathbf{n} = \langle 1, -1, 0 \rangle$.

12. Find an equation of the plane passing through the three points $A = (0, 0, 0)$, $B = (1, 1, 1)$, and $C = (1, 2, 3)$.

13. Determine whether the planes $x + y - z = 12$ and $3x - 4y - z = 9$ are parallel, orthogonal, or neither.

14. Find the distance between the point $(1, 1, 1)$ and the plane $x + 2y + z = 6$.

CHAPTER 11
Limits and an Introduction to Calculus

Section 11.1 Introduction to Limits **929**

Section 11.2 Techniques for Evaluating Limits **936**

Section 11.3 The Tangent Line Problem **947**

Section 11.4 Limits at Infinity and Limits of Sequences **959**

Section 11.5 The Area Problem **966**

Review Exercises **976**

Practice Test **989**

CHAPTER 11
Limits and an Introduction to Calculus

Section 11.1 Introduction to Limits

- If $f(x)$ becomes arbitrarily close to a unique number L as x approaches c from either side, then the limit of $f(x)$ as x approaches c is L:

  $$\lim_{x \to c} f(x) = L.$$

- You should be able to use a calculator to find a limit.
- You should be able to use a graph to find a limit.
- You should understand how limits can fail to exist:
  (a) $f(x)$ approaches a different number from the right of c than it approaches from the left of c.
  (b) $f(x)$ increases or decreases without bound as x approaches c.
  (c) $f(x)$ oscillates between two fixed values as x approaches c.
- You should know and be able to use the elementary properties of limits.

Vocabulary Check

1. limit **2.** oscillates **3.** direct substitution

1. (a)

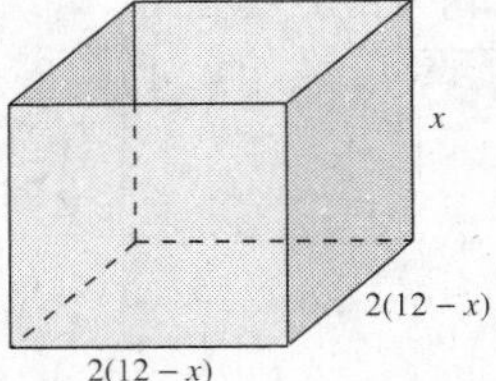

(b) $V = (\text{base})\text{height} = (24 - 2x)^2 x = 4x(12 - x)^2$

(c) $\lim_{x \to 4} V = 1024$

x	3	3.5	3.9	4	4.1	4.5	5
V	972.0	1011.5	1023.5	1024.0	1023.5	1012.5	980.0

(d)

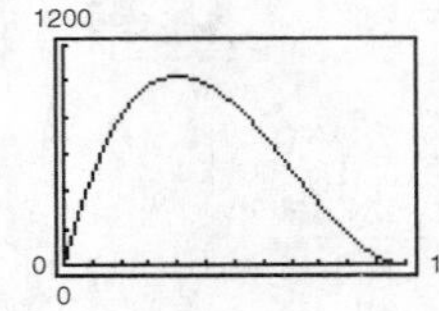

Maximum at $x = 4$

2. (a)

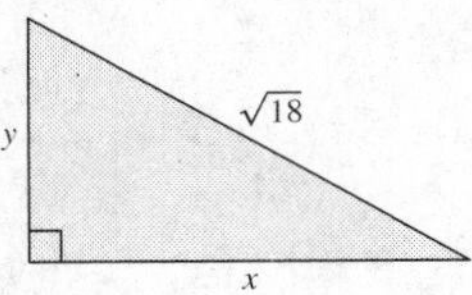

(b) $x^2 + y^2 = 18 \Rightarrow y = \sqrt{18 - x^2}$

Area $= \frac{1}{2}bh = \frac{1}{2}x\sqrt{18 - x^2}$

(c) $\lim_{x \to 3} A(x) = 4.5$

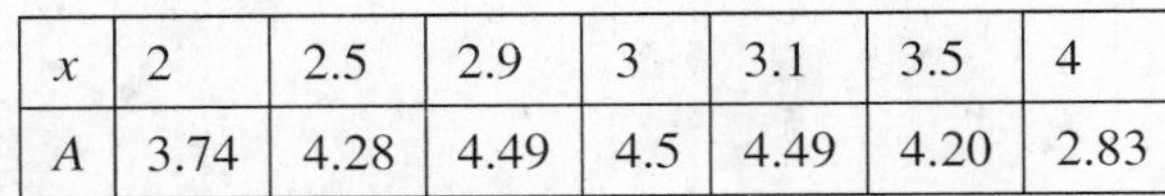

x	2	2.5	2.9	3	3.1	3.5	4
A	3.74	4.28	4.49	4.5	4.49	4.20	2.83

(d)

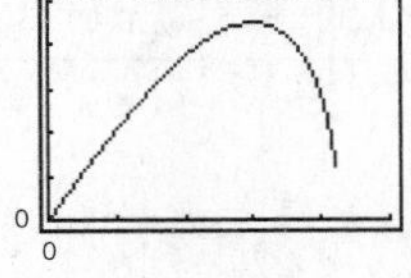

3. $\lim_{x \to 2} (5x + 4) = 14$

x	1.9	1.99	1.999	2	2.001	2.01	2.1
$f(x)$	13.5	13.95	13.995	14	14.005	14.05	14.5

The limit is reached.

4. $\lim_{x \to 1} (2x^2 + x - 4) = -1$

x	0.9	0.99	0.999	1	1.001	1.01	1.1
$f(x)$	−1.48	−1.0498	−1.0050	−1	−0.9950	−0.9498	−0.48

The limit is reached.

5. $\lim_{x \to 3} \frac{x - 3}{x^2 - 9} = \frac{1}{6}$

x	2.9	2.99	2.999	3	3.001	3.01	3.1
$f(x)$	0.1695	0.1669	0.16669	Error	0.16664	0.1664	0.1639

The limit is not reached.

6. $\lim_{x \to -1} \frac{x + 1}{x^2 - x - 2} = -\frac{1}{3}$

x	−1.1	−1.01	−1.001	−1.0	−0.999	−0.99	−0.9
$f(x)$	−0.3226	−0.3322	−0.3332	Error	−0.3334	−0.3344	−0.3348

The limit is not reached.

7. $\lim_{x \to 0} \frac{\sin 2x}{x} = 2$

x	−0.1	−0.01	−0.001	0	0.001	0.01	0.1
$f(x)$	1.9867	1.99987	1.9999987	Error	1.9999987	1.99987	1.987

The limit is not reached.

8. $\lim_{x \to 0} \frac{\tan x}{2x} = \frac{1}{2}$

x	−0.1	−0.01	−0.001	0	0.001	0.01	0.1
$f(x)$	0.5017	0.50002	0.5	Error	0.5	0.50002	0.5017

The limit is not reached.

9. $\lim_{x \to 0} \frac{e^{2x} - 1}{x} = 2$

x	-0.1	-0.01	-0.001	0	0.001	0.01	0.1
$f(x)$	1.8127	1.9801	1.9980	Error	2.0020	2.0201	2.2140

The limit is not reached.

10. $\lim_{x \to 1} \frac{\ln x}{x - 1} = 1$

x	0.9	0.99	0.999	1	1.001	1.01	1.1
$f(x)$	1.0536	1.0050	1.0005	Error	0.9995	0.9950	0.9531

The limit is not reached.

11. $\lim_{x \to 1} \frac{x - 1}{x^2 + 2x - 3} = \frac{1}{4}$

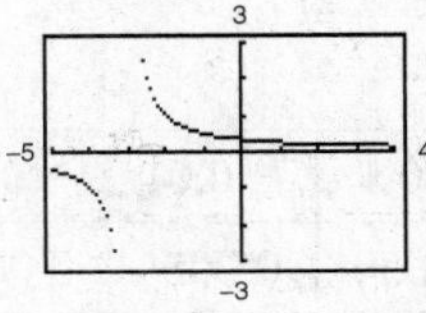

x	0.9	0.99	0.999	1.0	1.001	1.01	1.1
$f(x)$	0.2564	0.2506	0.2501	Error	0.2499	0.2494	0.2439

12. $\lim_{x \to -2} \frac{x + 2}{x^2 + 5x + 6} = 1$

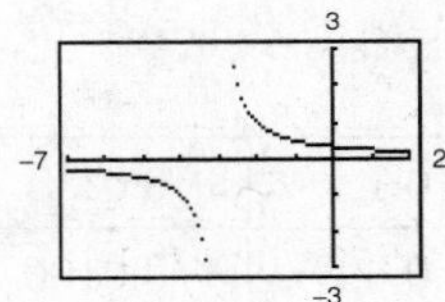

x	-2.1	-2.01	-2.001	-2.0	-1.999	-1.99	-1.9
$f(x)$	1.1111	1.0101	1.0010	Error	0.9990	0.9901	0.9091

13. $\lim_{x \to 0} \frac{\sqrt{x + 5} - \sqrt{5}}{x} \approx 0.2236$ $\left(\text{Actual limit is } \frac{1}{2\sqrt{5}}.\right)$

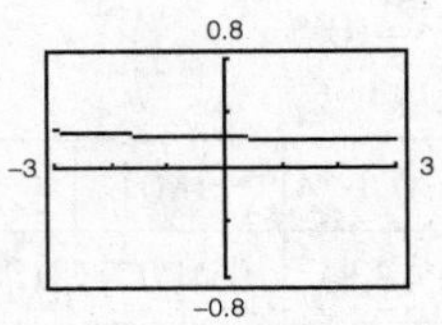

x	-0.1	-0.01	-0.001	0	0.001	0.01	0.1
$f(x)$	0.2247	0.2237	0.2236	Error	0.2236	0.2235	0.2225

14. $\lim_{x \to -3} \frac{\sqrt{1 - x} - 2}{x + 3} = -\frac{1}{4}$

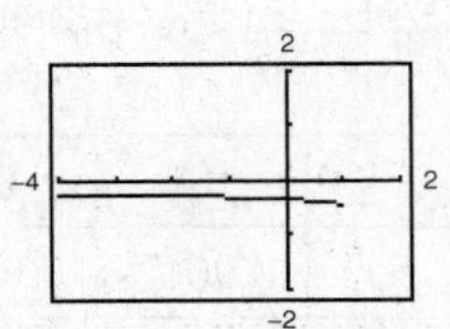

x	-3.1	-3.01	-3.001	-3.0	-2.999	-2.99	-2.9
$f(x)$	-0.2485	-0.2498	-0.25	Error	-0.25	-0.2502	-0.2516

15. $\lim_{x \to -4} \frac{[x/(x + 2)] - 2}{x + 4} = \frac{1}{2}$

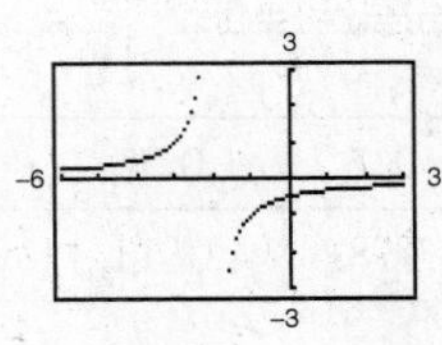

x	-4.1	-4.01	-4.001	-4.0	-3.999	-3.99	-3.9
$f(x)$	0.4762	0.4975	0.4998	Error	0.5003	0.5025	0.5263

16. $\lim_{x \to 2} \dfrac{\dfrac{1}{x+2} - \dfrac{1}{4}}{x-2} = -\dfrac{1}{16}$

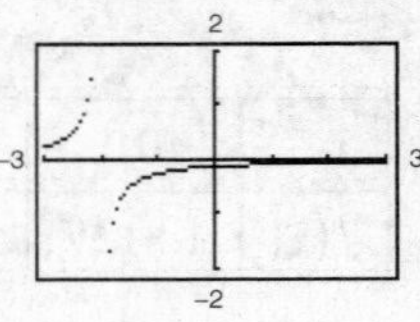

x	1.9	1.99	1.999	2.0	2.001	2.01	2.1
$f(x)$	−0.0641	−0.0627	−0.0625	Error	−0.0625	−0.0623	−0.0610

17. Make sure your calculator is set in radian mode.

$\lim_{x \to 0} \dfrac{\sin x}{x} = 1$

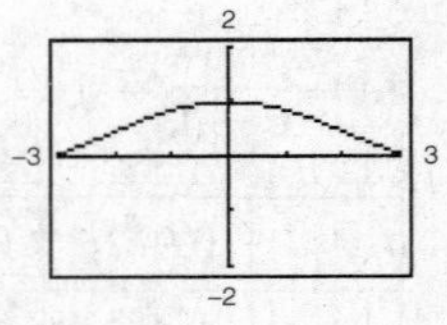

x	−0.1	−0.01	−0.001	0	0.001	0.01	0.1
$f(x)$	0.9983	0.99998	0.9999998	Error	0.9999998	0.99998	0.9983

18. $\lim_{x \to 0} \dfrac{\cos x - 1}{x} = 0$

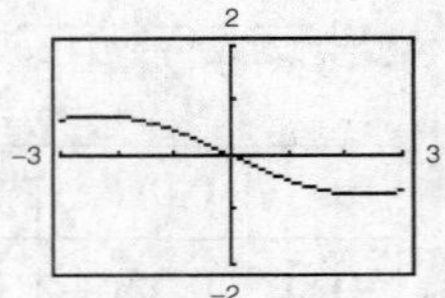

x	−0.1	−0.01	−0.001	0	0.001	0.01	0.1
$f(x)$	0.050	0.005	0.0005	Error	−0.0005	−0.005	−0.050

19. $\lim_{x \to 0} \dfrac{\sin^2 x}{x} = 0$

x	−0.1	−0.01	−0.001	0	0.001	0.01	0.1
$f(x)$	−0.0997	−0.0100	−0.0010	Error	0.0010	0.0100	0.0997

20. $\lim_{x \to 0} \dfrac{2x}{\tan 4x} = 0.5$

x	−0.1	−0.01	−0.001	0	0.001	0.01	0.1
$f(x)$	0.4730	0.4997	0.499997	Error	0.499997	0.4997	0.4730

21. $\lim_{x \to 0} \dfrac{e^{2x} - 1}{2x} = 1.0$

x	−0.1	−0.01	−0.001	0	0.001	0.01	0.1
$f(x)$	0.9063	0.9901	0.9990	Error	1.0010	1.0101	1.1070

22. $\lim_{x \to 0} \dfrac{1 - e^{-4x}}{x} = 4.0$

x	−0.1	−0.01	−0.001	0	0.001	0.01	0.1
$f(x)$	4.9182	4.0811	4.0080	Error	3.9920	3.9211	3.2968

23. $\lim_{x \to 1} \frac{\ln(2x - 1)}{x - 1} = 2$

x	0.9	0.99	0.999	1	1.001	1.01	1.1
$f(x)$	2.2314	2.0203	2.0020	Error	1.9980	1.9803	1.8232

24. $\lim_{x \to 1} \frac{\ln x^2}{x - 1} = 2.0$

x	0.9	0.99	0.999	1	1.001	1.01	1.1
$f(x)$	2.1072	2.0101	2.0010	Error	1.9990	1.9901	1.9062

25. $f(x) = \begin{cases} 2x + 1, & x < 2 \\ x + 3, & x \geq 2 \end{cases}$

The limit exists as x approaches 2:

$\lim_{x \to 2} f(x) = 5$

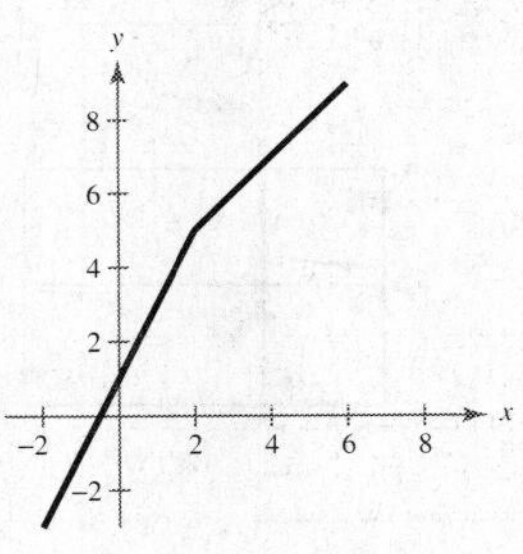

26. $\lim_{x \to 2} f(x) = 4$

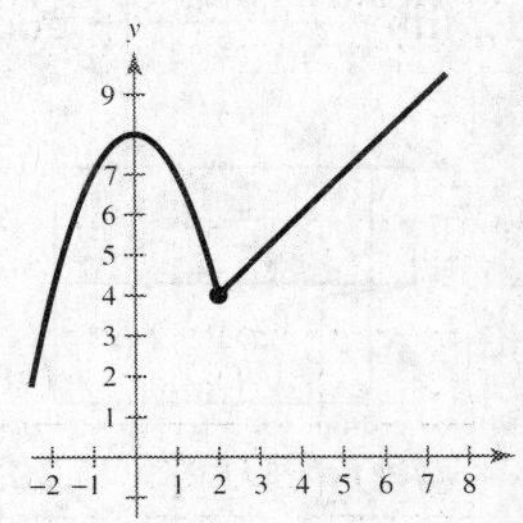

27. $\lim_{x \to 2} f(x)$ does not exist.

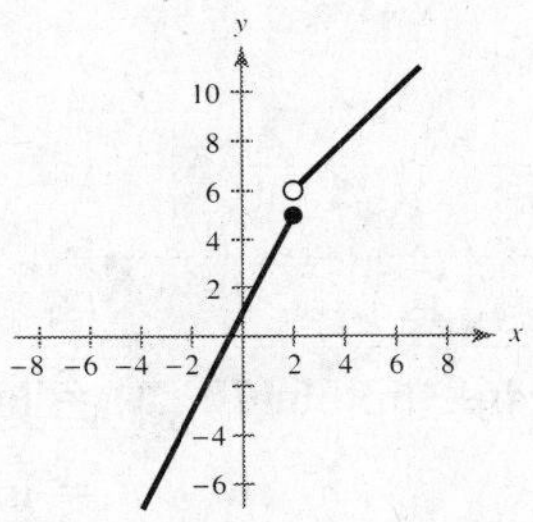

28. $\lim_{x \to 2} f(x)$ does not exist.

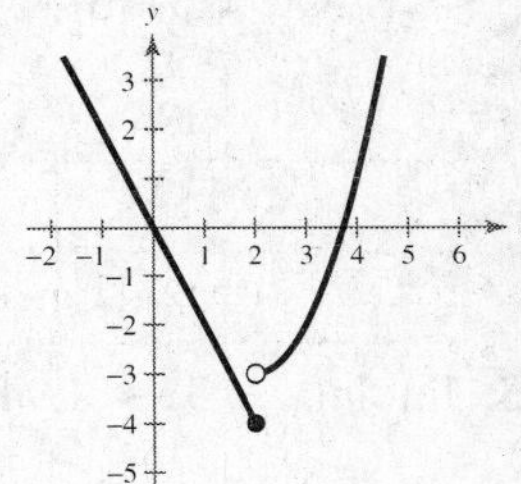

29. $\lim_{x \to -4} (x^2 - 3) = 13$

30. $\lim_{x \to 2} \frac{3x^2 - 12}{x - 2} = 12$

31. $\lim_{x \to -2} \frac{|x + 2|}{x + 2}$ does not exist. $f(x) = \frac{|x + 2|}{x + 2}$ equals -1 to the left of -2, and equals 1 to the right of -2.

32. The limit does not exist because $f(x)$ does not approach a real number as x approaches 1.

33. The limit does not exist because $f(x)$ oscillates between 2 and -2.

34. $\lim_{x \to -1} \sin\left(\frac{\pi x}{2}\right) = -1$

35. $\lim_{x \to \pi/2} \tan x$ does not exist.

36. $\lim_{x \to \pi/2} \sec x$ does not exist.

37. $\lim_{x\to 0} \dfrac{5}{2 + e^{1/x}}$ does not exist.

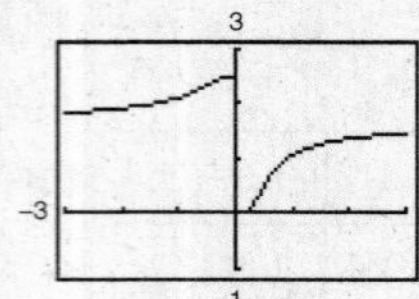

38. $\lim_{x\to 0} \dfrac{e^x - 1}{x} = 1$

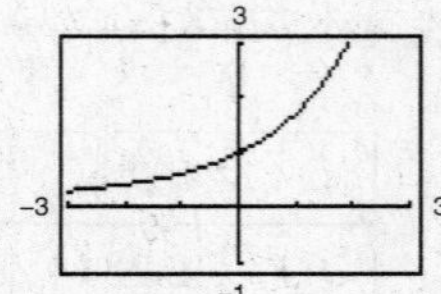

39. $\lim_{x\to 0} \cos \dfrac{1}{x}$ does not exist.

The graph oscillates between -1 and 1.

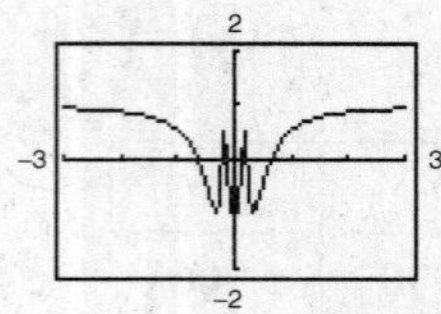

40. $\lim_{x\to -1} \sin \pi x = 0$

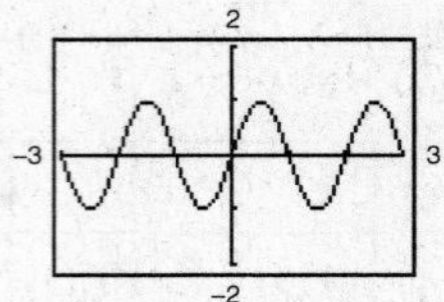

41. $\lim_{x\to 4} \dfrac{\sqrt{x + 3} - 1}{x - 4}$ does not exist.

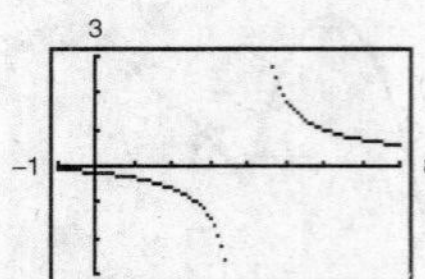

42. $\lim_{x\to 2} \dfrac{\sqrt{x + 5} - 4}{x - 2}$ does not exist.

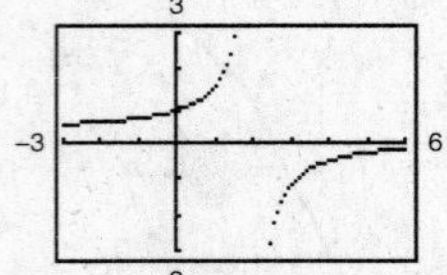

43. $\lim_{x\to 1} \dfrac{x - 1}{x^2 - 4x + 3} = -\dfrac{1}{2}$

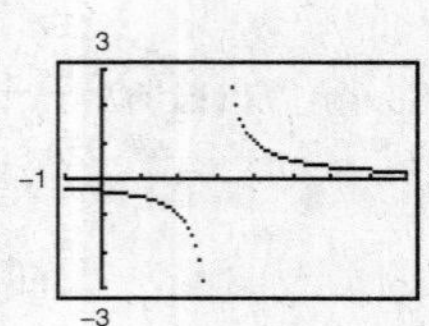

44. $\lim_{x\to 3} \dfrac{7}{x - 3}$ does not exist.

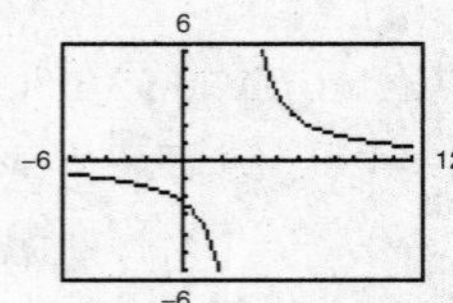

45. $\lim_{x\to 4} \ln(x + 3) \approx 1.946$ (Exact limit is ln 7.)

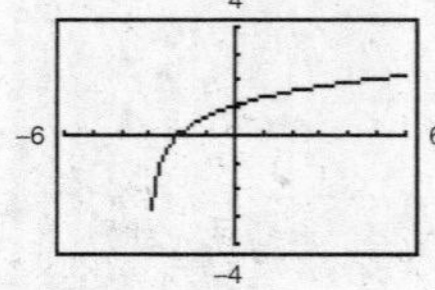

46. $\lim_{x\to -1} \ln(7 - x) = \ln(7 - (-1))$

$= \ln 8$

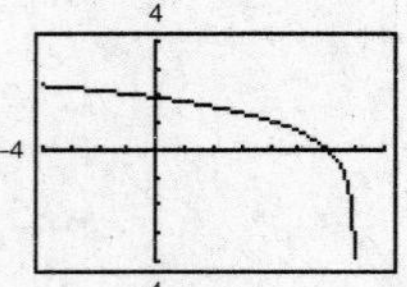

47. (a) $\lim_{x\to c} [-2g(x)] = -2(6) = -12$

(b) $\lim_{x\to c} [f(x) + g(x)] = 3 + 6 = 9$

(c) $\lim_{x\to c} \dfrac{f(x)}{g(x)} = \dfrac{3}{6} = \dfrac{1}{2}$

(d) $\lim_{x\to c} \sqrt{f(x)} = \sqrt{3}$

48. (a) $\lim_{x\to c} [f(x) + g(x)]^2 = (5 - 2)^2 = 9$

(b) $\lim_{x\to c} [6f(x)g(x)] = 6(5)(-2) = -60$

(c) $\lim_{x\to c} \dfrac{5g(x)}{4f(x)} = \dfrac{5(-2)}{4(5)} = -\dfrac{1}{2}$

(d) $\lim_{x\to c} \dfrac{1}{\sqrt{f(x)}} = \dfrac{1}{\sqrt{5}} = \dfrac{\sqrt{5}}{5}$

49. (a) $\lim_{x\to 2} f(x) = 2^3 = 8$

(b) $\lim_{x\to 2} g(x) = \dfrac{\sqrt{2^2 + 5}}{2(2^2)} = \dfrac{3}{8}$

(c) $\lim_{x\to 2} [f(x)g(x)] = 8\left(\dfrac{3}{8}\right) = 3$

(d) $\lim_{x\to 2} [g(x) - f(x)] = \dfrac{3}{8} - 8 = -\dfrac{61}{8}$

50. (a) $\lim_{x\to 2} f(x) = \frac{2}{3-2} = 2$

(b) $\lim_{x\to 2} g(x) = \sin(\pi 2) = 0$

(c) $\lim_{x\to 2} [f(x)g(x)] = 2(0) = 0$

(d) $\lim_{x\to 2} [g(x) - f(x)] = 0 - 2 = -2$

51. $\lim_{x\to 5} (10 - x^2) = 10 - 5^2 = -15$

52. $\lim_{x\to -2} \left(\frac{1}{2}x^3 - 5x\right) = \frac{1}{2}(-2)^3 - 5(-2) = 6$

53. $\lim_{x\to -3} (2x^2 + 4x + 1) = 2(-3)^2 + 4(-3) + 1 = 7$

54. $\lim_{x\to -2} (x^3 - 6x + 5) = (-2)^3 - 6(-2) + 5 = 9$

55. $\lim_{x\to 3} \left(-\frac{9}{x}\right) = -\frac{9}{3} = -3$

56. $\lim_{x\to -5} \frac{6}{x+2} = \frac{6}{-5+2} = \frac{6}{-3} = -2$

57. $\lim_{x\to -3} \frac{3x}{x^2+1} = -\frac{9}{10}$

58. $\lim_{x\to 4} \frac{x-1}{x^2+2x+3} = \frac{4-1}{16+8+3} = \frac{3}{27} = \frac{1}{9}$

59. $\lim_{x\to -2} \frac{5x+3}{2x-9} = \frac{5(-2)+3}{2(-2)-9} = \frac{-7}{-13} = \frac{7}{13}$

60. $\lim_{x\to 3} \frac{x^2+1}{x} = \frac{9+1}{3} = \frac{10}{3}$

61. $\lim_{x\to -1} \sqrt{x+2} = \sqrt{-1+2} = 1$

62. $\lim_{x\to 3} \sqrt[3]{x^2-1} = \sqrt[3]{9-1} = 2$

63. $\lim_{x\to 7} \frac{5x}{\sqrt{x+2}} = \frac{5(7)}{\sqrt{7+2}} = \frac{35}{3}$

64. $\lim_{x\to 8} \frac{\sqrt{x+1}}{x-4} = \frac{\sqrt{8+1}}{x-4} = \frac{3}{4}$

65. $\lim_{x\to 3} e^x = e^3 \approx 20.0855$

66. $\lim_{x\to e} \ln x = \ln e = 1$

67. $\lim_{x\to \pi} \sin 2x = \sin 2\pi = 0$

68. $\lim_{x\to \pi} \tan x = \tan \pi = 0$

69. $\lim_{x\to 1/2} \arcsin x = \arcsin \frac{1}{2} = \frac{\pi}{6} \approx 0.5236$

70. $\lim_{x\to 1} \arccos \frac{x}{2} = \arccos \frac{1}{2} = \frac{\pi}{3} \approx 1.0472$

71. True

72. True (assuming the limits exist).

73. Answers will vary.

74. In general, you cannot use a graphing utility to determine whether a limit can be reached. It is important to analyze a function analytically.

75. (a) No. The limit may or may not exist, and if it does exist, it may not equal 4.

(b) No. $f(2)$ may or may not exist, and if $f(2)$ exists, it may not equal 4.

76. $\lim_{x\to 5} f(x) = 12$ means that the values of f approach 12 as x approaches 5.

77. $\dfrac{5-x}{3x-15} = \dfrac{5-x}{-3(5-x)} = -\dfrac{1}{3},\ x \neq 5$

78. $\dfrac{x^2-81}{9-x} = \dfrac{(x-9)(x+9)}{9-x} = -x-9,\ x \neq 9$

79. $\dfrac{15x^2+7x-4}{15x^2+x-2} = \dfrac{(3x-1)(5x+4)}{(3x-1)(5x+2)}$

$= \dfrac{5x+4}{5x+2},\ x \neq \dfrac{1}{3}$

80. $\dfrac{x^2-12x+36}{x^2-7x+6} = \dfrac{(x-6)(x-6)}{(x-6)(x-1)} = \dfrac{x-6}{x-1},\ x \neq 6$

81. $\dfrac{x^3+27}{x^2+x-6} = \dfrac{(x+3)(x^2-3x+9)}{(x+3)(x-2)}$

$= \dfrac{x^2-3x+9}{x-2},\ x \neq -3$

82. $\dfrac{x^3-8}{x^2-4} = \dfrac{(x-2)(x^2+2x+4)}{(x-2)(x+2)}$

$= \dfrac{x^2+2x+4}{x+2},\ x \neq 2$

Section 11.2 Techniques for Evaluating Limits

- You can use direct substitution to find the limit of a polynomial function $p(x)$:
  $\lim_{x\to c} p(x) = p(c)$.
- You can use direct substitution to find the limit of a rational function $r(x) = \dfrac{p(x)}{q(x)}$, as long as $q(c) \neq 0$:
  $\lim_{x\to c} r(x) = r(c) = \dfrac{p(c)}{q(c)},\ q(c) \neq 0.$
- You should be able to use cancellation techniques to find a limit.
- You should know how to use rationalization techniques to find a limit.
- You should know how to use technology to find a limit.
- You should be able to calculate one-sided limits.

Vocabulary Check

1. dividing out technique
2. indeterminate form
3. one-sided limit
4. difference quotient

1. $g(x) = \dfrac{-2x^2+x}{x},\ g_2(x) = -2x+1$

(a) $\lim_{x\to 0} g(x) = 1$

(b) $\lim_{x\to -1} g(x) = 3$

(c) $\lim_{x\to -2} g(x) = 5$

2. $h(x) = \dfrac{x^2-3x}{x},\ h_2(x) = x-3$

(a) $\lim_{x\to -2} h(x) = -5$

(b) $\lim_{x\to 0} h(x) = -3$

(c) $\lim_{x\to 3} h(x) = 0$

3. $g(x) = \dfrac{x^3 - x}{x - 1}, g_2(x) = x^2 + x = x(x + 1)$

(a) $\lim\limits_{x\to 1} g(x) = 2$

(b) $\lim\limits_{x\to -1} g(x) = 0$

(c) $\lim\limits_{x\to 0} g(x) = 0$

4. $f(x) = \dfrac{x^2 - 1}{x + 1}, f_2(x) = x - 1$

(a) $\lim\limits_{x\to 1} f(x) = 0$

(b) $\lim\limits_{x\to 2} f(x) = 1$

(c) $\lim\limits_{x\to -1} f(x) = -2$

5. $$\lim_{x\to 6} \frac{x - 6}{x^2 - 36} = \lim_{x\to 6} \frac{x - 6}{(x - 6)(x + 6)} = \lim_{x\to 6} \frac{1}{x + 6} = \frac{1}{12}$$

6. $$\lim_{x\to 9} \frac{9 - x}{x^2 - 81} = \lim_{x\to 9} \frac{9 - x}{(x - 9)(x + 9)} = \lim_{x\to 9} \frac{-1}{x + 9} = \frac{-1}{18}$$

7. $$\lim_{x\to -1} \frac{1 - 2x - 3x^2}{1 + x} = \lim_{x\to -1} \frac{(1 + x)(1 - 3x)}{1 + x} = \lim_{x\to -1} (1 - 3x) = 4$$

8. $$\lim_{x\to -4} \frac{2x^2 + 7x - 4}{x + 4} = \lim_{x\to -4} \frac{(x + 4)(2x - 1)}{x + 4} = \lim_{x\to -4} (2x - 1) = -9$$

9. $$\lim_{t\to 2} \frac{t^3 - 8}{t - 2} = \lim_{t\to 2} \frac{(t - 2)(t^2 + 2t + 4)}{t - 2} = \lim_{t\to 2} (t^2 + 2t + 4) = 4 + 4 + 4 = 12$$

10. $$\lim_{a\to -4} \frac{a^3 + 64}{a + 4} = \lim_{a\to -4} \frac{(a + 4)(a^2 - 4a + 16)}{a + 4} = \lim_{a\to -4} (a^2 - 4a + 16) = 16 + 16 + 16 = 48$$

11. $$\lim_{x\to 1} \frac{x^4 - 1}{x^4 - 3x^2 - 4} = \frac{0}{-6} = 0$$

12. $$\lim_{x\to 2} \frac{x^4 - 2x^2 - 8}{x^4 - 6x^2 + 8} = \lim_{x\to 2} \frac{(x - 2)(x + 2)(x^2 + 2)}{(x - 2)(x + 2)(x^2 - 2)} = \lim_{x\to 2} \frac{(x + 2)(x^2 + 2)}{(x + 2)(x^2 - 2)} = \frac{4(6)}{4(2)} = 3$$

13. $$\lim_{x\to -1} \frac{x^3 + 2x^2 - x - 2}{x^3 + 4x^2 - x - 4} = \lim_{x\to -1} \frac{(x - 1)(x + 1)(x + 2)}{(x - 1)(x + 1)(x + 4)} = \lim_{x\to -1} \frac{(x - 1)(x + 2)}{(x - 1)(x + 4)} = \frac{(-2)(1)}{(-2)(3)} = \frac{1}{3}$$

14. $$\lim_{x\to -3} \frac{x^3 + 2x^2 - 9x - 18}{x^3 + x^2 - 9x - 9} = \lim_{x\to -3} \frac{(x - 3)(x + 2)(x + 3)}{(x - 3)(x + 1)(x + 3)} = \lim_{x\to -3} \frac{x + 2}{x + 1} = \frac{-1}{-2} = \frac{1}{2}$$

15. $\lim_{x\to 2} \dfrac{x^3 + 2x^2 - 5x - 6}{x^3 - 7x + 6} = \lim_{x\to 2} \dfrac{(x-2)(x+1)(x+3)}{(x-2)(x-1)(x+3)}$

$= \lim_{x\to 2} \dfrac{x+1}{x-1}$

$= \dfrac{3}{1} = 3$

16. $\lim_{x\to 3} \dfrac{x^3 - 4x^2 - 3x + 18}{x^3 - 4x^2 + x + 6} = \lim_{x\to 3} \dfrac{(x-3)^2(x+2)}{(x-3)(x-2)(x+1)}$

$= \lim_{x\to 3} \dfrac{(x-3)(x+2)}{(x-2)(x+1)}$

$= \dfrac{0}{4} = 0$

17. $\lim_{y\to 0} \dfrac{\sqrt{5+y} - \sqrt{5}}{y} = \lim_{y\to 0} \dfrac{\sqrt{5+y} - \sqrt{5}}{y} \cdot \dfrac{\sqrt{5+y} + \sqrt{5}}{\sqrt{5+y} + \sqrt{5}}$

$= \lim_{y\to 0} \dfrac{(5+y) - 5}{y\left(\sqrt{5+y} + \sqrt{5}\right)}$

$= \lim_{y\to 0} \dfrac{1}{\sqrt{5+y} + \sqrt{5}}$

$= \dfrac{1}{2\sqrt{5}} = \dfrac{\sqrt{5}}{10}$

18. $\lim_{z\to 0} \dfrac{\sqrt{7-z} - \sqrt{7}}{z}\left(\dfrac{\sqrt{7-z} + \sqrt{7}}{\sqrt{7-z} + \sqrt{7}}\right) = \lim_{z\to 0} \dfrac{(7-z) - 7}{z\left(\sqrt{7-z} + \sqrt{7}\right)}$

$= \lim_{z\to 0} \dfrac{-1}{\sqrt{7-z} + \sqrt{7}}$

$= \dfrac{-1}{2\sqrt{7}} = -\dfrac{\sqrt{7}}{14}$

19. $\lim_{x\to -3} \dfrac{\sqrt{x+7} - 2}{x+3} = \lim_{x\to -3} \dfrac{\sqrt{x+7} - 2}{x+3} \cdot \dfrac{\sqrt{x+7} + 2}{\sqrt{x+7} + 2}$

$= \lim_{x\to -3} \dfrac{(x+7) - 4}{(x+3)\left(\sqrt{x+7} + 2\right)}$

$= \lim_{x\to -3} \dfrac{1}{\sqrt{x+7} + 2} = \dfrac{1}{4}$

20. $\lim_{x\to 2} \dfrac{4 - \sqrt{18-x}}{x-2} = \lim_{x\to 2} \dfrac{4 - \sqrt{18-x}}{x-2} \cdot \dfrac{4 + \sqrt{18-x}}{4 + \sqrt{18-x}}$

$= \lim_{x\to 2} \dfrac{16 - (18-x)}{(x-2)\left(4 + \sqrt{18-x}\right)}$

$= \lim_{x\to 2} \dfrac{1}{4 + \sqrt{18-x}} = \dfrac{1}{8}$

21. $\displaystyle \lim_{x\to 0} \frac{1/(1+x) - 1}{x} = \lim_{x\to 0} \frac{1-(1+x)}{(1+x)x}$

$\displaystyle = \lim_{x\to 0} \frac{-1}{1+x} = -1$

22. $\displaystyle \lim_{x\to 0} \frac{\dfrac{1}{x-8} + \dfrac{1}{8}}{x} = \lim_{x\to 0} \frac{8 + (x-8)}{(x-8)(8)x}$

$\displaystyle = \lim_{x\to 0} \frac{1}{(x-8)8} = -\frac{1}{64}$

23. $\displaystyle \lim_{x\to 0} \frac{\sec x}{\tan x} = \lim_{x\to 0} \frac{1}{\cos x} \cdot \frac{\cos x}{\sin x}$

$\displaystyle = \lim_{x\to 0} \frac{1}{\sin x}$, does not exist

24. $\displaystyle \lim_{x\to\pi/2} \frac{1-\sin x}{\cos x} = \lim_{x\to\pi/2} \frac{1-\sin x}{\cos x} \cdot \frac{1+\sin x}{1+\sin x}$

$\displaystyle = \lim_{x\to\pi/2} \frac{1-\sin^2 x}{\cos x(1+\sin x)}$

$\displaystyle = \lim_{x\to\pi/2} \frac{\cos^2 x}{\cos x(1+\sin x)}$

$\displaystyle = \lim_{x\to\pi/2} \frac{\cos x}{1+\sin x} = 0$

25. $\displaystyle \lim_{x\to 0} \frac{\cos 2x}{\cot 2x} = \lim_{x\to 0} \frac{\cos 2x}{(\cos 2x)/\sin(2x)}$

$\displaystyle = \lim_{x\to 0} \sin 2x = 0$

26. $\displaystyle \lim_{x\to 0} \frac{\sin x - x}{\sin x} = \lim_{x\to 0} \left(1 - \frac{x}{\sin x}\right)$

$= 1 - 1 = 0$

27. $\displaystyle \lim_{x\to\pi/2} \frac{\sin x - 1}{x} = \frac{1-1}{\pi/2} = 0$

28. $\displaystyle \lim_{x\to\pi} \frac{1+\cos x}{x} = \frac{1+(-1)}{\pi} = 0$

29. $\displaystyle f(x) = \frac{\sqrt{x+3} - \sqrt{3}}{x}$

$\displaystyle \lim_{x\to 0} f(x) \approx 0.2887$

$\left(\text{Exact limit: } \dfrac{1}{2\sqrt{3}}\right)$

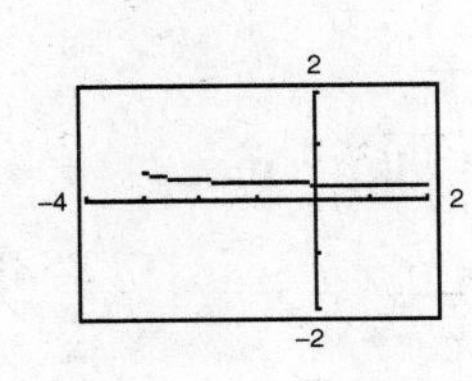

30. $\displaystyle \lim_{x\to 0} \frac{\sqrt{x+4} - 2}{x} \approx 0.25, \left(\frac{1}{4}\right)$

31. $\displaystyle f(x) = \frac{\sqrt{2x+1} - 1}{x}$

$\displaystyle \lim_{x\to 0} f(x) = 1$

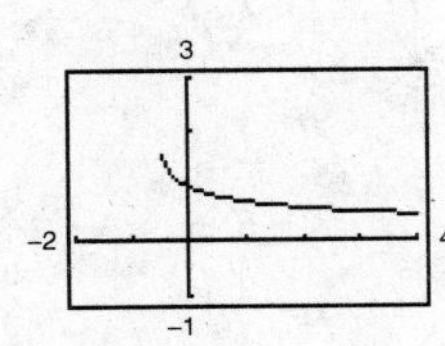

32. $\displaystyle \lim_{x\to 9} \frac{3 - \sqrt{x}}{x-9} = -0.1667, \left(-\frac{1}{6}\right)$

33. $\displaystyle \lim_{x\to 2} \frac{x^5 - 32}{x-2} = 80$

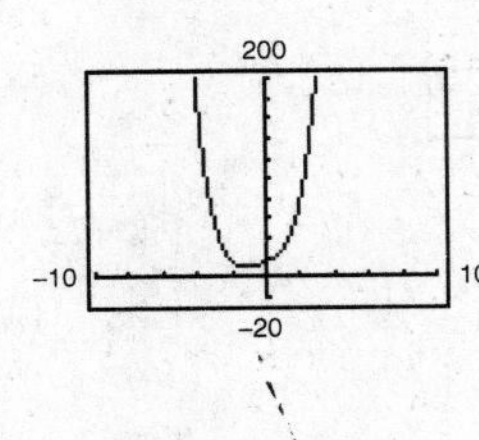

34. $\displaystyle \lim_{x\to 1} \frac{x^4 - 1}{x-1} = 4$

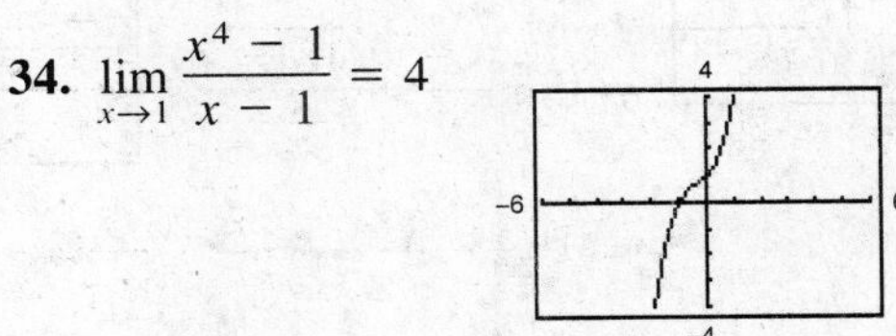

35. $f(x) = \dfrac{1/(x+4) - (1/4)}{x}$

$\lim\limits_{x\to 0} f(x) = -\dfrac{1}{16}, (-0.0625)$

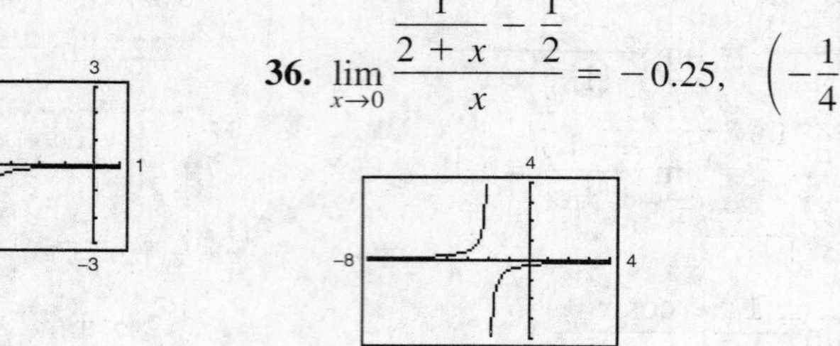

36. $\lim\limits_{x\to 0} \dfrac{\dfrac{1}{2+x} - \dfrac{1}{2}}{x} = -0.25, \left(-\dfrac{1}{4}\right)$

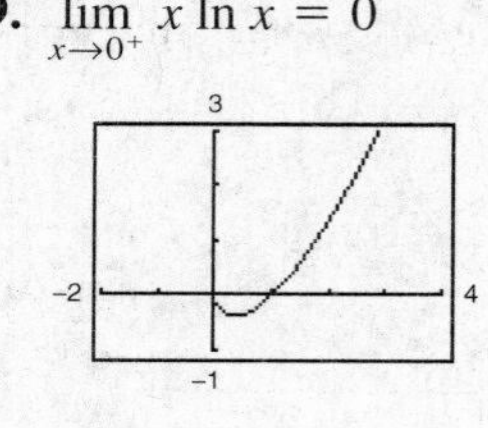

37. $f(x) = \dfrac{e^{2x} - 1}{x}$

$\lim\limits_{x\to 0} f(x) = 2$

38. $\lim\limits_{x\to 0} \dfrac{1 - e^{-x}}{x} = 1$

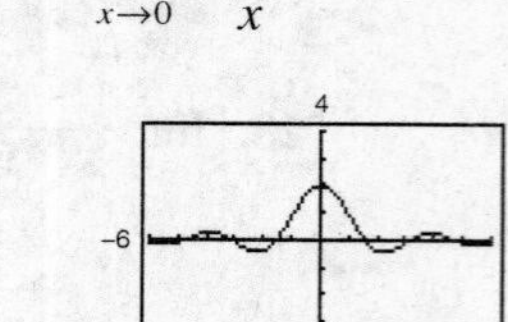

39. $\lim\limits_{x\to 0^+} x \ln x = 0$

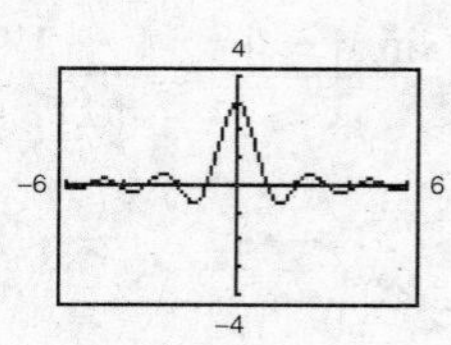

40. $\lim\limits_{x\to 0^+} x^2 \ln x = 0$

41. $\lim\limits_{x\to 0} \dfrac{\sin 2x}{x} = 2$

42. $\lim\limits_{x\to 0} \dfrac{\sin 3x}{x} = 3$

43. $\lim\limits_{x\to 0} \dfrac{\tan x}{x} = 1$

44. $\lim\limits_{x\to 0} \dfrac{1 - \cos 2x}{x} = 0$

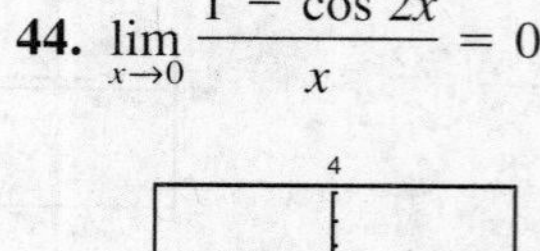

45. $\lim\limits_{x\to 1} \dfrac{1 - \sqrt[3]{x}}{1 - x} = \dfrac{1}{3} \approx 0.333$

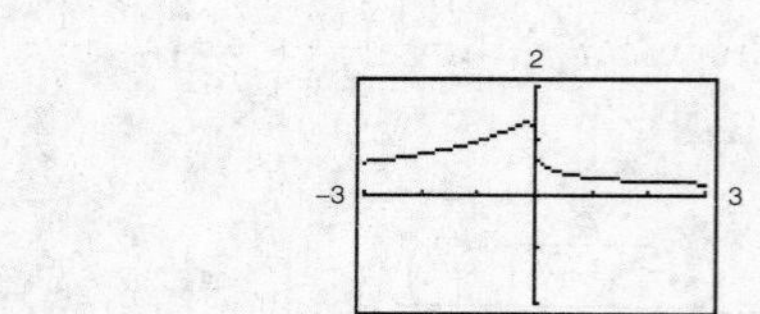

46. $\lim\limits_{x\to 1} \dfrac{\sqrt[3]{x} - x}{x - 1} \approx -0.667, \left(-\dfrac{2}{3}\right)$

47. $f(x) = (1 - x)^{2/x}$

$\lim\limits_{x\to 0} f(x) \approx 0.135$

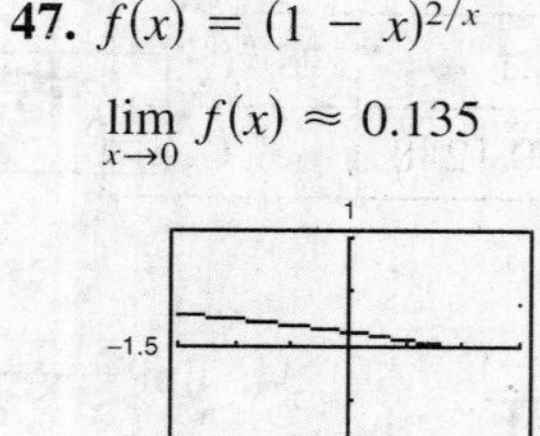

48. $\lim\limits_{x\to 0} (1 + 2x)^{1/x} \approx 7.389$

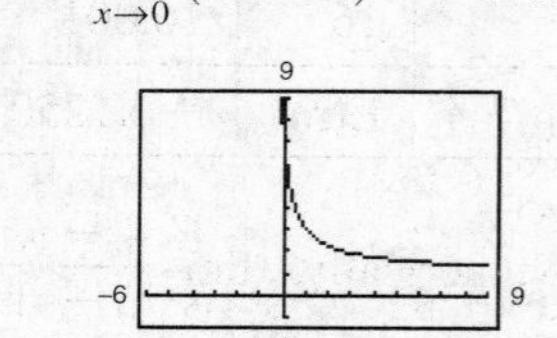

49. $f(x) = \dfrac{x-1}{x^2-1}$

(a) Graphically, $\lim\limits_{x \to 1^-} \dfrac{x-1}{x^2-1} = \dfrac{1}{2}$.

(b)

x	0.5	0.9	0.99	0.999	1
$f(x)$	0.6667	0.5263	0.5025	0.5003	Error

Numerically, $\lim\limits_{x \to 1^-} \dfrac{x-1}{x^2-1} = \dfrac{1}{2}$.

(c) Algebraically, $\lim\limits_{x \to 1^-} \dfrac{x-1}{x^2-1} = \lim\limits_{x \to 1^-} \dfrac{x-1}{(x-1)(x+1)} = \lim\limits_{x \to 1^-} \dfrac{1}{x+1} = \dfrac{1}{2}$.

50. $\lim\limits_{x \to 5^+} \dfrac{5-x}{25-x^2} = 0.1$

(a)

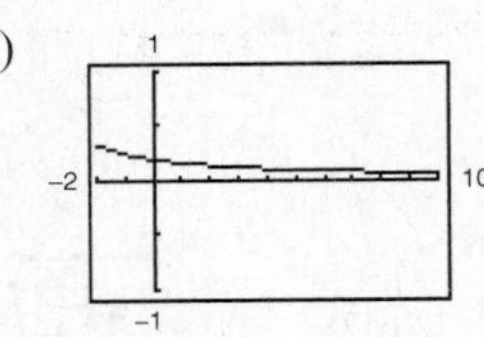

(b)

x	5.1	5.01	5.001	5
$f(x)$	0.099	0.0999	0.09999	Error

(c) Algebraically,

$$\lim_{x \to 5^+} \frac{5-x}{25-x^2} = \lim_{x \to 5^+} \frac{(5-x)}{(5-x)(5+x)}$$

$$= \lim_{x \to 5^+} \frac{1}{5+x} = \frac{1}{10}.$$

51. $f(x) = \dfrac{4-\sqrt{x}}{x-16}$

(a) Graphically, $\lim\limits_{x \to 16^+} \dfrac{4-\sqrt{x}}{x-16} = -\dfrac{1}{8}$.

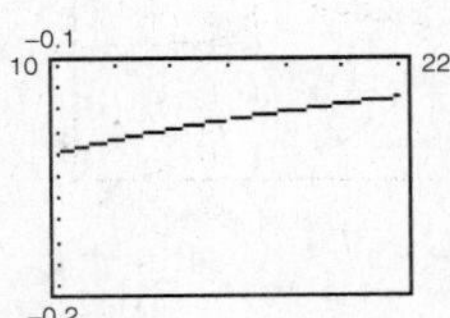

(b)

x	16	16.001	16.01	16.1	16.5
$f(x)$	Error	−0.1250	−0.1250	−0.1248	−0.1240

Numerically, $\lim\limits_{x \to 16^+} \dfrac{4-\sqrt{x}}{x-16} = -0.125$.

(c) Algebraically,

$$\lim_{x \to 16^+} \frac{4-\sqrt{x}}{x-16} = \lim_{x \to 16^+} \frac{4-\sqrt{x}}{\left(\sqrt{x}-4\right)\left(\sqrt{x}+4\right)}$$

$$= \lim_{x \to 16^+} \frac{-1}{\sqrt{x}+4} = \frac{-1}{4+4} = -\frac{1}{8}.$$

52. $\lim_{x\to 0^-} \dfrac{\sqrt{x+2}-\sqrt{2}}{x} \approx 0.3536$

(a)

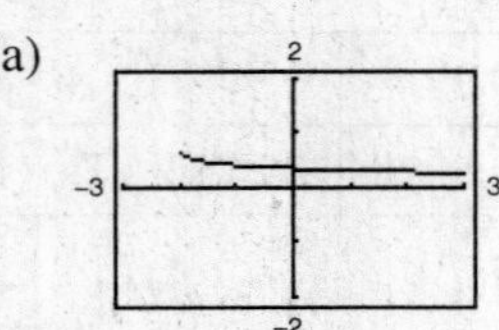

(b)

x	−1.0	−0.1	−0.01	−0.001	0
$f(x)$	0.4142	0.3581	0.3540	0.3536	?

(c) Algebraically,

$$\lim_{x\to 0^-} \frac{\sqrt{x+2}-\sqrt{2}}{x} \cdot \frac{\sqrt{x+2}+\sqrt{2}}{\sqrt{x+2}+\sqrt{2}} = \lim_{x\to 0^-} \frac{(x+2)-2}{x\left(\sqrt{x+2}+\sqrt{2}\right)}$$

$$= \lim_{x\to 0^-} \frac{1}{\sqrt{x+2}+\sqrt{2}} = \frac{1}{2\sqrt{2}} = \frac{\sqrt{2}}{4} \approx 0.3536.$$

53. $f(x) = \dfrac{|x-6|}{x-6}$

$\lim_{x\to 6^+} f(x) = 1$

$\lim_{x\to 6^-} f(x) = -1$

Limit does not exist.

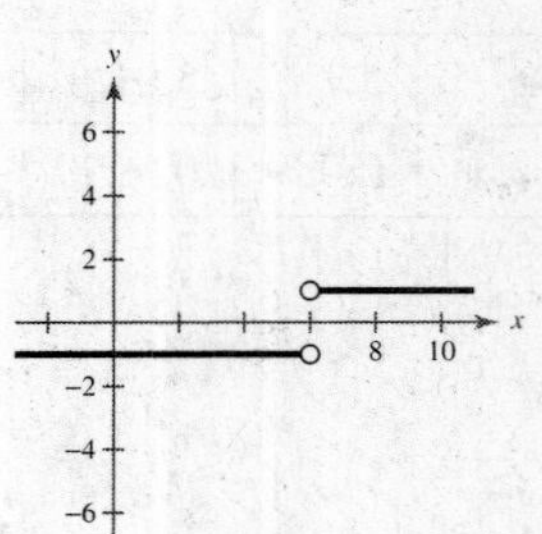

54. $\lim_{x\to 2^-} \dfrac{|x-2|}{x-2} = -1$

$\lim_{x\to 2^+} \dfrac{|x-2|}{x-2} = 1$

$\lim_{x\to 2} \dfrac{|x-2|}{x-2} = 1$

Limit does not exist.

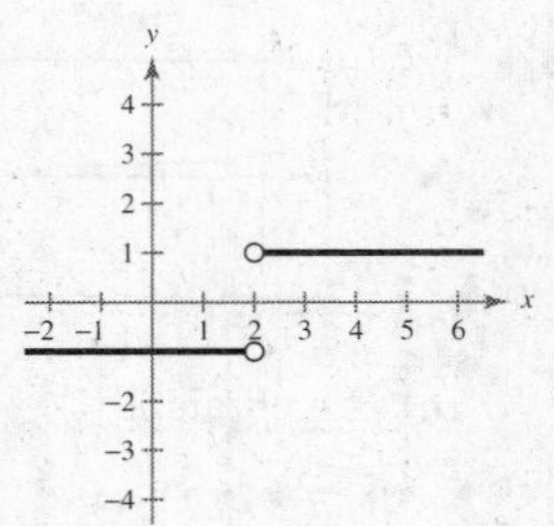

55. $f(x) = \dfrac{1}{x^2+1}$

$\lim_{x\to 1^-} \dfrac{1}{x^2+1} = \lim_{x\to 1^+} \dfrac{1}{x^2+1}$

$= \lim_{x\to 1} \dfrac{1}{x^2+1}$

$= \dfrac{1}{2}$

56. $\lim_{x\to 1^-} \dfrac{1}{x^2-1}$ does not exist.

$\lim_{x\to 1^+} \dfrac{1}{x^2-1}$ does not exist.

$\lim_{x\to 1} \dfrac{1}{x^2-1}$ does not exist.

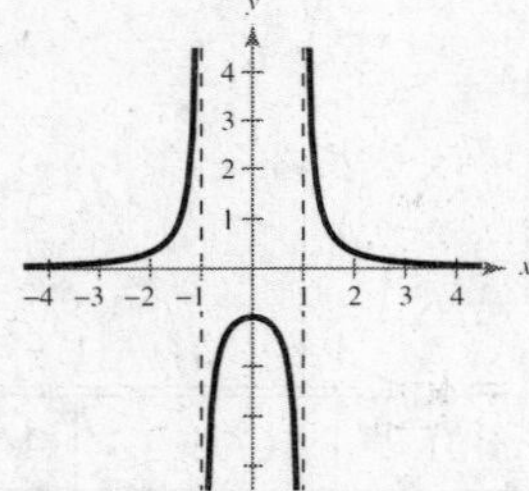

57. $\lim_{x\to 2^-} f(x) = 2 - 1 = 1$

$\lim_{x\to 2^+} f(x) = 2(2) - 3 = 1$

$\lim_{x\to 2} f(x) = 1$

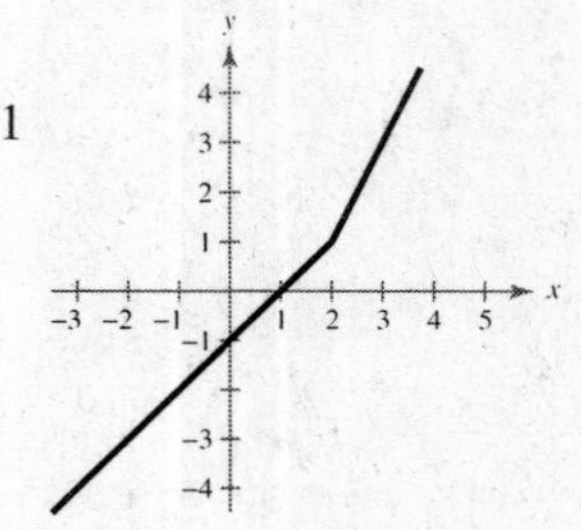

58. $\lim_{x\to 1^-} f(x) = 2(1) + 1 = 3$

$\lim_{x\to 1^+} f(x) = 4 - 1 = 3$

$\lim_{x\to 1} f(x) = 3$

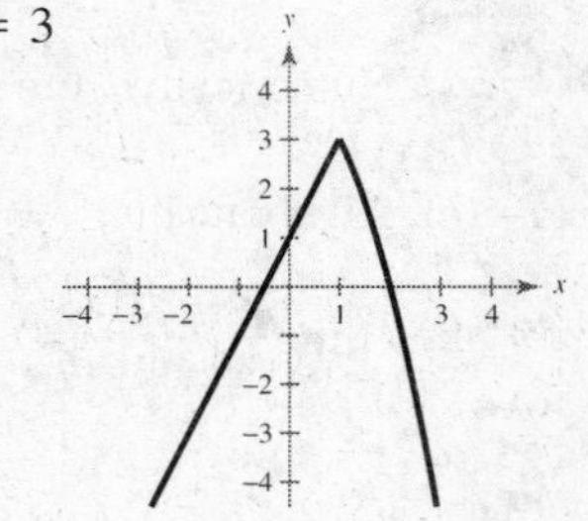

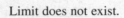

59. $f(x) = \begin{cases} 4 - x^2, & x \le 1 \\ 3 - x, & x > 1 \end{cases}$

$\lim\limits_{x \to 1^-} f(x) = 4 - 1 = 3$

$\lim\limits_{x \to 1^+} f(x) = 3 - 1 = 2$

$\lim\limits_{x \to 1} f(x)$ does not exist.

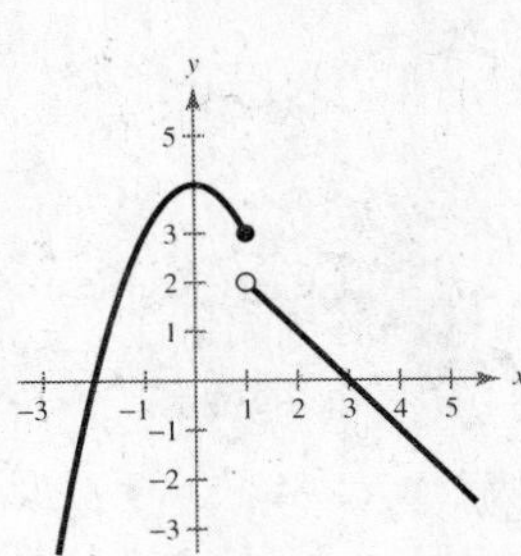

60. $\lim\limits_{x \to 0^-} f(x) = 4 - 0 = 4$

$\lim\limits_{x \to 0^+} f(x) = 0 + 4 = 4$

$\lim\limits_{x \to 0} f(x) = 4$

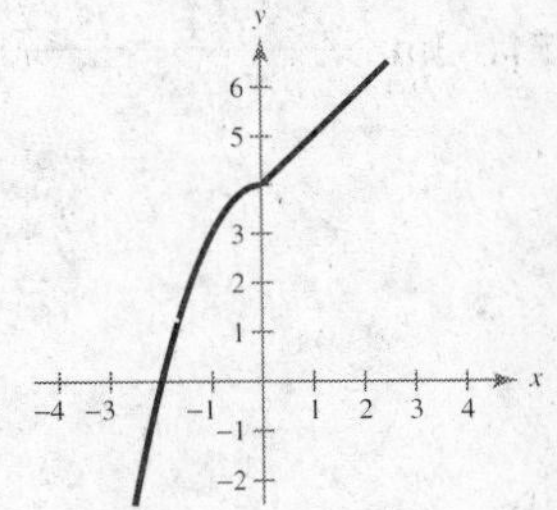

61.

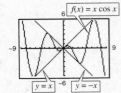

$\lim\limits_{x \to 0} f(x) = 0$

62.

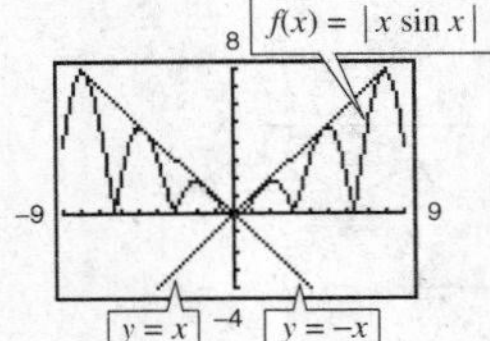

$\lim\limits_{x \to 0} f(x) = 0$

63.

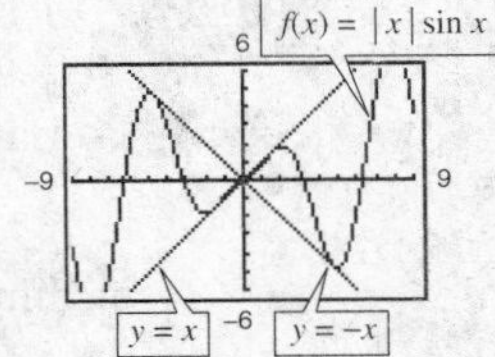

$\lim\limits_{x \to 0} f(x) = 0$

64.

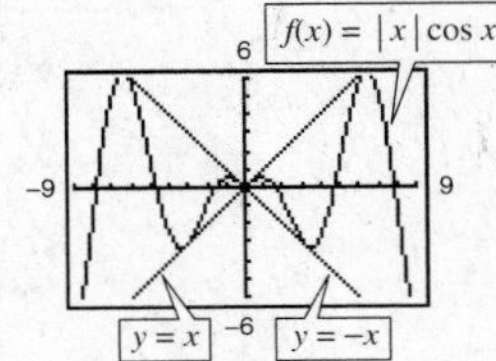

$\lim\limits_{x \to 0} f(x) = 0$

65.

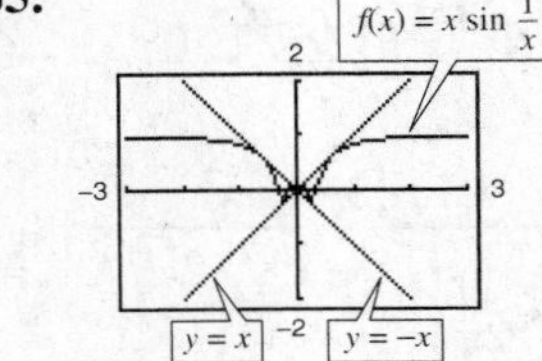

$\lim\limits_{x \to 0} f(x) = 0$

66.

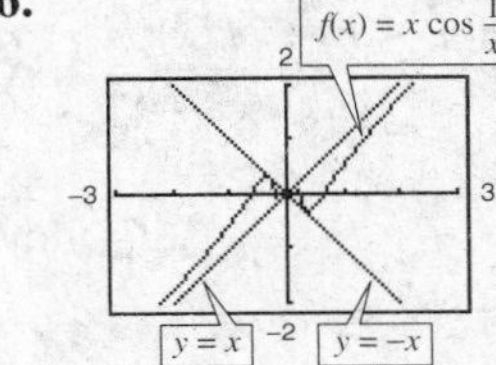

$\lim\limits_{x \to 0} f(x) = 0$

67. (a) Can be evaluated by direct substitution:

$\lim\limits_{x \to 0} x^2 \sin x^2 = 0^2 \sin 0^2 = 0$

(b) Cannot be evaluated by direct substitution:

$\lim\limits_{x \to 0} \dfrac{\sin x^2}{x^2} = 1$

68. (a) Can be evaluated by direct substitution.

$\lim\limits_{x \to 0} \dfrac{x}{\cos x} = \dfrac{0}{\cos 0} = 0$

(b) Cannot be evaluated by direct substitution.

$\lim\limits_{x \to 0} \dfrac{1 - \cos x}{x} = 0$

(See Section 11.1, Exercise 18.)

69.
$$\lim_{h \to 0} \frac{f(x+h) - f(x)}{h} = \lim_{h \to 0} \frac{3(x+h) - 1 - (3x - 1)}{h}$$
$$= \lim_{h \to 0} \frac{3x + 3h - 1 - 3x + 1}{h}$$
$$= \lim_{h \to 0} \frac{3h}{h} = 3$$

70.
$$\lim_{h \to 0} \frac{f(x+h) - f(x)}{h} = \lim_{h \to 0} \frac{[5 - 6(x+h)] - (5 - 6x)}{h}$$
$$= \lim_{h \to 0} -\frac{6h}{h} = -6$$

71. $\lim_{h\to 0}\frac{f(x+h)-f(x)}{h} = \lim_{h\to 0}\frac{\sqrt{x+h}-\sqrt{x}}{h}\cdot\left(\frac{\sqrt{x+h}+\sqrt{x}}{\sqrt{x+h}+\sqrt{x}}\right)$

$$= \lim_{h\to 0}\frac{(x+h)-x}{h\left(\sqrt{x+h}+\sqrt{x}\right)}$$

$$= \lim_{h\to 0}\frac{1}{\sqrt{x+h}+\sqrt{x}} = \frac{1}{2\sqrt{x}}$$

72. $\lim_{h\to 0}\frac{f(x+h)-f(x)}{h} = \lim_{h\to 0}\frac{\sqrt{x+h-2}-\sqrt{x-2}}{h}\cdot\frac{\sqrt{x+h-2}+\sqrt{x-2}}{\sqrt{x+h-2}+\sqrt{x-2}}$

$$= \lim_{h\to 0}\frac{(x+h-2)-(x-2)}{h\left[\sqrt{x+h-2}+\sqrt{x-2}\right]}$$

$$= \lim_{h\to 0}\frac{1}{\sqrt{x+h-2}+\sqrt{x-2}}$$

$$= \frac{1}{2\sqrt{x-2}}$$

73. $\lim_{h\to 0}\frac{f(x+h)-f(x)}{h} = \lim_{h\to 0}\frac{((x+h)^2-3(x+h))-(x^2-3x)}{h}$

$$= \lim_{h\to 0}\frac{x^2+2xh+h^2-3x-3h-x^2+3x}{h}$$

$$= \lim_{h\to 0}\frac{2xh+h^2-3h}{h}$$

$$= \lim_{h\to 0}(2x+h-3) = 2x-3$$

74. $\lim_{h\to 0}\frac{f(x+h)-f(x)}{h} = \lim_{h\to 0}\frac{[4-2(x+h)-(x+h)^2]-[4-2x-x^2]}{h}$

$$= \lim_{h\to 0}\frac{4-2x-2h-x^2-2xh-h^2-4+2x+x^2}{h}$$

$$= \lim_{h\to 0}\frac{-2h-2xh-h^2}{h}$$

$$= \lim_{h\to 0}(-2-2x-h) = -2-2x$$

75. $\lim_{h\to 0}\frac{f(x+h)-f(x)}{h} = \lim_{h\to 0}\frac{1/(x+h+2)-1/(x+2)}{h}$

$$= \lim_{h\to 0}\frac{(x+2)-(x+h+2)}{h(x+h+2)(x+2)}$$

$$= \lim_{h\to 0}\frac{-h}{h(x+h+2)(x+2)}$$

$$= \lim_{h\to 0}\frac{-1}{(x+h+2)(x+2)}$$

$$= \frac{-1}{(x+2)^2}$$

76. $\lim_{h\to 0} \frac{f(x+h)-f(x)}{h} = \lim_{h\to 0} \frac{\frac{1}{x+h-1} - \frac{1}{x-1}}{h}$

$= \lim_{h\to 0} \frac{x-1-(x+h-1)}{h(x+h-1)(x-1)}$

$= \lim_{h\to 0} \frac{-1}{(x+h-1)(x-1)}$

$= \frac{-1}{(x-1)^2}$

77. $\lim_{t\to 1} \frac{(-16(1)+128)-(-16t^2+128)}{1-t} = \lim_{t\to 1} \frac{16t^2-16}{1-t}$

$= \lim_{t\to 1} \frac{16(t-1)(t+1)}{1-t}$

$= \lim_{t\to 1} -16(t+1)$

$= -32 \frac{\text{ft}}{\text{sec}}$

78. $v(2) = \lim_{t\to 2} \frac{s(2)-s(t)}{2-t} = \lim_{t\to 2} \frac{(-64+128)-(-16t^2+128)}{2-t}$

$= \lim_{t\to 2} \frac{16t^2-64}{2-t} = \lim_{t\to 2} \frac{16(t+2)(t-2)}{2-t}$

$= \lim_{t\to 2} -16(t+2) = -64$ feet per second

79. $C(t) = 1.00 - 0.25[\![-(t-1)]\!]$

(a)

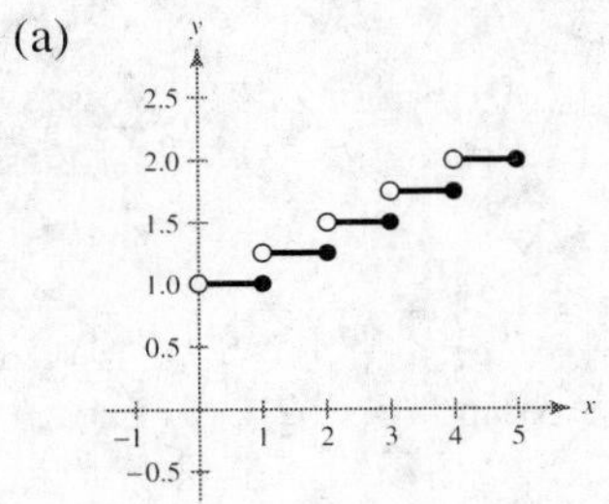

(b)

t	3	3.3	3.4	3.5	3.6	3.7	4
C	1.50	1.75	1.75	1.75	1.75	1.75	1.75

$\lim_{t\to 3.5} C(t) = 1.75$

(c)

t	2	2.5	2.9	3	3.1	3.5	4
C	1.25	1.50	1.50	1.50	1.75	1.75	1.75

$\lim_{t\to 3} C(t)$ does not exist. The one-sided limits do not agree.

80. $C(t) = 1.25 - 0.15[\![-(t - 1)]\!]$

(a)

(b)

t	3	3.3	3.4	3.5	3.6	3.7	4
C	1.55	1.70	1.70	1.70	1.70	1.70	1.70

$\lim_{t \to 3.5} C(t) = 1.70$

(c)

t	2	2.5	2.9	3	3.1	3.5	4
C	1.4	1.55	1.55	1.55	1.7	1.7	1.7

$\lim_{t \to 3} C(t)$ does not exist. The one-sided limits do not agree.

81. Answers will vary. As $t \to 2$ from the left, $f(t) \to 39.00$. As $t \to 2$ from the right, $f(t) \to 46.80$.

82. Answers will vary. As $x \to 1$ from the left, $f(x) \to 14.40$. As $x \to 1$ from the right, $f(x) \to 18.30$.

83. True

84. False. The value of f at c has no bearing on the limit.

85. Many answers possible

(a)

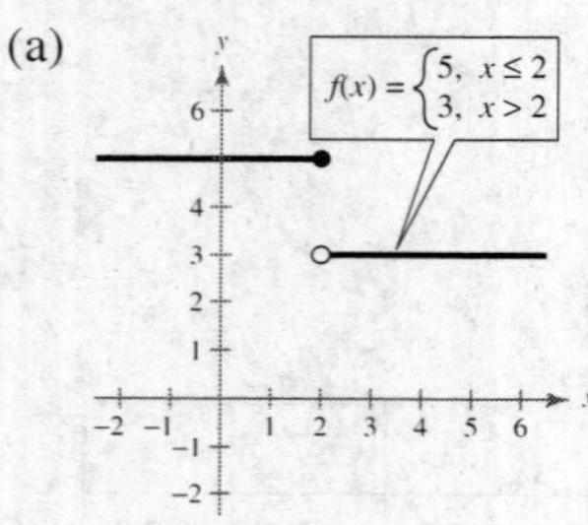

(b)

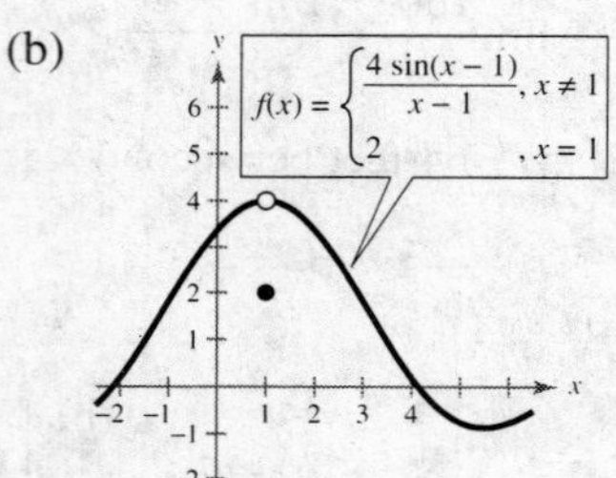

86. Answers will vary.

87. Slope of line through $(4, -6)$ and $(3, -4)$:

$$\frac{-6 + 4}{4 - 3} = -2$$

Slope of perpendicular line: $\frac{1}{2}$

Equation: $y + 10 = \frac{1}{2}(x - 6)$

$$2y - x + 26 = 0$$

88. Slope between $(3, -3)$ and $(5, -2)$:

$$\frac{-2 - (-3)}{5 - 3} = \frac{1}{2}$$

Line: $y + 1 = \frac{1}{2}(x - 1)$

$$2y + 2 = x - 1$$

$$2y - x + 3 = 0$$

89. $r = \dfrac{3}{1 + \cos\theta}$, $e = 1$, Parabola

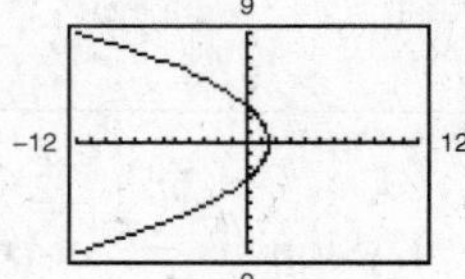

90. $r = \dfrac{12}{3 + 2\sin\theta} = \dfrac{4}{1 + (2/3)\sin\theta}$, $e = \dfrac{2}{3}$, Ellipse

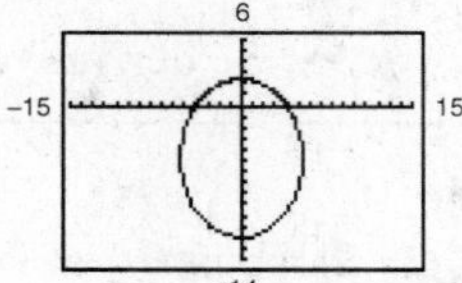

91. $r = \dfrac{9}{2 + 3\cos\theta} = \dfrac{9/2}{1 + (3/2)\cos\theta}$, $e = \dfrac{3}{2}$,

Hyperbola

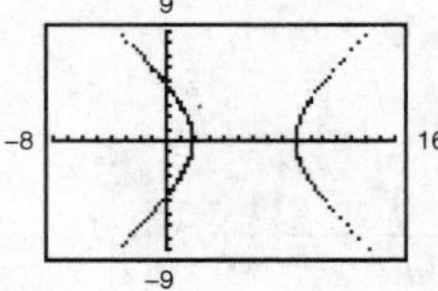

92. $r = \dfrac{4}{4 + \cos\theta} = \dfrac{1}{1 + (1/4)\cos\theta}$, $e = \dfrac{1}{4}$, Ellipse

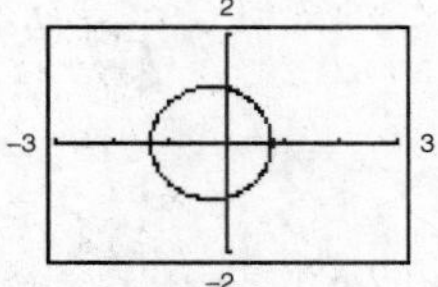

93. $r = \dfrac{5}{1 - \sin\theta}$, $e = 1$, Parabola

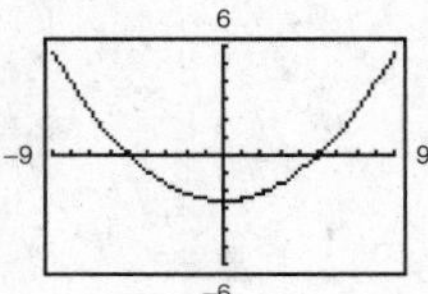

94. $r = \dfrac{6}{3 - 4\sin\theta} = \dfrac{2}{1 - (4/3)\sin\theta}$, $e = \dfrac{4}{3}$,

Hyperbola

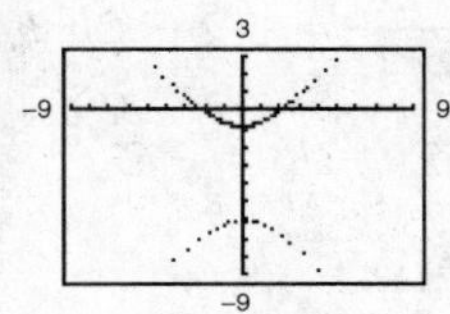

95. $\langle 7, -2, 3\rangle \cdot \langle -1, 4, 5\rangle = -7 - 8 + 15$

$= 0 \Rightarrow$ orthogonal

96. $\langle 5, 5, 0\rangle \cdot \langle 0, 5, 1\rangle = 25 \neq 0$

Not multiples of each other; neither parallel nor orthogonal

97. $-3\langle -4, 3, -6\rangle = \langle 12, -9, 18\rangle \Rightarrow$ parallel

98. $\langle 2, -3, 1\rangle \cdot \langle -2, 2, 2\rangle = -8 \neq 0$

Not multiples of each other; neither parallel nor orthogonal

Section 11.3 The Tangent Line Problem

- You should be able to visually approximate the slope of a graph.
- The slope m of the graph of f at the point $(x, f(x))$ is given by

  $$m = \lim_{h \to 0} \frac{f(x + h) - f(x)}{h}$$

  provided this limit exists.
- You should be able to use the limit definition to find the slope of a graph.
- The derivative of f at x is given by

  $$f'(x) = \lim_{h \to 0} \frac{f(x + h) - f(x)}{h}$$

  provided this limit exists. Notice that this is the same limit as that for the tangent line slope.
- You should be able to use the limit definition to find the derivative of a function.

Vocabulary Check

1. Calculus
2. tangent line
3. secant line
4. difference quotient
5. derivative

1. Slope is 0 at (x, y).

2. Slope is -1 at (x, y).

3. Slope is $\frac{1}{2}$ at (x, y).

4. Slope is -2 at (x, y).

5. $$m_{\text{sec}} = \frac{g(3+h) - g(3)}{h} = \frac{(3+h)^2 - 4(3+h) - (-3)}{h} = \frac{h^2 + 2h}{h}$$

$$m = \lim_{h\to 0} \frac{h^2 + 2h}{h} = \lim_{h\to 0} \frac{h(h+2)}{h} = \lim_{h\to 0} (h+2) = 2$$

6. $$m_{\text{sec}} = \frac{f(3+h) - f(3)}{h}$$

$$= \frac{10(3+h) - 2(3+h)^2 - 12}{h}$$

$$= \frac{-2h - 2h^2}{h} = -2 - 2h, h \neq 0$$

$$m = \lim_{h\to 0} (-2 - 2h) = -2$$

7. $$m_{\text{sec}} = \frac{g(1+h) - g(1)}{h}$$

$$= \frac{5 - 2(1+h) - 3}{h} = \frac{-2h}{h}$$

$$m = \lim_{h\to 0} \frac{-2h}{h} = -2$$

8. $$m_{\text{sec}} = \frac{h(-1+k) - h(-1)}{k} = \frac{2(-1+k) + 5 - 3}{k} = \frac{2k}{k}$$

$$m = \lim_{k\to 0} \frac{2k}{k} = 2$$

9. $$m_{\text{sec}} = \frac{g(2+h) - g(2)}{h} = \frac{[4/(2+h)] - 2}{h} = \frac{4 - 2(2+h)}{(2+h)h} = \frac{-2}{2+h}, h \neq 0$$

$$m = \lim_{h\to 0}\left(\frac{-2}{2+h}\right) = -1$$

10. $$m_{\text{sec}} = \frac{g(4+h) - g(4)}{h} = \frac{\frac{1}{4+h-2} - \frac{1}{2}}{h} = \frac{\frac{1}{2+h} - \frac{1}{2}}{h} = \frac{-h}{(2+h)2h} = \frac{-1}{2(2+h)}, h \neq 0$$

$$m = \lim_{h\to 0}\left(\frac{-1}{2(2+h)}\right) = -\frac{1}{4}$$

11. $$m_{\text{sec}} = \frac{h(9+k) - h(9)}{k} = \frac{\sqrt{9+k} - 3}{k} \cdot \frac{\sqrt{9+k} + 3}{\sqrt{9+k} + 3} = \frac{(9+k) - 9}{k[\sqrt{9+k} + 3]} = \frac{1}{\sqrt{9+k} + 3}, k \neq 0$$

$$m = \lim_{k\to 0} \frac{1}{\sqrt{9+k} + 3} = \frac{1}{6}$$

12. $$m_{\text{sec}} = \frac{h(-1+k) - h(-1)}{k} = \frac{\sqrt{-1+k+10} - 3}{k} \cdot \frac{\sqrt{k+9} + 3}{\sqrt{k+9} + 3} = \frac{(k+9) - 9}{k\left[\sqrt{k+9} + 3\right]} = \frac{1}{\sqrt{k+9} + 3}, k \neq 0$$

$$m = \lim_{k\to 0} \frac{1}{\sqrt{k+9} + 3} = \frac{1}{6}$$

13. $m_{\text{sec}} = \dfrac{g(x+h) - g(x)}{h} = \dfrac{4 - (x+h)^2 - (4 - x^2)}{h} = \dfrac{-2xh - h^2}{h} = -2x - h,\ h \neq 0$

$m = \lim\limits_{h \to 0}(-2x - h) = -2x$

(a) At $(0, 4)$, $m = -2(0) = 0$.

(b) At $(-1, 3)$, $m = -2(-1) = 2$.

14. $m_{\text{sec}} = \dfrac{g(x+h) - g(x)}{h} = \dfrac{(x+h)^3 - x^3}{h} = \dfrac{3x^2h + 3xh^2 + h^3}{h}$

$= 3x^2 + 3xh + h^2,\ h \neq 0$

$m = \lim\limits_{h \to 0}(3x^2 + 3xh + h^2) = 3x^2$

(a) At $(1, 1)$, $m = 3(1)^2 = 3$.

(b) At $(-2, -8)$, $m = 3(-2)^2 = 12$.

15. $m_{\text{sec}} = \dfrac{g(x+h) - g(x)}{h} = \dfrac{\dfrac{1}{x+h+4} - \dfrac{1}{x+4}}{h} = \dfrac{(x+4) - (x+4+h)}{(x+h+4)(x+4)(h)}$

$= \dfrac{-h}{(x+h+4)(x+4)h} = \dfrac{-1}{(x+h+4)(x+4)},\ h \neq 0$

$m = \lim\limits_{h \to 0} \dfrac{-1}{(x+h+4)(x+4)} = \dfrac{-1}{(x+4)^2}$

(a) At $\left(0, \dfrac{1}{4}\right)$, $m = \dfrac{-1}{(0+4)^2} = \dfrac{-1}{16}$.

(b) At $\left(-2, \dfrac{1}{2}\right)$, $m = \dfrac{-1}{(-2+4)^2} = \dfrac{-1}{4}$.

16. $m_{\text{sec}} = \dfrac{f(x+h) - f(x)}{h} = \dfrac{\dfrac{1}{x+h+2} - \dfrac{1}{x+2}}{h} = \dfrac{(x+2) - (x+h+2)}{h(x+h+2)(x+2)}$

$= \dfrac{-h}{h(x+h+2)(x+2)}$

$m = \lim\limits_{h \to 0} \dfrac{-h}{h(x+h+2)(x+2)} = \dfrac{-1}{(x+2)^2}$

(a) At $\left(0, \dfrac{1}{2}\right)$, $m = \dfrac{1}{(0+2)^2} = \dfrac{-1}{4}$.

(b) At $(-1, 1)$, $m = \dfrac{1}{(-1+2)^2} = -1$.

17. $m_{\text{sec}} = \dfrac{g(x+h) - g(x)}{h} = \dfrac{\sqrt{x+h-1} - \sqrt{x-1}}{h} \cdot \dfrac{\sqrt{x+h+1} + \sqrt{x-1}}{\sqrt{x+h-1} + \sqrt{x-1}}$

$= \dfrac{(x+h-1) - (x-1)}{h\left(\sqrt{x+h-1} + \sqrt{x-1}\right)} = \dfrac{1}{\sqrt{x+h-1} + \sqrt{x-1}},\ h \neq 0$

$m = \lim\limits_{h \to 0}\left(\dfrac{1}{\sqrt{x+h-1} + \sqrt{x-1}}\right) = \dfrac{1}{2\sqrt{x-1}}$

(a) At $(5, 2)$, $m = \dfrac{1}{2\sqrt{5-1}} = \dfrac{1}{4}$.

(b) At $(10, 3)$, $m = \dfrac{1}{2\sqrt{10-1}} = \dfrac{1}{6}$.

18. $m_{\text{sec}} = \dfrac{f(x+h) - f(x)}{h} = \dfrac{\sqrt{x+h-4} - \sqrt{x-4}}{h} \cdot \dfrac{\sqrt{x+h-4} + \sqrt{x-4}}{\sqrt{x+h-4} + \sqrt{x-4}}$

$= \dfrac{(x+h-4) - (x-4)}{h\left[\sqrt{x+h-4} + \sqrt{x-4}\right]}$

$m = \lim\limits_{h\to 0} \dfrac{h}{h\left[\sqrt{x+h-4} + \sqrt{x-4}\right]} = \dfrac{1}{2\sqrt{x-4}}$

(a) At $(5, 1)$, $m = \dfrac{1}{2}$.

(b) At $(8, 2)$, $m = \dfrac{1}{4}$.

19.

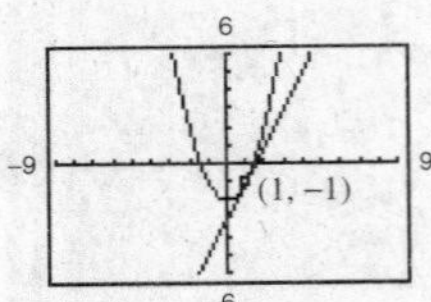

Slope at $(1, -1)$ is 2.

20.

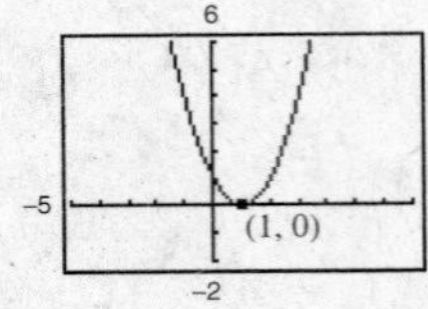

Slope ≈ 0

21.

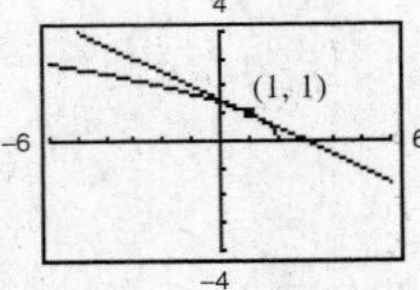

Slope at $(1, 1)$ is $-\frac{1}{2}$.

22.

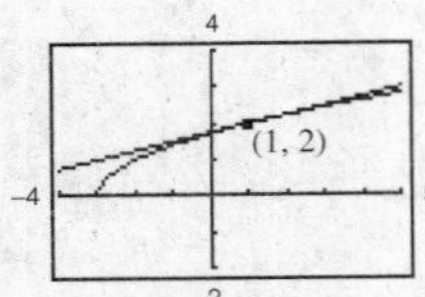

At $(1, 2)$, slope $\approx \frac{1}{4}$.

23.

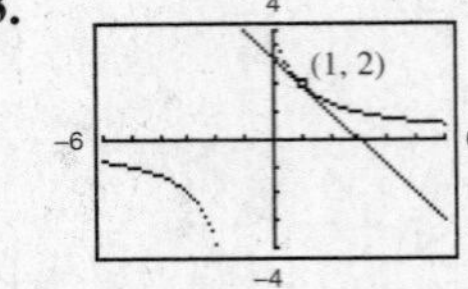

Slope at $(1, 2)$ is -1.

24.

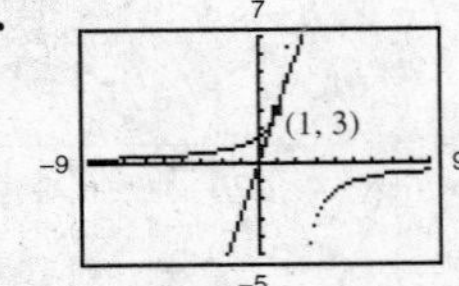

Slope ≈ 3

25. $f'(x) = \lim\limits_{h\to 0} \dfrac{f(x+h) - f(x)}{h} = \lim\limits_{h\to 0} \dfrac{5-5}{h} = 0$

26. $f'(x) = \lim\limits_{h\to 0} \dfrac{f(x+h) - f(x)}{h}$

$= \lim\limits_{h\to 0} \dfrac{(-1) - (-1)}{h} = 0$

27. $g'(x) = \lim\limits_{h\to 0} \dfrac{g(x+h) - g(x)}{h}$

$= \lim\limits_{h\to 0} \dfrac{\left[9 - \frac{1}{3}(x+h)\right] - \left[9 - \frac{1}{3}x\right]}{h}$

$= \lim\limits_{h\to 0} \dfrac{-\frac{1}{3}h}{h} = -\dfrac{1}{3}$

28. $f'(x) = \lim\limits_{h\to 0} \dfrac{f(x+h) - f(x)}{h}$

$= \lim\limits_{h\to 0} \dfrac{\left[-5(x+h) + 2\right] - (-5x+2)}{h}$

$= \lim\limits_{h\to 0} \dfrac{-5h}{h} = -5$

29. $f'(x) = \lim\limits_{h\to 0} \dfrac{f(x+h) - f(x)}{h} = \lim\limits_{h\to 0} \dfrac{\left[4 - 3(x+h)^2\right] - (4 - 3x^2)}{h}$

$= \lim\limits_{h\to 0} \dfrac{-3(x^2 + 2xh + h^2) + 3x^2}{h} = \lim\limits_{h\to 0} \dfrac{-6xh - 3h^2}{h} = \lim\limits_{h\to 0}(-6x - 3h) = -6x$

30. $f'(x) = \lim\limits_{h\to 0} \dfrac{f(x+h) - f(x)}{h} = \lim\limits_{h\to 0} \dfrac{\left[(x+h)^2 - 3(x+h) + 4\right] - (x^2 - 3x + 4)}{h}$

$= \lim\limits_{h\to 0} \dfrac{x^2 + 2xh + h^2 - 3h - x^2}{h}$

$= \lim\limits_{h\to 0} (2x + h - 3) = 2x - 3$

31. $f'(x) = \lim_{h\to 0} \frac{f(x+h) - f(x)}{h}$

$= \lim_{h\to 0} \frac{\frac{1}{(x+h)^2} - \frac{1}{x^2}}{h}$

$= \lim_{h\to 0} \frac{x^2 - (x^2 + 2xh + h^2)}{(x+h)^2 x^2 h}$

$= \lim_{h\to 0} \frac{-2x - h}{(x+h)^2 x^2} = -\frac{2x}{x^4} = -\frac{2}{x^3}$

32. $f'(x) = \lim_{h\to 0} \frac{f(x+h) - f(x)}{h} = \lim_{h\to 0} \frac{\frac{1}{(x+h)^3} - \frac{1}{x^3}}{h}$

$= \lim_{h\to 0} \frac{x^3 - (x^3 + 3x^2h + 3xh^2 + h^3)}{h(x+h)^3 x^3}$

$= \lim_{h\to 0} \frac{-3x^2h - 3xh^2 - h^3}{h(x+h)^3 x^3}$

$= \lim_{h\to 0} \frac{-3x^2 - 3xh - h^2}{(x+h)^3 x^3}$

$= \frac{-3x^2}{x^6} = \frac{-3}{x^4}$

33. $f'(x) = \lim_{h\to 0} \frac{f(x+h) - f(x)}{h}$

$= \lim_{h\to 0} \frac{\sqrt{x+h-4} - \sqrt{x-4}}{h} \cdot \frac{\sqrt{x+h-4} + \sqrt{x-4}}{\sqrt{x+h-4} + \sqrt{x-4}}$

$= \lim_{h\to 0} \frac{(x+h-4) - (x-4)}{h\left[\sqrt{x+h-4} + \sqrt{x-4}\right]}$

$= \lim_{h\to 0} \frac{1}{\sqrt{x+h-4} + \sqrt{x-4}}$

$= \frac{1}{2\sqrt{x-4}}$

34. $f'(x) = \lim_{h\to 0} \frac{f(x+h) - f(x)}{h}$

$= \lim_{h\to 0} \frac{\sqrt{x+h+8} - \sqrt{x+8}}{h} \cdot \frac{\sqrt{x+h+8} + \sqrt{x+8}}{\sqrt{x+h+8} + \sqrt{x+8}}$

$= \lim_{h\to 0} \frac{(x+h+8) - (x+8)}{h\left[\sqrt{x+h+8} + \sqrt{x+8}\right]}$

$= \lim_{h\to 0} \frac{1}{\sqrt{x+h+8} + \sqrt{x+8}}$

$= \frac{1}{2\sqrt{x+8}}$

35. $f'(x) = \lim_{h\to 0} \frac{f(x+h) - f(x)}{h}$

$= \lim_{h\to 0} \frac{\frac{1}{(x+h+2)} - \frac{1}{x+2}}{h}$

$= \lim_{h\to 0} \frac{(x+2) - (x+h+2)}{h(x+h+2)(x+2)}$

$= \lim_{h\to 0} \frac{-1}{(x+h+2)(x+2)}$

$= \frac{-1}{(x+2)^2}$

36. $f'(x) = \lim_{h\to 0} \frac{f(x+h) - f(x)}{h}$

$= \lim_{h\to 0} \frac{\frac{1}{(x+h-5)} - \frac{1}{x-5}}{h}$

$= \lim_{h\to 0} \frac{(x-5) - (x+h-5)}{h(x+h-5)(x-5)}$

$= \lim_{h\to 0} \frac{-1}{(x+h-5)(x-5)}$

$= \frac{-1}{(x-5)^2}$

37. $$f'(x) = \lim_{h\to 0}\frac{f(x+h)-f(x)}{h} = \lim_{h\to 0}\frac{\dfrac{1}{\sqrt{x+h-9}}-\dfrac{1}{\sqrt{x-9}}}{h}\cdot\frac{\dfrac{1}{\sqrt{x+h-9}}+\dfrac{1}{\sqrt{x-9}}}{\dfrac{1}{\sqrt{x+h-9}}+\dfrac{1}{\sqrt{x-9}}}$$

$$= \lim_{h\to 0}\frac{\dfrac{1}{(x+h-9)}-\dfrac{1}{(x-9)}}{h\left[\dfrac{1}{\sqrt{x+h-9}}+\dfrac{1}{\sqrt{x-9}}\right]} = \lim_{h\to 0}\frac{(x-9)-(x+h-9)}{h(x+h-9)(x-9)\left[\dfrac{1}{\sqrt{x+h-9}}+\dfrac{1}{\sqrt{x-9}}\right]}$$

$$= \lim_{h\to 0}\frac{-1}{(x+h-9)(x-9)\left[\dfrac{1}{\sqrt{x+h-9}}+\dfrac{1}{\sqrt{x-9}}\right]} = \frac{-1}{(x-9)^2\left[\dfrac{2}{\sqrt{x-9}}\right]} = \frac{-1}{2(x-9)^{3/2}}$$

38. $$f'(x) = \lim_{h\to 0}\frac{f(x+h)-f(x)}{h} = \lim_{h\to 0}\frac{\dfrac{1}{\sqrt{x+h+1}}-\dfrac{1}{\sqrt{x+1}}}{h}$$

$$= \lim_{h\to 0}\frac{\sqrt{x+1}-\sqrt{x+h+1}}{h\sqrt{x+h+1}\sqrt{x+1}}\cdot\frac{\sqrt{x+1}+\sqrt{x+h+1}}{\sqrt{x+1}+\sqrt{x+h+1}}$$

$$= \lim_{h\to 0}\frac{(x+1)-(x+h+1)}{h\sqrt{x+h+1}\sqrt{x+1}\left[\sqrt{x+1}+\sqrt{x+h+1}\right]}$$

$$= \lim_{h\to 0}\frac{-1}{\sqrt{x+h+1}\sqrt{x+1}\left[\sqrt{x+1}+\sqrt{x+h+1}\right]}$$

$$= \frac{-1}{\sqrt{x+1}\sqrt{x+1}\left[2\sqrt{x+1}\right]}$$

$$= \frac{-1}{2(x+1)^{3/2}}$$

39. (a) $$m_{\text{sec}} = \frac{f(2+h)-f(2)}{h}$$

$$= \frac{(2+h)^2-1-3}{h}$$

$$= \frac{4+4h+h^2-4}{h}$$

$$= 4+h,\ h\neq 0$$

$$m = \lim_{h\to 0}(4+h) = 4$$

(b) $y-3 = 4(x-2)$

$y = 4x-5$

(c)

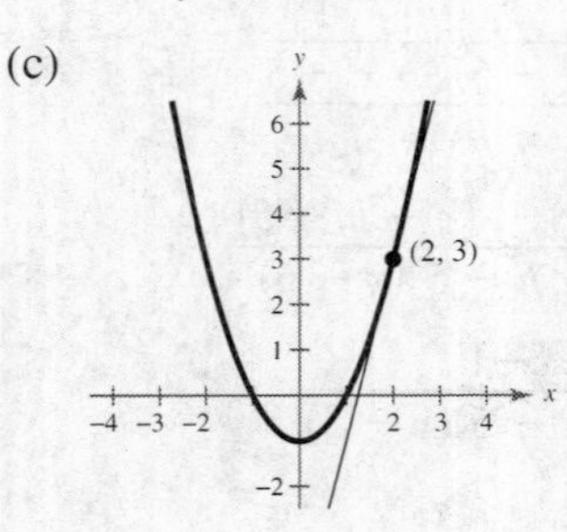

40. (a) $$m_{\text{sec}} = \frac{f(1+h)-f(1)}{h}$$

$$= \frac{4-(1+h)^2-3}{h}$$

$$= \frac{4-(1+2h+h^2)-3}{h}$$

$$= \frac{-h^2-2h}{h} = -h-2,\ h\neq 0$$

$$m = \lim_{h\to 0}(-h-2) = -2$$

(b) $y-3 = -2(x-1)$

$y = -2x+5$

(c)

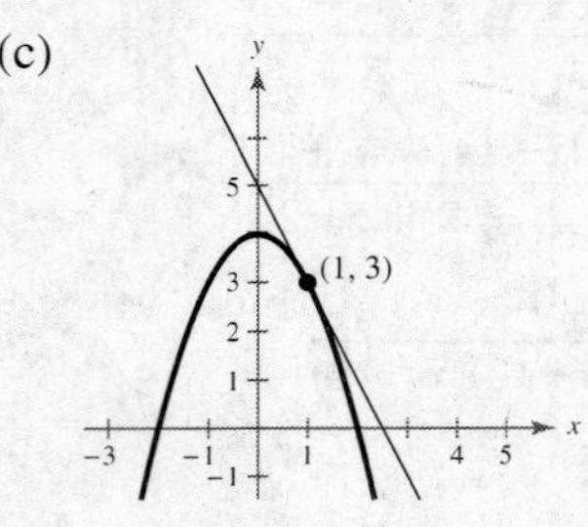

41. (a) $m_{\text{sec}} = \dfrac{f(1+h) - f(1)}{h}$

$= \dfrac{(1+h)^3 - 2(1+h) - (-1)}{h}$

$= \dfrac{1 + 3h + 3h^2 + h^3 - 2 - 2h + 1}{h}$

$= \dfrac{h^3 + 3h^2 + h}{h} = h^2 + 3h + 1, \; h \neq 0$

$m = \lim\limits_{h \to 0} (h^2 + 3h + 1) = 1$

(b) $y - (-1) = 1(x - 1)$

$y = x - 2$

(c)

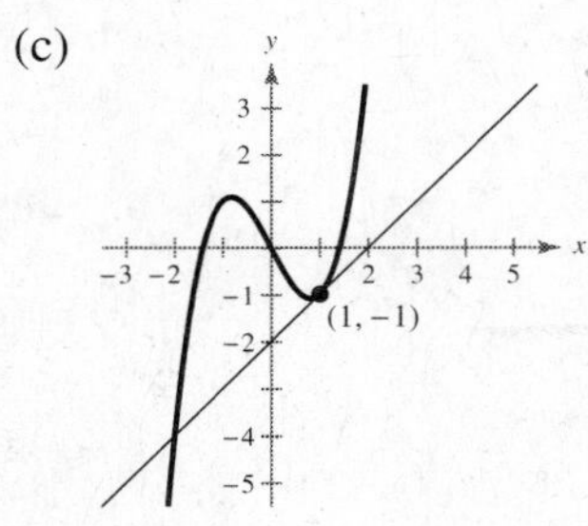

42. (a) $m_{\text{sec}} = \dfrac{f(2+h) - f(2)}{h}$

$= \dfrac{(2+h)^3 - (2+h) - 6}{h}$

$= \dfrac{h^3 + 6h^2 + 12h + 8 - 2 - h - 6}{h}$

$= \dfrac{h^3 + 6h^2 + 11h}{h}$

$= h^2 + 6h + 11, \; h \neq 0$

$m = \lim\limits_{h \to 0} (h^2 + 6h + 11) = 11$

(b) $y - 6 = 11(x - 2)$

$y = 11x - 16$

(c)

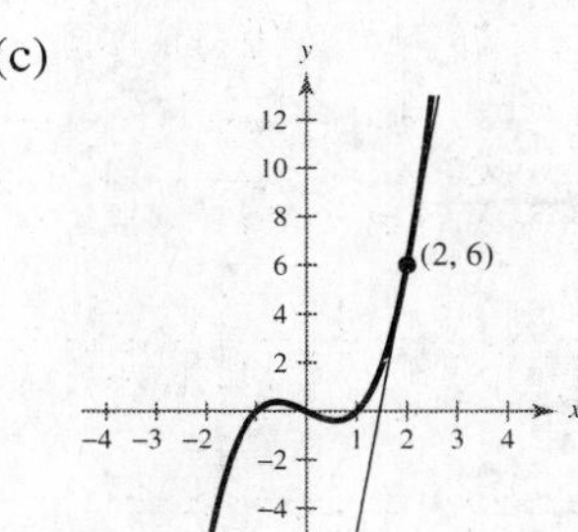

43. (a) $m_{\text{sec}} = \dfrac{f(3+h) - f(3)}{h} = \dfrac{\sqrt{3+h+1} - 2}{h}$

$= \dfrac{\sqrt{4+h} - 2}{h} \cdot \dfrac{\sqrt{4+h} + 2}{\sqrt{4+h} + 2}$

$= \dfrac{4 + h - 4}{h\left[\sqrt{4+h} + 2\right]}$

$= \dfrac{1}{\sqrt{4+h} + 2}$

$m = \lim\limits_{h \to 0} \dfrac{1}{\sqrt{4+h} + 2} = \dfrac{1}{4}$

(b) $y - 2 = \dfrac{1}{4}(x - 3)$

$y = \dfrac{1}{4}x + \dfrac{5}{4}$

(c)

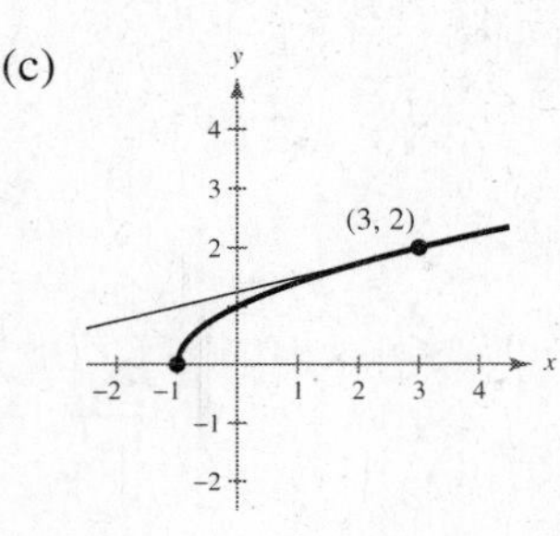

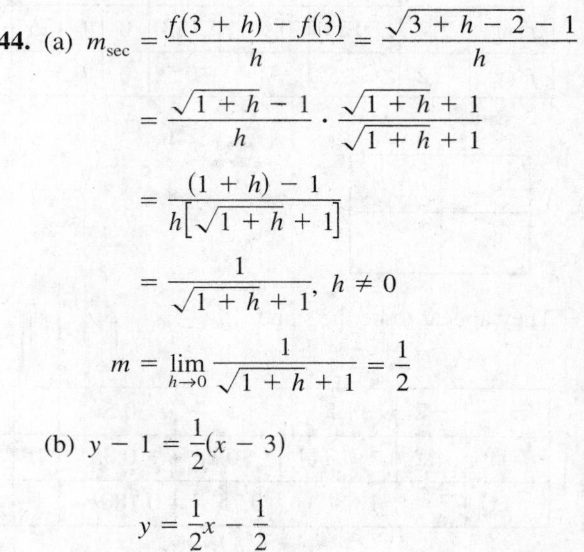

44. (a) $m_{\text{sec}} = \dfrac{f(3+h) - f(3)}{h} = \dfrac{\sqrt{3+h-2} - 1}{h}$

$= \dfrac{\sqrt{1+h} - 1}{h} \cdot \dfrac{\sqrt{1+h} + 1}{\sqrt{1+h} + 1}$

$= \dfrac{(1+h) - 1}{h\left[\sqrt{1+h} + 1\right]}$

$= \dfrac{1}{\sqrt{1+h} + 1}, \; h \neq 0$

$m = \lim\limits_{h \to 0} \dfrac{1}{\sqrt{1+h} + 1} = \dfrac{1}{2}$

(b) $y - 1 = \dfrac{1}{2}(x - 3)$

$y = \dfrac{1}{2}x - \dfrac{1}{2}$

(c)

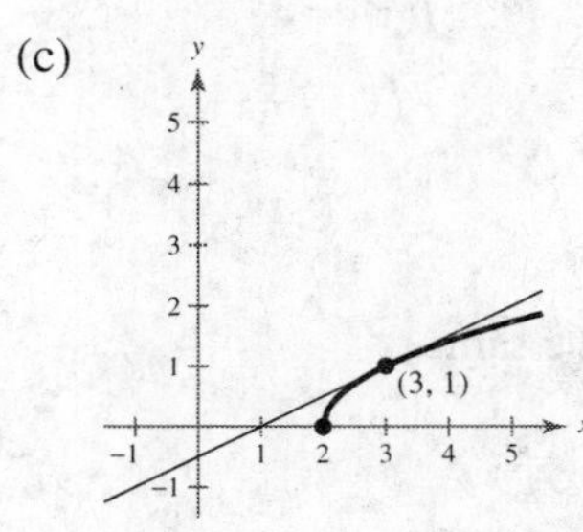

45. (a) $m_{\text{sec}} = \dfrac{f(-4+h) - f(-4)}{h}$

$$= \frac{\dfrac{1}{-4+h+5} - 1}{h}$$

$$= \frac{1+4-h-5}{h(-4+h+5)} = \frac{-1}{h+1},\ h \neq 0$$

$$m = \lim_{h \to 0} \frac{-1}{h+1} = -1$$

(b) $y - 1 = -1(x + 4)$

$y = -x - 3$

(c)

46. (a) $m_{\text{sec}} = \dfrac{f(4+h) - f(4)}{h}$

$$= \frac{\dfrac{1}{4+h-3} - 1}{h}$$

$$= \frac{1-4-h+3}{h(4+h-3)} = \frac{-1}{h+1},\ h \neq 0$$

$$m = \lim_{h \to 0} \frac{-1}{h+1} = -1$$

(b) $y - 1 = -1(x - 4)$

$y = -x + 5$

(c)

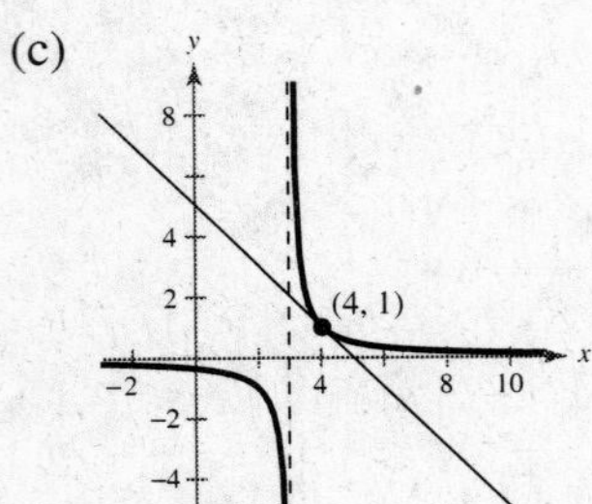

47.

x	-2	-1.5	-1	-0.5	0	0.5	1	1.5	2
$f(x)$	2	1.125	0.5	0.125	0	0.125	0.5	1.125	2
$f'(x)$	-2	-1.5	-1	-0.5	0	0.5	1	1.5	2

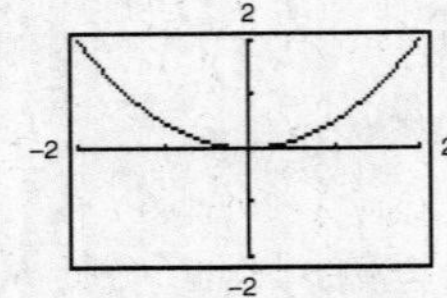

$f(x) = \frac{1}{2}x^2$

$f'(x) = x$

They appear to be the same.

48.

x	-2	-1.5	-1	-0.5	0	0.5	1	1.5	2
$f(x)$	-2	-0.844	-0.25	-0.031	0	0.031	0.25	0.844	2
$f'(x)$	3	1.688	0.75	0.188	0	0.188	0.75	1.688	3

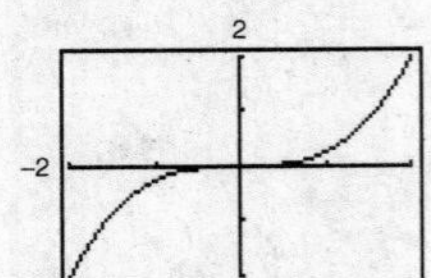

$f(x) = \frac{1}{4}x^3$

$f'(x) = \frac{3}{4}x^2$

They appear to be the same.

49.

x	-2	-1.5	-1	-0.5	0	0.5	1	1.5	2
$f(x)$	1	1.225	1.414	1.581	1.732	1.871	2	2.121	2.236
$f'(x)$	0.5	0.408	0.354	0.316	0.289	0.267	0.25	0.236	0.224

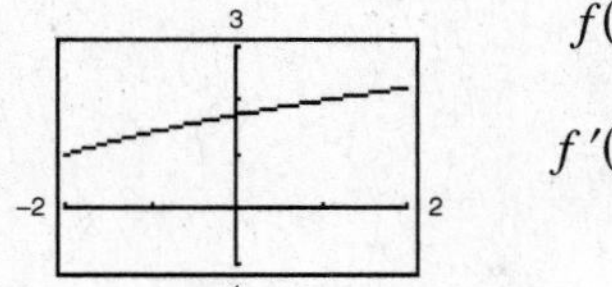

$$f(x) = \sqrt{x+3}$$

$$f'(x) = \frac{1}{2\sqrt{x+3}}$$

They appear to be the same.

50.

x	-2	-1.5	-1	-0.5	0	0.5	1	1.5	2
$f(x)$	0	-0.7	-1	-1.071	-1	-0.833	-0.6	-0.318	0
$f'(x)$	-2	-0.92	-0.333	0.020	0.25	0.407	0.52	0.603	0.667

$$f(x) = \frac{x^2-4}{x+4}$$

$$f'(x) = \frac{x^2+8x+4}{(x+4)^2}$$

They appear to be the same.

51. $f'(x) = \lim_{h\to 0} \frac{f(x+h)-f(x)}{h} = \lim_{h\to 0} \frac{[(x+h)^2 - 4(x+h) + 3] - [x^2 - 4x + 3]}{h}$

$$= \lim_{h\to 0} \frac{(x^2 + 2xh + h^2 - 4x - 4h + 3) - (x^2 - 4x + 3)}{h}$$

$$= \lim_{h\to 0} \frac{2xh + h^2 - 4h}{h} = \lim_{h\to 0} 2x + h - 4 = 2x - 4$$

$f'(x) = 0 = 2x - 4 \Rightarrow x = 2$

f has a horizontal tangent at $(2, -1)$.

52. $f'(x) = \lim_{h\to 0} \frac{f(x+h)-f(x)}{h}$

$$= \lim_{h\to 0} \frac{(x+h)^2 - 6(x+h) + 4 - (x^2 - 6x + 4)}{h}$$

$$= \lim_{h\to 0} \frac{x^2 + 2xh + h^2 - 6x - 6h - x^2 + 6x}{h}$$

$$= \lim_{h\to 0} \frac{2xh + h^2 - 6hh}{h} = 2x - 6$$

$f'(x) = 2x = 6$

$f'(x) = 0 \Rightarrow x = 3$

f has a horizontal tangent at $(3, -5)$.

53. $f'(x) = \lim_{h\to 0} \dfrac{f(x+h) - f(x)}{h} = \lim_{h\to 0} \dfrac{[3(x+h)^3 - 9(x+h)] - [3x^3 - 9x]}{h}$

$= \lim_{h\to 0} \dfrac{3(x^3 + 3x^2h + 3xh^2 + h^3) - 9x - 9h - 3x^3 + 9x}{h}$

$= \lim_{h\to 0} \dfrac{9x^2h + 9xh^2 + 3h^3 - 9h}{h}$

$= \lim_{h\to 0} (9x^2 + 9xh + 3h - 9) = 9x^2 - 9$

$f'(x) = 0 = 9x^2 - 9 = 9(x+1)(x-1) \implies x = \pm 1$

Horizontal tangents at $(1, -6)$ and $(-1, 6)$

54. $f'(x) = \lim_{h\to 0} \dfrac{f(x+h) - f(x)}{h} = \lim_{h\to 0} \dfrac{(x+h)^3 + 3(x+h) - (x^3 + 3x)}{h}$

$= \lim_{h\to 0} \dfrac{x^3 + 3x^2h + 3xh^2 + h^3 + 3x + 3h - x^3 - 3x}{h}$

$= \lim_{h\to 0} \dfrac{3x^2h + 3xh^2 + h^3 + 3h}{h}$

$= \lim_{h\to 0} (3x^2 + 3xh + h^2 + 3) = 3x^2 + 3$

$f'(x) = 3x^2 + 3 = 0,$ Impossible

No horizontal tangents

55. $f'(x) = 4x^3 - 4x = 0$

$4x(x-1)(x+1) = 0$

$x = 0, 1, -1$

$(0, 0), (1, -1), (-1, -1)$

56. $f'(x) = 12x^3 + 12x^2$

$f'(x) = 0 = 12x^3 + 12x^2 = 12x^2(x+1) \implies 0, -1$

f has horizontal tangents at $(0, 0)$ and $(-1, -1)$.

57. $f'(x) = -2\sin x + 1 = 0$

$\sin x = \dfrac{1}{2}$

$x = \dfrac{\pi}{6}, \dfrac{5\pi}{6}$

$\left(\dfrac{\pi}{6}, \sqrt{3} + \dfrac{\pi}{6}\right), \left(\dfrac{5\pi}{6}, \dfrac{5\pi}{6} - \sqrt{3}\right)$

58. $f'(x) = 1 - 2\cos x = 0$

$\cos x = \dfrac{1}{2}$

$x = \dfrac{\pi}{3}, \dfrac{5\pi}{3}$

$\left(\dfrac{\pi}{3}, \dfrac{\pi}{3} - \sqrt{3}\right), \left(\dfrac{5\pi}{3}, \dfrac{5\pi}{3} + \sqrt{3}\right)$

59. $f'(x) = x^2e^x + 2xe^x = 0$

$$xe^x(x + 2) = 0$$

$$x = 0, -2$$

$(0, 0), (-2, 4e^{-2})$

60. $f'(x) = e^{-x} - xe^{-x} = 0$

$$e^{-x}(1 - x) = 0$$

$$x = 1$$

$(1, e^{-1})$

61. $f'(x) = \ln x + 1 = 0$

$$\ln x = -1$$

$$x = e^{-1}$$

$(e^{-1}, -e^{-1})$

62. $f'(x) = \dfrac{1 - \ln x}{x^2} = 0$

$$1 - \ln x = 0$$

$$x = e$$

$\left(e, \dfrac{1}{e}\right)$

63. (a) $P(t) = -0.63t^2 + 63.3t + 8448$

(b)

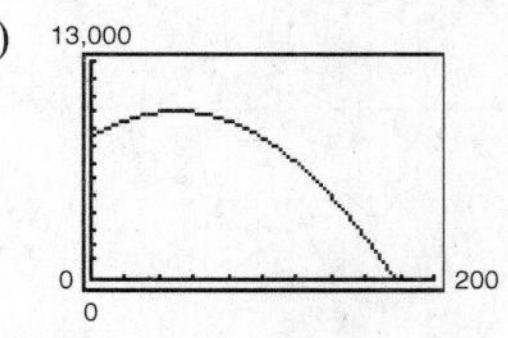

$P'(20) \approx 38$

At time 2020, the population is increasing at approximately 38,000 per year.

(c) Using the limit definition,

$$P'(t) = -1.26t + 63.3$$

$$P'(20) = -1.26(20) + 63.3 = 38.1.$$

(d) Answers will vary.

64. (a) $N = 1.04p^2 - 81.50p + 1613.31$

(b)

Slope $= -50.3$ for $p = 15$.

Slope $= -19.1$ for $p = 30$.

(c)

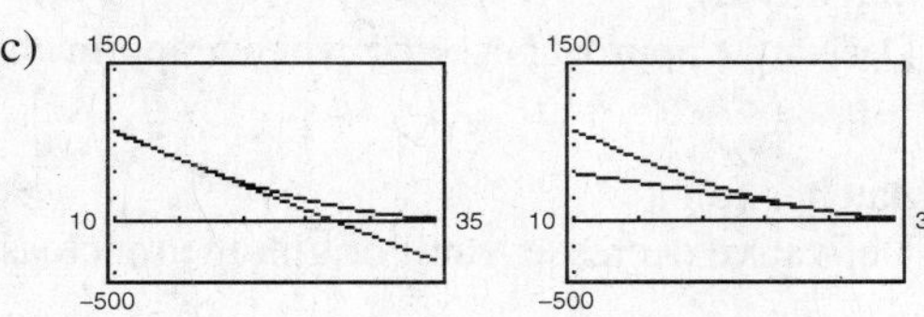

(d) The rate of decrease in sales decreases as the price increases.

65. (a) $V = \dfrac{4}{3}\pi r^3$

$$V'(r) = \lim_{h\to 0} \frac{V(r + h) - V(r)}{h}$$

$$= \lim_{h\to 0} \frac{(4/3)\pi(r + h)^3 - (4/3)\pi r^3}{h}$$

$$= \lim_{h\to 0} \left(\frac{4}{3}\pi\right)\frac{r^3 + 3r^2h + 3rh^2 + h^3 - r^3}{h}$$

$$= \lim_{h\to 0} \frac{4}{3}\pi(3r^2 + 3rh + h^2) = 4\pi r^2$$

(b) $V'(4) = 4\pi(4)^2 \approx 201.06$

(c) Cubic inches per inch; Answers will vary.

66. $S(r) = 4\pi r^2$

(a) Using the limit definition, $S'(r) = 8\pi r$.

(b) $S'(2) = 8\pi(2) = 16\pi \approx 50.27$

(c) Square millimeters per millimeter

67. $s(t) = -16t^2 + 64t + 80$

(a) Using the limit definition, $s'(t) = -32t + 64$.

(b) $s(0) = 80, s(3) = 128$

$$\text{Average rate of change} = \frac{128 - 80}{3}$$

$$= \frac{48}{3} = 16 \text{ ft/sec}$$

(c) $s'(t) = -32t + 64 = 0 \Rightarrow t = 2$ seconds

Answers will vary.

(d) $s(t) = -16t^2 + 64t + 80$

$= 0 \Rightarrow t = 5$ seconds

$s'(5) = -32(5) + 64 = -96$ ft/sec

(e)

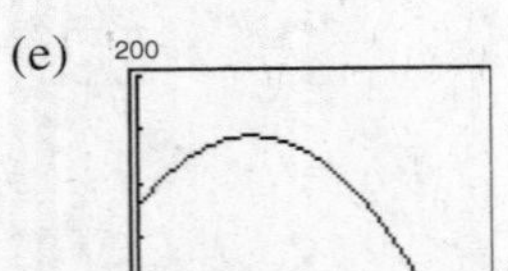

68. $s(t) = -16t^2 + 120$

(a) Using the limit definition, $s'(t) = -32t$.

(b) $\text{Average} = \dfrac{s(2) - s(0)}{2 - 0}$

$$= \frac{56 - 120}{2} = -32 \text{ ft/sec}$$

(c) $s(t) = -16t^2 + 120 = 0 \Rightarrow t = \sqrt{7.5}$

$s'(\sqrt{7.5}) = -32\sqrt{7.5} \approx -87.64$ ft/sec

(d) $-32t = -60$

$$t = \frac{60}{32} = 1.875 \text{ seconds}$$

(e)

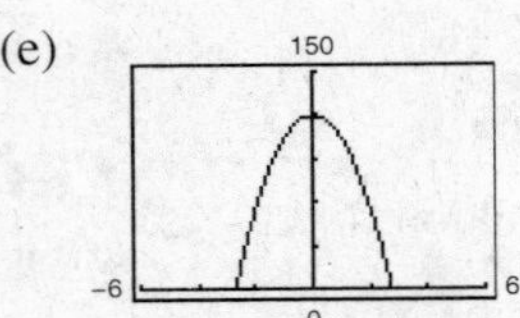

69. True. The slope is $2x$, which is different for all x.

70. False. For example, the tangent line to $y = x^3$ at $(1, 1)$ intersects the curve at $(-2, -8)$.

71. Matches (b).
(Derivative is always positive, but decreasing.)

72. Matches (a).
(Derivative approaches $-\infty$ when x approaches 0.)

73. Matches (d).
(Derivative is -1 for $x < 0$, 1 for $x > 0$.)

74. Matches (c).
(Derivative decreases until origin, then increases.)

75. Answers will vary.

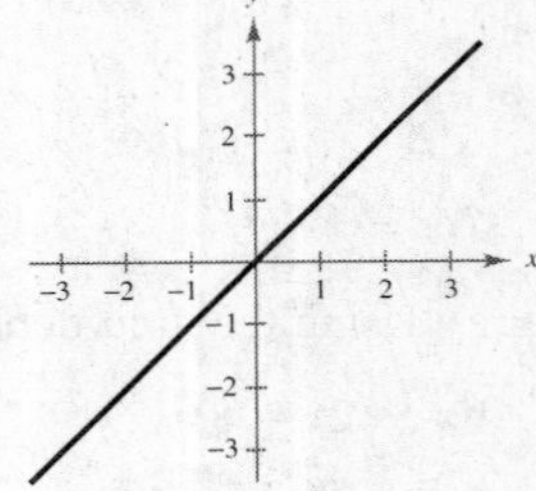

76. Answers not unique

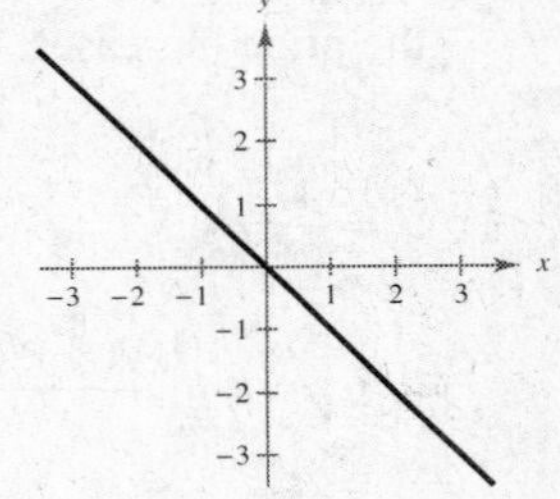

77. $f(x) = \dfrac{1}{x^2 - x - 2} = \dfrac{1}{(x + 1)(x - 2)}$

Intercept: $\left(0, -\dfrac{1}{2}\right)$

Vertical asymptotes: $x = -1, x = 2$

Horizontal asymptote: $y = 0$

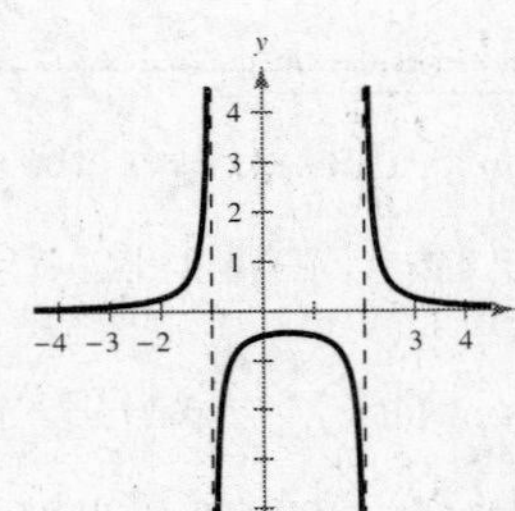

78. $f(x) = \dfrac{x-2}{x^2-4x+3} = \dfrac{x-2}{(x-3)(x-1)}$

Intercepts: $(2, 0), \left(0, -\dfrac{2}{3}\right)$

Vertical asymptotes: $x = 1, x = 3$

Horizontal asymptote: $y = 0$

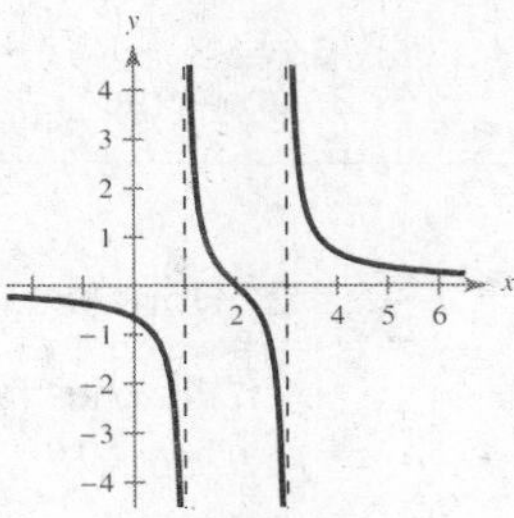

79. $f(x) = \dfrac{x^2-x-2}{x-2} = \dfrac{(x-2)(x+1)}{x-2} = x+1,\ x \neq 2$

Line with hole at $(2, 3)$

Intercepts: $(0, 1), (-1, 0)$

Slant asymptote: $y = x + 1$

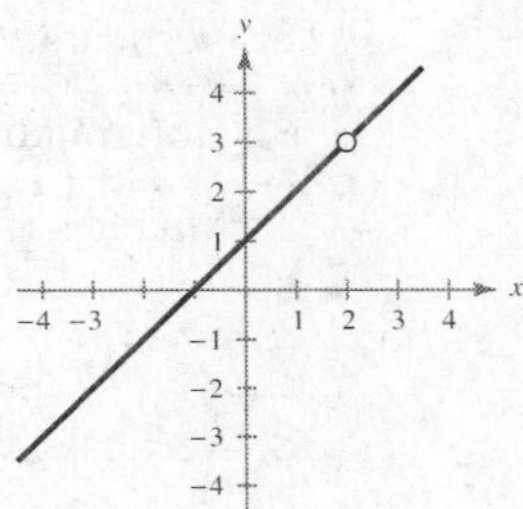

80. $f(x) = \dfrac{x^2-16}{x+4} = \dfrac{(x+4)(x-4)}{x+4} = x-4,\ x \neq -4$

Line with hole at $(-4, -8)$

Intercepts: $(0, -4), (4, 0)$

Slant asymptote: $y = x - 4$

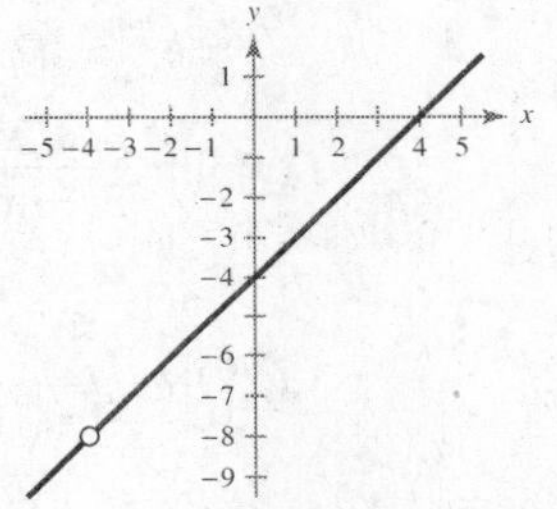

81. $\langle 1, 1, 1\rangle \times \langle 2, 1, -1\rangle = \begin{vmatrix} \mathbf{i} & \mathbf{j} & \mathbf{k} \\ 1 & 1 & 1 \\ 2 & 1 & -1 \end{vmatrix}$

$= \langle -2, 3, -1\rangle$

82. $\mathbf{u} \times \mathbf{v} = \begin{vmatrix} \mathbf{i} & \mathbf{j} & \mathbf{k} \\ -10 & 0 & 6 \\ 7 & 0 & 0 \end{vmatrix} = \langle 0, 42, 0\rangle$

83. $\langle -4, 10, 0\rangle \times \langle 4, -1, 0\rangle = \begin{vmatrix} \mathbf{i} & \mathbf{j} & \mathbf{k} \\ -4 & 10 & 0 \\ 4 & -1 & 0 \end{vmatrix}$

$= \langle 0, 0, -36\rangle$

84. $\mathbf{u} \times \mathbf{v} = \begin{vmatrix} \mathbf{i} & \mathbf{j} & \mathbf{k} \\ 8 & -7 & 14 \\ -1 & 8 & 4 \end{vmatrix} = \langle -140, -46, 57\rangle$

Section 11.4 Limits at Infinity and Limits of Sequences

- The limit at infinity $\lim_{x\to\infty} f(x) = L$ means that $f(x)$ get arbitrarily close to L as x increases without bound.
- Similarly, the limit at infinity $\lim_{x\to-\infty} f(x) = L$ means that $f(x)$ get arbitrarily close to L as x decreases without bound.
- You should be able to calculate limits at infinity, especially those arising from rational functions.
- Limits of functions can be used to evaluate limits of sequences. If f is a function such that $\lim_{x\to\infty} f(x) = L$ and if a_n is a sequence such that $f(n) = a_n$, then $\lim_{n\to\infty} a_n = L$.

Vocabulary Check

1. limit, infinity

2. converge

3. diverge

1. Intercept: $(0, 0)$

Horizontal asymptote: $y = 4$

Matches (c).

2. Horizontal asymptote: $y = 1$

Matches (a).

3. Horizontal asymptote: $y = 4$

Vertical asymptote: $x = 0$

Matches (d).

4. $f(x) = x + \dfrac{1}{x}$

No horizontal asymptote

Matches (b).

5. Vertical asymptotes: $x = \pm 1$

Horizontal asymptote: $y = 1$

Matches (f).

6. Vertical asymptote: $x = 2$

Horizontal asymptote: $y = 2$

Matches (g).

7. Vertical asymptote: $x = 2$

Horizontal asymptote: $y = -2$

Matches (h).

8. Vertical asymptote: $x = \pm 2$

Horizontal asymptote: $y = -4$

Matches (e).

9. $\displaystyle\lim_{x\to\infty} \frac{3}{x^2} = 0$

10. $\displaystyle\lim_{x\to\infty} \frac{5}{2x} = 0$

11. $\displaystyle\lim_{x\to\infty} \frac{3 + x}{3 - x} = -1$

12. $\displaystyle\lim_{x\to\infty} \frac{2 - 7x}{2 + 3x} = -\frac{7}{3}$

13. $\displaystyle\lim_{x\to-\infty} \frac{5x - 2}{6x + 1} = \frac{5}{6}$

14. $\displaystyle\lim_{x\to-\infty} \frac{5 - 3x}{x + 4} = -3$

15. $\displaystyle\lim_{x\to-\infty} \frac{4x^2 - 3}{2 - x^2} = \frac{4}{-1} = -4$

16. $\displaystyle\lim_{x\to-\infty} \frac{x^2 + 3}{5x^2 - 4} = \frac{1}{5}$

17. $\displaystyle\lim_{t\to\infty} \frac{t^2}{t + 3}$ does not exist.

18. $\displaystyle\lim_{y\to\infty} \frac{4y^4}{y^2 + 3}$ does not exist.

19. $\displaystyle\lim_{t\to\infty} \frac{4t^2 + 3t - 1}{3t^2 + 2t - 5} = \frac{4}{3}$

20. $\displaystyle\lim_{x\to\infty} \frac{5 - 6x - 3x^2}{2x^2 + x + 4} = -\frac{3}{2}$

21. $\displaystyle\lim_{y\to-\infty} \frac{3 + 8y - 4y^2}{3 - y - 2y^2} = \frac{-4}{-2} = 2$

22. $\displaystyle\lim_{t\to-\infty} \frac{t^2 + 9t - 10}{2 + 4t - 3t^2} = \frac{1}{-3} = -\frac{1}{3}$

23. $\displaystyle\lim_{x\to-\infty} \frac{-(x^2 + 3)}{(2 - x)^2} = \lim_{x\to-\infty} \frac{-x^2 - 3}{x^2 - 4x + 4} = -1$

24. $\displaystyle\lim_{x\to\infty} \frac{2x^2 - 6}{(x - 1)^2} = \lim_{x\to\infty} \frac{2x^2 - 6}{x^2 - 2x + 1} = 2$

25. $\displaystyle\lim_{x\to-\infty} \left[\frac{x}{(x + 1)^2} - 4\right] = 0 - 4 = -4$

26. $\displaystyle\lim_{x\to\infty} \left[7 + \frac{2x^2}{(x + 3)^2}\right] = 7 + 2 = 9$

27. $\displaystyle\lim_{t\to\infty} \left(\frac{1}{3t^2} - \frac{5t}{t + 2}\right) = 0 - 5 = -5$

28. $\displaystyle\lim_{x\to\infty} \left[\frac{x}{2x + 1} + \frac{3x^2}{(x - 3)^2}\right] = \frac{1}{2} + 3 = \frac{7}{2}$

29. $y = \dfrac{3x}{1 - x}$

Horizontal asymptote: $y = -3$

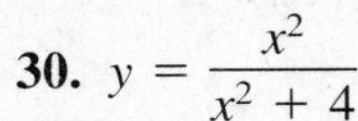

30. $y = \dfrac{x^2}{x^2 + 4}$

Horizontal asymptote: $y = 1$

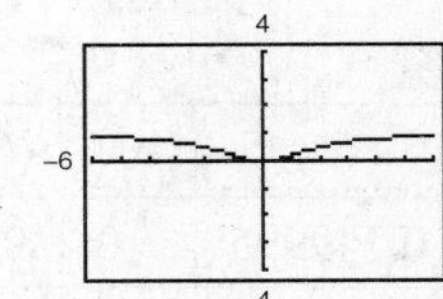

31. $y = \dfrac{2x}{1 - x^2}$

Horizontal asymptote: $y = 0$

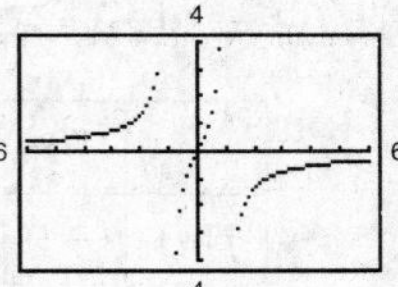

32. $y = \dfrac{2x + 1}{x^2 - 1}$

Horizontal asymptote: $y = 0$

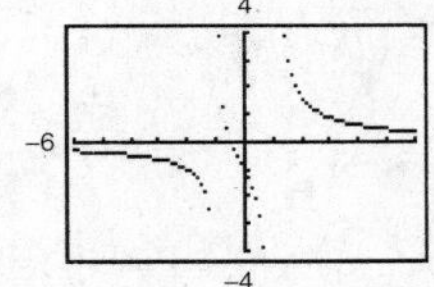

33. $y = 1 - \dfrac{3}{x^2}$

Horizontal asymptote: $y = 1$

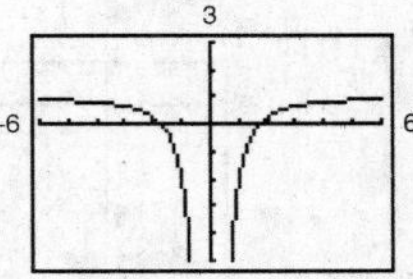

34. $y = 2 + \dfrac{1}{x}$

Horizontal asymptote: $y = 2$

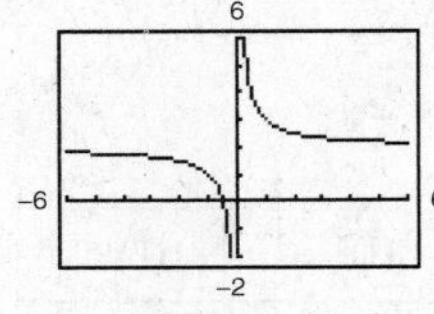

35. $f(x) = x - \sqrt{x^2 + 2}$

(a)

x	10^0	10^1	10^2	10^3	10^4	10^5	10^6
$f(x)$	-0.7321	-0.0995	-0.0100	-0.0010	-1.0×10^{-4}	-1.0×10^{-5}	-1.0×10^{-6}

$\lim_{x \to \infty} f(x) = 0$

(b)

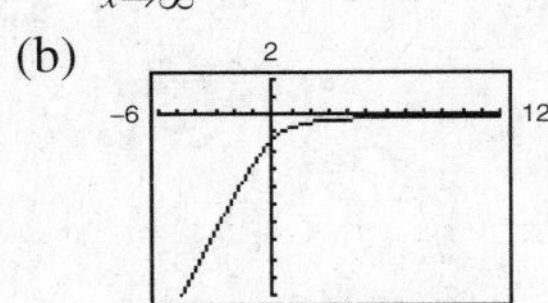

$\lim_{x \to \infty} f(x) = 0$

36. $f(x) = 3x - \sqrt{9x^2 + 1}$

(a)

x	10^0	10^1	10^2	10^3	10^4	10^5	10^6
$f(x)$	-0.1623	-0.0167	-0.0017	-1.67×10^{-4}	-1.67×10^{-5}	-1.67×10^{-6}	-1.67×10^{-7}

$\lim_{x \to \infty} f(x) = 0$

(b)

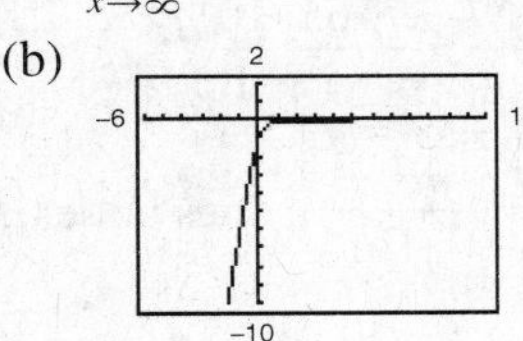

$\lim_{x \to \infty} f(x) = 0$

37. $f(x) = 3\left(2x - \sqrt{4x^2 + x}\right)$

(a)

x	10^0	10^1	10^2	10^3	10^4	10^5	10^6
$f(x)$	-0.7082	-0.7454	-0.7495	-0.74995	-0.749995	-0.7499995	-0.75

$\lim_{x\to\infty} f(x) = -0.75$

(b)

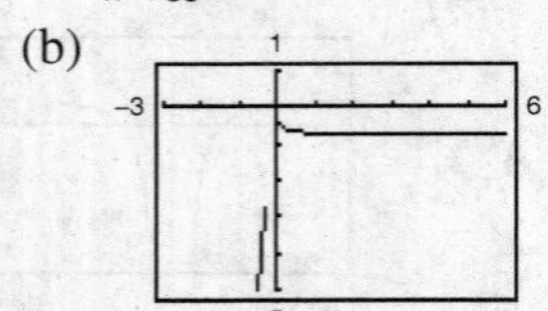

$\lim_{x\to\infty} f(x) = -0.75$

38. $f(x) = 4\left(4x - \sqrt{16x^2 - x}\right)$

(a)

x	10^0	10^1	10^2	10^3	10^4	10^5	10^6
$f(x)$	0.5081	0.5008	0.5001	0.5000	0.5000	0.5000	0.5000

$\lim_{x\to\infty} f(x) = 0.5$

(b)

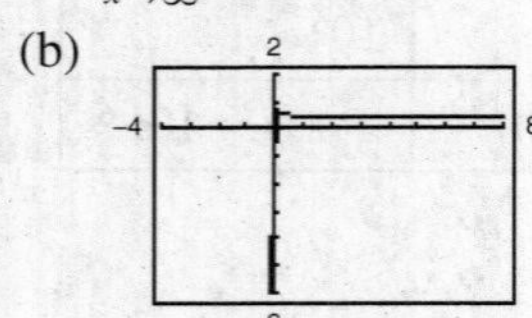

$\lim_{x\to\infty} f(x) = 0.5$

39. $a_n = \dfrac{n+1}{n^2+1}$

$1, \frac{3}{5}, \frac{2}{5}, \frac{5}{17}, \frac{3}{13}$

$\lim_{n\to\infty} a_n = 0$

40. $a_n = \dfrac{n}{n^2+1}$

$\frac{1}{2}, \frac{2}{5}, \frac{3}{10}, \frac{4}{17}, \frac{5}{26}$

$\lim_{n\to\infty} \dfrac{n}{n^2+1} = 0$

41. $a_n = \dfrac{n}{2n+1}$

$\frac{1}{3}, \frac{2}{5}, \frac{3}{7}, \frac{4}{9}, \frac{5}{11}$

$\lim_{n\to\infty} a_n = \dfrac{1}{2}$

42. $a_n = \dfrac{4n-1}{n+3}$

$\frac{3}{4}, \frac{7}{5}, \frac{11}{6}, \frac{15}{7}, \frac{19}{8}$

$\lim_{n\to\infty} \dfrac{4n-1}{n+3} = 4$

43. $a_n = \dfrac{n^2}{3n+2}$

$\frac{1}{5}, \frac{1}{2}, \frac{9}{11}, \frac{8}{7}, \frac{25}{17}$

$\lim_{n\to\infty} \dfrac{n^2}{3n+2}$ does not exist.

44. $a_n = \dfrac{4n^2+1}{2n}$

$\frac{5}{2}, \frac{17}{4}, \frac{37}{6}, \frac{65}{8}, \frac{101}{10}$

$\lim_{n\to\infty} \dfrac{4n^2+1}{2n}$ does not exist.

45. $a_n = \dfrac{(n+1)!}{n!}$

2, 3, 4, 5, 6

$\lim_{n\to\infty} \dfrac{(n+1)!}{n!} = \lim_{n\to\infty} (n+1)$ does not exist.

46. $a_n = \dfrac{(3n-1)!}{(3n+1)!} = \dfrac{1}{(3n+1)(3n)}$

$\frac{1}{12}, \frac{1}{42}, \frac{1}{90}, \frac{1}{156}, \frac{1}{240}$

$\lim_{n\to\infty} \dfrac{(3n-1)!}{(3n+1)!} = 0$

47. $a_n = \dfrac{(-1)^n}{n}$

$-1, \dfrac{1}{2}, -\dfrac{1}{3}, \dfrac{1}{4}, -\dfrac{1}{5}$

$\lim\limits_{n\to\infty} \dfrac{(-1)^n}{n} = 0$

48. $a_n = \dfrac{(-1)^{n+1}}{n^2}$

$1, -\dfrac{1}{4}, \dfrac{1}{9}, -\dfrac{1}{16}, \dfrac{1}{25}$

$\lim\limits_{n\to\infty} \dfrac{(-1)^{n+1}}{n^2} = 0$

49.

n	10^0	10^1	10^2	10^3	10^4	10^5	10^6
a_n	2	1.55	1.505	1.5005	1.5001	1.500	1.500

$\lim\limits_{n\to\infty} a_n = 1.5$

$$a_n = \frac{1}{n}\left(n + \frac{1}{n}\left[\frac{n(n+1)}{2}\right]\right) = 1 + \frac{1}{n^2}\left[\frac{n^2+n}{2}\right] = 1 + \frac{n^2+n}{2n^2}$$

$$\lim_{n\to\infty} a_n = 1 + \frac{1}{2} = \frac{3}{2}$$

50.

n	10^0	10^1	10^2	10^3	10^4	10^5	10^6
a_n	20	12.8	12.08	12.008	12.0008	12.0001	12.0000

$\lim\limits_{n\to\infty} a_n = 12.0$

$$a_n = \frac{4}{n}\left(n + \frac{4}{n}\left[\frac{n(n+1)}{2}\right]\right) = 4 + \frac{16}{n^2}\left[\frac{n^2+n}{2}\right] = 4 + \frac{8(n^2+n)}{n^2}$$

$$\lim_{n\to\infty} a_n = 4 + 8 = 12$$

51.

n	10^0	10^1	10^2	10^3	10^4	10^5	10^6
a_n	16	6.16	5.4136	5.3413	5.3341	5.3334	5.3333

$\lim\limits_{n\to\infty} a_n = 5.33$

$$a_n = \frac{16}{n^3}\left[\frac{n(n+1)(2n+1)}{6}\right] = \left(\frac{8}{3}\right)\frac{n(n+1)(2n+1)}{n^3}$$

$$\lim_{n\to\infty} a_n = \frac{16}{3}$$

52.

n	10^0	10^1	10^2	10^3	10^4	10^5	10^6
a_n	1	0.7975	0.7550	0.7505	0.7501	0.7500	0.7500

$\lim\limits_{n\to\infty} a_n = 0.75$

$$a_n = \frac{n(n+1)}{n^2} - \frac{1}{n^4}\left[\frac{n(n+1)}{2}\right]^2 = \frac{n^2+n}{n^2} - \left(\frac{1}{4}\right)\frac{(n^2+n)^2}{n^4}$$

$$\lim_{n\to\infty} a_n = 1 - \frac{1}{4} = \frac{3}{4}$$

53. (a) Average cost $= \overline{C} = \dfrac{C}{x} = 13.50 + \dfrac{45{,}750}{x}$

(b) $\overline{C}(100) = \$471$

$\overline{C}(1000) = \$59.25$

(c) $\displaystyle\lim_{x\to\infty} C(x) = 13.50$

As more units are produced, the fixed costs (45,750) become less dominant.

54. $C = 1.25x + 10{,}500$

(a) Average cost $= \overline{C} = \dfrac{C}{x} = 1.25 + \dfrac{10{,}500}{x}$

(b) $\overline{C}\,(100) = \$106.25$

$\overline{C}\,(1000) = \$11.75$

(c) As $x \to \infty$, $\overline{C} \to \$1.25$.

As the number of tons gets very large, the average cost approaches \$1.25 per ton.

55. (a)

(b) For 2004, $t = 14$ and $E(14) \approx 72.0$ million.

For 2008, $t = 18$ and $E(18) \approx 73.8$ million.

(c) $\displaystyle\lim_{t\to\infty} E(t) = \frac{0.702}{0.009} = 78$

The enrollment approaches 78 million.

(d) Answers will vary.

56. (a)

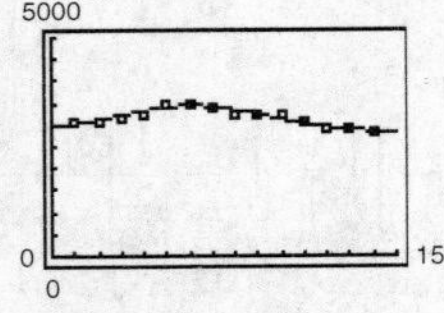

(b) For 2006, $t = 16$ and $N \approx 2772$ thousand.

For 2010, $t = 20$ and $N \approx 2696$ thousand.

(c) $\displaystyle\lim_{t\to\infty} N(t) = \frac{40.8189}{0.0157} \approx 2600$

The number of injuries approaches 2600 thousand.

(d) Answers will vary.

57. False. $f(x) = \dfrac{x^2 + 1}{1}$ does not have a horizontal asymptote.

58. False. The limit does not exist.

59. True

60. False

61. For example, let $f(x) = \dfrac{1}{x^2}$ and $g(x) = \dfrac{1}{x^2}$.

Then, $\displaystyle\lim_{x\to 0} \frac{1}{x^2}$ increases without bound, but $\displaystyle\lim_{x\to 0} [f(x) - g(x)] = 0$.

62.

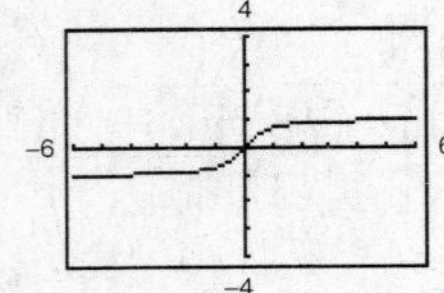

Two horizontal asymptotes: $y = \pm 1$

63. Converges to 0

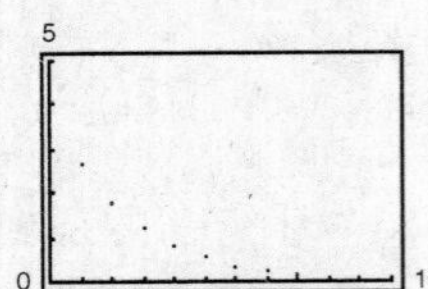

64. Diverges

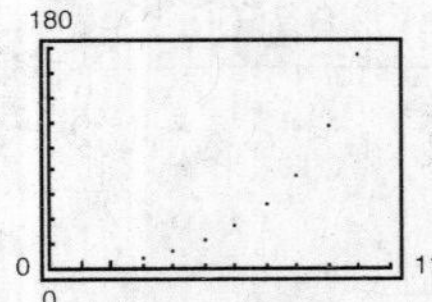

65. Diverges

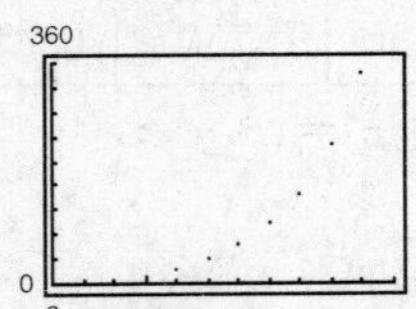

66. Converges to 6

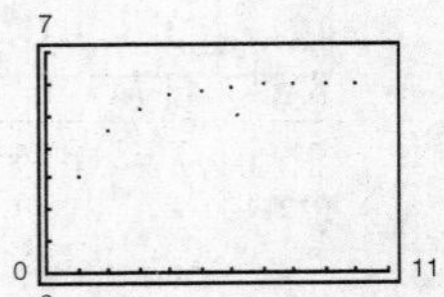

67. $y = x^4$

(a) $f(x) = (x + 3)^4$

(b) $f(x) = x^4 - 1$

(c) $f(x) = -2 + x^4$

(d) $f(x) = \frac{1}{2}(x - 4)^4$

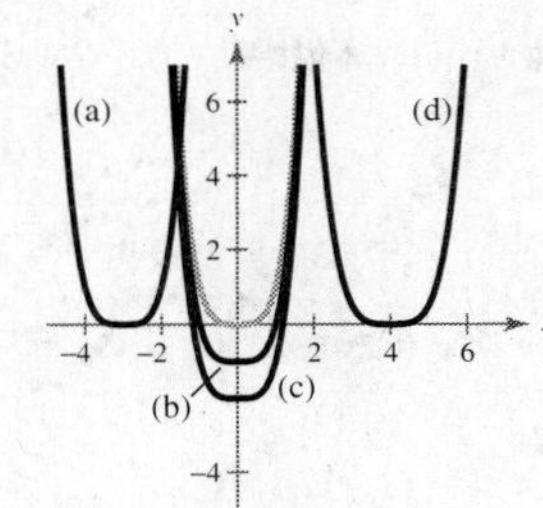

68. $y = x^3$

(a) $f(x) = (x + 2)^3$

(b) $f(x) = 3 + x^3$

(c) $f(x) = 2 - \frac{1}{4}x^3$

(d) $f(x) = 3(x + 1)^3$

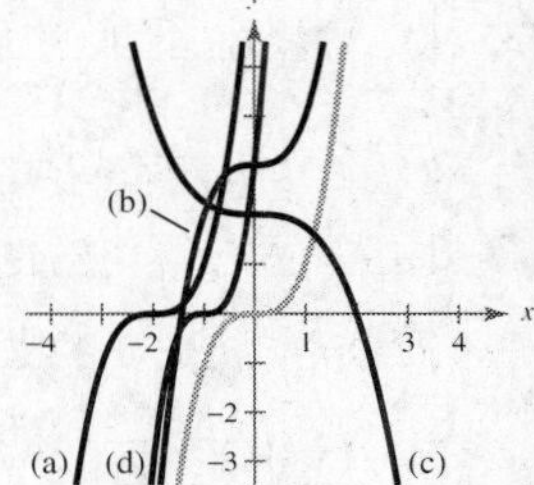

69.

$$\begin{array}{r}
x^2 + 2x + 1 \\
x^2 - 4 \overline{\smash{)}\, x^4 + 2x^3 - 3x^2 - 8x - 4} \\
\underline{x^4 \qquad - 4x^2} \qquad\qquad \\
2x^3 + x^2 \qquad\qquad \\
\underline{2x^3 \qquad - 8x} \qquad \\
x^2 \qquad - 4
\end{array}$$

$$x^4 + 2x^3 - 3x^2 - 8x - 4 = (x^2 - 4)(x^2 + 2x + 1)$$

70.

$$\begin{array}{r}
2x^3 + 4x^2 - 2x - 8 \\
x^2 - 2x + 1 \overline{\smash{)}\, 2x^5 \qquad - 8x^3 \qquad + 4x - 1} \\
\underline{2x^5 - 4x^4 + 2x^3} \qquad\qquad\qquad\qquad \\
4x^4 - 10x^3 \qquad\qquad\qquad \\
\underline{4x^4 - 8x^3 + 4x^2} \qquad\qquad \\
-2x^3 - 4x^2 + 4x \qquad \\
\underline{-2x^3 + 4x^2 - 2x} \qquad \\
-8x^2 + 6x - 1 \\
\underline{-8x^2 + 16x - 8} \\
-10x + 7
\end{array}$$

$$\frac{2x^5 - 8x^3 + 4x - 1}{x^2 - 2x + 1} = 2x^3 + 4x^2 - 2x - 8 + \frac{-10x + 7}{x^2 - 2x + 1}$$

71.

$$\begin{array}{r}
x^3 + 5x^2 \qquad - 3 \\
3x + 2 \overline{\smash{)}\, 3x^4 + 17x^3 + 10x^2 - 9x - 8} \\
\underline{3x^4 + 2x^3} \qquad\qquad\qquad\qquad \\
15x^3 + 10x^2 \qquad\qquad \\
\underline{15x^3 + 10x^2} \qquad\qquad \\
-9x - 8 \\
\underline{-9x - 6} \\
-2
\end{array}$$

$$\frac{3x^4 + 17x^3 + 10x^2 - 9x - 8}{3x + 2} = x^3 + 5x^2 - 3 + \frac{-2}{3x + 2}$$

72.

$$\begin{array}{r} 2x^2 + 11x + 14 \\ 5x - 2 \overline{\smash{)}\, 10x^3 + 51x^2 + 48x - 28} \\ \underline{10x^3 - 4x^2 } \\ 55x^2 + 48x \\ \underline{55x^2 - 22x } \\ 70x - 28 \\ \underline{70x - 28} \end{array}$$

$$\frac{10x^3 + 51x^2 + 48x - 28}{5x - 2} = 2x^2 + 11x + 14, \quad x \neq \frac{2}{5}$$

73. $f(x) = x^4 - x^3 - 20x^2$

$= x^2(x^2 - x - 20)$

$= x^2(x - 5)(x + 4)$

Real zeros: 0, 0, 5, −4

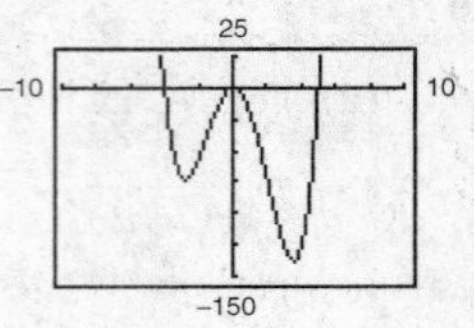

74. $x^5 + x^3 - 6x = x(x^4 + x^2 - 6)$

$= x(x^2 + 3)(x^2 - 2)$

Real zeros: $0, \pm\sqrt{2}$

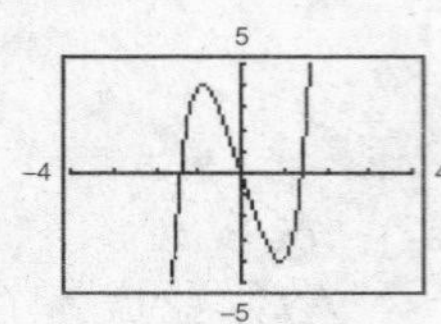

75. $f(x) = x^3 - 3x^2 + 2x - 6$

$= x^2(x - 3) + 2(x - 3)$

$= (x - 3)(x^2 + 2)$

Real zero: 3

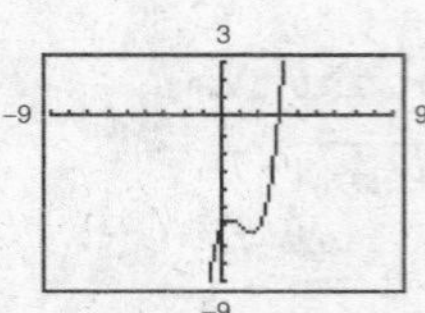

76. $x^3 - 4x^2 - 25x + 100 = x^2(x - 4) - 25(x - 4)$

$= (x^2 - 25)(x - 4)$

Real zeros: $\pm 5, 4$

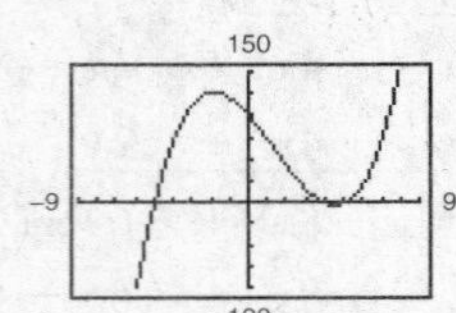

77. $\displaystyle\sum_{i=1}^{6} (2i + 3) = 5 + 7 + 9 + 11 + 13 + 15 = 60$

78. $\displaystyle\sum_{i=0}^{4} 5i^2 = 0 + 5 + 20 + 45 + 80 = 150$

79. $\displaystyle\sum_{k=1}^{10} 15 = 10(15) = 150$

80. $\displaystyle\sum_{k=0}^{8} \frac{3}{k^2 + 1} \approx 5.8791$

Section 11.5 The Area Problem

- You should know the following summation formulas and properties.

  (a) $\displaystyle\sum_{i=1}^{n} c = cn$ (b) $\displaystyle\sum_{i=1}^{n} i = \frac{n(n + 1)}{2}$ (c) $\displaystyle\sum_{i=1}^{n} i^2 = \frac{n(n + 1)(2n + 1)}{6}$

  (d) $\displaystyle\sum_{i=1}^{n} i^3 = \frac{n^2(n + 1)^2}{4}$ (e) $\displaystyle\sum_{i=1}^{n} (a_i \pm b_i) = \sum_{i=1}^{n} a_i \pm \sum_{i=1}^{n} b_i$ (f) $\displaystyle\sum_{i=1}^{n} ka_i = k\sum_{i=1}^{n} a_i$
- You should be able to evaluate a limit of a summation, $\displaystyle\lim_{n\to\infty} S(n)$.
- You should be able to approximate the area of a region using rectangles. By increasing the number of rectangles, the approximation improves.

—CONTINUED—

—CONTINUED—

- The area of a plane region above the x-axis bounded by f between $x = a$ and $x = b$ is the limit of the sum of the approximating rectangles:

$$A = \lim_{n\to\infty} \sum_{i=1}^{n} f\left(a + \frac{(b-a)i}{n}\right)\left(\frac{b-a}{n}\right)$$

- You should be able to use the limit definition of area to find the area bounded by simple functions in the plane.

Vocabulary Check

1. $\dfrac{n(n+1)}{2}$

2. $\dfrac{n^2(n+1)^2}{4}$

3. area

1. $\displaystyle\sum_{i=1}^{60} 7 = 7(60) = 420$

2. $\displaystyle\sum_{i=1}^{45} 3 = 3(45) = 135$

3. $\displaystyle\sum_{i=1}^{20} i^3 = \frac{20^2(21)^2}{4} = 44{,}100$

4. $\displaystyle\sum_{i=1}^{30} i^2 = \frac{n(n+1)(2n+1)}{6}$

$\displaystyle = \frac{30(31)(61)}{6} = 9455$

5. $\displaystyle\sum_{k=1}^{20} (k^3 + 2) = \frac{20^2(21)^2}{4} + 2(20)$

$= 44{,}100 + 40$

$= 44{,}140$

6. $\displaystyle\sum_{k=1}^{50} (2k+1) = 2\sum_{k=1}^{50} k + \sum_{k=1}^{50} 1$

$\displaystyle = 2\frac{50(51)}{2} + 50$

$= 2600$

7. $\displaystyle\sum_{j=1}^{25} (j^2 + j) = \frac{25(26)(51)}{6} + \frac{25(26)}{2} = 5850$

8. $\displaystyle\sum_{j=1}^{10} (j^3 - 3j^2) = \frac{10^2(11)^2}{4} - 3\left(\frac{10(11)(21)}{6}\right) = 1870$

9. (a) $\displaystyle S(n) = \sum_{i=1}^{n} \frac{i^3}{n^4} = \frac{1}{n^4}\left[\frac{n^2(n+1)^2}{4}\right] = \frac{n^2 + 2n + 1}{4n^2}$

(b)

n	10^0	10^1	10^2	10^3	10^4
$S(n)$	1	0.3025	0.255025	0.25050025	0.25005

(c) $\displaystyle\lim_{n\to\infty} S(n) = \frac{1}{4}$

10. (a) $\displaystyle S(n) = \sum_{i=1}^{n} \frac{i}{n^2} = \frac{1}{n^2}\frac{n(n+1)}{2} = \frac{n+1}{2n}$

(b)

n	10^0	10^1	10^2	10^3	10^4
$S(n)$	1	0.55	0.505	0.5005	0.50005

(c) $\displaystyle\lim_{n\to\infty} S(n) = \frac{1}{2}$

11. (a) $\displaystyle S(n) = \sum_{i=1}^{n} \frac{3}{n^3}(1 + i^2) = \frac{3}{n^3}\left[n + \frac{n(n+1)(2n+1)}{6}\right] = \frac{3}{n^2} + \frac{6n^2 + 9n + 3}{6n^2} = \frac{2n^2 + 3n + 7}{2n^2}$

(b)

n	10^0	10^1	10^2	10^3	10^4
$S(n)$	6	1.185	1.0154	1.0015	1.00015

(c) $\displaystyle\lim_{n\to\infty} S(n) = 1$

12. (a) $S(n) = \sum_{i=1}^{n} \frac{2i+3}{n^2} = \frac{1}{n^2}\left(2\left(\frac{n(n+1)}{2}\right) + 3n\right) = \frac{n+1}{n} + \frac{3}{n} = \frac{n+4}{n}$

(b)

n	10^0	10^1	10^2	10^3	10^4
$S(n)$	5	1.4	1.04	1.004	1.0004

(c) $\lim_{n\to\infty} S(n) = 1$

13. (a) $S(n) = \sum_{i=1}^{n}\left(\frac{i^2}{n^3} + \frac{2}{n}\right)\left(\frac{1}{n}\right) = \frac{1}{n}\left[\frac{n(n+1)(2n+1)}{6n^3} + \frac{2n}{n}\right] = \frac{1}{6n^3}(2n^2 + 3n + 1) + \frac{2}{n} = \frac{14n^2 + 3n + 1}{6n^3}$

(b)

n	10^0	10^1	10^2	10^3	10^4
$S(n)$	3	0.2385	0.02338	0.00233	0.0002333

(c) $\lim_{n\to\infty} S(n) = 0$

14. (a) $S(n) = \sum_{i=1}^{n}\left[3 - 2\left(\frac{i}{n}\right)\right]\frac{1}{n} = \frac{1}{n}\left[3n - \frac{2}{n}\,\frac{n(n+1)}{2}\right] = 3 - \frac{n+1}{n} = \frac{2n-1}{n}$

(b)

n	10^0	10^1	10^2	10^3	10^4
$S(n)$	1	1.9	1.99	1.999	1.9999

(c) $\lim_{n\to\infty} S(n) = 2$

15. (a) $S(n) = \sum_{i=1}^{n}\left[1 - \left(\frac{i}{n}\right)^2\right]\left(\frac{1}{n}\right) = \frac{1}{n}\left[n - \frac{1}{n^2}\left(\frac{n(n+1)(2n+1)}{6}\right)\right] = 1 - \frac{2n^2 + 3n + 1}{6n^2} = \frac{4n^2 - 3n - 1}{6n^2}$

(b)

n	10^0	10^1	10^2	10^3	10^4
$S(n)$	0	0.615	0.66165	0.66617	0.666617

(c) $\lim_{n\to\infty} S(n) = \frac{2}{3}$

16. (a) $S(n) = \sum_{i=1}^{n}\left(\frac{4}{n} + \frac{2i}{n^2}\right)\left(\frac{2i}{n}\right) = \frac{2}{n}\left[\frac{4}{n}\,\frac{n(n+1)}{2} + \frac{2}{n^2}\,\frac{n(n+1)(2n+1)}{6}\right]$

$= \frac{2}{n}\left[\frac{4n^2 + 4n}{2n} + \frac{2(2n^2 + 3n + 1)}{6n}\right] = \frac{16n^2 + 18n + 2}{3n^2}$

(b)

n	10^0	10^1	10^2	10^3	10^4
$S(n)$	12.0	5.94	5.3934	5.3393	5.33393

(c) $\lim_{n\to\infty} S(n) = \frac{16}{3}$

17. $f(x) = x + 4$, $[-1, 2]$, $n = 6$, width $= \frac{1}{2}$

Area $\approx \frac{1}{2}[3.5 + 4 + 4.5 + 5 + 5.5 + 6] = 14.25$ square units

18. $f(x) = 2 - x^2$, $-1 \le x \le 1$, $n = 4$, width $= \frac{1}{2}$

Area $\approx \frac{1}{2}\left[\left(2 - \left(-\frac{1}{2}\right)^2\right) + (2 - 0^2) + \left(2 - \left(\frac{1}{2}\right)^2\right) + (2 - 1^2)\right]$

$= \frac{1}{2}[1.75 + 2 + 1.75 + 1]$

$= 3.25$ square units

19. The width of each rectangle is $\frac{1}{4}$. The height is obtained by evaluating f at the right-hand endpoint of each interval.

$$A \approx \sum_{i=1}^{8} f\left(\frac{i}{4}\right)\left(\frac{1}{4}\right) = \sum_{i=1}^{8} \frac{1}{4}\left(\frac{i}{4}\right)^3\left(\frac{1}{4}\right)$$

$$= 1.265625 \text{ square units}$$

20. $\text{Area} \approx \frac{1}{2}\left[\frac{1}{16} + \frac{1}{2} + \frac{27}{16} + 4\right]$

$= 3.125$ square units

21. Width of each rectangle is $12/n$. The height is

$$f\left(\frac{12}{n}i\right) = -\frac{1}{3}\left(\frac{12}{n}i\right) + 4.$$

$$A = \sum_{i=1}^{n}\left[-\frac{1}{3}\left(\frac{12i}{n}\right) + 4\right]\left(\frac{12}{n}\right)$$

Note: Exact area is 24.

n	4	8	20	50
Approximate area	18	21	22.8	23.52

22. The width of each rectangle is $3/n$. The height is

$$f\left(\frac{3i}{n}\right) = 9 - \left(\frac{3i}{n}\right)^2.$$

$$A \approx \sum_{i=1}^{n}\left(9 - \left(\frac{3i}{n}\right)^2\right)\frac{3}{n}$$

Note: Exact area is 18.

n	4	8	20	50
Approximate area	14.344	16.242	17.314	17.7282

23. The width of each rectangle is $3/n$. The height is

$$\frac{1}{9}\left(\frac{3i}{n}\right)^3.$$

$$A \approx \sum_{i=1}^{n}\frac{1}{9}\left(\frac{3i}{n}\right)^3\left(\frac{3}{n}\right)$$

n	4	8	20	50
Approximate area	3.52	2.85	2.48	2.34

24. The width of each rectangle is $(2 - (-1))/n = 3/n$. The height is

$$f\left(-1 + \frac{3i}{n}\right) = 3 - \frac{1}{4}\left(-1 + \frac{3i}{n}\right)^3.$$

$$A \approx \sum_{i=1}^{n}\left[3 - \frac{1}{4}\left(-1 + \frac{3i}{n}\right)^3\right]\frac{3}{n}$$

Note: Exact area is $8\frac{1}{16} = 8.0625$.

n	4	8	20	50
Approximate area	7.113	7.614	7.8895	7.994

25. $f(x) = 2x + 5,\ [0, 4]$

The width of each rectangle is $4/n$. The height is

$$f\left(\frac{4i}{n}\right) = 2\left(\frac{4i}{n}\right) + 5 = \frac{8i}{n} + 5.$$

$$A \approx \sum_{i=1}^{n}\left(\frac{8i}{n} + 5\right)\left(\frac{4}{n}\right)$$

n	4	8	20	50	100	∞
Area	40	38	36.8	36.32	36.16	36

—CONTINUED—

25. —CONTINUED—

$$A \approx \sum_{i=1}^{n}\left(\frac{8i}{n} + 5\right)\left(\frac{4}{n}\right) = \sum_{i=1}^{n}\left(\frac{20}{n} + \frac{32}{n^2}i\right) \approx \frac{20}{n}(n) + \frac{32}{n^2}\left(\frac{n(n+1)}{2}\right) = 20 + 16\left(\frac{n^2+n}{n^2}\right)$$

$$A = \lim_{n\to\infty}\left[20 + 16\left(\frac{n^2+n}{n^2}\right)\right] = 20 + 16 = 36$$

26. $f(x) = 3x + 1,\ [0, 4]$

The width of each rectangle is $4/n$. The height is

$$f\left(\frac{4i}{n}\right) = 3\left(\frac{4i}{n}\right) + 1.$$

n	4	8	20	50	100	∞
Area	34	31	29.2	28.48	28.24	28

$$A \approx \sum_{i=1}^{n}\left(\frac{12i}{n} + 1\right)\frac{4}{n}$$

$$A \approx \sum_{i=1}^{n}\left(\frac{48i}{n^2} + \frac{4}{n}\right) = \frac{48}{n^2}\left(\frac{n(n+1)}{2}\right) + \frac{4}{n}(n) = 24\left(\frac{n^2+n}{n^2}\right) + 4$$

$$A = \lim_{n\to\infty}\left[24\left(\frac{n^2+n}{n^2}\right) + 4\right] = 28$$

27. $f(x) = 16 - 2x,\ [1, 5]$

The width of each rectangle is $4/n$. The height is

$$f\left(1 + \frac{4i}{n}\right) = 16 - 2\left(1 + \frac{4i}{n}\right) = 14 - \frac{8i}{n}.$$

n	4	8	20	50	100	∞
Area	36	38	39.2	39.68	39.84	40

$$A \approx \sum_{i=1}^{n}\left(14 - \frac{8i}{n}\right)\frac{4}{n}$$

$$A \approx \sum_{i=1}^{n}\left(\frac{56}{n} - \frac{32i}{n^2}\right) = \frac{56}{n}(n) - \frac{32}{n^2}\left(\frac{n(n+1)}{2}\right) = 56 - 16\left(\frac{n(n+1)}{n^2}\right)$$

$$A = \lim_{n\to\infty}\left[56 - 16\left(\frac{n(n+1)}{n^2}\right)\right] = 56 - 16 = 40$$

28. $f(x) = 20 - 2x,\ [2, 6]$

The width of each rectangle is $4/n$. The height is

$$f\left(2 + \frac{4i}{n}\right) = 20 - 2\left(2 + \frac{4i}{n}\right) = 16 - \frac{8i}{n}.$$

n	4	8	20	50	100	∞
Area	44	46	47.2	47.68	47.84	48

$$A \approx \sum_{i=1}^{n}\left(16 - \frac{8i}{n}\right)\frac{4}{n}$$

$$A \approx \sum_{i=1}^{n}\left(\frac{64}{n} - \frac{32i}{n^2}\right) = \frac{64}{n}(n) - \frac{32}{n^2}\left(\frac{n(n+1)}{2}\right) = 64 - 16\left(\frac{n(n+1)}{n^2}\right)$$

$$A = \lim_{n\to\infty}\left[64 - 16\left(\frac{n(n+1)}{n^2}\right)\right] = 64 - 16 = 48$$

29. $f(x) = 9 - x^2,\ [0, 2]$

The width of each rectangle is $2/n$. The height is

$$f\left(\frac{2i}{n}\right) = 9 - \left(\frac{2i}{n}\right)^2 = 9 - \frac{4i^2}{n^2}.$$

$$A \approx \sum_{i=1}^{n}\left(9 - \frac{4i^2}{n^2}\right)\left(\frac{2}{n}\right)$$

n	4	8	20	50	100	∞
Area	14.25	14.8125	15.13	15.2528	15.2932	$\frac{46}{3}$

$$A \approx \sum_{i=1}^{n}\left(\frac{18}{n} - \frac{8i^2}{n^3}\right) = \left(\frac{18}{n}\right)n - \frac{8}{n^3}\left[\frac{n(n+1)(2n+1)}{6}\right] = 18 - \frac{4}{3}\left[\frac{n(n+1)(2n+1)}{n^3}\right]$$

$$A = \lim_{n\to\infty}\left[18 - \frac{4}{3}\left(\frac{n(n+1)(2n+1)}{n^3}\right)\right] = 18 - \frac{8}{3} = \frac{46}{3}$$

30. $f(x) = x^2 + 1,\ [4, 6]$

The width of each rectangle is $2/n$. The height is

$$f\left(4 + \frac{2i}{n}\right) = \left(4 + \frac{2i}{n}\right)^2 + 1 = 17 + \frac{16i}{n} + \frac{4i^2}{n^2}.$$

$$A \approx \sum_{i=1}^{n}\left(17 + \frac{16i}{n} + \frac{4i^2}{n^2}\right)\left(\frac{2}{n}\right)$$

n	4	8	20	50	100	∞
Area	57.75	55.1875	53.67	53.0672	52.8668	$\frac{158}{3}$

$$A \approx \sum_{i=1}^{n}\left(\frac{34}{n} + \frac{32i}{n^2} + \frac{8i^2}{n^3}\right) = \left(\frac{34}{n}\right)n + \left(\frac{32}{n^2}\right)\frac{n(n+1)}{2} + \left(\frac{8}{n^3}\right)\frac{n(n+1)(2n+1)}{6}$$

$$= 34 + 16\left(\frac{n^2+n}{n^2}\right) + \frac{4}{3}\left[\frac{n(n+1)(2n+1)}{n^3}\right]$$

$$A = \lim_{n\to\infty}\left[34 + 16\left(\frac{n^2+n}{n^2}\right) + \frac{4}{3}\left(\frac{n(n+1)(2n+1)}{n^3}\right)\right] = 34 + 16 + \frac{8}{3} = \frac{158}{3}$$

31. $f(x) = \frac{1}{2}x + 4,\ [-1, 3]$

The width of each rectangle is $4/n$. The height is

$$f\left(-1 + \frac{4i}{n}\right) = \frac{1}{2}\left(-1 + \frac{4i}{n}\right) + 4 = \frac{7}{2} + \frac{2i}{n}.$$

n	4	8	20	50	100	∞
Area	19	18.5	18.2	18.08	18.04	18

$$A \approx \sum_{i=1}^{n}\left(\frac{7}{2} + \frac{2i}{n}\right)\left(\frac{4}{n}\right)$$

$$A \approx \sum_{i=1}^{n}\left(\frac{14}{n} + \frac{8i}{n^2}\right) = \left(\frac{14}{n}\right)n + \frac{8}{n^2}\left(\frac{n(n+1)}{2}\right)$$

$$A = \lim_{n\to\infty}\left[14 + \frac{4}{n^2}\left(\frac{n(n+1)}{1}\right)\right] = 14 + 4 = 18$$

32. $f(x) = \frac{1}{2}x + 1,\ [-2, 2]$

The width of each rectangle is $4/n$. The height is

$$f\left(-2 + \frac{4i}{n}\right) = \frac{1}{2}\left(-2 + \frac{4i}{n}\right) + 1 = \frac{2i}{n}.$$

$$A \approx \sum_{i=1}^{n}\left(\frac{2i}{n}\right)\left(\frac{4}{n}\right) = \sum_{i=1}^{n}\frac{8i}{n^2}$$

$$A \approx \sum_{i=1}^{n}\frac{8i}{n^2} = \frac{8}{n^2}\left(\frac{n(n+1)}{2}\right)$$

$$A = \lim_{n\to\infty}\left[\frac{8}{n^2}\left(\frac{n(n+1)}{2}\right)\right] = 4$$

n	4	8	20	50	100	∞
Area	5	4.5	4.2	4.08	4.04	4

33. $A \approx \sum_{i=1}^{n} f\left(\frac{i}{n}\right)\left(\frac{1}{n}\right)$

$$= \sum_{i=1}^{n}\left[4\left(\frac{i}{n}\right) + 1\right]\left(\frac{1}{n}\right)$$

$$= \frac{1}{n}\sum_{i=1}^{n}\left[\frac{4}{n}i + 1\right]$$

$$= \frac{1}{n}\left[\frac{4}{n}\frac{n(n+1)}{2} + n\right]$$

$$= \frac{1}{n}[2(n+1) + n]$$

$$= \frac{3n+2}{n}$$

$$A = \lim_{n\to\infty}\frac{3n+2}{n} = 3 \text{ square units}$$

34. $A \approx \sum_{i=1}^{n} f\left(\frac{2i}{n}\right)\left(\frac{2}{n}\right)$

$$= \sum_{i=1}^{n}\left[3\left(\frac{2i}{n}\right) + 2\right]\frac{2}{n}$$

$$= \frac{2}{n}\sum_{i=1}^{n}\left(\frac{6}{n}i + 2\right)$$

$$= \frac{2}{n}\left[\frac{6}{n}\frac{n(n+1)}{2} + 2n\right]$$

$$= 6\left(\frac{n+1}{n}\right) + 4$$

$$A = \lim_{n\to\infty}\left[6\frac{n+1}{n} + 4\right] = 10 \text{ square units}$$

35. $A \approx \sum_{i=1}^{n} f\left(\frac{i}{n}\right)\left(\frac{1}{n}\right)$

$$= \sum_{i=1}^{n}\left[-2\left(\frac{i}{n}\right) + 3\right]\left(\frac{1}{n}\right)$$

$$= \frac{1}{n}\sum_{i=1}^{n}\left[-\frac{2i}{n} + 3\right]$$

$$= \frac{1}{n}\left[-\frac{2}{n}\frac{n(n+1)}{2} + 3n\right]$$

$$= \frac{1}{n}[2n - 1]$$

$$A = \lim_{n\to\infty}\frac{2n-1}{n} = 2 \text{ square units}$$

36. $A \approx \sum_{i=1}^{n} f\left(2 + \frac{3i}{n}\right)\left(\frac{3}{n}\right)$

$$= \sum_{i=1}^{n}\left[3\left(2 + \frac{3i}{n}\right) - 4\right]\frac{3}{n}$$

$$= \frac{3}{n}\sum_{i=1}^{n}\left[2 + \frac{9}{n}i\right]$$

$$= \frac{3}{n}\left[2n + \frac{9}{n}\frac{n(n+1)}{2}\right]$$

$$= 6 + \frac{27}{2}\frac{(n+1)}{n}$$

$$A = \lim_{n\to\infty}\left[6 + \frac{27}{2}\frac{(n+1)}{n}\right] = \frac{39}{2} \text{ square units}$$

37. $A \approx \sum_{i=1}^{n} f\left(-1 + \frac{2i}{n}\right)\left(\frac{2}{n}\right)$

$$= \sum_{i=1}^{n} \left[2 - \left(-1 + \frac{2i}{n}\right)^2\right]\frac{2}{n}$$

$$= \sum_{i=1}^{n}\left[2 - 1 + \frac{4i}{n} - \frac{4i^2}{n^2}\right]\left(\frac{2}{n}\right)$$

$$= \frac{2}{n}\sum_{i=1}^{n} 1 + \frac{8}{n^2}\sum_{i=1}^{n} i - \frac{8}{n^3}\sum_{i=1}^{n} i^2$$

$$= \frac{2}{n}(n) + \frac{8}{n^2}\frac{n(n+1)}{2} - \frac{8}{n^3}\frac{n(n+1)(2n+1)}{6}$$

$$A = \lim_{n\to\infty}\left[2 + 4\frac{n(n+1)}{n^2} - \frac{4}{3}\frac{n(n+1)(2n+1)}{n^3}\right]$$

$$= 2 + 4 - \frac{8}{3} = \frac{10}{3} \text{ square units}$$

38. $A \approx \sum_{n=1}^{\infty} f\left(\frac{i}{n}\right)\left(\frac{1}{n}\right)$

$$= \sum_{n=1}^{\infty}\left[\left(\frac{i}{n}\right)^2 + 2\right]\frac{1}{n}$$

$$= \frac{1}{n}\left[\frac{1}{n^2}\frac{n(n+1)(2n+1)}{6} + 2n\right]$$

$$= \frac{(n+1)(2n+1)}{6n^2} + 2$$

$$A = \lim_{n\to\infty}\left[\frac{(n+1)(2n+1)}{6n^2} + 2\right] = \frac{7}{3} \text{ square units}$$

39. $A \approx \sum_{i=1}^{n} g\left(1 + \frac{i}{n}\right)\left(\frac{1}{n}\right)$

$$= \sum_{i=1}^{n}\left[8 - \left(1 + \frac{i}{n}\right)^3\right]\frac{1}{n}$$

$$= \sum_{i=1}^{n}\left[7 - \frac{3i}{n} - \frac{3i^2}{n^2} - \frac{i^3}{n^3}\right]\frac{1}{n}$$

$$= \frac{7}{n}\sum_{i=1}^{n} 1 - \frac{3}{n^2}\sum_{i=1}^{n} i - \frac{3}{n^3}\sum_{i=1}^{n} i^2 - \frac{1}{n^4}\sum_{i=1}^{n} i^3$$

$$= \frac{7}{n}(n) - \frac{3}{n^2}\frac{n(n+1)}{2} - \frac{3}{n^3}\frac{n(n+1)(2n+1)}{6} - \frac{1}{n^4}\frac{n^2(n+1)^2}{4}$$

$$A = \lim_{n\to\infty}\left[7 - \frac{3}{2}\frac{n(n+1)}{n^2} - \frac{1}{2n^3}n(n+1)(2n+1) - \frac{1}{n^4}\frac{n^2(n+1)^2}{4}\right] = 7 - \frac{3}{2} - 1 - \frac{1}{4} = \frac{17}{4} \text{ square units}$$

40. $A \approx \sum_{i=1}^{n} g\left(1 + \frac{3i}{n}\right)\left(\frac{3}{n}\right)$

$$= \sum_{i=1}^{n}\left[64 - \left(1 + \frac{3i}{n}\right)^3\right]\frac{3}{n}$$

$$= \frac{3}{n}\sum_{i=1}^{n}\left[63 - \frac{9i}{n} - \frac{27i^2}{n^2} - \frac{27i^3}{n^3}\right]$$

$$= \frac{3}{n}\left[63n - \frac{9n(n+1)}{2n} - \frac{27n(n+1)(2n+1)}{6n^2} - \frac{27n^2(n+1)^2}{4n^3}\right]$$

$$= 189 - \frac{27(n+1)}{2n} - \frac{27(n+1)(2n+1)}{2n^2} - \frac{81(n+1)^2}{4n^2}$$

$$A = \lim_{n\to\infty}\left[189 - \frac{27(n+1)}{2n} - \frac{27(n+1)(2n+1)}{2n^2} - \frac{81(n+1)^2}{4n^2}\right] = \frac{513}{4} \text{ square units}$$

41. $A \approx \sum_{i=1}^{n} g\left(\frac{i}{n}\right)\left(\frac{1}{n}\right)$

$= \sum_{i=1}^{n}\left[2\left(\frac{i}{n}\right) - \left(\frac{i}{n}\right)^3\right]\left(\frac{1}{n}\right)$

$= \frac{1}{n}\sum_{i=1}^{n}\left[\frac{2}{n}i - \frac{1}{n^3}i^3\right]$

$= \frac{1}{n}\left[\frac{2}{n}\frac{n(n+1)}{2} - \frac{1}{n^3}\frac{n^2(n+1)^2}{4}\right]$

$= \frac{n+1}{n} - \frac{(n+1)^2}{4n^2}$

$A = \lim_{n\to\infty}\left[\frac{n+1}{n} - \frac{(n+1)^2}{4n^2}\right]$

$= 1 - \frac{1}{4} = \frac{3}{4}$ square units

42. $A \approx \sum_{i=1}^{n} g\left(2\frac{i}{n}\right)\left(\frac{2}{n}\right)$

$= \sum_{i=1}^{n}\left[4\left(\frac{2i}{n}\right) - \left(\frac{2i}{n}\right)^3\right]\left(\frac{2}{n}\right)$

$= \frac{16}{n^2}\sum_{i=1}^{n} i - \frac{16}{n^4}\sum_{i=1}^{n} i^3$

$= \frac{16}{n^2}\frac{n(n+1)}{2} - \frac{16}{n^4}\frac{n^2(n+1)^2}{4}$

$A = \lim_{n\to\infty}\left[8\frac{n(n+1)}{n^2} - 4\frac{n^2(n+1)^2}{n^4}\right]$

$= 8 - 4 = 4$ square units

43. $A \approx \sum_{i=1}^{n} f\left(1 + \frac{3i}{n}\right)\left(\frac{3}{n}\right)$

$= \sum_{i=1}^{n}\left[\frac{1}{4}\left(1 + \frac{3i}{n}\right)^2 + \left(1 + \frac{3i}{n}\right)\right]\left(\frac{3}{n}\right)$

$= \sum_{i=1}^{n}\left(\frac{1}{4} + \frac{3}{2}\frac{i}{n} + \frac{9}{4}\frac{i^2}{n^2} + 1 + \frac{3i}{n}\right)\left(\frac{3}{n}\right)$

$= \frac{15}{4n}\sum_{i=1}^{n} 1 + \frac{27}{2n^2}\sum_{i=1}^{n} i + \frac{27}{4n^3}\sum_{i=1}^{n} i^2$

$= \frac{15}{4n}(n) + \frac{27}{2n^2}\left(\frac{n(n+1)}{2}\right) + \frac{27}{4n^3}\frac{n(n+1)(2n+1)}{6}$

$A = \lim_{n\to\infty}\left[\frac{15}{4} + \frac{27}{4}\frac{n(n+1)}{n^2} + \frac{9}{8n^3}n(n+1)(2n+1)\right]$

$= \frac{15}{4} + \frac{27}{4} + \frac{9}{4} = \frac{51}{4}$ square units

44. $A \approx \sum_{i=1}^{n} f\left(-1 + \frac{2i}{n}\right)\left(\frac{2}{n}\right)$

$= \sum_{i=1}^{n}\left[\left(-1 + \frac{2i}{n}\right)^2 - \left(-1 + \frac{2i}{n}\right)^3\right]\left(\frac{2}{n}\right)$

$= \sum_{i=1}^{n}\left[\left(1 - \frac{4i}{n} + \frac{4i^2}{n^2}\right) - \left(-1 + \frac{6i}{n} - \frac{12i^2}{n^2} + \frac{8i^3}{n^3}\right)\right]\frac{2}{n}$

$= \sum_{i=1}^{n}\left[2 - \frac{10i}{n} + \frac{16i^2}{n^2} - \frac{8i^3}{n^3}\right]\frac{2}{n}$

$= \frac{4}{n}\sum_{i=1}^{n} 1 - \frac{20}{n^2}\sum_{i=1}^{n} i + \frac{32}{n^3}\sum_{i=1}^{n} i^2 - \frac{16}{n^4}\sum_{i=1}^{n} i^3$

$= \frac{4}{n}(n) - \frac{20}{n^2}\frac{n(n+1)}{2} + \frac{32}{n^3}\frac{n(n+1)(2n+1)}{6} - \frac{16}{n^4}\frac{n^2(n+1)^2}{4}$

$\lim_{n\to\infty} A = 4 - 10 + \frac{32}{3} - 4 = \frac{2}{3}$ square units

45. $y = (-3.0 \cdot 10^{-6})x^3 + 0.002x^2 - 1.05x + 400$

Note that $y = 0$ when $x = 500$.

Area $\approx$ 105,208.33 square feet $\approx$ 2.4153 acres

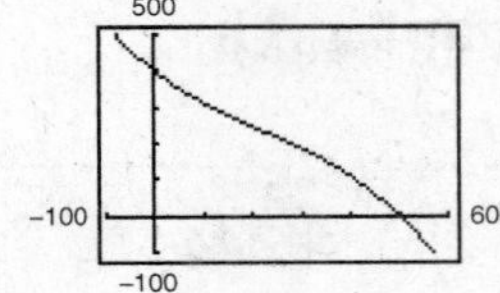

46. (a) $-4.089 \times 10^{-5}x^3 + 0.01615x^2 - 2.6716x + 452.9286$

(b)

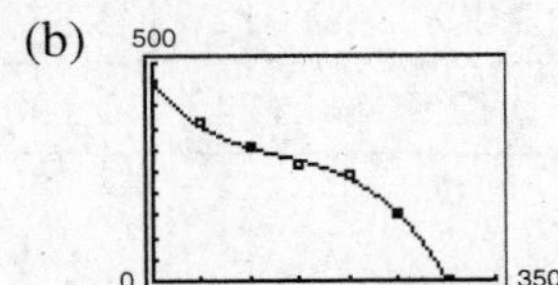

(c) Using a graphing utility to integrate from 0 to 300 gives Area $\approx$ 78,204 square feet.

(Answers will vary.)

47. True. See Formula 2, page 820.

48. False. n approaches infinity.

49. Answers will vary.

50. Area is approximately a triangle of base 2 and height 3.

Area $\approx$ 4; (c)

51. $2 \tan x = \tan 2x = \dfrac{2 \tan x}{1 - \tan^2 x}$

$\tan x = 0 \Rightarrow x = n\pi$

52.

$$\cos 2x - 3 \sin x = 2$$
$$1 - 2\sin^2 x - 3 \sin x = 2$$
$$2\sin^2 x + 3 \sin x + 1 = 0$$
$$(2 \sin x + 1)(\sin x + 1) = 0$$
$$\sin x = \frac{-1}{2} \Rightarrow x = \frac{7\pi}{6} + 2n\pi, \frac{11\pi}{6} + 2n\pi$$
$$\sin x = -1 \Rightarrow x = \frac{3\pi}{2} + 2n\pi$$

53. $(\mathbf{u} \cdot \mathbf{v})\mathbf{u} = (\langle 4, -5\rangle \cdot \langle -1, -2\rangle)\langle 4, -5\rangle$

$= 6\langle 4, -5\rangle$

$= \langle 24, -30\rangle$

54. $3\mathbf{u} \cdot \mathbf{v} = 3\langle 4, -5\rangle \cdot \langle -1, -2\rangle = 3(-4 + 10)$

$= 18$

55. $\|\mathbf{v}\| - 2 = \sqrt{5} - 2$

56. $\|\mathbf{u}\|^2 - \|\mathbf{v}\|^2 = (4^2 + (-5)^2) - ((-1)^2 + (-2)^2)$

$= (16 + 25) - (1 + 4)$

$= 36$

Review Exercises for Chapter 11

1. $\lim_{x\to 3} (6x - 1)$

The limit (17) can be reached.

x	2.9	2.99	2.999	3	3.001	3.01	3.1
$f(x)$	16.4	16.94	16.994	17	17.006	17.06	17.6

2. $f(x) = \dfrac{x-2}{3x^2 - 4x - 4}$

x	1.9	1.99	1.999	2	2.001	2.01	2.1
$f(x)$	0.1299	0.1255	0.1250	Undef.	0.1250	0.1245	0.1205

$\lim_{x\to 2} f(x) = \dfrac{1}{8}$

The limit cannot be reached.

3. $f(x) = \dfrac{1 - e^{-x}}{x}$

x	−0.1	−0.01	−0.001	0	0.001	0.01	0.1
$f(x)$	1.0517	1.0050	1.0005	Error	0.9995	0.9950	0.9516

$\lim_{x\to 0} \dfrac{1 - e^{-x}}{x} = 1$

The limit cannot be reached.

4. $f(x) = \dfrac{\ln(1 - x)}{x}$

x	−0.1	−0.01	−0.001	0	0.001	0.01	0.1
$f(x)$	−0.9531	−0.9950	−0.9995	Error	−1.0005	−1.0050	−1.0536

$\lim_{x\to 0} \dfrac{\ln(1 - x)}{x} = -1$

The limit cannot be reached.

5. $\lim_{x\to 1} (3 - x) = 2$

6. Limit does not exist.

7. $\lim_{x\to 1} \dfrac{x^2 - 1}{x - 1} = 2$

8. $\lim_{x\to -1} (2x^2 + 1) = 3$

9. (a) $\lim_{x\to c} [f(x)]^3 = 4^3 = 64$

(b) $\lim_{x\to c} [3f(x) - g(x)] = 3(4) - 5 = 7$

(c) $\lim_{x\to c} [f(x)g(x)] = (4)(5) = 20$

(d) $\lim_{x\to c} \dfrac{f(x)}{g(x)} = \dfrac{4}{5}$

10. (a) $\lim_{x\to c} \sqrt[3]{f(x)} = \sqrt[3]{27} = 3$

(b) $\lim_{x\to c} \dfrac{f(x)}{18} = \dfrac{27}{18} = \dfrac{3}{2}$

(c) $\lim_{x\to c} [f(x)\, g(x)] = (27)(12) = 324$

(d) $\lim_{x\to c} [f(x) - 2g(x)] = 27 - 2(12) = 3$

11. $\lim_{x\to 4} \left(\frac{1}{2}x + 3\right) = \frac{1}{2}(4) + 3 = 5$

12. $\lim_{x\to 3} (5x - 4) = 5(3) - 4 = 11$

13. $\lim_{x\to 2} (5x - 3)(3x + 5) = (5(2) - 3)(3(2) + 5)$

$= (7)(11) = 77$

14. $\lim_{x\to -2} (5 - 2x - x^2) = 5 - 2(-2) - (-2)^2 = 5$

15. $\lim_{t\to 3} \dfrac{t^2 + 1}{t} = \dfrac{9 + 1}{3} = \dfrac{10}{3}$

16. $\lim_{x\to 2} \dfrac{3x + 5}{5x - 3} = \dfrac{3(2) + 5}{5(2) - 3} = \dfrac{11}{7}$

17. $\lim_{x\to-2} \sqrt[3]{4x} = (-8)^{1/3} = -2$

18. $\lim_{x\to-1} \sqrt{5-x} = \sqrt{5-(-1)} = \sqrt{6}$

19. $\lim_{x\to\pi} \sin 3x = \sin 3\pi = 0$

20. $\lim_{x\to0} \tan x = \tan 0 = 0$

21. $\lim_{x\to-1} 2e^x = 2e^{-1} = \dfrac{2}{e}$

22. $\lim_{x\to4} \ln x = \ln 4$

23. $\lim_{x\to-1/2} \arcsin x = \arcsin\left(-\dfrac{1}{2}\right) = -\dfrac{\pi}{6}$

24. $\lim_{x\to0} \arctan x = \arctan 0 = 0$

25. $$\lim_{t\to-2} \frac{t+2}{t^2-4} = \lim_{t\to-2} \frac{t+2}{(t+2)(t-2)} = \lim_{t\to-2} \frac{1}{t-2} = -\frac{1}{4}$$

26. $$\lim_{t\to3} \frac{t^2-9}{t-3} = \lim_{t\to3} \frac{(t-3)(t+3)}{t-3} = \lim_{t\to3}(t+3) = 6$$

27. $$\lim_{x\to5} \frac{x-5}{x^2+5x-50} = \lim_{x\to5} \frac{x-5}{(x-5)(x+10)} = \lim_{x\to5} \frac{1}{x+10} = \frac{1}{15}$$

28. $$\lim_{x\to-1} \frac{x+1}{(x^2-5x-6)} = \lim_{x\to-1} \frac{(x+1)}{(x+1)(x-6)} = \lim_{x\to-1} \frac{1}{x-6} = -\frac{1}{7}$$

29. $$\lim_{x\to-2} \frac{x^2-4}{x^3+8} = \lim_{x\to-2} \frac{(x+2)(x-2)}{(x+2)(x^2-2x+4)} = \lim_{x\to-2} \frac{x-2}{x^2-2x+4} = \frac{-4}{12} = \frac{-1}{3}$$

30. $$\lim_{x\to4} \frac{x^3-64}{x^2-16} = \lim_{x\to4} \frac{(x-4)(x^2+4x+16)}{(x-4)(x+4)} = \lim_{x\to4} \frac{x^2+4x+16}{x+4} = \frac{16+16+16}{8} = 6$$

31. $$\lim_{x\to-1} \frac{1/(x+2)-1}{x+1} = \lim_{x\to-1} \frac{1-(x+2)}{(x+2)(x+1)} = \lim_{x\to-1} \frac{-(x+1)}{(x+2)(x+1)} = \lim_{x\to-1} \frac{-1}{(x+2)} = -1$$

32. $$\lim_{x\to0} \frac{(1/(1+x)-1)}{x} = \lim_{x\to0} \frac{1-(1+x)}{x(1+x)} = \lim_{x\to0} \frac{-x}{x(1+x)} = -1$$

33. $$\lim_{u\to0} \frac{\sqrt{4+u}-2}{u} = \lim_{u\to0} \frac{\sqrt{4+u}-2}{u} \cdot \frac{\sqrt{4+u}+2}{\sqrt{4+u}+2} = \lim_{u\to0} \frac{(4+u)-4}{u\left(\sqrt{4+u}+2\right)} = \lim_{u\to0} \frac{1}{\sqrt{4+u}+2} = \frac{1}{4}$$

34. $$\lim_{v\to0} \frac{\sqrt{v+9}-3}{v} = \lim_{v\to0} \frac{\sqrt{v+9}-3}{v} \cdot \frac{\sqrt{v+9}+3}{\sqrt{v+9}+3} = \lim_{v\to0} \frac{(v+9)-9}{v\left[\sqrt{v+9}+3\right]} = \lim_{v\to0} \frac{1}{\sqrt{v+9}+3} = \frac{1}{6}$$

35. $$\lim_{x\to5}\frac{\sqrt{x-1}-2}{x-5}=\lim_{x\to5}\frac{\sqrt{x-1}-2}{x-5}\cdot\frac{\sqrt{x-1}+2}{\sqrt{x-1}+2}$$
$$=\lim_{x\to5}\frac{(x-1)-4}{(x-5)\left(\sqrt{x-1}+2\right)}$$
$$=\lim_{x\to5}\frac{1}{\sqrt{x-1}+2}=\frac{1}{2+2}=\frac{1}{4}$$

36. $$\lim_{x\to1}\frac{\sqrt{3}-\sqrt{x+2}}{1-x}=\lim_{x\to1}\frac{\sqrt{3}-\sqrt{x+2}}{1-x}\cdot\frac{\sqrt{3}+\sqrt{x+2}}{\sqrt{3}+\sqrt{x+2}}$$
$$=\lim_{x\to1}\frac{3-(x+2)}{(1-x)\left(\sqrt{3}+\sqrt{x+2}\right)}$$
$$=\lim_{x\to1}\frac{1}{\sqrt{3}+\sqrt{x+2}}=\frac{1}{2\sqrt{3}}=\frac{\sqrt{3}}{6}$$

37. (a)

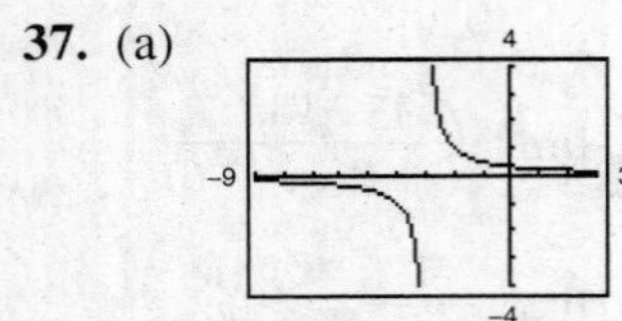

$\lim_{x\to3}\frac{x-3}{x^2-9}=\frac{1}{6}$

(b)

x	2.9	2.99	3	3.01	3.1
$f(x)$	0.1695	0.1669	Error	0.1664	0.1639

38. (a)

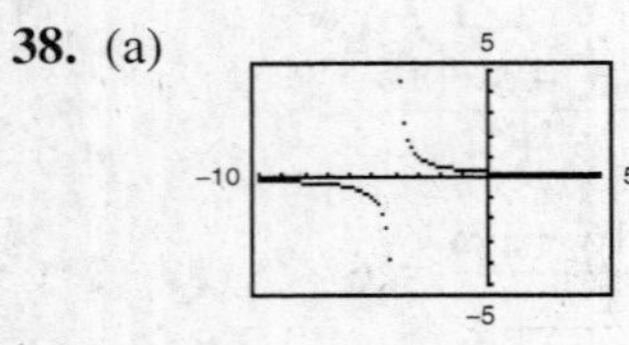

$\lim_{x\to4}\frac{4-x}{16-x^2}=\frac{1}{8}$

(b)

x	3.99	3.999	4	4.001	4.01
y_1	0.12516	0.12502	Error	0.12498	0.12484

39. (a)

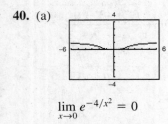

$\lim_{x\to0}e^{-2/x}$ does not exist.

(b) Answers will vary.

x	-0.1	-0.01	-0.001	0	0.001	0.01	0.1
y_1	4.85 E 8	7.2 E 86	Error	Error	0	1 E -87	2.1 E -9

40. (a)

$\lim_{x\to0}e^{-4/x^2}=0$

(b)

x	-0.01	-0.001	0	0.001	0.01
y_1	0	0	Error	0	0

41. (a)

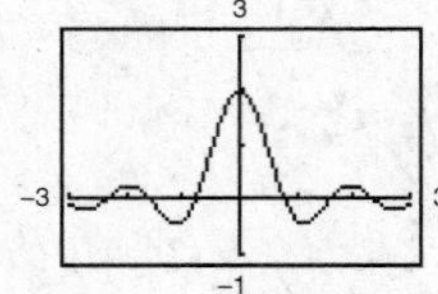

$\lim_{x\to 0} \frac{\sin 4x}{2x} = 2$

(b)

x	−0.1	−0.01	−0.001	0	0.001	0.01	0.1
y_1	1.9471	1.9995	1.999995	error	1.999995	1.995	1.9471

42. (a)

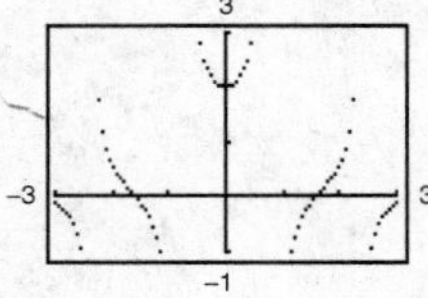

$\lim_{x\to 0} \frac{\tan 2x}{x} = 2$

(b)

x	−0.01	−0.001	0	0.001	0.01
y_1	2.0003	2	Error	2	2.0003

43. (a)

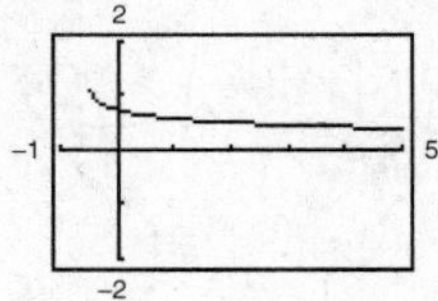

$\lim_{x\to 1^+} \frac{\sqrt{2x+1}-\sqrt{3}}{x-1} \approx 0.577$

$\left(\text{Exact value: } \frac{\sqrt{3}}{3}\right)$

(b)

x	1.1	1.01	1.001	1.0001
$f(x)$	0.5680	0.5764	0.5773	0.5773

44. (a)

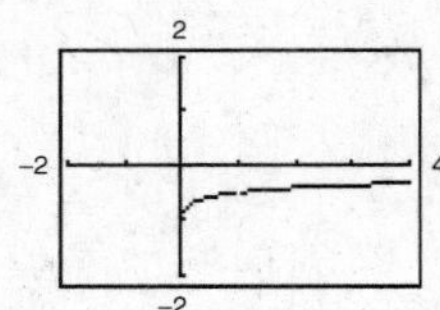

$\lim_{x\to 1^+} \frac{1-\sqrt{x}}{x-1} = -\frac{1}{2}$

(b)

x	1.1	1.01	1.001	1.0001
$f(x)$	−0.4881	−0.4988	−0.4999	−0.5000

45. $f(x) = \frac{|x-3|}{x-3}$

Limit does not exist because

$\lim_{x\to 3^+} f(x) = 1$ and

$\lim_{x\to 3^-} f(x) = -1.$

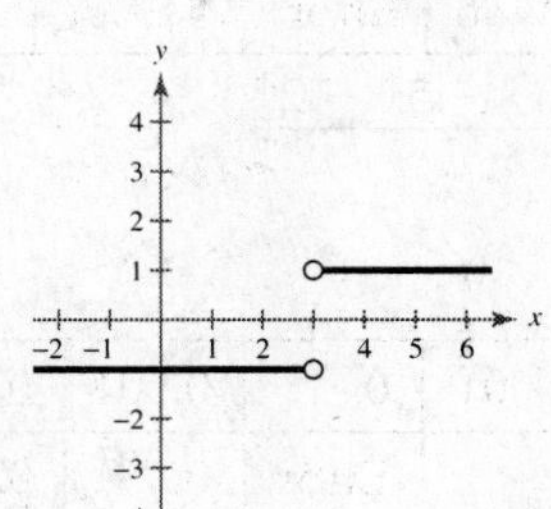

46. $\lim_{x\to 8^-} \frac{|8-x|}{8-x} = 1$

$\lim_{x\to 8^+} \frac{|8-x|}{8-x} = -1$

$\lim_{x\to 8} \frac{|8-x|}{8-x}$ does not exist.

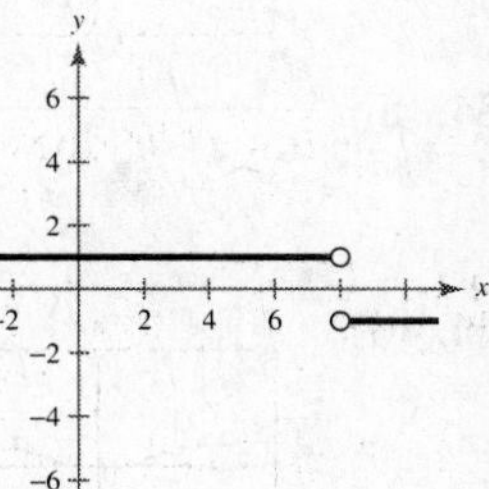

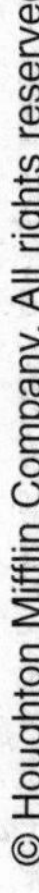

47. 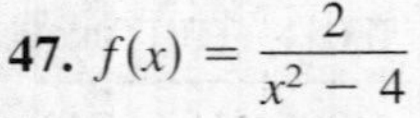 $f(x) = \dfrac{2}{x^2 - 4}$

Limit does not exist.

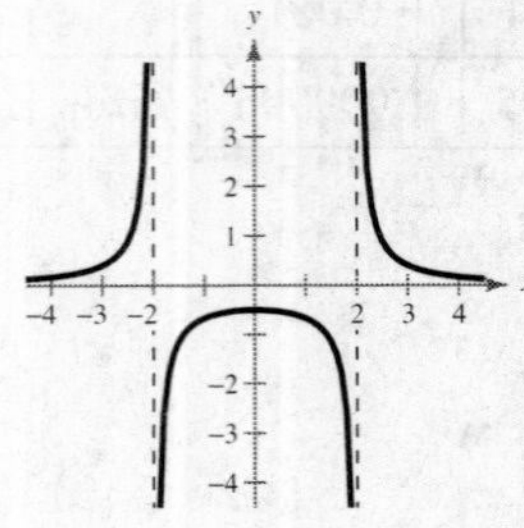

48. $\lim\limits_{x \to -3} \dfrac{1}{x^2 + 9} = \dfrac{1}{(-3)^2 + 9} = \dfrac{1}{18}$

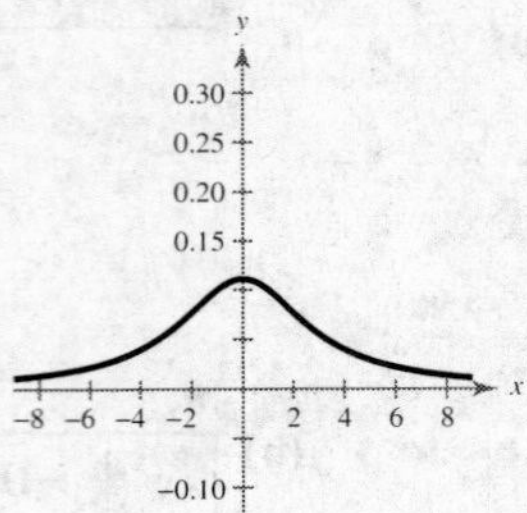

49. $\lim\limits_{x \to 5} \dfrac{|x - 5|}{x - 5}$ does not exist.

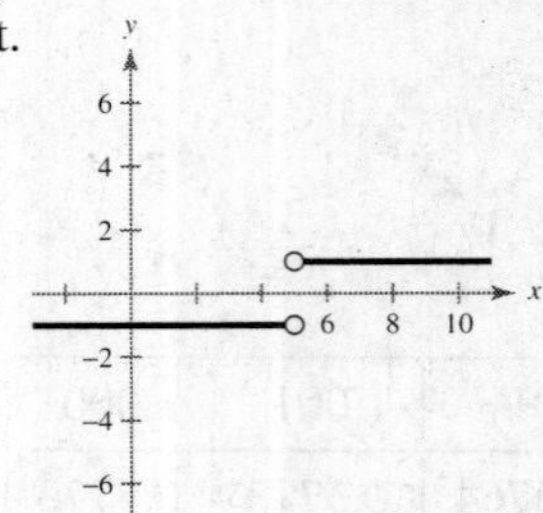

50. $\lim\limits_{x \to -2^-} \dfrac{|x + 2|}{x + 2} = -1$

$\lim\limits_{x \to -2^+} \dfrac{|x + 2|}{x + 2} = 1$

$\lim\limits_{x \to -2} \dfrac{|x + 2|}{x + 2}$ does not exist.

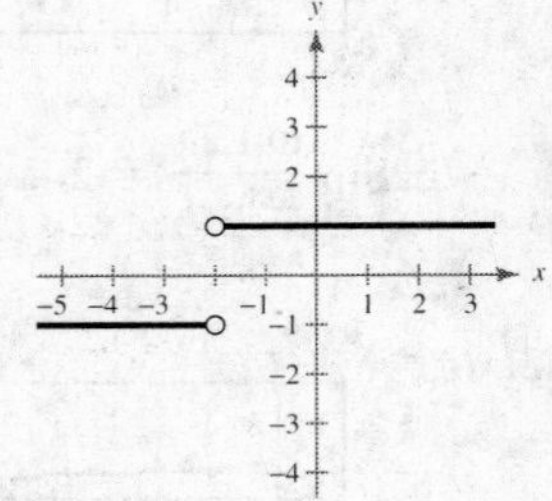

51. $\lim\limits_{x \to 2} f(x)$ does not exist.

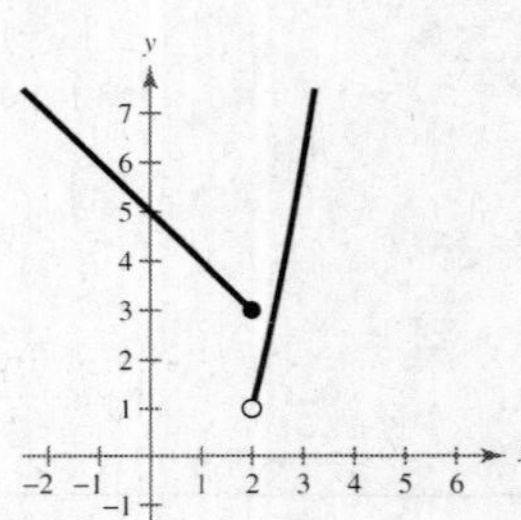

52. $\lim\limits_{x \to 0^-} f(x) = -4$

$\lim\limits_{x \to 0^+} f(x) = -6$

$\lim\limits_{x \to 0} f(x)$ does not exist.

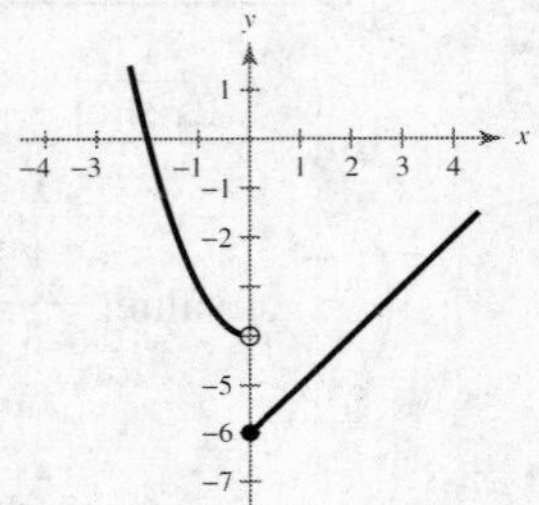

53.
$$\lim_{h \to 0} \frac{f(x + h) - f(x)}{h} = \lim_{h \to 0} \frac{3(x + h) - (x + h)^2 - (3x - x^2)}{h}$$
$$= \lim_{h \to 0} \frac{3x + 3h - x^2 - 2xh - h^2 - 3x + x^2}{h} = \lim_{h \to 0} \frac{3h - 2xh - h^2}{h}$$
$$= \lim_{h \to 0} (3 - 2x - h) = 3 - 2x$$

54.
$$\lim_{h \to 0} \frac{f(x + h) - f(x)}{h} = \lim_{h \to 0} \frac{[(x + h)^2 - 5(x + h) - 2] - [x^2 - 5x - 2]}{h}$$
$$= \lim_{h \to 0} \frac{2xh + h^2 - 5h}{h}$$
$$= \lim_{h \to 0} [2x + h - 5] = 2x - 5$$

55. Slope ≈ 2

Answers will vary.

56. Slope $= 0$

57.

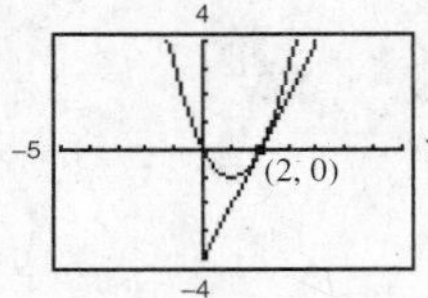

Slope at $(2, f(2))$ is approximately 2.

58. At $(2, f(2)) = (2, 2)$.

Slope $= -4$

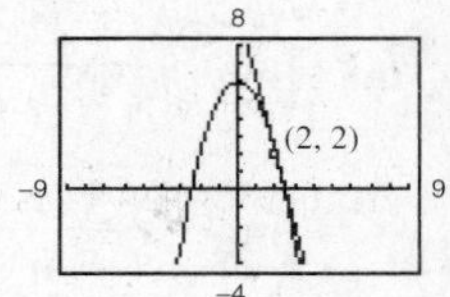

59.

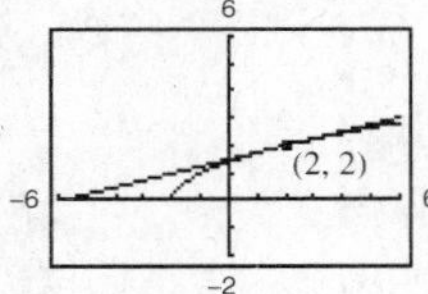

Slope is $\frac{1}{4}$ at $(2, 2)$.

60. At $(2, f(2)) = (2, 3)$.

Slope $= \frac{2}{3}$

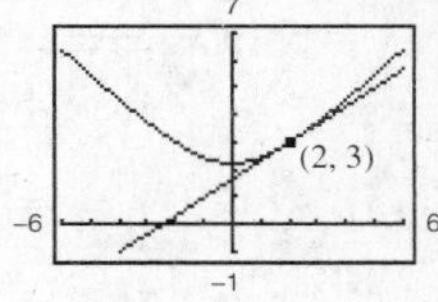

61.

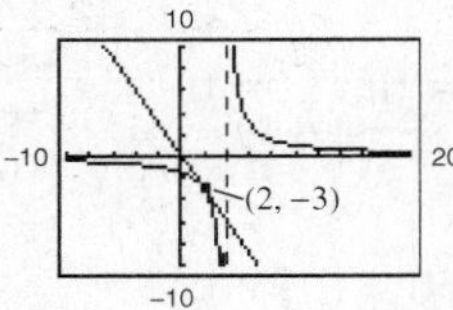

At $(2, f(2)) = (2, -3)$, the slope is approximately -1.5.

62.

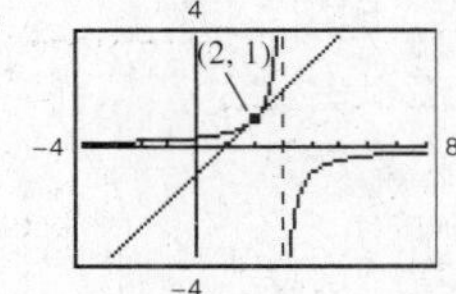

At $(2, f(2)) = (2, 1)$, the slope is approximately 1.

63.
$$\begin{aligned} m &= \lim_{h\to 0}\frac{f(x+h)-f(x)}{h} \\ &= \lim_{h\to 0}\frac{(x+h)^2-4(x+h)-(x^2-4x)}{h} \\ &= \lim_{h\to 0}\frac{x^2+2xh+h^2-4x-4h-x^2-4x}{h} \\ &= \lim_{h\to 0}\frac{2xh+h^2-4h}{h} \\ &= \lim_{h\to 0}(2x+h-4) = 2x-4 \end{aligned}$$

(a) At $(0, 0)$, $m = 2(0) - 4 = -4$.

(b) At $(5, 5)$, $m = 2(5) - 4 = 6$.

64.
$$\begin{aligned} m &= \lim_{h\to 0}\frac{f(x+h)-f(x)}{h} \\ &= \lim_{h\to 0}\frac{(1/4)(x+h)^4-(1/4)x^4}{h} \\ &= \lim_{h\to 0}\frac{(1/4)[x^4+4x^3h+6x^2h^2+4xh^3+h^4-x^4]}{h} \\ &= \lim_{h\to 0}\frac{1}{4}[4x^3+6x^2h+4xh^2+h^3] = x^3 \end{aligned}$$

(a) At $(-2, 4)$, $m = (-2)^3 = -8$.

(b) At $\left(1, \frac{1}{4}\right)$, $m = (1)^3 = 1$.

65.
$$\begin{aligned} m &= \lim_{h\to 0}\frac{f(x+h)-f(x)}{h} = \lim_{h\to 0}\frac{\dfrac{4}{x+h-6}-\dfrac{4}{x-6}}{h} \\ &= \lim_{h\to 0}\frac{4(x-6)-4(x+h-6)}{(x+h-6)(x-6)h} \\ &= \lim_{h\to 0}\frac{-4h}{(x+h-6)(x-6)h} \\ &= \lim_{h\to 0}\frac{-4}{(x+h-6)(x-6)} = \frac{-4}{(x-6)^2} \end{aligned}$$

(a) At $(7, 4)$, $m = \dfrac{-4}{(7-6)^2} = -4$.

(b) At $(8, 2)$, $m = \dfrac{-4}{(8-6)^2} = -1$.

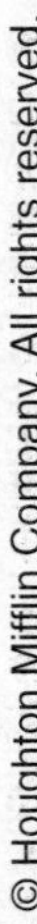

66. $m = \lim_{h\to 0} \frac{f(x+h) - f(x)}{h}$

$= \lim_{h\to 0} \frac{\sqrt{x+h} - \sqrt{x}}{h} \cdot \frac{\sqrt{x+h} + \sqrt{x}}{\sqrt{x+h} + \sqrt{x}}$

$= \lim_{h\to 0} \frac{(x+h) - x}{h\left[\sqrt{x+h} + \sqrt{x}\right]}$

$= \lim_{h\to 0} \frac{1}{\sqrt{x+h} + \sqrt{x}} = \frac{1}{2\sqrt{x}}$

(a) At $(1, 1)$, $m = \frac{1}{2\sqrt{1}} = \frac{1}{2}$.

(b) At $(4, 2)$, $m = \frac{1}{2\sqrt{4}} = \frac{1}{4}$.

67. $f'(x) = \lim_{h\to 0} \frac{f(x+h) - f(x)}{h} = \lim_{h\to 0} \frac{5-5}{h} = 0$

68. $g'(x) = \lim_{h\to 0} \frac{g(x+h) - g(x)}{h}$

$= \lim_{h\to 0} \frac{-3 - (-3)}{h} = \lim_{h\to 0} \frac{0}{h} = 0$

69. $h'(x) = \lim_{k\to 0} \frac{h(x+k) - h(x)}{k}$

$= \lim_{k\to 0} \frac{\left[5 - \frac{1}{2}(x+k)\right] - \left[5 - \frac{1}{2}x\right]}{k}$

$= \lim_{k\to 0} \frac{-\frac{1}{2}k}{k} = -\frac{1}{2}$

70. $f'(x) = \lim_{h\to 0} \frac{f(x+h) - f(x)}{h}$

$= \lim_{h\to 0} \frac{3(x+h) - 3x}{h} = 3$

71. $g'(x) = \lim_{h\to 0} \frac{g(x+h) - g(x)}{h}$

$= \lim_{h\to 0} \frac{2(x+h)^2 - 1 - (2x^2 - 1)}{h}$

$= \lim_{h\to 0} \frac{2x^2 + 4xh + 2h^2 - 2x^2}{h}$

$= \lim_{h\to 0} (4x + 2h)$

$= 4x$

72. $f'(x) = \lim_{h\to 0} \frac{f(x+h) - f(x)}{h} = \lim_{h\to 0} \frac{-(x+h)^3 + 4(x+h) - (-x^3 + 4x)}{h}$

$= \lim_{h\to 0} \frac{-x^3 - 3x^2h - 3xh^2 - h^3 + 4x + 4h + x^3 - 4x}{h}$

$= \lim_{h\to 0} \frac{-3x^2h - 3xh^2 - h^3 + 4h}{h}$

$= \lim_{h\to 0} (-3x^2 - 3xh - h^2 + 4)$

$= -3x^2 + 4$

73. $$f'(t) = \lim_{h\to 0} \frac{f(t+h) - f(t)}{h}$$
$$= \lim_{h\to 0} \frac{\sqrt{t+h+5} - \sqrt{t+5}}{h} \cdot \frac{\sqrt{t+h+5} + \sqrt{t+5}}{\sqrt{t+h+5} + \sqrt{t+5}}$$
$$= \lim_{h\to 0} \frac{(t+h+5) - (t+5)}{h\left(\sqrt{t+h+5} + \sqrt{t+5}\right)}$$
$$= \lim_{h\to 0} \frac{1}{\sqrt{t+h+5} + \sqrt{t+5}}$$
$$= \frac{1}{2\sqrt{t+5}}$$

74. $$g'(t) = \lim_{h\to 0} \frac{g(t+h) - g(t)}{h}$$
$$= \lim_{h\to 0} \frac{\sqrt{t+h-3} - \sqrt{t-3}}{h} \cdot \frac{\sqrt{t+h-3} + \sqrt{t-3}}{\sqrt{t+h-3} + \sqrt{t-3}}$$
$$= \lim_{h\to 0} \frac{(t+h-3) - (t-3)}{h\left(\sqrt{t+h-3} + \sqrt{t-3}\right)}$$
$$= \lim_{h\to 0} \frac{1}{\sqrt{t+h-3} + \sqrt{t-3}}$$
$$= \frac{1}{2\sqrt{t-3}}$$

75. $$g'(s) = \frac{g(s+h) - g(s)}{h}$$
$$= \lim_{h\to 0} \frac{\dfrac{4}{s+h+5} - \dfrac{4}{s+5}}{h}$$
$$= \lim_{h\to 0} \frac{4s + 20 - 4s - 4h - 20}{(s+h+5)(s+5)h}$$
$$= \lim_{h\to 0} \frac{-4h}{(s+h+5)(s+5)h}$$
$$= \lim_{h\to 0} \frac{-4}{(s+h+5)(s+5)}$$
$$= \frac{-4}{(s+5)^2}$$

76. $$g'(t) = \lim_{h\to 0} \frac{g(t+h) - g(t)}{h}$$
$$= \lim_{h\to 0} \frac{\dfrac{6}{5-(t+h)} - \dfrac{6}{5-t}}{h}$$
$$= \lim_{h\to 0} \frac{30 - 6t - 30 + 6t + 6h}{h(5-t-h)(5-t)}$$
$$= \lim_{h\to 0} \frac{6}{(5-t-h)(5-t)}$$
$$= \frac{6}{(5-t)^2}$$

77. $$g'(x) = \lim_{h \to 0} \frac{g(x+h) - g(x)}{h}$$

$$= \lim_{h \to 0} \frac{\frac{1}{\sqrt{x+h+4}} - \frac{1}{\sqrt{x+4}}}{h}$$

$$= \lim_{h \to 0} \frac{\sqrt{x+4} - \sqrt{x+h+4}}{h\sqrt{x+h+4}\sqrt{x+4}} \cdot \frac{\sqrt{x+4} + \sqrt{x+h+4}}{\sqrt{x+4} + \sqrt{x+h+4}}$$

$$= \lim_{h \to 0} \frac{(x+4) - (x+h+4)}{h\sqrt{x+h+4}\sqrt{x+4}\left[\sqrt{x+4} + \sqrt{x+h+4}\right]}$$

$$= \lim_{h \to 0} \frac{-1}{\sqrt{x+h+4}\sqrt{x+4}\left[\sqrt{x+4} + \sqrt{x+h+4}\right]}$$

$$= \frac{-1}{(x+4)2\sqrt{x+4}}$$

$$= \frac{-1}{2(x+4)^{3/2}}$$

78. $$f'(x) = \lim_{h \to 0} \frac{f(x+h) - f(x)}{h} = \lim_{h \to 0} \frac{\frac{1}{\sqrt{12-x-h}} - \frac{1}{\sqrt{12-x}}}{h}$$

$$= \lim_{h \to 0} \frac{\sqrt{12-x} - \sqrt{12-x-h}}{h\left[\sqrt{12-x-h}\sqrt{12-x}\right]} \cdot \frac{\sqrt{12-x} + \sqrt{12-x-h}}{\sqrt{12-x} + \sqrt{12-x-h}}$$

$$= \lim_{h \to 0} \frac{(12-x) - (12-x-h)}{h\left[\sqrt{12-x-h}\sqrt{12-x}\right]} \cdot \frac{1}{\left[\sqrt{12-x} + \sqrt{12-x-h}\right]}$$

$$= \lim_{h \to 0} \frac{1}{\left[\sqrt{12-x-h}\sqrt{12-x}\right]\left[\sqrt{12-x} + \sqrt{12-x-h}\right]}$$

$$= \frac{1}{(12-x)2\sqrt{12-x}}$$

$$= \frac{1}{2(12-x)^{3/2}}$$

79. $\displaystyle\lim_{x \to \infty} \frac{4x}{2x-3} = \frac{4}{2} = 2$

80. $\displaystyle\lim_{x \to \infty} \frac{7x}{14x+2} = \frac{7}{14} = \frac{1}{2}$

81. $\displaystyle\lim_{x \to -\infty} \frac{2x}{x^2-25} = 0$

82. $\displaystyle\lim_{x \to -\infty} \frac{3x}{(1-x)^3} = 0$

83. $\displaystyle\lim_{x \to \infty} \frac{x^2}{2x+3}$ does not exist.

84. $\displaystyle\lim_{y \to \infty} \frac{3y^4}{y^2+1}$ does not exist.

85. $\displaystyle\lim_{x \to \infty} \left[\frac{x}{(x-2)^2} + 3\right] = 0 + 3 = 3$

86. $\displaystyle\lim_{x \to \infty} \left[2 - \frac{2x^2}{(x+1)^2}\right] = 2 - 2 = 0$

87. $a_n = \frac{2n-3}{5n+4}$

$a_1 = -\frac{1}{9}$ $\quad a_4 = \frac{5}{24}$

$a_2 = \frac{1}{14}$ $\quad a_5 = \frac{7}{29}$

$a_3 = \frac{3}{19}$

$\lim_{n\to\infty} a_n = \frac{2}{5}$

88. $a_n = \frac{2n}{n^2+1}$

$a_1 = \frac{2}{2} = 1$ $\quad a_4 = \frac{8}{17}$

$a_2 = \frac{4}{5}$ $\quad a_5 = \frac{10}{26} = \frac{5}{13}$

$a_3 = \frac{6}{10} = \frac{3}{5}$

$\lim_{n\to\infty} a_n = 0$

89. $a_n = \frac{(-1)^n}{n^3}$

$a_1 = -1$ $\quad a_4 = \frac{1}{64}$

$a_2 = \frac{1}{8}$ $\quad a_5 = -\frac{1}{125}$

$a_3 = -\frac{1}{27}$

$\lim_{n\to\infty} a_n = 0$

90. $a_n = \frac{(-1)^{n+1}}{n}$

$a_1 = 1$ $\quad a_4 = -\frac{1}{4}$

$a_2 = -\frac{1}{2}$ $\quad a_5 = \frac{1}{5}$

$a_3 = \frac{1}{3}$

$\lim_{n\to\infty} a_n = 0$

91. $a_n = \frac{1}{2n^2}[3 - 2n(n+1)] = \frac{3}{2n^2} - \frac{n+1}{n}$

$-0.5, -1.125, -1.16\overline{6}, -1.15625, -1.14$

$\lim_{n\to\infty} a_n = 0 - 1 = -1$

92. $a_n = 2 + \frac{2}{n}(n-1) - \frac{4}{n} = 4 - \frac{6}{n}$

$-2, 1, 2, \frac{5}{2}, \frac{14}{5}$

$\lim_{n\to\infty} a_n = \lim_{n\to\infty}\left(4 - \frac{6}{n}\right) = 4$

93. (a) $\sum_{i=1}^{n}\left(\frac{4i^2}{n^2} - \frac{i}{n}\right)\frac{1}{n} = \frac{4}{n^3}\sum_{i=1}^{n} i^2 - \frac{1}{n^2}\sum_{i=1}^{n} i$

$$= \frac{4}{n^3}\frac{n(n+1)(2n+1)}{6} - \frac{1}{n^2}\frac{n(n+1)}{2}$$

$$= \frac{4n(n+1)(2n+1) - 3n^2(n+1)}{6n^3}$$

$$= \frac{n(n+1)(8n+4-3n)}{6n^3}$$

$$= \frac{(n+1)(5n+4)}{6n^2}$$

(b)

n	10^0	10^1	10^2	10^3	10^4
$S(n)$	3	0.99	0.8484	0.8348	0.8335

(c) $\lim_{n\to\infty} S(n) = \frac{5}{6}$

94. (a) $\sum_{i=1}^{n}\left[4-\left(\frac{3i}{n}\right)^2\right]\left(\frac{3i}{n^2}\right) = \frac{12}{n^2}\sum_{i=1}^{n} i - \frac{27}{n^4}\sum_{i=1}^{n} i^3 = \frac{12}{n^2}\frac{n(n+1)}{2} - \frac{27}{n^4}\frac{n^2(n+1)^2}{4}$

$$= \frac{24n^2+24n-27(n^2+2n+1)}{4n^2}$$

$$= \frac{-3n^2-30n-27}{4n^2} = \frac{-3}{4n^2}(n^2+10n+9)$$

$$= \frac{-3(n+1)(n+9)}{4n^2}$$

(b)

n	10^0	10^1	10^2	10^3	10^4
$S(n)$	-15	-1.5675	-0.8257	-0.7575	-0.7508

(c) $\lim_{n\to\infty} Sn = -\frac{3}{4}$

95. Area $\approx \frac{1}{2}\left(\frac{7}{2}+3+\frac{5}{2}+2+\frac{3}{2}+1\right)$

$= \frac{1}{2}\left(\frac{27}{2}\right) = \frac{27}{4} = 6.75$

96. Width of rectangle: $\frac{1}{4}$

Height is f evaluated at right endpoint

Area $\approx \frac{1}{4}\left[f\left(\frac{1}{4}\right)+f\left(\frac{1}{2}\right)+f\left(\frac{3}{4}\right)+f(1)\right]$

$= \frac{1}{4}\left[4-\left(\frac{1}{4}\right)^2+4-\left(\frac{1}{2}\right)^2+4-\left(\frac{3}{4}\right)^2+4-1\right]$

$= \frac{1}{4}\left[15-\frac{14}{16}\right] = \frac{113}{32} = 3.53125$

97. $f(x) = \frac{1}{4}x^2,\ b-a = 4-0 = 4$

$A \approx \sum_{i=1}^{n} f\left(\frac{4i}{n}\right)\left(\frac{4}{n}\right)$

$= \sum_{i=1}^{n}\frac{1}{4}\left(\frac{4i}{n}\right)^2\left(\frac{4}{n}\right)$

$= \frac{1}{n}\sum_{i=1}^{n}\frac{16}{n^2}i^2$

$= \frac{16}{n^3}\frac{n(n+1)(2n+1)}{6}$

$= \frac{8(n+1)(2n+1)}{3n^2}$

n	4	8	20	50
Approximate area	7.5	6.375	5.74	5.4944

$\left(\text{Exact area is } \frac{16}{3} \approx 5.33.\right)$

98. $f(x) = 4x - x^2$

n	4	8	20	50
Approximate area	10	10.5	10.64	10.6624

$\left(\text{Exact area is } 10\frac{2}{3}.\right)$

99. $A = \lim_{n\to\infty}\sum_{i=1}^{n}\left(10-\frac{10i}{n}\right)\left(\frac{10}{n}\right)$

$= \lim_{n\to\infty}\left[\frac{100}{n}\sum_{i=1}^{n}1 - \frac{100}{n^2}\sum_{i=1}^{n}i\right]$

$= \lim_{n\to\infty}\left[\frac{100}{n}(n) - \frac{100}{n^2}\left(\frac{n(n+1)}{2}\right)\right]$

$= \lim_{n\to\infty}\left[100 - 50\frac{n(n+1)}{n^2}\right]$

$= 100 - 50 = 50$, exact area

100. $A = \lim_{n\to\infty} \sum_{i=1}^{n} \left[2\left(3 + \frac{3i}{n}\right) - 6\right]\left(\frac{3}{n}\right)$

$= \lim_{n\to\infty} \sum_{i=1}^{n} \frac{18i}{n^2} = \lim_{n\to\infty} \frac{18}{n^2} \sum_{i=1}^{n} i$

$= \lim_{n\to\infty} \frac{18}{n^2} \frac{n(n+1)}{2} = 9$, exact area

101. $A = \lim_{n\to\infty} \sum_{i=1}^{n} \left[\left(-1 + \frac{3i}{n}\right)^2 + 4\right]\left(\frac{3}{n}\right)$

$= \lim_{n\to\infty} \sum_{i=1}^{n} \left[5 - \frac{6i}{n} + \frac{9i^2}{n^2}\right]\frac{3}{n}$

$= \lim_{n\to\infty} \left[\frac{15}{n} \sum_{i=1}^{n} 1 - \frac{18}{n^2} \sum_{i=1}^{n} i + \frac{27}{n^3} \sum_{i=1}^{n} i^2\right]$

$= \lim_{n\to\infty} \left[\frac{15}{n}(n) - \frac{18}{n^2} \frac{n(n+1)}{2} + \frac{27}{n^3} \frac{n(n+1)(2n+1)}{6}\right]$

$= 15 - 9 + 9 = 15$, exact area

102. $A = \lim_{n\to\infty} \sum_{i=1}^{n} 8\left(\left(\frac{i}{n}\right) - \left(\frac{i}{n}\right)^2\right)\frac{1}{n}$

$= \lim_{n\to\infty} \left[\frac{8}{n^2} \sum_{i=1}^{n} i - \frac{8}{n^3} \sum i^2\right]$

$= \lim_{n\to\infty} \left[\frac{8}{n^2} \frac{n(n+1)}{2} - \frac{8}{n^3} \frac{n(n+1)(2n+1)}{6}\right]$

$= 4 - \frac{8}{3} = \frac{4}{3}$, exact area

103. $f(x) = x^3 + 1,\ [0, 2]$

The width of each rectangle is $2/n$. The height is

$f\left(\frac{2i}{n}\right) = \left(\frac{2i}{n}\right)^3 + 1.$

$A \approx \sum_{i=1}^{n} \left[\left(\frac{2i}{n}\right)^3 + 1\right]\left(\frac{2}{n}\right)$

$= \sum_{i=1}^{n} \left[\frac{16i^3}{n^4} + \frac{2}{n}\right]$

$= \left(\frac{16}{n^4}\right)\frac{n^2(n+1)^2}{4} + \left(\frac{2}{n}\right)n$

$= \frac{4}{n^2}(n+1)^2 + 2$

$A = \lim_{n\to\infty} \left[\frac{4}{n^2}(n+1)^2 + 2\right] = 4 + 2 = 6$

104. $f(x) = 1 - x^3,\ [-3, -1]$

The width of each rectangle is $2/n$. The height is

$f\left(-3 + \frac{2i}{n}\right) = 1 - \left(-3 + \frac{2i}{n}\right)^3$

$= 28 - 54\frac{i}{n} + \frac{36i^2}{n^2} - \frac{8i^3}{n^3}.$

$A \approx \sum_{i=1}^{n} \left[28 - \frac{54}{n}i + \frac{36}{n^2}i^2 - \frac{8}{n^3}i^3\right]\left(\frac{2}{n}\right)$

$= \frac{56}{n}(n) - \frac{108}{n^2} \frac{n(n+1)}{2} + \frac{72}{n^3} \frac{n(n+1)(2n+1)}{6} - \frac{16}{n^4} \frac{n^2(n+1)^2}{4}$

$A = \lim_{n\to\infty} \left[56 - 54\frac{n(n+1)}{n^2} + 12\frac{n(n+1)(2n+1)}{n^3} - \frac{4n^2(n+1)^2}{n^4}\right]$

$= 56 - 54 + 24 - 4 = 22$

105. $f(x) = 3(x^3 - x^2)$, $[1, 3]$

The width of each rectangle is $2/n$. The height is

$$f\left(1 + \frac{2i}{n}\right) = 3\left[\left(1 + \frac{2i}{n}\right)^3 - \left(1 + \frac{2i}{n}\right)^2\right]$$

$$= \frac{6i}{n} + \frac{24i^2}{n^2} + \frac{24i^3}{n^3}.$$

$$A \approx \sum_{i=1}^{n}\left[\frac{6i}{n} + \frac{24i^2}{n^2} + \frac{24i^3}{n^3}\right]\left(\frac{2}{n}\right)$$

$$= \frac{12}{n^2}\frac{n(n+1)}{2} + \frac{48}{n^3}\frac{n(n+1)(2n+1)}{6} + \frac{48}{n^4}\frac{n^2(n+1)^2}{4}$$

$$A = \lim_{n\to\infty}\left[6 + 8\frac{n(n+1)(2n+1)}{n^3} + 12\frac{n^2(n+1)^2}{n^4}\right]$$

$$= 6 + 16 + 12 = 34$$

106. $f(x) = 5 - (x + 2)^2$, $[-2, 0]$

The width of each rectangle is $2/n$. The height is

$$f\left(-2 + \frac{2i}{n}\right) = 5 - \left[\left(-2 + \frac{2i}{n}\right) + 2\right]^2$$

$$= 5 - \left(\frac{2i}{n}\right)^2$$

$$= 5 - \frac{4i^2}{n^2}.$$

$$A \approx \sum_{i=1}^{n}\left[5 - \frac{4i^2}{n^2}\right]\left(\frac{2}{n}\right) = \sum_{i=1}^{n}\left[\frac{10}{n} - \frac{8}{n^3}i^2\right]$$

$$A = \lim_{n\to\infty}\left[\frac{10}{n}(n) - \frac{8}{n^3}\frac{n(n+1)(2n+1)}{6}\right] = 10 - \frac{8}{3} = \frac{22}{3}$$

107. (a) $y = -3.376 \times 10^{-7}x^3 + 3.753 \times 10^{-4}x^2 - 0.168x + 132.168$

(b)

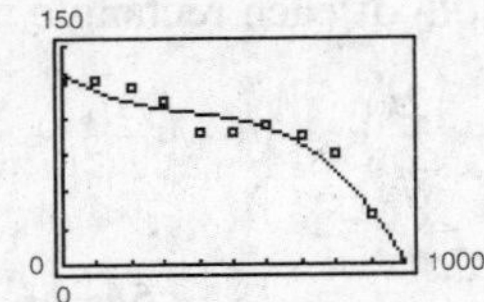

(c) Area $\approx$ 88,868 square feet; answers will vary.

108. True (assuming all the limits exist)

109. False. The limit does not exist.

110. Answers will vary.

Chapter 11 Practice Test

1. Use a graphing utility to complete the table and use the result to estimate the limit

$$\lim_{x \to 3} \frac{x - 3}{x^2 - 9}.$$

x	2.9	2.99	3	3.01	3.1
$f(x)$			?		

2. Graph the function

$$f(x) = \frac{\sqrt{x + 4} - 2}{x}$$

and estimate the limit

$$\lim_{x \to 0} \frac{\sqrt{x + 4} - 2}{x}.$$

3. Find the limit $\lim_{x \to 2} e^{x-2}$ by direct substitution.

4. Find the limit $\lim_{x \to 1} \frac{x^3 - 1}{x - 1}$ analytically.

5. Use a graphing utility to estimate the limit

$$\lim_{x \to 0} \frac{\sin 5x}{2x}.$$

6. Find the limit

$$\lim_{x \to -2} \frac{|x + 2|}{x + 2}.$$

7. Use the limit process to find the slope of the graph of $f(x) = \sqrt{x}$ at the point $(4, 2)$.

8. Find the derivative of the function $f(x) = 3x - 1$.

9. Find the limits.

(a) $\lim_{x \to \infty} \frac{3}{x^4}$ (b) $\lim_{x \to -\infty} \frac{x^2}{x^2 + 3}$ (c) $\lim_{x \to \infty} \frac{|x|}{1 - x}$

10. Write the first four terms of the sequence $a_n = \frac{1 - n^2}{2n^2 + 1}$ and find the limit of the sequence.

11. Find the sum $\sum_{i=1}^{25} (i^2 + i)$.

12. Write the sum $\sum_{i=1}^{n} \frac{i^2}{n^3}$ as a rational function $S(n)$, and find $\lim_{n \to \infty} S(n)$.

13. Find the area of the region bounded by $f(x) = 1 - x^2$ over the interval $0 \le x \le 1$.

APPENDICES

Appendix B Prerequisites **991**

B.1 The Cartesian Plane **991**

B.2 Graphs of Equations **1000**

B.3 Solving Equations Algebraically and Graphically **1009**

B.4 Solving Inequalities Algebraically and Graphically **1034**

B.5 Representing Data Graphically **1045**

Appendix C Concepts in Statistics **1048**

C.1 Measures of Central Tendency and Dispersion **1048**

C.2 Least Squares Regression **1052**

Appendix D Variation **1053**

Appendix E Solving Linear Equations and Inequalities **1059**

Appendix F Systems of Inequalities **1061**

F.1 Solving Systems of Inequalities **1061**

F.2 Linear Programming **1071**

APPENDIX B
Prerequisites

Appendix B.1 The Cartesian Plane

- You should be able to plot points.
- You should know that the distance between (x_1, y_1) and (x_2, y_2) in the plane is
  $d = \sqrt{(x_2 - x_1)^2 + (y_2 - y_1)^2}$.
- You should know that the midpoint of the line segment joining (x_1, y_1) and (x_2, y_2) is
  $\left(\frac{x_1 + x_2}{2}, \frac{y_1 + y_2}{2}\right)$.
- You should know the equation of a circle: $(x - h)^2 + (y - k)^2 = r^2$.
- You should be able to translate points in the plane.

Vocabulary Check

1. (a) iii (b) vi (c) i (d) iv (e) v (f) ii

2. Cartesian

3. Distance Formula

4. Midpoint Formula

5. $(x - h)^2 + (y - k)^2 = r^2$, center, radius

1. A: $(2, 6)$, B: $(-6, -2)$, C: $(4, -4)$, D: $(-3, 2)$

2. A: $\left(\frac{3}{2}, -4\right)$; B: $(0, -2)$; C: $\left(-3, \frac{5}{2}\right)$; D: $(-6, 0)$

3.

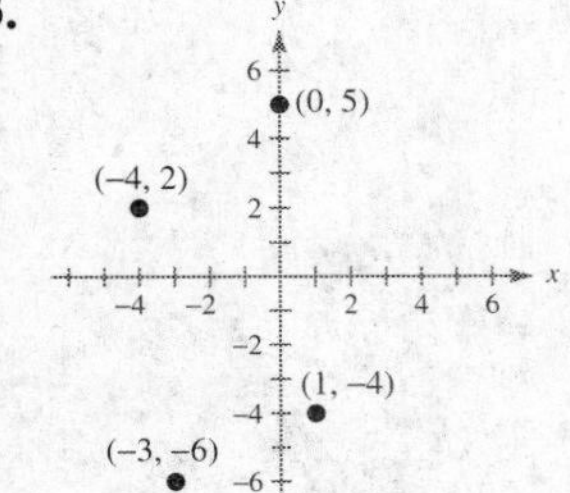

4.

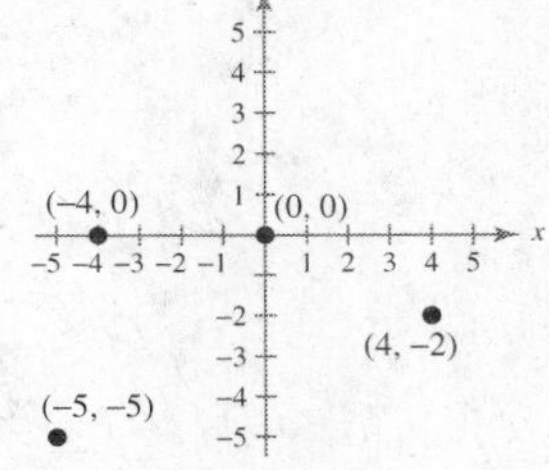

5.

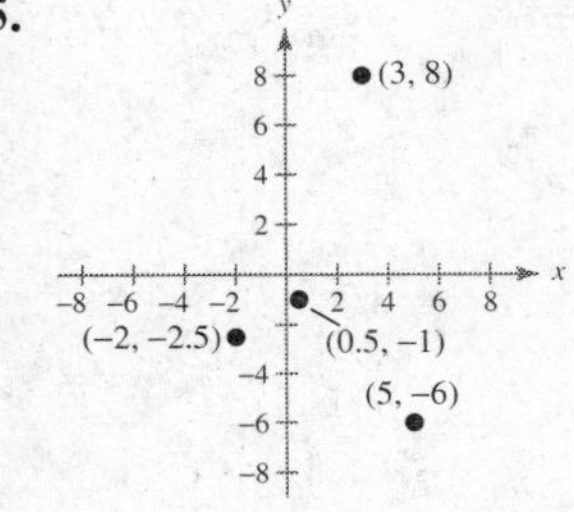

6.

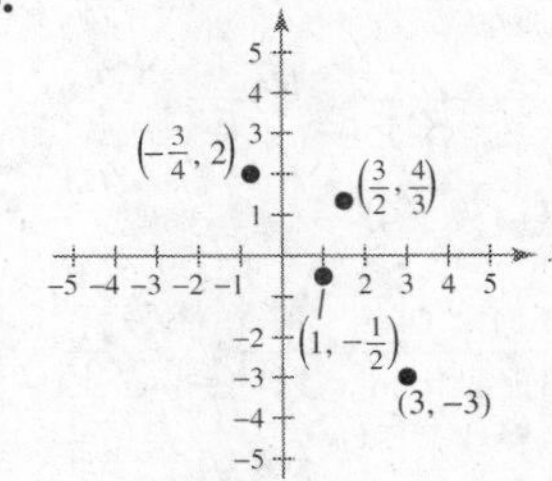

7. $(-5, 4)$

8. $(2, -3)$

9. $(-6, -6)$

10. $(-10, 0)$

11. $x > 0 \Rightarrow$ The point lies in Quadrant I or in Quadrant IV.

$y < 0 \Rightarrow$ The point lies in Quadrant III or in Quadrant IV.

$x > 0$ and $y < 0 \Rightarrow (x, y)$ lies in Quadrant IV.

12. If $x < 0$ and $y < 0$ then (x, y) is in Quadrant III.

13. $x = -4 \Rightarrow$ x is negative $\Rightarrow$ The point lies in Quadrant II or in Quadrant III.

$y > 0 \Rightarrow$ The point lies in Quadrant I or Quadrant II.

$x = -4$ and $y > 0 \Rightarrow (x, y)$ lies in Quadrant II.

14. If $x > 2$ and $y = 3$ then $(x, 3)$ is in Quadrant I.

15. $y < -5 \Rightarrow y$ is negative $\Rightarrow$ The point lies in either Quadrant III or Quadrant IV.

16. If $x > 4$ then (x, y) is in Quadrants I or IV.

17. If $-y > 0$, then $y < 0$.

$x < 0 \Rightarrow$ The point lies in Quadrant II or in Quadrant III.

$y < 0 \Rightarrow$ The point lies in Quadrant III or in Quadrant IV.

$x < 0$ and $y < 0 \Rightarrow (x, y)$ lies in Quadrant III.

18. If $(-x, y)$ is in Quadrant IV, then (x, y) must be in Quadrant III.

19. If $xy > 0$, then either x and y are both positive, or both negative. Hence, (x, y) lies in either Quadrant I or Quadrant III.

20. If $xy < 0$, then x and y have opposite signs. This happens in Quadrants II and IV.

21.

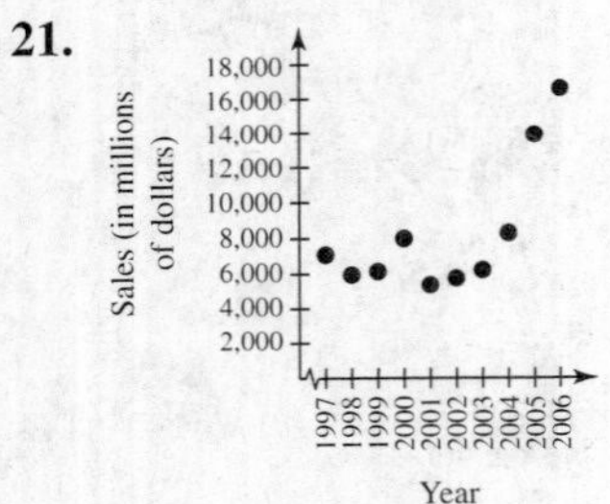

22.

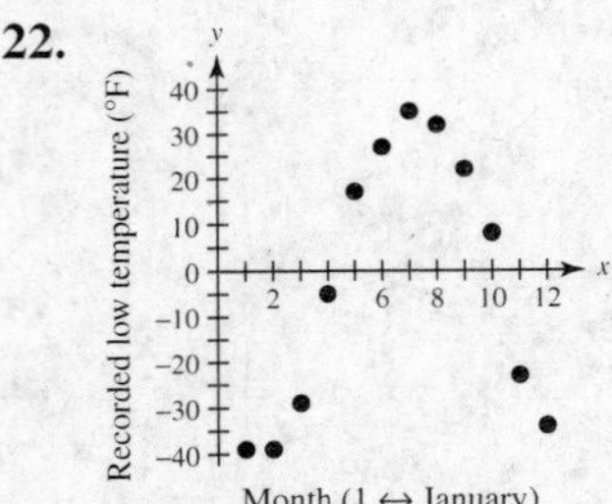

23. $(6, -3), (6, 5)$

$d = \sqrt{(6-6)^2 + (5-(-3))^2} = \sqrt{64} = 8$

24. $d = |8 - 1| = 7$

25. $(-3, -1), (2, -1)$

$d = \sqrt{(2-(-3))^2 + (-1-(-1))^2} = \sqrt{25} = 5$

26. $d = |6 - (-4)| = |6 + 4| = 10$

27. $d = \sqrt{(3-(-2))^2 + (-6-6)^2} = \sqrt{5^2 + (-12)^2}$

$= \sqrt{25 + 144} = \sqrt{169} = 13$

28. $d = \sqrt{(0-8)^2 + (20-5)^2} = \sqrt{8^2 + 15^2}$

$= \sqrt{64 + 225} = \sqrt{289} = 17$

29. $\left(\frac{1}{2}, \frac{4}{3}\right), (2, -1)$

$$d = \sqrt{\left(\frac{1}{2} - 2\right)^2 + \left(\frac{4}{3} + 1\right)^2}$$
$$= \sqrt{\frac{9}{4} + \frac{49}{9}}$$
$$= \sqrt{\frac{277}{36}} = \frac{\sqrt{277}}{6} \approx 2.77$$

30. $d = \sqrt{\left(-\frac{2}{3} + 1\right)^2 + \left(3 - \frac{5}{4}\right)^2}$

$$= \sqrt{\frac{1}{9} + \frac{49}{16}}$$
$$= \sqrt{\frac{457}{144}} = \frac{\sqrt{457}}{12} \approx 1.78$$

31. $(-4.2, 3.1), (-12.5, 4.8)$

$$d = \sqrt{(-4.2 + 12.5)^2 + (3.1 - 4.8)^2}$$
$$= \sqrt{68.89 + 2.89}$$
$$= \sqrt{71.78} \approx 8.47$$

32. $d = \sqrt{(9.5 + 3.9)^2 + (-2.6 - 8.2)^2}$

$$= \sqrt{179.56 + 116.64}$$
$$= \sqrt{296.2} \approx 17.21$$

33. (a) The distance between $(0, 2)$ and $(4, 2)$ is 4.

The distance between $(4, 2)$ and $(4, 5)$ is 3.

The distance between $(0, 2)$ and $(4, 5)$ is

$$\sqrt{(4 - 0)^2 + (5 - 2)^2} = \sqrt{16 + 9}$$
$$= \sqrt{25} = 5.$$

(b) $4^2 + 3^2 = 16 + 9 = 25 = 5^2$

34. (a) $(1, 0), (13, 5)$

$$d = \sqrt{(13 - 1)^2 + (5 - 0)^2}$$
$$= \sqrt{12^2 + 5^2}$$
$$= \sqrt{169} = 13$$

$(13, 5), (13, 0)$

$$d = |5 - 0| = |5| = 5$$

$(1, 0), (13, 0)$

$$d = |1 - 13| = |-12| = 12$$

(b) $5^2 + 12^2 = 25 + 144 = 169 = 13^2$

35. (a) The distance between $(-1, 1)$ and $(9, 1)$ is 10.

The distance between $(9, 1)$ and $(9, 4)$ is 3.

The distance between $(-1, 1)$ and $(9, 4)$ is

$$\sqrt{(9 - (-1))^2 + (4 - 1)^2} = \sqrt{100 + 9}$$
$$= \sqrt{109}.$$

(b) $10^2 + 3^2 = 109 = \left(\sqrt{109}\right)^2$

36. (a) $(1, 5), (5, -2)$

$$d = \sqrt{(1 - 5)^2 + (5 - (-2))^2}$$
$$= \sqrt{(-4)^2 + (7)^2}$$
$$= \sqrt{16 + 49} = \sqrt{65}$$

$(1, 5), (1, -2)$

$$d = |5 - (-2)| = |5 + 2| = |7| = 7$$

$(1, -2), (5, -2)$

$$d = |1 - 5| = |-4| = 4$$

(b) $4^2 + 7^2 = 65 = \left(\sqrt{65}\right)^2$

37. Find distances between pairs of points.

$$d_1 = \sqrt{(4 - 2)^2 + (0 - 1)^2} = \sqrt{5}$$
$$d_2 = \sqrt{(4 + 1)^2 + (0 + 5)^2} = \sqrt{50}$$
$$d_3 = \sqrt{(2 + 1)^2 + (1 + 5)^2} = \sqrt{45}$$
$$\left(\sqrt{5}\right)^2 + \left(\sqrt{45}\right)^2 = \left(\sqrt{50}\right)^2$$

Because $d_1^2 + d_3^2 = d_2^2$, the triangle is a right triangle.

38. Find the distances between pairs of points.

$$d_1 = \sqrt{(3 - (-1))^2 + (5 - 3)^2}$$
$$= \sqrt{16 + 4} = \sqrt{20}$$
$$d_2 = \sqrt{(5 - 3)^2 + (1 - 5)^2}$$
$$= \sqrt{4 + 16} = \sqrt{20}$$
$$d_3 = \sqrt{(5 - (-1))^2 + (1 - 3)^2}$$
$$= \sqrt{36 + 4} = \sqrt{40}$$

Because $d_1^2 + d_2^2 = d_3^2$, the triangle is a right triangle.

39. $d_1 = \sqrt{(1-3)^2 + (-3-2)^2} = \sqrt{4+25} = \sqrt{29}$

$d_2 = \sqrt{(3+2)^2 + (2-4)^2} = \sqrt{25+4} = \sqrt{29}$

$d_3 = \sqrt{(1+2)^2 + (-3-4)^2} = \sqrt{9+49} = \sqrt{58}$

$d_1 = d_2$. Triangle is isosceles.

40. Find the distances between pairs of points.

$d_1 = \sqrt{(4-2)^2 + (9-3)^2}$

$= \sqrt{4+36} = \sqrt{40} = 2\sqrt{10}$

$d_2 = \sqrt{(-2-4)^2 + (7-9)^2}$

$= \sqrt{36+4} = \sqrt{40} = 2\sqrt{10}$

$d_3 = \sqrt{(-2-2)^2 + (7-3)^2}$

$= \sqrt{16+16} = \sqrt{32} = 4\sqrt{2}$

Because $d_1 = d_2$, the triangle is isosceles.

41. Find distances between pairs of points.

$d_1 = \sqrt{(0-2)^2 + (9-5)^2} = \sqrt{4+16} = \sqrt{20} = 2\sqrt{5}$

$d_2 = \sqrt{(-2-0)^2 + (0-9)^2} = \sqrt{4+81} = \sqrt{85}$

$d_3 = \sqrt{(0-(-2))^2 + (-4-0)^2} = \sqrt{4+16} = \sqrt{20} = 2\sqrt{5}$

$d_4 = \sqrt{(0-2)^2 + (-4-5)^2} = \sqrt{4+81} = \sqrt{85}$

Opposite sides have equal lengths of $2\sqrt{5}$ and $\sqrt{85}$, so the figure is a parallelogram.

42. $d_1 = \sqrt{(0-3)^2 + (1-7)^2} = \sqrt{9+36} = \sqrt{45} = 3\sqrt{5}$

$d_2 = \sqrt{(3-4)^2 + (7-4)^2} = \sqrt{1+9} = \sqrt{10}$

$d_3 = \sqrt{(4-1)^2 + (4+2)^2} = \sqrt{9+36} = \sqrt{45} = 3\sqrt{5}$

$d_4 = \sqrt{(0-1)^2 + (1+2)^2} = \sqrt{1+9} = \sqrt{10}$

Opposite sides have equal lengths of $3\sqrt{5}$ and $\sqrt{10}$. The figure is a parallelogram.

43. First show that the diagonals are equal in length.

$d_1 = \sqrt{(0-(-3))^2 + (8-1)^2} = \sqrt{9+49} = \sqrt{58}$

$d_2 = \sqrt{(2-(-5))^2 + (3-6)^2} = \sqrt{49+9} = \sqrt{58}$

Now use the Pythagorean Theorem to verify that at least one angle is 90° (and, hence, they are all right angles).

$d_3 = \sqrt{(0-(-5))^2 + (8-6)^2} = \sqrt{25+4} = \sqrt{29}$

$d_4 = \sqrt{(-3-(-5))^2 + (1-6)^2} = \sqrt{4+25} = \sqrt{29}$

Thus, $d_3^2 + d_4^2 = d_1^2$.

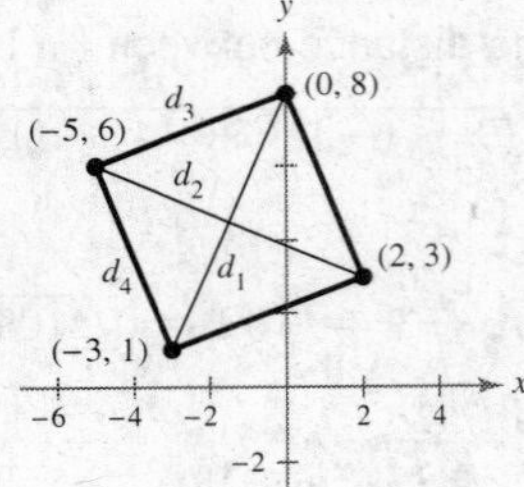

44. First show that the diagonals are equal in length.

$d_1 = \sqrt{(3-2)^2 + (1-4)^2} = \sqrt{1+9} = \sqrt{10}$

$d_2 = \sqrt{(4-1)^2 + (3-2)^2} = \sqrt{9+1} = \sqrt{10}$

Now use the Pythagorean Theorem to verify that at least one angle is 90°.

$d_3 = \sqrt{(4-2)^2 + (3-4)^2} = \sqrt{4+1} = \sqrt{5}$

$d_4 = \sqrt{(2-1)^2 + (4-2)^2} = \sqrt{1+4} = \sqrt{5}$

Thus, $d_3^2 + d_4^2 = d_1^2$.

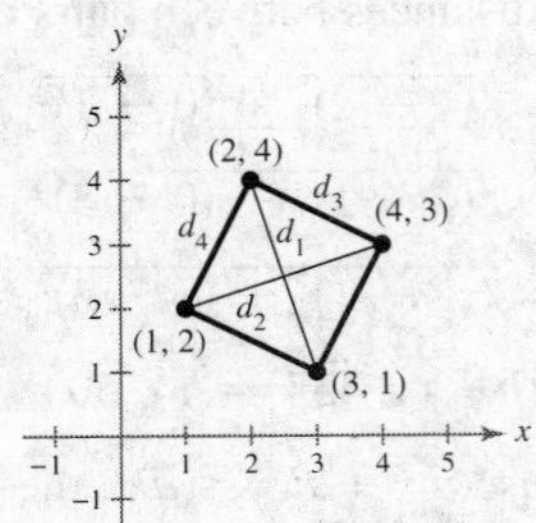

45. (a)

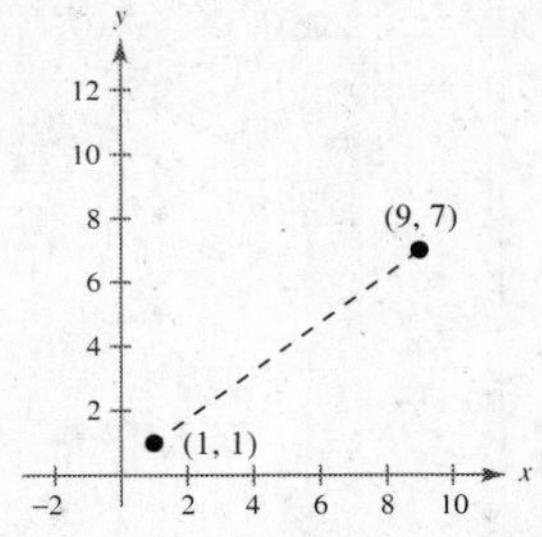

(b) $d = \sqrt{(9-1)^2 + (7-1)^2}$

$= \sqrt{64 + 36} = 10$

(c) $\left(\dfrac{9+1}{2}, \dfrac{7+1}{2}\right) = (5, 4)$

46. (a)

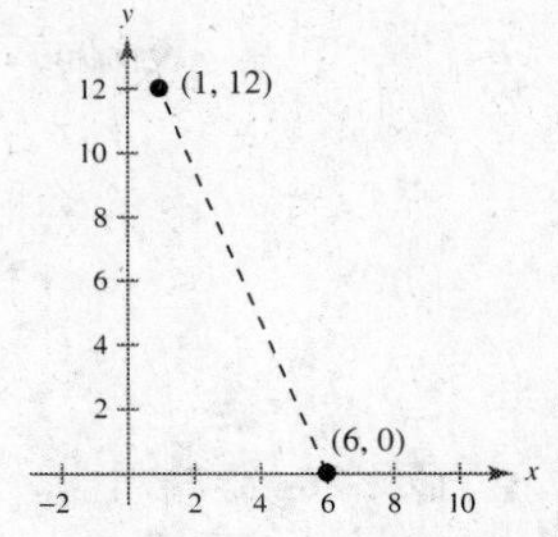

(b) $d = \sqrt{(1-6)^2 + (12-0)^2}$

$= \sqrt{25 + 144} = 13$

(c) $\left(\dfrac{1+6}{2}, \dfrac{12+0}{2}\right) = \left(\dfrac{7}{2}, 6\right)$

47. (a)

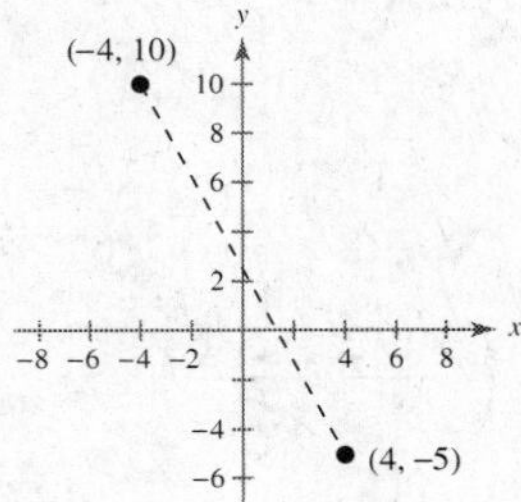

(b) $d = \sqrt{(4+4)^2 + (-5-10)^2}$

$= \sqrt{64 + 225} = 17$

(c) $\left(\dfrac{4-4}{2}, \dfrac{-5+10}{2}\right) = \left(0, \dfrac{5}{2}\right)$

48. (a)

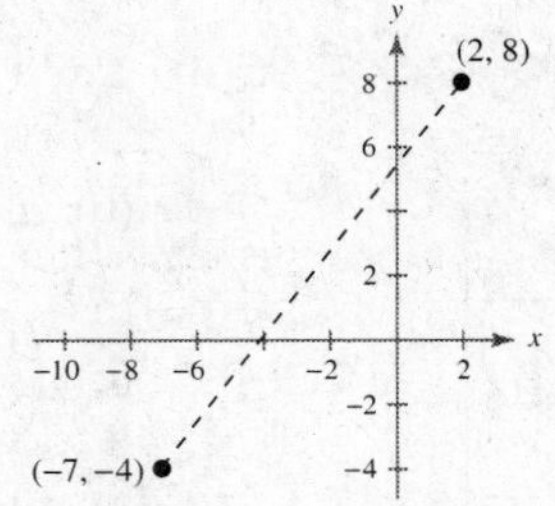

(b) $d = \sqrt{(-7-2)^2 + (-4-8)^2}$

$= \sqrt{81 + 144} = 15$

(c) $\left(\dfrac{-7+2}{2}, \dfrac{-4+8}{2}\right) = \left(-\dfrac{5}{2}, 2\right)$

49. (a)

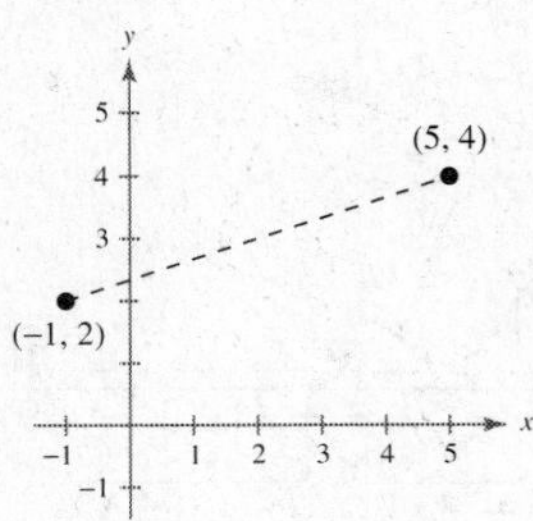

(b) $d = \sqrt{(5+1)^2 + (4-2)^2}$

$= \sqrt{36 + 4} = \sqrt{40} = 2\sqrt{10}$

(c) $\left(\dfrac{-1+5}{2}, \dfrac{2+4}{2}\right) = (2, 3)$

50. (a)

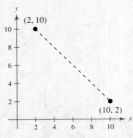

(b) $d = \sqrt{(2-10)^2 + (10-2)^2}$

$= \sqrt{64 + 64} = 8\sqrt{2}$

(c) $\left(\dfrac{2+10}{2}, \dfrac{10+2}{2}\right) = (6, 6)$

51. (a)

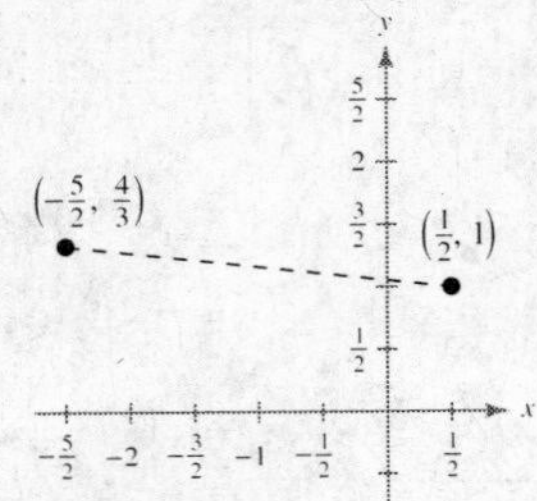

(b) $d = \sqrt{\left(\dfrac{1}{2} + \dfrac{5}{2}\right)^2 + \left(1 - \dfrac{4}{3}\right)^2}$

$d = \sqrt{9 + \dfrac{1}{9}} = \dfrac{\sqrt{82}}{3}$

(c) $\left(\dfrac{-\frac{5}{2} + \frac{1}{2}}{2}, \dfrac{\frac{4}{3} + 1}{2}\right) = \left(-1, \dfrac{7}{6}\right)$

52. (a)

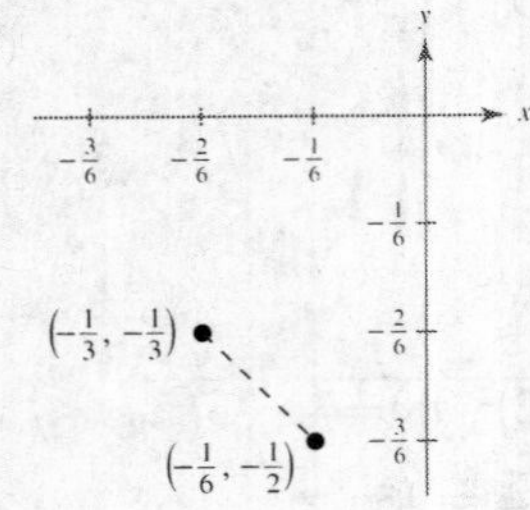

(b) $d = \sqrt{\left(-\dfrac{1}{3} + \dfrac{1}{6}\right)^2 + \left(-\dfrac{1}{3} + \dfrac{1}{2}\right)^2} = \sqrt{\dfrac{1}{36} + \dfrac{1}{36}} = \dfrac{\sqrt{2}}{6}$

(c) $\left(\dfrac{(-1/3) - (1/6)}{2}, \dfrac{(-1/3) - (1/2)}{2}\right) = \left(\dfrac{-1/2}{2}, \dfrac{-5/6}{2}\right)$

$= \left(-\dfrac{1}{4}, -\dfrac{5}{12}\right)$

53. (a)

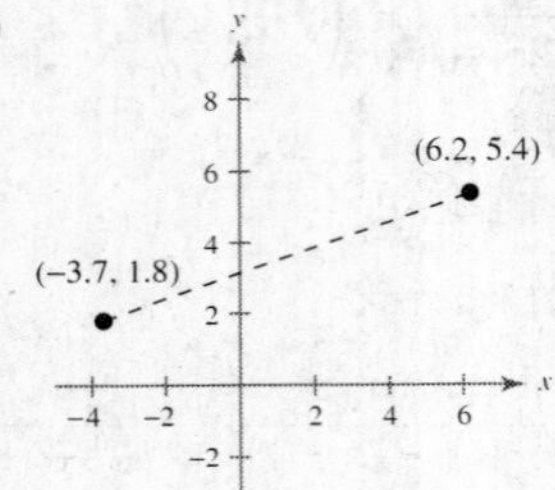

(b) $d = \sqrt{(6.2 + 3.7)^2 + (5.4 - 1.8)^2}$

$= \sqrt{98.01 + 12.96} = \sqrt{110.97}$

(c) $\left(\dfrac{6.2 - 3.7}{2}, \dfrac{5.4 + 1.8}{2}\right) = (1.25, 3.6)$

54. (a)

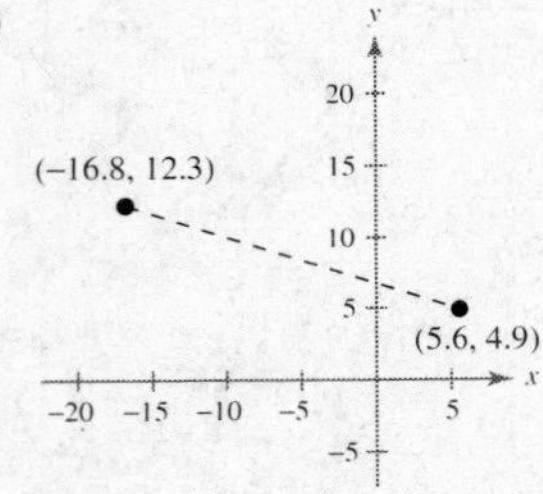

(b) $d = \sqrt{(-16.8 - 5.6)^2 + (12.3 - 4.9)^2}$

$= \sqrt{501.76 + 54.76} = \sqrt{556.52}$

(c) $\left(\dfrac{-16.8 + 5.6}{2}, \dfrac{12.3 + 4.9}{2}\right) = (-5.6, 8.6)$

55. Calculate the midpoint:

$\left(\dfrac{2000 + 2006}{2}, \dfrac{2237 + 3950}{2}\right) = (2003, 3093.5)$

The sales in 2003 are \$3093.5 million.

56. Calculate the midpoint:

$\left(\dfrac{2000 + 2006}{2}, \dfrac{945 + 1005}{2}\right) = (2003, 975)$

The sales in 2003 are \$975 million.

57. Since $x_m = \dfrac{x_1 + x_2}{2}$ and $y_m = \dfrac{y_1 + y_2}{2}$ we have:

$$2x_m = x_1 + x_2 \qquad 2y_m = y_1 + y_2$$

$$2x_m - x_1 = x_2 \qquad 2y_m - y_1 = y_2$$

So, $(x_2, y_2) = (2x_m - x_1, 2y_m - y_1)$.

(a) $(x_2, y_2) = (2x_m - x_1, 2y_m - y_1) = (2(4) - 1, 2(-1) - (-2)) = (7, 0)$

(b) $(x_2, y_2) = (2x_m - x_1, 2y_m - y_1) = (2(2) - (-5), 2(4) - 11) = (9, -3)$

58. (a) $\left(\dfrac{3x_1 + x_2}{4}, \dfrac{3y_1 + y_2}{4}\right) = \left(\dfrac{3(1) + 4}{4}, \dfrac{3(-2) - 1}{4}\right) = \left(\dfrac{7}{4}, \dfrac{-7}{4}\right)$

$\left(\dfrac{x_1 + x_2}{2}, \dfrac{y_1 + y_2}{2}\right) = \left(\dfrac{1 + 4}{2}, \dfrac{-2 - 1}{2}\right) = \left(\dfrac{5}{2}, \dfrac{-3}{2}\right)$

$\left(\dfrac{x_1 + 3x_2}{4}, \dfrac{y_1 + 3y_2}{4}\right) = \left(\dfrac{1 + 3(4)}{4}, \dfrac{-2 + 3(-1)}{4}\right) = \left(\dfrac{13}{4}, \dfrac{-5}{4}\right)$

(b) $\left(\dfrac{3x_1 + x_2}{4}, \dfrac{3y_1 + y_2}{4}\right) = \left(\dfrac{3(-2) + 0}{4}, \dfrac{3(-3) + 0}{4}\right) = \left(\dfrac{-3}{2}, \dfrac{-9}{4}\right)$

$\left(\dfrac{x_1 + x_2}{2}, \dfrac{y_1 + y_2}{2}\right) = \left(\dfrac{-2 + 0}{2}, \dfrac{-3 + 0}{2}\right) = \left(-1, \dfrac{-3}{2}\right)$

$\left(\dfrac{x_1 + 3x_2}{4}, \dfrac{y_1 + 3y_2}{4}\right) = \left(\dfrac{-2 + 0}{4}, \dfrac{-3 + 0}{4}\right) = \left(\dfrac{-1}{2}, \dfrac{-3}{4}\right)$

59. $(x - 0)^2 + (y - 0)^2 = 3^2$

$x^2 + y^2 = 9$

60. $(x - 0)^2 + (y - 0)^2 = 6^2$

$x^2 + y^2 = 36$

61. $(x - 2)^2 + (y + 1)^2 = 4^2$

$(x - 2)^2 + (y + 1)^2 = 16$

62. $(x - 0)^2 + \left(y - \frac{1}{3}\right)^2 = \left(\frac{1}{3}\right)^2$

$x^2 + \left(y - \frac{1}{3}\right)^2 = \frac{1}{9}$

63. $(x + 1)^2 + (y - 2)^2 = r^2$

$(0 + 1)^2 + (0 - 2)^2 = r^2 \implies r^2 = 5$

$(x + 1)^2 + (y - 2)^2 = 5$

64. $r = \sqrt{(3 - (-1))^2 + (-2 - 1)^2} = \sqrt{16 + 9} = 5$

$(x - 3)^2 + (y + 2)^2 = 5^2 = 25$

65. $r = \dfrac{1}{2}\sqrt{(6 - 0)^2 + (8 - 0)^2} = \dfrac{1}{2}\sqrt{100} = 5$

Center: $\left(\dfrac{0 + 6}{2}, \dfrac{0 + 8}{2}\right) = (3, 4)$

$(x - 3)^2 + (y - 4)^2 = 25$

66. Center: $\left(\dfrac{-4 + 4}{2}, \dfrac{-1 + 1}{2}\right) = (0, 0)$

$r = \sqrt{(4 - 0)^2 + (1 - 0)^2} = \sqrt{17}$

$x^2 + y^2 = 17$

67. Because the circle is tangent to the x-axis, the radius is 1.

$(x + 2)^2 + (y - 1)^2 = 1$

68. Because the circle is tangent to the y-axis, the radius is 3.

$(x - 3)^2 + (y + 2)^2 = 9$

69. The center is the midpoint of one of the diagonals of the square.

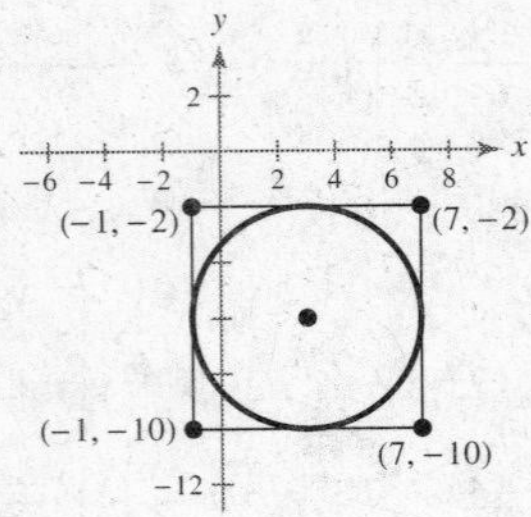

Center: $\left(\dfrac{7 + (-1)}{2}, \dfrac{-2 + (-10)}{2}\right) = (3, -6)$

The radius is one half the length of a side of the square.

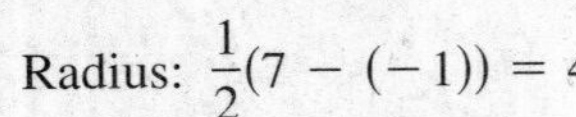

Radius: $\dfrac{1}{2}(7 - (-1)) = 4$

Circle: $(x - 3)^2 + (y + 6)^2 = 16$

70. The center is the midpoint of one of the diagonals of the square.

Center: $\left(\dfrac{8 + (-12)}{2}, \dfrac{10 + (-10)}{2}\right) = (-2, 0)$

The radius is one half the length of a side of the square.

Radius: $\dfrac{1}{2}(8 - (-12)) = 10$

Circle: $(x + 2)^2 + y^2 = 100$

71. $(x - 2)^2 + (y + 1)^2 = 16$

72. $(x + 3)^2 + (y - 1)^2 = 25$

73. $x^2 + y^2 = 25$

Center: $(0, 0)$

Radius: 5

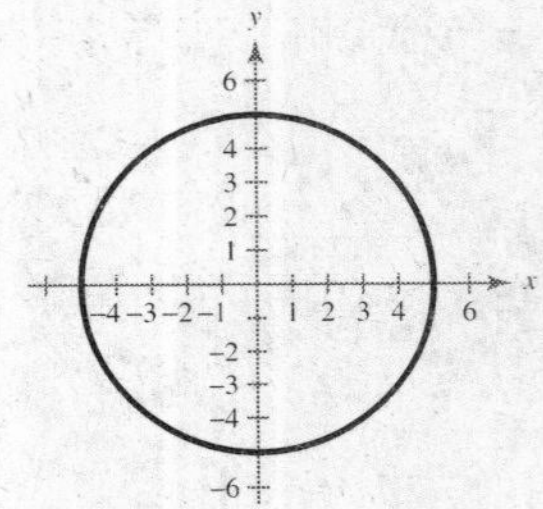

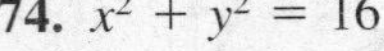

74. $x^2 + y^2 = 16$

Center: $(0, 0)$

Radius: $\sqrt{16} = 4$

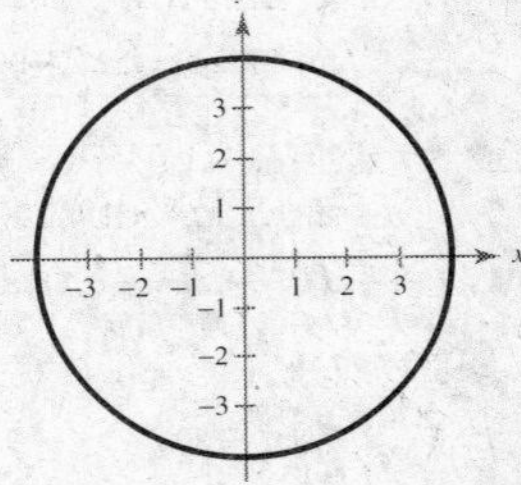

75. Center: $(1, -3)$

Radius: 2

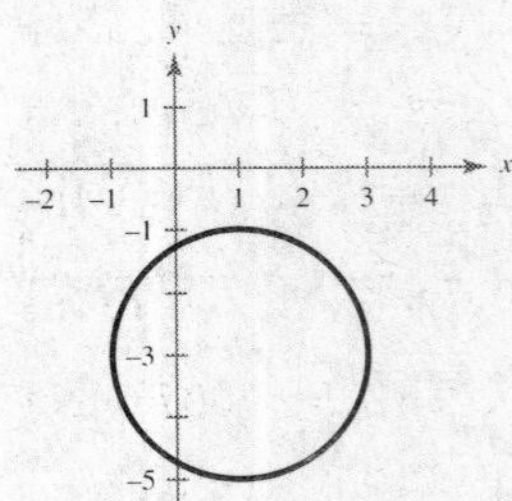

76. $x^2 + (y - 1)^2 = 49$

Center: $(0, 1)$

Radius: $\sqrt{49} = 7$

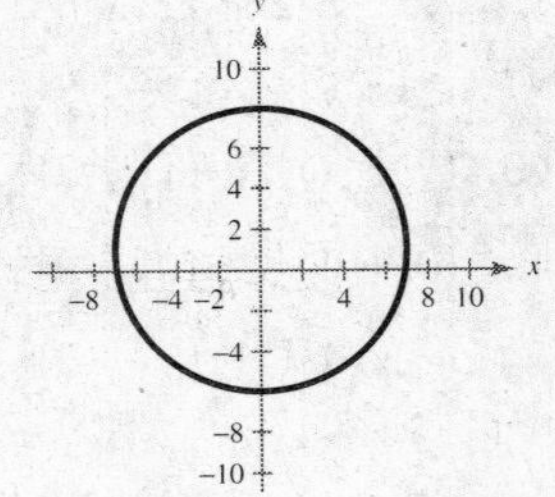

77. Center: $\left(\frac{1}{2}, \frac{1}{2}\right)$

Radius: $\frac{3}{2}$

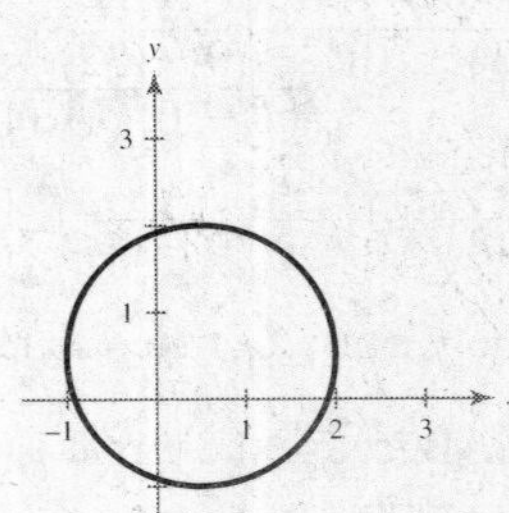

78. $\left(x - \frac{2}{3}\right)^2 + \left(y + \frac{1}{4}\right)^2 = \frac{25}{9}$

Center: $\left(\frac{2}{3}, -\frac{1}{4}\right)$

Radius: $\frac{5}{3}$

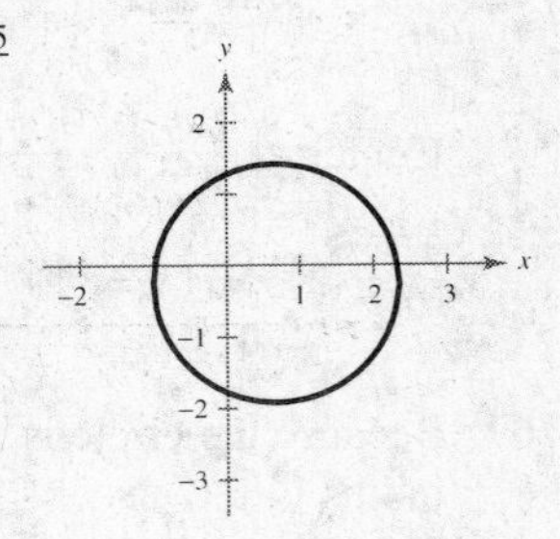

79. The x-coordinates are increased by 2, and the y-coordinates are increased by 5.

Old vertex	*Shifted vertex*
$(-1, -1)$	$(1, 4)$
$(-2, -4)$	$(0, 1)$
$(2, -3)$	$(4, 2)$

80. $(-3 + 6, 6 - 3) = (3, 3)$

$(-5 + 6, 3 - 3) = (1, 0)$

$(-3 + 6, 0 - 3) = (3, -3)$

$(-1 + 6, 3 - 3) = (5, 0)$

81.

Old vertex	*Shifted vertex*
$(0, 2)$	$(-1, 5)$
$(3, 5)$	$(2, 8)$
$(5, 2)$	$(4, 5)$
$(2, -1)$	$(1, 2)$

82. $(1 - 3, -1 - 2) = (-2, -3)$

$(3 - 3, 2 - 2), = (0, 0)$

$(1 - 3, -2 - 2) = (-2, -4)$

83. The point (65, 83) represents an entrance exam score of 65.

84. No, there are many variables that will affect the final exam score.

85. (a) Sample answer: The number of artists inducted each year seems to be nearly steady except for the first few years.
Estimate: Between 5 and 7 new members

(b) Sample answer: The Rock and Roll Hall of Fame was opened in 1986.

86. Let (0, 0) represent the point of departure, Naples, and (120, 150) represent the destination, Rome.

$$d = \sqrt{(120 - 0)^2 + (150 - 0)^2}$$

$$= \sqrt{36{,}900} \approx 192.1 \text{ km}$$

87. $d = \sqrt{(45 - 10)^2 + (40 - 15)^2} = \sqrt{35^2 + 25^2} = \sqrt{1850} = 5\sqrt{74} \approx 43$ yards

88.

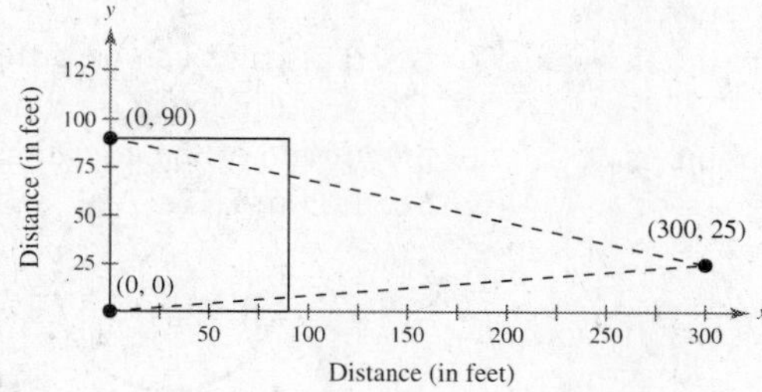

Distance from (300, 25) to home plate:

$$d_1 = \sqrt{(300 - 0)^2 + (25 - 0)^2}$$

$$= \sqrt{90{,}625} \approx 301.0 \text{ feet}$$

Distance from (300, 25) to third base:

$$d_2 = \sqrt{(300 - 0)^2 + (25 - 90)^2}$$

$$= \sqrt{94{,}225} \approx 307.0 \text{ feet}$$

89. (a)

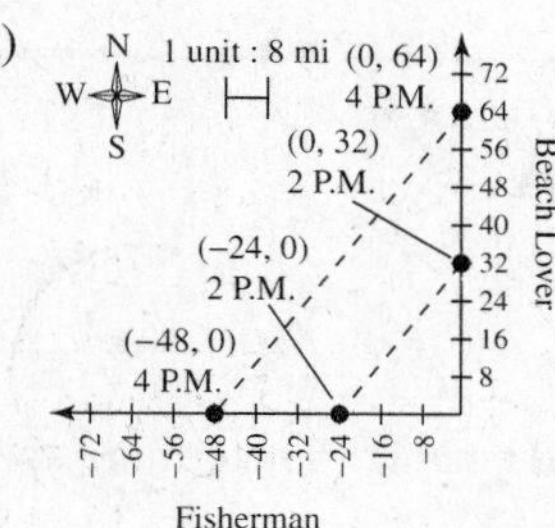

(b) Distance at 2 P.M.:

$\sqrt{(-24 - 0)^2 + (0 - 32)^2} = \sqrt{1600} = 40$ miles

Distance at 4 P.M.:

$\sqrt{(-48 - 0)^2 + (0 - 64)^2} = \sqrt{6400} = 80$ miles

Yes, the yachts are twice as far from each other.

90. (a)

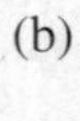

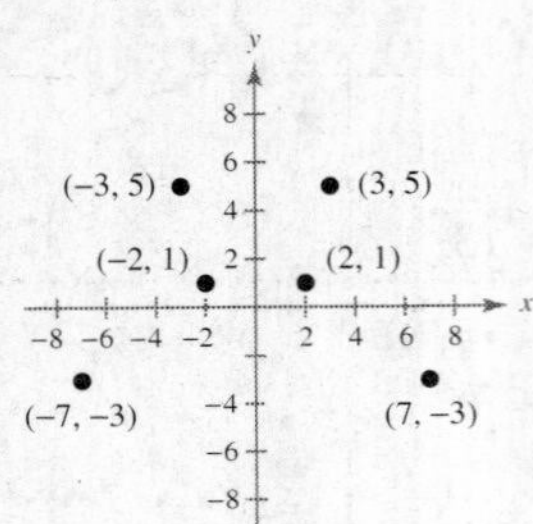

The points are reflected through the y-axis.

(b)

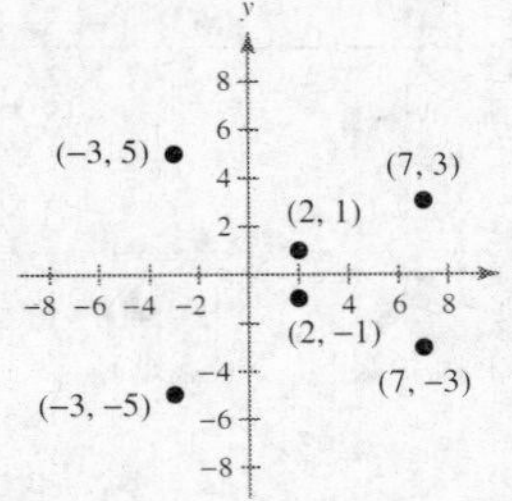

The points are reflected through the x-axis.

(c)

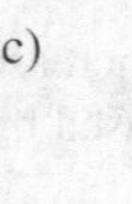

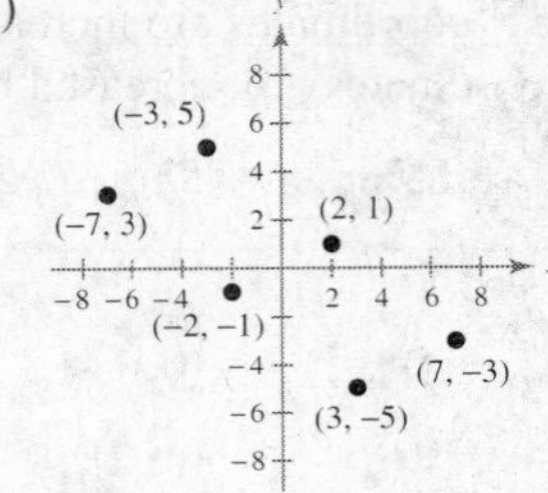

The points are rotated 180° about the origin (reflected through the origin).

91. Find the distances between pairs of points.

$d_1 = \sqrt{(2 + 2\sqrt{3} - 2)^2 + (0 - 6)^2} = \sqrt{12 + 36} = \sqrt{48} = 4\sqrt{3}$

$d_2 = \sqrt{((2 + 2\sqrt{3}) - (2 - 2\sqrt{3}))^2 + (0 - 0)^2} = 4\sqrt{3}$

$d_3 = \sqrt{(2 - 2\sqrt{3} - 2)^2 + (0 - 6)^2} = \sqrt{12 + 36} = 4\sqrt{3}$

Because $d_1 = d_2 = d_3$, the triangle is equilateral.

92. $d_1 = \sqrt{(4 - (-2))^2 + (7 - (-1))^2} = \sqrt{36 + 64} = \sqrt{100} = 10$

$d_2 = \sqrt{(4 - 2)^2 + (7 - (-4))^2} = \sqrt{4 + 121} = \sqrt{125} = 5\sqrt{5}$

$d_3 = \sqrt{(2 - (-2))^2 + (-4 - (-1))^2} = \sqrt{16 + 9} = \sqrt{25} = 5$

$d_1^2 + d_3^2 = 100 + 25 = 125 = d_2^2$

By the Pythagorean Theorem, the triangle is a right triangle.

93. False. It would be sufficient to use the midpoint formula 15 times.

94. True. The side joining $(-8, 4)$ and $(2, 11)$ has length $\sqrt{(-8 - 2)^2 + (4 - 11)^2} = \sqrt{149}$.

The side joining $(2, 11)$ and $(-5, 1)$ has length $\sqrt{(2 + 5)^2 + (11 - 1)^2} = \sqrt{149}$.

95. False. The polygon could be a rhombus. For example, consider the points $(4, 0)$, $(0, 6)$, $(-4, 0)$ and $(0, -6)$.

96. The y-coordinate of a point on the x-axis is 0. The x-coordinate of a point on the y-axis is 0.

97. No, the scales can be different. The scales depend on the magnitude of the coordinates. See Figure P.13.

Appendix B.2 Graphs of Equations

- You should be able to use the point-plotting method of graphing.
- You should be able to find x- and y-intercepts.
  (a) To find the x-intercepts, let $y = 0$ and solve for x.
  (b) To find the y-intercepts, let $x = 0$ and solve for y.
- You should know how to graph an equation with a graphing utility. You should be able to determine an appropriate viewing rectangle.
- You should be able to use the zoom and trace features of a graphing utility.

Vocabulary Check

1. solution point
2. graph
3. intercepts

1. $y = \sqrt{x + 4}$

(a) $(0, 2)$: $2 \stackrel{?}{=} \sqrt{0 + 4}$

$2 = 2$ ✓

Yes, the point *is* on the graph.

(b) $(5, 3)$: $3 \stackrel{?}{=} \sqrt{5 + 4}$

$3 = \sqrt{9}$ ✓

Yes, the point *is* on the graph.

2. $y = x^2 - 3x + 2$

(a) $(2, 0)$: $(2)^2 - 3(2) + 2 \stackrel{?}{=} 0$

$4 - 6 + 2 \stackrel{?}{=} 0$

$0 = 0$

Yes, the point *is* on the graph.

(b) $(-2, 8)$: $(-2)^2 - 3(-2) + 2 \stackrel{?}{=} 8$

$4 + 6 + 2 \stackrel{?}{=} 8$

$12 \neq 8$

No, the point *is not* on the graph.

3. $y = 4 - |x - 2|$

(a) $(1, 5)$: $5 \stackrel{?}{=} 4 - |1 - 2|$

$5 \neq 4 - 1$

No, the point *is not* on the graph.

(b) $(1.2, 3.2)$: $3.2 \stackrel{?}{=} 4 - |1.2 - 2|$

$3.2 \stackrel{?}{=} 4 - |-0.8|$

$3.2 \stackrel{?}{=} 4 - 0.8$

$3.2 \stackrel{?}{=} 3.2$ ✓

Yes, the point *is* on the graph.

4. $2x - y - 3 = 0$

(a) $(1, 2)$: $2(1) - 2 - 3 \stackrel{?}{=} 0$

$-3 \neq 0$

No, the point *is not* on the graph.

(b) $(1, -1)$: $2(1) - (-1) - 3 \stackrel{?}{=} 0$

$0 = 0$

Yes, the point *is* on the graph.

5. $x^2 + y^2 = 20$

(a) $(3, -2)$: $3^2 + (-2)^2 \stackrel{?}{=} 20$

$9 + 4 \stackrel{?}{=} 20$

$13 \neq 20$

No, the point *is not* on the graph.

(b) $(-4, 2)$: $(-4)^2 + 2^2 \stackrel{?}{=} 20$

$16 + 4 \stackrel{?}{=} 20$

$20 = 20$

Yes, the point *is* on the graph.

6. $y = \frac{1}{3}x^3 - 2x^2$

(a) $\left(2, -\frac{16}{3}\right)$: $\frac{1}{3}(2)^3 - 2(2)^2 \stackrel{?}{=} -\frac{16}{3}$

$\frac{1}{3} \cdot 8 - 2 \cdot 4 \stackrel{?}{=} -\frac{16}{3}$

$\frac{8}{3} - 8 \stackrel{?}{=} -\frac{16}{3}$

$\frac{8}{3} - \frac{24}{3} \stackrel{?}{=} -\frac{16}{3}$

$-\frac{16}{3} = -\frac{16}{3}$

Yes, the point is on the graph.

(b) $(-3, 9)$: $\frac{1}{3}(-3)^3 - 2(-3)^2 \stackrel{?}{=} 9$

$\frac{1}{3}(-27) - 2(9) \stackrel{?}{=} 9$

$-9 - 18 \stackrel{?}{=} 9$

$-27 \neq 9$

No, the point is not on the graph.

7. $y = \frac{3}{2}x - 1$

x	-2	0	$\frac{2}{3}$	1	2
y	-4	-1	0	$\frac{1}{2}$	2
Solution point	$(-2, -4)$	$(0, -1)$	$\left(\frac{3}{2}, 0\right)$	$\left(1, \frac{1}{2}\right)$	$(2, 2)$

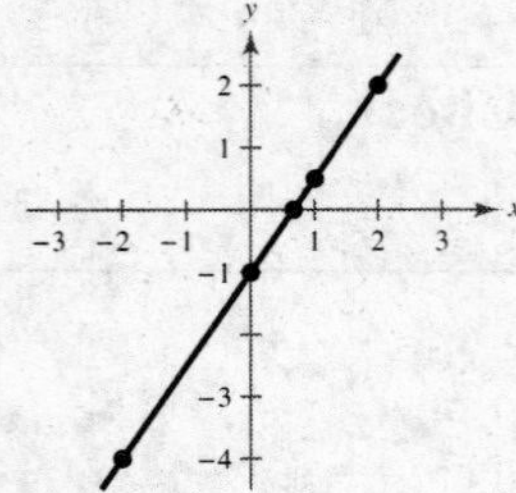

8. $y = x^2 - 2x$

x	-1	0	1	2	3
y	3	0	-1	0	3
Solution point	$(-1, 3)$	$(0, 0)$	$(1, -1)$	$(2, 0)$	$(3, 3)$

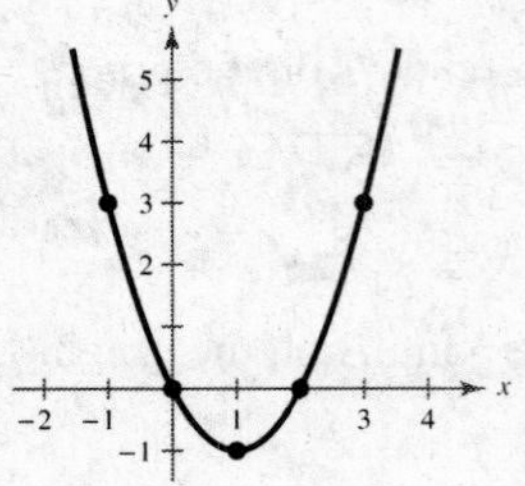

9. (a) $y = \frac{1}{4}x - 3$

x	-2	-1	0	1	2
y	$-\frac{7}{2}$	$-\frac{13}{4}$	-3	$-\frac{11}{4}$	$-\frac{5}{2}$

(b)

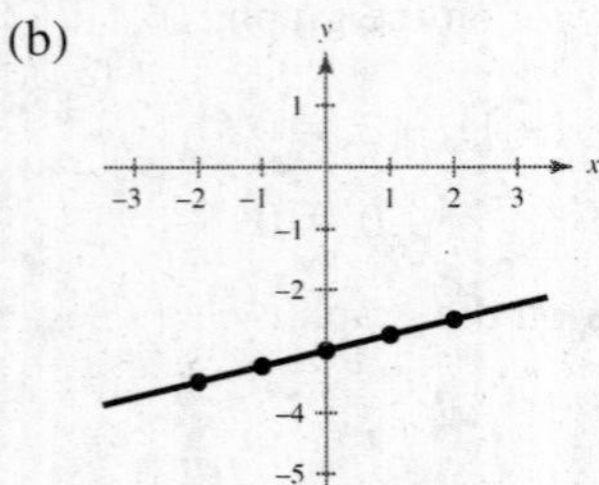

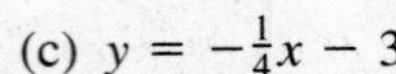

(c) $y = -\frac{1}{4}x - 3$

x	-2	-1	0	1	2
y	$-\frac{5}{2}$	$-\frac{11}{4}$	-3	$-\frac{13}{4}$	$-\frac{7}{2}$

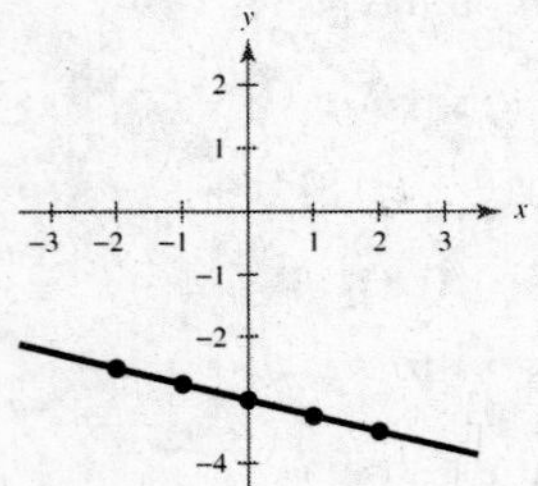

Both graphs are lines. The first graph rises to the right, whereas the second falls. Both pass through $(0, -3)$.

10. (a) $y = \dfrac{6x}{x^2 + 1}$

x	-2	-1	0	1	2
y	-2.4	-3	0	3	2.4

(b)

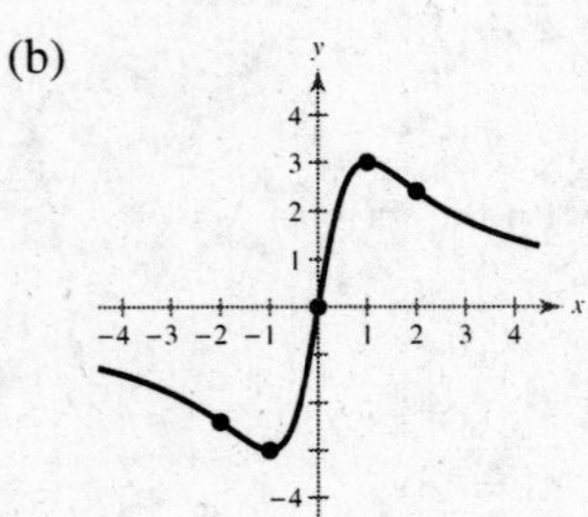

(c)

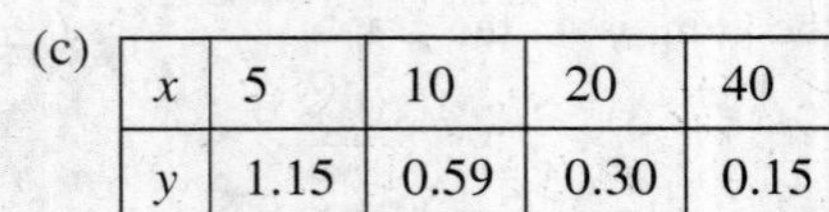

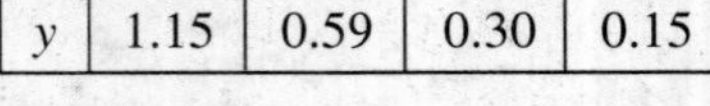

x	5	10	20	40
y	1.15	0.59	0.30	0.15

The y-values are approaching 0.

No, y cannot be negative for positive values of x because $6x > 0$ and $x^2 + 1 > 0$.

11. $y = 2x + 3$ has intercepts $(0, 3)$ and $\left(-\frac{3}{2}, 0\right)$.

Matches graph (e).

12. $y = 4 - x^2$ has intercepts $(0, 4)$, $(2, 0)$ and $(-2, 0)$.

Matches graph (f).

13. $y = x^2 - 2x$ has intercepts $(0, 0)$ and $(2, 0)$.

Matches graph (b).

14. $y = \sqrt{9 - x^2}$ has intercepts $(0, 3)$, $(-3, 0)$ and $(3, 0)$.

Matches graph (d).

15. $y = 2\sqrt{x}$ has one intercept $(0, 0)$.

Matches graph (c).

16. $y = |x| - 3$ has intercepts $(0, -3)$, $(3, 0)$ and $(-3, 0)$.

Matches graph (a).

17. $y = -4x + 1$

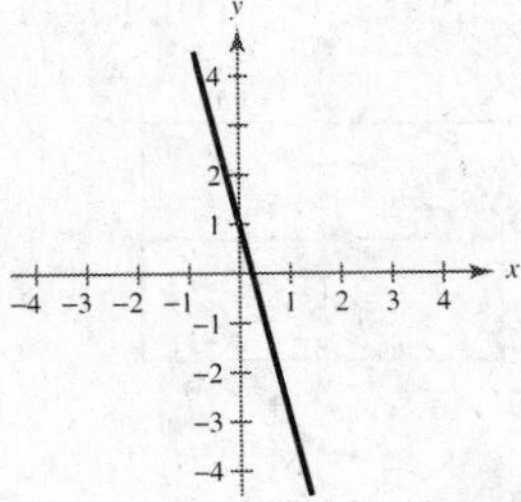

18. $y = 2x - 3$

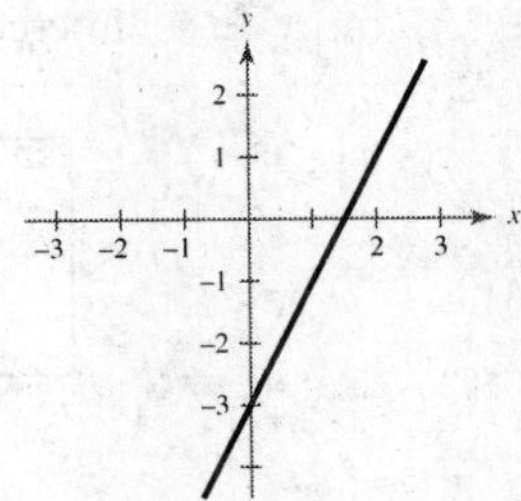

19. $y = 2 - x^2$

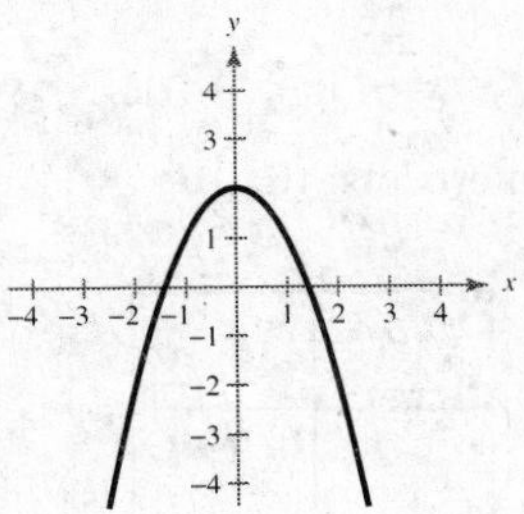

20. $y = x^2 - 1$

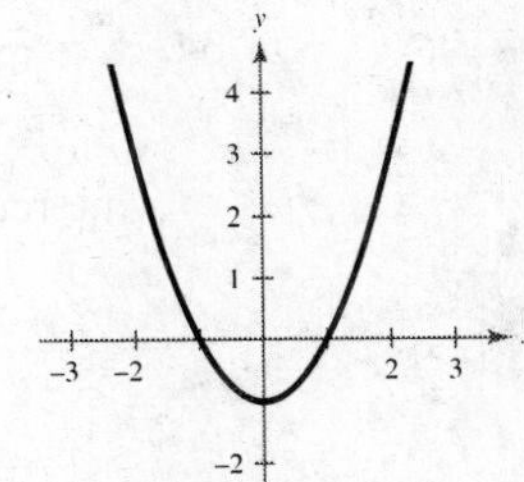

21. $y = x^2 - 3x$

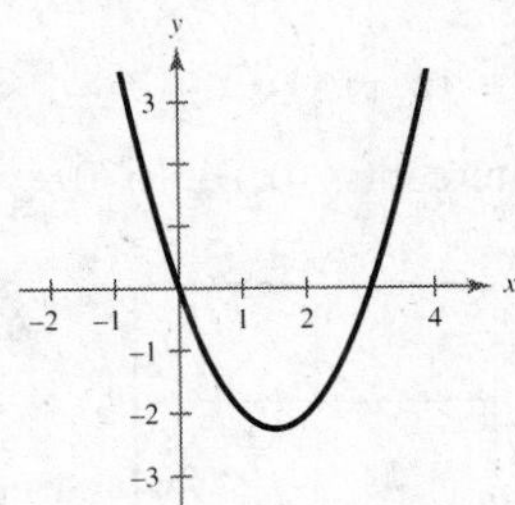

22. $y = -x^2 - 4x$

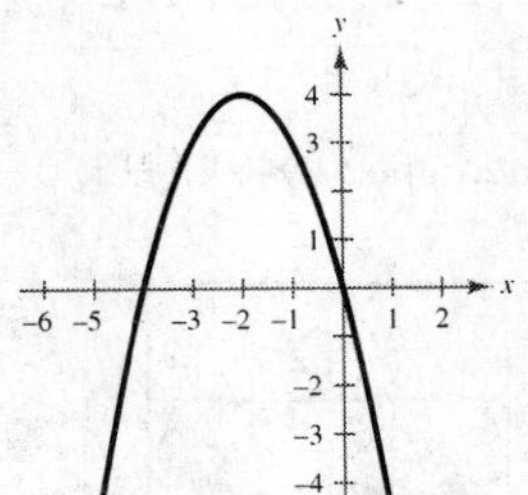

23. $y = x^3 + 2$

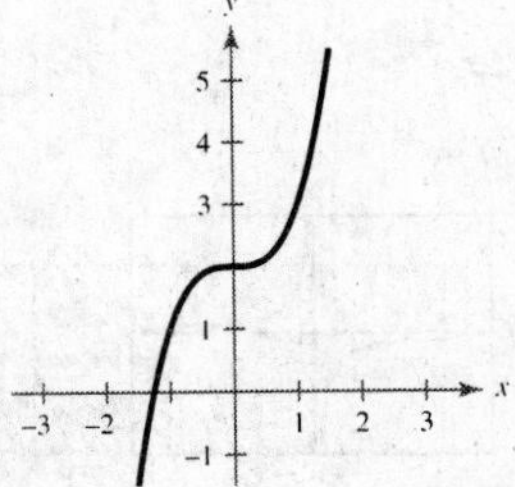

24. $y = x^3 - 3$

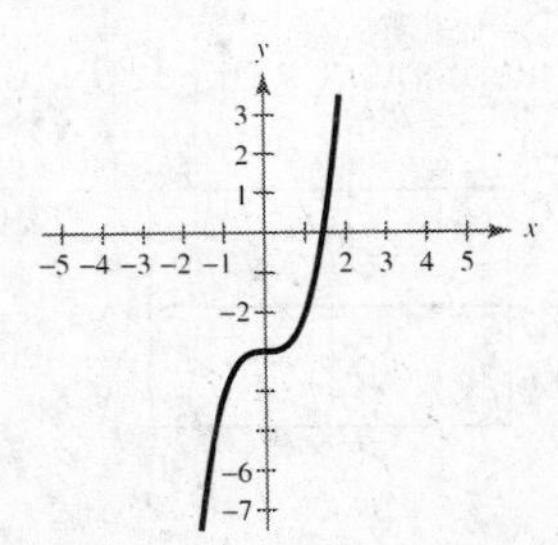

25. $y = \sqrt{x - 3}$

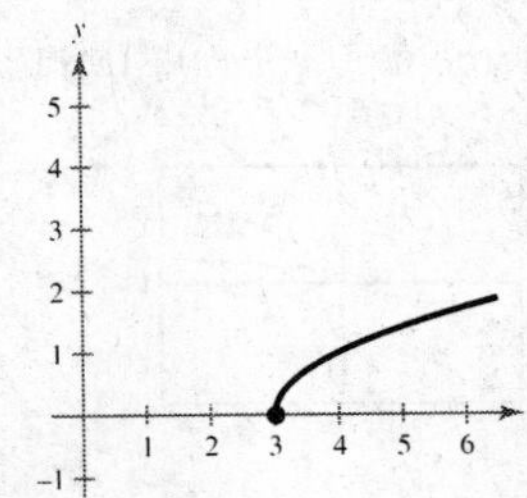

26. $y = \sqrt{1 - x}$

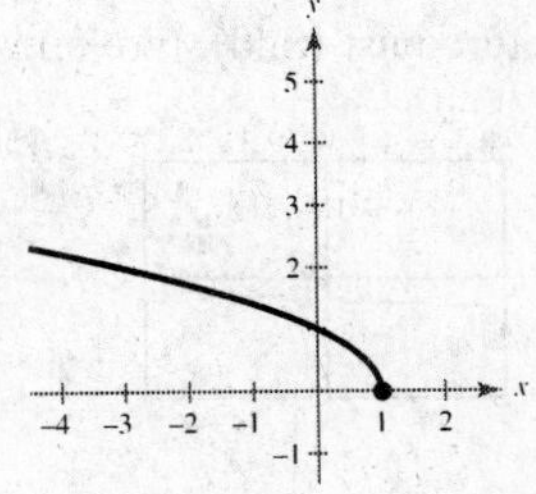

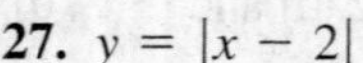

27. $y = |x - 2|$

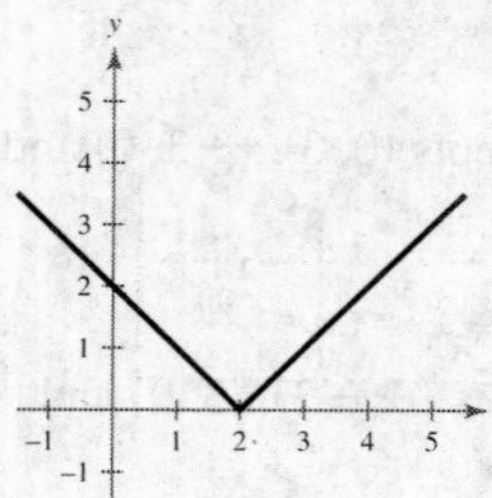

28. $y = 5 - |x|$

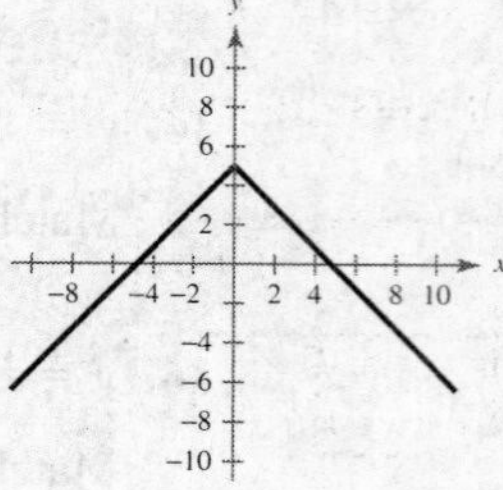

29. $x = y^2 - 1$

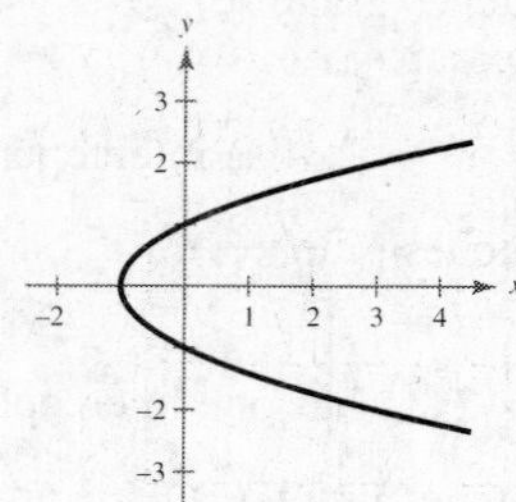

30. $x = y^2 + 4$

Intercept: $(4, 0)$

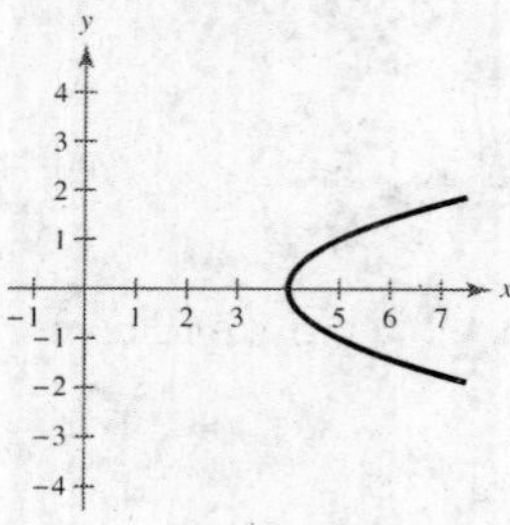

31. $y = x - 7$

Intercepts: $(0, -7), (7, 0)$

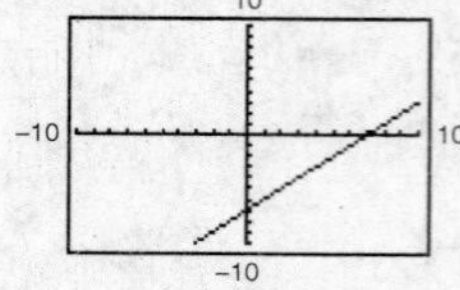

32. $y = x + 1$

Intercepts: $(-1, 0), (0, 1)$

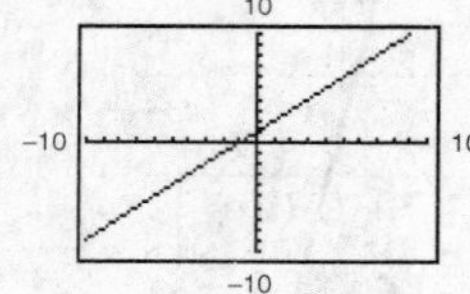

33. $y = 3 - \frac{1}{2}x$

Intercepts: $(6, 0), (0, 3)$

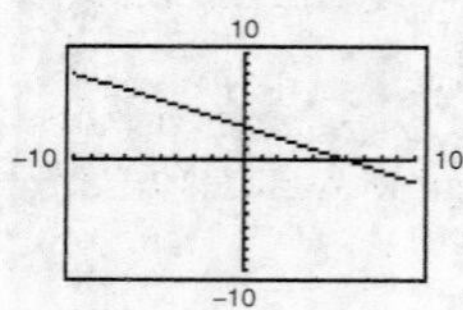

34. $y = \frac{2}{3}x - 1$

Intercepts: $(0, -1), \left(\frac{3}{2}, 0\right)$

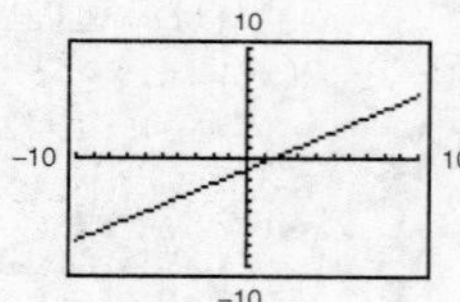

35. $y = \frac{2x}{x - 1}$

Intercepts: $(0, 0)$

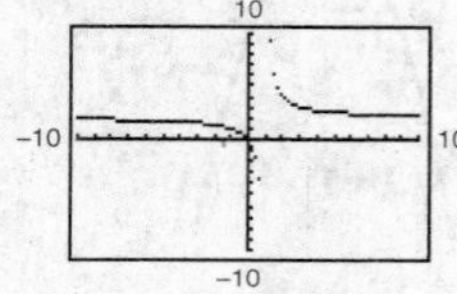

36. $y = \frac{4}{x}$

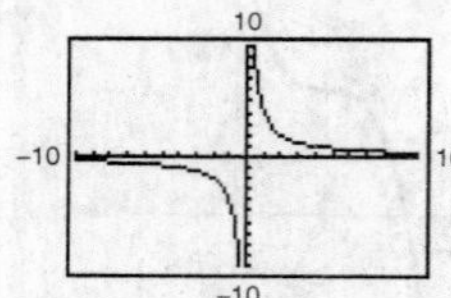

37. $y = x\sqrt{x + 3}$

Intercepts: $(0, 0), (-3, 0)$

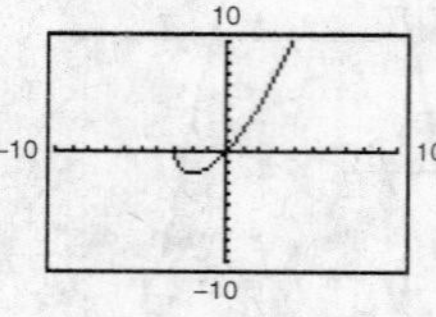

38. $y = (6 - x)\sqrt{x}$

Intercepts: $(0, 0), (6, 0)$

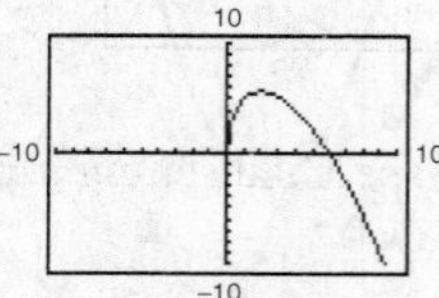

39. $y = \sqrt[3]{x - 8}$

Intercepts: $(8, 0), (0, -2)$

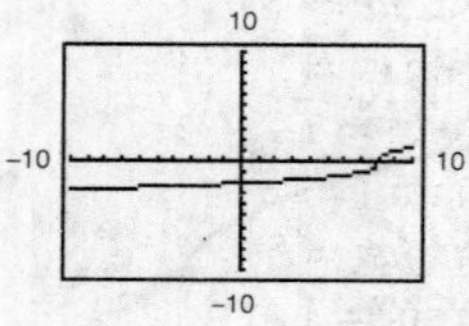

40. $y = \sqrt[3]{x + 1}$

Intercepts: $(-1, 0), (0, 1)$

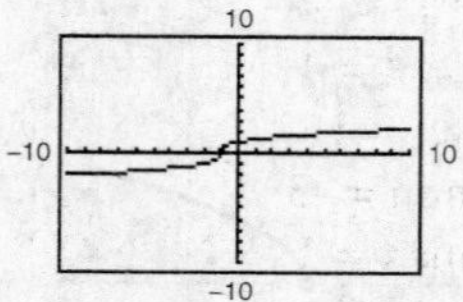

41. $y = x^2 - 4x + 3$

Intercepts: $(3, 0), (1, 0), (0, 3)$

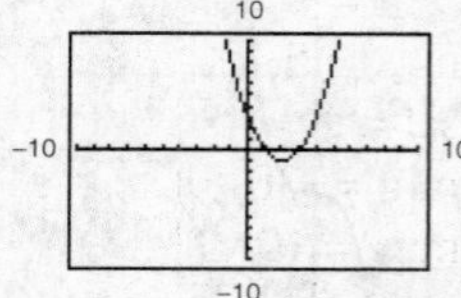

42. $y = \dfrac{x^2 + 2x - 8}{2}$

Intercepts:

$(2, 0), (-4, 0), (0, -4)$

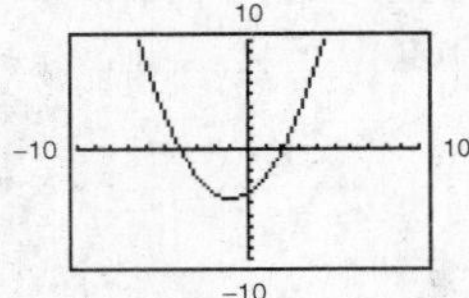

43. $y = x^2(x - 4) + 4x$

$= x^3 - 4x^2 + 4x$

Intercepts: $(0, 0), (2, 0)$

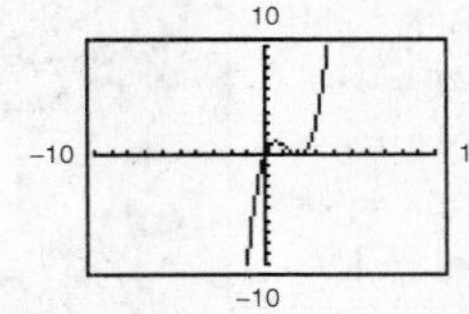

44. $y = 1 - x^3$

Intercepts: $(0, 1), (1, 0)$

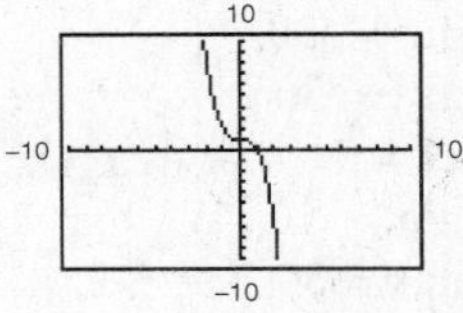

45. $y = \frac{5}{2}x + 5$

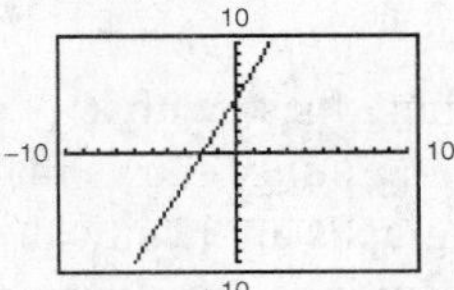

The first setting shows the line and its intercepts. The first setting is better.

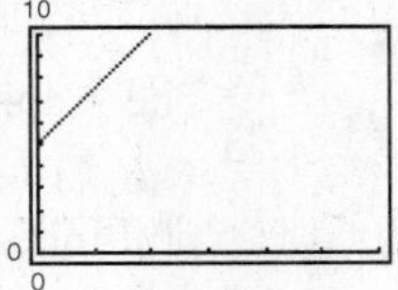

The second setting does not show the x-intercept $(-2, 0)$.

46. $y = -3x + 50$

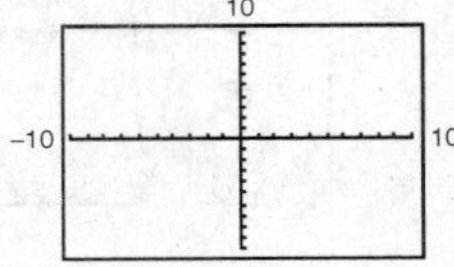

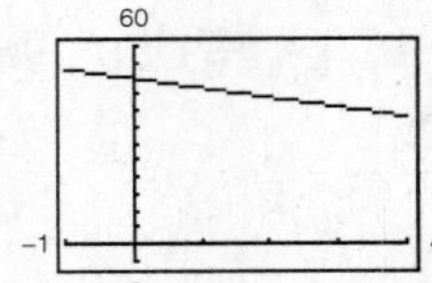

The specified setting gives a more complete graph. (The y-intercept is visible.)

47. $y = -x^2 + 10x - 5$

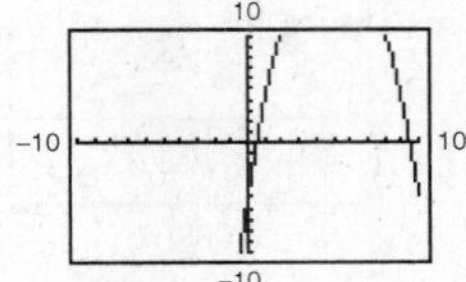

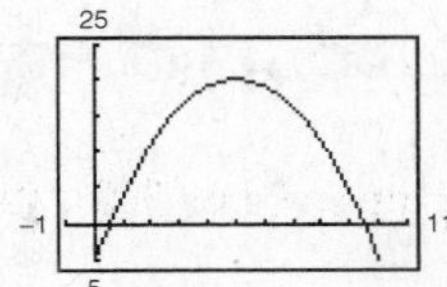

The second viewing window is better because it shows more of the essential features of the function.

48. $y = 4(x + 5)\sqrt{4 - x}$

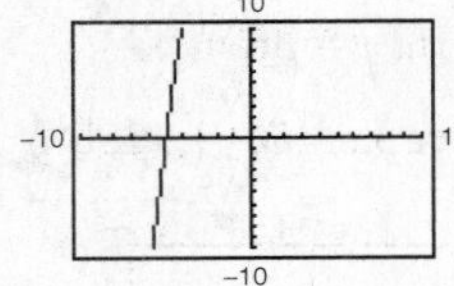

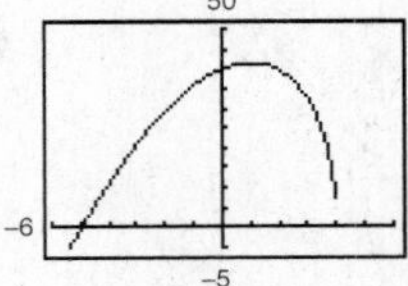

The specified setting gives a more complete graph.

49. $y = -10x + 50$

Range/Window

Xmin = -10
Xmax = 10
Xscl = 2
Ymin = -50
Ymax = 100
Yscl = 25

50. $y = 4x^2 - 25$

Range/Window

Xmin = -5
Xmax = 5
Xscl = 1
Ymin = -30
Ymax = 10
Yscl = 5

51. $y = \sqrt{x + 2} - 1$

Range/Window

Xmin = -5
Xmax = 1
Xscl = 1
Ymin = -3
Ymax = 1
Yscl = 1

52. $y = x^3 - 3x^2 + 4$

Range/Window

Xmin = -3
Xmax = 5
Xscl = 1
Ymin = -3
Ymax = 5
Yscl = 1

53. $y = |x| + |x - 10|$

Range/Window

Xmin = -30
Xmax = 30
Xscl = 5
Ymin = -10
Ymax = 50
Yscl = 5

54. $y = 8\sqrt[3]{x - 6}$

Range/Window

Xmin = -40
Xmax = 40
Xscl = 10
Ymin = -40
Ymax = 40
Yscl = 10

55. $y_1 = \frac{1}{4}(x^2 - 8)$

$y_2 = \frac{1}{4}x^2 - 2$

The graphs are identical.

The Distributive Property is illustrated.

56. $y_1 = \frac{1}{2}x + (x + 1)$

$y_2 = \frac{3}{2}x + 1$

Graphing these with a graphing utility shows that their graphs are identical. The Associative Property of Addition is illustrated.

57. $y_1 = \frac{1}{5}[10(x^2 - 1)]$

$y_2 = 2(x^2 - 1)$

The graphs are identical.

The Associative Property of Multiplication is illustrated.

58. $y_1 = (x - 3) \cdot \frac{1}{x - 3}$

$y_2 = 1$

Graphing these with a graphing utility shows that their graphs are identical. The Multiplicative Inverse Property is illustrated (except for hole at $x = 3$ for y_1).

59. $y = \sqrt{5 - x}$

(a) $(2, y) \approx (2, 1.73)$

(b) $(x, 3) = (-4, 3)$

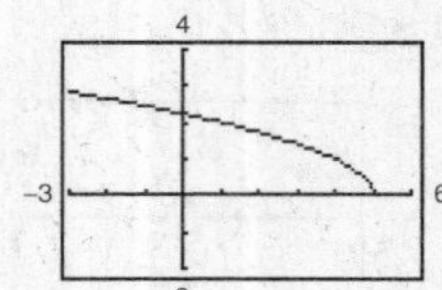

60. (a) $(2.25, -8.54)$

(b) $(-1.63, 20), (3.48, 20)$

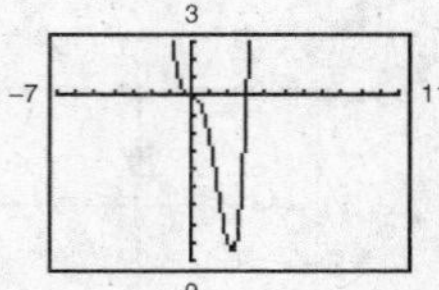

61. $y = x^5 - 5x$

(a) $(-0.5, y) \approx (-0.5, 2.47)$

(b) $(x, -4) = (1, -4)$ or $(x, -4) \approx (-1.65, -4)$

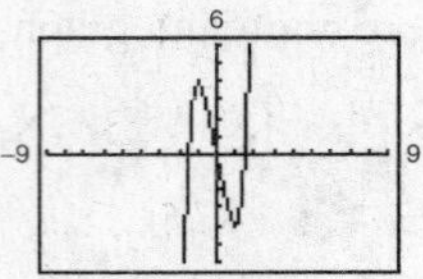

62.

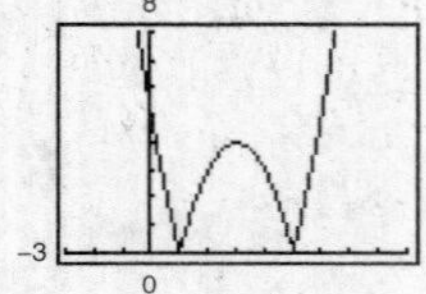

(a) $(2, 3)$

(b) $(0.65, 1.5), (1.42, 1.5)$

$(4.58, 1.5), (5.35, 1.5)$

63. $x^2 + y^2 = 16$

$y^2 = 16 - x^2$

$y = \pm\sqrt{16 - x^2}$

Use $y_1 = \sqrt{16 - x^2}$

$y_2 = -\sqrt{16 - x^2}$

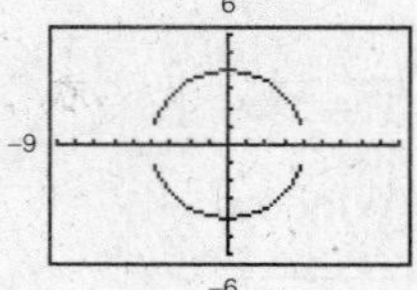

64. $x^2 + y^2 = 36$

$y^2 = 36 - x^2$

$y = \pm\sqrt{36 - x^2}$

Use $y_1 = \sqrt{36 - x^2}$

$y_2 = -\sqrt{36 - x^2}$

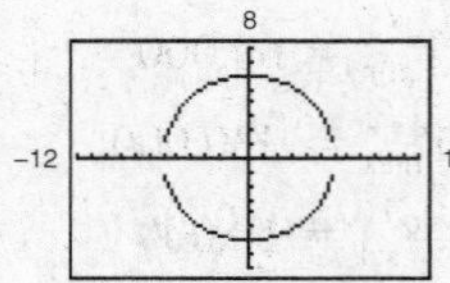

65. $(x - 1)^2 + (y - 2)^2 = 4$

$$(y - 2)^2 = 4 - (x - 1)^2$$

$$y - 2 = \pm\sqrt{4 - (x - 1)^2}$$

$$y = 2 \pm \sqrt{4 - (x - 1)^2}$$

Use $y_1 = 2 + \sqrt{4 - (x - 1)^2}$

$y_2 = 2 - \sqrt{4 - (x - 1)^2}$

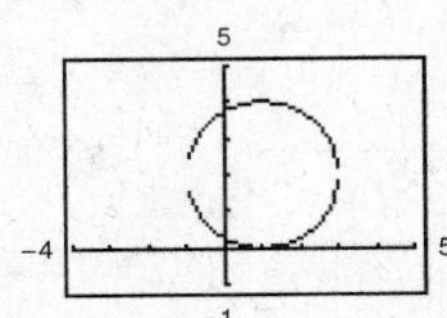

66.
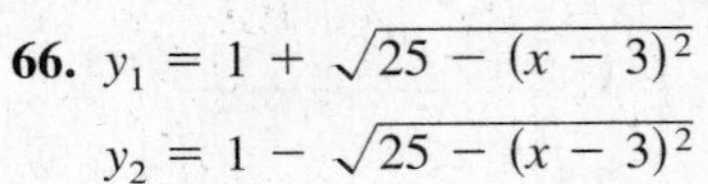
$y_1 = 1 + \sqrt{25 - (x - 3)^2}$

$y_2 = 1 - \sqrt{25 - (x - 3)^2}$

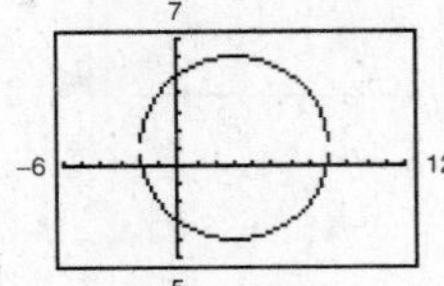

67. The center is in the first quadrant and the circle is tangent to the x-axis.
Matches (a).

68. The center is in the second quadrant and the circle intercepts the axes.
Matches (c).

69. $(x - 1)^2 + (y - 2)^2 = 25$

(a) $(1 - 1)^2 + (2 - 2)^2 = 0 \neq 25$ No

(b) $(-2 - 1)^2 + (6 - 2)^2 = 9 + 16 = 25$ Yes

(c) $(5 - 1)^2 + (-1 - 2)^2 = 16 + 9 = 25$ Yes

(d) $(0 - 1)^2 + (2 + 2\sqrt{6} - 2)^2 = 1 + 24 = 25$ Yes

70. $(x + 2)^2 + (y - 3)^2 = 25$

(a) $(-2 + 2)^2 + (3 - 3)^2 = 0 \neq 25$ No

(b) $(0 + 2)^2 + (0 - 3)^2 = 4 + 9 = 13 \neq 25$ No

(c) $(1 + 2)^2 + (-1 - 3)^2 = 9 + 16 = 25$ Yes

(d) $(-1 + 2)^2 + (3 - 2\sqrt{6} - 3)^2 = 1 + 24 = 25$ Yes

71. (a) $y = 225{,}000 - 20{,}000t$, $0 \le t \le 8$

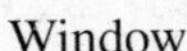

Window

$X_{min} = 0$

$X_{max} = 8$

$X_{scl} = 1$

$Y_{min} = 60{,}000$

$Y_{max} = 230{,}000$

$Y_{scl} = 10{,}000$

230,000
0
8
60,000

(b) When $t = 5.8$, $y = 109{,}000$. Algebraically, $225{,}000 - 20{,}000(5.8) = \$109{,}000$.

(c) When $t = 2.35$, $y = 178{,}000$. Algebraically, $225{,}000 - 20{,}000(2.35) = \$178{,}000$.

72. (a)

Xmin = 0
Xmax = 6
Xscl = 1
Ymin = 2500
Ymax = 8500
Yscl = 500

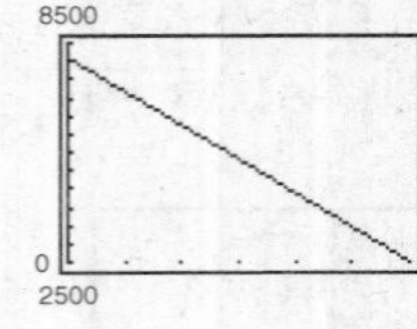

(b) For $y = 5545.25$, $t = 2.75$. Algebraically,

$$8100 - 929t = 5545.25$$
$$2554.75 = 929t$$
$$t = 2.75 \text{ years.}$$

(c) For $t = 5.5$, $y = 2990.5$. Algebraically, $y = 8100 - 929(5.5) = \$2990.5$.

73. (a) Model: $y = -0.0049t^3 + 0.443t^2 - 0.75t + 116.7, \quad 5 \le t \le 14$

t	5	6	7	8	9	10	11	12	13	14
Model	123.4	127.1	131.5	136.5	142.3	148.6	155.5	163.0	171.1	179.6

The model is a good fit.

(b)

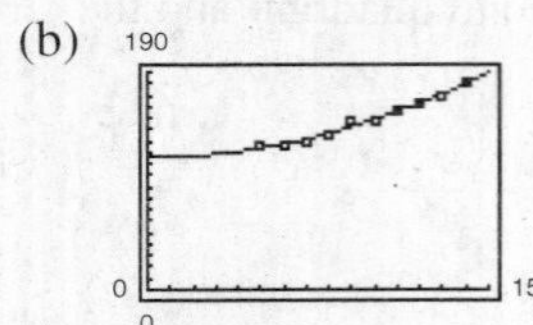

The model is a good fit.

(c) For 2008, $t = 18$ and $y \approx 218.2$ thousand dollars. For 2010, $t = 20$ and $y \approx 239.7$ thousand dollars. These values seem reasonable.

(d) For $y = 150$, $t \approx 10.2$, or 2000.

74. (a)

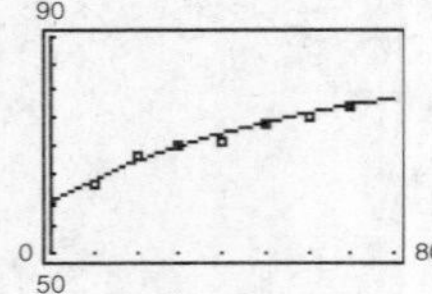

The model is a good fit.

(b) The y-intercept represents the life expectancy for the year 1930.

(c) $y = 73.2$ for $t \approx 45$, or 1975

(d) For 1948, $t = 18$ and $y \approx 66.5$ years.

$$\text{Algebraically, } y = \frac{59.617 + 1.18(18)}{1 + 0.012(18)}$$
$$= \frac{80.857}{1.216} \approx 66.5$$

(e) For 2010, $t = 80$ and $y \approx 78.6$ years.

75. (a)

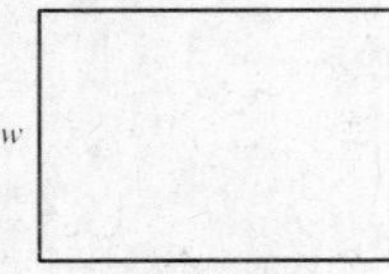

(b) Perimeter: $12 = 2x + 2w$

$$12 = 2(x + w)$$
$$6 = x + w$$

Thus, $w = 6 - x$.

Area: $xw = x(6 - x) \Rightarrow A = x(6 - x)$

(c)

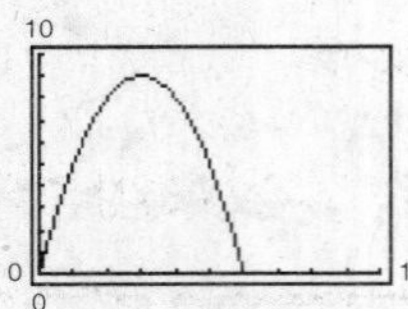

(d) When $w = 4.9$, $x = 1.1$ and Area $= 5.39$ square meters.

Algebraically,
Area $= xw = (1.1)(4.9) = 5.39$ square meters.

(e) The maximum area corresponds to the highest point on the graph, which appears to be $(3, 9)$. Thus, $x = 3$ and $w = 3$, and the rectangle is a square.

76. Center $= \left(\frac{0+4}{2}, \frac{0-6}{2}\right) = (2, -3)$

Radius $= \frac{1}{2}\sqrt{(0-4)^2 + (0+6)^2}$

$= \frac{1}{2}\sqrt{16+36} = \frac{1}{2}\sqrt{52} = \sqrt{13}$

Circle: $(x-2)^2 + (y+3)^2 = 13$

77. False. $y = 1 - x^2$ has two x-intercepts, $(1, 0)$ and $(-1, 0)$. Also, $y = x^2 + 1$ has no x-intercepts.

78. False. The line $y = 0$ has an infinite number of x-intercepts.

79. Answers will vary.

80. Option 1: $w_1 = 3000 + 0.07x$

Option 2: $w_2 = 3400 + 0.05x$

(x is amount of sales)

$w_1 = w_2$

$3000 + 0.07x = 3400 + 0.05x$

$0.02x = 400$

$x = 20{,}000$

If sales equal 20,000, the options are equivalent. For sales less than 20,000, choose option 2. For sales greater than 20,000, choose option 1.

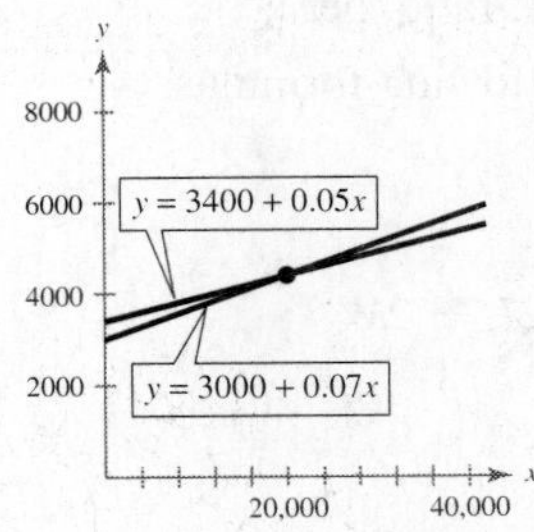

81. Answers will vary. Sample answer: $y = 250x + 1000$ could represent the amount of money in someone's checking account after x months if they deposited an initial \$1000 and added \$250 per month.

82. Answers will vary. Sample answer: The equation could represent the amount of points for turning in a 10 point assignment x days late.

Appendix B.3 Solving Equations Algebraically and Graphically

- You should know how to solve linear equations: $ax + b = 0$.
- An identity is an equation whose solution consists of every real number in its domain.
- To solve an equation you can:
  (a) Add or subtract the same quantity from both sides.
  (b) Multiply or divide both sides by the same nonzero quantity.
- To solve an equation that can be simplified to a linear equation:
  (a) Remove all symbols of grouping and all fractions. (b) Combine like terms.
  (c) Solve by algebra. (d) Check the answer.
- A "solution" that does not satisfy the original equation is called an extraneous solution.
- You should be able to set up mathematical models to solve problems.

—CONTINUED—

Appendix B.3 —CONTINUED—

- You should be able to translate key words and phrases.
  - (a) Equality:
    Equals, equal to, is, are, was, will be, represents
  - (b) Addition:
    Sum, plus, greater, increased by, more than, exceeds, total of
  - (c) Subtraction:
    Difference, minus, less than, decreased by, subtracted from, reduced by, the remainder
  - (d) Multiplication:
    Product, multiplied by, twice, times, percent of
  - (e) Division:
    Quotient, divided by, ratio, per
  - (f) Consecutive:
    Next, subsequent
- You should know the following formulas:
  - (a) Perimeter:
    1. Square: $P = 4s$
    2. Rectangle: $P = 2L + 2W$
    3. Circle: $C = 2\pi r$
  - (b) Area:
    1. Square: $A = s^2$
    2. Rectangle: $A = LW$
    3. Circle: $A = \pi r^2$
    4. Triangle: $A = \left(\frac{1}{2}\right)bh$
  - (c) Volume
    1. Cube: $V = s^3$
    2. Rectangular solid: $V = LWH$
    3. Cylinder: $V = \pi r^2 h$
    4. Sphere: $V = \left(\frac{4}{3}\right)\pi r^3$
  - (d) Simple Interest: $I = Prt$
  - (e) Compound Interest: $A = P\left(1 + \frac{r}{n}\right)^{nt}$
  - (f) Distance: $D = r \cdot t$
  - (g) Temperature: $F = \frac{9}{5}C + 32$
- You should be able to solve word problems. Study the examples in the text carefully.

1. $\frac{5}{2x} - \frac{4}{x} = 3$

(a) $\frac{5}{2(-1/2)} - \frac{4}{(-1/2)} \stackrel{?}{=} 3$

$3 = 3$

$x = -\frac{1}{2}$ *is* a solution.

(b) $\frac{5}{2(4)} - \frac{4}{4} \stackrel{?}{=} 3$

$-\frac{3}{8} \neq 3$

$x = 4$ *is not* a solution.

(c) $\frac{5}{2(0)} - \frac{4}{0}$ is undefined.

$x = 0$ *is not* a solution.

(d) $\frac{5}{2(1/4)} - \frac{4}{1/4} \stackrel{?}{=} 3$

$-6 \neq 3$

$x = \frac{1}{4}$ *is not* a solution.

2. $\dfrac{x}{2} + \dfrac{6x}{7} = \dfrac{19}{14}$

(a) $x = -2$

$$\frac{-2}{2} + \frac{6(-2)}{7} \stackrel{?}{=} \frac{19}{14}$$

$$\frac{-14 - 24}{14} \stackrel{?}{=} \frac{19}{14}$$

$$\frac{-38}{14} \stackrel{?}{=} \frac{19}{14}$$

$x = -2$ is not a solution.

(b) $x = 1$

$$\frac{1}{2} + \frac{6(1)}{7} \stackrel{?}{=} \frac{19}{14}$$

$$\frac{19}{14} = \frac{19}{14}$$

$x = 1$ is a solution.

(c) $x = \dfrac{1}{2}$

$$\frac{1/2}{2} + \frac{6(1/2)}{7} \stackrel{?}{=} \frac{19}{14}$$

$$\frac{(7/2) + 6}{14} \stackrel{?}{=} \frac{19}{14}$$

$$\frac{19}{28} \neq \frac{19}{14}$$

$x = \frac{1}{2}$ is not a solution.

(d) $x = 7$

$$\frac{7}{2} + \frac{6(7)}{7} = \frac{19}{14}$$

$$\frac{7}{2} + 6 = \frac{19}{14}$$

$$\frac{19}{2} \stackrel{?}{=} \frac{19}{14}$$

$x = 7$ is not a solution.

3. $3 + \dfrac{1}{x + 2} = 4$

(a) $3 + \dfrac{1}{(-1) + 2} \stackrel{?}{=} 4$

$$4 = 4$$

$x = -1$ *is* a solution.

(b) $3 + \dfrac{1}{(-2) + 2} = 3 + \dfrac{1}{0}$ is undefined.

$x = -2$ *is not* a solution.

(c) $3 + \dfrac{1}{0 + 2} \stackrel{?}{=} 4$

$$\frac{7}{2} \neq 4$$

$x = 0$ *is not* a solution.

(d) $3 + \dfrac{1}{5 + 2} \stackrel{?}{=} 4$

$$\frac{22}{7} = 4$$

$x = 5$ *is not* a solution.

4. $\dfrac{(x+5)(x-3)}{2} = 24$

(a) $x = -3$

$$\frac{(-3+5)(-3-3)}{2} \stackrel{?}{=} 24$$

$$\frac{-12}{2} \stackrel{?}{=} 24$$

$$-6 \neq 24$$

$x = -3$ is not a solution.

(b) $x = -2$

$$\frac{(-2+5)(-2-3)}{2} \stackrel{?}{=} 24$$

$$\frac{-15}{2} \neq 24$$

$x = -2$ is not a solution.

(c) $x = 7$

$$\frac{(7+5)(7-3)}{2} \stackrel{?}{=} 24$$

$$24 = 24$$

$x = 7$ is a solution.

(d) $x = 9$

$$\frac{(9+5)(9-3)}{2} \stackrel{?}{=} 24$$

$$42 \neq 24$$

$x = 9$ is not a solution.

5. $\dfrac{\sqrt{x+4}}{6} + 3 = 4$

(a) $\dfrac{\sqrt{-3+4}}{6} + 3 \stackrel{?}{=} 4$

$$\frac{19}{6} \neq 4$$

$x = -3$ *is not* a solution.

(b) $\dfrac{\sqrt{0+4}}{6} + 3 \stackrel{?}{=} 4$

$$\frac{10}{3} \neq 4$$

$x = 0$ *is not* a solution.

(c) $\dfrac{\sqrt{21+4}}{6} + 3 \stackrel{?}{=} 4$

$$\frac{23}{6} \neq 4$$

$x = 21$ *is not* a solution.

(d) $\dfrac{\sqrt{32+4}}{6} + 3 \stackrel{?}{=} 4$

$$4 = 4$$

$x = 32$ *is* a solution.

6. $\dfrac{\sqrt[3]{x-8}}{3} = -\dfrac{2}{3}$

(a) $x = -16$

$$\frac{\sqrt[3]{-16-8}}{3} \stackrel{?}{=} -\frac{2}{3}$$

$$\sqrt[3]{-24} \neq -2$$

$x = -16$ is not a solution.

(b) $x = 0$

$$\frac{\sqrt[3]{0-8}}{3} \stackrel{?}{=} -\frac{2}{3}$$

$$-2 = -2$$

$x = 0$ is a solution.

(c) $x = 9$

$$\frac{\sqrt[3]{9-8}}{3} \stackrel{?}{=} -\frac{2}{3}$$

$$1 \neq -2$$

$x = 9$ is not a solution.

(d) $x = 16$

$$\frac{\sqrt[3]{16-8}}{3} \stackrel{?}{=} -\frac{2}{3}$$

$$2 \neq -2$$

$x = 16$ is not a solution.

7. $2(x - 1) = 2x - 2$ is an *identity* by the Distributive Property. It is true for all real values of x.

8. $-7(x - 3) + 4x = 3(7 - x)$ is an *identity* by simplification. It is true for all real values of x.

$$\begin{aligned} -7(x - 3) + 4x &= -7x + 21 + 4x \\ &= 21 - 3x \\ &= 3(7 - x) \end{aligned}$$

9. $x^2 - 8x + 5 = (x - 4)^2 - 11$ is an *identity* since

$$\begin{aligned} (x - 4)^2 - 11 &= x^2 - 8x + 16 - 11 \\ &= x^2 - 8x + 5. \end{aligned}$$

10. $x^2 + 2(3x - 2) = x^2 + 6x - 4$ is an *identity* by simplification. It is true for all real values of x.

11. $3 + \frac{1}{x + 1} = \frac{4x}{x + 1}$ is *conditional*. There are real values of x for which the equation is not true.

12. $\frac{5}{x} + \frac{3}{x} = 24$ is *conditional*. There are real values of x for which the equation is not true (for example, $x = 1$).

13. *Method 1:*

$$\begin{aligned} \frac{3x}{8} - \frac{4x}{3} &= 4 \\ \frac{9x - 32x}{24} &= 4 \\ -23x &= 96 \\ x &= -\frac{96}{23} \end{aligned}$$

Method 2: Graph $y_1 = \frac{3x}{8} - \frac{4x}{3}$ and $y_2 = 4$ in the same viewing window. These lines intersect at

$$x \approx -4.1739 \approx -\frac{96}{23}.$$

14. *Method 1:*

$$\begin{aligned} \frac{3z}{8} - \frac{z}{10} &= 6 \\ z\left(\frac{3}{8} - \frac{1}{10}\right) &= 6 \\ z\left(\frac{22}{80}\right) &= 6 \\ z = \frac{6(80)}{22} &= \frac{240}{11} \approx 21.8182 \end{aligned}$$

Method 2: Graph $y_1 = \frac{3x}{8} - \frac{x}{10}$ and $y_2 = 6$ in the same viewing window. These lines intersect at

$$x \approx 21.8182 \approx \frac{240}{11}.$$

15. *Method 1:*

$$\begin{aligned} \frac{2x}{5} + 5x &= \frac{4}{3} \\ \frac{2x + 25x}{5} &= \frac{4}{3} \\ 27x &= \frac{20}{3} \\ x = \frac{20}{3(27)} &= \frac{20}{81} \end{aligned}$$

Method 2: Graph $y_1 = \frac{2x}{5} + 5x$ and $y_2 = \frac{4}{3}$ in the same viewing window. These lines intersect at $x \approx 0.2469 \approx \frac{20}{81}$.

16. *Method 1:*

$$\begin{aligned} \frac{4y}{3} - 2y &= \frac{16}{5} \\ \frac{4y - 6y}{3} &= \frac{16}{5} \\ -2y &= \frac{48}{5} \\ y &= \frac{-24}{5} \end{aligned}$$

Method 2: Graph $y_1 = \frac{4x}{3} - 2x$ and $y_2 = \frac{16}{5}$ in the same viewing window. These lines intersect at $x = -4.8 = \frac{-24}{5}$.

17. $3x - 5 = 2x + 7$

$3x - 2x = 7 + 5$

$x = 12$

18. $5x + 3 = 6 - 2x$

$5x + 2x = 6 - 3$

$7x = 3$

$x = \frac{3}{7}$

19. $4y + 2 - 5y = 7 - 6y$

$-y + 2 = 7 - 6y$

$6y - y = 7 - 2$

$5y = 5$

$y = 1$

20. $5y + 1 = 8y - 5 + 6y$

$5y + 1 = 14y - 5$

$6 = 9y$

$y = \frac{2}{3}$

21. $3(y - 5) = 3 + 5y$

$3y - 15 = 3 + 5y$

$-18 = 2y$

$y = -9$

22. $5(z - 4) + 4z = 5 - 6z$

$5z - 20 + 4z = 5 - 6z$

$9z - 20 = 5 - 6z$

$15z = 25$

$z = \frac{25}{15} = \frac{5}{3}$

23. $\frac{x}{5} - \frac{x}{2} = 3$

$\frac{2x - 5x}{10} = 3$

$-3x = 30$

$x = -10$

24. $\frac{5x}{4} + \frac{1}{2} = x - \frac{1}{2}$

$\frac{5x}{4} - x = -\frac{1}{2} - \frac{1}{2}$

$\frac{1}{4}x = -1$

$x = -4$

25. $\frac{3}{2}(z + 5) - \frac{1}{4}(z + 24) = 0$

$4\left(\frac{3}{2}\right)(z + 5) - 4\left(\frac{1}{4}\right)(z + 24) = 4(0)$

$6(z + 5) - (z + 24) = 0$

$6z + 30 - z - 24 = 0$

$5z = -6$

$z = -\frac{6}{5}$

26. $\frac{3x}{2} + \frac{1}{4}(x - 2) = 10$

$(4)\left(\frac{3x}{2}\right) + (4)\frac{1}{4}(x - 2) = (4)10$

$6x + (x - 2) = 40$

$7x - 2 = 40$

$7x = 42$

$x = 6$

27. $\frac{2(z - 4)}{5} + 5 = 10z$

$\frac{(2z - 8) + 25}{5} = 10z$

$2z + 17 = 50z$

$17 = 48z$

$z = \frac{17}{48}$

28. $\frac{5}{3} + 2(y + 1) = \frac{10}{3}$

$5 + 6(y + 1) = 10$

$6y + 6 = 5$

$6y = -1$

$y = -\frac{1}{6}$

29. $$\frac{100 - 4u}{3} = \frac{5u + 6}{4} + 6$$

$$12\left(\frac{100 - 4u}{3}\right) = 12\left(\frac{5u + 6}{4}\right) + 12(6)$$

$$4(100 - 4u) = 3(5u + 6) + 72$$

$$400 - 16u = 15u + 18 + 72$$

$$-31u = -310$$

$$u = 10$$

30. $$\frac{17 + y}{y} + \frac{32 + y}{y} = 100$$

$$(y)\frac{17 + y}{y} + (y)\frac{32 + y}{y} = 100(y)$$

$$17 + y + 32 + y = 100y$$

$$49 + 2y = 100y$$

$$49 = 98y$$

$$\frac{1}{2} = y$$

31. $$\frac{5x - 4}{5x + 4} = \frac{2}{3}$$

$$3(5x - 4) = 2(5x + 4)$$

$$15x - 12 = 10x + 8$$

$$5x = 20$$

$$x = 4$$

32. $$\frac{10x + 3}{5x + 6} = \frac{1}{2}$$

$$20x + 6 = 5x + 6$$

$$15x = 0$$

$$x = 0$$

33. $$\frac{1}{x - 3} + \frac{1}{x + 3} = \frac{10}{x^2 - 9}$$

$$\frac{(x + 3) + (x - 3)}{x^2 - 9} = \frac{10}{x^2 - 9}$$

$$2x = 10$$

$$x = 5$$

34. $$\frac{1}{x - 2} + \frac{3}{x + 3} = \frac{4}{x^2 + x - 6}$$

$$(x^2 + x - 6)\frac{1}{x - 2} + (x^2 + x - 6)\frac{3}{x + 3} = (x^2 + x - 6)\frac{4}{x^2 + x - 6}$$

$$(x + 3) + 3(x - 2) = 4$$

$$x + 3 + 3x - 6 = 4$$

$$4x - 3 = 4$$

$$4x = 7$$

$$x = \frac{7}{4}$$

35. $$\frac{7}{2x + 1} - \frac{8x}{2x - 1} = -4$$

$$7(2x - 1) - 8x(2x + 1) = -4(2x + 1)(2x - 1)$$

$$14x - 7 - 16x^2 - 8x = -16x^2 + 4$$

$$6x = 11$$

$$x = \frac{11}{6}$$

36. $$\frac{x}{x + 4} + \frac{4}{x + 4} + 2 = 0$$

$$\frac{x + 4}{x + 4} + 2 = 0$$

$$1 + 2 = 0$$

Impossible

No solution

37. $\dfrac{1}{x} + \dfrac{2}{x-5} = 0$

$1(x-5) + 2x = 0$

$3x - 5 = 0$

$3x = 5$

$x = \dfrac{5}{3}$

38. $3 = 2 + \dfrac{2}{z+2}$

$1 = \dfrac{2}{z+2}$

$z + 2 = 2$

$z = 0$

39. $\dfrac{3}{x(x-3)} + \dfrac{4}{x} = \dfrac{1}{x-3}$

$3 + 4(x-3) = x$

$3 + 4x - 12 = x$

$3x = 9$

$x = 3$

A check reveals that $x = 3$ is an extraneous solution, so there is no solution.

40. $\dfrac{6}{x} - \dfrac{2}{x+3} = \dfrac{3(x+5)}{x(x+3)}$

$x(x+3)\dfrac{6}{x} - x(x+3)\dfrac{2}{x+3} = x(x+3)\dfrac{3(x+5)}{x(x+3)}$

$6(x+3) - 2x = 3(x+5)$

$6x + 18 - 2x = 3x + 15$

$4x + 18 = 3x + 15$

$x = -3$

Check: $\dfrac{6}{-3} - \dfrac{2}{-3+3} = \dfrac{3(-3+5)}{-3(-3+3)}$

$-2 - \dfrac{2}{0} = \dfrac{6}{-3(0)}$

Division by zero is undefined. Thus, $x = -3$ is not a solution, and the original equation has no solution.

41. $y = x - 5$

Let $y = 0$: $0 = x - 5 \Rightarrow x = 5 \Rightarrow (5, 0)$ x-intercept

Let $x = 0$: $y = 0 - 5 \Rightarrow y = -5 \Rightarrow (0, -5)$ y-intercept

42. $y = -\frac{3}{4}x - 3$

Let $y = 0$: $0 = -\frac{3}{4}x - 3 \Rightarrow \frac{3}{4}x = -3 \Rightarrow x = -4 \Rightarrow (-4, 0)$ x-intercept

Let $x = 0$: $y = -\frac{3}{4}(0) - 3 = -3 \Rightarrow (0, -3)$ y-intercept

43. $y = x^2 + x - 2$

Let $y = 0$: $(x^2 + x - 2) = (x+2)(x-1) = 0 \Rightarrow x = -2, 1 \Rightarrow (-2, 0), (1, 0)$ x-intercepts

Let $x = 0$: $y = 0^2 + 0 - 2 = -2 \Rightarrow (0, -2)$ y-intercept

44. $y = 4 - x^2$

Let $y = 0$: $0 = 4 - x^2 \Rightarrow x = 2, -2 \Rightarrow (2, 0), (-2, 0)$ x-intercepts

Let $x = 0$: $y = 4 - 0^2 = 4 \Rightarrow (0, 4)$ y-intercept

45. $y = x\sqrt{x+2}$

Let $y = 0$: $0 = x\sqrt{x+2} \Rightarrow x = 0, -2 \Rightarrow (0, 0), (-2, 0)$ x-intercepts

Let $x = 0$: $y = 0\sqrt{0+2} = 0 \Rightarrow (0, 0)$ y-intercept

46. $y = -\frac{1}{2}x\sqrt{x+3} + 1$

Let $y = 0$: $0 = -\frac{1}{2}x\sqrt{x+3} + 1 \Rightarrow \frac{1}{2}x\sqrt{x+3} = 1 \Rightarrow x\sqrt{x+3} = 2$

$\Rightarrow x^2(x+3) = 4 \Rightarrow x^3 + 3x^2 - 4 = 0$

$\Rightarrow (x-1)(x^2 + 4x + 4) = 0 \Rightarrow (x-1)(x+2)^2 = 0$

$\Rightarrow x = 1 \Rightarrow (1, 0)$ ($x = -2$ is impossible.)

Let $x = 0 \Rightarrow y = 1 \Rightarrow (0, 1)$ y-intercept

47. $xy = 4$

If $x = 0$, then $0y = 0 = 4$, which is impossible. Similarly, $y = 0$ is impossible. Hence there are no intercepts.

48. $4xy = 3x - 1$

Let $y = 0$: $0 = 3x - 1 \Rightarrow x = \frac{1}{3} \Rightarrow \left(\frac{1}{3}, 0\right)$ x-intercept

Let $x = 0$: $0 = -1$ is impossible. No y-intercepts

49. $y = |x - 2| - 4$

Let $y = 0$: $|x - 2| - 4 = 0 \Rightarrow |x - 2| = 4 \Rightarrow x = -2, 6 \Rightarrow (-2, 0), (6, 0)$ x-intercepts

Let $x = 0$: $|0 - 2| - 4 = |-2| - 4 = 2 - 4 = -2 = y \Rightarrow (0, -2)$ y-intercept

50. $y = 3 - \frac{1}{2}|x + 1|$

Let $y = 0$: $0 = 3 - \frac{1}{2}|x + 1| \Rightarrow \frac{1}{2}|x + 1| = 3 \Rightarrow |x + 1| = 6$

$\Rightarrow x = 5, -7 \Rightarrow (5, 0), (-7, 0)$ x-intercepts

Let $x = 0$: $y = 3 - \frac{1}{2} = 2.5, \left(0, \frac{5}{2}\right)$ y-intercept

51. $xy - 2y - x + 1 = 0$

Let $y = 0$:

$-x + 1 = 0 \Rightarrow x = 1 \Rightarrow (1, 0)$ x-intercept

Let $x = 0$:

$-2y + 1 = 0 \Rightarrow y = \frac{1}{2} \Rightarrow \left(0, \frac{1}{2}\right)$ y-intercept

52. $xy - x + 4y = 0$

Let $y = 0$:

$-x = 0 \Rightarrow x = 0 \Rightarrow (0, 0)$ x-intercept

Let $x = 0$:

$4y = 0 \Rightarrow y = 0 \Rightarrow (0, 0)$ y-intercept

53.

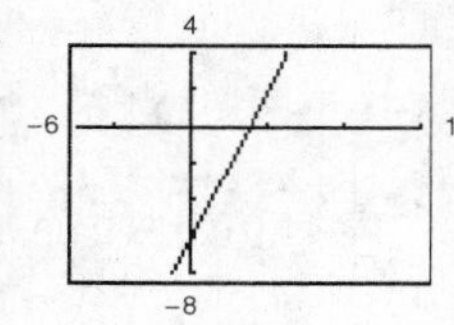

$y = 0 = 2(x - 1) - 4$

$= 2x - 2 - 4$

$= 2x - 6 \Rightarrow 2x = 6 \Rightarrow x = 3$

$(3, 0)$

54. $y = 4(x + 3) - 2$

$0 = 4(x + 3) - 2$

$0 = 4x + 10$

$4x = -10$

$x = -\frac{5}{2}$

$\left(-\frac{5}{2}, 0\right)$

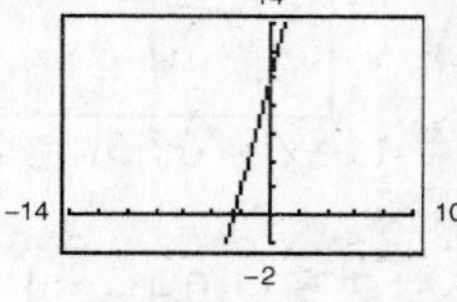

55.

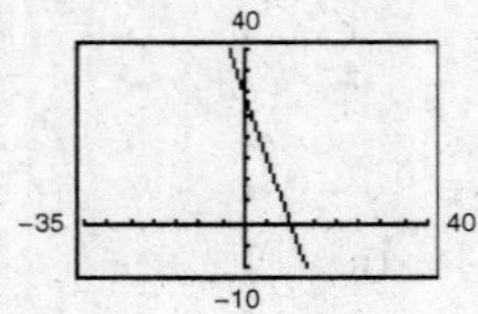

$$y = 0 = 20 - (3x - 10)$$
$$= 20 - 3x + 10$$
$$= 30 - 3x \Rightarrow 3x = 30 \Rightarrow x = 10$$

$(10, 0)$

56.

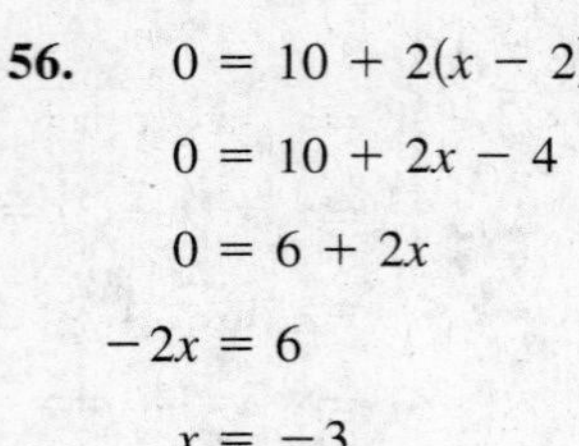

$$0 = 10 + 2(x - 2)$$
$$0 = 10 + 2x - 4$$
$$0 = 6 + 2x$$
$$-2x = 6$$
$$x = -3$$

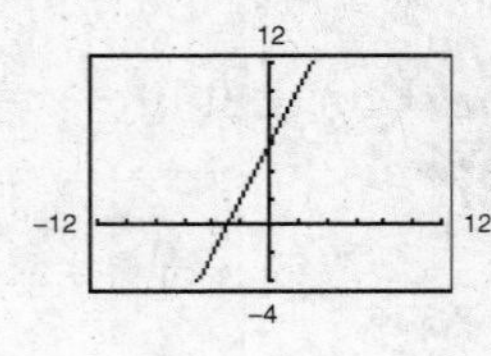

Intercept: $(-3, 0)$

The solution to $0 = 10 + 2(x - 2)$ is the same as the x-intercept of $0 = 10 + 2(x - 2)$. They are both $x = -3$.

57. $f(x) = 5(4 - x)$

$$5(4 - x) = 0$$
$$4 - x = 0$$
$$x = 4$$

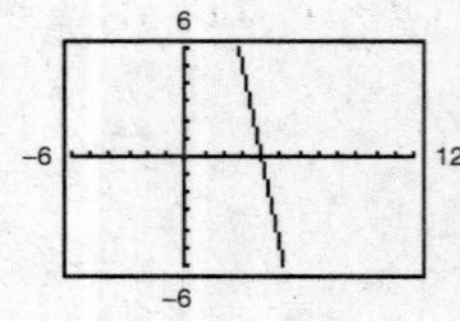

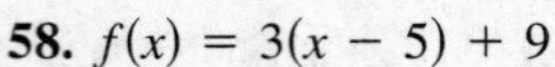

58. $f(x) = 3(x - 5) + 9$

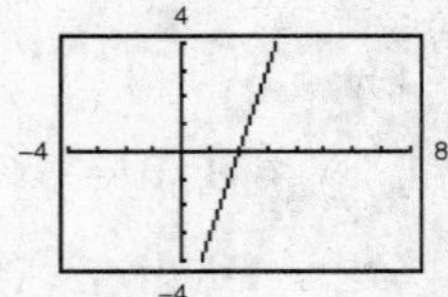

59. $f(x) = x^3 - 6x^2 + 5x$

$$x^3 - 6x^2 + 5x = 0$$
$$x(x^2 - 6x + 5) = 0$$
$$x(x - 5)(x - 1) = 0$$
$$x = 0, 5, 1$$

60. $f(x) = x^3 - 9x^2 + 18x$

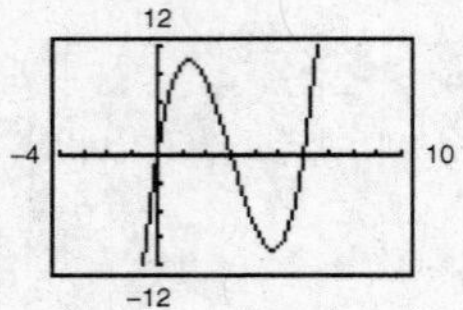

61. $f(x) = \dfrac{x + 2}{3} - \dfrac{x - 1}{5} - 1$

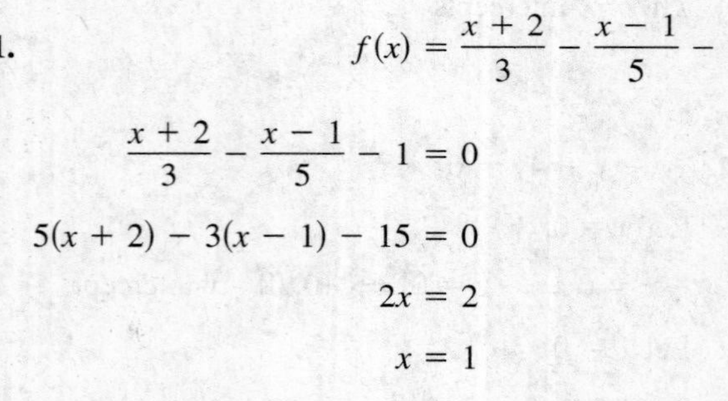

$$\frac{x + 2}{3} - \frac{x - 1}{5} - 1 = 0$$
$$5(x + 2) - 3(x - 1) - 15 = 0$$
$$2x = 2$$
$$x = 1$$

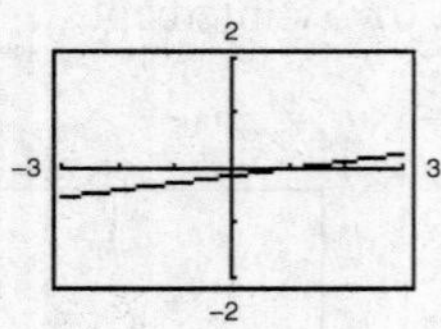

62. $f(x) = x - 3 - \dfrac{10}{x}$

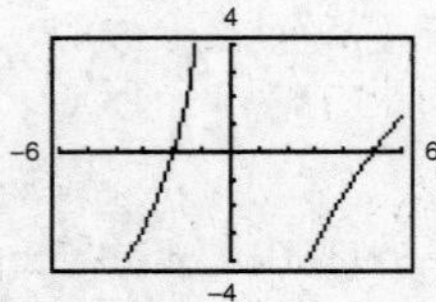

63. $2.7x - 0.4x = 1.2$

$$2.3x = 1.2$$
$$x = \frac{1.2}{2.3} \approx 0.522$$

$f(x) = 2.7x - 0.4x - 1.2 = 0$

$x \approx 0.522$

64. $3.5x - 8 = 0.5x$

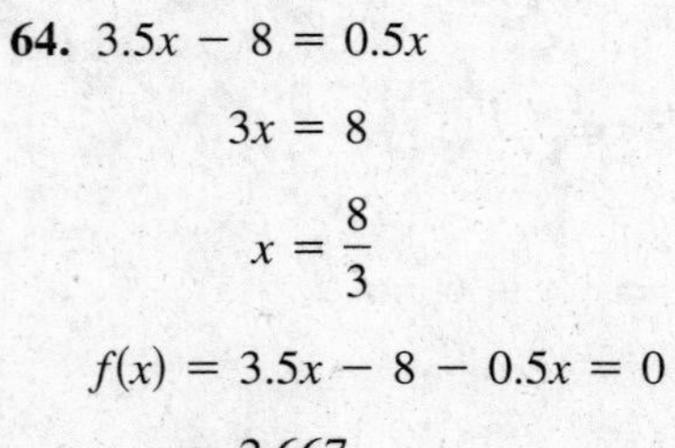

$$3x = 8$$
$$x = \frac{8}{3}$$

$f(x) = 3.5x - 8 - 0.5x = 0$

$x = 2.667$

65. $25(x - 3) = 12(x + 2) - 10$

$25x - 75 = 12x + 24 - 10$

$13x - 89 = 0$

$x = \frac{89}{13}$

$f(x) = 25(x - 3) - 12(x + 2) + 10 = 0$

$x = 6.846$

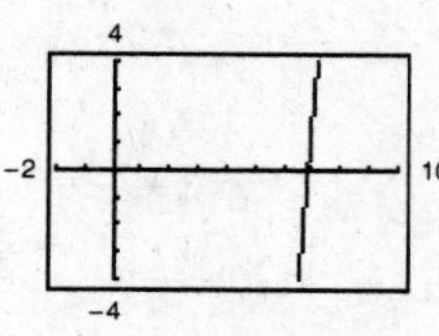

66. $1200 = 300 + 2(x - 500)$

$900 = 2x - 1000$

$1900 = 2x$

$x = 950$

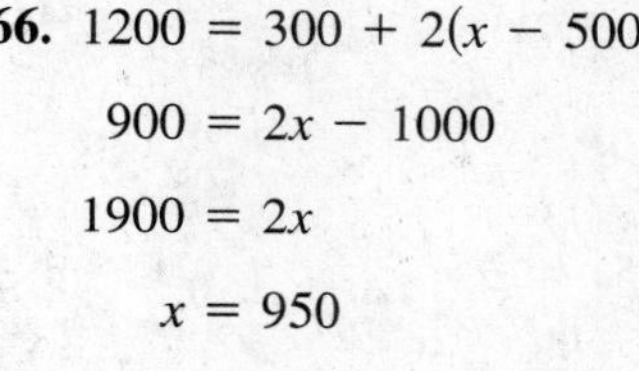

67. $\frac{3x}{2} + \frac{1}{4}(x - 2) = 10$

$\frac{6x}{4} + \frac{x}{4} = 10 + \frac{1}{2}$

$\frac{7x}{4} = \frac{21}{2}$

$x = 6$

$f(x) = \frac{3x}{2} + \frac{1}{4}(x - 2) - 10 = 0$

$x = 6.0$

68. $\frac{2x}{3} + \frac{1}{2}(x - 5) = 6$

$\left(\frac{2}{3} + \frac{1}{2}\right)x = \frac{5}{2} + 6$

$\frac{7}{6}x = \frac{17}{2}$

$x = \frac{51}{7} \approx 7.286$

69. $0.60x + 0.40(100 - x) = 1.2$

$0.60x + 40 - 0.40x = 1.2$

$0.20x = -38.8$

$x = -194$

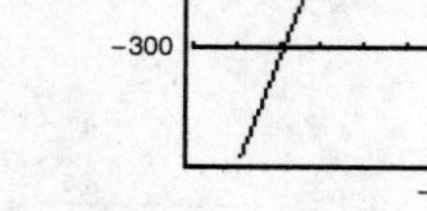

$f(x) = 0.60x + 0.40(100 - x) - 1.2 = 0$

$x = -194$

70. $0.75x + 0.2(80 - x) = 20$

$(0.75 - 0.2)x = 20 - 16$

$0.55x = 4$

$x = \frac{4}{0.55} = \frac{80}{11} \approx 7.273$

71. $\frac{2x}{3} = 10 - \frac{24}{x}$

$\frac{2x}{3}(3x) = 10(3x) - \frac{24}{x}(3x)$

$2x^2 = 30x - 72$

$2x^2 - 30x + 72 = 0$

$x^2 - 15x + 36 = 0$

$(x - 3)(x - 12) = 0$

$x = 3, 12$

$f(x) = \frac{2x}{3} - 10 + \frac{24}{x}$

$x = 3, 12$

72. $\dfrac{x-3}{25} = \dfrac{x-5}{12}$

$12(x-3) = 25(x-5)$

$12x - 36 = 25x - 125$

$13x = 89$

$x = \dfrac{89}{13} \approx 6.846$

73. $\dfrac{3}{x+2} - \dfrac{4}{x-2} = 5$

$3(x-2) - 4(x+2) = 5(x+2)(x-2)$

$3x - 6 - 4x - 8 = 5(x^2 - 4)$

$0 = 5x^2 + x - 6$

$0 = (x-1)(5x+6)$

$x = 1, -\dfrac{6}{5}$

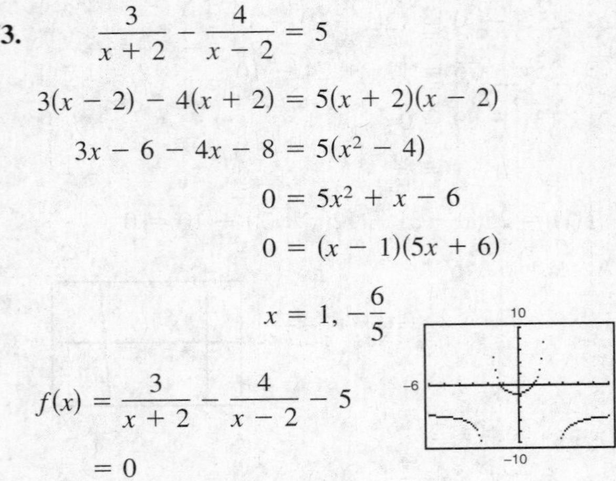

$f(x) = \dfrac{3}{x+2} - \dfrac{4}{x-2} - 5$

$= 0$

$x = 1.0, -1.2$

74. $\dfrac{6}{x} + \dfrac{8}{x+5} = 3$

$6(x+5) + 8x = 3x(x+5)$

$6x + 30 + 8x = 3x^2 + 15x$

$0 = 3x^2 + x - 30$

$= (x-3)(3x+10)$

$x = 3, -\dfrac{10}{3}$

75. $(x+2)^2 = x^2 - 6x + 1$

$x^2 + 4x + 4 = x^2 - 6x + 1$

$10x = -3$

$x = -\dfrac{3}{10}$

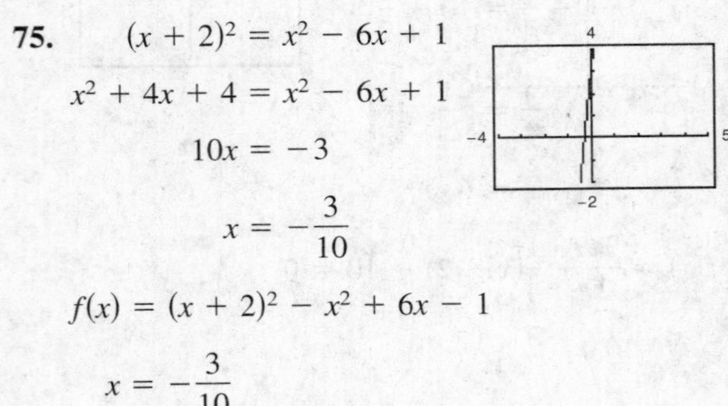

$f(x) = (x+2)^2 - x^2 + 6x - 1$

$x = -\dfrac{3}{10}$

76. $(x+1)^2 + 2(x-2) = (x+1)(x-2)$

$x^2 + 2x + 1 + 2x - 4 = x^2 - x - 2$

$5x = 1$

$x = \frac{1}{5}$

77. $2x^3 - x^2 - 18x + 9 = 0$

$x = -3.0, 0.5, 3.0$

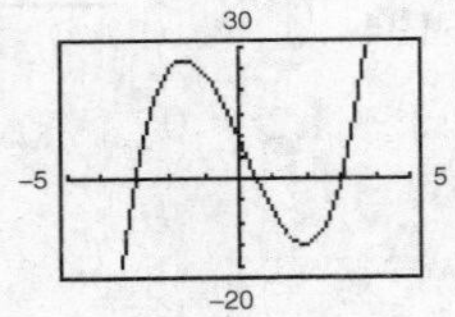

78. $4x^3 + 12x^2 - 26x - 24 = 0$

$x = -4.206, -0.735, 1.941$

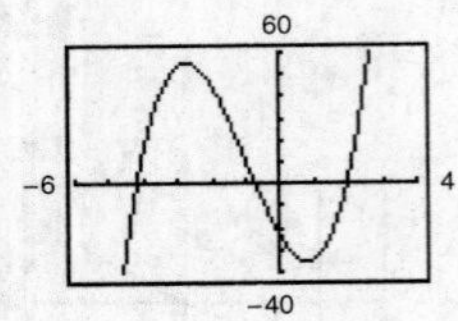

79. $x^4 = 2x^3 + 1$

$x^4 - 2x^3 - 1 = 0$

$x \approx -0.717, 2.107$

80. $x^5 = 3 + 2x^3$

$x^5 - 3 - 2x^3 = 0$

$x = 1.638$

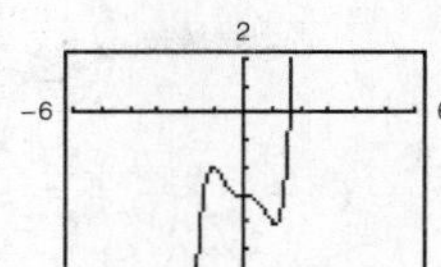

81. $\dfrac{2}{x+2} = 3$

$\dfrac{2}{x+2} - 3 = 0$

$x = -\dfrac{4}{3}$

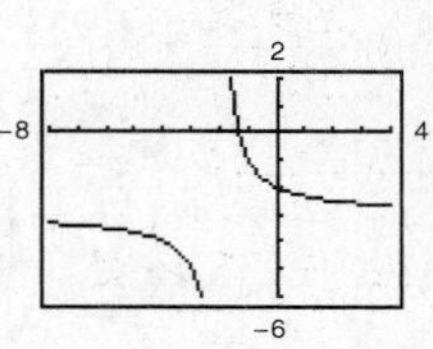

82. $\dfrac{5}{x} = 1 + \dfrac{3}{x+2}$

$\dfrac{5}{x} - 1 - \dfrac{3}{x+2} = 0$

$x = -3.162, 3.162$

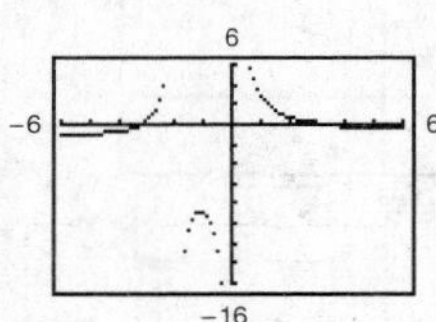

83. $|x - 3| = 4$

$|x - 3| - 4 = 0$

$x = -1, 7$

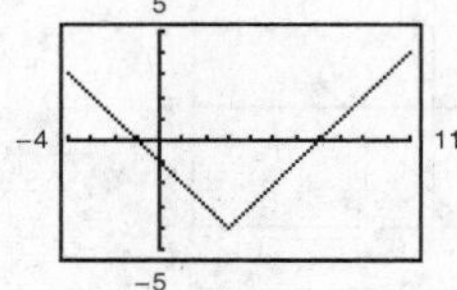

84. $|x + 1| = 6$

$x + 1 = 6$ or $x + 1 = -6$

$x = 5$ or $x = -7$

85. $\sqrt{x-2} = 3$

$\sqrt{x-2} - 3 = 0$

$x = 11$

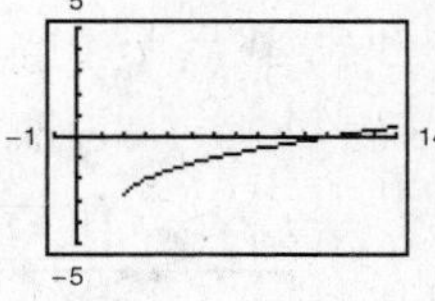

86. $\sqrt{x-4} = 8$

$x - 4 = 64$

$x = 68$

87. $y = 2 - x$

$y = 2x - 1$

$2 - x = 2x - 1$

$3 = 3x$

$x = 1, y = 2 - 1 = 1$

$(x, y) = (1, 1)$

88. $y = x + 4$

$y = \frac{5}{2} - \frac{1}{2}x$

$x + 4 = \frac{5}{2} - \frac{1}{2}x$

$2x + 8 = 5 - x$

$3x = -3$

$x = -1$

$y = -1 + 4 = 3$

Solution: $(-1, 3)$

89. $x - y = -4 \Rightarrow y = x + 4$

$x^2 - y = -2 \Rightarrow y = x^2 + 2$

$x^2 + 2 = x + 4$

$x^2 - x - 2 = 0$

$(x - 2)(x + 1) = 0$

$x = 2, y = 6$

$x = -1, y = 3$

$(2, 6), (-1, 3)$

90. $3x + y = 2 \Rightarrow y = 2 - 3x$

$x^3 + y = 0 \Rightarrow y = -x^3$

$2 - 3x = -x^3$

$x^3 - 3x + 2 = 0$

$(x - 1)(x^2 + x - 2) = 0$

$(x - 1)(x + 2)(x - 1) = 0$

$x = 1, -2$

$(x, y) = (1, -1), (-2, 8)$

91.
$$y = x^2 - x + 1$$
$$y = x^2 + 2x + 4$$
$$x^2 - x + 1 = x^2 + 2x + 4$$
$$-3 = 3x$$
$$x = -1$$
$$y = (-1)^2 - (-1) + 1 = 3$$
$$(x, y) = (-1, 3)$$

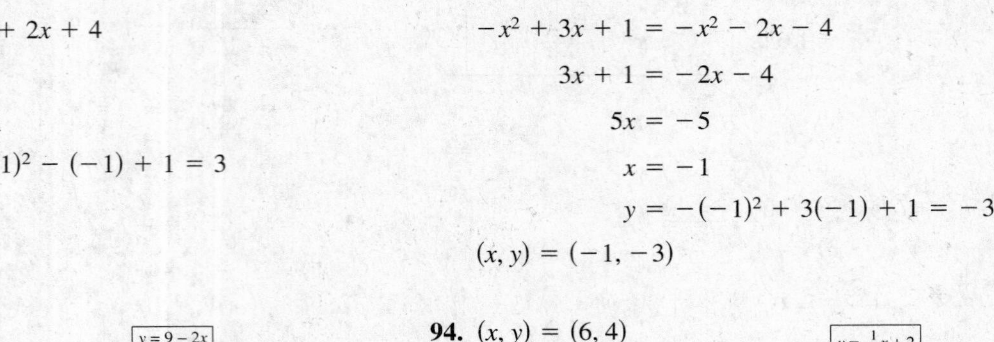

92.
$$y = -x^2 + 3x + 1$$
$$y = -x^2 - 2x - 4$$
$$-x^2 + 3x + 1 = -x^2 - 2x - 4$$
$$3x + 1 = -2x - 4$$
$$5x = -5$$
$$x = -1$$
$$y = -(-1)^2 + 3(-1) + 1 = -3$$
$$(x, y) = (-1, -3)$$

93. $y = 9 - 2x$

$y = x - 3$

$(4, 1)$

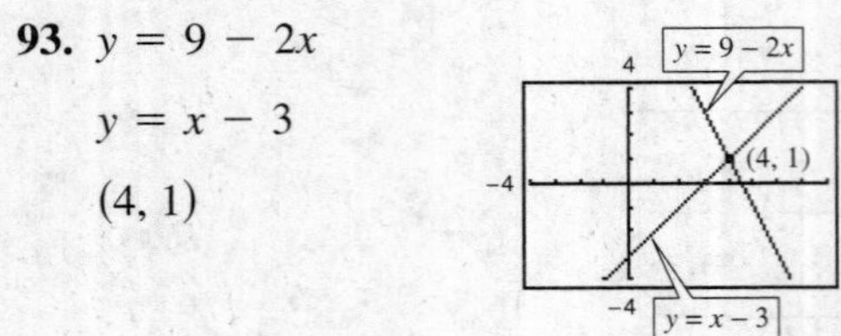

94. $(x, y) = (6, 4)$

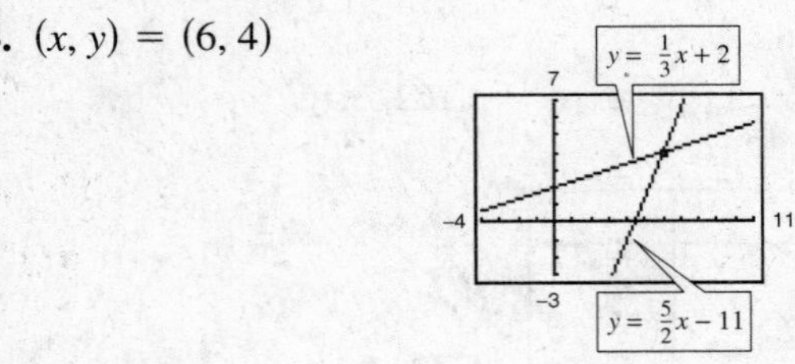

95. $y = 4 - x^2$

$y = 2x - 1$

$(x, y) = (1.449, 1.898), (-3.449, -7.899)$

96. $(x, y) = (1.670, 1.660)$

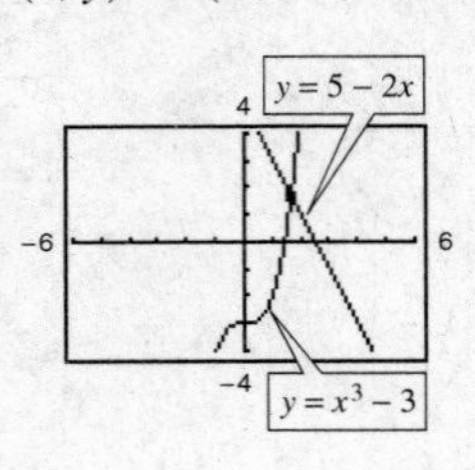

97. $y = 2x^2$

$y = x^4 - 2x^2$

$(x, y) = (0, 0), (2, 8), (-2, 8)$

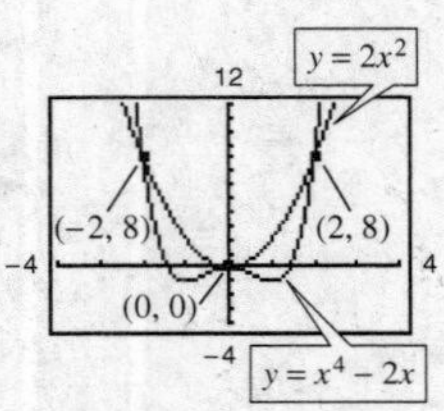

98. $(x, y) = (0, 0), (3, -3)$

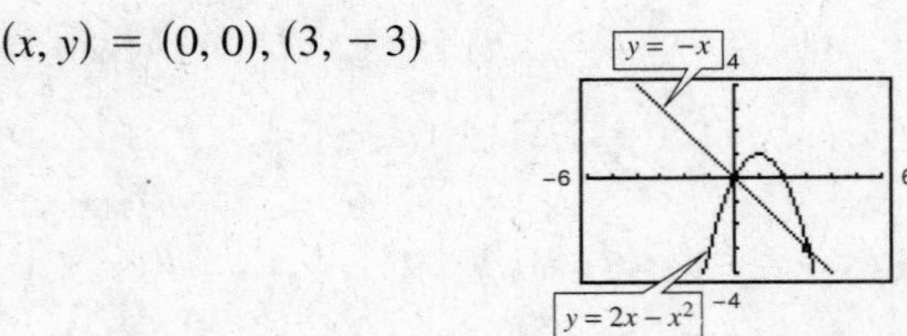

99.
$$6x^2 + 3x = 0$$
$$3x(2x + 1) = 0$$
$$3x = 0 \text{ or } 2x + 1 = 0$$
$$x = 0 \text{ or } x = -\tfrac{1}{2}$$

100.
$$9x^2 - 1 = 0$$
$$(3x + 1)(3x - 1) = 0$$
$$3x + 1 = 0 \Rightarrow x = -\tfrac{1}{3}$$
$$3x - 1 = 0 \Rightarrow x = \tfrac{1}{3}$$

101.
$$x^2 - 2x - 8 = 0$$
$$(x - 4)(x + 2) = 0$$
$$x - 4 = 0 \text{ or } x + 2 = 0$$
$$x = 4 \text{ or } x = -2$$

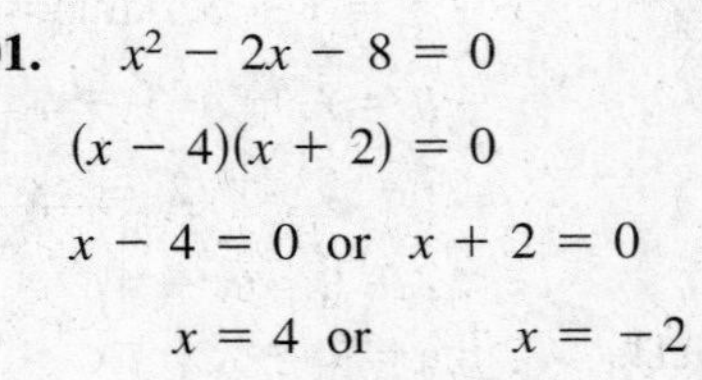

102.
$$x^2 - 10x + 9 = 0$$
$$(x - 9)(x - 1) = 0$$
$$x - 9 = 0 \Rightarrow x = 9$$
$$x - 1 = 0 \Rightarrow x = 1$$

103.
$$3 + 5x - 2x^2 = 0$$
$$(3 - x)(1 + 2x) = 0$$
$$3 - x = 0 \text{ or } 1 + 2x = 0$$
$$x = 3 \text{ or } x = -\tfrac{1}{2}$$

104.
$$2x^2 = 19x + 33$$
$$2x^2 - 19x - 33 = 0$$
$$(2x + 3)(x - 11) = 0$$
$$2x + 3 = 0 \Rightarrow x = -\tfrac{3}{2}$$
$$x - 11 = 0 \Rightarrow x = 11$$

105. $x^2 + 4x = 12$

$x^2 + 4x - 12 = 0$

$(x + 6)(x - 2) = 0$

$x + 6 = 0$ or $x - 2 = 0$

$x = -6$ or $x = 2$

106. $-x^2 + 8x = 12$

$x^2 - 8x + 12 = 0$

$(x - 2)(x - 6) = 0$

$x = 2, 6$

107. $(x + a)^2 - b^2 = 0$

$[(x + a) + b][(x + a) - b] = 0$

$x + a + b = 0 \Rightarrow x = -a - b$

$x + a - b = 0 \Rightarrow x = -a + b$

108. $x^2 + 2ax + a^2 = 0$

$(x + a)^2 = 0$

$x = -a$

109. $x^2 = 49$

$x = \pm\sqrt{49} = \pm 7$

110. $x^2 = 144$

$x = \pm\sqrt{144} = \pm 12$

111. $(x - 12)^2 = 16$

$x - 12 = \pm\sqrt{16} = \pm 4$

$x = 12 \pm 4$

$x = 16, 8$

112. $(x - 5)^2 = 25$

$x - 5 = \pm 5$

$x = 5 \pm 5$

$x = 10, 0$

113. $(3x - 1)^2 + 6 = 0$

$(3x - 1)^2 = -6$

$3x - 1 = \pm\sqrt{-6} = \pm\sqrt{6}i$

$x = \frac{1}{3} \pm \frac{\sqrt{6}}{3}i \approx 0.33 \pm 0.82i$

114. $(2x + 3)^2 + 25 = 0$

$(2x + 3)^2 = -25$

$2x + 3 = \pm\sqrt{-25} = \pm 5i$

$x = -\frac{3}{2} \pm \frac{5}{2}i = -1.5 \pm 2.5i$

115. $(2x - 1)^2 = 12$

$2x - 1 = \pm\sqrt{12} = \pm 2\sqrt{3}$

$2x = 1 \pm 2\sqrt{3}$

$x = \frac{1}{2} \pm \sqrt{3}$

$x = 2.23, -1.23$

116. $(4x + 7)^2 = 44$

$4x + 7 = \pm\sqrt{44} = \pm 2\sqrt{11}$

$4x = -7 \pm 2\sqrt{11}$

$x = -\frac{7}{4} \pm \frac{1}{2}\sqrt{11}$

$x \approx -3.41, -0.09$

117. $(x - 7)^2 = (x + 3)^2$

$x - 7 = \pm(x + 3)$

$x - 7 = x + 3$, impossible

$x - 7 = -(x + 3) \Rightarrow 2x = 4$

$\Rightarrow x = 2$

118. $(x + 5)^2 = (x + 4)^2$

$x + 5 = x + 4$, impossible

$x + 5 = -(x + 4)$

$2x = -9$

$x = -\frac{9}{2} = -4.5$

119. $x^2 + 4x = 32$

$x^2 + 4x + 4 = 32 + 4$

$(x + 2)^2 = 36$

$x + 2 = \pm 6$

$x = -2 \pm 6$

$x = -8, 4$

120. $x^2 - 2x - 3 = 0$

$x^2 - 2x + 1 = 3 + 1$

$(x - 1)^2 = 4$

$x - 1 = \pm 2$

$x = 1 \pm 2$

$x = 3, -1$

121. $x^2 + 6x + 2 = 0$

$x^2 + 6x = -2$

$x^2 + 6x + 3^2 = -2 + 3^2$

$(x + 3)^2 = 7$

$x + 3 = \pm\sqrt{7}$

$x = -3 \pm \sqrt{7}$

122. $x^2 + 8x + 14 = 0$

$$x^2 + 8x = -14$$
$$x^2 + 8x + 4^2 = -14 + 16$$
$$(x + 4)^2 = 2$$
$$x + 4 = \pm\sqrt{2}$$
$$x = -4 \pm \sqrt{2}$$

123. $9x^2 - 18x + 3 = 0$

$$x^2 - 2x + \frac{1}{3} = 0$$
$$x^2 - 2x = -\frac{1}{3}$$
$$x^2 - 2x + 1^2 = -\frac{1}{3} + 1^2$$
$$(x - 1)^2 = \frac{2}{3}$$
$$x - 1 = \pm\sqrt{\frac{2}{3}}$$
$$x = 1 \pm \sqrt{\frac{2}{3}}$$
$$x = 1 \pm \frac{\sqrt{6}}{3}$$

124. $4x^2 - 4x - 99 = 0$

$$4\left(x^2 - x + \frac{1}{4}\right) = 99 + 1$$
$$4\left(x - \frac{1}{2}\right)^2 = 100$$
$$\left(x - \frac{1}{2}\right)^2 = 25$$
$$x - \frac{1}{2} = \pm 5$$
$$x = \frac{1}{2} \pm 5$$
$$x = -\frac{9}{2}, \frac{11}{2}$$

125. $-6 + 2x - x^2 = 0$

$$(x^2 - 2x + 1) = -6 + 1$$
$$(x - 1)^2 = -5$$
$$x - 1 = \pm\sqrt{-5}$$
$$= \pm\sqrt{5}i$$
$$x = 1 \pm \sqrt{5}i$$

126. $-x^2 + x - 1 = 0$

$$x^2 - x + \frac{1}{4} = -1 + \frac{1}{4}$$
$$\left(x - \frac{1}{2}\right)^2 = -\frac{3}{4}$$
$$x - \frac{1}{2} = \pm\frac{\sqrt{3}}{2}i$$
$$x = \frac{1}{2} \pm \frac{\sqrt{3}}{2}i$$

127. $2x^2 + 5x - 8 = 0$

$$x^2 + \frac{5}{2}x - 4 = 0$$
$$x^2 + \frac{5}{2}x + \frac{25}{16} = 4 + \frac{25}{16}$$
$$\left(x + \frac{5}{4}\right)^2 = \frac{89}{16}$$
$$x + \frac{5}{4} = \pm\frac{\sqrt{89}}{4}$$
$$x = \frac{-5}{4} \pm \frac{\sqrt{89}}{4}$$

128. $9x^2 - 12x = 14$

$$x^2 - \frac{4}{3}x = \frac{14}{9}$$
$$x^2 - \frac{4}{3}x + \left(\frac{2}{3}\right)^2 = \frac{14}{9} + \frac{4}{9}$$
$$\left(x - \frac{2}{3}\right)^2 = \frac{18}{9}$$
$$\left(x - \frac{2}{3}\right)^2 = 2$$
$$x - \frac{2}{3} = \pm\sqrt{2}$$
$$x = \frac{2}{3} \pm \sqrt{2}$$

129. $-x^2 + 2x + 2 = 0$

$$x = \frac{-b \pm \sqrt{b^2 - 4ac}}{2a}$$
$$= \frac{-2 \pm \sqrt{2^2 - 4(-1)(2)}}{2(-1)}$$
$$= \frac{-2 \pm 2\sqrt{3}}{-2} = 1 \pm \sqrt{3}$$

130. $x^2 - 10x + 22 = 0$

$$x = \frac{-b \pm \sqrt{b^2 - 4ac}}{2a}$$

$$= \frac{-(-10) \pm \sqrt{(-10)^2 - 4(1)(22)}}{2(1)}$$

$$= \frac{10 \pm \sqrt{100 - 88}}{2}$$

$$= \frac{10 \pm 2\sqrt{3}}{2} = 5 \pm \sqrt{3}$$

131. $x^2 + 8x - 4 = 0$

$$x = \frac{-b \pm \sqrt{b^2 - 4ac}}{2a}$$

$$= \frac{-8 \pm \sqrt{8^2 - 4(1)(-4)}}{2(1)}$$

$$= \frac{-8 \pm 4\sqrt{5}}{2} = -4 \pm 2\sqrt{5}$$

132. $4x^2 - 4x - 4 = 0$

$$x^2 - x - 1 = 0$$

$$x = \frac{-b \pm \sqrt{b^2 - 4ac}}{2a}$$

$$= \frac{-(-1) \pm \sqrt{(-1)^2 - 4(1)(-1)}}{2(1)}$$

$$= \frac{1 \pm \sqrt{1 + 4}}{2}$$

$$= \frac{1}{2} \pm \frac{\sqrt{5}}{2}$$

133. $x^2 + 3x + 8 = 0$

$$x = \frac{-3 \pm \sqrt{9 - 4(8)}}{2}$$

$$= \frac{-3 \pm \sqrt{-23}}{2}$$

$$= -\frac{3}{2} \pm \frac{\sqrt{23}i}{2}$$

134. $x^2 + 5x + 16 = 0$

$$x = \frac{-5 \pm \sqrt{25 - 4(16)}}{2}$$

$$= \frac{-5 \pm \sqrt{-39}}{2}$$

$$= -\frac{5}{2} \pm \frac{\sqrt{39}}{2}i$$

135. $28x - 49x^2 = 4$

$$-49x^2 + 28x - 4 = 0$$

$$x = \frac{-b \pm \sqrt{b^2 - 4ac}}{2a}$$

$$= \frac{-28 \pm \sqrt{28^2 - 4(-49)(-4)}}{2(-49)}$$

$$= \frac{-28 \pm 0}{-98} = \frac{2}{7}$$

136. $9x^2 + 24x + 16 = 0$

$$x = \frac{-b \pm \sqrt{b^2 - 4ac}}{2a}$$

$$= \frac{-24 \pm \sqrt{24^2 - 4(9)(16)}}{2(9)}$$

$$= \frac{-24 \pm \sqrt{576 - 576}}{18}$$

$$= -\frac{4}{3}$$

137. $4x^2 + 16x + 17 = 0$

$$x = \frac{-b \pm \sqrt{b^2 - 4ac}}{2a}$$

$$= \frac{-16 \pm \sqrt{16^2 - 4(4)(17)}}{2(4)}$$

$$= \frac{-16 \pm \sqrt{-16}}{8}$$

$$= \frac{-16 \pm 4i}{8}$$

$$= -2 \pm \frac{1}{2}i$$

138. $9x^2 - 6x + 37 = 0$

$$x = \frac{-b \pm \sqrt{b^2 - 4ac}}{2a}$$

$$= \frac{6 \pm \sqrt{36 - 1332}}{18}$$

$$= \frac{1}{3} \pm 2i$$

139. $x^2 - 2x - 1 = 0$

$$x^2 - 2x = 1$$

$$x^2 - 2x + 1^2 = 1 + 1^2$$

$$(x - 1)^2 = 2$$

$$x - 1 = \pm\sqrt{2}$$

$$x = 1 \pm \sqrt{2}$$

140. $11x^2 + 33x = 0$

$$11(x^2 + 3x) = 0$$

$$x(x + 3) = 0$$

$$x = 0$$

$$x + 3 = 0 \Rightarrow x = -3$$

141. $(x + 3)^2 = 81$

$$x + 3 = \pm 9$$

$$x + 3 = 9 \text{ or } x + 3 = -9$$

$$x = 6 \text{ or } \quad x = -12$$

142. $(x - 1)^2 = -1$

$$x - 1 = \pm\sqrt{-1} = \pm i$$

$$x = 1 \pm i$$

143. $x^2 - 14x + 49 = 0$

$$(x - 7)^2 = 0$$

$$x = 7$$

144. $x^2 - 2x + \frac{13}{4} = 0$

$$x = \frac{2 \pm \sqrt{4 - 4(13/4)}}{2}$$

$$= \frac{2 \pm \sqrt{-9}}{2}$$

$$= 1 \pm \frac{3}{2}i$$

145. $x^2 - x - \frac{11}{4} = 0$

$$x^2 - x + \frac{1}{4} = \frac{11}{4} + \frac{1}{4}$$

$$\left(x - \frac{1}{2}\right)^2 = 3$$

$$x - \frac{1}{2} = \pm\sqrt{3}$$

$$x = \frac{1}{2} \pm \sqrt{3}$$

$$x = \frac{1}{2} \pm \sqrt{3}$$

146. $x^2 + 3x - \frac{3}{4} = 0$

$$x^2 + 3x + \left(\frac{3}{2}\right)^2 = \frac{3}{4} + \frac{9}{4}$$

$$\left(x + \frac{3}{2}\right)^2 = 3$$

$$x + \frac{3}{2} = \pm\sqrt{3}$$

$$x = -\frac{3}{2} \pm \sqrt{3}$$

147. $(x + 1)^2 = x^2$

$$(x + 1)^2 - x^2 = 0$$

$$(x + 1 - x)(x + 1 + x) = 0$$

$$2x + 1 = 0$$

$$2x = -1$$

$$x = -\frac{1}{2}$$

148. $a^2x^2 - b^2 = 0, \ a \neq 0$

$$a^2x^2 = b^2$$

$$x^2 = \frac{b^2}{a^2}$$

$$x = \pm\frac{b}{a}$$

(If $b = 0$, then $x = 0$.)

149. $4x^4 - 16x^2 = 0$

$$4x^2(x^2 - 4) = 0$$

$$4x^2(x - 2)(x + 2) = 0$$

$$x = 0, \pm 2$$

150. $8x^4 - 18x^2 = 0$

$$2x^2(4x^2 - 9) = 0$$

$$2x^2(2x + 3)(2x - 3) = 0$$

$$x = 0, \pm\tfrac{3}{2}$$

151. $5x^3 + 30x^2 + 45x = 0$

$$5x(x^2 + 6x + 9) = 0$$

$$5x(x + 3)^2 = 0$$

$$5x = 0 \Rightarrow x = 0$$

$$x + 3 = 0 \Rightarrow x = -3$$

152. $9x^4 - 24x^3 + 16x^2 = 0$

$$x^2(9x^2 - 24x + 16) = 0$$

$$x^2(3x - 4)^2 = 0$$

$$x^2 = 0 \Rightarrow x = 0$$

$$3x - 4 = 0 \Rightarrow x = \tfrac{4}{3}$$

153. $4x^4 - 18x^2 = 0$

$2x^2(2x^2 - 9) = 0$

$2x^2 = 0 \Rightarrow x = 0$

$2x^2 - 9 = 0 \Rightarrow x = \pm\dfrac{3\sqrt{2}}{2}$

154. $20x^3 - 125x = 0$

$5x(4x^2 - 25) = 0$

$5x(2x + 5)(2x - 5) = 0$

$5x = 0 \Rightarrow x = 0$

$2x + 5 = 0 \Rightarrow x = -\dfrac{5}{2}$

$2x - 5 = 0 \Rightarrow x = \dfrac{5}{2}$

155. $x^4 - 4x^2 + 3 = 0$

$(x^2 - 3)(x^2 - 1) = 0$

$(x + \sqrt{3})(x - \sqrt{3})(x + 1)(x - 1) = 0$

$x + \sqrt{3} = 0 \Rightarrow x = -\sqrt{3}$

$x - \sqrt{3} = 0 \Rightarrow x = \sqrt{3}$

$x + 1 = 0 \Rightarrow x = -1$

$x - 1 = 0 \Rightarrow x = 1$

156. $x^4 + 5x^2 - 36 = 0$

$(x^2 + 9)(x^2 - 4) = 0$

$(x^2 + 9)(x + 2)(x - 2) = 0$

$x^2 + 9 = 0 \Rightarrow x = \pm 3i$

$x + 2 = 0 \Rightarrow x = -2$

$x - 2 = 0 \Rightarrow x = 2$

157. $x^3 - 3x^2 - x + 3 = 0$

$x^2(x - 3) - (x - 3) = 0$

$(x - 3)(x^2 - 1) = 0$

$(x - 3)(x + 1)(x - 1) = 0$

$x - 3 = 0 \Rightarrow x = 3$

$x + 1 = 0 \Rightarrow x = -1$

$x - 1 = 0 \Rightarrow x = 1$

158. $x^4 + 2x^3 - 8x - 16 = 0$

$x^3(x + 2) - 8(x + 2) = 0$

$(x^3 - 8)(x + 2) = 0$

$(x - 2)(x^2 + 2x + 4)(x + 2) = 0$

$x - 2 = 0 \Rightarrow x = 2$

$x^2 + 2x + 4 = 0 \Rightarrow x = -1 \pm \sqrt{3}i$

$x + 2 = 0 \Rightarrow x = -2$

159. $4x^4 - 65x^2 + 16 = 0$

$(4x^2 - 1)(x^2 - 16) = 0$

$(2x + 1)(2x - 1)(x + 4)(x - 4) = 0$

$2x + 1 = 0 \Rightarrow x = -\frac{1}{2}$

$2x - 1 = 0 \Rightarrow x = \frac{1}{2}$

$x + 4 = 0 \Rightarrow x = -4$

$x - 4 = 0 \Rightarrow x = 4$

160. $36t^4 + 29t^2 - 7 = 0$

$(36t^2 - 7)(t^2 + 1) = 0$

$(6t + \sqrt{7})(6t - \sqrt{7})(t^2 + 1) = 0$

$6t + \sqrt{7} = 0 \Rightarrow t = -\frac{\sqrt{7}}{6}$

$6t - \sqrt{7} = 0 \Rightarrow t = \frac{\sqrt{7}}{6}$

$t^2 + 1 = 0 \Rightarrow t = \pm i$

161. $\frac{1}{t^2} + \frac{8}{t} + 15 = 0$

$1 + 8t + 15t^2 = 0$

$(1 + 3t)(1 + 5t) = 0$

$1 + 3t = 0 \Rightarrow t = -\frac{1}{3}$

$1 + 5t = 0 \Rightarrow t = -\frac{1}{5}$

162. $6 - \frac{1}{x} - \frac{1}{x^2} = 0$

$6x^2 - x - 1 = 0$

$(3x + 1)(2x - 1) = 0$

$x = -\frac{1}{3}, \frac{1}{2}$

163. $6\left(\frac{s}{s+1}\right)^2 + 5\left(\frac{s}{s+1}\right) - 6 = 0$

Let $u = \frac{s}{(s+1)}$.

$6u^2 + 5u - 6 = 0$

$(3u - 2)(2u + 3) = 0$

$3u - 2 = 0 \Rightarrow u = \frac{2}{3}$

$2u + 3 = 0 \Rightarrow u = -\frac{3}{2}$

$\frac{s}{s+1} = \frac{2}{3} \Rightarrow s = 2$

$\frac{s}{s+1} = -\frac{3}{2} \Rightarrow s = -\frac{3}{5}$

164. $8\left(\frac{t}{t-1}\right)^2 - 2\left(\frac{t}{t-1}\right) - 3 = 0$

Let $\frac{t}{t-1} = x$. Then:

$8x^2 - 2x - 3 = 0$

$(2x + 1)(4x - 3) = 0$

$x = -\frac{1}{2}, x = \frac{3}{4}$

$\frac{t}{t-1} = -\frac{1}{2} \Rightarrow 2t = -t + 1 \Rightarrow t = \frac{1}{3}$

$\frac{t}{t-1} = \frac{3}{4} \Rightarrow 4t = 3t - 3 \Rightarrow t = -3$

165. $2x + 9\sqrt{x} - 5 = 0$

$(2\sqrt{x} - 1)(\sqrt{x} + 5) = 0$

$\sqrt{x} = \frac{1}{2} \Rightarrow x = \frac{1}{4}$

($\sqrt{x} = -5$ is not possible.)

Note: You can see graphically that there is only one solution.

166. $6x - 7\sqrt{x} - 3 = 0$

Let $z = \sqrt{x}$. Then:

$6z^2 - 7z - 3 = 0$

$(2z - 3)(3z + 1) = 0$

$z = \frac{3}{2}, -\frac{1}{3}$

Hence, $x = \frac{9}{4}$. (The other value is extraneous.)

167. $\sqrt{x-10}-4=0$

$\sqrt{x-10}=4$

$x-10=16$

$x=26$

168. $\sqrt{2x+5}+3=0$

$\sqrt{2x+5}=-3$, impossible

No solution

169. $\sqrt{x+1}-3x=1$

$\sqrt{x+1}=3x+1$

$x+1=9x^2+6x+1$

$0=9x^2+5x$

$0=x(9x+5)$

$x=0$

$9x+5=0 \Rightarrow x=-\frac{5}{9}$, extraneous

170. $\sqrt{x+5}-2x=3$

$\sqrt{x+5}=2x+3$

$x+5=4x^2+12x+9$

$4x^2+11x+4=0$

$x=\dfrac{-11\pm\sqrt{121-64}}{8}=\dfrac{-11\pm\sqrt{57}}{8}$

171. $\sqrt[3]{2x+1}+8=0$

$\sqrt[3]{2x+1}=-8$

$2x+1=-512$

$2x=-513$

$x=-\frac{513}{2}=-256.5$

172. $\sqrt[3]{4x-3}+2=0$

$(4x-3)^{1/3}=-2$

$4x-3=-8$

$4x=-5$

$x=-\frac{5}{4}$

173. $\sqrt{x}-\sqrt{x-5}=1$

$\sqrt{x}=1+\sqrt{x-5}$

$\left(\sqrt{x}\right)^2=\left(1+\sqrt{x-5}\right)^2$

$x=1+2\sqrt{x-5}+x-5$

$4=2\sqrt{x-5}$

$2=\sqrt{x-5}$

$4=x-5$

$9=x$

174. $\sqrt{x}+\sqrt{x-20}=10$

$\sqrt{x}=10-\sqrt{x-20}$

$\left(\sqrt{x}\right)^2=\left(10-\sqrt{x-20}\right)^2$

$x=100-20\sqrt{x-20}+x-20$

$-80=-20\sqrt{x-20}$

$4=\sqrt{x-20}$

$16=x-20$

$36=x$

175. $(x-5)^{2/3}=16$

$x-5=\pm16^{3/2}$

$x-5=\pm64$

$x=69,-59$

176. $(x^2-x-22)^{4/3}=16$

$x^2-x-22=\pm16^{3/4}$

$x^2-x-22=\pm8$

$x^2-x-30=0 \Rightarrow x=-5, 6$

$x^2-x-14=0 \Rightarrow x=\dfrac{1\pm\sqrt{57}}{2}$

177. $3x(x-1)^{1/2} + 2(x-1)^{3/2} = 0$

$(x-1)^{1/2}[3x + 2(x-1)] = 0$

$(x-1)^{1/2}(5x-2) = 0$

$(x-1)^{1/2} = 0 \Rightarrow x - 1 = 0 \Rightarrow x = 1$

$5x - 2 = 0 \Rightarrow x = \frac{2}{5}$ which is extraneous.

178. $4x^2(x-1)^{1/3} + 6x(x-1)^{4/3} = 0$

$2x[2x(x-1)^{1/3} + 3(x-1)^{4/3}] = 0$

$2x(x-1)^{1/3}[2x + 3(x-1)] = 0$

$2x(x-1)^{1/3}(5x-3) = 0$

$2x = 0 \Rightarrow x = 0$

$x - 1 = 0 \Rightarrow x = 1$

$5x - 3 = 0 \Rightarrow x = \frac{3}{5}$

179. $\frac{1}{x} - \frac{1}{x+1} = 3$

$x(x+1)\frac{1}{x} - x(x+1)\frac{1}{x+1} = x(x+1)(3)$

$x + 1 - x = 3x(x+1)$

$1 = 3x^2 + 3x$

$0 = 3x^2 + 3x - 1;\ a = 3,\ b = 3,\ c = -1$

$x = \frac{-3 \pm \sqrt{(3)^2 - 4(3)(-1)}}{2(3)} = \frac{-3 \pm \sqrt{21}}{6}$

180. $\frac{x}{x^2-4} + \frac{1}{x+2} = 3$

$(x+2)(x-2)\frac{x}{x^2-4} + (x+2)(x-2)\frac{1}{x+2} = 3(x+2)(x-2)$

$x + x - 2 = 3x^2 - 12$

$3x^2 - 2x - 10 = 0$

$a = 3,\ b = -2,\ c = -10$

$x = \frac{-(-2) \pm \sqrt{(-2)^2 - 4(3)(-10)}}{2(3)} = \frac{2 \pm \sqrt{124}}{6} = \frac{2 \pm 2\sqrt{31}}{6} = \frac{1 \pm \sqrt{31}}{3}$

181. $x = \frac{3}{x} + \frac{1}{2}$

$(2x)(x) = (2x)\left(\frac{3}{x}\right) + (2x)\left(\frac{1}{2}\right)$

$2x^2 = 6 + x$

$2x^2 - x - 6 = 0$

$(2x+3)(x-2) = 0$

$2x + 3 = 0 \Rightarrow x = -\frac{3}{2}$

$x - 2 = 0 \Rightarrow x = 2$

182. $4x + 1 = \frac{3}{x}$

$(x)4x + (x)1 = (x)\frac{3}{x}$

$4x^2 + x = 3$

$4x^2 + x - 3 = 0$

$(4x-3)(x+1) = 0$

$4x - 3 = 0 \Rightarrow x = \frac{3}{4}$

$x + 1 = 0 \Rightarrow x = -1$

183. $|2x - 1| = 5$

$2x - 1 = 5 \Rightarrow x = 3$

$-(2x-1) = 5 \Rightarrow x = -2$

184. $|3x + 2| = 7$

$3x + 2 = 7 \Rightarrow x = \frac{5}{3}$

$-(3x+2) = 7$

$-3x - 2 = 7 \Rightarrow x = -3$

185. $|x| = x^2 + x - 3$

$x = x^2 + x - 3$ OR $-x = x^2 + x - 3$

$x^2 - 3 = 0$ $\qquad$ $x^2 + 2x - 3 = 0$

$x = \pm\sqrt{3}$ $\qquad$ $(x - 1)(x + 3) = 0$

$x - 1 = 0 \Rightarrow x = 1$

$x + 3 = 0 \Rightarrow x = -3$

Only $x = \sqrt{3}$, and $x = -3$ are solutions to the original equation. $x = -\sqrt{3}$ and $x = 1$ are extraneous. Note that the graph of $y = x^2 + x - 3 - |x|$ has two x-intercepts.

186. $|x - 10| = x^2 - 10x$

First equation:

$x - 10 = x^2 - 10x$

$0 = x^2 - 11x + 10$

$0 = (x - 1)(x - 10)$

$0 = x - 1 \Rightarrow x = 1$, not a solution

$0 = x - 10 \Rightarrow x = 10$

Second equation:

$-(x - 10) = x^2 - 10x$

$0 = x^2 - 9x - 10$

$0 = (x - 10)(x + 1)$

$0 = x - 10 \Rightarrow x = 10$

$0 = x + 1 \Rightarrow x = -1$

187. $y = x^3 - 2x^2 - 3x$

(a)

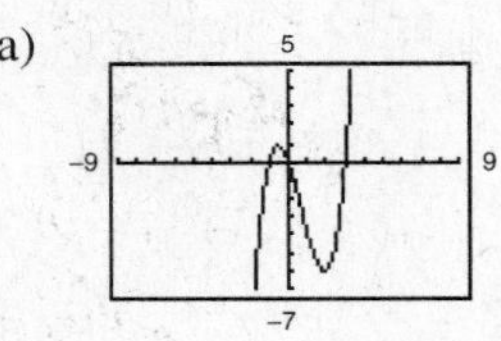

(b) x-intercepts: $(-1, 0), (0, 0), (3, 0)$

(c) $0 = x^3 - 2x^2 - 3x$

$0 = x(x + 1)(x - 3)$

$x = 0$

$x + 1 = 0 \Rightarrow x = -1$

$x - 3 = 0 \Rightarrow x = 3$

(d) The x-intercepts are the same as the solutions.

188. $y = x^4 - 10x^2 + 9$

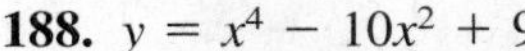

(a)

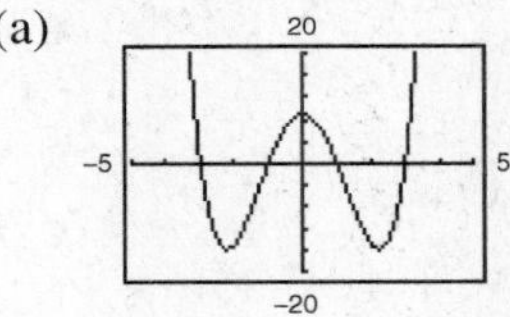

(b) x-intercepts: $(\pm 1, 0), (\pm 3, 0)$

(c) $0 = x^4 - 10x^2 + 9$

$0 = (x^2 - 1)(x^2 - 9)$

$0 = (x + 1)(x - 1)(x + 3)(x - 3)$

$x + 1 = 0 \Rightarrow x = -1$

$x - 1 = 0 \Rightarrow x = 1$

$x + 3 = 0 \Rightarrow x = -3$

$x - 3 = 0 \Rightarrow x = 3$

(d) The x-intercepts are the same as the solutions.

189. $y = \sqrt{11x - 30} - x$

(a)

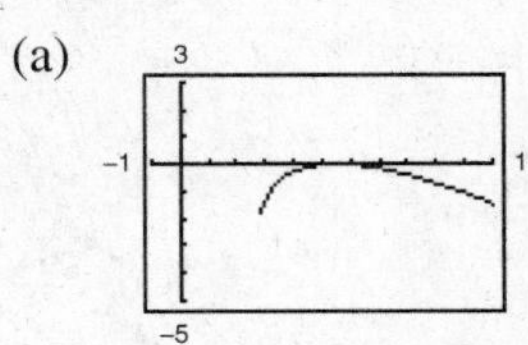

(b) x-intercepts: $(5, 0), (6, 0)$

—CONTINUED—

189. —CONTINUED—

(c)
$$0 = \sqrt{11x - 30} - x$$
$$x = \sqrt{11x - 30}$$
$$x^2 = 11x - 30$$
$$x^2 - 11x + 30 = 0$$
$$(x - 5)(x - 6) = 0$$
$$x - 5 = 0 \Rightarrow x = 5$$
$$x - 6 = 0 \Rightarrow x = 6$$

(d) The x-intercepts and the solutions are the same.

190. $y = 2x - \sqrt{15 - 4x}$

(a)

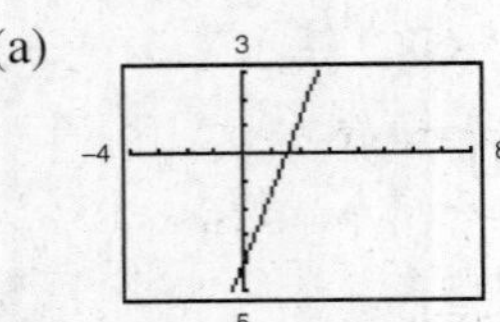

(b) x-intercept: $\left(\frac{3}{2}, 0\right)$

(c) $0 = 2x - \sqrt{15 - 4x}$
$$\sqrt{15 - 4x} = 2x$$
$$15 - 4x = 4x^2$$
$$0 = 4x^2 + 4x - 15$$
$$0 = (2x + 5)(2x - 3)$$
$$0 = 2x + 5 \Rightarrow x = -\frac{5}{2}$$
$$0 = 2x - 3 \Rightarrow x = \frac{3}{2}$$

$x = -\frac{5}{2}$ is extraneous. The x-intercept is $\left(\frac{3}{2}, 0\right)$.

(d) Same as intercept

191. $y = \dfrac{1}{x} - \dfrac{4}{x - 1} - 1$

(a)

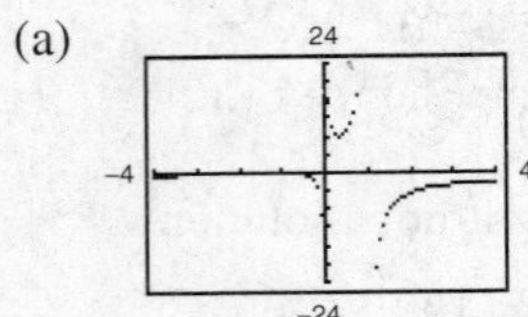

(b) x-intercept: $(-1, 0)$

(c)
$$0 = \frac{1}{x} - \frac{4}{x - 1} - 1$$
$$0 = (x - 1) - 4x - x(x - 1)$$
$$0 = x - 1 - 4x - x^2 + x$$
$$0 = -x^2 - 2x - 1$$
$$0 = x^2 + 2x + 1$$
$$x + 1 = 0 \Rightarrow x = -1$$

(d) The x-intercepts and the solutions are the same.

192. $y = x + \dfrac{9}{x + 1} - 5$

(a)

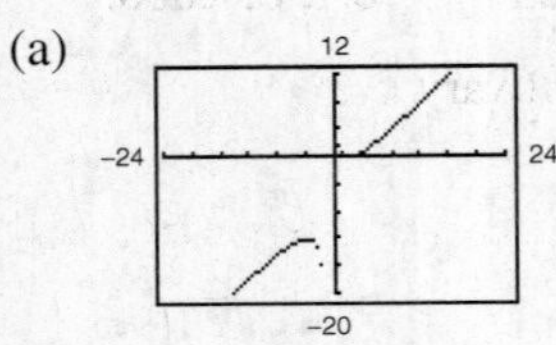

(b) x-intercept: $(2, 0)$

(c) $0 = x + \dfrac{9}{x + 1} - 5$
$$0 = x(x + 1) + (x + 1)\frac{9}{x + 1} - 5(x + 1)$$
$$0 = x^2 + x + 9 - 5x - 5$$
$$0 = x^2 - 4x + 4$$
$$0 = (x - 2)(x - 2)$$
$$0 = x - 2 \Rightarrow x = 2$$

x-intercept: $(2, 0)$

(d) Same as intercept

193. $y = |x + 1| - 2$

(a)

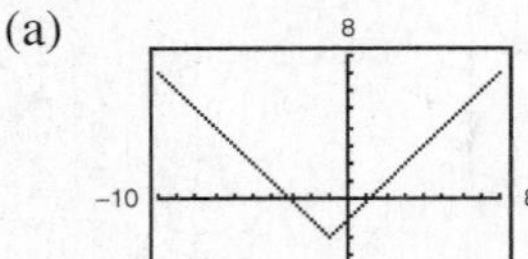

(b) x-intercept: $(1, 0), (-3, 0)$

(c) $0 = |x + 1| - 2$

$2 = |x + 1|$

$x + 1 = 2$ or $-(x + 1) = 2$

$x = 1$ or $-x - 1 = 2$

$-x = 3$

$x = -3$

(d) The x-intercepts and the solutions are the same.

194. $y = |x - 2| - 3$

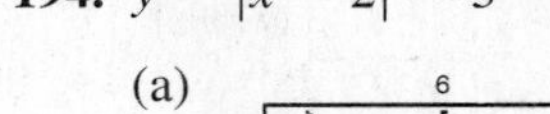

(a)

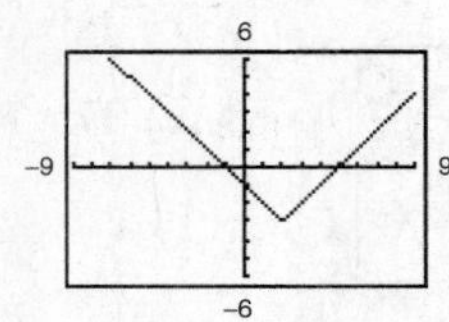

(b) x-intercepts: $(5, 0), (-1, 0)$

(c) $0 = |x - 2| - 3$

$3 = |x - 2|$

First equation:

$x - 2 = 3 \Rightarrow x = 5$

Second equation:

$-(x - 2) = 3$

$-x + 2 = 3 \Rightarrow x = -1$

x-intercepts: $(5, 0), (-1, 0)$

(d) Same as intercepts

195. (a)

6000
0 24
2000

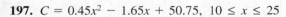

Intersection: $(6.7, 3388.7)$

(b) $45.2t + 3087 = 128.2t + 2533$

$83t = 554$

$t \approx 6.7$

$A = S \approx 3388.7$

The point $(6.7, 3388.7)$ indicates the year, 1986, in which the two populations were the same, about 3388.7 thousand.

(c) The slopes indicate the change in population per year. Arizona's population is growing faster.

(d) For 2010, $t = 30$ and $S \approx 4443$ thousand and $A \approx 6379$ thousand. Answers will vary.

196. (a) $P = 0.1220t^2 + 1.529t + 18.72 = 40$

$0.122t^2 + 1.529t - 21.28 = 0$

$$t = \frac{-1.529 \pm \sqrt{(1.529)^2 - 4(0.122)(-21.28)}}{2(0.122)}$$

$$= \frac{-1.529 \pm \sqrt{12.7225}}{0.244}$$

$t \approx 8.35, -20.89$

Taking the positive root, $t \approx 8.35$ or 1998. Similarly, $P = 50$ yields 10.93, or 2000.

(b) Answers will vary.

(c)

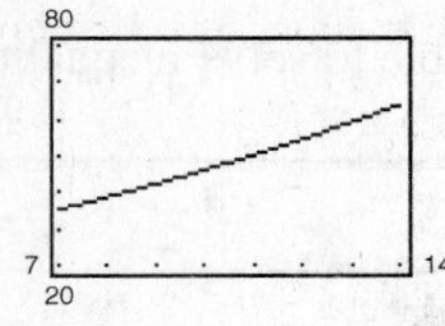

(d) $P = 75$ when $t \approx 16.1$, or 2006.

(e) Answers will vary.

197. $C = 0.45x^2 - 1.65x + 50.75,\ 10 \le x \le 25$

(a)

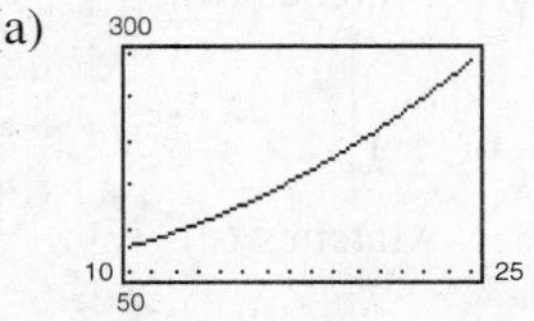

(b) If $C = 150$, then $x = 16.797$ degrees.

(c) If the temperature is increased 10° to 20°, then C increases from 79.25 to 197.75, a factor of 2.5.

198. $T = 75.82 - 2.11x + 43.51\sqrt{x},\ 5 \le x \le 40$

(a)

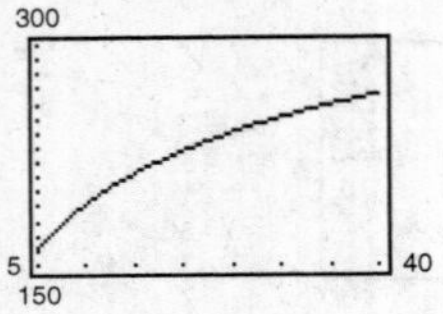

(b) For $x = 14.696$, $T \approx 211.6°\text{F}$.

(c) For $T = 240°\text{F}$, $x \approx 24.725$ pounds/in.^{2}.

199. False. Two linear equations could have an infinite number of points of intersection. For example, $x + y = 1$ and $2x + 2y = 2$.

200. False. An equation can have any number of extraneous solutions. For example, $|x| = x^2 + x + 3$.

201. $2x - 5c = 10 + 3c - 3x, \quad x = 3$

$2(3) - 5c = 10 + 3c - 3(3)$

$6 - 5c = 1 + 3c$

$5 = 8c$

$c = \frac{5}{8}$

202. $5x + 2c = 12 + 4x - 2c, \quad x = 2$

$5(2) + 2c = 12 + 4(2) - 2c$

$10 + 2c = 20 - 2c$

$4c = 10$

$c = \frac{5}{2}$

203. (a) $ax^2 + bx = 0$

$x(ax + b) = 0$

$x = 0$

$x = -b/a$

(b) $ax^2 - ax = 0$

$ax(x - 1) = 0$

$x = 0$

$x = 1$

Appendix B.4 Solving Inequalities Algebraically and Graphically

- You should be able to solve an inequality algebraically using the Properties of Inequalities.
- You should be able to solve inequalities involving absolute values.
- You should be able to solve polynomial inequalities using critical numbers and test intervals.
- You should be able to solve rational inequalities.
- You should be able to solve inequalities using a graphing utility.

Vocabulary Check

1. negative
2. double
3. $-a \le x \le a$
4. $x \le -a,\ x \ge a$
5. zeros, undefined values

1. $x < 3$

Matches (f).

2. $x \ge 5$

Matches (a).

3. $-3 < x \le 4$

Matches (d).

4. $0 \le x \le \frac{9}{2}$

Matches (b).

5. $-1 \le x \le \frac{5}{2}$

Matches (e).

6. $-1 < x < \frac{5}{2}$

Matches (c).

7. (a) $x = 3$

$5(3) - 12 \overset{?}{>} 0$

$3 > 0$

Yes, $x = 3$ is a solution.

(b) $x = -3$

$5(-3) - 12 \overset{?}{>} 0$

$-27 \not> 0$

No, $x = -3$ is not a solution.

(c) $x = \frac{5}{2}$

$5\left(\frac{5}{2}\right) - 12 \overset{?}{>} 0$

$\frac{1}{2} > 0$

Yes, $x = \frac{5}{2}$ is a solution.

(d) $x = \frac{3}{2}$

$5\left(\frac{3}{2}\right) - 12 \overset{?}{>} 0$

$-\frac{9}{2} \not> 0$

No, $x = \frac{3}{2}$ is not a solution.

8. $-5 < 2x - 1 \le 1$

(a) $x = -\frac{1}{2}$

$-5 \overset{?}{<} 2\left(-\frac{1}{2}\right) - 1 \overset{?}{\le} 1$

$-5 \overset{?}{<} -1 - 1 \overset{?}{\le} 1$

$-5 \overset{?}{<} -2 \overset{?}{\le} 1$

Yes, $x = -\frac{1}{2}$ is a solution.

(b) $x = -\frac{5}{2}$

$-5 \overset{?}{<} 2\left(-\frac{5}{2}\right) - 1 \overset{?}{\le} 1$

$-5 \overset{?}{<} -6 \overset{?}{\le} 1$

No, $x = -\frac{5}{2}$ is not a solution.

(c) $x = \frac{4}{3}$

$-5 \overset{?}{<} 2\left(\frac{4}{3}\right) - 1 \overset{?}{\le} 1$

$-5 \overset{?}{<} \frac{8}{3} - 1 \overset{?}{\le} 1$

$-5 \overset{?}{<} \frac{5}{3} \overset{?}{\le} 1$

No, $x = \frac{4}{3}$ is not a solution.

(d) $x = 0$

$-5 \overset{?}{<} 2(0) - 1 \overset{?}{\le} 1$

$-5 < -1 \overset{?}{\le} 1$

Yes, $x = 0$ is a solution.

9. $-1 < \dfrac{3 - x}{2} \le 1$

(a) $x = 0$

$-1 \overset{?}{<} \dfrac{3 - 0}{2} \overset{?}{\le} 1$

$-1 \overset{?}{<} \dfrac{3}{2} \overset{?}{\le} 1$

No, $x = 0$ is not a solution.

(b) $x = \sqrt{5}$

$-1 \overset{?}{<} \dfrac{3 - \sqrt{5}}{2} \overset{?}{\le} 1$

$-1 \overset{?}{<} 0.382 \overset{?}{\le} 1$

Yes, $x = \sqrt{5}$ is a solution.

(c) $x = 1$

$-1 \overset{?}{<} \dfrac{3 - 1}{2} \overset{?}{\le} 1$

$-1 \overset{?}{<} 1 \overset{?}{\le} 1$

Yes, $x = 1$ is a solution.

(d) $x = 5$

$-1 \overset{?}{<} \dfrac{3 - 5}{2} \le 1$

$-1 \overset{?}{<} -1 \overset{?}{\le} 1$

No, $x = 5$ is not a solution.

10. $|x - 10| \geq 3$

(a) $x = 13$

$|13 - 10| \stackrel{?}{\geq} 3$

$3 \geq 3$

Yes, $x = 13$ is a solution.

(b) $x = -1$

$|-1 - 10| \stackrel{?}{\geq} 3$

$|-11| \stackrel{?}{\geq} 3$

$11 \geq 3$

Yes, $x = -1$ is a solution.

(c) $x = 14$

$|14 - 10| \stackrel{?}{\geq} 3$

$4 \geq 3$

Yes, $x = 14$ is a solution.

(d) $x = 9$

$|9 - 10| \stackrel{?}{\geq} 3$

$1 \stackrel{?}{\geq} 3$

No, $x = 9$ is not a solution.

11. $-10x < 40$

$-\frac{1}{10}(-10x) > -\frac{1}{10}(40)$

$x > -4$

12. $6x > 15$

$2x > 5$

$x > \frac{5}{2}$

13. $4(x + 1) < 2x + 3$

$4x + 4 < 2x + 3$

$2x < -1$

$x < -\frac{1}{2}$

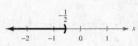

14. $2x + 7 < 3(x - 4)$

$2x + 7 < 3x - 12$

$19 < x$

15. $\frac{3}{4}x - 6 \leq x - 7$

$1 \leq \frac{1}{4}x$

$4 \leq x$

$x \geq 4$

16. $3 + \frac{2}{7}x > x - 2$

$21 + 2x > 7x - 14$

$35 > 5x$

$7 > x$

$x < 7$

17. $-8 \leq 1 - 3(x - 2) < 13$

$-8 \leq 1 - 3x + 6 < 13$

$-8 \leq -3x + 7 < 13$

$-15 \leq -3x < 6$

$5 \geq x > -2 \Rightarrow -2 < x \leq 5$

18. $0 \leq 2 - 3(x + 1) < 20$

$0 \leq -3x - 1 < 20$

$1 \leq -3x < 21$

$-\frac{1}{3} \geq x > -7$

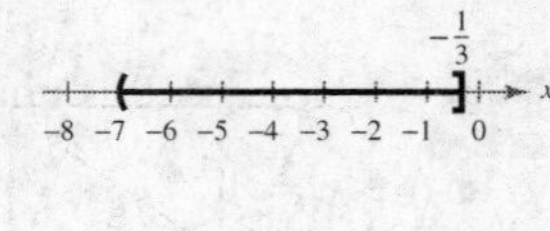

19. $-4 < \dfrac{2x - 3}{3} < 4$

$-12 < 2x - 3 < 12$

$-9 < 2x < 15$

$-\dfrac{9}{2} < x < \dfrac{15}{2}$

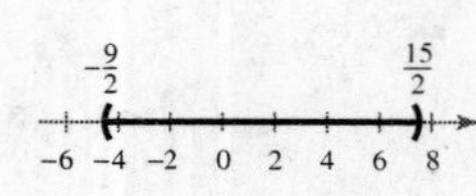

20. $0 \leq \dfrac{x + 3}{2} < 5$

$0 \leq x + 3 < 10$

$-3 \leq x < 7$

21. $5 - 2x \geq 1$

$-2x \geq -4$

$x \leq 2$

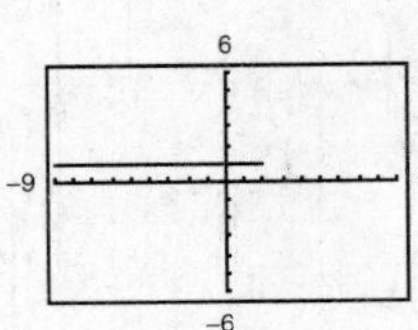

22. $20 < 6x - 1$

$x > \frac{7}{2}$

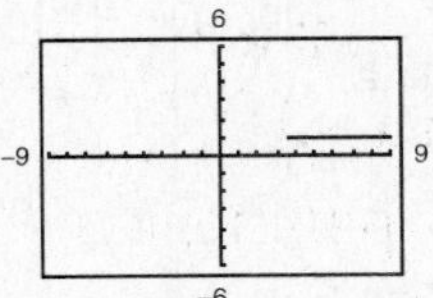

23. $3(x + 1) < x + 7$

$3x + 3 < x + 7$

$2x < 4$

$x < 2$

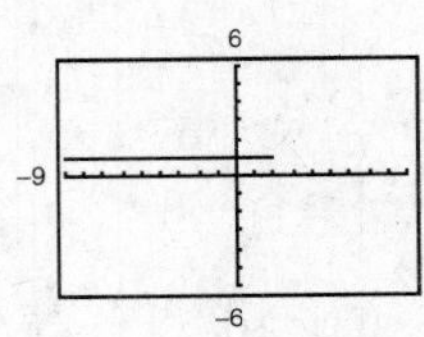

24. $4(x - 3) \leq 8 - x$

$x \leq 4$

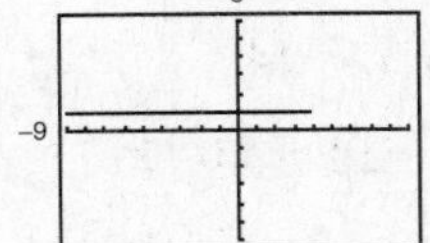

25.

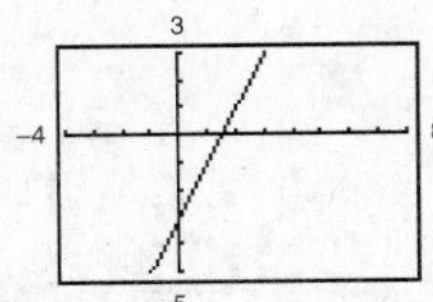

Using the graph, (a) $y \geq 1$ for $x \geq 2$ and (b) $y \leq 0$ for $x \leq \frac{3}{2}$.
Algebraically:

(a) $y \geq 1$

$2x - 3 \geq 1$

$2x \geq 4$

$x \geq 2$

(b) $y \leq 0$

$2x - 3 \leq 0$

$2x \leq 3$

$x \leq \frac{3}{2}$

26.

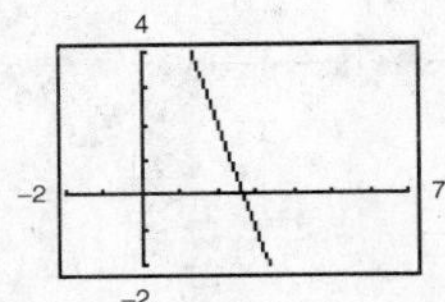

Using the graph, (a) $-1 \leq y \leq 3$ for $\frac{5}{3} \leq x \leq 3$, and (b) $y \leq 0$ for $x \geq \frac{8}{3}$.
Algebraically:

(a) $-1 \leq y \leq 3$

$-1 \leq -3x + 8 \leq 3$

$-9 \leq -3x \leq -5$

$3 \geq x \geq \frac{5}{3}$

(b) $y \leq 0$

$-3x + 8 \leq 0$

$8 \leq 3x$

$\frac{8}{3} \leq x$

27.

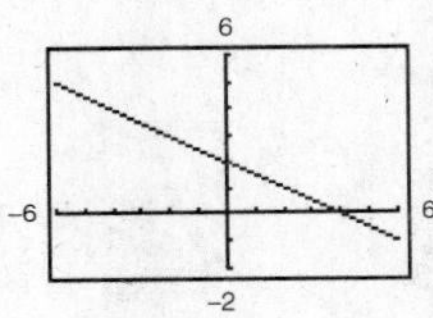

Using the graph, (a) $0 \leq y \leq 3$ for $-2 \leq x \leq 4$ and (b) $y \geq 0$ for $x \leq 4$.
Algebraically:

(a) $0 \leq y \leq 3$

$0 \leq -\frac{1}{2}x + 2 \leq 3$

$-2 \leq -\frac{1}{2}x \leq 1$

$4 \geq x \geq -2$

(b) $y \geq 0$

$-\frac{1}{2}x + 2 \geq 0$

$2 \geq \frac{1}{2}x$

$4 \geq x$

28.

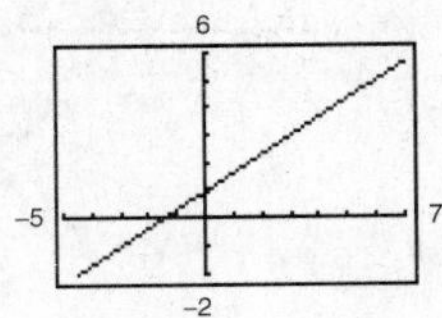
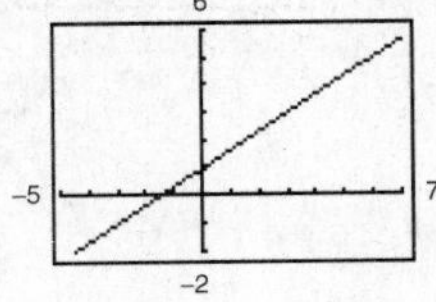

Using the graph, (a) $y \leq 5$ for $x \leq 6$, and (b) $y \geq 0$ for $x \geq -\frac{3}{2}$.
Algebraically:

(a) $y \leq 5$

$\frac{2}{3}x + 1 \leq 5$

$\frac{2}{3}x \leq 4$

$x \leq 6$

(b) $y \geq 0$

$\frac{2}{3}x + 1 \geq 0$

$\frac{2}{3}x \geq -1$

$x \geq -\frac{3}{2}$

29. $|5x| > 10$

$5x < -10$ or $5x > 10$

$x < -2$ or $x > 2$

$-3 \quad -2 \quad -1 \quad 0 \quad 1 \quad 2 \quad 3 \quad x$

30. $\left|\frac{x}{2}\right| \le 1$

$|x| \le 2$

$-2 \le x \le 2$

31. $|x - 7| < 6$

$-6 < x - 7 < 6$

$1 < x < 13$

32. $|x - 20| \ge 4$

$x - 20 \ge 4 \quad \text{or} \quad x - 20 \le -4$

$x \ge 24 \quad \text{or} \quad x \le 16$

33. $|x + 14| + 3 > 17$

$|x + 14| > 14$

$x + 14 < -14 \quad \text{or} \quad x + 14 > 14$

$x < -28 \quad \text{or} \quad x > 0$

34. $\left|\frac{x - 3}{2}\right| \ge 5$

$|x - 3| \ge 10$

$x - 3 \ge 10 \quad \text{or} \quad x - 3 \le -10$

$x \ge 13 \quad \text{or} \quad x \le -7$

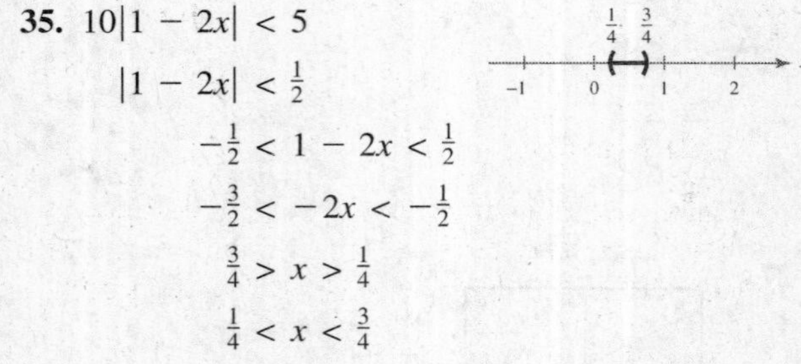

35. $10|1 - 2x| < 5$

$|1 - 2x| < \frac{1}{2}$

$-\frac{1}{2} < 1 - 2x < \frac{1}{2}$

$-\frac{3}{2} < -2x < -\frac{1}{2}$

$\frac{3}{4} > x > \frac{1}{4}$

$\frac{1}{4} < x < \frac{3}{4}$

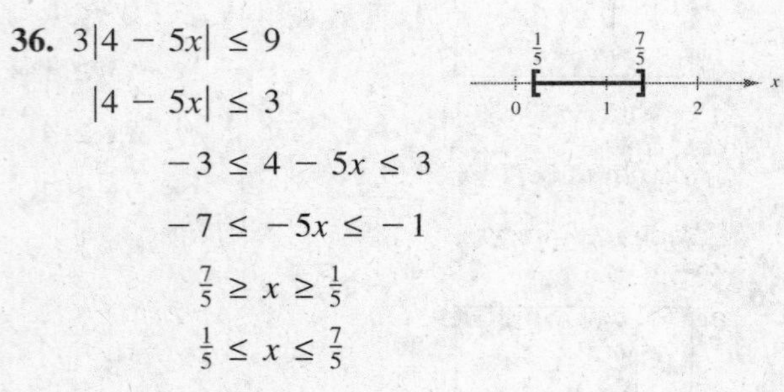

36. $3|4 - 5x| \le 9$

$|4 - 5x| \le 3$

$-3 \le 4 - 5x \le 3$

$-7 \le -5x \le -1$

$\frac{7}{5} \ge x \ge \frac{1}{5}$

$\frac{1}{5} \le x \le \frac{7}{5}$

37. $y = |x - 3|$

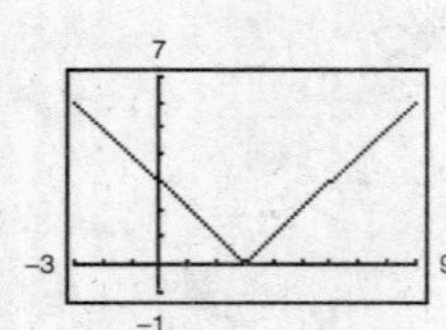

Graphically, (a) $y \le 2$ for $1 \le x \le 5$ and (b) $y \ge 4$ for $x \le -1$ or $x \ge 7$.

Algebraically:

(a) $y \le 2$

$|x - 3| \le 2$

$-2 \le x - 3 \le 2$

$1 \le x \le 5$

(b) $y \ge 4$

$|x - 3| \ge 4$

$x - 3 \le -4 \quad \text{or} \quad x - 3 \ge 4$

$x \le -1 \quad \text{or} \quad x \ge 7$

38. $y = \left|\frac{1}{2}x + 1\right|$

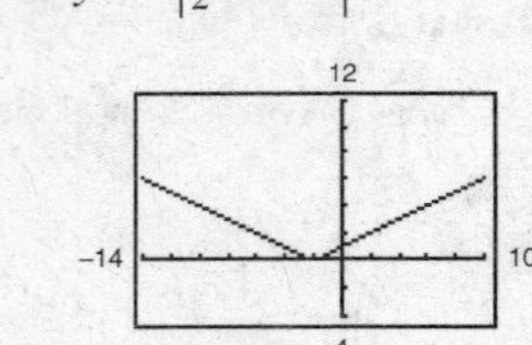

Algebraically:

(a) $y \le 4$

$\left|\frac{1}{2}x + 1\right| \le 4$

$-4 \le \frac{1}{2}x \le 4$

$-5 \le \frac{1}{2}x \le 3$

$-10 \le x \le 6$

(b) $y \ge 1$

$\left|\frac{1}{2}x + 1\right| \ge 1$

$\frac{1}{2}x + 1 \le -1 \quad \text{or} \quad \frac{1}{2}x + 1 \ge 1$

$\frac{1}{2}x \le -2 \quad \text{or} \quad \frac{1}{2}x \ge 0$

$x \le -4 \quad \text{or} \quad x \ge 0$

39. The midpoint of the interval $[-3, 3]$ is 0. The interval represents all real numbers x no more than three units from 0.

$|x - 0| \leq 3$

$|x| \leq 3$

40. The graph shows all real numbers no more than four units from -1.

$|x + 1| \leq 4$

41. The midpoint of the interval $[-3, 3]$ is 0. The two intervals represent all numbers x more than three units from 0.

$|x - 0| > 3$

$|x| > 3$

42. The graph shows all real numbers at least three units from 7.

$|x - 7| \geq 3$

43. All real numbers within 10 units of 7

$|x - 7| \leq 10$

44. $|x + 5| \leq 8$

45. All real numbers at least five units from 3

$|x - 3| \geq 5$

46. All real numbers more than three units from -1

$|x + 1| > 3$

47. $x^2 - 4x - 5 > 0$

$(x - 5)(x + 1) > 0$

Critical numbers: $-1, 5$

Testing the intervals $(-\infty, -1)$, $(-1, 5)$ and $(5, \infty)$, we have $x^2 - 4x - 5 > 0$ on $(-\infty, -1)$ and $(5, \infty)$. Similarly, $x^2 - 4x - 5 < 0$ on $(-1, 5)$.

48. $x^2 - 3x - 4 > 0$

$(x - 4)(x + 1) > 0$

Critical numbers: $-1, 4$

Testing the intervals $(-\infty, -1)$, $(-1, 4)$, and $(4, \infty)$, we have $x^2 - 3x - 4 > 0$ on $(-\infty, -1)$ and $(4, \infty)$. Similarly, $x^2 - 3x - 4 < 0$ on $(-1, 4)$.

49. $2x^2 - 4x - 3 = 0$

$$x = \frac{4 \pm \sqrt{16 + 24}}{4} = 1 \pm \frac{\sqrt{10}}{2}$$

Entirely negative: $\left(1 - \frac{\sqrt{10}}{2}, 1 + \frac{\sqrt{10}}{2}\right) \approx (-0.581, 2.581)$

Entirely positive: $\left(-\infty, 1 - \frac{\sqrt{10}}{2}\right) \cup \left(1 + \frac{\sqrt{10}}{2}, \infty\right)$

50. $2x^2 - x - 5 = 0$

$$x = \frac{1 \pm \sqrt{1 - 4(2)(-5)}}{2(2)} = \frac{1 \pm \sqrt{41}}{4}, \text{ critical numbers}$$

Test intervals: $\left(-\infty, \frac{1}{4} - \frac{\sqrt{41}}{4}\right), \left(\frac{1}{4} - \frac{\sqrt{41}}{4}, \frac{1}{4} + \frac{\sqrt{41}}{4}\right)$, and $\left(\frac{1}{4} + \frac{\sqrt{41}}{4}, \infty\right)$

Testing these intervals, we have

$2x^2 - x - 5 > 0$ on $\left(-\infty, \frac{1}{4} - \frac{\sqrt{41}}{4}\right)$ and $\left(\frac{1}{4} + \frac{\sqrt{41}}{4}, \infty\right)$,

$2x^2 - x - 5 < 0$ on $\left(\frac{1}{4} - \frac{\sqrt{41}}{4}, \frac{1}{4} + \frac{\sqrt{41}}{4}\right)$.

51. $x^2 - 4x + 5 > 0$ for all x. There are no critical numbers because $x^2 - 4x + 5 \neq 0$. The only test interval is $(-\infty, \infty)$.

52. $-x^2 + 6x - 10 < 0$ for all x. There are no critical numbers because $-x^2 + 6x - 10 \neq 0$. The only test interval is $(-\infty, \infty)$.

53. $(x + 2)^2 < 25$

$x^2 + 4x + 4 < 25$

$x^2 + 4x - 21 < 0$

$(x + 7)(x - 3) < 0$

Critical numbers: $x = -7, x = 3$

Test intervals: $(-\infty, -7), (-7, 3), (3, \infty)$

Test: Is $(x + 7)(x - 3) < 0$?

Solution set: $(-7, 3)$

54. $(x - 3)^2 \geq 1$

$x - 3 \geq 1$ or $x - 3 \leq -1$

$x \geq 4$ or $x \leq 2$

55. $x^2 + 4x + 4 \geq 9$

$x^2 + 4x - 5 \geq 0$

$(x + 5)(x - 1) \geq 0$

Critical numbers: $x = -5, x = 1$

Test intervals: $(-\infty, -5), (-5, 1), (1, \infty)$

Test: Is $(x + 5)(x - 1) \geq 0$?

Solution set: $(-\infty, -5] \cup [1, \infty)$

56. $x^2 - 6x + 9 < 16$

$x^2 - 6x - 7 < 0$

$(x + 1)(x - 7) < 0$

Critical numbers: $x = -1, x = 7$

Test intervals: $(-\infty, -1) \Rightarrow (x + 1)(x - 7) > 0$

$(-1, 7) \Rightarrow (x + 1)(x - 7) < 0$

$(7, \infty) \Rightarrow (x + 1)(x - 7) > 0$

Solution interval: $(-1, 7)$

57. $x^3 - 4x \geq 0$

$x(x + 2)(x - 2) \geq 0$

Critical number: $x = 0, x = \pm 2$

Test intervals: $(-\infty, -2), (-2, 0), (0, 2), (2, \infty)$

Test: Is $x(x + 2)(x - 2) \geq 0$?

Solution set: $[-2, 0] \cup [2, \infty)$

58. $x^4(x - 3) \leq 0$

Critical numbers: $x = 0, x = 3$

Test intervals: $(-\infty, 0) \Rightarrow x^4(x - 3) < 0$

$(0, 3) \Rightarrow x^4(x - 3) < 0$

$(3, \infty) \Rightarrow x^4(x - 3) > 0$

Solution intervals: $(-\infty, 0] \cup [0, 3]$ or $(-\infty, 3]$

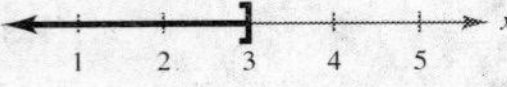

59. $3x^2 - 11x + 16 \leq 0$

Since $b^2 - 4ac = -71 < 0$, there are no real solutions to $3x^2 - 11x + 16 = 0$. In fact, $3x^2 - 11x + 16 > 0$ for all x.

No solution

60. $4x^2 + 12x + 9 \leq 0$

$(2x + 3)^2 \leq 0$

$2x + 3 = 0$

$x = -\frac{3}{2}$

61. $2x^3 + 5x^2 - 6x - 9 > 0$

$(x + 1)(x + 3)(2x - 3) > 0$

Critical numbers: $-3, -1, \frac{3}{2}$

Testing the four intervals, we see that $2x^3 + 5x^2 - 6x - 9 > 0$ on $(-3, -1)$ and $\left(\frac{3}{2}, \infty\right)$.

62. $2x^3 + 3x^2 - 11x - 6 < 0$

$(x - 2)(x + 3)(2x + 1) < 0$

Critical numbers: $-3, -\frac{1}{2}, 2$

Testing the four intervals, we see that $2x^3 + 3x^2 - 11x - 6 < 0$ on $(-\infty, -3)$ and $\left(-\frac{1}{2}, 2\right)$.

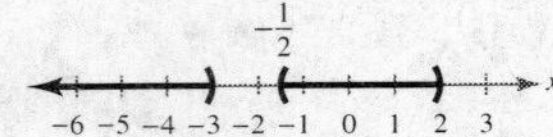

63. (a) $f(x) = g(x)$ when $x = 1$.

(b) $f(x) \geq g(x)$ when $x \geq 1$.

(c) $f(x) > g(x)$ when $x > 1$.

64. (a) $f(x) = g(x)$ when $x = -1$ or $x = 3$.

(b) $f(x) \geq g(x)$ when $x \leq -1$ or $x \geq 3$.

(c) $f(x) > g(x)$ when $x < -1$ or $x > 3$.

65. $y = -x^2 + 2x + 3$

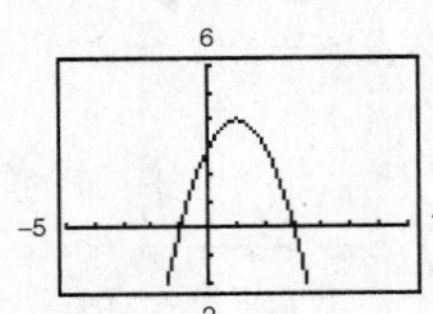

(a) $y \leq 0$ when $x \leq -1$ or $x \geq 3$.

(b) $y \geq 3$ when $0 \leq x \leq 2$.

Algebraically,

$$-x^2 + 2x + 3 \leq 0$$
$$x^2 - 2x - 3 \geq 0$$
$$(x - 3)(x + 1) \geq 0$$

Critical numbers: $x = -1, x = 3$

Testing the intervals $(-\infty, -1)$, $(-1, 3)$, and $(3, \infty)$, you obtain $x \leq -1$ or $x \geq 3$.

$$-x^2 + 2x + 3 \geq 3$$
$$-x^2 + 2x \geq 0$$
$$x^2 - 2x \leq 0$$
$$x(x - 2) \leq 0$$

Critical numbers: $x = 0, x = 2$

Testing the intervals $(-\infty, 0)$, $(0, 2)$, and $(2, \infty)$, you obtain $0 \leq x \leq 2$.

66. $y = x^3 - x^2 - 16x + 16$

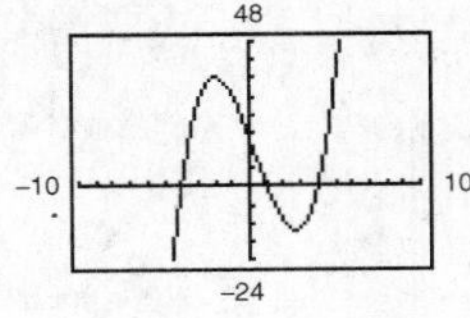

(a) $y \leq 0$

$$x^3 - x^2 - 16x + 16 \leq 0$$
$$x^2(x - 1) - 16(x - 1) \leq 0$$
$$(x - 1)(x^2 - 16) \leq 0$$

$y \leq 0$ when $-\infty < x \leq -4, 1 \leq x \leq 4$.

(b) $y \geq 36$

$$x^3 - x^2 - 16x + 16 \geq 36$$
$$x^3 - x^2 - 16x - 20 \geq 0$$
$$(x + 2)(x - 5)(x + 2) \geq 0$$

$y \geq 36$ when $x = -2, 5 \leq x < \infty$.

67. $\dfrac{1}{x} - x > 0$

$$\frac{1 - x^2}{x} > 0$$

Critical numbers: $x = 0, x = \pm 1$

Test intervals: $(-\infty, -1), (-1, 0), (0, 1), (1, \infty)$

Test: Is $\dfrac{1 - x^2}{x} > 0$?

Solution set: $(-\infty, -1) \cup (0, 1)$

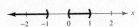

68. $\dfrac{1}{x} - 4 < 0$

$$\frac{1 - 4x}{x} < 0$$

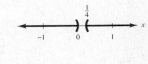

Critical numbers: $x = 0, x = \dfrac{1}{4}$

Test intervals: $(-\infty, 0) \Rightarrow \dfrac{1 - 4x}{x} < 0$

$\left(0, \dfrac{1}{4}\right) \Rightarrow \dfrac{1 - 4x}{x} > 0$

$\left(\dfrac{1}{4}, \infty\right) \Rightarrow \dfrac{1 - 4x}{x} < 0$

Solution interval: $(-\infty, 0) \cup \left(\dfrac{1}{4}, \infty\right)$

69. $\dfrac{x+6}{x+1} - 2 < 0$

$$\frac{x+6-2(x+1)}{x+1} < 0$$

$$\frac{4-x}{x+1} < 0$$

Critical numbers: $x = -1, x = 4$

Test intervals: $(-\infty, -1), (-1, 4), (4, \infty)$

Test: Is $\dfrac{4-x}{x+1} < 0$?

Solution set: $(-\infty, -1) \cup (4, \infty)$

70. $\dfrac{x+12}{x+2} - 3 \geq 0$

$$\frac{x+12-3(x+2)}{x+2} \geq 0$$

$$\frac{6-2x}{x+2} \geq 0$$

Critical numbers: $x = -2, x = 3$

Test intervals: $(-\infty, -2) \Rightarrow \dfrac{6-2x}{x+2} < 0$

$(-2, 3) \Rightarrow \dfrac{6-2x}{x+2} > 0$

$(3, \infty) \Rightarrow \dfrac{6-2x}{x+2} < 0$

Solution interval: $(-2, 3]$

71. $y = \dfrac{3x}{x-2}$

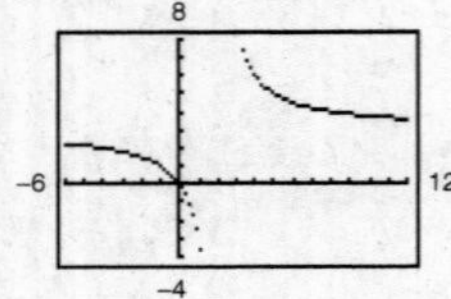

(a) $y \leq 0$ when $0 \leq x < 2$.

(b) $y \geq 6$ when $2 < x \leq 4$.

72. $y = \dfrac{5x}{x^2+4}$

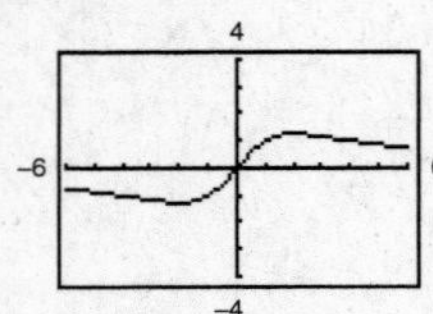

(a) $y \geq 1$

$$\frac{5x}{x^2+4} \geq 1$$

$$\frac{5x-(x^2+4)}{(x^2+4)} \geq 0$$

$$\frac{(x-4)(x-1)}{x^2+4} \leq 0$$

$y \geq 1$ when $1 \leq x \leq 4$.

(b) $y \leq 0$

$$\frac{5x}{x^2+4} \leq 0$$

$y \leq 0$ when $-\infty < x \leq 0$.

73. $\sqrt{x-5}$

Need: $x - 5 \geq 0$

$x \geq 5$

Domain: $[5, \infty)$

74. $\sqrt[4]{6x+15}$

$6x + 15 \geq 0$

$6x \geq -15$

$x \geq -\frac{15}{6}$

$x \geq -\frac{5}{2}$

$\left[-\frac{5}{2}, \infty\right)$

75. $\sqrt[3]{6-x}$

Domain: all real x

76. $\sqrt[3]{2x^2-8}$

Domain: all real x

77. $\sqrt{x^2 - 4}$

Need: $x^2 - 4 \geq 0$

$(x + 2)(x - 2) \geq 0$

$x \leq -2$ or $x \geq 2$

Domain: $(-\infty, -2] \cup [2, \infty)$

78. $\sqrt[4]{4 - x^2}$

Need: $4 - x^2 \geq 0$

$x^2 - 4 \leq 0$

$(x - 2)(x + 2) \leq 0$

Testing each interval, the solution is $-2 \leq x \leq 2$.

Domain: $[-2, 2]$

79. (a) $P(t) = 1000$

This occurs at the point of intersection, $t \approx 4$, or 1994.

(b) Less than one million: $P(t) < 1000$
This occurs for $t < 4$, or before 1994.

Greater than one million: $P(t) > 1000$
This occurs for $t > 4$, or after 1994.

80. (a) $p(t) = 2450$ for $t \approx 8$, or 1998

(b) $p(t) < 2450$ for (1998, 2004), and $p(t) > 2450$ for (1993, 1998).

81. (a) $s = -16t^2 + v_0t + s_0$

$s = -16t^2 + 160t$

$s = 16t(10 - t)$

$s = 0$ when $t = 10$ seconds.

(b) $s = -16t^2 + 160t > 384$

$16t^2 - 160t + 384 < 0$

$16(t - 6)(t - 4) < 0$

$s > 384$ when $4 < t < 6$.

82. (a) $s = -16t^2 + v_0t + s_0$

$= -16t^2 + 128t$

$= 16t(8 - t)$

$t = 8$ seconds

(b) $-16t^2 + 128t < 128$

$16t^2 - 128t + 128 < 0$

Critical numbers: 1.17, 6.83

(0, 1.17), (6.83, 8)

83. (a)

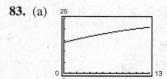

(b) $15 < D < 20$ for $1.28 < t < 10.09$, or between 1991 and 2000

(c) $15 < D < 20$

$15 < -0.0165t^2 + 0.755t + 14.06 < 20$

To solve these inequalities, find the critical numbers.

$0.0165t^2 - 0.755t + 0.94 = 0$

$$t = \frac{0.755 \pm \sqrt{(-0.755)^2 - 4(0.0165)(0.94)}}{2(0.0165)}$$

$$= \frac{0.755 \pm \sqrt{0.507985}}{0.033}$$

Because $0 < t < 13$, select the negative sign, $t \approx 1.28$. Hence, $15 < D$ for $1.28 < t$. Similarly, $D < 20$ for $t < 10.09$.

(d) No. $D(t) < 30$ for all t.

84. (a), (b)

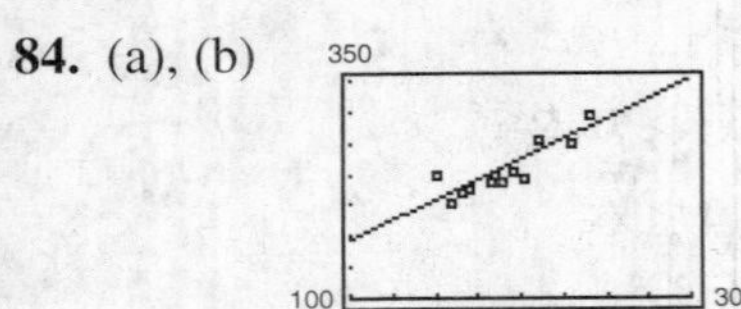

(c) For $y \geq 200$, $x \geq 181.5$ pounds.

(d) The model is not accurate. The data is not linear. Other factors include muscle strength, height, physical condition, etc.

85.

$$V(t) \geq 65$$
$$3.37t + 57.9 \geq 65$$
$$3.37t \geq 7.1$$
$$t \geq 2.11$$

The number of hours playing video games exceeded 65 in 2002.

86.

$$N(t) \leq 175$$
$$-2.51t + 179.6 \leq 175$$
$$4.6 \leq 2.51t$$
$$1.83 \leq t$$

The number of hours reading daily newspapers was below 175 at the end of 2001.

87.

$$V(t) = N(t)$$
$$3.37t + 57.9 = -2.51t + 179.6$$
$$5.88t = 121.7$$
$$t \approx 20.7$$

According to these models, the number of hours reading daily newspapers and playing video games will be the same in 2020.

88.

$$V(t) > N(t)$$
$$3.37t + 57.9 > -2.51t + 179.6$$
$$5.88t > 121.7$$
$$t > 20.7$$

According to these models, the number of hours playing video games will exceed the number of hours reading daily newspapers in 2020.

89. When $t = 2$, $v \approx 333$ vibrations per second.

90. For $v = 600$, $t \approx 3.6$ mm.

91. When $200 \leq v \leq 400$, $1.2 < t < 2.4$.

92. For $t < 3$, $0 < v < 500$.

93. (a) Option A: $A(t) = 0.15t + 12$

Option B: $B(t) = 0.20t$

(b)

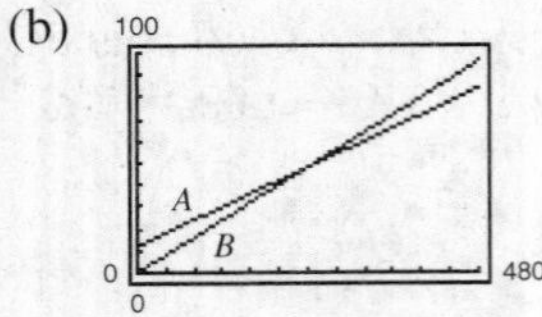

(c) $A(t) = B(t)$ when $t = 240$. $B(t)$ is the better choice if you use less than 240 minutes. $A(t)$ is the better choice if you use more than 240 minutes.

(d) Answers will vary.

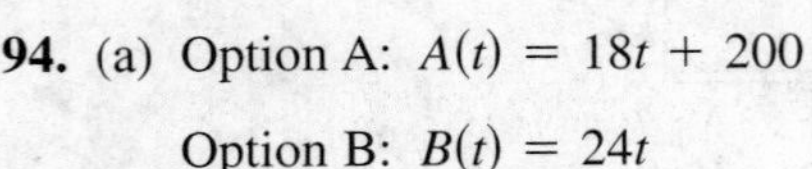

94. (a) Option A: $A(t) = 18t + 200$

Option B: $B(t) = 24t$

(b)

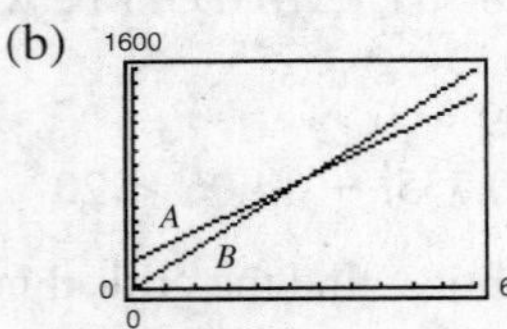

(c) $A(t) = B(t)$ when $t \approx 33.3$. $B(t)$ is the better choice if the move takes less than 33.3 hours. $A(t)$ is the better choice if the move takes more than 33.3 hours.

(d) Answers will vary.

95. False. If $-10 \leq x \leq 8$, then $10 \geq -x$ and $-x \geq -8$.

96. True. $\frac{3}{2}x^2 + 3x + 6 \geq 0$ for all x.

97. The polynomial $f(x) = (x - a)(x - b)$ is zero at $x = a$ and $x = b$.

98. For $(-\infty, a)$, $(x - a) < 0$, $(x - b) < 0$, and $(x - a)(x - b) > 0$.

For (a, b), $(x - a) > 0$, $(x - b) < 0$, and $(x - a)(x - b) < 0$.

For (b, ∞), $(x - a) > 0$, $(x - b) > 0$, and $(x - a)(x - b) > 0$.

The polynomial changes signs at the zeros, $x = a$ and $x = b$.

99. (iv) $a < b$

(ii) $2a < 2b$

(iii) $2a < a + b < 2b$

(i) $a < \dfrac{a + b}{2} < b$

100. (ii) $0 < a < b$

(i) $a^2 < ab < b^2$

(iii) $a < \sqrt{ab} < b$

Appendix B.5 Representing Data Graphically

- You should be able to construct line plots.
- You should be able to construct histograms or frequency distributions.
- You should be able to construct bar graphs.
- You should be able to construct line graphs.

Vocabulary Check

1. Statistics **2.** Line plots **3.** histogram

4. frequency distribution **5.** bar graph **6.** Line graphs

1. (a) The price 2.569 occurred with the greatest frequency (6).

(b) The prices range from 2.459 to 2.649. The range is $2.649 - 2.459 = 0.19$.

2. (a) The weight of 900 pounds occurred with the greatest frequency (9).

(b) The weights range from 600 to 1300 pounds. The range of weights is $1300 - 600 = 700$ pounds.

3.

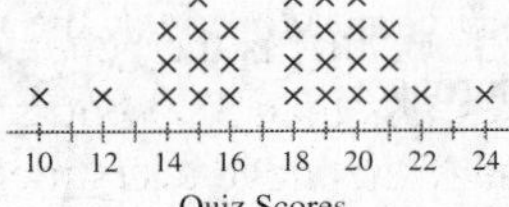

The score of 15 occurred with the greatest frequency.

4.

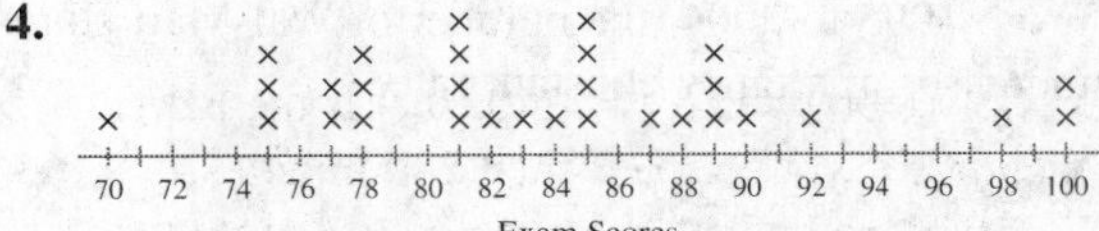

The scores 81 and 85 occurred with the greatest frequency.

5. (Answers will depend on intervals selected.)

Interval	*Tally*
[0, 25)	𝍸 𝍸 𝍸 |||
[25, 50)	𝍸 𝍸 𝍸 |
[50, 75)	𝍸 |
[75, 100)	𝍸 |||
[100, 125)	|
[125, 150)	
[150, 175)	
[175, 200)	
[200, 225)	
[225, 250)	|

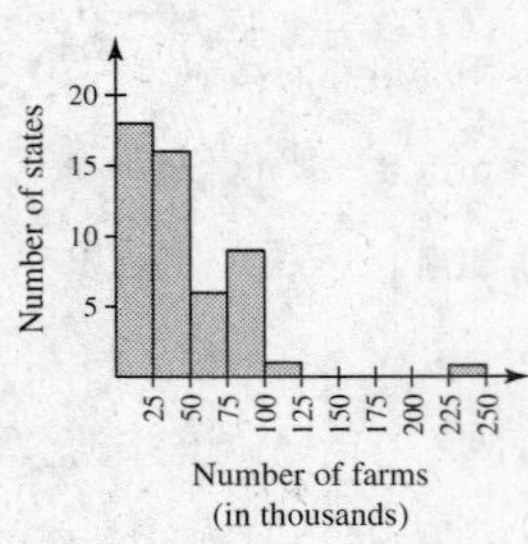

6. Sample answer:

Interval	*Tally*
[0, 40)	𝍸 𝍸 𝍸 𝍸 𝍸 ||||
[40, 80)	𝍸 𝍸 |||
[80, 120)	|||
[120, 160)	||||
[160, 200)	
[200, 240)	|
[240, 280)	
[280, 320)	
[320, 360)	|

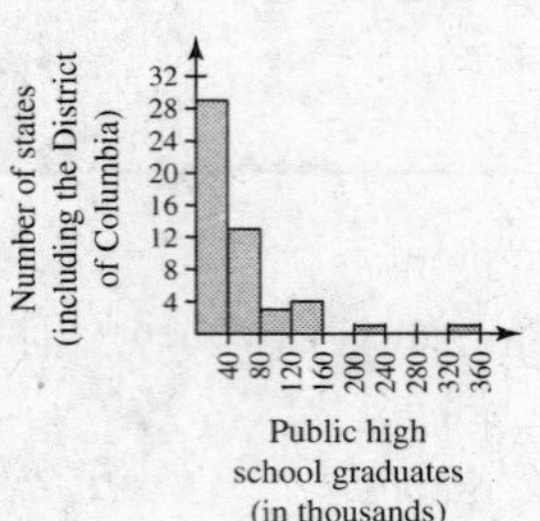

7.

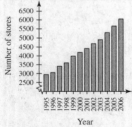

From 1995 to 2006, the number of Wal-Mart stores increases at a fairly constant rate.

8.

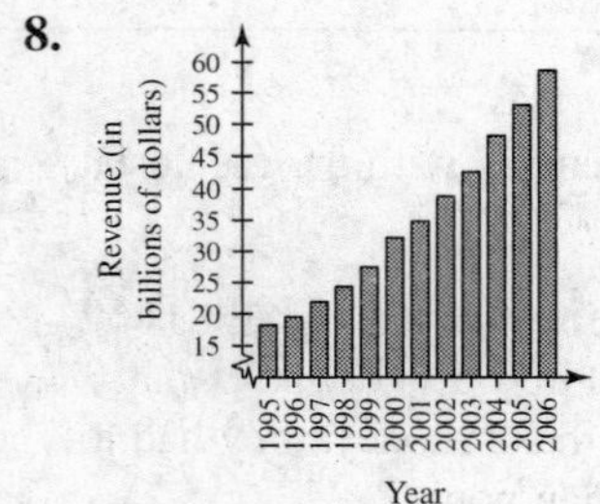

From 1995 to 2006, the revenue of Costco Wholesale increases every year. Moreover, the rate of increase appears to increase.

9. 1999: 13,428 − 2430 = \$10,998

2000: 14,081 − 2506 = \$11,575

2001: 15,000 − 2562 = \$12,438

2002: 15,742 − 2700 = \$13,042

2003: 16,383 − 2903 = \$13,480

2004: 17,442 − 3313 = \$14,129

10.

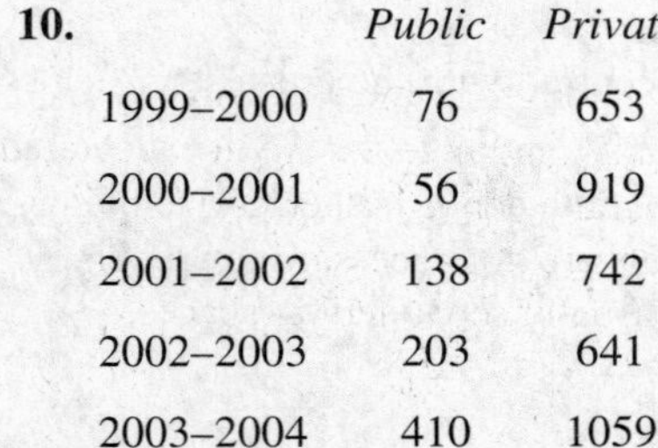

	Public	*Private*
1999–2000	76	653
2000–2001	56	919
2001–2002	138	742
2002–2003	203	641
2003–2004	410	1059

11.

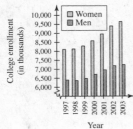

12.

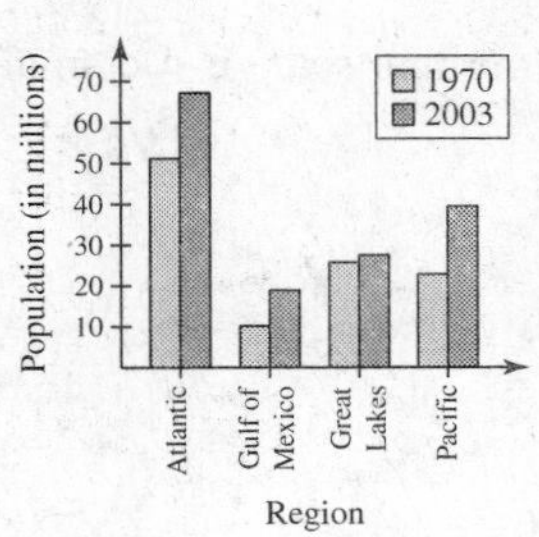

13. From 1996 to 2005:

$$\frac{2400 - 1100}{1100} \approx 1.18, \text{ or } 118\%$$

14. (a) 1995 to 1999: $1600 - 1180 = 420$, or \$420,000 increase

(b) 2000 to 2005: $2400 - 2200 = 200$, or \$200,000 increase

15. Highest price was \$2.59 in January.

16. $2.59 - 2.46 = \$0.13$

17.

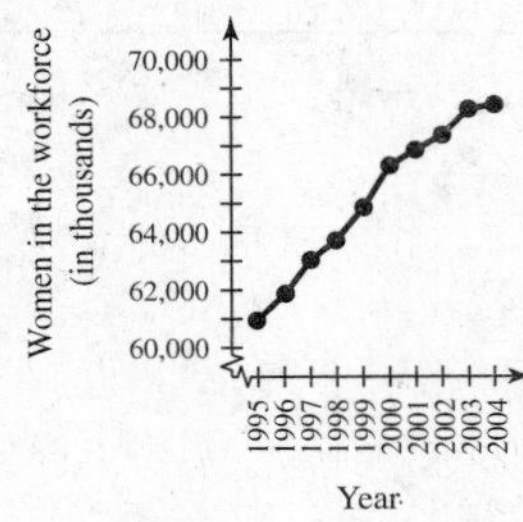

From 1995 to 2004, the total number of women in the work force increases at a fairly constant rate.

18.

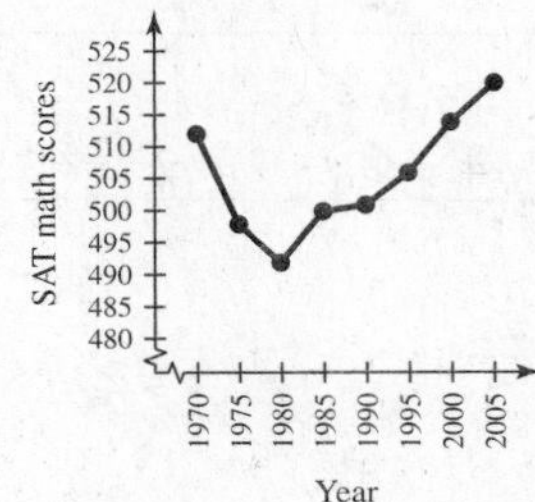

From 1970 to 1980, the SAT math scores decreased, and from 1980 to 2003 they increased.

19.

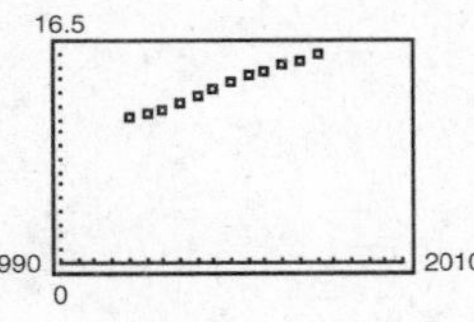

20.

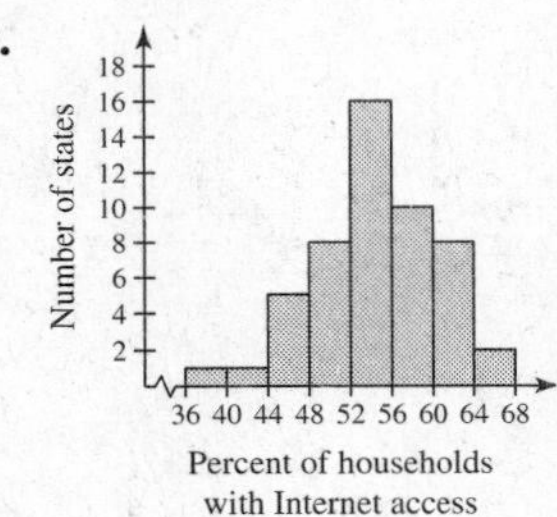

Answers will vary.

21.

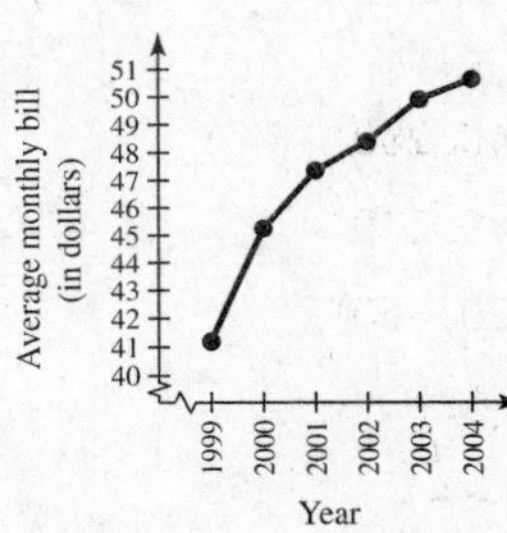

Answers will vary.

22. In 1990, cell phone bills might have been high because they were still new and not so popular. In order for providers to make money, they had to charge higher prices than now.

23.

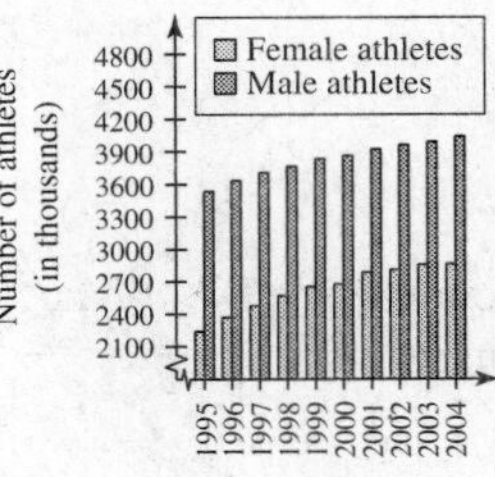

Answers will vary.

24. A histogram has a portion of the real number line as its horizontal axis, and the bars are not separated by spaces. A bar graph can be either horizontal or vertical. The labels are not necessarily numbers, and the bars are usually separated by spaces.

25. Answers will vary. Line plots are useful for ordering small sets of data. Histograms or bar graphs can be used to organize larger sets.

26. The second graph is misleading because the vertical scale is too small which makes small changes look large. Answers will vary.

APPENDIX C
Concepts in Statistics

Appendix C.1 Measures of Central Tendency and Dispersion

Vocabulary Check

1. measure, central tendency

2. modes, bimodal

3. variance, standard deviation

4. Quartiles

1. Mean $= \dfrac{5 + 12 + 7 + 14 + 8 + 9 + 7}{7} = \dfrac{62}{7} \approx 8.86$

Median: 8

Mode: 7

2. Mean $= \dfrac{30 + 37 + 32 + 39 + 33 + 34 + 32}{7} = \dfrac{237}{7} \approx 33.86$

Median: 33

Mode: 32

3. Mean $= \dfrac{5 + 12 + 7 + 24 + 8 + 9 + 7}{7} = \dfrac{72}{7} \approx 10.29$

Median: 8

Mode: 7

4. Mean $= \dfrac{20 + 37 + 32 + 39 + 33 + 34 + 32}{7} = \dfrac{227}{7} \approx 32.43$

Median: 33

Mode: 32

5. Mean $= \dfrac{5 + 12 + 7 + 14 + 9 + 7}{6} = \dfrac{54}{6} = 9$

Median: $\dfrac{7 + 9}{2} = 8$

Mode: 7

6. Mean $= \dfrac{30 + 37 + 32 + 39 + 34 + 32}{6} = \dfrac{204}{6} = 34$

Median: $\dfrac{32 + 34}{2} = 33$

Mode: 32

7. (a) The mean is sensitive to extreme values

(b) Mean: 14.86

Median: 14

Mode: 13

Each is increased by 6.

(c) Each will increase by k.

8. Mean $= \dfrac{805.69}{12} = \$67.14$

Median: $65.35

9. Mean $= \dfrac{410 + 260 + 320 + 320 + 460 + 150}{6} = \dfrac{1920}{6} = 320$

Median: 320

Mode: 320

10. Mean $= \dfrac{0(1) + 1(24) + 2(45) + 3(54) + 4(50) + 5(19) + 6(7)}{1 + 24 + 45 + 54 + 50 + 19 + 7} = \dfrac{613}{200} \approx 3.07$

Median: 3

Mode: 3

11. (a) Jay: $\dfrac{181 + 222 + 196}{3} = 199\frac{2}{3}$

Hank: $\dfrac{199 + 195 + 205}{3} = 199\frac{2}{3}$

Buck: $\dfrac{202 + 251 + 235}{3} = 229\frac{1}{3}$

(b) Adding all nine numbers, you obtain

Mean $= \dfrac{1886}{9} = 209\frac{5}{9}$.

(c) Median = 202 (four scores below 202 and four scores above 202)

12. (a) Mean $= \dfrac{5{,}510{,}000}{12} \approx \$459{,}167$

Mode: $500,000, $550,000, and $425,000

Median: $\dfrac{450{,}000 + 475{,}000}{2} = 462{,}500$

(b) Answers will vary.

13. There are many possible answers. For example: {4, 4, 10}

14. There are many correct answers. One possible set: {4, 4, 6, 7.5, 8.5}

15. The mean is 76.55 and the median is 82. The median is the best description.

16. Median and mode give most representative descriptions.

17. (a) Mean = 12, $\sigma \approx 2.83$

(b) Mean = 20, $\sigma \approx 2.83$

(c) Mean = 12, $\sigma \approx 1.41$

(d) Mean = 9, $\sigma \approx 1.41$

18. (a) $\bar{x} = 15$, $\sigma \approx 3.19$

(b) $\bar{x} = 15$, $\sigma \approx 2.83$

(c) $\bar{x} = 25$, $\sigma \approx 2.83$

(d) $\bar{x} = 5$, $\sigma \approx 3.19$

19. $\bar{x} = 6$, $v = 10$, $\sigma \approx 3.16$

20. $\bar{x} = 7$, $v = 22$, $\sigma \approx 4.69$

21. $\bar{x} = 2$, $v = \frac{4}{3}$, $\sigma \approx 1.15$

22. $\bar{x} = 2$, $v = 0$, $\sigma = 0$

23. $\bar{x} = 4$, $v = 4$, $\sigma \approx 2$

24. $\bar{x} = 3$, $v = 4$, $\sigma = 2$

25. $\bar{x} = 47$, $v = 226$, $\sigma \approx 15.03$

26. $\bar{x} = 1.1$, $v = 0.38$, $\sigma \approx 0.616$

27. $\bar{x} = 6$

$$\sigma = \sqrt{\frac{2^2 + 4^2 + 6^2 + 6^2 + 13^2 + 5^2}{6} - 6^2}$$
$$= \sqrt{\frac{286}{6} - 36}$$
$$= \sqrt{\frac{35}{3}} \approx 3.42$$

28. $\bar{x} = 300$

$$\sigma = \sqrt{\frac{246^2 + 336^2 + 473^2 + 167^2 + 219^2 + 359^2}{6} - 300^2}$$
$$= \sqrt{\frac{601{,}872}{6} - 300^2}$$
$$= \sqrt{10{,}312} \approx 101.55$$

29. $\bar{x} = 5.8$

$$\sigma = \sqrt{\frac{8.1^2 + 6.9^2 + 3.7^2 + 4.2^2 + 6.1^2}{5} - 5.8^2}$$
$$= \sqrt{2.712} \approx 1.65$$

30. $\bar{x} = 6.64$

$$\sigma = \sqrt{\frac{9^2 + 7.5^2 + 3.3^2 + 7.4^2 + 6^2}{5} - 6.64^2}$$
$$= \sqrt{\frac{238.9}{5} - 6.64^2}$$
$$= \sqrt{3.6904} \approx 1.92$$

31. $\bar{x} = 12$ and $|x_i - 12| = 8$ for all x_i. Hence, $\sigma = 8$.

32. All the numbers must be equal.

33. The mean will increase by 5. The standard deviation will not change.

34. Mean $\approx$ 362.46

Variance $\approx$ 2665.48

Standard deviation $\approx$ 51.63

100% of the data lies within two standard deviations of the mean.

[**Note:** Some graphing utilities give variance $\approx$ 2554.41 and standard deviation $\approx$ 50.54.]

35. $\bar{x} = 235$

$\sigma = 28$

$n = 600$

$1 - \frac{1}{2^2} = \frac{3}{4}$ lies within two standard deviations:

$[235 - 2(28), 235 + 2(28)] = [179, 291]$.

$1 - \frac{1}{3^2} = \frac{8}{9}$ lies within three standard deviations:

$[235 - 3(28), 235 + 3(28)] = [151, 319]$.

If $\sigma = 16$, then

$[235 - 2(16), 235 + 2(16)] = [203, 267]$

$[235 - 3(16), 235 + 3(16)] = [187, 283]$.

36. The first histogram has a smaller standard deviation.

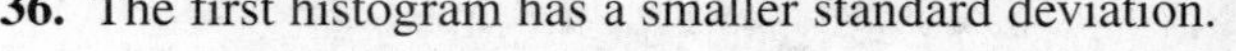

37. (a) 12, 13, 13, 14, 14, 15, 20, 23, 23

Median: 14

Lower quartile is median of $\{12, 13, 13\} = 13$.

Upper quartile is median of $\{15, 20, 23, 23\} = 21.5$.

(b)

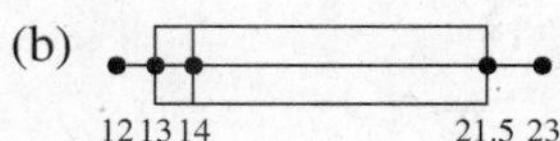

38. (a) 8, 10, 11, 11, 11, 14, 14, 14, 16, 17, 20

Median: 14

Lower quartile is median of $\{8, 10, 11, 11, 11\} = 11$.

Upper quartile is median of $\{14, 14, 16, 17, 20\} = 16$.

(b)

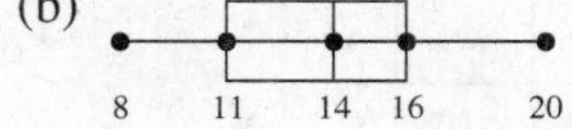

39. (a) 46, 47, 47, 48, 48, 49, 50, 51, 52, 53

Median: $\frac{48 + 49}{2} = 48.5$

Lower quartile is median of $\{46, 47, 47, 48, 48\} = 47$.

Upper quartile is median of $\{49, 50, 51, 52, 53\} = 51$.

(b)

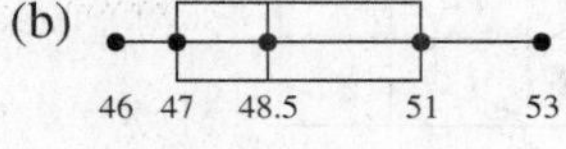

40. (a) 19, 20, 21, 22, 24, 25, 25, 27, 28, 28, 28, 29

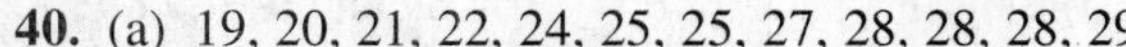

Median: 25

Lower quartile is median of $\{19, 20, 21, 22, 24, 25\} = 21.5$.

Upper quartile is median of $\{27, 28, 28, 28, 29\} = 28$.

(b)

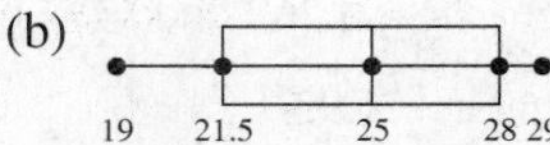

41. 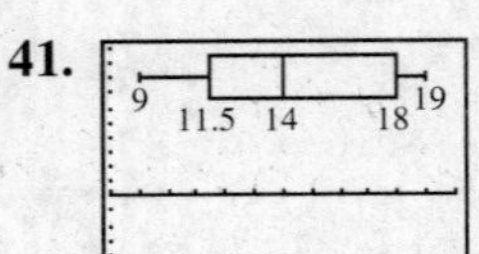

42. 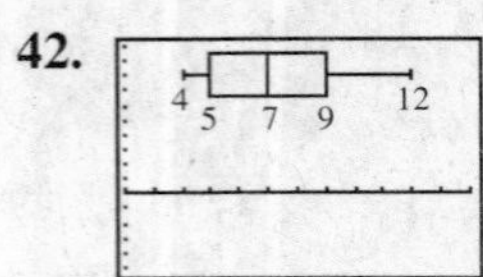

43. 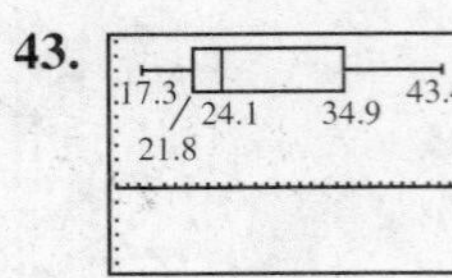

44.

37.1 78.1 107.5
70.55 91.75

45. 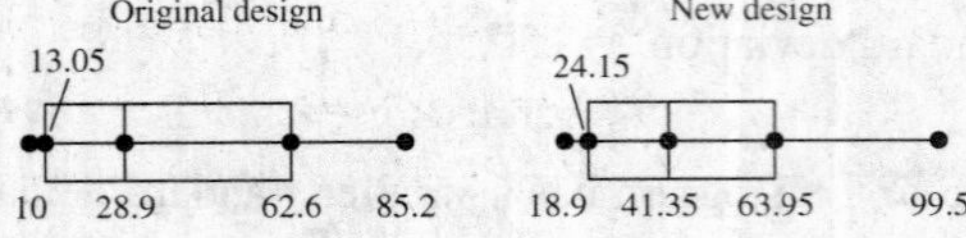

From the plots, you can see that the lifetimes of the units in the new design are greater than the original design. The median increased by over 12 months.

Appendix C.2 Least Squares Regression

1.

	x	y	xy	x^2
	-4	1	-4	16
	-3	3	-9	9
	-2	4	-8	4
	-1	6	-6	1
Total	-10	14	-27	30

$n = 4$

$4b + (-10)a = 14$

$(-10)b + 30a = -27$

Solving this system, $a = 1.6$ and $b = 7.5$.

Answer: $y = 1.6x + 7.5$

2.

	x	y	xy	x^2
	0	-1	0	0
	2	0	0	4
	4	3	12	16
	6	5	30	36
Total	12	7	42	56

$n = 4$

$4b + 12a = 7$

$12b + 56a = 42$

Solving this system, $b = -1.4$ and $a = 1.05$.

Answer: $y = 1.05x - 1.4$

3.

	x	y	xy	x^2
	-3	1	-3	9
	-1	2	-2	1
	1	2	2	1
	4	3	12	16
Total	1	8	9	27

$n = 4$

$4b + a = 8$

$b + 27a = 9$

Solving this system, $a \approx 0.262$ and $b \approx 1.93$.

Answer: $y = 0.262x + 1.93$

4.

	x	y	xy	x^2
	0	-1	0	0
	2	1	2	4
	3	2	6	9
	5	3	15	25
Total	10	5	23	38

$n = 4$

$4b + 10a = 5$

$10b + 38a = 23$

Solving this system, $b \approx -0.769$ and $a \approx 0.808$.

Answer: $y = 0.808x - 0.769$

Appendix D Variation

Vocabulary Check

1. directly proportional **2.** constant, variation **3.** directly proportional

4. inverse **5.** combined **6.** jointly proportional

1.
$$y = kx$$
$$12 = k(5)$$
$$\tfrac{12}{5} = k$$
$$y = \tfrac{12}{5}x$$

2.
$$y = kx$$
$$14 = k(2)$$
$$7 = k$$
$$y = 7x$$

3.
$$y = kx$$
$$2050 = k(10)$$
$$205 = k$$
$$y = 205x$$

4.
$$y = kx$$
$$580 = k(6)$$
$$\tfrac{290}{3} = k$$
$$y = \tfrac{290}{3}x$$

5.
$$y = kx$$
$$33 = k(13)$$
$$\tfrac{33}{13} = k$$
$$y = \tfrac{33}{13}x$$

When $x = 10$ inches, $y \approx 25.4$ centimeters.

When $x = 20$ inches, $y \approx 50.8$ centimeters.

6.
$$y = kx$$
$$53 = k(14)$$
$$\tfrac{53}{14} = k$$
$$y = \tfrac{53}{14}x$$

5 gallons: $y = \tfrac{53}{14}(5) \approx 18.9$ liters

25 gallons: $y = \tfrac{53}{14}(25) \approx 94.6$ liters

7.
$$y = kx$$
$$5520 = k(150{,}000)$$
$$0.0368 = k$$
$$y = 0.0368x$$
$$y = 0.0368(200{,}000)$$
$$= \$7360$$

The property tax is \$7360.

8.
$$y = kx$$
$$10.22 = k(145.99)$$
$$0.07 \approx k$$
$$y = 0.07x$$
$$y = 0.07(540.50)$$
$$y \approx 37.84$$

The sales tax is \$37.84.

9.
$$d = kF$$
$$0.15 = k(265)$$
$$\tfrac{3}{5300} = k$$
$$d = \tfrac{3}{5300}F$$

(a) $d = \tfrac{3}{5300}(90) \approx 0.05$ meter

(b) $0.1 = \tfrac{3}{5300}F$

$$\tfrac{530}{3} = F$$
$$F = 176\tfrac{2}{3} \text{ newtons}$$

10.
$$d = kF$$
$$0.12 = k(220)$$
$$\tfrac{3}{5500} = k$$
$$d = \tfrac{3}{5500}F$$
$$0.16 = \tfrac{3}{5500}F$$
$$\tfrac{880}{3} = F$$

The required force is $293\tfrac{1}{3}$ newtons.

11. $k = 1$

x	2	4	6	8	10
$y = kx^2$	4	16	36	64	100

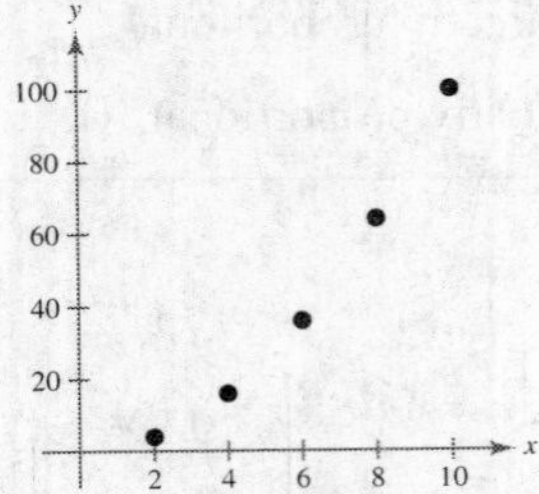

12. $k = 2$

x	2	4	6	8	10
$y = kx^2$	8	32	72	128	200

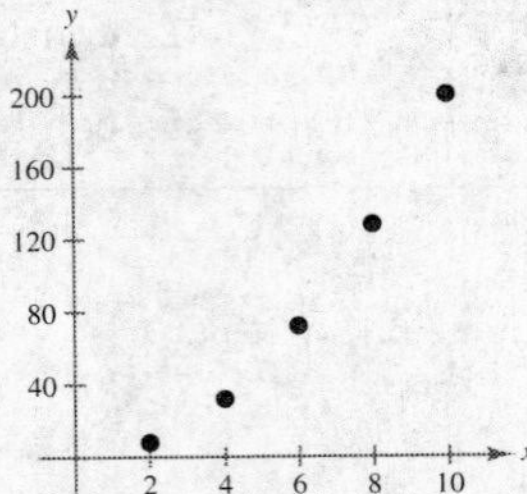

13. $k = \frac{1}{2}$

x	2	4	6	8	10
$y = kx^2$	2	8	18	32	50

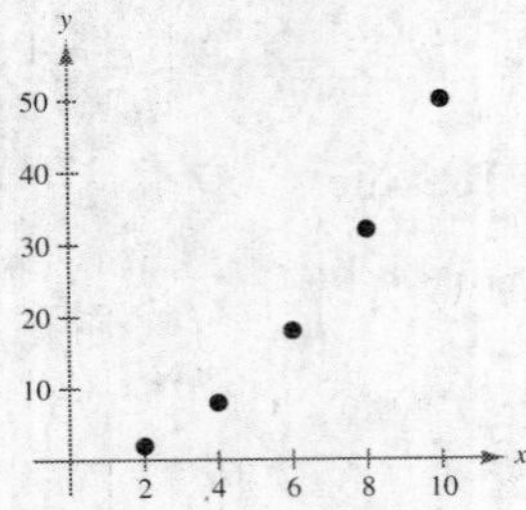

14. $k = \frac{1}{4}$

x	2	4	6	8	10
$y = kx^2$	1	4	9	16	25

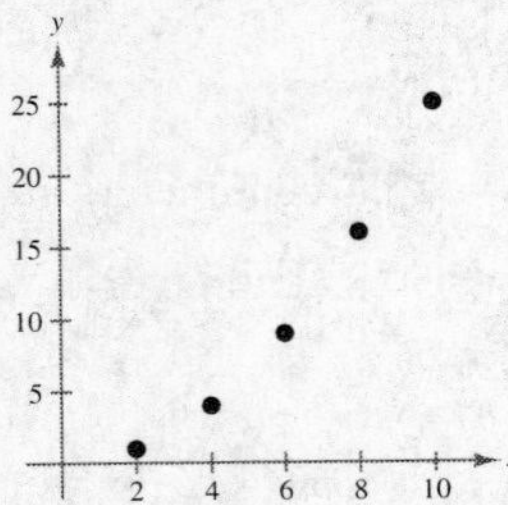

15. $d = kv^2$

$$0.02 = k\left(\frac{1}{4}\right)^2$$

$$k = 0.32$$

$$d = 0.32v^2$$

$$0.12 = 0.32v^2$$

$$v^2 = \frac{0.12}{0.32} = \frac{3}{8}$$

$$v = \frac{\sqrt{3}}{2\sqrt{2}} = \frac{\sqrt{6}}{4} \approx 0.61 \text{ mi/hr}$$

16. $d = kv^2$

If the velocity is doubled:

$$d = k(2v)^2$$

$$d = k \cdot 4v^2$$

$$\frac{4kv^2}{kv^2} = 4$$

d increases by a factor of 4 when velocity is doubled.

17. $k = 2$

x	2	4	6	8	10
$y = \frac{k}{x^2}$	$\frac{1}{2}$	$\frac{1}{8}$	$\frac{1}{18}$	$\frac{1}{32}$	$\frac{1}{50}$

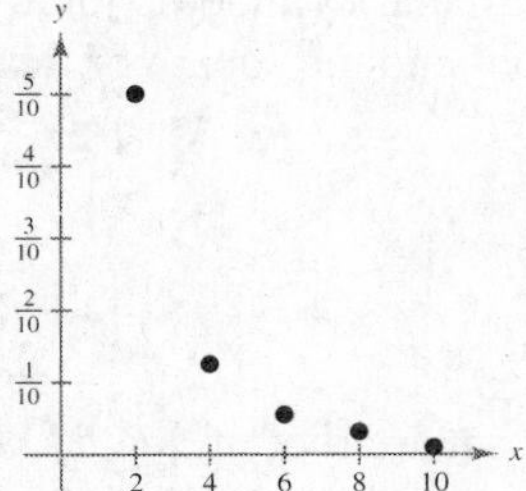

18. $k = 5$

x	2	4	6	8	10
$y = \frac{k}{x^2}$	$\frac{5}{4}$	$\frac{5}{16}$	$\frac{5}{36}$	$\frac{5}{64}$	$\frac{1}{20}$

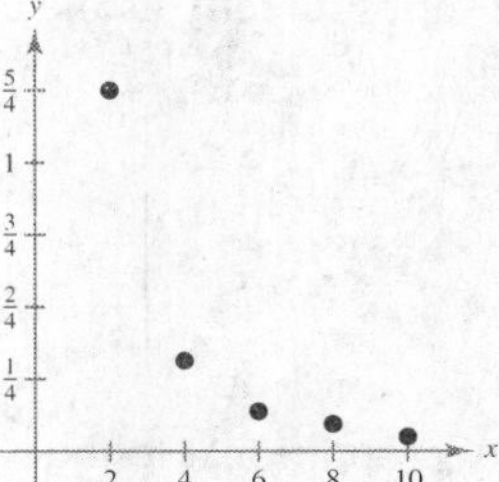

19. $k = 10$

x	2	4	6	8	10
$y = \frac{k}{x^2}$	$\frac{5}{2}$	$\frac{5}{8}$	$\frac{5}{18}$	$\frac{5}{32}$	$\frac{1}{10}$

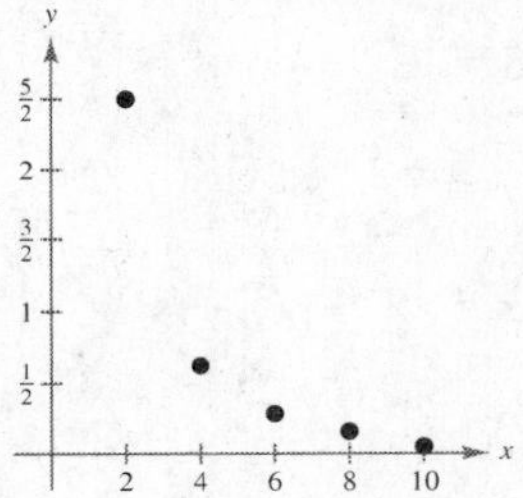

20. $k = 20$

x	2	4	6	8	10
$y = \frac{k}{x^2}$	5	$\frac{5}{4}$	$\frac{5}{9}$	$\frac{5}{16}$	$\frac{1}{5}$

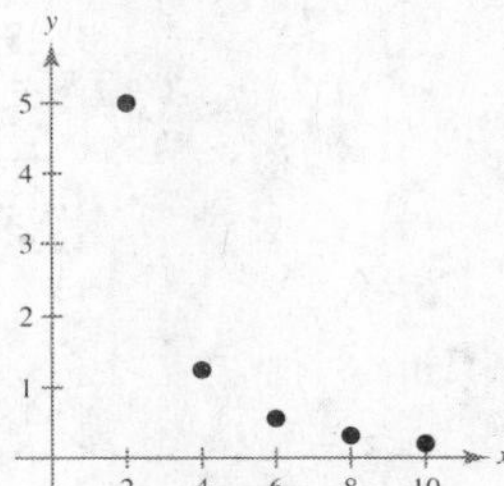

21. The table represents the equation $y = 5/x$.

22. The table represents the equation $y = \frac{2}{5}x$.

23.
$$y = kx$$
$$-7 = k(10)$$
$$-\frac{7}{10} = k$$
$$y = -\frac{7}{10}x$$

This equation checks with the other points given in the table.

24.
$$y = \frac{k}{x}$$
$$24 = \frac{k}{5}$$
$$120 = k$$

Thus, $y = 120/x$. This equation checks with the other points given in the table.

25. $A = kr^2$

26. $V = ke^3$

27. $y = \frac{k}{x^2}$

28. $h = \frac{k}{\sqrt{s}}$

29. $F = \frac{kg}{r^2}$

30. $z = kx^2y^3$

31. $P = \frac{k}{V}$

32. $R = kS(S - L)$

33. $R = k(T - T_e)$

34. $F = \frac{km_1m_2}{r^2}$

35. $A = \frac{1}{2}bh$

The area of a triangle is jointly proportional to its base and height.

36. $S = 4\pi r^2$

The surface area of a sphere varies directly as the square of the radius r.

37. $V = \frac{4}{3}\pi r^3$

The volume of a sphere varies directly as the cube of its radius.

38. $V = \pi r^2 h$

The volume of a right circular cylinder is jointly proportional to the height and the square of the radius.

39. $r = \dfrac{d}{t}$

Average speed is directly proportional to the distance and inversely proportional to the time.

40. $\omega = \sqrt{\dfrac{kg}{W}}$

ω varies directly as the square root of g and inversely as the square root of W.

(**Note:** The constant of proportionality is $\sqrt{k}$.)

41.
$$A = kr^2$$
$$9\pi = k(3)^2$$
$$\pi = k$$
$$A = \pi r^2$$

42.
$$y = \frac{k}{x}$$
$$3 = \frac{k}{25}$$
$$75 = k$$
$$y = \frac{75}{x}$$

43.
$$y = \frac{k}{x}$$
$$7 = \frac{k}{4}$$
$$28 = k$$
$$y = \frac{28}{x}$$

44.
$$z = kxy$$
$$64 = k(4)(8)$$
$$2 = k$$
$$z = 2xy$$

45.
$$F = krs^3$$
$$4158 = k(11)(3)^3$$
$$k = 14$$
$$F = 14rs^3$$

46.
$$P = \frac{kx}{y^2}$$
$$\frac{28}{3} = \frac{k(42)}{9^2}$$
$$\frac{28}{3} \cdot \frac{81}{42} = k$$
$$\frac{2 \cdot 27}{3} = k$$
$$18 = k$$
$$P = \frac{18x}{y^2}$$

47.
$$z = \frac{kx^2}{y}$$
$$6 = \frac{k(6)^2}{4}$$
$$\frac{24}{36} = k$$
$$\frac{2}{3} = k$$
$$z = \frac{2/3x^2}{y} = \frac{2x^2}{3y}$$

48.
$$v = \frac{kpq}{s^2}$$
$$1.5 = \frac{k(4.1)(6.3)}{(1.2)^2}$$
$$\frac{(1.5)(1.44)}{(4.1)(6.3)} = k$$
$$\frac{2.16}{25.83} = k$$
$$k = \frac{24}{287}$$
$$v = \frac{24pq}{287s^2}$$

49.

$$r = \frac{kl}{A},\ A = \pi r^2 = \frac{\pi d^2}{4}$$

$$r = \frac{4kl}{\pi d^2}$$

$$66.17 = \frac{4(1000)k}{\pi\left(\frac{0.0126}{12}\right)^2}$$

$$k \approx 5.73 \times 10^{-8}$$

$$r = \frac{4(5.73 \times 10^{-8})l}{\pi\left(\frac{0.0126}{12}\right)^2}$$

$$33.5 = \frac{4(5.73 \times 10^{-8})l}{\pi\left(\frac{0.0126}{12}\right)^2}$$

$$\frac{33.5\pi\left(\frac{0.0126}{12}\right)^2}{4(5.73 \times 10^{-8})} = l$$

$$l \approx 506 \text{ feet}$$

50. From Exercise 49:

$$k \approx 5.73 \times 10^{-8}$$

$$r = \frac{4(5.73 \times 10^{-8})l}{\pi d^2}$$

$$d = \sqrt{\frac{4(5.73 \times 10^{-8})l}{\pi r}}$$

$$d = \sqrt{\frac{4(5.73 \times 10^{-8})(14)}{\pi(0.05)}}$$

$$d \approx 0.0045 \text{ feet} = 0.054 \text{ inch}$$

51.

$$W = kmh$$

$$2116.8 = k(120)(1.8)$$

$$k = \frac{2116.8}{(120)(1.8)} = 9.8$$

$$W = 9.8mh$$

When $m = 100$ kilograms and $h = 1.5$ meters, we have $W = 9.8(100)(1.5) = 1470$ joules.

52.

$$P = kA = k(\pi r^2) = k\pi\left(\frac{d}{2}\right)^2$$

$$8.78 = k\pi\left(\frac{9}{2}\right)^2$$

$$\frac{4(8.78)}{81\pi} = k$$

$$k \approx 0.138$$

However, we do not obtain \$11.78 when $d = 12$ inches.

$$P = 0.138\pi\left(\frac{12}{2}\right)^2 \approx \$15.61$$

Instead, $k = \frac{11.78}{36\pi} \approx 0.104$.

For the 15-inch pizza, we have $k = \frac{4(14.18)}{225\pi} \approx 0.080$.

The price is not directly proportional to the surface area. The best buy is the 15-inch pizza.

53. $v = \frac{k}{A}$

$$v = \frac{k}{0.75A} = \frac{4}{3}\left(\frac{k}{A}\right)$$

The velocity is increased by one-third.

54. Load $= \dfrac{kwd^2}{l}$

(a) Load $= \dfrac{k(2w)d^2}{2l} = \dfrac{kwd^2}{l}$

The safe load is unchanged.

(b) Load $= \dfrac{k(2w)(2d)^2}{l} = \dfrac{8kwd^2}{l}$

The safe load is eight times as great.

(c) Load $= \dfrac{k(2w)(2d)^2}{2l} = \dfrac{4kwd^2}{l}$

The safe load is four times as great.

(d) Load $= \dfrac{kw(d/2)^2}{l} = \dfrac{(1/4)kwd^2}{l}$

The safe load is one-fourth as great.

55. (a)

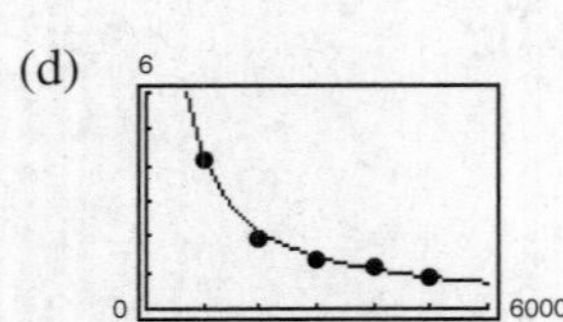

(b) Yes, the data appears to be modeled (approximately) by the inverse proportion model.

$4.2 = \dfrac{k_1}{1000}$ $\quad 1.9 = \dfrac{k_2}{2000}$ $\quad 1.4 = \dfrac{k_3}{3000}$ $\quad 1.2 = \dfrac{k_4}{4000}$ $\quad 0.9 = \dfrac{k_5}{5000}$

$4200 = k_1$ $\quad 3800 = k_2$ $\quad 4200 = k_3$ $\quad 4800 = k_4$ $\quad 4500 = k_5$

(c) Mean: $k = \dfrac{4200 + 3800 + 4200 + 4800 + 4500}{5} = 4300$, Model: $C = \dfrac{4300}{d}$

(d)

(e) $3 = \dfrac{4300}{d}$

$d = \dfrac{4300}{3} = 1433\frac{1}{3}$ meters

56. (a)

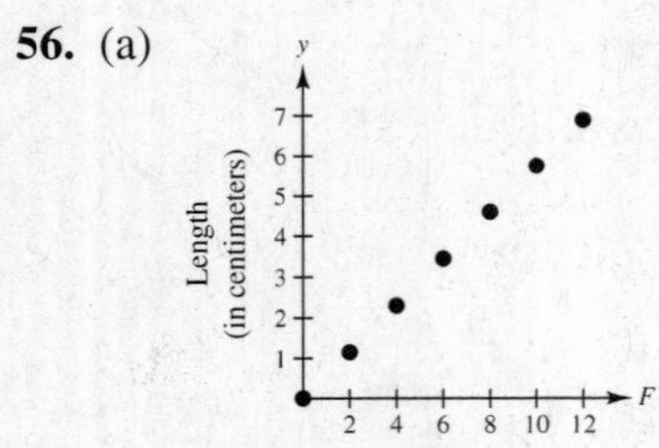

(b) It appears to fit Hooke's Law.

$k \approx \dfrac{6.9}{12} = 0.575$

(c) $y = kF$

$9 = 0.575F$

$F \approx 15.7$ pounds

57. False. y will increase if k is positive and y will decrease if k is negative.

58. False. E is jointly proportional (not "directly proportional") to the mass of an object and the square of its velocity.

59. The graph appears to represent $y = 4/x$, so y varies inversely as x.

60. The graph appears to represent $y = \frac{3}{2}x$ which is a direct variation.

APPENDIX E
Solving Linear Equations and Inequalities

Vocabulary Check

1. linear

2. equivalent inequalities

1. $x + 11 = 15$
$x = 15 - 11$
$x = 4$

2. $x + 3 = 9$
$x = 9 - 3$
$x = 6$

3. $x - 2 = 5$
$x = 5 + 2$
$x = 7$

4. $x - 5 = 1$
$x = 1 + 5$
$x = 6$

5. $3x = 12$
$x = \frac{12}{3}$
$x = 4$

6. $2x = 6$
$x = \frac{6}{2}$
$x = 3$

7. $\frac{x}{5} = 4$
$x = 4(5)$
$x = 20$

8. $\frac{x}{4} = 5$
$x = 5(4)$
$x = 20$

9. $8x + 7 = 39$
$8x = 32$
$x = 4$

10. $12x - 5 = 43$
$12x = 48$
$x = 4$

11. $24 - 7x = 3$
$-7x = -21$
$x = 3$

12. $13 + 6x = 61$
$6x = 48$
$x = 8$

13. $8x - 5 = 3x + 20$
$5x = 25$
$x = 5$

14. $7x + 3 = 3x - 17$
$4x = -20$
$x = -5$

15. $-2(x + 5) = 10$
$-2x - 10 = 10$
$-2x = 20$
$x = -10$

16. $4(3 - x) = 9$
$12 - 4x = 9$
$-4x = -3$
$x = \frac{3}{4}$

17. $2x + 3 = 2x - 2$
$3 = -2$
No solution

18. $8(x - 2) = 4(2x - 4)$
$8x - 16 = 8x - 16$
True for all real numbers.

19. $\frac{3}{2}(x + 5) - \frac{1}{4}(x + 24) = 0$
$\frac{3}{2}(x + 5) = \frac{1}{4}(x + 24)$
$12(x + 5) = 2(x + 24)$
$12x + 60 = 2x + 48$
$10x = -12$
$x = -\frac{12}{10}$
$x = -\frac{6}{5}$

20. $\frac{3}{2}x + \frac{1}{4}(x - 2) = 10$
$\frac{3}{2}x + \frac{1}{4}x - \frac{1}{2} = 10$
$\frac{7}{4}x = \frac{21}{2}$
$x = \frac{21}{2} \cdot \frac{4}{7}$
$x = 6$

21. $0.25x + 0.75(10 - x) = 3$

$25x + 75(10 - x) = 300$

$25x + 750 - 75x = 300$

$-50x = -450$

$x = 9$

22. $0.60x + 0.40(100 - x) = 50$

$0.60x + 40 - 0.40x = 50$

$0.20x = 10$

$x = \frac{10}{0.2}$

$= 50$

23. $x + 6 < 8$

$x < 8 - 6$

$x < 2$

24. $3 + x > -10$

$x > -10 - 3$

$x > -13$

25. $-x - 8 > -17$

$17 - 8 > x$

$9 > x$

$x < 9$

26. $-3 + x < 19$

$x < 19 + 3$

$x < 22$

27. $6 + x \le -8$

$x \le -8 - 6$

$x \le -14$

28. $x - 10 \ge -6$

$x \ge -6 + 10$

$x \ge 4$

29. $\frac{4}{5}x > 8$

$x > \frac{5}{4}(8)$

$x > 10$

30. $\frac{2}{3}x < -4$

$x < \frac{3}{2}(-4)$

$x < -6$

31. $-\frac{3}{4}x > -3$

$\frac{3}{4}x < 3$

$x < 4$

32. $-\frac{1}{6}x < -2$

$\frac{1}{6}x > 2$

$x > 12$

33. $4x < 12$

$x < 3$

34. $10x > -40$

$x > -\frac{40}{10}$

$x > -4$

35. $-11x \le -22$

$11x \ge 22$

$x \ge 2$

36. $-7x \ge 21$

$x \le \frac{21}{(-7)}$

$x \le -3$

37. $x - 3(x + 1) \ge 7$

$x - 3x - 3 \ge 7$

$-2x \ge 10$

$x \le -5$

38. $2(4x - 5) - 3x \le -15$

$8x - 10 - 3x \le -15$

$5x \le -5$

$x \le -1$

39. $7x - 12 < 4x + 6$

$3x < 18$

$x < 6$

40. $11 - 6x \le 2x + 7$

$4 \le 8x$

$\frac{1}{2} \le x$

$x \ge \frac{1}{2}$

41. $\frac{3}{4}x - 6 \le x - 7$

$1 \le \frac{1}{4}x$

$4 \le x$

$x \ge 4$

42. $3 + \frac{2}{7}x > x - 2$

$5 > \frac{5}{7}x$

$7 > x$

$x < 7$

43. $3.6x + 11 \ge -3.4$

$3.6x \ge -14.4$

$x \ge \frac{-14.4}{3.6}$

$x \ge -4$

44. $15.6 - 1.3x < -5.2$

$20.8 < 1.3x$

$16 < x$

$x > 16$

APPENDIX F
Systems of Inequalities

Appendix F.1 Solving Systems of Inequalities

Vocabulary Check

1. solution **2.** graph **3.** linear **4.** point, equilibrium

1. $x < 2$

Vertical boundary; Matches graph (g).

2. $y \geq 3$

Region above or on horizontal line $y = 3$; Matches (d).

3. $2x + 3y \geq 6$

$y \geq -\frac{2}{3}x + 2$

Line with negative slope; Matches (a).

4. $2x - y \leq -2 \Rightarrow y \geq 2x + 2$

Region above or on line $y = 2x + 2$; Matches (h).

5. $x^2 + y^2 < 9$

Circular boundary; Matches (e).

6. $(x - 2)^2 + (y - 3)^2 > 9$

Region outside circle; Matches (b).

7. $xy > 1$ or $y > \dfrac{1}{x}$

Matches (f).

8. $y \leq 1 - x^2$

Region below or on parabola; Matches (c).

9. $y < 2 - x^2$

Graph the parabola $y = 2 - x^2$. The region lies below the parabola.

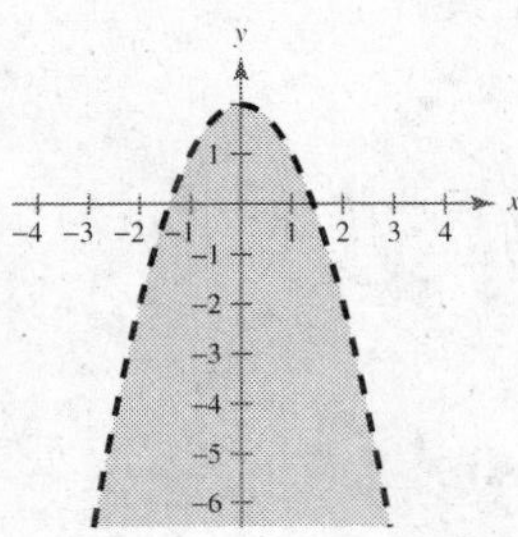

10. $y - 4 \leq x^2$

$y \leq 4 + x^2$

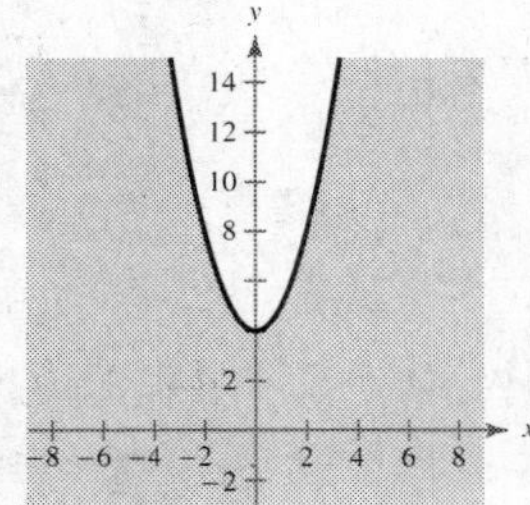

11. $y^2 + 1 \geq x$

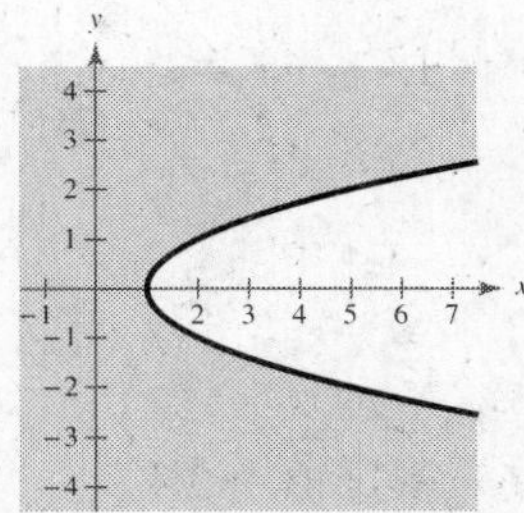

12. $y^2 - x < 0$

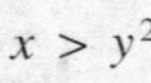

$x > y^2$

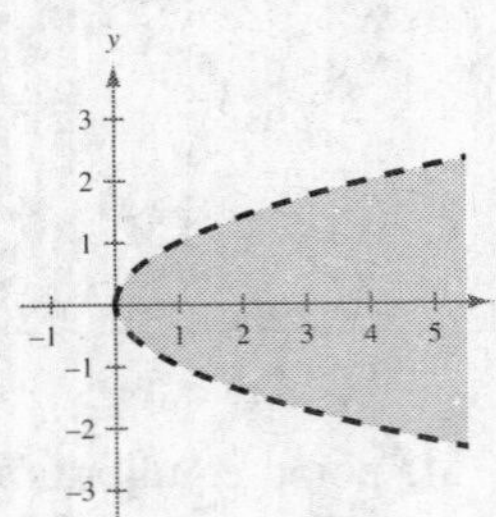

13. $x \geq 4$

Using a solid line, graph the vertical line $x = 4$ and shade to the right of this line.

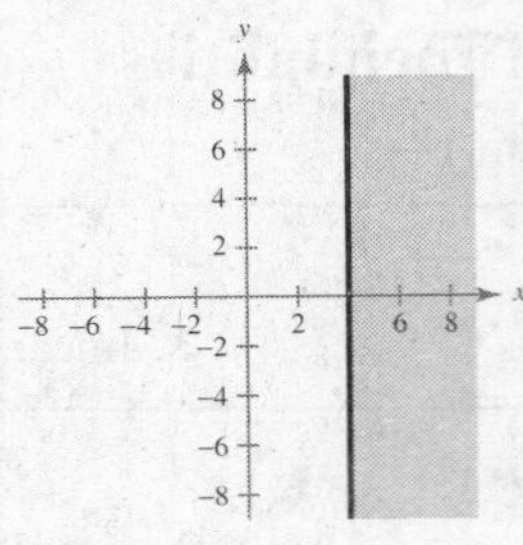

14. $x \leq -5$

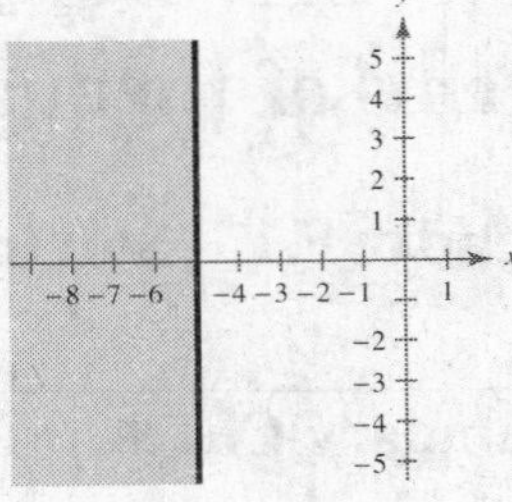

15. $y \geq -1$

Using a solid line, graph the horizontal line $y = -1$ and shade above this line.

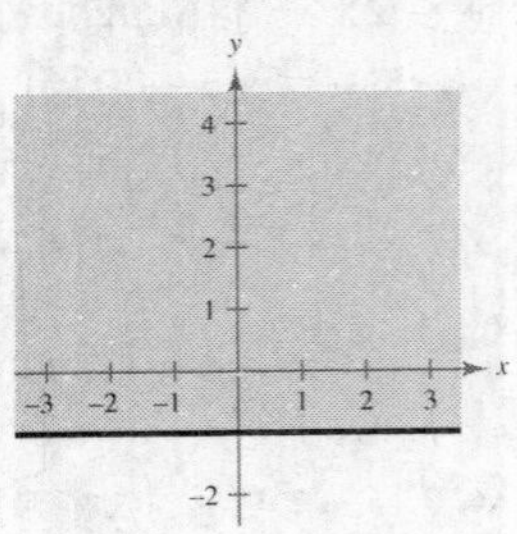

16. $y \leq 3$

Using a solid line, graph the horizontal line $y = 3$, and shade below this line.

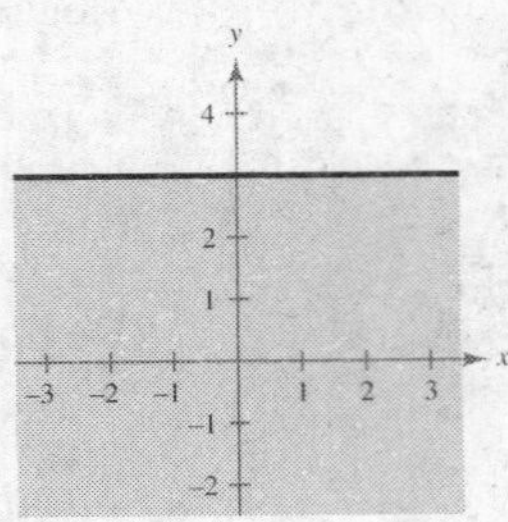

17. $2y - x \geq 4$

Using a solid line, graph $2y - x = 4$, and then shade above the line. (Use $(0, 0)$ as a test point.)

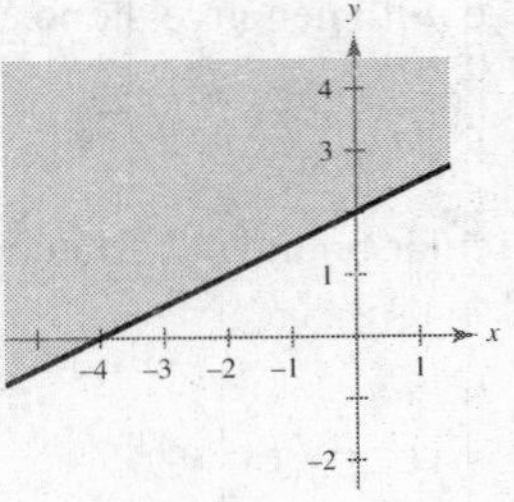

18. $5x + 3y \geq -15$

Using a solid line, graph $5x + 3y = -15$, and shade above the line. (Use $(0, 0)$ as a test point.)

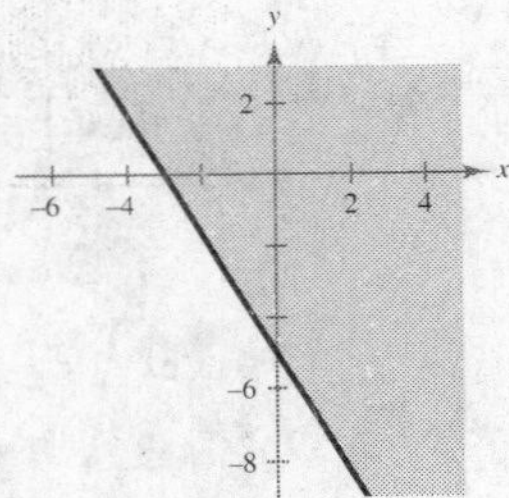

19. $2x + 3y < 6$

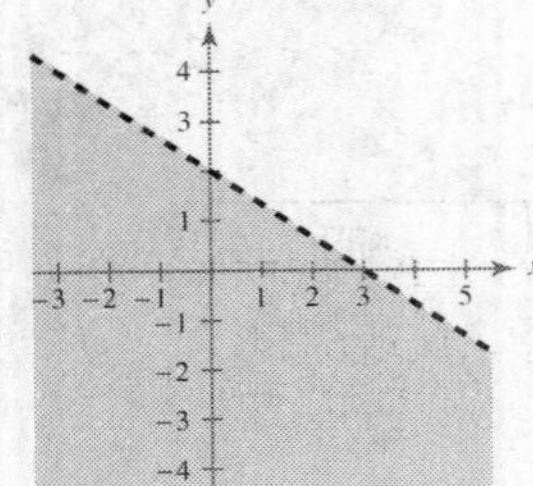

20. $5x - 2y > 10$

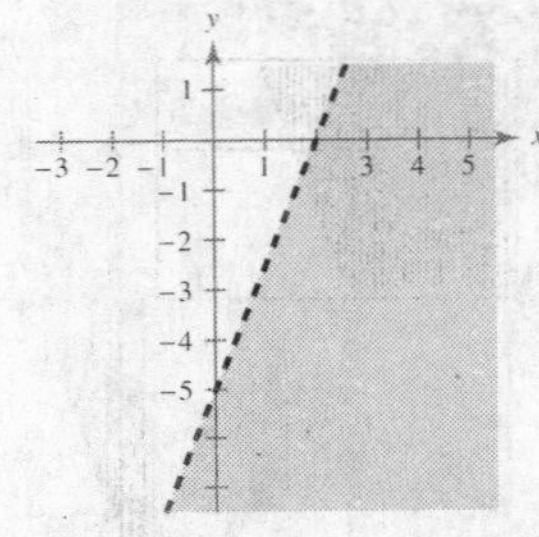

21. $4x - 3y \leq 24$

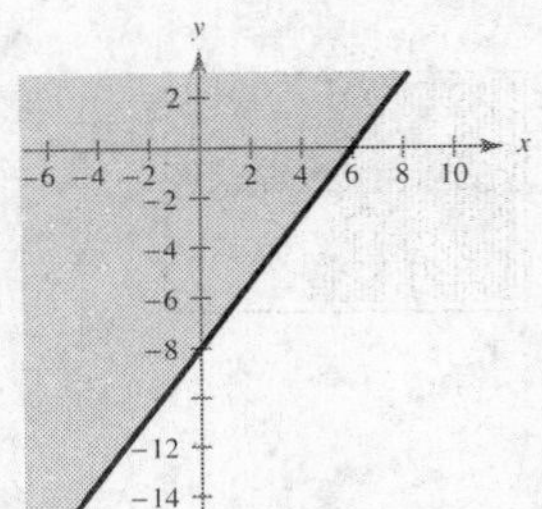

22. $2x + 7y \leq 28$

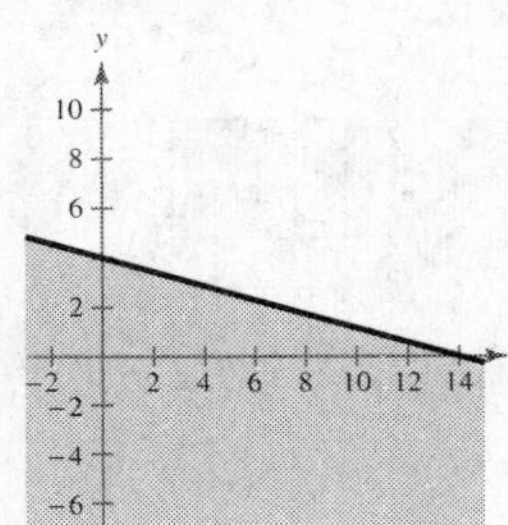

23. $y > 3x^2 + 1$

Sketch the parabola $y = 3x^2 + 1$. The region lies above the parabola.

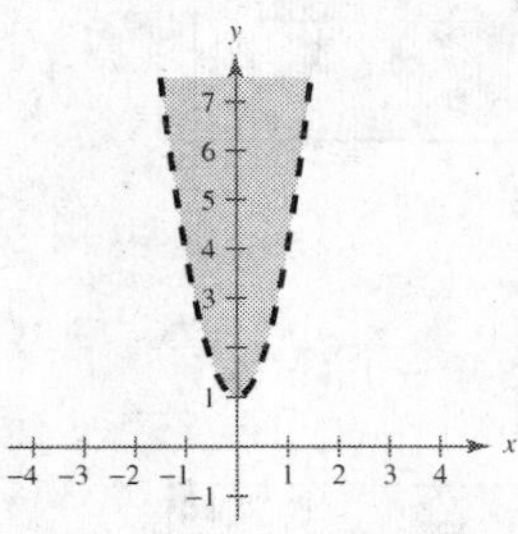

24. $y + 9 \geq x^2$

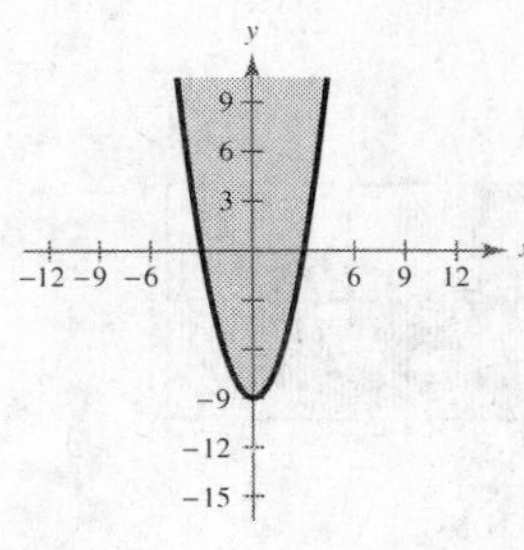

25. $2x - y^2 > 0$

$2x > y^2$

26. $4x + y^2 > 1$

Region to right of parabola

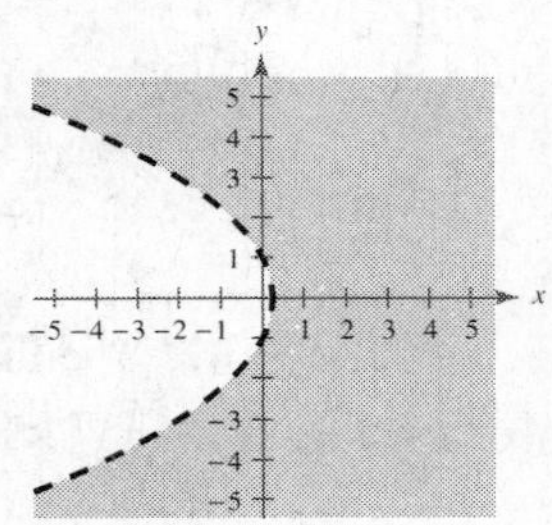

27. $(x + 1)^2 + y^2 < 9$

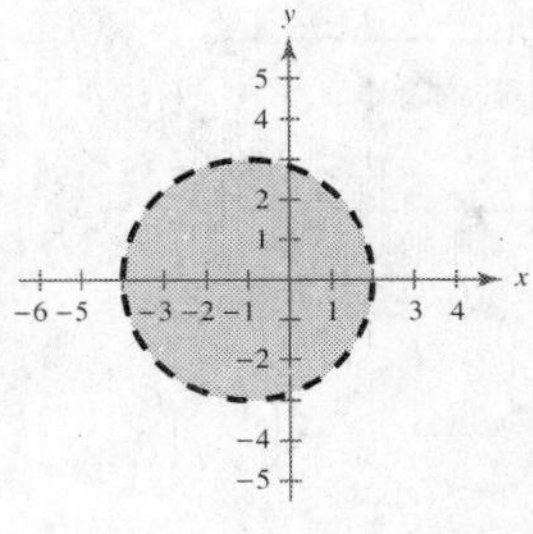

28. $(x - 1)^2 + (y - 4)^2 > 9$

Region outside of circle

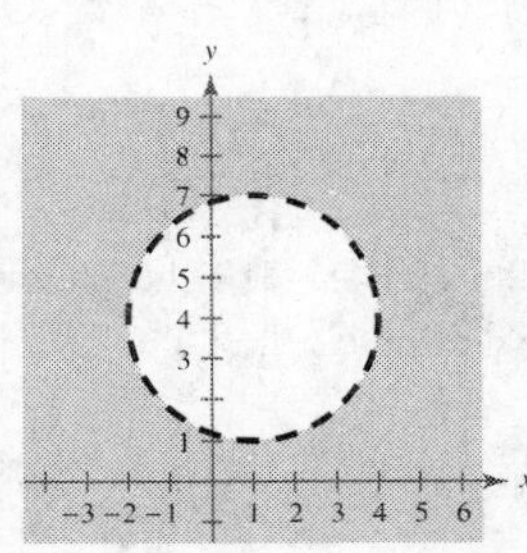

29. $y \geq \frac{2}{3}x - 1$

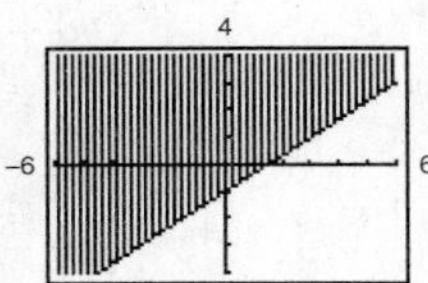

30. $y \leq 6 - \frac{3}{2}x$

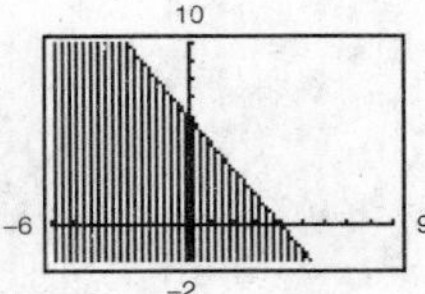

31. $y < -3.8x + 1.1$

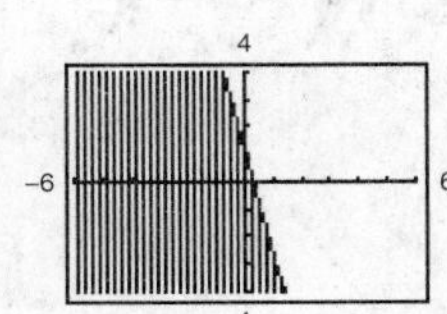

32. $y \geq -20.74 + 2.66x$

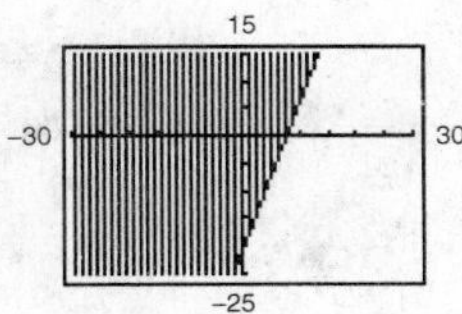

33. $x^2 + 5y - 10 \leq 0$

$y \leq 2 - \frac{x^2}{5}$

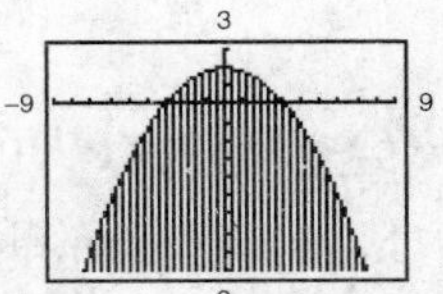

34. $2x^2 - y - 3 > 0$

$y < 2x^2 - 3$

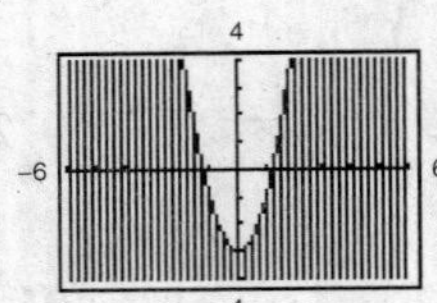

35. $y \le \dfrac{1}{1 + x^2}$

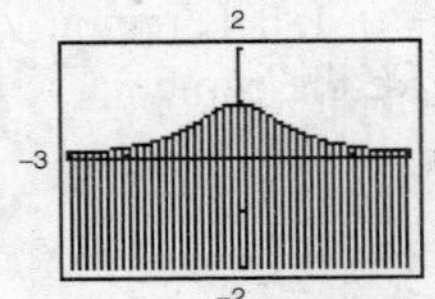

36. $y > \dfrac{-10}{x^2 + x + 4}$

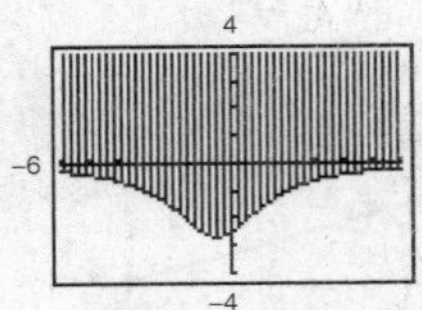

37. $y < \ln x$

Using a dashed line, graph $y = \ln x$, and shade to the right of the curve. (Use (2, 0) as a test point.)

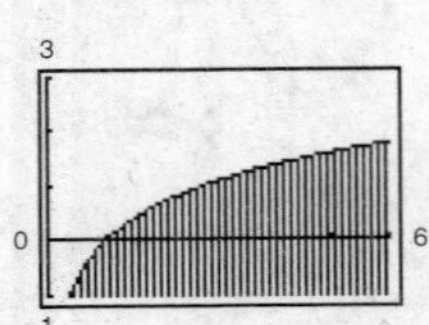

38. $y \ge 4 - \ln(x + 5)$

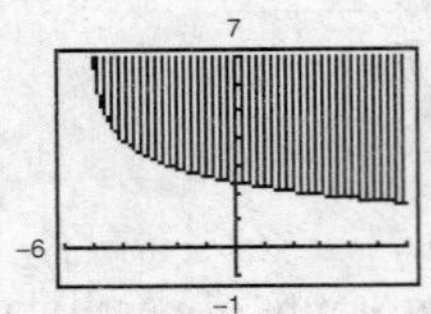

39. $y > 3^{-x-4}$

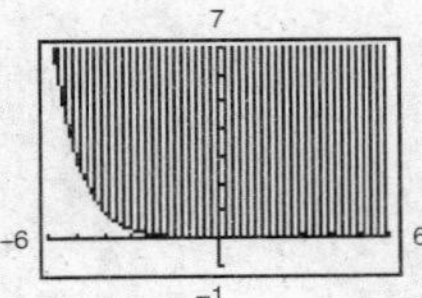

40. $y \le 2^{2x-1} - 3$

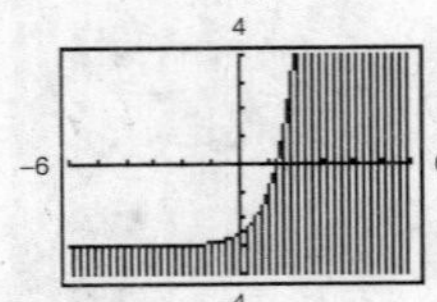

41. The line through (0, 2) and (3, 0) is $y = -\frac{2}{3}x + 2$. For the shaded region above the line, we have:

$$y > -\frac{2}{3}x + 2$$

$$3y > -2x + 6$$

$$2x + 3y > 6$$

$$\frac{x}{3} + \frac{y}{2} > 1$$

42. The parabola through $(-2, 0)$, $(0, -4)$, $(2, 0)$ is $y = x^2 - 4$. For the shaded region inside the parabola, we have $y \ge x^2 - 4$.

43. The circle shown is $x^2 + y^2 = 9$. For the shaded region inside the circle, we have $x^2 + y^2 \le 9$.

44. The region to the right of the vertical line $x = 5$. Thus, $x > 5$.

45. (a) (0, 2) is a solution: $-2(0) + 5(2) \ge 3$

$2 < 4$

$-4(0) + 2(2) < 7$

(b) $(-6, 4)$ is not a solution: $4 \nless 4$

(c) $(-8, -2)$ is not a solution: $-4(-8) + 2(-2) \nless 7$

(d) $(-3, 2)$ is not a solution: $-4(-3) + 2(2) \nless 7$

46. $x^2 + y^2 \ge 36$

$-3x + y \le 10$

$\frac{2}{3}x - y \ge 5$

(a) $(-1, 7)$ is not a solution because $(-1)^2 + 7^2 = 50 < 36$.

(b) $(-5, 1)$ is not a solution because $-3(-5) + 1 = 16 > 10$.

(c) (6, 0) is not a solution because $\frac{2}{3}(6) - 0 = 4 < 5$.

(d) $(4, -8)$ is a solution.

47. 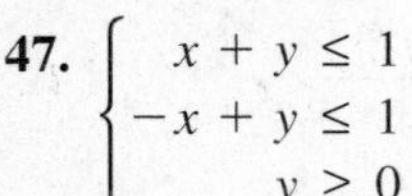
$$\begin{cases} x + y \le 1 \\ -x + y \le 1 \\ y \ge 0 \end{cases}$$

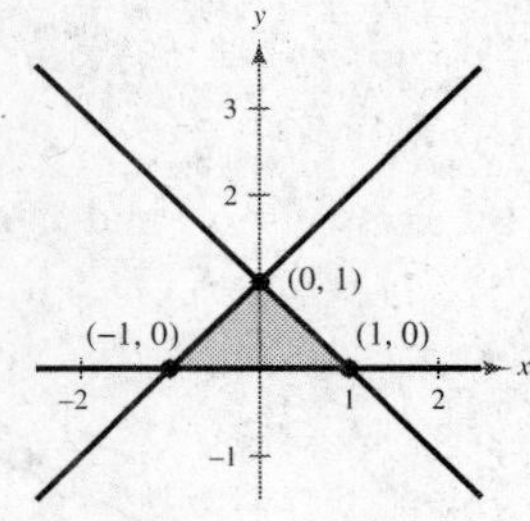

First, find the points of intersection of each pair of equations.

Vertex A	*Vertex B*	*Vertex C*
$\begin{cases} x + y = 1 \\ -x + y = 1 \end{cases}$	$\begin{cases} x + y = 1 \\ y = 0 \end{cases}$	$\begin{cases} -x + y = 1 \\ y = 0 \end{cases}$
(0, 1)	(1, 0)	$(-1, 0)$

48. $\begin{cases} 3x + 2y < 6 \\ x < 0 \\ y < 0 \end{cases}$

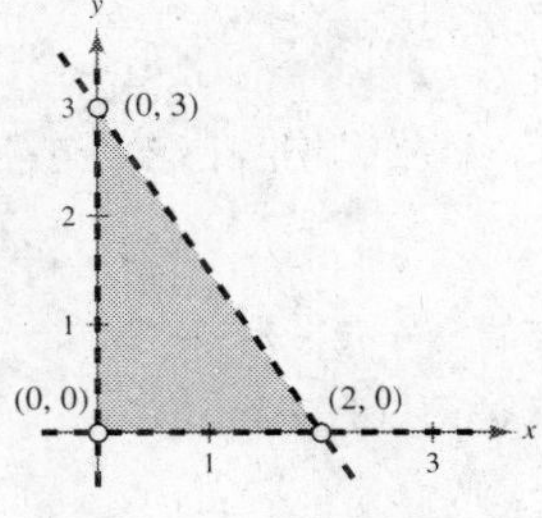

First, find the points of intersection of each pair of equations.

Vertex A	*Vertex B*	*Vertex C*
$\begin{cases} 3x + 2y = 6 \\ x = 0 \end{cases}$	$\begin{cases} x = 0 \\ y = 0 \end{cases}$	$\begin{cases} 3x + 2y = 6 \\ y = 0 \end{cases}$
(0, 3)	(0, 0)	(2, 0)

49. $\begin{cases} -3x + 2y < 6 \\ x - 4y > -2 \\ 2x + y < 3 \end{cases}$

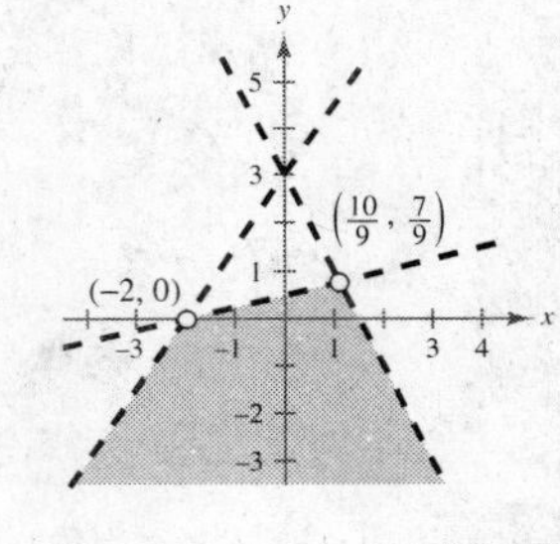

First, find the points of intersection of each pair of equations.

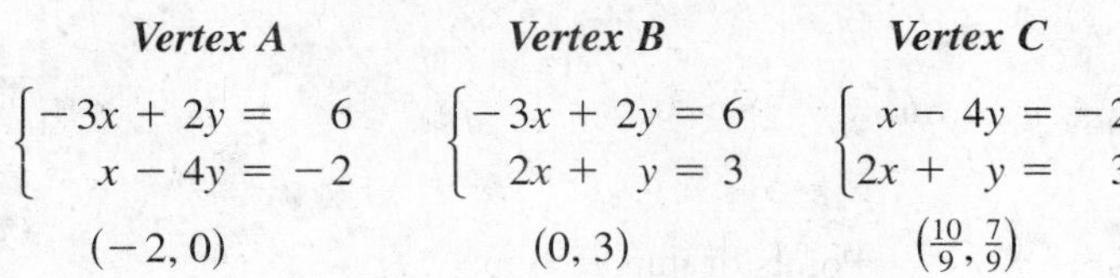

Vertex A	*Vertex B*	*Vertex C*
$\begin{cases} -3x + 2y = 6 \\ x - 4y = -2 \end{cases}$	$\begin{cases} -3x + 2y = 6 \\ 2x + y = 3 \end{cases}$	$\begin{cases} x - 4y = -2 \\ 2x + y = 3 \end{cases}$
$(-2, 0)$	(0, 3)	$\left(\frac{10}{9}, \frac{7}{9}\right)$

50. $\begin{cases} x - 7y > -36 \\ 5x + 2y > 5 \\ 6x - 5y > 6 \end{cases}$

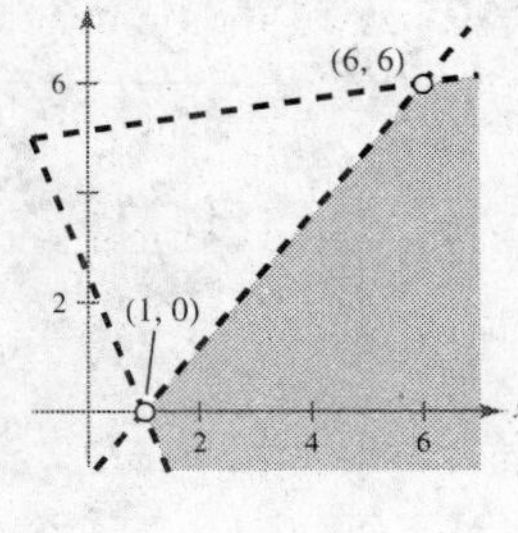

First, find the points of intersection of each pair of equations.

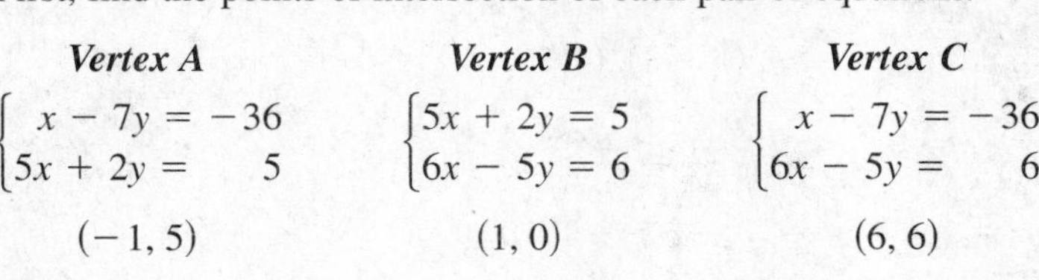

Vertex A	*Vertex B*	*Vertex C*
$\begin{cases} x - 7y = -36 \\ 5x + 2y = 5 \end{cases}$	$\begin{cases} 5x + 2y = 5 \\ 6x - 5y = 6 \end{cases}$	$\begin{cases} x - 7y = -36 \\ 6x - 5y = 6 \end{cases}$
$(-1, 5)$	(1, 0)	(6, 6)

51. $3x + y \le y^2$

$x - y > 0$

The curves given by $3x + y = y^2$ and $x - y = 0$ intersect as follows:

$3x + x = x^2$

$4x = x^2$

$x = 0, 4$

Intersection points:
$(0, 0), (4, 4)$

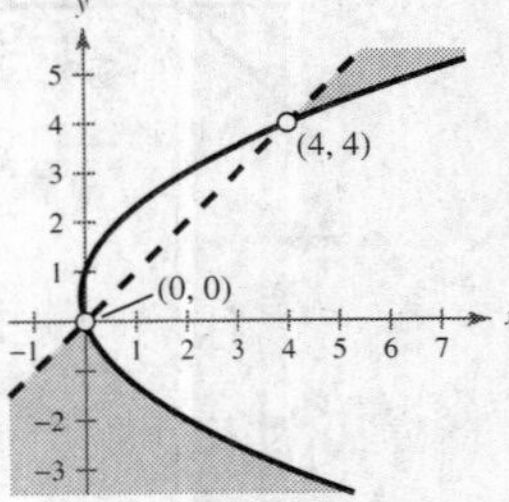

52. $y^2 - 3x \ge 9 \implies x \le \dfrac{y^2}{3} - 3$

$x + y \ge -3 \implies x \ge -y - 3$

The curves intersect where

$\dfrac{y^2}{3} - 3 = -y - 3$

$y^2 + 3y = 0$

$y(y + 3) = 0$

$y = 0, -3.$

Intersection points:

$(-3, 0), (0, -3)$

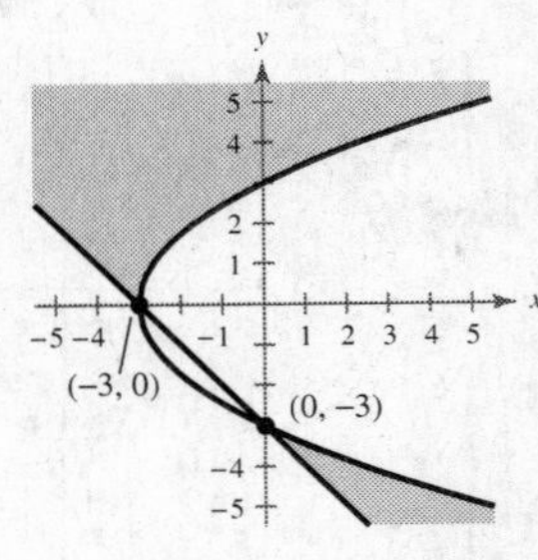

53. $2x + y < 2 \implies y < 2 - 2x$

$x + 3y > 2 \implies y > \frac{1}{3}(2 - x)$

$2 - 2x = \frac{1}{3}(2 - x)$

$6 - 6x = (2 - x)$

$4 = 5x$

$x = \frac{4}{5}$

Intersection: $\left(\frac{4}{5}, \frac{2}{5}\right)$

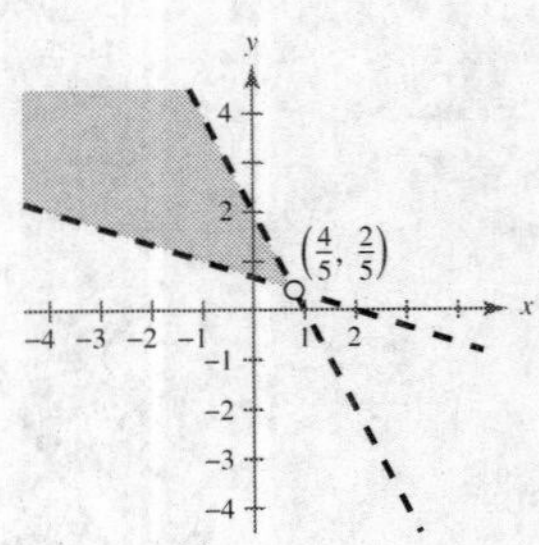

54. $x - 2y{-}6 \implies y > \frac{1}{2}x + 3$

$2x - 4y{-}9 \implies y < \frac{1}{2}x + \frac{9}{4}$

No solution

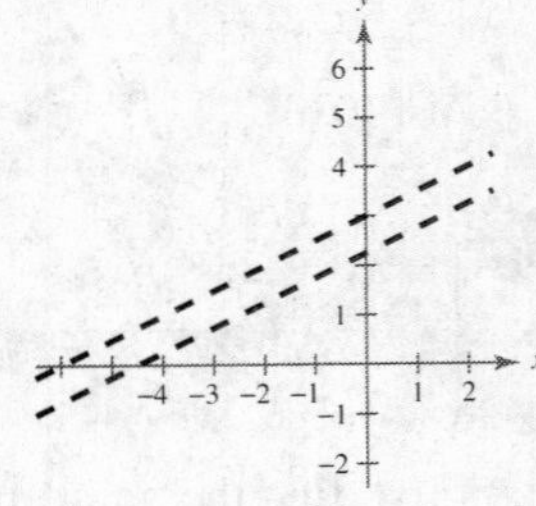

55. $\begin{cases} x < y^2 \\ x > y + 2 \end{cases}$

Points of intersection:

$y^2 = y + 2$

$y^2 - y - 2 = 0$

$(y + 1)(y - 2) = 0$

$y = -1, 2$

$(1, -1), (4, 2)$

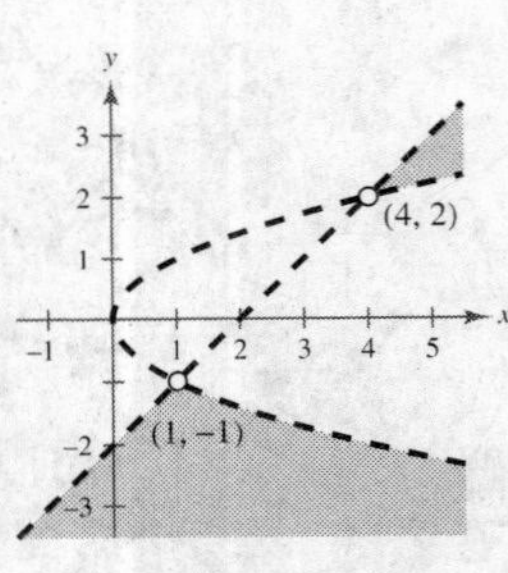

56. $x - y^2 > 0$

$x - y < 2$

Points of intersection:

$y^2 = y + 2$

$y^2 - y - 2 = 0$

$(y + 1)(y - 2) = 0$

$y = -1, 2$

$(1, -1), (4, 2)$

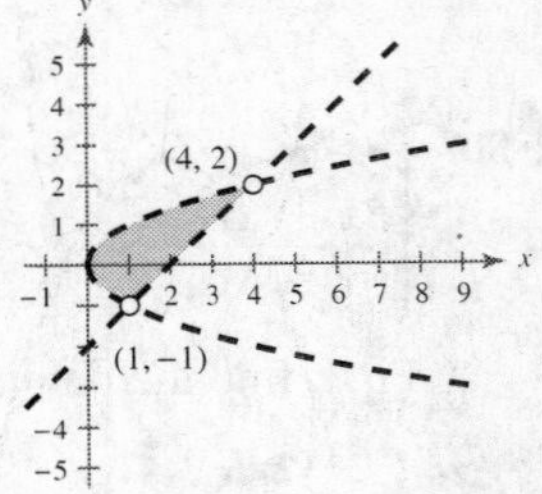

57. $\begin{cases} x^2 + y^2 \le 9 \\ x^2 + y^2 \ge 1 \end{cases}$

There are no points of intersection. The region in common to both inequalities is the region between the circles.

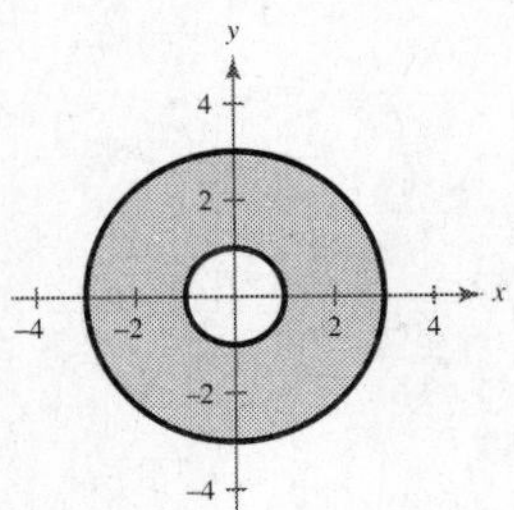

58. 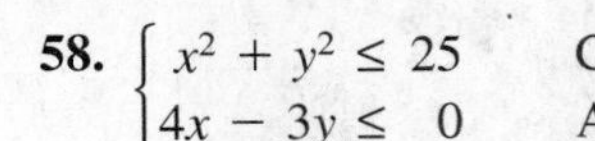

$\begin{cases} x^2 + y^2 \le 25 \\ 4x - 3y \le 0 \end{cases}$ Circle and interior
Above line

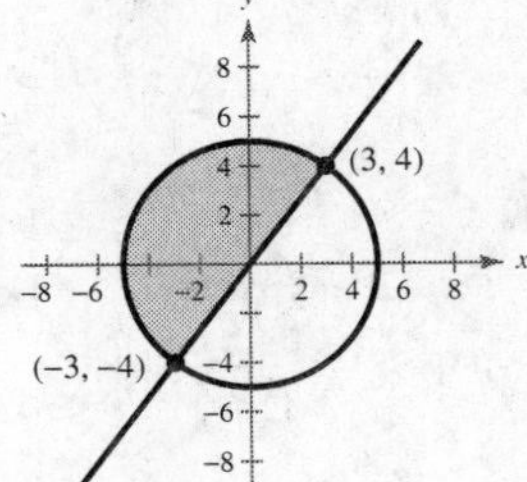

59. $\begin{cases} y \le \sqrt{3x} + 1 \\ y \ge x^2 + 1 \end{cases}$

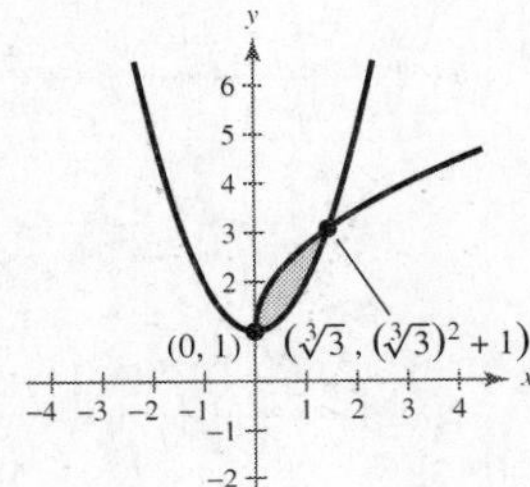

60. $\begin{cases} y < -x^2 + 2x + 3 \\ y > x^2 - 4x + 3 \end{cases}$

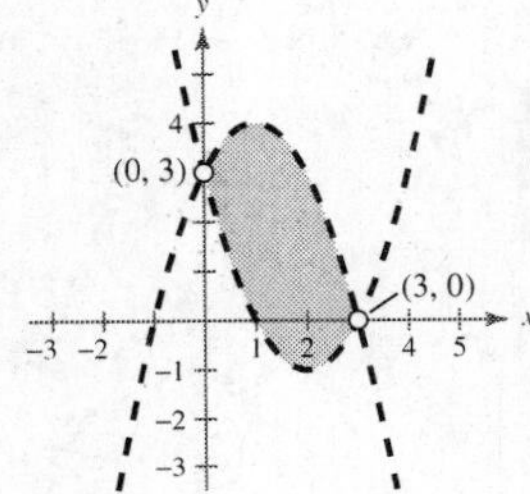

61. $\begin{cases} y < x^3 - 2x + 1 \\ y > -2x \\ x \le 1 \end{cases}$

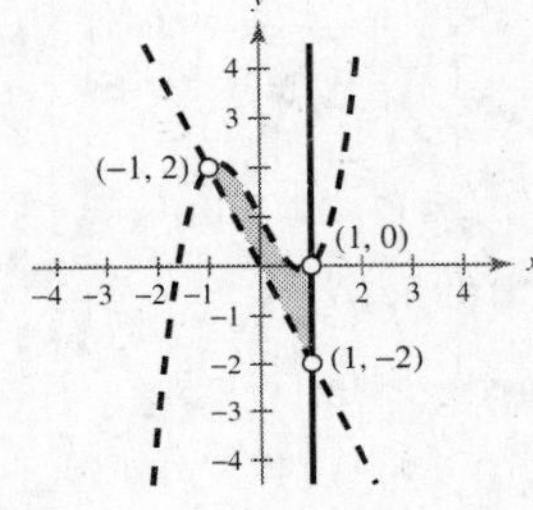

62. $\begin{cases} y \ge x^4 - 2x^2 + 1 \\ y \le 1 - x^2 \end{cases}$

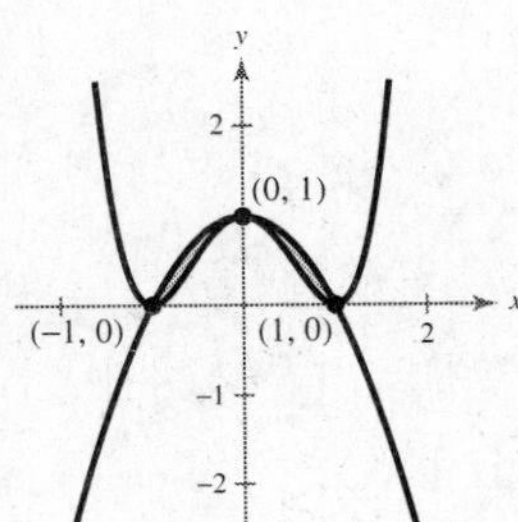

63. $\begin{cases} x^2y \ge 1 \\ 0 < x \le 4 \\ y \le 4 \end{cases}$

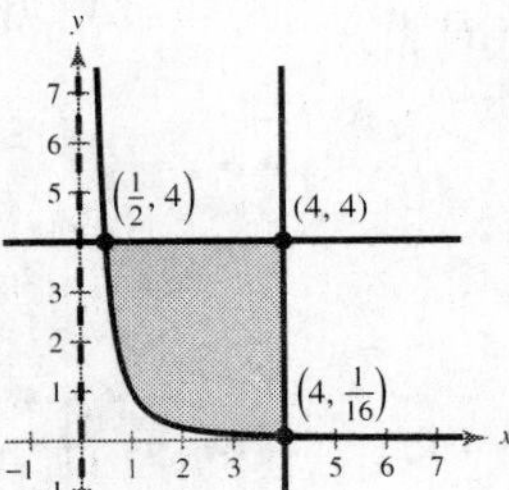

64. $\begin{cases} y \le e^{-x^2/2} \\ y \ge 0 \\ -2 \le x \le 2 \end{cases}$

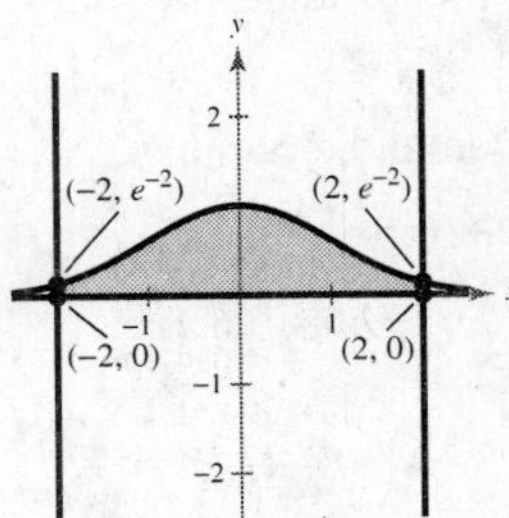

65. $y < -x + 4 \Rightarrow \dfrac{x}{4} + \dfrac{y}{4} < 1$

$x \ge 0$ $\qquad x \ge 0$

$y \ge 0$ $\qquad y \ge 0$

66. (0, 6), (3, 0)

Line: $y \le 6 - 2x$

(0, −3), (3, 0)

Line: $y \ge x - 3$

$x \ge 1$

67. (0, 4), (4, 0)

Line: $y \le 4 - x$

(0, 2), (8, 0)

Line: $y \le -\dfrac{1}{4}x + 2$

$x \ge 0,\ y \ge 0$

68. The lines have equations $y = -\frac{1}{3}x + 2$ and $y = 4 - x$. They intersect at $(3, 1)$.

$$x + 3y < 6$$
$$x + y < 4$$
$$x \geq 0$$
$$y \geq 0$$

69. Circle of radius 2 and center $(0, 2)$

$$x^2 + (y - 2)^2 \leq 4$$

70. Circle: $x^2 + y^2 > 4$

71. $\begin{cases} x \geq 2 \\ x \leq 5 \\ y \geq 1 \\ y \leq 7 \end{cases}$

Thus,
$2 \leq x \leq 5, 1 \leq y \leq 7.$

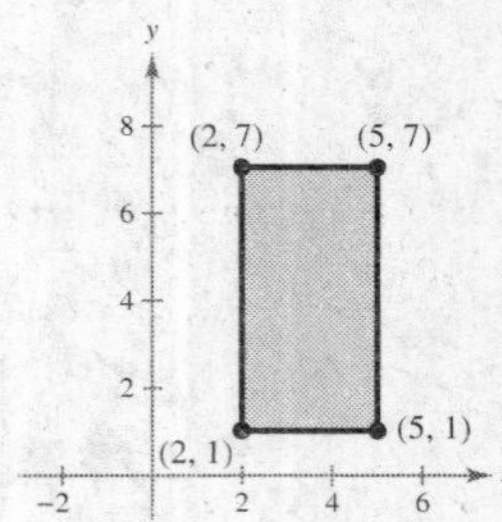

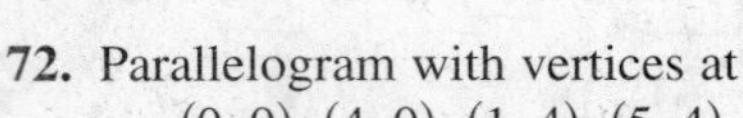

72. Parallelogram with vertices at $(0, 0), (4, 0), (1, 4), (5, 4)$

$(0, 0), (4, 0)$: $y \geq 0$

$(4, 0), (5, 4)$: $4x - y \leq 16$

$(1, 4), (5, 4)$: $y \leq 4$

$(0, 0), (1, 4)$: $4x - y \geq 0$

$$4x - y \geq 0$$
$$4x - y \leq 16$$
$$0 \leq y \leq 4$$

73. $(0, 0), (5, 0)$

Line: $y \geq 0$

$(0, 0), (2, 3)$

Line: $y \leq \frac{3}{2}x$

$(2, 3), (5, 0)$

Line: $y \leq -x + 5$

74. Triangle with vertices at $(-1, 0), (1, 0), (0, 1)$

$(-1, 0), (1, 0)$: $y \geq 0$

$(-1, 0), (0, 1)$: $y \leq x + 1$

$(0, 1), (1, 0)$: $y \leq -x + 1$

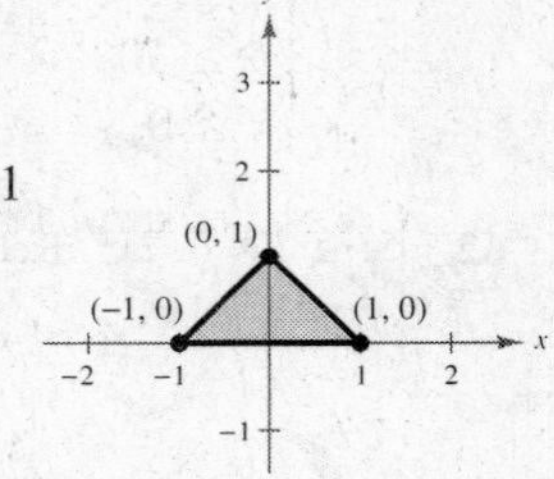

75. Demand = Supply

$$50 - 0.5x = 0.125x$$
$$50 = 0.625x$$
$$x = 80$$
$$p = 10$$

Point of equilibrium: $(80, 10)$

Consumer surplus $= \frac{1}{2}(40)(80) = 1600$

Producer surplus $= \frac{1}{2}(10)(80) = 400$

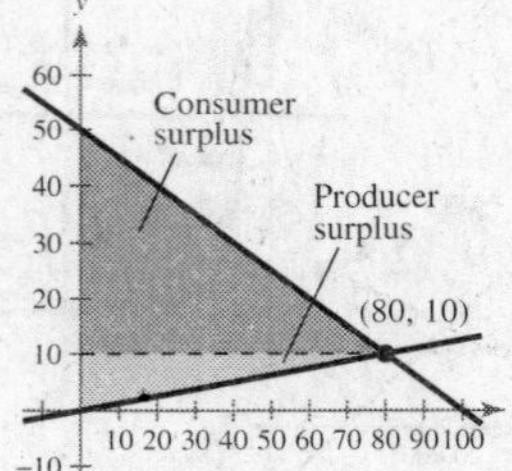

76. Demand = Supply

$$100 - 0.05x = 25 + 0.1x$$
$$75 = 0.15x$$
$$x = 500$$
$$p = 75$$

Consumer surplus $= \frac{1}{2}(500)(25) = 6250$

Producer surplus $= \frac{1}{2}(500)(50) = 12{,}500$

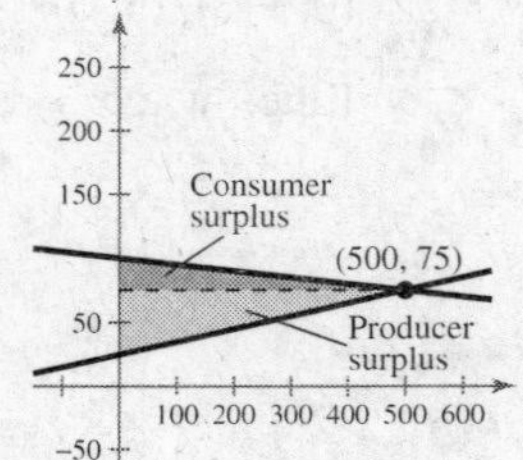

77. Demand = Supply

$$300 - 0.0002x = 225 + 0.0005x$$

$$75 = 0.0007x$$

$$x = \frac{75}{0.0007} = \frac{750{,}000}{7}$$

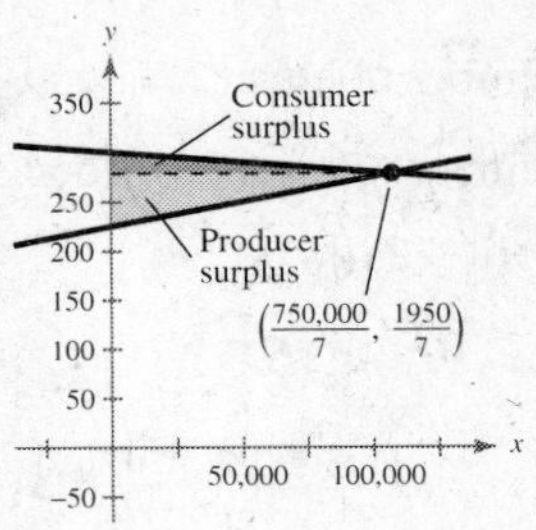

Equilibrium point: $\left(\dfrac{750{,}000}{7}, \dfrac{1950}{7}\right) \approx (107{,}142.86, 278.57)$

Consumer surplus: $\dfrac{(107{,}142.86)(300 - 278.57)}{2} \approx 1{,}148{,}036$

Producer surplus: $\dfrac{(107{,}142.86)(278.57 - 225)}{2} \approx 2{,}869{,}822$

78. Demand = Supply

$$140 - 0.00002x = 80 + 0.00001x$$

$$60 = 0.00003x$$

$$2{,}000{,}000 = x$$

$$100 = p$$

Point of equilibrium: $(2{,}000{,}000, 100)$

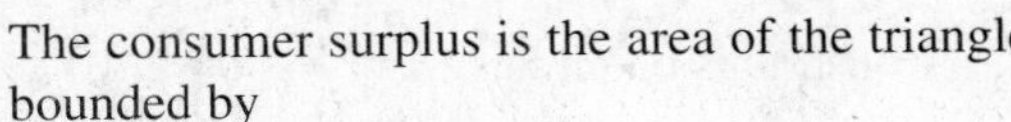

The consumer surplus is the area of the triangle bounded by

$$\begin{cases} p \le 140 - 0.00002x \\ p \ge 100 \\ x \ge 0. \end{cases}$$

Consumer surplus $= \frac{1}{2}(\text{base})(\text{height})$

$= \frac{1}{2}(2{,}000{,}000)(40)$

$= 40{,}000{,}000$ or \$40 million

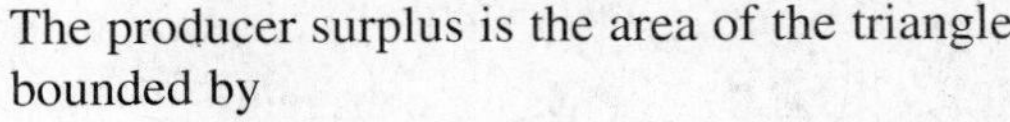

The producer surplus is the area of the triangle bounded by

$$\begin{cases} p \ge 80 + 0.00001x \\ p \le 100 \\ x \ge 0. \end{cases}$$

Producer surplus $= \frac{1}{2}(\text{base})(\text{height})$

$= \frac{1}{2}(2{,}000{,}000)(20)$

$= 20{,}000{,}000$ or \$20 million

79. $x + y \le 30{,}000$

$x \ge 7500$

$y \ge 7500$

$x \ge 2y$

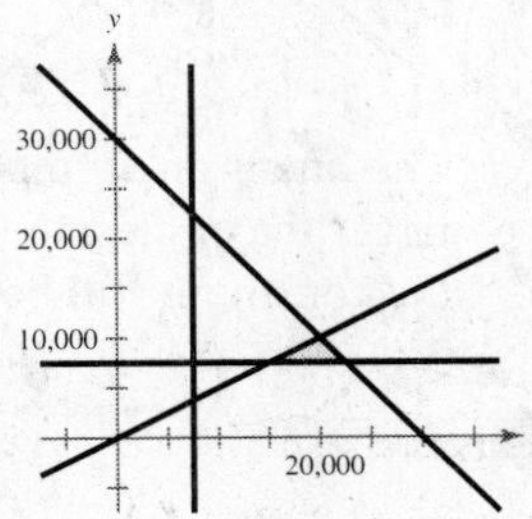

80. Let x be the number of \$20 tickets.

Let y be the number of \$35 tickets.

$x + y \ge 20{,}000$

$x \ge 10{,}000$

$y \ge 5{,}000$

$20x + 35y \ge 300{,}000$

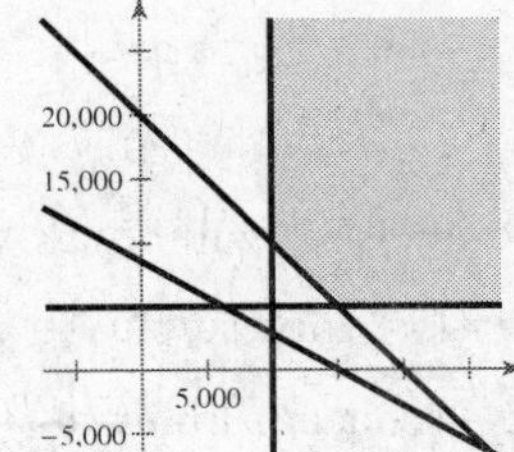

81. (a) Let x = number of ounces of food X.

Let y = number of ounces of food Y.

Calcium: $20x + 10y \geq 280$

Iron: $15x + 10y \geq 160$

Vitamin B: $10x + 20y \geq 180$

$x \geq 0$

$y \geq 0$

(b)

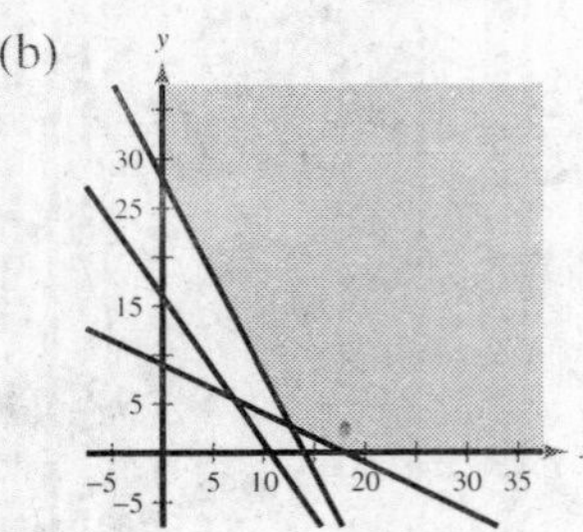

82. x = number of model A

y = number of model B

Demand: $x \geq 2y$

Cost: $8x + 12y \leq 200$

Inventory: $x \geq 4$

$y \geq 2$

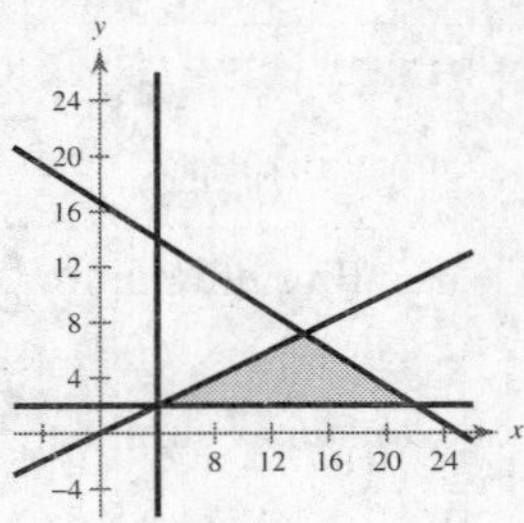

83. (a)

$xy \geq 500$ Body-building space

$2x + \pi y \geq 125$ Track (two semi-circles and two lengths)

$x \geq 0$ Physical constraint

$y \geq 0$ Physical constraint

(b)

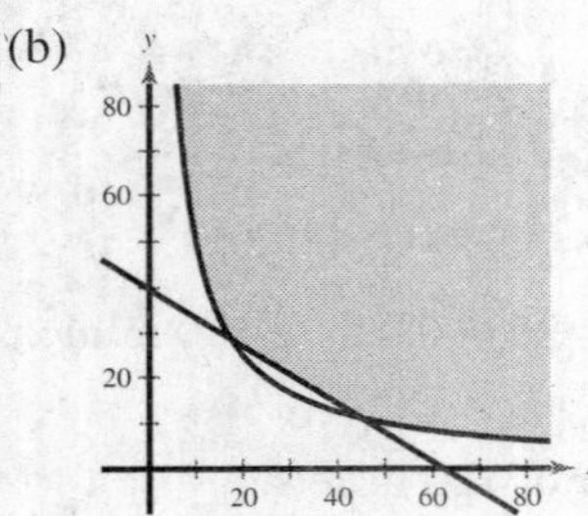

84. Let x = radius of smaller circle.

Let y = radius of larger circle.

(a) Constraints on circles: $\pi y^2 - \pi x^2 \geq 10$

$x > 0$

$y > x$

(b)

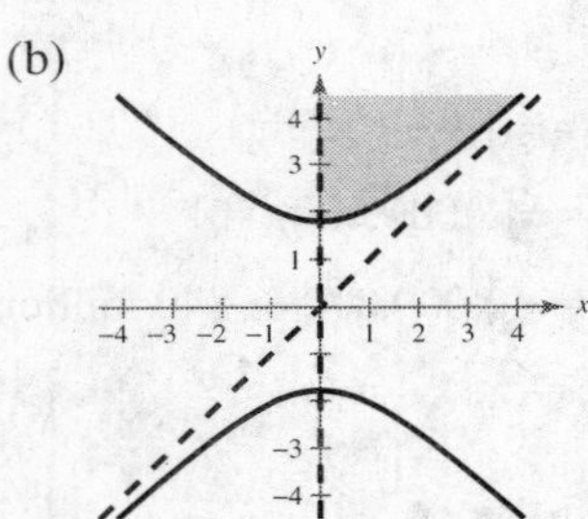

(c) The line is an asymptote to the boundary. The larger the circles, the closer the radii can be and the constraint still be satisfied.

85. Area $= 9 \cdot 11 = 99$ square units

True

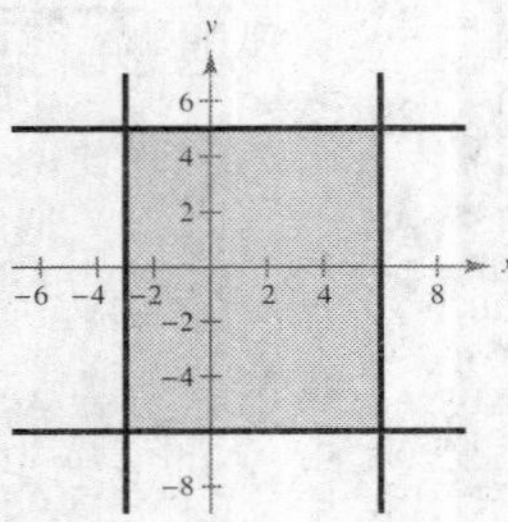

86. False

$3x + y^2 \geq 2$ is outside the parabola $3x = 2 - y^2$.

87. Test a point on either side of the boundary.

88. Answers will vary.

Appendix F.2 Linear Programming

Vocabulary Check

1. optimization

2. objective function

3. constraints, feasible solutions

1. $z = 3x + 5y$

At $(0, 6)$: $z = 3(0) + 5(6) = 30$

At $(0, 0)$: $z = 3(0) + 5(0) = 0$

At $(6, 0)$: $z = 3(6) + 5(0) = 18$

The minimum value is 0 at $(0, 0)$.

The maximum value is 30 at $(0, 6)$.

2. $z = 2x + 8y$

At $(0, 4)$: $z = 2(0) + 8(4) = 32$

At $(0, 0)$: $z = 2(0) + 8(0) = 0$

At $(2, 0)$: $z = 2(2) + 8(0) = 4$

The maximum value is 32 at $(0, 4)$.

The minimum value is 0 at $(0, 0)$.

3. $z = 10x + 7y$

At $(0, 6)$: $z = 10(0) + 7(6) = 42$

At $(0, 0)$: $z = 10(0) + 7(0) = 0$

At $(6, 0)$: $z = 10(6) + 7(0) = 60$

The minimum value is 0 at $(0, 0)$.

The maximum value is 60 at $(6, 0)$.

4. $z = 7x + 3y$

At $(0, 4)$: $z = 7(0) + 3(4) = 12$

At $(0, 0)$: $z = 7(0) + 3(0) = 0$

At $(2, 0)$: $z = 7(2) + 3(0) = 14$

The maximum value is 14 at $(2, 0)$.

The minimum value is 0 at $(0, 0)$.

5. $z = 3x + 2y$

$x + 3y = 15 \Rightarrow y = \frac{1}{3}(15 - x)$

$4x + y = 16 \Rightarrow y = (16 - 4x)$

$\frac{1}{3}(15 - x) = 16 - 4x$

$(15 - x) = 48 - 12x$

$11x = 33$

$x = 3$

$y = 4$

At $(0, 0)$: $z = 0$

At $(0, 5)$: $z = 10$

At $(4, 0)$: $z = 12$

At $(3, 4)$: $z = 17$

The minimum value is 0 at $(0, 0)$.

The maximum value is 17 at $(3, 4)$.

6. $z = 4x + 3y$

At $(0, 4)$: $z = 4(0) + 3(4) = 12$

At $(3, 0)$: $z = 4(3) + 3(0) = 12$

At $(5, 3)$: $z = 4(5) + 3(3) = 29$

At $(0, 2)$: $z = 4(0) + 3(2) = 6$

The maximum value is 29 at $(5, 3)$.

The minimum value is 6 at $(0, 2)$.

7. $z = 5x + 0.5y$

At $(0, 0)$: $z = 0$

At $(0, 5)$: $z = 2.5$

At $(4, 0)$: $z = 20$

At $(3, 4)$: $z = 17$

The minimum value is 0 at $(0, 0)$.

The maximum value is 20 at $(4, 0)$.

8. $z = x + 6y$

At $(0, 4)$: $z = 0 + 6(4) = 24$

At $(3, 0)$: $z = 3 + 6(0) = 3$

At $(5, 3)$: $z = 5 + 6(3) = 23$

At $(0, 2)$: $z = 0 + 6(2) = 12$

The maximum value is 24 at $(0, 4)$.

The minimum value is 3 at $(3, 0)$.

9. $z = 10x + 7y$

At $(0, 45)$: $z = 10(0) + 7(45) = 315$

At $(30, 45)$: $z = 10(30) + 7(45) = 615$

At $(60, 20)$: $z = 10(60) + 7(20) = 740$

At $(60, 0)$: $z = 10(60) + 7(0) = 600$

At $(0, 0)$: $z = 10(0) + 7(0) = 0$

The minimum value is 0 at $(0, 0)$.

The maximum value is 740 at $(60, 20)$.

10. $z = 50x + 35y$

At $(0, 800)$: $z = 50(0) + 35(800) = 28{,}000$

At $(900, 0)$: $z = 50(900) + 35(0) = 45{,}000$

At $(675, 0)$: $z = 50(675) + 35(0) = 33{,}750$

At $(0, 600)$: $z = 50(0) + 35(600) = 21{,}000$

The maximum value is 45,000 at $(900, 0)$.

The minimum value is 21,000 at $(0, 600)$.

11. $z = 25x + 30y$

At $(0, 45)$: $z = 25(0) + 30(45) = 1350$

At $(30, 45)$: $z = 25(30) + 30(45) = 2100$

At $(60, 20)$: $z = 25(60) + 30(20) = 2100$

At $(60, 0)$: $z = 25(60) + 30(0) = 1500$

At $(0, 0)$: $z = 25(0) + 30(0) = 0$

The minimum value is 0 at $(0, 0)$.

The maximum value is 2100 at any point along the line segment connecting $(30, 45)$ and $(60, 20)$.

12. $z = 15x + 20y$

At $(0, 800)$: $z = 16{,}000$

At $(900, 0)$: $z = 13{,}500$

At $(675, 0)$: $z = 10{,}125$

At $(0, 600)$: $z = 12{,}000$

The minimum value is 10,125 at $(675, 0)$.

The maximum value is 16,000 at $(0, 800)$.

13. $z = 6x + 10y$

At $(0, 2)$: $z = 6(0) + 10(2) = 20$

At $(5, 0)$: $z = 6(5) + 10(0) = 30$

At $(0, 0)$: $z = 6(0) + 10(0) = 0$

The minimum value is 0 at $(0, 0)$.

The maximum value is 30 at $(5, 0)$.

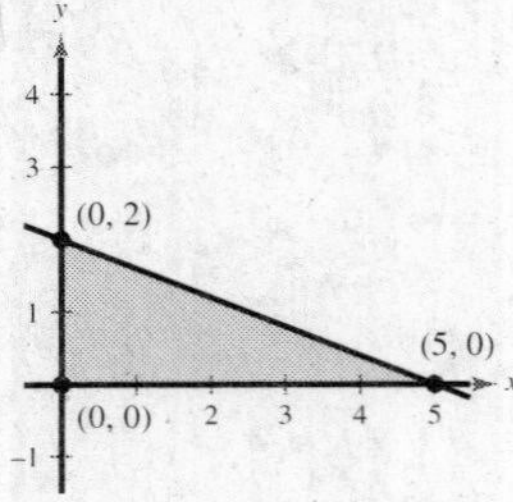

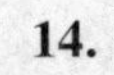

14. $x \geq 0$

$y \geq 0$

$x + \frac{1}{2}y \leq 4$

$z = 7x + 8y$

At $(0, 0)$: $z = 0$

At $(4, 0)$: $z = 28$

At $(0, 8)$: $z = 64$

The maximum value is 64 at $(0, 8)$.

The minimum value is 0 at $(0, 0)$.

15. $z = 3x + 4y$

At $(0, 0)$: $z = 0$

At $(7, 0)$: $z = 21$

At $(0, 10)$: $z = 40$

At $(5, 8)$: $z = 47$

The minimum value is 0 at $(0, 0)$.

The maximum value is 47 at $(5, 8)$.

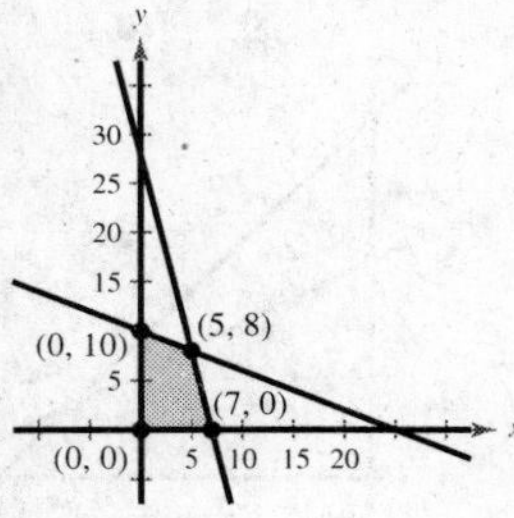

16. $z = 4x + 5y$

At $(0, 0)$: $z = 4(0) + 5(0) = 0$

At $(5, 0)$: $z = 4(5) + 5(0) = 20$

At $(4, 1)$: $z = 4(4) + 5(1) = 21$

At $(0, 3)$: $z = 4(0) + 5(3) = 15$

The maximum value is 21 at $(4, 1)$.

The minimum value is 0 at $(0, 0)$.

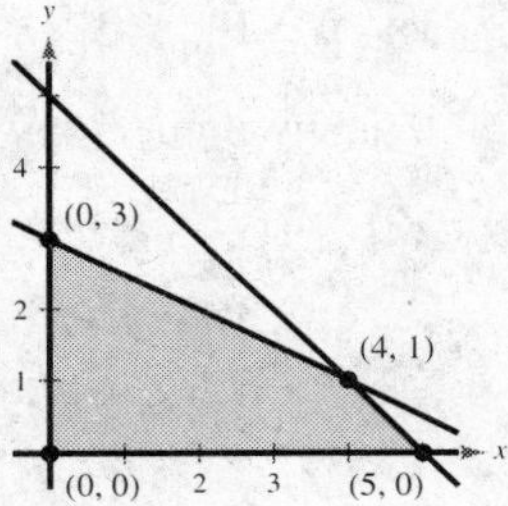

17. $z = x + 2y$

At $(0, 0)$: $z = 0 + 2(0) = 0$

At $(0, 10)$: $z = 0 + 2(10) = 20$

At $(5, 8)$: $z = 5 + 2(8) = 21$

At $(7, 0)$: $z = 7 + 2(0) = 7$

The minimum value is 0 at $(0, 0)$.

The maximum value is 21 at $(5, 8)$.

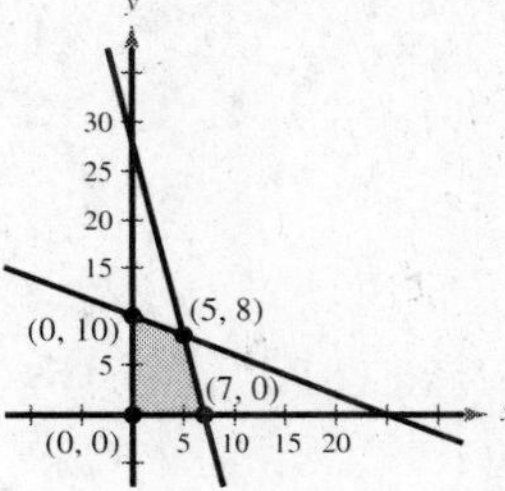

18. $z = 2x + 4y$

At $(0, 0)$: $z = 2(0) + 4(0) = 0$

At $(0, 3)$: $z = 2(0) + 4(3) = 12$

At $(4, 1)$: $z = 2(4) + 4(1) = 12$

At $(5, 0)$: $z = 2(5) + 4(0) = 10$

The minimum value is 0 at $(0, 0)$.

The maximum value is 12 at any point on the line segment joining $(0, 3)$ and $(4, 1)$.

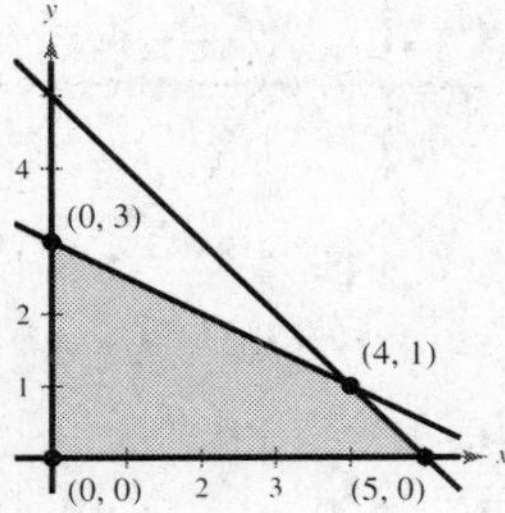

19. $z = 2x$

At $(0, 0)$: $z = 2(0) = 0$

At $(0, 10)$: $z = 2(0) = 0$

At $(5, 8)$: $z = 2(5) = 10$

At $(7, 0)$: $z = 2(7) = 14$

The maximum value is 14 at $(7, 0)$.

The minimum value is 0 along the line segment joining $(0, 0)$ and $(0, 10)$.

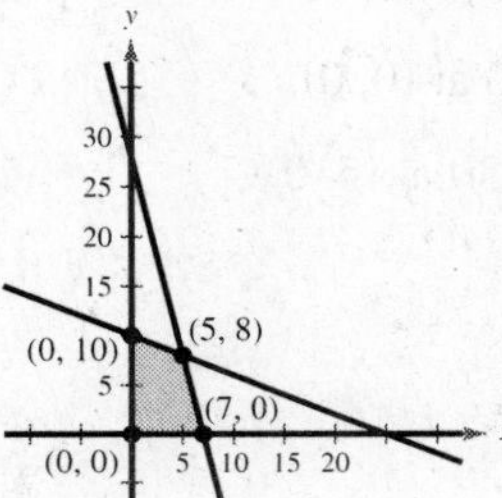

20. $z = 3y$

At $(0, 0)$: $z = 3(0) = 0$

At $(0, 3)$: $z = 3(3) = 9$

At $(4, 1)$: $z = 3(1) = 3$

At $(5, 0)$: $z = 3(0) = 0$

The maximum value is 9 at $(0, 3)$.

The minimum value is 0 at any point on the line segment joining $(0, 0)$ and $(5, 0)$.

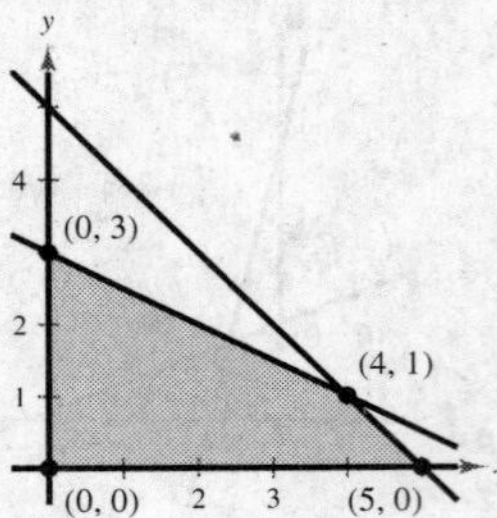

21. $z = 4x + y$

At $(36, 0)$: $z = 4(36) + 0 = 144$

At $(40, 0)$: $z = 4(40) + 0 = 160$

At $(24, 8)$: $z = 4(24) + 8 = 104$

The minimum value is 104 at $(24, 8)$.

The maximum value is 160 at $(40, 0)$.

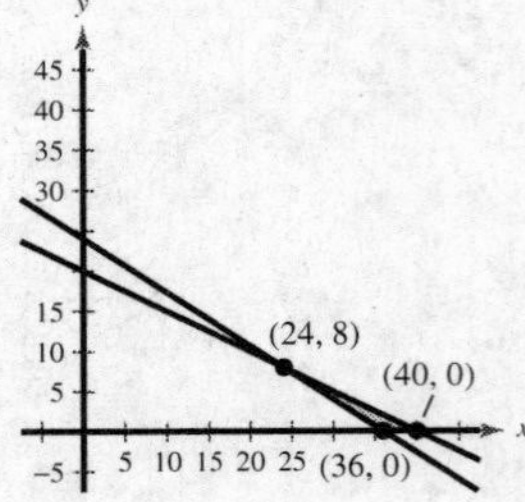

22. $z = x$

At $(0, 0)$: $z = 0$

At $(12, 0)$: $z = 12$

At $(10, 8)$: $z = 10$

At $(6, 16)$: $z = 6$

At $(0, 20)$: $z = 0$

The maximum value is 12 at $(12, 0)$. The minimum value is 0 at any point along the line segment connecting $(0, 0)$ and $(0, 20)$.

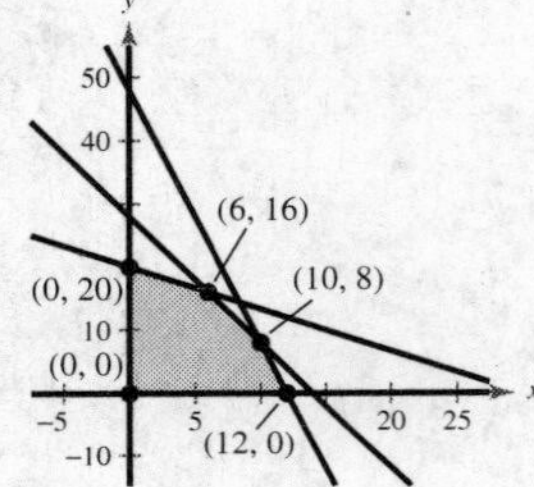

23. $z = x + 4y$

At $(36, 0)$: $z = 36 + 4(0) = 36$

At $(40, 0)$: $z = 40 + 4(0) = 40$

At $(24, 8)$: $z = 24 + 4(8) = 56$

The minimum value is 36 at $(36, 0)$.

The maximum value is 56 at $(24, 8)$.

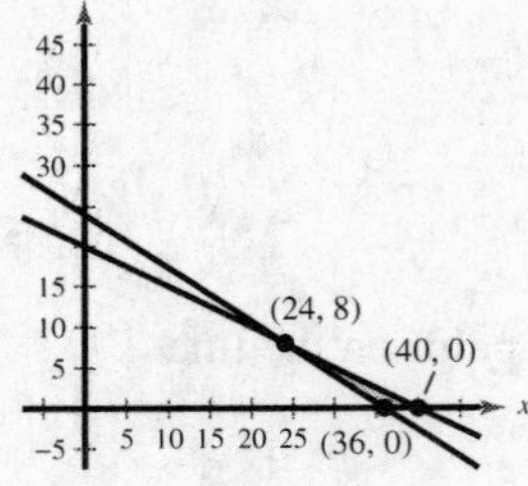

24. $z = y$

At $(0, 0)$: $z = 0$

At $(12, 0)$: $z = 0$

At $(10, 8)$: $z = 8$

At $(6, 16)$: $z = 16$

At $(0, 20)$: $z = 20$

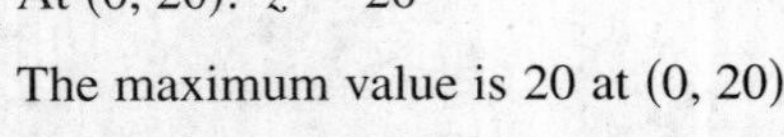

The maximum value is 20 at $(0, 20)$.

The minimum value is 0 at any point along the line segment connecting $(0, 0)$ and $(12, 0)$.

25. $z = 2x + 3y$

At $(36, 0)$: $z = 2(36) + 3(0) = 72$

At $(40, 0)$: $z = 2(40) + 3(0) = 80$

At $(24, 8)$: $z = 2(24) + 3(8) = 72$

The minimum value is 72 at any point on the line segment joining $(36, 0)$ and $(24, 8)$.

The maximum value is 80 at $(40, 0)$.

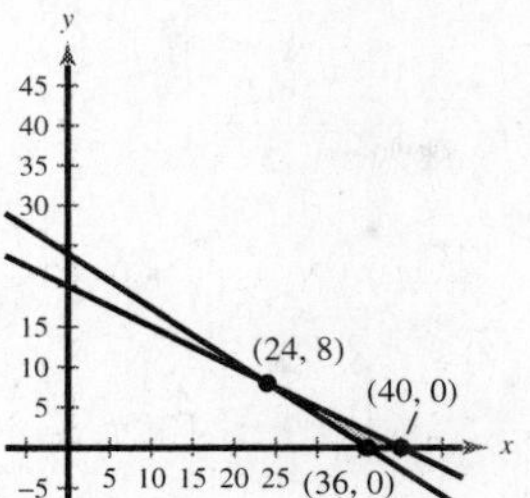

26. $z = 3x + 2y$

At $(0, 0)$: $z = 0$

At $(12, 0)$: $z = 36$

At $(10, 8)$: $z = 46$

At $(6, 16)$: $z = 50$

At $(0, 20)$: $z = 40$

The maximum value is 50 at $(6, 16)$.

The minimum value is 0 at $(0, 0)$.

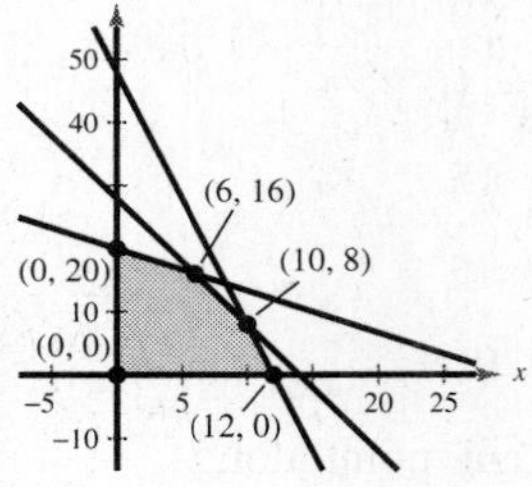

27. $z = 2x + y$

(a), (b)

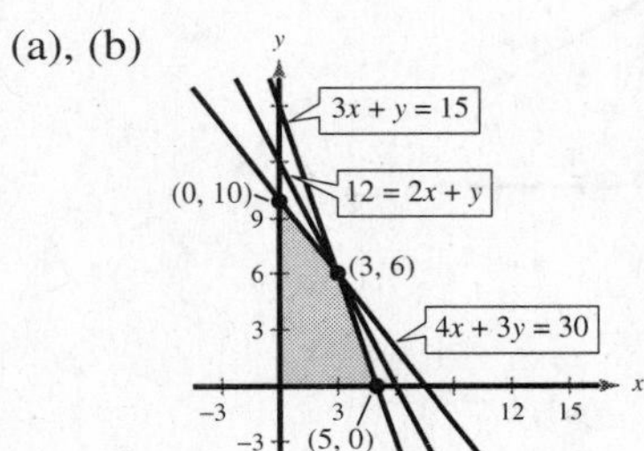

(c) At $(0, 10)$: $z = 2(0) + (10) = 10$

At $(3, 6)$: $z = 2(3) + (6) = 12$

At $(5, 0)$: $z = 2(5) + (0) = 10$

At $(0, 0)$: $z = 2(0) + (0) = 0$

The maximum value is 12 at $(3, 6)$.

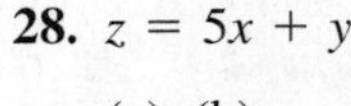

28. $z = 5x + y$

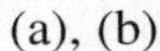

(a), (b)

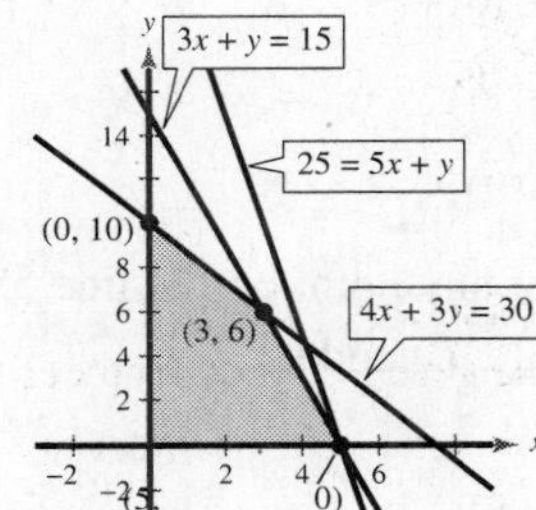

(c) At $(0, 10)$: $z = 5(0) + (10) = 10$

At $(3, 6)$: $z = 5(3) + (6) = 21$

At $(5, 0)$: $z = 5(5) + (0) = 25$

At $(0, 0)$: $z = 5(0) + (0) = 0$

The maximum value is 25 at $(5, 0)$.

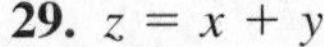

29. $z = x + y$

(a), (b)

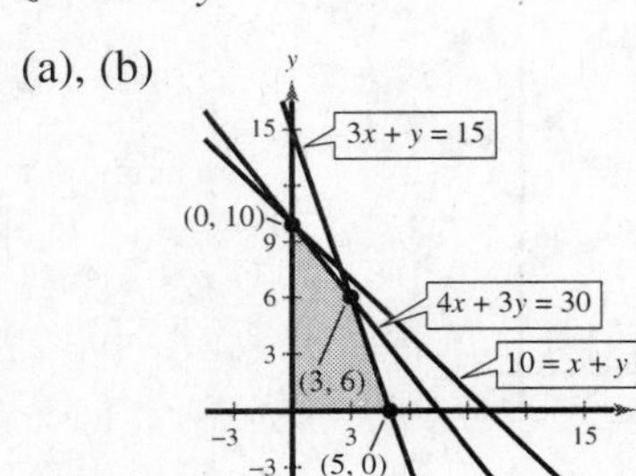

(c) At $(0, 10)$: $z = (0) + (10) = 10$

At $(3, 6)$: $z = (3) + (6) = 9$

At $(5, 0)$: $z = (5) + (0) = 5$

At $(0, 0)$: $z = (0) + (0) = 0$

The maximum value is 10 at $(0, 10)$.

30. $z = 3x + y$

(a), (b)

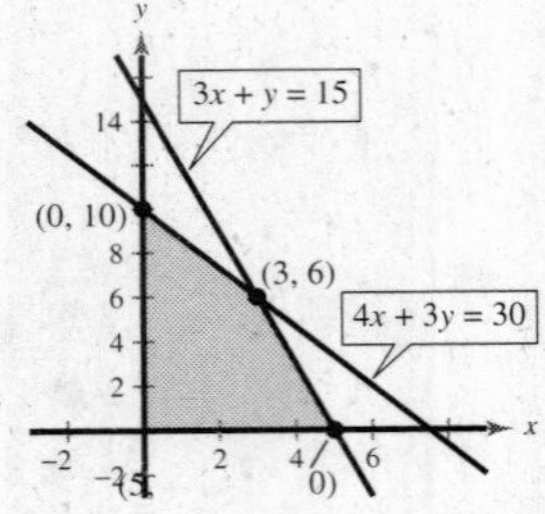

(c) At $(0, 10)$: $z = 3(0) + (10) = 10$

At $(3, 6)$: $z = 3(3) + (6) = 15$

At $(5, 0)$: $z = 3(5) + (0) = 15$

At $(0, 0)$: $z = 3(0) + (0) = 0$

The maximum value is 15 at any point along the line segment connecting $(3, 6)$ and $(5, 0)$.

31. $-x + y \le 1 \Rightarrow y \le x + 1$

$-x + 2y \le 4 \Rightarrow y \le \frac{1}{2}x + 2$

Intersection: $(2, 3)$

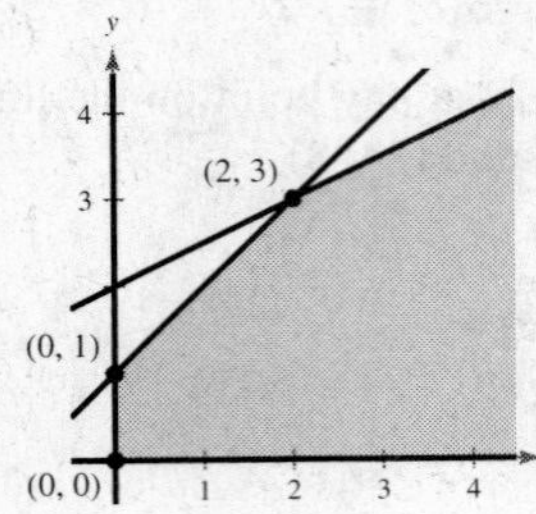

The constraints do not form a closed set of points. Therefore, $z = x + y$ is unbounded.

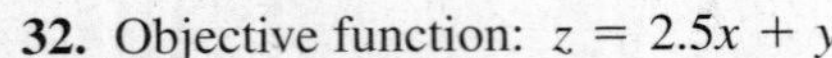

32. Objective function: $z = 2.5x + y$

Constraints: $x \ge 0, y \ge 0, 3x + 5y \le 15, 5x + 2y \le 10$

At $(0, 0)$: $z = 2.5(0) + 0 = 0$

At $(2, 0)$: $z = 2.5(2) + 0 = 5$

At $\left(\frac{20}{19}, \frac{45}{19}\right)$: $z = 2.5\left(\frac{20}{19}\right) + \frac{45}{19} = \frac{95}{19} = 5$

At $(0, 3)$: $z = 2.5(0) + 3 = 3$

z is the maximum at any point on the line $5x + 2y = 10$ between the points $(2, 0)$ and $\left(\frac{20}{19}, \frac{45}{19}\right)$.

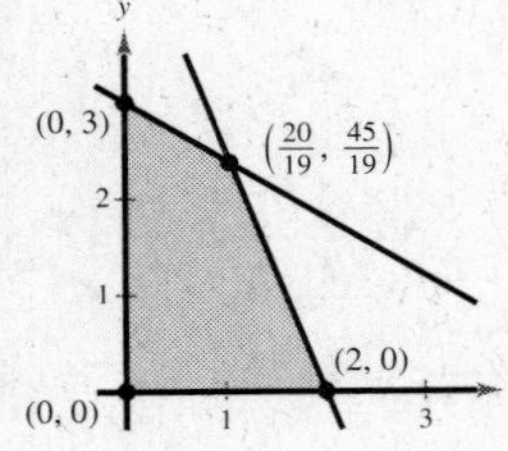

33. $-x + y \le 0 \Rightarrow y \le x$

$-3x + y \ge 3 \Rightarrow y \ge 3x + 3$

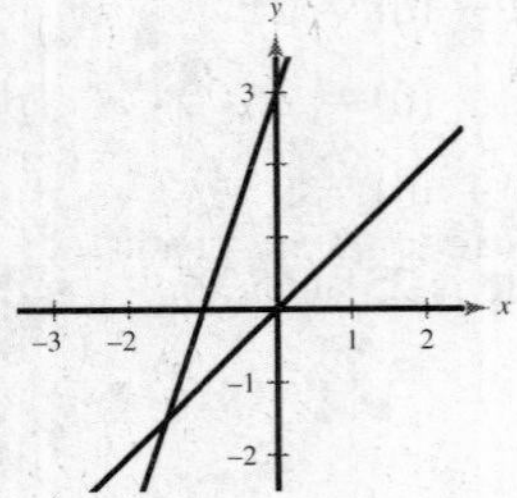

The feasible set is empty.

34. Objective function: $z = -x + 2y$

Constraints: $x \ge 0, y \ge 0, x \le 10, x + y \le 7$

At $(0, 0)$: $z = -0 + 2(0) = 0$

At $(0, 7)$: $z = -0 + 2(7) = 14$

At $(7, 0)$: $z = -7 + 2(0) = -7$

The constraint $x \le 10$ is extraneous.

The maximum value of 14 occurs at $(0, 7)$.

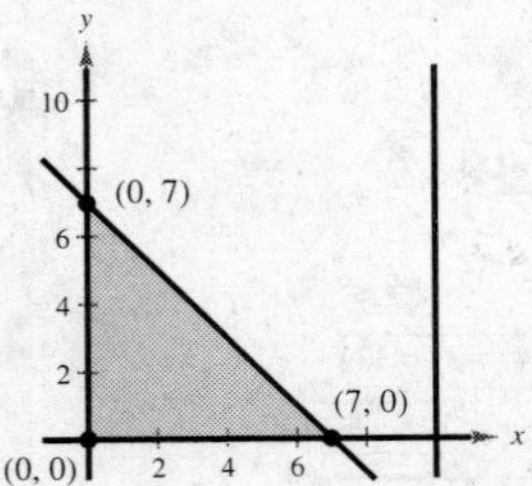

35. Let x = number of audits.

Let y = number of tax returns.

Constraints: $100x + 12.5y \le 800$

$8x + 2y \le 96$

$x \ge 0$

$y \ge 0$

Objective function: $R = 2000x + 300y$

Vertices of feasible region: (0, 0), (8, 0), (0, 48), (4, 32)

At (0, 0): $R = 0$

At (8, 0): $R = 16{,}000$

At (0, 48): $R = 14{,}400$

At (4, 32): $R = 17{,}600$

4 audits, 32 tax returns yields maximum revenue of \$17,600.

36. x = amount of Model A

y = amount of Model B

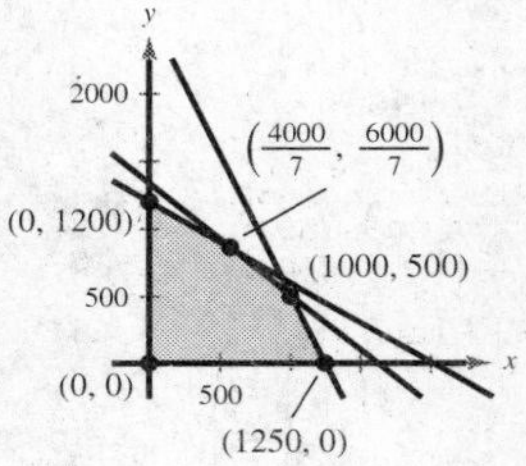

Constraints: $2.5x + 3y \le 4000$

$2x + y \le 2500$

$0.75x + 1.25y \le 1500$

$x \ge 0$

$y \ge 0$

Objective function: $P = 50x + 52y$

Vertices: (0, 0), (0, 1200), $\left(\frac{4000}{7}, \frac{6000}{7}\right)$, (1000, 500), (1250, 0)

At (0, 0): $P = (50)(0) + 52(0) = 0$

At (0, 1200): $P = 50(0) + 52(1200) = 62{,}400$

At $\left(\frac{4000}{7}, \frac{6000}{7}\right)$: $P = 50\left(\frac{4000}{7}\right) + 52\left(\frac{6000}{7}\right) \approx 73{,}142.86$

At (1000, 500): $P = 50(1000) + 52(500) = 76{,}000$

At (1250, 0): $P = 50(1250) + 52(0) = 62{,}500$

The maximum profit (\$76,000) occurs when 1000 units of Model A and 500 units of Model B are produced.

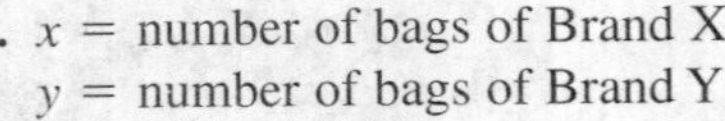

37. x = number of bags of Brand X
y = number of bags of Brand Y

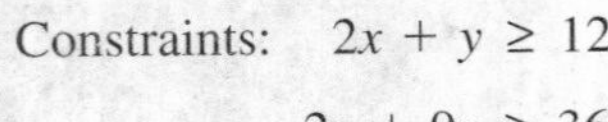

Constraints: $2x + y \geq 12$

$2x + 9y \geq 36$

$2x + 3y \geq 24$

$x \geq 0$

$y \geq 0$

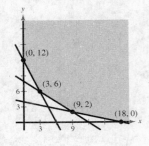

Objective function: $C = 25x + 20y$

Vertices: (0, 12), (3, 6), (9, 2), (18, 0)

At (0, 12): $C = 25(0) + 20(12) = 240$

At (3, 6): $C = 25(3) + 20(6) = 195$

At (9, 2): $C = 25(9) + 20(2) = 265$

At (18, 0): $C = 25(18) + 20(0) = 450$

To minimize cost, use three bags of Brand X and six bags of Brand Y for a total cost of $195.

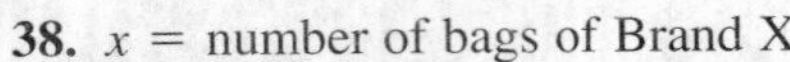

38. x = number of bags of Brand X

y = number of bags of Brand Y

Constraints: $8x + 2y \geq 16$

$x + y \geq 5$

$2x + 7y \geq 20$

$x \geq 0$

$y \geq 0$

$C = 15x + 30y$

At (0, 8): $C = 240$

At (1, 4): $C = 135$

At (3, 2): $C = 105$

At (10, 0): $C = 150$

The minimum cost is $105.

Use 3 bags of Brand X and 2 bags of Brand Y.

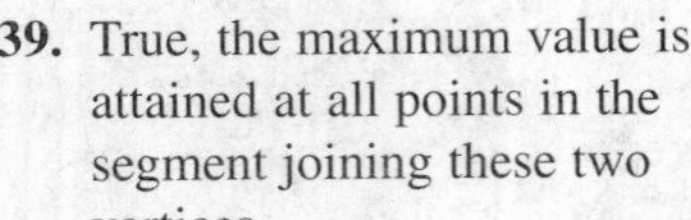

39. True, the maximum value is attained at all points in the segment joining these two vertices.

40. True, the maximum value is attained at all points on the segment joining these two vertices.

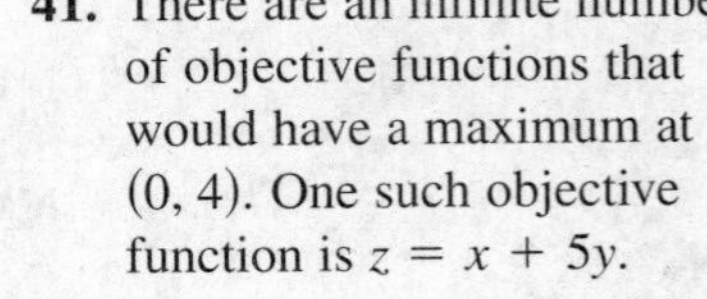

41. There are an infinite number of objective functions that would have a maximum at (0, 4). One such objective function is $z = x + 5y$.

42. There are an infinite number of objective functions that would have a maximum at (4, 3). One such objective function is $z = x + y$.

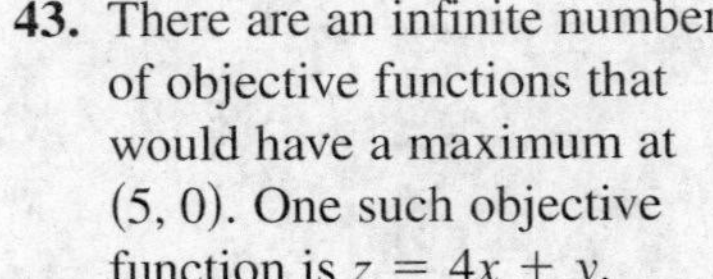

43. There are an infinite number of objective functions that would have a maximum at (5, 0). One such objective function is $z = 4x + y$.

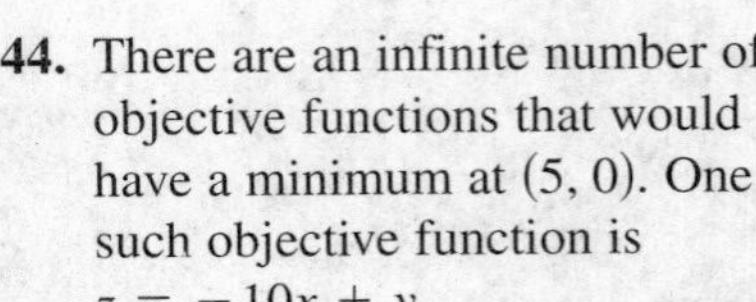

44. There are an infinite number of objective functions that would have a minimum at (5, 0). One such objective function is $z = -10x + y$.

45. Constraints: $x \geq 0, y \geq 0, x + 3y \leq 15, 4x + y \leq 16$

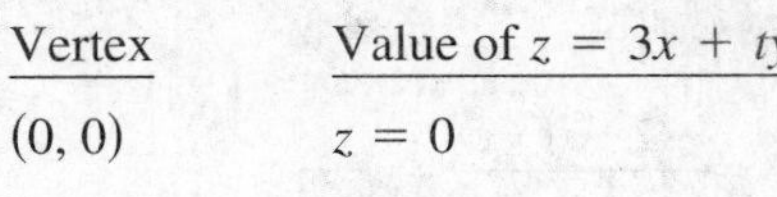

Vertex	Value of $z = 3x + ty$
(0, 0)	$z = 0$
(0, 5)	$z = 5t$
(3, 4)	$z = 9 + 4t$
(4, 0)	$z = 12$

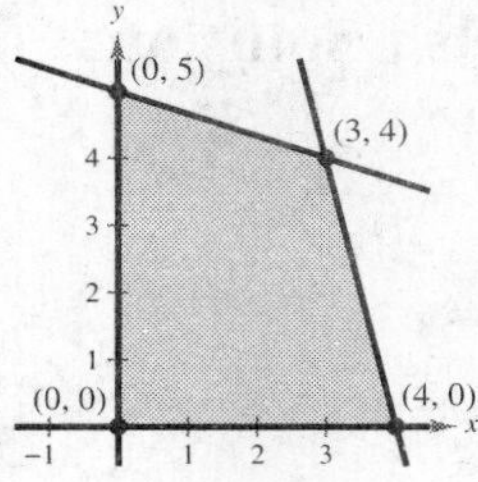

(a) For the maximum value to be at (0, 5), $z = 5t$ must be greater than

$z = 9 + 4t$ and $z = 12.$

$5t > 9 + 4t$ and $5t > 12$

$t > 9$ $\qquad t > \frac{12}{5}$

Thus, $t > 9$.

(b) For the maximum value to be at (3, 4), $z = 9 + 4t$ must be greater than $z = 5t$ and $z = 12$.

$9 + 4t > 5t$ and $9 + 4t > 12$

$9 > t$ $\qquad t > 3$

$\qquad t > \frac{3}{4}$

Thus, $\frac{3}{4} < t < 9$.

46. Constraints: $x \geq 0, y \geq 0, x + 2y \leq 4, x - y \leq 1$

$z = 3x + ty$

At (0, 0): $z = 3(0) + t(0) = 0$

At (1, 0): $z = 3(1) + t(0) = 3$

At (2, 1): $z = 3(2) + t(1) = 6 + t$

At (0, 2): $z = 3(0) + t(2) = 2t$

(a) For the maximum value to be at (2, 1), $z = 6 + t$ must be greater than $z = 2t$ and $z = 3$.

$6 + t > 2t$ and $6 + t > 3$

$6 > t$ $\qquad t > -3$

Thus, $-3 < t < 6$.

(b) For maximum value to be at (0, 2), $z = 2t$ must be greater than $z = 6 + t$ and $z = 3$.

$2t > 6 + t$ and $2t > 3$

$t > 6$ $\qquad t > \frac{3}{2}$

Thus, $t > 6$.

Chapter 1 Practice Test Solutions

1. $m = \dfrac{3 - 2}{1 - (-2)} = \dfrac{1}{3}$

2. Slope $= \dfrac{-2 - (-5)}{3 - 4} = \dfrac{3}{-1} = -3$

$y + 2 = -3(x - 3)$

$y + 2 = -3x + 9$

$y + 3x = 7$ or $y = -3x + 7$

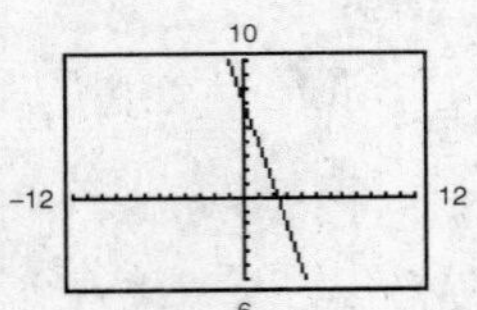

3. $y - 5 = -3(x + 1)$

$y - 5 = -3x - 3$

$y + 3x = 2$ or $y = -3x + 2$

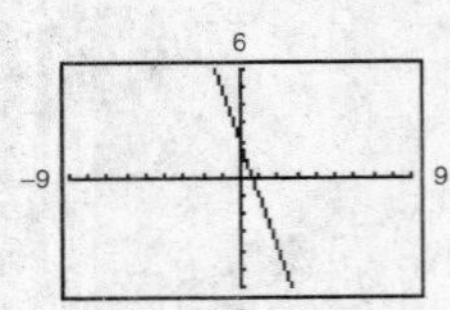

4. $3x + 5y = 7$

$5y = -3x + 7$

$y = -\frac{3}{5}x + \frac{7}{5}$

Slope of perpendicular line is $m = \frac{5}{3}$.

$y - 2 = \frac{5}{3}(x + 3)$

$y = \frac{5}{3}x + 7$

5. No, y is not a function of x. For example, $(0, 2)$ and $(0, -2)$ both satisfy the equation.

6. $f(0) = \dfrac{|0 - 2|}{(0 - 2)} = \dfrac{2}{-2} = -1$

$f(2)$ is not defined.

$f(4) = \dfrac{|4 - 2|}{(4 - 2)} = \dfrac{2}{2} = 1$

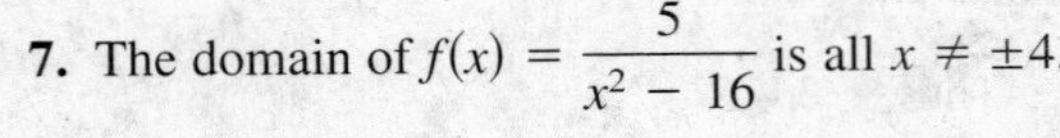

7. The domain of $f(x) = \dfrac{5}{x^2 - 16}$ is all $x \neq \pm 4$.

8. The domain of $g(t) = \sqrt{4 - t}$ consists of all t satisfying

$4 - t \geq 0$ or $t \leq 4$.

9.

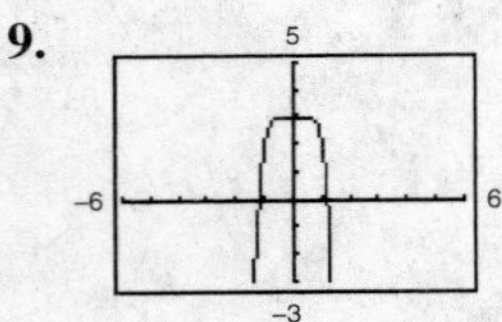

$f(x) = 3 - x^6$ is even.

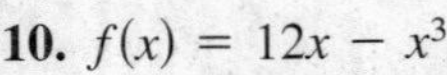

10. $f(x) = 12x - x^3$

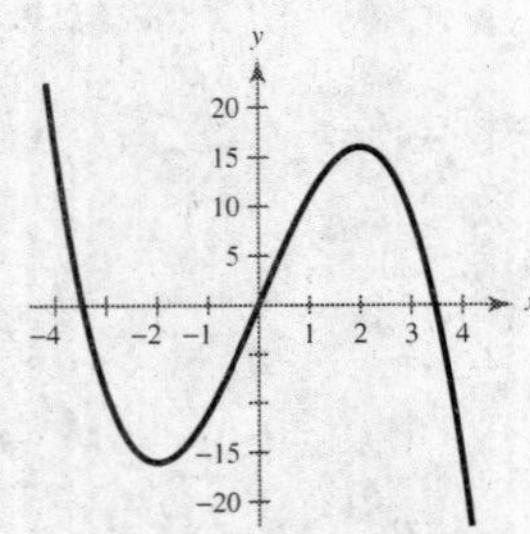

f is increasing on $(-2, 2)$.

11.

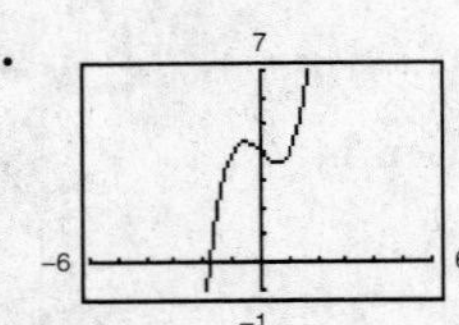

Relative minimum: $(0.577, 3.615)$

Relative maximum: $(-0.577, 4.385)$

12. $f(x) = x^3 - 3$ is a vertical shift of three units downward of $y = x^3$.

13. $f(x) = \sqrt{x - 6}$ is a horizontal shift six units to the right of $y = \sqrt{x}$.

14. $(g \circ f)(x) = g(f(x))$

$$= g(\sqrt{x}) = (\sqrt{x})^2 - 2 = x - 2$$

Domain: $x \ge 0$

15. $\left(\dfrac{f}{g}\right)(x) = \dfrac{f(x)}{g(x)} = \dfrac{3x^2}{16 - x^4}$

The domain is all $x \neq \pm 2$.

16. $(f \circ g)(x) = f\left(\dfrac{x - 1}{3}\right)$

$$= 3\left(\frac{x - 1}{3}\right) + 1 = (x - 1) + 1 = x$$

$$(g \circ f)(x) = g(3x + 1) = \frac{(3x + 1) - 1}{3} = \frac{3x}{3} = x$$

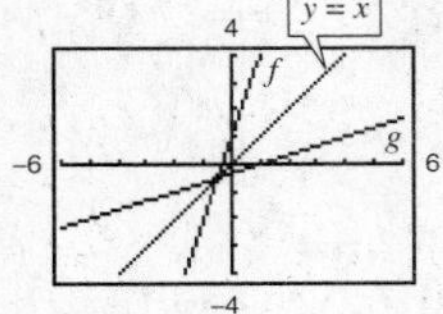

17. $y = \sqrt{9 - x^2}, \quad 0 \le x \le 3$

$$x = \sqrt{9 - y^2}$$

$$x^2 = 9 - y^2$$

$$y^2 = 9 - x^2$$

$$y = \sqrt{9 - x^2}$$

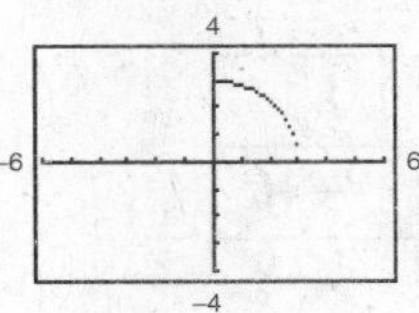

18. $y = 0.882 + 0.912x$

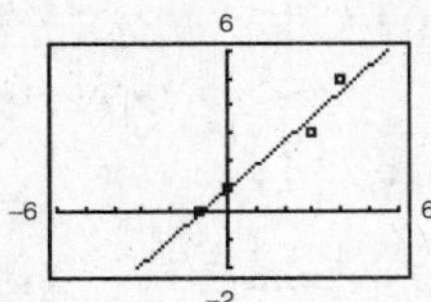

Chapter 2 Practice Test Solutions

1. x-intercepts: $(1, 0), (5, 0)$

y-intercept: $(0, 5)$

Vertex: $(3, -4)$

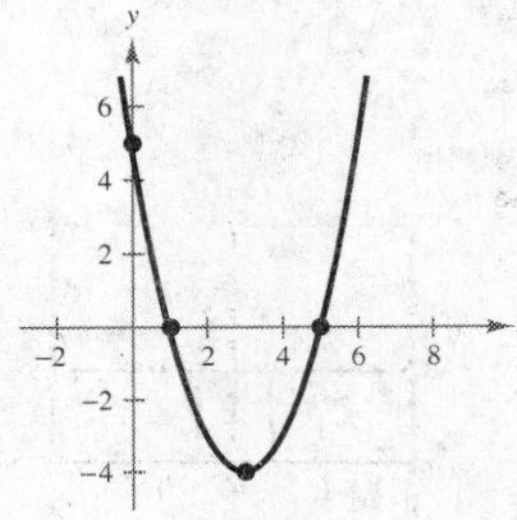

2. $a = 0.01, b = -90$

$$\frac{-b}{2a} = \frac{90}{2(.01)} = 4500 \text{ units}$$

3. Vertex: $(1, 7)$

Opening downward through $(2, 5)$

$y = a(x - 1)^2 + 7$ Standard form

$5 = a(2 - 1)^2 + 7$

$5 = a + 7$

$a = -2$

$y = -2(x - 1)^2 + 7 = -2(x^2 - 2x + 1) + 7 = -2x^2 + 4x + 5$

4. $y = \pm a(x - 2)(3x - 4)$ where a is any real number.

$y = \pm(3x^2 - 10x + 8)$

5. Leading coefficient: -3

Degree: 5

Moves down to the right and up to the left.

6.
$$\begin{aligned} 0 &= x^5 - 5x^3 + 4x \\ &= x(x^4 - 5x^2 + 4) \\ &= x(x^2 - 1)(x^2 - 4) \\ &= x(x + 1)(x - 1)(x + 2)(x - 2) \end{aligned}$$

$x = 0, x = \pm 1, x = \pm 2$

7.
$$\begin{aligned} f(x) &= x(x - 3)(x + 2) \\ &= x(x^2 - x - 6) \\ &= x^3 - x^2 - 6x \end{aligned}$$

8. Intercepts: $(0, 0), (\pm 2\sqrt{3}, 0)$

Moves up to the right.

Moves down to the left.

x	-2	-1	0	1	2
y	16	11	0	-11	-16

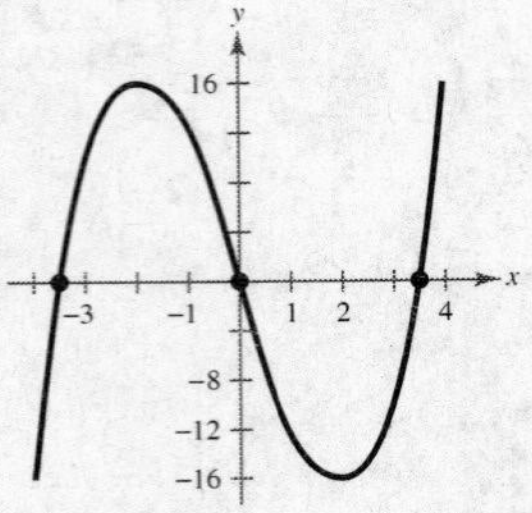

9.
$$\begin{array}{r} 3x^3 + 9x^2 + 20x + 62 + \dfrac{176}{x - 3} \\ x - 3 \overline{)\, 3x^4 + 0x^3 - 7x^2 + 2x - 10} \\ \underline{3x^4 - 9x^3} \\ 9x^3 - 7x^2 \\ \underline{9x^3 - 27x^2} \\ 20x^2 + 2x \\ \underline{20x^2 - 60x} \\ 62x - 10 \\ \underline{62x - 186} \\ 176 \end{array}$$

10.
$$\begin{array}{r} x - 2 + \dfrac{5x - 13}{x^2 + 2x - 1} \\ x^2 + 2x - 1 \overline{)\, x^3 + 0x^2 + 0x - 11} \\ \underline{x^3 + 2x^2 - x} \\ -2x^2 + x - 11 \\ \underline{-2x^2 - 4x + 2} \\ 5x - 13 \end{array}$$

11.
$$\begin{array}{r|rrrrrr} -5 & 3 & 13 & 0 & 0 & 12 & -1 \\ & & -15 & 10 & -50 & 250 & -1310 \\ \hline & 3 & -2 & 10 & -50 & 262 & -1311 \end{array}$$

$$\frac{3x^5 + 13x^4 + 12x - 1}{x + 5} = 3x^4 - 2x^3 + 10x^2 - 50x + 262 - \frac{1311}{x + 5}$$

12.
$$\begin{array}{r|rrrr} -6 & 7 & 40 & -12 & 15 \\ & & -42 & 12 & 0 \\ \hline & 7 & -2 & 0 & 15 \end{array}$$

$f(-6) = 15$

13. $0 = x^3 - 19x - 30$

Possible rational roots:

$\pm1, \pm2, \pm3, \pm5, \pm6, \pm10, \pm15, \pm30$

$$\begin{array}{r|rrrr} -2 & 1 & 0 & -19 & -30 \\ & & -2 & 4 & 30 \\ \hline & 1 & -2 & -15 & 0 \end{array}$$

-2 is a zero.

$0 = (x + 2)(x^2 - 2x - 15)$

$0 = (x + 2)(x + 3)(x - 5)$

Zeros: $x = -2, x = -3, x = 5$

14. $0 = x^4 + x^3 - 8x^2 - 9x - 9$

Possible rational roots: $\pm1, \pm3, \pm9$

$$\begin{array}{r|rrrrr} 3 & 1 & 1 & -8 & -9 & -9 \\ & & 3 & 12 & 12 & 9 \\ \hline & 1 & 4 & 4 & 3 & 0 \end{array}$$

$x = 3$ is a zero.

$0 = (x - 3)(x^3 + 4x^2 + 4x + 3)$

Possible rational roots of $x^3 + 4x^2 + 4x + 3$: $\pm1, \pm3$

$$\begin{array}{r|rrrr} -3 & 1 & 4 & 4 & 3 \\ & & -3 & -3 & -3 \\ \hline & 1 & 1 & 1 & 0 \end{array}$$

$x = -3$ is a zero.

$0 = (x - 3)(x + 3)(x^2 + x + 1)$

The zeros of $x^2 + x + 1$ are $x = \dfrac{-1 \pm \sqrt{3}i}{2}$.

Zeros: $x = 3, x = -3,$

$$x = -\frac{1}{2} + \frac{\sqrt{3}}{2}i, x = -\frac{1}{2} - \frac{\sqrt{3}}{2}i$$

15. $0 = 6x^3 - 5x^2 + 4x - 15$

Possible rational roots: $\pm1, \pm3, \pm5, \pm15, \pm\frac{1}{2}, \pm\frac{3}{2}, \pm\frac{5}{2}, \pm\frac{15}{2}, \pm\frac{1}{3}, \pm\frac{5}{3}, \pm\frac{1}{6}, \pm\frac{5}{6}$

16. $0 = x^3 - \frac{20}{3}x^2 + 9x - \frac{10}{3}$

$0 = 3x^3 - 20x^2 + 27x - 10$

Possible rational roots:

$\pm1, \pm2, \pm5, \pm10, \pm\frac{1}{3}, \pm\frac{2}{3}, \pm\frac{5}{3}, \pm\frac{10}{3}$

$$\begin{array}{r|rrrr} 1 & 3 & -20 & 27 & -10 \\ & & 3 & -17 & 10 \\ \hline & 3 & -17 & 10 & 0 \end{array}$$

$x = 1$ is a zero.

$0 = (x - 1)(3x^2 - 17x + 10)$

$0 = (x - 1)(3x - 2)(x - 5)$

Zeros: $x = 1, x = \frac{2}{3}, x = 5$

17. $f(x) = x^4 + x^3 + 3x^2 + 5x - 10$

Possible rational roots: $\pm1, \pm2, \pm5, \pm10$

$$\begin{array}{r|rrrrr} 1 & 1 & 1 & 3 & 5 & -10 \\ & & 1 & 2 & 5 & 10 \\ \hline & 1 & 2 & 5 & 10 & 0 \end{array}$$

$x = 1$ is a zero.

$$\begin{array}{r|rrrr} -2 & 1 & 2 & 5 & 10 \\ & & -2 & 0 & -10 \\ \hline & 1 & 0 & 5 & 0 \end{array}$$

$x = -2$ is a zero.

$f(x) = (x - 1)(x + 2)(x^2 + 5)$

$= (x - 1)(x + 2)(x + \sqrt{5}i)(x - \sqrt{5}i)$

18. $\dfrac{2}{1 + i} = \dfrac{2}{1 + i} \cdot \dfrac{1 - i}{1 - i}$

$= \dfrac{2 - 2i}{1 + 1}$

$= 1 - i$

19. $\dfrac{3 + i}{2} - \dfrac{i + 1}{4} = \dfrac{6 + 2i - i - 1}{4} = \dfrac{5}{4} + \dfrac{1}{4}i$

20. $f(x) = (x - 2)[x - (3 + i)][x - (3 - i)][x - (3 - 2i)][x - (3 + 2i)]$
$= (x - 2)[(x - 3)^2 + 1][(x - 3)^2 + 4]$
$= (x - 2)(x^2 - 6x + 10)(x^2 - 6x + 13)$
$= x^5 - 14x^4 + 83x^3 - 256x^2 + 406x - 260$

21.

$3i$	1	4	9	36
		$3i$	$12i - 9$	-36
	1	$4 + 3i$	$12i$	0

22. $z = \dfrac{kx^2}{\sqrt{y}}$

23. $f(x) = \dfrac{x - 1}{2x}$

Vertical asymptote: $x = 0$

Horizontal asymptote: $y = \dfrac{1}{2}$

x-intercept: $(1, 0)$

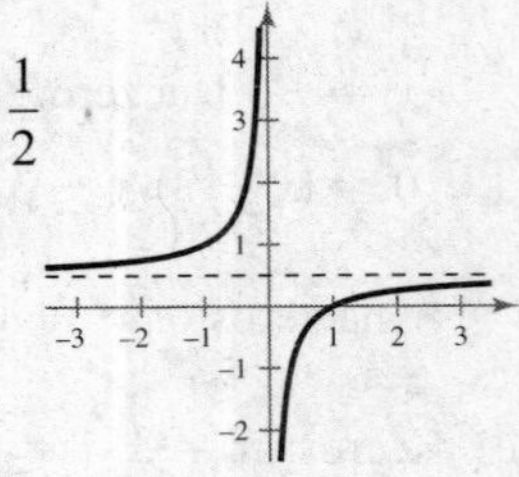

24. $f(x) = \dfrac{3x^2 - 4}{x}$

Vertical asymptote: $x = 0$

Slant asymptote: $y = 3x$

x-intercepts: $\left(\pm\dfrac{2}{\sqrt{3}}, 0\right)$

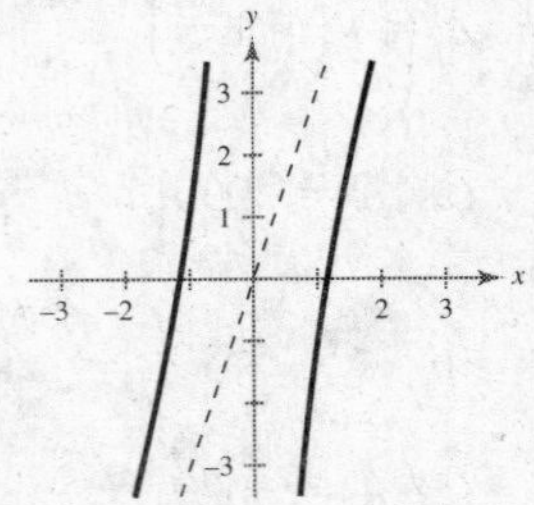

25. $y = 8$ is a horizontal asymptote since the degree of the numerator equals the degree of the denominator. There are no vertical asymptotes.

26. $x = 1$ is a vertical asymptote.

$$\frac{4x^2 - 2x + 7}{x - 1} = 4x + 2 + \frac{9}{x - 1}$$

so $y = 4x + 2$ is a slant asymptote.

27. $f(x) = \dfrac{x - 5}{(x - 5)^2} = \dfrac{1}{x - 5}$

Vertical asymptote: $x = 5$
Horizontal asymptote: $y = 0$
y-intercept: $\left(0, -\dfrac{1}{5}\right)$

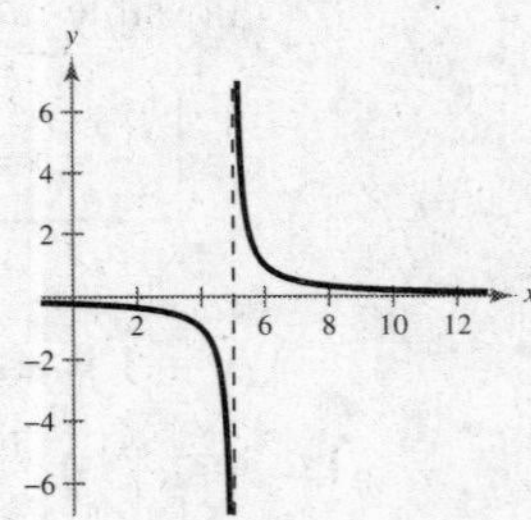

Chapter 3 Practice Test Solutions

1. $x^{3/5} = 8$
$x = 8^{5/3}$
$= \left(\sqrt[3]{8}\right)^5 = 2^5 = 32$

2. $3^{x-1} = \frac{1}{81}$
$3^{x-1} = 3^{-4}$
$x - 1 = -4$
$x = -3$

3. $f(x) = 2^{-x} = \left(\frac{1}{2}\right)^x$

x	-2	-1	0	1	2
$f(x)$	4	2	1	$\frac{1}{2}$	$\frac{1}{4}$

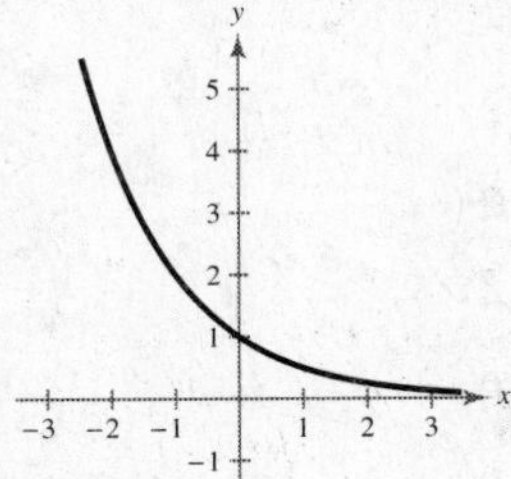

4. $g(x) = e^x + 1$

x	-2	-1	0	1	2
$g(x)$	1.14	1.37	2	3.72	8.39

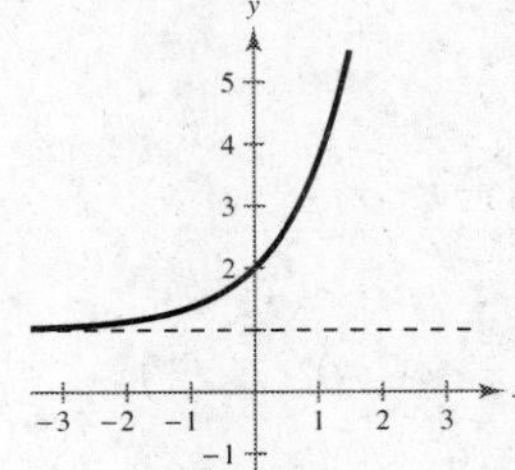

5. $A = P\left(1 + \frac{r}{n}\right)^{nt}$

(a) $A = 5000\left(1 + \frac{0.09}{12}\right)^{12(3)} \approx \$6543.23$

(b) $A = 5000\left(1 + \frac{0.09}{4}\right)^{4(3)} \approx \$6530.25$

(c) $A = 5000e^{(0.09)(3)} \approx \$6549.82$

6. $7^{-2} = \frac{1}{49}$

$\log_7 \frac{1}{49} = -2$

7. $x - 4 = \log_2 \frac{1}{64}$

$2^{x-4} = \frac{1}{64}$

$2^{x-4} = 2^{-6}$

$x - 4 = -6$

$x = -2$

8. $\log_b \sqrt[4]{\frac{8}{25}} = \frac{1}{4} \log_b \frac{8}{25}$

$= \frac{1}{4}[\log_b 8 - \log_b 25]$

$= \frac{1}{4}[\log_b 2^3 - \log_b 5^2]$

$= \frac{1}{4}[3 \log_b 2 - 2 \log_b 5]$

$= \frac{1}{4}[3(0.3562) - 2(0.8271)]$

$= -0.1464$

9. $5 \ln x - \frac{1}{2} \ln y + 6 \ln z = \ln x^5 - \ln \sqrt{y} + \ln z^6 = \ln\left(\frac{x^5 z^6}{\sqrt{y}}\right)$

10. $\log_9 28 = \frac{\log 28}{\log 9} \approx 1.5166$

11. $\log_{10} N = 0.6646$

$N = 10^{0.6646} \approx 4.62$

12.

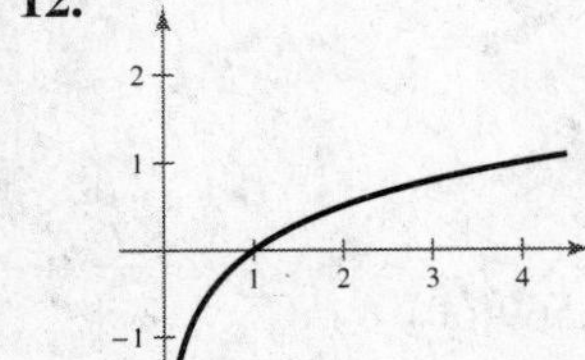

13. Domain:

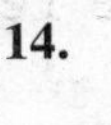

$x^2 - 9 > 0$

$(x + 3)(x - 3) > 0$

$x < -3$ or $x > 3$

14.

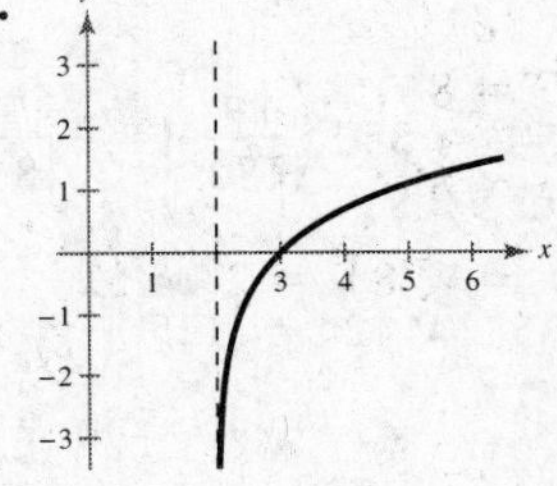

15. $\frac{\ln x}{\ln y} \neq \ln(x - y)$ since $\frac{\ln x}{\ln y} = \log_y x$.

16. $5^x = 41$

$$x = \log_5 41 = \frac{\ln 41}{\ln 5} \approx 2.3074$$

17. $x - x^2 = \log_5 \frac{1}{25}$

$$5^{x-x^2} = \frac{1}{25}$$
$$5^{x-x^2} = 5^{-2}$$
$$x - x^2 = -2$$
$$0 = x^2 - x - 2$$
$$0 = (x + 1)(x - 2)$$
$$x = -1 \text{ or } x = 2$$

18. $\log_2 x + \log_2(x - 3) = 2$

$$\log_2[x(x - 3)] = 2$$
$$x(x - 3) = 2^2$$
$$x^2 - 3x = 4$$
$$x^2 - 3x - 4 = 0$$
$$(x + 1)(x - 4) = 0$$
$$x = 4$$
$$x = -1 \quad \text{(extraneous solution)}$$

19. $\frac{e^x + e^{-x}}{3} = 4$

$$e^x(e^x + e^{-x}) = 12e^x$$
$$e^{2x} + 1 = 12e^x$$
$$e^{2x} - 12e^x + 1 = 0$$
$$e^x = \frac{12 \pm \sqrt{144 - 4}}{2}$$

$e^x \approx 11.9161$ or $e^x \approx 0.08392$

$x \approx \ln 11.9161$ $\qquad$ $x \approx \ln 0.08392$

$x \approx 2.4779$ $\qquad$ $x \approx -2.4779$

20. $A = Pe^{rt}$

$$12{,}000 = 6000e^{0.13t}$$
$$2 = e^{0.13t}$$
$$\ln 2 = 0.13t$$
$$\frac{\ln 2}{0.13} = t$$
$$t \approx 5.3319 \text{ yr or } 5 \text{ yr } 4 \text{ mo}$$

21. There are two points of intersection:

(0.0169, −2.983),
(1.731, 1.647)

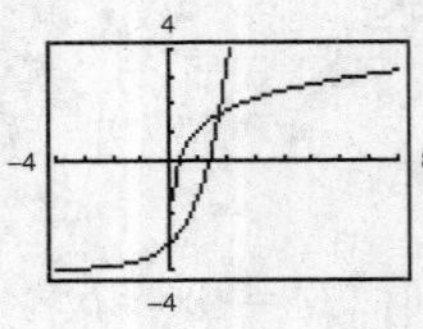

22. $y = 1.0597x^{1.9792}$

Chapter 4 Practice Test Solutions

1. $350° = 350°\left(\frac{\pi}{180°}\right) = \frac{35\pi}{18}$

2. $\frac{5\pi}{9} = \frac{5\pi}{9} \cdot \frac{180°}{\pi} = 100°$

3. $135°\ 14'\ 12'' = \left(135 + \frac{14}{60} + \frac{12}{3600}\right)°$

$$\approx 135.2367°$$

4. $-22.569° = -(22° + 0.569(60)')$

$$= -22°\ 34.14'$$
$$= -(22°\ 34' + 0.14(60)'')$$
$$\approx -22°\ 34'\ 8''$$

5. $\cos\theta = \dfrac{2}{3}$

$x = 2,\ r = 3,\ y = \pm\sqrt{9-4} = \pm\sqrt{5}$

$\tan\theta = \dfrac{y}{x} = \pm\dfrac{\sqrt{5}}{2}$

6. $\sin\theta = 0.9063$

$\theta = \arcsin 0.9063$

$\theta \approx 65°$ or $\dfrac{13\pi}{36}$

7. $\tan 20° = \dfrac{35}{x}$

$x = \dfrac{35}{\tan 20°} \approx 96.1617$

8. $\theta = \dfrac{6\pi}{5}$, θ is in Quadrant III.

Reference angle: $\dfrac{6\pi}{5} - \pi = \dfrac{\pi}{5}$ or $36°$

9. $\csc 3.92 = \dfrac{1}{\sin 3.92} \approx -1.4242$

10. $\tan\theta = 6 = \dfrac{6}{1}$, θ lies in Quadrant III.

$y = -6,\ x = -1,\ r = \sqrt{36+1} = \sqrt{37}$, so

$\sec\theta = \dfrac{\sqrt{37}}{-1} \approx -6.0828.$

11. Period: 4π

Amplitude: 3

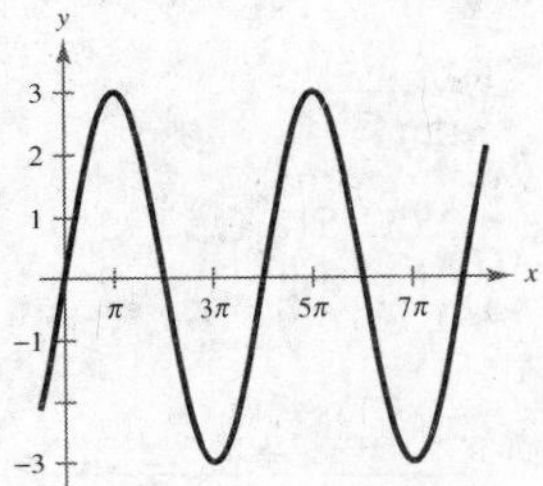

12. Period: 2π

Amplitude: 2

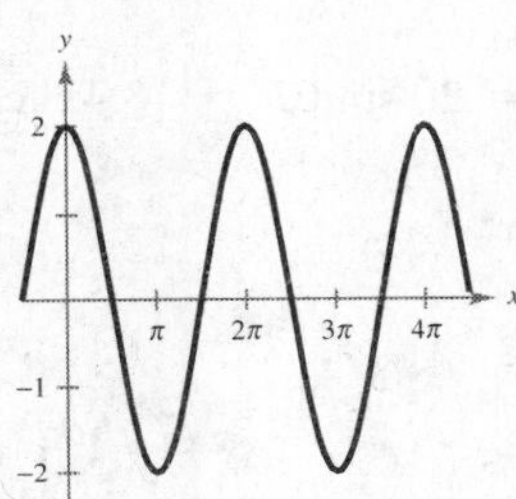

13. Period: $\dfrac{\pi}{2}$

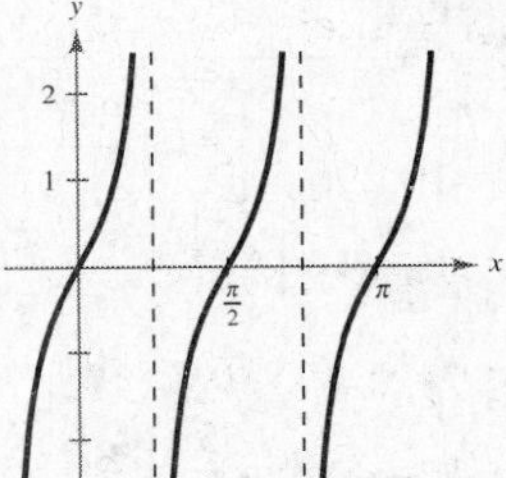

14. Period: 2π

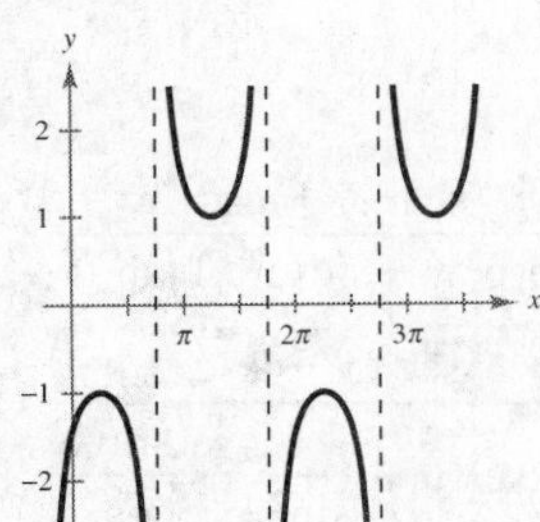

15.

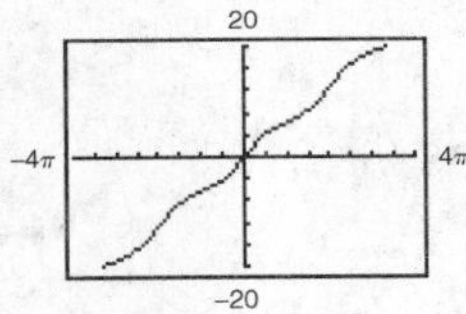

16.

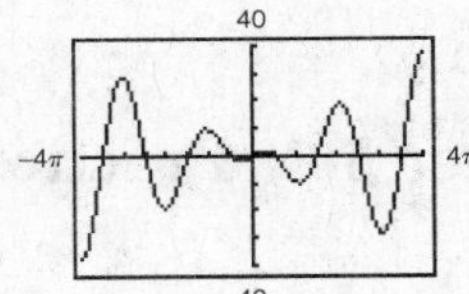

17. $\theta = \arcsin 1$

$\sin\theta = 1$

$\theta = \dfrac{\pi}{2}$

18. $\theta = \arctan(-3)$

$\tan\theta = -3$

$\theta \approx -1.249$ or $-71.565°$

19. $\sin\left(\arccos \dfrac{4}{\sqrt{35}}\right)$

$\sin\theta = \dfrac{\sqrt{19}}{\sqrt{35}} \approx 0.7368$

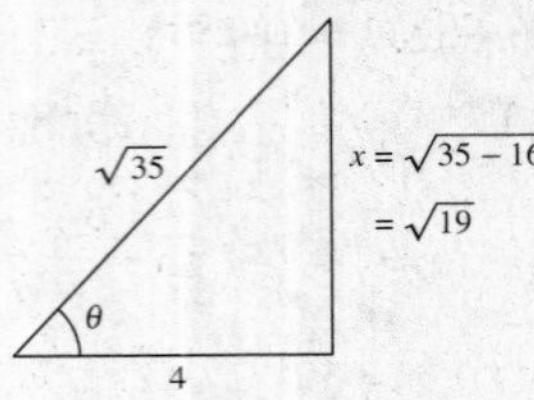

20. $\cos\left(\arcsin \dfrac{x}{4}\right)$

$\cos\theta = \dfrac{\sqrt{16 - x^2}}{4}$

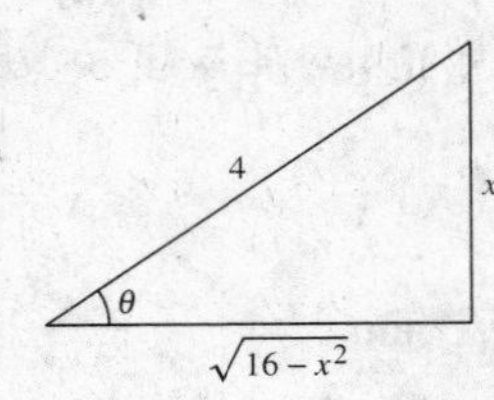

21. Given $A = 40°,\ c = 12$

$B = 90° - 40° = 50°$

$\sin 40° = \dfrac{a}{12}$

$a = 12 \sin 40° \approx 7.713$

$\cos 40° = \dfrac{b}{12}$

$b = 12 \cos 40° \approx 9.193$

22. Given $B = 6.84°,\ a = 21.3$

$A = 90° - 6.84° = 83.16°$

$\sin 83.16° = \dfrac{21.3}{c}$

$c = \dfrac{21.3}{\sin 83.16°} \approx 21.453$

$\tan 83.16° = \dfrac{21.3}{b}$

$b = \dfrac{21.3}{\tan 83.16°} \approx 2.555$

23. Given $a = 5,\ b = 9$

$c = \sqrt{25 + 81} = \sqrt{106}$

≈ 10.296

$\tan A = \dfrac{5}{9}$

$A = \arctan \dfrac{5}{9} \approx 29.055°$

$B = 90° - 29.055° = 60.945°$

24. $\sin 67° = \dfrac{x}{20}$

$x = 20 \sin 67° \approx 18.41$ feet

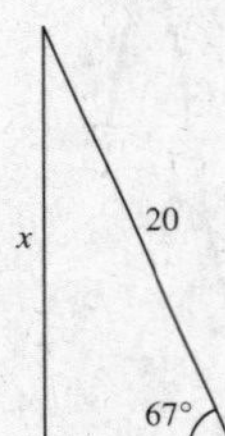

25. $\tan 5° = \dfrac{250}{x}$

$x = \dfrac{250}{\tan 5°}$

≈ 2857.513 feet

≈ 0.541 mi

Chapter 5 Practice Test Solutions

1. $\tan x = \dfrac{4}{11},\ \sec x < 0 \implies x$ is in Quadrant III.

$y = -4,\ \bar{x} = -11,\ r = \sqrt{16 + 121} = \sqrt{137}$

$\sin x = -\dfrac{4}{\sqrt{137}} = -\dfrac{4\sqrt{137}}{137}$ $\qquad \csc x = -\dfrac{\sqrt{137}}{4}$

$\cos x = -\dfrac{11}{\sqrt{137}} = -\dfrac{11\sqrt{137}}{137}$ $\qquad \sec x = -\dfrac{\sqrt{137}}{11}$

$\tan x = \dfrac{4}{11}$ $\qquad \cot x = \dfrac{11}{4}$

2. $\dfrac{\sec^2 x + \csc^2 x}{\csc^2 x(1 + \tan^2 x)} = \dfrac{\sec^2 x + \csc^2 x}{\csc^2 x + (\csc^2 x)\tan^2 x}$

$= \dfrac{\sec^2 x + \csc^2 x}{\csc^2 x + \dfrac{1}{\sin^2 x} \cdot \dfrac{\sin^2 x}{\cos^2 x}}$

$= \dfrac{\sec^2 x + \csc^2 x}{\csc^2 x + \dfrac{1}{\cos^2 x}}$

$= \dfrac{\sec^2 x + \csc^2 x}{\csc^2 x + \sec^2 x} = 1$

3. $\ln|\tan\theta| - \ln|\cot\theta| = \ln\dfrac{|\tan\theta|}{|\cot\theta|}$

$= \ln\left|\dfrac{\sin\theta/\cos\theta}{\cos\theta/\sin\theta}\right| = \ln\left|\dfrac{\sin^2\theta}{\cos^2\theta}\right|$

$= \ln|\tan^2\theta| = 2\ln|\tan\theta|$

4. $\cos\left(\dfrac{\pi}{2} - x\right) = \dfrac{1}{\csc x}$ is true since

$\cos\left(\dfrac{\pi}{2} - x\right) = \sin x = \dfrac{1}{\csc x}.$

5. $\sin^4 x + (\sin^2 x)\cos^2 x = \sin^2 x(\sin^2 x + \cos^2 x)$

$= \sin^2 x(1) = \sin^2 x$

6. $(\csc x + 1)(\csc x - 1) = \csc^2 x - 1 = \cot^2 x$

7. $\dfrac{\cos^2 x}{1 - \sin x} \cdot \dfrac{1 + \sin x}{1 + \sin x} = \dfrac{\cos^2 x(1 + \sin x)}{1 - \sin^2 x} = \dfrac{\cos^2 x(1 + \sin x)}{\cos^2 x} = 1 + \sin x$

8. $\dfrac{1 + \cos\theta}{\sin\theta} + \dfrac{\sin\theta}{1 + \cos\theta} = \dfrac{(1 + \cos\theta)^2 + \sin^2\theta}{\sin\theta(1 + \cos\theta)}$

$= \dfrac{1 + 2\cos\theta + \cos^2\theta + \sin^2\theta}{\sin\theta(1 + \cos\theta)}$

$= \dfrac{2 + 2\cos\theta}{\sin\theta(1 + \cos\theta)} = \dfrac{2}{\sin\theta} = 2\csc\theta$

9. $\tan^4 x + 2\tan^2 x + 1 = (\tan^2 x + 1)^2 = (\sec^2 x)^2 = \sec^4 x$

10. (a) $\sin 105° = \sin(60° + 45°)$

$= \sin 60°\cos 45° + \cos 60°\sin 45°$

$= \dfrac{\sqrt{3}}{2} \cdot \dfrac{\sqrt{2}}{2} + \dfrac{1}{2} \cdot \dfrac{\sqrt{2}}{2}$

$= \dfrac{\sqrt{2}}{4}(\sqrt{3} + 1)$

(b) $\tan 15° = \tan(60° - 45°) = \dfrac{\tan 60° - \tan 45°}{1 + \tan 60°\tan 45°}$

$= \dfrac{\sqrt{3} - 1}{1 + \sqrt{3}} \cdot \dfrac{1 - \sqrt{3}}{1 - \sqrt{3}} = \dfrac{2\sqrt{3} - 1 - 3}{1 - 3}$

$= \dfrac{2\sqrt{3} - 4}{-2} = 2 - \sqrt{3}$

11. $(\sin 42°)\cos 38° - (\cos 42°)\sin 38° = \sin(42° - 38°) = \sin 4°$

12. $\tan\left(\theta + \dfrac{\pi}{4}\right) = \dfrac{\tan\theta + \tan(\pi/4)}{1 - (\tan\theta)\tan(\pi/4)} = \dfrac{\tan\theta + 1}{1 - \tan\theta(1)} = \dfrac{1 + \tan\theta}{1 - \tan\theta}$

13. $\sin(\arcsin x - \arccos x) = \sin(\arcsin x)\cos(\arccos x) - \cos(\arcsin x)\sin(\arccos x)$

$= (x)(x) - \left(\sqrt{1 - x^2}\right)\left(\sqrt{1 - x^2}\right) = x^2 - (1 - x^2) = 2x^2 - 1$

14. (a) $\cos(120°) = \cos[2(60°)] = 2\cos^2 60° - 1 = 2\left(\dfrac{1}{2}\right)^2 - 1 = -\dfrac{1}{2}$

(b) $\tan(300°) = \tan[2(150°)] = \dfrac{2\tan 150°}{1 - \tan^2 150°} = \dfrac{-2\sqrt{3}/3}{1 - (1/3)} = -\sqrt{3}$

15. (a) $\sin 22.5^\circ = \sin \frac{45^\circ}{2} = \sqrt{\frac{1 - \cos 45^\circ}{2}} = \sqrt{\frac{1 - \sqrt{2}/2}{2}} = \frac{\sqrt{2 - \sqrt{2}}}{2}$

(b) $\tan \frac{\pi}{12} = \tan \frac{\pi/6}{2} = \frac{\sin(\pi/6)}{1 + \cos(\pi/6)} = \frac{1/2}{1 + \sqrt{3}/2} = \frac{1}{2 + \sqrt{3}} = 2 - \sqrt{3}$

16. $\sin \theta = \frac{4}{5}$, θ lies in Quadrant II $\Rightarrow \cos \theta = -\frac{3}{5}$.

$$\cos \frac{\theta}{2} = \sqrt{\frac{1 + \cos \theta}{2}} = \sqrt{\frac{1 - (3/5)}{2}}$$

$$= \sqrt{\frac{2}{10}} = \frac{1}{\sqrt{5}} = \frac{\sqrt{5}}{5}$$

17. $(\sin^2 x) \cos^2 x = \frac{1 - \cos 2x}{2} \cdot \frac{1 + \cos 2x}{2}$

$$= \frac{1}{4}[1 - \cos^2 2x]$$

$$= \frac{1}{4}\left[1 - \frac{1 + \cos 4x}{2}\right]$$

$$= \frac{1}{8}[2 - (1 + \cos 4x)]$$

$$= \frac{1}{8}[1 - \cos 4x]$$

18. $6(\sin 5\theta) \cos 2\theta = 6\left\{\frac{1}{2}[\sin(5\theta + 2\theta) + \sin(5\theta - 2\theta)]\right\} = 3[\sin 7\theta + \sin 3\theta]$

19. $\sin(x + \pi) + \sin(x - \pi) = 2\left(\sin \frac{[(x + \pi) + (x - \pi)]}{2}\right) \cos \frac{[(x + \pi) - (x - \pi)]}{2} = 2 \sin x \cos \pi = -2 \sin x$

20. $\frac{\sin 9x + \sin 5x}{\cos 9x - \cos 5x} = \frac{2 \sin 7x \cos 2x}{-2 \sin 7x \sin 2x} = -\frac{\cos 2x}{\sin 2x} = -\cot 2x$

21. $\frac{1}{2}[\sin(u + v) - \sin(u - v)] = \frac{1}{2}\{(\sin u) \cos v + (\cos u) \sin v - [(\sin u) \cos v - (\cos u) \sin v]\}$

$$= \frac{1}{2}[2(\cos u) \sin v] = (\cos u) \sin v$$

22. $4 \sin^2 x = 1$

$$\sin^2 x = \frac{1}{4}$$

$$\sin x = \pm\frac{1}{2}$$

$\sin x = \frac{1}{2}$ or $\sin x = -\frac{1}{2}$

$x = \frac{\pi}{6}$ or $\frac{5\pi}{6}$ $\qquad x = \frac{7\pi}{6}$ or $\frac{11\pi}{6}$

23. $\tan^2 \theta + \left(\sqrt{3} - 1\right) \tan \theta - \sqrt{3} = 0$

$$(\tan \theta - 1)\left(\tan \theta + \sqrt{3}\right) = 0$$

$\tan \theta = 1$ or $\tan \theta = -\sqrt{3}$

$\theta = \frac{\pi}{4}$ or $\frac{5\pi}{4}$ $\qquad \theta = \frac{2\pi}{3}$ or $\frac{5\pi}{3}$

24. $\sin 2x = \cos x$

$$2(\sin x) \cos x - \cos x = 0$$

$$\cos x(2 \sin x - 1) = 0$$

$\cos x = 0$ or $\sin x = \frac{1}{2}$

$x = \frac{\pi}{2}$ or $\frac{3\pi}{2}$ $\qquad x = \frac{\pi}{6}$ or $\frac{5\pi}{6}$

25. $\tan^2 x - 6\tan x + 4 = 0$

$$\tan x = \frac{-(-6) \pm \sqrt{(-6)^2 - 4(1)(4)}}{2(1)}$$

$$\tan x = \frac{6 \pm \sqrt{20}}{2} = 3 \pm \sqrt{5}$$

$\tan x = 3 + \sqrt{5}$ or $\tan x = 3 - \sqrt{5}$

$x \approx 1.3821$ or 4.5237 $\quad$ $x = 0.6524$ or 3.7940

Chapter 6 Practice Test Solutions

1. $C = 180° - (40° + 12°) = 128°$

$$a = \sin 40°\left(\frac{100}{\sin 12°}\right) \approx 309.164$$

$$c = \sin 128°\left(\frac{100}{\sin 12°}\right) \approx 379.012$$

2. $\sin A = 5\left(\frac{\sin 150°}{20}\right) = 0.125$

$A \approx 7.181°$

$B \approx 180° - (150° + 7.181°) = 22.819°$

$$b = \sin 22.819°\left(\frac{20}{\sin 150°}\right) \approx 15.513$$

3. $\text{Area} = \frac{1}{2}ab \sin C$

$= \frac{1}{2}(3)(6)\sin 130°$

≈ 6.894 square units

4. $h = b \sin A = 35 \sin 22.5° \approx 13.394$

$a = 10$

Since $a < h$ and A is acute, the triangle has no solution.

5. $$\cos A = \frac{(53)^2 + (38)^2 - (49)^2}{2(53)(38)} \approx 0.4598$$

$A \approx 62.627°$

$$\cos B = \frac{(49)^2 + (38)^2 - (53)^2}{2(49)(38)} \approx 0.2782$$

$B \approx 73.847°$

$C \approx 180° - (62.627° + 73.847°) = 43.526°$

6. $c^2 = (100)^2 + (300)^2 - 2(100)(300)\cos 29°$

$\approx 47{,}522.8176$

$c \approx 218$

$$\cos A = \frac{(300)^2 + (218)^2 - (100)^2}{2(300)(218)} \approx 0.97495$$

$A \approx 12.85°$

$B \approx 180° - (12.85° + 29°) = 138.15°$

7. $$s = \frac{a + b + c}{2} = \frac{4.1 + 6.8 + 5.5}{2} = 8.2$$

$\text{Area} = \sqrt{s(s-a)(s-b)(s-c)}$

$= \sqrt{8.2(8.2 - 4.1)(8.2 - 6.8)(8.2 - 5.5)}$

$= 11.273$ square units

8. $x^2 = (40)^2 + (70)^2 - 2(40)(70)\cos 168°$

$\approx 11{,}977.6266$

$x \approx 190.442$ miles

9. $\mathbf{w} = 4(3\mathbf{i} + \mathbf{j}) - 7(-\mathbf{i} + 2\mathbf{j}) = 19\mathbf{i} - 10\mathbf{j}$

10. $$\frac{\mathbf{v}}{\|\mathbf{v}\|} = \frac{5\mathbf{i} - 3\mathbf{j}}{\sqrt{25 + 9}} = \frac{5}{\sqrt{34}}\mathbf{i} - \frac{3}{\sqrt{34}}\mathbf{j}$$

$$= \frac{5\sqrt{34}}{34}\mathbf{i} - \frac{3\sqrt{34}}{34}\mathbf{j}$$

11. $\mathbf{u} = 6\mathbf{i} + 5\mathbf{j},\ \mathbf{v} = 2\mathbf{i} - 3\mathbf{j}$

$\mathbf{u} \cdot \mathbf{v} = 6(2) + 5(-3) = -3$

$\|\mathbf{u}\| = \sqrt{61},\ \|\mathbf{v}\| = \sqrt{13}$

$\cos\theta = \dfrac{-3}{\sqrt{61}\sqrt{13}}$

$\theta \approx 96.116°$

12. $4(\mathbf{i}\cos 30° + \mathbf{j}\sin 30°) = 4\left(\dfrac{\sqrt{3}}{2}\mathbf{i} + \dfrac{1}{2}\mathbf{j}\right) = \langle 4\sqrt{3}, 2\rangle$

13. $\text{proj}_{\mathbf{v}}\mathbf{u} = \left(\dfrac{\mathbf{u}\cdot\mathbf{v}}{\|\mathbf{v}\|^2}\right)\mathbf{v} = \dfrac{-10}{20}\langle -2, 4\rangle = \langle 1, -2\rangle$

14. $r = \sqrt{25 + 25} = \sqrt{50} = 5\sqrt{2}$

$\tan\theta = \dfrac{-5}{5} = -1$

Since z is in Quadrant IV,

$\theta = 315°$

$z = 5\sqrt{2}(\cos 315° + i\sin 315°)$.

15. $\cos 225° = -\dfrac{\sqrt{2}}{2}\ \sin 225° = -\dfrac{\sqrt{2}}{2}$

$z = 6\left(-\dfrac{\sqrt{2}}{2} - i\dfrac{\sqrt{2}}{2}\right)$

$= -3\sqrt{2} - 3\sqrt{2}i$

16. $[7(\cos 23° + i\sin 23°)][4(\cos 7° + i\sin 7°)] = 7(4)[\cos(23° + 7°) + i\sin(23° + 7°)]$

$= 28(\cos 30° + i\sin 30°) = 14\sqrt{3} + 14i$

17. $\dfrac{9\left(\cos\dfrac{5\pi}{4} + i\sin\dfrac{5\pi}{4}\right)}{3(\cos\pi + i\sin\pi)} = \dfrac{9}{3}\left[\cos\left(\dfrac{5\pi}{4} - \pi\right) + i\sin\left(\dfrac{5\pi}{4} - \pi\right)\right] = 3\left(\cos\dfrac{\pi}{4} + i\sin\dfrac{\pi}{4}\right) = \dfrac{3\sqrt{2}}{2} + \dfrac{3\sqrt{2}}{2}i$

18. $(2 + 2i)^8 = [2\sqrt{2}(\cos 45° + i\sin 45°)]^8 = \left(2\sqrt{2}\right)^8[\cos(8)(45°) + i\sin(8)(45°)]$

$= 4096[\cos 360° + i\sin 360°] = 4096$

19. $z = 8\left(\cos\dfrac{\pi}{3} + i\sin\dfrac{\pi}{3}\right),\ n = 3$

The cube roots of z are:

For $k = 0$, $\sqrt[3]{8}\left[\cos\dfrac{\pi/3}{3} + i\sin\dfrac{\pi/3}{3}\right] = 2\left(\cos\dfrac{\pi}{9} + i\sin\dfrac{\pi}{9}\right)$.

For $k = 1$, $\sqrt[3]{8}\left[\cos\dfrac{\pi/3 + 2\pi}{3} + i\sin\dfrac{\pi/3 + 2\pi}{3}\right] = 2\left(\cos\dfrac{7\pi}{9} + i\sin\dfrac{7\pi}{9}\right)$.

For $k = 2$, $\sqrt[3]{8}\left[\cos\dfrac{\pi/3 + 4\pi}{3} + i\sin\dfrac{\pi/3 + 4\pi}{3}\right] = 2\left(\cos\dfrac{13\pi}{9} + i\sin\dfrac{13\pi}{9}\right)$.

20. $x^4 = -i = 1\left(\cos\frac{3\pi}{2} + i\sin\frac{3\pi}{2}\right)$

For $k = 0$, $\cos\frac{3\pi/2}{4} + i\sin\frac{3\pi/2}{4} = \cos\frac{3\pi}{8} + i\sin\frac{3\pi}{8}$.

For $k = 1$, $\cos\frac{3\pi/2 + 2\pi}{4} + i\sin\frac{3\pi/2 + 2\pi}{4} = \cos\frac{7\pi}{8} + i\sin\frac{7\pi}{8}$.

For $k = 2$, $\cos\frac{3\pi/2 + 4\pi}{4} + i\sin\frac{3\pi/2 + 4\pi}{4} = \cos\frac{11\pi}{8} + i\sin\frac{11\pi}{8}$.

For $k = 3$, $\cos\frac{3\pi/2 + 6\pi}{4} + i\sin\frac{3\pi/2 + 6\pi}{4} = \cos\frac{15\pi}{8} + i\sin\frac{15\pi}{8}$.

Chapter 7 Practice Test Solutions

1. $\begin{cases} x + y = 1 \\ 3x - y = 15 \end{cases} \Rightarrow y = 3x - 15$

$x + (3x - 15) = 1$

$4x = 16$

$x = 4$

$y = -3$

2. $\begin{cases} x - 3y = -3 \\ x^2 + 6y = 5 \end{cases} \Rightarrow x = 3y - 3$

$(3y - 3)^2 + 6y = 5$

$9y^2 - 18y + 9 + 6y = 5$

$9y^2 - 12y + 4 = 0$

$(3y - 2)^2 = 0$

$y = \frac{2}{3}$

$x = -1$

3. $\begin{cases} x + y + z = 6 \\ 2x - y + 3z = 0 \\ 5x + 2y - z = -3 \end{cases}$ $\Rightarrow z = 6 - x - y$

$2x - y + 3(6 - x - y) = 0 \Rightarrow -x - 4y = -18$

$5x + 2y - (6 - x - y) = -3 \Rightarrow 6x + 3y = 3$

$x = 18 - 4y$

$6(18 - 4y) + 3y = 3$

$-21y = -105$

$y = 5$

$x = 18 - 4y = -2$

$z = 6 - x - y = 3$

4. $\begin{cases} x + y = 110 \\ xy = 2800 \end{cases} \Rightarrow y = 110 - x$

$x(110 - x) = 2800$

$0 = x^2 - 110x + 2800$

$0 = (x - 40)(x - 70)$

$x = 40$ or $x = 70$

$y = 70$ $\quad y = 40$

5. $\begin{cases} 2x + 2y = 170 \\ xy = 1500 \end{cases} \Rightarrow y = \frac{170 - 2x}{2} = 85 - x$

$x(85 - x) = 1500$

$0 = x^2 - 85x + 1500$

$0 = (x - 25)(x - 60)$

$x = 25$ or $x = 60$

$y = 60$ $\quad y = 25$

Dimensions: $60' \times 25'$

6. $\begin{cases} 2x + 15y = 4 \Rightarrow 2x + 15y = 4 \\ x - 3y = 23 \Rightarrow 5x - 15y = 115 \end{cases}$

$$7x = 119$$

$$x = 17$$

$$y = \frac{x - 23}{3} = -2$$

7. $\begin{cases} x + y = 2 \Rightarrow 19x + 19y = 38 \\ 38x - 19y = 7 \Rightarrow 38x - 19y = 7 \end{cases}$

$$57x = 45$$

$$x = \frac{45}{57} = \frac{15}{19}$$

$$y = 2 - x$$

$$= \frac{38}{19} - \frac{15}{19}$$

$$= \frac{23}{19}$$

8. $y_1 = 2(0.112 - 0.4x)$

$$y_2 = \frac{(0.131 + 0.3x)}{0.7}$$

$\begin{cases} 0.4x + 0.5y = 0.112 \Rightarrow 0.28x + 0.35y = 0.0784 \\ 0.3x - 0.7y = -0.131 \Rightarrow 0.15x - 0.35y = -0.0655 \end{cases}$

$$0.43x = 0.0129$$

$$x = \frac{0.0129}{0.43} = 0.03$$

$$y = (2)(0.112 - 0.4x) = 0.20$$

9. Let x = amount in 11% fund and y = amount in 13% fund.

$\begin{cases} x + y = 17{,}000 \Rightarrow y = 17{,}000 - x \\ 0.11x + 0.13y = 2080 \end{cases}$

$$0.11x + 0.13(17{,}000 - x) = 2080$$

$$-0.02x = -130$$

$$x = \$6500$$

$$y = \$10{,}500$$

10. Using a graphing utility, you obtain $y = 0.7857x - 0.1429$. Analytically, $(4, 3)$, $(1, 1)$, $(-1, -2)$, $(-2, -1)$.

$$n = 4, \sum_{i=1}^{4} x_i = 2, \sum_{i=1}^{4} y_i = 1, \sum_{i=1}^{4} x_i^2 = 22, \sum_{i=1}^{4} x_i y_i = 17$$

$4b + 2a = 1 \Rightarrow 4b + 2a = 1$

$2b + 22a = 17 \Rightarrow -4b - 44a = -34$

$$-42a = -33$$

$$a = \tfrac{33}{42} = \tfrac{11}{14}$$

$$b = \tfrac{1}{4}\left(1 - 2\left(\tfrac{33}{42}\right)\right) = -\tfrac{1}{7}$$

$$y = ax + b = \tfrac{11}{14}x - \tfrac{1}{7}$$

11.
$x + y = -2$ Equation 1
$2x - y + z = 11$ Equation 2
$4y - 3z = -20$ Equation 3

$\begin{cases} x + y = -2 \\ -3y + z = 15 \quad -2\text{Eq.1} + \text{Eq.2} \\ 4y - 3z = -20 \end{cases}$

$\begin{cases} x + y = -2 \\ -3y + z = 15 \\ -5y = 25 \quad 3\text{Eq.2} + \text{Eq.3} \end{cases}$

Answer: $y = -5$
$x = 3$
$z = 0$

12. $4x - y + 5z = 4$ Equation 1
$2x + y - z = 0$ Equation 2
$2x + 4y + 8z = 0$ Equation 3

$$\begin{cases} 4x - y + 5z = 4 & \\ -3y + 7z = 4 & \text{Eq.1} - 2\text{Eq.2} \\ 3y + 9z = 0 & -\text{Eq.2} + \text{Eq.3} \end{cases}$$

$$\begin{cases} 4x - y + 5z = 4 & \\ -3y + 7z = 4 & \\ 16z = 4 & \text{Eq.2} + \text{Eq.3} \end{cases}$$

Answer: $z = \frac{1}{4}$

$y = -\frac{3}{4}$

$x = \frac{1}{2}$

13. $\begin{cases} 3x + 2y - z = 5 \implies 6x + 4y - 2z = 10 \\ 6x - y + 5z = 2 \implies -6x + y - 5z = -2 \end{cases}$

$5y - 7z = 8$

$y = \dfrac{8 + 7z}{5}$

$3x + 2y - z = 5$
$12x - 2y + 10z = 4$
$15x + 9z = 9$

$x = \dfrac{9 - 9z}{15} = \dfrac{3 - 3z}{5}$

Let $z = a$, then $x = \dfrac{3 - 3a}{5}$ and $y = \dfrac{8 + 7a}{5}$.

14. $y = ax^2 + bx + c$ passes through $(0, -1)$, $(1, 4)$, and $(2, 13)$.

At $(0, -1)$: $-1 = a(0)^2 + b(0) + c \implies c = -1$

At $(1, 4)$: $4 = a(1)^2 + b(1) - 1 \implies 5 = a + b \implies 5 = a + b$

At $(2, 13)$: $13 = a(2)^2 + b(2) - 1 \implies 14 = 4a + 2b \implies -7 = -2a - b$

$-2 = -a$

$a = 2$

$b = 3$

Thus, $y = 2x^2 + 3x - 1$.

15. $s = \frac{1}{2}at^2 + v_0t + s_0$ passes through $(1, 12)$, $(2, 5)$, and $(3, 4)$.

At $(1, 12)$: $12 = \frac{1}{2}a + v_0 + s_0 \implies$
At $(2, 5)$: $5 = 2a + 2v_0 + s_0 \implies$
At $(3, 4)$: $4 = \frac{9}{2}a + 3v_0 + s_0 \implies$

$$\begin{cases} \frac{1}{2}a + v_0 + s_0 = 12 & \\ -a + s_0 = 19 & 2\text{Eq.1} - \text{Eq.2} \\ -3a + s_0 = 7 & 3\text{Eq.2} - 2\text{Eq.3} \end{cases}$$

$$\begin{cases} \frac{1}{2}a + v_0 + s_0 = 12 & \\ -a + s_0 = 19 & \\ -2a = -12 & -\text{Eq.2} + \text{Eq.3} \end{cases}$$

$a = 6$

$s_0 = 25$

$v_0 = -16$

Thus,

$s = \frac{1}{2}(6)t^2 - 16t + 25 = 3t^2 - 16t + 25$.

16. $\begin{bmatrix} 1 & -2 & 4 \\ 3 & -5 & 9 \end{bmatrix}$

$-3R_1 + R_2 \rightarrow \begin{bmatrix} 1 & -2 & 4 \\ 0 & 1 & -3 \end{bmatrix}$

$2R_2 + R_1 \rightarrow \begin{bmatrix} 1 & 0 & -2 \\ 0 & 1 & -3 \end{bmatrix}$

17. $3x + 5y = 3$

$2x - y = -11$

$$\begin{bmatrix} 3 & 5 & \vdots & 3 \\ 2 & -1 & \vdots & -11 \end{bmatrix}$$

$$\begin{matrix} -R_2 + R_1 \rightarrow \\ \ \end{matrix} \begin{bmatrix} 1 & 6 & \vdots & 14 \\ 2 & -1 & \vdots & -11 \end{bmatrix}$$

$$\begin{matrix} \ \\ -2R_1 + R_2 \rightarrow \end{matrix} \begin{bmatrix} 1 & 6 & \vdots & 14 \\ 0 & -13 & \vdots & -39 \end{bmatrix}$$

$$\begin{matrix} \ \\ -\frac{1}{13}R_2 \rightarrow \end{matrix} \begin{bmatrix} 1 & 6 & \vdots & 14 \\ 0 & 1 & \vdots & 3 \end{bmatrix}$$

$$\begin{matrix} -6R_2 + R_1 \rightarrow \\ \ \end{matrix} \begin{bmatrix} 1 & 0 & \vdots & -4 \\ 0 & 1 & \vdots & 3 \end{bmatrix}$$

Answer: $x = -4, y = 3$

18. $\begin{cases} 2x + 3y = -3 \\ 3x + 2y = 8 \\ x + y = 1 \end{cases}$

$$\begin{bmatrix} 2 & 3 & \vdots & -3 \\ 3 & 2 & \vdots & 8 \\ 1 & 1 & \vdots & 1 \end{bmatrix}$$

$$\begin{matrix} R_3 \\ \updownarrow \\ R_1 \end{matrix} \begin{bmatrix} 1 & 1 & \vdots & 1 \\ 3 & 2 & \vdots & 8 \\ 2 & 3 & \vdots & -3 \end{bmatrix}$$

$$\begin{matrix} \ \\ -3R_1 + R_2 \rightarrow \\ -2R_1 + R_3 \rightarrow \end{matrix} \begin{bmatrix} 1 & 1 & \vdots & 1 \\ 0 & -1 & \vdots & 5 \\ 0 & 1 & \vdots & -5 \end{bmatrix}$$

$$\begin{matrix} R_2 + R_1 \rightarrow \\ -R_2 \rightarrow \\ -R_2 + R_3 \rightarrow \end{matrix} \begin{bmatrix} 1 & 0 & \vdots & 6 \\ 0 & 1 & \vdots & -5 \\ 0 & 0 & \vdots & 0 \end{bmatrix}$$

Answer: $x = 6, y = -5$

19. $\begin{cases} x + 3z = -5 \\ 2x + y = 0 \\ 3x + y - z = 3 \end{cases}$

$$\begin{bmatrix} 1 & 0 & 3 & \vdots & -5 \\ 2 & 1 & 0 & \vdots & 0 \\ 3 & 1 & -1 & \vdots & 3 \end{bmatrix}$$

$$\begin{matrix} \ \\ -2R_1 + R_2 \rightarrow \\ -3R_1 + R_3 \rightarrow \end{matrix} \begin{bmatrix} 1 & 0 & 3 & \vdots & -5 \\ 0 & 1 & -6 & \vdots & 10 \\ 0 & 1 & -10 & \vdots & 18 \end{bmatrix}$$

$$\begin{matrix} \ \\ \ \\ -R_2 + R_3 \rightarrow \end{matrix} \begin{bmatrix} 1 & 0 & 3 & \vdots & -5 \\ 0 & 1 & -6 & \vdots & 10 \\ 0 & 0 & -4 & \vdots & 8 \end{bmatrix}$$

$$\begin{matrix} -3R_3 + R_1 \rightarrow \\ 6R_3 + R_2 \rightarrow \\ -\frac{1}{4}R_3 \rightarrow \end{matrix} \begin{bmatrix} 1 & 0 & 0 & \vdots & 1 \\ 0 & 1 & 0 & \vdots & -2 \\ 0 & 0 & 1 & \vdots & -2 \end{bmatrix}$$

Answer: $x = 1, y = -2, z = -2$

20. $$\begin{bmatrix} 1 & 4 & 5 \\ 2 & 0 & -3 \end{bmatrix} \begin{bmatrix} 1 & 6 \\ 0 & -7 \\ -1 & 2 \end{bmatrix} = \begin{bmatrix} -4 & -12 \\ 5 & 6 \end{bmatrix}$$

21. $$3A - 5B = 3\begin{bmatrix} 9 & 1 \\ -4 & 8 \end{bmatrix} - 5\begin{bmatrix} 6 & -2 \\ 3 & 5 \end{bmatrix}$$

$$= \begin{bmatrix} -3 & 13 \\ -27 & -1 \end{bmatrix}$$

22. $$f(A) = \begin{bmatrix} 3 & 0 \\ 7 & 1 \end{bmatrix}^2 - 7\begin{bmatrix} 3 & 0 \\ 7 & 1 \end{bmatrix} + 8\begin{bmatrix} 1 & 0 \\ 0 & 1 \end{bmatrix}$$

$$= \begin{bmatrix} 3 & 0 \\ 7 & 1 \end{bmatrix}\begin{bmatrix} 3 & 0 \\ 7 & 1 \end{bmatrix} - \begin{bmatrix} 21 & 0 \\ 49 & 7 \end{bmatrix} + \begin{bmatrix} 8 & 0 \\ 0 & 8 \end{bmatrix}$$

$$= \begin{bmatrix} 9 & 0 \\ 28 & 1 \end{bmatrix} - \begin{bmatrix} 21 & 0 \\ 49 & 7 \end{bmatrix} + \begin{bmatrix} 8 & 0 \\ 0 & 8 \end{bmatrix}$$

$$= \begin{bmatrix} -4 & 0 \\ -21 & 2 \end{bmatrix}$$

23. False

$(A + B)(A + 3B) = A(A + 3B) + B(A + 3B)$

$= A^2 + 3AB + BA + 3B^2$

24. $\left[\begin{array}{cc|cc} 1 & 2 & 1 & 0 \\ 3 & 5 & 0 & 1 \end{array}\right]$

$\begin{array}{r} \\ -3R_1 + R_2 \rightarrow \end{array} \left[\begin{array}{cc|cc} 1 & 2 & 1 & 0 \\ 0 & -1 & -3 & 1 \end{array}\right]$

$\begin{array}{r} 2R_2 + R_1 \rightarrow \\ -R_2 \rightarrow \end{array} \left[\begin{array}{cc|cc} 1 & 0 & -5 & 2 \\ 0 & 1 & 3 & -1 \end{array}\right]$

$A^{-1} = \begin{bmatrix} -5 & 2 \\ 3 & -1 \end{bmatrix}$

25. $\left[\begin{array}{ccc|ccc} 1 & 1 & 1 & 1 & 0 & 0 \\ 3 & 6 & 5 & 0 & 1 & 0 \\ 6 & 10 & 8 & 0 & 0 & 1 \end{array}\right]$

$\begin{array}{r} \\ -3R_1 + R_2 \rightarrow \\ -6R_1 + R_3 \rightarrow \end{array} \left[\begin{array}{ccc|ccc} 1 & 1 & 1 & 1 & 0 & 0 \\ 0 & 3 & 2 & -3 & 1 & 0 \\ 0 & 4 & 2 & -6 & 0 & 1 \end{array}\right]$

$\begin{array}{r} -\frac{1}{3}R_2 + R_1 \rightarrow \\ \frac{1}{3}R_2 \rightarrow \\ -4R_2 + R_3 \rightarrow \end{array} \left[\begin{array}{ccc|ccc} 1 & 0 & \frac{1}{3} & 2 & -\frac{1}{3} & 0 \\ 0 & 1 & \frac{2}{3} & -1 & \frac{1}{3} & 0 \\ 0 & 0 & -\frac{2}{3} & -2 & -\frac{4}{3} & 1 \end{array}\right]$

$\begin{array}{r} \frac{1}{2}R_3 + R_1 \rightarrow \\ R_3 + R_2 \rightarrow \\ -\frac{3}{2}R_3 \rightarrow \end{array} \left[\begin{array}{ccc|ccc} 1 & 0 & 0 & 1 & -1 & \frac{1}{2} \\ 0 & 1 & 0 & -3 & -1 & 1 \\ 0 & 0 & 1 & 3 & 2 & -\frac{3}{2} \end{array}\right]$

$A^{-1} = \begin{bmatrix} 1 & -1 & \frac{1}{2} \\ -3 & -1 & 1 \\ 3 & 2 & -\frac{3}{2} \end{bmatrix}$

26. (a) $x + 2y = 4$

$3x + 5y = 1$

$\left[\begin{array}{cc|cc} 1 & 2 & 1 & 0 \\ 3 & 5 & 0 & 1 \end{array}\right]$

$\begin{array}{r} \\ -3R_1 + R_2 \rightarrow \end{array} \left[\begin{array}{cc|cc} 1 & 2 & 1 & 0 \\ 0 & -1 & -3 & 1 \end{array}\right]$

$\begin{array}{r} -2R_2 + R_1 \rightarrow \\ -R_2 \rightarrow \end{array} \left[\begin{array}{cc|cc} 1 & 0 & -5 & 2 \\ 0 & 1 & 3 & -1 \end{array}\right]$

$X = A^{-1}B = \begin{bmatrix} -5 & 2 \\ 3 & -1 \end{bmatrix}\begin{bmatrix} 4 \\ 1 \end{bmatrix} = \begin{bmatrix} -18 \\ 11 \end{bmatrix}$

$x = -18, y = 11$

(b) $x + 2y = 3$

$3x + 5y = -2$

$X = A^{-1}B - \begin{bmatrix} -5 & 2 \\ 3 & -1 \end{bmatrix}\begin{bmatrix} 3 \\ -2 \end{bmatrix} = \begin{bmatrix} -19 \\ 11 \end{bmatrix}$

$x = -19, y = 11$

27. $\begin{vmatrix} 6 & -1 \\ 3 & 4 \end{vmatrix} = 24 - (-3) = 27$

28. $\begin{vmatrix} 1 & 3 & -1 \\ 5 & 9 & 0 \\ 6 & 2 & -5 \end{vmatrix} = 1(-45) + (-3)(-25) + (-1)(-44)$

$= 74$

29. $\begin{vmatrix} 1 & 4 & 2 & 3 \\ 0 & 1 & -2 & 0 \\ 3 & 5 & -1 & 1 \\ 2 & 0 & 6 & 1 \end{vmatrix} = -7$

30. $\begin{vmatrix} 6 & 4 & 3 & 0 & 6 \\ 0 & 5 & 1 & 4 & 8 \\ 0 & 0 & 2 & 7 & 3 \\ 0 & 0 & 0 & 9 & 2 \\ 0 & 0 & 0 & 0 & 1 \end{vmatrix} = 6(5)(2)(9)(1) = 540$

31. Area $= \frac{1}{2}\begin{vmatrix} 0 & 7 & 1 \\ 5 & 0 & 1 \\ 3 & 9 & 1 \end{vmatrix} = \frac{1}{2}(31)$

$= 15.5$ square units

32. $\begin{vmatrix} x & y & 1 \\ 2 & 7 & 1 \\ -1 & 4 & 1 \end{vmatrix} = 3x - 3y + 15 = 0$

or $x - y + 5 = 0$

33. $x = \dfrac{\begin{vmatrix} 4 & -7 \\ 11 & 5 \end{vmatrix}}{\begin{vmatrix} 6 & -7 \\ 2 & 5 \end{vmatrix}} = \dfrac{97}{44}$

34. $z = \dfrac{\begin{vmatrix} 3 & 0 & 1 \\ 0 & 1 & 3 \\ 1 & -1 & 2 \end{vmatrix}}{\begin{vmatrix} 3 & 0 & 1 \\ 0 & 1 & 4 \\ 1 & -1 & 0 \end{vmatrix}} = \dfrac{14}{11}$

35. $y = \dfrac{\begin{vmatrix} 721.4 & 33.77 \\ 45.9 & 19.85 \end{vmatrix}}{\begin{vmatrix} 721.4 & -29.1 \\ 45.9 & 105.6 \end{vmatrix}}$

$= \dfrac{12{,}769.747}{77{,}515.530} \approx 0.1647$

Chapter 8 Practice Test Solutions

1. $a_n = \dfrac{2n}{(n+2)!}$

$a_1 = \dfrac{2(1)}{3!} = \dfrac{2}{6} = \dfrac{1}{3}$

$a_2 = \dfrac{2(2)}{4!} = \dfrac{4}{24} = \dfrac{1}{6}$

$a_3 = \dfrac{2(3)}{5!} = \dfrac{6}{120} = \dfrac{1}{20}$

$a_4 = \dfrac{2(4)}{6!} = \dfrac{8}{720} = \dfrac{1}{90}$

$a_5 = \dfrac{2(5)}{7!} = \dfrac{10}{5040} = \dfrac{1}{504}$

Terms: $\dfrac{1}{3}, \dfrac{1}{6}, \dfrac{1}{20}, \dfrac{1}{90}, \dfrac{1}{504}$

2. $a_n = \dfrac{n+3}{3^n}$

3. $\displaystyle\sum_{i=1}^{6} (2i - 1) = 1 + 3 + 5 + 7 + 9 + 11 = 36$

4. $a_1 = 23,\ d = -2$

$a_2 = a_1 + d = 21$

$a_3 = a_2 + d = 19$

$a_4 = a_3 + d = 17$

$a_5 = a_4 + d = 15$

Terms: 23, 21, 19, 17, 15

5. $a_1 = 12, d = 3, n = 50$

$a_n = a_1 + (n-1)d$

$a_{50} = 12 + (50 - 1)3 = 159$

6. $a_1 = 1$

$a_{200} = 200$

$S_n = \dfrac{n}{2}(a_1 + a_n)$

$S_{200} = \dfrac{200}{2}(1 + 200) = 20{,}100$

7. $a_1 = 7, r = 2$

$a_2 = a_1 r = 14$

$a_3 = a_1 r^2 = 28$

$a_4 = a_1 r^3 = 56$

$a_5 = a_1 r^4 = 112$

Terms: 7, 14, 28, 56, 112

8. $\sum_{n=0}^{9} 6\left(\frac{2}{3}\right)^n, a_1 = 6, r = \frac{2}{3}, n = 10$

$$S_n = \frac{a_1(1 - r^n)}{1 - r} = \frac{6\left(1 - (2/3)^{10}\right)}{1 - (2/3)} \approx 17.6879$$

9. $\sum_{n=0}^{\infty} (0.03)^n, a_1 = 1, r = 0.03$

$$S = \frac{a_1}{1 - r} = \frac{1}{1 - 0.03} = \frac{1}{0.97} = \frac{100}{97} \approx 1.0309$$

10. For $n = 1, 1 = \frac{1(1 + 1)}{2}$. Assume that $1 + 2 + 3 = 4 + \cdot \cdot \cdot + k = \frac{k(k + 1)}{2}$. Now for $n = k + 1$,

$$\begin{aligned} 1 + 2 + 3 + 4 + \cdot \cdot \cdot + k + (k + 1) &= \frac{k(k + 1)}{2} + k + 1 \\ &= \frac{k(k + 1)}{2} + \frac{2(k + 1)}{2} \\ &= \frac{(k + 1)(k + 2)}{2}. \end{aligned}$$

Thus, $1 + 2 + 3 + 4 + \cdot \cdot \cdot + n = \frac{n(n + 1)}{2}$ for all integers $n \geq 1$.

11. For $n = 4, 4! > 2^4$. Assume that $k! > 2^k$. Then

$$\begin{aligned} (k + 1)! = (k + 1)(k!) &> (k + 1)2^k > 2 \cdot 2^k \\ &= 2^{k+1}. \end{aligned}$$

Thus, $n! > 2^n$ for all integers $n \geq 4$.

12. ${}_{13}C_4 = \frac{13!}{(13 - 4)!4!} = 715$

13.
$$\begin{aligned} (x + 3)^5 &= x^5 + 5x^4(3) + 10x^3(3)^2 + 10x^2(3)^3 + 5x(3)^4 + (3)^5 \\ &= x^5 + 15x^4 + 90x^3 + 270x^2 + 405x + 243 \end{aligned}$$

14. ${}_{12}C_5 x^7(-2)^5 = -25{,}344x^7$

15. ${}_{30}P_4 = \frac{30!}{(30 - 4)!} = 657{,}720$

16. $6! = 720$ ways

17. ${}_{12}P_3 = 1320$

18.
$$\begin{aligned} P(2) + P(3) + P(4) &= \tfrac{1}{36} + \tfrac{2}{36} + \tfrac{3}{36} \\ &= \tfrac{6}{36} = \tfrac{1}{6} \end{aligned}$$

19. $P(K, B10) = \frac{4}{52} \cdot \frac{2}{51} = \frac{2}{663}$

20. Let A = probability of no faulty units.

$P(A) = \left(\frac{997}{1000}\right)^{50} \approx 0.8605$

$P(A') = 1 - P(A) \approx 0.1395$

Chapter 9 Practice Test Solutions

1. $x^2 - 6x - 4y + 1 = 0$

$$x^2 - 6x + 9 = 4y - 1 + 9$$

$$(x - 3)^2 = 4y + 8$$

$$(x - 3)^2 = 4(1)(y + 2) \Rightarrow p = 1$$

Vertex: $(3, -2)$

Focus: $(3, -1)$

Directrix: $y = -3$

2. Vertex: $(2, -5)$

Focus: $(2, -6)$

Vertical axis; opens downward with $p = -1$

$$(x - h)^2 = 4p(y - k)$$

$$(x - 2)^2 = 4(-1)(y + 5)$$

$$x^2 - 4x + 4 = -4y - 20$$

$$x^2 - 4x + 4y + 24 = 0$$

3. $x^2 + 4y^2 - 2x + 32y + 61 = 0$

$$(x^2 - 2x + 1) + 4(y^2 + 8y + 16) = -61 + 1 + 64$$

$$(x - 1)^2 + 4(y + 4)^2 = 4$$

$$\frac{(x - 1)^2}{4} + \frac{(y + 4)^2}{1} = 1$$

$a = 2, b = 1, c = \sqrt{3}$

Horizontal major axis

Center: $(1, -4)$

Foci: $\left(1 \pm \sqrt{3}, -4\right)$

Vertices: $(3, -4), (-1, -4)$

Eccentricity: $e = \dfrac{\sqrt{3}}{2}$

4. Vertices: $(0, \pm 6)$

Eccentricity: $e = \dfrac{1}{2}$

Center: $(0, 0)$

Vertical major axis

$a = 6, e = \dfrac{c}{a} = \dfrac{c}{6} = \dfrac{1}{2} \Rightarrow c = 3$

$b^2 = (6)^2 - (3)^2 = 27$

$$\frac{x^2}{27} + \frac{y^2}{36} = 1$$

5. $16y^2 - x^2 - 6x - 128y + 231 = 0$

$$16(y^2 - 8y + 16) - (x^2 + 6x + 9) = -231 + 256 - 9$$

$$16(y - 4)^2 - (x + 3)^2 = 16$$

$$\frac{(y - 4)^2}{1} - \frac{(x + 3)^2}{16} = 1$$

$a = 1, b = 4, c = \sqrt{17}$

Center: $(-3, 4)$

Vertical transverse axis

Vertices: $(-3, 5), (-3, 3)$

Foci: $\left(-3, 4 \pm \sqrt{17}\right)$

Asymptotes: $y = 4 \pm \dfrac{1}{4}(x + 3)$

6. Vertices: $(\pm 3, 2)$

Foci: $(\pm 5, 2)$

Center: $(0, 2)$

Horizontal transverse axis

$a = 3, c = 5, b = 4$

$$\frac{(x - 0)^2}{9} - \frac{(y - 2)^2}{16} = 1$$

$$\frac{x^2}{9} - \frac{(y - 2)^2}{16} = 1$$

7. $5x^2 + 2xy + 5y^2 - 10 = 0$

$A = 5, B = 2, C = 5$

$\cot 2\theta = \dfrac{5-5}{2} = 0$

$2\theta = \dfrac{\pi}{2} \Rightarrow \theta = \dfrac{\pi}{4}$

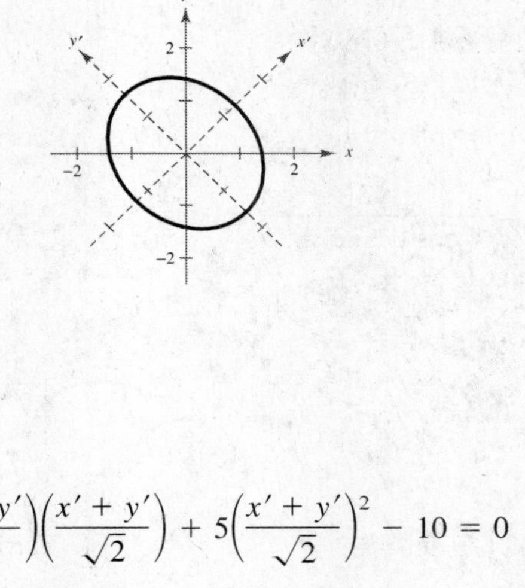

$x = x'\cos\dfrac{\pi}{4} - y'\sin\dfrac{\pi}{4} = \dfrac{x'-y'}{\sqrt{2}}$

$y = x'\sin\dfrac{\pi}{4} + y'\cos\dfrac{\pi}{4} = \dfrac{x'+y'}{\sqrt{2}}$

$$5\left(\frac{x'-y'}{\sqrt{2}}\right)^2 + 2\left(\frac{x'-y'}{\sqrt{2}}\right)\left(\frac{x'+y'}{\sqrt{2}}\right) + 5\left(\frac{x'+y'}{\sqrt{2}}\right)^2 - 10 = 0$$

$$\frac{5(x')^2}{2} - \frac{10x'y'}{2} + \frac{5(y')^2}{2} + (x')^2 - (y')^2 + \frac{5(x')^2}{2} + \frac{10x'y'}{2} + \frac{5(y')^2}{2} - 10 = 0$$

$$6(x')^2 + 4(y')^2 - 10 = 0$$

$$\frac{3(x')^2}{5} + \frac{2(y')^2}{5} = 1$$

$$\frac{(x')^2}{5/3} + \frac{(y')^2}{5/2} = 1$$

Ellipse centered at the origin

8. (a) $6x^2 - 2xy + y^2 = 0$

$A = 6, B = -2, C = 1$

$B^2 - 4AC = (-2)^2 - 4(6)(1) = -20 < 0$

Ellipse

(b) $x^2 + 4xy + 4y^2 - x - y + 17 = 0$

$A = 1, B = 4, C = 4$

$B^2 - 4AC = (4)^2 - 4(1)(4) = 0$

Parabola

9. $x = 3 - 2\sin\theta, y = 1 + 5\cos\theta$

$\dfrac{x-3}{-2} = \sin\theta, \dfrac{y-1}{5} = \cos\theta$

$\left(\dfrac{x-3}{-2}\right)^2 + \left(\dfrac{y-1}{5}\right)^2 = 1$

$\dfrac{(x-3)^2}{4} + \dfrac{(y-1)^2}{25} = 1$

10. $x = e^{2t}, y = e^{4t}$

$x > 0, y > 0$

$y = (e^{2t})^2 = (x)^2 = x^2, x > 0, y > 0$

11. Polar: $\left(\sqrt{2}, \dfrac{3\pi}{4}\right)$

$x = \sqrt{2}\cos\dfrac{3\pi}{4} = \sqrt{2}\left(-\dfrac{1}{\sqrt{2}}\right) = -1$

$y = \sqrt{2}\sin\dfrac{3\pi}{4} = \sqrt{2}\left(\dfrac{1}{\sqrt{2}}\right) = 1$

Rectangular: $(-1, 1)$

12. Rectangular: $\left(\sqrt{3}, -1\right)$

$r = \pm\sqrt{(\sqrt{3})^2 + (-1)^2} = \pm 2$

$\tan\theta = \dfrac{-1}{\sqrt{3}} = -\dfrac{\sqrt{3}}{3}$

$\theta = \dfrac{5\pi}{6}$ or $\theta = \dfrac{11\pi}{6}$

Polar: $\left(-2, \dfrac{5\pi}{6}\right)$ or $\left(2, \dfrac{11\pi}{6}\right)$

13. Rectangular: $4x - 3y = 12$

Polar: $4r\cos\theta - 3r\sin\theta = 12$

$r(4\cos\theta - 3\sin\theta) = 12$

$$r = \frac{12}{4\cos\theta - 3\sin\theta}$$

14. Polar: $r = 5\cos\theta$

$r^2 = 5r\cos\theta$

Rectangular: $x^2 + y^2 = 5x$

$x^2 + y^2 - 5x = 0$

15. $r = 1 - \cos\theta$

Cardioid

Symmetry: Polar axis

Maximum value of $|r|$: $r = 2$ when $\theta = \pi$.

Zero of r: $r = 0$ when $\theta = 0$.

θ	0	$\frac{\pi}{2}$	π	$\frac{3\pi}{2}$
r	0	1	2	1

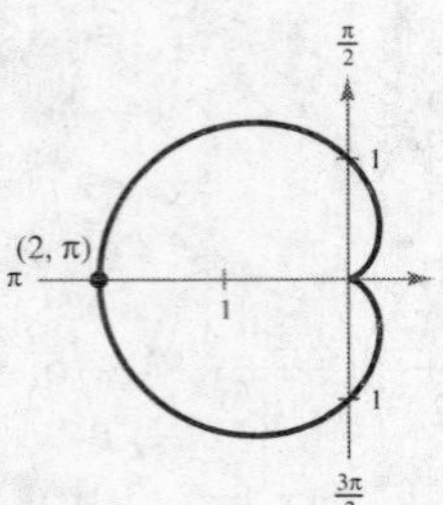

16. $r = 5\sin 2\theta$

Rose curve with four petals

Symmetry: Polar axis, $\theta = \frac{\pi}{2}$, and pole

Maximum value of $|r|$: $|r| = 5$ when $\theta = \frac{\pi}{4}, \frac{3\pi}{4}, \frac{5\pi}{4}, \frac{7\pi}{4}$.

Zeros of r: $r = 0$ when $\theta = 0, \frac{\pi}{2}, \pi, \frac{3\pi}{2}$.

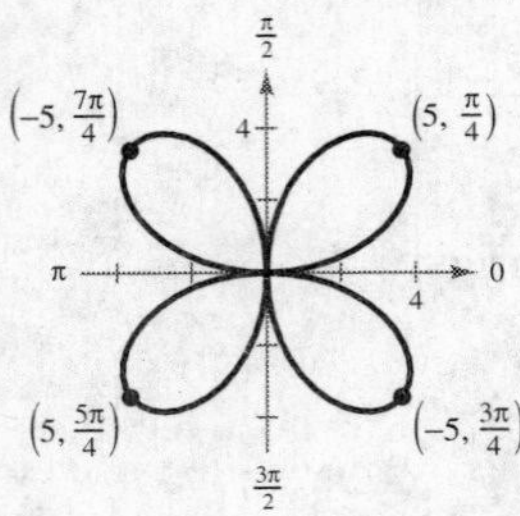

17. $r = \dfrac{3}{6 - \cos\theta}$

$r = \dfrac{1/2}{1 - (1/6)\cos\theta}$

$e = \dfrac{1}{6} < 1$, so the graph is an ellipse.

θ	0	$\frac{\pi}{2}$	π	$\frac{3\pi}{2}$
r	$\frac{3}{5}$	$\frac{1}{2}$	$\frac{3}{7}$	$\frac{1}{2}$

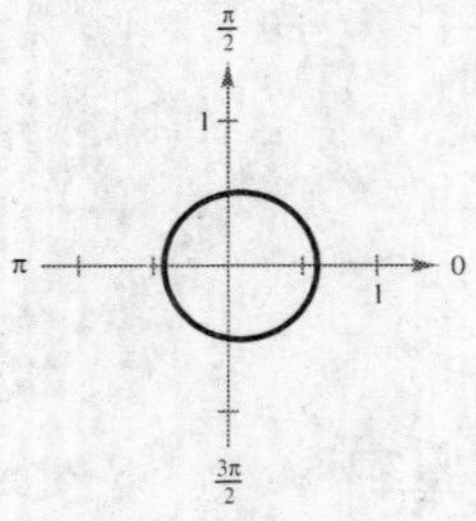

18. Parabola

Vertex: $\left(6, \frac{\pi}{2}\right)$

Focus: $(0, 0)$

$e = 1$

$r = \dfrac{ep}{1 + e\sin\theta}$

$r = \dfrac{p}{1 + \sin\theta}$

$6 = \dfrac{p}{1 + \sin(\pi/2)}$

$6 = \dfrac{p}{2}$

$12 = p$

$r = \dfrac{12}{1 + \sin\theta}$

Chapter 10 Practice Test Solutions

1. Let $A = (0, 0, 0)$, $B = (1, 2, -4)$, $C = (0, -2, -1)$.

Side AB: $\sqrt{1^2 + 2^2 + 4^2} = \sqrt{21}$

Side AC: $\sqrt{0^2 + 2^2 + 1^2} = \sqrt{5}$

Side BC: $\sqrt{(-1)^2 + (-2 - 2)^2 + (-1 + 4)^2} = \sqrt{1 + 16 + 9} = \sqrt{26}$

$BC^2 = AB^2 + AC^2$

$26 = 21 + 5$

2. $(x - 0)^2 + (y - 4)^2 + (z - 1)^2 = 5^2$

$x^2 + (y - 4)^2 + (z - 1)^2 = 25$

3. $(x^2 + 2x + 1) + y^2 + (z^2 - 4z + 4) = 1 + 4 + 11$

$(x + 1)^2 + y^2 + (z - 2)^2 = 16$

Center: $(-1, 0, 2)$

Radius: 4

4. $\mathbf{u} - 3\mathbf{v} = \langle 1, 0, -1\rangle - 3\langle 4, 3, -6\rangle$

$= \langle 1, 0, -1\rangle - \langle 12, 9, -18\rangle$

$= \langle -11, -9, 17\rangle$

5. $\frac{1}{2}\mathbf{v} = \frac{1}{2}\langle 2, 4, -6\rangle = \langle 1, 2, -3\rangle$

$\left\|\frac{1}{2}\mathbf{v}\right\| = \sqrt{1^2 + 2^2 + (-3)^2} = \sqrt{14}$

6. $\mathbf{u} \cdot \mathbf{v} = \langle 2, 1, -3\rangle \cdot \langle 1, 1, -2\rangle$

$= 2 + 1 + 6 = 9$

7. Because $\mathbf{v} = \langle -3, -3, 3\rangle = -3\langle 1, 1, -1\rangle = -3\mathbf{u}$, $\mathbf{u}$ and $\mathbf{v}$ are parallel.

8. $\mathbf{u} \times \mathbf{v} = \begin{vmatrix} \mathbf{i} & \mathbf{j} & \mathbf{k} \\ -1 & 0 & 2 \\ 1 & -1 & 3 \end{vmatrix} = \langle 2, 5, 1\rangle$

$\mathbf{v} \times \mathbf{u} = -(\mathbf{u} \times \mathbf{v}) = \langle -2, -5, -1\rangle$

9. $\mathbf{u} \cdot (\mathbf{v} \times \mathbf{w}) = \begin{vmatrix} 1 & 1 & 1 \\ 0 & -1 & 1 \\ 1 & 0 & 4 \end{vmatrix}$

$= 1(-4) - 1(-1) + 1(1)$

$= -4 + 1 + 1 = -2$

Volume $= |\mathbf{u} \cdot (\mathbf{v} \times \mathbf{w})| = |-2| = 2$

10. $\mathbf{v} = \langle (2 - 0), -3 - (-3), 4 - 3\rangle = \langle 2, 0, 1\rangle$

$x = 2 + 2t, y = -3, z = 4 + t$

11. $1(x - 1) - 1(y - 2) + 0(z - 3) = 0$

$x - 1 - y + 2 = 0$

$x - y + 1 = 0$

12. $\overrightarrow{AB} = \langle 1, 1, 1\rangle, \overrightarrow{AC} = \langle 1, 2, 3\rangle$

$\mathbf{n} = \overrightarrow{AB} \times \overrightarrow{AC} = \begin{vmatrix} \mathbf{i} & \mathbf{j} & \mathbf{k} \\ 1 & 1 & 1 \\ 1 & 2 & 3 \end{vmatrix} = \langle 1, -2, 1\rangle$

Plane: $1(x - 0) - 2(y - 0) + (z - 0) = 0$

$x - 2y + z = 0$

13. $\mathbf{n}_1 = \langle 1, 1, -1\rangle, \mathbf{n}_2 = \langle 3, -4, -1\rangle$

$\mathbf{n}_1 \cdot \mathbf{n}_2 = 3 - 4 + 1 = 0 \Rightarrow$ Orthogonal planes

14. $\mathbf{n} = \langle 1, 2, 1\rangle, Q = (1, 1, 1), P = (0, 0, 6)$ on plane, $\overrightarrow{PQ} = \langle 1, 1, -5\rangle$

$D = \frac{|\overrightarrow{PQ} \cdot \mathbf{n}|}{\|\mathbf{n}\|} = \frac{|1 + 2 - 5|}{\sqrt{1 + 4 + 1}} = \frac{2}{\sqrt{6}} = \frac{\sqrt{6}}{3}$

Chapter 11 Practice Test Solutions

1.

x	2.9	2.99	3	3.01	3.1
$f(x)$	0.1695	0.1669	?	0.1664	0.1639

$\lim_{x\to 3} \dfrac{x-3}{x^2-9} \approx 0.1667$

2. $\lim_{x\to 0} \dfrac{\sqrt{x+4}-2}{x} \approx \dfrac{1}{4}$

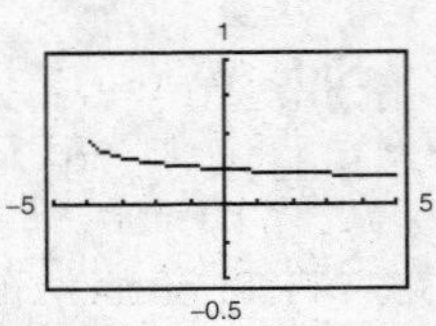

3. $\lim_{x\to 2} e^{x-2} = e^{2-2} = e^0 = 1$

4. $\lim_{x\to 1} \dfrac{x^3-1}{x-1} = \lim_{x\to 1} \dfrac{(x-1)(x^2+x+1)}{x-1}$

$= \lim_{x\to 1} (x^2+x+1) = 3$

5. $\lim_{x\to 0} \dfrac{\sin 5x}{2x} \approx 2.5$

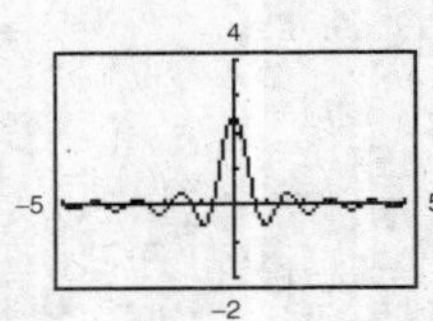

6. The limit does not exist. If

$f(x) = \dfrac{|x+2|}{x+2},$

then $f(x) = 1$ for $x > -2$, and $f(x) = -1$ for $x < -2$.

7. $m_{\text{sec}} = \dfrac{f(4+h)-f(4)}{h}$

$= \dfrac{\sqrt{4+h}-2}{h}$

$= \dfrac{\sqrt{4+h}-2}{h} \cdot \dfrac{\sqrt{4+h}+2}{\sqrt{4+h}+2}$

$= \dfrac{(4+h)-4}{h\left[\sqrt{4+h}+2\right]}$

$= \dfrac{h}{h\left[\sqrt{4+h}+2\right]}$

$= \dfrac{1}{\sqrt{4+h}+2},\ h \neq 0$

$m = \lim_{h\to 0} \dfrac{1}{\sqrt{4+h}+2} = \dfrac{1}{\sqrt{4}+2} = \dfrac{1}{4}$

8. $f'(x) = \lim_{h\to 0} \dfrac{f(x+h)-f(x)}{h}$

$= \lim_{h\to 0} \dfrac{[3(x+h)-1]-[3x-1]}{h}$

$= \lim_{h\to 0} \dfrac{3x+3h-1-3x+1}{h}$

$= \lim_{h\to 0} \dfrac{3h}{h} = \lim_{h\to 0} 3 = 3$

9. (a) $\lim_{x\to\infty} \dfrac{3}{x^4} = 0$

(b) $\lim_{x\to -\infty} \dfrac{x^2}{x^2+3} = 1$

(c) $\lim_{x\to\infty} \dfrac{|x|}{1-x} = -1$

10. $a_1 = 0,\ a_2 = \dfrac{1-4}{8+1} = -\dfrac{1}{3},\ a_3 = \dfrac{1-9}{18+1} = -\dfrac{8}{19},$

$a_4 = \dfrac{1-16}{33} = -\dfrac{15}{33}$

$\lim_{n\to\infty} a_n = \lim_{n\to\infty} \dfrac{1-n^2}{2n^2+1} = -\dfrac{1}{2}$

11. $\sum_{i=1}^{25} i^2 + \sum_{i=1}^{25} i = \dfrac{25(26)(51)}{6} + \dfrac{25(26)}{2} = \dfrac{25(26)}{6}[51+3] = \dfrac{25(26)(54)}{6} = 5850$

12. $\displaystyle\sum_{i=1}^{n} \frac{i^2}{n^3} = \frac{1}{n^3}\sum_{i=1}^{n} i^2 = \frac{1}{n^3}\left[\frac{n(n+1)(2n+1)}{6}\right] = \frac{2n^2+3n+1}{6n^2} = S(n)$

$\displaystyle\lim_{n\to\infty} S(n) = \frac{1}{3}$

13. Width of rectangles: $\displaystyle\frac{b-a}{n} = \frac{1}{n}$

Height: $\displaystyle f\left(a + \frac{(b-a)i}{n}\right) = f\left(\frac{i}{n}\right) = 1 - \left(\frac{i}{n}\right)^2$

$\displaystyle A_n \approx \sum_{i=1}^{n}\left[1 - \frac{i^2}{n^2}\right]\frac{1}{n} = \sum_{i=1}^{n}\frac{1}{n} - \sum_{i=1}^{n}\frac{i^2}{n^3} = 1 - \frac{1}{n^2}\,\frac{n(n+1)(2n+1)}{6}$

$\displaystyle A = \lim_{n\to\infty} A_n = 1 - \frac{1}{3} = \frac{2}{3}$

PART II

Chapter 1 Chapter Test Solutions

1. $5x + 2y = 3$

$2y = -5x + 3$

$y = -\frac{5}{2}x + \frac{3}{2}$

Slope $= -\frac{5}{2}$

(a) Parallel line

$y - 4 = -\frac{5}{2}(x - 0)$

$y = -\frac{5}{2}x + 4$

$5x + 2y - 8 = 0$

(b) Perpendicular line

$y - 4 = \frac{2}{5}(x - 0)$

$y = \frac{2}{5}x + 4$

$2x - 5y + 20 = 0$

2. Slope $= \dfrac{4 - (-1)}{-3 - 2} = \dfrac{5}{-5} = -1$

$y + 1 = -1(x - 2)$

$y = -x + 1$

3. No, for some x there corresponds more than one value of y. For instance, if $x = 1$, $y = \pm 1/\sqrt{3}$.

4. $f(x) = |x + 2| - 15$

(a) $f(-8) = |-8 + 2| - 15 = 6 - 15 = -9$

(b) $f(14) = |14 + 2| - 15 = 16 - 15 = 1$

(c) $f(t - 6) = |t - 6 + 2| - 15 = |t - 4| - 15$

5. $3 - x \geq 0 \implies$ domain is all $x \leq 3$.

6. $C = 5.60x + 24{,}000$

$P = R - C$

$= 99.50x - (5.60x + 24{,}000)$

$= 93.9x - 24{,}000$

7. $f(-x) = 2(-x)^3 - 3(-x)$

$= -2x^3 + 3x = -f(x)$

Odd

8. $f(-x) = 3(-x)^4 + 5(-x)^2$

$= 3x^4 + 5x^2 = f(x)$

Even

9. $h(x) = \frac{1}{4}x^4 - 2x^2 = \frac{1}{4}x^2(x^2 - 8)$

By graphing h, you see that the graph is increasing on $(-2, 0)$ and $(2, \infty)$ and decreasing on $(-\infty, -2)$ and $(0, 2)$.

10. $g(t) = |t + 2| - |t - 2|$

By graphing g, you see that the graph is increasing on $(-2, 2)$, and constant on $(-\infty, -2)$ and $(2, \infty)$.

11. Relative minimum: $(-3.33, -6.52)$

Relative maximum: $(0, 12)$

12. Relative minimum: $(0.77, 1.81)$

Relative maximum: $(-0.77, 2.19)$

13. (a) Parent function $f(x) = x^3$

(b) g is obtained from f by a horizontal shift five units to the right, a vertical stretch of 2, a reflection in the x-axis, and a vertical shift three units upward.

(c)

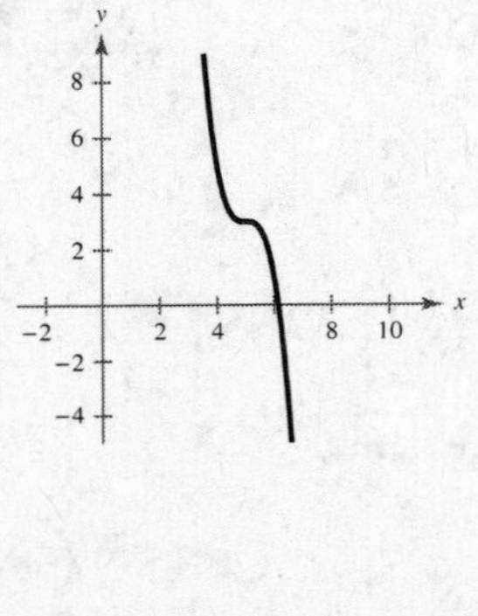

14. (a) Parent function $f(x) = \sqrt{x}$

(b) g is obtained from f by a reflection in the y-axis, and a horizontal shift seven units to the left.

(c)

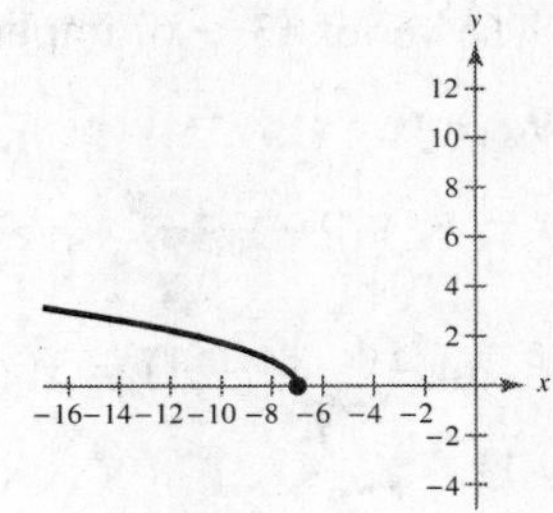

15. (a) Parent function $f(x) = |x|$

(b) $g(x) = 4|-x| - 7 = 4|x| - 7$ is obtained from f by a vertical stretch of 4 followed by a vertical shift seven units downward.

(c)

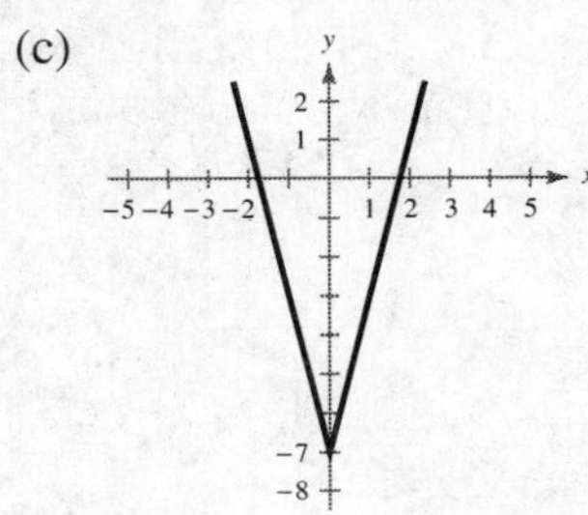

16. (a) $(f - g)(x) = x^2 - \sqrt{2 - x}$

Domain: $x \le 2$

(b) $\left(\frac{f}{g}\right)(x) = \frac{x^2}{\sqrt{2 - x}}$

Domain: $x < 2$

(c) $(f \circ g)(x) = f(\sqrt{2-x}) = 2 - x$

Domain: $x \le 2$

(d) $(g \circ f)x = g(x^2) = \sqrt{2 - x^2}$

Domain: $-\sqrt{2} \le x \le \sqrt{2}$

17. $f(x) = x^3 + 8$

Yes, f is one-to-one and has an inverse function.

$$y = x^3 + 8$$
$$x = y^3 + 8$$
$$x - 8 = y^3$$
$$\sqrt[3]{x - 8} = y$$
$$f^{-1}(x) = \sqrt[3]{x - 8}$$

18. $f(x) = x^2 + 6$

No, f is not one-to-one, and does not have an inverse function.

19. $f(x) = \frac{3x\sqrt{x}}{8}$

Yes, f is one-to-one and has an inverse function.

$$y = \tfrac{3}{8}x^{3/2},\ x \ge 0, y \ge 0$$
$$x = \tfrac{3}{8}y^{3/2},\ y \ge 0,\ x \ge 0$$
$$\tfrac{8}{3}x = y^{3/2}$$
$$\left(\tfrac{8}{3}x\right)^{2/3} = y$$
$$f^{-1}(x) = \left(\tfrac{8}{3}x\right)^{2/3},\quad x \ge 0$$

20. $y = 18.30t - 76.2,\ r \approx 0.99622$

$y = 200$ for $t \approx 15$, or 2005

Chapter 2 Chapter Test Solutions

1. $y = x^2 + 4x + 3 = x^2 + 4x + 4 - 1 = (x + 2)^2 - 1$

Vertex: $(-2, -1)$

$x = 0 \Rightarrow y = 3$

$y = 0 \Rightarrow x^2 + 4x + 3 = 0 \Rightarrow (x + 3)(x + 1) = 0 \Rightarrow x = -1, -3$

Intercepts: $(0, 3), (-1, 0), (-3, 0)$

2. Let $y = a(x - h)^2 + k$. The vertex $(3, -6)$ implies that $y = a(x - 3)^2 - 6$. For $(0, 3)$ you obtain

$3 = a(0 - 3)^2 - 6 = 9a - 6 \Rightarrow a = 1.$

Thus, $y = (x - 3)^2 - 6 = x^2 - 6x + 3.$

3. $f(x) = 4x^3 + 4x^2 + x = x(4x^2 + 4x + 1) = x(2x + 1)^2$

Zeros: 0 (multiplicity 1)

$-\frac{1}{2}$ (multiplicity 2)

4. $f(x) = -x^3 + 7x + 6$

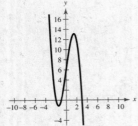

5.
$$\begin{array}{r} 3x \\ x^2 + 1 \overline{\smash{)}\, 3x^3 + 0x^2 + 4x - 1} \\ \underline{3x^3 + 3x } \\ x - 1 \end{array}$$

$$3x + \frac{x - 1}{x^2 + 1}$$

6.
$$\begin{array}{r|rrrrr} 2 & 2 & 0 & -5 & 0 & -3 \\ & & 4 & 8 & 6 & 12 \\ \hline & 2 & 4 & 3 & 6 & 9 \end{array}$$

$$2x^3 + 4x^2 + 3x + 6 + \frac{9}{x - 2}$$

7.
$$\begin{array}{r|rrrrr} -2 & 3 & 0 & -6 & 5 & -1 \\ & & -6 & 12 & -12 & 14 \\ \hline & 3 & -6 & 6 & -7 & 13 \end{array}$$

$f(-2) = 13$

8. Possible rational zeros:

$\pm 24, \pm 12, \pm 8, \pm 6, \pm 4, \pm 3, \pm 2, \pm 1, \pm\frac{3}{2}, \pm\frac{1}{2}$

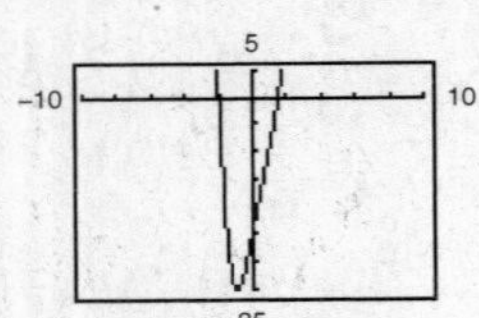

Rational zeros: $-2, \frac{3}{2}$

9. Possible rational zeros: $\pm 2, \pm 1, \pm\frac{2}{3}, \pm\frac{1}{3}$

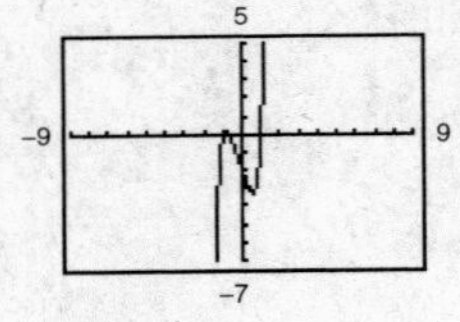

Rational zeros: $\pm 1, -\frac{2}{3}$

10. $f(x) = x^3 - 7x^2 + 11x + 19$

$= (x + 1)(x^2 - 8x + 19)$

For the quadratic,

$$x = \frac{8 \pm \sqrt{64 - 4(19)}}{2} = 4 \pm \sqrt{3}i.$$

Zeros: $-1, 4 \pm \sqrt{3}i$

$f(x) = (x + 1)(x - 4 + \sqrt{3}i)(x - 4 - \sqrt{3}i)$

11. $(-8 - 3i) + (-1 - 15i) = -9 - 18i$

12. $(10 + \sqrt{-20}) - (4 - \sqrt{-14}) = 6 + 2\sqrt{5}i + \sqrt{14}i = 6 + (2\sqrt{5} + \sqrt{14})i$

13. $(2 + i)(6 - i) = 12 + 6i - 2i + 1 = 13 + 4i$

14. $(4 + 3i)^2 - (5 + i)^2 = (16 + 24i - 9) - (25 + 10i - 1) = -17 + 14i$

15. $\dfrac{8 + 5i}{6 - i} \cdot \dfrac{6 + i}{6 + i} = \dfrac{48 + 30i + 8i - 5}{36 + 1} = \dfrac{43}{37} + \dfrac{38}{37}i$

16. $\dfrac{5i}{2 + i} \cdot \dfrac{2 - i}{2 - i} = \dfrac{10i + 5}{4 + 1} = 1 + 2i$

17. $\dfrac{(2i - 1)}{(3i + 2)} \cdot \dfrac{2 - 3i}{2 - 3i} = \dfrac{6 - 2 + 4i + 3i}{4 + 9}$

$= \dfrac{4}{13} + \dfrac{7}{13}i$

18.

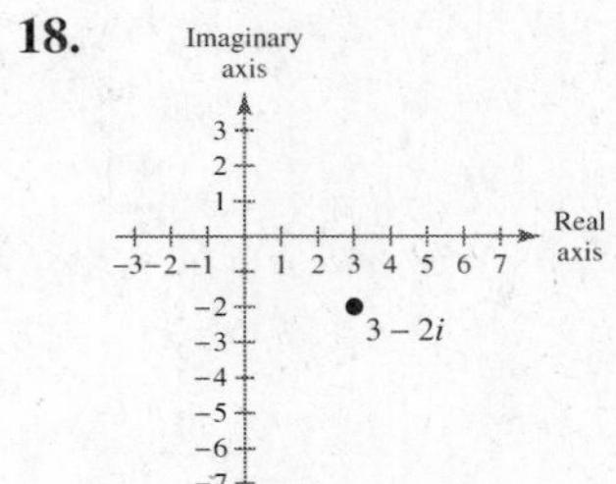

19.

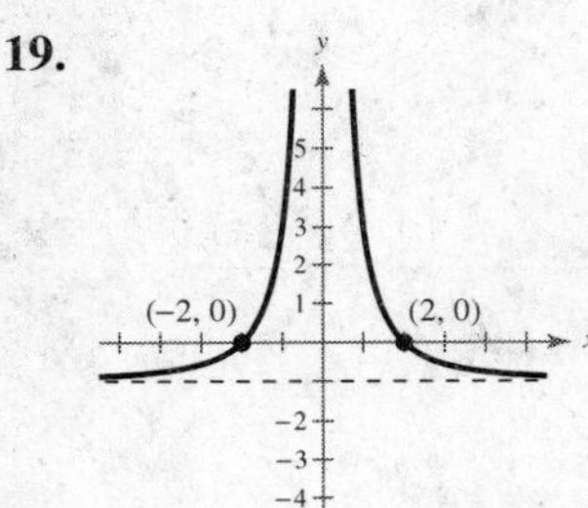

Vertical asymptote: $x = 0$

Intercepts: $(2, 0), (-2, 0)$

Symmetry: y-axis

Horizontal asymptote: $y = -1$

20. $g(x) = \dfrac{x^2 + 2}{x - 1} = x + 1 + \dfrac{3}{x - 1}$

Vertical asymptote: $x = 1$

Intercept: $(0, -2)$

Slant asymptote: $y = x + 1$

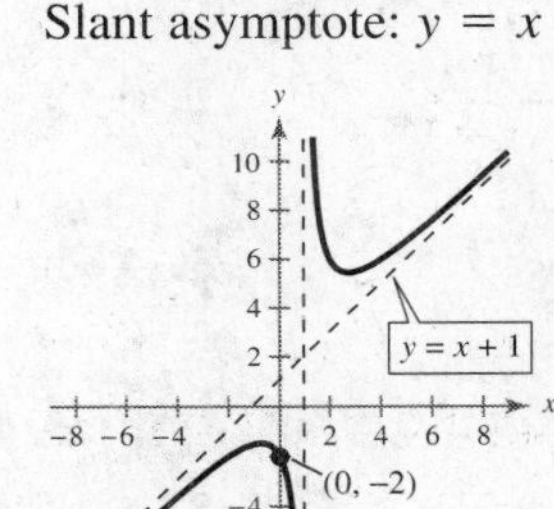

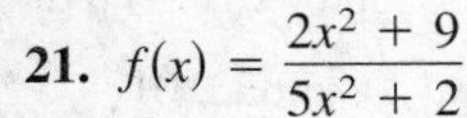

21. $f(x) = \dfrac{2x^2 + 9}{5x^2 + 2}$

Horizontal asymptote: $y = \dfrac{2}{5}$

y-axis symmetry

Intercept: $\left(0, \dfrac{9}{2}\right)$

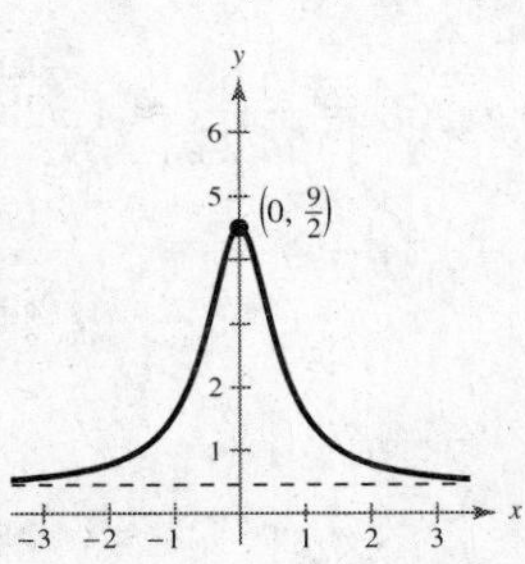

22. (a)

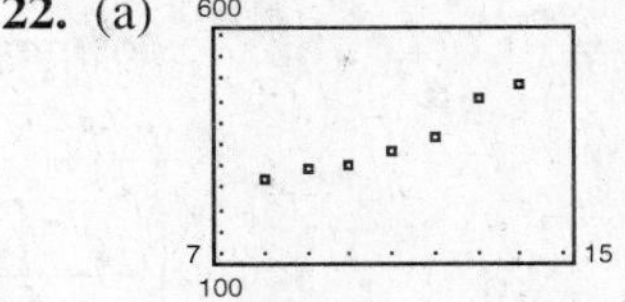

(b) $y = 5.582t^2 - 85.53t + 602.0$

(c)

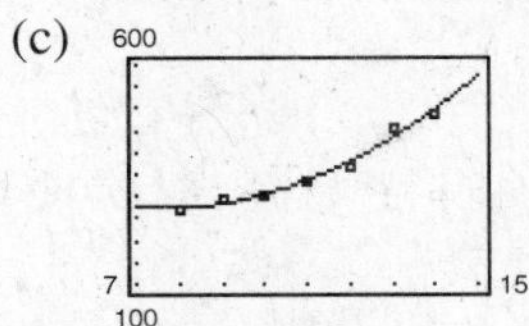

Yes, the model is a good fit.

(d) For 2005, $t = 15$ and $y \approx \$575$ billion.

For 2010, $t = 20$ and $y \approx \$1124$ billion.

(e) Answers will vary.

Chapter 3 Chapter Test Solutions

1.

x	-2	-1	0	1	2
$f(x)$	100	10	1	0.1	0.01

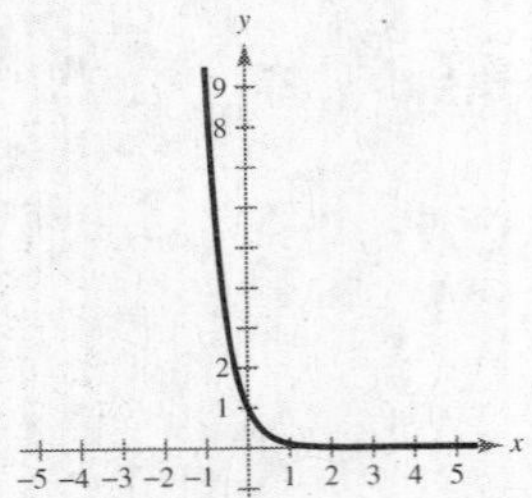

$f(x) = 10^{-x}$

Horizontal asymptote: $y = 0$

Intercept: $(0, 1)$

2.

x	0	2	3	4
$f(x)$	-0.03	-1	-6	-36

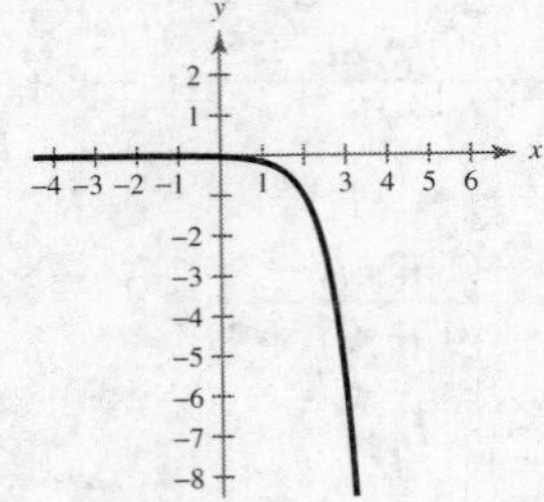

$f(x) = -6^{x-2}$

Horizontal asymptote: $y = 0$

Intercept: $\left(0, -\frac{1}{36}\right)$

3.

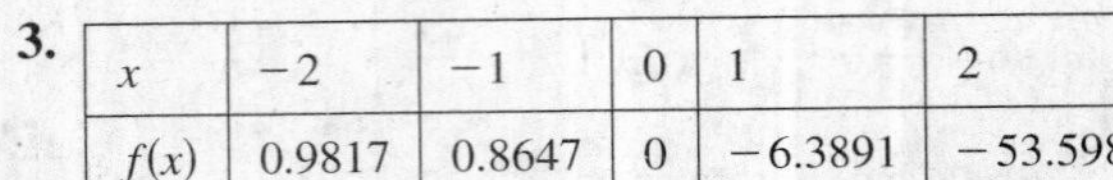

x	-2	-1	0	1	2
$f(x)$	0.9817	0.8647	0	-6.3891	-53.5982

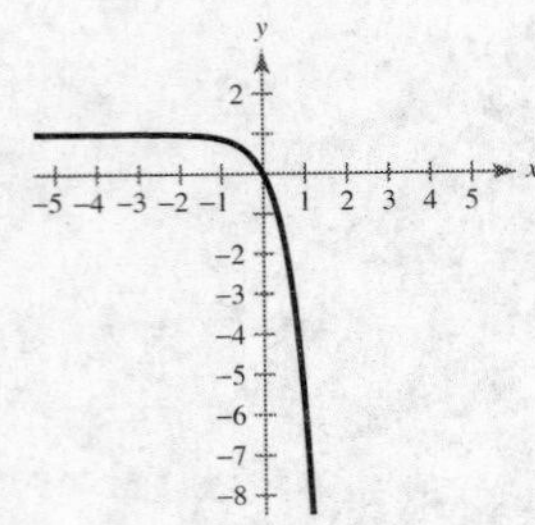

$f(x) = 1 - e^{2x}$

Horizontal asymptote: $y = 1$

Intercept: $(0, 0)$

4. $\log_7 7^{-0.89} = -0.89 \log_7 7$
$= -0.89$

5. $4.6 \ln e^2 = 4.6(2) \ln e = 9.2$

6. $2 - \log_{10} 100 = 2 - 2 = 0$

7. $f(x) = -\log_{10} x - 6$

Domain: $x > 0$

Vertical asymptote: $x = 0$

x-intercept: $(10^{-6}, 0) \approx (0, 0)$

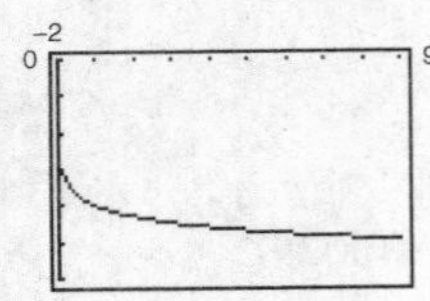

8. $f(x) = \ln(x - 4)$

Domain: $x > 4$

Vertical asymptote: $x = 4$

x-intercept: $(5, 0)$

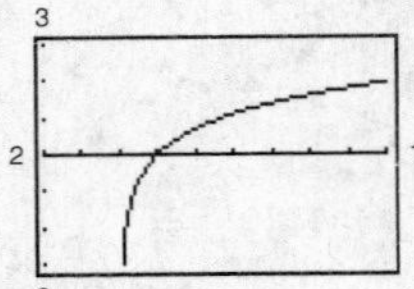

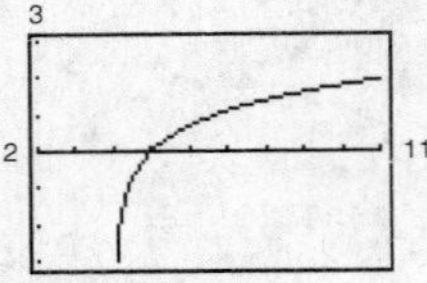

9. $f(x) = 1 + \ln(x + 6)$

Domain: $x > -6$

Vertical asymptote: $x = -6$

x-intercept: $(-5.632, 0)$

10. $\log_7 44 = \dfrac{\ln 44}{\ln 7} \approx 1.945$

11. $\log_{2/5}(0.9) = \dfrac{\ln(0.9)}{\ln(2/5)} \approx 0.115$

12. $\log_{24} 68 = \dfrac{\ln 68}{\ln 24} \approx 1.328$

13. $\log_2 3a^4 = \log_2 3 + \log_2 a^4 = \log_2 3 + 4 \log_2 a$

14. $\ln \frac{5\sqrt{x}}{6} = \ln 5 + \ln\sqrt{x} - \ln 6$

$= \ln 5 + \frac{1}{2}\ln x - \ln 6$

15. $\ln \frac{x\sqrt{x+1}}{2e^4} = \ln x + \ln\sqrt{x+1} - \ln(2) - \ln e^4$

$= \ln x + \frac{1}{2}\ln(x+1) - \ln 2 - 4$

16. $\log_3 13 + \log_3 y = \log_3(13y)$

17. $4\ln x - 4\ln y = \ln x^4 - \ln y^4 = \ln\left(\frac{x^4}{y^4}\right) = \ln\left(\frac{x}{y}\right)^4$

18. $\ln x - \ln(x+2) + \ln(2x-3) = \ln\left[\frac{x(2x-3)}{x+2}\right]$

19. $3^x = 81 = 3^4$

$x = 4$

20. $5^{2x} = 2500$

$2x\ln 5 = \ln 2500$

$x = \frac{1}{2}\frac{\ln 2500}{\ln 5} \approx 2.431$

21. $\log_7 x = 3$

$7^3 = x$

$x = 343$

22. $\log_{10}(x-4) = 5$

$10^5 = x - 4$

$x = 10^5 + 4$

$= 100{,}004$

23. $\frac{1025}{8 + e^{4x}} = 5$

$1025 = 40 + 5e^{4x}$

$985 = 5e^{4x}$

$e^{4x} = 197$

$4x = \ln(197)$

$x = \frac{1}{4}\ln(197) \approx 1.321$

24. $-xe^{-x} + e^{-x} = 0$

$e^{-x}(1 - x) = 0$

$x = 1$

25. $\log_{10} x - \log_{10}(8 - 5x) = 2$

$\log_{10}\left(\frac{x}{8-5x}\right) = 2$

$10^2 = \frac{x}{8-5x}$

$800 - 500x = x$

$800 = 501x$

$x = \frac{800}{501} \approx 1.597$

26. $2x\ln x - x = 0$

$2\ln x = 1, \quad (x \neq 0)$

$\ln x = \frac{1}{2}$

$x = e^{1/2} \approx 1.649$

27. $\frac{1}{2} = 1e^{k(22)}$ (half-life is 22 years)

$\ln\frac{1}{2} = 22k$

$k = \frac{1}{22}\ln\frac{1}{2} = -\frac{1}{22}\ln 2 \approx -0.03151$

$A = e^{-0.03151(19)} \approx 0.54953$ or 55% remains

28. (a) Quadratic model: $R = -0.092t^2 + 3.29t + 38.1$

Exponential model: $R = 46.99(1.026)^t$

Power model: $R = 36.00t^{0.233}$

(b) 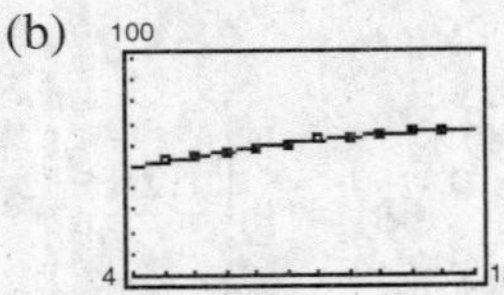

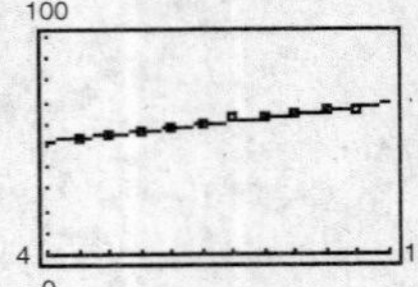

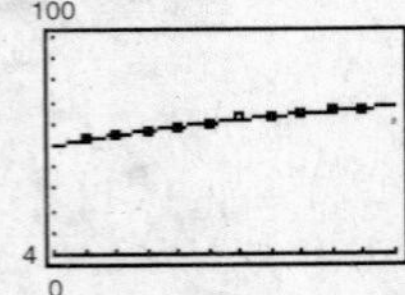

(c) The quadratic model is best for 2010, $t = 20$, and $R \approx 67.1$ billion dollars.

Chapters 1–3 Cumulative Test Solutions

1. (a) $\text{Slope} = \dfrac{8-4}{-5-(-1)} = \dfrac{4}{-4} = -1$

$y - 8 = -1(x - (-5)) = -x - 5$

$x + y - 3 = 0$

(b) Sample answers: $(0, 3), (1, 2), (2, 1)$

2. (a) $y - 1 = -2\left(x + \dfrac{1}{2}\right)$

$y - 1 = -2x - 1$

$y = -2x$

$y + 2x = 0$

(b) Three additional points: $(0, 0), (1, -2), (2, -4)$

3. (a) Vertical line: $x = -\dfrac{3}{7}$ or $x + \dfrac{3}{7} = 0$

(b) Three additional points:

$\left(-\dfrac{3}{7}, 0\right), \left(-\dfrac{3}{7}, 1\right), \left(-\dfrac{3}{7}, 2\right)$

4. $f(x) = \dfrac{x}{x-2}$

(a) $f(5) = \dfrac{5}{5-2} = \dfrac{5}{3}$

(b) $f(2)$ is undefined (division by 0).

(c) $f(5 + 4s) = \dfrac{5+4s}{(5+4s)-2} = \dfrac{5+4s}{3+4s}$

5. $f(x) = \begin{cases} 3x - 8, & x < 0 \\ x^2 + 4, & x \ge 0 \end{cases}$

(a) $f(-8) = 3(-8) - 8 = -32$

(b) $f(0) = 0^2 + 4 = 4$

(c) $f(4) = 4^2 + 4 = 20$

6. No, for some x there corresponds two values of y.

7. 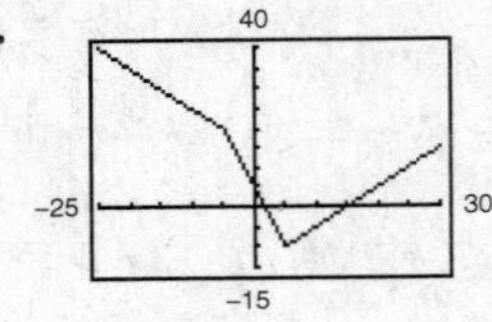

Decreasing on $(-\infty, 5)$,
Increasing on $(5, \infty)$

8. (a) $r(x) = \frac{1}{2}\sqrt[3]{x}$ is a vertical shrink of $y = \sqrt[3]{x}$.

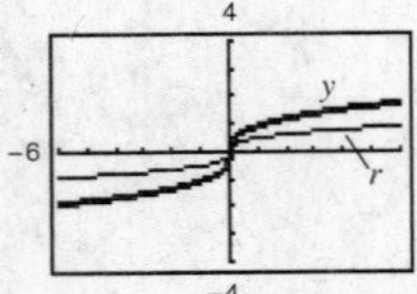

(b) $h(x) = \sqrt[3]{x} + 2$ is a vertical shift two units upward.

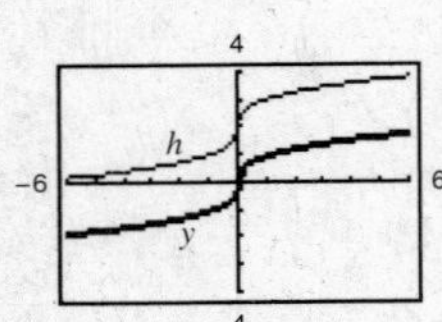

—CONTINUED—

8. —CONTINUED—

(c) $f(x) = \sqrt[3]{x}$

$g(x) = -\sqrt[3]{x + 2}$

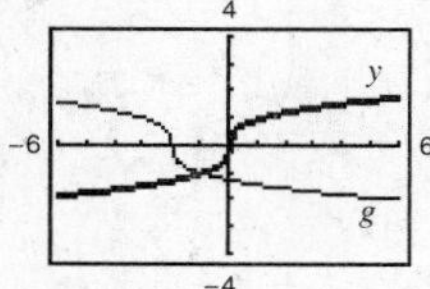

g is a horizontal shift two units to the left followed by a reflection in the x-axis.

9. $(f + g)(-4) = f(-4) + g(-4) = [-(-4)^2 + 3(-4) - 10] + [4(-4) + 1]$

$= -38 - 15 = -53$

10. $(g - f)\left(\frac{3}{4}\right) = \left[4\left(\frac{3}{4}\right) + 1\right] - \left[-\left(\frac{3}{4}\right)^2 + 3\left(\frac{3}{4}\right) - 10\right]$

$= 4 - (-8.3125) = 12.3125 = \frac{197}{16}$

11. $(g \circ f)(-2) = g(f(-2)) = g(-20) = 4(-20) + 1 = -79$

12. $(fg)(-1) = f(-1)g(-1) = (-14)(-3) = 42$

13. Yes, $h(x) = 5x - 2$ has an inverse function.

$y = 5x - 2$

$x = 5y - 2$

$x + 2 = 5y$

$\frac{x + 2}{5} = y$

$h^{-1}(x) = \frac{x + 2}{5}$

14. $f(x) = -\frac{1}{2}(x^2 + 4x)$

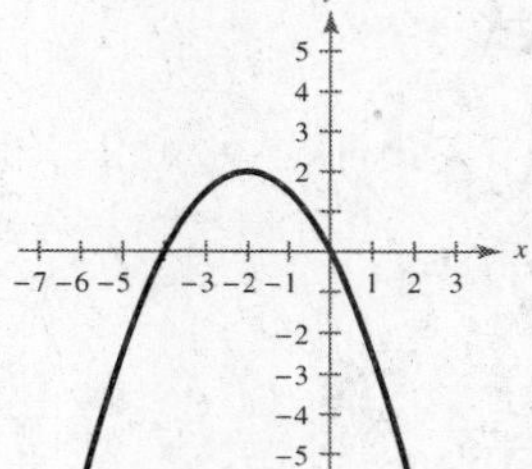

15. $f(x) = \frac{1}{4}x(x - 2)^2$

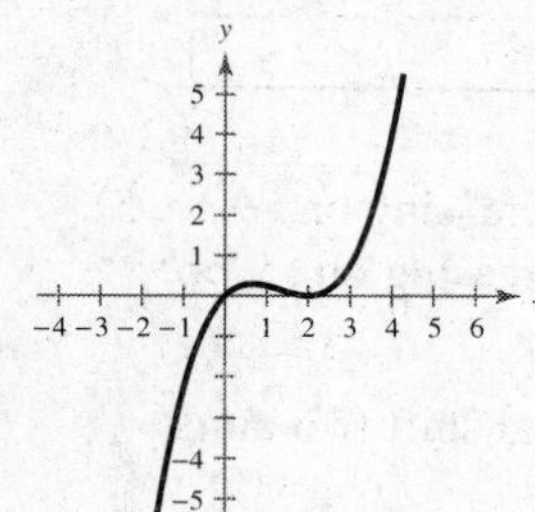

16.

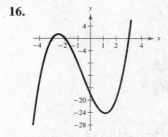

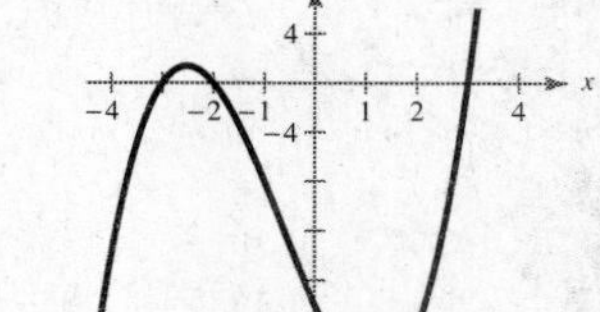

17. $x^3 + 2x^2 + 4x + 8 = (x + 2)(x^2 + 4)$

Zeros: $-2, \pm 2i$

18. Using a graphing utility, $x \approx 1.424$.

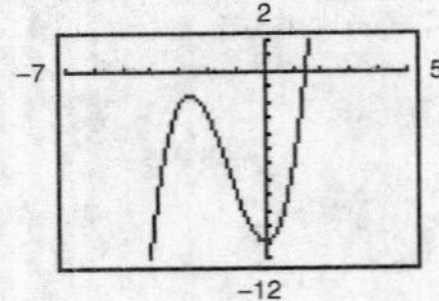

19.

$$\begin{array}{r} 4x + 2 \\ x + 3 \overline{\big) 4x^2 + 14x - 9} \\ \underline{4x^2 + 12x} \\ 2x - 9 \\ \underline{2x + 6} \\ -15 \end{array}$$

$$\frac{4x^2 + 14x - 9}{x + 3} = 4x + 2 - \frac{15}{x + 3}$$

20.

$$\begin{array}{r|rrrr} 6 & 2 & -5 & 6 & -20 \\ & & 12 & 42 & 288 \\ \hline & 2 & 7 & 48 & 268 \end{array}$$

$$\frac{2x^3 - 5x^2 + 6x - 20}{x - 6} = 2x^2 + 7x + 48 + \frac{268}{x - 6}$$

21.

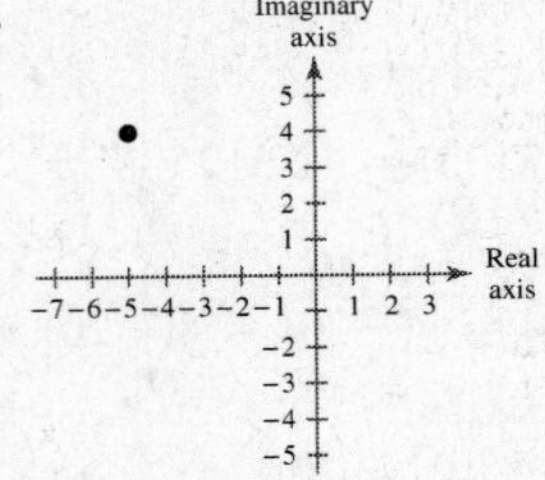

22. $f(x) = (x - 0)(x + 3)\left[x - \left(1 + \sqrt{5}i\right)\right]\left[x - \left(1 - \sqrt{5}i\right)\right]$

$= x(x + 3)[(x - 1)^2 + 5]$

$= (x^2 + 3x)(x^2 - 2x + 6)$

$= x^4 + x^3 + 18x$

23. $f(x) = \dfrac{2x}{x - 3}$

Vertical asymptote: $x = 3$

Horizontal asymptote: $y = 2$

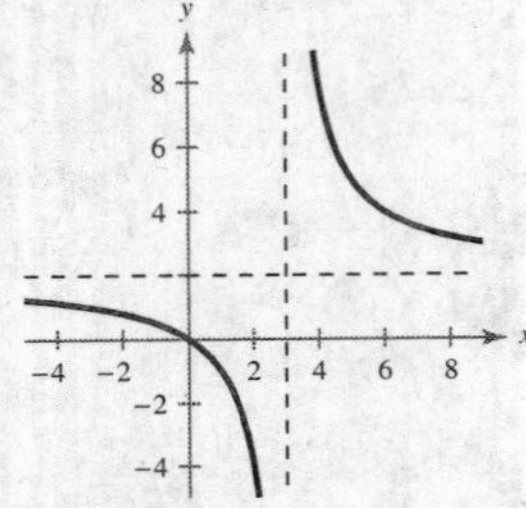

24. $f(x) = \dfrac{5x}{x^2 + x - 6} = \dfrac{5x}{(x + 3)(x - 2)}$

Vertical asymptotes: $x = -3, 2$

Horizontal asymptote: $y = 0$

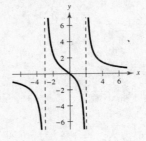

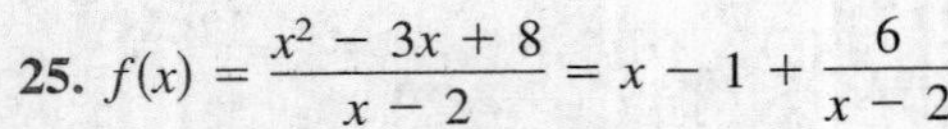

25. $f(x) = \dfrac{x^2 - 3x + 8}{x - 2} = x - 1 + \dfrac{6}{x - 2}$

Vertical asymptote: $x = 2$

Slant asymptote: $y = x - 1$

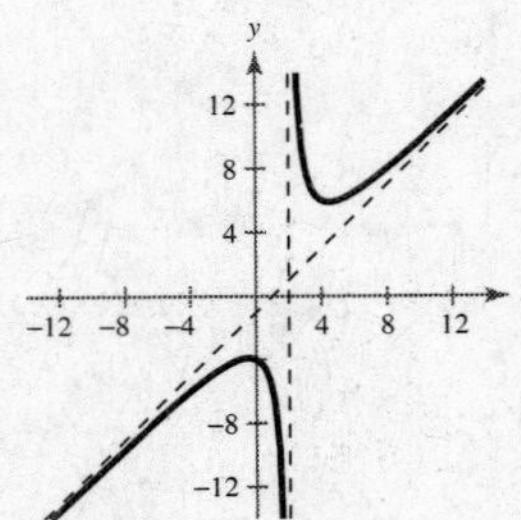

26. $(1.85)^{3.1} \approx 6.733$

27. $58^{\sqrt{5}} \approx 8772.934$

28. $e^{-20/11} \approx 0.162$

29. $4e^{2.56} \approx 51.743$

30. $f(x) = -3^{x+4} - 5$

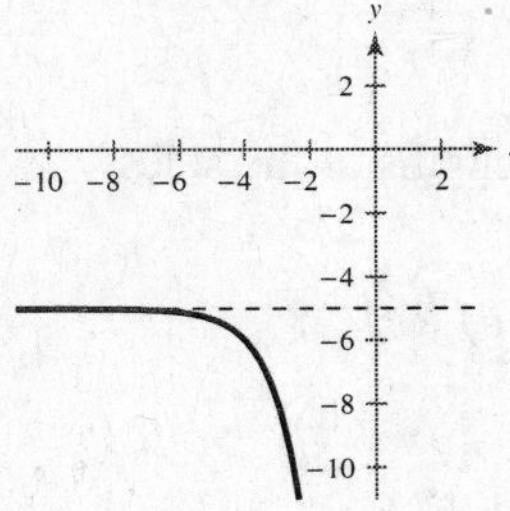

31. $f(x) = -\left(\frac{1}{2}\right)^{-x} - 3$

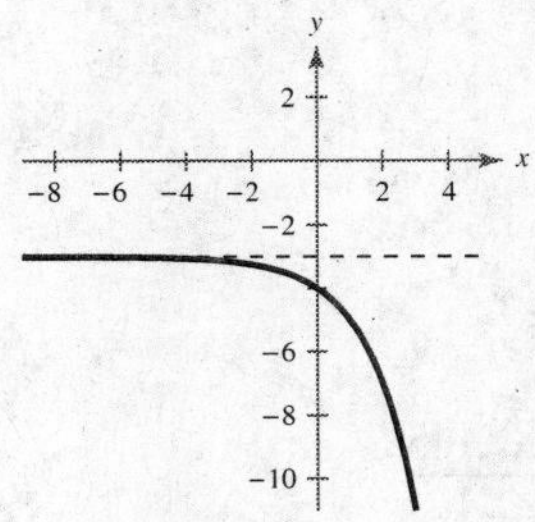

32. $f(x) = 4 + \log_{10}(x - 3)$

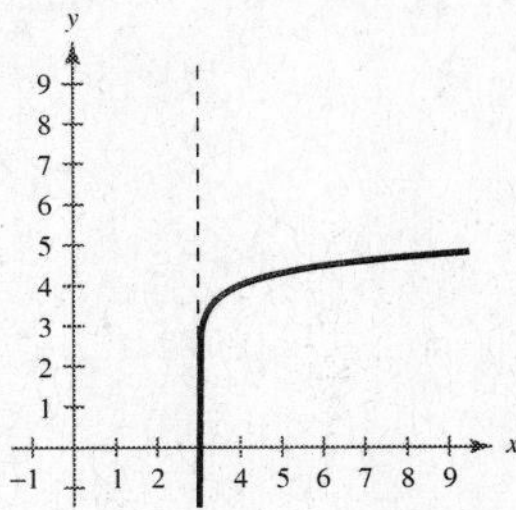

33. $f(x) = \ln(4 - x)$

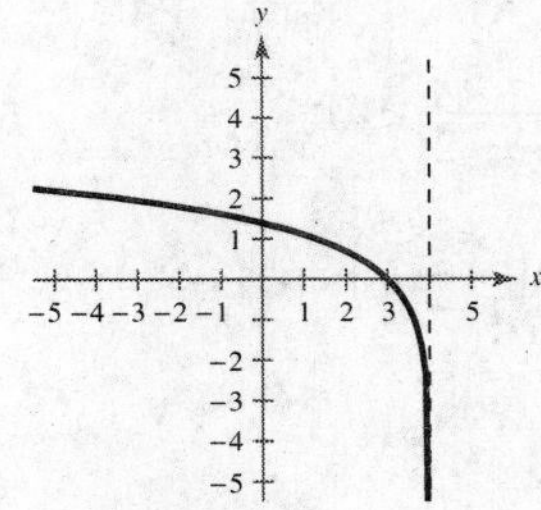

34. $\log_5 21 = \dfrac{\ln 21}{\ln 5} \approx 1.892$

35. $\log_9 6.8 = \dfrac{\ln 6.8}{\ln 9} \approx 0.872$

36. $\log_2\left(\dfrac{3}{2}\right) = \dfrac{\ln\left(\frac{3}{2}\right)}{\ln 2} \approx 0.585$

37.
$$\ln\left(\frac{x^2 - 4}{x^2 + 1}\right) = \ln[(x - 2)(x + 2)] - \ln(x^2 + 1)$$
$$= \ln(x - 2) + \ln(x + 2) - \ln(x^2 + 1)$$

38. $2 \ln x - \ln(x - 1) + \ln(x + 1) = \ln\left[x^2\left(\dfrac{x + 1}{x - 1}\right)\right]$

39.
$$6e^{2x} = 72$$
$$e^{2x} = 12$$
$$2x = \ln 12$$
$$x = \frac{1}{2}\ln 12 \approx 1.242$$

40.
$$4^{x-5} + 21 = 30$$
$$4^{x-5} = 9$$
$$(x - 5)\ln 4 = \ln 9$$
$$x - 5 = \frac{\ln 9}{\ln 4}$$
$$x = 5 + \frac{\ln 9}{\ln 4} \approx 6.585$$

41.
$$\log_2 x + \log_2 5 = 6$$
$$\log_2 5x = 6$$
$$5x = 2^6 = 64$$
$$x = \frac{64}{5} = 12.8$$

42. $250e^{0.05x} = 500{,}000$

$e^{0.05x} = 2000$

$0.05x = \ln 2000$

$x = 20 \ln 2000$

≈ 152.018

43. $2x^2e^{2x} - 2xe^{2x} = 0$

$(2x^2 - 2x)e^{2x} = 0$

$2x^2 - 2x = 0$

$2x(x - 1) = 0$

$x = 0, 1$

44. $\ln(2x - 5) - \ln x = 1$

$$\ln \frac{2x - 5}{x} = 1$$

$$e = \frac{2x - 5}{x}$$

$$ex = 2x - 5$$

$$x(e - 2) = -5$$

$$x = \frac{-5}{e - 2} < 0$$

No solution because $\ln\left(\frac{-5}{e - 2}\right)$ does not exist.

45. (a) Let x and y be the lengths of the sides

$2x + 2y = 546 \implies y = 273 - x.$

$A = xy = x(273 - x)$

(b) 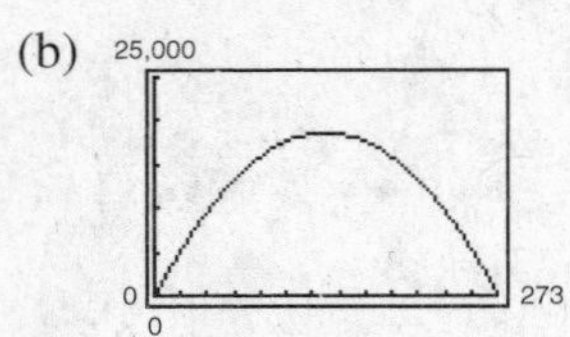

Domain: $0 < x < 273$

(c) If $A = 15{,}000$, then $x = 76.23$ or 196.77.

Dimensions in feet:

76.23×196.77 or 196.77×76.23

46. (a) Quadratic model: $y = 0.0707x^2 - 0.183x + 1.45$, Coefficient of determination: 0.99871

Exponential model: $y = 0.8915(1.2106)^x$, Coefficient of determination: 0.99862

Power model: $y = 0.7865x^{0.6762}$, Coefficient of determination: 0.93130

(b) Quadratic model: Exponential model: Power model:

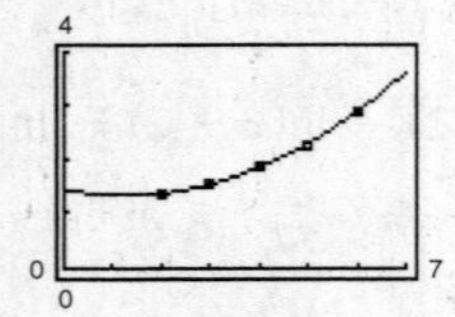

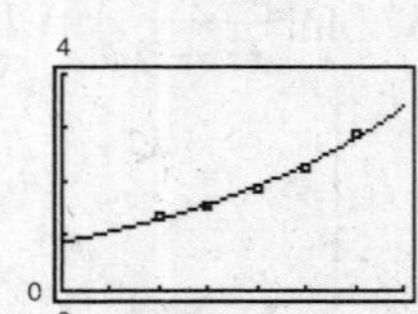

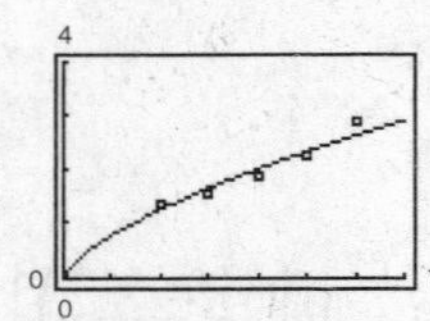

(c) The quadratic model is best because its coefficient of determination is closest to 1.

(d) For 2008, $x = 8$ and $y \approx \$4.51$. For 2010, $x = 10$ and $y \approx \$6.69$. Answers will vary.

Chapter 4 Chapter Test Solutions

1. (a) 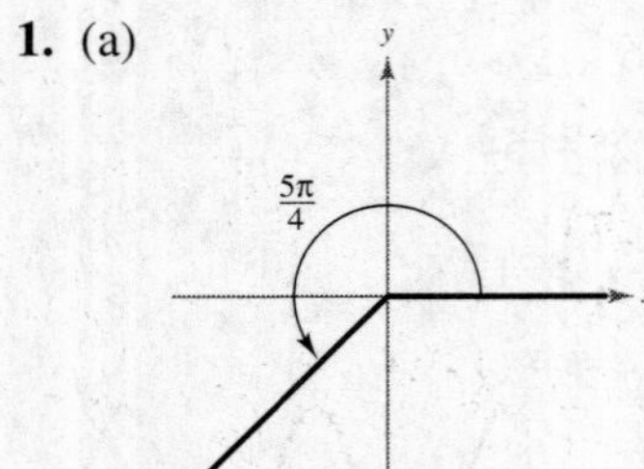

(b) $\frac{5\pi}{4} + 2\pi = \frac{13\pi}{4}$; $\frac{5\pi}{4} - 2\pi = -\frac{3\pi}{4}$

(c) $\frac{5\pi}{4} \cdot \frac{180}{\pi} = 225°$

2. $90 \text{ km/hr} = \dfrac{90 \text{ km/hr}}{60 \text{ min/h}} \cdot 1000 \text{ m/km}$

$= 1500 \text{ m/min}$

$1500 = \dfrac{s}{t} = \dfrac{r\theta}{t} \Longrightarrow \text{angular speed} = \dfrac{\theta}{t} = \dfrac{1500}{r} = \dfrac{1500}{1.25/2} = 2400 \text{ rad/min}$

3. $\sin \theta = \dfrac{4}{\sqrt{17}} = \dfrac{4\sqrt{17}}{17}$ $\csc \theta = \dfrac{\sqrt{17}}{4}$

$\cos \theta = -\dfrac{1}{\sqrt{17}} = -\dfrac{\sqrt{17}}{17}$ $\sec \theta = -\sqrt{17}$

$\tan \theta = -4$ $\cot \theta = -\dfrac{1}{4}$

4. $\tan \theta = \dfrac{7}{2}$

$\tan^2 \theta + 1 = \sec^2 \theta \Longrightarrow \sec \theta = \sqrt{\dfrac{49}{4} + 1} = \dfrac{\sqrt{53}}{2}$

$\cos \theta = \dfrac{2}{\sqrt{53}} = \dfrac{2\sqrt{53}}{53}$

$\sin \theta = \tan \theta \cos \theta = \dfrac{7\sqrt{53}}{53}$

$\csc \theta = \dfrac{53}{7\sqrt{53}} = \dfrac{\sqrt{53}}{7}$

$\cot \theta = \dfrac{2}{7}$

$\sec \theta = \dfrac{\sqrt{53}}{2}$

5. $\theta = 255°$

$\theta' = 255° - 180° = 75°$

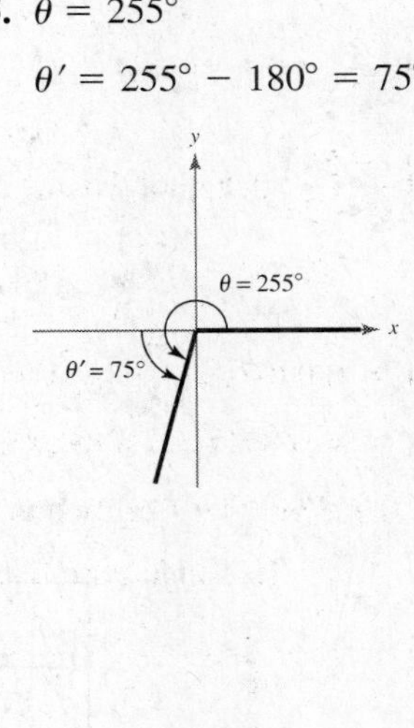

6. $\sec \theta = \dfrac{1}{\cos \theta} < 0 \Longrightarrow$ Quadrants II or III

$\tan \theta > 0 \Longrightarrow$ Quadrants I or III

Hence, Quadrant III.

7. $\cos \theta = -\dfrac{\sqrt{2}}{2}$

$\theta = 135°, 225°$

8. $\csc \theta = \dfrac{1}{\sin \theta} = 1.030 \Longrightarrow \sin \theta = \dfrac{1}{1.030}$ and θ in Quadrant I or II.

Using a calculator, $\theta = 1.33, 1.81$ radians.

9. $\cos \theta = -\dfrac{3}{5}$, $\sin \theta > 0$, Quadrant II

$\sin \theta = \dfrac{4}{5}$ $\tan \theta = -\dfrac{4}{3}$

$\sec \theta = -\dfrac{5}{3}$ $\csc \theta = \dfrac{5}{4}$

$\cot \theta = -\dfrac{3}{4}$

10. $g(x) = -2 \sin\left(x - \dfrac{\pi}{4}\right)$

Amplitude: 2, shifted $\pi/4$ to the right

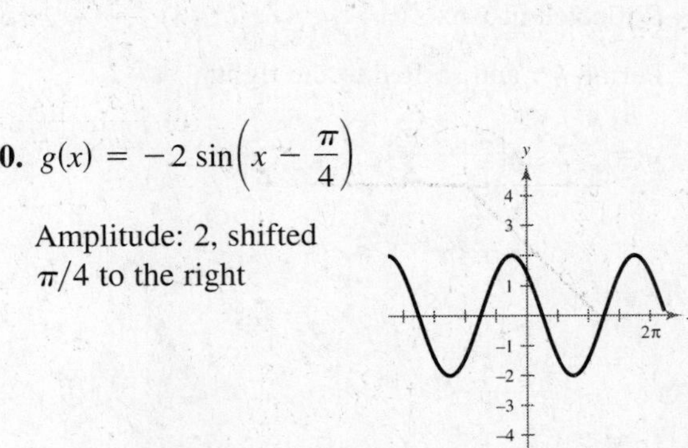

11. $f(x) = \frac{1}{2}\tan 4x$

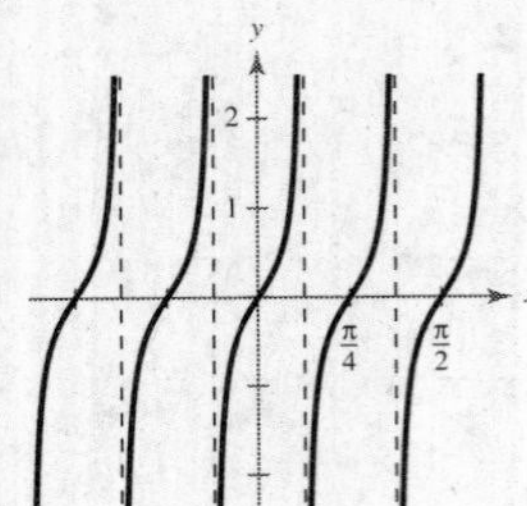

12. $f(x) = \frac{1}{2}\sec(x - \pi)$ is $y = \frac{1}{2}\sec x$ shifted π to the right.

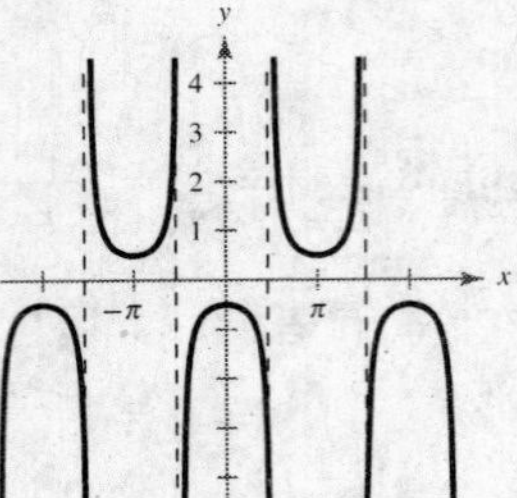

13. $f(x) = 2\cos(\pi - 2x) + 3 = 2\cos(2x - \pi) + 3$

Amplitude: 2

Shifted $\frac{\pi}{2}$ to the right, period π

Shifted vertically upward 3

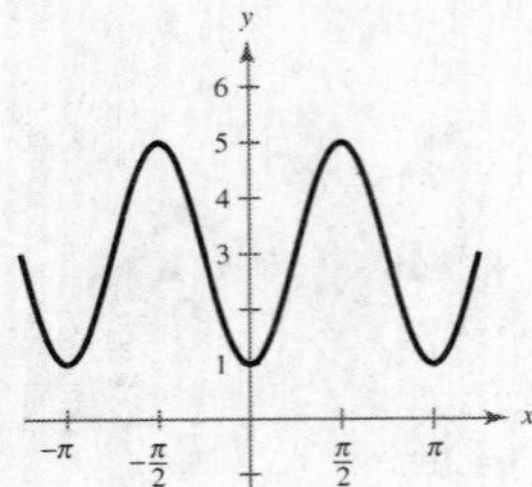

14. $f(x) = 2\csc\left(x + \frac{\pi}{2}\right)$

Shifted $\frac{\pi}{2}$ to the left

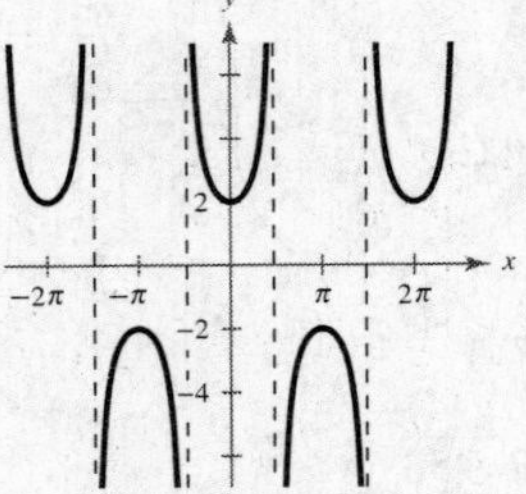

15. $f(x) = 2\cot\left(x - \frac{\pi}{2}\right)$

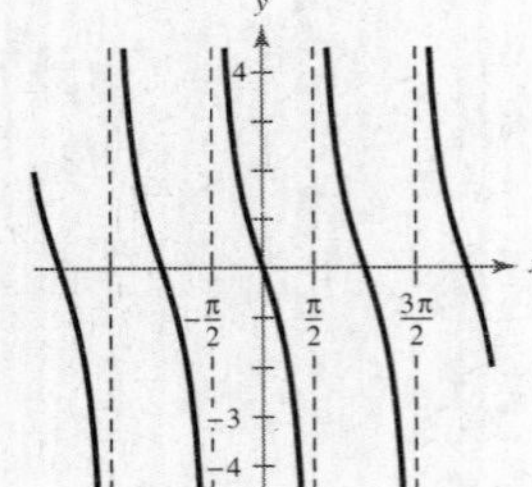

16.

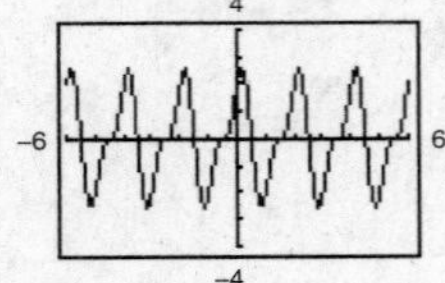

Period is 2.

17.

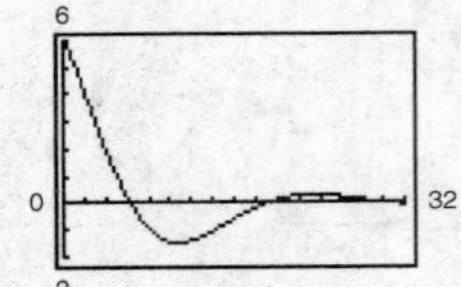

Not periodic

18. Amplitude: 2

Reflected in x-axis $\Rightarrow a = -2$

Period 4π and shifted to the right:

$y = -2\sin\left(\frac{x}{2} - \frac{\pi}{4}\right)$

19. Let $u = \arccos\frac{2}{3} \Rightarrow \cos u = \frac{2}{3}$.

Then $\tan\left(\arccos\frac{2}{3}\right) = \tan u = \frac{\sqrt{5}}{2}$.

20. $f(x) = 2 \arcsin\left(\frac{1}{2}x\right)$

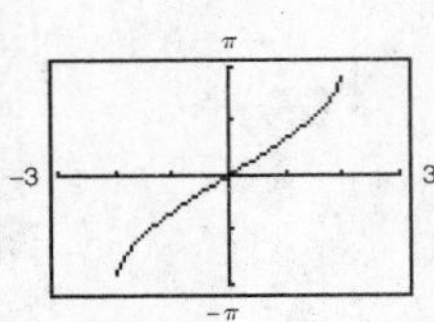

21. $f(x) = 2 \arccos x$

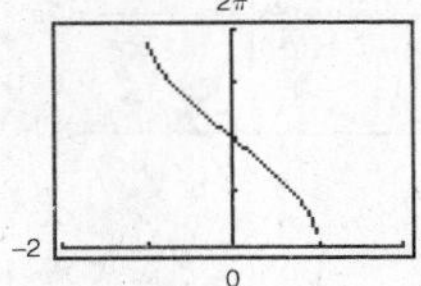

22. $f(x) = \arctan\left(\frac{x}{2}\right)$

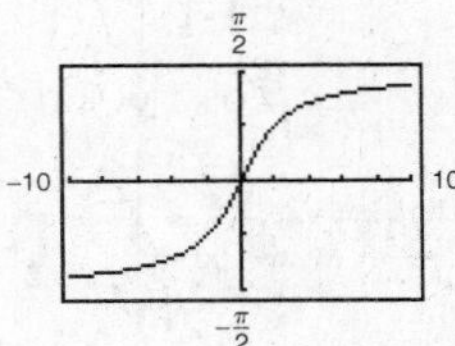

23. $\tan \theta = \frac{110}{160} \implies \theta \approx 34.5°$

Bearing: 214.5°

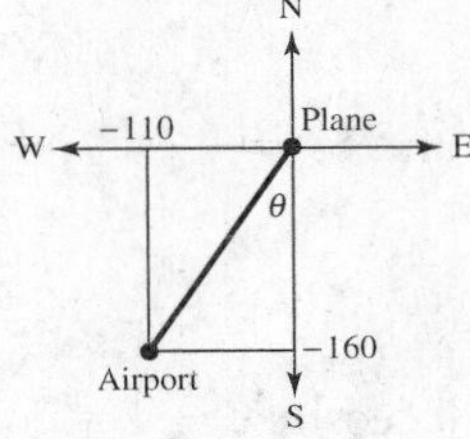

Chapter 5 Chapter Test Solutions

1. $\tan \theta = \frac{3}{2}, \cos \theta < 0 \implies \theta$ in Quadrant III

$$\sec^2 \theta = \tan^2 \theta + 1 = \frac{9}{4} + 1 = \frac{13}{4} \implies \sec \theta = -\frac{\sqrt{13}}{2}$$

$$\cos \theta = -\frac{2}{\sqrt{13}} = -\frac{2\sqrt{13}}{13}$$

$$\sin \theta = \tan \theta \cos \theta = \frac{3}{2}\left(-\frac{2\sqrt{13}}{13}\right) = -\frac{3\sqrt{13}}{13}$$

$$\csc \theta = -\frac{13}{3\sqrt{13}} = -\frac{\sqrt{13}}{3}$$

$$\cot \theta = \frac{2}{3}$$

2. $\csc^2 \beta(1 - \cos^2 \beta) = \frac{1}{\sin^2 \beta} \cdot \sin^2 \beta = 1$

3. $\dfrac{\sec^4 x - \tan^4 x}{\sec^2 x + \tan^2 x} = \dfrac{[(\sec^2 x) + (\tan^2 x)][\sec^2 x - \tan^2 x]}{\sec^2 x + \tan^2 x} = \sec^2 x - \tan^2 x = 1$

4. $\dfrac{\cos \theta}{\sin \theta} + \dfrac{\sin \theta}{\cos \theta} = \dfrac{\cos^2 \theta + \sin^2 \theta}{\sin \theta \cos \theta} = \dfrac{1}{\sin \theta \cos \theta} = \csc \theta \sec \theta$

5. Since $\tan^2 \theta = \sec^2 \theta - 1$ for all θ, then $\tan \theta = -\sqrt{\sec^2 \theta - 1}$ in Quadrants II and IV.

Thus, $\frac{\pi}{2} < \theta \le \pi$ and $\frac{3\pi}{2} < \theta < 2\pi$.

6. Conjecture: $y_1 = y_2$

Algebraically,

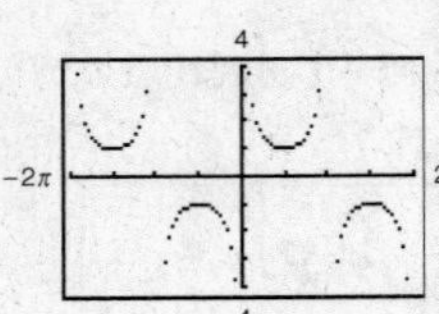

$$y_1 = \sin x + \cos x \cot x = \sin x + \frac{\cos^2 x}{\sin x}$$

$$= \frac{\sin^2 x + \cos^2 x}{\sin x}$$

$$= \frac{1}{\sin x} = \csc x.$$

7. $\sin \theta \cdot \sec \theta = \sin \theta \frac{1}{\cos \theta} = \tan \theta$

8. $\sec^2 x \tan^2 x + \sec^2 x = \sec^2 x(\tan^2 x + 1) = \sec^4 x$

9. $$\frac{\csc \alpha + \sec \alpha}{\sin \alpha + \cos \alpha} = \frac{\frac{1}{\sin \alpha} + \frac{1}{\cos \alpha}}{\sin \alpha + \cos \alpha} = \frac{\frac{\cos \alpha + \sin \alpha}{\sin \alpha \cdot \cos \alpha}}{(\sin \alpha + \cos \alpha)}$$

$$= \frac{1}{\sin \alpha \cos \alpha} = \frac{\cos^2 \alpha + \sin^2 \alpha}{\sin \alpha \cos \alpha}$$

$$= \frac{\cos \alpha}{\sin \alpha} + \frac{\sin \alpha}{\cos \alpha} = \cot \alpha + \tan \alpha$$

10. $$\cos\left(x + \frac{\pi}{2}\right) = \cos x \cos \frac{\pi}{2} - \sin x \sin \frac{\pi}{2}$$

$$= 0 - \sin x = -\sin x$$

11. $$\sin(n\pi + \theta) = \sin n\pi \cos \theta + \cos n\pi \sin \theta$$

$$= 0 + (-1)^n \sin \theta$$

$$= (-1)^n \sin \theta$$

12. $$(\sin x + \cos x)^2 = \sin^2 x + \cos^2 x + 2 \sin x \cos x$$

$$= 1 + \sin 2x$$

13. $$\tan 105° = \tan(45° + 60°)$$

$$= \frac{\tan 45° + \tan 60°}{1 - \tan 45° \tan 60°}$$

$$= \frac{1 + \sqrt{3}}{1 - \sqrt{3}} = -2 - \sqrt{3}$$

14. $$\sin^4 x \tan^2 x = \frac{\sin^6 x}{\cos^2 x}$$

$$= \frac{1}{32} \cdot \frac{(10 - 15 \cos 2x + 6 \cos 4x - \cos 6x)}{(1 + \cos 2x)/2}$$

$$= \frac{1}{16}\left[\frac{10 - 15 \cos 2x + 6 \cos 4x - \cos 6x}{1 + \cos 2x}\right]$$

15. $$\frac{\sin 4\theta}{1 + \cos 4\theta} = \tan \frac{4\theta}{2} = \tan 2\theta$$

16. $$4 \cos 2\theta \sin 4\theta = 4\left(\frac{1}{2}\right)[\sin(2\theta + 4\theta) - \sin(2\theta - 4\theta)]$$

$$= 2[\sin 6\theta - \sin(-2\theta)]$$

$$= 2[\sin 6\theta + \sin 2\theta]$$

17. $\sin 3\theta - \sin 4\theta = 2\cos\left(\frac{3\theta + 4\theta}{2}\right)\sin\left(\frac{3\theta - 4\theta}{2}\right)$

$= 2\cos\left(\frac{7\theta}{2}\right)\sin\left(\frac{-\theta}{2}\right)$

$= -2\cos\frac{7\theta}{2}\sin\frac{\theta}{2}$

18. $\tan^2 x + \tan x = 0$

$\tan x(\tan x + 1) = 0$

$\tan x = 0 \Rightarrow x = 0, \pi$

$\tan x + 1 = 0 \Rightarrow \tan x = -1 \Rightarrow x = \frac{3\pi}{4}, \frac{7\pi}{4}$

19. $\sin 2\alpha - \cos\alpha = 0$

$2\sin\alpha\cos\alpha - \cos\alpha = 0$

$\cos\alpha(2\sin\alpha - 1) = 0$

$\cos\alpha = 0 \Rightarrow a = \frac{\pi}{2}, \frac{3\pi}{2}$

$2\sin\alpha - 1 = 0 \Rightarrow \sin a = \frac{1}{2} \Rightarrow \alpha = \frac{\pi}{6}, \frac{5\pi}{6}$

20. $4\cos^2 x - 3 = 0$

$\cos^2 x = \frac{3}{4}$

$\cos x = \pm\frac{\sqrt{3}}{2}$

$x = \frac{\pi}{6}, \frac{5\pi}{6}, \frac{7\pi}{6}, \frac{11\pi}{6}$

21. $\csc^2 x - \csc x - 2 = 0$

$(\csc x - 2)(\csc x + 1) = 0$

$\csc x - 2 = 0 \Rightarrow \csc x = 2 \Rightarrow \sin x = \frac{1}{2} \Rightarrow x = \frac{\pi}{6}, \frac{5\pi}{6}$

$\csc x + 1 = 0 \Rightarrow \csc x = -1 \Rightarrow \sin x = -1 \Rightarrow x = \frac{3\pi}{2}$

22. $3\cos x - x = 0$

$x \approx 1.170, -2.663, -2.938$

23. $\sin 2u = 2\sin u\cos u = 2\frac{2}{\sqrt{5}} \cdot \frac{1}{\sqrt{5}} = \frac{4}{5}$

$\tan 2u = \frac{2\tan u}{1 - \tan^2 u} = \frac{2(2)}{1 - 2^2} = -\frac{4}{3}$

$\cos 2u = 1 - 2\sin^2 u = 1 - 2\left(\frac{2}{\sqrt{5}}\right)^2 = -\frac{3}{5}$

24. $n = \frac{\sin[(\theta/2) + (\alpha/2)]}{\sin(\theta/2)}$

$\frac{3}{2} = \frac{\sin[(\theta/2) + 30°]}{\sin(\theta/2)}$

$3\sin\frac{\theta}{2} = 2\left[\sin\frac{\theta}{2}\cos 30° + \cos\frac{\theta}{2}\sin 30°\right]$

$3\sin\frac{\theta}{2} = \sqrt{3}\sin\frac{\theta}{2} + \cos\frac{\theta}{2}$

$(3 - \sqrt{3})\sin\frac{\theta}{2} = \cos\frac{\theta}{2}$

$\tan\frac{\theta}{2} = \frac{1}{3 - \sqrt{3}}$

$\frac{\theta}{2} = \arctan\left(\frac{1}{3 - \sqrt{3}}\right) \approx 38.26°$

$\theta \approx 76.52°$

Chapter 6 Chapter Test Solutions

1. $A = 36°, B = 98°, c = 16$

$C = 180° - 36° - 98° = 46°$

$a = \frac{c}{\sin C}\sin A \approx 13.07$

$b = \frac{a}{\sin A}\sin B \approx 22.03$

2. $a = 4, b = 8, c = 10$

$\cos C = \frac{a^2 + b^2 - c^2}{2ab} = \frac{-20}{64} \Rightarrow C \approx 108.21°$

$\cos B = \frac{a^2 + c^2 - b^2}{2ac} = \frac{52}{80} \Rightarrow B \approx 49.46°$

$A = 180° - C - B \approx 22.33°$

3. $A = 35°, b = 8, c = 12$

$a^2 = b^2 + c^2 - 2\,bc \cdot \cos A$

$= 64 + 144 - 2(8)(12)\cos 35° \approx 50.7228$

$a \approx 7.12$

$\sin B = \frac{\sin A}{a} b \approx 0.6443 \Rightarrow B \approx 40.11°$

$C = 180° - A - B \approx 104.89°$

4. $A = 25°, b = 28, a = 18$

$\sin B = \frac{\sin A}{a} b = \frac{(\sin 25°)28}{18} \approx 0.6574$

$B_1 \approx 41.10°$ or $B_2 \approx 180° - 41.1° \approx 138.90°$

Case 1: $B_1 = 41.10°$

$C = 180° - A - B_1 \approx 113.90°$

$c = \frac{a}{\sin A}\sin C \approx 38.94$

Case 2: $B_2 = 138.90°$

$C = 180° - A - B_2 \approx 16.10°$

$c = \frac{a}{\sin A}\sin C \approx 11.81$

5. No triangle possible $(5.2 \leq 10.1)$

6. $\sin B = \frac{\sin A}{a} b = \frac{\sin 150°}{9.4} 4.8$

$\approx 0.2553 \Rightarrow B \approx 14.8°$

$C = 180° - A - B = 15.2°$

$c = \frac{a}{\sin A}\sin C \approx 4.9$

7. Law of Cosines:

$a^2 = b^2 + c^2 - 2bc\cos\theta$

$= 480^2 + 565^2 - 2(480)(565)\cos 80°$

$= 455{,}438.2 \Rightarrow a \approx 674.9$ ft

8. $s = \frac{a + b + c}{2} = \frac{55 + 85 + 100}{2} = 120$

$A = \sqrt{s(s - a)(s - b)(s - c)}$

$= \sqrt{120(65)(35)(20)}$

≈ 2336.7 square meters

9. $\mathbf{w} = \langle 4 - (-8), 1 - (-12)\rangle = \langle 12, 13\rangle$

$\|\mathbf{w}\| = \sqrt{12^2 + 13^2} = \sqrt{313} \approx 17.69$

10. (a) $2\mathbf{v} + \mathbf{u} = 2\langle -2, -8\rangle + \langle 0, -4\rangle = \langle -4, -20\rangle$

(b) $\mathbf{u} - 3\mathbf{v} = \langle 0, -4\rangle - 3\langle -2, -8\rangle = \langle 6, 20\rangle$

(c) $5\mathbf{u} - \mathbf{v} = 5\langle 0, -4\rangle - \langle -2, -8\rangle = \langle 2, -12\rangle$

11. (a) $2\mathbf{v} + \mathbf{u} = 2\langle -1, -10\rangle + \langle -2, -3\rangle$

$= \langle -4, -23\rangle$

(b) $\mathbf{u} - 3\mathbf{v} = \langle -2, -3\rangle - 3\langle -1, -10\rangle = \langle 1, 27\rangle$

(c) $5\mathbf{u} - \mathbf{v} = 5\langle -2, -3\rangle - \langle -1, -10\rangle$

$= \langle -9, -5\rangle$

12. (a) $2\mathbf{v} + \mathbf{u} = 2(6\mathbf{i} + 9\mathbf{j}) + (\mathbf{i} - \mathbf{j}) = 13\mathbf{i} + 17\mathbf{j}$

(b) $\mathbf{u} - 3\mathbf{v} = (\mathbf{i} - \mathbf{j}) - 3(6\mathbf{i} + 9\mathbf{j}) = -17\mathbf{i} - 28\mathbf{j}$

(c) $5\mathbf{u} - \mathbf{v} = 5(\mathbf{i} - \mathbf{j}) - (6\mathbf{i} + 9\mathbf{j}) = -\mathbf{i} - 14\mathbf{j}$

13. (a) $2\mathbf{v} + \mathbf{u} = 2(-\mathbf{i} - 2\mathbf{j}) + (2\mathbf{i} + 3\mathbf{j}) = -\mathbf{j}$

(b) $\mathbf{u} - 3\mathbf{v} = (2\mathbf{i} + 3\mathbf{j}) - 3(-\mathbf{i} - 2\mathbf{j}) = 5\mathbf{i} + 9\mathbf{j}$

(c) $5\mathbf{u} - \mathbf{v} = 5(2\mathbf{i} + 3\mathbf{j}) - (-\mathbf{i} - 2\mathbf{j}) = 11\mathbf{i} + 17\mathbf{j}$

14. Unit vector $= \dfrac{\mathbf{v}}{\|\mathbf{v}\|} = \dfrac{1}{\sqrt{49 + 16}}\langle 7, 4\rangle$

$= \left\langle \dfrac{7}{\sqrt{65}}, \dfrac{4}{\sqrt{65}} \right\rangle = \dfrac{\sqrt{65}}{65}\langle 7, 4\rangle$

15. $12\dfrac{\langle 3, -5\rangle}{\|\langle 3, -5\rangle\|} = \dfrac{12}{\sqrt{34}}\langle 3, -5\rangle = \left\langle \dfrac{36}{\sqrt{34}}, \dfrac{-60}{\sqrt{34}} \right\rangle$

$= \left\langle \dfrac{18\sqrt{34}}{17}, \dfrac{-30\sqrt{34}}{17} \right\rangle$

16. $250(\cos 45°\mathbf{i} + \sin 45°\mathbf{j})$, first force

$130(\cos(-60°)\mathbf{i} + \sin(-60°)\mathbf{j})$, second force

Resultant: $\left[250\left(\dfrac{\sqrt{2}}{2}\right) + 130\left(\dfrac{1}{2}\right)\right]\mathbf{i} + \left[250\left(\dfrac{\sqrt{2}}{2}\right) + 130\left(-\dfrac{\sqrt{3}}{2}\right)\right]\mathbf{j}$

$= \left(125\sqrt{2} + 65\right)\mathbf{i} + \left(125\sqrt{2} - 65\sqrt{3}\right)\mathbf{j}$

Magnitude: $\sqrt{\left(125\sqrt{2} + 65\right)^2 + \left(125\sqrt{2} - 65\sqrt{3}\right)^2} \approx 250.15$

Direction: $\theta = \arctan\left(\dfrac{125\sqrt{2} - 65\sqrt{3}}{125\sqrt{2} + 65}\right) \Rightarrow \theta \approx 14.9°$

17. $\mathbf{u} \cdot \mathbf{v} = \langle -9, 4\rangle \cdot \langle 1, 3\rangle = -9 + 12 = 3$

18. $\cos\theta = \dfrac{\mathbf{u} \cdot \mathbf{v}}{\|\mathbf{u}\|\,\|\mathbf{v}\|} = \dfrac{-8}{\sqrt{53}(4)} \Rightarrow \theta \approx 105.9°$

19. No, the dot product is 24, not 0.

20. $\text{proj}_{\mathbf{v}}\mathbf{u} = \dfrac{-37}{26}\langle -5, -1\rangle = \left\langle \dfrac{185}{26}, \dfrac{37}{26} \right\rangle = \mathbf{w}_1$

$\mathbf{w}_2 = \mathbf{u} - \mathbf{w}_1 = \langle 6, 7\rangle - \left\langle \dfrac{185}{26}, \dfrac{37}{26} \right\rangle = \left\langle \dfrac{-29}{26}, \dfrac{145}{26} \right\rangle$

$\mathbf{u} = \mathbf{w}_1 + \mathbf{w}_2$

21. $|z| = 2\sqrt{2}$

$z = 2\sqrt{2}\left(\cos\dfrac{3\pi}{4} + i\sin\dfrac{3\pi}{4}\right)$

22. $100(\cos 240° + i\sin 240°) = -50 - 50\sqrt{3}i$

23. $\left[3\left(\cos\dfrac{5\pi}{6} + i\sin\dfrac{5\pi}{6}\right)\right]^8 = 3^8\left(\cos\dfrac{40\pi}{6} + i\sin\dfrac{40\pi}{6}\right)$

$= 3^8\left(-\dfrac{1}{2} + \dfrac{\sqrt{3}}{2}i\right)$

$= -3280.5 + 3280.5\sqrt{3}i = -\dfrac{6561}{2} + \dfrac{6561}{2}\sqrt{3}i$

24. $(3 - 3i)^6 = \left[3\sqrt{2}\left(\cos\dfrac{7\pi}{4} + i\sin\dfrac{7\pi}{4}\right)\right]^6$

$= 5832\left(\cos\dfrac{42\pi}{4} + i\sin\dfrac{42\pi}{4}\right) = 5832i$

25. $128(1 + \sqrt{3}i) = 256\left(\frac{1}{2} + \frac{\sqrt{3}}{2}i\right) = 256\left(\cos\frac{\pi}{3} + i\sin\frac{\pi}{3}\right)$

Fourth roots: $\sqrt[4]{256}\left(\cos\frac{(\pi/3) + 2\pi k}{4} + i\sin\frac{(\pi/3) + 2k\pi}{4}\right),\ k = 0, 1, 2, 3$

Four roots are: $4\left(\cos\frac{\pi}{12} + i\sin\frac{\pi}{12}\right) \approx 3.8637 + 1.0353i$

$4\left(\cos\frac{7\pi}{12} + i\sin\frac{7\pi}{12}\right) \approx -1.0353 + 3.8637i$

$4\left(\cos\frac{13\pi}{12} + i\sin\frac{13\pi}{12}\right) \approx -3.8637 - 1.0353i$

$4\left(\cos\frac{19\pi}{12} + i\sin\frac{19\pi}{12}\right) \approx 1.0353 - 3.8637i$

26. $x^4 = 625i$

Fourth roots of $625i = 625\left(\cos\frac{\pi}{2} + i\sin\frac{\pi}{2}\right)$

$\sqrt[4]{625}\left[\cos\left(\frac{(\pi/2) + 2\pi k}{4}\right) + i\sin\left(\frac{(\pi/2) + 2\pi k}{4}\right)\right],\ k = 0, 1, 2, 3$

Four roots are: $5\left(\cos\frac{\pi}{8} + i\sin\frac{\pi}{8}\right)$

$5\left(\cos\frac{5\pi}{8} + i\sin\frac{5\pi}{8}\right)$

$5\left(\cos\frac{9\pi}{8} + i\sin\frac{9\pi}{8}\right)$

$5\left(\cos\frac{13\pi}{8} + i\sin\frac{13\pi}{8}\right)$

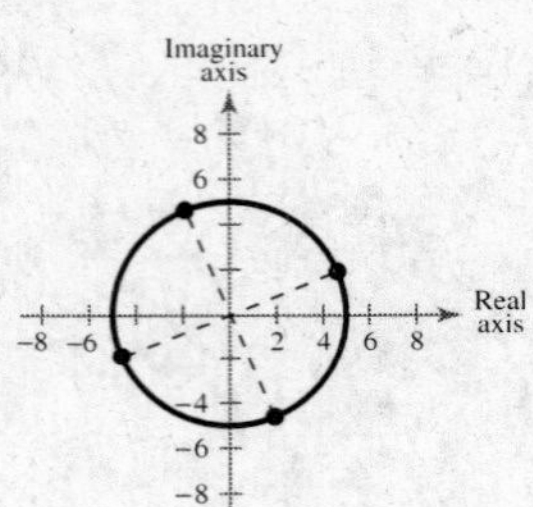

Chapters 4–6 Cumulative Test Solutions

1. $\theta = -150°$

(a)

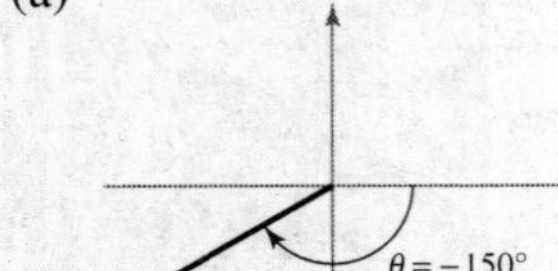

(b) $-150° + 360° = 210°$

(c) $(-150°)\frac{\pi}{180°} = -\frac{5}{6}\pi$ radians

(d) $\theta' = 30°$

(e) $\sin\theta = -\frac{1}{2}$ $\qquad \csc\theta = -2$

$\cos\theta = -\frac{\sqrt{3}}{2}$ $\qquad \sec\theta = -\frac{2}{\sqrt{3}} = -\frac{2\sqrt{3}}{3}$

$\tan\theta = \frac{\sqrt{3}}{3}$ $\qquad \cot\theta = \frac{3}{\sqrt{3}} = \sqrt{3}$

2. $2.55 \text{ rad} = 2.55\left(\dfrac{180°}{\pi}\right) \approx 146.1°$

3. $\sec^2\theta = 1 + \tan^2\theta = 1 + \left(-\dfrac{12}{5}\right)^2 = \dfrac{169}{25}$

$\sec\theta = -\dfrac{13}{5}$ (since θ in Quadrant II)

$\cos\theta = -\dfrac{5}{13}$

4. $f(x) = 3 - 2\sin \pi x$

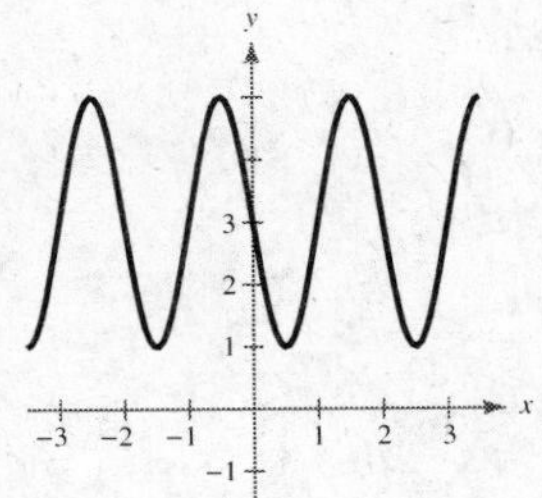

5. $f(x) = \tan(3x)$

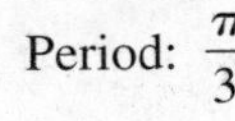

Period: $\dfrac{\pi}{3}$

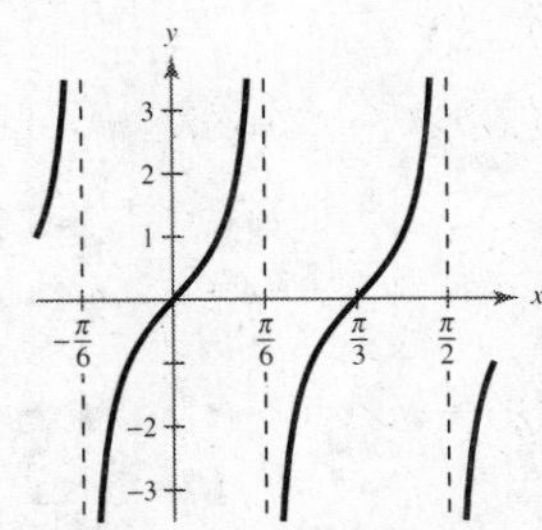

6. $f(x) = \dfrac{1}{2}\sec(x + \pi)$

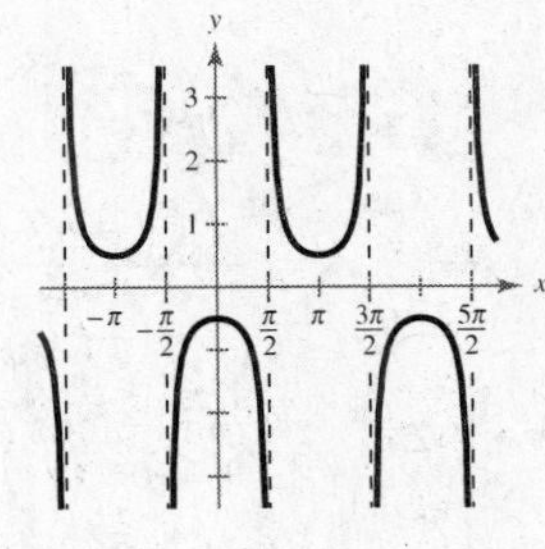

7. Amplitude: 3

Cosine curve reflected about the x-axis

Period: $2 \implies h(x) = -3\cos(\pi x)$

Answer: $a = -3, b = \pi, c = 0$

8. Let $\theta = \arctan\dfrac{3}{4}$.

$\tan\theta = \dfrac{3}{4}$

$\sin\left(\arctan\dfrac{3}{4}\right) = \dfrac{3}{5}$

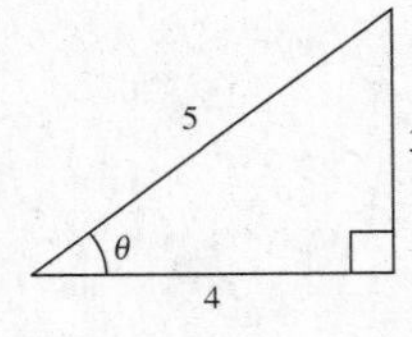

9. Let $\arcsin\left(-\dfrac{1}{2}\right) = \theta$.

$\sin\theta = -\dfrac{1}{2}$

$\theta = -\dfrac{\pi}{6}$

$\tan\left(-\dfrac{\pi}{6}\right) = -\dfrac{\sqrt{3}}{3}$

10. Let $\theta = \arctan 2x$.

$\tan\theta = 2x$

$\sin(\arctan 2x) = \sin\theta = \dfrac{2x}{\sqrt{1 + 4x^2}}$

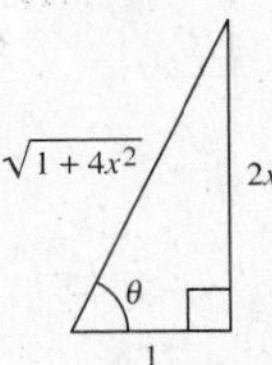

11. $\dfrac{\sin\theta - 1}{\cos\theta} - \dfrac{\cos\theta}{\sin\theta - 1} = \dfrac{\sin^2\theta - 2\sin\theta + 1 - \cos^2\theta}{\cos\theta(\sin\theta - 1)}$

$= \dfrac{\sin^2\theta - 2\sin\theta + \sin^2\theta}{\cos\theta(\sin\theta - 1)}$

$= \dfrac{2\sin\theta(\sin\theta - 1)}{\cos\theta(\sin\theta - 1)} = 2\tan\theta$

12. $\cot^2\alpha(\sec^2\alpha - 1) = \cot^2\alpha(\tan^2\alpha) = 1$

13. $\sin(x + y)\sin(x - y) = [\sin x \cos y + \cos x \sin y][\sin x \cos y - \sin y \cos x]$

$$= \sin^2 x \cos^2 y - \sin^2 y \cos^2 x$$
$$= \sin^2 x(1 - \sin^2 y) - \sin^2 y(1 - \sin^2 x)$$
$$= \sin^2 x - \sin^2 x \sin^2 y - \sin^2 y + \sin^2 y \sin^2 x$$
$$= \sin^2 x - \sin^2 y$$

14. $\sin^2 x \cos^2 x = \frac{1}{4}(2 \sin x \cos x)^2$

$$= \frac{1}{4}(\sin 2x)^2$$
$$= \frac{1}{4} \cdot \frac{1 - \cos 4x}{2}$$
$$= \frac{1}{8}(1 - \cos 4x)$$

15. $\sin^2 x + 2 \sin x + 1 = 0$

$$(\sin x + 1)^2 = 0$$
$$\sin x + 1 = 0$$
$$\sin x = -1$$
$$x = \frac{3\pi}{2} + 2n\pi$$

16. $3 \tan \theta - \cot \theta = 0$

$$3 \tan \theta - \frac{1}{\tan \theta} = 0$$
$$3 \tan^2 \theta - 1 = 0$$
$$\tan \theta = \pm\frac{1}{\sqrt{3}} \implies \theta = \frac{\pi}{6} + n\pi, \frac{5\pi}{6} + n\pi$$

17. Graph $y = \cos^2 x - 5 \cos x - 1$ on $[0, 2\pi)$.

Roots are $x \approx 1.7646, 4.5186$.

18.

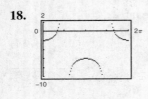

Zeros: $x \approx 1.047, 5.236$

Algebraically:
$$\frac{1 + \sin x}{\cos x} + \frac{\cos x}{1 + \sin x} = 4$$
$$\frac{1 + 2 \sin x + \sin^2 x + \cos^2 x}{\cos x(1 + \sin x)} = 4$$
$$\frac{2 + 2 \sin x}{\cos x(1 + \sin x)} = 4$$
$$\frac{2}{\cos x} = 4$$
$$\cos x = \frac{1}{2}$$
$$x = \frac{\pi}{3}, \frac{5\pi}{3}$$

19.

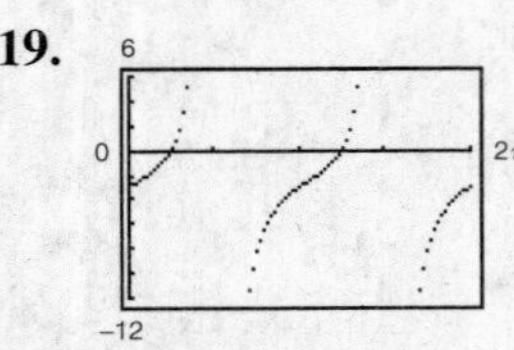

Zeros: $x \approx 0.785, 3.927$

Algebraically:
$$\tan^3 x - \tan^2 x + 3 \tan x - 3 = 0$$
$$\tan^2 x(\tan x - 1) + 3(\tan x - 1) = 0$$
$$(\tan^2 x + 3)(\tan x - 1) = 0$$
$$\tan x = 1 \implies x = \frac{\pi}{4}, \frac{5\pi}{4}$$

20. $\sin u = \dfrac{12}{13} \Rightarrow \cos u = \dfrac{5}{13} \Rightarrow \tan u = \dfrac{12}{5}$

$\cos v = \dfrac{3}{5} \Rightarrow \sin v = \dfrac{4}{5} \Rightarrow \tan v = \dfrac{4}{3}$

$\tan(u - v) = \dfrac{\tan u - \tan v}{1 + \tan u \tan v} = \dfrac{(12/5) - (4/3)}{1 + (12/5)(4/3)} = \dfrac{16}{63}$

21. $\tan(2\theta) = \dfrac{2 \tan \theta}{1 - \tan^2 \theta} = \dfrac{2(1/2)}{1 - (1/4)} = \dfrac{4}{3}$

22. $\sec^2 \theta = \tan^2 \theta + 1 = \dfrac{25}{9} \Rightarrow \sec \theta = -\dfrac{5}{3} \Rightarrow \cos \theta = -\dfrac{3}{5}$ (Quadrant III)

$\sin \dfrac{\theta}{2} = \pm\sqrt{\dfrac{1 - \cos \theta}{2}} = \pm\dfrac{2}{\sqrt{5}} = \pm\dfrac{2\sqrt{5}}{5}$

$\dfrac{\theta}{2}$ in Quadrant II: $\sin \dfrac{\theta}{2} = \dfrac{2\sqrt{5}}{5}$

23. $\cos 8x + \cos 4x = 2 \cos\left(\dfrac{8x + 4x}{2}\right) \cos\left(\dfrac{8x - 4x}{2}\right)$

$= 2 \cos 6x \cos 2x$

24. $\tan x(1 - \sin^2 x) = \dfrac{\sin x}{\cos x} \cos^2 x = \sin x \cos x$

$= \dfrac{1}{2}(2 \sin x \cos x) = \dfrac{1}{2} \sin 2x$

25. $\sin 3\theta \sin \theta = \frac{1}{2}[\cos(3\theta - \theta) - \cos(3\theta + \theta)]$

$= \frac{1}{2}(\cos 2\theta - \cos 4\theta)$

26. $\sin 3x \cos 2x = \frac{1}{2}(\sin(3x + 2x) + \sin(3x - 2x))$

$= \frac{1}{2}(\sin 5x + \sin x)$

27. $\dfrac{2 \cos 3x}{\sin 4x - \sin 2x} = \dfrac{2 \cos 3x}{2 \cos 3x \cdot \sin x} = \dfrac{1}{\sin x} = \csc x$

28. $\sin B = \dfrac{\sin A}{a} b = 0.2569 \Rightarrow B \approx 14.9°$

$C = 180° - 46° - 14.9° = 119.1°$

$c = \dfrac{a}{\sin A}(\sin C) \approx 17.0$

29. $A = 32°, b = 8, c = 10$

$a^2 = b^2 + c^2 - 2bc \cos A$

$= 64 + 100 - 2(8)(10) \cos 32°$

$= 28.3123 \Rightarrow a \approx 5.32$

$\sin B = \dfrac{b \sin A}{a} \approx 0.7967 \Rightarrow B \approx 52.82°$

$C = 180° - B - A = 95.18°$

30. $B = 180° - 24° - 101° = 55°$

$b = \dfrac{a}{\sin A} \sin B \approx 20.14$

$c = \dfrac{a}{\sin A} \sin C \approx 24.13$

31. $\cos A = \dfrac{b^2 + c^2 - a^2}{2bc} = 0.8982 \Rightarrow A \approx 26.1°$

$\cos B = \dfrac{a^2 + c^2 - b^2}{2ac} = 0.8355 \Rightarrow B \approx 33.3°$

$C = 180° - 26.1° - 33.3° = 120.6°$

32. $A = \dfrac{1}{2}bh = \dfrac{1}{2}\, 19 \cdot 14 \sin 82°$

≈ 131.7 sq. in.

33. $s = \frac{12 + 16 + 18}{2} = 23$

$\text{Area} = \sqrt{s(s-a)(s-b)(s-c)}$

$= \sqrt{23(11)(7)(5)} \approx 94.10$ sq. in.

34. $\mathbf{u} = \langle 3, 5\rangle = 3\mathbf{i} + 5\mathbf{j}$

35. $\mathbf{v} = \mathbf{i} - 2\mathbf{j}$

$\|\mathbf{v}\| = \sqrt{1+4} = \sqrt{5}$

Unit vector: $\frac{1}{\sqrt{5}}\mathbf{i} - \frac{2}{\sqrt{5}}\mathbf{j} = \left\langle \frac{\sqrt{5}}{5}, \frac{-2\sqrt{5}}{5}\right\rangle$

36. $\mathbf{u} \cdot \mathbf{v} = 3(1) + 4(-2) = -5$

37.

$$\begin{aligned} \mathbf{u} \cdot \mathbf{v} &= 0 \\ \langle 1, 2k\rangle \cdot \langle 2, -1\rangle &= 0 \\ 2 - 2k &= 0 \\ k &= 1 \end{aligned}$$

38. $\text{proj}_{\mathbf{v}}\mathbf{u} = \frac{8-10}{26}\langle 1, 5\rangle = \left\langle -\frac{1}{13}, -\frac{5}{13}\right\rangle = \mathbf{w}_1$

$\mathbf{w}_2 = \mathbf{u} - \mathbf{w}_1 = \langle 8, -2\rangle - \left\langle -\frac{1}{13}, -\frac{5}{13}\right\rangle$

$= \left\langle \frac{105}{13}, -\frac{21}{13}\right\rangle$

$\mathbf{u} = \mathbf{w}_1 + \mathbf{w}_2$

39. $|z| = 3\sqrt{2},\ \theta = \frac{3\pi}{4}$: $3\sqrt{2}\left(\cos\frac{3\pi}{4} + i\sin\frac{3\pi}{4}\right)$

40. $8\left(-\frac{\sqrt{3}}{2} + \frac{1}{2}i\right) = -4\sqrt{3} + 4i$

41.

$$\begin{aligned} [4(\cos 30^\circ + i\sin 30^\circ)][6(\cos 120^\circ + i\sin 120^\circ)] &= 24(\cos(30 + 120^\circ) + i\sin(30^\circ + 120^\circ)) \\ &= 24(\cos 150^\circ + i\sin 150^\circ) \\ &= 24\left(-\frac{\sqrt{3}}{2} + i\frac{1}{2}\right) = -12\sqrt{3} + 12i \end{aligned}$$

42. $2 + i = \sqrt{5}(\cos\theta + i\sin\theta)$, where $\tan\theta = \frac{1}{2} \Rightarrow \theta \approx 0.4636$

Square roots: $z_1 = 5^{1/4}\left(\cos\frac{\theta}{2} + i\sin\frac{\theta}{2}\right)$

$z_2 = 5^{1/4}\left(\cos\left(\frac{\theta + 2\pi}{2}\right) + i\sin\left(\frac{\theta + 2\pi}{2}\right)\right)$

$z_1 \approx 1.4533 + 0.3436i$

$z_2 \approx -1.4553 - 0.3436i$

43. $1 = 1(\cos 0 + i\sin 0)$

$\cos\left(\frac{0 + 2\pi k}{3}\right) + i\sin\left(\frac{0 + 2\pi k}{3}\right),\quad k = 0, 1, 2$

$k = 0$: $\cos 0 + i\sin 0 = 1$

$k = 1$: $\cos\frac{2\pi}{3} + i\sin\frac{2\pi}{3} = -\frac{1}{2} + \frac{\sqrt{3}}{2}i$

$k = 2$: $\cos\frac{4\pi}{3} + i\sin\frac{4\pi}{3} = -\frac{1}{2} - \frac{\sqrt{3}}{2}i$

44. $x^5 = -243$

Five fifth roots of $-243 = 243(\cos\pi + i\sin\pi)$ are:

$$\sqrt[5]{243}\left(\cos\frac{\pi + 2\pi k}{5} + i\sin\frac{\pi + 2\pi k}{5}\right);\ k = 0, 1, 2, 3, 4$$

$$3\left(\cos\frac{\pi}{5} + i\sin\frac{\pi}{5}\right)$$

$$3\left(\cos\frac{3\pi}{5} + i\sin\frac{3\pi}{5}\right)$$

$$3\left(\cos\frac{5\pi}{5} + i\sin\frac{5\pi}{5}\right) = -3$$

$$3\left(\cos\frac{7\pi}{5} + i\sin\frac{7\pi}{5}\right)$$

$$3\left(\cos\frac{9\pi}{5} + i\sin\frac{9\pi}{5}\right)$$

45. $\tan 18° = \dfrac{h}{200}$

$\tan 16° 45' = \dfrac{k}{200}$

Hence,

$f = h - k = 200\tan 18° - 200\tan 16° 45'$

$\approx 4.8 \approx 5$ feet.

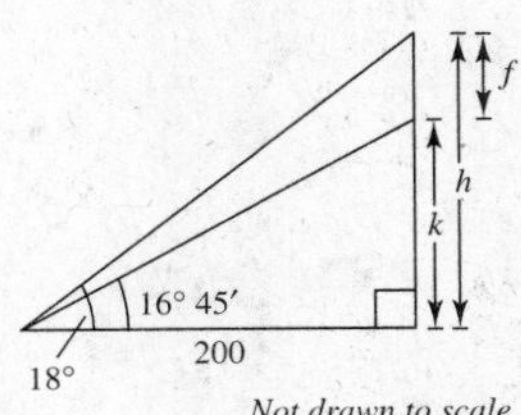

Not drawn to scale

46. $y = 4\cos\left(\frac{\pi}{4}t\right)$ or $y = 4\sin\left(\frac{\pi}{4}t\right)$

Amplitude: 4

Period $\dfrac{2\pi}{(\pi/4)} = 8$

47. Add the two vectors:

$500(\cos 60°\mathbf{i} + \sin 60°\mathbf{j}) + 50(\cos 30°\mathbf{i} + \sin 30°\mathbf{j}) = \left(250 + 25\sqrt{3}\right)\mathbf{i} + \left(250\sqrt{3} + 25\right)\mathbf{j}$

$\tan\theta = \dfrac{250\sqrt{3} + 25}{250 + 25\sqrt{3}} \approx 1.56 \Rightarrow \theta \approx 57.4°$

Direction: N 32.6° E or 32.6° in airplane navigation

Speed $= \sqrt{\left(250 + 25\sqrt{3}\right)^2 + \left(250\sqrt{3} + 25\right)^2} \approx 543.9$ km/hr

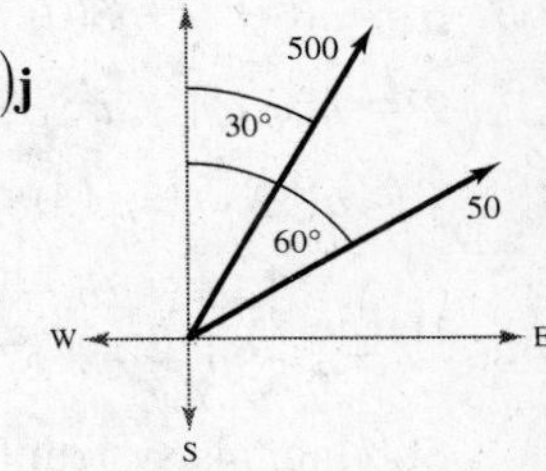

48. $\cos A = \dfrac{60^2 + 125^2 - 100^2}{2(60)(125)} = 0.615 \Rightarrow A \approx 52.05°$

$\cos B = \dfrac{100^2 + 125^2 - 60^2}{2(100)(125)} = 0.881 \Rightarrow B \approx 28.24$

Angle between vectors $= A + B \approx 80.3°$

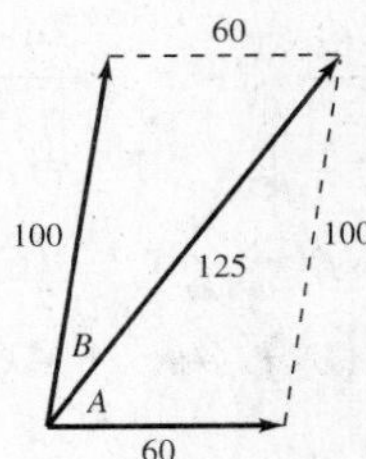

Chapter 7 Chapter Test Solutions

1. $x - y = 6 \Rightarrow y = x - 6$. Then

$3x + 5(x - 6) = 2 \Rightarrow$

$8x = 32 \Rightarrow x = 4, y = 4 - 6 = -2.$

Answer: $(4, -2)$

2. $y = x - 1 = (x - 1)^3 \Rightarrow x = 1$ or

$1 = (x - 1)^2 = x^2 - 2x + 1 \Rightarrow x^2 - 2x = 0.$

Thus, $x = 1$ or $x(x - 2) = 0 \Rightarrow x = 0, 1, 2.$

Answer: $(0, -1), (1, 0), (2, 1)$

3. $x - y = 3 \Rightarrow y = x - 3 \Rightarrow 4x - (x - 3)^2 = 7$

$$4x - (x^2 - 6x + 9) = 7$$
$$x^2 - 10x + 16 = 0$$
$$(x - 2)(x - 8) = 0$$

$x = 2, 8$

Answer: $(2, -1), (8, 5)$

4. $\begin{cases} 2x + 5y = -11 & \text{Equation 1} \\ 5x - y = 19 & \text{Equation 2} \end{cases}$

$-\frac{5}{2}$ times Eq. 1 added to Eq. 2 produces

$-\frac{27}{2}y = \frac{93}{2} \Rightarrow y = -\frac{31}{9}$.

Then $2x + 5\left(-\frac{31}{9}\right) = -11 \Rightarrow x = \frac{28}{9}$.

Answer: $\left(\frac{28}{9}, -\frac{31}{9}\right)$

5. $\begin{cases} 3x - 2y + z = 0 \\ 6x + 2y + 3z = -2 \\ 3x - 4y + 5z = 5 \end{cases}$

$\begin{cases} 3x - 2y + z = 0 \\ 6y + z = -2 \\ -2y + 4z = 5 \end{cases}$

$\begin{cases} 3x - 2y + z = 0 \\ y - 2z = -\frac{5}{2} \\ 13z = 13 \end{cases}$

$z = 1$

$y = 2(1) - \frac{5}{2} = -\frac{1}{2}$

$x = \frac{1}{3}\left(-1 + 2\left(-\frac{1}{2}\right)\right) = \frac{1}{3}(-2) = -\frac{2}{3}$

Answer: $\left(-\frac{2}{3}, -\frac{1}{2}, 1\right)$

6. $\begin{cases} x - 4y - z = 3 \\ 2x - 5y + z = 0 \\ 3x - 3y + 2z = -1 \end{cases}$

$\begin{cases} x - 4y - z = 3 \\ 3y + 3z = -6 \\ 9y + 5z = -10 \end{cases}$

$\begin{cases} x - 4y - z = 3 \\ y + z = -2 \\ -4z = 8 \end{cases}$

$z = -2$

$y = -2 - (-2) = 0$

$x = 3 + 4(0) + (-2) = 1$

Answer: $(1, 0, -2)$

7. $6 = a(0)^2 + b(0) + c \Rightarrow c = 6$

$2 = a(-2)^2 + b(-2) + c$

$\frac{9}{2} = a(3)^2 + b(3) + c$

Hence, $\begin{cases} 4a - 2b + 6 = 2 \text{ or } 2a - b = -2 \\ 9a + 3b + 6 = \frac{9}{2} \text{ or } 9a + 3b = -\frac{3}{2} \end{cases}$.

Solving this system for a and b, you obtain

$a = -\frac{1}{2}, b = 1$. Thus, $y = -\frac{1}{2}x^2 + x + 6$.

8. $\dfrac{5x - 2}{(x - 1)^2} = \dfrac{A}{x - 1} + \dfrac{B}{(x - 1)^2}$

$5x - 2 = A(x - 1) + B = Ax + (-A + B)$

$\begin{cases} A = 5 \\ -A + B = -2 \Rightarrow B = 3 \end{cases}$

$\dfrac{5x - 2}{(x - 1)^2} = \dfrac{5}{x - 1} + \dfrac{3}{(x - 1)^2}$

9. $\dfrac{x^3 + x^2 + x + 2}{x^4 + x^2} = \dfrac{A}{x} + \dfrac{B}{x^2} + \dfrac{Cx + D}{x^2 + 1}$

$$x^3 + x^2 + x + 2 = Ax(x^2 + 1) + B(x^2 + 1) + (Cx + D)x^2$$
$$= (A + C)x^3 + (B + D)x^2 + Ax + B$$

$\begin{cases} A + C = 1 \\ B + D = 1 \\ A = 1 \\ B = 2 \end{cases}$

$A = 1, C = 0, B = 2, D = -1$

$\dfrac{x^3 + x^2 + x + 2}{x^4 + x^2} = \dfrac{1}{x} + \dfrac{2}{x^2} - \dfrac{1}{x^2 + 1}$

10. $\begin{bmatrix} 2 & 1 & 2 & \vdots & 4 \\ 2 & 2 & 0 & \vdots & 5 \\ 2 & -1 & 6 & \vdots & 2 \end{bmatrix}$ row reduces to $\begin{bmatrix} 1 & 0 & 2 & \vdots & 1.5 \\ 0 & 1 & -2 & \vdots & 1 \\ 0 & 0 & 0 & \vdots & 0 \end{bmatrix}$.

Infinite number of solutions. Let $z = a$, $y = 2a + 1$, $x = 1.5 - 2a$.

Answer: $(1.5 - 2a, 1 + 2a, a)$, where a is any real number

11. $\begin{bmatrix} 2 & 3 & 1 & \vdots & 10 \\ 2 & -3 & -3 & \vdots & 22 \\ 4 & -2 & 3 & \vdots & -2 \end{bmatrix}$ row reduces to $\begin{bmatrix} 1 & 0 & 0 & \vdots & 5 \\ 0 & 1 & 0 & \vdots & 2 \\ 0 & 0 & 1 & \vdots & -6 \end{bmatrix}$.

Answer: $(5, 2, -6)$

12. (a) $A - B = \begin{bmatrix} 1 & 0 & 4 \\ -7 & -6 & -1 \\ 0 & 4 & 0 \end{bmatrix}$

(b) $3A = \begin{bmatrix} 15 & 12 & 12 \\ -12 & -12 & 0 \\ 3 & 6 & 0 \end{bmatrix}$

(c) $3A - 2B = \begin{bmatrix} 7 & 4 & 12 \\ -18 & -16 & -2 \\ 1 & 10 & 0 \end{bmatrix}$

(d) $AB = \begin{bmatrix} 36 & 20 & 4 \\ -28 & -24 & -4 \\ 10 & 8 & 2 \end{bmatrix}$

13. $\begin{bmatrix} -2 & 2 & 3 & \vdots & 1 & 0 & 0 \\ 1 & -1 & 0 & \vdots & 0 & 1 & 0 \\ 0 & 1 & 4 & \vdots & 0 & 0 & 1 \end{bmatrix}$

reduces to

$\begin{bmatrix} 1 & 0 & 0 & \vdots & -\frac{4}{3} & -\frac{5}{3} & 1 \\ 0 & 1 & 0 & \vdots & -\frac{4}{3} & -\frac{8}{3} & 1 \\ 0 & 0 & 1 & \vdots & \frac{1}{3} & \frac{2}{3} & 0 \end{bmatrix}$.

$$A^{-1} = \begin{bmatrix} -\frac{4}{3} & -\frac{5}{3} & 1 \\ -\frac{4}{3} & -\frac{8}{3} & 1 \\ \frac{1}{3} & \frac{2}{3} & 0 \end{bmatrix}$$

$$A^{-1}\begin{bmatrix} 7 \\ -5 \\ -1 \end{bmatrix} = \begin{bmatrix} -2 \\ 3 \\ -1 \end{bmatrix}$$

Answer: $(-2, 3, -1)$

14. $\begin{vmatrix} -25 & 18 \\ 6 & -7 \end{vmatrix} = (-25)(-7) - 6(18) = 67$

15. $\det(A) = \begin{vmatrix} 4 & 0 & 3 \\ 1 & -8 & 2 \\ 3 & 2 & 2 \end{vmatrix} = 4(-16 - 4) - 0 + 3(2 + 24)$

$= -80 + 78 = -2$

16. $\begin{vmatrix} x_1 & y_1 & 1 \\ x_2 & y_2 & 1 \\ x_3 & y_3 & 1 \end{vmatrix} = \begin{vmatrix} -1 & 1 & 1 \\ 4 & 11 & 1 \\ -1 & -5 & 1 \end{vmatrix}$

$= -1(16) - 1(4 + 1) + 1(-20 + 11)$

$= -16 - 5 - 9 = -30$

Area $= |-30| = 30$ square units

17. $x = \dfrac{\begin{vmatrix} 3 & -2 \\ -1 & 4 \end{vmatrix}}{\begin{vmatrix} 2 & -2 \\ 1 & 4 \end{vmatrix}} = \dfrac{10}{10} = 1$

$y = \dfrac{\begin{vmatrix} 2 & 3 \\ 1 & -1 \end{vmatrix}}{\begin{vmatrix} 2 & -2 \\ 1 & 4 \end{vmatrix}} = \dfrac{-5}{10} = -\dfrac{1}{2}$

Answer: $\left(1, -\dfrac{1}{2}\right)$

18. Upper left: $400 + x_2 = x_1$

Upper right: $x_1 + x_3 = x_4 + 600$

Lower left: $300 = x_2 + x_3 + x_5$

Lower right: $x_5 + x_4 = 100$

$$\begin{cases} x_1 - x_2 \qquad\qquad\qquad = 400 \\ x_1 \qquad + x_3 - x_4 \qquad = 600 \\ \qquad x_2 + x_3 \qquad + x_5 = 300 \\ \qquad\qquad\qquad x_4 + x_5 = 100 \end{cases}$$

Solving this system:

$$\begin{bmatrix} 1 & -1 & 0 & 0 & 0 & \vdots & 400 \\ 1 & 0 & 1 & -1 & 0 & \vdots & 600 \\ 0 & 1 & 1 & 0 & 1 & \vdots & 300 \\ 0 & 0 & 0 & 1 & 1 & \vdots & 100 \end{bmatrix} \rightarrow \begin{bmatrix} 1 & 0 & 1 & 0 & 1 & \vdots & 700 \\ 0 & 1 & 1 & 0 & 1 & \vdots & 300 \\ 0 & 0 & 0 & 1 & 1 & \vdots & 100 \\ 0 & 0 & 0 & 0 & 0 & \vdots & 0 \end{bmatrix}$$

Letting $x_3 = a$ and $x_5 = b$ be real numbers, we have:

$x_5 = b$

$x_4 = 100 - b$

$x_3 = a$

$x_2 = 300 - a - b$

$x_1 = 700 - b - a$

Chapter 8 Chapter Test Solutions

1. $a_n = \left(-\frac{2}{3}\right)^{n-1}$

$a_1 = \left(-\frac{2}{3}\right)^{1-1} = \left(-\frac{2}{3}\right)^0 = 1$

$a_2 = -\frac{2}{3}$

$a_3 = \left(-\frac{2}{3}\right)^2 = \frac{4}{9}$

$a_4 = \left(-\frac{2}{3}\right)^3 = -\frac{8}{27}$

$a_5 = \left(-\frac{2}{3}\right)^4 = \frac{16}{81}$

2. $a_1 = 12,\ a_{k+1} = a_k + 4$

$a_2 = 12 + 4 = 16$

$a_3 = 16 + 4 = 20$

$a_4 = 20 + 4 = 24$

$a_5 = 24 + 4 = 28$

3. $b_1 = -x$

$b_2 = \dfrac{x^2}{2}$

$b_3 = -\dfrac{x^3}{3}$

$b_4 = \dfrac{x^4}{4}$

$b_5 = -\dfrac{x^5}{5}$

4. $b_1 = -\dfrac{x^3}{3!} = -\dfrac{x^3}{6}$

$b_2 = -\dfrac{x^5}{5!} = -\dfrac{x^5}{120}$

$b_3 = -\dfrac{x^7}{7!}$

$b_4 = -\dfrac{x^9}{9!}$

$b_5 = -\dfrac{x^{11}}{11!}$

5. $\dfrac{11!4!}{4!7!} = \dfrac{11!}{7!}$

$= \dfrac{11 \cdot 10 \cdot 9 \cdot 8 \cdot 7!}{7!}$

$= 11 \cdot 10 \cdot 9 \cdot 8$

$= 7920$

6. $\dfrac{n!}{(n+1)!} = \dfrac{n!}{(n+1)n!} = \dfrac{1}{n+1}$

7. $\dfrac{2n!}{(n-1)!} = \dfrac{2n(n-1)!}{(n-1)!} = 2n$

8. $a_n = n^2 + 1,\ n = 1, 2, 3, \ldots$

9. $a_n = dn + c$

$c = a_1 - d = 5000 - (-100) = 5100 \Rightarrow$

$a_n = -100n + 5100 = 5000 - 100(n-1)$

10. $a_n = a_1r^{n-1},\ a_1 = 4,\ r = \frac{1}{2} \Rightarrow a_n = 4\left(\frac{1}{2}\right)^{n-1}$

11. $\displaystyle\sum_{n=1}^{12} \frac{2}{3n+1}$

12. $\displaystyle 2 + \frac{1}{2} + \frac{1}{8} + \frac{1}{32} + \cdots = \sum_{n=1}^{\infty} 2\left(\frac{1}{4}\right)^{n-1}$

$\displaystyle = \sum_{n=0}^{\infty} \frac{1}{2^{2n-1}}$

13. $\displaystyle\sum_{n=1}^{7}(8n-5) = 8\left(\frac{7(8)}{2}\right) - 5(7) = 224 - 35 = 189$

14. $\displaystyle\sum_{n=1}^{8} 24\left(\frac{1}{6}\right)^{n-1} = 24\left(\frac{1-(1/6)^8}{1-(1/6)}\right)$

$= 24\left(\frac{6}{5}\right)\left(1 - \left(\frac{1}{6}\right)^8\right)$

$\approx 28.79998 \approx 28.80$

15. $\displaystyle\sum_{n=0}^{\infty} \frac{(-1)^n 2^n}{5^{n-1}} = \sum_{n=0}^{\infty} 5\left(\frac{(-1)2}{5}\right)^n$

$= 5\left(\dfrac{1}{1-(-2/5)}\right)$

$= 5\left(\dfrac{5}{7}\right)$

$= \dfrac{25}{7}$

16. (1) For $n = 1$, $3 = \dfrac{3(1)(1+1)}{2}$.

(2) Assume $S_k = 3 + 6 + \cdots + 3k = \dfrac{3k(k+1)}{2}$.

Then $S_{k+1} = 3 + 6 + \cdots + 3k + 3(k+1)$

$= S_k + 3(k+1)$

$= \dfrac{3k(k+1)}{2} + 3(k+1)$

$= \dfrac{k+1}{2}[3k+6]$

$= \dfrac{3(k+1)(k+2)}{2}$.

Therefore, the formula is true for all positive integers n.

17. $(2a - 5b)^4 = (2a)^4 - 4(2a)^3(5b) + 6(2a)^2(5b)^2 - 4(2a)(5b)^3 + (5b)^4$

$= 16a^4 - 160a^3b + 600a^2b^2 - 1000ab^3 + 625b^4$

18. ${}_9C_3 = 84$

19. ${}_{20}C_3 = 1140$

20. ${}_9P_2 = \dfrac{9!}{7!} = 9 \cdot 8 = 72$

21. ${}_{70}P_3 = \dfrac{70!}{67!}$

$= 70 \cdot 69 \cdot 68$

$= 328{,}440$

22. $4 \cdot {}_nP_3 = {}_{n+1}P_4$

$4\dfrac{n!}{(n-3)!} = \dfrac{(n+1)!}{(n-3)!}$

$4n! = (n+1)!$

$n = 3$

23. $26 \cdot 10 \cdot 10 \cdot 10 = 26{,}000$ ways

24. ${}_{25}C_4 = \dfrac{25!}{21!\,4!} = \dfrac{25 \cdot 24 \cdot 23 \cdot 22}{24} = 12{,}650$ ways

25. There are six red face cards $\Longrightarrow$

probability $= \dfrac{6}{52} = \dfrac{3}{26}$.

26. $\dfrac{1}{{}_{11}C_6} = \dfrac{1}{462}$

27. (a) $\left(\frac{30}{60}\right)\left(\frac{30}{60}\right) = \frac{1}{2} \cdot \frac{1}{2} = \frac{1}{4}$

(b) $\frac{11}{60} \cdot \frac{11}{60} = \frac{121}{3600} \approx 0.0336$

(c) $\frac{1}{60} \approx 0.0167$

28. $1 - 0.75 = 0.25 = 25\%$

Chapter 9 Chapter Test Solutions

1. $y^2 = 8x = 2(4)x$

Parabola

Vertex: $(0, 0)$

Focus: $(2, 0)$

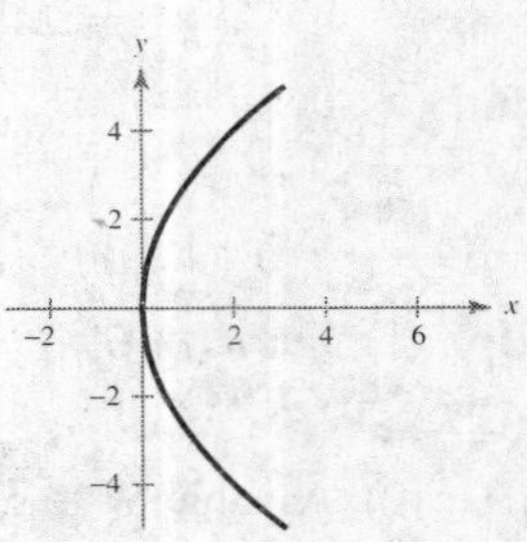

2. $y^2 - 4x + 4 = 0$

$y^2 = 4x - 4$

$y^2 = 4(x - 1)$

Parabola

Vertex: $(1, 0)$

Focus: $(2, 0)$

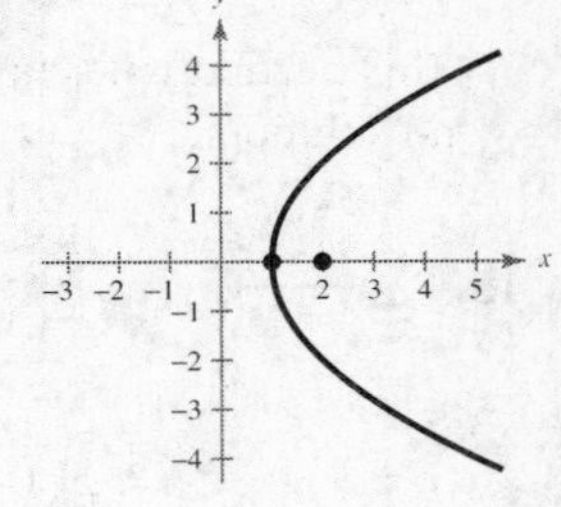

3.

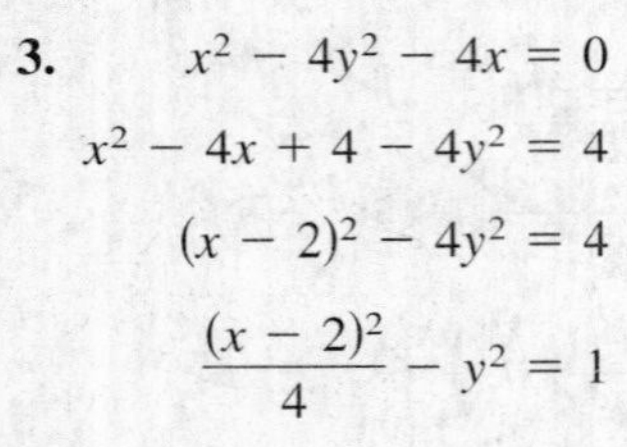

$$x^2 - 4y^2 - 4x = 0$$
$$x^2 - 4x + 4 - 4y^2 = 4$$
$$(x - 2)^2 - 4y^2 = 4$$
$$\frac{(x - 2)^2}{4} - y^2 = 1$$

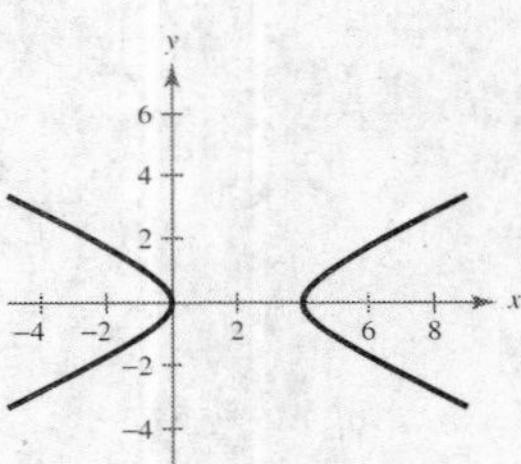

Hyperbola

Center: $(2, 0)$

$a = 2, b = 1, c = \sqrt{5}$

Vertices: $(0, 0), (4, 0)$

Foci: $\left(2 \pm \sqrt{5}, 0\right)$

4. Vertex: $(6, -2), p = 2$

$(y + 2)^2 = 4(2)(x - 6)$

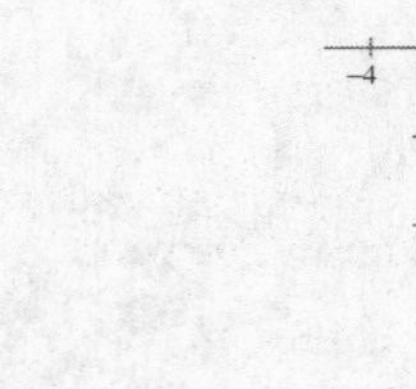

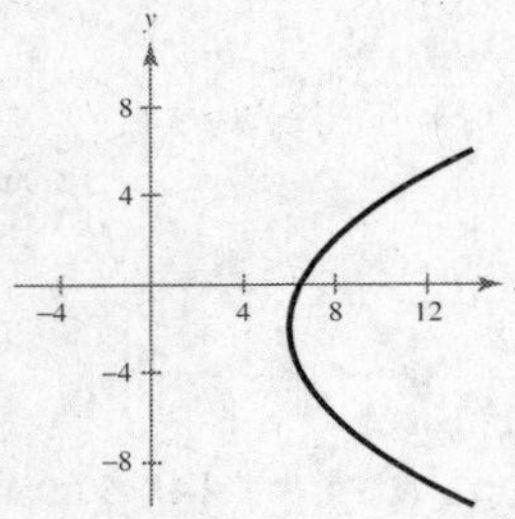

5. Center: $(-6, 3)$

$a = 7, b = 4$

$$\frac{(x + 6)^2}{16} + \frac{(y - 3)^2}{49} = 1$$

6. $a = 3, \dfrac{3}{2} = \dfrac{a}{b} \Longrightarrow b = 2$

$$\frac{y^2}{9} - \frac{x^2}{4} = 1$$

7. $x^2 - \dfrac{y^2}{4} = 1$

$$\frac{y^2}{4} = x^2 - 1$$
$$y = \pm 2\sqrt{x^2 - 1}$$

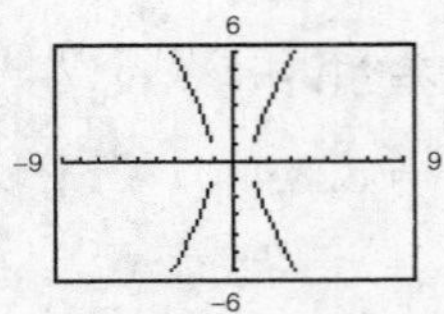

8. (a) $\cot 2\theta = \dfrac{A - C}{B} = \dfrac{1 - 1}{6} = 0 \implies \theta = \dfrac{\pi}{4}$ or $45°$

(b) $B^2 - 4AC = 36 - 4 = 32 > 0 \implies$ Hyperbola

$y^2 + 6xy + (x^2 - 6) = 0$

$$y = \frac{-6x \pm \sqrt{36x^2 - 4(x^2 - 6)}}{2}$$

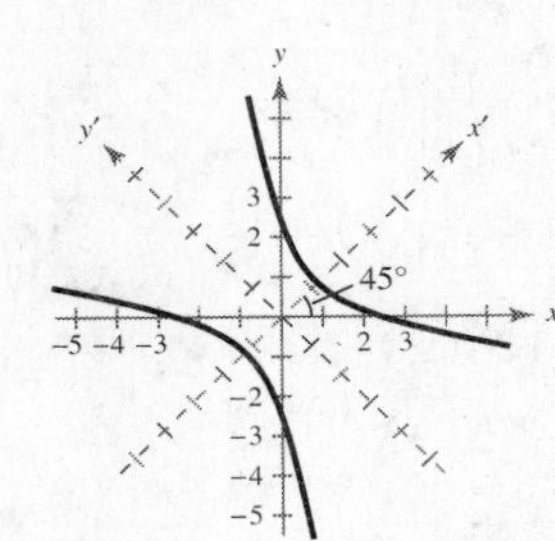

9. $x^2 + 2y^2 - 4x + 6y - 5 = 0$

$x + y + 5 = 0$

$y = -x - 5$:

$x^2 + 2(-x - 5)^2 - 4x + 6(-x - 5) - 5 = 0$

$x^2 + 2x^2 + 20x + 50 - 4x - 6x - 30 - 5 = 0$

$3x^2 + 10x + 15 = 0$

This quadratic has no real solutions. Therefore, no solution.

10. $x = t^2 - 6$

$y = \frac{1}{2}t - 1 \implies t = 2(y + 1)$

$x = [2(y + 1)]^2 - 6 = 4y^2 + 8y - 2$

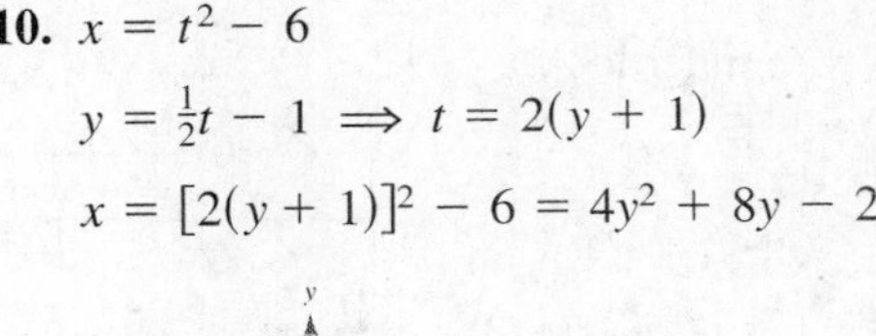

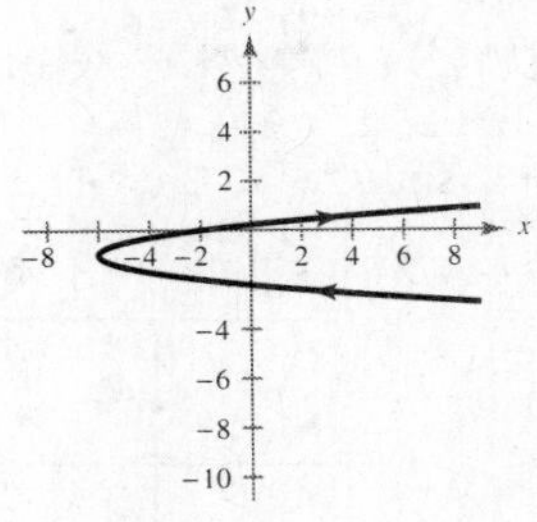

Parabola

$x = 4y^2 + 8y - 2$ or $(y + 1)^2 = \frac{1}{4}(x + 6)$

11. $x = \sqrt{t^2 + 2}$

$y = \dfrac{t}{4} \implies t = 4y$

$x = \sqrt{16y^2 + 2}$

$x^2 = 16y^2 + 2$

Right-hand portion of hyperbola

12. $x = 2 + 3\cos\theta$

$y = 2\sin\theta$

$\left(\dfrac{x - 2}{3}\right)^2 + \left(\dfrac{y}{2}\right)^2 = 1$

$\dfrac{(x - 2)^2}{9} + \dfrac{y^2}{4} = 1$

Ellipse

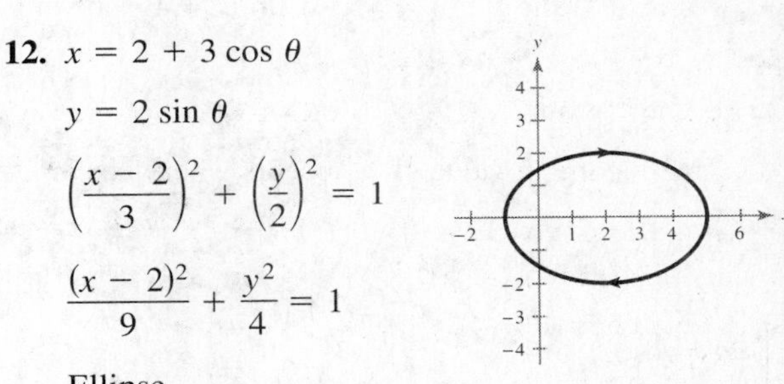

13. $x = t, \quad y = t^2 + 10$

$x = -t, \quad y = t^2 + 10$

14. Sample answers:

$x = 4 - t^2$

$y = t$

$x = 4 - 4t^2$

$y = 2t$

15. Sample answers:

$x = \pm\sqrt{16 - 4t^2}$

$y = t$

$x = \pm\sqrt{16 - t^2}$

$y = \frac{1}{2}t$

16. $(r, \theta) = \left(-14, \dfrac{5\pi}{3}\right) \implies (x, y) = \left(-7, 7\sqrt{3}\right)$

17. $(x, y) = (2, -2), r = \sqrt{8} = 2\sqrt{2}, \theta = \dfrac{7\pi}{4}$

$(r, \theta) = \left(2\sqrt{2}, \dfrac{7\pi}{4}\right) = \left(2\sqrt{2}, -\dfrac{\pi}{4}\right) = \left(-2\sqrt{2}, \dfrac{3\pi}{4}\right)$

18. $x^2 + y^2 - 12y = 0$

$r^2 - 12\, r \sin\theta = 0$

$r^2 = 12\, r \sin\theta$

$r = 12 \sin\theta$

19. $r = 2\sin\theta$

$r^2 = 2r\sin\theta$

$x^2 + y^2 = 2y$

$x^2 + y^2 - 2y + 1 = 1$

$x^2 + (y - 1)^2 = 1$, Circle

20. $r = 2 + 3\sin\theta$

Limaçon with inner loop

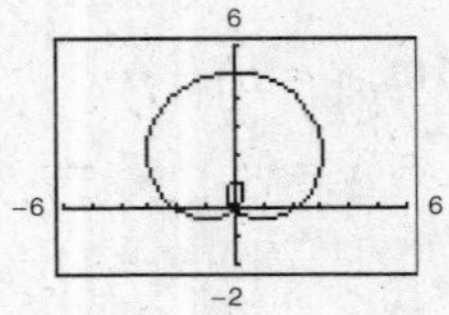

21. $r = \dfrac{1}{1 - \cos\theta}$

$e = 1 \Rightarrow$ Parabola

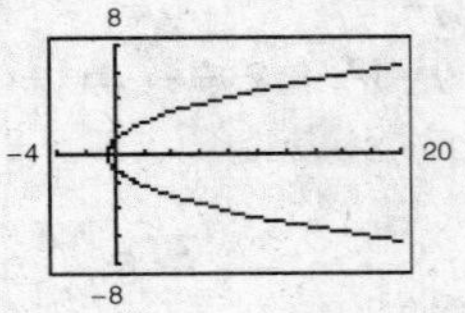

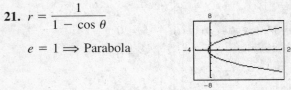

22. $r = \dfrac{4}{2 + 3\sin\theta} = \dfrac{2}{1 + \frac{3}{2}\sin\theta}$

$e = \dfrac{3}{2} \Rightarrow$ Hyperbola

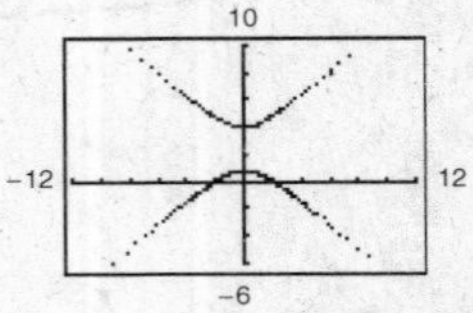

23. $r = \dfrac{ep}{1 + e\sin\theta} = \dfrac{(1/4)(4)}{1 + (1/4)\sin\theta}$

$r = \dfrac{4}{4 + \sin\theta} = \dfrac{1}{1 + (1/4)\sin\theta}$

24. $r = \dfrac{ep}{1 + e\sin\theta} = \dfrac{(5/4)(2)}{1 + (5/4)\sin\theta} = \dfrac{10}{4 + 5\sin\theta}$

25. $r = 8\cos 3\theta$

The maximum value of $|r|$ occurs when $|\cos 3\theta| = 1$. Hence, the maximum is $8 = |r|$.

$r = 0 \Rightarrow \cos 3\theta = 0$

$\Rightarrow 3\theta = \dfrac{\pi}{2} + n\pi$

$\Rightarrow \theta = \dfrac{\pi}{6} + \dfrac{n\pi}{3}$

On the interval $0 \le \theta \le \pi$, $\theta = \dfrac{\pi}{6}, \dfrac{\pi}{2}, \dfrac{5\pi}{6}$.

Chapters 7–9 Cumulative Test Solutions

1. $\begin{bmatrix} -1 & -3 & \vdots & 5 \\ 4 & 2 & \vdots & 10 \end{bmatrix}$ row reduces to $\begin{bmatrix} 1 & 0 & \vdots & 4 \\ 0 & 1 & \vdots & -3 \end{bmatrix}$.

Answer: $(4, -3)$

2. $2x - y^2 = 0$

$$x - y = 4 \Rightarrow x = y + 4$$
$$2(y + 4) - y^2 = 0$$
$$y^2 - 2y - 8 = 0$$
$$(y - 4)(y + 2) = 0$$
$$y = 4,\ x = 8$$
$$y = -2,\ x = 2$$

Solutions: $(2, -2), (8, 4)$

3. $\begin{bmatrix} 2 & -3 & 1 & \vdots & 13 \\ -4 & 1 & -2 & \vdots & -6 \\ 1 & -3 & 3 & \vdots & 12 \end{bmatrix}$ row reduces to

$$\begin{bmatrix} 1 & 0 & 0 & \vdots & \frac{3}{5} \\ 0 & 1 & 0 & \vdots & -4 \\ 0 & 0 & 1 & \vdots & -\frac{1}{5} \end{bmatrix}.$$

Answer: $\left(\frac{3}{5}, -4, -\frac{1}{5}\right)$

4. $\begin{bmatrix} 1 & -4 & 3 & \vdots & 5 \\ 5 & 2 & -1 & \vdots & 1 \\ -2 & -8 & 0 & \vdots & 30 \end{bmatrix}$ row reduces to

$$\begin{bmatrix} 1 & 0 & 0 & \vdots & 1 \\ 0 & 1 & 0 & \vdots & -4 \\ 0 & 0 & 1 & \vdots & -4 \end{bmatrix}.$$

Solution: $(1, -4, -4)$

5. $3A - B = \begin{bmatrix} -7 & -10 & -16 \\ -6 & 18 & 9 \\ -12 & 16 & 7 \end{bmatrix}$

6. $5A + 3B = \begin{bmatrix} -18 & 15 & -14 \\ 28 & 11 & 34 \\ -20 & 52 & -1 \end{bmatrix}$

7. $AB = \begin{bmatrix} 3 & -31 & 2 \\ 22 & 18 & 6 \\ 52 & -40 & 14 \end{bmatrix}$

8. $BA = \begin{bmatrix} 5 & 36 & 31 \\ -36 & 12 & -36 \\ 16 & 0 & 18 \end{bmatrix}$

9. (a) $\begin{bmatrix} 1 & 2 & -1 \\ 3 & 7 & -10 \\ -5 & -7 & -15 \end{bmatrix}^{-1} = \begin{bmatrix} -175 & 37 & -13 \\ 95 & -20 & 7 \\ 14 & -3 & 1 \end{bmatrix}$

(b) $\det(A) = \begin{vmatrix} 1 & 2 & -1 \\ 3 & 7 & -10 \\ -5 & -7 & -15 \end{vmatrix} = 1(-105 - 70) - 2(-45 - 50) - 1(-21 + 35)$

$$= -175 + 190 - 14 = 1$$

10. $\begin{vmatrix} 0 & 0 & 1 \\ 6 & 2 & 1 \\ 8 & 10 & 1 \end{vmatrix} = 44 \Rightarrow \text{Area} = \frac{1}{2}(44) = 22 \text{ sq. units}$

11. (a) $a_1 = \dfrac{(-1)^{1+1}}{2(1) + 3} = \dfrac{1}{5}$

$a_2 = -\dfrac{1}{7}$

$a_3 = \dfrac{1}{9}$

$a_4 = -\dfrac{1}{11}$

$a_5 = \dfrac{1}{13}$

(b) $a_1 = 3(2)^{1-1} = 3$

$a_2 = 6$

$a_3 = 12$

$a_4 = 24$

$a_5 = 48$

12. $\displaystyle\sum_{k=1}^{6} (7k - 2) = \frac{7(6)(7)}{2} - 2(6) = 135$

13. $\displaystyle\sum_{k=1}^{4} \frac{2}{k^2 + 4} = \frac{2}{1 + 4} + \frac{2}{4 + 4} + \frac{2}{9 + 4} + \frac{2}{16 + 4}$

$$\approx 0.9038$$

14. $\sum_{n=0}^{10} 9\left(\frac{3}{4}\right)^n = 9\left(\frac{1-(3/4)^{11}}{1-(3/4)}\right) \approx 34.4795$

15. $\sum_{n=0}^{50} 100\left(-\frac{1}{2}\right)^n = \sum_{n=1}^{51} 100\left(-\frac{1}{2}\right)^{n-1}$

$= 100\frac{1-(-1/2)^{51}}{1-(-1/2)}$

$\approx \frac{2}{3}(100) \approx 66.67$

16. $\sum_{n=0}^{\infty} 3\left(-\frac{3}{5}\right)^n = \frac{3}{1-(-3/5)} = \frac{3}{8/5} = \frac{15}{8}$

17. $\sum_{n=1}^{\infty} 5(-0.02)^n = 5(-0.02)\frac{1}{1-(-0.02)}$

$= \frac{-0.1}{1.02} = \frac{-5}{51}$

18. $4 - 2 + 1 - \frac{1}{2} + \frac{1}{4} - \cdots = \sum_{n=0}^{\infty} 4\left(-\frac{1}{2}\right)^n = \frac{4}{1-(-1/2)} = \frac{8}{3}$

19. For $n = 1$, $3 = 1(2 + 1)$ and the formula is true. Assume true for k, and consider

$$\begin{aligned} 3 + 7 + \cdots + (4k - 1) + (4(k + 1) - 1) &= 3 + 7 + \cdots + (4k - 1) + (4k + 3) \\ &= k(2k + 1) + (4k + 3) \\ &= 2k^2 + 5k + 3 \\ &= (k + 1)(2k + 3) \\ &= (k + 1)(2(k + 1) + 1) \end{aligned}$$

which shows that the formula is true for $k + 1$.

20. $(x + 3)^4 = x^4 + 12x^3 + 54x^2 + 108x + 81$

21. $(2x + y^2)^5 = 32x^5 + 80x^4y^2 + 80x^3y^4 + 40x^2y^6 + 10xy^8 + y^{10}$

22. $(x - 2y)^6 = x^6 - 12x^5y + 60x^4y^2 - 160x^3y^3 + 240x^2y^4 - 192xy^5 + 64y^6$

23. $(3a - 4b)^8 = 6561a^8 - 69{,}984a^7b + 326{,}592a^6b^2 - 870{,}912a^5b^3 + 1{,}451{,}520a^4b^4 - 1{,}548{,}288a^3b^5$
$+ 1{,}032{,}192a^2b^6 - 393{,}216ab^7 + 65{,}536b^8$

24. $\frac{5!}{2!2!1!} = \frac{120}{4} = 30$

25. $\frac{6!}{3!} = 6 \cdot 5 \cdot 4 = 120$

26. $\frac{10!}{2!2!2!} = 453{,}600$

27. $\frac{10!}{3!2!2!} = 151{,}200$

28. Hyperbola with center $(5, -3)$

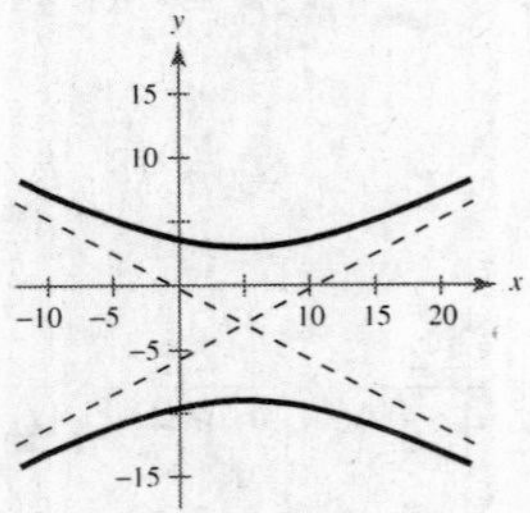

29. Ellipse with center $(2, -1)$

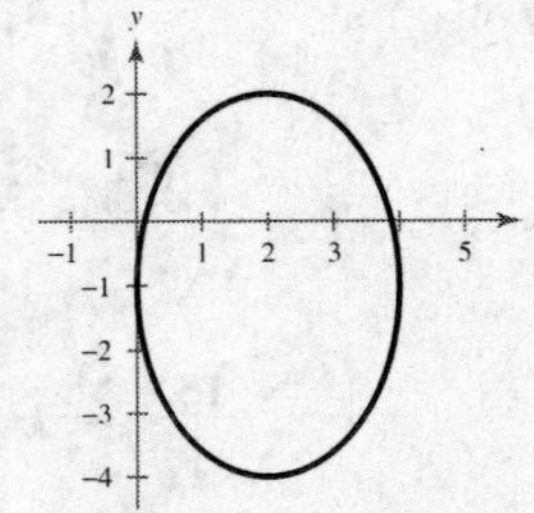

30. Hyperbola with center $(0, 0)$

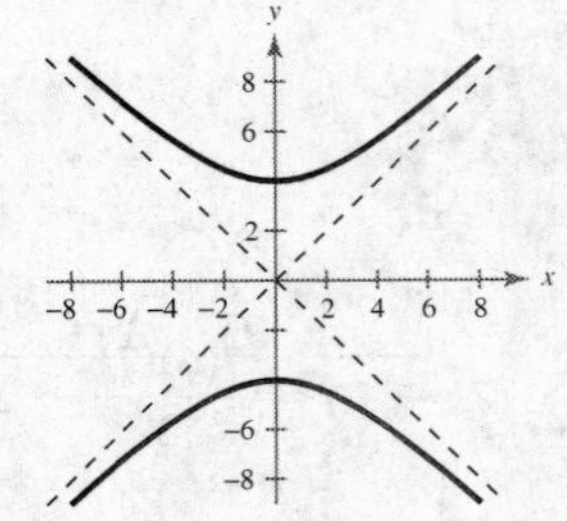

31. $(x^2 - 2x + 1) + (y^2 - 4y + 4) = -1 + 1 + 4$

$$(x - 1)^2 + (y - 2)^2 = 4$$

Circle

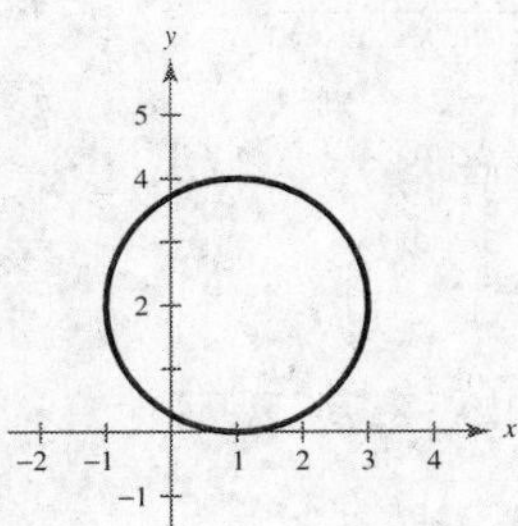

32. $(x - 2)^2 = 4p(y - 3)$

$(0, 0)$: $4 = 4p(-3) \Rightarrow p = -\frac{1}{3}$

$(x - 2)^2 = 4\left(-\frac{1}{3}\right)(y - 3)$

$(x - 2)^2 = -\frac{4}{3}(y - 3)$

33. Center: $(1, 4)$

$a = 5, b = 2$

$$\frac{(x - 1)^2}{25} + \frac{(y - 4)^2}{4} = 1$$

34. Center: $(0, -4)$; $a = 2$

$$\frac{(y + 4)^2}{4} - \frac{x^2}{b^2} = 1$$

$(4, 0)$: $4 - \dfrac{16}{b^2} = 1 \Rightarrow \dfrac{16}{b^2} = 3 \Rightarrow b^2 = \dfrac{16}{3}$

$$\frac{(y + 4)^2}{4} - \frac{x^2}{16/3} = 1$$

35. $B^2 - 4AC = 16 - 8 = 8 \Rightarrow$ Hyperbola

$\cot 2\theta = \dfrac{1 - 2}{-4} = \dfrac{1}{4} \Rightarrow \theta \approx 38°$

Graph as:

$2y^2 - 4xy + (x^2 - 6) = 0$

$$y = \frac{4x \pm \sqrt{16x^2 - 8(x^2 - 6)}}{4}$$

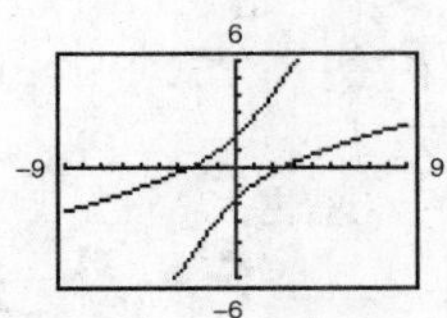

36. $x = 2t + 1, y = t^2$

(a), (b)

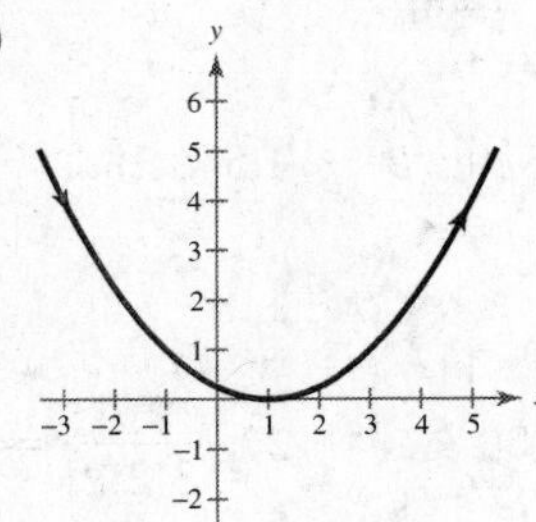

(c) $t = \dfrac{x - 1}{2} \Rightarrow y = \left(\dfrac{x - 1}{2}\right)^2 = \dfrac{1}{4}(x - 1)^2$

37. $x = \cos\theta, y = 2\sin^2\theta$

(a), (b)

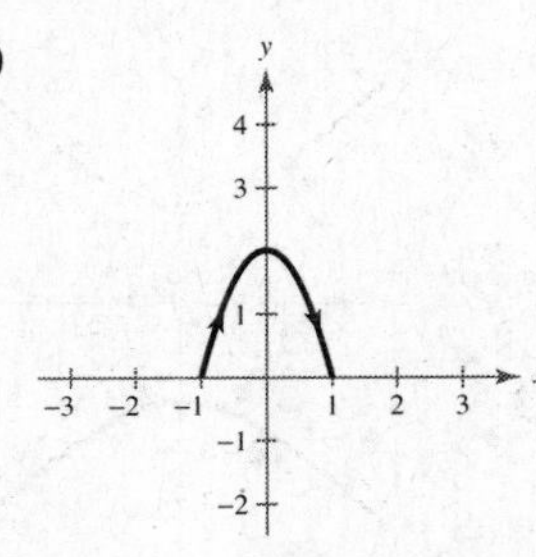

(c) $y = 2\sin^2\theta$

$= 2(1 - \cos^2\theta)$

$= 2(1 - x^2), \ -1 \le x \le 1$

38. $x = 4 \ln t, y = \frac{1}{2}t^2$

(a), (b)

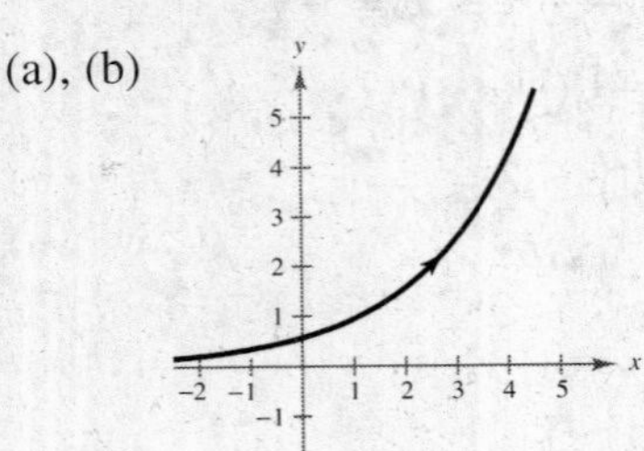

(c) $t = e^{x/4} \Longrightarrow y = \frac{1}{2}e^{x/2}$

39. $y = 3x - 2$

Sample answers:

$x = t$

$y = 3t - 2$

$x = -t$

$y = -3t - 2$

40. Sample answers:

$x = \pm\sqrt{t^2 + 16}$

$y = t$

$x = t$

$y = \pm\sqrt{t^2 - 16}$

41. $y = \dfrac{2}{x}$

Sample answers:

$x = t$

$y = \dfrac{2}{t}$

$x = -t$

$y = -\dfrac{2}{t}$

42. Sample answers:

$x = t$

$y = \dfrac{e^{2t}}{e^{2t} + 1}$

$x = \dfrac{1}{2}t$

$y = \dfrac{e^t}{e^t + 1}$

43. $(r, \theta) = \left(8, \dfrac{5\pi}{6}\right)$

$\left(8, -\dfrac{7\pi}{6}\right), \left(-8, -\dfrac{\pi}{6}\right), \left(-8, \dfrac{11\pi}{6}\right)$

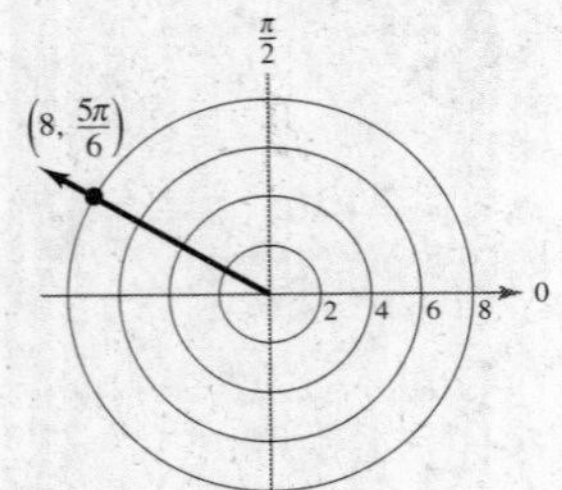

44. $(r, \theta) = \left(5, -\dfrac{3\pi}{4}\right)$

$\left(5, \dfrac{5\pi}{4}\right), \left(-5, \dfrac{\pi}{4}\right), \left(-5, -\dfrac{7\pi}{4}\right)$

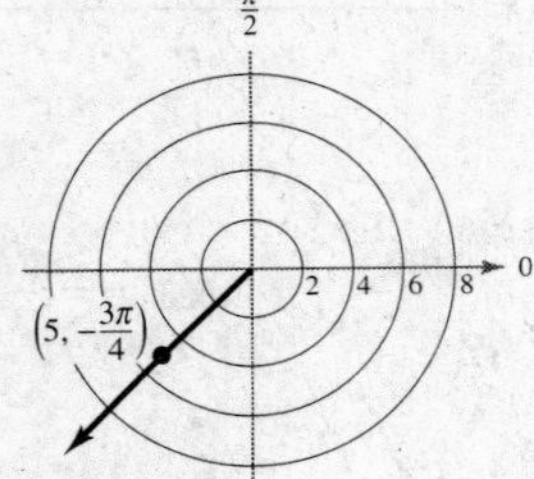

45. $(r, \theta) = \left(-2, \dfrac{5\pi}{4}\right)$

$\left(-2, -\dfrac{3\pi}{4}\right), \left(2, \dfrac{\pi}{4}\right), \left(2, -\dfrac{7\pi}{4}\right)$

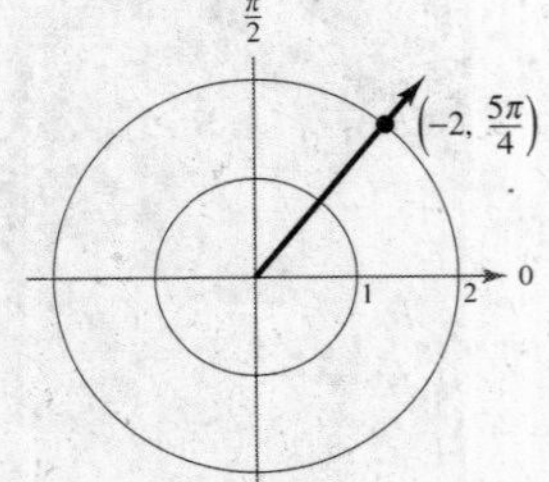

46. $(r, \theta) = \left(-3, -\dfrac{11\pi}{6}\right)$

$\left(-3, \dfrac{\pi}{6}\right), \left(3, \dfrac{7\pi}{6}\right), \left(3, -\dfrac{5\pi}{6}\right)$

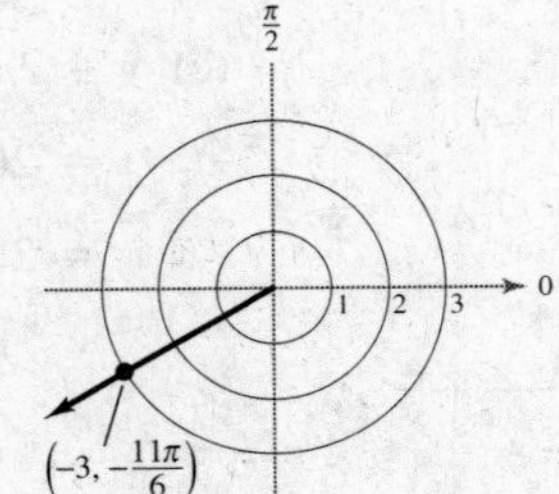

47. $4x + 4y + 1 = 0$

$4r\cos\theta + 4r\sin\theta + 1 = 0$

$r[4\cos\theta + 4\sin\theta] = -1$

$r = \dfrac{-1}{4\cos\theta + 4\sin\theta}$

48. $r = 2\cos\theta$

$r^2 = 2r\cos\theta$

$x^2 + y^2 = 2x$

$x^2 - 2x + 1 + y^2 = 1$

$(x - 1)^2 + y^2 = 1$, Circle

49. $r = \dfrac{2}{4 - 5\cos\theta}$

$4r - 5r\cos\theta = 2$

$4(x^2 + y^2)^{1/2} - 5x = 2$

$16(x^2 + y^2) = (5x + 2)^2 = 25x^2 + 20x + 4$

$16y^2 - 9x^2 - 20x = 4$

50. $r = -\dfrac{\pi}{6}$, Circle

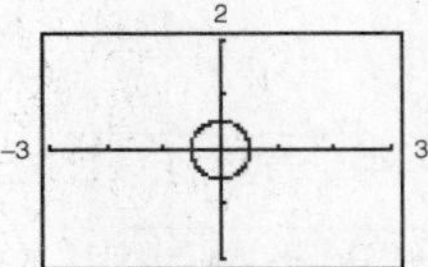

51. $r = 3 - 2\sin\theta$

Limaçon

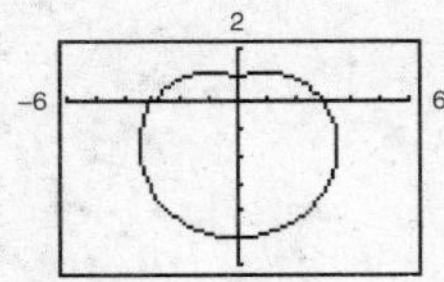

52. $r = 2 + 5\cos\theta$

Limaçon

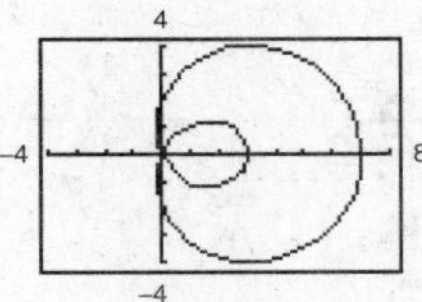

53. $32{,}500 + 32{,}500(1.05) + \cdots + 32{,}500(1.05)^{14} = \sum_{n=1}^{15} 32{,}500(1.05)^{n-1}$

$= 32{,}500\left(\dfrac{1 - 1.05^{15}}{1 - 1.05}\right) \approx \$701{,}303.32$

54. There are two ways to select the first digit (4 or 5), and two ways for the second digit. Hence, $p = \frac{1}{4}$.

55. Let $y = -ax^2 + 16$.

$(6, 14)$: $14 = -a(6)^2 + 16$

$36a = 2$

$a = \frac{1}{18}$

$y = -\frac{1}{18}x^2 + 16$

$y = 0$: $16 = \frac{1}{18}x^2$

$x^2 = 288$

$x = 12\sqrt{2}$

Width: $24\sqrt{2}$ meters

Chapter 10 Chapter Test Solutions

1.

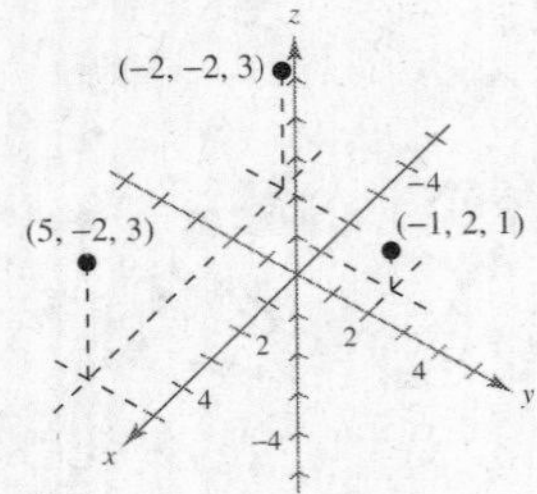

2. $AB = \sqrt{(8-6)^2 + (-2-4)^2 + (5+1)^2} = \sqrt{76}$

$AC = \sqrt{(8+4)^2 + (-2-3)^2 + (5-0)^2} = \sqrt{144 + 25 + 25} = \sqrt{194}$

$BC = \sqrt{(6+4)^2 + (4-3)^2 + (-1-0)^2} = \sqrt{100 + 1 + 1} = \sqrt{102}$

No. $(\sqrt{76})^2 + (\sqrt{102})^2 \neq (\sqrt{194})^2$

3. Midpoint $= \left(\dfrac{8+6}{2}, \dfrac{-2+4}{2}, \dfrac{5-1}{2}\right) = (7, 1, 2)$

4. Diameter $= \sqrt{(8-6)^2 + (-2-4)^2 + (5+1)^2}$

$= \sqrt{4 + 36 + 36} = \sqrt{76}$

Radius $= \sqrt{19}$

$(x-7)^2 + (y-1)^2 + (z-2)^2 = 19$

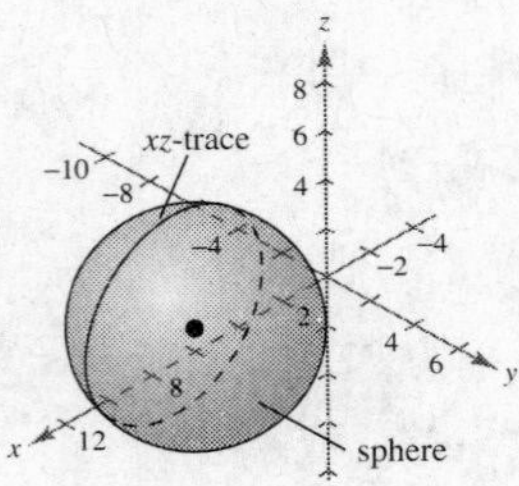

5. $\mathbf{v} = \langle 4-2, 4-(-1), -7-3\rangle = \langle 2, 5, -10\rangle$

$\|\mathbf{v}\| = \sqrt{2^2 + 5^2 + (-10)^2} = \sqrt{129}$

6. $\mathbf{v} = \langle 3-6, -3-2, 8-0\rangle = \langle -3, -5, 8\rangle$

$\|\mathbf{v}\| = \sqrt{(-3)^2 + (-5)^2 + 8^2} = \sqrt{98} = 7\sqrt{2}$

7. $\mathbf{u} = \langle 6-8, 4-(-2), -1-5\rangle = \langle -2, 6, -6\rangle$

$\mathbf{v} = \langle -4-8, 3-(-2), 0-5\rangle = \langle -12, 5, -5\rangle$

8. (a) $\|\mathbf{v}\| = \sqrt{(-12)^2 + 5^2 + (-5)^2} = \sqrt{194}$

(b) $\mathbf{u}\cdot\mathbf{v} = (-2)(-12) + 6(5) + (-6)(-5) = 84$

(c) $\mathbf{u}\times\mathbf{v} = \begin{vmatrix} \mathbf{i} & \mathbf{j} & \mathbf{k} \\ -2 & 6 & -6 \\ -12 & 5 & -5 \end{vmatrix} = \langle 0, 62, 62\rangle$

9. $\cos\theta = \dfrac{\mathbf{u}\cdot\mathbf{v}}{\|\mathbf{u}\|\,\|\mathbf{v}\|} = \dfrac{84}{\sqrt{76}\sqrt{194}} \approx 0.6918 \implies \theta \approx 46.23^\circ$ or 0.8068 radians

10. (a) $x = 8 - 2t, y = -2 + 6t, z = 5 - 6t$

(b) $\dfrac{x-8}{-2} = \dfrac{y+2}{6} = \dfrac{z-5}{-6}$

11. $\mathbf{u}\cdot\mathbf{v} = 0 - 2 - 6 \neq 0$ and $\mathbf{u} \neq c\mathbf{v} \implies$ neither

12. $\mathbf{u}\cdot\mathbf{v} = -2 + 3 - 1 = 0 \implies$ orthogonal

13. First two points: $\mathbf{v} = \langle 4, 8, -2 \rangle$

Last two points: $\mathbf{w} = \langle 4, 8, -2 \rangle$

Opposite sides are parallel and equal length.

Adjacent sides: $\mathbf{v}$ and $\mathbf{u} = \langle 1, -3, 3 \rangle$

Area $= \|\mathbf{u} \times \mathbf{v}\|$

$$\mathbf{u} \times \mathbf{v} = \begin{vmatrix} \mathbf{i} & \mathbf{j} & \mathbf{k} \\ 1 & -3 & 3 \\ 4 & 8 & -2 \end{vmatrix} = \langle -18, 14, 20 \rangle$$

$$\|\mathbf{u} \times \mathbf{v}\| = \sqrt{18^2 + 14^2 + 20^2} = 2\sqrt{230} \approx 30.33 \text{ square units}$$

14. $\mathbf{u} = \langle 0, 8, -1 \rangle$, $\mathbf{v} = \langle 4, 5, -4 \rangle$

$$\mathbf{n} = \mathbf{u} \times \mathbf{v} = \begin{vmatrix} \mathbf{i} & \mathbf{j} & \mathbf{k} \\ 0 & 8 & -1 \\ 4 & 5 & -4 \end{vmatrix} = \langle -27, -4, -32 \rangle$$

$$\text{Plane: } -27(x + 3) - 4(y + 4) - 32(z - 2) = 0$$
$$-27x - 4y - 32z - 33 = 0$$
$$27x + 4y + 32z + 33 = 0$$

15. Let $A(0, 0, 5)$ be the vertex.

$\mathbf{u} = \overrightarrow{AD} = \langle 4, 0, 0 \rangle$, $\mathbf{v} = \overrightarrow{AB} = \langle 0, 10, 0 \rangle$,

$\mathbf{w} = \overrightarrow{AE} = \langle 0, 1, -5 \rangle$

$$\mathbf{u} \cdot (\mathbf{v} \times \mathbf{w}) = \begin{vmatrix} 4 & 0 & 0 \\ 0 & 10 & 0 \\ 0 & 1 & -5 \end{vmatrix} = 4(-50) = -200$$

Volume $= |-200| = 200$ cubic units

16. $2x + 3y + 4z = 12$

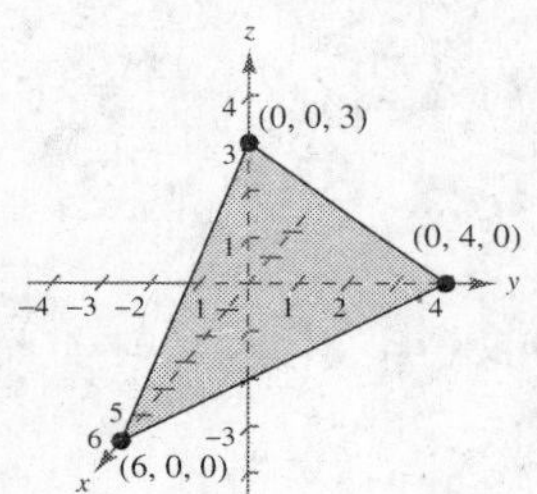

17. $5x - y - 2z = 10$

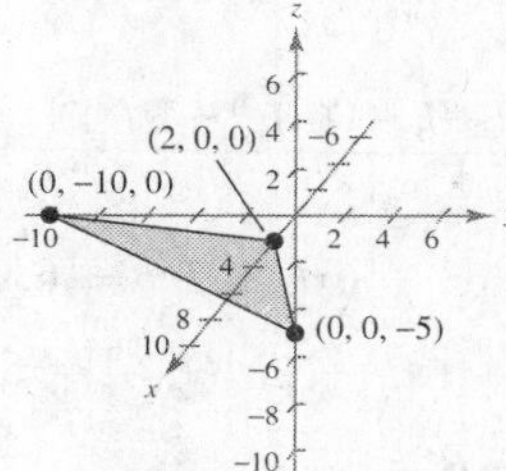

18. $\mathbf{n} = \langle 3, -2, 1 \rangle$, $Q = (2, -1, 6)$, $P = (0, 0, 6)$ in plane, $\overrightarrow{PQ} = \langle 2, -1, 0 \rangle$

$$D = \frac{|\overrightarrow{PQ} \cdot \mathbf{n}|}{\|\mathbf{n}\|} = \frac{|8|}{\sqrt{14}} = \frac{4\sqrt{14}}{7}$$

Chapter 11 Chapter Test Solutions

1. $\displaystyle\lim_{x \to -2} \frac{x^2 - 1}{2x} = \frac{(-2)^2 - 1}{2(-2)} = -\frac{3}{4}$

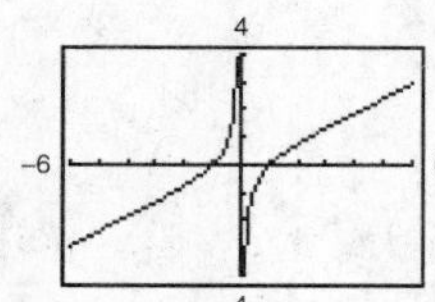

Limit is -0.75.

2.

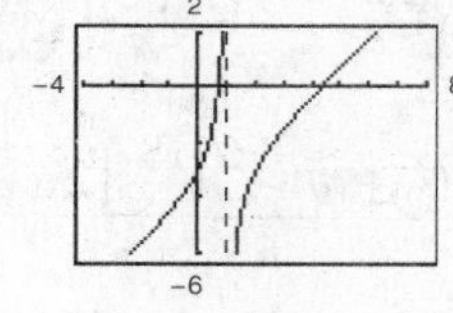

The limit does not exist.

$\displaystyle\lim_{x \to 1} \frac{-x^2 + 5x - 3}{1 - x}$ does not exist.

$x = 1$ is a vertical asymptote.

3.

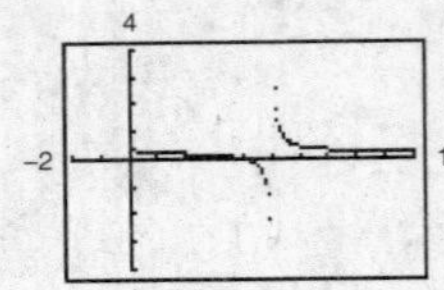

$\lim_{x\to 5} \frac{\sqrt{x}-2}{x-5}$ does not exist.

4.

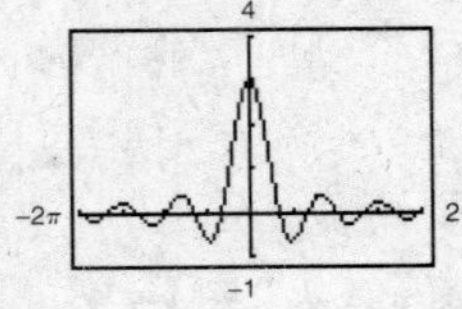

$\lim_{x\to 0} \frac{\sin 3x}{x} = 3$

$f(x) = \frac{\sin 3x}{x}$

5.

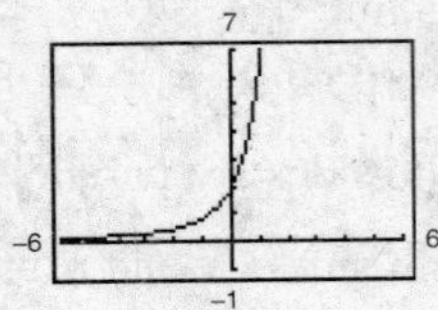

$\lim_{x\to 0} \frac{e^{2x}-1}{x} = 2$

$f(x) = \frac{e^{2x}-1}{x}$

6. (a) $\frac{f(x+h)-f(x)}{h} = \frac{3(x+h)^2 - 5(x+h) - 2 - (3x^2 - 5x - 2)}{h}$

$= \frac{3x^2 + 6xh + 3h^2 - 5h - 3x^2}{h}$

$= 6x + 3h - 5$

$f'(x) = \lim_{h\to 0} [6x + 3h - 5] = 6x - 5$

$f'(2) = 6(2) - 5 = 7$

(b) $\frac{f(x+h)-f(x)}{h} = \frac{[2(x+h)^3 + 6(x+h)] - [2x^3 + 6x]}{h}$

$= \frac{2x^3 + 6x^2h + 6xh^2 + 2h^3 + 6x + 6h - 2x^3 - 6x}{h}$

$= \frac{6x^2h + 6xh^2 + 2h^3 + 6h}{h}$

$= 6x^2 + 6xh + 2h^2 + 6, \ h \neq 0$

$f'(x) = \lim_{h\to 0} [6x^2 + 6xh + 2h^2 + 6] = 6x^2 + 6$

$f'(-1) = 6(-1)^2 + 6 = 12$

7. $f'(x) = \lim_{h\to 0} \frac{f(x+h)-f(x)}{h}$

$= \lim_{h\to 0} \frac{5 - (2/5)(x+h) - (5 - (2/5)x)}{h}$

$= \lim_{h\to 0} \frac{-(2/5)h}{h} = -\frac{2}{5}$

8. $f'(x) = \lim_{h\to 0} \frac{f(x+h)-f(x)}{h}$

$= \lim_{h\to 0} \frac{2(x+h)^2 + 4(x+h) - 1 - [2x^2 + 4x - 1]}{h}$

$= \lim_{h\to 0} \frac{2x^2 + 4xh + 2h^2 + 4h - 2x^2}{h}$

$= \lim_{h\to 0} (4x + 2h + 4) = 4x + 4$

9. $f'(x) = \lim_{h \to 0} \frac{f(x+h) - f(x)}{h}$

$$= \lim_{h \to 0} \frac{\frac{1}{x+3+h} - \frac{1}{x+3}}{h}$$

$$= \lim_{h \to 0} \frac{(x+3) - (x+3+h)}{h(x+3+h)(x+3)}$$

$$= \lim_{h \to 0} \frac{-1}{(x+3+h)(x+3)}$$

$$= \frac{-1}{(x+3)^2}$$

10. $\lim_{x \to \infty} \frac{6}{5x - 1} = 0$

11. $\lim_{x \to \infty} \frac{1 - 3x^2}{x^2 - 5} = -3$

12. $\lim_{x \to -\infty} \frac{x^2}{3x + 2}$ does not exist.

$f(x) = \frac{x^2}{3x + 2}$ decreases without bound as $x \to -\infty$.

13. $0, \frac{3}{4}, \frac{14}{19}, \frac{12}{17}, \frac{36}{53}$

$\lim_{n \to \infty} a_n = \frac{1}{2}$

14. $0, 1, 0, \frac{1}{2}, 0$

$\lim_{n \to \infty} a_n = 0$

15. Width of each rectangle: $\frac{1}{2}$

Heights: $8, \frac{15}{2}, 6, \frac{7}{2}$

Area $\approx \frac{1}{2}\left[8 + \frac{15}{2} + 6 + \frac{7}{2}\right] = \frac{25}{2}$

16. Width: $\frac{4}{n}$, Height: $f\left(-2 + \frac{4i}{n}\right) = \left(-2 + \frac{4i}{n}\right) + 2 = \frac{4i}{n}$

$$A \approx \sum_{i=1}^{n} \left(\frac{4i}{n}\right)\left(\frac{4}{n}\right) = \frac{16}{n^2} \sum_{i=1}^{n} i = \frac{16}{n^2} \frac{n(n+1)}{2}$$

$$A = \lim_{n \to \infty} \frac{16}{n^2} \cdot \frac{n(n+1)}{2} = 8$$

17. $f(x) = 3 - x^2$, $[-1, 1]$

The width of each rectangle is $\frac{2}{n}$. The height is

$$f\left(-1 + \frac{2i}{n}\right) = 3 - \left[-1 + \frac{2i}{n}\right]^2$$

$$= 2 + \frac{4}{n}i - \frac{4}{n^2}i^2.$$

$$A \approx \sum_{i=1}^{n} \left[2 + \frac{4}{n}i - \frac{4}{n^2}i^2\right]\left(\frac{2}{n}\right)$$

$$= \sum_{i=1}^{n} \left[\frac{4}{n} + \frac{8}{n^2}i - \frac{8}{n^3}i^2\right]$$

$$A = \lim_{n \to \infty} \left[\frac{4}{n}(n) + \frac{8}{n^2}\frac{n(n+1)}{2} - \frac{8}{n^3}\frac{n(n+1)(2n+1)}{6}\right]$$

$$= 4 + 4 - \frac{8}{3} = \frac{16}{3}$$

18. (a) $y = 8.79x^2 - 6.2x - 0.4$

(b) Velocity = Derivative = $17.58x - 6.2$

At $x = 5$, velocity ≈ 81.7 ft/sec.

Chapters 10–11 Cumulative Test Solutions

1. $(-6, 1, 3)$

2. $(0, -4, 0)$

3. $d = \sqrt{(4-(-2))^2 + (-5-3)^2 + (1-(-6))^2}$

$= \sqrt{36 + 64 + 49}$

$= \sqrt{149}$

4. $d_1 = 3, d_2 = 4, d_3 = \sqrt{4^2 + 3^2} = 5$

$d_1^2 + d_2^2 = d_3^2$

5. Midpoint: $\left(\frac{3-5}{2}, \frac{4+0}{2}, \frac{-1+2}{2}\right) = \left(-1, 2, \frac{1}{2}\right)$

6. Center $= (2, 2, 4)$

Radius $= \sqrt{2^2 + 2^2 + 4^2} = \sqrt{24}$

$(x-2)^2 + (y-2)^2 + (z-4)^2 = 24$

7. xy-trace: $(z = 0)$

$(x-2)^2 + (y+1)^2 = 4$, Circle

yz-trace: $(x = 0)$

$4 + (y+1)^2 + z^2 = 4$ or $(y+1)^2 + z^2 = 0$, Point

$(0, -1, 0)$, Point

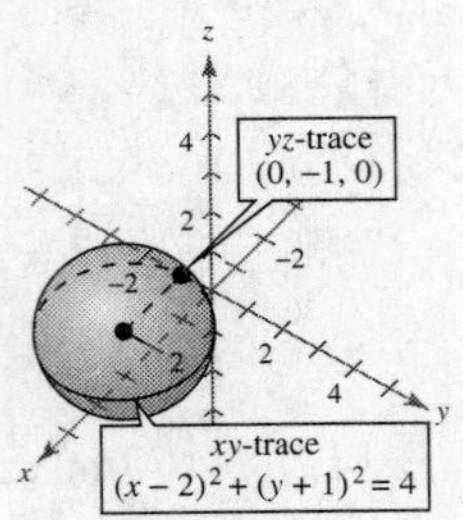

8. $\mathbf{u} \cdot \mathbf{v} = \langle 2, -6, 0 \rangle \cdot \langle -4, 5, 3 \rangle$

$= -8 - 30 = -38$

$\mathbf{u} \times \mathbf{v} = \begin{vmatrix} \mathbf{i} & \mathbf{j} & \mathbf{k} \\ 2 & -6 & 0 \\ -4 & 5 & 3 \end{vmatrix} = \langle -18, -6, -14 \rangle$

9. $\mathbf{u} \cdot \mathbf{v} \neq 0, \mathbf{u} \neq c\mathbf{v} \implies$ neither

10. $\mathbf{u} \cdot \mathbf{v} = -8 - 12 + 20 = 0 \implies$ orthogonal

11. $3\mathbf{u} = \langle -3, 18, -9 \rangle = -\mathbf{v} \implies$ parallel

12. $\overrightarrow{DA} = \langle 0, 2, 0 \rangle, \overrightarrow{DC} = \langle 2, 1, 0 \rangle, \overrightarrow{DH} = \langle 0, 0, 3 \rangle$

$\begin{vmatrix} 0 & 2 & 0 \\ 2 & 1 & 0 \\ 0 & 0 & 3 \end{vmatrix} = 12$ cubic units

13. (a) Vector is $\langle 5+2, 8-3, 25-0 \rangle = \langle 7, 5, 25 \rangle$.

$x = -2 + 7t, y = 3 + 5t, z = 25t$

(b) $\frac{x+2}{7} = \frac{y-3}{5} = \frac{z}{25}$

14. $\mathbf{v} = \langle 2, -4, 1 \rangle$ and $P = (-1, 2, 0)$

$x = -1 + 2t$

$y = 2 - 4t$

$z = t$

15. $\mathbf{u} = \langle -2, 3, 0 \rangle, \mathbf{v} = \langle 5, 8, 25 \rangle$

$\mathbf{u} \times \mathbf{v} = \begin{vmatrix} \mathbf{i} & \mathbf{j} & \mathbf{k} \\ -2 & 3 & 0 \\ 5 & 8 & 25 \end{vmatrix} = \langle 75, 50, -31 \rangle$

Normal to plane

Plane: $75x + 50y - 31z = 0$

16.

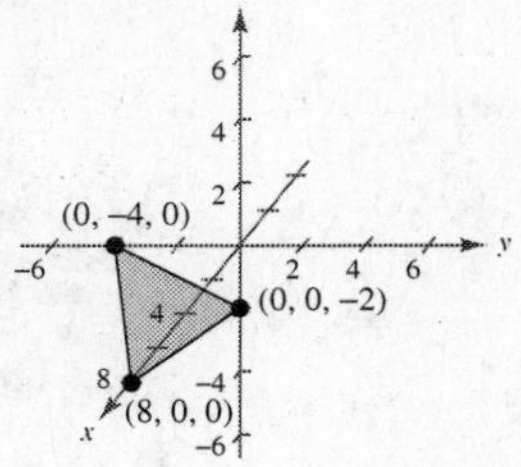

17. $\mathbf{n} = \langle 2, -5, 1\rangle, Q = (0, 0, 25), P = (0, 0, 10)$ in plane, $\overrightarrow{PQ} = \langle 0, 0, 15\rangle$

$$D = \frac{|\overrightarrow{PQ} \cdot \mathbf{n}|}{\|\mathbf{n}\|} = \frac{15}{\sqrt{30}} = \frac{\sqrt{30}}{2} \approx 2.74$$

18. Normal to plane containing: $(-1, -1, 3)$, $(0, 0, 0)$ and $(2, 0, 0)$ is

$$\langle -1, -1, 3\rangle \times \langle 2, 0, 0\rangle = \begin{vmatrix} \mathbf{i} & \mathbf{j} & \mathbf{k} \\ -1 & -1 & 3 \\ 2 & 0 & 0 \end{vmatrix} = \langle 0, 6, 2\rangle \text{ or } \mathbf{n}_1 = \langle 0, 3, 1\rangle$$

Normal to front face is: $\langle 1, -1, 3\rangle \times \langle 0, 2, 0\rangle = \begin{vmatrix} \mathbf{i} & \mathbf{j} & \mathbf{k} \\ 1 & -1 & 3 \\ 0 & 2 & 0 \end{vmatrix} = \langle -6, 0, 2\rangle$ or $\mathbf{n}_2 = \langle -3, 0, 1\rangle$

Angle between sides: $\cos\theta = \dfrac{|\mathbf{n}_1 \cdot \mathbf{n}_2|}{\|\mathbf{n}_1\|\,\|\mathbf{n}_2\|} = \dfrac{1}{\sqrt{10}\sqrt{10}} = \dfrac{1}{10} \implies \theta \approx 84.26°$

19. $\lim\limits_{x\to 4} (5x - x^2) = 5(4) - 4^2 = 4$

20. $\lim\limits_{x\to -2^+} \dfrac{x+2}{(x+2)(x-1)} = \lim\limits_{x\to -2^+} \dfrac{1}{x-1} = -\dfrac{1}{3}$

21. $\lim\limits_{x\to 7} \dfrac{x-7}{(x-7)(x+7)} = \lim\limits_{x\to 7} \dfrac{1}{x+7} = \dfrac{1}{14}$

22. $\lim\limits_{x\to 0} \dfrac{\sqrt{x+4}-2}{x} \cdot \dfrac{\sqrt{x+4}+2}{\sqrt{x+4}+2} = \lim\limits_{x\to 0} \dfrac{(x+4)-4}{x(\sqrt{x+4}+2)} = \lim\limits_{x\to 0} \dfrac{1}{\sqrt{x+4}+2} = \dfrac{1}{2+2} = \dfrac{1}{4}$

23. $\lim\limits_{x\to 4^-} \dfrac{|x-4|}{x-4} = -1$

24. $\lim\limits_{x\to 0} \sin\left(\dfrac{\pi}{x}\right)$ does not exist.

25. $\lim\limits_{x\to 0} \dfrac{\dfrac{1}{x+2} - \dfrac{1}{2}}{x} = \lim\limits_{x\to 0} \dfrac{2-(x+2)}{x(x+2)2}$

$= \lim\limits_{x\to 0} \dfrac{-1}{(x+2)2} = -\dfrac{1}{4}$

26. $\lim\limits_{x\to 0} \dfrac{\sqrt{x+1}-1}{x} \cdot \dfrac{\sqrt{x+1}+1}{\sqrt{x+1}+1} = \lim\limits_{x\to 0} \dfrac{(x+1)-1}{x\left[\sqrt{x+1}+1\right]}$

$= \lim\limits_{x\to 0} \dfrac{1}{\sqrt{x+1}+1} = \dfrac{1}{2}$

27. $\lim\limits_{x\to 2^-} \dfrac{x-2}{x^2-4} = \lim\limits_{x\to 2^-} \dfrac{x-2}{(x-2)(x+2)}$

$= \lim\limits_{x\to 2^-} \dfrac{1}{x+2} = \dfrac{1}{4}$

28. $f'(x) = \lim_{h \to 0} \frac{f(x+h) - f(x)}{h}$

$= \lim_{h \to 0} \frac{4 - (x+h)^2 - (4 - x^2)}{h}$

$= \lim_{h \to 0} \frac{4 - x^2 - 2xh - h^2 - 4 + x^2}{h}$

$= \lim_{h \to 0} \frac{-2xh - h^2}{h}$

$= \lim_{h \to 0} (-2x - h) = -2x$, Slope

At $(0, 4)$, $m = 0$.

29. $f(x) = \sqrt{x+3}$

$m = \lim_{h \to 0} \frac{f(x+h) - f(x)}{h}$

$= \lim_{h \to 0} \frac{\sqrt{x+h+3} - \sqrt{x+3}}{h} \cdot \frac{\sqrt{x+h+3} + \sqrt{x+3}}{\sqrt{x+h+3} + \sqrt{x+3}}$

$= \lim_{h \to 0} \frac{(x+h+3) - (x+3)}{h\left[\sqrt{x+h+3} + \sqrt{x+3}\right]}$

$= \lim_{h \to 0} \frac{1}{\sqrt{x+h+3} + \sqrt{x+3}} = \frac{1}{2\sqrt{x+3}}$

At $(-2, 1)$, $m = \frac{1}{2}$.

30. $f(x) = \frac{1}{x+3}$

$m = \lim_{h \to 0} \frac{f(x+h) - f(x)}{h}$

$= \lim_{h \to 0} \frac{\frac{1}{x+h+3} - \frac{1}{x+3}}{h}$

$= \lim_{h \to 0} \frac{(x+3) - (x+h+3)}{h(x+h+3)(x+3)}$

$= \lim_{h \to 0} \frac{-1}{(x+h+3)(x+3)}$

$= \frac{-1}{(x+3)^2}$

At $\left(1, \frac{1}{4}\right)$, $m = -\frac{1}{16}$.

31. $f'(x) = \lim_{h \to 0} \frac{f(x+h) - f(x)}{h}$

$= \lim_{h \to 0} \frac{(x+h)^2 - (x+h) - (x^2 - x)}{h}$

$= \lim_{h \to 0} \frac{x^2 + 2xh + h^2 - x - h - x^2 + x}{h}$

$= \lim_{h \to 0} \frac{2xh + h^2 - h}{h}$

$= \lim_{h \to 0} (2x + h - 1) = 2x - 1$, Slope

At $(1, 0)$, $m = 1$.

32. $\lim_{x \to \infty} \frac{x^3}{x^2 - 9}$ does not exist.

Function increases without bound.

33. $\lim_{x \to \infty} \frac{3 - 7x}{x + 4} = -7$

34. $\lim_{x \to \infty} \frac{3x^2 + 1}{x^2 + 4} = 3$

35. $\lim_{x\to\infty} \frac{2x}{x^2 + 3x - 2} = 0$

36. $\lim_{x\to\infty} \frac{3 - x}{x^2 + 1} = 0$

37. $\lim_{x\to\infty} \frac{3 + 4x - x^3}{2x^2 + 3}$

does not exist. Function decreases without bound.

38. $\sum_{i=1}^{50} (1 - i^2) = 50 - \frac{50(51)(101)}{6} = -42{,}875$

39. $\sum_{k=1}^{20} (3k^2 - 2k) = 3\,\frac{20(21)(41)}{6} - 2\,\frac{20(21)}{2}$

$= 8610 - 420 = 8190$

40. $\sum_{i=1}^{40} (12 + i^3) = 12(40) + \frac{40^2(41)^2}{4}$

$= 480 + 672{,}400 = 672{,}880$

41. Area $\approx \frac{1}{2}[1 + 2 + 3 + 4 + 5 + 6]$

$= \frac{21}{2}$ square units

42. Area $\approx \frac{1}{2}[4.875 + 4.5 + 3.875 + 3]$

$= 8.125$ square units

43. Area $\approx \frac{1}{2}\left[\frac{9}{16} + 1 + \frac{25}{16} + \frac{9}{4}\right] = \frac{43}{16} = 2.6875$

44. Area $\approx \frac{1}{4}\left[\frac{1}{1 + \left(-\frac{3}{4}\right)^2} + \frac{1}{1 + \left(-\frac{1}{2}\right)^2} + \frac{1}{1 + \left(-\frac{1}{4}\right)^2} + \frac{1}{1 + 0} + \frac{1}{1 + \left(\frac{1}{4}\right)^2} + \frac{1}{1 + \left(\frac{1}{2}\right)^2} + \frac{1}{1 + \left(\frac{3}{4}\right)^2} + \frac{1}{1 + 1^2}\right]$

$= \frac{1}{4}\left[2(0.64) + 2(0.8) + 2(0.941176) + 1 + \frac{1}{2}\right]$

≈ 1.566 square units

45. $f(x) = x + 2,\ [0, 1]$

The width of each rectangle is $1/n$. The height is

$f\left(\frac{i}{n}\right) = \frac{i}{n} + 2.$

$A \approx \sum_{i=1}^{n}\left[\frac{i}{n} + 2\right]\frac{1}{n} = \sum_{i=1}^{n}\left(\frac{1}{n^2}i + \frac{2}{n}\right)$

$A = \lim_{n\to\infty}\left[\frac{1}{n^2}\frac{n(n + 1)}{2} + \frac{2}{n}(n)\right]$

$= \frac{1}{2} + 2 = \frac{5}{2}$

46. $f(x) = 8 - 2x, [-4, 4]$

The width of each rectangle is $8/n$. The height is

$f\left(-4 + \frac{8i}{n}\right) = 8 - 2\left(-4 + \frac{8i}{n}\right) = 16 - \frac{16i}{n}.$

$A \approx \sum_{i=1}^{n}\left(16 - \frac{16i}{n}\right)\left(\frac{8}{n}\right)$

$= \sum_{i=1}^{n}\left(\frac{128}{n} - \frac{128i}{n^2}\right)$

$A = \lim_{n\to\infty}\left[\frac{128}{n}(n) - \frac{128}{n^2}\frac{n(n + 1)}{2}\right]$

$= 128 - 64 = 64$

47. $f(x) = 2x + 5,\ [-1, 3]$

The width of each rectangle is $4/n$. The height is

$$f\left(-1 + \frac{4i}{n}\right) = 2\left(-1 + \frac{4i}{n}\right) + 5 = 3 + \frac{8i}{n}.$$

$$A \approx \sum_{i=1}^{n}\left(3 + \frac{8i}{n}\right)\left(\frac{4}{n}\right) = \sum_{i=1}^{n}\left(\frac{12}{n} + \frac{32}{n^2}i\right)$$

$$A = \lim_{n\to\infty}\left[\frac{12}{n}(n) + \frac{32}{n^2}\frac{n(n+1)}{2}\right]$$

$$= 12 + 16 = 28$$

48. $f(x) = x^2 + 1, [0, 4]$

The width of each rectangle is $4/n$. The height is

$$f\left(\frac{4i}{n}\right) = \left(\frac{4i}{n}\right)^2 + 1.$$

$$A \approx \sum_{i=1}^{n}\left(\frac{16i^2}{n^2} + 1\right)\left(\frac{4}{n}\right) = \sum_{i=1}^{n}\left(\frac{64}{n^3}i^2 + \frac{4}{n}\right)$$

$$A = \lim_{n\to\infty}\left[\frac{64}{n^3}\frac{n(n+1)(2n+1)}{6} + \frac{4}{n}(n)\right]$$

$$= \frac{64}{3} + 4 = \frac{76}{3}$$

49. $f(x) = 4 - x^2,\ [0, 2]$

The width of each rectangle is $2/n$. The height is

$$f\left(\frac{2i}{n}\right) = 4 - \left(\frac{2i}{n}\right)^2.$$

$$A \approx \sum_{i=1}^{n}\left[4 - \frac{4i^2}{n^2}\right]\left(\frac{2}{n}\right) = \sum_{i=1}^{n}\left(\frac{8}{n} - \frac{8i^2}{n^3}\right)$$

$$A = \lim_{n\to\infty}\left[\frac{8}{n}(n) - \frac{8}{n^3}\frac{n(n+1)(2n+1)}{6}\right]$$

$$= 8 - \frac{8}{3} = \frac{16}{3}$$

50. Width: $\frac{1}{n}$, Height: $f\left(\frac{i}{n}\right) = 1 - \left(\frac{i}{n}\right)^3$

$$A \approx \sum_{i=1}^{n}\left(1 - \left(\frac{i}{n}\right)^3\right)\left(\frac{1}{n}\right) = \frac{1}{n}\sum_{i=1}^{n}1 - \frac{1}{n^4}\sum_{i=1}^{n}i^3$$

$$= \frac{1}{n}(n) - \frac{1}{n^4}\left[\frac{n^2(n+1)^2}{4}\right]$$

$$A = \lim_{n\to\infty}\left[1 - \frac{1}{n^4}\left(\frac{n^2(n+1)^2}{4}\right)\right] = 1 - \frac{1}{4} = \frac{3}{4}$$